ALGEBRA

Exponents and Radicals

$$x^a x^b = x^{a+b} \qquad \frac{x^a}{x^b} = x^{a-b} \qquad x^{-a} = \frac{1}{x^a} \qquad (x^a)^b = x^{ab} \qquad \left(\frac{x}{y}\right)^a = \frac{x^a}{y^a}$$

$$x^{1/n} = \sqrt[n]{x} \qquad x^{m/n} = \sqrt[n]{x^m} = (\sqrt[n]{x})^m \qquad \sqrt[n]{xy} = \sqrt[n]{x}\sqrt[n]{y} \qquad \sqrt[n]{x/y} = \sqrt[n]{x}/\sqrt[n]{y}$$

Factoring Formulas

$$a^2 - b^2 = (a - b)(a + b) \qquad a^2 + b^2 \text{ does not factor over real numbers.}$$
$$a^3 - b^3 = (a - b)(a^2 + ab + b^2) \qquad a^3 + b^3 = (a + b)(a^2 - ab + b^2)$$
$$a^n - b^n = (a - b)(a^{n-1} + a^{n-2}b + a^{n-3}b^2 + \cdots + ab^{n-2} + b^{n-1})$$

Binomials

$$(a \pm b)^2 = a^2 \pm 2ab + b^2$$
$$(a \pm b)^3 = a^3 \pm 3a^2b + 3ab^2 \pm b^3$$

Binomial Theorem

$$(a + b)^n = a^n + \binom{n}{1}a^{n-1}b + \binom{n}{2}a^{n-2}b^2 + \cdots + \binom{n}{n-1}ab^{n-1} + b^n,$$

$$\text{where } \binom{n}{k} = \frac{n(n-1)(n-2)\cdots(n-k+1)}{k(k-1)(k-2)\cdots 3\cdot 2\cdot 1} = \frac{n!}{k!(n-k)!}$$

Quadratic Formula

The solutions of $ax^2 + bx + c = 0$ are

$$x = \frac{-b \pm \sqrt{b^2 - 4ac}}{2a}.$$

GEOMETRY

Parallelogram

$$A = bh$$

Triangle

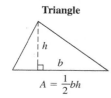

$$A = \frac{1}{2}bh$$

Trapezoid

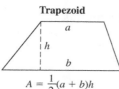

$$A = \frac{1}{2}(a + b)h$$

Circle

$$A = \pi r^2$$
$$C = 2\pi r$$

Sector

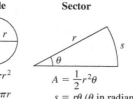

$$A = \frac{1}{2}r^2\theta$$
$$s = r\theta \text{ (θ in radians)}$$

Cylinder

$$V = \pi r^2 h$$
$$S = 2\pi rh$$
(lateral surface area)

Cone

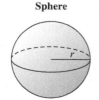

$$V = \frac{1}{3}\pi r^2 h$$
$$S = \pi r\ell$$
(lateral surface area)

Sphere

$$V = \frac{4}{3}\pi r^3$$
$$S = 4\pi r^2$$

Equations of Lines and Circles

$$m = \frac{y_2 - y_1}{x_2 - x_1}$$ slope of line through (x_1, y_1) and (x_2, y_2)

$$y - y_1 = m(x - x_1)$$ point–slope form of line through (x_1, y_1) with slope m

$$y = mx + b$$ slope–intercept form of line with slope m and y-intercept $(0, b)$

$$(x - h)^2 + (y - k)^2 = r^2$$ circle of radius r with center (h, k)

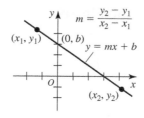

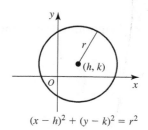

$$(x - h)^2 + (y - k)^2 = r^2$$

TRIGONOMETRY

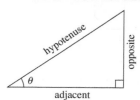

$$\cos\theta = \frac{\text{adj}}{\text{hyp}} \qquad \sin\theta = \frac{\text{opp}}{\text{hyp}} \qquad \tan\theta = \frac{\text{opp}}{\text{adj}}$$

$$\sec\theta = \frac{\text{hyp}}{\text{adj}} \qquad \csc\theta = \frac{\text{hyp}}{\text{opp}} \qquad \cot\theta = \frac{\text{adj}}{\text{opp}}$$

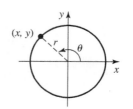

$$\cos\theta = \frac{x}{r} \qquad \sec\theta = \frac{r}{x}$$
$$\sin\theta = \frac{y}{r} \qquad \csc\theta = \frac{r}{y}$$
$$\tan\theta = \frac{y}{x} \qquad \cot\theta = \frac{x}{y}$$

(Continued)

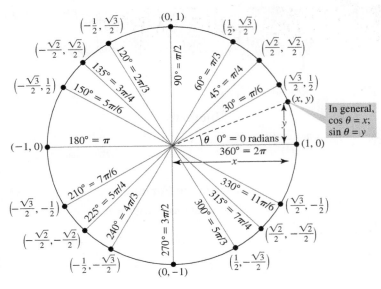

Reciprocal Identities

$$\tan \theta = \frac{\sin \theta}{\cos \theta} \qquad \cot \theta = \frac{\cos \theta}{\sin \theta} \qquad \sec \theta = \frac{1}{\cos \theta} \qquad \csc \theta = \frac{1}{\sin \theta}$$

Pythagorean Identities

$$\sin^2 \theta + \cos^2 \theta = 1 \qquad \tan^2 \theta + 1 = \sec^2 \theta \qquad 1 + \cot^2 \theta = \csc^2 \theta$$

Sign Identities

$$\sin (-\theta) = -\sin \theta \qquad \cos (-\theta) = \cos \theta \qquad \tan (-\theta) = -\tan \theta$$
$$\csc (-\theta) = -\csc \theta \qquad \sec (-\theta) = \sec \theta \qquad \cot (-\theta) = -\cot \theta$$

In general, $\cos \theta = x$; $\sin \theta = y$

Double-Angle Identities

$$\sin 2\theta = 2 \sin \theta \cos \theta$$

$$\cos 2\theta = \cos^2 \theta - \sin^2 \theta$$
$$= 2 \cos^2 \theta - 1$$
$$= 1 - 2 \sin^2 \theta$$

$$\tan 2\theta = \frac{2 \tan \theta}{1 - \tan^2 \theta}$$

Half-Angle Formulas

$$\cos^2 \theta = \frac{1 + \cos 2\theta}{2} \qquad \sin^2 \theta = \frac{1 - \cos 2\theta}{2}$$

Addition Formulas

$$\sin (\alpha + \beta) = \sin \alpha \cos \beta + \cos \alpha \sin \beta$$
$$\cos (\alpha + \beta) = \cos \alpha \cos \beta - \sin \alpha \sin \beta$$
$$\tan (\alpha + \beta) = \frac{\tan \alpha + \tan \beta}{1 - \tan \alpha \tan \beta}$$

$$\sin (\alpha - \beta) = \sin \alpha \cos \beta - \cos \alpha \sin \beta$$
$$\cos (\alpha - \beta) = \cos \alpha \cos \beta + \sin \alpha \sin \beta$$
$$\tan (\alpha - \beta) = \frac{\tan \alpha - \tan \beta}{1 + \tan \alpha \tan \beta}$$

Law of Sines

$$\frac{\sin \alpha}{a} = \frac{\sin \beta}{b} = \frac{\sin \gamma}{c}$$

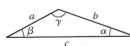

Law of Cosines

$$a^2 = b^2 + c^2 - 2bc \cos \alpha$$

Graphs of Trigonometric Functions and Their Inverses

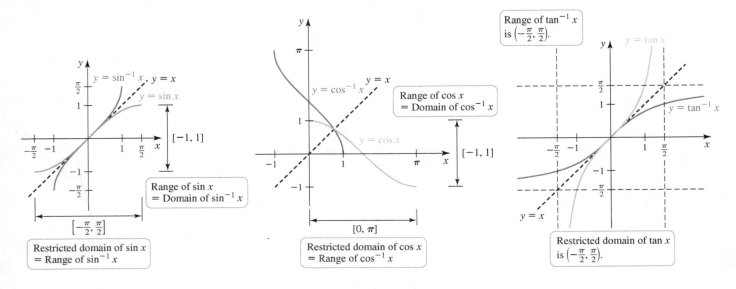

William Briggs • Lyle Cochran • Bernard Gillett

Calculus
Early Transcendentals
Volume II

Custom Edition for Oakton Community College

Taken from:
Calculus: Early Transcendentals, Second Edition
by William Briggs, Lyle Cochran, and Bernard Gillett

Cover Art: Courtesy of Photodisc/Getty Images.

Taken from:

Calculus: Early Transcendentals, Second Edition
by William Briggs, Lyle Cochran, and Bernard Gillett
Copyright © 2015, 2011 by Pearson Education, Inc.
Boston, Massachusetts 02116

This special edition published in cooperation with Pearson Learning Solutions.

Pearson Learning Solutions, 501 Boylston Street, Suite 900, Boston, MA 02116
A Pearson Education Company
www.pearsoned.com

Printed in the United States of America

1 2 3 4 5 6 7 8 9 10 V092 15 14

000200010271885523

SK

ISBN 10: 1-269-86807-1
ISBN 13: 978-1-269-86807-5

Contents

Preface

The second edition of *Calculus: Early Transcendentals* supports a three-semester or four-quarter calculus sequence typically taken by students studying mathematics, engineering, the natural sciences, or economics. The second edition has the same goals as the first edition:

• to motivate the essential ideas of calculus with a lively narrative, demonstrating the utility of calculus with applications in diverse fields;

• to introduce new topics through concrete examples, applications, and analogies, appealing to students' intuition and geometric instincts to make calculus natural and believable; and

• once this intuitive foundation is established, to present generalizations and abstractions and to treat theoretical matters in a rigorous way.

The second edition both builds on the success and addresses the inevitable deficiencies of the first edition. We have listened to and learned from the instructors who used the first edition. They have given us wise guidance about how to make the second edition an even more effective learning tool for students and a more powerful resource for instructors. Users of the book continue to tell us that it mirrors the course they teach—and more importantly, that students actually read it! Of course, the second edition also benefits from our own experiences using the book, as well as our experiences teaching mathematics at diverse institutions over the past 30 years.

We are grateful to users of the first edition—for their courage in adopting a first edition book, for their enthusiastic response to the book, and for their invaluable advice and feedback. They deserve much of the credit for the improvements that we have made in the second edition.

New in the Second Edition

Narrative

The second edition of this book has undergone a thorough cover-to-cover polishing of the narrative, making the presentation of material even more concise and lucid. Occasionally, we discovered new ways to present material to make the exposition clearer for students and more efficient for instructors.

Figures

The figures—already dynamic and informative in the first edition—were thoroughly reviewed and revised when necessary. The figures enrich the overall spirit of the book and tell as much of the calculus story as the words do. The path-breaking interactive figures in the companion eBook have been refined, and they still represent a revolutionary way to communicate mathematics. See page xii, eBook with Interactive Figures, for more information.

Exercises

The comprehensive 7656 exercises in the first edition were thoroughly reviewed and refined. Then 19% more basic skills and mid-level exercises were added. The exercises at the end of each section are still efficiently organized in the following categories.

- *Review Questions* begin each exercise set and check students' conceptual understanding of the essential ideas from the section.

- *Basic Skills* exercises are confidence-building problems that provide a solid foundation for the more challenging exercises to follow. Each example in the narrative is linked directly to a block of *Basic Skills* exercises via *Related Exercises* references at the end of the example solution.

- *Further Explorations* exercises expand on the *Basic Skills* exercises by challenging students to think creatively and to generalize newly acquired skills.

- *Applications* exercises connect skills developed in previous exercises to applications and modeling problems that demonstrate the power and utility of calculus.

- *Additional Exercises* are generally the most difficult and challenging problems; they include proofs of results cited in the narrative.

Each chapter concludes with a comprehensive set of *Review Exercises*.

Answers

The answers in the back of the book have been reviewed and thoroughly checked for accuracy. The reliability that we achieved in the first edition has been maintained—if not improved.

New Topics

We have added new material on Newton's method, surface area of solids of revolution, hyperbolic functions, and TNB frames. Based on our own teaching experience, we also added a brief new introductory section to the chapter on Techniques of Integration. We felt it makes sense to introduce students to some general integration strategies before diving into the standard techniques of integration by parts, partial fraction, and various substitutions.

MyMathLab

We (together with the team at Pearson) have made many improvements to the MyMathLab course for the second edition. Hundreds of new algorithmic exercises that correspond to those in the text were added to the course. Cumulative review exercises have been added, providing an opportunity for students to get "mixed practice" with important skills such as finding derivatives. New step-by-step exercises for key skills provide support for students in their first attempts at new and important problems. Real-world exerciess now require that students provide units with their answer. We've added more exercises that call for student manipulation and analysis of the Interactive Figures. We have greatly increased the number of instructional videos. The graphing functionality in MyMathLab has become more sophisticated and the answer-checking algorithms are more refined.

Differential Equations

This book has a single robust section devoted to an overview of differential equations. However, for schools that require more expansive coverage of differential equations, we provide complete online chapters on both first- and second-order differential equations, available in MyMathLab as well as through the Pearson Math and Stats Resource page at **www.pearsonhighered.com/mathstatsresources**.

Pedagogical Features

Figures

Given the power of graphics software and the ease with which many students assimilate visual images, we devoted considerable time and deliberation to the figures in this book. Whenever possible, we let the figures communicate essential ideas using annotations

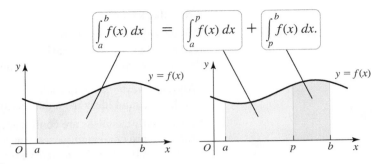

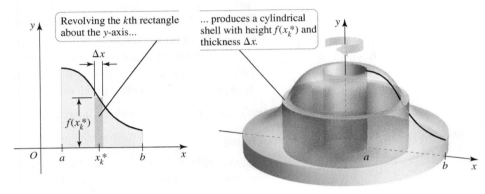

Figure 5.29

Figure 6.40

reminiscent of an instructor's voice at the board. Readers will quickly find that the figures facilitate learning in new ways.

Quick Check and Margin Notes

The narrative is interspersed with *Quick Check* questions that encourage students to read with pencil in hand. These questions resemble the kinds of questions instructors pose in class. Answers to the *Quick Check* questions are found at the end of the section in which they occur. *Margin Notes* offer reminders, provide insight, and clarify technical points.

Guided Projects

The *Instructor's Resource Guide and Test Bank* contains 78 *Guided Projects*. These projects allow students to work in a directed, step-by-step fashion, with various objectives: to carry out extended calculations, to derive physical models, to explore related theoretical topics, or to investigate new applications of calculus. The *Guided Projects* vividly demonstrate the breadth of calculus and provide a wealth of mathematical excursions that go beyond the typical classroom experience. A list of suggested *Guided Projects* is included at the end of each chapter. Students may access the *Guided Projects* within MyMathLab.

Technology

We believe that a calculus text should help students strengthen their analytical skills and demonstrate how technology can extend (not replace) those skills. Calculators and graphing utilities are additional tools in the kit, and students must learn when and when not to use them. Our goal is to accommodate the different policies about technology that various instructors may use.

Throughout the book, exercises marked with **T** indicate that the use of technology— ranging from plotting a function with a graphing calculator to carrying out a calculation using a computer algebra system—may be needed. See page xiv for information regarding our technology resource manuals covering Maple, Mathematica and Texas Instruments graphing calculators.

eBook with Interactive Figures

The textbook is supported by a groundbreaking and award-winning electronic book, created by Eric Schulz of Walla Walla Community College. This "live book" contains the complete text of the print book plus interactive versions of approximately 700 figures. Instructors can use these interactive figures in the classroom to illustrate the important ideas of calculus, and students can explore them while they are reading the textbook. Our experience confirms that the interactive figures help build students' geometric intuition of calculus. The authors have written Interactive Figure Exercises that can be assigned via MyMathLab so that students can engage with the figures outside of class in a directed way. Additionally, the authors have created short videos, accessed through the eBook, that tell the story of key Interactive Figures. Available only within MyMathLab, the eBook provides instructors with powerful new teaching tools that expand and enrich the learning experience for students.

Content Highlights

In writing this text, we identified content in the calculus curriculum that consistently presents challenges to our students. We made organizational changes to the standard presentation of these topics or slowed the pace of the narrative to facilitate students' comprehension of material that is traditionally difficult. Two noteworthy modifications to the traditional table of contents for this course appear in the material for Calculus II and Calculus III.

Often appearing near the end of the term, the topics of sequences and series are the most challenging in Calculus II. By splitting this material into two chapters, we have given these topics a more deliberate pace and made them more accessible without adding significantly to the length of the narrative.

There is a clear and logical path through multivariate calculus, which is not apparent in many textbooks. We have carefully separated functions of several variables from vector-valued functions, so that these ideas are distinct in the minds of students. The book culminates when these two threads are joined in the last chapter, which is devoted to vector calculus.

Additional Resources

Instructor's Resource Guide and Test Bank

ISBN 0-321-95429-7 | 978-0-321-95429-9
Bernard Gillett, University of Colorado at Boulder

This guide represents significant contributions by the textbook authors and contains a variety of classroom support materials for instructors.

- Seventy-eight *Guided Projects*, correlated to specific chapters of the text, can be assigned to students for individual or group work. The *Guided Projects* vividly demonstrate the breadth of calculus and provide a wealth of mathematical excursions that go beyond the typical classroom experience.

- *Lecture Support Notes* give an *Overview* of the material to be taught in each section of the text, and helpful classroom *Teaching Tips*. *Connections* among various sections of the text are also pointed out, and *Additional Activities* are provided.

- *Quick Quizzes* for each section in the text consist of multiple-choice questions that can be used as in-class quiz material or as Active Learning Questions. These Quick Quizzes can also be found at the end of each section in the interactive eBook.

- *Chapter Reviews* provide a list of key concepts from each chapter, followed by a set of chapter review questions.

- *Chapter Test Banks* consist of between 25 and 30 questions that can be used for in-class exams, take-home exams, or additional review material.

- *Learning Objectives Lists* and an *Index of Applications* are tools to help instructors gear the text to their course goals and students' interests.

- *Student Study Cards*, consisting of key concepts for both single-variable and multivariable calculus, are included for instructors to photocopy and distribute to their students as convenient study tools.

- *Answers* are provided for all exercises in the manual, including the *Guided Projects*.

Instructor's Solutions Manuals

Mark Woodard, Furman University
Single Variable Calculus (Chapters 1–10) ISBN 0-321-95422-X | 978-0-321-95422-0
Multivariable Calculus (Chapters 8–14) ISBN 0-321-95430-0 | 978-0-321-95430-5

The *Instructor's Solutions Manual* contains complete solutions to all the exercises in the text.

Student's Solutions Manuals

Mark Woodard, Furman University
Single Variable Calculus (Chapters 1–10) ISBN 0-321-95432-7 | 978-0-321-95432-9
Multivariable Calculus (Chapters 8–14) ISBN 0-321-95431-9 | 978-0-321-95431-2

The *Student's Solutions Manual* is designed for the student and contains complete solutions to all the odd-numbered exercises in the text.

Just-in-Time Algebra and Trigonometry for Early Transcendentals Calculus, Fourth Edition

ISBN 0-321-67103-1 | 978-0-321-67103-5
Guntram Mueller and Ronald I. Brent, University of Massachusetts—Lowell

Sharp algebra and trigonometry skills are critical to mastering calculus, and *Just-in-Time Algebra and Trigonometry for Early Transcendentals Calculus* is designed to bolster these skills while students study calculus. As students make their way through calculus, this text is with them every step of the way, showing them the necessary algebra or trigonometry topics and pointing out potential problem spots. The easy-to-use table of contents has algebra and trigonometry topics arranged in the order in which students will need them as they study calculus.

Technology Resource Manuals

Maple Manual by Marie Vanisko, Carroll College
Mathematica Manual by Marie Vanisko, Carroll College
TI-Graphing Calculator Manual by Elaine McDonald-Newman, Sonoma State University

These manuals cover Maple™ 17, Mathematica® 8, and the TI-83 Plus/TI-84 Plus and TI-89, respectively. Each manual provides detailed guidance for integrating a specific software package or graphing calculator throughout the course, including syntax and commands. These manuals are available to instructors and students through the Pearson Math and Stats Resources page, **www.pearsonhighered.com/mathstatsresources**, and MyMathLab®.

MyMathLab® Online Course (access code required)

MyMathLab from Pearson is the world's leading online resource in mathematics, integrating interactive homework, assessment, and media in a flexible, easy-to-use format. MyMathLab delivers **proven results** in helping individual students succeed. It provides **engaging experiences** that personalize, stimulate, and measure learning for each student. And it comes from an **experienced partner** with educational expertise and an eye on the future.

MyMathLab for *Calculus: Early Transcendentals* contains the groundbreaking **eBook featuring over 700 Interactive Figures** that can be manipulated to illuminate difficult-to-convey concepts. Instructors can use these interactive figures in the classroom to illustrate the important ideas of calculus, and students can manipulate the interactive figures while they are using MyMathLab. In each case, these interactive figures help build geometric intuition of calculus. Exercises for the Interactive Figures can be assigned as homework to encourage students to explore the concepts presented.

The MyMathLab course for this text contains over 7500 assignable algorithmic exercises. To learn more about how MyMathLab combines proven learning applications with powerful assessment, visit **www.mymathlab.com** or contact your Pearson representative.

MathXL® Online Course (access code required)

MathXL® is the homework and assessment engine that runs MyMathLab. (MyMathLab is MathXL plus a learning management system.)

With MathXL, instructors can:

- Create, edit, and assign online homework and tests using algorithmically generated exercises correlated at the objective level to the textbook.
- Create and assign their own online exercises.
- Maintain records of all student work tracked in MathXL's online gradebook.

With MathXL, students can:

- Work through the **Getting Ready for Calculus** chapter, which includes hundreds of exercises that address prerequisite skills in algebra and trigonometry, and receive remediation for those skills with which they need help.
- Take chapter tests in MathXL and receive personalized study plans and/or personalized homework assignments based on their test results.
- Use the study plan and/or the homework to link directly to tutorial exercises for the objectives they need to study.
- Access supplemental animations and video clips directly from selected exercises.

MathXL is available to qualified adopters. For more information, visit our website at **www.mathxl.com** or contact your Pearson representative.

TestGen®

TestGen® (**www.pearsoned.com/testgen**) enables instructors to build, edit, print, and administer tests using a computerized bank of questions developed to cover all the objectives of the text. TestGen is algorithmically based, allowing instructors to create multiple but equivalent versions of the same question or test with the click of a button. Instructors can also modify test bank questions or add new questions. The software and testbank are available for download from Pearson Education's online catalog, **www.pearsonhighered.com/irc**.

Video Resources

The Video Lectures With Optional Captioning feature an engaging team of mathematics instructors who present comprehensive coverage of topics in the text. The lecturers' presentations include illustrative examples and exercises and support an approach that emphasizes visualization and problem solving. Available only through MyMathLab and MathXL.

PowerPoint® Lecture Slides

These PowerPoint slides contain key concepts, definitions, figures, and tables from the textbook. These files are available to qualified instructors through the Pearson Instructor Resource Center, **www.pearsonhighered.com/irc**, and MyMathLab.

Acknowledgments

We would like to express our thanks to the people who made many valuable contributions to this edition as it evolved through its many stages:

Accuracy Checkers

Lisa Collette

Blaise DeSesa

Patricia Espinoza-Toro

David Grinstein

Ebony Harvey

Michele Jean-Louis

Nickolas Mavrikidis

Renato Mirollo

Patricia Nelson

John Samons

Joan Saniuk

Tom Wegleitner

Gary Williams

Reviewers

Jay Paul Abramson, *Arizona State University*

Anthony Barcellos, *American River College*

Maurino Bautista, *Rochester Institute of Technology*

Nick Belloit, *Florida State College at Jacksonville, Kent Campus*

Patrice D. Benson, *The United States Military Academy*

Nadine Bluett, *Front Range Community College, Westminster*

Maritza M. Branker, *Niagara College*

Tim Britt, *Jackson State Community College*

Zhixiong Chen, *New Jersey City University*

Marcela Chiorescu, *Georgia College and State University*

Ray E. Collins, *Georgia Perimeter College*

Robert Diaz, *Fullerton College*

Vincent D. Dimiceli, *Oral Roberts University*

Paul Drelles, *West Shore Community College*

Lori Dunlop-Pyle, *University of Central Florida*

Keith Erickson, *Georgia Highlands College*

Justin Fitzpatrick, *Vanderbilt University*

Laurie Huffman, *Georgia College and State University*

Michelle Knox, *Midwestern State University*

Christy Koelling, *Davidson County Community College*

John M. Livermore, *Cazenovia College*

Mike Long, *Shippensburg University*

Gabriel Melendez, *Mohawk Valley Community College*

Susan Miller, *Richland College*

Renato Mirollo, *Boston College*

Val Mohanakumar, *Hillsborough Community College*

Nathan T. Moyer, *Whitworth University*

Lloyd Moyo, *Henderson State University*

Mihai Putinar, *University of California at Santa Barbara*

Marc Renault, *Shippensburg University*

Michael Rosenthal, *Florida International University*

Jennifer Strehler, *Oakton Community College*

V. Lee Turner, *Southern Nazarene University*

Larissa Williamson, *University of Florida*

Deborah Ziegler, *Hannibal-LaGrange University*

Calculus MyMathLab Advisory Board

Maria Capursi, *University Central Florida*

Jacqueline Donofrio, *Monroe Community College*

Allen Guest, *Clemson University*

Debbie Korth, *University of Arkansas*

Nela Lakos, *Ohio State University*

Elizabeth Miller, *Ohio State University*

Stephen Scarborough, *Oregon State University*

German Vargas, *College of Coastal Georgia*

Janet Woodland, *University of Arkansas*

Class Testers, Focus Group Participants

Martha Gady, *Whitworth University*

Nathan T. Moyer, *Whitworth University*

Donna M. Pierce, *Whitworth University*

Michael J. Rempe, *Whitworth University*

Anne A. Trefry, *Whitworth University*

Credits

Chapter opener art: Petr Vaclavek/Shutterstock

Chapter 6

Page 414, Thomas, George B; Weir, Maurice D; Hass, Joel; Giordano, Frank R., THOMAS' CALCULUS, EARLY TRANSCENDENTALS, MEDIA UPGRADE, 11th edition © 2008. Printed and Electronically reproduced by permission of Pearson Education, Inc., Upper Saddle River, New Jersey. **Page 419,** Mathematics Magazine 81, No. 2, Apr. 2008. **Pages 421, 425, 426, 433, 435,** Thomas, George B.; Weir, Maurice D.; Hass Joel; Giordano, Frank R., THOMAS' CALCULUS, EARLY TRANSCENDENTALS, MEDIA UP. GRADE, 11th edition, © 2008. Printed and Electronically reproduced by permission of Pearson Education, Inc., Upper Saddle River, New Jersey. **Page 490,** Adapted from Putnam Exam 1939. **Page 490,** "A Theory of Competitive Running," Joe Keller, Physics Today 26 Sept. 1973.

Chapter 7

Page 515, The College Mathematics Journal 32, No. 5, Nov. 2001, **Page 540,** The College Mathematics Journal, Vol. 34, No. 3 © 2003 Mathematical Association of America. Reproduced by permission. All rights reserved. **Page 550,** The College Mathematics Journal 32, No. 5, Nov. 2001. **Page 556,** The College Mathematics Journal 33, 4, Sept. 2004. **Page 562,** U.S. Energy Information Administration. **Page 562,** U.S. Energy Information Administration. **Page 563,** Collecte Localisation Satellites/Centre National d'études Spatiales/Legos. **Page 569,** U.S. Energy Information Administration. **Page 580,** P. Weidman, I. Pinelis, Comptes Rendu Méchanique 332 2004: 571–584. **Page 581,** Mathematics Magazine 59, 1, Feb. 1986. **Page 595,** Mathematics Magazine 81, No 2, Apr. 2008: 152–154.

Chapter 8

Page 639, The College Mathematics Journal 24, 5, Nov. 1993. **Page 640,** The College Mathematics Journal 30, No. 1 Jan. 1999. **Page 640,** Steve Kifowit 2006 and H. Chen, C. Kennedy, Harmonic series meets Fibonacci sequence, The College Mathematics Journal, 43 May 2012.

Chapter 10

Pages 718, and **719,** N. Brannen, The Sun, the Moon, and Convexity in The College Mathematics Journal, 32, 4 Sept. 2001. **Page 727,** T.H. Fay, American Mathematical Monthly 96 1989, revived in Wagon and Packel, Animating Calculus, Freeman, 1994. **Pages 737 and 747,** Thomas, George B.; Weir, Maurice D.; Hass, Joel; Giordano, Frank R. THOMAS'S CALCULUS, EARLY TRANSCENDENTALS, MEDIA UPGRADE, 11th © 2008, Printed and Electronically reproduced by permission of Pearson Education, Inc., Upper Saddle River, New Jersey.

6

Applications of Integration

Chapter Preview Now that we have some basic techniques for evaluating integrals, we turn our attention to the uses of integration, which are virtually endless. We first illustrate the general rule that if the rate of change of a quantity is known, then integration can be used to determine the net change or the future value of that quantity over a certain time interval. Next, we explore some rich geometric applications of integration: computing the area of regions bounded by several curves, the volume and surface area of three-dimensional solids, and the length of curves. A variety of physical applications of integration include finding the work done by a variable force and computing the total force exerted by water behind a dam. All of these applications are unified by their use of the *slice-and-sum* strategy. We end this chapter by revisiting the logarithmic function, exploring the many applications of the exponential function, and introducing hyperbolic functions.

6.1 Velocity and Net Change

In previous chapters, we established the relationship between the position and velocity of an object moving along a line. With integration, we can now say much more about this relationship. Once we relate velocity and position through integration, we can make analogous observations about a variety of other practical problems, which include fluid flow, population growth, manufacturing costs, and production and consumption of natural resources. The ideas in this section come directly from the Fundamental Theorem of Calculus, and they are among the most powerful applications of calculus.

Velocity, Position, and Displacement

Suppose you are driving along a straight highway and your position relative to a reference point or origin is $s(t)$ for times $t \geq 0$. Your *displacement* over a time interval $[a, b]$ is the change in the position $s(b) - s(a)$ (Figure 6.1). If $s(b) > s(a)$, then your displacement is positive; when $s(b) < s(a)$, your displacement is negative.

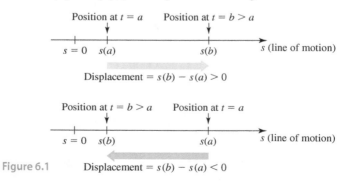

Figure 6.1

Now assume that $v(t)$ is the velocity of the object at a particular time t. Recall from Chapter 3 that $v(t) = s'(t)$, which means that s is an antiderivative of v. From the Fundamental Theorem of Calculus, it follows that

$$\int_a^b v(t)\, dt = \int_a^b s'(t)\, dt = s(b) - s(a) = \text{displacement.}$$

We see that the definite integral $\int_a^b v(t)\, dt$ is the displacement (change in position) between times $t = a$ and $t = b$. Equivalently, the displacement over the time interval $[a, b]$ is the net area under the velocity curve over $[a, b]$ (Figure 6.2a).

Not to be confused with the displacement is the *distance traveled* over a time interval, which is the total distance traveled by the object, independent of the direction of motion. If the velocity is positive, the object moves in the positive direction and the displacement equals the distance traveled. However, if the velocity changes sign, then the displacement and the distance traveled are not generally equal.

QUICK CHECK 1 A police officer leaves his station on a north-south freeway at 9 A.M., traveling north (the positive direction) for 40 mi between 9 A.M. and 10 A.M. From 10 A.M. to 11 A.M., he travels south to a point 20 mi south of the station. What are the distance traveled and the displacement between 9 A.M. and 11 A.M.? ◄

To compute the distance traveled, we need the magnitude, but not the sign, of the velocity. The magnitude of the velocity $|v(t)|$ is called the *speed*. The distance traveled over a small time interval dt is $|v(t)|\, dt$ (speed multiplied by elapsed time). Summing these distances, the distance traveled over the time interval $[a, b]$ is the integral of the speed; that is,

$$\text{distance traveled} = \int_a^b |v(t)|\, dt.$$

As shown in Figure 6.2b, integrating the speed produces the area (not net area) bounded by the velocity curve and the t-axis, which corresponds to the distance traveled. The distance traveled is always nonnegative.

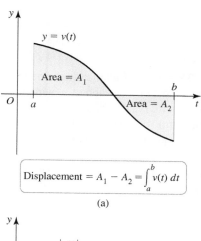

$$\text{Displacement} = A_1 - A_2 = \int_a^b v(t)\, dt$$

(a)

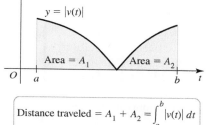

$$\text{Distance traveled} = A_1 + A_2 = \int_a^b |v(t)|\, dt$$

(b)

Figure 6.2

DEFINITION Position, Velocity, Displacement, and Distance

1. The **position** of an object moving along a line at time t, denoted $s(t)$, is the location of the object relative to the origin.

2. The **velocity** of an object at time t is $v(t) = s'(t)$.

3. The **displacement** of the object between $t = a$ and $t = b > a$ is

$$s(b) - s(a) = \int_a^b v(t)\, dt.$$

4. The **distance traveled** by the object between $t = a$ and $t = b > a$ is

$$\int_a^b |v(t)|\, dt,$$

where $|v(t)|$ is the **speed** of the object at time t.

QUICK CHECK 2 Describe a possible motion of an object along a line for $0 \le t \le 5$ for which the displacement and the distance traveled are different. ◄

EXAMPLE 1   Displacement from velocity A jogger runs along a straight road with velocity (in mi/hr) $v(t) = 2t^2 - 8t + 6$, for $0 \le t \le 3$, where t is measured in hours.

a. Graph the velocity function over the interval $[0, 3]$. Determine when the jogger moves in the positive direction and when she moves in the negative direction.

b. Find the displacement of the jogger (in miles) on the time intervals $[0, 1]$, $[1, 3]$, and $[0, 3]$. Interpret these results.

c. Find the distance traveled over the interval $[0, 3]$.

SOLUTION

a. By solving $v(t) = 2t^2 - 8t + 6 = 2(t - 1)(t - 3) = 0$, we find that the velocity is zero at $t = 1$ and $t = 3$; these values are the t-intercepts of the graph of v, which is an upward-opening parabola with a v-intercept of 6 (Figure 6.3a). The velocity is positive on the interval $0 \le t < 1$, which means the jogger moves in the positive s direction. For $1 < t < 3$, the velocity is negative and the jogger moves in the negative s direction.

b. The displacement (in miles) over the interval $[0, 1]$ is

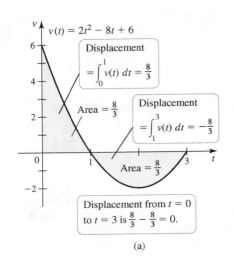

$$s(1) - s(0) = \int_0^1 v(t)\, dt$$

$$= \int_0^1 (2t^2 - 8t + 6)\, dt \qquad \text{Substitute for } v.$$

$$= \left(\frac{2}{3}t^3 - 4t^2 + 6t \right)\Big|_0^1 = \frac{8}{3}. \qquad \text{Evaluate integral.}$$

A similar calculation shows that the displacement over the interval $[1, 3]$ is

$$s(3) - s(1) = \int_1^3 v(t)\, dt = -\frac{8}{3}.$$

Over the interval $[0, 3]$, the displacement is $\frac{8}{3} + \left(-\frac{8}{3}\right) = 0$, which means the jogger returns to the starting point after three hours.

c. From part (b), we can deduce the total distance traveled by the jogger. On the interval $[0, 1]$, the distance traveled is $\frac{8}{3}$ mi; on the interval $[1, 3]$, the distance traveled is also $\frac{8}{3}$ mi. Therefore, the distance traveled on $[0, 3]$ is $\frac{16}{3}$ mi. Alternatively (Figure 6.3b), we can integrate the speed and get the same result:

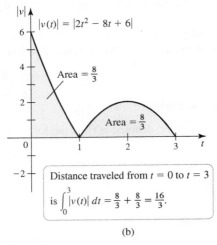

$$\int_0^3 |v(t)|\, dt = \int_0^1 (2t^2 - 8t + 6)\, dt + \int_1^3 (-(2t^2 - 8t + 6))\, dt \qquad \text{Definition of } |v(t)|$$

$$= \left(\frac{2}{3}t^3 - 4t^2 + 6t \right)\Big|_0^1 + \left(-\frac{2}{3}t^3 + 4t^2 - 6t \right)\Big|_1^3 \qquad \text{Evaluate integrals.}$$

$$= \frac{16}{3}. \qquad \text{Simplify.}$$

Related Exercises 7–14 ◄

Figure 6.3

Future Value of the Position Function

To find the displacement of an object, we do not need to know its initial position. For example, whether an object moves from $s = -20$ to $s = -10$ or from $s = 50$ to $s = 60$, its displacement is 10 units. What happens if we are interested in the actual *position* of the object at some future time?

Suppose we know the velocity of an object and its initial position $s(0)$. The goal is to find the position $s(t)$ at some future time $t \geq 0$. The Fundamental Theorem of Calculus gives us the answer directly. Because the position s is an antiderivative of the velocity v, we have

> Note that t is the independent variable of the position function. Therefore, another (dummy) variable, in this case x, must be used as the variable of integration.

$$\int_0^t v(x)\, dx = \int_0^t s'(x)\, dx = s(x)\Big|_0^t = s(t) - s(0).$$

Rearranging this expression leads to the following result.

THEOREM 6.1   Position from Velocity

Given the velocity $v(t)$ of an object moving along a line and its initial position $s(0)$, the position function of the object for future times $t \geq 0$ is

$$\underbrace{s(t)}_{\substack{\text{position} \\ \text{at } t}} = \underbrace{s(0)}_{\substack{\text{initial} \\ \text{position}}} + \underbrace{\int_0^t v(x)\, dx}_{\substack{\text{displacement} \\ \text{over } [0, t]}}.$$

> Theorem 6.1 is a consequence (actually a statement) of the Fundamental Theorem of Calculus.

Theorem 6.1 says that to find the position $s(t)$, we add the displacement over the interval $[0, t]$ to the initial position $s(0)$.

QUICK CHECK 3 Is the position $s(t)$ a number or a function? For fixed times $t = a$ and $t = b$, is the displacement $s(b) - s(a)$ a number or a function? ◄

There are two *equivalent* ways to determine the position function:

• Using antiderivatives (Section 4.9)
• Using Theorem 6.1

The latter method is usually more efficient, but either method produces the same result. The following example illustrates both approaches.

EXAMPLE 2   Position from velocity A block hangs at rest from a massless spring at the origin $(s = 0)$. At $t = 0$, the block is pulled downward $\frac{1}{4}$ m to its initial position $s(0) = -\frac{1}{4}$ and released (Figure 6.4). Its velocity (in m/s) is given by $v(t) = \frac{1}{4} \sin t$, for $t \geq 0$. Assume that the upward direction is positive.

a. Find the position of the block, for $t \geq 0$.

b. Graph the position function, for $0 \leq t \leq 3\pi$.

c. When does the block move through the origin for the first time?

d. When does the block reach its highest point for the first time and what is its position at that time? When does the block return to its lowest point?

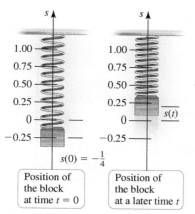

Figure 6.4

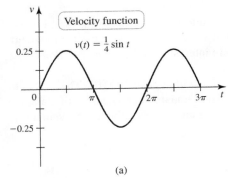

(a)

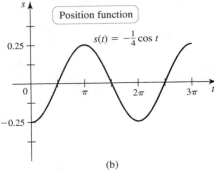

(b)

Figure 6.5

> ➤ It is worth repeating that to find the displacement, we need to know only the velocity. To find the position, we must know both the velocity and the initial position $s(0)$.

SOLUTION

a. The velocity function (Figure 6.5a) is positive for $0 < t < \pi$, which means the block moves in the positive (upward) direction. At $t = \pi$, the block comes to rest momentarily; for $\pi < t < 2\pi$, the block moves in the negative (downward) direction. We let $s(t)$ be the position at time $t \geq 0$ with the initial position $s(0) = -\frac{1}{4}$ m.

Method 1: Using antiderivatives Because the position is an antiderivative of the velocity, we have

$$s(t) = \int v(t)\, dt = \int \frac{1}{4} \sin t\, dt = -\frac{1}{4} \cos t + C.$$

To determine the arbitrary constant C, we substitute the initial condition $s(0) = -\frac{1}{4}$ into the expression for $s(t)$:

$$-\frac{1}{4} = -\frac{1}{4} \cos 0 + C.$$

Solving for C, we find that $C = 0$. Therefore, the position for any time $t \geq 0$ is

$$s(t) = -\frac{1}{4} \cos t.$$

Method 2: Using Theorem 6.1 Alternatively, we may use the relationship

$$s(t) = s(0) + \int_0^t v(x)\, dx.$$

Substituting $v(x) = \frac{1}{4} \sin x$ and $s(0) = -\frac{1}{4}$, the position function is

$$
\begin{aligned}
s(t) &= \underbrace{-\frac{1}{4}}_{s(0)} + \int_0^t \underbrace{\frac{1}{4} \sin x}_{v(x)} dx \\
&= -\frac{1}{4} - \left(\frac{1}{4} \cos x \right)\Big|_0^t \qquad \text{Evaluate integral.} \\
&= -\frac{1}{4} - \frac{1}{4} (\cos t - 1) \qquad \text{Simplify.} \\
&= -\frac{1}{4} \cos t. \qquad \text{Simplify.}
\end{aligned}
$$

b. The graph of the position function is shown in Figure 6.5b. We see that $s(0) = -\frac{1}{4}$ m, as prescribed.

c. The block initially moves in the positive s direction (upward), reaching the origin $(s = 0)$ when $s(t) = -\frac{1}{4} \cos t = 0$. So the block arrives at the origin for the first time when $t = \pi/2$.

d. The block moves in the positive direction and reaches its high point for the first time when $t = \pi$; the position at that moment is $s(\pi) = \frac{1}{4}$ m. The block then reverses direction and moves in the negative (downward) direction, reaching its low point at $t = 2\pi$. This motion repeats every 2π seconds.

Related Exercises 15–24 ◀

QUICK CHECK 4 Without doing further calculations, what are the displacement and distance traveled by the block in Example 2 over the interval $[0, 2\pi]$? ◀

> The terminal velocity of an object depends on its density, shape, size, and the medium through which it falls. Estimates for human beings in free fall in the lower atmosphere vary from 120 mi/hr (54 m/s) to 180 mi/hr (80 m/s).

EXAMPLE 3 **Skydiving** Suppose a skydiver leaps from a hovering helicopter and falls in a straight line. He reaches a terminal velocity of 80 m/s at $t = 0$ and falls for 19 seconds, at which time he opens his parachute. The velocity decreases linearly to 6 m/s over a two-second period and then remains constant until he reaches the ground at $t = 40$ s. The motion is described by the velocity function

$$v(t) = \begin{cases} 80 & \text{if } 0 \le t < 19 \\ 783 - 37t & \text{if } 19 \le t < 21 \\ 6 & \text{if } 21 \le t \le 40. \end{cases}$$

Determine the height above the ground from which the skydiver jumped.

SOLUTION We let the position of the skydiver increase *downward* with the origin ($s = 0$) corresponding to the position of the helicopter. The velocity is positive, so the distance traveled by the skydiver equals the displacement, which is

$$\int_0^{40} |v(t)|\, dt = \int_0^{19} 80\, dt + \int_{19}^{21} (783 - 37t)\, dt + \int_{21}^{40} 6\, dt$$

$$= 80t \Big|_0^{19} + \left(783t - \frac{37t^2}{2}\right)\Big|_{19}^{21} + 6t \Big|_{21}^{40} \qquad \text{Fundamental Theorem}$$

$$= 1720. \qquad \text{Evaluate and simplify.}$$

The skydiver jumped from 1720 m above the ground. Notice that the displacement of the skydiver is the area under the velocity curve (Figure 6.6).

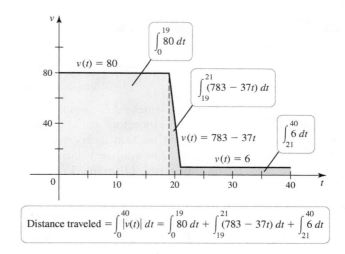

Figure 6.6

Related Exercises 25–26 ◄

QUICK CHECK 5 Suppose (unrealistically) in Example 3 that the velocity of the skydiver is 80 m/s, for $0 \le t < 20$, and then it changes instantaneously to 6 m/s, for $20 \le t \le 40$. Sketch the velocity function and, without integrating, find the distance the skydiver falls in 40 s. ◄

Acceleration

Because the acceleration of an object moving along a line is given by $a(t) = v'(t)$, the relationship between velocity and acceleration is the same as the relationship between position and velocity. Given the acceleration of an object, the change in velocity over an interval $[a, b]$ is

$$\text{change in velocity} = v(b) - v(a) = \int_a^b v'(t)\, dt = \int_a^b a(t)\, dt.$$

Furthermore, if we know the acceleration and initial velocity $v(0)$, then the velocity at future times can also be found.

> ➤ Theorem 6.2 is a consequence of the Fundamental Theorem of Calculus.

THEOREM 6.2   Velocity from Acceleration
Given the acceleration $a(t)$ of an object moving along a line and its initial velocity $v(0)$, the velocity of the object for future times $t \geq 0$ is

$$v(t) = v(0) + \int_0^t a(x)\, dx.$$

EXAMPLE 4   Motion in a gravitational field An artillery shell is fired directly upward with an initial velocity of 300 m/s from a point 30 m above the ground (Figure 6.7). Assume that only the force of gravity acts on the shell and it produces an acceleration of 9.8 m/s². Find the velocity of the shell while it is in the air.

SOLUTION We let the positive direction be upward with the origin ($s = 0$) corresponding to the ground. The initial velocity of the shell is $v(0) = 300$ m/s. The acceleration due to gravity is downward; therefore, $a(t) = -9.8$ m/s². Integrating the acceleration, the velocity is

$$v(t) = \underbrace{v(0)}_{300\text{ m/s}} + \int_0^t \underbrace{a(x)}_{-9.8\text{ m/s}^2}\, dx = 300 + \int_0^t (-9.8)\, dx = 300 - 9.8t.$$

The velocity decreases from its initial value of 300 m/s, reaching zero at the high point of the trajectory when $v(t) = 300 - 9.8t = 0$, or at $t \approx 30.6$ s (Figure 6.8). At this point, the velocity becomes negative, and the shell begins its descent to Earth.

Knowing the velocity function, you could now find the position function using the methods of Example 3.

Related Exercises 27–37 ◀

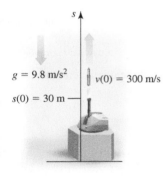

Figure 6.7

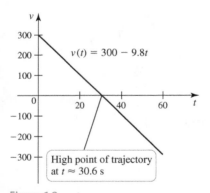

Figure 6.8

Net Change and Future Value

Everything we have said about velocity, position, and displacement carries over to more general situations. Suppose you are interested in some quantity Q that changes over *time*; Q may represent the amount of water in a reservoir, the population of a cell culture, or the amount of a resource that is consumed or produced. If you are given the rate Q' at which Q changes, then integration allows you to calculate either the net change in the quantity Q or the future value of Q.

We argue just as we did for velocity and position: Because $Q(t)$ is an antiderivative of $Q'(t)$, the Fundamental Theorem of Calculus tells us that

$$\int_a^b Q'(t)\, dt = Q(b) - Q(a) = \text{net change in } Q \text{ over } [a, b].$$

> ➤ Note that the units in the integral are consistent. For example, if Q' has units of gallons/second, and t and x have units of seconds, then $Q'(x)\, dx$ has units of (gallons/second)(seconds) = gallons, which are the units of Q.

Geometrically, the net change in Q over the time interval $[a, b]$ is the net area under the graph of Q' over $[a, b]$. We interpret the product $Q'(t)\, dt$ as a change in Q over a small increment of time. Integrating $Q'(t)$ accumulates, or adds up, these small changes over the interval $[a, b]$. The result is the net change in Q between $t = a$ and $t = b$. We see that accumulating the rate of change of a quantity over the interval gives the net change in that quantity over the interval.

Alternatively, suppose we are given both the rate of change Q' and the initial value $Q(0)$. Integrating over the interval $[0, t]$, where $t \geq 0$, we have

$$\int_0^t Q'(x)\, dx = Q(t) - Q(0).$$

Rearranging this equation, we write the value of Q at any future time $t \geq 0$ as

$$Q(t) = \underbrace{Q(0)}_{\substack{\text{initial} \\ \text{value}}} + \underbrace{\int_0^t Q'(x)\, dx}_{\substack{\text{net change} \\ \text{over } [0, t]}}.$$

$\underbrace{Q(t)}_{\substack{\text{future} \\ \text{value}}}$

> At the risk of being repetitious, Theorem 6.3 is also a consequence of the Fundamental Theorem of Calculus. We assume that Q' is an integrable function.

THEOREM 6.3   Net Change and Future Value

Suppose a quantity Q changes over time at a known rate Q'. Then the **net change** in Q between $t = a$ and $t = b > a$ is

$$\underbrace{Q(b) - Q(a)}_{\text{net change in } Q} = \int_a^b Q'(t)\, dt.$$

Given the initial value $Q(0)$, the **future value** of Q at time $t \geq 0$ is

$$Q(t) = Q(0) + \int_0^t Q'(x)\, dx.$$

The correspondences between velocity–displacement problems and more general problems are shown in Table 6.1.

Table 6.1

Velocity–Displacement Problems	General Problems
Position $s(t)$	Quantity $Q(t)$ (such as volume or population)
Velocity: $s'(t) = v(t)$	Rate of change: $Q'(t)$
Displacement: $s(b) - s(a) = \int_a^b v(t)\, dt$	Net change: $Q(b) - Q(a) = \int_a^b Q'(t)\, dt$
Future position: $s(t) = s(0) + \int_0^t v(x)\, dx$	Future value of Q: $Q(t) = Q(0) + \int_0^t Q'(x)\, dx$

EXAMPLE 5   Cell growth A culture of cells in a lab has a population of 100 cells when nutrients are added at time $t = 0$. Suppose the population $N(t)$ (in cells/hr) increases at a rate given by

> Although N is a positive integer (the number of cells), we treat it as a continuous variable in this example.

$$N'(t) = 90e^{-0.1t}.$$

Find $N(t)$, for $t \geq 0$.

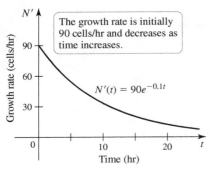

Figure 6.9

SOLUTION As shown in Figure 6.9, the growth rate is large when t is small (plenty of food and space) and decreases as t increases. Knowing that the initial population is $N(0) = 100$ cells, we can find the population $N(t)$ at any future time $t \geq 0$ using Theorem 6.3:

$$N(t) = N(0) + \int_0^t N'(x)\, dx$$

$$= \underbrace{100}_{N(0)} + \int_0^t \underbrace{90e^{-0.1x}}_{N'(x)}\, dx$$

$$= 100 + \left[\left(\frac{90}{-0.1} \right) e^{-0.1x} \right] \Big|_0^t \qquad \text{Fundamental Theorem}$$

$$= 1000 - 900e^{-0.1t}. \qquad \text{Simplify.}$$

The graph of the population function (Figure 6.10) shows that the population increases, but at a decreasing rate. Note that the initial condition $N(0) = 100$ cells is satisfied and that the population size approaches 1000 cells as $t \to \infty$.

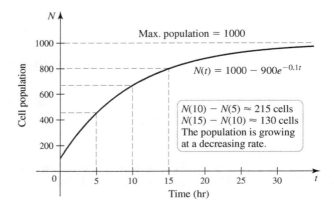

Figure 6.10

Related Exercises 38–44 ◀

EXAMPLE 6   Production costs A book publisher estimates that the marginal cost of a particular title (in dollars/book) is given by

$$C'(x) = 12 - 0.0002x,$$

where $0 \leq x \leq 50{,}000$ is the number of books printed. What is the cost of producing the 12,001st through the 15,000th book?

SOLUTION Recall from Section 3.6 that the cost function $C(x)$ is the cost required to produce x units of a product. The marginal cost $C'(x)$ is the approximate cost of producing one additional unit after x units have already been produced. The cost of producing books $x = 12{,}001$ through $x = 15{,}000$ is the cost of producing 15,000 books minus the cost of producing the first 12,000 books. Therefore, the cost in dollars of producing books 12,001 through 15,000 is

▶ Although x is a positive integer (the number of books produced), we treat it as a continuous variable in this example.

$$C(15{,}000) - C(12{,}000) = \int_{12{,}000}^{15{,}000} C'(x)\, dx$$

$$= \int_{12{,}000}^{15{,}000} (12 - 0.0002x)\, dx \qquad \text{Substitute for } C'(x).$$

$$= (12x - 0.0001x^2) \Big|_{12{,}000}^{15{,}000} \qquad \text{Fundamental Theorem}$$

$$= 27{,}900. \qquad \text{Simplify.}$$

QUICK CHECK 6 Is the cost of increasing the production from 9000 books to 12,000 books in Example 6 more or less than the cost of increasing the production from 12,000 books to 15,000 books? Explain. ◀

Related Exercises 45–48 ◀

SECTION 6.1 EXERCISES

Review Questions

1. Explain the meaning of position, displacement, and distance traveled as they apply to an object moving along a line.

2. Suppose the velocity of an object moving along a line is positive. Are displacement and distance traveled equal? Explain.

3. Given the velocity function v of an object moving along a line, explain how definite integrals can be used to find the displacement of the object.

4. Explain how to use definite integrals to find the net change in a quantity, given the rate of change of that quantity.

5. Given the rate of change of a quantity Q and its initial value $Q(0)$, explain how to find the value of Q at a future time $t \geq 0$.

6. What is the result of integrating a population growth rate between times $t = a$ and $t = b$, where $b > a$?

Basic Skills

7. **Displacement and distance from velocity** Consider the graph shown in the figure, which gives the velocity of an object moving along a line. Assume time is measured in hours and distance is measured in miles. The areas of three regions bounded by the velocity curve and the t-axis are also given.

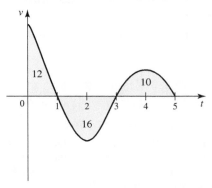

a. On what intervals is the object moving in the positive direction?
b. What is the displacement of the object over the interval $[0, 3]$?
c. What is the total distance traveled by the object over the interval $[1, 5]$?
d. What is the displacement of the object over the interval $[0, 5]$?
e. Describe the position of the object relative to its initial position after 5 hours.

8. **Displacement and distance from velocity** Consider the velocity function shown below of an object moving along a line. Assume time is measured in seconds and distance is measured in meters. The areas of four regions bounded by the velocity curve and the t-axis are also given.

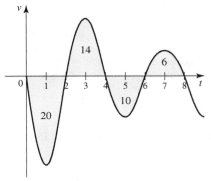

a. On what intervals is the object moving in the negative direction?
b. What is the displacement of the object over the interval $[2, 6]$?
c. How far does the object travel over the interval $[0, 6]$?
d. What is the displacement of the object over the interval $[0, 8]$?
e. Describe the position of the object relative to its initial position after 8 hours.

T 9–14. Displacement from velocity *Assume t is time measured in seconds and velocities have units of m/s.*

a. *Graph the velocity function over the given interval. Then determine when the motion is in the positive direction and when it is in the negative direction.*
b. *Find the displacement over the given interval.*
c. *Find the distance traveled over the given interval.*

9. $v(t) = 6 - 2t$ on $0 \leq t \leq 6$

10. $v(t) = 10 \sin 2t$ on $0 \leq t \leq 2\pi$

11. $v(t) = t^2 - 6t + 8$ on $0 \leq t \leq 5$

12. $v(t) = -t^2 + 5t - 4$ on $0 \leq t \leq 5$

13. $v(t) = t^3 - 5t^2 + 6t$ on $0 \leq t \leq 5$

14. $v(t) = 50e^{-2t}$ on $0 \leq t \leq 4$

T 15–20. Position from velocity *Consider an object moving along a line with the following velocities and initial positions.*

a. *Graph the velocity function on the given interval and determine when the object is moving in the positive direction and when it is moving in the negative direction.*
b. *Determine the position function, for $t \geq 0$, using both the antiderivative method and the Fundamental Theorem of Calculus (Theorem 6.1). Check for agreement between the two methods.*
c. *Graph the position function on the given interval.*

15. $v(t) = \sin t$ on $[0, 2\pi]$; $s(0) = 1$

16. $v(t) = -t^3 + 3t^2 - 2t$ on $[0, 3]$; $s(0) = 4$

17. $v(t) = 6 - 2t$ on $[0, 5]$; $s(0) = 0$

18. $v(t) = 3 \sin \pi t$ on $[0, 4]$; $s(0) = 1$

19. $v(t) = 9 - t^2$ on $[0, 4]$; $s(0) = -2$

20. $v(t) = 1/(t + 1)$ on $[0, 8]$; $s(0) = -4$

T 21. Oscillating motion A mass hanging from a spring is set in motion, and its ensuing velocity is given by $v(t) = 2\pi \cos \pi t$, for $t \geq 0$. Assume that the positive direction is upward and that $s(0) = 0$.

a. Determine the position function, for $t \geq 0$.
b. Graph the position function on the interval $[0, 4]$.
c. At what times does the mass reach its low point the first three times?
d. At what times does the mass reach its high point the first three times?

22. **Cycling distance** A cyclist rides down a long straight road at a velocity (in m/min) given by $v(t) = 400 - 20t$, for $0 \leq t \leq 10$, where t is measured in minutes.

a. How far does the cyclist travel in the first 5 min?
b. How far does the cyclist travel in the first 10 min?
c. How far has the cyclist traveled when her velocity is 250 m/min?

23. Flying into a headwind The velocity (in mi/hr) of an airplane flying into a headwind is given by $v(t) = 30(16 - t^2)$, for $0 \le t \le 3$. Assume that $s(0) = 0$ and t is measured in hours.

   a. Determine and graph the position function, for $0 \le t \le 3$.

   b. How far does the airplane travel in the first 2 hr?

   c. How far has the airplane traveled at the instant its velocity reaches 400 mi/hr?

24. Day hike The velocity (in mi/hr) of a hiker walking along a straight trail is given by $v(t) = 3 \sin^2(\pi t/2)$, for $0 \le t \le 4$. Assume that $s(0) = 0$ and t is measured in hours.

   a. Determine and graph the position function, for $0 \le t \le 4$. (*Hint:* $\sin^2 t = \frac{1}{2}(1 - \cos 2t)$.)

   b. What is the distance traveled by the hiker in the first 15 min of the hike?

   c. What is the hiker's position at $t = 3$?

25. Piecewise velocity The velocity of a (fast) automobile on a straight highway is given by the function

$$v(t) = \begin{cases} 3t & \text{if } 0 \le t < 20 \\ 60 & \text{if } 20 \le t < 45 \\ 240 - 4t & \text{if } t \ge 45, \end{cases}$$

where t is measured in seconds and v has units of m/s.

   a. Graph the velocity function, for $0 \le t \le 70$. When is the velocity a maximum? When is the velocity zero?

   b. What is the distance traveled by the automobile in the first 30 s?

   c. What is the distance traveled by the automobile in the first 60 s?

   d. What is the position of the automobile when $t = 75$?

26. Probe speed A data collection probe is dropped from a stationary balloon, and it falls with a velocity (in m/s) given by $v(t) = 9.8t$, neglecting air resistance. After 10 s, a chute deploys and the probe immediately slows to a constant speed of 10 m/s, which it maintains until it enters the ocean.

   a. Graph the velocity function.

   b. How far does the probe fall in the first 30 s after it is released?

   c. If the probe was released from an altitude of 3 km, when does it enter the ocean?

27–34. Position and velocity from acceleration *Find the position and velocity of an object moving along a straight line with the given acceleration, initial velocity, and initial position.*

27. $a(t) = -32, v(0) = 70, s(0) = 10$

28. $a(t) = -32, v(0) = 50, s(0) = 0$

29. $a(t) = -9.8, v(0) = 20, s(0) = 0$

30. $a(t) = e^{-t}, v(0) = 60, s(0) = 40$

31. $a(t) = -0.01t, v(0) = 10, s(0) = 0$

32. $a(t) = \dfrac{20}{(t + 2)^2}, v(0) = 20, s(0) = 10$

33. $a(t) = \cos 2t, v(0) = 5, s(0) = 7$

34. $a(t) = \dfrac{2t}{(t^2 + 1)^2}, v(0) = 0, s(0) = 0$

35. Acceleration A drag racer accelerates at $a(t) = 88$ ft/s². Assume that $v(0) = 0$, $s(0) = 0$, and t is measured in seconds.

   a. Determine and graph the position function, for $t \ge 0$.

   b. How far does the racer travel in the first 4 seconds?

   c. At this rate, how long will it take the racer to travel $\frac{1}{4}$ mi?

   d. How long does it take the racer to travel 300 ft?

   e. How far has the racer traveled when it reaches a speed of 178 ft/s?

36. Deceleration A car slows down with an acceleration of $a(t) = -15$ ft/s². Assume that $v(0) = 60$ ft/s, $s(0) = 0$, and t is measured in seconds.

   a. Determine and graph the position function, for $t \ge 0$.

   b. How far does the car travel in the time it takes to come to rest?

37. Approaching a station At $t = 0$, a train approaching a station begins decelerating from a speed of 80 mi/hr according to the acceleration function $a(t) = -1280(1 + 8t)^{-3}$, where $t \ge 0$ is measured in hours. How far does the train travel between $t = 0$ and $t = 0.2$? Between $t = 0.2$ and $t = 0.4$? The units of acceleration are mi/hr².

38. Peak oil extraction The owners of an oil reserve begin extracting oil at time $t = 0$. Based on estimates of the reserves, suppose the projected extraction rate is given by $Q'(t) = 3t^2(40 - t)^2$, where $0 \le t \le 40$, Q is measured in millions of barrels, and t is measured in years.

   a. When does the peak extraction rate occur?

   b. How much oil is extracted in the first 10, 20, and 30 years?

   c. What is the total amount of oil extracted in 40 years?

   d. Is one-fourth of the total oil extracted in the first one-fourth of the extraction period? Explain.

39. Oil production An oil refinery produces oil at a variable rate given by

$$Q'(t) = \begin{cases} 800 & \text{if } 0 \le t < 30 \\ 2600 - 60t & \text{if } 30 \le t < 40 \\ 200 & \text{if } t \ge 40, \end{cases}$$

where t is measured in days and Q is measured in barrels.

   a. How many barrels are produced in the first 35 days?

   b. How many barrels are produced in the first 50 days?

   c. Without using integration, determine the number of barrels produced over the interval $[60, 80]$.

40–43. Population growth

40. Starting with an initial value of $P(0) = 55$, the population of a prairie dog community grows at a rate of $P'(t) = 20 - t/5$ (prairie dogs/month), for $0 \le t \le 200$, where t is measured in months.

   a. What is the population 6 months later?

   b. Find the population $P(t)$, for $0 \le t \le 200$.

41. When records were first kept ($t = 0$), the population of a rural town was 250 people. During the following years, the population grew at a rate of $P'(t) = 30(1 + \sqrt{t})$, where t is measured in years.

   a. What is the population after 20 years?

   b. Find the population $P(t)$ at any time $t \ge 0$.

42. The population of a community of foxes is observed to fluctuate on a 10-year cycle due to variations in the availability of prey. When population measurements began ($t = 0$), the population was 35 foxes. The growth rate in units of foxes/year was observed to be

$$P'(t) = 5 + 10 \sin \frac{\pi t}{5}.$$

   a. What is the population 15 years later? 35 years later?

   b. Find the population $P(t)$ at any time $t \ge 0$.

43. A culture of bacteria in a Petri dish has an initial population of 1500 cells and grows at a rate (in cells/day) of $N'(t) = 100e^{-0.25t}$. Assume t is measured in days.

  a. What is the population after 20 days? After 40 days?
  b. Find the population $N(t)$ at any time $t \geq 0$.

44. Flow rates in the Spokane River The daily discharge of the Spokane River as it flows through Spokane, Washington, in April and June is modeled by the functions

$$r_1(t) = 0.25t^2 + 37.46t + 722.47 \ (\text{April}) \quad \text{and}$$
$$r_2(t) = 0.90t^2 - 69.06t + 2053.12 \ (\text{June}),$$

where the discharge is measured in millions of cubic feet per day and $t = 1$ corresponds to the first day of the month (see figure).

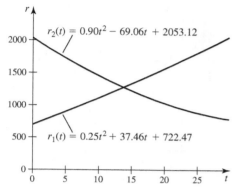

  a. Determine the total amount of water that flows through Spokane in April (30 days).
  b. Determine the total amount of water that flows through Spokane in June (30 days).
  c. The Spokane River flows out of Lake Coeur d'Alene, which contains approximately $0.67 \ \text{mi}^3$ of water. Determine the percentage of Lake Coeur d'Alene's volume that flows through Spokane in April and June.

45–48. Marginal cost *Consider the following marginal cost functions.*

a. *Find the additional cost incurred in dollars when production is increased from 100 units to 150 units.*
b. *Find the additional cost incurred in dollars when production is increased from 500 units to 550 units.*

45. $C'(x) = 2000 - 0.5x$ **46.** $C'(x) = 200 - 0.05x$

47. $C'(x) = 300 + 10x - 0.01x^2$

48. $C'(x) = 3000 - x - 0.001x^2$

Further Explorations

49. Explain why or why not Determine whether the following statements are true and give an explanation or counterexample.

  a. The distance traveled by an object moving along a line is the same as the displacement of the object.
  b. When the velocity is positive on an interval, the displacement and the distance traveled on that interval are equal.
  c. Consider a tank that is filled and drained at a flow rate of $V'(t) = 1 - t^2/100$ (gal/min), for $t \geq 0$, where t is measured in minutes. It follows that the volume of water in the tank increases for 10 min and then decreases until the tank is empty.
  d. A particular marginal cost function has the property that it is positive and decreasing. The cost of increasing production from A units to $2A$ units is greater than the cost of increasing production from $2A$ units to $3A$ units.

50–51. Velocity graphs *The figures show velocity functions for motion along a straight line. Assume the motion begins with an initial position of $s(0) = 0$. Determine the following:*

a. *The displacement between $t = 0$ and $t = 5$*
b. *The distance traveled between $t = 0$ and $t = 5$*
c. *The position at $t = 5$*
d. *A piecewise function for $s(t)$*

50.

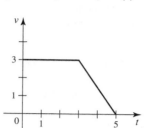

51.

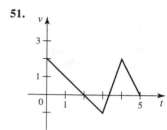

52–55. Equivalent constant velocity *Consider the following velocity functions. In each case, complete the sentence: The same distance could have been traveled over the given time period at a <u>constant</u> velocity of _____.*

52. $v(t) = 2t + 6$, for $0 \leq t \leq 8$

53. $v(t) = 1 - t^2/16$, for $0 \leq t \leq 4$

54. $v(t) = 2 \sin t$, for $0 \leq t \leq \pi$

55. $v(t) = t(25 - t^2)^{1/2}$, for $0 \leq t \leq 5$

56. Where do they meet? Kelly started at noon ($t = 0$) riding a bike from Niwot to Berthoud, a distance of 20 km, with velocity $v(t) = 15/(t + 1)^2$ (decreasing because of fatigue). Sandy started at noon ($t = 0$) riding a bike in the opposite direction from Berthoud to Niwot with velocity $u(t) = 20/(t + 1)^2$ (also decreasing because of fatigue). Assume distance is measured in kilometers and time is measured in hours.

  a. Make a graph of Kelly's distance from Niwot as a function of time.
  b. Make a graph of Sandy's distance from Berthoud as a function of time.
  c. When do they meet? How far has each person traveled when they meet?
  d. More generally, if the riders' speeds are $v(t) = A/(t + 1)^2$ and $u(t) = B/(t + 1)^2$ and the distance between the towns is D, what conditions on A, B, and D must be met to ensure that the riders will pass each other?
  e. Looking ahead: With the velocity functions given in part (d), make a conjecture about the maximum distance each person can ride (given unlimited time).

57. Bike race Theo and Sasha start at the same place on a straight road, riding bikes with the following velocities (measured in mi/hr). Assume t is measured in hours.

  Theo: $v_T(t) = 10$, for $t \geq 0$

  Sasha: $v_S(t) = 15t$, for $0 \leq t \leq 1$ and $v_S(t) = 15$, for $t > 1$

  a. Graph the velocity functions for both riders.
  b. If the riders ride for 1 hr, who rides farther? Interpret your answer geometrically using the graphs of part (a).
  c. If the riders ride for 2 hr, who rides farther? Interpret your answer geometrically using the graphs of part (a).

d. Which rider arrives first at the 10-, 15-, and 20-mile markers of the race? Interpret your answer geometrically using the graphs of part (a).

e. Suppose Sasha gives Theo a head start of 0.2 mi and the riders ride for 20 mi. Who wins the race?

f. Suppose Sasha gives Theo a head start of 0.2 hr and the riders ride for 20 mi. Who wins the race?

58. Two runners At noon ($t = 0$), Alicia starts running along a long straight road at 4 mi/hr. Her velocity decreases according to the function $v(t) = 4/(t + 1)$, for $t \geq 0$. At noon, Boris also starts running along the same road with a 2-mi head start on Alicia; his velocity is given by $u(t) = 2/(t + 1)$, for $t \geq 0$. Assume t is measured in hours.

a. Find the position functions for Alicia and Boris, where $s = 0$ corresponds to Alicia's starting point.

b. When, if ever, does Alicia overtake Boris?

59. Running in a wind A strong west wind blows across a circular running track. Abe and Bess start running at the south end of the track, and at the same time, Abe starts running clockwise and Bess starts running counterclockwise. Abe runs with a speed (in units of mi/hr) given by $u(\varphi) = 3 - 2 \cos \varphi$ and Bess runs with a speed given by $v(\theta) = 3 + 2 \cos \theta$, where φ and θ are the central angles of the runners.

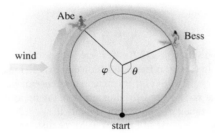

a. Graph the speed functions u and v, and explain why they describe the runners' speeds (in light of the wind).

b. Compute the average value of u and v with respect to the central angle.

c. Challenge: If the track has a radius of $\frac{1}{10}$ mi, how long does it take each runner to complete one lap and who wins the race?

Applications

60. Filling a tank A 2000-liter cistern is empty when water begins flowing into it (at $t = 0$) at a rate (in L/min) given by $Q'(t) = 3\sqrt{t}$, where t is measured in minutes.

a. How much water flows into the cistern in 1 hour?

b. Find and graph the function that gives the amount of water in the tank at any time $t \geq 0$.

c. When will the tank be full?

61. Depletion of natural resources Suppose that $r(t) = r_0 e^{-kt}$, with $k > 0$, is the rate at which a nation extracts oil, where $r_0 = 10^7$ barrels/yr is the current rate of extraction. Suppose also that the estimate of the total oil reserve is 2×10^9 barrels.

a. Find $Q(t)$, the total amount of oil extracted by the nation after t years.

b. Evaluate $\lim_{t \to \infty} Q(t)$ and explain the meaning of this limit.

c. Find the minimum decay constant k for which the total oil reserves will last forever.

d. Suppose $r_0 = 2 \times 10^7$ barrels/yr and the decay constant k is the minimum value found in part (c). How long will the total oil reserves last?

62. Snowplow problem With snow on the ground and falling at a constant rate, a snowplow began plowing down a long straight road at noon. The plow traveled twice as far in the first hour as it did in the second hour. At what time did the snow start falling? Assume the plowing rate is inversely proportional to the depth of the snow.

Ⓣ 63. Filling a reservoir A reservoir with a capacity of 2500 m³ is filled with a single inflow pipe. The reservoir is empty when the inflow pipe is opened at $t = 0$. Letting $Q(t)$ be the amount of water in the reservoir at time t, the flow rate of water into the reservoir (in m³/hr) oscillates on a 24-hr cycle (see figure) and is given by

$$Q'(t) = 20\left(1 + \cos \frac{\pi t}{12}\right).$$

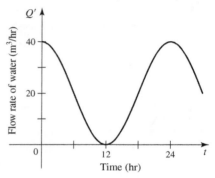

a. How much water flows into the reservoir in the first 2 hr?

b. Find and graph the function that gives the amount of water in the reservoir over the interval $[0, t]$, where $t \geq 0$.

c. When is the reservoir full?

64. Blood flow A typical human heart pumps 70 mL of blood with each stroke (stroke volume). Assuming a heart rate of 60 beats/min (1 beat/s), a reasonable model for the outflow rate of the heart is $V'(t) = 70(1 + \sin 2\pi t)$, where $V(t)$ is the amount of blood (in milliliters) pumped over the interval $[0, t]$, $V(0) = 0$, and t is measured in seconds.

a. Graph the outflow rate function.

b. Verify that the amount of blood pumped over a one-second interval is 70 mL.

c. Find the function that gives the total blood pumped between $t = 0$ and a future time $t > 0$.

d. What is the cardiac output over a period of 1 min? (Use calculus; then check your answer with algebra.)

65. Air flow in the lungs A simple model (with different parameters for different people) for the flow of air in and out of the lungs is

$$V'(t) = -\frac{\pi}{2} \sin \frac{\pi t}{2},$$

where $V(t)$ (measured in liters) is the volume of air in the lungs at time $t \geq 0$, t is measured in seconds, and $t = 0$ corresponds to a time at which the lungs are full and exhalation begins. Only a fraction of the air in the lungs in exchanged with each breath. The amount that is exchanged is called the *tidal volume*.

a. Find and graph the volume function V assuming that $V(0) = 6$ L.

b. What is the breathing rate in breaths/min?

c. What is the tidal volume and what is the total capacity of the lungs?

66. Oscillating growth rates Some species have growth rates that oscillate with an (approximately) constant period P. Consider the growth rate function

$$N'(t) = r + A \sin \frac{2\pi t}{P}$$

where A and r are constants with units of individuals/yr, and t is measured in years. A species becomes extinct if its population ever reaches 0 after $t = 0$.

a. Suppose $P = 10$, $A = 20$, and $r = 0$. If the initial population is $N(0) = 10$, does the population ever become extinct? Explain.

b. Suppose $P = 10$, $A = 20$, and $r = 0$. If the initial population is $N(0) = 100$, does the population ever become extinct? Explain.

c. Suppose $P = 10$, $A = 50$, and $r = 5$. If the initial population is $N(0) = 10$, does the population ever become extinct? Explain.

d. Suppose $P = 10$, $A = 50$, and $r = -5$. Find the initial population $N(0)$ needed to ensure that the population never becomes extinct.

67. Power and energy Power and energy are often used interchangeably, but they are quite different. **Energy** is what makes matter move or heat up and is measured in units of **joules** (J) or **Calories** (Cal), where 1 Cal = 4184 J. One hour of walking consumes roughly 10^6 J, or 250 Cal. On the other hand, **power** is the rate at which energy is used and is measured in **watts** (W; 1 W = 1 J/s). Other useful units of power are **kilowatts** (1 kW = 10^3 W) and **megawatts** (1 MW = 10^6 W). If energy is used at a rate of 1 kW for 1 hr, the total amount of energy used is 1 **kilowatt-hour** (kWh), which is 3.6×10^6 J.

Suppose the power function of a large city over a 24-hr period is given by

$$P(t) = E'(t) = 300 - 200 \sin \frac{\pi t}{12},$$

where P is measured in megawatts and $t = 0$ corresponds to 6:00 P.M. (see figure).

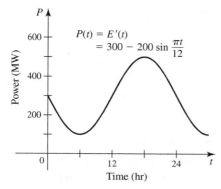

a. How much energy is consumed by this city in a typical 24-hr period? Express the answer in megawatt-hours and in joules.

b. Burning 1 kg of coal produces about 450 kWh of energy. How many kg of coal are required to meet the energy needs of the city for 1 day? For 1 year?

c. Fission of 1 g of uranium-235 (U-235) produces about 16,000 kWh of energy. How many grams of uranium are needed to meet the energy needs of the city for 1 day? For 1 year?

d. A typical wind turbine can generate electrical power at a rate of about 200 kW. Approximately how many wind turbines are needed to meet the average energy needs of the city?

68. Variable gravity At Earth's surface, the acceleration due to gravity is approximately $g = 9.8$ m/s^2 (with local variations). However, the acceleration decreases with distance from the surface according to Newton's law of gravitation. At a distance of y meters from Earth's surface, the acceleration is given by

$$a(y) = -\frac{g}{(1 + y/R)^2},$$

where $R = 6.4 \times 10^6$ m is the radius of Earth.

a. Suppose a projectile is launched upward with an initial velocity of v_0 m/s. Let $v(t)$ be its velocity and $y(t)$ its height (in meters) above the surface t seconds after the launch. Neglecting forces such as air resistance, explain why $\frac{dv}{dt} = a(y)$ and $\frac{dy}{dt} = v(t)$.

b. Use the Chain Rule to show that $\frac{dv}{dt} = \frac{1}{2}\frac{d}{dy}(v^2)$.

c. Show that the equation of motion for the projectile is $\frac{1}{2}\frac{d}{dy}(v^2) = a(y)$, where $a(y)$ is given previously.

d. Integrate both sides of the equation in part (c) with respect to y using the fact that when $y = 0$, $v = v_0$. Show that

$$\frac{1}{2}(v^2 - v_0^2) = g R\left(\frac{1}{1 + y/R} - 1\right).$$

e. When the projectile reaches its maximum height, $v = 0$. Use this fact to determine that the maximum height is

$$y_{max} = \frac{Rv_0^2}{2gR - v_0^2}.$$

f. Graph y_{max} as a function of v_0. What is the maximum height when $v_0 = 500$ m/s, 1500 m/s, and 5 km/s?

g. Show that the value of v_0 needed to put the projectile into orbit (called the escape velocity) is $\sqrt{2gR}$.

Additional Exercises

69–72. Another look at the Fundamental Theorem

69. Suppose that f and g have continuous derivatives on an interval $[a, b]$. Prove that if $f(a) = g(a)$ and $f(b) = g(b)$, then $\int_a^b f'(x)\, dx = \int_a^b g'(x)\, dx$.

70. Use Exercise 69 to prove that if two runners start and finish at the same time and place, then *regardless of the velocities at which they run*, their displacements are equal.

71. Use Exercise 69 to prove that if two trails start at the same place and finish at the same place, then *regardless of the ups and downs of the trails*, they have the same net change in elevation.

72. Without evaluating integrals, prove that

$$\int_0^2 \frac{d}{dx}(12 \sin \pi x^2)\, dx = \int_0^2 \frac{d}{dx}(x^{10}(2 - x)^3)\, dx.$$

QUICK CHECK ANSWERS

1. Displacement $= -20$ mi (20 mi south); distance traveled $= 100$ mi   **2.** Suppose the object moves in the positive direction, for $0 \le t \le 3$, and then moves in the negative direction, for $3 < t \le 5$.   **3.** A function; a number   **4.** Displacement $= 0$; distance traveled $= 1$ **5.** 1720 m   **6.** The production cost would increase more between 9000 and 12,000 books than between 12,000 and 15,000 books. Graph C' and look at the area under the curve. ◄

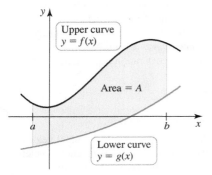

Figure 6.11

6.2 Regions Between Curves

In this section, the method for finding the area of a region bounded by a single curve is generalized to regions bounded by two or more curves. Consider two functions f and g continuous on an interval $[a, b]$ on which $f(x) \geq g(x)$ (Figure 6.11). The goal is to find the area A of the region bounded by the two curves and the vertical lines $x = a$ and $x = b$.

Once again, we rely on the *slice-and-sum* strategy (Section 5.2) for finding areas by Riemann sums. The interval $[a, b]$ is partitioned into n subintervals using uniformly spaced grid points separated by a distance $\Delta x = (b - a)/n$ (Figure 6.12). On each subinterval, we build a rectangle extending from the lower curve to the upper curve. On the kth subinterval, a point x_k^* is chosen, and the height of the corresponding rectangle is taken to be $f(x_k^*) - g(x_k^*)$. Therefore, the area of the kth rectangle is $(f(x_k^*) - g(x_k^*)) \Delta x$ (Figure 6.13). Summing the areas of the n rectangles gives an approximation to the area of the region between the curves:

$$A \approx \sum_{k=1}^{n} (f(x_k^*) - g(x_k^*)) \, \Delta x.$$

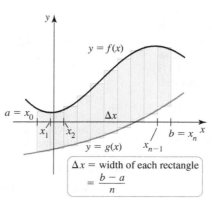

Figure 6.12

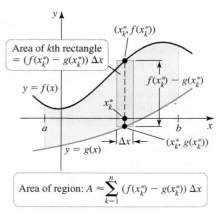

Figure 6.13

As the number of grid points increases, Δx approaches zero and these sums approach the area of the region between the curves; that is,

$$A = \lim_{n \to \infty} \sum_{k=1}^{n} (f(x_k^*) - g(x_k^*)) \Delta x.$$

The limit of these Riemann sums is a definite integral of the function $f - g$.

▶ It is helpful to interpret the area formula: $f(x) - g(x)$ is the length of a rectangle and dx represents its width. We sum (integrate) the areas of the rectangles $(f(x) - g(x)) \, dx$ to obtain the area of the region.

DEFINITION Area of a Region Between Two Curves

Suppose that f and g are continuous functions with $f(x) \geq g(x)$ on the interval $[a, b]$. The area of the region bounded by the graphs of f and g on $[a, b]$ is

$$A = \int_a^b (f(x) - g(x)) \, dx.$$

QUICK CHECK 1 In the area formula for a region between two curves, verify that if the lower curve is $g(x) = 0$, the formula becomes the usual formula for the area of the region bounded by $y = f(x)$ and the x-axis. ◀

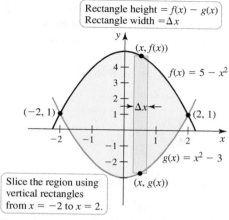

Rectangle height = $f(x) - g(x)$
Rectangle width = Δx

Slice the region using vertical rectangles from $x = -2$ to $x = 2$.

Figure 6.14

EXAMPLE 1 **Area between curves** Find the area of the region bounded by the graphs of $f(x) = 5 - x^2$ and $g(x) = x^2 - 3$ (Figure 6.14).

SOLUTION A key step in the solution of many area problems is finding the intersection points of the boundary curves, which often determine the limits of integration. The intersection points of these two curves satisfy the equation $5 - x^2 = x^2 - 3$. The solutions of this equation are $x = -2$ and $x = 2$, which become the lower and upper limits of integration, respectively. The graph of f is the upper curve and the graph of g is the lower curve on the interval $[-2, 2]$. Therefore, the area of the region is

$$A = \int_{-2}^{2} (\underbrace{(5 - x^2)}_{f(x)} - \underbrace{(x^2 - 3)}_{g(x)}) \, dx \qquad \text{Substitute for } f \text{ and } g.$$

$$= 2 \int_{0}^{2} (8 - 2x^2) \, dx \qquad \text{Simplify and use symmetry.}$$

$$= 2 \left(8x - \frac{2}{3}x^3 \right) \Big|_{0}^{2} \qquad \text{Fundamental Theorem}$$

$$= \frac{64}{3}. \qquad \text{Simplify.}$$

Notice how the symmetry of the problem simplifies the integration. Additionally, note that the area formula $A = \int_{a}^{b} (f(x) - g(x)) \, dx$ is valid even if one or both curves lie below the x-axis, as long as $f(x) \geq g(x)$ on $[a, b]$.

Related Exercises 5–14 ◄

QUICK CHECK 2 Interpret the area formula when written in the form $A = \int_{a}^{b} f(x) \, dx - \int_{a}^{b} g(x) \, dx$, where $f(x) \geq g(x) \geq 0$ on $[a, b]$. ◄

EXAMPLE 2 **Compound region** Find the area of the region bounded by the graphs of $f(x) = -x^2 + 3x + 6$ and $g(x) = |2x|$ (Figure 6.15a).

SOLUTION The lower boundary of the region is bounded by two different branches of the absolute value function. In situations like this, the region is divided into two (or more) subregions whose areas are found independently and then summed; these subregions are labeled R_1 and R_2 (Figure 6.15b). By the definition of absolute value,

$$g(x) = |2x| = \begin{cases} 2x & \text{if } x \geq 0 \\ -2x & \text{if } x < 0. \end{cases}$$

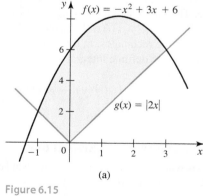

$$\text{Area} = \int_{-1}^{0} ((-x^2 + 3x + 6) - (-2x)) \, dx$$

$$\text{Area} = \int_{0}^{3} ((-x^2 + 3x + 6) - 2x) \, dx$$

(a) (b)

Figure 6.15

➤ The solution $x = 6$ corresponds to the intersection of the parabola $y = -x^2 + 3x + 6$ and the line $y = -2x$ in the fourth quadrant, not shown in Figure 6.15 because $g(x) = -2x$ only when $x < 0$.

The left intersection point of f and g satisfies $-2x = -x^2 + 3x + 6$, or $x^2 - 5x - 6 = 0$. Solving for x, we find that $(x + 1)(x - 6) = 0$, which implies $x = -1$ or $x = 6$; only the first solution is relevant. The right intersection point of f and g satisfies $2x = -x^2 + 3x + 6$; you should verify that the relevant solution in this case is $x = 3$.

Given these points of intersection, we see that the region R_1 is bounded by $y = -x^2 + 3x + 6$ and $y = -2x$ on the interval $[-1, 0]$. Similarly, region R_2 is bounded by $y = -x^2 + 3x + 6$ and $y = 2x$ on $[0, 3]$ (Figure 6.15b). Therefore,

$$A = \underbrace{\int_{-1}^{0} ((-x^2 + 3x + 6) - (-2x))\, dx}_{\text{area of region } R_1} + \underbrace{\int_{0}^{3} ((-x^2 + 3x + 6) - 2x)\, dx}_{\text{area of region } R_2}$$

$$= \int_{-1}^{0} (-x^2 + 5x + 6)\, dx + \int_{0}^{3} (-x^2 + x + 6)\, dx \qquad \text{Simplify.}$$

$$= \left(-\frac{x^3}{3} + \frac{5}{2}x^2 + 6x \right)\Big|_{-1}^{0} + \left(-\frac{x^3}{3} + \frac{1}{2}x^2 + 6x \right)\Big|_{0}^{3} \qquad \text{Fundamental Theorem}$$

$$= 0 - \left(\frac{1}{3} + \frac{5}{2} - 6 \right) + \left(-9 + \frac{9}{2} + 18 \right) - 0 = \frac{50}{3}. \qquad \text{Simplify.}$$

Related Exercises 15–22 ◄

Integrating with Respect to y

There are occasions when it is convenient to reverse the roles of x and y. Consider the regions shown in Figure 6.16 that are bounded by the graphs of $x = f(y)$ and $x = g(y)$, where $f(y) \geq g(y)$, for $c \leq y \leq d$ (which implies that the graph of f lies to the right of the graph of g). The lower and upper boundaries of the regions are $y = c$ and $y = d$, respectively.

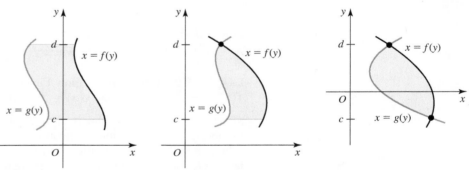

Figure 6.16

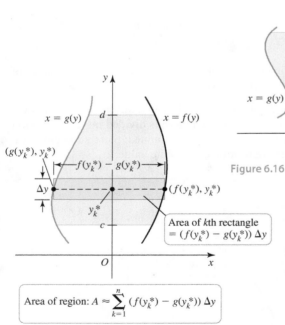

Area of region: $A \approx \sum_{k=1}^{n} (f(y_k^*) - g(y_k^*))\, \Delta y$

Figure 6.17

▶ This area formula is analogous to the one given on page 412; it is now expressed with respect to the y-axis. In this case, $f(y) - g(y)$ is the length of a rectangle and dy represents its width. We sum (integrate) the areas of the rectangles $(f(y) - g(y))\, dy$ to obtain the area of the region.

In cases such as these, we treat y as the independent variable and divide the interval $[c, d]$ into n subintervals of width $\Delta y = (d - c)/n$ (Figure 6.17). On the kth subinterval, a point y_k^* is selected, and we construct a rectangle that extends from the left curve to the right curve. The kth rectangle has length $f(y_k^*) - g(y_k^*)$, so the area of the kth rectangle is $(f(y_k^*) - g(y_k^*))\Delta y$. The area of the region is approximated by the sum of the areas of the rectangles. In the limit as $n \to \infty$ and $\Delta y \to 0$, the area of the region is given as the definite integral

$$A = \lim_{n \to \infty} \sum_{k=1}^{n} (f(y_k^*) - g(y_k^*))\Delta y = \int_{c}^{d} (f(y) - g(y))\, dy.$$

DEFINITION Area of a Region Between Two Curves with Respect to y

Suppose that f and g are continuous functions with $f(y) \geq g(y)$ on the interval $[c, d]$. The area of the region bounded by the graphs $x = f(y)$ and $x = g(y)$ on $[c, d]$ is

$$A = \int_{c}^{d} (f(y) - g(y))\, dy.$$

EXAMPLE 3 **Integrating with respect to y** Find the area of the region R bounded by the graphs of $y = x^3$, $y = x + 6$, and the x-axis.

SOLUTION The area of this region could be found by integrating with respect to x. But this approach requires splitting the region into two pieces (Figure 6.18). Alternatively, we can view y as the independent variable, express the bounding curves as functions of y, and make horizontal slices parallel to the x-axis (Figure 6.19).

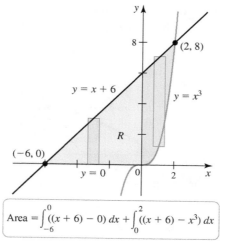

$$\text{Area} = \int_{-6}^{0} ((x+6) - 0)\, dx + \int_{0}^{2} ((x+6) - x^3)\, dx$$

Figure 6.18

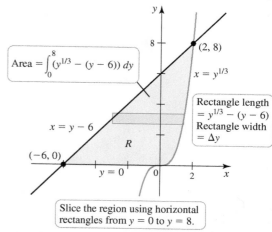

$$\text{Area} = \int_{0}^{8} (y^{1/3} - (y-6))\, dy$$

Rectangle length
$= y^{1/3} - (y-6)$
Rectangle width
$= \Delta y$

Slice the region using horizontal rectangles from $y = 0$ to $y = 8$.

Figure 6.19

▶ You may use synthetic division or a root finder to factor the cubic polynomial in Example 3. Then the quadratic formula shows that the equation

$$y^2 - 10y + 27 = 0$$

has no real roots.

Solving for x in terms of y, the right curve $y = x^3$ becomes $x = f(y) = y^{1/3}$. The left curve $y = x + 6$ becomes $x = g(y) = y - 6$. The intersection point of the curves satisfies the equation $y^{1/3} = y - 6$, or $y = (y - 6)^3$. Expanding this equation gives the cubic equation

$$y^3 - 18y^2 + 107y - 216 = (y - 8)(y^2 - 10y + 27) = 0,$$

whose only real root is $y = 8$. As shown in Figure 6.19, the areas of the slices through the region are summed from $y = 0$ to $y = 8$. Therefore, the area of the region is given by

$$\int_{0}^{8} (y^{1/3} - (y - 6))\, dy = \left(\frac{3}{4}y^{4/3} - \frac{y^2}{2} + 6y\right)\Big|_{0}^{8} \qquad \text{Fundamental Theorem}$$

$$= \left(\frac{3}{4} \cdot 16 - 32 + 48\right) - 0 = 28. \qquad \text{Simplify.}$$

Related Exercises 23–32 ◄

QUICK CHECK 3 The region R is bounded by the curve $y = \sqrt{x}$, the line $y = x - 2$, and the x-axis. Express the area of R in terms of (a) integral(s) with respect to x and (b) integral(s) with respect to y. ◄

EXAMPLE 4 **Calculus and geometry** Find the area of the region R in the first quadrant bounded by the curves $y = x^{2/3}$ and $y = x - 4$ (Figure 6.20).

SOLUTION Slicing the region vertically and integrating with respect to x requires two integrals. Slicing the region horizontally requires a single integral with respect to y. The second approach appears to involve less work.

Slicing horizontally, the right bounding curve is $x = y + 4$ and the left bounding curve is $x = y^{3/2}$. The two curves intersect at $(8, 4)$, so the limits of integration are $y = 0$ and $y = 4$. The area of R is

$$\int_{0}^{4} (\underbrace{(y + 4)}_{\text{right curve}} - \underbrace{y^{3/2}}_{\text{left curve}})\, dy = \left(\frac{y^2}{2} + 4y - \frac{2}{5}y^{5/2}\right)\Big|_{0}^{4} = \frac{56}{5}.$$

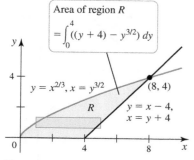

Area of region R
$$= \int_{0}^{4} ((y + 4) - y^{3/2})\, dy$$

$y = x^{2/3}, x = y^{3/2}$

$(8, 4)$

R

$y = x - 4,$
$x = y + 4$

Figure 6.20

➤ To find the point of intersection in Example 4, solve $y^{3/2} = y + 4$ by first squaring both sides of the equation.

Can this area be found using a different approach? Sometimes it helps to use geometry. Notice that the region R can be formed by taking the entire region under the curve $y = x^{2/3}$ on the interval $[0, 8]$ and then removing a triangle whose base is the interval $[4, 8]$ (Figure 6.21). The area of the region R_1 under the curve $y = x^{2/3}$ is

$$\int_0^8 x^{2/3} \, dx = \frac{3}{5} x^{5/3} \Big|_0^8 = \frac{96}{5}.$$

The triangle R_2 has a base of length 4 and a height of 4, so its area is $\frac{1}{2} \cdot 4 \cdot 4 = 8$. Therefore, the area of R is $\frac{96}{5} - 8 = \frac{56}{5}$, which agrees with the first calculation.

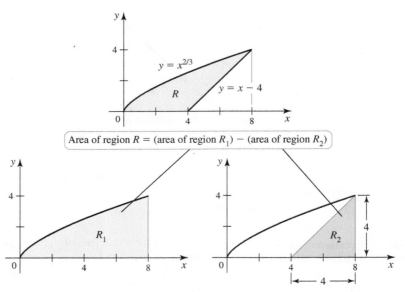

Figure 6.21

Related Exercises 33–38 ◄

QUICK CHECK 4 An alternative way to determine the area of the region in Example 3 (Figure 6.18) is to compute $18 + \int_0^2 (x + 6 - x^3) \, dx$. Why? ◄

SECTION 6.2 EXERCISES

Review Questions

1. Draw the graphs of two functions f and g that are continuous and intersect exactly twice on $(-\infty, \infty)$. Explain how to use integration to find the area of the region bounded by the two curves.

2. Draw the graphs of two functions f and g that are continuous and intersect exactly three times on $(-\infty, \infty)$. How is integration used to find the area of the region bounded by the two curves?

3. Make a sketch to show a case in which the area bounded by two curves is most easily found by integrating with respect to x.

4. Make a sketch to show a case in which the area bounded by two curves is most easily found by integrating with respect to y.

Basic Skills

5–8. Finding area *Determine the area of the shaded region in the following figures.*

5.

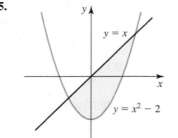

6.

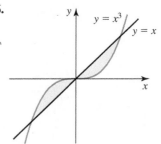

7.

8.

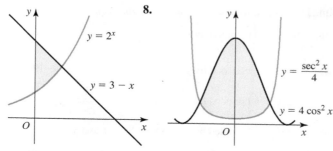

(*Hint:* Find the intersection point by inspection.)

9–14. Regions between curves *Sketch the region and find its area.*

9. The region bounded by $y = 2(x + 1)$, $y = 3(x + 1)$, and $x = 4$

10. The region bounded by $y = \cos x$ and $y = \sin x$ between $x = \pi/4$ and $x = 5\pi/4$

11. The region bounded by $y = e^x$, $y = e^{-2x}$, and $x = \ln 4$

12. The region bounded by $y = 2x$ and $y = x^2 + 3x - 6$

13. The region bounded by $y = \dfrac{2}{1 + x^2}$ and $y = 1$

14. The region bounded by $y = 24\sqrt{x}$ and $y = 3x^2$

15–22. Compound regions *Sketch each region (if a figure is not given) and then find its total area.*

15. The region bounded by $y = \sin x$, $y = \cos x$, and the x-axis between $x = 0$ and $x = \pi/2$

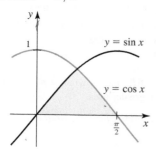

16. The regions between $y = \sin x$ and $y = \sin 2x$, for $0 \le x \le \pi$

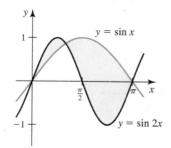

17. The region bounded by $y = x$, $y = 1/x$, $y = 0$, and $x = 2$

18. The regions in the first quadrant on the interval $[0, 2]$ bounded by $y = 4x - x^2$ and $y = 4x - 4$.

19. The region bounded by $y = 2 - |x|$ and $y = x^2$

20. The regions bounded by $y = x^3$ and $y = 9x$

21. The region bounded by $y = |x - 3|$ and $y = x/2$

22. The regions bounded by $y = x^2(3 - x)$ and $y = 12 - 4x$

23–26. Integrating with respect to y *Sketch each region (if a figure is not given) and find its area by integrating with respect to y.*

23. The region bounded by $y = \sqrt{\dfrac{x}{2} + 1}$, $y = \sqrt{1 - x}$, and $y = 0$.

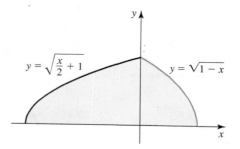

24. The region bounded by $x = \cos y$ and $x = -\sin 2y$

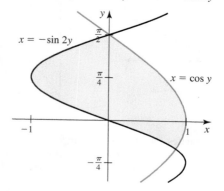

25. The region bounded by $x = y^2 - 3y + 12$ and $x = -2y^2 - 6y + 30$

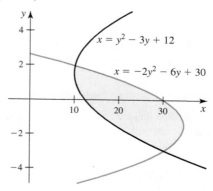

26. Both regions bounded by $x = y^3 - 4y^2 + 3y$ and $x = y^2 - y$

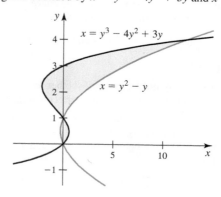

27–30. Two approaches *Express the area of the following shaded regions in terms of (a) one or more integrals with respect to x and (b) one or more integrals with respect to y. You do not need to evaluate the integrals.*

27.

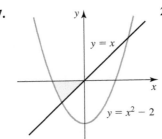

$y = x$

$y = x^2 - 2$

28.

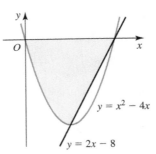

O

$y = x^2 - 4x$

$y = 2x - 8$

29.

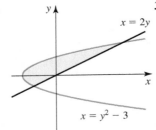

$x = 2y$

$x = y^2 - 3$

30.

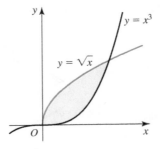

$y = x^3$

$y = \sqrt{x}$

O

31–32. Two approaches *Find the area of the following regions by (a) integrating with respect to x and (b) integrating with respect to y. Be sure your results agree. Sketch the bounding curves and the region in question.*

31. The region bounded by $y = 2 - \dfrac{x}{2}$ and $x = 2y^2$

32. The region bounded by $x = 2 - y^2$ and $x = |y|$

33–38. Any method *Use any method (including geometry) to find the area of the following regions. In each case, sketch the bounding curves and the region in question.*

33. The region in the first quadrant bounded by $y = x^{2/3}$ and $y = 4$

34. The region in the first quadrant bounded by $y = 2$ and $y = 2 \sin x$ on the interval $[0, \pi/2]$

35. The region bounded by $y = e^x$, $y = 2e^{-x} + 1$, and $x = 0$

T 36. The region below the line $y = 2$ and above the curve $y = \sec^2 x$ on the interval $[0, \pi/4]$

T 37. The region between the line $y = x$ and the curve $y = 2x\sqrt{1 - x^2}$ in the first quadrant

38. The region bounded by $x = y^2 - 4$ and $y = x/3$

Further Explorations

39. Explain why or why not Determine whether the following statements are true and give an explanation or counterexample.

   a. The area of the region bounded by $y = x$ and $x = y^2$ can be found only by integrating with respect to x.

   b. The area of the region between $y = \sin x$ and $y = \cos x$ on the interval $[0, \pi/2]$ is $\int_0^{\pi/2} (\cos x - \sin x)\, dx$.

   c. $\int_0^1 (x - x^2)\, dx = \int_0^1 (\sqrt{y} - y)\, dy$.

40–43. Regions between curves *Sketch the region and find its area.*

40. The region bounded by $y = \sin x$ and $y = x(x - \pi)$, for $0 \le x \le \pi$

41. The region bounded by $y = (x - 1)^2$ and $y = 7x - 19$

42. The region bounded by $y = 2$ and $y = \dfrac{1}{\sqrt{1 - x^2}}$

43. The region bounded by $y = x^2 - 2x + 1$ and $y = 5x - 9$

44–50. Either method *Use the most efficient strategy for computing the area of the following regions.*

44. The region bounded by $x = y(y - 1)$ and $x = -y(y - 1)$

45. The region bounded by $x = y(y - 1)$ and $y = x/3$

46. The region bounded by $y = x^3$, $y = -x^3$, and $3y - 7x - 10 = 0$

47. The region bounded by $y = \sqrt{x}$, $y = 2x - 15$, and $y = 0$

48. The region bounded by $y = x^2 - 4$, $4y - 5x - 5 = 0$, and $y = 0$, for $y \ge 0$

49. The region in the first quadrant bounded by $y = \dfrac{5}{2} - \dfrac{1}{x}$ and $y = x$

50. The region in the first quadrant bounded by $y = x^{-1}$, $y = 4x$, and $y = x/4$

51. Comparing areas Let $f(x) = x^p$ and $g(x) = x^{1/q}$, where $p > 1$ and $q > 1$ are positive integers. Let R_1 be the region in the first quadrant between $y = f(x)$ and $y = x$ and let R_2 be the region in the first quadrant between $y = g(x)$ and $y = x$.

   a. Find the area of R_1 and R_2 when $p = q$, and determine which region has the greater area.

   b. Find the area of R_1 and R_2 when $p > q$, and determine which region has the greater area.

   c. Find the area of R_1 and R_2 when $p < q$, and determine which region has the greater area.

52–55. Complicated regions *Find the area of the regions shown in the following figures.*

52.

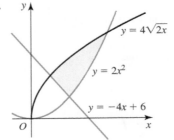

$y = 4\sqrt{2x}$

$y = 2x^2$

$y = -4x + 6$

O

53.

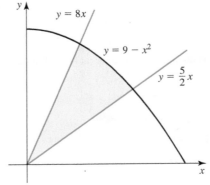

$y = 8x$

$y = 9 - x^2$

$y = \dfrac{5}{2}x$

T 54.

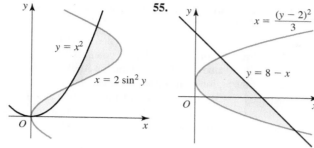

55.

$$x = \frac{(y-2)^2}{3}$$

$y = 8 - x$

56–59. Roots and powers *Find the area of the following regions, expressing your results in terms of the positive integer $n \geq 2$.*

56. The region bounded by $f(x) = x$ and $g(x) = x^n$, for $x \geq 0$

57. The region bounded by $f(x) = x$ and $g(x) = x^{1/n}$, for $x \geq 0$

58. The region bounded by $f(x) = x^{1/n}$ and $g(x) = x^n$, for $x \geq 0$

59. Let A_n be the area of the region bounded by $f(x) = x^{1/n}$ and $g(x) = x^n$ on the interval $[0, 1]$, where n is a positive integer. Evaluate $\lim\limits_{n \to \infty} A_n$ and interpret the result.

60–63. Bisecting regions *For each region R, find the horizontal line $y = k$ that divides R into two subregions of equal area.*

60. R is the region bounded by $y = 1 - x$, the x-axis, and the y-axis.

61. R is the region bounded by $y = 1 - |x - 1|$ and the x-axis.

62. R is the region bounded by $y = 4 - x^2$ and the x-axis.

T 63. R is the region bounded by $y = \sqrt{x}$ and $y = x$.

Applications

64. Geometric probability Suppose a dartboard occupies the square $\{(x, y): 0 \leq |x| \leq 1, 0 \leq |y| \leq 1\}$. A dart is thrown randomly at the board many times (meaning it is equally likely to land at any point in the square). What fraction of the dart throws land closer to the edge of the board than the center? Equivalently, what is the probability that the dart lands closer to the edge of the board than the center? Proceed as follows.

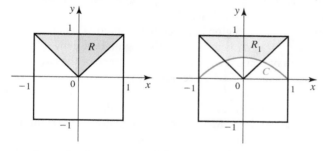

a. Argue that by symmetry, it is necessary to consider only one quarter of the board, say the region R: $\{(x, y): |x| \leq y \leq 1\}$.

b. Find the curve C in this region that is equidistant from the center of the board and the top edge of the board (see figure).

c. The probability that the dart lands closer to the edge of the board than the center is the ratio of the area of the region R_1 above C to the area of the entire region R. Compute this probability.

T 65. Lorenz curves and the Gini index A **Lorenz curve** is given by $y = L(x)$, where $0 \leq x \leq 1$ represents the lowest fraction of the population of a society in terms of wealth and $0 \leq y \leq 1$ represents the fraction of the total wealth that is owned by that fraction of the society. For example, the Lorenz curve in the figure shows that $L(0.5) = 0.2$, which means that the lowest 0.5 (50%) of the society owns 0.2 (20%) of the wealth. (See the Guided Project *Distribution of Wealth* for more on Lorenz curves.)

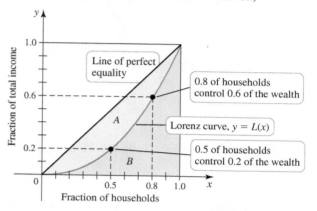

a. A Lorenz curve $y = L(x)$ is accompanied by the line $y = x$, called the **line of perfect equality**. Explain why this line is given this name.

b. Explain why a Lorenz curve satisfies the conditions $L(0) = 0, L(1) = 1, L(x) \leq x$, and $L'(x) \geq 0$ on $[0, 1]$.

c. Graph the Lorenz curves $L(x) = x^p$ corresponding to $p = 1.1, 1.5, 2, 3, 4$. Which value of p corresponds to the *most* equitable distribution of wealth (closest to the line of perfect equality)? Which value of p corresponds to the *least* equitable distribution of wealth? Explain.

d. The information in the Lorenz curve is often summarized in a single measure called the **Gini index**, which is defined as follows. Let A be the area of the region between $y = x$ and $y = L(x)$ (see figure) and let B be the area of the region between $y = L(x)$ and the x-axis. Then the Gini index is

$$G = \frac{A}{A + B}.$$ Show that $G = 2A = 1 - 2\int_0^1 L(x)\, dx.$

e. Compute the Gini index for the cases $L(x) = x^p$ and $p = 1.1, 1.5, 2, 3, 4$.

f. What is the smallest interval $[a, b]$ on which values of the Gini index lie for $L(x) = x^p$ with $p \geq 1$? Which endpoints of $[a, b]$ correspond to the least and most equitable distribution of wealth?

g. Consider the Lorenz curve described by $L(x) = 5x^2/6 + x/6$. Show that it satisfies the conditions $L(0) = 0, L(1) = 1$, and $L'(x) \geq 0$ on $[0, 1]$. Find the Gini index for this function.

Additional Exercises

66. Equal area properties for parabolas Consider the parabola $y = x^2$. Let P, Q, and R be points on the parabola with R between P and Q on the curve. Let ℓ_P, ℓ_Q, and ℓ_R be the lines tangent to the parabola at P, Q, and R, respectively (see figure). Let P' be the intersection point of ℓ_Q and ℓ_R, let Q' be the intersection point of ℓ_P and ℓ_R, and let R' be the intersection point of ℓ_P and ℓ_Q. Prove that Area $\triangle PQR = 2 \cdot$ Area $\triangle P'Q'R'$ in the following cases. (In fact, the property holds for any three points on any parabola.) (*Source: Mathematics Magazine* 81, 2, Apr 2008)

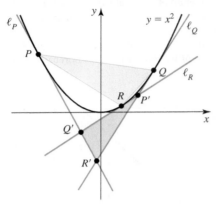

a. $P(-a, a^2)$, $Q(a, a^2)$, and $R(0, 0)$, where a is a positive real number

b. $P(-a, a^2)$, $Q(b, b^2)$, and $R(0, 0)$, where a and b are positive real numbers

c. $P(-a, a^2)$, $Q(b, b^2)$, and R is any point between P and Q on the curve

67. Minimum area Graph the curves $y = (x + 1)(x - 2)$ and $y = ax + 1$ for various values of a. For what value of a is the area of the region between the two curves a minimum?

68. An area function Graph the curves $y = a^2 x^3$ and $y = \sqrt{x}$ for various values of $a > 0$. Note how the area $A(a)$ between the curves varies with a. Find and graph the area function $A(a)$. For what value of a is $A(a) = 16$?

69. Area of a curve defined implicitly Determine the area of the shaded region bounded by the curve $x^2 = y^4(1 - y^3)$ (see figure).

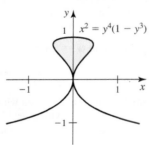

70. Rewrite first Find the area of the region bounded by the curve $x = \dfrac{1}{2y} - \sqrt{\dfrac{1}{4y^2} - 1}$ and the line $x = 1$ in the first quadrant.

(*Hint:* Express y in terms of x.)

71. Area function for a cubic Consider the cubic polynomial $f(x) = x(x - a)(x - b)$, where $0 \leq a \leq b$.

a. For a fixed value of b, find the function $F(a) = \int_0^b f(x)\, dx$. For what value of a (which depends on b) is $F(a) = 0$?

b. For a fixed value of b, find the function $A(a)$ that gives the area of the region bounded by the graph of f and the x-axis between $x = 0$ and $x = b$. Graph this function and show that it has a minimum at $a = b/2$. What is the maximum value of $A(a)$, and where does it occur (in terms of b)?

72. Differences of even functions Assume f and g are even, integrable functions on $[-a, a]$, where $a > 1$. Suppose $f(x) > g(x) > 0$ on $[-a, a]$ and the area bounded by the graphs of f and g on $[-a, a]$ is 10. What is the value of $\int_0^{\sqrt{a}} x(f(x^2) - g(x^2))\, dx$?

73. Roots and powers Consider the functions $f(x) = x^n$ and $g(x) = x^{1/n}$, where $n \geq 2$ is a positive integer.

a. Graph f and g for $n = 2, 3$, and 4, for $x \geq 0$.

b. Give a geometric interpretation of the area function $A_n(x) = \int_0^x (f(s) - g(s))\, ds$, for $n = 2, 3, 4, \ldots$ and $x > 0$.

c. Find the positive root of $A_n(x) = 0$ in terms of n. Does the root increase or decrease with n?

74. Shifting sines Consider the functions $f(x) = a \sin 2x$ and $g(x) = (\sin x)/a$, where $a > 0$ is a real number.

a. Graph the two functions on the interval $[0, \pi/2]$, for $a = \frac{1}{2}, 1$, and 2.

b. Show that the curves have an intersection point x^* (other than $x = 0$) on $[0, \pi/2]$ that satisfies $\cos x^* = 1/(2a^2)$, provided $a > 1/\sqrt{2}$.

c. Find the area of the region between the two curves on $[0, x^*]$ when $a = 1$.

d. Show that as $a \to 1/\sqrt{2}^+$, the area of the region between the two curves on $[0, x^*]$ approaches zero.

QUICK CHECK ANSWERS

1. If $g(x) = 0$ and $f(x) \geq 0$, then the area between the curves is $\int_a^b (f(x) - 0)\, dx = \int_a^b f(x)\, dx$, which is the area between $y = f(x)$ and the x-axis.   **2.** $\int_a^b f(x)\, dx$ is the area of the region between the graph of f and the x-axis. $\int_a^b g(x)\, dx$ is the area of the region between the graph of g and the x-axis. The difference of the two integrals is the area of the region between the graphs of f and g.   **3. a.** $\int_0^2 \sqrt{x}\, dx + \int_2^4 (\sqrt{x} - x + 2)\, dx$ **b.** $\int_0^2 (y + 2 - y^2)\, dy$ **4.** The area of the triangle to the left of the y-axis is 18. The area of the region to the right of the y-axis is given by the integral. ◄

6.3 Volume by Slicing

We have seen that integration is used to compute the area of two-dimensional regions bounded by curves. Integrals are also used to find the volume of three-dimensional regions (or solids). Once again, the slice-and-sum method is the key to solving these problems.

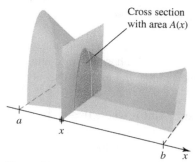

Cross section with area $A(x)$

Figure 6.22

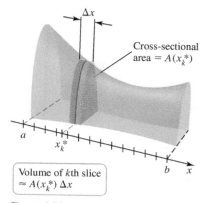

Δx

Cross-sectional area $= A(x_k^*)$

x_k^*

Volume of kth slice $\approx A(x_k^*)\,\Delta x$

Figure 6.23

General Slicing Method

Consider a solid object that extends in the x-direction from $x = a$ to $x = b$. Imagine cutting through the solid, perpendicular to the x-axis at a particular point x, and suppose the area of the cross section created by the cut is given by a known integrable function A (Figure 6.22).

To find the volume of this solid, we first divide $[a, b]$ into n subintervals of length $\Delta x = (b - a)/n$. The endpoints of the subintervals are the grid points $x_0 = a, x_1, x_2, \ldots, x_n = b$. We now make vertical cuts through the solid perpendicular to the x-axis at each grid point, which produces n slices of thickness Δx. (Imagine cutting a loaf of bread to create n slices of equal width.) On each subinterval, an arbitrary point x_k^* is identified. The kth slice through the solid has a thickness Δx, and we take $A(x_k^*)$ as a representative cross-sectional area of the slice. Therefore, the volume of the kth slice is approximately $A(x_k^*)\Delta x$ (Figure 6.23). Summing the volumes of the slices, the approximate volume of the solid is

$$V \approx \sum_{k=1}^{n} A(x_k^*)\Delta x.$$

As the number of slices increases ($n \to \infty$) and the thickness of each slice goes to zero ($\Delta x \to 0$), the exact volume V is obtained in terms of a definite integral (Figure 6.24):

$$V = \lim_{n \to \infty} \sum_{k=1}^{n} A(x_k^*)\Delta x = \int_a^b A(x)\,dx.$$

Increase the number of slices.

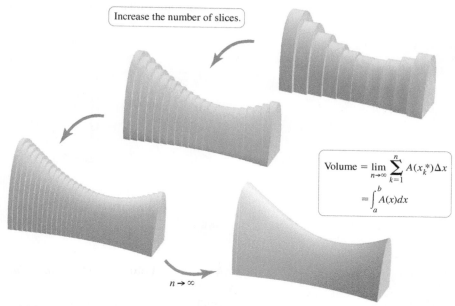

Volume $= \lim_{n \to \infty} \sum_{k=1}^{n} A(x_k^*)\Delta x$
$= \int_a^b A(x)dx$

$n \to \infty$

Figure 6.24

We summarize the important general slicing method, which is also the basis of other volume formulas to follow.

▶ The factors in this volume integral have meaning: $A(x)$ is the cross-sectional area of a slice and dx represents its thickness. Summing (integrating) the volumes of the slices $A(x)\,dx$ gives the volume of the solid.

General Slicing Method

Suppose a solid object extends from $x = a$ to $x = b$ and the cross section of the solid perpendicular to the x-axis has an area given by a function A that is integrable on $[a, b]$. The volume of the solid is

$$V = \int_a^b A(x)\,dx.$$

QUICK CHECK 1 Why is the volume, as given by the general slicing method, equal to the average value of the area function A on $[a, b]$ multiplied by $b - a$? ◄

EXAMPLE 1   Volume of a "parabolic cube" Let R be the region in the first quadrant bounded by the coordinate axes and the curve $y = 1 - x^2$. A solid has a base R, and cross sections through the solid perpendicular to the base and parallel to the y-axis are squares (Figure 6.25a). Find the volume of the solid.

SOLUTION Focus on a cross section through the solid at a point x, where $0 \leq x \leq 1$. That cross section is a square with sides of length $1 - x^2$. Therefore, the area of a typical cross section is $A(x) = (1 - x^2)^2$. Using the general slicing method, the volume of the solid is

$$V = \int_0^1 A(x)\, dx \qquad \text{General slicing method}$$

$$= \int_0^1 (1 - x^2)^2\, dx \qquad \text{Substitute for } A(x).$$

$$= \int_0^1 (1 - 2x^2 + x^4)\, dx \qquad \text{Expand integrand.}$$

$$= \frac{8}{15}. \qquad \text{Evaluate.}$$

The actual solid with a square cross section is shown in Figure 6.25b.

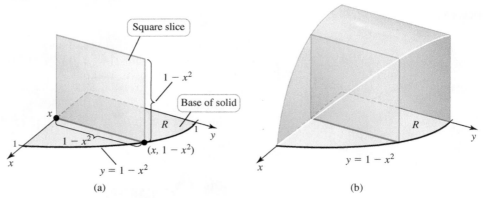

(a)   (b)

Figure 6.25

Related Exercises 7–16 ◄

EXAMPLE 2   Volume of a "parabolic hemisphere" A solid has a base that is bounded by the curves $y = x^2$ and $y = 2 - x^2$ in the xy-plane. Cross sections through the solid perpendicular to the base and parallel to the y-axis are semicircular disks. Find the volume of the solid.

SOLUTION Because a typical cross section perpendicular to the x-axis is a semicircular disk (Figure 6.26), the area of a cross section is $\frac{1}{2}\pi r^2$, where r is the radius of the cross section.

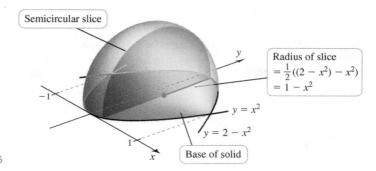

Figure 6.26

The key observation is that this radius is one-half of the distance between the upper bounding curve $y = 2 - x^2$ and the lower bounding curve $y = x^2$. So the radius at the point x is

$$r = \frac{1}{2}\left((2 - x^2) - x^2\right) = 1 - x^2.$$

This means that the area of the semicircular cross section at the point x is

$$A(x) = \frac{1}{2}\pi r^2 = \frac{\pi}{2}(1 - x^2)^2.$$

The intersection points of the two bounding curves satisfy $2 - x^2 = x^2$, which has solutions $x = \pm 1$. Therefore, the cross sections lie between $x = -1$ and $x = 1$. Integrating the cross-sectional areas, the volume of the solid is

$$V = \int_{-1}^{1} A(x)\,dx \qquad \text{General slicing method}$$

$$= \int_{-1}^{1} \frac{\pi}{2}(1 - x^2)^2\,dx \qquad \text{Substitute for } A(x).$$

$$= \frac{\pi}{2}\int_{-1}^{1}(1 - 2x^2 + x^4)\,dx \qquad \text{Expand integrand.}$$

$$= \frac{8\pi}{15}. \qquad \text{Evaluate.}$$

Related Exercises 7–16 ◄

QUICK CHECK 2 In Example 2, what is the cross-sectional area function $A(x)$ if cross sections perpendicular to the base are squares rather than semicircles? ◄

The Disk Method

We now consider a specific type of solid known as a **solid of revolution**. Suppose f is a continuous function with $f(x) \geq 0$ on an interval $[a, b]$. Let R be the region bounded by the graph of f, the x-axis, and the lines $x = a$ and $x = b$ (Figure 6.27). Now revolve R around the x-axis. As R revolves once about the x-axis, it sweeps out a three-dimensional solid of revolution (Figure 6.28). The goal is to find the volume of this solid, and it may be done using the general slicing method.

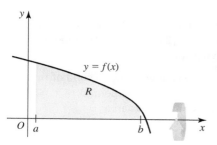

Figure 6.27

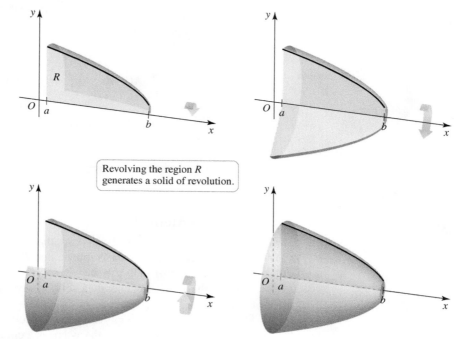

Revolving the region R generates a solid of revolution.

Figure 6.28

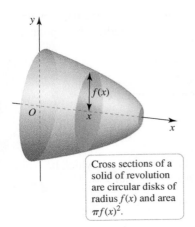

Cross sections of a solid of revolution are circular disks of radius $f(x)$ and area $\pi f(x)^2$.

Figure 6.29

QUICK CHECK 3 What solid results when the region R is revolved about the x-axis if (a) R is a square with vertices $(0, 0)$, $(0, 2)$, $(2, 0)$, and $(2, 2)$, and (b) R is a triangle with vertices $(0, 0)$, $(0, 2)$, and $(2, 0)$? ◄

With a solid of revolution, the cross-sectional area function has a special form because all cross sections perpendicular to the x-axis are *circular disks* with radius $f(x)$ (Figure 6.29). Therefore, the cross section at the point x, where $a \leq x \leq b$, has area

$$A(x) = \pi(\text{radius})^2 = \pi f(x)^2.$$

By the general slicing method, the volume of the solid is

$$V = \int_a^b A(x)\, dx = \int_a^b \pi f(x)^2\, dx.$$

Because each slice through the solid is a circular disk, the resulting method is called the *disk method*.

Disk Method about the x-Axis

Let f be continuous with $f(x) \geq 0$ on the interval $[a, b]$. If the region R bounded by the graph of f, the x-axis, and the lines $x = a$ and $x = b$ is revolved about the x-axis, the volume of the resulting solid of revolution is

$$V = \int_a^b \pi f(x)^2\, dx.$$

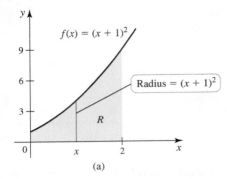

(a)

EXAMPLE 3 Disk method at work Let R be the region bounded by the curve $f(x) = (x + 1)^2$, the x-axis, and the lines $x = 0$ and $x = 2$ (Figure 6.30a). Find the volume of the solid of revolution obtained by revolving R about the x-axis.

SOLUTION When the region R is revolved about the x-axis, it generates a solid of revolution (Figure 6.30b). A cross section perpendicular to the x-axis at the point $0 \leq x \leq 2$ is a circular disk of radius $f(x)$. Therefore, a typical cross section has area

$$A(x) = \pi f(x)^2 = \pi((x + 1)^2)^2.$$

Integrating these cross-sectional areas between $x = 0$ and $x = 2$ gives the volume of the solid:

$$V = \int_0^2 A(x)\, dx = \int_0^2 \pi((x + 1)^2)^2\, dx \quad \text{Substitute for } A(x).$$

$$= \int_0^2 \pi(x + 1)^4\, dx \quad \text{Simplify.}$$

$$= \pi \frac{u^5}{5}\bigg|_1^3 = \frac{242\,\pi}{5}. \quad \text{Let } u = x + 1 \text{ and evaluate.}$$

Related Exercises 17–26 ◄

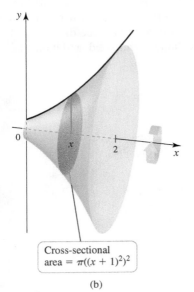

Cross-sectional area = $\pi((x + 1)^2)^2$

(b)

Figure 6.30

Washer Method

A slight variation on the disk method enables us to compute the volume of more exotic solids of revolution. Suppose that R is the region bounded by the graphs of f and g between $x = a$ and $x = b$, where $f(x) \geq g(x) \geq 0$ (Figure 6.31). If R is revolved about the x-axis to generate a solid of revolution, the resulting solid generally has a hole through it.

Once again we apply the general slicing method. In this case, a cross section through the solid perpendicular to the x-axis is a circular *washer* with an outer radius of $R = f(x)$

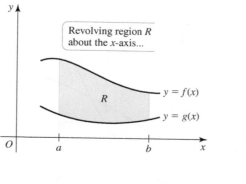

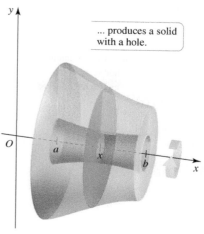

Figure 6.31

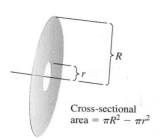

Cross-sectional
area $= \pi R^2 - \pi r^2$

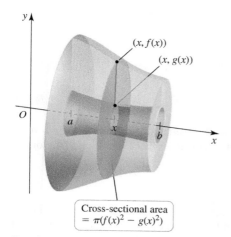

Cross-sectional area
$= \pi(f(x)^2 - g(x)^2)$

Figure 6.32

and an inner radius of $r = g(x)$, where $a \le x \le b$. The area of the cross section is the area of the entire disk minus the area of the hole, or

$$A(x) = \pi(R^2 - r^2) = \pi(f(x)^2 - g(x)^2)$$

(Figure 6.32). The general slicing method gives the area of the solid.

Washer Method about the x-Axis

Let f and g be continuous functions with $f(x) \ge g(x) \ge 0$ on $[a, b]$. Let R be the region bounded by $y = f(x)$, $y = g(x)$, and the lines $x = a$ and $x = b$. When R is revolved about the x-axis, the volume of the resulting solid of revolution is

$$V = \int_a^b \pi(f(x)^2 - g(x)^2)\, dx.$$

QUICK CHECK 4 Show that when $g(x) = 0$ in the washer method, the result is the disk method. ◄

EXAMPLE 4 **Volume by the washer method** The region R is bounded by the graphs of $f(x) = \sqrt{x}$ and $g(x) = x^2$ between $x = 0$ and $x = 1$. What is the volume of the solid that results when R is revolved about the x-axis?

SOLUTION The region R is bounded by the graphs of f and g with $f(x) \ge g(x)$ on $[0, 1]$, so the washer method is applicable (Figure 6.33). The area of a typical cross section at the point x is

$$A(x) = \pi(f(x)^2 - g(x)^2) = \pi((\sqrt{x})^2 - (x^2)^2) = \pi(x - x^4).$$

Therefore, the volume of the solid is

$$V = \int_0^1 \pi(x - x^4)\, dx \qquad \text{Washer method}$$

$$= \pi\left(\frac{x^2}{2} - \frac{x^5}{5}\right)\Big|_0^1 = \frac{3\pi}{10}. \qquad \text{Fundamental Theorem}$$

> The washer method is really two applications of the disk method. We compute the volume of the entire solid without the hole (by the disk method) and then subtract the volume of the hole (also computed by the disk method).

▶ Ignoring the factor of π, the integrand in the washer method integral is $f(x)^2 - g(x)^2$, which is not equal to $(f(x) - g(x))^2$.

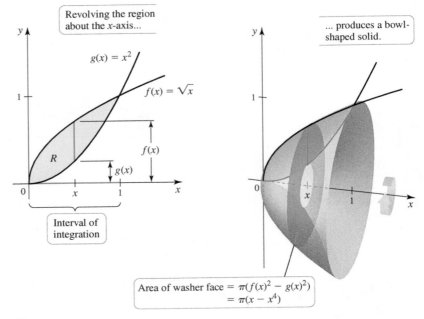

Revolving the region about the x-axis...

$g(x) = x^2$

$f(x) = \sqrt{x}$

R

$f(x)$

$g(x)$

Interval of integration

... produces a bowl-shaped solid.

Area of washer face $= \pi(f(x)^2 - g(x)^2)$
$= \pi(x - x^4)$

Figure 6.33

Related Exercises 27–34 ◀

QUICK CHECK 5 Suppose the region in Example 4 is revolved about the line $y = -1$ instead of the x-axis. (a) What is the inner radius of a typical washer? (b) What is the outer radius of a typical washer? ◀

Revolving about the y-Axis

Everything you learned about revolving regions about the x-axis applies to revolving regions about the y-axis. Consider a region R bounded by the curve $x = p(y)$ on the right, the curve $x = q(y)$ on the left, and the horizontal lines $y = c$ and $y = d$ (Figure 6.34a).

To find the volume of the solid generated when R is revolved about the y-axis, we use the general slicing method—now with respect to the y-axis (Figure 6.34b). The area of a typical cross section is $A(y) = \pi(p(y)^2 - q(y)^2)$, where $c \leq y \leq d$. As before, integrating these cross-sectional areas of the solid gives the volume.

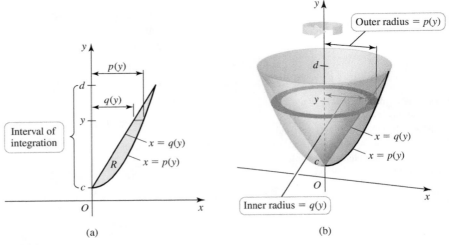

Interval of integration

$p(y)$

$q(y)$

$x = q(y)$

$x = p(y)$

R

(a)

Outer radius $= p(y)$

$x = q(y)$

$x = p(y)$

Inner radius $= q(y)$

(b)

Figure 6.34

▶ The disk/washer method about the
y-axis is the disk/washer method about
the x-axis with x replaced with y.

Disk and Washer Methods about the y-Axis

Let p and q be continuous functions with $p(y) \geq q(y) \geq 0$ on $[c, d]$. Let R be the region bounded by $x = p(y)$, $x = q(y)$, and the lines $y = c$ and $y = d$. When R is revolved about the y-axis, the volume of the resulting solid of revolution is given by

$$V = \int_c^d \pi (p(y)^2 - q(y)^2) \, dy.$$

If $q(y) = 0$, the disk method results:

$$V = \int_c^d \pi p(y)^2 \, dy.$$

EXAMPLE 5   Which solid has greater volume? Let R be the region in the first quadrant bounded by the graphs of $x = y^3$ and $x = 4y$. Which is greater, the volume of the solid generated when R is revolved about the x-axis or the y-axis?

SOLUTION Solving $y^3 = 4y$, or equivalently, $y(y^2 - 4) = 0$, we find that the bounding curves of R intersect at the points $(0, 0)$ and $(8, 2)$. When the region R (Figure 6.35a) is revolved about the y-axis, it generates a funnel with a curved inner surface (Figure 6.35b). Washer-shaped cross sections perpendicular to the y-axis extend from $y = 0$ to $y = 2$. The outer radius of the cross section at the point y is determined by the line $x = p(y) = 4y$. The inner radius of the cross section at the point y is determined by the curve $x = q(y) = y^3$. Applying the washer method, the volume of this solid is

$$V = \int_0^2 \pi (p(y)^2 - q(y)^2) \, dy \qquad \text{Washer method}$$

$$= \int_0^2 \pi (16y^2 - y^6) \, dy \qquad \text{Substitute for } p \text{ and } q.$$

$$= \pi \left(\frac{16}{3} y^3 - \frac{y^7}{7} \right) \Big|_0^2 \qquad \text{Fundamental Theorem}$$

$$= \frac{512\pi}{21}. \qquad \text{Evaluate.}$$

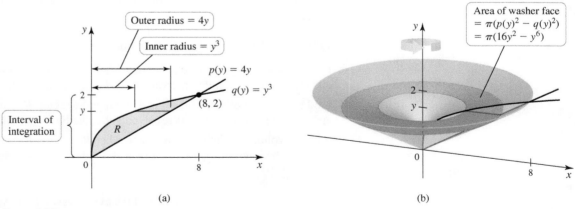

Figure 6.35

When the region R is revolved about the x-axis, it generates a different funnel (Figure 6.36). Vertical slices through the solid between $x = 0$ and $x = 8$ produce washers. The outer radius of the washer at the point x is determined by the curve $x = y^3$, or

$y = f(x) = x^{1/3}$. The inner radius is determined by $x = 4y$, or $y = g(x) = x/4$. The volume of the resulting solid is

$$V = \int_0^8 \pi(f(x)^2 - g(x)^2)\, dx \qquad \text{Washer method}$$

$$= \int_0^8 \pi\left(x^{2/3} - \frac{x^2}{16}\right) dx \qquad \text{Substitute for } f \text{ and } g.$$

$$= \pi\left(\frac{3}{5}x^{5/3} - \frac{x^3}{48}\right)\Big|_0^8 \qquad \text{Fundamental Theorem}$$

$$= \frac{128\pi}{15}. \qquad \text{Evaluate.}$$

We see that revolving the region about the y-axis produces a solid of greater volume.

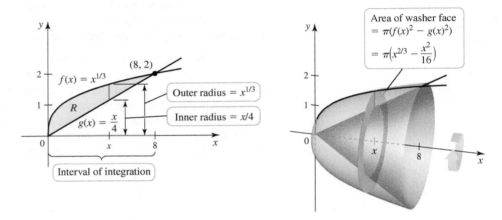

Figure 6.36

Related Exercises 35–44 ◀

QUICK CHECK 6 The region in the first quadrant bounded by $y = x$ and $y = x^3$ is revolved about the y-axis. Give the integral for the volume of the solid that is generated. ◀

The disk and washer methods may be generalized to handle situations in which a region R is revolved about a line parallel to one of the coordinate axes. The next example discusses three such cases.

EXAMPLE 6 **Revolving about other lines** Let $f(x) = \sqrt{x} + 1$ and $g(x) = x^2 + 1$.

a. Find the volume of the solid generated when the region R_1 bounded by the graph of f and the line $y = 2$ on the interval $[0, 1]$ is revolved about the line $y = 2$.

b. Find the volume of the solid generated when the region R_2 bounded by the graphs of f and g on the interval $[0, 1]$ is revolved about the line $y = -1$.

c. Find the volume of the solid generated when the region R_2 bounded by the graphs of f and g on the interval $[0, 1]$ is revolved about the line $x = 2$.

SOLUTION

a. Figure 6.37a shows the region R_1 and the axis of revolution. Applying the disk method, we see that a disk located at a point x has a radius of $2 - f(x) = 2 - (\sqrt{x} + 1) = 1 - \sqrt{x}$. Therefore, the volume of the solid generated when R_1 is revolved about $y = 2$ is

$$\int_0^1 \pi(1 - \sqrt{x})^2\, dx = \pi\int_0^1 (1 - 2\sqrt{x} + x)\, dx = \frac{\pi}{6}.$$

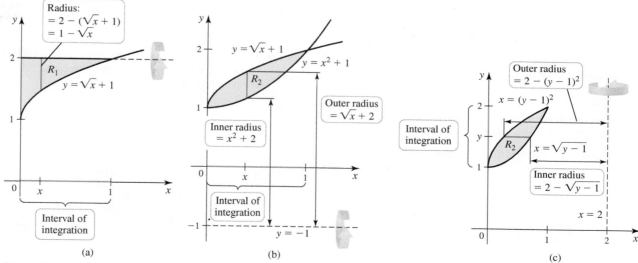

Figure 6.37

b. When the graph of f is revolved about $y = -1$, it sweeps out a solid of revolution whose radius at a point x is $f(x) + 1 = \sqrt{x} + 2$. Similarly, when the graph of g is revolved about $y = -1$, it sweeps out a solid of revolution whose radius at a point x is $g(x) + 1 = x^2 + 2$ (Figure 6.37b). Using the washer method, the volume of the solid generated when R_2 is revolved about $y = -1$ is

$$\int_0^1 \pi((\sqrt{x} + 2)^2 - (x^2 + 2)^2) \, dx$$

$$= \pi \int_0^1 (-x^4 - 4x^2 + x + 4\sqrt{x}) \, dx$$

$$= \frac{49\pi}{30}.$$

c. When the region R_2 is revolved about the line $x = 2$, we use the washer method and integrate in the y-direction. First note that the graph of f is described by $y = \sqrt{x} + 1$, or equivalently, $x = (y - 1)^2$, for $y \geq 1$. Also, the graph of g is described by $y = x^2 + 1$, or equivalently, $x = \sqrt{y - 1}$ for $y \geq 1$ (Figure 6.37c). When the graph of f is revolved about the line $x = 2$, the radius of a typical disk at a point y is $2 - (y - 1)^2$. Similarly, when the graph of g is revolved about $x = 2$, the radius of a typical disk at a point y is $2 - \sqrt{y - 1}$. Finally, observe that the extent of the region R_2 in the y-direction is the interval $1 \leq y \leq 2$.

   Applying the washer method, simplifying the integrand, and integrating powers of y, the volume of the solid of revolution is

$$\int_1^2 \pi\left((2 - (y - 1)^2)^2 - (2 - \sqrt{y - 1})^2\right) dy = \frac{31\pi}{30}.$$

Related Exercises 45–52 ◄

SECTION 6.3 EXERCISES

Review Questions

1. Suppose a cut is made through a solid object perpendicular to the x-axis at a particular point x. Explain the meaning of $A(x)$.

2. A solid has a circular base and cross sections perpendicular to the base are squares. What method should be used to find the volume of the solid?

3. The region bounded by the curves $y = 2x$ and $y = x^2$ is revolved about the x-axis. Give an integral for the volume of the solid that is generated.

4. The region bounded by the curves $y = 2x$ and $y = x^2$ is revolved about the y-axis. Give an integral for the volume of the solid that is generated.

5. Why is the disk method a special case of the general slicing method?

6. The region R bounded by the graph of $y = f(x) \geq 0$ and the x-axis on $[a, b]$ is revolved about the line $y = -2$ to form a solid of revolution whose cross sections are washers. What are the inner and outer radii of the washer at a point x in $[a, b]$?

Basic Skills

7–16. General slicing method *Use the general slicing method to find the volume of the following solids.*

7. The solid whose base is the region bounded by the curves $y = x^2$ and $y = 2 - x^2$, and whose cross sections through the solid perpendicular to the x-axis are squares

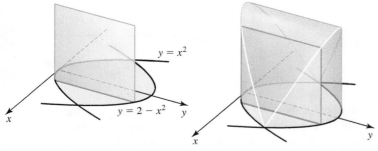

8. The solid whose base is the region bounded by the semicircle $y = \sqrt{1 - x^2}$ and the x-axis, and whose cross sections through the solid perpendicular to the x-axis are squares

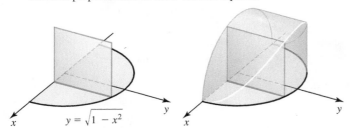

9. The solid whose base is the region bounded by the curve $y = \sqrt{\cos x}$ and the x-axis on $[-\pi/2, \pi/2]$, and whose cross sections through the solid perpendicular to the x-axis are isosceles right triangles with a horizontal leg in the xy-plane and a vertical leg above the x-axis

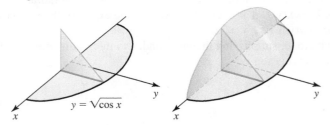

10. The solid with a circular base of radius 5 whose cross sections perpendicular to the base and parallel to the x-axis are equilateral triangles

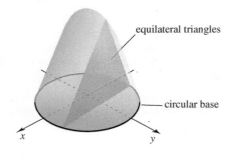

equilateral triangles

circular base

11. The solid with a semicircular base of radius 5 whose cross sections perpendicular to the base and parallel to the diameter are squares

12. The solid whose base is the region bounded by $y = x^2$ and the line $y = 1$, and whose cross sections perpendicular to the base and parallel to the x-axis are squares

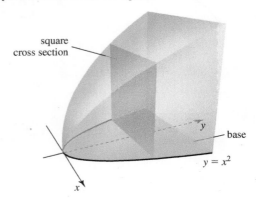

square cross section

base

$y = x^2$

13. The solid whose base is the triangle with vertices $(0, 0)$, $(2, 0)$, and $(0, 2)$, and whose cross sections perpendicular to the base and parallel to the y-axis are semicircles

14. The pyramid with a square base 4 m on a side and a height of 2 m (Use calculus.)

15. The tetrahedron (pyramid with four triangular faces), all of whose edges have length 4

16. A circular cylinder of radius r and height h whose axis is at an angle of $\pi/4$ to the base

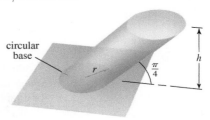

circular base

r

$\frac{\pi}{4}$

h

17–26. Disk method *Let R be the region bounded by the following curves. Use the disk method to find the volume of the solid generated when R is revolved about the x-axis.*

17. $y = 2x, y = 0, x = 3$ (Verify that your answer agrees with the volume formula for a cone.)

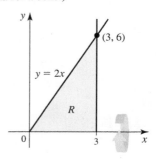

18. $y = 2 - 2x, y = 0, x = 0$ (Verify that your answer agrees with the volume formula for a cone.)

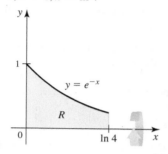

19. $y = e^{-x}, y = 0, x = 0, x = \ln 4$

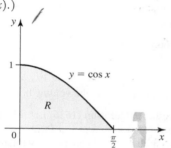

20. $y = \cos x$ on $[0, \pi/2], y = 0, x = 0$ (Recall that $\cos^2 x = \frac{1}{2}(1 + \cos 2x)$.)

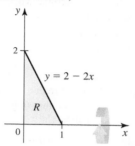

21. $y = \sin x$ on $[0, \pi], y = 0$ (Recall that $\sin^2 x = \frac{1}{2}(1 - \cos 2x)$.)

22. $y = \sqrt{25 - x^2}, y = 0$ (Verify that your answer agrees with the volume formula for a sphere.)

23. $y = \dfrac{1}{\sqrt[4]{1 - x^2}}, y = 0, x = 0,$ and $x = \frac{1}{2}$

24. $y = \sec x, y = 0, x = 0,$ and $x = \frac{\pi}{4}$

25. $y = \dfrac{1}{\sqrt{1 + x^2}}, y = 0, x = -1,$ and $x = 1$

26. $y = \dfrac{1}{\sqrt[4]{1 - x^2}}, y = 0, x = -\frac{1}{2},$ and $x = \frac{1}{2}$

27–34. Washer method *Let R be the region bounded by the following curves. Use the washer method to find the volume of the solid generated when R is revolved about the x-axis.*

27. $y = x, y = 2\sqrt{x}$

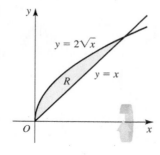

28. $y = x, y = \sqrt[4]{x}$

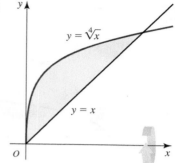

29. $y = e^{x/2}, y = e^{-x/2}, x = \ln 2, x = \ln 3$

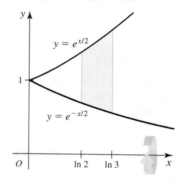

30. $y = x, y = x + 2, x = 0, x = 4$

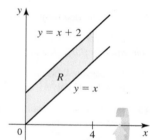

31. $y = x + 3, y = x^2 + 1$

32. $y = \sqrt{\sin x}, y = 1, x = 0$

33. $y = \sin x, y = \sqrt{\sin x},$ for $0 \le x \le \pi/2$

34. $y = |x|, y = 2 - x^2$

35–40. Disks / washers about the y-axis *Let R be the region bounded by the following curves. Use the disk or washer method to find the volume of the solid generated when R is revolved about the y-axis.*

35. $y = x, y = 2x, y = 6$

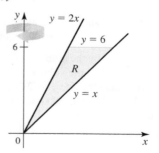

36. $y = 0, y = \ln x, y = 2, x = 0$

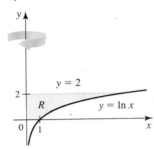

37. $y = x^3, y = 0, x = 2$

38. $y = \sqrt{x}, y = 0, x = 4$

39. $x = \sqrt{4 - y^2}, x = 0$

40. $y = \sin^{-1} x, x = 0, y = \pi/4$

41–44. Which is greater? *For the following regions R, determine which is greater—the volume of the solid generated when R is revolved about the x-axis or about the y-axis.*

41. R is bounded by $y = 2x$, the x-axis, and $x = 5$.

42. R is bounded by $y = 4 - 2x$, the x-axis, and the y-axis.

43. R is bounded by $y = 1 - x^3$, the x-axis, and the y-axis.

44. R is bounded by $y = x^2$ and $y = \sqrt{8x}$.

45–52. Revolution about other axes *Find the volume of the solid generated in the following situations.*

45. The region R bounded by the graphs of $x = 0$, $y = \sqrt{x}$, and $y = 1$ is revolved around the line $y = 1$.

46. The region R bounded by the graphs of $x = 0$, $y = \sqrt{x}$, and $y = 2$ is revolved around the line $x = 4$.

47. The region R bounded by the graph of $y = 2 \sin x$ and the x-axis on $[0, \pi]$ is revolved about the line $y = -2$.

48. The region R bounded by the graph of $y = \ln x$ and the y-axis on the interval $0 \le y \le 1$ is revolved about the line $x = -1$.

49. The region R bounded by the graphs of $y = \sin x$ and $y = 1 - \sin x$ on $\left[\dfrac{\pi}{6}, \dfrac{5\pi}{6} \right]$ is revolved about the line $y = -1$.

50. The region R in the first quadrant bounded by the graphs of $y = x$ and $y = 1 + \dfrac{x}{2}$ is revolved about the line $y = 3$.

51. The region R in the first quadrant bounded by the graphs of $y = 2 - x$ and $y = 2 - 2x$ is revolved about the line $x = 3$.

52. The region R is bounded by the graph of $f(x) = 2x(2 - x)$ and the x-axis. Which is greater, the volume of the solid generated when R is revolved about the line $y = 2$ or the volume of the solid generated when R is revolved about the line $y = 0$? Use integration to justify your answer.

Further Explorations

53. Explain why or why not Determine whether the following statements are true and give an explanation or counterexample.

    a. A pyramid is a solid of revolution.

    b. The volume of a hemisphere can be computed using the disk method.

    c. Let R_1 be the region bounded by $y = \cos x$ and the x-axis on $[-\pi/2, \pi/2]$. Let R_2 be the region bounded by $y = \sin x$ and the x-axis on $[0, \pi]$. The volumes of the solids generated when R_1 and R_2 are revolved about the x-axis are equal.

54–60. Solids of revolution *Find the volume of the solid of revolution. Sketch the region in question.*

54. The region bounded by $y = (\ln x)/\sqrt{x}$, $y = 0$, and $x = 2$ revolved about the x-axis

55. The region bounded by $y = 1/\sqrt{x}$, $y = 0$, $x = 2$, and $x = 6$ revolved about the x-axis

56. The region bounded by $y = \dfrac{1}{\sqrt{x^2 + 1}}$ and $y = \dfrac{1}{\sqrt{2}}$ revolved about the x-axis

57. The region bounded by $y = e^x$, $y = 0$, $x = 0$, and $x = 2$ revolved about the x-axis

58. The region bounded by $y = e^{-x}$, $y = e^x$, $x = 0$, and $x = \ln 4$ revolved about the x-axis

59. The region bounded by $y = \ln x$, $y = \ln x^2$, and $y = \ln 8$ revolved about the y-axis

60. The region bounded by $y = e^{-x}$, $y = 0$, $x = 0$, and $x = p > 0$ revolved about the x-axis (Is the volume bounded as $p \to \infty$?)

61. Fermat's volume calculation (1636) Let R be the region bounded by the curve $y = \sqrt{x + a}$ (with $a > 0$), the y-axis, and the x-axis. Let S be the solid generated by rotating R about the y-axis. Let T be the inscribed cone that has the same circular base as S and height $\sqrt{a}$. Show that volume(S)/volume$(T) = \frac{8}{5}$.

62. Solid from a piecewise function Let

$$f(x) = \begin{cases} x & \text{if } 0 \le x \le 2 \\ 2x - 2 & \text{if } 2 < x \le 5 \\ -2x + 18 & \text{if } 5 < x \le 6. \end{cases}$$

Find the volume of the solid formed when the region bounded by the graph of f, the x-axis, and the line $x = 6$ is revolved about the x-axis.

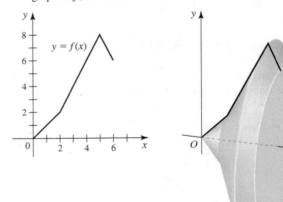

63. Solids from integrals Sketch a solid of revolution whose volume by the disk method is given by the following integrals. Indicate the function that generates the solid. Solutions are not unique.

a. $\int_0^\pi \pi \sin^2 x \, dx$

b. $\int_0^2 \pi(x^2 + 2x + 1) \, dx$

Applications

T 64. Volume of a wooden object A solid wooden object turned on a lathe has a length of 50 cm and diameters (measured in cm) shown in the figure. (A lathe is a tool that spins and cuts a block of wood so that it has circular cross sections.) Use left Riemann sums with uniformly spaced grid points to estimate the volume of the object.

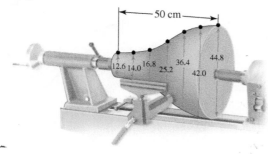

65. Cylinder, cone, hemisphere A right circular cylinder with height R and radius R has a volume of $V_C = \pi R^3$ (height = radius).

a. Find the volume of the cone that is inscribed in the cylinder with the same base as the cylinder and height R. Express the volume in terms of V_C.

b. Find the volume of the hemisphere that is inscribed in the cylinder with the same base as the cylinder. Express the volume in terms of V_C.

66. Water in a bowl A hemispherical bowl of radius 8 inches is filled to a depth of h inches, where $0 \le h \le 8$. Find the volume of water in the bowl as a function of h. (Check the special cases $h = 0$ and $h = 8$.)

T 67. A torus (doughnut) Find the volume of the torus formed when the circle of radius 2 centered at $(3, 0)$ is revolved about the y-axis. Use geometry to evaluate the integral.

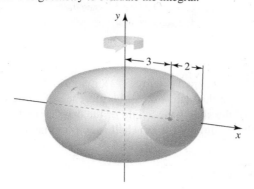

68. Which is greater? Let R be the region bounded by $y = x^2$ and $y = \sqrt{x}$. Use integration to determine which is greater, the volume of the solid generated when R is revolved about the x-axis or about the line $y = 1$.

Additional Exercises

69. Cavalieri's principle *Cavalieri's principle* states that if two solids of equal altitudes have the same cross-sectional areas at every height, then they have equal volumes (see figure).

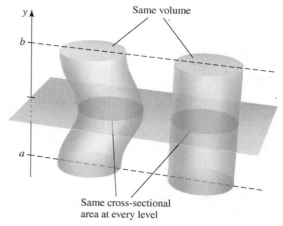

a. Use the theory of this section to justify Cavalieri's principle.

b. Find the radius of a circular cylinder of height 10 m that has the same volume as a box whose dimensions in meters are $2 \times 2 \times 10$.

70. Limiting volume Consider the region R in the first quadrant bounded by $y = x^{1/n}$ and $y = x^n$, where $n > 1$ is a positive number.

a. Find the volume $V(n)$ of the solid generated when R is revolved about the x-axis. Express your answer in terms of n.

b. Evaluate $\lim_{n \to \infty} V(n)$. Interpret this limit geometrically.

QUICK CHECK ANSWERS

1. The average value of A on $[a, b]$ is $\overline{A} = \dfrac{1}{b - a} \int_a^b A(x) \, dx$. Therefore, $V = (b - a)\overline{A}$.   2. $A(x) = (2 - 2x^2)^2$
3. **(a)** A cylinder with height 2 and radius 2; **(b)** a cone with height 2 and base radius 2   4. When $g(x) = 0$, the washer method $V = \int_a^b \pi(f(x)^2 - g(x)^2) \, dx$ reduces to the disk method $V = \int_a^b \pi(f(x)^2) \, dx$.   5. **(a)** Inner radius $= x^2 + 1$ **(b)** outer radius $= \sqrt{x} + 1$;
6. $\int_0^1 \pi(y^{2/3} - y^2) \, dy$ ◄

6.4 Volume by Shells

You can solve many challenging volume problems using the disk/washer method. There are, however, some volume problems that are difficult to solve with this method. For this reason, we extend our discussion of volume problems to the *shell method*, which—like the disk/washer method—is used to compute the volume of solids of revolution.

Cylindrical Shells

➤ Why another method? Suppose R is the region in the first quadrant bounded by the graph of $y = x^2 - x^3$ and the x-axis (Figure 6.38). When R is revolved about the y-axis, the resulting solid has a volume that is difficult to compute using the washer method. The volume is much easier to compute using the shell method.

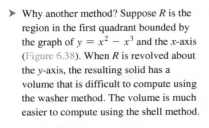

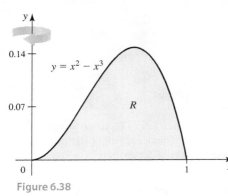

Figure 6.38

Let R be a region bounded by the graph of f, the x-axis, and the lines $x = a$ and $x = b$, where $0 \le a < b$ and $f(x) \ge 0$ on $[a, b]$. When R is revolved about the y-axis, a solid is generated (Figure 6.39) whose volume is computed with the slice-and-sum strategy.

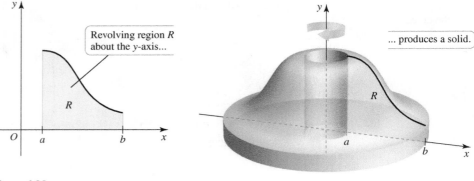

Figure 6.39

We divide $[a, b]$ into n subintervals of length $\Delta x = (b - a)/n$ and identify an arbitrary point x_k^* on the kth subinterval, for $k = 1, \ldots, n$. Now observe the rectangle built on the kth subinterval with a height of $f(x_k^*)$ and a width Δx (Figure 6.40). As it revolves about the y-axis, this rectangle sweeps out a thin *cylindrical shell*.

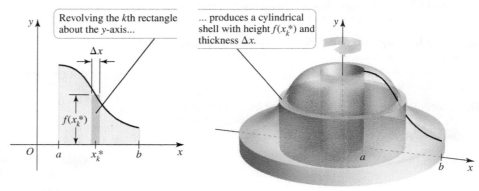

Figure 6.40

When the kth cylindrical shell is unwrapped (Figure 6.41), it approximates a thin rectangular slab. The approximate length of the slab is the circumference of a circle with radius x_k^*, which is $2\pi x_k^*$. The height of the slab is the height of the original rectangle $f(x_k^*)$ and its thickness is Δx; therefore, the volume of the kth shell is approximately

$$\underbrace{2\pi x_k^*}_{\text{length}} \cdot \underbrace{f(x_k^*)}_{\text{height}} \cdot \underbrace{\Delta x}_{\text{thickness}} = 2\pi x_k^* f(x_k^*) \Delta x.$$

Summing the volumes of the n cylindrical shells gives an approximation to the volume of the entire solid:

$$V \approx \sum_{k=1}^{n} 2\pi x_k^* f(x_k^*) \Delta x.$$

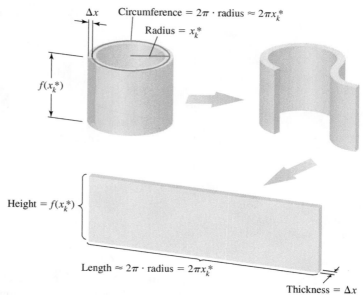

Figure 6.41

As n increases and as Δx approaches 0 (Figure 6.42), we obtain the exact volume of the solid as a definite integral:

$$V = \lim_{n \to \infty} \sum_{k=1}^{n} \underbrace{2\pi \, x_k^*}_{\substack{\text{shell} \\ \text{circumference}}} \overbrace{f(x_k^*)}^{\substack{\text{shell} \\ \text{height}}} \underbrace{\Delta x}_{\substack{\text{shell} \\ \text{thickness}}} = \int_a^b 2\pi x f(x) \, dx.$$

➤ Rather than memorizing, think of the meaning of the factors in this formula: $f(x)$ is the height of a single cylindrical shell, $2\pi x$ is the circumference of the shell, and dx corresponds to the thickness of a shell. Therefore, $2\pi x f(x) \, dx$ represents the volume of a single shell, and we sum the volumes from $x = a$ to $x = b$. Notice that the integrand for the shell method is the function $A(x)$ that gives the surface area of the shell of radius x, for $a \le x \le b$.

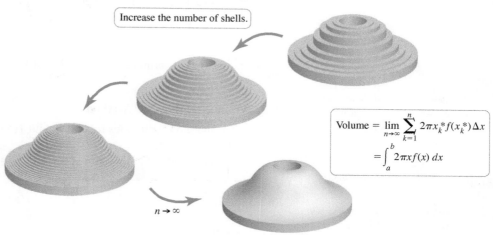

Increase the number of shells.

$$\text{Volume} = \lim_{n \to \infty} \sum_{k=1}^{n} 2\pi x_k^* f(x_k^*) \Delta x$$
$$= \int_a^b 2\pi x f(x) \, dx$$

$n \to \infty$

Figure 6.42

Before doing examples, we generalize this method as we did for the disk method. Suppose that the region R is bounded by two curves, $y = f(x)$ and $y = g(x)$, where $f(x) \ge g(x)$ on $[a, b]$ (Figure 6.43). What is the volume of the solid generated when R is revolved about the y-axis?

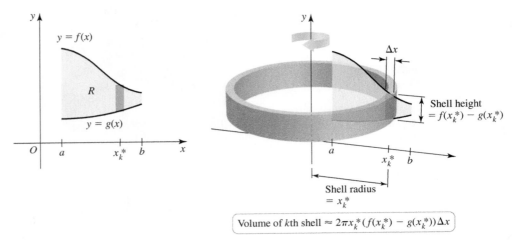

Figure 6.43

The situation is similar to the case we just considered. A typical rectangle in R sweeps out a cylindrical shell, but now the height of the kth shell is $f(x_k^*) - g(x_k^*)$, for $k = 1, \ldots, n$. As before, we take the radius of the kth shell to be x_k^*, which means the volume of the kth shell is approximated by $2\pi x_k^*(f(x_k^*) - g(x_k^*))\Delta x$ (Figure 6.43). Summing the volumes of all the shells gives an approximation to the volume of the entire solid:

$$V \approx \sum_{k=1}^{n} \underbrace{2\pi x_k^*}_{\substack{\text{shell} \\ \text{circumference}}} \underbrace{(f(x_k^*) - g(x_k^*))}_{\substack{\text{shell} \\ \text{height}}} \Delta x.$$

Taking the limit as $n \to \infty$ (which implies that $\Delta x \to 0$), the exact volume is the definite integral

$$V = \lim_{n \to \infty} \sum_{k=1}^{n} 2\pi x_k^*(f(x_k^*) - g(x_k^*))\Delta x = \int_a^b 2\pi x(f(x) - g(x))\, dx.$$

We now have the formula for the shell method.

> An analogous formula for the shell method when R is revolved about the x-axis is obtained by reversing the roles of x and y:
>
> $$V = \int_c^d 2\pi y(p(y) - q(y))\, dy.$$
>
> We assume R is bounded by the curves $x = p(y)$ and $x = q(y)$, where $p(y) \ge q(y)$ on $[c, d]$.

Volume by the Shell Method

Let f and g be continuous functions with $f(x) \ge g(x)$ on $[a, b]$. If R is the region bounded by the curves $y = f(x)$ and $y = g(x)$ between the lines $x = a$ and $x = b$, the volume of the solid generated when R is revolved about the y-axis is

$$V = \int_a^b 2\pi x(f(x) - g(x))\, dx.$$

EXAMPLE 1   A sine bowl Let R be the region bounded by the graph of $f(x) = \sin x^2$, the x-axis, and the vertical line $x = \sqrt{\pi/2}$ (Figure 6.44). Find the volume of the solid generated when R is revolved about the y-axis.

SOLUTION Revolving R about the y-axis produces a bowl-shaped region (Figure 6.45). The radius of a typical cylindrical shell is x and its height is $f(x) = \sin x^2$. Therefore, the volume by the shell method is

$$V = \int_a^b \underbrace{2\pi x}_{\substack{\text{shell} \\ \text{circumference}}} \underbrace{f(x)}_{\substack{\text{shell} \\ \text{height}}} dx = \int_0^{\sqrt{\pi/2}} 2\pi x \sin x^2\, dx.$$

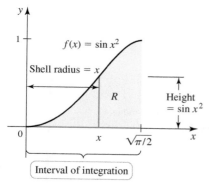

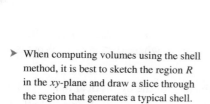

Figure 6.44

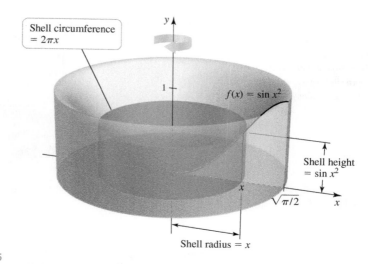

Figure 6.45

> When computing volumes using the shell method, it is best to sketch the region R in the xy-plane and draw a slice through the region that generates a typical shell.

Now we make the change of variables $u = x^2$, which means that $du = 2x\,dx$. The lower limit $x = 0$ becomes $u = 0$ and the upper limit $x = \sqrt{\pi/2}$ becomes $u = \pi/2$. The volume of the solid is

$$V = \int_0^{\sqrt{\pi/2}} 2\pi x \sin x^2 \, dx = \pi \int_0^{\pi/2} \sin u \, du \qquad u = x^2,\ du = 2x\,dx$$

$$= \pi(-\cos u)\Big|_0^{\pi/2} \qquad \text{Fundamental Theorem}$$

$$= \pi(0 - (-1)) = \pi. \qquad \text{Simplify.}$$

Related Exercises 5–14 ◄

QUICK CHECK 1 The triangle bounded by the x-axis, the line $y = 2x$, and the line $x = 1$ is revolved about the y-axis. Give an integral that equals the volume of the resulting solid using the shell method. ◄

EXAMPLE 2 **Shells about the x-axis** Let R be the region in the first quadrant bounded by the graph of $y = \sqrt{x - 2}$ and the line $y = 2$. Find the volume of the solid generated when R is revolved about the x-axis.

SOLUTION The revolution is about the x-axis, so the integration in the shell method is with respect to y. A typical shell runs parallel to the x-axis and has radius y, where $0 \le y \le 2$; the shells extend from the y-axis to the curve $y = \sqrt{x - 2}$ (Figure 6.46). Solving $y = \sqrt{x - 2}$ for x, we have $x = y^2 + 2$, which is the height of the shell at the point y (Figure 6.47). Integrating with respect to y, the volume of the solid is

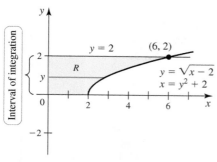

Figure 6.46

$$V = \int_0^2 \underbrace{2\pi y}_{\substack{\text{shell} \\ \text{circumference}}} \underbrace{(y^2 + 2)}_{\substack{\text{shell} \\ \text{height}}} dy = 2\pi \int_0^2 (y^3 + 2y) \, dy = 16\pi.$$

➤ In Example 2, we could use the disk/washer method to compute the volume, but notice that this approach requires splitting the region into two subregions. A better approach is to use the shell method and integrate along the y-axis.

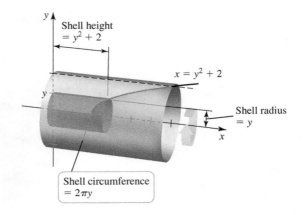

Figure 6.47

Related Exercises 15–26 ◀

EXAMPLE 3   Volume of a drilled sphere A cylindrical hole with radius r is drilled symmetrically through the center of a sphere with radius a, where $0 \le r \le a$. What is the volume of the remaining material?

SOLUTION The y-axis is chosen to coincide with the axis of the cylindrical hole. We let R be the region in the xy-plane bounded above by $f(x) = \sqrt{a^2 - x^2}$, the upper half of a circle of radius a, and bounded below by $g(x) = -\sqrt{a^2 - x^2}$, the lower half of a circle of radius a, for $r \le x \le a$ (Figure 6.48a). Slices are taken perpendicular to the x-axis from $x = r$ to $x = a$. When a slice is revolved about the y-axis, it sweeps out a cylindrical shell that is concentric with the hole through the sphere (Figure 6.48b). The radius of a typical shell is x and its height is $f(x) - g(x) = 2\sqrt{a^2 - x^2}$. Therefore, the volume of the material that remains in the sphere is

$$V = \int_r^a 2\pi x \left(2\sqrt{a^2 - x^2}\right) dx$$

$$= -2\pi \int_{a^2 - r^2}^0 \sqrt{u}\, du \quad u = a^2 - x^2,\, du = -2x\, dx$$

$$= 2\pi \left(\frac{2}{3} u^{3/2}\right)\Big|_0^{a^2 - r^2} \quad \text{Fundamental Theorem}$$

$$= \frac{4\pi}{3}(a^2 - r^2)^{3/2}. \quad \text{Simplify.}$$

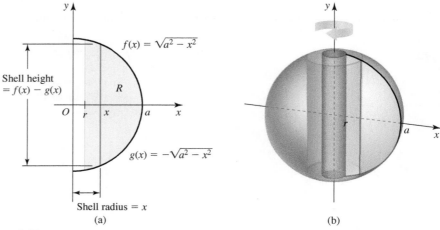

(a)

(b)

Figure 6.48

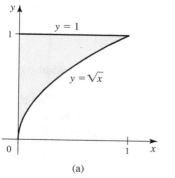

(a)

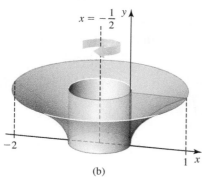

(b)

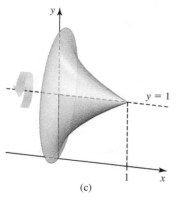

(c)

Figure 6.49

> If we instead revolved about the y-axis
($x = 0$), the radius of the shell would be
x. Because we are revolving about the line
$x = -\frac{1}{2}$, the radius of the shell is $x + \frac{1}{2}$.

> The disk/washer method can also be used
for part (a), and the shell method can also
be used for part (b).

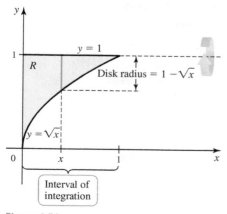

Figure 6.51

It is important to check the result by examining special cases. In the case that $r = a$ (the radius of the hole equals the radius of the sphere), our calculation gives a volume of 0, which is correct. In the case that $r = 0$ (no hole in the sphere), our calculation gives the correct volume of a sphere, $\frac{4}{3}\pi a^3$.

Related Exercises 27–32 ◄

EXAMPLE 4   Revolving about other lines Let R be the region bounded by the curve $y = \sqrt{x}$, the line $y = 1$, and the y-axis (Figure 6.49a).

a. Use the shell method to find the volume of the solid generated when R is revolved about the line $x = -\frac{1}{2}$ (Figure 6.49b).

b. Use the disk/washer method to find the volume of the solid generated when R is revolved about the line $y = 1$ (Figure 6.49c).

SOLUTION

a. Using the shell method, we must imagine taking slices through R parallel to the y-axis. A typical slice through R at a point x, where $0 \le x \le 1$, has length $1 - \sqrt{x}$. When that slice is revolved about the line $x = -\frac{1}{2}$, it sweeps out a cylindrical shell with a radius of $x + \frac{1}{2}$ and a height of $1 - \sqrt{x}$ (Figure 6.50). A slight modification of the standard shell method gives the volume of the solid:

$$\int_0^1 \underbrace{2\pi\left(x + \frac{1}{2}\right)}_{\substack{\text{shell}\\\text{circumference}}}\underbrace{(1 - \sqrt{x})}_{\substack{\text{shell}\\\text{height}}}\,dx = 2\pi\int_0^1\left(x - x^{3/2} + \frac{1}{2} - \frac{x^{1/2}}{2}\right)dx \qquad \begin{array}{l}\text{Expand}\\\text{integrand.}\end{array}$$

$$= 2\pi\left(\frac{1}{2}x^2 - \frac{2}{5}x^{5/2} + \frac{1}{2}x - \frac{1}{3}x^{3/2}\right)\Big|_0^1 = \frac{8\pi}{15}. \quad \begin{array}{l}\text{Evaluate}\\\text{integral.}\end{array}$$

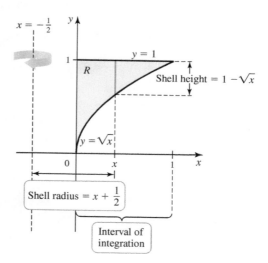

Figure 6.50

b. Using the disk/washer method, we take slices through R parallel to the y-axis. Consider a typical slice at a point x, where $0 \le x \le 1$. Its length, now measured with respect to the line $y = 1$, is $1 - \sqrt{x}$. When that slice is revolved about the line $y = 1$, it sweeps out a disk of radius $1 - \sqrt{x}$ (Figure 6.51). By the disk/washer method, the volume of the solid is

$$\int_0^1 \pi\underbrace{(1 - \sqrt{x})^2}_{\substack{\text{radius of}\\\text{disk}}}dx = \pi\int_0^1(1 - 2\sqrt{x} + x)\,dx \quad \text{Expand integrand.}$$

$$= \pi\left(x - \frac{4}{3}x^{3/2} + \frac{1}{2}x^2\right)\Big|_0^1 \quad \text{Evaluate integral.}$$

$$= \frac{\pi}{6}.$$

Related Exercises 33–40 ◄

QUICK CHECK 2 Write the volume integral in Example 4b in the case that R is revolved about the line $y = -5$. ◄

Restoring Order

After working with slices, disks, washers, and shells, you may feel somewhat overwhelmed. How do you choose a method, and which method is best?

Notice that the disk method is just a special case of the washer method. So for solids of revolution, the choice is between the washer method and the shell method. In *principle*, either method can be used. In *practice*, one method usually produces an integral that is easier to evaluate than the other method. The following table summarizes these methods.

SUMMARY Disk/Washer and Shell Methods	
Integration with respect to x 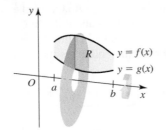	**Disk/washer method about the x-axis** Disks/washers are *perpendicular* to the x-axis. $$\int_a^b \pi(f(x)^2 - g(x)^2)\, dx$$
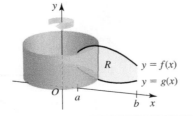	**Shell method about the y-axis** Shells are *parallel* to the y-axis. $$\int_a^b 2\pi x(f(x) - g(x))\, dx$$
Integration with respect to y 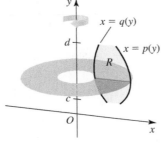	**Disk/washer method about the y-axis** Disks/washers are *perpendicular* to the y-axis. $$\int_c^d \pi(p(y)^2 - q(y)^2)\, dy$$
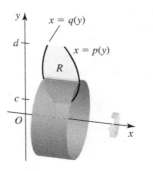	**Shell method about the x-axis** Shells are *parallel* to the x-axis. $$\int_c^d 2\pi y(p(y) - q(y))\, dy$$

The following example shows that while two methods may be used on the same problem, one of them may be preferable.

EXAMPLE 5   Volume by which method? The region R is bounded by the graphs of $f(x) = 2x - x^2$ and $g(x) = x$ on the interval $[0, 1]$ (Figure 6.52). Use the washer method and the shell method to find the volume of the solid formed when R is revolved about the x-axis.

SOLUTION Solving $f(x) = g(x)$, we find that the curves intersect at the points $(0, 0)$ and $(1, 1)$. Using the washer method, the upper bounding curve is the graph of f, the lower bounding curve is the graph of g, and a typical washer is perpendicular to the x-axis (Figure 6.53). Therefore, the volume is

$$V = \int_0^1 \pi((2x - x^2)^2 - x^2)\, dx \quad \text{Washer method}$$

$$= \pi \int_0^1 (x^4 - 4x^3 + 3x^2)\, dx \quad \text{Expand integrand.}$$

$$= \pi \left(\frac{x^5}{5} - x^4 + x^3 \right)\Big|_0^1 = \frac{\pi}{5}. \quad \text{Evaluate integral.}$$

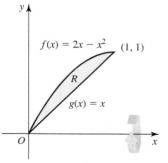

Figure 6.52

> ➤ To solve $y = 2x - x^2$ for x, write the equation as $x^2 - 2x + y = 0$ and complete the square or use the quadratic formula.

The shell method requires expressing the bounding curves in the form $x = p(y)$ for the right curve and $x = q(y)$ for the left curve. The right curve is $x = y$. Solving $y = 2x - x^2$ for x, we find that $x = 1 - \sqrt{1 - y}$ describes the left curve. A typical shell is parallel to the x-axis (Figure 6.54). Therefore, the volume is

$$V = \int_0^1 2\pi y \underbrace{(y}_{p(y)} - \underbrace{(1 - \sqrt{1 - y}))}_{q(y)}\, dy.$$

This integral equals $\frac{\pi}{5}$, but it is more difficult to evaluate than the integral required by the washer method. In this case, the washer method is preferable. Of course, the shell method may be preferable for other problems.

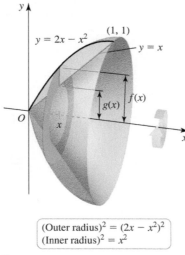

(Outer radius)$^2 = (2x - x^2)^2$
(Inner radius)$^2 = x^2$

Figure 6.53

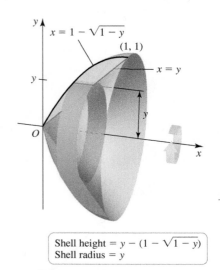

Shell height $= y - (1 - \sqrt{1 - y})$
Shell radius $= y$

Figure 6.54

Related Exercises 41–48 ◄

QUICK CHECK 3 Suppose the region in Example 5 is revolved about the y-axis. Which method (washer or shell) leads to an easier integral? ◄

SECTION 6.4 EXERCISES

Review Questions

1. Assume f and g are continuous with $f(x) \geq g(x)$ on $[a, b]$. The region bounded by the graphs of f and g and the lines $x = a$ and $x = b$ is revolved about the y-axis. Write the integral given by the shell method that equals the volume of the resulting solid.

2. Fill in the blanks: A region R is revolved about the y-axis. The volume of the resulting solid could (in principle) be found using the disk/washer method and integrating with respect to _____ or using the shell method and integrating with respect to _____.

3. Fill in the blanks: A region R is revolved about the x-axis. The volume of the resulting solid could (in principle) be found using the disk/washer method and integrating with respect to _____ or using the shell method and integrating with respect to _____.

4. Are shell method integrals easier to evaluate than washer method integrals? Explain.

Basic Skills

5–14. Shell method *Let R be the region bounded by the following curves. Use the shell method to find the volume of the solid generated when R is revolved about the y-axis.*

5. $y = x - x^2, y = 0$

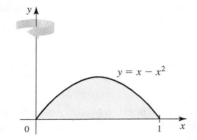

6. $y = -x^2 + 4x + 2, y = x^2 - 6x + 10$

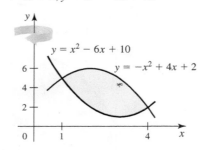

7. $y = (1 + x^2)^{-1}, y = 0, x = 0,$ and $x = 2$

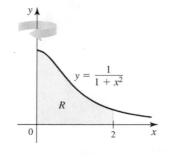

8. $y = 6 - x, y = 0, x = 2,$ and $x = 4$

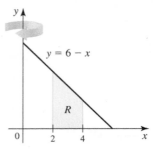

9. $y = 3x, y = 3,$ and $x = 0$ (Use integration and check your answer using the volume formula for a cone.)

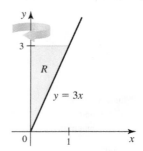

10. $y = 1 - x^2, x = 0,$ and $y = 0,$ in the first quadrant

11. $y = x^3 - x^8 + 1, y = 1$

12. $y = \sqrt{x}, y = 0,$ and $x = 1$

13. $y = \cos x^2, y = 0,$ for $0 \leq x \leq \sqrt{\pi/2}$

14. $y = \sqrt{4 - 2x^2}, y = 0,$ and $x = 0,$ in the first quadrant

15–26. Shell method *Let R be the region bounded by the following curves. Use the shell method to find the volume of the solid generated when R is revolved about the x-axis.*

15. $y = \sqrt{x}, y = 0,$ and $x = 4$

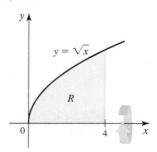

16. $y = 8, y = 2x + 2, x = 0,$ and $x = 2$

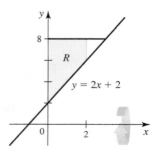

17. $y = 4 - x$, $y = 2$, and $x = 0$

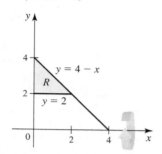

18. $x = \dfrac{4}{y + y^3}$, $x = \dfrac{1}{\sqrt{3}}$, and $y = 1$

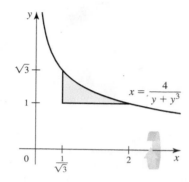

19. $y = x$, $y = 2 - x$, and $y = 0$ **20.** $x = y^2$, $x = 4$, and $y = 0$

21. $x = y^2$, $x = 0$, and $y = 3$ **22.** $y = x^3$, $y = 1$, and $x = 0$

23. $y = 2x^{-3/2}$, $y = 2$, $y = 16$, and $x = 0$

24. $y = \sqrt{\sin^{-1} x}$, $y = \sqrt{\pi/2}$, and $x = 0$

25. $y = \sqrt{\cos^{-1} x}$, in the first quadrant

26. $y = \sqrt{50 - 2x^2}$, in the first quadrant

27–32. Shell method *Use the shell method to find the volume of the following solids.*

27. A right circular cone of radius 3 and height 8

28. The solid formed when a hole of radius 2 is drilled symmetrically along the axis of a right circular cylinder of height 6 and radius 4

29. The solid formed when a hole of radius 3 is drilled symmetrically along the axis of a right circular cone of radius 6 and height 9

30. The solid formed when a hole of radius 3 is drilled symmetrically through the center of a sphere of radius 6

31. The *ellipsoid* formed when that part of the ellipse $x^2 + 2y^2 = 4$ with $x \geq 0$ is revolved about the y-axis

32. A hole of radius $r \leq R$ is drilled symmetrically along the axis of a bullet. The bullet is formed by revolving the parabola
$y = 6\left(1 - \dfrac{x^2}{R^2}\right)$ about the y-axis, where $0 \leq x \leq R$.

33–36. Shell method about other lines *Let R be the region bounded by $y = x^2$, $x = 1$, and $y = 0$. Use the shell method to find the volume of the solid generated when R is revolved about the following lines.*

33. $x = -2$ **34.** $x = -1$ **35.** $y = -2$ **36.** $y = 2$

37–40. Different axes of revolution *Use either the washer or shell method to find the volume of the solid that is generated when the region in the first quadrant bounded by $y = x^2$, $y = 1$, and $x = 0$ is revolved about the following lines.*

37. $y = -2$ **38.** $x = -1$ **39.** $y = 6$ **40.** $x = 2$

41–48. Washers vs. shells *Let R be the region bounded by the following curves. Let S be the solid generated when R is revolved about the given axis. If possible, find the volume of S by both the disk/washer and shell methods. Check that your results agree and state which method is easier to apply.*

41. $y = x$, $y = x^{1/3}$ in the first quadrant; revolved about the x-axis

42. $y = x^2$, $y = 2 - x$, and $x = 0$ in the first quadrant; revolved about the y-axis

43. $y = 1/(x + 1)$, $y = 1 - x/3$; revolved about the x-axis

44. $y = (x - 2)^3 - 2$, $x = 0$, and $y = 25$; revolved about the y-axis

45. $y = \sqrt{\ln x}$, $y = \sqrt{\ln x^2}$, and $y = 1$; revolved about the x-axis

46. $y = 6/(x + 3)$, $y = 2 - x$; revolved about the x-axis

47. $y = x - x^4$, $y = 0$; revolved about the x-axis

48. $y = x - x^4$, $y = 0$; revolved about the y-axis

Further Explorations

49. Explain why or why not Determine whether the following statements are true and give an explanation or counterexample.

   a. When using the shell method, the axis of the cylindrical shells is parallel to the axis of revolution.

   b. If a region is revolved about the y-axis, then the shell method must be used.

   c. If a region is revolved about the x-axis, then in principle, it is possible to use the disk/washer method and integrate with respect to x or the shell method and integrate with respect to y.

50–54. Solids of revolution *Find the volume of the following solids of revolution. Sketch the region in question.*

50. The region bounded by $y = (\ln x)/x^2$, $y = 0$, and $x = 3$ revolved about the y-axis

51. The region bounded by $y = 1/x^2$, $y = 0$, $x = 2$, and $x = 8$ revolved about the y-axis

52. The region bounded by $y = 1/(x^2 + 1)$, $y = 0$, $x = 1$, and $x = 4$ revolved about the y-axis

53. The region bounded by $y = e^x/x$, $y = 0$, $x = 1$, and $x = 2$ revolved about the y-axis

54. The region bounded by $y^2 = \ln x$, $y^2 = \ln x^3$, and $y = 2$ revolved about the x-axis

55–62. Choose your method *Find the volume of the following solids using the method of your choice.*

55. The solid formed when the region bounded by $y = x^2$ and $y = 2 - x^2$ is revolved about the x-axis

56. The solid formed when the region bounded by $y = \sin x$ and $y = 1 - \sin x$ between $x = \pi/6$ and $x = 5\pi/6$ is revolved about the x-axis

57. The solid formed when the region bounded by $y = x$, $y = 2x + 2$, $x = 2$, and $x = 6$ is revolved about the y-axis

58. The solid formed when the region bounded by $y = x^3$, the x-axis, and $x = 2$ is revolved about the x-axis

59. The solid whose base is the region bounded by $y = x^2$ and the line $y = 1$, and whose cross sections perpendicular to the base and parallel to the x-axis are semicircles

60. The solid formed when the region bounded by $y = 2$, $y = 2x + 2$, and $x = 6$ is revolved about the y-axis

61. The solid whose base is the square with vertices $(1, 0)$, $(0, 1)$, $(-1, 0)$, and $(0, -1)$, and whose cross sections perpendicular to the base and perpendicular to the x-axis are semicircles

62. The solid formed when the region bounded by $y = \sqrt{x}$, the x-axis, and $x = 4$ is revolved about the x-axis

T 63. Equal volumes Consider the region R bounded by the curves $y = ax^2 + 1$, $y = 0$, $x = 0$, and $x = 1$, for $a \geq -1$. Let S_1 and S_2 be solids generated when R is revolved about the x- and y-axes, respectively.

  a. Find V_1 and V_2, the volumes of S_1 and S_2, as functions of a.

  b. What are the values of $a \geq -1$ for which $V_1(a) = V_2(a)$?

64. A hemisphere by three methods Let R be the region in the first quadrant bounded by the circle $x^2 + y^2 = r^2$ and the coordinate axes. Find the volume of a hemisphere of radius r in the following ways.

  a. Revolve R about the x-axis and use the disk method.

  b. Revolve R about the x-axis and use the shell method.

  c. Assume the base of the hemisphere is in the xy-plane and use the general slicing method with slices perpendicular to the xy-plane and parallel to the x-axis.

65. A cone by two methods Verify that the volume of a right circular cone with a base radius of r and a height of h is $\pi r^2 h/3$. Use the region bounded by the line $y = rx/h$, the x-axis, and the line $x = h$, where the region is rotated about the x-axis. Then (a) use the disk method and integrate with respect to x, and (b) use the shell method and integrate with respect to y.

66. A spherical cap by three methods Consider the cap of thickness h that has been sliced from a sphere of radius r (see figure). Verify that the volume of the cap is $\pi h^2 (3r - h)/3$ using (a) the washer method, (b) the shell method, and (c) the general slicing method. Check for consistency among the three methods and check the special cases $h = r$ and $h = 0$.

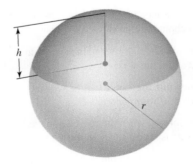

Applications

67. Water in a bowl A hemispherical bowl of radius 8 inches is filled to a depth of h inches, where $0 \leq h \leq 8$ ($h = 0$ corresponds to an empty bowl). Use the shell method to find the volume of water in the bowl as a function of h. (Check the special cases $h = 0$ and $h = 8$.)

68. Wedge from a tree Imagine a cylindrical tree of radius a. A wedge is cut from the tree by making two cuts: one in a horizontal plane P perpendicular to the axis of the cylinder and one that makes an angle θ with P, intersecting P along a diameter of the tree (see figure). What is the volume of the wedge?

T 69. A torus (doughnut) Find the volume of the torus formed when a circle of radius 2 centered at $(3, 0)$ is revolved about the y-axis. Use the shell method. You may need a computer algebra system or table of integrals to evaluate the integral.

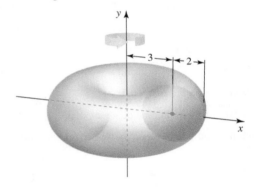

Additional Exercises

70. Different axes of revolution Suppose R is the region bounded by $y = f(x)$ and $y = g(x)$ on the interval $[a, b]$, where $f(x) \geq g(x)$.

  a. Show that if R is revolved about the vertical line $x = x_0$, where $x_0 < a$, then by the shell method, the volume of the resulting solid is $V = \int_a^b 2\pi(x - x_0)(f(x) - g(x))\, dx$.

  b. How is this formula changed if $x_0 > b$?

71. Different axes of revolution Suppose R is the region bounded by $y = f(x)$ and $y = g(x)$ on the interval $[a, b]$, where $f(x) \geq g(x) \geq 0$.

  a. Show that if R is revolved about the horizontal line $y = y_0$ that lies below R, then by the washer method, the volume of the resulting solid is

$$V = \int_a^b \pi\left((f(x) - y_0)^2 - (g(x) - y_0)^2\right) dx.$$

  b. How is this formula changed if the line $y = y_0$ lies above R?

72. **Ellipsoids** An ellipse centered at the origin is described by the equation $x^2/a^2 + y^2/b^2 = 1$. If an ellipse R is revolved about either axis, the resulting solid is an *ellipsoid.*

    a. Find the volume of the ellipsoid generated when R is revolved about the x-axis (in terms of a and b).

    b. Find the volume of the ellipsoid generated when R is revolved about the y-axis (in terms of a and b).

    c. Should the results of parts (a) and (b) agree? Explain.

73. **Change of variables** Suppose $f(x) > 0$ for all x and $\int_0^4 f(x)\, dx = 10$. Let R be the region in the first quadrant bounded by the coordinate axes, $y = f(x^2)$, and $x = 2$. Find the volume of the solid generated by revolving R about the y-axis.

74. **Equal integrals** Without evaluating integrals, explain the following equalities. (*Hint:* Draw pictures.)

    a. $\pi \int_0^4 (8 - 2x)^2\, dx = 2\pi \int_0^8 y\left(4 - \dfrac{y}{2}\right) dy$

    b. $\int_0^2 (25 - (x^2 + 1)^2)\, dx = 2 \int_1^5 y\sqrt{y - 1}\, dy$

75. **Volumes without calculus** Solve the following problems with *and* without calculus. A good picture helps.

    a. A cube with side length r is inscribed in a sphere, which is inscribed in a right circular cone, which is inscribed in a right circular cylinder. The side length (slant height) of the cone is equal to its diameter. What is the volume of the cylinder?

    b. A cube is inscribed in a right circular cone with a radius of 1 and a height of 3. What is the volume of the cube?

    c. A cylindrical hole 10 in long is drilled symmetrically through the center of a sphere. How much material is left in the sphere? (Enough information *is* given.)

QUICK CHECK ANSWERS

1. $\int_0^1 2\pi x(2x)\, dx$ 2. $V = \int_0^1 \pi(36 - (\sqrt{x} + 5)^2)\, dx$
3. The shell method is easier. ◀

6.5 Length of Curves

The space station orbits Earth in an elliptical path. How far does it travel in one orbit? A baseball slugger launches a home run into the upper deck and the sportscaster claims it landed 480 feet from home plate. But how far did the ball actually travel along its flight path? These questions deal with the length of trajectories or, more generally, with *arc length*. As you will see, their answers can be found by integration.

There are two common ways to formulate problems about arc length: The curve may be given explicitly in the form $y = f(x)$ or it may be defined *parametrically*. In this section, we deal with the first case. Parametric curves are introduced in Section 10.1, and the associated arc length problem is discussed in Section 11.8.

Arc Length for $y = f(x)$

Suppose a curve is given by $y = f(x)$, where f is a function with a continuous first derivative on the interval $[a, b]$. The goal is to determine how far you would travel if you walked along the curve from $(a, f(a))$ to $(b, f(b))$. This distance is the arc length, which we denote L.

▶ More generally, we may choose any point in the kth subinterval and Δx may vary from one subinterval to the next. Using right endpoints, as we do here, simplifies the discussion and leads to the same result.

As shown in Figure 6.55, we divide $[a, b]$ into n subintervals of length $\Delta x = (b - a)/n$, where x_k is the right endpoint of the kth subinterval, for $k = 1, \ldots, n$. Joining the corresponding points on the curve by line segments, we obtain a polygonal line with n line segments. If n is large and Δx is small, the length of the polygonal line is a good approximation to the length of the actual curve. The strategy is to find the length of the polygonal line and then let n increase, while Δx goes to zero, to get the exact length of the curve.

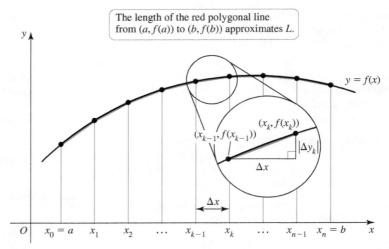

Figure 6.55

Consider the kth subinterval $[x_{k-1}, x_k]$ and the line segment between the points $(x_{k-1}, f(x_{k-1}))$ and $(x_k, f(x_k))$. We let the change in the y-coordinate between these points be

$$\Delta y_k = f(x_k) - f(x_{k-1}).$$

The kth line segment is the hypotenuse of a right triangle with sides of length Δx and $|\Delta y_k| = |f(x_k) - f(x_{k-1})|$. The length of each line segment is

$$\sqrt{(\Delta x)^2 + |\Delta y_k|^2}, \quad \text{for} \quad k = 1, 2, \ldots, n.$$

Summing these lengths, we obtain the length of the polygonal line, which approximates the length L of the curve:

$$L \approx \sum_{k=1}^{n} \sqrt{(\Delta x)^2 + |\Delta y_k|^2}.$$

> Notice that Δx is the same for each subinterval, but Δy_k depends on the subinterval.

In previous applications of the integral, we would, at this point, take the limit as $n \to \infty$ and $\Delta x \to 0$ to obtain a definite integral. However, because of the presence of the Δy_k term, we must complete one additional step before taking a limit. Notice that the slope of the line segment on the kth subinterval is $\Delta y_k / \Delta x$ (rise over run). By the Mean Value Theorem (see the margin figure and Section 4.6), this slope equals $f'(x_k^*)$ for some point x_k^* on the kth subinterval. Therefore,

$$
\begin{aligned}
L &\approx \sum_{k=1}^{n} \sqrt{(\Delta x)^2 + |\Delta y_k|^2} \\
&= \sum_{k=1}^{n} \sqrt{(\Delta x)^2 \left(1 + \left(\frac{\Delta y_k}{\Delta x}\right)^2\right)} \qquad \text{Factor out } (\Delta x)^2. \\
&= \sum_{k=1}^{n} \sqrt{1 + \left(\frac{\Delta y_k}{\Delta x}\right)^2} \, \Delta x \qquad \text{Bring } \Delta x \text{ out of the square root.} \\
&= \sum_{k=1}^{n} \sqrt{1 + f'(x_k^*)^2} \, \Delta x. \qquad \text{Mean Value Theorem}
\end{aligned}
$$

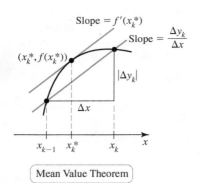

Mean Value Theorem

Now we have a Riemann sum. As n increases and as Δx approaches zero, the sum approaches a definite integral, which is also the exact length of the curve. We have

$$L = \lim_{n \to \infty} \sum_{k=1}^{n} \sqrt{1 + f'(x_k^*)^2} \, \Delta x = \int_a^b \sqrt{1 + f'(x)^2} \, dx.$$

▶ Note that $1 + f'(x)^2$ is positive, so the square root in the integrand is defined whenever f' exists. To ensure that $\sqrt{1 + f'(x)^2}$ is integrable on $[a, b]$, we require that f' be continuous.

> **DEFINITION Arc Length for $y = f(x)$**
>
> Let f have a continuous first derivative on the interval $[a, b]$. The length of the curve from $(a, f(a))$ to $(b, f(b))$ is
>
> $$L = \int_a^b \sqrt{1 + f'(x)^2}\, dx.$$

QUICK CHECK 1 What does the arc length formula give for the length of the line $y = x$ between $x = 0$ and $x = a$, where $a \geq 0$? ◄

EXAMPLE 1   Arc length Find the length of the curve $f(x) = x^{3/2}$ between $x = 0$ and $x = 4$ (Figure 6.56).

SOLUTION Notice that $f'(x) = \frac{3}{2} x^{1/2}$, which is continuous on the interval $[0, 4]$. Using the arc length formula, we have

$$L = \int_a^b \sqrt{1 + f'(x)^2}\, dx = \int_0^4 \sqrt{1 + \left(\frac{3}{2} x^{1/2}\right)^2}\, dx \quad \text{Substitute for } f'(x).$$

$$= \int_0^4 \sqrt{1 + \frac{9}{4} x}\, dx \qquad\qquad \text{Simplify.}$$

$$= \frac{4}{9} \int_1^{10} \sqrt{u}\, du \qquad\qquad u = 1 + \frac{9x}{4},\ du = \frac{9}{4} dx$$

$$= \frac{4}{9} \left(\frac{2}{3} u^{3/2}\right)\Big|_1^{10} \qquad\qquad \text{Fundamental Theorem}$$

$$= \frac{8}{27} (10^{3/2} - 1). \qquad\qquad \text{Simplify.}$$

The length of the curve is $\frac{8}{27} (10^{3/2} - 1) \approx 9.1$ units.

Related Exercises 3–16 ◄

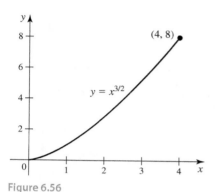

Figure 6.56

EXAMPLE 2   Arc length of an exponential curve Find the length of the curve $f(x) = 2e^x + \frac{1}{8} e^{-x}$ on the interval $[0, \ln 2]$.

SOLUTION We first calculate $f'(x) = 2e^x - \frac{1}{8} e^{-x}$ and $f'(x)^2 = 4e^{2x} - \frac{1}{2} + \frac{1}{64} e^{-2x}$. The length of the curve on the interval $[0, \ln 2]$ is

$$L = \int_0^{\ln 2} \sqrt{1 + f'(x)^2}\, dx = \int_0^{\ln 2} \sqrt{1 + \left(4e^{2x} - \frac{1}{2} + \frac{1}{64} e^{-2x}\right)}\, dx$$

$$= \int_0^{\ln 2} \sqrt{4e^{2x} + \frac{1}{2} + \frac{1}{64} e^{-2x}}\, dx \qquad\qquad \text{Simplify.}$$

$$= \int_0^{\ln 2} \sqrt{\left(2e^x + \frac{1}{8} e^{-x}\right)^2}\, dx \qquad\qquad \text{Factor.}$$

$$= \int_0^{\ln 2} \left(2e^x + \frac{1}{8} e^{-x}\right) dx \qquad\qquad \text{Simplify.}$$

$$= \left(2e^x - \frac{1}{8} e^{-x}\right)\Big|_0^{\ln 2} = \frac{33}{16}. \qquad\qquad \text{Evaluate the integral.}$$

Related Exercises 3–16 ◄

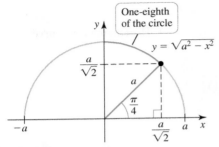

Figure 6.57

EXAMPLE 3   Circumference of a circle Confirm that the circumference of a circle of radius a is $2\pi a$.

SOLUTION The upper half of a circle of radius a centered at $(0, 0)$ is given by the function $f(x) = \sqrt{a^2 - x^2}$ for $|x| \le a$ (Figure 6.57). So we might consider using the arc length formula on the interval $[-a, a]$ to find the length of a semicircle. However, the circle has vertical tangent lines at $x = \pm a$ and $f'(\pm a)$ is undefined, which prevents us from using the arc length formula. An alternative approach is to use symmetry and avoid the points $x = \pm a$. For example, let's compute the length of one-eighth of the circle on the interval $[0, a/\sqrt{2}]$ (Figure 6.57).

We first determine that $f'(x) = -\dfrac{x}{\sqrt{a^2 - x^2}}$, which is continuous on $[0, a/\sqrt{2}]$.

The length of one-eighth of the circle is

$$\int_0^{a/\sqrt{2}} \sqrt{1 + f'(x)^2}\, dx = \int_0^{a/\sqrt{2}} \sqrt{1 + \left(-\frac{x}{\sqrt{a^2 - x^2}}\right)^2}\, dx$$

$$= \int_0^{a/\sqrt{2}} \sqrt{\frac{a^2}{a^2 - x^2}}\, dx \qquad\qquad \text{Simplify.}$$

$$= a \int_0^{a/\sqrt{2}} \frac{dx}{\sqrt{a^2 - x^2}} \qquad\qquad \text{Simplify; } a > 0.$$

$$= a \sin^{-1}\frac{x}{a}\Big|_0^{a/\sqrt{2}} \qquad\qquad \text{Integrate.}$$

$$= a\left(\sin^{-1}\frac{1}{\sqrt{2}} - 0\right) \qquad\qquad \text{Evaluate.}$$

$$= \frac{\pi a}{4}. \qquad\qquad\qquad\qquad \text{Simplify.}$$

> The arc length integral for the semicircle on $[-a, a]$ is an example of an *improper integral*, a topic considered in Section 7.8.

It follows that the circumference of the full circle is $8(\pi a/4) = 2\pi a$ units.
Related Exercises 3–16 ◄

EXAMPLE 4   Looking ahead Consider the segment of the parabola $f(x) = x^2$ on the interval $[0, 2]$.

a. Write the integral for the length of the curve.

b. Use a calculator to evaluate the integral.

SOLUTION

a. Noting that $f'(x) = 2x$, the arc length integral is

$$\int_0^2 \sqrt{1 + f'(x)^2}\, dx = \int_0^2 \sqrt{1 + 4x^2}\, dx.$$

> When relying on technology, it is a good idea to check whether an answer is plausible. In Example 4, we found that the arc length of $y = x^2$ on $[0, 2]$ is approximately 4.647. The straight-line distance between $(0, 0)$ and $(2, 4)$ is $\sqrt{20} \approx 4.472$, so our answer is reasonable.

b. Using integration techniques presented so far, this integral cannot be evaluated (the required method is given in Section 7.4). This is typical of arc length integrals—even simple functions can lead to arc length integrals that are difficult to evaluate analytically. Without an analytical method, we may use numerical integration to *approximate* the value of a definite integral (Section 7.7). Many calculators have built-in functions for this purpose. For this integral, the approximate arc length is

$$\int_0^2 \sqrt{1 + 4x^2}\, dx \approx 4.647.$$

Related Exercises 17–26 ◄

Arc Length for $x = g(y)$

Sometimes it is advantageous to describe a curve as a function of y—that is, $x = g(y)$. The arc length formula in this case is derived exactly as in the case of $y = f(x)$, switching the roles of x and y. The result is the following arc length formula.

> **DEFINITION Arc Length for $x = g(y)$**
>
> Let $x = g(y)$ have a continuous first derivative on the interval $[c, d]$. The length of the curve from $(g(c), c)$ to $(g(d), d)$ is
>
> $$L = \int_c^d \sqrt{1 + g'(y)^2}\, dy.$$

QUICK CHECK 2 What does the arc length formula give for the length of the line $x = y$ between $y = c$ and $y = d$, where $d \geq c$? Is the result consistent with the result given by the Pythagorean theorem? ◄

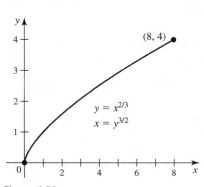

Figure 6.58

QUICK CHECK 3 Write the integral for the length of the curve $x = \sin y$ on the interval $0 \leq y \leq \pi$. ◄

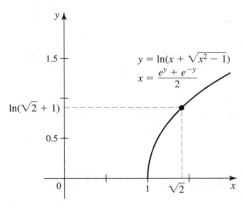

Figure 6.59

▶ The function $\frac{1}{2}(e^y + e^{-y})$ is the **hyperbolic cosine**, denoted cosh y. The function $\frac{1}{2}(e^y - e^{-y})$ is the **hyperbolic sine**, denoted sinh y. See Section 6.10.

EXAMPLE 5   Arc length Find the length of the curve $y = f(x) = x^{2/3}$ between $x = 0$ and $x = 8$ (Figure 6.58).

SOLUTION The derivative of $f(x) = x^{2/3}$ is $f'(x) = \frac{2}{3}x^{-1/3}$, which is undefined at $x = 0$. Therefore, the arc length formula with respect to x cannot be used, yet the curve certainly appears to have a well-defined length.

The key is to describe the curve with y as the independent variable. Solving $y = x^{2/3}$ for x, we have $x = g(y) = \pm y^{3/2}$. Notice that when $x = 8$, $y = 8^{2/3} = 4$, which says that we should use the positive branch of $\pm y^{3/2}$. Therefore, finding the length of the curve $y = f(x) = x^{2/3}$ from $x = 0$ to $x = 8$ is equivalent to finding the length of the curve $x = g(y) = y^{3/2}$ from $y = 0$ to $y = 4$. This is precisely the problem solved in Example 1. The arc length is $\frac{8}{27}(10^{3/2} - 1) \approx 9.1$ units.

Related Exercises 27–30 ◄

EXAMPLE 6   Ingenuity required Find the length of the curve $y = f(x) = \ln(x + \sqrt{x^2 - 1})$ on the interval $[1, \sqrt{2}]$ (Figure 6.59).

SOLUTION Calculating f' shows that the graph of f has a vertical tangent line at $x = 1$. Therefore, the integrand in the arc length integral is undefined at $x = 1$. An alternative strategy is to express the function in the form $x = g(y)$ and evaluate the arc length integral with respect to y. Noting that $x \geq 1$ and $y \geq 0$, we solve $y = \ln(x + \sqrt{x^2 - 1})$ for x in the following steps:

$$e^y = x + \sqrt{x^2 - 1} \qquad \text{Exponentiate both sides.}$$
$$e^y - x = \sqrt{x^2 - 1} \qquad \text{Subtract } x \text{ from both sides.}$$
$$e^{2y} - 2e^y x = -1 \qquad \text{Square both sides and cancel } x^2.$$
$$x = \frac{e^{2y} + 1}{2e^y} = \frac{e^y + e^{-y}}{2}. \qquad \text{Solve for } x.$$

We conclude that the given curve is also described by the function $x = g(y) = \dfrac{e^y + e^{-y}}{2}$. The interval $1 \leq x \leq \sqrt{2}$ corresponds to the interval $0 \leq y \leq \ln(\sqrt{2} + 1)$ (Figure 6.59). Note that $g'(y) = \dfrac{e^y - e^{-y}}{2}$ is continuous on $[0, \ln(\sqrt{2} + 1)]$. The arc length is

$$\int_0^{\ln(\sqrt{2}+1)} \sqrt{1 + g'(y)^2}\, dy = \int_0^{\ln(\sqrt{2}+1)} \sqrt{1 + \left(\frac{e^y - e^{-y}}{2}\right)^2}\, dy \quad \text{Substitute for } g'(y).$$

$$= \frac{1}{2}\int_0^{\ln(\sqrt{2}+1)} (e^y + e^{-y})\, dy \qquad \text{Expand and simplify.}$$

$$= \frac{1}{2}(e^y - e^{-y})\Big|_0^{\ln(\sqrt{2}+1)} = 1. \qquad \text{Fundamental Theorem}$$

Related Exercises 27–30 ◄

SECTION 6.5 EXERCISES

Review Questions

1. Explain the steps required to find the length of a curve $y = f(x)$ between $x = a$ and $x = b$.

2. Explain the steps required to find the length of a curve $x = g(y)$ between $y = c$ and $y = d$.

Basic Skills

3–6. Setting up arc length integrals *Write and simplify, but do not evaluate, an integral with respect to x that gives the length of the following curves on the given interval.*

3. $y = x^3 + 2$ on $[-2, 5]$

4. $y = 2\cos 3x$ on $[-\pi, \pi]$

5. $y = e^{-2x}$ on $[0, 2]$

6. $y = \ln x$ on $[1, 10]$

7–16. Arc length calculations *Find the arc length of the following curves on the given interval by integrating with respect to x.*

7. $y = 2x + 1$ on $[1, 5]$ (Use calculus.)

8. $y = 4 - 3x$ on $[-3, 2]$ (Use calculus.)

9. $y = -8x - 3$ on $[-2, 6]$ (Use calculus.)

10. $y = \frac{1}{2}(e^x + e^{-x})$ on $[-\ln 2, \ln 2]$

11. $y = \frac{1}{3}x^{3/2}$ on $[0, 60]$

12. $y = 3\ln x - \frac{x^2}{24}$ on $[1, 6]$

13. $y = \frac{(x^2 + 2)^{3/2}}{3}$ on $[0, 1]$

14. $y = \frac{x^{3/2}}{3} - x^{1/2}$ on $[4, 16]$

15. $y = \frac{x^4}{4} + \frac{1}{8x^2}$ on $[1, 2]$

16. $y = \frac{2}{3}x^{3/2} - \frac{1}{2}x^{1/2}$ on $[1, 9]$

☐ 17–26. Arc length by calculator

a. *Write and simplify the integral that gives the arc length of the following curves on the given interval.*

b. *If necessary, use technology to evaluate or approximate the integral.*

17. $y = x^2$ on $[-1, 1]$

18. $y = \sin x$ on $[0, \pi]$

19. $y = \ln x$ on $[1, 4]$

20. $y = \frac{x^3}{3}$ on $[-1, 1]$

21. $y = \sqrt{x - 2}$ on $[3, 4]$

22. $y = \frac{8}{x^2}$ on $[1, 4]$

23. $y = \cos 2x$ on $[0, \pi]$

24. $y = 4x - x^2$ on $[0, 4]$

25. $y = \frac{1}{x}$ on $[1, 10]$

26. $y = \frac{1}{x^2 + 1}$ on $[-5, 5]$

27–30. Arc length calculations with respect to y *Find the arc length of the following curves by integrating with respect to y.*

27. $x = 2y - 4$, for $-3 \leq y \leq 4$ (Use calculus.)

28. $y = \ln(x - \sqrt{x^2 - 1})$, for $1 \leq x \leq \sqrt{2}$

29. $x = \frac{y^4}{4} + \frac{1}{8y^2}$, for $1 \leq y \leq 2$

30. $x = 2e^{\sqrt{2}y} + \frac{1}{16}e^{-\sqrt{2}y}$, for $0 \leq y \leq \frac{\ln 2}{\sqrt{2}}$

Further Explorations

31. **Explain why or why not** Determine whether the following statements are true and give an explanation or counterexample.

a. $\int_a^b \sqrt{1 + f'(x)^2}\, dx = \int_a^b (1 + f'(x))\, dx$.

b. Assuming f' is continuous on the interval $[a, b]$, the length of the curve $y = f(x)$ on $[a, b]$ is the area under the curve $y = \sqrt{1 + f'(x)^2}$ on $[a, b]$.

c. Arc length may be negative if $f(x) < 0$ on part of the interval in question.

32. **Arc length for a line** Consider the segment of the line $y = mx + c$ on the interval $[a, b]$. Use the arc length formula to show that the length of the line segment is $(b - a)\sqrt{1 + m^2}$. Verify this result by computing the length of the line segment using the distance formula.

33. **Functions from arc length** What differentiable functions have an arc length on the interval $[a, b]$ given by the following integrals? Note that the answers are not unique. Give a family of functions that satisfy the conditions.

a. $\int_a^b \sqrt{1 + 16x^4}\, dx$

b. $\int_a^b \sqrt{1 + 36\cos^2 2x}\, dx$

34. **Function from arc length** Find a curve that passes through the point $(1, 5)$ and has an arc length on the interval $[2, 6]$ given by $\int_2^6 \sqrt{1 + 16x^{-6}}\, dx$.

☐ 35. **Cosine vs. parabola** Which curve has the greater length on the interval $[-1, 1]$, $y = 1 - x^2$ or $y = \cos(\pi x/2)$?

36. **Function defined as an integral** Write the integral that gives the length of the curve $y = f(x) = \int_0^x \sin t\, dt$ on the interval $[0, \pi]$.

Applications

☐ 37. **Golden Gate cables** The profile of the cables on a suspension bridge may be modeled by a parabola. The central span of the Golden Gate Bridge (see figure) is 1280 m long and 152 m high. The parabola $y = 0.00037x^2$ gives a good fit to the shape of the cables, where $|x| \leq 640$, and x and y are measured in meters. Approximate the length of the cables that stretch between the tops of the two towers.

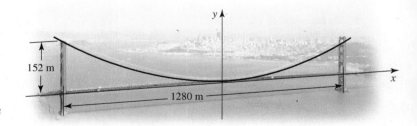

☐ 38. **Gateway Arch** The shape of the Gateway Arch in St. Louis (with a height and a base length of 630 ft) is modeled by the function $y = -630\cosh(x/239.2) + 1260$, where $|x| \leq 315$, and x and y are measured in feet (see figure). The function $\cosh x$ is the **hyperbolic cosine**, defined by $\cosh x = \dfrac{e^x + e^{-x}}{2}$ (see Section 6.10

for more on hyperbolic functions). Estimate the length of the
Gateway Arch.

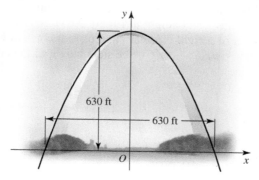

630 ft

630 ft

O

x

Additional Exercises

39. Lengths of related curves Suppose the graph of f on the interval
$[a, b]$ has length L, where f' is continuous on $[a, b]$. Evaluate the
following integrals in terms of L.

a. $\displaystyle\int_{a/2}^{b/2} \sqrt{1 + f'(2x)^2}\, dx$ **b.** $\displaystyle\int_{a/c}^{b/c} \sqrt{1 + f'(cx)^2}\, dx$ if $c \ne 0$

40. Lengths of symmetric curves Suppose a curve is described
by $y = f(x)$ on the interval $[-b, b]$, where f' is continuous on
$[-b, b]$. Show that if f is symmetric about the origin (f is odd) *or*
f is symmetric about the y-axis (f is even), then the length of the
curve $y = f(x)$ from $x = -b$ to $x = b$ is twice the length of the
curve from $x = 0$ to $x = b$. Use a geometric argument and prove
it using integration.

41. A family of exponential functions

a. Show that the arc length integral for the function $f(x) =$
$Ae^{ax} + \dfrac{1}{4Aa^2}\, e^{-ax}$, where $a > 0$ and $A > 0$, may be
integrated using methods you already know.

b. Verify that the arc length of the curve $y = f(x)$ on the interval
$[0, \ln 2]$ is

$$A(2^a - 1) - \frac{1}{4a^2 A}(2^{-a} - 1).$$

T 42. Bernoulli's "parabolas" Johann Bernoulli (1667–1748) evaluated the arc length of curves of the form $y = x^{(2n+1)/2n}$, where n
is a positive integer, on the interval $[0, a]$.

a. Write the arc length integral.

b. Make the change of variables $u^2 = 1 + \left(\dfrac{2n + 1}{2n}\right)^2 x^{1/n}$ to

obtain a new integral with respect to u.

c. Use the Binomial Theorem to expand this integrand and evaluate the integral.

d. The case $n = 1$ ($y = x^{3/2}$) was done in Example 1. With
$a = 1$, compute the arc length in the cases $n = 2$ and $n = 3$.
Does the arc length increase or decrease with n?

e. Graph the arc length of the curves for $a = 1$ as a function of n.

QUICK CHECK ANSWERS
1. $\sqrt{2}a$ (The length of the line segment joining the points)
2. $\sqrt{2}(d - c)$ (The length of the line segment joining the
points)   3. $L = \int_0^\pi \sqrt{1 + \cos^2 y}\, dy$ ◄

6.6 Surface Area

In Sections 6.3 and 6.4, we introduced solids of revolution and presented methods for
computing the volume of such solids. We now consider a related problem: computing the
area of the surface of a solid of revolution. Surface area calculations are important in aero-
dynamics (computing the lift on an airplane wing) and biology (computing transport rates
across cell membranes), to name just two applications. Here is an interesting observation:
A surface area problem is "between" a volume problem (which is three-dimensional) and
an arc length problem (which is one-dimensional). For this reason, you will see ideas that
appear in both volume and arc length calculations as we develop the surface area integral.

Some Preliminary Calculations

Consider a curve $y = f(x)$ on an interval $[a, b]$, where f is a nonnegative function with a
continuous first derivative on $[a, b]$. Now imagine revolving the curve about the x-axis to
generate a *surface of revolution* (Figure 6.60). Our objective is to find the area of this surface.

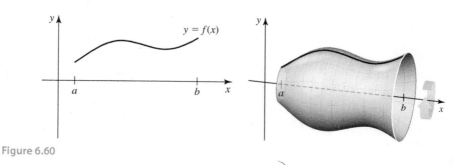

$y = f(x)$

Figure 6.60

▶ One way to derive the formula for the surface area of a cone (not including the base) is to cut the cone on a line from its base to its vertex. When the cone is unfolded, it forms a sector of a circular disk of radius ℓ with a curved edge of length $2\pi r$. This sector is a fraction

$$\frac{2\pi r}{2\pi \ell} = \frac{r}{\ell} \text{ of a full circular disk of radius } \ell.$$

So the area of the sector, which is also the surface area of the cone, is

$$\pi \ell^2 \cdot \frac{r}{\ell} = \pi r \ell.$$

Curved edge length $= 2\pi r$

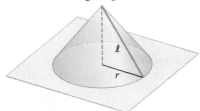

Curved edge length $= 2\pi r$

Before tackling this problem, we consider a preliminary problem upon which we build a general surface area formula. First consider the graph of $f(x) = rx/h$ on the interval $[0, h]$, where $h > 0$ and $r > 0$. When this line segment is revolved about the x-axis, it generates the surface of a cone of radius r and height h (Figure 6.61). A formula from geometry states that the surface area of a right circular cone of radius r and height h (excluding the base) is $\pi r \sqrt{r^2 + h^2} = \pi r \ell$, where ℓ is the slant height of the cone (the length of the slanted "edge" of the cone).

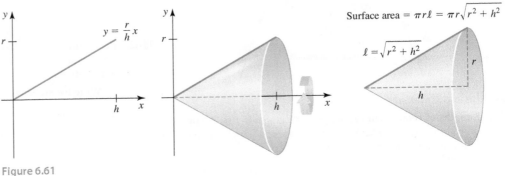

Figure 6.61

QUICK CHECK 1 Which is greater, the surface area of a cone of height 10 and radius 20 or the surface area of a cone of height 20 and radius 10 (excluding the bases)? ◄

With this result, we can solve a preliminary problem that will be useful. Consider the linear function $f(x) = cx$ on the interval $[a, b]$, where $0 < a < b$ and $c > 0$. When this line segment is revolved about the x-axis, it generates a *frustum of a cone* (a cone whose top has been sliced off). The goal is to find S, the surface area of the frustum. Figure 6.62 shows that S is the difference between the surface area S_b of the cone that extends over the interval $[0, b]$ and the surface area S_a of the cone that extends over the interval $[0, a]$.

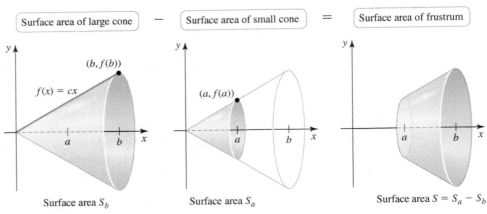

Figure 6.62

Notice that the radius of the cone on $[0, b]$ is $r = f(b) = cb$, and its height is $h = b$. Therefore, this cone has surface area

$$S_b = \pi r \sqrt{r^2 + h^2} = \pi (bc) \sqrt{(bc)^2 + b^2} = \pi b^2 c \sqrt{c^2 + 1}.$$

Similarly, the cone on $[0, a]$ has radius $r = f(a) = ca$ and height $h = a$, so its surface area is

$$S_a = \pi (ac) \sqrt{(ac)^2 + a^2} = \pi a^2 c \sqrt{c^2 + 1}.$$

The difference of the surface areas $S_b - S_a$ is the surface area S of the frustum on $[a, b]$:

$$S = S_b - S_a = \pi b^2 c \sqrt{c^2 + 1} - \pi a^2 c \sqrt{c^2 + 1}$$
$$= \pi c (b^2 - a^2) \sqrt{c^2 + 1}.$$

Surface area of frustum:
$$S = \pi (f(b) + f(a)) \ell$$
$$= \pi (r_2 + r_1) \ell$$

A slightly different form of this surface area formula will be useful. Observe that the line segment from $(a, f(a))$ to $(b, f(b))$ (which is the slant height of the frustum in Figure 6.62) has length

$$\ell = \sqrt{(b - a)^2 + (bc - ac)^2} = (b - a)\sqrt{c^2 + 1}.$$

Therefore, the surface area of the frustum can also be written

$$
\begin{aligned}
S &= \pi c(b^2 - a^2)\sqrt{c^2 + 1} \\
&= \pi c(b + a)(b - a)\sqrt{c^2 + 1} \qquad \text{Factor } b^2 - a^2. \\
&= \pi \Big(\underbrace{cb}_{f(b)} + \underbrace{ca}_{f(a)} \Big) \underbrace{(b - a)\sqrt{c^2 + 1}}_{\ell} \qquad \text{Expand } c(b + a). \\
&= \pi(f(b) + f(a))\ell.
\end{aligned}
$$

This result can be generalized to *any* linear function $g(x) = cx + d$ that is positive on the interval $[a, b]$. That is, the surface area of the frustum generated by revolving the line segment between $(a, g(a))$ and $(b, g(b))$ about the x-axis is given by $\pi(g(b) + g(a))\ell$ (Exercise 36).

QUICK CHECK 2 What is the surface area of the frustum of a cone generated when the graph of $f(x) = 3x$ on the interval $[2, 5]$ is revolved about the x-axis? ◄

Surface Area Formula

With the surface area formula for a frustum of a cone, we now derive a general area formula for a surface of revolution. We assume the surface is generated by revolving the graph of a positive, differentiable function f on the interval $[a, b]$ about the x-axis. We begin by subdividing the interval $[a, b]$ into n subintervals of equal length $\Delta x = \dfrac{b - a}{n}$.

The grid points in this partition are

$$x_0 = a, x_1, x_2, \dots, x_{n-1}, x_n = b.$$

Now consider the kth subinterval $[x_{k-1}, x_k]$ and the line segment between the points $(x_{k-1}, f(x_{k-1}))$ and $(x_k, f(x_k))$ (Figure 6.63). We let the change in the y-coordinates between these points be $\Delta y_k = f(x_k) - f(x_{k-1})$.

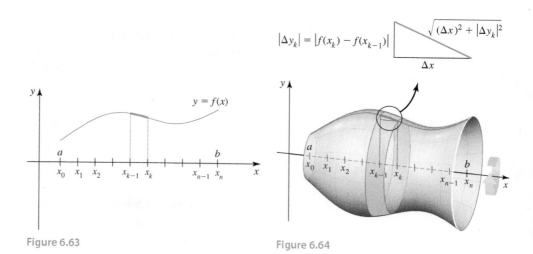

Figure 6.63

Figure 6.64

When this line segment is revolved about the x-axis, it generates a frustum of a cone (Figure 6.64). The slant height of this frustum is the length of the hypotenuse of a right triangle whose sides have lengths Δx and $|\Delta y_k|$. Therefore, the slant height of the kth frustum is

$$\sqrt{(\Delta x)^2 + |\Delta y_k|^2} = \sqrt{(\Delta x)^2 + (\Delta y_k)^2}$$

and its surface area is

$$S_k = \pi(f(x_k) + f(x_{k-1}))\sqrt{(\Delta x)^2 + (\Delta y_k)^2}.$$

It follows that the area S of the entire surface of revolution is approximately the sum of the surface areas of the individual frustums S_k, for $k = 1, \ldots, n$; that is,

$$S \approx \sum_{k=1}^{n} S_k = \sum_{k=1}^{n} \pi(f(x_k) + f(x_{k-1}))\sqrt{(\Delta x)^2 + (\Delta y_k)^2}.$$

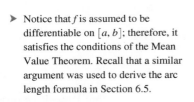

➤ Notice that f is assumed to be differentiable on $[a, b]$; therefore, it satisfies the conditions of the Mean Value Theorem. Recall that a similar argument was used to derive the arc length formula in Section 6.5.

We would like to identify this sum as a Riemann sum. However, one more step is required to put it in the correct form. We apply the Mean Value Theorem on the kth subinterval $[x_{k-1}, x_k]$ and observe that

$$\frac{f(x_k) - f(x_{k-1})}{\Delta x} = f'(x_k^*),$$

for some number x_k^* in the interval (x_{k-1}, x_k), for $k = 1, \ldots, n$. It follows that $\Delta y_k = f(x_k) - f(x_{k-1}) = f'(x_k^*)\Delta x$.

We now replace Δy_k with $f'(x_k^*)\Delta x$ in the expression for the approximate surface area. The result is

$$S \approx \sum_{k=1}^{n} S_k = \sum_{k=1}^{n} \pi(f(x_k) + f(x_{k-1}))\sqrt{(\Delta x)^2 + (\Delta y_k)^2}$$

$$= \sum_{k=1}^{n} \pi(f(x_k) + f(x_{k-1}))\sqrt{(\Delta x)^2(1 + f'(x_k^*)^2)} \qquad \text{Mean Value Theorem}$$

$$= \sum_{k=1}^{n} \pi(f(x_k) + f(x_{k-1}))\sqrt{1 + f'(x_k^*)^2}\,\Delta x. \qquad \text{Factor out } \Delta x.$$

When Δx is small, we have $x_{k-1} \approx x_k \approx x_k^*$, and by the continuity of f, it follows that $f(x_{k-1}) \approx f(x_k) \approx f(x_k^*)$, for $k = 1, \ldots, n$. These observations allow us to write

$$S \approx \sum_{k=1}^{n} \pi(f(x_k^*) + f(x_k^*))\sqrt{1 + f'(x_k^*)^2}\,\Delta x$$

$$= \sum_{k=1}^{n} 2\pi f(x_k^*)\sqrt{1 + f'(x_k^*)^2}\,\Delta x.$$

This approximation to S, which has the form of a Riemann sum, improves as the number of subintervals increases and as the length of the subintervals approaches 0. Specifically, as $n \to \infty$ and as $\Delta x \to 0$, we obtain an integral for the surface area:

$$S = \lim_{n \to \infty} \sum_{k=1}^{n} 2\pi f(x_k^*)\sqrt{1 + f'(x_k^*)^2}\,\Delta x$$

$$= \int_a^b 2\pi f(x)\sqrt{1 + f'(x)^2}\,dx.$$

DEFINITION Area of a Surface of Revolution

Let f be a nonnegative function with a continuous first derivative on the interval $[a, b]$. The area of the surface generated when the graph of f on the interval $[a, b]$ is revolved about the x-axis is

$$S = \int_a^b 2\pi f(x)\sqrt{1 + f'(x)^2}\,dx.$$

QUICK CHECK 3 Let $f(x) = c$, where $c > 0$. What surface is generated when the graph of f on $[a, b]$ is revolved about the x-axis? Without using calculus, what is the area of the surface? ◄

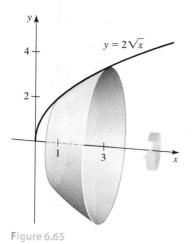

Figure 6.65

EXAMPLE 1 Using the surface area formula The graph of $f(x) = 2\sqrt{x}$ on the interval $[1, 3]$ is revolved about the x-axis. What is the area of the surface generated (Figure 6.65)?

SOLUTION Noting that $f'(x) = \dfrac{1}{\sqrt{x}}$, the surface area formula gives

$$S = \int_a^b 2\pi f(x)\sqrt{1 + f'(x)^2}\,dx$$

$$= 2\pi \int_1^3 2\sqrt{x}\sqrt{1 + \frac{1}{x}}\,dx \qquad \text{Substitute for } f \text{ and } f'.$$

$$= 4\pi \int_1^3 \sqrt{x + 1}\,dx \qquad \text{Simplify.}$$

$$= \frac{8\pi}{3}(x + 1)^{3/2}\Big|_1^3 = \frac{16\pi}{3}(4 - \sqrt{2}). \quad \text{Integrate and simplify.}$$

Related Exercises 5–14 ◄

EXAMPLE 2 Surface area of a spherical cap A spherical cap is produced when a sphere of radius a is sliced by a horizontal plane that is a vertical distance h below the north pole of the sphere, where $0 \le h \le 2a$ (Figure 6.66a). We take the spherical cap to be that part of the sphere above the plane, so that h is the depth of the cap. Show that the area of a spherical cap of depth h cut from a sphere of radius a is $2\pi ah$.

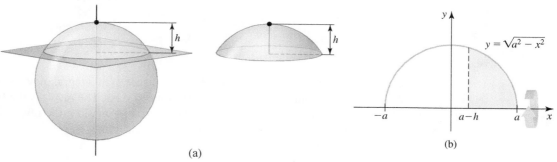

(a)

(b)

Figure 6.66

▶ Notice that f is not differentiable at $\pm a$. Nevertheless, in this case, the surface area integral can be evaluated using methods you know.

SOLUTION To generate the spherical surface, we revolve the curve $f(x) = \sqrt{a^2 - x^2}$ on the interval $[-a, a]$ about the x-axis (Figure 6.66b). The spherical cap of height h corresponds to that part of the sphere on the interval $[a - h, a]$, for $0 \le h \le 2a$. Noting that $f'(x) = -x(a^2 - x^2)^{-1/2}$, the surface area of the spherical cap of height h is

$$S = \int_a^b 2\pi f(x)\sqrt{1 + f'(x)^2}\,dx$$

$$= 2\pi \int_{a-h}^a \sqrt{a^2 - x^2}\sqrt{1 + (-x(a^2 - x^2)^{-1/2})^2}\,dx \quad \text{Substitute for } f \text{ and } f'.$$

$$= 2\pi \int_{a-h}^a \sqrt{a^2 - x^2}\sqrt{\frac{a^2}{a^2 - x^2}}\,dx \qquad \text{Simplify.}$$

$$= 2\pi \int_{a-h}^a a\,dx = 2\pi ah. \qquad \text{Simplify and integrate.}$$

▶ The surface area of a sphere of radius a is $4\pi a^2$.

It is worthwhile to check this result with three special cases. With $h = 2a$, we have a complete sphere, so $S = 4\pi a^2$. The case $h = a$ corresponds to a hemispherical cap, so $S = (4\pi a^2)/2 = 2\pi a^2$. The case $h = 0$ corresponds to no spherical cap, so $S = 0$.

Related Exercises 5–14 ◄

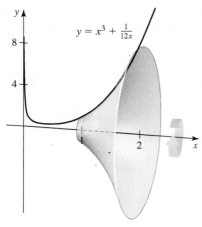

Figure 6.67

EXAMPLE 3   Painting a funnel The curved surface of a funnel is generated by revolving the graph of $y = f(x) = x^3 + \dfrac{1}{12x}$ on the interval $[1, 2]$ about the x-axis (Figure 6.67). Approximately what volume of paint is needed to cover the outside of the funnel with a layer of paint 0.05 cm thick? Assume that x and y are measured in centimeters.

SOLUTION Note that $f'(x) = 3x^2 - \dfrac{1}{12x^2}$. Therefore, the surface area of the funnel in cm^2 is

$$S = \int_a^b 2\pi f(x)\sqrt{1 + f'(x)^2}\, dx$$

$$= 2\pi \int_1^2 \left(x^3 + \frac{1}{12x}\right)\sqrt{1 + \left(3x^2 - \frac{1}{12x^2}\right)^2}\, dx \quad \text{Substitute for } f \text{ and } f'.$$

$$= 2\pi \int_1^2 \left(x^3 + \frac{1}{12x}\right)\sqrt{\left(3x^2 + \frac{1}{12x^2}\right)^2}\, dx \quad \text{Expand and factor under square root.}$$

$$= 2\pi \int_1^2 \left(x^3 + \frac{1}{12x}\right)\left(3x^2 + \frac{1}{12x^2}\right) dx \quad \text{Simplify.}$$

$$= \frac{12{,}289}{192}\,\pi. \quad \text{Evaluate integral.}$$

Because the paint layer is 0.05 cm thick, the approximate volume of paint needed is

$$\left(\frac{12{,}289\pi}{192}\ \text{cm}^2\right)(0.05\ \text{cm}) \approx 10.1\ \text{cm}^3.$$

Related Exercises 15–16 ◄

The derivation that led to the surface area integral may be used when a curve is revolved about the y-axis (rather than the x-axis). The result is the same integral with x replaced with y. For example, if the curve $x = g(y)$ on the interval $[c, d]$ is revolved about the y-axis, the area of the surface generated is

$$S = \int_c^d 2\pi g(y)\sqrt{1 + g'(y)^2}\, dy.$$

To use this integral, we must first describe the given curve as a differentiable function of y.

EXAMPLE 4   Change of perspective Consider the function $y = \ln\left(\dfrac{x + \sqrt{x^2 - 1}}{2}\right)$. Find the area of the surface generated when the part of the curve between the points $\left(\frac{5}{4}, 0\right)$ and $\left(\frac{17}{8}, \ln 2\right)$ is revolved about the y-axis (Figure 6.68).

SOLUTION We solve for x in terms of y in the following steps:

$$y = \ln\left(\frac{x + \sqrt{x^2 - 1}}{2}\right)$$

$$e^y = \frac{x + \sqrt{x^2 - 1}}{2} \quad \text{Exponentiate both sides.}$$

$$2e^y - x = \sqrt{x^2 - 1} \quad \text{Rearrange terms.}$$

$$4e^{2y} - 4xe^y + x^2 = x^2 - 1 \quad \text{Square both sides.}$$

$$x = g(y) = e^y + \frac{1}{4}e^{-y}. \quad \text{Solve for } x.$$

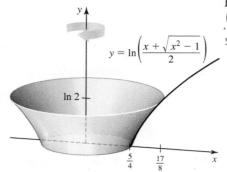

Figure 6.68

Note that $g'(y) = e^y - \frac{1}{4}e^{-y}$ and that the interval of integration on the y-axis is $[0, \ln 2]$. The area of the surface is

$$
\begin{aligned}
S &= \int_c^d 2\pi g(y)\sqrt{1 + g'(y)^2}\, dy \\
&= 2\pi \int_0^{\ln 2}\left(e^y + \frac{1}{4}e^{-y}\right)\sqrt{1 + \left(e^y - \frac{1}{4}e^{-y}\right)^2}\, dy \quad &\text{Substitute for } g \text{ and } g'. \\
&= 2\pi \int_0^{\ln 2}\left(e^y + \frac{1}{4}e^{-y}\right)\sqrt{\left(e^y + \frac{1}{4}e^{-y}\right)^2}\, dy \quad &\text{Expand and factor.} \\
&= 2\pi \int_0^{\ln 2}\left(e^y + \frac{1}{4}e^{-y}\right)^2 dy \quad &\text{Simplify.} \\
&= 2\pi \int_0^{\ln 2}\left(e^{2y} + \frac{1}{2} + \frac{1}{16}e^{-2y}\right) dy \quad &\text{Expand.} \\
&= \pi\left(\frac{195}{64} + \ln 2\right). \quad &\text{Integrate.}
\end{aligned}
$$

Related Exercises 17–20 ◄

SECTION 6.6 EXERCISES

Review Questions

1. What is the area of the curved surface of a right circular cone of radius 3 and height 4?

2. A frustum of a cone is generated by revolving the graph of $y = 4x$ on the interval $[2, 6]$ about the x-axis. What is the area of the surface of the frustum?

3. Suppose f is positive and differentiable on $[a, b]$. The curve $y = f(x)$ on $[a, b]$ is revolved about the x-axis. Explain how to find the area of the surface that is generated.

4. Suppose g is positive and differentiable on $[c, d]$. The curve $x = g(y)$ on $[c, d]$ is revolved about the y-axis. Explain how to find the area of the surface that is generated.

Basic Skills

5–14. Computing surface areas *Find the area of the surface generated when the given curve is revolved about the x-axis.*

5. $y = 3x + 4$ on $[0, 6]$

6. $y = 12 - 3x$ on $[1, 3]$

7. $y = 8\sqrt{x}$ on $[9, 20]$

8. $y = x^3$ on $[0, 1]$

9. $y = x^{3/2} - \dfrac{x^{1/2}}{3}$ on $[1, 2]$

10. $y = \sqrt{4x + 6}$ on $[0, 5]$

11. $y = \dfrac{1}{4}(e^{2x} + e^{-2x})$ on $[-2, 2]$

12. $y = \dfrac{x^4}{8} + \dfrac{1}{4x^2}$ on $[1, 2]$

13. $y = \dfrac{x^3}{3} + \dfrac{1}{4x}$ on $\left[\dfrac{1}{2}, 2\right]$

14. $y = \sqrt{5x - x^2}$ on $[1, 4]$

15–16. Painting surfaces *A 1.5-mm layer of paint is applied to one side of the following surfaces. Find the approximate volume of paint needed. Assume that x and y are measured in meters.*

15. The spherical zone generated when the curve $y = \sqrt{8x - x^2}$ on the interval $[1, 7]$ is revolved about the x-axis

16. The spherical zone generated when the upper portion of the circle $x^2 + y^2 = 100$ on the interval $[-8, 8]$ is revolved about the x-axis

17–20. Revolving about the y-axis *Find the area of the surface generated when the given curve is revolved about the y-axis.*

17. $y = (3x)^{1/3}$, for $0 \le x \le \dfrac{8}{3}$

18. $y = \dfrac{x^2}{4}$, for $2 \le x \le 4$

19. The part of the curve $y = 4x - 1$ between the points $(1, 3)$ and $(4, 15)$

20. The part of the curve $y = \frac{1}{2}\ln\left(2x + \sqrt{4x^2 - 1}\right)$ between the points $\left(\frac{1}{2}, 0\right)$ and $\left(\frac{17}{16}, \ln 2\right)$

Further Explorations

21. **Explain why or why not** Determine whether the following statements are true and give an explanation or counterexample.

a. If the curve $y = f(x)$ on the interval $[a, b]$ is revolved about the y-axis, the area of the surface generated is

$$\int_{f(a)}^{f(b)} 2\pi f(y)\sqrt{1 + f'(y)^2}\, dy.$$

b. If f is not one-to-one on the interval $[a, b]$, then the area of the surface generated when the graph of f on $[a, b]$ is revolved about the x-axis is not defined.

c. Let $f(x) = 12x^2$. The area of the surface generated when the graph of f on $[-4, 4]$ is revolved about the x-axis is twice the area of the surface generated when the graph of f on $[0, 4]$ is revolved about the x-axis.

d. Let $f(x) = 12x^2$. The area of the surface generated when the graph of f on $[-4, 4]$ is revolved about the y-axis is twice the area of the surface generated when the graph of f on $[0, 4]$ is revolved about the y-axis.

22–25. Surface area calculations *Use the method of your choice to determine the area of the surface generated when the following curves are revolved about the indicated axis.*

22. $x = \sqrt{12y - y^2}$, for $2 \le y \le 10$; about the y-axis

23. $x = 4y^{3/2} - \dfrac{y^{1/2}}{12}$, for $1 \le y \le 4$; about the y-axis

24. $y = 1 + \sqrt{1 - x^2}$ between the points $(1, 1)$ and $\left(\dfrac{\sqrt{3}}{2}, \dfrac{3}{2}\right)$; about the y-axis

T 25. $y = 9x^{2/3} - \dfrac{x^{4/3}}{32}$, for $1 \le x \le 8$; about the x-axis

T 26–29. Surface area using technology *Consider the following curves on the given intervals.*

a. *Write the integral that gives the area of the surface generated when the curve is revolved about the x-axis.*

b. *Use a calculator or software to approximate the surface area.*

26. $y = x^5$ on $[0, 1]$ **27.** $y = \cos x$ on $\left[0, \dfrac{\pi}{2}\right]$

28. $y = \ln x^2$ on $[1, \sqrt{e}]$ **29.** $y = \tan x$ on $\left[0, \dfrac{\pi}{4}\right]$

30. Cones and cylinders The volume of a cone of radius r and height h is one-third the volume of a cylinder with the same radius and height. Does the surface area of a cone of radius r and height h equal one-third the surface area of a cylinder with the same radius and height? If not, find the correct relationship. Exclude the bases of the cone and cylinder.

31. Revolving an astroid Consider the upper half of the astroid described by $x^{2/3} + y^{2/3} = a^{2/3}$, where $a > 0$ and $|x| \le a$. Find the area of the surface generated when this curve is revolved about the x-axis. Use symmetry. Note that the function describing the curve is not differentiable at 0. However, the surface area integral can be evaluated using methods you know.

Applications

32. Surface area of a torus When the circle $x^2 + (y - a)^2 = r^2$ on the interval $[-r, r]$ is revolved about the x-axis, the result is the surface of a torus, where $0 < r < a$. Show that the surface area of the torus is $S = 4\pi^2 ar$.

33. Zones of a sphere Suppose a sphere of radius r is sliced by two horizontal planes h units apart (see figure). Show that the surface area of the resulting zone on the sphere is $2\pi r h$, independent of the location of the cutting planes.

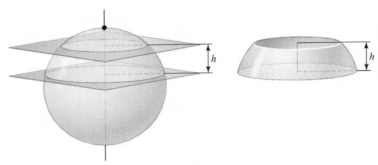

34. Surface area of an ellipsoid If the top half of the ellipse $\dfrac{x^2}{a^2} + \dfrac{y^2}{b^2} = 1$ is revolved about the x-axis, the result is an *ellipsoid* whose axis along the x-axis has length $2a$, whose axis along the y-axis has length $2b$, and whose axis perpendicular to the xy-plane has length $2b$. We assume that $0 < b < a$ (see figure). Use the following steps to find the surface area S of this ellipsoid.

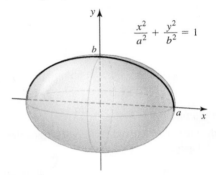

a. Use the surface area formula to show that
$$S = \frac{4\pi b}{a} \int_0^a \sqrt{a^2 - c^2 x^2}\, dx, \text{ where } c^2 = 1 - \frac{b^2}{a^2}.$$

b. Use the change of variables $u = cx$ to show that
$$S = \frac{4\pi b}{\sqrt{a^2 - b^2}} \int_0^{\sqrt{a^2 - b^2}} \sqrt{a^2 - u^2}\, du.$$

c. A table of integrals shows that
$$\int \sqrt{a^2 - u^2}\, du = \frac{1}{2}\left(u\sqrt{a^2 - u^2} + a^2 \sin^{-1}\frac{u}{a}\right) + C.$$
Use this fact to show that the surface area of the ellipsoid is
$$S = 2\pi b\left(b + \frac{a^2}{\sqrt{a^2 - b^2}} \sin^{-1}\frac{\sqrt{a^2 - b^2}}{a}\right).$$

d. If a and b have units of length (say, meters), what are the units of S according to this formula?

e. Use part (a) to show that if $a = b$, then $S = 4\pi a^2$, which is the surface area of a sphere of radius a.

35. Surface-area-to-volume ratio (SAV) In the design of solid objects (both artificial and natural), the ratio of the surface area to the volume of the object is important. Animals typically generate heat at a rate proportional to their volume and lose heat at a rate proportional to their surface area. Therefore, animals with a low SAV ratio tend to retain heat, whereas animals with a high SAV ratio (such as children and hummingbirds) lose heat relatively quickly.

a. What is the SAV ratio of a cube with side lengths a?

b. What is the SAV ratio of a ball with radius a?

c. Use the result of Exercise 34 to find the SAV ratio of an ellipsoid whose long axis has length $2a\sqrt[3]{4}$, for $a \geq 1$, and whose other two axes have half the length of the long axis. (This scaling is used so that, for a given value of a, the volumes of the ellipsoid and the ball of radius a are equal.) The volume of a general ellipsoid is $V = \dfrac{4\pi}{3}ABC$, where the axes have lengths $2A$, $2B$, and $2C$.

d. Graph the SAV ratio of the ball of radius $a \geq 1$ as a function of a (part (b)) and graph the SAV ratio of the ellipsoid described in (part (c)) on the same set of axes. Which object has the smaller SAV ratio?

e. Among all ellipsoids of a fixed volume, which one would you choose for the shape of an animal if the goal is to minimize heat loss?

Additional Exercises

36. Surface area of a frustum Show that the surface area of the frustum of a cone generated by revolving the line segment between $(a, g(a))$ and $(b, g(b))$ about the x-axis is $\pi(g(b) + g(a))\ell$, for

any linear function $g(x) = cx + d$ that is positive on the interval $[a, b]$, where ℓ is the slant height of the frustum.

37. Scaling surface area Let f be a nonnegative function with a continuous first derivative on $[a, b]$ and suppose that $g(x) = cf(x)$ and $h(x) = f(cx)$, where $c > 0$. When the curve $y = f(x)$ on $[a, b]$ is revolved about the x-axis, the area of the resulting surface is A. Evaluate the following integrals in terms of A and c.

a. $\displaystyle\int_a^b 2\pi g(x)\sqrt{c^2 + g'(x)^2}\,dx$ **b.** $\displaystyle\int_{a/c}^{b/c} 2\pi h(x)\sqrt{c^2 + h'(x)^2}\,dx$

38. Surface plus cylinder Suppose f is a nonnegative function with a continuous first derivative on $[a, b]$. Let L equal the length of the graph of f on $[a, b]$ and let S be the area of the surface generated by revolving the graph of f on $[a, b]$ about the x-axis. For a positive constant C, assume the curve $y = f(x) + C$ is revolved about the x-axis. Show that the area of the resulting surface equals the sum of S and the surface area of a right circular cylinder of radius C and height L.

QUICK CHECK ANSWERS

1. The surface area of the first cone $(200\sqrt{5}\pi)$ is twice as great as the surface area of the second cone $(100\sqrt{5}\pi)$.
2. The surface area is $63\sqrt{10}\pi$. **3.** The surface is a cylinder of radius c and height $b - a$. The area of the curved surface is $2\pi c(b - a)$. ◄

6.7 Physical Applications

We continue this chapter on applications of integration with several problems from physics and engineering. The physical themes in these problems are mass, work, force, and pressure. The common mathematical theme is the use of the slice-and-sum strategy, which always leads to a definite integral.

Density and Mass

Density is the concentration of mass in an object and is usually measured in units of mass per volume (for example, g/cm^3). An object with *uniform* density satisfies the basic relationship

$$\text{mass} = \text{density} \cdot \text{volume}.$$

When the density of an object *varies*, this formula no longer holds, and we must appeal to calculus.

In this section, we introduce mass calculations for thin objects that can be viewed as line segments (such as wires or thin bars). The bar shown in Figure 6.69 has a density ρ that varies along its length. For one-dimensional objects, we use *linear density* with units of mass per length (for example, g/cm). What is the mass of such an object?

> In Chapter 13, we return to mass calculations for two- and three-dimensional objects (plates and solids).

$x = a$ $x = b$

Figure 6.69

QUICK CHECK 1 In Figure 6.69, suppose $a = 0$, $b = 3$, and the density of the rod in g/cm is $\rho(x) = (4 - x)$. (a) Where is the rod lightest and heaviest? (b) What is the density at the middle of the bar? ◄

We begin by dividing the bar, represented by the interval $a \leq x \leq b$, into n subintervals of equal length $\Delta x = (b - a)/n$ (Figure 6.70). Let x_k^* be any point in the kth subinterval, for $k = 1, \ldots, n$. The mass of the kth segment of the bar m_k is approximately the density at x_k^* multiplied by the length of the interval, or $m_k \approx \rho(x_k^*)\Delta x$. So the approximate mass of the entire bar is

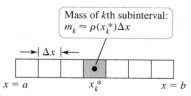

Mass of kth subinterval:
$m_k \approx \rho(x_k^*)\Delta x$

$x = a$ x_k^* $x = b$

Figure 6.70

$$\sum_{k=1}^{n} m_k \approx \sum_{k=1}^{n} \underbrace{\rho(x_k^*)\Delta x}_{m_k}.$$

The exact mass is obtained by taking the limit as $n \to \infty$ and as $\Delta x \to 0$, which produces a definite integral.

> ➤ Note that the units of the integral work out as they should: ρ has units of mass per length and dx has units of length, so $\rho(x)\,dx$ has units of mass.

> ➤ Another interpretation of the mass integral is that mass equals the average value of the density multiplied by the length of the bar $b - a$.

DEFINITION Mass of a One-Dimensional Object

Suppose a thin bar or wire is represented by the interval $a \le x \le b$ with a density function ρ (with units of mass per length). The **mass** of the object is

$$m = \int_a^b \rho(x)\,dx.$$

EXAMPLE 1   Mass from variable density A thin 2-m bar, represented by the interval $0 \le x \le 2$, is made of an alloy whose density in units of kg/m is given by $\rho(x) = (1 + x^2)$. What is the mass of the bar?

SOLUTION The mass of the bar in kilograms is

$$m = \int_a^b \rho(x)\,dx = \int_0^2 (1 + x^2)\,dx = \left(x + \frac{x^3}{3}\right)\Bigg|_0^2 = \frac{14}{3}.$$

Related Exercises 9–16 ◄

QUICK CHECK 2 A thin bar occupies the interval $0 \le x \le 2$ and has a density in kg/m of $\rho(x) = (1 + x^2)$. Using the minimum value of the density, what is a lower bound for the mass of the object? Using the maximum value of the density, what is an upper bound for the mass of the object? ◄

Work

Work can be described as the change in energy when a force causes a displacement of an object. When you carry a basket of laundry up a flight of stairs or push a stalled car, you apply a force that results in the displacement of an object, and work is done. If a *constant* force F displaces an object a distance d in the direction of the force, the work done is the force multiplied by the distance:

$$\text{work} = \text{force} \cdot \text{distance}.$$

It is easiest to use metric units for force and work. A newton (N) is the force required to give a 1-kg mass an acceleration of 1 m/s^2. A joule (J) is 1 newton-meter (N-m), the work done by a 1-N force over a distance of 1 m.

Calculus enters the picture with *variable* forces. Suppose an object is moved along the x-axis by a variable force F that is directed along the x-axis (Figure 6.71). How much work is done in moving the object between $x = a$ and $x = b$? Once again, we use the slice-and-sum strategy.

The interval $[a, b]$ is divided into n subintervals of equal length $\Delta x = (b - a)/n$. We let x_k^* be any point in the kth subinterval, for $k = 1, \ldots, n$. On that subinterval, the force is approximately constant with a value of $F(x_k^*)$. Therefore, the work done in moving the object across the kth subinterval is approximately $F(x_k^*)\Delta x$ (force · distance). Summing the work done over each of the n subintervals, the total work over the interval $[a, b]$ is approximately

$$W \approx \sum_{k=1}^n F(x_k^*)\Delta x.$$

This approximation becomes exact when we take the limit as $n \to \infty$ and $\Delta x \to 0$. The total work done is the integral of the force over the interval $[a, b]$ (or, equivalently, the net area under the force curve in Figure 6.71).

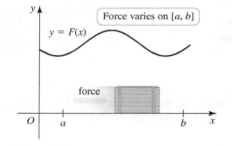

Figure 6.71

QUICK CHECK 3 Explain why the sum of the work over n subintervals is only an approximation of the total work. ◄

DEFINITION Work

The work done by a variable force F moving an object along a line from $x = a$ to $x = b$ in the direction of the force is

$$W = \int_a^b F(x)\, dx.$$

An application of force and work that is easy to visualize is the stretching and compression of a spring. Suppose an object is attached to a spring on a frictionless horizontal surface; the object slides back and forth under the influence of the spring. We say that the spring is at *equilibrium* when it is neither compressed nor stretched. It is convenient to let x be the position of the object, where $x = 0$ is the equilibrium position (Figure 6.72).

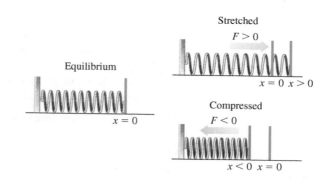

Figure 6.72

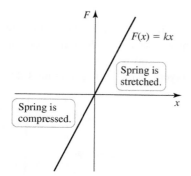

Figure 6.73

According to **Hooke's law**, the force required to keep the spring in a compressed or stretched position x units from the equilibrium position is $F(x) = kx$, where the positive spring constant k measures the stiffness of the spring. Note that to stretch the spring to a position $x > 0$, a force $F > 0$ (in the positive direction) is required. To compress the spring to a position $x < 0$, a force $F < 0$ (in the negative direction) is required (Figure 6.73). In other words, the force required to displace the spring is always in the direction of the displacement.

EXAMPLE 2 Compressing a spring Suppose a force of 10 N is required to stretch a spring 0.1 m from its equilibrium position and hold it in that position.

a. Assuming that the spring obeys Hooke's law, find the spring constant k.

b. How much work is needed to *compress* the spring 0.5 m from its equilibrium position?

c. How much work is needed to *stretch* the spring 0.25 m from its equilibrium position?

d. How much additional work is required to stretch the spring 0.25 m if it has already been stretched 0.1 m from its equilibrium position?

SOLUTION

➤ Hooke's law was proposed by the English scientist Robert Hooke (1635–1703), who also coined the biological term *cell*. Hooke's law works well for springs made of many common materials. However, some springs obey more complicated spring laws (see Exercise 51).

a. The fact that a force of 10 N is required to keep the spring stretched at $x = 0.1$ m means (by Hooke's law) that $F(0.1) = k(0.1 \text{ m}) = 10$ N. Solving for the spring constant, we find that $k = 100$ N/m. Therefore, Hooke's law for this spring is $F(x) = 100x$.

b. The work in joules required to compress the spring from $x = 0$ to $x = -0.5$ is

$$W = \int_a^b F(x)\, dx = \int_0^{-0.5} 100x\, dx = 50x^2 \Big|_0^{-0.5} = 12.5.$$

> Notice again that the units in the integral are consistent. If F has units of N and x has units of m, then W has units of $F \, dx$, or N-m, which are the units of work ($1 \text{ N-m} = 1 \text{ J}$).

c. The work in joules required to stretch the spring from $x = 0$ to $x = 0.25$ is

$$W = \int_a^b F(x) \, dx = \int_0^{0.25} 100x \, dx = 50x^2 \Big|_0^{0.25} = 3.125.$$

d. The work in joules required to stretch the spring from $x = 0.1$ to $x = 0.35$ is

$$W = \int_a^b F(x) \, dx = \int_{0.1}^{0.35} 100x \, dx = 50x^2 \Big|_{0.1}^{0.35} = 5.625.$$

QUICK CHECK 4 In Example 2, explain why more work is needed in part (d) than in part (c), even though the displacement is the same. ◄

Comparing parts (c) and (d), we see that more work is required to stretch the spring 0.25 m starting at $x = 0.1$ than starting at $x = 0$.   *Related Exercises 17–26* ◄

Lifting Problems   Another common work problem arises when the motion is vertical and the force is the gravitational force. The gravitational force exerted on an object with mass m is $F = mg$, where $g \approx 9.8 \text{ m/s}^2$ is the acceleration due to gravity near the surface of Earth. The work in joules required to lift an object of mass m a vertical distance of y meters is

$$\text{work} = \text{force} \cdot \text{distance} = mgy.$$

This type of problem becomes interesting when the object being lifted is a body of water, a rope, or a chain. In these situations, different parts of the object are lifted different distances—so integration is necessary. Here is a typical situation and the strategy used.

Suppose a fluid such as water is pumped out of a tank to a height h above the bottom of the tank. How much work is required, assuming the tank is full of water? Three key observations lead to the solution.

- Water from different levels of the tank is lifted different vertical distances, requiring different amounts of work.

- Two equal volumes of water from the same horizontal plane are lifted the same distance and require the same amount of work.

> The choice of a coordinate system is somewhat arbitrary and may depend on the geometry of the problem. You can let the y-axis point upward or downward, and there are usually several logical choices for the location of $y = 0$. You should experiment with different coordinate systems.

- A volume V of water has mass ρV, where $\rho = 1 \text{ g/cm}^3 = 1000 \text{ kg/m}^3$ is the density of water.

To solve this problem, we let the y-axis point upward with $y = 0$ at the bottom of the tank. The body of water that must be lifted extends from $y = 0$ to $y = b$ (which *may* be the top of the tank). The level to which the water must be raised is $y = h$, where $h \geq b$ (Figure 6.74). We now slice the water into n horizontal layers, each having thickness Δy.

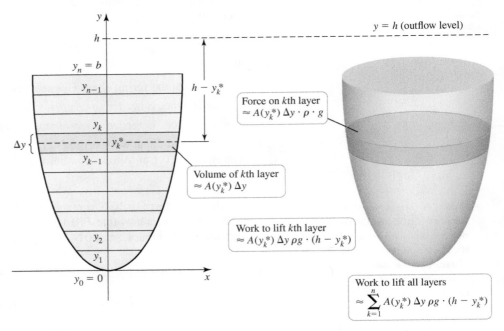

Figure 6.74

The kth layer occupying the interval $[y_{k-1}, y_k]$, for $k = 1, \ldots, n$, is approximately y_k^* units above the bottom of the tank, where y_k^* is any point in $[y_{k-1}, y_k]$.

The cross-sectional area of the kth layer at y_k^*, denoted $A(y_k^*)$, is determined by the shape of the tank; the solution depends on being able to find A for all values of y. Because the volume of the kth layer is approximately $A(y_k^*)\Delta y$, the force on the kth layer (its weight) is

$$F_k = mg \approx \underbrace{\underbrace{A(y_k^*)\Delta y}_{\text{volume}} \cdot \overbrace{\rho}^{\text{mass}} \cdot g}_{} \cdot g.$$

To reach the level $y = h$, the kth layer is lifted an approximate distance $(h - y_k^*)$ (Figure 6.74). So the work in lifting the kth layer to a height h is approximately

$$W_k = \underbrace{A(y_k^*)\Delta y \rho g}_{\text{force}} \cdot \underbrace{(h - y_k^*)}_{\text{distance}}.$$

Summing the work required to lift all the layers to a height h, the total work is

$$W \approx \sum_{k=1}^{n} W_k = \sum_{k=1}^{n} A(y_k^*)\rho g(h - y_k^*)\Delta y.$$

This approximation becomes more accurate as the width of the layers Δy tends to zero and the number of layers tends to infinity. In this limit, we obtain a definite integral from $y = 0$ to $y = b$. The total work required to empty the tank is

$$W = \lim_{n \to \infty} \sum_{k=1}^{n} A(y_k^*)\rho g(h - y_k^*)\Delta y = \int_0^b \rho g A(y)(h - y)\, dy.$$

This derivation assumes that the *bottom* of the tank is at $y = 0$, in which case the distance that the slice at level y must be lifted is $D(y) = h - y$. If you choose a different location for the origin, the function D will be different. Here is a general procedure for any choice of origin.

PROCEDURE   **Solving Lifting Problems**

1. Draw a y-axis in the vertical direction (parallel to gravity) and choose a convenient origin. Assume the interval $[a, b]$ corresponds to the vertical extent of the fluid.

2. For $a \le y \le b$, find the cross-sectional area $A(y)$ of the horizontal slices and the distance $D(y)$ the slices must be lifted.

3. The work required to lift the water is

$$W = \int_a^b \rho g A(y) D(y)\, dy.$$

We now use this procedure to solve two pumping problems.

EXAMPLE 3   **Pumping water**   How much work is needed to pump all the water out of a cylindrical tank with a height of 10 m and a radius of 5 m? The water is pumped to an outflow pipe 15 m above the bottom of the tank.

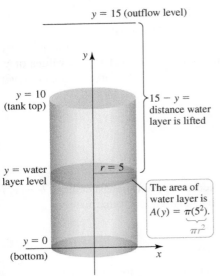

$y = 15$ (outflow level)

y

$y = 10$
(tank top)

$15 - y =$
distance water
layer is lifted

$y = $ water
layer level

$r = 5$

The area of
water layer is
$A(y) = \pi(5^2)$.
$\underbrace{\quad}_{\pi r^2}$

$y = 0$
(bottom)

x

Figure 6.75

➤ Recall that $g \approx 9.8 \text{ m/s}^2$. You should
verify that the units are consistent in this
calculation: The units of $\rho, g, A(y), D(y)$,
and dy are $\text{kg/m}^3, \text{m/s}^2, \text{m}^2, \text{m}$, and m,
respectively. The resulting units of W are
$\text{kg m}^2/\text{s}^2$, or J. A more convenient unit
for large amounts of work and energy is
the kilowatt-hour, which is 3.6 million
joules.

SOLUTION Figure 6.75 shows the cylindrical tank filled to capacity and the outflow 15 m
above the bottom of the tank. We let $y = 0$ represent the bottom of the tank and $y = 10$
represent the top of the tank. In this case, all horizontal slices are circular disks of radius
$r = 5$ m. Therefore, for $0 \le y \le 10$, the cross-sectional area is

$$A(y) = \pi r^2 = \pi 5^2 = 25\pi.$$

Note that the water is pumped to a level $h = 15$ m above the bottom of the tank, so the
lifting distance is $D(y) = 15 - y$. The resulting work integral is

$$W = \int_0^{10} \rho g \underbrace{A(y)}_{25\pi} \underbrace{D(y)}_{15 - y} \, dy = 25\pi\rho g \int_0^{10} (15 - y) \, dy.$$

Substituting $\rho = 1000 \text{ kg/m}^3$ and $g = 9.8 \text{ m/s}^2$, the total work in joules is

$$W = 25\pi\rho g \int_0^{10} (15 - y) \, dy$$

$$= 25\pi \underbrace{(1000)}_{\rho} \underbrace{(9.8)}_{g} \left(15y - \frac{1}{2}y^2 \right) \Big|_0^{10}$$

$$\approx 7.7 \times 10^7.$$

The work required to pump the water out of the tank is approximately 77 million joules.

Related Exercises 27–37 ◀

QUICK CHECK 5 In the previous example, how would the integral change if the outflow
pipe were at the top of the tank? ◀

EXAMPLE 4   Pumping gasoline A cylindrical tank with a length of 10 m and a radius
of 5 m is on its side and half-full of gasoline (Figure 6.76). How much work is required
to empty the tank through an outlet pipe at the top of the tank? (The density of gasoline is
$\rho \approx 737 \text{ kg/m}^3$.)

The equation of the
right side of the
circle is $x = \sqrt{25 - y^2}$.

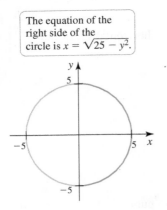

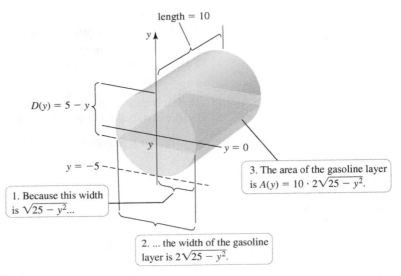

length $= 10$

y

$D(y) = 5 - y$

y

$y = 0$

$y = -5$

3. The area of the gasoline layer
is $A(y) = 10 \cdot 2\sqrt{25 - y^2}$.

1. Because this width
is $\sqrt{25 - y^2}$...

2. ... the width of the gasoline
layer is $2\sqrt{25 - y^2}$.

Figure 6.76

➤ Again, there are several choices for the
location of the origin. The location in this
example makes $A(y)$ easy to compute.

SOLUTION In this problem, we choose a different origin by letting $y = 0$ and $y = -5$
correspond to the center and the bottom of the tank, respectively. For $-5 \le y \le 0$, a horizontal layer of gasoline located at a depth y is a rectangle with a length of 10 and width of
$2\sqrt{25 - y^2}$ (Figure 6.76). Therefore, the cross-sectional area of the layer at depth y is

$$A(y) = 20\sqrt{25 - y^2}.$$

The distance the layer at level y must be lifted to reach the top of the tank is $D(y) = 5 - y$, where $5 \le D(y) \le 10$. The resulting work integral is

$$W = \underbrace{737}_{\rho}\underbrace{(9.8)}_{g} \int_{-5}^{0} \underbrace{20\sqrt{25 - y^2}}_{A(y)} \underbrace{(5 - y)}_{D(y)} \, dy = 144{,}452 \int_{-5}^{0} \sqrt{25 - y^2}\,(5 - y) \, dy.$$

This integral is evaluated by splitting the integrand into two pieces and recognizing that one piece is the area of a quarter circle of radius 5:

$$\int_{-5}^{0} \sqrt{25 - y^2}\,(5 - y)\,dy = 5 \underbrace{\int_{-5}^{0} \sqrt{25 - y^2}\,dy}_{\text{area of quarter circle}} - \underbrace{\int_{-5}^{0} y\sqrt{25 - y^2}\,dy}_{\text{let } u = 25 - y^2;\, du = -2y\,dy}$$

$$= 5 \cdot \frac{25\pi}{4} + \frac{1}{2}\int_{0}^{25} \sqrt{u}\,du$$

$$= \frac{125\pi}{4} + \frac{1}{3}u^{3/2}\Big|_{0}^{25} = \frac{375\pi + 500}{12}.$$

Multiplying this result by $20\,\rho g = 144{,}452$, we find that the work required is approximately 20.2 million joules.

Related Exercises 27–37 ◄

Force and Pressure

Another application of integration deals with the force exerted on a surface by a body of water. Again, we need a few physical principles.

Pressure is a force per unit area, measured in units such as newtons per square meter (N/m^2). For example, the pressure of the atmosphere on the surface of Earth is about 14 lb/in^2 (approximately 100 kilopascals, or $10^5\,\text{N/m}^2$). As another example, if you stood on the bottom of a swimming pool, you would feel pressure due to the weight (force) of the column of water above your head. If your head is flat and has surface area A m^2 and it is h meters below the surface, then the column of water above your head has volume Ah m^3. That column of water exerts a force (its weight)

$$F = \text{mass} \cdot \text{acceleration} = \underbrace{\text{volume} \cdot \text{density}}_{\text{mass}} \cdot g = Ah\rho g,$$

where ρ is the density of water and g is the acceleration due to gravity. Therefore, the pressure on your head is the force divided by the surface area of your head:

$$\text{pressure} = \frac{\text{force}}{A} = \frac{Ah\rho g}{A} = \rho g h.$$

This pressure is called **hydrostatic pressure** (meaning the pressure of *water at rest*), and it has the following important property: *It has the same magnitude in all directions.* Specifically, the hydrostatic pressure on a vertical wall of the swimming pool at a depth h is also $\rho g h$. This is the only fact needed to find the total force on vertical walls such as dams. We assume that the water completely covers the face of the dam.

The first step in finding the force on the face of the dam is to introduce a coordinate system. We choose a y-axis pointing upward with $y = 0$ corresponding to the base of the dam and $y = a$ corresponding to the top of the dam (Figure 6.77). Because the pressure varies with depth (y-direction), the dam is sliced horizontally into n strips of equal thickness Δy. The kth strip corresponds to the interval $[y_{k-1}, y_k]$, and we let y_k^* be any point in that interval. The depth of that strip is approximately $h = a - y_k^*$, so the hydrostatic pressure on that strip is approximately $\rho g(a - y_k^*)$.

The crux of any dam problem is finding the width of the strips as a function of y, which we denote $w(y)$. Each dam has its own width function; however, once the width function is known, the solution follows directly. The approximate area of the kth strip is

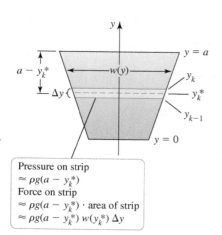

Pressure on strip
$\approx \rho g(a - y_k^*)$
Force on strip
$\approx \rho g(a - y_k^*) \cdot$ area of strip
$\approx \rho g(a - y_k^*)\,w(y_k^*)\,\Delta y$

Figure 6.77

its width multiplied by its thickness, or $w(y_k^*)\Delta y$. The force on the kth strip (which is the area of the strip multiplied by the pressure) is approximately

$$F_k = \underbrace{\rho g(a - y_k^*)}_{\text{pressure}}\underbrace{w(y_k^*)\Delta y}_{\text{area of strip}}.$$

Summing the forces over the n strips, the total force is

$$F \approx \sum_{k=1}^{n} F_k = \sum_{k=1}^{n} \rho g(a - y_k^*)w(y_k^*)\Delta y.$$

To find the exact force, we let the thickness of the strips tend to zero and the number of strips tend to infinity, which produces a definite integral. The limits of integration correspond to the base $(y = 0)$ and top $(y = a)$ of the dam. Therefore, the total force on the dam is

$$F = \lim_{n \to \infty} \sum_{k=1}^{n} \rho g(a - y_k^*)w(y_k^*)\Delta y = \int_{0}^{a} \rho g(a - y)w(y)\, dy.$$

➤ We have chosen $y = 0$ to be the base of the dam. Depending on the geometry of the problem, it may be more convenient (less computation) to let $y = 0$ be at the top of the dam. Experiment with different choices.

PROCEDURE   Solving Force Problems

1. Draw a y-axis on the face of the dam in the vertical direction and choose a convenient origin (often taken to be the base of the dam).

2. Find the width function $w(y)$ for each value of y on the face of the dam.

3. If the base of the dam is at $y = 0$ and the top of the dam is at $y = a$, then the total force on the dam is

$$F = \int_{0}^{a} \rho g \underbrace{(b - y)}_{\text{depth}}\underbrace{w(y)}_{\text{width}}\, dy.$$

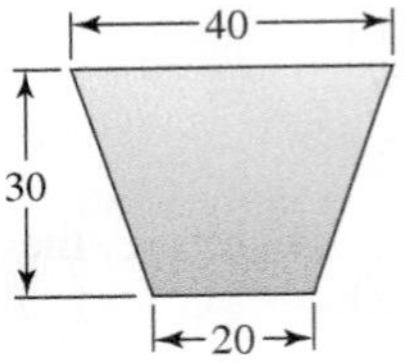

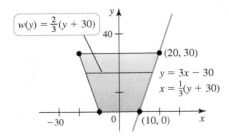

Figure 6.78

➤ You should check the width function: $w(0) = 20$ (the width of the dam at its base) and $w(30) = 40$ (the width of the dam at its top).

EXAMPLE 5   Force on a dam A large vertical dam in the shape of a symmetric trapezoid has a height of 30 m, a width of 20 m at its base, and a width of 40 m at the top (Figure 6.78). What is the total force on the face of the dam when the reservoir is full?

SOLUTION We place the origin at the center of the base of the dam (Figure 6.79). The right slanted edge of the dam is a segment of the line that passes through the points $(10, 0)$ and $(20, 30)$. An equation of that line is

$$y - 0 = \frac{30}{10}(x - 10) \quad \text{or} \quad y = 3x - 30 \quad \text{or} \quad x = \frac{1}{3}(y + 30).$$

Notice that at a depth of y, where $0 \le y \le 30$, the width of the dam is

$$w(y) = 2x = \frac{2}{3}(y + 30).$$

Figure 6.79

Using $\rho = 1000 \text{ kg/m}^3$ and $g = 9.8 \text{ m/s}^2$, the total force on the dam (in newtons) is

$$F = \int_0^a \rho g(a - y)w(y)\,dy \qquad \text{Force integral}$$

$$= \rho g \int_0^{30} \underbrace{(30 - y)}_{a-y}\,\underbrace{\frac{2}{3}(y + 30)}_{w(y)}\,dy \quad \text{Substitute.}$$

$$= \frac{2}{3}\rho g \int_0^{30} (900 - y^2)\,dy \qquad \text{Simplify.}$$

$$= \frac{2}{3}\rho g\left(900y - \frac{y^3}{3}\right)\Big|_0^{30} \qquad \text{Fundamental Theorem}$$

$$\approx 1.18 \times 10^8.$$

The force of 1.18×10^8 N on the dam amounts to about 26 million pounds, or 13,000 tons.

Related Exercises 38–48 ◄

SECTION 6.7 EXERCISES

Review Questions

1. Suppose a 1-m cylindrical bar has a constant density of 1 g/cm for its left half and a constant density 2 g/cm for its right half. What is its mass?

2. Explain how to find the mass of a one-dimensional object with a variable density ρ.

3. How much work is required to move an object from $x = 0$ to $x = 5$ (measured in meters) in the presence of a constant force of 5 N acting along the x-axis?

4. Why is integration used to find the work done by a variable force?

5. Why is integration used to find the work required to pump water out of a tank?

6. Why is integration used to find the total force on the face of a dam?

7. What is the pressure on a horizontal surface with an area of 2 m² that is 4 m underwater?

8. Explain why you integrate in the vertical direction (parallel to the acceleration due to gravity) rather than the horizontal direction to find the force on the face of a dam.

Basic Skills

9–16. Mass of one-dimensional objects *Find the mass of the following thin bars with the given density function.*

9. $\rho(x) = 1 + \sin x$; for $0 \le x \le \pi$

10. $\rho(x) = 1 + x^3$; for $0 \le x \le 1$

11. $\rho(x) = 2 - x/2$; for $0 \le x \le 2$

12. $\rho(x) = 5e^{-2x}$; for $0 \le x \le 4$

13. $\rho(x) = x\sqrt{2 - x^2}$; for $0 \le x \le 1$

14. $\rho(x) = \begin{cases} 1 & \text{if } 0 \le x \le 2 \\ 2 & \text{if } 2 < x \le 3 \end{cases}$

15. $\rho(x) = \begin{cases} 1 & \text{if } 0 \le x \le 2 \\ 1 + x & \text{if } 2 < x \le 4 \end{cases}$

16. $\rho(x) = \begin{cases} x^2 & \text{if } 0 \le x \le 1 \\ x(2 - x) & \text{if } 1 < x \le 2 \end{cases}$

17. **Work from force** How much work is required to move an object from $x = 0$ to $x = 3$ (measured in meters) in the presence of a force (in N) given by $F(x) = 2x$ acting along the x-axis?

18. **Work from force** How much work is required to move an object from $x = 1$ to $x = 3$ (measured in meters) in the presence of a force (in N) given by $F(x) = 2/x^2$ acting along the x-axis?

19. **Compressing and stretching a spring** Suppose a force of 30 N is required to stretch and hold a spring 0.2 m from its equilibrium position.

   a. Assuming the spring obeys Hooke's law, find the spring constant k.
   b. How much work is required to compress the spring 0.4 m from its equilibrium position?
   c. How much work is required to stretch the spring 0.3 m from its equilibrium position?
   d. How much additional work is required to stretch the spring 0.2 m if it has already been stretched 0.2 m from its equilibrium position?

20. **Compressing and stretching a spring** Suppose a force of 15 N is required to stretch and hold a spring 0.25 m from its equilibrium position.

   a. Assuming the spring obeys Hooke's law, find the spring constant k.
   b. How much work is required to compress the spring 0.2 m from its equilibrium position?
   c. How much additional work is required to stretch the spring 0.3 m if it has already been stretched 0.25 m from its equilibrium position?

21. **Work done by a spring** A spring on a horizontal surface can be stretched and held 0.5 m from its equilibrium position with a force of 50 N.

   a. How much work is done in stretching the spring 1.5 m from its equilibrium position?
   b. How much work is done in compressing the spring 0.5 m from its equilibrium position?

22. **Shock absorber** A heavy-duty shock absorber is compressed 2 cm from its equilibrium position by a mass of 500 kg. How much work is required to compress the shock absorber 4 cm from its equilibrium position? (A mass of 500 kg exerts a force (in newtons) of 500 g, where $g \approx 9.8 \text{ m/s}^2$.)

23. **Calculating work for different springs** Calculate the work required to stretch the following springs 0.5 m from their equilibrium positions. Assume Hooke's law is obeyed.

   a. A spring that requires a force of 50 N to be stretched 0.2 m from its equilibrium position
   b. A spring that requires 50 J of work to be stretched 0.2 m from its equilibrium position

24. **Calculating work for different springs** Calculate the work required to stretch the following springs 0.4 m from their equilibrium positions. Assume Hooke's law is obeyed.

   a. A spring that requires a force of 50 N to be stretched 0.1 m from its equilibrium position
   b. A spring that requires 2 J of work to be stretched 0.1 m from its equilibrium position

25. **Calculating work for different springs** Calculate the work required to stretch the following springs 1.25 m from their equilibrium positions. Assume Hooke's law is obeyed.

   a. A spring that requires 100 J of work to be stretched 0.5 m from its equilibrium position
   b. A spring that requires a force of 250 N to be stretched 0.5 m from its equilibrium

26. **Work function** A spring has a restoring force given by $F(x) = 25x$. Let $W(x)$ be the work required to stretch the spring from its equilibrium position ($x = 0$) to a variable distance x. Find and graph the work function. Compare the work required to stretch the spring x units from equilibrium to the work required to compress the spring x units from equilibrium.

27. **Emptying a swimming pool** A swimming pool has the shape of a box with a base that measures 25 m by 15 m and a uniform depth of 2.5 m. How much work is required to pump the water out of the pool when it is full?

28. **Emptying a cylindrical tank** A cylindrical water tank has height 8 m and radius 2 m (see figure).

   a. If the tank is full of water, how much work is required to pump the water to the level of the top of the tank and out of the tank?
   b. Is it true that it takes half as much work to pump the water out of the tank when it is half full as when it is full? Explain.

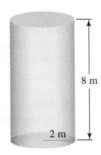

8 m

2 m

29. **Emptying a half-full cylindrical tank** Suppose the water tank in Exercise 28 is half full of water. Determine the work required to empty the tank by pumping the water to a level 2 m above the top of the tank.

30. **Emptying a partially filled swimming pool** If the water in the swimming pool in Exercise 27 is 2 m deep, then how much work is required to pump all the water to a level 3 m above the bottom of the pool?

31. **Emptying a conical tank** A water tank is shaped like an inverted cone with height 6 m and base radius 1.5 m (see figure).

   a. If the tank is full, how much work is required to pump the water to the level of the top of the tank and out of the tank?
   b. Is it true that it takes half as much work to pump the water out of the tank when it is filled to half its depth as when it is full? Explain.

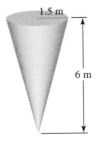

1.5 m

6 m

32. **Emptying a real swimming pool** A swimming pool is 20 m long and 10 m wide, with a bottom that slopes uniformly from a depth of 1 m at one end to a depth of 2 m at the other end (see figure). Assuming the pool is full, how much work is required to pump the water to a level 0.2 m above the top of the pool?

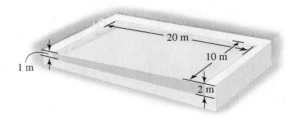

20 m

10 m

1 m

2 m

33. **Filling a spherical tank** A spherical water tank with an inner radius of 8 m has its lowest point 2 m above the ground. It is filled by a pipe that feeds the tank at its lowest point (see figure).

   a. Neglecting the volume of the inflow pipe, how much work is required to fill the tank if it is initially empty?
   b. Now assume that the inflow pipe feeds the tank at the top of the tank. Neglecting the volume of the inflow pipe, how much work is required to fill the tank if it is initially empty?

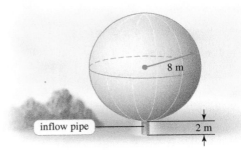

8 m

inflow pipe

2 m

34. Emptying a water trough A water trough has a semicircular cross section with a radius of 0.25 m and a length of 3 m (see figure).

a. How much work is required to pump the water out of the trough when it is full?

b. If the length is doubled, is the required work doubled? Explain.

c. If the radius is doubled, is the required work doubled? Explain.

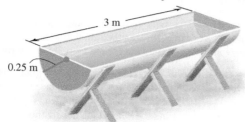

35. Emptying a water trough A cattle trough has a trapezoidal cross section with a height of 1 m and horizontal sides of length $\frac{1}{2}$ m and 1 m. Assume the length of the trough is 10 m (see figure).

a. How much work is required to pump the water out of the trough (to the level of the top of the trough) when it is full?

b. If the length is doubled, is the required work doubled? Explain.

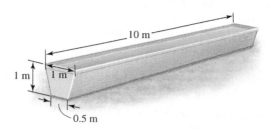

36. Pumping water Suppose the tank in Example 4 is full of water (rather than half full of gas). Determine the work required to pump all the water to an outlet pipe 15 m above the bottom of the tank.

37. Emptying a conical tank An inverted cone is 2 m high and has a base radius of $\frac{1}{2}$ m. If the tank is full, how much work is required to pump the water to a level 1 m above the top of the tank?

38–41. Force on dams *The following figures show the shape and dimensions of small dams. Assuming the water level is at the top of the dam, find the total force on the face of the dam.*

38.

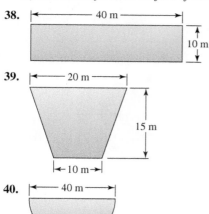

39.

40.

41.

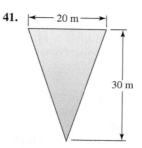

42. Parabolic dam The lower edge of a dam is defined by the parabola $y = x^2/16$ (see figure). Use a coordinate system with $y = 0$ at the bottom of the dam to determine the total force on the dam. Lengths are measured in meters. Assume the water level is at the top of the dam.

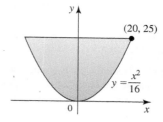

43. Orientation and force A plate shaped like an isosceles triangle with a height of 1 m is placed on a vertical wall 1 m below the surface of a pool filled with water (see figure). Compute the force on the plate.

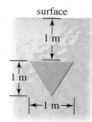

44. Force on the end of a tank Determine the force on a circular end of the tank in Figure 6.76 if the tank is full of gasoline. The density of gasoline is $\rho = 737 \text{ kg/m}^3$.

45. Force on a building A large building shaped like a box is 50 m high with a face that is 80 m wide. A strong wind blows directly at the face of the building, exerting a pressure of 150 N/m^2 at the ground and increasing with height according to $P(y) = 150 + 2y$, where y is the height above the ground. Calculate the total force on the building, which is a measure of the resistance that must be included in the design of the building.

46–48. Force on a window *A diving pool that is 4 m deep and full of water has a viewing window on one of its vertical walls. Find the force on the following windows.*

46. The window is a square, 0.5 m on a side, with the lower edge of the window on the bottom of the pool.

47. The window is a square, 0.5 m on a side, with the lower edge of the window 1 m from the bottom of the pool.

48. The window is a circle, with a radius of 0.5 m, tangent to the bottom of the pool.

Further Explorations

49. Explain why or why not Determine whether the following statements are true and give an explanation or counterexample.

  a. The mass of a thin wire is the length of the wire times its average density over its length.

  b. The work required to stretch a linear spring (that obeys Hooke's law) 100 cm from equilibrium is the same as the work required to compress it 100 cm from equilibrium.

  c. The work required to lift a 10-kg object vertically 10 m is the same as the work required to lift a 20-kg object vertically 5 m.

  d. The total force on a 10-ft^2 region on the (horizontal) floor of a pool is the same as the total force on a 10-ft^2 region on a (vertical) wall of the pool.

50. Mass of two bars Two bars of length L have densities $\rho_1(x) = 4e^{-x}$ and $\rho_2(x) = 6e^{-2x}$, for $0 \le x \le L$.

  a. For what values of L is bar 1 heavier than bar 2?

  b. As the lengths of the bars increase, do their masses increase without bound? Explain.

51. A nonlinear spring Hooke's law is applicable to idealized (linear) springs that are not stretched or compressed too far. Consider a nonlinear spring whose restoring force is given by $F(x) = 16x - 0.1x^3$, for $|x| \le 7$.

  a. Graph the restoring force and interpret it.

  b. How much work is done in stretching the spring from its equilibrium position $(x = 0)$ to $x = 1.5$?

  c. How much work is done in compressing the spring from its equilibrium position $(x = 0)$ to $x = -2$?

52. A vertical spring A 10-kg mass is attached to a spring that hangs vertically and is stretched 2 m from the equilibrium position of the spring. Assume a linear spring with $F(x) = kx$.

  a. How much work is required to compress the spring and lift the mass 0.5 m?

  b. How much work is required to stretch the spring and lower the mass 0.5 m?

53. Drinking juice A glass has circular cross sections that taper (linearly) from a radius of 5 cm at the top of the glass to a radius of 4 cm at the bottom. The glass is 15 cm high and full of orange juice. How much work is required to drink all the juice through a straw if your mouth is 5 cm above the top of the glass? Assume the density of orange juice equals the density of water.

54. Upper and lower half A cylinder with height 8 m and radius 3 m is filled with water and must be emptied through an outlet pipe 2 m above the top of the cylinder.

  a. Compute the work required to empty the water in the top half of the tank.

  b. Compute the work required to empty the (equal amount of) water in the lower half of the tank.

  c. Interpret the results of parts (a) and (b).

Applications

55. Work in a gravitational field For large distances from the surface of Earth, the gravitational force is given by $F(x) = GMm/(x + R)^2$, where $G = 6.7 \times 10^{-11}$ N-m^2/kg^2 is the gravitational constant, $M = 6 \times 10^{24}$ kg is the mass of Earth, m is the mass of the object in the gravitational field, $R = 6.378 \times 10^6$ m is the radius of Earth, and $x \ge 0$ is the distance above the surface of Earth (in meters).

  a. How much work is required to launch a rocket with a mass of 500 kg in a vertical flight path to a height of 2500 km (from Earth's surface)?

  b. Find the work required to launch the rocket to a height of x kilometers, for $x > 0$.

  c. How much work is required to reach outer space $(x \to \infty)$?

  d. Equate the work in part (c) to the initial kinetic energy of the rocket, $\frac{1}{2}mv^2$, to compute the escape velocity of the rocket.

56. Work by two different integrals A rigid body with a mass of 2 kg moves along a line due to a force that produces a position function $x(t) = 4t^2$, where x is measured in meters and t is measured in seconds. Find the work done during the first 5 s in two ways.

  a. Note that $x''(t) = 8$; then use Newton's second law $(F = ma = mx''(t))$ to evaluate the work integral $W = \int_{x_0}^{x_f} F(x)\, dx$, where x_0 and x_f are the initial and final positions, respectively.

  b. Change variables in the work integral and integrate with respect to t. Be sure your answer agrees with part (a).

57. Winding a chain A 30-m-long chain hangs vertically from a cylinder attached to a winch. Assume there is no friction in the system and the chain has a density of 5 kg/m.

  a. How much work is required to wind the entire chain onto the cylinder using the winch?

  b. How much work is required to wind the chain onto the cylinder if a 50-kg block is attached to the end of the chain?

58. Coiling a rope A 60-m-long, 9.4-mm-diameter rope hangs free from a ledge. The density of the rope is 55 g/m. How much work is needed to pull the entire rope to the ledge?

59. Lifting a pendulum A body of mass m is suspended by a rod of length L that pivots without friction (see figure). The mass is slowly lifted along a circular arc to a height h.

  a. Assuming that the only force acting on the mass is the gravitational force, show that the component of this force acting along the arc of motion is $F = mg \sin \theta$.

  b. Noting that an element of length along the path of the pendulum is $ds = L\, d\theta$, evaluate an integral in θ to show that the work done in lifting the mass to a height h is mgh.

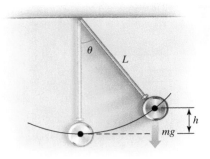

60. Orientation and force A plate shaped like an equilateral triangle 1 m on a side is placed on a vertical wall 1 m below the surface of a pool filled with water. On which plate in the figure is the force greater? Try to anticipate the answer and then compute the force on each plate.

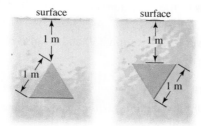

61. Orientation and force A square plate 1 m on a side is placed on a vertical wall 1 m below the surface of a pool filled with water. On which plate in the figure is the force greater? Try to anticipate the answer and then compute the force on each plate.

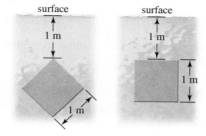

62. A calorie-free milkshake? Suppose a cylindrical glass with a diameter of $\frac{1}{12}$ m and a height of $\frac{1}{10}$ m is filled to the brim with a 400-Cal milkshake. If you have a straw that is 1.1 m long (so the top of the straw is 1 m above the top of the glass), do you burn off all the calories in the milkshake in drinking it? Assume that the density of the milkshake is 1 g/cm^3 $(1 \text{ Cal} = 4184 \text{ J})$.

63. Critical depth A large tank has a plastic window on one wall that is designed to withstand a force of 90,000 N. The square window is 2 m on a side, and its lower edge is 1 m from the bottom of the tank.

a. If the tank is filled to a depth of 4 m, will the window withstand the resulting force?

b. What is the maximum depth to which the tank can be filled without the window failing?

64. Buoyancy Archimedes' principle says that the buoyant force exerted on an object that is (partially or totally) submerged in water is equal to the weight of the water displaced by the object (see figure). Let $\rho_w = 1 \text{ g/cm}^3 = 1000 \text{ kg/m}^3$ be the density of water and let ρ be the density of an object in water. Let $f = \rho/\rho_w$. If $0 < f \leq 1$, then the object floats with a fraction f of its volume submerged; if $f > 1$, then the object sinks.

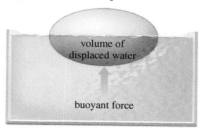

Consider a cubical box with sides 2 m long floating in water with one-half of its volume submerged $(\rho = \rho_w/2)$. Find the force required to fully submerge the box (so its top surface is at the water level).

(See the Guided Project *Buoyancy and Archimedes' Principle* for further explorations of buoyancy problems.)

QUICK CHECK ANSWERS

1. a. The bar is heaviest at the left end and lightest at the right end. **b.** $\rho = 2.5 \text{ g/cm}$. **2.** Minimum mass = 2 kg; maximum mass = 10 kg **3.** We assume that the force is constant over each subinterval, when, in fact, it varies over each subinterval. **4.** The restoring force of the spring increases as the spring is stretched $(f(x) = 100x)$. Greater restoring forces are encountered on the interval $[0.1, 0.35]$ than on the interval $[0, 0.25]$. **5.** The factor $(15 - y)$ in the integral is replaced with $(10 - y)$. ◄

6.8 Logarithmic and Exponential Functions Revisited

Earlier in the text, we made several claims about exponential and logarithmic functions, but we did not prove them. (For example, these functions are continuous and differentiable on their domains.) Our objective in this section is to place these important functions on a solid foundation by presenting a more rigorous development of their properties.

Before embarking on this program, we offer a roadmap to help guide you through the section. We carry out the following four steps.

1. We first define the natural logarithm function in terms of an integral, and then derive the properties of ln x directly from this new definition.

2. The natural exponential function e^x is introduced as the inverse of $\ln x$, and the properties of e^x are developed by appealing to this inverse relationship. We also present derivative and integral formulas associated with these functions.

3. Next, we define the general exponential function b^x in terms of e^x, and the general logarithmic function $\log_b x$ in terms of $\ln x$. The derivative and integral results stated in Section 3.9 follow immediately.

4. Finally, we revisit the General Power Rule (Section 3.9) and we also derive a limit that can be used to approximate e.

Step 1: The Natural Logarithm

Our aim is to develop the properties of the natural logarithm using definite integrals. It all begins with the following definition.

DEFINITION The Natural Logarithm

The **natural logarithm** of a number $x > 0$, is $\ln x = \displaystyle\int_1^x \frac{1}{t}\, dt.$

All the familiar geometric and algebraic properties of the natural logarithmic function follow directly from this new integral definition.

Properties of the Natural Logarithm

Domain, range, and sign Because the natural logarithm is defined as a definite integral, its value is the net area under the curve $y = 1/t$ between $t = 1$ and $t = x$. The integrand is undefined at $t = 0$, so the domain of $\ln x$ is $(0, \infty)$. On the interval $(1, \infty)$, $\ln x$ is positive because the net area of the region under the curve is positive (Figure 6.80a). On

$(0, 1)$, we have $\displaystyle\int_1^x \frac{1}{t}\, dt = -\int_x^1 \frac{1}{t}\, dt$, which implies $\ln x$ is negative (Figure 6.80b). As

expected, when $x = 1$, we have $\ln 1 = \displaystyle\int_1^1 \frac{1}{t}\, dt = 0$. The net area interpretation of $\ln x$

also implies that the range of $\ln x$ is $(-\infty, \infty)$ (see Exercise 72 for an outline of a proof).

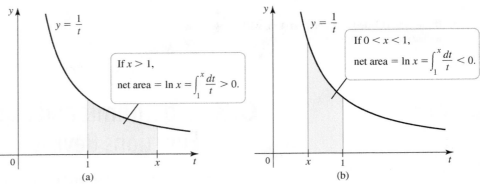

Figure 6.80

> By the Fundamental Theorem of Calculus,
>
> $$\frac{d}{dx}\int_a^x f(t)\, dt = f(x).$$

Derivative The derivative of the natural logarithm follows immediately from its definition and the Fundamental Theorem of Calculus:

$$\frac{d}{dx}(\ln x) = \frac{d}{dx}\int_1^x \frac{dt}{t} = \frac{1}{x}, \text{ for } x > 0.$$

We have two important consequences.

- Because its derivative is defined for $x > 0$, $\ln x$ is a differentiable function for $x > 0$, which means it is continuous on its domain (Theorem 3.1).
- Because $1/x > 0$ for $x > 0$, $\ln x$ is strictly increasing and one-to-one on its domain; therefore, it has a well-defined inverse.

The Chain Rule allows us to extend the derivative property to all nonzero real numbers (Exercise 70). By differentiating $\ln(-x)$ for $x < 0$, we find that

$$\frac{d}{dx}(\ln|x|) = \frac{1}{x}, \quad \text{for } x \neq 0.$$

QUICK CHECK 1 What is the domain of $\ln|x|$? ◄

More generally, by the Chain Rule,

$$\frac{d}{dx}(\ln|u(x)|) = \frac{1}{u(x)}u'(x) = \frac{u'(x)}{u(x)}.$$

Graph of ln x As noted before, $\ln x$ is continuous and strictly increasing for $x > 0$. The second derivative, $\dfrac{d^2}{dx^2}(\ln x) = -\dfrac{1}{x^2}$, is negative for $x > 0$, which implies the graph of $\ln x$ is concave down for $x > 0$. As demonstrated in Exercise 72,

$$\lim_{x \to \infty} \ln x = \infty, \quad \text{and} \quad \lim_{x \to 0^+} \ln x = -\infty.$$

This information, coupled with the fact that $\ln 1 = 0$, gives the graph of $y = \ln x$ (Figure 6.81).

Logarithm of a product The familiar logarithm property

$$\ln xy = \ln x + \ln y, \quad \text{for } x > 0, \quad y > 0,$$

may be proved using the integral definition:

$$\ln xy = \int_1^{xy} \frac{dt}{t} \qquad \text{Definition of } \ln xy$$

$$= \int_1^x \frac{dt}{t} + \int_x^{xy} \frac{dt}{t} \qquad \text{Additive property of integrals}$$

$$= \int_1^x \frac{dt}{t} + \int_1^y \frac{du}{u} \qquad \text{Substitute } u = t/x \text{ in second integral.}$$

$$= \ln x + \ln y. \qquad \text{Definition of } \ln$$

Logarithm of a quotient Assuming $x > 0$ and $y > 0$, the product property and a bit of algebra give

$$\ln x = \ln\left(y \cdot \frac{x}{y}\right) = \ln y + \ln\frac{x}{y}.$$

Solving for $\ln(x/y)$, we have

$$\ln\frac{x}{y} = \ln x - \ln y,$$

which is the quotient property for logarithms.

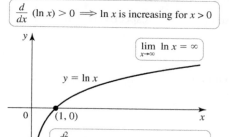

$\dfrac{d}{dx}(\ln x) > 0 \Rightarrow \ln x$ is increasing for $x > 0$

$\lim_{x \to \infty} \ln x = \infty$

$y = \ln x$

$(1, 0)$

$\dfrac{d^2}{dx^2}(\ln x) < 0 \Rightarrow$ concave down

$\lim_{x \to 0^+} \ln x = -\infty$

Figure 6.81

Logarithm of a power Assuming $x > 0$ and p is rational, we have

$$\ln x^p = \int_1^{x^p} \frac{dt}{t} \qquad \text{Definition of } \ln x^p$$

$$= p \int_1^x \frac{du}{u} \qquad \text{Let } t = u^p; \; dt = pu^{p-1}\,du.$$

$$= p \ln x. \qquad \text{By definition, } \ln x = \int_1^x \frac{du}{u}.$$

This argument relies on the Power Rule $(dt = pu^{p-1}\,du)$, which we proved only for rational exponents. Later in this section, we prove that $\ln x^p = p \ln x$, for all real values of p.

Integrals Because $\dfrac{d}{dx}(\ln |x|) = \dfrac{1}{x}$, we have

$$\int \frac{1}{x}\,dx = \ln |x| + C.$$

We have shown that the familiar properties of $\ln x$ follow from its new integral definition.

THEOREM 6.4   Properties of the Natural Logarithm

1. The domain and range of $\ln x$ are $(0, \infty)$ and $(-\infty, \infty)$, respectively.
2. $\ln xy = \ln x + \ln y$, for $x > 0$ and $y > 0$
3. $\ln (x/y) = \ln x - \ln y$, for $x > 0$ and $y > 0$
4. $\ln x^p = p \ln x$, for $x > 0$ and p a rational number
5. $\dfrac{d}{dx}(\ln |x|) = \dfrac{1}{x}$, for $x \neq 0$
6. $\dfrac{d}{dx}(\ln |u(x)|) = \dfrac{u'(x)}{u(x)}$, for $u(x) \neq 0$
7. $\displaystyle\int \frac{1}{x}\,dx = \ln |x| + C$

EXAMPLE 1   Integrals with ln x Evaluate $\displaystyle\int_0^4 \frac{x}{x^2 + 9}\,dx$.

SOLUTION

$$\int_0^4 \frac{x}{x^2 + 9}\,dx = \frac{1}{2}\int_9^{25} \frac{du}{u} \qquad \text{Let } u = x^2 + 9; \; du = 2x\,dx.$$

$$= \frac{1}{2}\ln |u| \Big|_9^{25} \qquad \text{Fundamental Theorem}$$

$$= \frac{1}{2}(\ln 25 - \ln 9) \qquad \text{Evaluate.}$$

$$= \ln \frac{5}{3} \qquad \text{Properties of logarithms}$$

Related Exercises 7–20 ◄

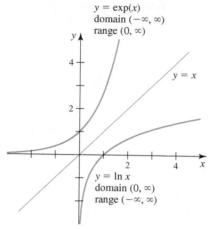

Figure 6.82

Step 2: The Exponential Function

We have established that $f(x) = \ln x$ is a continuous, increasing function on the interval $(0, \infty)$. Therefore, it is one-to-one and its inverse function exists on $(0, \infty)$. We denote the inverse function $f^{-1}(x) = \exp(x)$. Its graph is obtained by reflecting the graph of $f(x) = \ln x$ about the line $y = x$ (Figure 6.82). The domain of $\exp(x)$ is $(-\infty, \infty)$ because the range of $\ln x$ is $(-\infty, \infty)$, and the range of $\exp(x)$ is $(0, \infty)$ because the domain of $\ln x$ is $(0, \infty)$.

The usual relationships between a function and its inverse also hold:

- $y = \exp(x)$ if and only if $x = \ln y$;
- $\exp(\ln x) = x$, for $x > 0$, and $\ln(\exp(x)) = x$, for all x.

We now appeal to the properties of $\ln x$ and use the inverse relations between $\ln x$ and $\exp(x)$ to show that $\exp(x)$ satisfies the expected properties of any exponential function. For example, if $x_1 = \ln y_1$ and $x_2 = \ln y_2$, then it follows that $y_1 = \exp(x_1)$, $y_2 = \exp(x_2)$, and

$$\exp(x_1 + x_2) = \exp(\underbrace{\ln y_1 + \ln y_2}_{\ln y_1 y_2}) \quad \text{Substitute } x_1 = \ln y_1, x_2 = \ln y_2.$$

$$= \exp(\ln y_1 y_2) \quad \text{Properties of logarithms}$$

$$= y_1 y_2 \quad \text{Inverse property of } \exp(x) \text{ and } \ln x$$

$$= \exp(x_1)\exp(x_2). \quad y_1 = \exp(x_1), y_2 = \exp(x_2)$$

Therefore, $\exp(x)$ satisfies the property of exponential functions $b^{x_1+x_2} = b^{x_1}b^{x_2}$. Similar arguments show that $\exp(x)$ satisfies other characteristic properties of exponential functions (Exercise 71):

$$\exp(0) = 1,$$

$$\exp(x_1 - x_2) = \frac{\exp(x_1)}{\exp(x_2)}, \quad \text{and}$$

$$(\exp(x))^p = \exp(px), \text{ for rational numbers } p.$$

Suspecting that $\exp(x)$ is an exponential function, the next task is to identify its base. Let's consider the real number $\exp(1)$, and with a bit of forethought, call it e. The inverse relationship between $\ln x$ and $\exp(x)$ implies that

$$\text{if } e = \exp(1), \text{ then } \ln e = \ln(\exp(1)) = 1.$$

Using the fact that $\ln e = 1$ and the integral definition of $\ln x$, we now formally define e.

DEFINITION The Number e

The number e is the real number that satisfies $\ln e = \displaystyle\int_1^e \frac{dt}{t} = 1$.

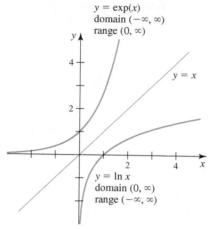

Figure 6.83

$$\ln e = \int_1^e \frac{dt}{t} = 1$$

$$\text{area} = \ln e = 1$$

$$\ln 2 < 1 \qquad \ln 3 > 1$$

▶ We give a limit definition that provides a good approximation to e at the end of this section.

The number e has the property that the area of the region bounded by the graph of $y = \dfrac{1}{t}$ and the t-axis on the interval $[1, e]$ is 1 (Figure 6.83). Note that $\ln 2 < 1$ and $\ln 3 > 1$ (Exercise 73). Because $\ln x$ is continuous on its domain, the Intermediate Value Theorem ensures that there is a number e with $2 < e < 3$ such that $\ln e = 1$.

We can now show that indeed $\exp(x)$ is the exponential function e^x. Assume that p is a rational number and note that $e^p > 0$. By property 4 of Theorem 6.4 we have

$$\ln e^p = p \underbrace{\ln e}_{1} = p.$$

Using the inverse relationship between $\ln x$ and $\exp(x)$, we also know that

$$\ln \exp(p) = p.$$

Equating these two expressions for p, we conclude that $\ln e^p = \ln \exp(p)$. Because $\ln x$ is a one-to-one function, it follows that

$$e^p = \exp(p), \text{ for rational numbers } p,$$

and we conclude that $\exp(x)$ is the exponential function with base e.

We already know how to evaluate e^x when x is rational. For example, $e^3 = e \cdot e \cdot e$, $e^{-2} = \dfrac{1}{e \cdot e}$, and $e^{1/2} = \sqrt{e}$. But how do we evaluate e^x when x is irrational? We proceed as follows. The function $x = \ln y$ is defined for $y > 0$ and its range is all real numbers. Therefore, the domain of its inverse $y = \exp(x)$ is all real numbers; that is, $\exp(x)$ is defined for all real numbers. We now define e^x to be $\exp(x)$ when x is irrational.

DEFINITION The Exponential Function

For any real number x, $y = e^x = \exp(x)$, where $x = \ln y$.

We may now dispense with the notation $\exp(x)$ and use e^x as the inverse of $\ln x$. The usual inverse relationships between e^x and $\ln x$ hold, and the properties of $\exp(x)$ can now be written for e^x.

THEOREM 6.5 Properties of e^x

The exponential function e^x satisfies the following properties, all of which result from the integral definition of $\ln x$. Let x and y be real numbers.

1. $e^{x+y} = e^x e^y$
2. $e^{x-y} = e^x / e^y$
3. $(e^x)^p = e^{xp}$, where p is a rational number
4. $\ln(e^x) = x$
5. $e^{\ln x} = x$, for $x > 0$

▶ The restriction on p in property 3 will be lifted shortly.

QUICK CHECK 2 Simplify $e^{\ln 2x}$, $\ln(e^{2x})$, $e^{2\ln x}$, and $\ln(2e^x)$. ◀

Derivatives and Integrals   By Theorem 3.23 (derivatives of inverse functions), the derivative of the exponential function exists for all x. To compute $\dfrac{d}{dx}(e^x)$, we observe that $\ln(e^x) = x$ and then differentiate both sides with respect to x:

$$\frac{d}{dx}(\ln e^x) = \underbrace{\frac{d}{dx}(x)}_{1}$$

$$\frac{1}{e^x}\frac{d}{dx}(e^x) = 1 \qquad \frac{d}{dx}(\ln u(x)) = \frac{u'(x)}{u(x)} \text{ (Chain Rule)}$$

$$\frac{d}{dx}(e^x) = e^x. \qquad \text{Solve for } \frac{d}{dx}(e^x).$$

QUICK CHECK 3 What is the slope of the curve $y = e^x$ at $x = \ln 2$? What is the area of the region bounded by the graph of $y = e^x$ and the x-axis between $x = 0$ and $x = \ln 2$? ◄

Once again, we obtain the remarkable result that the exponential function is its own derivative. It follows that e^x is its own antiderivative up to a constant; that is,

$$\int e^x \, dx = e^x + C.$$

Extending these results using the Chain Rule, we have the following theorem.

THEOREM 6.6 Derivative and Integral of the Exponential Function

For real numbers x,

$$\frac{d}{dx}\left(e^{u(x)}\right) = e^{u(x)}u'(x) \quad \text{and} \quad \int e^x \, dx = e^x + C.$$

EXAMPLE 2 Integrals with e^x Evaluate $\int \dfrac{e^x}{1 + e^x} \, dx$.

SOLUTION The change of variables $u = 1 + e^x$ implies $du = e^x \, dx$:

$$\int \underbrace{\frac{1}{1 + e^x}}_{u} \underbrace{e^x \, dx}_{du} = \int \frac{1}{u} \, du \qquad u = 1 + e^x, \, du = e^x \, dx$$

$$= \ln|u| + C \qquad \text{Antiderivative of } u^{-1}$$

$$= \ln(1 + e^x) + C. \qquad \text{Replace } u \text{ with } 1 + e^x.$$

Note that the absolute value may be removed from $\ln|u|$ because $1 + e^x > 0$, for all x.

Related Exercises 21–26 ◄

Step 3: General Logarithmic and Exponential Functions

We now turn to exponential and logarithmic functions with a general positive base b. The first step is to define the exponential function b^x for positive bases with $b \neq 1$ and for all real numbers x. We use property 3 of Theorem 6.5 and the fact that $b = e^{\ln b}$. If x is a rational number, then

$$b^x = \underbrace{\left(e^{\ln b}\right)^x}_{b} = e^{x \ln b};$$

this important relationship expresses b^x in terms of e^x. Because e^x is defined for all real x, we use this relationship to define b^x for all real x.

DEFINITION Exponential Functions with General Bases

Let b be a positive real number with $b \neq 1$. Then for all real x,

$$b^x = e^{x \ln b}.$$

This definition fills the gap in property 4 of Theorem 6.4 ($\ln x^p = p \ln x$). We use the definition of b^x to write

$$x^p = e^{p \ln x}, \text{ for } x > 0 \text{ and } p \text{ real.}$$

Taking the natural logarithm of both sides and using the inverse relationship between e^x and $\ln x$, we find that

$$\ln x^p = \ln e^{p \ln x} = p \ln x, \text{ for } x > 0 \text{ and } p \text{ real.}$$

In this way, we extend property 4 of Theorem 6.4 to real powers.

Just as b^x is defined in terms of e^x, logarithms with base $b > 1$ and $b \neq 1$ may be expressed in terms of $\ln x$. All that is needed is the change of base formula (Section 1.3)

$$\log_b x = \frac{\ln x}{\ln b}.$$

➤ Knowing that $\ln x^p = p \ln x$ for real p, we can also extend property 3 of Theorem 6.5 to real numbers. For real x and y, we take the natural logarithm of both sides of $z = (e^x)^y$, which gives $\ln z = y \ln e^x = xy$, or $z = e^{xy}$. Therefore, $(e^x)^y = e^{xy}$.

Theorems 3.18 and 3.20 give us the derivative results for exponential and logarithmic functions with a general base $b > 0$. Extending those results with the Chain Rule, we have the following derivatives and integrals.

SUMMARY   Derivatives and Integrals with Other Bases

Let $b > 0$ and $b \neq 1$. Then

$$\frac{d}{dx}\left(\log_b |u(x)|\right) = \frac{u'(x)}{u(x)\ln b}, \text{ for } u(x) \neq 0 \text{ and } \frac{d}{dx}\left(b^{u(x)}\right) = (\ln b)b^{u(x)}u'(x).$$

For $b > 0$ and $b \neq 1$, $\displaystyle\int b^x\, dx = \frac{1}{\ln b}b^x + C.$

QUICK CHECK 4 Verify that the derivative and integral results for a general base b reduce to the expected results when $b = e$. ◄

EXAMPLE 3   Integrals involving exponentials with other bases Evaluate the following integrals.

a. $\displaystyle\int x\, 3^{x^2}\, dx$ **b.** $\displaystyle\int_1^4 \frac{6^{-\sqrt{x}}}{\sqrt{x}}\, dx$

SOLUTION

a. $\displaystyle\int x\, 3^{x^2}\, dx = \frac{1}{2}\int 3^u\, du$ $u = x^2,\, du = 2x\, dx$

$\qquad\qquad\quad = \frac{1}{2}\frac{1}{\ln 3}3^u + C$ Integrate.

$\qquad\qquad\quad = \frac{1}{2\ln 3}3^{x^2} + C$ Substitute $u = x^2$.

b. $\displaystyle\int_1^4 \frac{6^{-\sqrt{x}}}{\sqrt{x}}\, dx = -2\int_{-1}^{-2} 6^u\, du$ $u = -\sqrt{x},\, du = -\dfrac{1}{2\sqrt{x}}\, dx$

$\qquad\qquad\quad = -\frac{2}{\ln 6}6^u\Big|_{-1}^{-2}$ Fundamental Theorem

$\qquad\qquad\quad = \frac{5}{18\ln 6}$ Simplify.

Related Exercises 27–32 ◄

Step 4: General Power Rule

With the identity $x^p = e^{p\ln x}$, we can state and prove the final version of the Power Rule. In Chapter 3, we showed that

$$\frac{d}{dx}(x^p) = px^{p-1}$$

when p is a rational number. This result is extended to all real values of p by differentiating $x^p = e^{p\ln x}$:

$$\frac{d}{dx}(x^p) = \frac{d}{dx}\left(e^{p\ln x}\right)\quad x^p = e^{p\ln x}$$

$$= \underbrace{e^{p\ln x}}_{x^p}\frac{p}{x}\quad \text{Chain Rule}$$

$$= x^p\frac{p}{x}\quad e^{p\ln x} = x^p$$

$$= px^{p-1}.\quad \text{Simplify.}$$

> **THEOREM 6.7 General Power Rule**
> For any real number p,
> $$\frac{d}{dx}(x^p) = px^{p-1} \quad \text{and} \quad \frac{d}{dx}(u(x)^p) = pu(x)^{p-1}u'(x).$$

EXAMPLE 4 Derivative of a tower function Evaluate the derivative of $f(x) = x^{2x}$.

SOLUTION We use the inverse relationship $e^{\ln x} = x$ to write $x^{2x} = e^{\ln(x^{2x})} = e^{2x\ln x}$. It follows that

$$\frac{d}{dx}(x^{2x}) = \frac{d}{dx}(e^{2x\ln x})$$

$$= e^{2x\ln x}\underbrace{}_{x^{2x}}\frac{d}{dx}(2x\ln x) \qquad \frac{d}{dx}(e^{u(x)}) = e^{u(x)}u'(x)$$

$$= x^{2x}\left(2\ln x + 2x\cdot\frac{1}{x}\right) \qquad \text{Product Rule}$$

$$= 2x^{2x}(1 + \ln x). \qquad \text{Simplify.}$$

Related Exercises 33–40 ◄

Computing e

We have shown that the number e serves as a base for both $\ln x$ and e^x, but how do we approximate its value? Recall that the derivative of $\ln x$ at $x = 1$ is 1. By the definition of the derivative, it follows that

$$1 = \frac{d}{dx}(\ln x)\bigg|_{x=1} = \lim_{h\to 0}\frac{\ln(1+h) - \ln 1}{h} \qquad \text{Derivative of } \ln x \text{ at } x = 1$$

$$= \lim_{h\to 0}\frac{\ln(1+h)}{h} \qquad \ln 1 = 0$$

$$= \lim_{h\to 0}\ln(1+h)^{1/h}. \qquad p\ln x = \ln x^p$$

> Because $\frac{d}{dx}(\ln x) = \frac{1}{x}$,
> $$\frac{d}{dx}(\ln x)\bigg|_{x=1} = \frac{1}{1} = 1.$$

> We rely on Theorem 2.12 of Section 2.6 here. If f is continuous at $g(a)$ and $\lim_{x\to a}g(x)$ exists, then $\lim_{x\to a}f(g(x)) = f(\lim_{x\to a}g(x))$.

The natural logarithm is continuous for $x > 0$, so it is permissible to interchange the order of $\lim_{h\to 0}$ and the evaluation of $\ln(1+h)^{1/h}$. The result is that

$$\ln\left(\underbrace{\lim_{h\to 0}(1+h)^{1/h}}_{e}\right) = 1.$$

Observe that the limit within the brackets is e because $\ln e = 1$ and only one number satisfies this equation. Therefore, we have isolated e as a limit:

$$e = \lim_{h\to 0}(1+h)^{1/h}.$$

It is evident from Table 6.2 that $(1+h)^{1/h} \to 2.718282\ldots$ as $h \to 0$. The value of this limit is e, and it has been computed to millions of digits. A better approximation,

$$e \approx 2.718281828459045,$$

is obtained by methods introduced in Chapter 9.

Table 6.2

h	$(1+h)^{1/h}$	h	$(1+h)^{1/h}$
10^{-1}	2.593742	-10^{-1}	2.867972
10^{-2}	2.704814	-10^{-2}	2.731999
10^{-3}	2.716924	-10^{-3}	2.719642
10^{-4}	2.718146	-10^{-4}	2.718418
10^{-5}	2.718268	-10^{-5}	2.718295
10^{-6}	2.718280	-10^{-6}	2.718283
10^{-7}	2.718282	-10^{-7}	2.718282

SECTION 6.8 EXERCISES

Review Questions

1. What are the domain and range of $\ln x$?

2. Give a geometrical interpretation of the function $\ln x = \int_1^x \frac{dt}{t}$.

3. Evaluate $\int 4^x \, dx$.

4. What is the inverse function of $\ln x$, and what are its domain and range?

5. Express 3^x, x^π, and $x^{\sin x}$ using the base e.

6. Evaluate $\dfrac{d}{dx}(3^x)$.

Basic Skills

7–12. Derivatives with $\ln x$ *Evaluate the following derivatives.*

7. $\dfrac{d}{dx}(x \ln x^3)\Big|_{x=1}$

8. $\dfrac{d}{dx}(\ln (\ln x))$

9. $\dfrac{d}{dx}(\sin (\ln x))$

10. $\dfrac{d}{dx}(\ln (\cos^2 x))$

11. $\dfrac{d}{dx}((\ln 2x)^{-5})$

12. $\dfrac{d}{dx}(\ln^3 (3x^2 + 2))$

13–20. Integrals with $\ln x$ *Evaluate the following integrals. Include absolute values only when needed.*

13. $\displaystyle\int_0^3 \frac{2x-1}{x+1} \, dx$

14. $\displaystyle\int \tan 10x \, dx$

15. $\displaystyle\int_e^{e^2} \frac{dx}{x \ln^3 x}$

16. $\displaystyle\int_0^{\pi/2} \frac{\sin x}{1 + \cos x} \, dx$

17. $\displaystyle\int \frac{e^{2x}}{4 + e^{2x}} \, dx$

18. $\displaystyle\int \frac{dx}{x \ln x \ln (\ln x)}$

19. $\displaystyle\int_{e^2}^{e^3} \frac{dx}{x \ln x \ln^2 (\ln x)}$

20. $\displaystyle\int_0^1 \frac{y \ln^4 (y^2 + 1)}{y^2 + 1} \, dy$

21–26. Integrals with e^x *Evaluate the following integrals.*

21. $\displaystyle\int_0^2 4 x e^{-x^2/2} \, dx$

22. $\displaystyle\int \frac{e^{\sin x}}{\sec x} \, dx$

23. $\displaystyle\int \frac{e^{\sqrt{x}}}{\sqrt{x}} \, dx$

24. $\displaystyle\int_{-2}^2 \frac{e^{z/2}}{e^{z/2} + 1} \, dz$

25. $\displaystyle\int \frac{e^x + e^{-x}}{e^x - e^{-x}} \, dx$

26. $\displaystyle\int_{\ln 2}^{\ln 3} \frac{e^x + e^{-x}}{e^{2x} - 2 + e^{-2x}} \, dx$

27–32. Integrals with general bases *Evaluate the following integrals.*

27. $\displaystyle\int_{-1}^1 10^x \, dx$

28. $\displaystyle\int_0^{\pi/2} 4^{\sin x} \cos x \, dx$

29. $\displaystyle\int_1^2 (1 + \ln x) x^x \, dx$

30. $\displaystyle\int_{1/3}^{1/2} \frac{10^{1/p}}{p^2} \, dp$

31. $\displaystyle\int x^2 \, 6^{x^3 + 8} \, dx$

32. $\displaystyle\int \frac{4^{\cot x}}{\sin^2 x} \, dx$

33–40. Derivatives *Evaluate the derivatives of the following functions.*

33. $f(x) = (2x)^{4x}$

34. $f(x) = x^\pi$

35. $h(x) = 2^{(x^2)}$

36. $h(t) = (\sin t)^{\sqrt{t}}$

37. $H(x) = (x + 1)^{2x}$

38. $p(x) = x^{-\ln x}$

39. $G(y) = y^{\sin y}$

40. $Q(t) = t^{1/t}$

Further Explorations

41. **Explain why or why not** Determine whether the following statements are true and give an explanation or counterexample. Assume $x > 0$ and $y > 0$.

    a. $\ln xy = \ln x + \ln y$.   b. $\ln 0 = 1$.
    c. $\ln (x + y) = \ln x + \ln y$.   d. $2^x = e^{2 \ln x}$.
    e. The area under the curve $y = 1/x$ and the x-axis on the interval $[1, e]$ is 1.

42. **Logarithm properties** Use the integral definition of the natural logarithm to prove that $\ln (x/y) = \ln x - \ln y$.

T **43–46. Calculator limits** *Use a calculator to make a table similar to Table 6.2 to approximate the following limits. Confirm your result with l'Hôpital's Rule.*

43. $\displaystyle\lim_{h \to 0} (1 + 2h)^{1/h}$

44. $\displaystyle\lim_{h \to 0} (1 + 3h)^{2/h}$

45. $\displaystyle\lim_{x \to 0} \frac{2^x - 1}{x}$

46. $\displaystyle\lim_{x \to 0} \frac{\ln (1 + x)}{x}$

47. **Zero net area** Consider the function $f(x) = \dfrac{1 - x}{x}$.

    a. Are there numbers $0 < a < 1$ such that $\displaystyle\int_{1-a}^{1+a} f(x) \, dx = 0$?

    b. Are there numbers $a > 1$ such that $\displaystyle\int_{1/a}^a f(x) \, dx = 0$?

T 48. **Behavior at the origin** Using calculus and accurate sketches, explain how the graphs of $f(x) = x^p \ln x$ differ as $x \to 0^+$ for $p = \frac{1}{2}, 1,$ and 2.

49. **Average value** What is the average value of $f(x) = 1/x$ on the interval $[1, p]$ for $p > 1$? What is the average value of f as $p \to \infty$?

50–57. Miscellaneous derivatives *Compute the following derivatives using the method of your choice.*

50. $\dfrac{d}{dx}(x^{2x})$

51. $\dfrac{d}{dx}(e^{-10x^2})$

52. $\dfrac{d}{dx}(x^{\tan x})$

53. $\dfrac{d}{dx}\left(\left(\dfrac{1}{x}\right)^x\right)$

54. $\dfrac{d}{dx}(x^e + e^x)$

55. $\dfrac{d}{dx}\left(1 + \dfrac{4}{x}\right)^x$

56. $\dfrac{d}{dx}(x^{(x^{10})})$

57. $\dfrac{d}{dx}(\cos(x^{2\sin x}))$

58–68. Miscellaneous integrals *Evaluate the following integrals.*

58. $\displaystyle\int 7^{2x}\,dx$

59. $\displaystyle\int 3^{-2x}\,dx$

60. $\displaystyle\int_0^5 5^{5x}\,dx$

61. $\displaystyle\int x^2 10^{x^3}\,dx$

62. $\displaystyle\int_0^\pi 2^{\sin x}\cos x\,dx$

63. $\displaystyle\int_1^{2e} \dfrac{3^{\ln x}}{x}\,dx$

64. $\displaystyle\int \dfrac{\sin(\ln x)}{4x}\,dx$

65. $\displaystyle\int_1^{e^2} \dfrac{(\ln x)^5}{x}\,dx$

66. $\displaystyle\int \dfrac{\ln^2 x + 2\ln x - 1}{x}\,dx$

67. $\displaystyle\int_0^{\ln 2} \dfrac{e^{3x} - e^{-3x}}{e^{3x} + e^{-3x}}\,dx$

68. $\displaystyle\int_0^1 \dfrac{16^x}{4^{2x}}\,dx$

Applications

69. Probability as an integral Two points P and Q are chosen randomly, one on each of two adjacent sides of a unit square (see figure). What is the probability that the area of the triangle formed by the sides of the square and the line segment PQ is less than one-fourth the area of the square? Begin by showing that x and y must satisfy $xy < \frac{1}{2}$ in order for the area condition to be met. Then argue that the required probability is $\dfrac{1}{2} + \displaystyle\int_{1/2}^1 \dfrac{dx}{2x}$ and evaluate the integral.

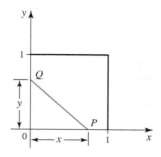

Additional Exercises

70. Derivative of $\ln|x|$ Differentiate $\ln x$ for $x > 0$ and differentiate $\ln(-x)$ for $x < 0$ to conclude that $\dfrac{d}{dx}(\ln|x|) = \dfrac{1}{x}$.

71. Properties of e^x Use the inverse relations between $\ln x$ and e^x ($\exp(x)$), and the properties of $\ln x$ to prove the following properties.

  a. $\exp(0) = 1$

  b. $\exp(x - y) = \dfrac{\exp(x)}{\exp(y)}$

  c. $(\exp(x))^p = \exp(px)$, p rational

72. $\ln x$ is unbounded Use the following argument to show that $\lim\limits_{x\to\infty} \ln x = \infty$ and $\lim\limits_{x\to 0^+} \ln x = -\infty$.

  a. Make a sketch of the function $f(x) = 1/x$ on the interval $[1, 2]$. Explain why the area of the region bounded by $y = f(x)$ and the x-axis on $[1, 2]$ is $\ln 2$.

  b. Construct a rectangle over the interval $[1, 2]$ with height $\frac{1}{2}$. Explain why $\ln 2 > \frac{1}{2}$.

  c. Show that $\ln 2^n > n/2$ and $\ln 2^{-n} < -n/2$.

  d. Conclude that $\lim\limits_{x\to\infty} \ln x = \infty$ and $\lim\limits_{x\to 0^+} \ln x = -\infty$.

73. Bounds on e Use a left Riemann sum with at least $n = 2$ subintervals of equal length to approximate $\ln 2 = \displaystyle\int_1^2 \dfrac{dt}{t}$ and show that $\ln 2 < 1$. Use a right Riemann sum with $n = 7$ subintervals of equal length to approximate $\ln 3 = \displaystyle\int_1^3 \dfrac{dt}{t}$ and show that $\ln 3 > 1$.

74. Alternative proof of product property Assume that $y > 0$ is fixed and that $x > 0$. Show that $\dfrac{d}{dx}(\ln xy) = \dfrac{d}{dx}(\ln x)$. Recall that if two functions have the same derivative, then they differ by an additive constant. Set $x = 1$ to evaluate the constant and prove that $\ln xy = \ln x + \ln y$.

75. Harmonic sum In Chapter 8, we will encounter the harmonic sum $1 + \dfrac{1}{2} + \dfrac{1}{3} + \cdots + \dfrac{1}{n}$. Use a left Riemann sum to approximate $\displaystyle\int_1^{n+1} \dfrac{dx}{x}$ (with unit spacing between the grid points) to show that $1 + \dfrac{1}{2} + \dfrac{1}{3} + \cdots + \dfrac{1}{n} > \ln(n + 1)$. Use this fact to conclude that $\lim\limits_{n\to\infty}\left(1 + \dfrac{1}{2} + \dfrac{1}{3} + \cdots + \dfrac{1}{n}\right)$ does not exist.

QUICK CHECK ANSWERS

1. $\{x: x \neq 0\}$ **2.** $2x, 2x, x^2, \ln 2 + x$ **3.** Slope $= 2$; area $= 1$ **4.** Note that when $b = e$, we have $\ln b = 1$.◄

6.9 Exponential Models

The uses of exponential functions are wide-ranging. In this section, you will see them applied to problems in finance, medicine, ecology, biology, economics, pharmacokinetics, anthropology, and physics.

Exponential Growth

Exponential growth functions have the form $y(t) = Ce^{kt}$, where C is a constant and the *rate constant* k is positive (Figure 6.84). If we start with this function and take its derivative, we find that

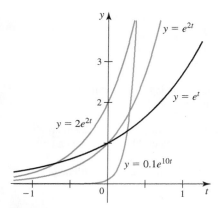

Figure 6.84

$$y'(t) = \frac{d}{dt}(Ce^{kt}) = C \cdot ke^{kt} = k\underbrace{(Ce^{kt})}_{y};$$

that is, $y'(t) = ky$. Here is the first insight about exponential functions: *Their rate of change is proportional to their value.* If y represents a population, then $y'(t)$ is the **growth rate** with units such as people/month or cells/hr. We see that the larger the population, the faster its growth.

Another way to talk about growth rates is to use the **relative growth rate**, which is the growth rate divided by the current value of that quantity, or $y'(t)/y(t)$. For example, if y is a population, the relative growth rate is the fraction or percentage by which the population grows each unit of time. Examples of relative growth rates are 5% *per year* or *a factor of* 1.2 *per month*. Therefore, when the equation $y'(t) = ky$ is written in the form $y'(t)/y = k$, it has another interpretation. It says *a quantity that grows exponentially has a constant relative growth rate.* Constant relative or percentage change is the hallmark of exponential growth.

▶ The derivative $\dfrac{dy}{dt}$ is the *absolute* growth rate but is usually simply called the *growth rate.*

▶ A consumer price index that increases at a constant rate of 4% per year increases exponentially. A currency that is devalued at a constant rate of 3% per month decreases exponentially. By contrast, linear growth is characterized by constant absolute growth rates, such as 500 people per year or $400 per month.

EXAMPLE 1   Linear versus exponential growth Suppose the population of the town of Pine is given by $P(t) = 1500 + 125t$, while the population of the town of Spruce is given by $S(t) = 1500e^{0.1t}$, where $t \geq 0$ is measured in years. Find the growth rate and the relative growth rate of each town.

SOLUTION Note that Pine grows according to a linear function, while Spruce grows exponentially (Figure 6.85). The growth rate of Pine is $\dfrac{dP}{dt} = 125$ people/year, which is constant for all times. The growth rate of Spruce is

$$\frac{dS}{dt} = 0.1\underbrace{(1500e^{0.1t})}_{S(t)} = 0.1S(t),$$

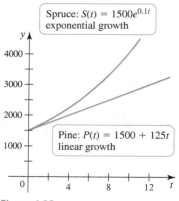

Figure 6.85

showing that the growth rate is proportional to the population. The relative growth rate of Pine is $\dfrac{1}{P}\dfrac{dP}{dt} = \dfrac{125}{1500 + 125t}$, which decreases in time. The relative growth rate of Spruce is

$$\frac{1}{S}\frac{dS}{dt} = \frac{0.1 \cdot 1500e^{0.1t}}{1500e^{0.1t}} = 0.1,$$

which is constant for all times. In summary, the linear population function has a *constant absolute growth rate* and the exponential population function has a *constant relative growth rate.*

Related Exercises 9–10 ◀

QUICK CHECK 1 Population A increases at a constant rate of 4%/yr. Population B increases at a constant rate of 500 people/yr. Which population exhibits exponential growth? What kind of growth is exhibited by the other population? ◀

The rate constant k in $y(t) = Ce^{kt}$ determines the growth rate of the exponential function. We adopt the convention that $k > 0$; then it is clear that $y(t) = Ce^{kt}$ describes exponential growth and $y(t) = Ce^{-kt}$ describes exponential decay, to be discussed shortly. For problems that involve time, the units of k are time^{-1}; for example, if t is measured in months, the units of k are month^{-1}. In this way, the exponent kt is dimensionless (without units).

> The unit time^{-1} is read *per unit time*. For example, month^{-1} is read *per month*.

Unless there is good reason to do otherwise, it is customary to take $t = 0$ as the reference point for time. Notice that with $y(t) = Ce^{kt}$, we have $y(0) = C$. Therefore, C has a simple meaning: It is the **initial value** of the quantity of interest, which we denote y_0. In the examples that follow, two pieces of information are typically given: the initial value and clues for determining the rate constant k. The initial value and the rate constant determine an exponential growth function completely.

Exponential Growth Functions

Exponential growth is described by functions of the form $y(t) = y_0e^{kt}$. The initial value of y at $t = 0$ is $y(0) = y_0$, and the **rate constant** $k > 0$ determines the rate of growth. Exponential growth is characterized by a constant relative growth rate.

Because exponential growth is characterized by a constant relative growth rate, the time required for a quantity to double (a 100% increase) is constant. Therefore, one way to describe an exponentially growing quantity is to give its *doubling time*. To compute the time it takes the function $y(t) = y_0e^{kt}$ to double in value, say from y_0 to $2y_0$, we find the value of t that satisfies

$$y(t) = 2y_0 \quad \text{or} \quad y_0e^{kt} = 2y_0.$$

> Note that the initial value y_0 appears on both sides of this equation. It may be canceled, meaning that the doubling time is independent of the initial condition: *The doubling time is constant for all t.*

Canceling y_0 from the equation $y_0e^{kt} = 2y_0$ leaves the equation $e^{kt} = 2$. Taking logarithms of both sides, we have $\ln e^{kt} = \ln 2$, or $kt = \ln 2$, which has the solution $t = \dfrac{\ln 2}{k}$. We denote this doubling time T_2 so that $T_2 = \dfrac{\ln 2}{k}$. If y increases exponentially, the time it takes to double from 100 to 200 is the same as the time it takes to double from 1000 to 2000.

DEFINITION Doubling Time

The quantity described by the function $y(t) = y_0e^{kt}$, for $k > 0$, has a constant **doubling time** of $T_2 = \dfrac{\ln 2}{k}$, with the same units as t.

QUICK CHECK 2 Verify that the time needed for $y(t) = y_0e^{kt}$ to double from y_0 to $2y_0$ is the same as the time needed to double from $2y_0$ to $4y_0$. ◄

> **World population**

1804	1 billion
1927	2 billion
1960	3 billion
1974	4 billion
1987	5 billion
1999	6 billion
2011	7 billion
2050	9 billion (proj.)

EXAMPLE 2 World population Human population growth rates vary geographically and fluctuate over time. The overall growth rate for world population peaked at an annual rate of 2.1% per year in the 1960s. Assume a world population of 6.0 billion in 1999 ($t = 0$) and 6.9 billion in 2009 ($t = 10$).

a. Find an exponential growth function for the world population that fits the two data points.

b. Find the doubling time for the world population using the model in part (a).

c. Find the (absolute) growth rate $y'(t)$ and graph it, for $0 \le t \le 50$.

d. How fast was the population growing in 2014 ($t = 15$)?

> ➤ It is a common mistake to assume that if the annual growth rate is 1.4% per year, then $k = 1.4\% = 0.014$ year^{-1}. The rate constant k must be calculated, as it is in Example 2, to give $k = 0.013976$. For larger growth rates, the difference between k and the actual growth rate is greater.

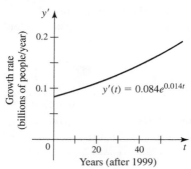

Figure 6.86

> ➤ Converted to a daily rate (dividing by 365), the world population in 2014 increased at a rate of roughly 284,000 people per day.

SOLUTION

a. Let $y(t)$ be world population measured in billions of people t years after 1999. We use the growth function $y(t) = y_0 e^{kt}$, where y_0 and k must be determined. The initial value is $y_0 = 6$ (billion). To determine the rate constant k, we use the fact that $y(10) = 6.9$. Substituting $t = 10$ into the growth function with $y_0 = 6$ implies

$$y(10) = 6e^{10k} = 6.9.$$

Solving for k yields the rate constant $k = \dfrac{\ln (6.9/6)}{10} \approx 0.013976 \approx 0.014$ year^{-1}. Therefore, the growth function is

$$y(t) = 6e^{0.014t}.$$

b. The doubling time of the population is

$$T_2 = \frac{\ln 2}{k} \approx \frac{\ln 2}{0.014} \approx 50 \text{ years.}$$

c. Working with the growth function $y(t) = 6e^{0.014t}$, we find that

$$y'(t) = 6\,(0.014)e^{0.014t} = 0.084e^{0.014t},$$

which has units of *billions of people/year*. As shown in Figure 6.86 the growth rate itself increases exponentially.

d. In 2014 ($t = 15$), the growth rate was

$$y'(15) = 0.084e^{(0.014)(15)} \approx 0.104 \text{ billion people/year,}$$

or roughly 104 million people/year.

Related Exercises 11–20 ◄

QUICK CHECK 3 Assume $y(t) = 100e^{0.05t}$. By (exactly) what percentage does y increase when t increases by 1 unit? ◄

A Financial Model   Exponential functions are used in many financial applications, several of which are explored in the exercises. For now, consider a simple savings account in which an initial deposit earns interest that is reinvested in the account. Interest payments are made on a regular basis (for example, annually, monthly, daily), or interest may be compounded continuously. In all cases, the balance in the account increases exponentially at a rate that can be determined from the advertised **annual percentage yield** (or **APY**) of the account. Assuming that no additional deposits are made, the balance in the account is given by the exponential growth function $y(t) = y_0 e^{kt}$, where y_0 is the initial deposit, t is measured in years, and k is determined by the annual percentage yield.

> ➤ The concept of continuous compounding was introduced in Exercise 109 of Section 4.7.

EXAMPLE 3   Compounding   The APY of a savings account is the percentage increase in the balance over the course of a year. Suppose you deposit $500 in a savings account that has an APY of 6.18% per year. Assume that the interest rate remains constant and that no additional deposits or withdrawals are made. How long will it take the balance to reach $2500?

> ➤ If the balance increases by 6.18% in one year, it increases by a factor of 1.0618 in one year.

SOLUTION   Because the balance grows by a fixed percentage every year, it grows exponentially. Letting $y(t)$ be the balance t years after the initial deposit of $y_0 = \$500$, we have $y(t) = y_0 e^{kt}$, where the rate constant k must be determined. Note that if the initial balance is y_0, one year later the balance is 6.18% more, or

$$y(1) = 1.0618\,y_0 = y_0 e^k.$$

Solving for k, we find that the rate constant is

$$k = \ln 1.0618 \approx 0.060 \text{ yr}^{-1}.$$

Therefore, the balance at any time $t \geq 0$ is $y(t) = 500e^{0.060t}$. To determine the time required for the balance to reach \$2500, we solve the equation

$$y(t) = 500e^{0.060t} = 2500.$$

Dividing by 500 and taking the natural logarithm of both sides yields

$$0.060t = \ln 5.$$

The balance reaches \$2500 in $t = (\ln 5)/0.060 \approx 26.8$ yr.

Related Exercises 11–20 ◄

Resource Consumption   Among the many resources that people use, energy is certainly one of the most important. The basic unit of energy is the **joule** (J), roughly the energy needed to lift a 0.1-kg object (say an orange) 1 m. The *rate* at which energy is consumed is called **power**. The basic unit of power is the **watt** (W), where $1\text{ W} = 1\text{ J/s}$. If you turn on a 100-W lightbulb for 1 min, the bulb consumes energy at a rate of 100 J/s, and it uses a total of $100\text{ J/s} \cdot 60\text{ s} = 6000$ J of energy.

    A more useful measure of energy for large quantities is the **kilowatt-hour** (kWh). A kilowatt is 1000 W or 1000 J/s. So if you consume energy at the rate of 1 kW for 1 hr (3600 s), you use a total of $1000\text{ J/s} \cdot 3600\text{ s} = 3.6 \times 10^6$ J, which is 1 kWh. A person running for one hour consumes roughly 1 kWh of energy. A typical house uses on the order of 1000 kWh of energy in a month.

    Assume that the total energy used (by a person, machine, or city) is given by the function $E(t)$. Because the power $P(t)$ is the rate at which energy is used, we have $P(t) = E'(t)$. Using the ideas of Section 6.1, the total amount of energy used between the times $t = a$ and $t = b$ is

$$\text{total energy used} = \int_a^b E'(t)\,dt = \int_a^b P(t)\,dt.$$

We see that energy is the area under the power curve. With this background, we can investigate a situation in which the rate of energy consumption increases exponentially.

EXAMPLE 4   **Energy consumption**   At the beginning of 2010, the rate of energy consumption for the city of Denver was 7000 megawatts (MW), where $1\text{ MW} = 10^6$ W. That rate is expected to increase at an annual growth rate of 2% per year.

a. Find the function that gives the power or rate of energy consumption for all times after the beginning of 2010.

b. Find the total amount of energy used during 2014.

c. Find the function that gives the total (cumulative) amount of energy used by the city between 2010 and any time $t \geq 0$.

SOLUTION

a. Let $t \geq 0$ be the number of years after the beginning of 2010 and let $P(t)$ be the power function that gives the rate of energy consumption at time t. Because P increases at a constant rate of 2% per year, it increases exponentially. Therefore, $P(t) = P_0 e^{kt}$, where $P_0 = 7000$ MW. We determine k as before by setting $t = 1$; after one year the power is

$$P(1) = P_0 e^k = 1.02 P_0.$$

Canceling P_0 and solving for k, we find that $k = \ln 1.02 \approx 0.0198$. Therefore, the power function (Figure 6.87) is

$$P(t) = 7000 e^{0.0198t}, \quad \text{for } t \geq 0.$$

> ► In one year, the power function increases by 2% or by a factor of 1.02.

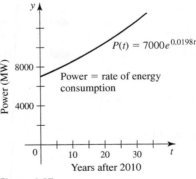

$P(t) = 7000e^{0.0198t}$

Power = rate of energy consumption

Power (MW)

Years after 2010

Figure 6.87

b. The entire year 2014 corresponds to the interval $4 \le t \le 5$. Substituting $P(t) = 7000e^{0.0198t}$, the total energy used in 2014 was

$$\int_4^5 P(t)\, dt = \int_4^5 7000e^{0.0198t}\, dt \quad \text{Substitute for } P(t).$$

$$= \frac{7000}{0.0198}\, e^{0.0198t}\Big|_4^5 \quad \text{Fundamental Theorem}$$

$$\approx 7652. \quad \text{Evaluate.}$$

Because the units of P are MW and t is measured in years, the units of energy are MW-yr. To convert to MWh, we multiply by 8760 hr/yr to get the total energy of about 6.7×10^7 MWh (or 6.7×10^{10} kWh).

c. The total energy used between $t = 0$ and any future time t is given by the future value formula (Section 6.1):

$$E(t) = E(0) + \int_0^t E'(s)\, ds = E(0) + \int_0^t P(s)\, ds.$$

Assuming $t = 0$ corresponds to the beginning of 2010, we take $E(0) = 0$. Substituting again for the power function P, the total energy (in MW-yr) at time t is

$$E(t) = E(0) + \int_0^t P(s)\, ds$$

$$= 0 + \int_0^t 7000e^{0.0198s}\, ds \quad \text{Substitute for } P(s) \text{ and } E(0).$$

$$= \frac{7000}{0.0198}\, e^{0.0198s}\Big|_0^t \quad \text{Fundamental Theorem}$$

$$\approx 353{,}535(e^{0.0198t} - 1). \quad \text{Evaluate.}$$

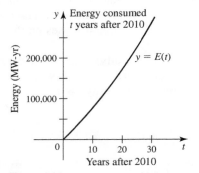

Figure 6.88

As shown in Figure 6.88, when the rate of energy consumption increases exponentially, the total amount of energy consumed also increases exponentially.

Related Exercises 11–20 ◄

Exponential Decay

Everything you have learned about exponential growth carries over directly to exponential decay. A function that decreases exponentially has the form $y(t) = y_0 e^{-kt}$, where $y_0 = y(0)$ is the initial value and $k > 0$ is the rate constant.

Exponential decay is characterized by a constant relative decay rate and by a constant *half-life*. For example, radioactive plutonium has a half-life of 24,000 years. An initial sample of 1 mg decays to 0.5 mg after 24,000 years and to 0.25 mg after 48,000 years. To compute the half-life, we determine the time required for the quantity $y(t) = y_0 e^{-kt}$ to reach one-half of its current value; that is, we solve $y_0 e^{-kt} = y_0/2$ for t. Canceling y_0 and taking logarithms of both sides, we find that

QUICK CHECK 4 If a quantity decreases by a factor of 8 every 30 years, what is its half-life? ◄

$$e^{-kt} = \frac{1}{2} \quad \Rightarrow \quad -kt = \ln\frac{1}{2} = -\ln 2 \quad \Rightarrow \quad t = \frac{\ln 2}{k}.$$

The half-life is given by the same formula as the doubling time.

Exponential Decay Functions

Exponential decay is described by functions of the form $y(t) = y_0 e^{-kt}$. The initial value of y is $y(0) = y_0$, and the rate constant $k > 0$ determines the rate of decay. Exponential decay is characterized by a constant relative decay rate. The constant **half-life** is $T_{1/2} = \dfrac{\ln 2}{k}$, with the same units as t.

Radiometric Dating A powerful method for estimating the age of ancient objects (for example, fossils, bones, meteorites, and cave paintings) relies on the radioactive decay of certain elements. A common version of radiometric dating uses the carbon isotope C-14, which is present in all living matter. When a living organism dies, it ceases to replace C-14, and the C-14 that is present decays with a half-life of about $T_{1/2} = 5730$ years. Comparing the C-14 in a living organism to the amount in a dead sample provides an estimate of its age.

EXAMPLE 5 Radiometric dating Researchers determine that a fossilized bone has 30% of the C-14 of a live bone. Estimate the age of the bone. Assume a half-life for C-14 of 5730 years.

SOLUTION The exponential decay function $y(t) = y_0 e^{-kt}$ represents the amount of C-14 in the bone t years after its owner died. By the half-life formula, $T_{1/2} = (\ln 2)/k$. Substituting $T_{1/2} = 5730$ yr, the rate constant is

$$k = \frac{\ln 2}{T_{1/2}} = \frac{\ln 2}{5730 \text{ yr}} \approx 0.000121 \text{ yr}^{-1}.$$

Assume that the amount of C-14 in a living bone is y_0. Over t years, the amount of C-14 in the fossilized bone decays to 30% of its initial value, or $0.3y_0$. Using the decay function, we have

$$0.3y_0 = y_0 e^{-0.000121t}.$$

Solving for t, the age of the bone (in years) is

$$t = \frac{\ln 0.3}{-0.000121} \approx 9950.$$

Related Exercises 21–26 ◄

Pharmacokinetics Pharmacokinetics describes the processes by which drugs are assimilated by the body. The elimination of most drugs from the body may be modeled by an exponential decay function with a known half-life (alcohol is a notable exception). The simplest models assume that an entire drug dose is immediately absorbed into the blood. This assumption is a bit of an idealization; more refined mathematical models account for the absorption process.

> **Half-lives of common drugs**

Penicillin	1 hr
Amoxicillin	1 hr
Nicotine	2 hr
Morphine	3 hr
Tetracycline	9 hr
Digitalis	33 hr
Phenobarbitol	2–6 days

EXAMPLE 6 Pharmacokinetics An exponential decay function $y(t) = y_0 e^{-kt}$ models the amount of drug in the blood t hr after an initial dose of $y_0 = 100$ mg is administered. Assume the half-life of the drug is 16 hours.

a. Find the exponential decay function that governs the amount of drug in the blood.

b. How much time is required for the drug to reach 1% of the initial dose (1 mg)?

c. If a second 100-mg dose is given 12 hr after the first dose, how much time is required for the drug level to reach 1 mg?

SOLUTION

a. Knowing that the half-life is 16 hr, the rate constant is

$$k = \frac{\ln 2}{T_{1/2}} = \frac{\ln 2}{16 \text{ hr}} \approx 0.0433 \text{ hr}^{-1}.$$

Therefore, the decay function is $y(t) = 100e^{-0.0433t}$.

b. The time required for the drug to reach 1 mg is the solution of

$$100e^{-0.0433t} = 1.$$

Solving for t, we have

$$t = \frac{\ln 0.01}{-0.0433 \text{ hr}^{-1}} \approx 106 \text{ hr}.$$

It takes more than 4 days for the drug to be reduced to 1% of the initial dose.

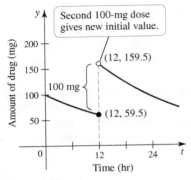

Figure 6.89

c. Using the exponential decay function of part (a), the amount of drug in the blood after 12 hr is

$$y(12) = 100e^{-0.0433 \cdot 12} \approx 59.5 \text{ mg.}$$

The second 100-mg dose given after 12 hr increases the amount of drug (assuming instantaneous absorption) to 159.5 mg. This amount becomes the new initial value for another exponential decay process (Figure 6.89). Measuring t from the time of the second dose, the amount of drug in the blood is

$$y(t) = 159.5e^{-0.0433t}.$$

The amount of drug reaches 1 mg when

$$y(t) = 159.5e^{-0.0433t} = 1,$$

which implies that

$$t = \frac{-\ln 159.5}{-0.0433 \text{ hr}^{-1}} = 117.1 \text{ hr.}$$

Approximately 117 hr after the second dose (or 129 hr after the first dose), the amount of drug reaches 1 mg.

Related Exercises 27–30 ◄

SECTION 6.9 EXERCISES

Review Questions

1. In terms of relative growth rate, what is the defining property of exponential growth?

2. Give two pieces of information that may be used to formulate an exponential growth or decay function.

3. Explain the meaning of doubling time.

4. Explain the meaning of half-life.

5. How are the rate constant and the doubling time related?

6. How are the rate constant and the half-life related?

7. Give two examples of processes that are modeled by exponential growth.

8. Give two examples of processes that are modeled by exponential decay.

Basic Skills

9–10. Absolute and relative growth rates *Two functions f and g are given. Show that the growth rate of the linear function is constant and the relative growth rate of the exponential function is constant.*

9. $f(t) = 100 + 10.5t,\ g(t) = 100e^{t/10}$

10. $f(t) = 2200 + 400t,\ g(t) = 400 \cdot 2^{t/20}$

11–16. Designing exponential growth functions *Devise the exponential growth function that fits the given data; then answer the accompanying questions. Be sure to identify the reference point $(t = 0)$ and units of time.*

11. **Population** The population of a town with a 2010 population of 90,000 grows at a rate of 2.4%/yr. In what year will the population double its initial value (to 180,000)?

12. **Population** The population of Clark County, Nevada, was 2 million in 2013. Assuming an annual growth rate of 4.5%/yr, what will the county population be in 2020?

13. **Population** The current population of a town is 50,000 and is growing exponentially. If the population is projected to be 55,000 in 10 years, then what will be the population 20 years from now?

14. **Savings account** How long will it take an initial deposit of $1500 to increase in value to $2500 in a saving account with an APY of 3.1%? Assume the interest rate remains constant and no additional deposits or withdrawals are made.

15. **Rising costs** Between 2005 and 2010, the average rate of inflation was about 3%/yr (as measured by the Consumer Price Index). If a cart of groceries cost $100 in 2005, what will it cost in 2018, assuming the rate of inflation remains constant?

16. **Cell growth** The number of cells in a tumor doubles every 6 weeks starting with 8 cells. After how many weeks does the tumor have 1500 cells?

17. **Projection sensitivity** According to the 2010 census, the U.S. population was 309 million with an estimated growth rate of 0.8%/yr.

    a. Based on these figures, find the doubling time and project the population in 2050.
    b. Suppose the actual growth rate is just 0.2 percentage point lower than 0.8%/yr (0.6%). What are the resulting doubling time and projected 2050 population? Repeat these calculations assuming the growth rate is 0.2 percentage point higher than 0.8%/yr.
    c. Comment on the sensitivity of these projections to the growth rate.

18. **Energy consumption** On the first day of the year $(t = 0)$, a city uses electricity at a rate of 2000 MW. That rate is projected to increase at a rate of 1.3% per year.

    a. Based on these figures, find an exponential growth function for the power (rate of electricity use) for the city.
    b. Find the total energy (in MW-yr) used by the city over four full years beginning at $t = 0$.
    c. Find a function that gives the total energy used (in MW-yr) between $t = 0$ and any future time $t > 0$.

19. **Population of Texas** Texas had the largest increase in population of any state in the United States from 2000 to 2010. During that decade, Texas grew from 20.9 million in 2000 to 25.1 million in 2010. Use an exponential growth model to predict the population of Texas in 2025.

20. **Oil consumption** Starting in 2010 ($t = 0$), the rate at which oil is consumed by a small country increases at a rate of 1.5%/yr, starting with an initial rate of 1.2 million barrels/yr.

    a. How much oil is consumed over the course of the year 2010 (between $t = 0$ and $t = 1$)?

    b. Find the function that gives the amount of oil consumed between $t = 0$ and any future time t.

    c. How many years after 2010 will the amount of oil consumed since 2010 reach 10 million barrels?

21–25. Designing exponential decay functions *Devise an exponential decay function that fits the following data; then answer the accompanying questions. Be sure to identify the reference point* ($t = 0$) *and units of time.*

21. **Crime rate** The homicide rate decreases at a rate of 3%/yr in a city that had 800 homicides/yr in 2010. At this rate, when will the homicide rate reach 600 homicides/yr?

22. **Drug metabolism** A drug is eliminated from the body at a rate of 15%/hr. After how many hours does the amount of drug reach 10% of the initial dose?

23. **Valium metabolism** The drug Valium is eliminated from the bloodstream with a half-life of 36 hr. Suppose that a patient receives an initial dose of 20 mg of Valium at midnight. How much Valium is in the patient's blood at noon the next day? When will the Valium concentration reach 10% of its initial level?

24. **China's population** China's one-child policy was implemented with a goal of reducing China's population to 700 million by 2050 (from 1.2 billion in 2000). Suppose China's population declines at a rate of 0.5%/yr. Will this rate of decline be sufficient to meet the goal?

25. **Population of Michigan** The population of Michigan decreased from 9.94 million in 2000 to 9.88 million in 2010. Use an exponential model to predict the population in 2020. Explain why an exponential (decay) model might not be an appropriate long-term model of the population of Michigan.

26. **Depreciation of equipment** A large die-casting machine used to make automobile engine blocks is purchased for $2.5 million. For tax purposes, the value of the machine can be depreciated by 6.8% of its current value each year.

    a. What is the value of the machine after 10 years?

    b. After how many years is the value of the machine 10% of its original value?

27. **Atmospheric pressure** The pressure of Earth's atmosphere at sea level is approximately 1000 millibars and decreases exponentially with elevation. At an elevation of 30,000 ft (approximately the altitude of Mt. Everest), the pressure is one-third the sea-level pressure. At what elevation is the pressure half the sea-level pressure? At what elevation is it 1% of the sea-level pressure?

28. **Carbon dating** The half-life of C-14 is about 5730 yr.

    a. Archaeologists find a piece of cloth painted with organic dyes. Analysis of the dye in the cloth shows that only 77% of

the C-14 originally in the dye remains. When was the cloth painted?

    b. A well-preserved piece of wood found at an archaeological site has 6.2% of the C-14 that it had when it was alive. Estimate when the wood was cut.

29. **Uranium dating** Uranium-238 (U-238) has a half-life of 4.5 billion years. Geologists find a rock containing a mixture of U-238 and lead, and determine that 85% of the original U-238 remains; the other 15% has decayed into lead. How old is the rock?

30. **Radioiodine treatment** Roughly 12,000 Americans are diagnosed with thyroid cancer every year, which accounts for 1% of all cancer cases. It occurs in women three times as frequently as in men. Fortunately, thyroid cancer can be treated successfully in many cases with radioactive iodine, or I-131. This unstable form of iodine has a half-life of 8 days and is given in small doses measured in millicuries.

    a. Suppose a patient is given an initial dose of 100 millicuries. Find the function that gives the amount of I-131 in the body after $t \geq 0$ days.

    b. How long does it take the amount of I-131 to reach 10% of the initial dose?

    c. Finding the initial dose to give a particular patient is a critical calculation. How does the time to reach 10% of the initial dose change if the initial dose is increased by 5%?

Further Explorations

31. **Explain why or why not** Determine whether the following statements are true and give an explanation or counterexample.

    a. A quantity that increases at 6%/yr obeys the growth function $y(t) = y_0 e^{0.06t}$.

    b. If a quantity increases by 10%/yr, it increases by 30% over 3 years.

    c. A quantity decreases by one-third every month. Therefore, it decreases exponentially.

    d. If the rate constant of an exponential growth function is increased, its doubling time is decreased.

    e. If a quantity increases exponentially, the time required to increase by a factor of 10 remains constant for all time.

32. **Tripling time** A quantity increases according to the exponential function $y(t) = y_0 e^{kt}$. What is the tripling time for the quantity? What is the time required for the quantity to increase p-fold?

33. **Constant doubling time** Prove that the doubling time for an exponentially increasing quantity is constant for all time.

34. **Overtaking** City A has a current population of 500,000 people and grows at a rate of 3%/yr. City B has a current population of 300,000 and grows at a rate of 5%/yr.

    a. When will the cities have the same population?

    b. Suppose City C has a current population of $y_0 < 500,000$ and a growth rate of $p > 3\%$/yr. What is the relationship between y_0 and p such that the Cities A and C have the same population in 10 years?

T 35. **A slowing race** Starting at the same time and place, Abe and Bob race, running at velocities $u(t) = 4/(t + 1)$ mi/hr and $v(t) = 4e^{-t/2}$ mi/hr, respectively, for $t \geq 0$.

    a. Who is ahead after $t = 5$ hr? After $t = 10$ hr?

    b. Find and graph the position functions of both runners. Which runner can run only a finite distance in an unlimited amount of time?

Applications

36. Law of 70 Bankers use the law of 70, which says that if an account increases at a fixed rate of $p\%$/yr, its doubling time is approximately $70/p$. Explain why and when this statement is true.

37. Compounded inflation The U.S. government reports the rate of inflation (as measured by the Consumer Price Index) both monthly and annually. Suppose that for a particular month, the *monthly* rate of inflation is reported as 0.8%. Assuming that this rate remains constant, what is the corresponding *annual* rate of inflation? Is the annual rate 12 times the monthly rate? Explain.

38. Acceleration, velocity, position Suppose the acceleration of an object moving along a line is given by $a(t) = -kv(t)$, where k is a positive constant and v is the object's velocity. Assume that the initial velocity and position are given by $v(0) = 10$ and $s(0) = 0$, respectively.

  a. Use $a(t) = v'(t)$ to find the velocity of the object as a function of time.
  b. Use $v(t) = s'(t)$ to find the position of the object as a function of time.
  c. Use the fact that $dv/dt = (dv/ds)(ds/dt)$ (by the Chain Rule) to find the velocity as a function of position.

T 39. Air resistance (adapted from Putnam Exam, 1939) An object moves in a straight line, acted on by air resistance, which is proportional to its velocity; this means its acceleration is $a(t) = -kv(t)$. The velocity of the object decreases from 1000 ft/s to 900 ft/s over a distance of 1200 ft. Approximate the time required for this deceleration to occur. (Exercise 38 may be useful.)

T 40. A running model A model for the startup of a runner in a short race results in the velocity function $v(t) = a(1 - e^{-t/c})$, where a and c are positive constants and v has units of m/s. (*Source: A Theory of Competitive Running*, Joe Keller, *Physics Today* 26, Sep 1973)

  a. Graph the velocity function for $a = 12$ and $c = 2$. What is the runner's maximum velocity?
  b. Using the velocity in part (a) and assuming $s(0) = 0$, find the position function $s(t)$, for $t \geq 0$.
  c. Graph the position function and estimate the time required to run 100 m.

41. Tumor growth Suppose the cells of a tumor are idealized as spheres each with a radius of 5 μm (micrometers). The number of cells has a doubling time of 35 days. Approximately how long will it take a single cell to grow into a multi-celled spherical tumor with a volume of 0.5 cm^3 (1 cm = 10,000 μm)? Assume that the tumor spheres are tightly packed.

42. Carbon emissions in China and the United States The burning of fossil fuels releases greenhouse gases (roughly 60% carbon dioxide) into the atmosphere. In 2010, the United States released approximately 5.8 billion metric tons of carbon dioxide (Environmental Protection Agency estimate), while China released approximately 8.2 billion metric tons (U.S. Department of Energy estimate). Reasonable estimates of the growth rate in carbon dioxide emissions are 4% per year for the United States and 9% per year for China. In 2010, the U.S. population was 309 million, growing at a rate of 0.7% per year, and the population of China was 1.3 billion, growing at a rate of 0.5% per year.

  a. Find exponential growth functions for the amount of carbon dioxide released by the United States and China. Let $t = 0$ correspond to 2010.
  b. According to the models in part (a), when will Chinese emissions double those of the United States?
  c. What was the amount of carbon dioxide released by the United States and China *per capita* in 2010?
  d. Find exponential growth functions for the per capita amount of carbon dioxide released by the United States and China. Let $t = 0$ correspond to 2010.
  e. Use the models of part (d) to determine the year in which per capita emissions in the two countries are equal.

43. A revenue model The owner of a clothing store understands that the demand for shirts decreases with the price. In fact, she has developed a model that predicts that at a price of x per shirt, she can sell $D(x) = 40e^{-x/50}$ shirts in a day. It follows that the revenue (total money taken in) in a day is $R(x) = xD(x)$ (x/shirt $\cdot D(x)$ shirts). What price should the owner charge to maximize revenue?

Additional Exercises

44. Geometric means A quantity grows exponentially according to $y(t) = y_0e^{kt}$. What is the relationship between m, n, and p such that $y(p) = \sqrt{y(m)y(n)}$?

45. Equivalent growth functions The same exponential growth function can be written in the forms $y(t) = y_0e^{kt}$, $y(t) = y_0(1 + r)^t$, and $y(t) = y_0 2^{t/T_2}$. Write k as a function of r, r as a function of T_2, and T_2 as a function of k.

46. General relative growth rates Define the relative growth rate of the function f over the time interval T to be the relative change in f over an interval of length T:

$$R_T = \frac{f(t + T) - f(t)}{f(t)}.$$

Show that for the exponential function $y(t) = y_0e^{kt}$, the relative growth rate R_T is constant for any T; that is, choose any T and show that R_T is constant for all t.

QUICK CHECK ANSWERS

1. Population A grows exponentially; population B grows linearly. **3.** The function $100e^{0.05t}$ increases by a factor of 1.0513, or by 5.13%, in 1 unit of time. **4.** 10 years ◄

6.10 Hyperbolic Functions

In this section, we introduce a new family of functions called the *hyperbolic* functions, which are closely related to both trigonometric functions and exponential functions. Hyperbolic functions find widespread use in applied problems in fluid dynamics, projectile motion, architecture, and electrical engineering, to name just a few areas. Hyperbolic functions are also important in the development of many theoretical results in mathematics.

Relationship Between Trigonometric and Hyperbolic Functions

The trigonometric functions defined in Chapter 1 are based on relationships involving a circle—for this reason, trigonometric functions are also known as *circular* functions. Specifically, $\cos t$ and $\sin t$ are equal to the x- and y-coordinates, respectively, of the point $P(x, y)$ on the unit circle that corresponds to an angle of t radians (Figure 6.90). We can also regard t as the length of the arc from $(1, 0)$ to the point $P(x, y)$.

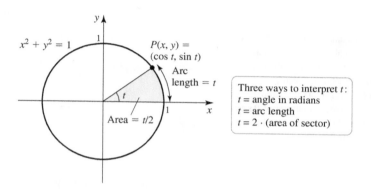

Figure 6.90

There is yet another way to interpret the number t, and it is this third interpretation that links the trigonometric and hyperbolic functions. Observe that t is twice the area of the circular sector in Figure 6.90. The functions $\cos t$ and $\sin t$ are still defined as the x- and y-coordinates of the point P, but now we associate P with a sector whose area is one-half of t.

The *hyperbolic cosine* and *hyperbolic sine* are defined in an analogous fashion using the hyperbola $x^2 - y^2 = 1$ instead of the circle $x^2 + y^2 = 1$. Consider the region bounded by the x-axis, the right branch of the unit hyperbola $x^2 - y^2 = 1$, and a line segment from the origin to a point $P(x, y)$ on the hyperbola (Figure 6.91); let t equal twice the area of this region.

The hyperbolic cosine of t, denoted $\cosh t$, is the x-coordinate of P and the hyperbolic sine of t, denoted $\sinh t$, is the y-coordinate of P. Expressing x and y in terms of t leads to the standard definitions of the hyperbolic functions. We accomplish this task by writing t, which is an area, as an integral that depends on the coordinates of P. In Exercise 112, we ask you to carry out the calculations to show that

$$x = \cosh t = \frac{e^t + e^{-t}}{2} \quad \text{and} \quad y = \sinh t = \frac{e^t - e^{-t}}{2}.$$

Everything that follows in this section is based on these two definitions.

> Recall that the area of a circular sector of radius r and angle θ is $A = \frac{1}{2} r^2 \theta$. With $r = 1$ and $\theta = t$, we have $A = \frac{1}{2}t$, which implies $t = 2A$.

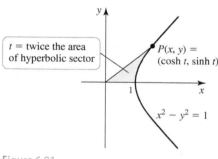

Figure 6.91

Definitions, Identities, and Graphs of the Hyperbolic Functions

Once the hyperbolic cosine and hyperbolic sine are defined, the four remaining hyperbolic functions follow in a manner analogous to the trigonometric functions.

> There is no universally accepted pronunciation of the names of the hyperbolic functions. In the United States, *cohsh x* (long *oh* sound) and *sinch x* are common choices for cosh x and sinh x. The pronunciations *tanch x, cotanch x, seech x* or *sech x*, and *coseech x* or *cosech x* are used for the other functions. International pronunciations vary as well.

DEFINITION Hyperbolic Functions

Hyperbolic cosine

$$\cosh x = \frac{e^x + e^{-x}}{2}$$

Hyperbolic sine

$$\sinh x = \frac{e^x - e^{-x}}{2}$$

Hyperbolic tangent

$$\tanh x = \frac{\sinh x}{\cosh x} = \frac{e^x - e^{-x}}{e^x + e^{-x}}$$

Hyperbolic cotangent

$$\coth x = \frac{\cosh x}{\sinh x} = \frac{e^x + e^{-x}}{e^x - e^{-x}}$$

Hyperbolic secant

$$\operatorname{sech} x = \frac{1}{\cosh x} = \frac{2}{e^x + e^{-x}}$$

Hyperbolic cosecant

$$\operatorname{csch} x = \frac{1}{\sinh x} = \frac{2}{e^x - e^{-x}}$$

The hyperbolic functions satisfy many important identities. Let's begin with the fundamental identity for hyperbolic functions, which is analogous to the familiar trigonometric identity $\cos^2 x + \sin^2 x = 1$:

$$\cosh^2 x - \sinh^2 x = 1.$$

> The fundamental identity for hyperbolic functions can also be understood in terms of the geometric definition of the hyperbolic functions. Because the point $P(\cosh t, \sinh t)$ is on the hyperbola $x^2 - y^2 = 1$, the coordinates of P satisfy the equation of the hyperbola, which leads immediately to
>
> $$\cosh^2 t - \sinh^2 t = 1.$$

This identity is verified by appealing to the definitions:

$$\cosh^2 x - \sinh^2 x = \left(\frac{e^x + e^{-x}}{2}\right)^2 - \left(\frac{e^x - e^{-x}}{2}\right)^2 \qquad \text{Definition of } \cosh x \text{ and } \sinh x$$

$$= \frac{e^{2x} + 2 + e^{-2x} - (e^{2x} - 2 + e^{-2x})}{4} \qquad \text{Expand and combine fractions.}$$

$$= \frac{4}{4} = 1. \qquad \text{Simplify.}$$

EXAMPLE 1 Deriving hyperbolic identities

a. Use the fundamental identity $\cosh^2 x - \sinh^2 x = 1$ to prove that $1 - \tanh^2 x = \operatorname{sech}^2 x$.

b. Derive the identity $\sinh 2x = 2 \sinh x \cosh x$.

SOLUTION

a. Dividing both sides of the fundamental identity $\cosh^2 x - \sinh^2 x = 1$ by $\cosh^2 x$ leads to the desired result:

$$\cosh^2 x - \sinh^2 x = 1 \qquad \text{Fundamental identity}$$

$$\underbrace{\frac{\cosh^2 x}{\cosh^2 x}}_{} - \underbrace{\frac{\sinh^2 x}{\cosh^2 x}}_{\tanh^2 x} = \underbrace{\frac{1}{\cosh^2 x}}_{\operatorname{sech}^2 x} \qquad \text{Divide both sides by } \cosh^2 x.$$

$$1 - \tanh^2 x = \operatorname{sech}^2 x. \qquad \text{Identify functions.}$$

b. Using the definition of the hyperbolic sine, we have

$$\sinh 2x = \frac{e^{2x} - e^{-2x}}{2} \qquad \text{Definition of sinh}$$

$$= \frac{(e^x - e^{-x})(e^x + e^{-x})}{2} \qquad \text{Factor; difference of perfect squares}$$

$$= 2 \sinh x \cosh x. \qquad \text{Identify functions.}$$

Related Exercises 11–18 ◄

The identities in Example 1 are just two of many useful hyperbolic identities, some of which we list next.

Hyperbolic Identities

$$\cosh^2 x - \sinh^2 x = 1 \qquad\qquad \cosh(-x) = \cosh x$$

$$1 - \tanh^2 x = \operatorname{sech}^2 x \qquad\qquad \sinh(-x) = -\sinh x$$

$$\coth^2 x - 1 = \operatorname{csch}^2 x \qquad\qquad \tanh(-x) = -\tanh x$$

$$\cosh(x + y) = \cosh x \cosh y + \sinh x \sinh y$$

$$\sinh(x + y) = \sinh x \cosh y + \cosh x \sinh y$$

$$\cosh 2x = \cosh^2 x + \sinh^2 x \qquad \sinh 2x = 2 \sinh x \cosh x$$

$$\cosh^2 x = \frac{\cosh 2x + 1}{2} \qquad\qquad \sinh^2 x = \frac{\cosh 2x - 1}{2}$$

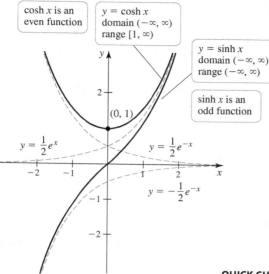

cosh x is an even function

$y = \cosh x$
domain $(-\infty, \infty)$
range $[1, \infty)$

$y = \sinh x$
domain $(-\infty, \infty)$
range $(-\infty, \infty)$

sinh x is an odd function

$(0, 1)$

$y = \frac{1}{2}e^x$

$y = \frac{1}{2}e^{-x}$

$y = -\frac{1}{2}e^{-x}$

Figure 6.92

Graphs of the hyperbolic functions are relatively easy to produce because they are based on the familiar graphs of e^x and e^{-x}. Recall that $\lim_{x \to \infty} e^{-x} = 0$ and that $\lim_{x \to -\infty} e^x = 0$. With these facts in mind, we see that the graph of $\cosh x$ (Figure 6.92) approaches the graph of $y = \frac{1}{2}e^x$ as $x \to \infty$ because $\cosh x = \dfrac{e^x + e^{-x}}{2} \approx \dfrac{e^x}{2}$ for large values of x. A similar argument shows that as $x \to -\infty$, $\cosh x$ approaches $y = \frac{1}{2}e^{-x}$. Note also that $\cosh x$ is an even function:

$$\cosh(-x) = \frac{e^{-x} + e^{-(-x)}}{2} = \frac{e^x + e^{-x}}{2} = \cosh x.$$

Finally, $\cosh 0 = \dfrac{e^0 + e^0}{2} = 1$, so its y-intercept is $(0, 1)$. The behavior of $\sinh x$, an odd function also shown in Figure 6.92, can be explained in much the same way.

QUICK CHECK 1 Use the definition of the hyperbolic sine to show that $\sinh x$ is an odd function. ◄

The graphs of the other four hyperbolic functions are shown in Figure 6.93. As a consequence of their definitions, we see that the domain of $\cosh x$, $\sinh x$, $\tanh x$, and $\operatorname{sech} x$ is $(-\infty, \infty)$, whereas the domain of $\coth x$ and $\operatorname{csch} x$ is the set of all real numbers excluding 0.

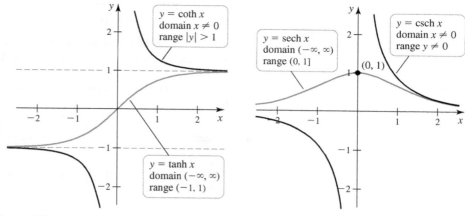

$y = \coth x$
domain $x \neq 0$
range $|y| > 1$

$y = \operatorname{sech} x$
domain $(-\infty, \infty)$
range $(0, 1]$

$y = \operatorname{csch} x$
domain $x \neq 0$
range $y \neq 0$

$(0, 1)$

$y = \tanh x$
domain $(-\infty, \infty)$
range $(-1, 1)$

Figure 6.93

QUICK CHECK 2 Explain why the graph of $\tanh x$ has the horizontal asymptotes $y = 1$ and $y = -1$. ◄

Derivatives and Integrals of Hyperbolic Functions

Because the hyperbolic functions are defined in terms of e^x and e^{-x}, computing their derivatives is straightforward. The derivatives of the hyperbolic functions are given in Theorem 6.8—reversing these formulas produces corresponding integral formulas.

▶ The identities, derivative formulas, and integral formulas for the hyperbolic functions are similar to the corresponding formulas for the trigonometric functions, which makes them easy to remember. However, be aware of some subtle differences in the signs associated with these formulas. For instance,

$$d/dx(\cos x) = -\sin x,$$

whereas

$$d/dx(\cosh x) = \sinh x.$$

THEOREM 6.8   Derivative and Integral Formulas

1. $\dfrac{d}{dx}(\cosh x) = \sinh x \quad \Rightarrow \quad \displaystyle\int \sinh x \, dx = \cosh x + C$

2. $\dfrac{d}{dx}(\sinh x) = \cosh x \quad \Rightarrow \quad \displaystyle\int \cosh x \, dx = \sinh x + C$

3. $\dfrac{d}{dx}(\tanh x) = \operatorname{sech}^2 x \quad \Rightarrow \quad \displaystyle\int \operatorname{sech}^2 x \, dx = \tanh x + C$

4. $\dfrac{d}{dx}(\coth x) = -\operatorname{csch}^2 x \quad \Rightarrow \quad \displaystyle\int \operatorname{csch}^2 x \, dx = -\coth x + C$

5. $\dfrac{d}{dx}(\operatorname{sech} x) = -\operatorname{sech} x \tanh x \quad \Rightarrow \quad \displaystyle\int \operatorname{sech} x \tanh x \, dx = -\operatorname{sech} x + C$

6. $\dfrac{d}{dx}(\operatorname{csch} x) = -\operatorname{csch} x \coth x \quad \Rightarrow \quad \displaystyle\int \operatorname{csch} x \coth x \, dx = -\operatorname{csch} x + C$

Proof: Using the definitions of $\cosh x$ and $\sinh x$, we have

$$\frac{d}{dx}(\cosh x) = \frac{d}{dx}\left(\frac{e^x + e^{-x}}{2}\right) = \frac{e^x - e^{-x}}{2} = \sinh x \quad \text{and}$$

$$\frac{d}{dx}(\sinh x) = \frac{d}{dx}\left(\frac{e^x - e^{-x}}{2}\right) = \frac{e^x + e^{-x}}{2} = \cosh x.$$

To prove formula (3), we begin with $\tanh x = \sinh x / \cosh x$ and then apply the Quotient Rule:

$$\frac{d}{dx}(\tanh x) = \frac{d}{dx}\left(\frac{\sinh x}{\cosh x}\right) \qquad \text{Definition of } \tanh x$$

$$= \frac{\cosh x(\cosh x) - \sinh x(\sinh x)}{\cosh^2 x} \qquad \text{Quotient Rule}$$

$$= \frac{1}{\cosh^2 x} \qquad \cosh^2 x - \sinh^2 x = 1$$

$$= \operatorname{sech}^2 x. \qquad \operatorname{sech} x = 1/\cosh x$$

The proofs of the remaining derivative formulas are assigned in Exercises 19–21. The integral formulas are a direct consequence of their corresponding derivative formulas. ◀

EXAMPLE 2   Derivatives and integrals of hyperbolic functions Evaluate the following derivatives and integrals.

a. $\dfrac{d}{dx}(\operatorname{sech} 3x)$

b. $\dfrac{d^2}{dx^2}(\operatorname{sech} 3x)$

c. $\displaystyle\int \frac{\operatorname{csch}^2 \sqrt{x}}{\sqrt{x}} \, dx$

d. $\displaystyle\int_0^{\ln 3} \sinh^3 x \cosh x \, dx$

SOLUTION

a. Combining formula (5) of Theorem 6.8 with the Chain Rule gives

$$\frac{d}{dx}(\text{sech } 3x) = -3 \text{ sech } 3x \tanh 3x.$$

b. Applying the Product Rule and Chain Rule to the result of part (a), we have

$$\frac{d^2}{dx^2}(\text{sech } 3x) = \frac{d}{dx}(-3 \text{ sech } 3x \tanh 3x)$$

$$= \underbrace{\frac{d}{dx}(-3 \text{ sech } 3x)}_{9 \text{ sech } 3x \tanh 3x} \cdot \tanh 3x + (-3 \text{ sech } 3x) \cdot \underbrace{\frac{d}{dx}(\tanh 3x)}_{3 \text{ sech}^2 3x} \quad \text{Product Rule}$$

$$= 9 \text{ sech } 3x \tanh^2 3x - 9 \text{ sech}^3 3x \qquad\qquad\qquad \text{Chain Rule}$$

$$= 9 \text{ sech } 3x(\tanh^2 3x - \text{ sech}^2 3x). \qquad\qquad\qquad \text{Simplify.}$$

c. The integrand suggests the substitution $u = \sqrt{x}$:

$$\int \frac{\text{csch}^2 \sqrt{x}}{\sqrt{x}} \, dx = 2 \int \text{csch}^2 u \, du \qquad \text{Let } u = \sqrt{x}; \, du = \frac{1}{2\sqrt{x}} \, dx.$$

$$= -2 \coth u + C \qquad \text{Formula (4), Theorem 6.8}$$

$$= -2 \coth \sqrt{x} + C. \qquad u = \sqrt{x}$$

d. The derivative formula $d/dx(\sinh x) = \cosh x$ suggests the substitution $u = \sinh x$:

$$\int_0^{\ln 3} \sinh^3 x \cosh x \, dx = \int_0^{4/3} u^3 \, du. \qquad \text{Let } u = \sinh x; \, du = \cosh x \, dx.$$

The new limits of integration are determined by the calculations

$$x = 0 \implies u = \sinh 0 = 0 \quad \text{and}$$

$$x = \ln 3 \implies u = \sinh(\ln 3) = \frac{e^{\ln 3} - e^{-\ln 3}}{2} = \frac{3 - 1/3}{2} = \frac{4}{3}.$$

We now evaluate the integral in the variable u:

$$\int_0^{4/3} u^3 \, du = \frac{1}{4} u^4 \Big|_0^{4/3}$$

$$= \frac{1}{4}\left(\left(\frac{4}{3}\right)^4 - 0^4\right) = \frac{64}{81}.$$

Related Exercises 19–40 ◄

QUICK CHECK 3 Find both the derivative and indefinite integral of $f(x) = 4 \cosh 2x.$ ◄

Theorem 6.9 presents integral formulas for the four hyperbolic functions not covered in Theorem 6.8.

THEOREM 6.9 Integrals of Hyperbolic Functions

1. $\displaystyle\int \tanh x \, dx = \ln \cosh x + C$ 　　　**2.** $\displaystyle\int \coth x \, dx = \ln|\sinh x| + C$

3. $\displaystyle\int \text{sech } x \, dx = \tan^{-1}(\sinh x) + C$ 　　**4.** $\displaystyle\int \text{csch } x \, dx = \ln|\tanh(x/2)| + C$

Proof: Formula (1) is derived by first writing $\tanh x$ in terms of $\sinh x$ and $\cosh x$:

$$\int \tanh x \, dx = \int \frac{\sinh x}{\cosh x} \, dx \qquad \text{Definition of } \tanh x$$

$$= \int \frac{1}{u} \, du \qquad \text{Let } u = \cosh x; \; du = \sinh x \, dx.$$

$$= \ln|u| + C \qquad \text{Evaluate integral.}$$

$$= \ln \cosh x + C. \qquad u = \cosh x > 0$$

Formula (2) is derived in a similar fashion (Exercise 44). The more challenging proofs of formulas (3) and (4) are considered in Exercises 107 and 108.   ◄

EXAMPLE 3 **Integrals involving hyperbolic functions** Determine the indefinite integral $\int x \coth (x^2) \, dx$.

SOLUTION The integrand suggests the substitution $u = x^2$:

$$\int x \coth x^2 \, dx = \frac{1}{2} \int \coth u \, du. \qquad \text{Let } u = x^2; \; du = 2x \, dx.$$

$$= \frac{1}{2} \ln|\sinh u| + C \qquad \text{Evaluate integral; use Theorem 6.9.}$$

$$= \frac{1}{2} \ln(\sinh x^2) + C. \qquad u = x^2; \sinh x^2 \geq 0$$

Related Exercises 41–44 ◄

QUICK CHECK 4 Determine the indefinite integral $\int \operatorname{csch} 2x \, dx$. ◄

Inverse Hyperbolic Functions

At present, we don't have the tools for evaluating an integral such as $\displaystyle\int \frac{dx}{\sqrt{x^2 + 4}}$. By studying inverse hyperbolic functions, we can discover new integration formulas. Inverse hyperbolic functions are also useful for solving equations involving hyperbolic functions.

Figures 6.92 and 6.93 show that the functions $\sinh x$, $\tanh x$, $\coth x$, and $\operatorname{csch} x$ are all one-to-one on their respective domains. This observation implies that each of these functions has a well-defined inverse. However, the function $y = \cosh x$ is not one-to-one on $(-\infty, \infty)$, so its inverse, denoted $y = \cosh^{-1} x$, exists only if we restrict the domain of $\cosh x$. Specifically, when $y = \cosh x$ is restricted to the interval $[0, \infty)$, it is one-to-one, and its inverse is defined as follows:

$$y = \cosh^{-1} x \quad \text{if and only if} \quad x = \cosh y, \text{ for } x \geq 1 \text{ and } 0 \leq y < \infty.$$

Figure 6.94a shows the graph of $y = \cosh^{-1} x$, obtained by reflecting the graph of $y = \cosh x$ on $[0, \infty)$ over the line $y = x$. The definitions and graphs of the other five inverse hyperbolic functions are also shown in Figure 6.94. Notice that the domain of $y = \operatorname{sech} x$ (Figure 6.94d) must be restricted to $[0, \infty)$ to ensure the existence of its inverse.

Because hyperbolic functions are defined in terms of exponential functions, we can find explicit formulas for their inverses in terms of logarithms. For example, let's start with the definition of the inverse hyperbolic sine. For all real x and y, we have

$$y = \sinh^{-1} x \quad \Longleftrightarrow \quad x = \sinh y.$$

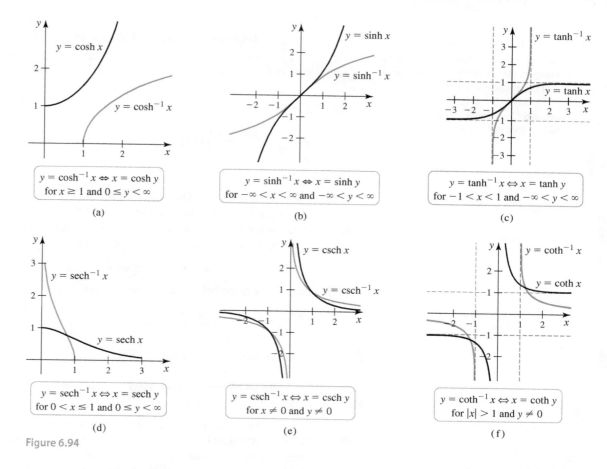

Figure 6.94

Following the procedure outlined in Section 1.3, we solve

$$x = \sinh y = \frac{e^y - e^{-y}}{2}$$

for y to give a formula for $\sinh^{-1} x$:

$$x = \frac{e^y - e^{-y}}{2} \quad \Rightarrow \quad e^y - 2x - e^{-y} = 0 \qquad \text{Rearrange equation.}$$

$$\Rightarrow \quad (e^y)^2 - 2xe^y - 1 = 0. \quad \text{Multiply by } e^y.$$

At this stage, we recognize a quadratic equation in e^y and solve for e^y using the quadratic formula, with $a = 1$, $b = -2x$, and $c = -1$:

$$e^y = \frac{2x \pm \sqrt{4x^2 + 4}}{2} = x \pm \sqrt{x^2 + 1} = \underbrace{x + \sqrt{x^2 + 1}}_{\text{choose positive root}}.$$

Because $e^y > 0$ and $\sqrt{x^2 + 1} > x$, the positive root must be chosen. We now solve for y by taking the natural logarithm of both sides:

$$e^y = x + \sqrt{x^2 + 1} \quad \Rightarrow \quad y = \ln(x + \sqrt{x^2 + 1}).$$

Therefore, the formula we seek is $\sinh^{-1} x = \ln(x + \sqrt{x^2 + 1})$.

A similar procedure can be carried out for the other inverse hyperbolic functions (Exercise 110). Theorem 6.10 lists the results of these calculations.

▶ Most calculators allow for the direct evaluation of the hyperbolic sine, cosine, and tangent, along with their inverses, but are not programmed to evaluate $\text{sech}^{-1} x$, $\text{csch}^{-1} x$, and $\text{coth}^{-1} x$. The formulas in Theorem 6.10 are useful for evaluating these functions on a calculator.

THEOREM 6.10   Inverses of the Hyperbolic Functions Expressed as Logarithms

$$\cosh^{-1} x = \ln\left(x + \sqrt{x^2 - 1}\right) (x \geq 1) \quad \text{sech}^{-1} x = \cosh^{-1}\frac{1}{x}\ (0 < x \leq 1)$$

$$\sinh^{-1} x = \ln\left(x + \sqrt{x^2 + 1}\right) \qquad\qquad \text{csch}^{-1} x = \sinh^{-1}\frac{1}{x}\ (x \neq 0)$$

$$\tanh^{-1} x = \frac{1}{2}\ln\left(\frac{1 + x}{1 - x}\right)(|x| < 1) \quad \text{coth}^{-1} x = \tanh^{-1}\frac{1}{x}\ (|x| > 1)$$

Notice that the formulas in Theorem 6.10 for the inverse hyperbolic secant, cosecant, and cotangent are given in terms of the inverses of their corresponding reciprocal functions. Justification for these formulas follows from the definitions of the inverse functions. For example, from the definition of $\text{csch}^{-1} x$, we have

$$y = \text{csch}^{-1} x \quad \Leftrightarrow \quad x = \text{csch } y \quad \Leftrightarrow \quad 1/x = \sinh y.$$

Applying the inverse hyperbolic sine to both sides of $1/x = \sinh y$ yields

$$\sinh^{-1}(1/x) = \underbrace{\sinh^{-1}(\sinh y)}_{y} \quad \text{or} \quad y = \text{csch}^{-1} x = \sinh^{-1}(1/x).$$

Similar derivations yield the other two formulas.

EXAMPLE 4   Points of intersection Find the points at which the curves $y = \cosh x$ and $y = \frac{5}{3}$ intersect (Figure 6.95).

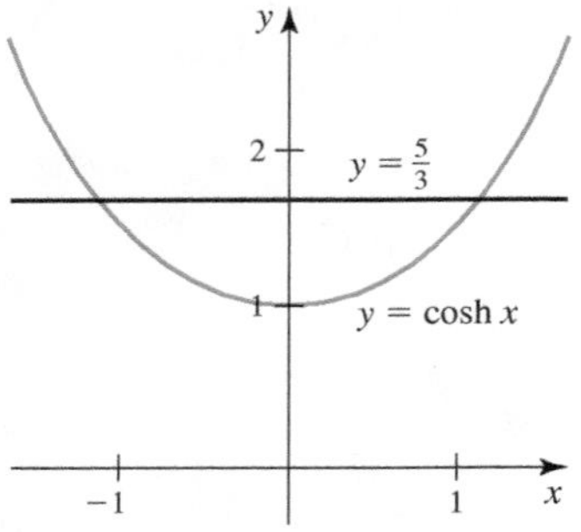

SOLUTION The x-coordinates of the points of intersection satisfy the equation $\cosh x = \frac{5}{3}$, which is solved by applying $\cosh^{-1}$ to both sides of the equation. However, evaluating $\cosh^{-1}(\cosh x)$ requires care—in Exercise 105, you are asked to show that $\cosh^{-1}(\cosh x) = |x|$. With this fact, the points of intersection can be found:

$$\cosh x = \tfrac{5}{3} \qquad\qquad\qquad \text{Set equations equal to one another.}$$

$$\cosh^{-1}(\cosh x) = \cosh^{-1}\tfrac{5}{3} \qquad \text{Apply } \cosh^{-1} \text{ to both sides.}$$

$$|x| = \ln\left(\tfrac{5}{3} + \sqrt{(\tfrac{5}{3})^2 - 1}\right) \quad \text{Simplify; use Theorem 6.10.}$$

$$x = \pm\ln 3. \qquad\qquad\qquad \text{Simplify.}$$

The points of intersection lie on the line $y = \frac{5}{3}$, so the points are $\left(-\ln 3, \frac{5}{3}\right)$ and $\left(\ln 3, \frac{5}{3}\right)$.

Related Exercises 45–46 ◀

Figure 6.95

QUICK CHECK 5 Use the results of Example 4 to write an integral for the area of the region bounded by $y = \cosh x$ and $y = \frac{5}{3}$ (Figure 6.95) and then evaluate the integral. ◀

Derivatives of the Inverse Hyperbolic Functions and Related Integral Formulas

The derivatives of the inverse hyperbolic functions can be computed directly from the logarithmic formulas given in Theorem 6.10. However, it is more efficient to use the definitions in Figure 6.94.

Recall that the inverse hyperbolic sine is defined by

$$y = \sinh^{-1} x \quad \Leftrightarrow \quad x = \sinh y.$$

We differentiate both sides of $x = \sinh y$ with respect to x and solve for dy/dx:

$$x = \sinh y \qquad\qquad y = \sinh^{-1} x \ \Leftrightarrow \ x = \sinh y$$

$$1 = (\cosh y)\frac{dy}{dx} \qquad\qquad \text{Use implicit differentiation.}$$

$$\frac{dy}{dx} = \frac{1}{\cosh y} \qquad\qquad \text{Solve for } dy/dx.$$

$$\frac{dy}{dx} = \frac{1}{\pm\sqrt{\sinh^2 y + 1}} \qquad \cosh^2 y - \sinh^2 y = 1$$

$$\frac{dy}{dx} = \frac{1}{\sqrt{x^2 + 1}}. \qquad\qquad x = \sinh y$$

In the last step, the positive root is chosen because $\cosh y > 0$ for all y.

The derivatives of the other inverse hyperbolic functions, listed in Theorem 6.11, are derived in a similar way (Exercise 106).

THEOREM 6.11   Derivatives of the Inverse Hyperbolic Functions

$$\frac{d}{dx}(\cosh^{-1}x) = \frac{1}{\sqrt{x^2-1}}\ (x>1) \qquad \frac{d}{dx}(\sinh^{-1}x) = \frac{1}{\sqrt{x^2+1}}$$

$$\frac{d}{dx}(\tanh^{-1}x) = \frac{1}{1-x^2}\ (|x|<1) \qquad \frac{d}{dx}(\coth^{-1}x) = \frac{1}{1-x^2}\ (|x|>1)$$

$$\frac{d}{dx}(\text{sech}^{-1}x) = -\frac{1}{x\sqrt{1-x^2}}\ (0<x<1) \quad \frac{d}{dx}(\text{csch}^{-1}x) = -\frac{1}{|x|\sqrt{1+x^2}}\ (x\neq0)$$

The restrictions associated with the formulas in Theorem 6.11 are a direct consequence of the domains of the inverse functions (Figure 6.94). Note that the derivative of both $\tanh^{-1}x$ and $\coth^{-1}x$ is $1/(1-x^2)$, although this result is valid on different domains ($|x|<1$ for $\tanh^{-1}x$ and $|x|>1$ for $\coth^{-1}x$). These facts have a bearing on formula (3) in the next theorem, which is a reversal of the derivative formulas in Theorem 6.11. Here we list integral results, where a is a positive constant; each formula can be verified by differentiation.

> The integrals in Theorem 6.12 appear again in Chapter 7 in terms of logarithms and with fewer restrictions on the variable of integration.

THEOREM 6.12   Integral Formulas

1. $\displaystyle\int \frac{dx}{\sqrt{x^2-a^2}} = \cosh^{-1}\frac{x}{a} + C,\ \text{for } x > a$

2. $\displaystyle\int \frac{dx}{\sqrt{x^2+a^2}} = \sinh^{-1}\frac{x}{a} + C,\ \text{for all } x$

3. $\displaystyle\int \frac{dx}{a^2-x^2} = \begin{cases} \frac{1}{a}\tanh^{-1}\frac{x}{a} + C, & \text{for } |x| < a \\ \frac{1}{a}\coth^{-1}\frac{x}{a} + C, & \text{for } |x| > a \end{cases}$

4. $\displaystyle\int \frac{dx}{x\sqrt{a^2-x^2}} = -\frac{1}{a}\text{sech}^{-1}\frac{x}{a} + C,\ \text{for } 0 < x < a$

5. $\displaystyle\int \frac{dx}{x\sqrt{a^2+x^2}} = -\frac{1}{a}\text{csch}^{-1}\frac{|x|}{a} + C,\ \text{for } x \neq 0$

EXAMPLE 5   Derivatives of inverse hyperbolic functions Compute dy/dx for each function.

a. $y = \tanh^{-1} 3x$ **b.** $y = x^2 \sinh^{-1} x$

SOLUTION

a. Using the Chain Rule, we have

$$\frac{dy}{dx} = \frac{d}{dx}(\tanh^{-1} 3x) = \frac{1}{1-(3x)^2}\cdot 3 = \frac{3}{1-9x^2}.$$

> The function $3/(1-9x^2)$ in the solution to Example 5a is defined for all $x \neq \pm 1/3$. However, the derivative formula $dy/dx = 3/(1-9x^2)$ is valid only on $-1/3 < x < 1/3$ because $\tanh^{-1} 3x$ is defined only on $-1/3 < x < 1/3$. The result of computing $d/dx(\coth^{-1} 3x)$ is the same, but valid on $(-\infty, -1/3) \cup (1/3, \infty)$.

b. $\displaystyle\frac{dy}{dx} = 2x\sinh^{-1}x + x^2\cdot\frac{1}{\sqrt{x^2+1}}$ Product Rule; Theorem 6.11

$\displaystyle = x\left(\frac{2\sqrt{x^2+1}\cdot\sinh^{-1}x + x}{\sqrt{x^2+1}}\right)$ Simplify.

Related Exercises 47–52 ◀

EXAMPLE 6   Integral computations

a. Compute the area of the region bounded by $y = 1/\sqrt{x^2 + 16}$ over the interval $[0, 3]$.

b. Evaluate $\displaystyle\int_9^{25} \frac{dx}{\sqrt{x}(4 - x)}$.

SOLUTION

a. The region in question is shown in Figure 6.96, and its area is given by

$\displaystyle\int_0^3 \frac{dx}{\sqrt{x^2 + 16}}$. Using formula (2) in Theorem 6.12 with $a = 4$, we have

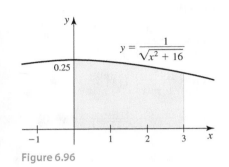

$y = \dfrac{1}{\sqrt{x^2 + 16}}$

0.25

Figure 6.96

$$\int_0^3 \frac{dx}{\sqrt{x^2 + 16}} = \sinh^{-1}\frac{x}{4}\bigg|_0^3 \qquad \text{Theorem 6.12}$$

$$= \sinh^{-1}\frac{3}{4} - \sinh^{-1} 0 \quad \text{Evaluate.}$$

$$= \sinh^{-1}\frac{3}{4}. \qquad \sinh^{-1} 0 = 0$$

A calculator gives an approximate result of $\sinh^{-1}(3/4) \approx 0.693$. The exact result can be written in terms of logarithms using Theorem 6.10:

$$\sinh^{-1}(3/4) = \ln(3/4 + \sqrt{(3/4)^2 + 1}) = \ln 2.$$

b. The integral doesn't match any of the formulas in Theorem 6.12, so we use the substitution $u = \sqrt{x}$:

$$\int_9^{25} \frac{dx}{\sqrt{x}(4 - x)} = 2\int_3^5 \frac{du}{4 - u^2}. \quad \text{Let } u = \sqrt{x}; du = \frac{dx}{2\sqrt{x}}.$$

The new integral now matches formula (3), with $a = 2$. We conclude that

$$2\int_3^5 \frac{du}{4 - u^2} = 2 \cdot \frac{1}{2}\coth^{-1}\frac{u}{2}\bigg|_3^5 \qquad \int \frac{dx}{a^2 - x^2} = \frac{1}{a}\coth^{-1}\frac{x}{a} + C$$

$$= \coth^{-1}\frac{5}{2} - \coth^{-1}\frac{3}{2}. \quad \text{Evaluate.}$$

The antiderivative involving $\coth^{-1} x$ was chosen because the interval of integration ($3 \le u \le 5$) satisfies $|u| > a = 2$. Theorem 6.10 is used to express the result in numerical form in case your calculator cannot evaluate $\coth^{-1} x$:

$$\coth^{-1}\frac{5}{2} - \coth^{-1}\frac{3}{2} = \tanh^{-1}\frac{2}{5} - \tanh^{-1}\frac{2}{3} \approx -0.381.$$

Related Exercises 53–64 ◄

QUICK CHECK 6 Evaluate $\displaystyle\int_0^1 \frac{du}{4 - u^2}$. ◄

Applications of Hyperbolic Functions

This section concludes with a brief look at two applied problems associated with hyperbolic functions. Additional applications are presented in the exercises.

The Catenary   When a free-hanging rope or flexible cable supporting only its own weight is attached to two points of equal height, it takes the shape of a curve known as a *catenary*. You can see catenaries in telephone wires, ropes strung across chasms for Tyrolean traverses (Example 7), and spider webs.

The equation for a general catenary is $y = a\cosh(x/a)$, where $a \ne 0$ is a real number. When $a < 0$, the curve is called an inverted catenary, sometimes used in the design of arches. Figure 6.97 illustrates catenaries for several values of a.

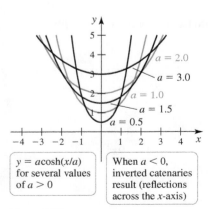

| $y = a\cosh(x/a)$ for several values of $a > 0$ | When $a < 0$, inverted catenaries result (reflections across the x-axis) |

Figure 6.97

> A Tyrolean traverse is used to pass over difficult terrain, such as a chasm between two cliffs or a raging river. A rope is strung between two anchor points, the climber clips onto the rope and then traverses the gap by pulling on the rope.

EXAMPLE 7   **Length of a catenary** A climber anchors a rope at two points of equal height, separated by a distance of 100 ft, in order to perform a *Tyrolean traverse*. The rope follows the catenary $f(x) = 200 \cosh(x/200)$ over the interval $[-50, 50]$ (Figure 6.98). Find the length of the rope between the two anchor points.

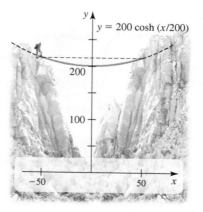

Figure 6.98

SOLUTION Recall from Section 6.5 that the arc length of the curve $y = f(x)$ over the interval $[a, b]$ is $L = \int_a^b \sqrt{1 + f'(x)^2} \, dx$. Also note that

> Using the principles of vector analysis introduced in Chapter 11, the tension in the rope and the forces acting upon the anchors in Example 7 can be computed. This is crucial information for anyone setting up a Tyrolean traverse; the *sag angle* (Exercise 68) figures into these calculations. Similar calculations are important for catenary lifelines used in construction and for rigging camera shots in Hollywood movies.

$$f'(x) = 200 \sinh\left(\frac{x}{200}\right) \cdot \frac{1}{200} = \sinh\frac{x}{200}.$$

Therefore, the length of the rope is

$$L = \int_{-50}^{50} \sqrt{1 + \sinh^2\left(\frac{x}{200}\right)} \, dx \qquad \text{Arc length formula}$$

$$= 2 \int_0^{50} \sqrt{1 + \sinh^2\left(\frac{x}{200}\right)} \, dx \qquad \text{Use symmetry.}$$

$$= 400 \int_0^{1/4} \sqrt{1 + \sinh^2 u} \, du \qquad \text{Let } u = \frac{x}{200}.$$

$$= 400 \int_0^{1/4} \cosh u \, du \qquad 1 + \sinh^2 u = \cosh^2 u$$

$$= 400 \sinh u \Big|_0^{1/4} \qquad \text{Evaluate integral.}$$

$$= 400\left(\sinh\frac{1}{4} - \sinh 0\right) \qquad \text{Simplify.}$$

$$\approx 101 \text{ ft.} \qquad \text{Evaluate.} \quad \textit{Related Exercises 65–68} \blacktriangleleft$$

Velocity of a Wave   To describe the characteristics of a traveling wave, researchers formulate a *wave equation* that reflects the known (or hypothesized) properties of the wave and that often takes the form of a differential equation (Section 7.9). Solving a wave equation produces additional information about the wave, and it turns out that hyperbolic functions may arise naturally in this context.

EXAMPLE 8   **Velocity of an ocean wave** The velocity v (in meters/second) of an idealized surface wave traveling on the ocean is modeled by the equation

$$v = \sqrt{\frac{g\lambda}{2\pi} \tanh\left(\frac{2\pi d}{\lambda}\right)},$$

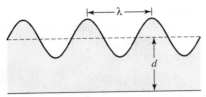

Figure 6.99

▶ In fluid dynamics, *water depth* is often discussed in terms of the depth-to-wavelength ratio d/λ, not the actual depth of the water. Three classifications are generally used:

shallow water: $d/\lambda < 0.05$

intermediate depth: $0.05 < d/\lambda < 0.5$

deep water: $d/\lambda > 0.5$

where $g = 9.8 \text{ m/s}^2$ is the acceleration due to gravity, λ is the wavelength measured in meters from crest to crest, and d is the depth of the undisturbed water, also measured in meters (Figure 6.99).

a. A sea kayaker observes several waves that pass beneath her kayak, and she estimates that $\lambda = 12$ m and $v = 4$ m/s. How deep is the water in which she is kayaking?

b. The *deep-water* equation for wave velocity is $v = \sqrt{\dfrac{g\lambda}{2\pi}}$, which is an approximation to the velocity formula given above. Waves are said to be in deep water if the depth-to-wavelength ratio d/λ is greater than $\dfrac{1}{2}$. Explain why $v = \sqrt{\dfrac{g\lambda}{2\pi}}$ is a good approximation when $d/\lambda > \dfrac{1}{2}$.

SOLUTION

a. We substitute $\lambda = 12$ and $v = 4$ into the velocity equation and solve for d.

$$4 = \sqrt{\frac{g \cdot 12}{2\pi} \tanh\left(\frac{2\pi d}{12}\right)} \quad \Rightarrow \quad 16 = \frac{6g}{\pi} \tanh\left(\frac{\pi d}{6}\right) \quad \text{Square both sides.}$$

$$\Rightarrow \quad \frac{8\pi}{3g} = \tanh\left(\frac{\pi d}{6}\right) \quad \text{Multiply by } \frac{\pi}{6g}.$$

In order to extract d from the argument of tanh, we apply $\tanh^{-1}$ to both sides of the equation and then use the property $\tanh^{-1}(\tanh x) = x$, for all x.

$$\tanh^{-1}\left(\frac{8\pi}{3g}\right) = \tanh^{-1}\left(\tanh\left(\frac{\pi d}{6}\right)\right) \quad \text{Apply } \tanh^{-1} \text{ to both sides.}$$

$$\tanh^{-1}\left(\frac{8\pi}{29.4}\right) = \frac{\pi d}{6} \quad \text{Simplify; } 3g = 29.4.$$

$$d = \frac{6}{\pi} \tanh^{-1}\left(\frac{8\pi}{29.4}\right) \approx 2.4 \text{ m} \quad \text{Solve for } d.$$

Therefore, the kayaker is in water that is about 2.4 m deep.

b. Recall that $y = \tanh x$ is an increasing function ($dy/dx = \text{sech}^2 x > 0$) whose values approach 1 as $x \to \infty$. Also notice that when $\dfrac{d}{\lambda} = \dfrac{1}{2}$, $\tanh\left(\dfrac{2\pi d}{\lambda}\right) = \tanh \pi \approx 0.996$, which is nearly equal to 1. These facts imply that whenever $\dfrac{d}{\lambda} > \dfrac{1}{2}$, we can replace $\tanh\left(\dfrac{2\pi d}{\lambda}\right)$ with 1 in the velocity formula, resulting in the deep-water velocity function $v = \sqrt{\dfrac{g\lambda}{2\pi}}$.

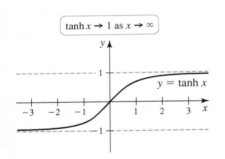

tanh $x \to 1$ as $x \to \infty$

$y = \tanh x$

QUICK CHECK 7 Explain why longer waves travel faster than shorter waves in deep water. ◄

Related Exercises 69–72 ◄

SECTION 6.10 EXERCISES

Review Questions

1. State the definition of the hyperbolic cosine and hyperbolic sine functions.

2. Sketch the graphs of $y = \cosh x$, $y = \sinh x$, and $y = \tanh x$ (include asymptotes), and state whether each function is even, odd, or neither.

3. What is the fundamental identity for hyperbolic functions?

4. How are the derivative formulas for the hyperbolic functions and the trigonometric functions alike? How are they different?

5. Express $\sinh^{-1} x$ in terms of logarithms.

6. What is the domain of $\text{sech}^{-1} x$? How is $\text{sech}^{-1} x$ defined in terms of the inverse hyperbolic cosine?

7. A calculator has a built-in $\sinh^{-1} x$ function, but no $\text{csch}^{-1} x$ function. How do you evaluate $\text{csch}^{-1} 5$ on such a calculator?

8. On what interval is the formula $d/dx(\tanh^{-1} x) = 1/(x^2 - 1)$ valid?

9. When evaluating the definite integral $\int_6^8 \frac{dx}{16 - x^2}$, why must you choose the antiderivative $\frac{1}{4} \coth^{-1} \frac{x}{4}$ rather than $\frac{1}{4} \tanh^{-1} \frac{x}{4}$?

10. How does the graph of the catenary $y = a \cosh(x/a)$ change as $a > 0$ increases?

Basic Skills

11–15. Verifying identities *Verify each identity using the definitions of the hyperbolic functions.*

11. $\tanh x = \dfrac{e^{2x} - 1}{e^{2x} + 1}$

12. $\tanh(-x) = -\tanh x$

13. $\cosh 2x = \cosh^2 x + \sinh^2 x$ (*Hint:* Begin with the right side of the equation.)

14. $2 \sinh(\ln(\sec x)) = \sin x \tan x$

15. $\cosh x + \sinh x = e^x$

16–18. Verifying identities *Use the given identity to verify the related identity.*

16. Use the fundamental identity $\cosh^2 x - \sinh^2 x = 1$ to verify the identity $\coth^2 x - 1 = \operatorname{csch}^2 x$.

17. Use the identity $\cosh 2x = \cosh^2 x + \sinh^2 x$ to verify the identities $\cosh^2 x = \dfrac{\cosh 2x + 1}{2}$ and $\sinh^2 x = \dfrac{\cosh 2x - 1}{2}$.

18. Use the identity $\cosh(x + y) = \cosh x \cosh y + \sinh x \sinh y$ to verify the identity $\cosh 2x = \cosh^2 x + \sinh^2 x$.

19–21. Derivative formulas *Derive the following derivative formulas given that $d/dx(\cosh x) = \sinh x$ and $d/dx(\sinh x) = \cosh x$.*

19. $d/dx(\coth x) = -\operatorname{csch}^2 x$

20. $d/dx(\operatorname{sech} x) = -\operatorname{sech} x \tanh x$

21. $d/dx(\operatorname{csch} x) = -\operatorname{csch} x \coth x$

22–30. Derivatives *Compute dy/dx for the following functions.*

22. $y = \sinh 4x$

23. $y = \cosh^2 x$

24. $y = -\sinh^3 4x$

25. $y = \tanh^2 x$

26. $y = \sqrt{\coth 3x}$

27. $y = \ln \operatorname{sech} 2x$

28. $y = x \tanh x$

29. $y = x^2 \cosh^2 3x$

30. $y = x/\operatorname{csch} x$

31–36. Indefinite integrals *Determine each indefinite integral.*

31. $\displaystyle\int \cosh 2x \, dx$

32. $\displaystyle\int \operatorname{sech}^2 x \tanh x \, dx$

33. $\displaystyle\int \frac{\sinh x}{1 + \cosh x} \, dx$

34. $\displaystyle\int \coth^2 x \operatorname{csch}^2 x \, dx$

35. $\displaystyle\int \tanh^2 x \, dx$ (*Hint:* Use an identity.)

36. $\displaystyle\int \sinh^2 x \, dx$ (*Hint:* Use an identity.)

37–40. Definite integrals *Evaluate each definite integral.*

37. $\displaystyle\int_0^1 \cosh^3 3x \sinh 3x \, dx$

38. $\displaystyle\int_0^4 \frac{\operatorname{sech}^2 \sqrt{x}}{\sqrt{x}} \, dx$

39. $\displaystyle\int_0^{\ln 2} \tanh x \, dx$

40. $\displaystyle\int_{\ln 2}^{\ln 3} \operatorname{csch} y \, dy$

41–42. Two ways *Evaluate the following integrals two ways.*
a. *Simplify the integrand first and then integrate.*
b. *Change variables (let $u = \ln x$), integrate, and then simplify your answer. Verify that both methods give the same answer.*

41. $\displaystyle\int \frac{\sinh(\ln x)}{x} \, dx$

42. $\displaystyle\int_1^{\sqrt{3}} \frac{\operatorname{sech}(\ln x)}{x} \, dx$

T 43. Visual approximation
a. Use a graphing utility to sketch the graph of $y = \coth x$ and then explain why $\int_5^{10} \coth x \, dx \approx 5$.
b. Evaluate $\int_5^{10} \coth x \, dx$ analytically and use a calculator to arrive at a decimal approximation to the answer. How large is the error in the approximation in part (a)?

44. **Integral proof** Prove the formula $\int \coth x \, dx = \ln|\sinh x| + C$ of Theorem 6.9.

45–46. Points of intersection and area
a. *Sketch the graphs of the functions f and g and find the x-coordinate of the points at which they intersect.*
b. *Compute the area of the region described.*

45. $f(x) = \operatorname{sech} x$, $g(x) = \tanh x$; the region bounded by the graphs of f, g, and the y-axis

46. $f(x) = \sinh x$, $g(x) = \tanh x$; the region bounded by the graphs of f, g, and $x = \ln 3$

47–52. Derivatives *Find the derivatives of the following functions.*

47. $f(x) = \cosh^{-1} 4x$

48. $f(t) = 2 \tanh^{-1} \sqrt{t}$

49. $f(v) = \sinh^{-1} v^2$

50. $f(x) = \operatorname{csch}^{-1}(2/x)$

51. $f(x) = x \sinh^{-1} x - \sqrt{x^2 + 1}$

52. $f(u) = \sinh^{-1}(\tan u)$

53–58. Indefinite integrals *Determine the following indefinite integrals.*

53. $\displaystyle\int \frac{dx}{8 - x^2}, x > 2\sqrt{2}$

54. $\displaystyle\int \frac{dx}{\sqrt{x^2 - 16}}$

55. $\displaystyle\int \frac{e^x}{36 - e^{2x}} \, dx, x < \ln 6$

56. $\displaystyle\int \frac{dx}{x\sqrt{16 + x^2}}$

57. $\displaystyle\int \frac{dx}{x\sqrt{4 - x^8}}$

58. $\displaystyle\int \frac{dx}{x\sqrt{1 + x^4}}$

59–64. Definite integrals *Evaluate the following definite integrals. Use Theorem 6.10 to express your answer in terms of logarithms.*

59. $\displaystyle\int_1^{e^2} \frac{dx}{x\sqrt{\ln^2 x + 1}}$

60. $\displaystyle\int_5^{3\sqrt{5}} \frac{dx}{\sqrt{x^2 - 9}}$

61. $\displaystyle\int_{-2}^2 \frac{dt}{t^2 - 9}$

62. $\displaystyle\int_{1/6}^{1/4} \frac{dt}{t\sqrt{1 - 4t^2}}$

63. $\displaystyle\int_{1/8}^1 \frac{dx}{x\sqrt{1 + x^{2/3}}}$

64. $\displaystyle\int_{\ln 5}^{\ln 9} \frac{\cosh x}{4 - \sinh^2 x} \, dx$

65. Catenary arch The portion of the curve $y = \frac{17}{15} - \cosh x$ that lies above the x-axis forms a catenary arch. Find the average height of the arch above the x-axis.

66. Length of a catenary Show that the arc length of the catenary $y = \cosh x$ over the interval $[0, a]$ is $L = \sinh a$.

67. Power lines A power line is attached at the same height to two utility poles that are separated by a distance of 100 ft; the power line follows the curve $f(x) = a \cosh(x/a)$. Use the following steps to find the value of a that produces a sag of 10 ft midway between the poles. Use a coordinate system that places the poles at $x = \pm 50$.

   a. Show that a satisfies the equation $\cosh(50/a) - 1 = 10/a$.

   b. Let $t = 10/a$, confirm that the equation in part (a) reduces to $\cosh 5t - 1 = t$, and solve for t using a graphing utility. Report your answer accurate to two decimal places.

   c. Use your answer in part (b) to find a and then compute the length of the power line.

68. Sag angle Imagine a climber clipping onto the rope described in Example 7 and pulling himself to the rope's midpoint. Because the rope is supporting the weight of the climber, it no longer takes the shape of the catenary $y = 200 \cosh(x/200)$. Instead, the rope (nearly) forms two sides of an isosceles triangle. Compute the *sag angle* θ illustrated in the figure, assuming that the rope does not stretch when weighted. Recall from Example 7 that the length of the rope is 101 ft.

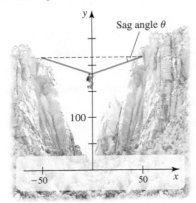

Sag angle θ

69. Wavelength The velocity of a surface wave on the ocean is given by $v = \sqrt{\dfrac{g\lambda}{2\pi} \tanh\left(\dfrac{2\pi d}{\lambda}\right)}$ (Example 8). Use a graphing utility or root finder to approximate the wavelength λ of an ocean wave traveling at $v = 7$ m/s in water that is $d = 10$ m deep.

70. Wave velocity Use Exercise 69 to do the following calculations.

   a. Find the velocity of a wave where $\lambda = 50$ m and $d = 20$ m.

   b. Determine the depth of the water if a wave with $\lambda = 15$ m is traveling at $v = 4.5$ m/s.

71. Shallow-water velocity equation

   a. Confirm that the linear approximation to $f(x) = \tanh x$ at $a = 0$ is $L(x) = x$.

   b. Recall that the velocity of a surface wave on the ocean is $v = \sqrt{\dfrac{g\lambda}{2\pi} \tanh \dfrac{2\pi d}{\lambda}}$. In fluid dynamics, *shallow water* refers to water where the depth-to-wavelength ratio $d/\lambda < 0.05$. Use your answer to part (a) to explain why the shallow water velocity equation is $v = \sqrt{gd}$.

   c. Use the shallow-water velocity equation to explain why waves tend to slow down as they approach the shore.

72. Tsunamis A tsunami is an ocean wave often caused by earthquakes on the ocean floor; these waves typically have long wavelengths, ranging between 150 to 1000 km. Imagine a tsunami traveling across the Pacific Ocean, which is the deepest ocean in the world, with an average depth of about 4000 m. Explain why the *shallow-water velocity equation* (Exercise 71) applies to tsunamis even though the actual depth of the water is large. What does the shallow-water equation say about the speed of a tsunami in the Pacific Ocean (use $d = 4000$ m)?

Further Explorations

73. Explain why or why not Determine whether the following statements are true and give an explanation or counterexample.

   a. $\dfrac{d}{dx}(\sinh \ln 3) = \dfrac{\cosh \ln 3}{3}$.

   b. $\dfrac{d}{dx}(\sinh x) = \cosh x$ and $\dfrac{d}{dx}(\cosh x) = -\sinh x$.

   c. Differentiating the velocity equation for an ocean wave
   $$v = \sqrt{\frac{g\lambda}{2\pi} \tanh\left(\frac{2\pi d}{\lambda}\right)}$$
   results in the acceleration of the wave.

   d. $\ln(1 + \sqrt{2}) = -\ln(-1 + \sqrt{2})$.

   e. $\displaystyle\int_0^1 \dfrac{dx}{4 - x^2} = \dfrac{1}{2}\left(\coth^{-1}\dfrac{1}{2} - \coth^{-1} 0\right)$.

74. Evaluating hyperbolic functions Use a calculator to evaluate each expression or state that the value does not exist. Report answers accurate to four decimal places.

   a. $\coth 4$ **b.** $\tanh^{-1} 2$ **c.** $\operatorname{csch}^{-1} 5$ **d.** $\operatorname{csch} x \big|_{1/2}^2$

   e. $\ln\left|\tanh\left(\dfrac{x}{2}\right)\right|\Big|_1^{10}$ **f.** $\tan^{-1}(\sinh x)\big|_{-3}^3$ **g.** $\dfrac{1}{4}\coth^{-1}\dfrac{x}{4}\Big|_{20}^{36}$

75. Evaluating hyperbolic functions Evaluate each expression without using a calculator or state that the value does not exist. Simplify answers to the extent possible.

   a. $\cosh 0$ **b.** $\tanh 0$ **c.** $\operatorname{csch} 0$ **d.** $\operatorname{sech}(\sinh 0)$

   e. $\coth(\ln 5)$ **f.** $\sinh(2\ln 3)$ **g.** $\cosh^2 1$ **h.** $\operatorname{sech}^{-1}(\ln 3)$

   i. $\cosh^{-1}(17/8)$ **j.** $\sinh^{-1}\left(\dfrac{e^2 - 1}{2e}\right)$

76. Confirming a graph The graph of $f(x) = \sinh x$ is shown in Figure 6.92. Use calculus to find the intervals of increase and decrease for f, and find the intervals on which f is concave up and concave down to confirm that the graph is correct.

77. Critical points Find the critical points of the function $f(x) = \sinh^2 x \cosh x$.

78. Critical points

   a. Show that the critical points of $f(x) = \dfrac{\cosh x}{x}$ satisfy $x = \coth x$.

   b. Use a root finder to approximate the critical points of f.

79. Points of inflection Find the x-coordinate of the point(s) of inflection of $f(x) = \tanh^2 x$.

80. Points of inflection Find the x-coordinate of the point(s) of inflection of $f(x) = \operatorname{sech} x$. Report exact answers in terms of logarithms (use Theorem 6.10).

81. Area of region Find the area of the region bounded by $y = \text{sech } x$, $x = 1$, and the unit circle.

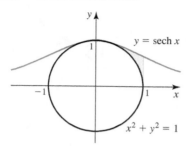

82. Solid of revolution Compute the volume of the solid of revolution that results when the region in Exercise 81 is revolved about the x-axis.

83. L'Hôpital loophole Explain why l'Hôpital's Rule fails when applied to the limit $\lim\limits_{x \to \infty} \dfrac{\sinh x}{\cosh x}$ and then find the limit another way.

84–87. Limits *Use l'Hôpital's Rule to evaluate the following limits.*

84. $\lim\limits_{x \to \infty} \dfrac{1 - \coth x}{1 - \tanh x}$

85. $\lim\limits_{x \to 0} \dfrac{\tanh^{-1} x}{\tan(\pi x/2)}$

86. $\lim\limits_{x \to 1^-} \dfrac{\tanh^{-1} x}{\tan(\pi x/2)}$

87. $\lim\limits_{x \to 0^+} (\tanh x)^x$

T 88. Slant asymptote The linear function $\ell(x) = mx + b$, for finite $m \neq 0$, is a slant asymptote of $f(x)$ if $\lim\limits_{x \to \infty} (f(x) - \ell(x)) = 0$.

    a. Use a graphing utility to make a sketch that shows $\ell(x) = x$ is a slant asymptote of $f(x) = x \tanh x$. Does f have any other slant asymptotes?

    b. Provide an intuitive argument showing that $f(x) = x \tanh x$ behaves like $\ell(x) = x$ as x gets large.

    c. Prove that $\ell(x) = x$ is a slant asymptote of f by confirming $\lim\limits_{x \to \infty} (x \tanh x - x) = 0$.

89–92. Additional integrals *Evaluate the following integrals.*

89. $\displaystyle\int \dfrac{\cosh z}{\sinh^2 z}\, dz$

90. $\displaystyle\int \dfrac{\cos \theta}{9 - \sin^2 \theta}\, d\theta$

91. $\displaystyle\int_{5/12}^{3/4} \dfrac{\sinh^{-1} x}{\sqrt{x^2 + 1}}\, dx$

92. $\displaystyle\int_{25}^{225} \dfrac{dx}{\sqrt{x^2 + 25x}}$ (*Hint:* $\sqrt{x^2 + 25x} = \sqrt{x}\sqrt{x + 25}$.)

Applications

93. Kiln design Find the volume interior to the inverted catenary kiln (an oven used to fire pottery) shown in the figure.

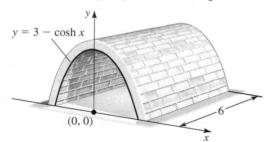

T 94. Newton's method Use Newton's method to find all local extreme values of $f(x) = x \text{ sech } x$.

95. Falling body When an object falling from rest encounters air resistance proportional to the square of its velocity, the distance it falls (in meters) after t seconds is given by
$$d(t) = \frac{m}{k} \ln\left(\cosh\left(\sqrt{\frac{kg}{m}}\, t \right) \right),$$
where m is the mass of the object in kilograms, $g = 9.8 \text{ m/s}^2$ is the acceleration due to gravity, and k is a physical constant.

    a. A BASE jumper ($m = 75$ kg) leaps from a tall cliff and performs a ten-second delay (she free-falls for 10 s and then opens her chute). How far does she fall in 10 s? Assume $k = 0.2$.

    b. How long does it take her to fall the first 100 m? The second 100 m? What is her average velocity over each of these intervals?

96. Velocity of falling body Refer to Exercise 95, which gives the position function for a falling body. Use $m = 75$ kg and $k = 0.2$.

    a. Confirm that the base jumper's velocity t seconds after jumping is $v(t) = d'(t) = \sqrt{\dfrac{mg}{k}} \tanh\left(\sqrt{\dfrac{kg}{m}}\, t \right)$.

    b. How fast is the BASE jumper falling at the end of a 10 s delay?

    c. How long does it take the BASE jumper to reach a speed of 45 m/s (roughly 100 mi/hr)?

97. Terminal velocity Refer to Exercises 95 and 96.

    a. Compute a jumper's *terminal velocity*, which is defined as
$$\lim\limits_{t \to \infty} v(t) = \lim\limits_{t \to \infty} \sqrt{\dfrac{mg}{k}} \tanh\left(\sqrt{\dfrac{kg}{m}}\, t \right).$$

    b. Find the terminal velocity for the jumper in Exercise 96 ($m = 75$ kg and $k = 0.2$).

    c. How long does it take any falling object to reach a speed equal to 95% of its terminal velocity? Leave your answer in terms of k, g, and m.

    d. How tall must a cliff be so that the BASE jumper ($m = 75$ kg and $k = 0.2$) reaches 95% of terminal velocity? Assume that the jumper needs at least 300 m at the end of free fall to deploy the chute and land safely.

98. Acceleration of a falling body

    a. Find the acceleration $a(t) = v'(t)$ of a falling body whose velocity is given in part (a) of Exercise 96.

    b. Compute $\lim\limits_{t \to \infty} a(t)$. Explain your answer as it relates to terminal velocity (Exercise 97).

99. Differential equations Hyperbolic functions are useful in solving differential equations (Section 7.9). Show that the functions $y = A \sinh kx$ and $y = B \cosh kx$, where A, B, and k are constants, satisfy the equation $y''(x) - k^2 y(x) = 0$.

100. Surface area of a catenoid When the catenary $y = a \cosh(x/a)$ is revolved about the x-axis, it sweeps out a surface of revolution called a *catenoid*. Find the area of the surface generated when $y = \cosh x$ on $[-\ln 2, \ln 2]$ is rotated around the x-axis.

Additional Exercises

101–104. Verifying identities *Verify the following identities.*

101. $\sinh(\cosh^{-1} x) = \sqrt{x^2 - 1}$, for $x \geq 1$

102. $\cosh(\sinh^{-1} x) = \sqrt{x^2 + 1}$, for all x

103. $\cosh(x + y) = \cosh x \cosh y + \sinh x \sinh y$

104. $\sinh(x + y) = \sinh x \cosh y + \cosh x \sinh y$

105. Inverse identity Show that $\cosh^{-1}(\cosh x) = |x|$ by using the formula $\cosh^{-1} t = \ln(t + \sqrt{t^2 - 1})$ and by considering the cases $x \geq 0$ and $x < 0$.

106. Theorem 6.11

a. The definition of the inverse hyperbolic cosine is
$y = \cosh^{-1} x \Leftrightarrow x = \cosh y$, for $x \geq 1, 0 \leq y < \infty$.
Use implicit differentiation to show that $\dfrac{d}{dx}(\cosh^{-1} x) = 1/\sqrt{x^2 - 1}$.

b. Differentiate $\sinh^{-1} x = \ln(x + \sqrt{x^2 + 1})$ to show that
$\dfrac{d}{dx}(\sinh^{-1} x) = 1/\sqrt{x^2 + 1}$.

107. Many formulas There are several ways to express the indefinite integral of $\text{sech } x$.

a. Show that $\int \text{sech } x \, dx = \tan^{-1}(\sinh x) + C$ (Theorem 6.9).
(*Hint:* Write $\text{sech } x = \dfrac{1}{\cosh x} = \dfrac{\cosh x}{\cosh^2 x} = \dfrac{\cosh x}{1 + \sinh^2 x}$ and then make a change of variables.)

b. Show that $\int \text{sech } x \, dx = \sin^{-1}(\tanh x) + C$. (*Hint:* Show that $\text{sech } x = \dfrac{\text{sech}^2 x}{\sqrt{1 - \tanh^2 x}}$ and then make a change of variables.)

c. Verify that $\int \text{sech } x \, dx = 2 \tan^{-1} e^x + C$ by proving
$\dfrac{d}{dx}(2 \tan^{-1} e^x) = \text{sech } x$.

108. Integral formula Carry out the following steps to derive the formula $\int \text{csch } x \, dx = \ln|\tanh(x/2)| + C$ (Theorem 6.9).

a. Change variables with the substitution $u = x/2$ to show that
$\int \text{csch } x \, dx = \int \dfrac{2 \, du}{\sinh 2u}$.

b. Use the identity for $\sinh 2u$ to show that $\dfrac{2}{\sinh 2u} = \dfrac{\text{sech}^2 u}{\tanh u}$.

c. Change variables again to determine $\int \dfrac{\text{sech}^2 u}{\tanh u} \, du$ and then express your answer in terms of x.

109. Arc length Use the result of Exercise 108 to find the arc length of $f(x) = \ln|\tanh(x/2)|$ on $[\ln 2, \ln 8]$.

110. Inverse hyperbolic tangent Recall that the inverse hyperbolic tangent is defined as $y = \tanh^{-1} x \Leftrightarrow x = \tanh y$, for $-1 < x < 1$ and all real y. Solve $x = \tanh y$ for y to express the formula for $\tanh^{-1} x$ in terms of logarithms.

111. Integral family Use the substitution $u = x^r$ to show that
$\int \dfrac{dx}{x\sqrt{1 - x^{2r}}} = -\dfrac{1}{r} \text{sech}^{-1} x^r + C$, for $r > 0$ and $0 < x < 1$.

112. Definitions of hyperbolic sine and cosine Complete the following steps to prove that when the x- and y-coordinates of a point on the hyperbola $x^2 - y^2 = 1$ are defined as $\cosh t$ and $\sinh t$, respectively, where t is twice the area of the shaded region in the figure, x and y can be expressed as
$$x = \cosh t = \frac{e^t + e^{-t}}{2} \text{ and } y = \sinh t = \frac{e^t - e^{-t}}{2}.$$

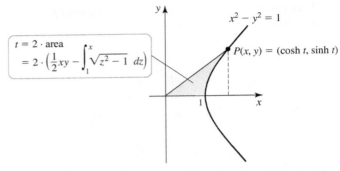

$$t = 2 \cdot \text{area} = 2 \cdot \left(\frac{1}{2}xy - \int_1^x \sqrt{z^2 - 1} \, dz\right)$$

$x^2 - y^2 = 1$

$P(x, y) = (\cosh t, \sinh t)$

a. Explain why twice the area of the shaded region is given by
$$t = 2 \cdot \left(\frac{1}{2} xy - \int_1^x \sqrt{z^2 - 1} \, dz\right)$$
$$= x\sqrt{x^2 - 1} - 2\int_1^x \sqrt{z^2 - 1} \, dz.$$

b. In Chapter 7, the formula for the integral in part (a) is derived:
$$\int \sqrt{z^2 - 1} \, dz = \frac{z}{2}\sqrt{z^2 - 1} - \frac{1}{2}\ln|z + \sqrt{z^2 - 1}| + C.$$
Evaluate this integral on the interval $[1, x]$, explain why the absolute value can be dropped, and combine the result with part (a) to show that
$$t = \ln(x + \sqrt{x^2 - 1}).$$

c. Solve the final result from part (b) for x to show that
$$x = \frac{e^t + e^{-t}}{2}.$$

d. Use the fact that $y = \sqrt{x^2 - 1}$ in combination with part (c) to show that $y = \dfrac{e^t - e^{-t}}{2}$.

QUICK CHECK ANSWERS

1. $\sinh(-x) = \dfrac{e^{-x} - e^{-(-x)}}{2} = -\dfrac{e^x - e^{-x}}{2} = -\sinh x$

2. Because $\tanh x = \dfrac{e^x - e^{-x}}{e^x + e^{-x}}$ and $\lim\limits_{x \to \infty} e^{-x} = 0$,
$\tanh x \approx \dfrac{e^x}{e^x} = 1$ for large x, which implies that $y = 1$ is a horizontal asymptote. A similar argument shows that $\tanh x \to -1$ as $x \to -\infty$, which means that $y = -1$ is also a horizontal asymptote.   **3.** $\dfrac{d}{dx}(4 \cosh 2x) = 8 \sinh 2x$;
$\int 4 \cosh 2x \, dx = 2 \sinh 2x + C$ **4.** $\dfrac{1}{2} \ln|\tanh x| + C$

5. Area $= 2\displaystyle\int_0^{\ln 3} \left(\frac{5}{3} - \cosh x\right) dx$
$= \dfrac{2}{3}(5 \ln 3 - 4) \approx 0.995$

6. $\displaystyle\int_0^1 \frac{du}{4 - u^2} = \frac{1}{2} \tanh^{-1} \frac{1}{2} \approx 0.275$ **7.** The deep-water velocity formula is $v = \sqrt{\dfrac{g\lambda}{2\pi}}$, which is an increasing function of the wavelength λ. Therefore, larger values of λ correspond with faster waves.◄

1. **Explain why or why not** Determine whether the following statements are true and give an explanation or counterexample.

    a. A region R is revolved about the y-axis to generate a solid S. To find the volume of S, you could use either the disk/washer method and integrate with respect to y or the shell method and integrate with respect to x.

    b. Given only the velocity of an object moving on a line, it is possible to find its displacement, but not its position.

    c. If water flows into a tank at a constant rate (for example, 6 gal/min), the volume of water in the tank increases according to a linear function of time.

    d. The variable $y = t + 1$ doubles in value whenever t increases by 1 unit.

    e. The function $y = Ae^{0.1t}$ increases by 10% when t increases by 1 unit.

    f. $\ln xy = (\ln x)(\ln y)$.

    g. $\sinh(\ln x) = \dfrac{x^2 - 1}{2x}$.

2. **Displacement from velocity** The velocity of an object moving along a line is given by $v(t) = 20 \cos \pi t$ (in ft/s). What is the displacement of the object after 1.5 s?

3. **Position, displacement, and distance** A projectile is launched vertically from the ground at $t = 0$, and its velocity in flight (in m/s) is given by $v(t) = 20 - 10t$. Find the position, displacement, and distance traveled after t seconds, for $0 \le t \le 4$.

4. **Deceleration** At $t = 0$, a car begins decelerating from a velocity of 80 ft/s at a constant rate of 5 ft/s². Find its position function assuming $s(0) = 0$.

5. **An oscillator** The acceleration of an object moving along a line is given by $a(t) = 2 \sin\left(\dfrac{\pi t}{4}\right)$. The initial velocity and position are

    $v(0) = -\dfrac{8}{\pi}$ and $s(0) = 0$.

    a. Find the velocity and position for $t \ge 0$.

    b. What are the minimum and maximum values of s?

    c. Find the average velocity and average position over the interval $[0, 8]$.

6. **A race** Starting at the same point on a straight road, Anna and Benny begin running with velocities (in mi/hr) given by $v_A(t) = 2t + 1$ and $v_B(t) = 4 - t$, respectively.

    a. Graph the velocity functions, for $0 \le t \le 4$.

    b. If the runners run for 1 hr, who runs farther? Interpret your conclusion geometrically using the graph in part (a).

    c. If the runners run for 6 mi, who wins the race? Interpret your conclusion geometrically using the graph in part (a).

7. **Fuel consumption** A small plane in flight consumes fuel at a rate (in gal/min) given by

    $$R'(t) = \begin{cases} 4t^{1/3} & \text{if } 0 \le t \le 8 \ \ (\text{take-off}) \\ 2 & \text{if } t > 8 \ \ (\text{cruising}). \end{cases}$$

    a. Find a function R that gives the total fuel consumed, for $0 \le t \le 8$.

    b. Find a function R that gives the total fuel consumed, for $t \ge 0$.

    c. If the fuel tank capacity is 150 gal, when does the fuel run out?

8. **Variable flow rate** Water flows out of a tank at a rate (in m³/hr) given by $V'(t) = 15/(t + 1)$. If the tank initially holds 75 m³ of water, when will the tank be empty?

T 9. **Decreasing velocity** A projectile is fired upward, and its velocity in m/s is given by $v(t) = 200e^{-t/10}$, for $t \ge 0$.

    a. Graph the velocity function for $t \ge 0$.

    b. When does the velocity reach 50 m/s?

    c. Find and graph the position function for the projectile for $t \ge 0$, assuming $s(0) = 0$.

    d. Given unlimited time, can the projectile travel 2500 m? If so, at what time does the distance traveled equal 2500 m?

T 10. **Decreasing velocity** A projectile is fired upward, and its velocity (in m/s) is given by $v(t) = \dfrac{200}{\sqrt{t + 1}}$, for $t \ge 0$.

    a. Graph the velocity function for $t \ge 0$.

    b. Find and graph the position function for the projectile, for $t \ge 0$, assuming $s(0) = 0$.

    c. Given unlimited time, can the projectile travel 2500 m? If so, at what time does the distance traveled equal 2500 m?

11. **An exponential bike ride** Tom and Sue took a bike ride, both starting at the same time and position. Tom started riding at 20 mi/hr, and his velocity decreased according to the function $v(t) = 20e^{-2t}$ for $t \ge 0$. Sue started riding at 15 mi/hr, and her velocity decreased according to the function $u(t) = 15e^{-t}$ for $t \ge 0$.

    a. Find and graph the position functions of Tom and Sue.

    b. Find the times at which the riders had the same position at the same time.

    c. Who ultimately took the lead and remained in the lead?

T **12–19. Areas of regions** *Use any method to find the area of the region described.*

12. The region in the first quadrant bounded by $y = x^p$ and $y = \sqrt[p]{x}$, where $p = 100$ and $p = 1000$

13. The region in the first quadrant bounded by $y = 4x$ and $y = x\sqrt{25 - x^2}$

14. The regions R_1 and R_2 (separately) shown in the figure, which are formed by the graphs of $y = 16 - x^2$ and $y = 5x - 8$

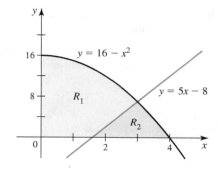

15. The regions R_1, R_2, and R_3 (separately) shown in the figure, which are formed by the graphs of $y = 2\sqrt{x}$, $y = 3 - x$, and $y = x(x - 3)$ (First find the intersection points by inspection.)

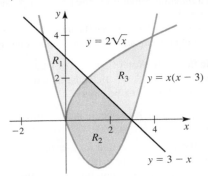

16. The region between $y = \sin x$ and $y = x$ on the interval $[0, 2\pi]$

17. The region bounded by $y = x^2$, $y = 2x^2 - 4x$, and $y = 0$

18. The region in the first quadrant bounded by the curve $\sqrt{x} + \sqrt{y} = 1$

19. The region in the first quadrant bounded by $y = x/6$ and $y = 1 - |x/2 - 1|$

20. An area function Let $R(x)$ be the area of the shaded region between the graphs of $y = f(t)$ and $y = g(t)$ on the interval $[a, x]$ (see figure).

   a. Sketch a plausible graph of R, for $a \le x \le c$.
   b. Give expressions for $R(x)$ and $R'(x)$, for $a \le x \le c$.

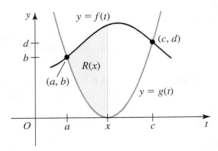

21. An area function Consider the functions $y = \dfrac{x^2}{a}$ and $y = \sqrt{\dfrac{x}{a}}$, where $a > 0$. Find $A(a)$, the area of the region between the curves.

22. Two methods The region R in the first quadrant bounded by the parabola $y = 4 - x^2$ and the coordinate axes is revolved about the y-axis to produce a dome-shaped solid. Find the volume of the solid in the following ways.

   a. Apply the disk method and integrate with respect to y.
   b. Apply the shell method and integrate with respect to x.

23–35. Volumes of solids *Choose the general slicing method, the disk/washer method, or the shell method to answer the following questions.*

23. What is the volume of the solid whose base is the region in the first quadrant bounded by $y = \sqrt{x}$, $y = 2 - x$, and the x-axis, and whose cross sections perpendicular to the base and parallel to the y-axis are squares?

24. What is the volume of the solid whose base is the region in the first quadrant bounded by $y = \sqrt{x}$, $y = 2 - x$, and the x-axis, and whose cross sections perpendicular to the base and parallel to the y-axis are semicircles?

25. What is the volume of the solid whose base is the region in the first quadrant bounded by $y = \sqrt{x}$, $y = 2 - x$, and the y-axis, and whose cross sections perpendicular to the base and parallel to the x-axis are square?

26. The region bounded by the curves $y = -x^2 + 2x + 2$ and $y = 2x^2 - 4x + 2$ is revolved about the x-axis. What is the volume of the solid that is generated?

27. The region bounded by the curves $y = 1 + \sqrt{x}$, $y = 1 - \sqrt{x}$, and the line $x = 1$ is revolved about the y-axis. Find the volume of the resulting solid by (a) integrating with respect to x and (b) integrating with respect to y. Be sure your answers agree.

28. The region bounded by the curves $y = 2e^{-x}$, $y = e^x$, and the y-axis is revolved about the x-axis. What is the volume of the solid that is generated?

29. The region bounded by the graphs of $x = 0$, $x = \sqrt{\ln y}$, and $x = \sqrt{2 - \ln y}$ in the first quadrant is revolved about the y-axis. What is the volume of the resulting solid?

30. The region bounded by the curves $y = \sec x$ and $y = 2$, for $0 \le x \le \frac{\pi}{3}$, is revolved around the x-axis. What is the volume of the solid that is generated?

31. The region bounded by $y = (1 - x^2)^{-1/2}$ and the x-axis over the interval $[0, \sqrt{3}/2]$ is revolved around the y-axis. What is the volume of the solid that is generated?

32. The region bounded by the graph of $y = 4 - x^2$ and the x-axis on the interval $[-2, 2]$ is revolved about the line $x = -2$. What is the volume of the solid that is generated?

33. The region bounded by the graphs of $y = (x - 2)^2$ and $y = 4$ is revolved about the line $y = 4$. What is the volume of the resulting solid?

34. The region bounded by the graphs of $y = 6x$ and $y = x^2 + 5$ is revolved about the line $y = -1$ and the line $x = -1$. Find the volumes of the resulting solids. Which one is greater?

35. The region bounded by the graphs of $y = 2x$, $y = 6 - x$, and $y = 0$ is revolved about the line $y = -2$ and the line $x = -2$. Find the volumes of the resulting solids. Which one is greater?

36. Area and volume The region R is bounded by the curves $x = y^2 + 2$, $y = x - 4$, and $y = 0$ (see figure).

   a. Write a single integral that gives the area of R.
   b. Write a single integral that gives the volume of the solid generated when R is revolved about the x-axis.
   c. Write a single integral that gives the volume of the solid generated when R is revolved about the y-axis.
   d. Suppose S is a solid whose base is R and whose cross sections perpendicular to R and parallel to the x-axis are semicircles. Write a single integral that gives the volume of S.

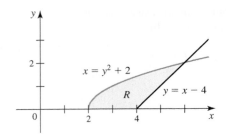

37. Comparing volumes Let R be the region bounded by $y = 1/x^p$ and the x-axis on the interval $[1, a]$, where $p > 0$ and $a > 1$ (see figure). Let V_x and V_y be the volumes of the solids generated when R is revolved about the x- and y-axes, respectively.

a. With $a = 2$ and $p = 1$, which is greater, V_x or V_y?
b. With $a = 4$ and $p = 3$, which is greater, V_x or V_y?
c. Find a general expression for V_x in terms of a and p. Note that $p = \frac{1}{2}$ is a special case. What is V_x when $p = \frac{1}{2}$?
d. Find a general expression for V_y in terms of a and p. Note that $p = 2$ is a special case. What is V_y when $p = 2$?
e. Explain how parts (c) and (d) demonstrate that

$$\lim_{h \to 0} \frac{a^h - 1}{h} = \ln a.$$

f. Find any values of a and p for which $V_x > V_y$.

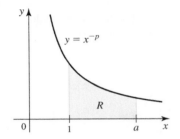

38. Multiple regions Determine the area of the region bounded by the curves $x = y^2$ and $x = (2 - y^2)^2$ (see figure).

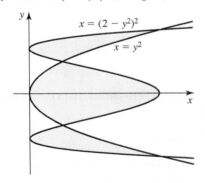

39. Comparing volumes Let R be the region bounded by the graph of $f(x) = cx(1 - x)$ and the x-axis on $[0, 1]$. Find the positive value of c such that the volume of the solid generated by revolving R about the x-axis equals the volume of the solid generated by revolving R about the y-axis.

40–45. Arc length *Find the length of the following curves.*

40. $y = 2x + 4$ on the interval $[-2, 2]$ (Use calculus.)

41. $y = \cosh^{-1} x$ on the interval $[\sqrt{2}, \sqrt{5}]$

42. $y = x^3/6 + 1/(2x)$ on the interval $[1, 2]$

43. $y = x^{1/2} - x^{3/2}/3$ on the interval $[1, 3]$

⊤ 44. $y = x^3/3 + x^2 + x + 1/(4x + 4)$ on the interval $[0, 4]$

⊤ 45. $y = \ln x$ between $x = 1$ and $x = b > 1$ given that

$$\int \frac{\sqrt{x^2 + a^2}}{x} \, dx = \sqrt{x^2 + a^2} - a \ln\left(\frac{a + \sqrt{x^2 + a^2}}{x}\right) + C.$$

Use any means to approximate the value of b for which the curve has length 2.

46. Surface area and volume Let $f(x) = \frac{1}{3}x^3$ and let R be the region bounded by the graph of f and the x-axis on the interval $[0, 2]$.

a. Find the area of the surface generated when the graph of f on $[0, 2]$ is revolved about the x-axis.
b. Find the volume of the solid generated when R is revolved about the y-axis.
c. Find the volume of the solid generated when R is revolved about the x-axis.

47. Surface area and volume Let $f(x) = \sqrt{3x - x^2}$ and let R be the region bounded by the graph of f and the x-axis on the interval $[0, 3]$.

a. Find the area of the surface generated when the graph of f on $[0, 3]$ is revolved about the x-axis.
b. Find the volume of the solid generated when R is revolved about the x-axis.

48. Surface area of a cone Find the surface area of a cone (excluding the base) with radius 4 and height 8 using integration and a surface area integral.

49. Surface area and more Let $f(x) = \dfrac{x^4}{2} + \dfrac{1}{16x^2}$ and let R be the region bounded by the graph of f and the x-axis on the interval $[1, 2]$.

a. Find the area of the surface generated when the graph of f on $[1, 2]$ is revolved about the x-axis.
b. Find the length of the curve $y = f(x)$ on $[1, 2]$.
c. Find the volume of the solid generated when R is revolved about the y-axis.
d. Find the volume of the solid generated when R is revolved about the x-axis.

50–52. Variable density in one dimension *Find the mass of the following thin bars.*

50. A bar on the interval $0 \le x \le 9$ with a density (in g/cm) given by $\rho(x) = 3 + 2\sqrt{x}$

51. A 3-m bar with a density (in g/m) of $\rho(x) = 150e^{-x/3}$, for $0 \le x \le 3$

52. A bar on the interval $0 \le x \le 6$ with a density

$$\rho(x) = \begin{cases} 1 & \text{if } 0 \le x < 2 \\ 2 & \text{if } 2 \le x < 4 \\ 4 & \text{if } 4 \le x \le 6. \end{cases}$$

53. Spring work

a. It takes 50 J of work to stretch a spring 0.2 m from its equilibrium position. How much work is needed to stretch it an additional 0.5 m?
b. It takes 50 N of force to stretch a spring 0.2 m from its equilibrium position. How much work is needed to stretch it an additional 0.5 m?

54. Pumping water A cylindrical water tank has a height of 6 m and a radius of 4 m. How much work is required to empty the full tank by pumping the water to an outflow pipe at the top of the tank?

55. Force on a dam Find the total force on the face of a semicircular dam with a radius of 20 m when its reservoir is full of water. The diameter of the semicircle is the top of the dam.

56–63. Integrals *Evaluate the following integrals.*

56. $\displaystyle\int \frac{e^x}{4e^x + 6}\,dx$

57. $\displaystyle\int_{e^2}^{e^8} \frac{dx}{x \ln x}$

58. $\displaystyle\int_1^4 \frac{10^{\sqrt{x}}}{\sqrt{x}}\,dx$

59. $\displaystyle\int \frac{x + 4}{x^2 + 8x + 25}\,dx$

60. $\displaystyle\int_{\ln 2}^{\ln 3} \coth s\,ds$

61. $\displaystyle\int \frac{dx}{\sqrt{x^2 - 9}},\ x > 3$

62. $\displaystyle\int \frac{e^x}{\sqrt{e^{2x} + 4}}\,dx$

63. $\displaystyle\int_0^1 \frac{x^2}{9 - x^6}\,dx$

64. Radioactive decay The mass of radioactive material in a sample has decreased by 30% since the decay began. Assuming a half-life of 1500 years, how long ago did the decay begin?

65. Population growth Growing from an initial population of 150,000 at a constant annual growth rate of 4%/yr, how long will it take a city to reach a population of 1 million?

66. Savings account A savings account advertises an annual percentage yield (APY) of 5.4%, which means that the balance in the account increases at an annual growth rate of 5.4%/yr.

   a. Find the balance in the account for $t \geq 0$ with an initial deposit of \$1500, assuming the APY remains fixed and no additional deposits or withdrawals are made.

   b. What is the doubling time of the balance?

   c. After how many years does the balance reach \$5000?

67–68. Curve sketching *Use the graphing techniques of Section 4.3 to graph the following functions on their domains. Identify local extreme points, inflection points, concavity, and end behavior. Use a graphing utility only to check your work.*

67. $f(x) = e^x(x^2 - x)$

68. $f(x) = \ln x - \ln^2 x$

T **69. Log-normal probability distribution** A commonly used distribution in probability and statistics is the log-normal distribution. (If the logarithm of a variable has a normal distribution, then the variable itself has a log-normal distribution.) The distribution function is

$$f(x) = \frac{1}{x\sigma\sqrt{2\pi}}\, e^{-\ln^2 x/(2\sigma^2)}, \quad \text{for } x > 0,$$

where $\ln x$ has zero mean and standard deviation $\sigma > 0$.

   a. Graph f for $\sigma = \frac{1}{2}$, 1, and 2. Based on your graphs, does $\displaystyle\lim_{x\to 0^+} f(x)$ appear to exist?

   b. Evaluate $\displaystyle\lim_{x\to 0^+} f(x)$. (*Hint:* Let $x = e^y$.)

   c. Show that f has a single local maximum at $x^* = e^{-\sigma^2}$.

   d. Evaluate $f(x^*)$ and express the result as a function of σ.

   e. For what value of $\sigma > 0$ in part (d) does $f(x^*)$ have a minimum?

70. Equal area property for parabolas Let $f(x) = ax^2 + bx + c$ be an arbitrary quadratic function and choose two points $x = p$ and $x = q$. Let L_1 be the line tangent to the graph of f at the point $(p, f(p))$ and let L_2 be the line tangent to the graph at the point $(q, f(q))$. Let $x = s$ be the vertical line through the intersection point of L_1 and L_2. Finally, let R_1 be the region bounded by $y = f(x)$, L_1, and the vertical line $x = s$, and let R_2 be the region bounded by $y = f(x)$, L_2, and the vertical line $x = s$. Prove that the area of R_1 equals the area of R_2.

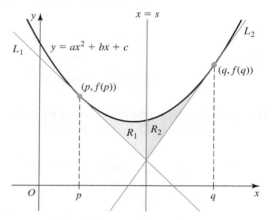

71. Derivatives of hyperbolic functions Compute the following derivatives.

   a. $d^6/dx^6(\cosh x)$

   b. $d/dx(x \operatorname{sech} x)$

72. Area of region Find the area of the region bounded by the curves $f(x) = 8\operatorname{sech}^2 x$ and $g(x) = \cosh x$.

73. Linear approximation Find the linear approximation to $f(x) = \cosh x$ at $a = \ln 3$ and then use it to approximate the value of $\cosh 1$.

74. Limit Evaluate $\displaystyle\lim_{x\to\infty} (\tanh x)^x$.

Chapter 6 Guided Projects

Applications of the material in this chapter and related topics can be found in the following Guided Projects. For additional information, see the Preface.

- Means and tangent lines
- Landing an airliner
- Geometric probability
- Mathematics of the CD player
- Designing a water clock
- Buoyancy and Archimedes' principle
- Dipstick problems
- Hyperbolic functions
- Optimizing fuel use
- Inverse sine from geometry

7

Integration Techniques

Chapter Preview In this chapter, we return to integration methods and present a variety of new strategies that supplement the substitution (or change of variables) method. The new techniques introduced here are integration by parts, trigonometric substitution, and partial fractions. Taken altogether, these *analytical methods* (pencil-and-paper methods) greatly enlarge the collection of integrals that we can evaluate. Nevertheless, it is important to recognize that these methods are limited because many integrals do not yield to them. For this reason, we also introduce table-based methods, which are used to evaluate many indefinite integrals, and computer-based methods for approximating definite integrals. The discussion then turns to integrals that have either infinite integrands or infinite intervals of integration. These integrals, called *improper integrals*, offer surprising results and have many practical applications. The chapter closes with an introductory survey of differential equations, a vast topic that has a central place in both the theory and applications of mathematics.

7.1 Basic Approaches

Before plunging into new integration techniques, we devote this section to two practical goals. The first is to review what you learned about the substitution method in Section 5.5. The other is to introduce several basic simplifying procedures that are worth keeping in mind for any integral that you might be working on. Table 7.1 will remind you of some frequently used indefinite integrals.

Table 7.1 Basic Integration Formulas

▶ Table 7.1 is similar to Tables 4.9 and 4.10 in Section 4.9. It is a subset of the table of integrals at the back of the book.

1. $\displaystyle\int k\, dx = kx + C, k \text{ real}$

2. $\displaystyle\int x^p\, dx = \frac{x^{p+1}}{p+1} + C, \, p \neq -1 \text{ real}$

3. $\displaystyle\int \cos ax\, dx = \frac{1}{a}\sin ax + C$

4. $\displaystyle\int \sin ax\, dx = -\frac{1}{a}\cos ax + C$

5. $\displaystyle\int \sec^2 ax\, dx = \frac{1}{a}\tan ax + C$

6. $\displaystyle\int \csc^2 ax\, dx = -\frac{1}{a}\cot ax + C$

7. $\displaystyle\int \sec ax \tan ax\, dx = \frac{1}{a}\sec ax + C$

8. $\displaystyle\int \csc ax \cot ax\, dx = -\frac{1}{a}\csc ax + C$

9. $\displaystyle\int e^{ax}\, dx = \frac{1}{a}e^{ax} + C$

10. $\displaystyle\int \frac{dx}{x} = \ln|x| + C$

11. $\displaystyle\int \frac{dx}{\sqrt{a^2 - x^2}} = \sin^{-1}\frac{x}{a} + C$

12. $\displaystyle\int \frac{dx}{a^2 + x^2} = \frac{1}{a}\tan^{-1}\frac{x}{a} + C$

13. $\displaystyle\int \frac{dx}{x\sqrt{x^2 - a^2}} = \frac{1}{a}\sec^{-1}\left|\frac{x}{a}\right| + C, a > 0$

> A common choice for a change of variables is a linear term of the form $ax + b$.

EXAMPLE 1 Substitution review Evaluate $\displaystyle\int_{-1}^{2} \frac{dx}{3 + 2x}$.

SOLUTION The expression $3 + 2x$ suggests the change of variables $u = 3 + 2x$, which implies that $du = 2\,dx$. Note that when $x = -1$, $u = 1$, and when $x = 2$, $u = 7$. The substitution may now be done:

$$\int_{-1}^{2} \frac{dx}{3 + 2x} = \int_{1}^{7} \frac{1}{u} \underbrace{\frac{du}{2}}_{dx} = \frac{1}{2} \ln |u| \, \Big|_{1}^{7} = \frac{1}{2} \ln 7.$$

Related Exercises 7–14 ◄

QUICK CHECK 1 What change of variable would you use for the integral $\int (6 + 5x)^8 \, dx$? ◄

> Example 2 shows the useful technique of multiplying the integrand by 1. In this case, $1 = \dfrac{e^x}{e^x}$. The idea is used again in Example 6.

EXAMPLE 2 Subtle substitution Evaluate $\displaystyle\int \frac{dx}{e^x + e^{-x}}$.

SOLUTION In this case, we see nothing in Table 7.1 that resembles the given integral. In a spirit of trial and error, we multiply numerator and denominator of the integrand by e^x:

$$\int \frac{dx}{e^x + e^{-x}} = \int \frac{e^x}{e^{2x} + 1} \, dx. \qquad e^x \cdot e^x = e^{2x}$$

This form of the integrand suggests the substitution $u = e^x$, which implies that $du = e^x \, dx$. Making these substitutions, the integral becomes

$$\int \frac{e^x}{e^{2x} + 1} \, dx = \int \frac{du}{u^2 + 1} \qquad \text{Substitute } u = e^x, \, du = e^x \, dx.$$

$$= \tan^{-1} u + C \qquad \text{Table 7.1}$$

$$= \tan^{-1} e^x + C. \qquad u = e^x$$

Related Exercises 15–22 ◄

EXAMPLE 3 Split up fractions Evaluate $\displaystyle\int \frac{\cos x + \sin^3 x}{\sec x} \, dx$.

SOLUTION Don't overlook the opportunity to split a fraction into two or more fractions. In this case, the integrand is simplified in a useful way:

$$\int \frac{\cos x + \sin^3 x}{\sec x} \, dx = \int \frac{\cos x}{\sec x} \, dx + \int \frac{\sin^3 x}{\sec x} \, dx \qquad \text{Split fraction.}$$

$$= \int \cos^2 x \, dx + \int \sin^3 x \cos x \, dx. \qquad \sec x = \frac{1}{\cos x}$$

> Half-angle formulas
> $$\cos^2 x = \frac{1 + \cos 2x}{2}$$
> $$\sin^2 x = \frac{1 - \cos 2x}{2}$$

The first of the resulting integrals is evaluated using a half-angle formula (Example 6 of Section 5.5). In the second integral, the substitution $u = \sin x$ is used:

$$\int \frac{\cos x + \sin^3 x}{\sec x} \, dx = \int \cos^2 x \, dx + \int \sin^3 x \cos x \, dx$$

$$= \int \frac{1 + \cos 2x}{2} \, dx + \int \sin^3 x \cos x \, dx \qquad \text{Half-angle formula}$$

$$= \frac{1}{2} \int dx + \frac{1}{2} \int \cos 2x \, dx + \int u^3 \, du \qquad u = \sin x, \, du = \cos x \, dx$$

$$= \frac{x}{2} + \frac{1}{4} \sin 2x + \frac{1}{4} \sin^4 x + C. \qquad \text{Evaluate integrals.}$$

Related Exercises 23–28 ◄

QUICK CHECK 2 Explain how to simplify the integrand of $\int \dfrac{x^3 + \sqrt{x}}{x^{3/2}}\, dx$ before integrating. ◄

EXAMPLE 4 **Division with rational functions** Evaluate $\int \dfrac{x^2 + 2x - 1}{x + 4}\, dx.$

SOLUTION When integrating rational functions (polynomials in the numerator and denominator), check to see whether the function is *improper* (the degree of the numerator is greater than or equal to the degree of the denominator). In this example, we have an improper rational function, and long division is used to simplify it. The integration is done as follows:

$$\int \frac{x^2 + 2x - 1}{x + 4}\, dx = \int (x - 2)\, dx + \int \frac{7}{x + 4}\, dx \quad \text{Long division}$$

$$= \frac{x^2}{2} - 2x + 7 \ln |x + 4| + C. \quad \text{Evaluate integrals.}$$

Related Exercises 29–32 ◄

$$
\begin{array}{r}
x - 2 \\
x + 4 \overline{)\,x^2 + 2x - 1} \\
\underline{x^2 + 4x} \\
-2x - 1 \\
\underline{-2x - 8} \\
7
\end{array}
$$

QUICK CHECK 3 Explain how to simplify the integrand of $\int \dfrac{x + 1}{x - 1}\, dx$ before integrating. ◄

EXAMPLE 5 **Complete the square** Evaluate $\displaystyle\int \frac{dx}{\sqrt{-x^2 - 8x - 7}}.$

SOLUTION We don't see an integral in Table 7.1 that looks like the given integral, so some preliminary work is needed. In this case, the key is to complete the square on the polynomial in the denominator. We find that

$$
\begin{aligned}
-x^2 - 8x - 7 &= -(x^2 + 8x + 7) \\
&= -(x^2 + \underbrace{8x + 16 - 16}_{\text{add and subtract 16}} + 7) \quad \text{Complete the square.} \\
&= -((x + 4)^2 - 9) \quad\quad\quad\ \text{Factor and combine terms.} \\
&= 9 - (x + 4)^2. \quad\quad\quad\quad\ \text{Rearrange terms.}
\end{aligned}
$$

After a change of variables, the integral is recognizable:

$$
\begin{aligned}
\int \frac{dx}{\sqrt{-7 - 8x - x^2}} &= \int \frac{dx}{\sqrt{9 - (x + 4)^2}} \quad \text{Complete the square.} \\
&= \int \frac{du}{\sqrt{9 - u^2}} \quad\quad\quad u = x + 4,\, du = dx \\
&= \sin^{-1} \frac{u}{3} + C \quad\quad\quad \text{Table 7.1} \\
&= \sin^{-1}\!\left(\frac{x + 4}{3}\right) + C. \quad \text{Replace } u \text{ with } x + 4.
\end{aligned}
$$

Related Exercises 33–36 ◄

QUICK CHECK 4 Express $x^2 + 6x + 16$ in terms of a perfect square. ◄

EXAMPLE 6 **Multiply by 1** Evaluate $\displaystyle\int \frac{dx}{1 + \cos x}.$

SOLUTION The key to evaluating this integral is admittedly not obvious, and the trick works only on special integrals. The idea is to multiply the integrand by 1, but the challenge is finding the appropriate representation of 1. In this case, we use

$$1 = \frac{1 - \cos x}{1 - \cos x}.$$

The integral is evaluated as follows:

$$\int \frac{dx}{1 + \cos x} = \int \frac{1}{1 + \cos x} \cdot \frac{1 - \cos x}{1 - \cos x}\, dx \qquad \text{Multiply by 1.}$$

$$= \int \frac{1 - \cos x}{1 - \cos^2 x}\, dx \qquad \text{Simplify.}$$

$$= \int \frac{1 - \cos x}{\sin^2 x}\, dx \qquad 1 - \cos^2 x = \sin^2 x$$

$$= \int \frac{1}{\sin^2 x}\, dx - \int \frac{\cos x}{\sin^2 x}\, dx \qquad \text{Split up the fraction.}$$

$$= \int \csc^2 x\, dx - \int \csc x \cot x\, dx \qquad \csc x = \frac{1}{\sin x}, \cot x = \frac{\cos x}{\sin x}$$

$$= -\cot x + \csc x + C. \qquad \text{Integrate using Table 7.1.}$$

Related Exercises 37–40 ◄

The techniques illustrated in this section are designed to transform or simplify an integrand before you apply a specific method. In fact, these ideas may help you recognize the best method to use. Keep them in mind as you learn new integration methods and improve your integration skills.

SECTION 7.1 EXERCISES

Review Questions

1. What change of variables would you use for the integral $\int (4 - 7x)^{-6}\, dx$?

2. Before integrating, how would you rewrite the integrand of $\int (x^4 + 2)^2\, dx$?

3. What trigonometric identity is useful in evaluating $\int \sin^2 x\, dx$?

4. Describe a first step in integrating $\int \frac{x^3 - 2x + 4}{x - 1}\, dx$.

5. Describe a first step in integrating $\int \frac{10}{x^2 - 4x + 5}\, dx$.

6. Describe a first step in integrating $\int \frac{x^{10} - 2x^4 + 10x^2 + 1}{3x^3}\, dx$.

Basic Skills

7–14. Substitution Review *Evaluate the following integrals.*

7. $\int \frac{dx}{(3 - 5x)^4}$

8. $\int (9x - 2)^{-3}\, dx$

9. $\int_0^{3\pi/8} \sin\left(2x - \frac{\pi}{4}\right) dx$

10. $\int e^{3 - 4x}\, dx$

11. $\int \frac{\ln 2x}{x}\, dx$

12. $\int_{-5}^0 \frac{dx}{\sqrt{4 - x}}$

13. $\int \frac{e^x}{e^x + 1}\, dx$

14. $\int \frac{e^{2\sqrt{y}+1}}{\sqrt{y}}\, dy$

15–22. Subtle substitutions *Evaluate the following integrals.*

15. $\int \frac{e^x}{e^x - 2e^{-x}}\, dx$

16. $\int \frac{e^{2z}}{e^{2z} - 4e^{-z}}\, dz$

17. $\int_1^{e^2} \frac{\ln^2(x^2)}{x}\, dx$

18. $\int \frac{\sin^3 x}{\cos^5 x}\, dx$

19. $\int \frac{\cos^4 x}{\sin^6 x}\, dx$

20. $\int_0^2 \frac{x(3x + 2)}{\sqrt{x^3 + x^2 + 4}}\, dx$

21. $\int \frac{dx}{x^{-1} + 1}$

22. $\int \frac{dy}{y^{-1} + y^{-3}}$

23–28. Splitting fractions *Evaluate the following integrals.*

23. $\int \frac{x + 2}{x^2 + 4}\, dx$

24. $\int_4^9 \frac{x^{5/2} - x^{1/2}}{x^{3/2}}\, dx$

25. $\int \frac{\sin t + \tan t}{\cos^2 t}\, dt$

26. $\int \frac{4 + e^{-2x}}{e^{3x}}\, dx$

27. $\int \frac{2 - 3x}{\sqrt{1 - x^2}}\, dx$

28. $\int \frac{3x + 1}{\sqrt{4 - x^2}}\, dx$

29–32. Division with rational functions *Evaluate the following integrals.*

29. $\int \frac{x + 2}{x + 4}\, dx$

30. $\int_2^4 \frac{x^2 + 2}{x - 1}\, dx$

31. $\int \frac{t^3 - 2}{t + 1}\, dt$

32. $\int \frac{6 - x^4}{x^2 + 4}\, dx$

33–36. Completing the square *Evaluate the following integrals.*

33. $\displaystyle\int \frac{dx}{x^2 - 2x + 10}$

34. $\displaystyle\int_0^2 \frac{x}{x^2 + 4x + 8}\, dx$

35. $\displaystyle\int \frac{d\theta}{\sqrt{27 - 6\theta - \theta^2}}$

36. $\displaystyle\int \frac{x}{x^4 + 2x^2 + 1}\, dx$

37–40. Multiply by 1 *Evaluate the following integrals.*

37. $\displaystyle\int \frac{d\theta}{1 + \sin\theta}$

38. $\displaystyle\int \frac{1 - x}{1 - \sqrt{x}}\, dx$

39. $\displaystyle\int \frac{dx}{\sec x - 1}$

40. $\displaystyle\int \frac{d\theta}{1 - \csc\theta}$

Further Explorations

41. Explain why or why not Determine whether the following statements are true and give an explanation or counterexample.

   a. $\displaystyle\int \frac{3}{x^2 + 4}\, dx = \int \frac{3}{x^2}\, dx + \int \frac{3}{4}\, dx.$

   b. Long division simplifies the evaluation of the integral
$\displaystyle\int \frac{x^3 + 2}{3x^4 + x}\, dx.$

   c. $\displaystyle\int \frac{dx}{\sin x + 1} = \ln|\sin x + 1| + C.$

   d. $\displaystyle\int \frac{dx}{e^x} = \ln e^x + C.$

42–54. Miscellaneous integrals *Use the approaches discussed in this section to evaluate the following integrals.*

42. $\displaystyle\int_4^9 \frac{dx}{1 - \sqrt{x}}$

43. $\displaystyle\int_{-1}^0 \frac{x}{x^2 + 2x + 2}\, dx$

44. $\displaystyle\int_0^1 \sqrt{1 + \sqrt{x}}\, dx$

45. $\displaystyle\int \sin x \sin 2x\, dx$

46. $\displaystyle\int_0^{\pi/2} \sqrt{1 + \cos 2x}\, dx$

47. $\displaystyle\int \frac{dx}{x^{1/2} + x^{3/2}}$

48. $\displaystyle\int_0^1 \frac{dp}{4 - \sqrt{p}}$

49. $\displaystyle\int \frac{x - 2}{x^2 + 6x + 13}\, dx$

50. $\displaystyle\int_0^{\pi/4} 3\sqrt{1 + \sin 2x}\, dx$

51. $\displaystyle\int \frac{e^x}{e^{2x} + 2e^x + 1}\, dx$

52. $\displaystyle\int_0^{\pi/8} \sqrt{1 - \cos 4x}\, dx$

53. $\displaystyle\int_1^3 \frac{2}{x^2 + 2x + 1}\, dx$

54. $\displaystyle\int_0^2 \frac{2}{s^3 + 3s^2 + 3s + 1}\, ds$

55. Different substitutions

   a. Evaluate $\int \tan x \sec^2 x\, dx$ using the substitution $u = \tan x$.

   b. Evaluate $\int \tan x \sec^2 x\, dx$ using the substitution $u = \sec x$.

   c. Reconcile the results in parts (a) and (b).

56. Different methods

   a. Evaluate $\int \cot x \csc^2 x\, dx$ using the substitution $u = \cot x$.

   b. Evaluate $\int \cot x \csc^2 x\, dx$ using the substitution $u = \csc x$.

   c. Reconcile the results in parts (a) and (b).

57. Different methods

   a. Evaluate $\displaystyle\int \frac{x^2}{x + 1}\, dx$ using the substitution $u = x + 1$.

   b. Evaluate $\displaystyle\int \frac{x^2}{x + 1}\, dx$ after first performing long division on the integrand.

   c. Reconcile the results in parts (a) and (b).

58. Different substitutions

   a. Show that $\displaystyle\int \frac{dx}{\sqrt{x - x^2}} = \sin^{-1}(2x - 1) + C$ using either $u = 2x - 1$ or $u = x - \frac{1}{2}$.

   b. Show that $\displaystyle\int \frac{dx}{\sqrt{x - x^2}} = 2\sin^{-1}\sqrt{x} + C$ using $u = \sqrt{x}$.

   c. Prove the identity $2\sin^{-1}\sqrt{x} - \sin^{-1}(2x - 1) = \dfrac{\pi}{2}$.

(Source: The College Mathematics Journal 32, 5, Nov 2001)

Applications

59. Area of a region between curves Find the area of the region bounded by the curves $y = \dfrac{x^2}{x^3 - 3x}$ and $y = \dfrac{1}{x^3 - 3x}$ on the interval $[2, 4]$.

60. Area of a region between curves Find the area of the entire region bounded by the curves $y = \dfrac{x^3}{x^2 + 1}$ and $y = \dfrac{8x}{x^2 + 1}$.

61. Volumes of solids Consider the region R bounded by the graph of $f(x) = \sqrt{x^2 + 1}$ and the x-axis on the interval $[0, 2]$.

   a. Find the volume of the solid formed when R is revolved about the x-axis.

   b. Find the volume of the solid formed when R is revolved about the y-axis.

62. Volumes of solids Consider the region R bounded by the graph of $f(x) = \dfrac{1}{x + 2}$ and the x-axis on the interval $[0, 3]$.

   a. Find the volume of the solid formed when R is revolved about the x-axis.

   b. Find the volume of the solid formed when R is revolved about the y-axis.

63. Arc length Find the length of the curve $y = x^{5/4}$ on the interval $[0, 1]$. (*Hint:* Write the arc length integral and let $u^2 = 1 + \left(\frac{5}{4}\right)^2 \sqrt{x}$.)

64. Surface area Find the area of the surface generated when the region bounded by the graph of $y = e^x + \frac{1}{4}e^{-x}$ on the interval $[0, \ln 2]$ is revolved about the x-axis.

65. Surface area Let $f(x) = \sqrt{x} + 1$. Find the area of the surface generated when the region bounded by the graph of f on the interval $[0, 1]$ is revolved about the x-axis.

66. Skydiving A skydiver in free fall subject to gravitational acceleration and air resistance has a velocity given by

$$v(t) = v_T\left(\frac{e^{at} - 1}{e^{at} + 1}\right),$$ where v_T is the terminal velocity and $a > 0$

is a physical constant. Find the distance that the skydiver falls after t seconds, which is $d(t) = \displaystyle\int_0^t v(y)\, dy$.

QUICK CHECK ANSWERS

1. Let $u = 6 + 5x$. **2.** Write the integrand as $x^{3/2} + x^{-1}$.

3. Use long division to write the integrand as $1 + \dfrac{2}{x - 1}$.

4. $(x + 3)^2 + 7$ ◄

7.2 Integration by Parts

The Substitution Rule (Section 5.5) arises when we reverse the Chain Rule for derivatives. In this section, we employ a similar strategy and reverse the Product Rule for derivatives. The result is an integration technique called *integration by parts*. To illustrate the importance of integration by parts, consider the indefinite integrals

$$\int e^x\, dx = e^x + C \quad \text{and} \quad \int xe^x\, dx = ?$$

The first integral is an elementary integral that we have already encountered. The second integral is only slightly different—and yet, the appearance of the product xe^x in the integrand makes this integral (at the moment) impossible to evaluate. Integration by parts is ideally suited for evaluating integrals of *products* of functions.

Integration by Parts for Indefinite Integrals

Given two differentiable functions u and v, the Product Rule states that

$$\frac{d}{dx}(u(x)v(x)) = u'(x)v(x) + u(x)v'(x).$$

By integrating both sides, we can write this rule in terms of an indefinite integral:

$$u(x)v(x) = \int (u'(x)v(x) + u(x)v'(x))\, dx.$$

Rearranging this expression in the form

$$\int u(x)\underbrace{v'(x)\, dx}_{dv} = u(x)v(x) - \int v(x)\underbrace{u'(x)\, dx}_{du}$$

leads to the basic relationship for *integration by parts*. It is expressed compactly by noting that $du = u'(x)\, dx$ and $dv = v'(x)\, dx$. Suppressing the independent variable x, we have

$$\int u\, dv = uv - \int v\, du.$$

The integral $\int u\, dv$ is viewed as the given integral, and we use integration by parts to express it in terms of a new integral $\int v\, du$. The technique is successful if the new integral can be evaluated.

> **Integration by Parts**
>
> Suppose that u and v are differentiable functions. Then
>
> $$\int u\, dv = uv - \int v\, du.$$

> ▶ The integration by parts calculation may be done without including the constant of integration—as long as it is included in the final result.

EXAMPLE 1 Integration by parts Evaluate $\int xe^x \, dx$.

SOLUTION The presence of *products* in the integrand often suggests integration by parts. We split the product xe^x into two factors, one of which must be identified as u and the other as dv (the latter always includes the differential dx). Powers of x are *often* good choices for u. The choice for dv should be easy to integrate. In this case, the choices $u = x$ and $dv = e^x \, dx$ are advisable. It follows that $du = dx$. The relationship $dv = e^x \, dx$ means that v is an antiderivative of e^x, which implies $v = e^x$. A table is helpful for organizing these calculations.

> ▶ The arrows in the table show how to combine factors in the integration by parts formula. The first arrow indicates the product uv; the second arrow indicates the integrand $v \, du$.

Functions in original integral	$u = x$	$dv = e^x \, dx$
Functions in new integral	$du = dx$	$v = e^x$

The integration by parts rule is now applied:

$$\int \underbrace{x}_{u} \; \underbrace{e^x \, dx}_{dv} = \underbrace{x}_{u} \; \underbrace{e^x}_{v} - \int \underbrace{e^x}_{v} \; \underbrace{dx}_{du}.$$

The original integral $\int xe^x \, dx$ has been replaced with the integral of e^x, which is easier to evaluate: $\int e^x \, dx = e^x + C$. The entire procedure looks like this:

$$\int xe^x \, dx = xe^x - \int e^x \, dx \quad \text{Integration by parts}$$

$$= xe^x - e^x + C. \quad \text{Evaluate the new integral.}$$

Related Exercises 7–22 ◀

EXAMPLE 2 Integration by parts Evaluate $\int x \sin x \, dx$.

SOLUTION Remembering that powers of x are often a good choice for u, we form the following table.

> ▶ To make the table, first write the functions in the original integral:
>
> $u = \underline{\hspace{1cm}}, dv = \underline{\hspace{1cm}}.$
>
> Then find the functions in the new integral by differentiating u and integrating dv:
>
> $du = \underline{\hspace{1cm}}, v = \underline{\hspace{1cm}}.$

$u = x$	$dv = \sin x \, dx$
$du = dx$	$v = -\cos x$

Applying integration by parts, we have

$$\int \underbrace{x}_{u} \; \underbrace{\sin x \, dx}_{dv} = \underbrace{x}_{u} \; \underbrace{(-\cos x)}_{v} - \int \underbrace{(-\cos x)}_{v} \; \underbrace{dx}_{du} \quad \text{Integration by parts}$$

$$= -x \cos x + \sin x + C. \quad \text{Evaluate } \int \cos x \, dx = \sin x.$$

Related Exercises 7–22 ◀

QUICK CHECK 1 What are the best choices for u and dv in evaluating $\int x \cos x \, dx$? ◀

In general, integration by parts works when we can easily integrate the choice for dv and when the new integral is easier to evaluate than the original. Integration by parts is often used for integrals of the form $\int x^n f(x) \, dx$, where n is a positive integer. Such integrals generally require the repeated use of integration by parts, as shown in the following example.

EXAMPLE 3 Repeated use of integration by parts

a. Evaluate $\int x^2 e^x \, dx$.

b. How would you evaluate $\int x^n e^x \, dx$, where n is a positive integer?

SOLUTION

a. The factor x^2 is a good choice for u, leaving $dv = e^x \, dx$. We then have

$u = x^2$	$dv = e^x \, dx$
$du = 2x \, dx$	$v = e^x$

$$\int \underbrace{x^2}_{u} \; \underbrace{e^x \, dx}_{dv} = \underbrace{x^2}_{u} \; \underbrace{e^x}_{v} - \int \underbrace{e^x}_{v} \; \underbrace{2x \, dx}_{du}.$$

Notice that the new integral on the right side is simpler than the original integral because the power of x has been reduced by one. In fact, the new integral was evaluated in Example 1. Therefore, after using integration by parts twice, we have

$$\int x^2 e^x \, dx = x^2 e^x - 2 \int x e^x \, dx \qquad \text{Integration by parts}$$

$$= x^2 e^x - 2(x e^x - e^x) + C \quad \text{Result of Example 1}$$
$$= e^x (x^2 - 2x + 2) + C. \quad \text{Simplify.}$$

b. We now let $u = x^n$ and $dv = e^x \, dx$. The integration takes the form

$$\int x^n e^x \, dx = x^n e^x - n \int x^{n-1} e^x \, dx.$$

We see that integration by parts reduces the power of the variable in the integrand. The integral in part (a) with $n = 2$ requires two uses of integration by parts. You can probably anticipate that evaluating the integral $\int x^n e^x \, dx$ requires n applications of integration by parts to reach the integral $\int e^x \, dx$, which is easily evaluated.

Related Exercises 23–30 ◄

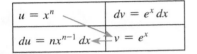

$$u = x^n \qquad dv = e^x \, dx$$
$$du = nx^{n-1} \, dx \qquad v = e^x$$

➤ An integral identity in which the power of a variable is reduced is called a **reduction formula**. Other examples of reduction formulas are explored in Exercises 44–47.

➤ In Example 4, we could also use $u = \sin x$ and $dv = e^{2x} \, dx$. In general, some trial and error may be required when using integration by parts. Effective choices come with practice.

EXAMPLE 4 Repeated use of integration by parts Evaluate $\int e^{2x} \sin x \, dx$.

SOLUTION The integrand consists of a product, which suggests integration by parts. In this case, there is no obvious choice for u and dv, so let's try the following choices.

$$u = e^{2x} \qquad dv = \sin x \, dx$$
$$du = 2e^{2x} \, dx \qquad v = -\cos x$$

The integral then becomes

$$\int e^{2x} \sin x \, dx = -e^{2x} \cos x + 2 \int e^{2x} \cos x \, dx. \qquad (1)$$

The original integral has been expressed in terms of a new integral, $\int e^{2x} \cos x \, dx$, which is no easier to evaluate than the original integral. It is tempting to start over with a new choice of u and dv, but a little persistence pays off. Suppose we evaluate $\int e^{2x} \cos x \, dx$ using integration by parts with the following choices.

➤ When using integration by parts, the acronym LIPET may help. If the integrand is the product of two or more functions, choose u to be the first function type that appears in the list

Logarithmic, **I**nverse trigonometric, **P**olynomial, **E**xponential, **T**rigonometric.

$$u = e^{2x} \qquad dv = \cos x \, dx$$
$$du = 2e^{2x} \, dx \qquad v = \sin x$$

Integrating by parts, we have

$$\int e^{2x} \cos x \, dx = e^{2x} \sin x - 2 \int e^{2x} \sin x \, dx. \qquad (2)$$

Now observe that equation (2) contains the original integral, $\int e^{2x} \sin x \, dx$. Substituting the result of equation (2) into equation (1), we find that

$$\int e^{2x} \sin x \, dx = -e^{2x} \cos x + 2 \int e^{2x} \cos x \, dx$$

➤ To solve for $\int e^{2x} \sin x \, dx$ in the equation $\int e^{2x} \sin x \, dx = -e^{2x} \cos x + 2e^{2x} \sin x - 4 \int e^{2x} \sin x \, dx$, add $4 \int e^{2x} \sin x \, dx$ to both sides of the equation and then divide both sides by 5.

$$= -e^{2x} \cos x + 2(e^{2x} \sin x - 2 \int e^{2x} \sin x \, dx) \quad \text{Substitute for } \int e^{2x} \cos x \, dx.$$

$$= -e^{2x} \cos x + 2e^{2x} \sin x - 4 \int e^{2x} \sin x \, dx. \quad \text{Simplify.}$$

Now it is a matter of solving for $\int e^{2x} \sin x \, dx$ and including the constant of integration:

$$\int e^{2x} \sin x \, dx = \frac{1}{5} e^{2x} (2 \sin x - \cos x) + C.$$

Related Exercises 23–30 ◄

Integration by Parts for Definite Integrals

Integration by parts with definite integrals presents two options. You can use the method outlined in Examples 1–4 to find an antiderivative and then evaluate it at the upper and lower limits of integration. Alternatively, the limits of integration can be incorporated directly into the integration by parts process. With the second approach, integration by parts for definite integrals has the following form.

> ▶ Integration by parts for definite integrals still has the form
>
> $$\int u \, dv = uv - \int v \, du.$$
>
> However, both definite integrals must be written with respect to x.

> **Integration by Parts for Definite Integrals**
>
> Let u and v be differentiable. Then
>
> $$\int_a^b u(x)v'(x) \, dx = u(x)v(x) \Big|_a^b - \int_a^b v(x)u'(x) \, dx.$$

EXAMPLE 5 **A definite integral** Evaluate $\int_1^2 \ln x \, dx$.

SOLUTION This example is instructive because the integrand does not appear to be a product. The key is to view the integrand as the product $(\ln x)(1 \, dx)$. Then the following choices are plausible.

$u = \ln x$	$dv = dx$
$du = \dfrac{1}{x} dx$	$v = x$

Using integration by parts, we have

$$\int_1^2 \underbrace{\ln x}_{u} \underbrace{dx}_{dv} = \left(\underbrace{(\ln x)}_{u} \underbrace{x}_{v} \right) \Big|_1^2 - \int_1^2 \underbrace{x}_{v} \underbrace{\frac{1}{x} dx}_{du} \qquad \text{Integration by parts}$$

$$= (x \ln x - x) \Big|_1^2 \qquad \text{Integrate and simplify.}$$

$$= (2 \ln 2 - 0) - (2 - 1) \qquad \text{Evaluate.}$$

$$= 2 \ln 2 - 1 \approx 0.386. \qquad \text{Simplify.}$$

Related Exercises 31–38 ◀

In Example 5, we evaluated a definite integral of $\ln x$. The corresponding indefinite integral can be added to our list of integration formulas.

QUICK CHECK 2 Verify by differentiation that $\int \ln x \, dx = x \ln x - x + C$. ◀

> **Integral of ln x**
>
> $$\int \ln x \, dx = x \ln x - x + C$$

We now apply integration by parts to a familiar geometry problem.

EXAMPLE 6 **Solids of revolution** Let R be the region bounded by $y = \ln x$, the x-axis, and the line $x = e$ (Figure 7.1). Find the volume of the solid that is generated when the region R is revolved about the x-axis.

SOLUTION Revolving R about the x-axis generates a solid whose volume is computed with the disk method (Section 6.3). Its volume is

$$V = \int_1^e \pi (\ln x)^2 \, dx.$$

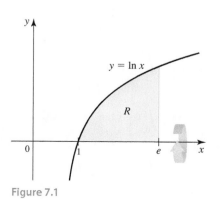

Figure 7.1

We integrate by parts with the following assignments.

$u = (\ln x)^2$	$dv = dx$
$du = \dfrac{2 \ln x}{x} dx$	$v = x$

▶ Recall that if $f(x) \geq 0$ on $[a, b]$ and the region bounded by the graph of f and the x-axis on $[a, b]$ is revolved about the x-axis, then the volume of the solid generated is $V = \displaystyle\int_a^b \pi f(x)^2 \, dx$.

The integration is carried out as follows, using the indefinite integral of $\ln x$ just given:

$$V = \int_1^e \pi (\ln x)^2 \, dx \qquad \text{Disk method}$$

$$= \pi \left(\underbrace{(\ln x)^2}_{u} \underbrace{x}_{v} \Big|_1^e - \int_1^e \underbrace{x}_{v} \underbrace{\frac{2 \ln x}{x}}_{du} \, dx \right) \qquad \text{Integration by parts}$$

$$= \pi \left(x(\ln x)^2 \Big|_1^e - 2 \int_1^e \ln x \, dx \right) \qquad \text{Simplify.}$$

$$= \pi \left(x(\ln x)^2 \Big|_1^e - 2(x \ln x - x) \Big|_1^e \right) \qquad \int \ln x \, dx = x \ln x - x + C$$

QUICK CHECK 3 How many times do you need to integrate by parts to reduce $\int_1^e (\ln x)^6 \, dx$ to an integral of $\ln x$? ◀

$$= \pi (e(\ln e)^2 - 2e \ln e + 2e - 2). \qquad \text{Evaluate and simplify.}$$

$$= \pi(e - 2) \approx 2.257 \qquad \text{Simplify.}$$

Related Exercises 39–42 ◀

SECTION 7.2 EXERCISES

Review Questions

1. On which derivative rule is integration by parts based?

2. How would you choose dv when evaluating $\int x^n e^{ax} \, dx$ using integration by parts?

3. How would you choose u when evaluating $\int x^n \cos ax \, dx$ using integration by parts?

4. Explain how integration by parts is used to evaluate a definite integral.

5. What type of integrand is a good candidate for integration by parts?

6. What choices for u and dv simplify $\int \tan^{-1} x \, dx$?

Basic Skills

7–22. Integration by parts *Evaluate the following integrals.*

7. $\displaystyle\int x \cos x \, dx$

8. $\displaystyle\int x \sin 2x \, dx$

9. $\displaystyle\int t e^t \, dt$

10. $\displaystyle\int 2x e^{3x} \, dx$

11. $\displaystyle\int \frac{x}{\sqrt{x+1}} \, dx$

12. $\displaystyle\int s e^{-2s} \, ds$

13. $\displaystyle\int x^2 \ln x^3 \, dx$

14. $\displaystyle\int \theta \sec^2 \theta \, d\theta$

15. $\displaystyle\int x^2 \ln x \, dx$

16. $\displaystyle\int x \ln x \, dx$

17. $\displaystyle\int \frac{\ln x}{x^{10}} \, dx$

18. $\displaystyle\int \sin^{-1} x \, dx$

19. $\displaystyle\int \tan^{-1} x \, dx$

20. $\displaystyle\int x \sec^{-1} x \, dx, \ x \geq 1$

21. $\displaystyle\int x \sin x \cos x \, dx$

22. $\displaystyle\int x \tan^{-1} x^2 \, dx$

23–30. Repeated integration by parts *Evaluate the following integrals.*

23. $\displaystyle\int t^2 e^{-t} \, dt$

24. $\displaystyle\int e^{3x} \cos 2x \, dx$

25. $\displaystyle\int e^{-x} \sin 4x \, dx$

26. $\displaystyle\int x^2 \ln^2 x \, dx$

27. $\displaystyle\int e^x \cos x \, dx$

28. $\displaystyle\int e^{-2\theta} \sin 6\theta \, d\theta$

29. $\displaystyle\int x^2 \sin 2x \, dx$

30. $\displaystyle\int x^2 e^{4x} \, dx$

31–38. Definite integrals *Evaluate the following definite integrals.*

31. $\displaystyle\int_0^\pi x \sin x \, dx$

32. $\displaystyle\int_1^e \ln 2x \, dx$

33. $\displaystyle\int_0^{\pi/2} x \cos 2x \, dx$

34. $\displaystyle\int_0^{\ln 2} x e^x \, dx$

35. $\displaystyle\int_1^{e^2} x^2 \ln x \, dx$

36. $\displaystyle\int_0^{1/\sqrt{2}} y \tan^{-1} y^2 \, dy$

37. $\displaystyle\int_{1/2}^{\sqrt{3}/2} \sin^{-1} y \, dy$

38. $\displaystyle\int_{2/\sqrt{3}}^2 z \sec^{-1} z \, dz$

39–42. Volumes of solids *Find the volume of the solid that is generated when the given region is revolved as described.*

39. The region bounded by $f(x) = e^{-x}$, $x = \ln 2$, and the coordinate axes is revolved about the y-axis.

40. The region bounded by $f(x) = \sin x$ and the x-axis on $[0, \pi]$ is revolved about the y-axis.

41. The region bounded by $f(x) = x \ln x$ and the x-axis on $[1, e^2]$ is revolved about the x-axis.

42. The region bounded by $f(x) = e^{-x}$ and the x-axis on $[0, \ln 2]$ is revolved about the line $x = \ln 2$.

Further Explorations

43. Explain why or why not Determine whether the following statements are true and give an explanation or counterexample.

a. $\displaystyle \int uv' \, dx = \left(\int u \, dx \right)\left(\int v' \, dx \right).$

b. $\displaystyle \int uv' \, dx = uv - \int vu' \, dx.$

c. $\displaystyle \int v \, du = uv - \int u \, dv.$

44–47. Reduction formulas *Use integration by parts to derive the following reduction formulas.*

44. $\displaystyle \int x^n e^{ax} \, dx = \frac{x^n e^{ax}}{a} - \frac{n}{a} \int x^{n-1} e^{ax} \, dx, \quad \text{for } a \neq 0$

45. $\displaystyle \int x^n \cos ax \, dx = \frac{x^n \sin ax}{a} - \frac{n}{a} \int x^{n-1} \sin ax \, dx, \quad \text{for } a \neq 0$

46. $\displaystyle \int x^n \sin ax \, dx = -\frac{x^n \cos ax}{a} + \frac{n}{a} \int x^{n-1} \cos ax \, dx, \quad \text{for } a \neq 0$

47. $\displaystyle \int \ln^n x \, dx = x \ln^n x - n \int \ln^{n-1} x \, dx$

48–51. Applying reduction formulas *Use the reduction formulas in Exercises 44–47 to evaluate the following integrals.*

48. $\displaystyle \int x^2 e^{3x} \, dx$

49. $\displaystyle \int x^2 \cos 5x \, dx$

50. $\displaystyle \int x^3 \sin x \, dx$

51. $\displaystyle \int \ln^4 x \, dx$

52–53. Integrals involving $\int \ln x \, dx$ *Use a substitution to reduce the following integrals to $\int \ln u \, du$. Then evaluate the resulting integral.*

52. $\displaystyle \int (\cos x) \ln (\sin x) \, dx$

53. $\displaystyle \int (\sec^2 x) \ln (\tan x + 2) \, dx$

54. Two methods

a. Evaluate $\int x \ln x^2 \, dx$ using the substitution $u = x^2$ and evaluating $\int \ln u \, du$.

b. Evaluate $\int x \ln x^2 \, dx$ using integration by parts.

c. Verify that your answers to parts (a) and (b) are consistent.

55. Logarithm base b Prove that

$$\int \log_b x \, dx = \frac{1}{\ln b} (x \ln x - x) + C.$$

56. Two integration methods Evaluate $\int \sin x \cos x \, dx$ using integration by parts. Then evaluate the integral using a substitution. Reconcile your answers.

57. Combining two integration methods Evaluate $\int \cos \sqrt{x} \, dx$ using a substitution followed by integration by parts.

58. Combining two integration methods Evaluate $\int_0^{\pi^2/4} \sin \sqrt{x} \, dx$ using a substitution followed by integration by parts.

59. Function defined as an integral Find the arc length of the function $f(x) = \int_e^x \sqrt{\ln^2 t - 1} \, dt$ on $[e, e^3]$.

60. A family of exponentials The curves $y = xe^{-ax}$ are shown in the figure for $a = 1, 2,$ and 3.

a. Find the area of the region bounded by $y = xe^{-x}$ and the x-axis on the interval $[0, 4]$.

b. Find the area of the region bounded by $y = xe^{-ax}$ and the x-axis on the interval $[0, 4]$, where $a > 0$.

c. Find the area of the region bounded by $y = xe^{-ax}$ and the x-axis on the interval $[0, b]$. Because this area depends on a and b, we call it $A(a, b)$, where $a > 0$ and $b > 0$.

d. Use part (c) to show that $A(1, \ln b) = 4A(2, (\ln b)/2)$.

e. Does this pattern continue? Is it true that $A(1, \ln b) = a^2 A(a, (\ln b)/a)$?

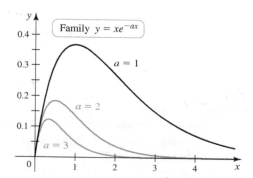

61. Solid of revolution Find the volume of the solid generated when the region bounded by $y = \cos x$ and the x-axis on the interval $[0, \pi/2]$ is revolved about the y-axis.

62. Between the sine and inverse sine Find the area of the region bounded by the curves $y = \sin x$ and $y = \sin^{-1} x$ on the interval $[0, \frac{1}{2}]$.

63. Comparing volumes Let R be the region bounded by $y = \sin x$ and the x-axis on the interval $[0, \pi]$. Which is greater, the volume of the solid generated when R is revolved about the x-axis or the volume of the solid generated when R is revolved about the y-axis?

64. Log integrals Use integration by parts to show that for $m \neq -1$,

$$\int x^m \ln x \, dx = \frac{x^{m+1}}{m+1} \left(\ln x - \frac{1}{m+1} \right) + C$$

and for $m = -1$,

$$\int \frac{\ln x}{x} \, dx = \frac{1}{2} \ln^2 x + C.$$

65. A useful integral

a. Use integration by parts to show that if f' is continuous,

$$\int x f'(x) \, dx = x f(x) - \int f(x) \, dx.$$

b. Use part (a) to evaluate $\int x e^{3x} \, dx$.

66. Integrating inverse functions Assume that f has an inverse on its domain.

a. Let $y = f^{-1}(x)$ and show that

$$\int f^{-1}(x)\, dx = \int y f'(y)\, dy.$$

b. Use part (a) to show that

$$\int f^{-1}(x)\, dx = y f(y) - \int f(y)\, dy.$$

c. Use the result of part (b) to evaluate $\int \ln x\, dx$ (express the result in terms of x).

d. Use the result of part (b) to evaluate $\int \sin^{-1} x\, dx$.

e. Use the result of part (b) to evaluate $\int \tan^{-1} x\, dx$.

67. Integral of $\sec^3 x$ Use integration by parts to show that

$$\int \sec^3 x\, dx = \frac{1}{2} \sec x \tan x + \frac{1}{2} \int \sec x\, dx.$$

68. Two useful exponential integrals Use integration by parts to derive the following formulas for real numbers a and b.

$$\int e^{ax} \sin bx\, dx = \frac{e^{ax}(a \sin bx - b \cos bx)}{a^2 + b^2} + C$$

$$\int e^{ax} \cos bx\, dx = \frac{e^{ax}(a \cos bx + b \sin bx)}{a^2 + b^2} + C$$

Applications

T 69. Oscillator displacements Suppose a mass on a spring that is slowed by friction has the position function $s(t) = e^{-t} \sin t$.

a. Graph the position function. At what times does the oscillator pass through the position $s = 0$?

b. Find the average value of the position on the interval $[0, \pi]$.

c. Generalize part (b) and find the average value of the position on the interval $[n\pi, (n + 1)\pi]$, for $n = 0, 1, 2, \ldots$.

d. Let a_n be the absolute value of the average position on the intervals $[n\pi, (n + 1)\pi]$, for $n = 0, 1, 2, \ldots$. Describe the pattern in the numbers $a_0, a_1, a_2, \ldots$.

Additional Exercises

70. Find the error Suppose you evaluate $\int \dfrac{dx}{x}$ using integration by parts. With $u = 1/x$ and $dv = dx$, you find that $du = -1/x^2\, dx$, $v = x$, and

$$\int \frac{dx}{x} = \left(\frac{1}{x}\right) x - \int x \left(-\frac{1}{x^2}\right) dx = 1 + \int \frac{dx}{x}.$$

You conclude that $0 = 1$. Explain the problem with the calculation.

71. Tabular integration Consider the integral $\int f(x) g(x)\, dx$, where f and g are sufficiently "smooth" to allow repeated differentiation and integration, respectively. Let G_k represent the result of calculating k indefinite integrals of g, where the constants of integration are omitted.

a. Show that integration by parts, when applied to $\int f(x) g(x)\, dx$ with the choices $u = f(x)$ and $dv = g(x)\, dx$, leads to $\int f(x) g(x)\, dx = f(x) G_1(x) - \int f'(x) G_1(x)\, dx$.

This formula can be remembered by utilizing the following table, where a right arrow represents a product of functions on the right side of the integration by parts formula, and a left arrow represents the *integral* of a product of functions (also appearing on the right side of the formula). Explain the significance of the signs associated with the arrows.

f and its derivatives	g and its integrals
$f(x)$	$g(x)$
$f'(x)$	$G_1(x)$

b. Perform integration by parts again on $\int f'(x) G_1(x)\, dx$ (from part (a)) with the choices $u = f'(x)$ and $dv = G_1(x)$ to show that $\int f(x) g(x)\, dx = f(x) G_1(x) - f'(x) G_2(x) + \int f''(x) G_2(x)\, dx$. Explain the connection between this integral formula and the following table, paying close attention to the signs attached to the arrows.

f and its derivatives	g and its integrals
$f(x)$	$g(x)$
$f'(x)$	$G_1(x)$
$f''(x)$	$G_2(x)$

c. Continue the pattern established in parts (a) and (b) and integrate by parts a third time. Write the integral formula that results from three applications of integration by parts, and construct the associated *tabular integration* table (include signs of the arrows).

d. The tabular integration table from part (c) is easily extended to allow for as many steps as necessary in the integration-by-parts process. Evaluate $\int x^2 e^{0.5x}\, dx$ by constructing an appropriate table, and explain why the process terminates after four rows of the table have been filled in.

e. Use tabular integration to evaluate $\int x^3 \cos x\, dx$. How many rows of the table are necessary? Why?

f. Explain why tabular integration is particularly suited to integrals of the form $\int p_n(x) g(x)\, dx$, where p_n is a polynomial of degree $n > 0$ (and where, as before, we assume g is easily integrated as many times as necessary).

72. Practice with tabular integration Evaluate the following integrals using tabular integration (refer to Exercise 71).

a. $\int x^4 e^x dx$

b. $\int 7x e^{3x} dx$

c. $\int_{-1}^{0} 2x^2 \sqrt{x + 1}\, dx$

d. $\int (x^3 - 2x) \sin 2x\, dx$

e. $\int \dfrac{2x^2 - 3x}{(x - 1)^3}\, dx$

f. $\int \dfrac{x^2 + 3x + 4}{\sqrt[3]{2x + 1}}\, dx$

g. Why doesn't tabular integration work well when applied to

$$\int \frac{x}{\sqrt{1 - x^2}}\, dx?$$ Evaluate this integral using a different method.

73. Tabular integration extended Refer to Exercise 71.

a. The following table shows the method of tabular integration applied to $\int e^x \cos x \, dx$. Use the table to express $\int e^x \cos x \, dx$ in terms of the sum of functions and an indefinite integral.

f and its derivatives	g and its integrals
e^x $+$	$\cos x$
e^x $-$	$\sin x$
e^x $+$	$-\cos x$

b. Solve the equation in part (a) for $\int e^x \cos x \, dx$.

c. Evaluate $\int e^{-2x} \sin 3x \, dx$ by applying the idea from parts (a) and (b).

74. Integrating derivatives Use integration by parts to show that if f' is continuous on $[a, b]$, then

$$\int_a^b f(x) f'(x) \, dx = \frac{1}{2} \left(f(b)^2 - f(a)^2 \right).$$

75. An identity Show that if f has a continuous second derivative on $[a, b]$ and $f'(a) = f'(b) = 0$, then

$$\int_a^b x f''(x) \, dx = f(a) - f(b).$$

76. An identity Show that if f and g have continuous second derivatives and $f(0) = f(1) = g(0) = g(1) = 0$, then

$$\int_0^1 f''(x) g(x) \, dx = \int_0^1 f(x) g''(x) \, dx.$$

77. Possible and impossible integrals Let $I_n = \int x^n e^{-x^2} \, dx$, where n is a nonnegative integer.

a. $I_0 = \int e^{-x^2} \, dx$ cannot be expressed in terms of elementary functions. Evaluate I_1.

b. Use integration by parts to evaluate I_3.

c. Use integration by parts and the result of part (b) to evaluate I_5.

d. Show that, in general, if n is odd, then $I_n = -\frac{1}{2} e^{-x^2} p_{n-1}(x)$, where p_{n-1} is a polynomial of degree $n - 1$.

e. Argue that if n is even, then I_n cannot be expressed in terms of elementary functions.

78. Looking ahead (to Chapter 9) Suppose that a function f has derivatives of all orders near $x = 0$. By the Fundamental Theorem of Calculus,

$$f(x) - f(0) = \int_0^x f'(t) \, dt.$$

a. Evaluate the integral using integration by parts to show that

$$f(x) = f(0) + x f'(0) + \int_0^x f''(t)(x - t) \, dt.$$

b. Show that integrating by parts n times gives

$$f(x) = f(0) + x f'(0) + \frac{1}{2!} x^2 f''(0) + \cdots + \frac{1}{n!} x^n f^{(n)}(0)$$
$$+ \frac{1}{n!} \int_0^x f^{(n+1)}(t)(x - t)^n \, dt + \cdots.$$

This expression, called the *Taylor series* for f at $x = 0$, is revisited in Chapter 9.

QUICK CHECK ANSWERS

1. Let $u = x$ and $dv = \cos x \, dx$.

2. $\dfrac{d}{dx}(x \ln x - x + C) = \ln x$

3. Integration by parts must be applied five times. ◄

7.3 Trigonometric Integrals

At the moment, our inventory of integrals involving trigonometric functions is rather limited. For example, we can integrate $\sin ax$ and $\cos ax$, where a is a constant, but missing from the list are integrals of $\tan ax$, $\cot ax$, $\sec ax$, and $\csc ax$. It turns out that integrals of powers of trigonometric functions, such as $\int \cos^5 x \, dx$ and $\int \cos^2 x \sin^4 x \, dx$, are also important. The goal of this section is to develop techniques for evaluating integrals involving trigonometric functions. These techniques are indispensable when we encounter *trigonometric substitutions* in the next section.

> Some of the techniques described in this section also work for negative powers of trigonometric functions.

Integrating Powers of sin x or cos x

Two strategies are employed when evaluating integrals of the form $\int \sin^m x \, dx$ or $\int \cos^n x \, dx$, where m and n are positive integers. Both strategies use trigonometric identities to recast the integrand, as shown in the first example.

EXAMPLE 1   Powers of sine or cosine Evaluate the following integrals.

a. $\int \cos^5 x \, dx$ **b.** $\int \sin^4 x \, dx$

▶ Pythagorean identities:

$$\cos^2 x + \sin^2 x = 1$$

$$1 + \tan^2 x = \sec^2 x$$

$$\cot^2 x + 1 = \csc^2 x$$

SOLUTION

a. Integrals involving odd powers of $\cos x$ (or $\sin x$) are most easily evaluated by splitting off a single factor of $\cos x$ (or $\sin x$). In this case, we rewrite $\cos^5 x$ as $\cos^4 x \cdot \cos x$. Notice that $\cos^4 x$ can be written in terms of $\sin x$ using the identity $\cos^2 x = 1 - \sin^2 x$. The result is an integrand that readily yields to the substitution $u = \sin x$:

$$
\begin{aligned}
\int \cos^5 x \, dx &= \int \cos^4 x \cdot \cos x \, dx && \text{Split off } \cos x. \\
&= \int (1 - \sin^2 x)^2 \cdot \cos x \, dx && \text{Pythagorean identity} \\
&= \int (1 - u^2)^2 \, du && \text{Let } u = \sin x;\, du = \cos x \, dx. \\
&= \int (1 - 2u^2 + u^4) \, du && \text{Expand.} \\
&= u - \frac{2}{3} u^3 + \frac{1}{5} u^5 + C && \text{Integrate.} \\
&= \sin x - \frac{2}{3} \sin^3 x + \frac{1}{5} \sin^5 x + C. && \text{Replace } u \text{ with } \sin x.
\end{aligned}
$$

▶ The half-angle formulas for $\sin^2 x$ and $\cos^2 x$ are easily confused. Use the phrase "sine is minus" to remember that a minus sign is associated with the half-angle formula for $\sin^2 x$, whereas a positive sign is used for $\cos^2 x$.

b. With even positive powers of $\sin x$ or $\cos x$, we use the half-angle formulas

$$\sin^2 x = \frac{1 - \cos 2x}{2} \quad \text{and} \quad \cos^2 x = \frac{1 + \cos 2x}{2}$$

to reduce the powers in the integrand:

$$
\int \sin^4 x \, dx = \int \underbrace{\left(\frac{1 - \cos 2x}{2} \right)^2}_{\sin^2 x} \, dx \qquad \text{Half-angle formula}
$$

$$
= \frac{1}{4} \int (1 - 2\cos 2x + \cos^2 2x) \, dx. \qquad \text{Expand the integrand.}
$$

Using the half-angle formula for $\cos^2 2x$, the evaluation may be completed:

$$
\int \sin^4 x \, dx = \frac{1}{4} \int \left(1 - 2\cos 2x + \underbrace{\frac{1 + \cos 4x}{2}}_{\cos^2 2x} \right) dx \quad \text{Half-angle formula}
$$

$$
= \frac{1}{4} \int \left(\frac{3}{2} - 2\cos 2x + \frac{1}{2}\cos 4x \right) dx \qquad \text{Simplify.}
$$

$$
= \frac{3x}{8} - \frac{1}{4}\sin 2x + \frac{1}{32}\sin 4x + C. \qquad \text{Evaluate the integrals.}
$$

Related Exercises 9–14 ◀

QUICK CHECK 1 Evaluate $\int \sin^3 x \, dx$ by splitting off a factor of $\sin x$, rewriting $\sin^2 x$ in terms of $\cos x$, and using an appropriate u-substitution. ◀

Integrating Products of Powers of $\sin x$ and $\cos x$

We now consider integrals of the form $\int \sin^m x \cos^n x \, dx$. If m is an odd, positive integer, we split off a factor of $\sin x$ and write the remaining even power of $\sin x$ in terms of cosine functions. This step prepares the integrand for the substitution $u = \cos x$, and the resulting integral is readily evaluated. A similar strategy is used when n is an odd, positive integer.

If both m and n are even positive integers, the half-angle formulas are used to transform the integrand into a polynomial in $\cos 2x$, each of whose terms can be integrated, as shown in Example 2.

EXAMPLE 2   Products of sine and cosine Evaluate the following integrals.

a. $\displaystyle\int \sin^4 x \cos^2 x \, dx$ **b.** $\displaystyle\int \sin^3 x \cos^{-2} x \, dx$

SOLUTION

a. When both powers are even positive integers, the half-angle formulas are used:

$$\int \sin^4 x \cos^2 x \, dx = \int \underbrace{\left(\frac{1 - \cos 2x}{2}\right)^2}_{\sin^2 x} \underbrace{\left(\frac{1 + \cos 2x}{2}\right)}_{\cos^2 x} dx \qquad \text{Half-angle formulas}$$

$$= \frac{1}{8} \int (1 - \cos 2x - \cos^2 2x + \cos^3 2x) \, dx. \quad \text{Expand.}$$

The third term in the integrand is rewritten with a half-angle formula. For the last term, a factor of $\cos 2x$ is split off, and the resulting even power of $\cos 2x$ is written in terms of $\sin 2x$ to prepare for a u-substitution:

$$\int \sin^4 x \cos^2 x \, dx =$$

$$\frac{1}{8} \int \left(1 - \cos 2x - \left(\overbrace{\frac{1 + \cos 4x}{2}}^{\cos^2 2x}\right)\right) dx + \frac{1}{8} \int \overbrace{(1 - \sin^2 2x)}^{\cos^2 2x} \cdot \cos 2x \, dx.$$

Finally, the integrals are evaluated, using the substitution $u = \sin 2x$ for the second integral. After simplification, we find that

$$\int \sin^4 x \cos^2 x \, dx = \frac{1}{16} x - \frac{1}{64} \sin 4x - \frac{1}{48} \sin^3 2x + C.$$

b. When at least one power is odd and positive, the following approach works:

$$\int \sin^3 x \cos^{-2} x \, dx = \int \sin^2 x \cos^{-2} x \cdot \sin x \, dx \qquad \text{Split off } \sin x.$$

$$= \int (1 - \cos^2 x) \cos^{-2} x \cdot \sin x \, dx \quad \text{Pythagorean identity}$$

$$= -\int (1 - u^2) u^{-2} \, du \qquad\qquad u = \cos x;\ du = -\sin x \, dx$$

$$= \int (1 - u^{-2}) \, du = u + \frac{1}{u} + C \quad \text{Evaluate the integral.}$$

$$= \cos x + \sec x + C. \qquad\qquad \text{Replace } u \text{ with } \cos x.$$

Related Exercises 15–24 ◄

QUICK CHECK 2 What strategy would you use to evaluate $\displaystyle\int \sin^3 x \cos^3 x \, dx$? ◄

Table 7.2 summarizes the techniques used to evaluate integrals of the form $\displaystyle\int \sin^m x \cos^n x \, dx$.

► If both m and n are odd, you may split off sin x or cos x; both choices are effective.

Table 7.2

$\int \sin^m x \cos^n x\, dx$	Strategy
m odd and positive, n real	Split off sin x, rewrite the resulting even power of sin x in terms of cos x, and then use $u = \cos x$.
n odd and positive, m real	Split off cos x, rewrite the resulting even power of cos x in terms of sin x, and then use $u = \sin x$.
m and n both even, nonnegative integers	Use half-angle formulas to transform the integrand into a polynomial in cos $2x$ and apply the preceding strategies once again to powers of cos $2x$ greater than 1.

Reduction Formulas

Evaluating an integral such as $\int \sin^8 x\, dx$ using the method of Example 1b is tedious, at best. For this reason, *reduction formulas* have been developed to ease the workload. A reduction formula equates an integral involving a power of a function with another integral in which the power is reduced; several reduction formulas were encountered in Exercises 44–47 of Section 7.2. Here are some frequently used reduction formulas for trigonometric integrals.

Reduction Formulas

Assume n is a positive integer.

1. $\displaystyle \int \sin^n x\, dx = -\frac{\sin^{n-1} x \cos x}{n} + \frac{n-1}{n} \int \sin^{n-2} x\, dx$

2. $\displaystyle \int \cos^n x\, dx = \frac{\cos^{n-1} x \sin x}{n} + \frac{n-1}{n} \int \cos^{n-2} x\, dx$

3. $\displaystyle \int \tan^n x\, dx = \frac{\tan^{n-1} x}{n-1} - \int \tan^{n-2} x\, dx, \ n \neq 1$

4. $\displaystyle \int \sec^n x\, dx = \frac{\sec^{n-2} x \tan x}{n-1} + \frac{n-2}{n-1} \int \sec^{n-2} x\, dx, \ n \neq 1$

Formulas 1, 3, and 4 are derived in Exercises 64–66. The derivation of formula 2 is similar to that of formula 1.

EXAMPLE 3   Powers of tan x Evaluate $\int \tan^4 x\, dx$.

SOLUTION Reduction formula 3 gives

$$\int \tan^4 x\, dx = \frac{1}{3} \tan^3 x - \underbrace{\int \tan^2 x\, dx}_{\text{use (3) again}}$$

$$= \frac{1}{3} \tan^3 x - \left(\tan x - \int \underbrace{\tan^0 x\, dx}_{=1} \right)$$

$$= \frac{1}{3} \tan^3 x - \tan x + x + C.$$

An alternative solution uses the identity $\tan^2 x = \sec^2 x - 1$:

$$\int \tan^4 x \, dx = \int \tan^2 x \underbrace{\left(\sec^2 x - 1\right)}_{\tan^2 x} dx$$

$$= \int \tan^2 x \sec^2 x \, dx - \int \tan^2 x \, dx.$$

The substitution $u = \tan x$, $du = \sec^2 x \, dx$ is used in the first integral, and the identity $\tan^2 x = \sec^2 x - 1$ is used again in the second integral:

$$\int \tan^4 x \, dx = \int \underbrace{\tan^2 x}_{u^2} \underbrace{\sec^2 x \, dx}_{du} - \int \tan^2 x \, dx$$

$$= \int u^2 \, du - \int \left(\sec^2 x - 1\right) dx \qquad \text{Substitution and identity}$$

$$= \frac{u^3}{3} - \tan x + x + C \qquad \text{Evaluate integrals.}$$

$$= \frac{1}{3} \tan^3 x - \tan x + x + C. \qquad u = \tan x$$

Related Exercises 25–30 ◄

Note that for odd powers of $\tan x$ and $\sec x$, the use of reduction formula 3 or 4 will eventually lead to $\int \tan x \, dx$ or $\int \sec x \, dx$. Theorem 7.1 gives these integrals, along with the integrals of $\cot x$ and $\csc x$.

THEOREM 7.1   Integrals of $\tan x$, $\cot x$, $\sec x$, and $\csc x$

$$\int \tan x \, dx = -\ln |\cos x| + C = \ln |\sec x| + C \qquad \int \cot x \, dx = \ln |\sin x| + C$$

$$\int \sec x \, dx = \ln |\sec x + \tan x| + C \qquad \int \csc x \, dx = -\ln |\csc x + \cot x| + C$$

Proof: In the first integral, $\tan x$ is expressed as the ratio of $\sin x$ and $\cos x$ to prepare for a standard substitution:

$$\int \tan x \, dx = \int \frac{\sin x}{\cos x} dx$$

$$= -\int \frac{1}{u} du \qquad u = \cos x;\ du = -\sin x \, dx$$

$$= -\ln |u| + C = -\ln |\cos x| + C.$$

Using properties of logarithms, the integral can also be written

$$\int \tan x \, dx = -\ln |\cos x| + C = \ln \left|(\cos x)^{-1}\right| + C = \ln |\sec x| + C.$$

To integrate $\sec x$, we utilize the technique of multiplying by 1 introduced in Section 7.1:

$$\int \sec x \, dx = \int \sec x \cdot \underbrace{\frac{\sec x + \tan x}{\sec x + \tan x}}_{1} \, dx \qquad \text{Multiply integrand by 1.}$$

$$= \int \frac{\sec^2 x + \sec x \tan x}{\sec x + \tan x} \, dx \qquad \text{Expand numerator.}$$

$$= \int \frac{du}{u} \qquad u = \sec x + \tan x; \, du = (\sec^2 x + \sec x \tan x) \, dx$$

$$= \ln |u| + C \qquad \text{Integrate.}$$

$$= \ln |\sec x + \tan x| + C. \qquad u = \sec x + \tan x$$

Derivations of the remaining integrals are left to Exercises 46–47. ◄

Integrating Products of Powers of $\tan x$ and $\sec x$

Integrals of the form $\int \tan^m x \sec^n x \, dx$ are evaluated using methods analogous to those used for $\int \sin^m x \cos^n x \, dx$. For example, if n is an even positive integer, we split off a factor of $\sec^2 x$ and write the remaining even power of $\sec x$ in terms of $\tan x$. This step prepares the integral for the substitution $u = \tan x$. If m is odd and positive, we split off a factor of $\sec x \tan x$ (the derivative of $\sec x$), which prepares the integral for the substitution $u = \sec x$. If m is even and n is odd, the integrand is expressed as a polynomial in $\sec x$, each of whose terms is handled by a reduction formula. Example 4 illustrates these techniques.

EXAMPLE 4 Products of $\tan x$ and $\sec x$ Evaluate the following integrals.

a. $\int \tan^3 x \sec^4 x \, dx$ **b.** $\int \tan^2 x \sec x \, dx$

SOLUTION

a. With an even power of $\sec x$, we split off a factor of $\sec^2 x$ and prepare the integral for the substitution $u = \tan x$:

$$\int \tan^3 x \sec^4 x \, dx = \int \tan^3 x \sec^2 x \cdot \sec^2 x \, dx$$

$$= \int \tan^3 x \, (\tan^2 x + 1) \cdot \sec^2 x \, dx \qquad \sec^2 x = \tan^2 x + 1$$

$$= \int u^3 (u^2 + 1) \, du \qquad u = \tan x; \, du = \sec^2 x \, dx$$

$$= \frac{1}{6} \tan^6 x + \frac{1}{4} \tan^4 x + C. \qquad \text{Evaluate; } u = \tan x.$$

> In Example 4a, the two methods produce results that look different, but are equivalent. This is common when evaluating trigonometric integrals. For instance, evaluate $\int \sin^4 x \, dx$ using reduction formula 1, and compare your answer to
>
> $$\frac{3x}{8} - \frac{1}{4} \sin 2x + \frac{1}{32} \sin 4x + C,$$
>
> the solution found in Example 1b.

Because the integrand also has an odd power of $\tan x$, an alternative solution is to split off a factor of $\sec x \tan x$ and prepare the integral for the substitution $u = \sec x$:

$$\int \tan^3 x \sec^4 x \, dx = \int \underbrace{\tan^2 x}_{\sec^2 x - 1} \sec^3 x \cdot \sec x \tan x \, dx$$

$$= \int (\sec^2 x - 1) \sec^3 x \cdot \sec x \tan x \, dx$$

$$= \int (u^2 - 1) u^3 \, du \qquad \begin{array}{l} u = \sec x; \\ du = \sec x \tan x \, dx \end{array}$$

$$= \frac{1}{6} \sec^6 x - \frac{1}{4} \sec^4 x + C. \qquad \text{Evaluate; } u = \sec x.$$

The apparent difference in the two solutions given here is reconciled by using the identity $1 + \tan^2 x = \sec^2 x$ to transform the second result into the first, the only difference being an additive constant, which is part of C.

b. In this case, we write the even power of $\tan x$ in terms of $\sec x$:

$$\int \tan^2 x \sec x \, dx = \int (\sec^2 x - 1) \sec x \, dx \qquad \tan^2 x = \sec^2 x - 1$$

$$= \int \sec^3 x \, dx - \int \sec x \, dx$$

$$\overbrace{}^{\text{reduction formula 4}}$$

$$= \frac{1}{2} \sec x \tan x + \frac{1}{2} \int \sec x \, dx - \int \sec x \, dx$$

$$= \frac{1}{2} \sec x \tan x - \frac{1}{2} \ln |\sec x + \tan x| + C. \qquad \begin{array}{l}\text{Add secant integrals;}\\ \text{use Theorem 7.1.}\end{array}$$

Related Exercises 31–44 ◄

Table 7.3 summarizes the methods used to integrate $\int \tan^m x \sec^n x \, dx$. Analogous techniques are used for $\int \cot^m x \csc^n x \, dx$.

Table 7.3

$\int \tan^m x \sec^n x \, dx$	Strategy
n even	Split off $\sec^2 x$, rewrite the remaining even power of $\sec x$ in terms of $\tan x$, and use $u = \tan x$.
m odd	Split off $\sec x \tan x$, rewrite the remaining even power of $\tan x$ in terms of $\sec x$, and use $u = \sec x$.
m even and n odd	Rewrite the even power of $\tan x$ in terms of $\sec x$ to produce a polynomial in $\sec x$; apply reduction formula 4 to each term.

SECTION 7.3 EXERCISES

Review Questions

1. State the half-angle identities used to integrate $\sin^2 x$ and $\cos^2 x$.

2. State the three Pythagorean identities.

3. Describe the method used to integrate $\sin^3 x$.

4. Describe the method used to integrate $\sin^m x \cos^n x$, for m even and n odd.

5. What is a reduction formula?

6. How would you evaluate $\int \cos^2 x \sin^3 x \, dx$?

7. How would you evaluate $\int \tan^{10} x \sec^2 x \, dx$?

8. How would you evaluate $\int \sec^{12} x \tan x \, dx$?

Basic Skills

9–14. Integrals of $\sin x$ or $\cos x$ *Evaluate the following integrals.*

9. $\displaystyle\int \sin^2 x \, dx$

10. $\displaystyle\int \sin^3 x \, dx$

11. $\displaystyle\int \cos^3 x \, dx$

12. $\displaystyle\int \cos^4 2\theta \, d\theta$

13. $\displaystyle\int \sin^5 x \, dx$

14. $\displaystyle\int \cos^3 20x \, dx$

15–24. Integrals of $\sin x$ and $\cos x$ *Evaluate the following integrals.*

15. $\displaystyle\int \sin^2 x \cos^2 x \, dx$

16. $\displaystyle\int \sin^3 x \cos^5 x \, dx$

17. $\displaystyle\int \sin^3 x \cos^2 x \, dx$

18. $\displaystyle\int \sin^2 \theta \cos^5 \theta \, d\theta$

19. $\displaystyle\int \cos^3 x \sqrt{\sin x} \, dx$

20. $\displaystyle\int \sin^3 \theta \cos^{-2} \theta \, d\theta$

21. $\displaystyle\int \sin^5 x \cos^{-2} x \, dx$

22. $\displaystyle\int \sin^{-3/2} x \cos^3 x \, dx$

23. $\displaystyle\int \sin^2 x \cos^4 x \, dx$

24. $\displaystyle\int \sin^3 x \cos^{3/2} x \, dx$

25–30. Integrals of $\tan x$ or $\cot x$ *Evaluate the following integrals.*

25. $\displaystyle\int \tan^2 x \, dx$

26. $\displaystyle\int 6 \sec^4 x \, dx$

27. $\displaystyle\int \cot^4 x \, dx$

28. $\displaystyle\int \tan^3 \theta \, d\theta$

29. $\displaystyle\int 20 \tan^6 x \, dx$

30. $\displaystyle\int \cot^5 3x \, dx$

31–44. Integrals involving tan x and sec x *Evaluate the following integrals.*

31. $\displaystyle\int 10\tan^9 x\sec^2 x\,dx$

32. $\displaystyle\int \tan^9 x\sec^4 x\,dx$

33. $\displaystyle\int \tan x\sec^3 x\,dx$

34. $\displaystyle\int \sqrt{\tan x}\sec^4 x\,dx$

35. $\displaystyle\int \tan^3 4x\,dx$

36. $\displaystyle\int \frac{\sec^2 x}{\tan^5 x}\,dx$

37. $\displaystyle\int \sec^2 x\tan^{1/2} x\,dx$

38. $\displaystyle\int \sec^{-2} x\tan^3 x\,dx$

39. $\displaystyle\int \frac{\csc^4 x}{\cot^2 x}\,dx$

40. $\displaystyle\int \csc^{10} x\cot x\,dx$

41. $\displaystyle\int_0^{\pi/4} \sec^4\theta\,d\theta$

42. $\displaystyle\int \tan^5\theta\sec^4\theta\,d\theta$

43. $\displaystyle\int_{\pi/6}^{\pi/3} \cot^3\theta\,d\theta$

44. $\displaystyle\int_0^{\pi/4} \tan^3\theta\sec^2\theta\,d\theta$

Further Explorations

45. Explain why or why not Determine whether the following statements are true and give an explanation or counterexample.

    a. If m is a positive integer, then $\int_0^\pi \cos^{2m+1} x\,dx = 0$.

    b. If m is a positive integer, then $\int_0^\pi \sin^m x\,dx = 0$.

46–47. Integrals of cot x and csc x

46. Use a change of variables to prove that
$\int \cot x\,dx = \ln|\sin x| + C$.

47. Prove that $\int \csc x\,dx = -\ln|\csc x + \cot x| + C$. (*Hint:* See the proof of Theorem 7.1.)

48. Comparing areas The region R_1 is bounded by the graph of $y = \tan x$ and the x-axis on the interval $[0, \pi/3]$. The region R_2 is bounded by the graph of $y = \sec x$ and the x-axis on the interval $[0, \pi/6]$. Which region has the greater area?

49. Region between curves Find the area of the region bounded by the graphs of $y = \tan x$ and $y = \sec x$ on the interval $[0, \pi/4]$.

50–57. Additional integrals *Evaluate the following integrals.*

50. $\displaystyle\int_0^{\sqrt{\pi/2}} x\sin^3(x^2)\,dx$

51. $\displaystyle\int \frac{\sec^4(\ln\theta)}{\theta}\,d\theta$

52. $\displaystyle\int_{\pi/6}^{\pi/2} \frac{dy}{\sin y}$

53. $\displaystyle\int_{-\pi/3}^{\pi/3} \sqrt{\sec^2\theta - 1}\,d\theta$

54. $\displaystyle\int_{-\pi/4}^{\pi/4} \tan^3 x\sec^2 x\,dx$

55. $\displaystyle\int_0^\pi (1 - \cos 2x)^{3/2}\,dx$

56. $\displaystyle\int \csc^{10} x\cot^3 x\,dx$

57. $\displaystyle\int e^x\sec(e^x + 1)\,dx$

58–61. Square roots *Evaluate the following integrals.*

58. $\displaystyle\int_{-\pi/4}^{\pi/4} \sqrt{1 + \cos 4x}\,dx$

59. $\displaystyle\int_0^{\pi/2} \sqrt{1 - \cos 2x}\,dx$

60. $\displaystyle\int_0^{\pi/8} \sqrt{1 - \cos 8x}\,dx$

61. $\displaystyle\int_0^{\pi/4} (1 + \cos 4x)^{3/2}\,dx$

62. Sine football Find the volume of the solid generated when the region bounded by the graph of $y = \sin x$ and the x-axis on the interval $[0, \pi]$ is revolved about the x-axis.

63. Arc length Find the length of the curve $y = \ln(\sec x)$, for $0 \le x \le \pi/4$.

64. A sine reduction formula Use integration by parts to obtain a reduction formula for positive integers n:

$$\int \sin^n x\,dx = -\sin^{n-1} x\cos x + (n-1)\int \sin^{n-2} x\cos^2 x\,dx.$$

Then use an identity to obtain the reduction formula

$$\int \sin^n x\,dx = -\frac{\sin^{n-1} x\cos x}{n} + \frac{n-1}{n}\int \sin^{n-2} x\,dx.$$

Use this reduction formula to evaluate $\int \sin^6 x\,dx$.

65. A tangent reduction formula Prove that for positive integers $n \ne 1$,

$$\int \tan^n x\,dx = \frac{\tan^{n-1} x}{n-1} - \int \tan^{n-2} x\,dx.$$

Use the formula to evaluate $\int_0^{\pi/4} \tan^3 x\,dx$.

66. A secant reduction formula Prove that for positive integers $n \ne 1$,

$$\int \sec^n x\,dx = \frac{\sec^{n-2} x\tan x}{n-1} + \frac{n-2}{n-1}\int \sec^{n-2} x\,dx.$$

(*Hint:* Integrate by parts with $u = \sec^{n-2} x$ and $dv = \sec^2 x\,dx$.)

Applications

67–71. Integrals of the form $\int \sin mx\cos nx\,dx$ *Use the following three identities to evaluate the given integrals.*

$$\sin mx\sin nx = \frac{1}{2}\left(\cos((m-n)x) - \cos((m+n)x)\right)$$

$$\sin mx\cos nx = \frac{1}{2}\left(\sin((m-n)x) + \sin((m+n)x)\right)$$

$$\cos mx\cos nx = \frac{1}{2}\left(\cos((m-n)x) + \cos((m+n)x)\right)$$

67. $\displaystyle\int \sin 3x\cos 7x\,dx$

68. $\displaystyle\int \sin 5x\sin 7x\,dx$

69. $\displaystyle\int \sin 3x\sin 2x\,dx$

70. $\displaystyle\int \cos x\cos 2x\,dx$

71. Prove the following **orthogonality relations** (which are used to generate *Fourier series*). Assume m and n are integers with $m \ne n$.

    a. $\displaystyle\int_0^\pi \sin mx\sin nx\,dx = 0$

    b. $\displaystyle\int_0^\pi \cos mx\cos nx\,dx = 0$

    c. $\displaystyle\int_0^\pi \sin mx\cos nx\,dx = 0$, for $|m + n|$ even

72. Mercator map projection The Mercator map projection was proposed by the Flemish geographer Gerardus Mercator (1512–1594). The stretching factor of the Mercator map as a function of the latitude θ is given by the function

$$G(\theta) = \int_0^{\theta} \sec x \, dx.$$

Graph G, for $0 \le \theta < \pi/2$. (See the Guided Project *Mercator projections* for a derivation of this integral.)

Additional Exercises

73. Exploring powers of sine and cosine

a. Graph the functions $f_1(x) = \sin^2 x$ and $f_2(x) = \sin^2 2x$ on the interval $[0, \pi]$. Find the area under these curves on $[0, \pi]$.
b. Graph a few more of the functions $f_n(x) = \sin^2 nx$ on the interval $[0, \pi]$, where n is a positive integer. Find the area under these curves on $[0, \pi]$. Comment on your observations.

c. Prove that $\int_0^{\pi} \sin^2(nx) \, dx$ has the same value for all positive integers n.
d. Does the conclusion of part (c) hold if sine is replaced with cosine?
e. Repeat parts (a), (b), and (c) with $\sin^2 x$ replaced with $\sin^4 x$. Comment on your observations.
f. Challenge problem: Show that for $m = 1, 2, 3, \ldots$,

$$\int_0^{\pi} \sin^{2m} x \, dx = \int_0^{\pi} \cos^{2m} x \, dx = \pi \cdot \frac{1 \cdot 3 \cdot 5 \cdots (2m-1)}{2 \cdot 4 \cdot 6 \cdots 2m}.$$

QUICK CHECK ANSWERS

1. $\frac{1}{3}\cos^3 x - \cos x + C$ **2.** Write $\int \sin^3 x \cos^3 x \, dx = \int \sin^2 x \cos^3 x \sin x \, dx = \int (1 - \cos^2 x) \cos^3 x \sin x \, dx$. Then use the substitution $u = \cos x$. Or begin by writing $\int \sin^3 x \cos^3 x \, dx = \int \sin^3 x \cos^2 x \cos x \, dx$. ◄

7.4 Trigonometric Substitutions

In Example 4 of Section 6.5, we wrote the arc length integral for the segment of the parabola $y = x^2$ on the interval $[0, 2]$ as

$$\int_0^2 \sqrt{1 + 4x^2} \, dx = \int_0^2 2\sqrt{\tfrac{1}{4} + x^2} \, dx.$$

At the time, we did not have the analytical methods needed to evaluate this integral. The difficulty with $\int_0^2 \sqrt{1 + 4x^2} \, dx$ is that the square root of a sum (or difference) of two squares is not easily simplified. On the other hand, the square root of a product of two squares is easily simplified: $\sqrt{A^2B^2} = |AB|$. If we could somehow replace $1 + 4x^2$ with a product of squares, this integral might be easier to evaluate. The goal of this section is to introduce techniques that transform sums of squares $a^2 + x^2$ (and the difference of squares $a^2 - x^2$ and $x^2 - a^2$) into products of squares.

Integrals similar to the arc length integral for the parabola arise in many different situations. For example, electrostatic, magnetic, and gravitational forces obey an inverse square law (their strength is proportional to $1/r^2$, where r is a distance). Computing these force fields in two dimensions leads to integrals such as $\displaystyle\int \frac{dx}{\sqrt{x^2 + a^2}}$ or $\displaystyle\int \frac{dx}{(x^2 + a^2)^{3/2}}$.

It turns out that integrals containing the terms $a^2 \pm x^2$ or $x^2 - a^2$, where a is a constant, can be simplified using somewhat unexpected substitutions involving trigonometric functions. The new integrals produced by these substitutions are often trigonometric integrals of the variety studied in the preceding section.

> To understand how a sum of squares is rewritten as a product of squares, think of the Pythagorean Theorem: $a^2 + b^2 = c^2$. A rearrangement of this theorem leads to the standard substitution for integrals involving the difference of squares $a^2 - x^2$. The term $\sqrt{a^2 - x^2}$ is the length of one side of a right triangle whose hypotenuse has length a and whose other side has length x. Labeling one acute angle θ, we see that $x = a \sin \theta$.

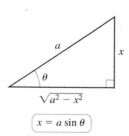

$x = a \sin \theta$

Integrals Involving $a^2 - x^2$

Suppose you are faced with an integral whose integrand contains the term $a^2 - x^2$, where a is a positive constant. Observe what happens when x is replaced with $a \sin \theta$:

$$
\begin{aligned}
a^2 - x^2 &= a^2 - (a \sin \theta)^2 &&\text{Replace } x \text{ with } a \sin \theta.\\
&= a^2 - a^2 \sin^2 \theta &&\text{Simplify.}\\
&= a^2 (1 - \sin^2 \theta) &&\text{Factor.}\\
&= a^2 \cos^2 \theta. &&1 - \sin^2 \theta = \cos^2 \theta
\end{aligned}
$$

QUICK CHECK 1 Use a substitution of the form $x = a \sin \theta$ to transform $9 - x^2$ into a product. ◄

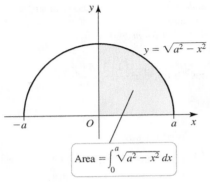

Figure 7.2

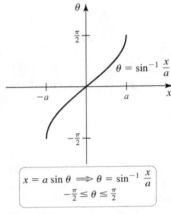

$$x = a \sin \theta \implies \theta = \sin^{-1} \frac{x}{a}$$
$$-\frac{\pi}{2} \leq \theta \leq \frac{\pi}{2}$$

Figure 7.3

➤ The key identities for integrating $\sin^2 \theta$ and $\cos^2 \theta$ are

$$\sin^2 \theta = \frac{1 - \cos 2\theta}{2} \quad \text{and}$$

$$\cos^2 \theta = \frac{1 + \cos 2\theta}{2}.$$

This calculation shows that the substitution $x = a \sin \theta$ turns the difference $a^2 - x^2$ into the product $a^2 \cos^2 \theta$. The resulting integral—now with respect to θ—is often easier to evaluate than the original integral. The details of this procedure are spelled out in the following examples.

EXAMPLE 1 Area of a circle Verify that the area of a circle of radius a is πa^2.

SOLUTION The function $f(x) = \sqrt{a^2 - x^2}$ describes the upper half of a circle centered at the origin with radius a (Figure 7.2). The region under this curve on the interval $[0, a]$ is a quarter-circle. Therefore, the area of the full circle is $4 \int_0^a \sqrt{a^2 - x^2} \, dx$.

Because the integrand contains the expression $a^2 - x^2$, we use the trigonometric substitution $x = a \sin \theta$. As with all substitutions, the differential associated with the substitution must be computed:

$$x = a \sin \theta \quad \text{implies that} \quad dx = a \cos \theta \, d\theta.$$

The substitution $x = a \sin \theta$ can also be written $\theta = \sin^{-1}(x/a)$, where $-\pi/2 \leq \theta \leq \pi/2$ (Figure 7.3). Notice that the new variable θ plays the role of an angle. Replacing x with $a \sin \theta$ in the integrand, we have

$$
\begin{aligned}
\sqrt{a^2 - x^2} &= \sqrt{a^2 - (a \sin \theta)^2} && \text{Replace } x \text{ with } a \sin \theta. \\
&= \sqrt{a^2 (1 - \sin^2 \theta)} && \text{Factor.} \\
&= \sqrt{a^2 \cos^2 \theta} && 1 - \sin^2 \theta = \cos^2 \theta \\
&= |a \cos \theta| && \sqrt{x^2} = |x| \\
&= a \cos \theta. && a > 0, \cos \theta \geq 0, \text{ for } -\frac{\pi}{2} \leq \theta \leq \frac{\pi}{2}
\end{aligned}
$$

We also change the limits of integration: When $x = 0$, $\theta = \sin^{-1} 0 = 0$; when $x = a$, $\theta = \sin^{-1}(a/a) = \sin^{-1} 1 = \pi/2$. Making these substitutions, the integral is evaluated as follows:

$$
\begin{aligned}
4 \int_0^a \sqrt{a^2 - x^2} \, dx &= 4 \int_0^{\pi/2} \underbrace{a \cos \theta \cdot a \cos \theta}_{\substack{\text{integrand} \\ \text{simplified}}} \underbrace{d\theta}_{dx} && x = a \sin \theta, dx = a \cos \theta \, d\theta \\
&= 4a^2 \int_0^{\pi/2} \cos^2 \theta \, d\theta && \text{Simplify.} \\
&= 4a^2 \left(\frac{\theta}{2} + \frac{\sin 2\theta}{4} \right) \Big|_0^{\pi/2} && \cos^2 \theta = \frac{1 + \cos 2\theta}{2} \\
&= 4a^2 \left(\left(\frac{\pi}{4} + 0 \right) - (0 + 0) \right) = \pi a^2. && \text{Simplify.}
\end{aligned}
$$

A similar calculation (Exercise 66) gives the area of an ellipse.

Related Exercises 7–16 ◄

EXAMPLE 2 Sine substitution Evaluate $\displaystyle \int \frac{dx}{(16 - x^2)^{3/2}}$.

SOLUTION The factor $16 - x^2$ has the form $a^2 - x^2$ with $a = 4$, so we use the substitution $x = 4 \sin \theta$. It follows that $dx = 4 \cos \theta \, d\theta$. We now simplify $(16 - x^2)^{3/2}$:

$$
\begin{aligned}
(16 - x^2)^{3/2} &= (16 - (4 \sin \theta)^2)^{3/2} && \text{Substitute } x = 4 \sin \theta. \\
&= (16 (1 - \sin^2 \theta))^{3/2} && \text{Factor.} \\
&= (16 \cos^2 \theta)^{3/2} && 1 - \sin^2 \theta = \cos^2 \theta \\
&= 64 \cos^3 \theta. && \text{Simplify.}
\end{aligned}
$$

Replacing the factors $(16 - x^2)^{3/2}$ and dx of the original integral with appropriate expressions in θ, we have

$$\int \frac{\overbrace{dx}^{4\cos\theta\,d\theta}}{\underbrace{(16 - x^2)^{3/2}}_{64\cos^3\theta}} = \int \frac{4\cos\theta}{64\cos^3\theta}\,d\theta$$

$$= \frac{1}{16}\int \frac{d\theta}{\cos^2\theta}$$

$$= \frac{1}{16}\int \sec^2\theta\,d\theta \quad \text{Simplify.}$$

$$= \frac{1}{16}\tan\theta + C. \quad \text{Evaluate the integral.}$$

The final step is to express this result in terms of x. In many integrals, this step is most easily done with a reference triangle showing the relationship between x and θ. Figure 7.4 shows a right triangle with an angle θ and with the sides labeled such that $x = 4\sin\theta$ (or $\sin\theta = x/4$). Using this triangle, we see that $\tan\theta = \dfrac{x}{\sqrt{16 - x^2}}$, which implies that

$$\int \frac{dx}{(16 - x^2)^{3/2}} = \frac{1}{16}\tan\theta + C = \frac{x}{16\sqrt{16 - x^2}} + C.$$

Related Exercises 7–16 ◄

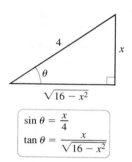

$$\sin\theta = \frac{x}{4}$$
$$\tan\theta = \frac{x}{\sqrt{16 - x^2}}$$

Figure 7.4

Integrals Involving $a^2 + x^2$ or $x^2 - a^2$

The additional trigonometric substitutions involving tangent and secant use a procedure similar to that used for the sine substitution. Figure 7.5 and Table 7.4 summarize the three basic trigonometric substitutions for real numbers $a > 0$.

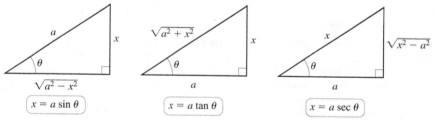

Figure 7.5

Table 7.4

The Integral Contains . . .	Corresponding Substitution	Useful Identity
$a^2 - x^2$	$x = a\sin\theta, -\dfrac{\pi}{2} \le \theta \le \dfrac{\pi}{2}$, for $|x| \le a$	$a^2 - a^2\sin^2\theta = a^2\cos^2\theta$
$a^2 + x^2$	$x = a\tan\theta, -\dfrac{\pi}{2} < \theta < \dfrac{\pi}{2}$	$a^2 + a^2\tan^2\theta = a^2\sec^2\theta$
$x^2 - a^2$	$x = a\sec\theta, \begin{cases} 0 \le \theta < \dfrac{\pi}{2}, \text{ for } x \ge a \\ \dfrac{\pi}{2} < \theta \le \pi, \text{ for } x \le -a \end{cases}$	$a^2\sec^2\theta - a^2 = a^2\tan^2\theta$

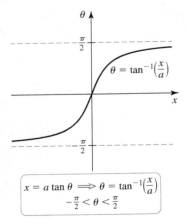

$$x = a \tan \theta \implies \theta = \tan^{-1}\left(\frac{x}{a}\right)$$
$$-\frac{\pi}{2} < \theta < \frac{\pi}{2}$$

Figure 7.6

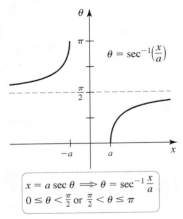

$$x = a \sec \theta \implies \theta = \sec^{-1}\frac{x}{a}$$
$$0 \le \theta < \frac{\pi}{2} \text{ or } \frac{\pi}{2} < \theta \le \pi$$

Figure 7.7

▶ Because we are evaluating a definite integral, we could change the limits of integration to $\theta = 0$ and $\theta = \tan^{-1} 4$. However, $\tan^{-1} 4$ is not a standard angle, so it is easier to express the antiderivative in terms of x and use the original limits of integration.

In order for the tangent substitution $x = a \tan \theta$ to be well defined, the angle θ must be restricted to the interval $-\pi/2 < \theta < \pi/2$, which is the range of $\tan^{-1}(x/a)$ (Figure 7.6). On this interval, $\sec \theta > 0$ and with $a > 0$, it is valid to write

$$\sqrt{a^2 + x^2} = \sqrt{a^2 + (a\tan\theta)^2} = \sqrt{a^2 \underbrace{(1 + \tan^2\theta)}_{\sec^2\theta}} = a\sec\theta.$$

With the secant substitution, there is a technicality. As discussed in Section 1.4, $\theta = \sec^{-1}(x/a)$ is defined for $x \ge a$, in which case $0 \le \theta < \pi/2$, *and* for $x \le -a$, in which case $\pi/2 < \theta \le \pi$ (Figure 7.7). These restrictions on θ must be treated carefully when simplifying integrands with a factor of $\sqrt{x^2 - a^2}$. Because $\tan \theta$ is positive in the first quadrant but negative in the second, we have

$$\sqrt{x^2 - a^2} = \sqrt{a^2 \underbrace{(\sec^2\theta - 1)}_{\tan^2\theta}} = |a\tan\theta| = \begin{cases} a\tan\theta & \text{if } 0 \le \theta < \dfrac{\pi}{2} \\ -a\tan\theta & \text{if } \dfrac{\pi}{2} < \theta \le \pi. \end{cases}$$

When evaluating a definite integral, you should check the limits of integration to see which of these two cases applies. For indefinite integrals, a piecewise formula is often needed, unless a restriction on the variable is given in the problem (see Exercises 85–88).

QUICK CHECK 2 What change of variables would you use for these integrals?

a. $\displaystyle\int \frac{x^2}{\sqrt{x^2 + 9}}\,dx$ b. $\displaystyle\int \frac{3}{x\sqrt{16 - x^2}}\,dx$? ◀

EXAMPLE 3 Arc length of a parabola Evaluate $\int_0^2 \sqrt{1 + 4x^2}\,dx$, the arc length of the segment of the parabola $y = x^2$ on $[0, 2]$.

SOLUTION Removing a factor of 4 from the square root, we have

$$\int_0^2 \sqrt{1 + 4x^2}\,dx = 2\int_0^2 \sqrt{\tfrac{1}{4} + x^2}\,dx = 2\int_0^2 \sqrt{\left(\tfrac{1}{2}\right)^2 + x^2}\,dx.$$

The integrand contains the expression $a^2 + x^2$, with $a = \tfrac{1}{2}$, which suggests the substitution $x = \tfrac{1}{2}\tan\theta$. It follows that $dx = \tfrac{1}{2}\sec^2\theta\,d\theta$, and

$$\sqrt{\left(\tfrac{1}{2}\right)^2 + x^2} = \sqrt{\left(\tfrac{1}{2}\right)^2 + \left(\tfrac{1}{2}\tan\theta\right)^2} = \frac{1}{2}\underbrace{\sqrt{1 + \tan^2\theta}}_{\sec^2\theta} = \frac{1}{2}\sec\theta.$$

Setting aside the limits of integration for the moment, we compute the antiderivative:

$$2\int \sqrt{\left(\tfrac{1}{2}\right)^2 + x^2}\,dx = 2\int \underbrace{\tfrac{1}{2}\sec\theta\,\tfrac{1}{2}\sec^2\theta\,d\theta}_{dx} \qquad \begin{aligned} x &= \tfrac{1}{2}\tan\theta, \\ dx &= \tfrac{1}{2}\sec^2\theta\,d\theta \end{aligned}$$

$$= \frac{1}{2}\int \sec^3\theta\,d\theta \qquad\qquad \text{Simplify.}$$

$$= \frac{1}{4}\left(\sec\theta\tan\theta + \ln|\sec\theta + \tan\theta|\right) + C. \quad \begin{aligned}&\text{Reduction formula 4,}\\&\text{Section 7.3}\end{aligned}$$

Using a reference triangle (Figure 7.8), we express the antiderivative in terms of the original variable x and evaluate the definite integral:

$$2\int_0^2 \sqrt{\left(\tfrac{1}{2}\right)^2 + x^2}\,dx = \frac{1}{4}\left(\underbrace{\sqrt{1 + 4x^2}}_{\sec\theta}\underbrace{2x}_{\tan\theta} + \ln\left|\underbrace{\sqrt{1 + 4x^2}}_{\sec\theta} + \underbrace{2x}_{\tan\theta}\right|\right)\Bigg|_0^2$$
$$\tan\theta = 2x, \ \sec\theta = \sqrt{1 + 4x^2}$$

$$= \frac{1}{4}\left(4\sqrt{17} + \ln\left(\sqrt{17} + 4\right)\right) \approx 4.65.$$

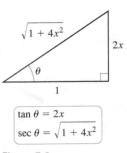

$$\tan\theta = 2x$$
$$\sec\theta = \sqrt{1 + 4x^2}$$

Figure 7.8

Related Exercises 17–56 ◀

QUICK CHECK 3 The integral $\int \dfrac{dx}{a^2 + x^2} = \dfrac{1}{a} \tan^{-1} \dfrac{x}{a} + C$ is given in Section 4.9. Verify this result with the appropriate trigonometric substitution. ◄

EXAMPLE 4 Another tangent substitution Evaluate $\int \dfrac{dx}{(1 + x^2)^2}$.

SOLUTION The factor $1 + x^2$ suggests the substitution $x = \tan \theta$. It follows that $\theta = \tan^{-1} x$, $dx = \sec^2 \theta \, d\theta$, and

$$(1 + x^2)^2 = \underbrace{(1 + \tan^2 \theta)^2}_{\sec^2 \theta} = \sec^4 \theta.$$

Substituting these factors leads to

$$\int \frac{dx}{(1 + x^2)^2} = \int \frac{\sec^2 \theta}{\sec^4 \theta} \, d\theta \qquad x = \tan \theta, \, dx = \sec^2 \theta \, d\theta$$

$$= \int \cos^2 \theta \, d\theta \qquad \text{Simplify.}$$

$$= \frac{\theta}{2} + \frac{\sin 2\theta}{4} + C. \qquad \text{Integrate } \cos^2 \theta = \frac{1 + \cos 2\theta}{2}.$$

The final step is to return to the original variable x. The first term $\theta/2$ is replaced with $\frac{1}{2} \tan^{-1} x$. The second term involving $\sin 2\theta$ requires the identity $\sin 2\theta = 2 \sin \theta \cos \theta$. The reference triangle (Figure 7.9) tells us that

$$\frac{1}{4} \sin 2\theta = \frac{1}{2} \sin \theta \cos \theta = \frac{1}{2} \cdot \frac{x}{\sqrt{1 + x^2}} \cdot \frac{1}{\sqrt{1 + x^2}} = \frac{x}{2(1 + x^2)}.$$

The integration can now be completed:

$$\int \frac{dx}{(1 + x^2)^2} = \frac{\theta}{2} + \frac{\sin 2\theta}{4} + C$$

$$= \frac{1}{2} \tan^{-1} x + \frac{x}{2(1 + x^2)} + C.$$

Related Exercises 17–56 ◄

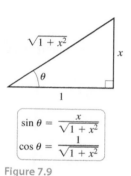

$$\sin \theta = \frac{x}{\sqrt{1 + x^2}}$$

$$\cos \theta = \frac{1}{\sqrt{1 + x^2}}$$

Figure 7.9

EXAMPLE 5 Multiple approaches Evaluate the integral $\int \dfrac{dx}{\sqrt{x^2 + 4}}$.

SOLUTION Our goal is to show that several different methods lead to the same end.

Solution 1: The term $x^2 + 4$ suggests the substitution $x = 2 \tan \theta$, which implies that $dx = 2 \sec^2 \theta \, d\theta$ and

$$\sqrt{x^2 + 4} = \sqrt{4 \tan^2 \theta + 4} = \sqrt{4(\tan^2 \theta + 1)} = 2\sqrt{\sec^2 \theta} = 2 \sec \theta.$$

Making these substitutions, the integral becomes

$$\int \frac{dx}{\sqrt{x^2 + 4}} = \int \frac{2 \sec^2 \theta}{2 \sec \theta} \, d\theta = \int \sec \theta \, d\theta = \ln |\sec \theta + \tan \theta| + C.$$

To express the indefinite integral in terms of x, notice that with $x = 2 \tan \theta$, we have

$$\tan \theta = \frac{x}{2} \quad \text{and} \quad \sec \theta = \sqrt{\tan^2 \theta + 1} = \frac{1}{2}\sqrt{x^2 + 4}.$$

Therefore,

$$\int \frac{dx}{\sqrt{x^2 + 4}} = \ln|\sec\theta + \tan\theta| + C$$

$$= \ln\left|\frac{1}{2}\sqrt{x^2 + 4} + \frac{x}{2}\right| + C \qquad \text{Substitute for } \sec\theta \text{ and } \tan\theta.$$

$$= \ln\left(\frac{1}{2}(\sqrt{x^2 + 4} + x)\right) + C \qquad \text{Factor; } \sqrt{x^2 + 4} + x > 0.$$

$$= \ln\frac{1}{2} + \ln(\sqrt{x^2 + 4} + x) + C \qquad \ln ab = \ln a + \ln b$$

$$= \ln(\sqrt{x^2 + 4} + x) + C. \qquad \text{Absorb constant in } C.$$

Solution 2: Using Theorem 6.12 of Section 6.10, we see that

$$\int \frac{dx}{\sqrt{x^2 + 4}} = \sinh^{-1}\frac{x}{2} + C.$$

By Theorem 6.10 of Section 6.10, we also know that

$$\sinh^{-1}\frac{x}{2} = \ln\left(\frac{x}{2} + \sqrt{\left(\frac{x}{2}\right)^2 + 1}\right) = \ln\left(\frac{1}{2}(\sqrt{x^2 + 4} + x)\right),$$

which leads to the same result as in Solution 1.

Solution 3: Yet another approach is to use the substitution $x = 2\sinh t$, which implies that $dx = 2\cosh t\, dt$ and

$$\sqrt{x^2 + 4} = \sqrt{4\sinh^2 t + 4} = \sqrt{4(\sinh^2 t + 1)} = 2\sqrt{\cosh^2 t} = 2\cosh t.$$

The original integral now becomes

$$\int \frac{dx}{\sqrt{x^2 + 4}} = \int \frac{2\cosh t}{2\cosh t}\, dt = \int dt = t + C.$$

Because $x = 2\sinh t$, we have $t = \sinh^{-1}\frac{x}{2}$, which, by Theorem 6.10, leads to the result found in Solution 2.

This example shows that some integrals may be evaluated by more than one method. With practice, you will learn to identify the best method for a given integral.

Related Exercises 17–56 ◀

▶ Recall that to complete the square with $x^2 + bx + c$, you add and subtract $(b/2)^2$ to the expression, and then factor to form a perfect square. You could also make the single substitution $x + 2 = 3\sec\theta$ in Example 6.

EXAMPLE 6   A secant substitution Evaluate $\displaystyle\int_1^4 \frac{\sqrt{x^2 + 4x - 5}}{x + 2}\, dx.$

SOLUTION This example illustrates a useful preliminary step first encountered in Section 7.1. The integrand does not contain any of the patterns in Table 7.4 that suggest a trigonometric substitution. Completing the square does, however, lead to one of those patterns. Noting that $x^2 + 4x - 5 = (x + 2)^2 - 9$, we change variables with $u = x + 2$ and write the integral as

$$\int_1^4 \frac{\sqrt{x^2 + 4x - 5}}{x + 2}\, dx = \int_1^4 \frac{\sqrt{(x + 2)^2 - 9}}{x + 2}\, dx \qquad \text{Complete the square.}$$

$$= \int_3^6 \frac{\sqrt{u^2 - 9}}{u}\, du. \qquad \begin{array}{l}u = x + 2, du = dx \\ \text{Change limits of integration.}\end{array}$$

▶ The substitution $u = 3 \sec \theta$ can be rewritten as $\theta = \sec^{-1}(u/3)$. Because $u \geq 3$ in the integral $\int_3^6 \dfrac{\sqrt{u^2 - 9}}{u}\, du$, we have $0 \leq \theta < \dfrac{\pi}{2}$.

This new integral calls for the secant substitution $u = 3 \sec \theta$ (where $0 \leq \theta < \pi/2$), which implies that $du = 3 \sec \theta \tan \theta\, d\theta$ and $\sqrt{u^2 - 9} = 3 \tan \theta$. We also change the limits of integration: When $u = 3$, $\theta = 0$, and when $u = 6$, $\theta = \pi/3$. The complete integration can now be done:

$$\int_1^4 \frac{\sqrt{x^2 + 4x - 5}}{x + 2}\, dx = \int_3^6 \frac{\sqrt{u^2 - 9}}{u}\, du \qquad u = x + 2,\, du = dx$$

$$= \int_0^{\pi/3} \frac{3 \tan \theta}{3 \sec \theta}\, 3 \sec \theta \tan \theta\, d\theta \quad u = 3 \sec \theta,\, du = 3 \sec \theta \tan \theta\, d\theta$$

$$= 3 \int_0^{\pi/3} \tan^2 \theta\, d\theta \qquad \text{Simplify.}$$

$$= 3 \int_0^{\pi/3} (\sec^2 \theta - 1)\, d\theta \qquad \tan^2 \theta = \sec^2 \theta - 1$$

$$= 3 (\tan \theta - \theta) \Big|_0^{\pi/3} \qquad \text{Evaluate integrals.}$$

$$= 3\sqrt{3} - \pi. \qquad \text{Simplify.}$$

Related Exercises 17–56 ◀

SECTION 7.4 EXERCISES

Review Questions

1. What change of variables is suggested by an integral containing $\sqrt{x^2 - 9}$?

2. What change of variables is suggested by an integral containing $\sqrt{x^2 + 36}$?

3. What change of variables is suggested by an integral containing $\sqrt{100 - x^2}$?

4. If $x = 4 \tan \theta$, express $\sin \theta$ in terms of x.

5. If $x = 2 \sin \theta$, express $\cot \theta$ in terms of x.

6. If $x = 8 \sec \theta$, express $\tan \theta$ in terms of x.

Basic Skills

7–16. Sine substitution *Evaluate the following integrals.*

7. $\displaystyle\int_0^{5/2} \frac{dx}{\sqrt{25 - x^2}}$

8. $\displaystyle\int_0^{3/2} \frac{dx}{(9 - x^2)^{3/2}}$

9. $\displaystyle\int_5^{10} \sqrt{100 - x^2}\, dx$

10. $\displaystyle\int_0^{\sqrt{2}} \frac{x^2}{\sqrt{4 - x^2}}\, dx$

11. $\displaystyle\int_0^{1/2} \frac{x^2}{\sqrt{1 - x^2}}\, dx$

12. $\displaystyle\int_{1/2}^1 \frac{\sqrt{1 - x^2}}{x^2}\, dx$

13. $\displaystyle\int \frac{dx}{(16 - x^2)^{1/2}}$

14. $\displaystyle\int \sqrt{36 - t^2}\, dt$

15. $\displaystyle\int \frac{\sqrt{9 - x^2}}{x}\, dx$

16. $\displaystyle\int (36 - 9x^2)^{-3/2}\, dx$

17–46. Trigonometric substitutions *Evaluate the following integrals.*

17. $\displaystyle\int \sqrt{64 - x^2}\, dx$

18. $\displaystyle\int \frac{dx}{\sqrt{x^2 - 49}},\, x > 7$

19. $\displaystyle\int \frac{dx}{(1 - x^2)^{3/2}}$

20. $\displaystyle\int \frac{dx}{(1 + x^2)^{3/2}}$

21. $\displaystyle\int \frac{dx}{x^2\sqrt{x^2 + 9}}$

22. $\displaystyle\int \frac{dt}{t^2\sqrt{9 - t^2}}$

23. $\displaystyle\int \frac{dx}{\sqrt{36 - x^2}}$

24. $\displaystyle\int \frac{dx}{\sqrt{16 + 4x^2}}$

25. $\displaystyle\int \frac{dx}{\sqrt{x^2 - 81}},\, x > 9$

26. $\displaystyle\int \frac{dx}{\sqrt{1 - 2x^2}}$

27. $\displaystyle\int \frac{dx}{(1 + 4x^2)^{3/2}}$

28. $\displaystyle\int \frac{dx}{(x^2 - 36)^{3/2}},\, x > 6$

29. $\displaystyle\int \frac{x^2}{\sqrt{16 - x^2}}\, dx$

30. $\displaystyle\int \frac{dx}{(81 + x^2)^2}$

31. $\displaystyle\int \frac{\sqrt{x^2 - 9}}{x}\, dx,\, x > 3$

32. $\displaystyle\int \sqrt{9 - 4x^2}\, dx$

33. $\displaystyle\int \frac{x^2}{\sqrt{4 + x^2}}\, dx$

34. $\displaystyle\int \frac{\sqrt{4x^2 - 1}}{x^2}\, dx,\, x > \frac{1}{2}$

35. $\displaystyle\int \frac{dx}{\sqrt{3 - 2x - x^2}}$

36. $\displaystyle\int \frac{y^4}{1 + y^2}\, dy$

37. $\displaystyle\int \frac{\sqrt{9x^2 - 25}}{x^3}\, dx,\, x > \frac{5}{3}$

38. $\displaystyle\int \frac{\sqrt{9 - x^2}}{x^2}\, dx$

39. $\displaystyle\int \frac{x^2}{(25 + x^2)^2}\, dx$

40. $\displaystyle\int \frac{dx}{x^2\sqrt{9x^2 - 1}},\, x > \frac{1}{3}$

41. $\displaystyle\int \frac{x^2}{(100 - x^2)^{3/2}}\, dx$

42. $\displaystyle\int \frac{dx}{x^3\sqrt{x^2 - 100}},\, x > 10$

43. $\displaystyle\int \frac{x^3}{(81 - x^2)^2}\, dx$

44. $\displaystyle\int \frac{dx}{x^3\sqrt{x^2 - 1}},\, x > 1$

45. $\displaystyle\int \frac{dx}{x(x^2-1)^{3/2}}, \; x > 1$

46. $\displaystyle\int \frac{x^3}{(x^2-16)^{3/2}}\, dx, \; x < -4$

47–56. Evaluating definite integrals *Evaluate the following definite integrals.*

47. $\displaystyle\int_0^1 \frac{dx}{\sqrt{x^2+16}}$

48. $\displaystyle\int_{8\sqrt{2}}^{16} \frac{dx}{\sqrt{x^2-64}}$

49. $\displaystyle\int_{1/\sqrt{3}}^1 \frac{dx}{x^2\sqrt{1+x^2}}$

50. $\displaystyle\int_1^{\sqrt{2}} \frac{dx}{x^2\sqrt{4-x^2}}$

51. $\displaystyle\int_0^{1/\sqrt{3}} \sqrt{x^2+1}\, dx$

52. $\displaystyle\int_{\sqrt{2}}^2 \frac{\sqrt{x^2-1}}{x}\, dx$

53. $\displaystyle\int_0^{1/3} \frac{dx}{(9x^2+1)^{3/2}}$

54. $\displaystyle\int_{10/\sqrt{3}}^{10} \frac{dy}{\sqrt{y^2-25}}$

55. $\displaystyle\int_{4/\sqrt{3}}^4 \frac{dx}{x^2(x^2-4)}$

56. $\displaystyle\int_6^{6\sqrt{3}} \frac{z^2}{(z^2+36)^2}\, dz$

Further Explorations

57. Explain why or why not Determine whether the following statements are true and give an explanation or counterexample.

a. If $x = 4\tan\theta$, then $\csc\theta = 4/x$.

b. The integral $\int_1^2 \sqrt{1-x^2}\, dx$ does not have a finite real value.

c. The integral $\int_1^2 \sqrt{x^2-1}\, dx$ does not have a finite real value.

d. The integral $\displaystyle\int \frac{dx}{x^2+4x+9}$ cannot be evaluated using a trigonometric substitution.

58–65. Completing the square *Evaluate the following integrals.*

58. $\displaystyle\int \frac{dx}{x^2-6x+34}$

59. $\displaystyle\int \frac{dx}{x^2+6x+18}$

60. $\displaystyle\int \frac{du}{2u^2-12u+36}$

61. $\displaystyle\int \frac{x^2-2x+1}{\sqrt{x^2-2x+10}}\, dx$

62. $\displaystyle\int \frac{x^2+2x+4}{\sqrt{x^2-4x}}\, dx, \; x > 4$

63. $\displaystyle\int \frac{x^2-8x+16}{(9+8x-x^2)^{3/2}}\, dx$

64. $\displaystyle\int_1^4 \frac{dt}{t^2-2t+10}$

65. $\displaystyle\int_{1/2}^{(\sqrt{2}+3)/(2\sqrt{2})} \frac{dx}{8x^2-8x+11}$

66. Area of an ellipse The upper half of the ellipse centered at the origin with axes of length $2a$ and $2b$ is described by $y = \dfrac{b}{a}\sqrt{a^2-x^2}$ (see figure). Find the area of the ellipse in terms of a and b.

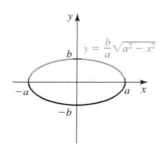

67. Area of a segment of a circle Use two approaches to show that the area of a cap (or segment) of a circle of radius r subtended by an angle θ (see figure) is given by

$$A_{seg} = \frac{1}{2}r^2(\theta - \sin\theta).$$

a. Find the area using geometry (no calculus).
b. Find the area using calculus.

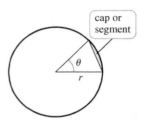

68. Area of a lune A lune is a crescent-shaped region bounded by the arcs of two circles. Let C_1 be a circle of radius 4 centered at the origin. Let C_2 be a circle of radius 3 centered at the point $(2, 0)$. Find the area of the lune (shaded in the figure) that lies inside C_1 and outside C_2.

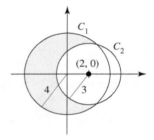

69. Area and volume Consider the function $f(x) = (9 + x^2)^{-1/2}$ and the region R on the interval $[0, 4]$ (see figure).

a. Find the area of R.
b. Find the volume of the solid generated when R is revolved about the x-axis.
c. Find the volume of the solid generated when R is revolved about the y-axis.

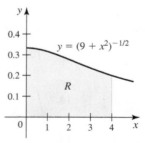

T 70. Area of a region Graph the function $f(x) = (16 + x^2)^{-3/2}$ and find the area of the region bounded by the curve and the x-axis on the interval $[0, 3]$.

71. Arc length of a parabola Find the length of the curve $y = ax^2$ from $x = 0$ to $x = 10$, where $a > 0$ is a real number.

72. Computing areas On the interval $[0, 2]$, the graphs of $f(x) = x^2/3$ and $g(x) = x^2(9 - x^2)^{-1/2}$ have similar shapes.

    a. Find the area of the region bounded by the graph of f and the x-axis on the interval $[0, 2]$.

    b. Find the area of the region bounded by the graph of g and the x-axis on the interval $[0, 2]$.

    c. Which region has greater area?

T 73–75. Using the integral of sec³ u *By reduction formula 4 in Section 7.3,*

$$\int \sec^3 u \, du = \frac{1}{2}(\sec u \tan u + \ln |\sec u + \tan u|) + C.$$

Graph the following functions and find the area under the curve on the given interval.

73. $f(x) = (9 - x^2)^{-2}, \ \left[0, \frac{3}{2}\right]$

74. $f(x) = (4 + x^2)^{1/2}, \ [0, 2]$

75. $f(x) = (x^2 - 25)^{1/2}, \ [5, 10]$

76–77. Asymmetric integrands *Evaluate the following integrals. Consider completing the square.*

76. $\displaystyle\int \frac{dx}{\sqrt{(x - 1)(3 - x)}}$

77. $\displaystyle\int_{2+\sqrt{2}}^{4} \frac{dx}{\sqrt{(x - 1)(x - 3)}}$

78. Clever substitution Evaluate $\displaystyle\int \frac{dx}{1 + \sin x + \cos x}$ using the substitution $x = 2 \tan^{-1} \theta$. The identities $\sin x = 2 \sin \frac{x}{2} \cos \frac{x}{2}$ and $\cos x = \cos^2 \frac{x}{2} - \sin^2 \frac{x}{2}$ are helpful.

Applications

79. A torus (doughnut) Find the volume of the solid torus formed when the circle of radius 4 centered at $(0, 6)$ is revolved about the x-axis.

80. Bagel wars Bob and Bruce bake bagels (shaped like tori). They both make bagels that have an inner radius of 0.5 in and an outer radius of 2.5 in. Bob plans to increase the volume of his bagels by decreasing the inner radius by 20% (leaving the outer radius unchanged). Bruce plans to increase the volume of his bagels by increasing the outer radius by 20% (leaving the inner radius unchanged). Whose new bagels will have the greater volume? Does this result depend on the size of the original bagels? Explain.

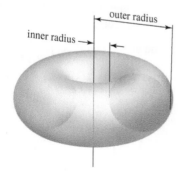

inner radius →   outer radius

81. Electric field due to a line of charge A total charge of Q is distributed uniformly on a line segment of length $2L$ along the y-axis (see figure). The x-component of the electric field at a point $(a, 0)$ is given by

$$E_x(a) = \frac{kQa}{2L} \int_{-L}^{L} \frac{dy}{(a^2 + y^2)^{3/2}},$$

where k is a physical constant and $a > 0$.

    a. Confirm that $E_x(a) = \dfrac{kQ}{a\sqrt{a^2 + L^2}}$.

    b. Letting $\rho = Q/2L$ be the charge density on the line segment, show that if $L \to \infty$, then $E_x(a) = 2k\rho/a$.

(See the Guided Project *Electric field integrals* for a derivation of this and other similar integrals.)

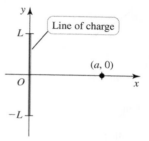

82. Magnetic field due to current in a straight wire A long, straight wire of length $2L$ on the y-axis carries a current I. According to the Biot-Savart Law, the magnitude of the magnetic field due to the current at a point $(a, 0)$ is given by

$$B(a) = \frac{\mu_0 I}{4\pi} \int_{-L}^{L} \frac{\sin \theta}{r^2} \, dy,$$

where μ_0 is a physical constant, $a > 0$, and θ, r, and y are related as shown in the figure.

    a. Show that the magnitude of the magnetic field at $(a, 0)$ is

$$B(a) = \frac{\mu_0 IL}{2\pi a\sqrt{a^2 + L^2}}.$$

    b. What is the magnitude of the magnetic field at $(a, 0)$ due to an infinitely long wire $(L \to \infty)$?

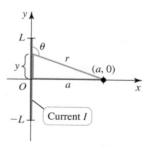

83. Fastest descent time The cycloid is the curve traced by a point on the rim of a rolling wheel. Imagine a wire shaped like an inverted cycloid (see figure). A bead sliding down this wire without friction has some remarkable properties. Among all wire shapes, the cycloid is the shape that produces the fastest descent time (see the Guided Project *The amazing cycloid* for more about the *brachistochrone property*). It can be shown that the descent time between any two points $0 \le a < b \le \pi$ on the curve is

$$\text{descent time} = \int_a^b \sqrt{\frac{1 - \cos t}{g(\cos a - \cos t)}}\, dt,$$

where g is the acceleration due to gravity, $t = 0$ corresponds to the top of the wire, and $t = \pi$ corresponds to the lowest point on the wire.

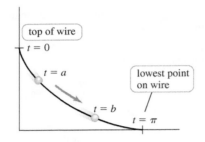

a. Find the descent time on the interval $[a, b]$ by making the substitution $u = \cos t$.

b. Show that when $b = \pi$, the descent time is the same for all values of a; that is, the descent time to the bottom of the wire is the same for all starting points.

T 84. Maximum path length of a projectile (Adapted from Putnam Exam 1940) A projectile is launched from the ground with an initial speed V at an angle θ from the horizontal. Assume that the x-axis is the horizontal ground and y is the height above the ground. Neglecting air resistance and letting g be the acceleration due to gravity, it can be shown that the trajectory of the projectile is given by

$$y = -\frac{1}{2}kx^2 + y_{\max}, \quad \text{where } k = \frac{g}{(V \cos \theta)^2}$$

$$\text{and } y_{\max} = \frac{(V \sin \theta)^2}{2g}.$$

a. Note that the high point of the trajectory occurs at $(0, y_{\max})$. If the projectile is on the ground at $(-a, 0)$ and $(a, 0)$, what is a?

b. Show that the length of the trajectory (arc length) is $2 \int_0^a \sqrt{1 + k^2 x^2}\, dx$.

c. Evaluate the arc length integral and express your result in terms of V, g, and θ.

d. For a fixed value of V and g, show that the launch angle θ that maximizes the length of the trajectory satisfies $(\sin \theta) \ln (\sec \theta + \tan \theta) = 1$.

e. Use a graphing utility to approximate the optimal launch angle.

Additional Exercises

85–88. Care with the secant substitution *Recall that the substitution $x = a \sec \theta$ implies either $x \ge a$ (in which case $0 \le \theta < \pi/2$ and $\tan \theta \ge 0$) or $x \le -a$ (in which case $\pi/2 < \theta \le \pi$ and $\tan \theta \le 0$).*

85. Show that $\displaystyle\int \frac{dx}{x\sqrt{x^2 - 1}} =$

$$\begin{cases} \sec^{-1} x + C = \tan^{-1} \sqrt{x^2 - 1} + C & \text{if } x > 1 \\ -\sec^{-1} x + C = -\tan^{-1} \sqrt{x^2 - 1} + C & \text{if } x < -1. \end{cases}$$

86. Evaluate for $\displaystyle\int \frac{\sqrt{x^2 - 1}}{x^3}\, dx$, for $x > 1$ and for $x < -1$.

T 87. Graph the function $f(x) = \dfrac{\sqrt{x^2 - 9}}{x}$ and consider the region bounded by the curve and the x-axis on $[-6, -3]$. Then evaluate $\displaystyle\int_{-6}^{-3} \frac{\sqrt{x^2 - 9}}{x}\, dx$. Be sure the result is consistent with the graph.

T 88. Graph the function $f(x) = \dfrac{1}{x\sqrt{x^2 - 36}}$ on its domain. Then find the area of the region R_1 bounded by the curve and the x-axis on $[-12, -12/\sqrt{3}]$ and the area of the region R_2 bounded by the curve and the x-axis on $[12/\sqrt{3}, 12]$. Be sure your results are consistent with the graph.

89. Visual proof Let $F(x) = \int_0^x \sqrt{a^2 - t^2}\, dt$. The figure shows that $F(x) =$ area of sector OAB + area of triangle OBC.

a. Use the figure to prove that

$$F(x) = \frac{a^2 \sin^{-1}(x/a)}{2} + \frac{x\sqrt{a^2 - x^2}}{2}.$$

b. Conclude that

$$\int \sqrt{a^2 - x^2}\, dx = \frac{a^2 \sin^{-1}(x/a)}{2} + \frac{x\sqrt{a^2 - x^2}}{2} + C.$$

(*Source: The College Mathematics Journal* 34, 3, May 2003)

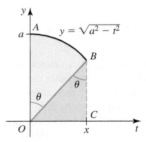

QUICK CHECK ANSWERS

1. Use $x = 3 \sin \theta$ to obtain $9 \cos^2 \theta$. **2.** (a) Use $x = 3 \tan \theta$. (b) Use $x = 4 \sin \theta$. **3.** Let $x = a \tan \theta$, so that $dx = a \sec^2 \theta\, d\theta$. The new integral is $\displaystyle\int \frac{a \sec^2 \theta\, d\theta}{a^2(1 + \tan^2 \theta)} = \frac{1}{a}\int d\theta = \frac{1}{a}\theta + C = \frac{1}{a}\tan^{-1}\frac{x}{a} + C.$ ◄

7.5 Partial Fractions

> Recall that a rational function has the form p/q, where p and q are polynomials.

Later in this chapter, we will see that finding the velocity of a skydiver requires evaluating an integral of the form $\int \dfrac{dv}{a - bv^2}$ and finding the population of a species that is limited in size involves an integral of the form $\int \dfrac{dP}{aP(1 - bP)}$, where a and b are constants in both cases. These integrals have the common feature that their integrands are rational functions. Similar integrals result from modeling mechanical and electrical networks. The goal of this section is to introduce the *method of partial fractions* for integrating rational functions. When combined with standard and trigonometric substitutions (Section 7.4), this method allows us (in principle) to integrate any rational function.

Method of Partial Fractions

Given a function such as

$$f(x) = \frac{1}{x - 2} + \frac{2}{x + 4},$$

it is a straightforward task to find a common denominator and write the equivalent expression

$$f(x) = \frac{(x + 4) + 2(x - 2)}{(x - 2)(x + 4)} = \frac{3x}{(x - 2)(x + 4)} = \frac{3x}{x^2 + 2x - 8}.$$

The purpose of partial fractions is to reverse this process. Given a rational function that is difficult to integrate, the method of partial fractions produces an equivalent function that is much easier to integrate.

Rational function		**Partial fraction decomposition**
$\dfrac{3x}{x^2 + 2x - 8}$	*method of partial fractions* $\longrightarrow$	$\dfrac{1}{x - 2} + \dfrac{2}{x + 4}$
Difficult to integrate		**Easy to integrate**
$\displaystyle\int \frac{3x}{x^2 + 2x - 8}\,dx$		$\displaystyle\int \left(\frac{1}{x - 2} + \frac{2}{x + 4}\right) dx$

QUICK CHECK 1 Find an antiderivative of $f(x) = \dfrac{1}{x - 2} + \dfrac{2}{x + 4}$. ◄

The Key Idea Working with the same function, $f(x) = \dfrac{3x}{(x - 2)(x + 4)}$, our objective is to write it in the form

$$\frac{A}{x - 2} + \frac{B}{x + 4},$$

> Notice that the numerator of the original rational function does not affect the form of the partial fraction decomposition. The constants A and B are called *undetermined coefficients*.

where A and B are constants to be determined. This expression is called the **partial fraction decomposition** of the original function; in this case, it has two terms, one for each factor in the denominator of the original function.

The constants A and B are determined using the condition that the original function f and its partial fraction decomposition must be equal for all values of x in the domain of f; that is,

$$\frac{3x}{(x - 2)(x + 4)} = \frac{A}{x - 2} + \frac{B}{x + 4}. \tag{1}$$

> ▶ This step requires that $x \neq 2$ and $x \neq -4$; both values are outside the domain of f.

Multiplying both sides of equation (1) by $(x - 2)(x + 4)$ gives

$$3x = A(x + 4) + B(x - 2).$$

Collecting like powers of x results in

$$3x = (A + B)x + (4A - 2B). \tag{2}$$

If equation (2) is to hold for all values of x, then

- the coefficients of x^1 on both sides of the equation must be equal, and
- the coefficients of x^0 (that is, the constants) on both sides of the equation must be equal.

$$3x + 0 = \underbrace{(A + B)}x + \underbrace{(4A - 2B)}$$

These observations lead to two equations for A and B.

Equate coefficients of x^1: $3 = A + B$
Equate coefficients of x^0: $0 = 4A - 2B$

The first equation says that $A = 3 - B$. Substituting $A = 3 - B$ into the second equation gives the equation $0 = 4(3 - B) - 2B$. Solving for B, we find that $6B = 12$, or $B = 2$. The value of A now follows; we have $A = 3 - B = 1$.

Substituting these values of A and B into equation (1), the partial fraction decomposition is

$$\frac{3x}{(x - 2)(x + 4)} = \frac{1}{x - 2} + \frac{2}{x + 4}.$$

Simple Linear Factors

> ▶ Like an ordinary fraction, a rational function is said to be in **reduced form** if the numerator and denominator have no common factors and it is said to be **proper** if the degree of the numerator is less than the degree of the denominator.

The previous calculation illustrates the method of partial fractions with **simple linear factors**, meaning the denominator of the original function consists only of linear factors of the form $(x - r)$, which appear to the first power and no higher power. Here is the general procedure for this case.

PROCEDURE   **Partial Fractions with Simple Linear Factors**

Suppose $f(x) = p(x)/q(x)$, where p and q are polynomials with no common factors and with the degree of p less than the degree of q. Assume that q is the product of simple linear factors. The partial fraction decomposition is obtained as follows.

Step 1. **Factor the denominator q** in the form $(x - r_1)(x - r_2) \cdots (x - r_n)$, where $r_1, \ldots, r_n$ are real numbers.

Step 2. **Partial fraction decomposition** Form the partial fraction decomposition by writing

$$\frac{p(x)}{q(x)} = \frac{A_1}{(x - r_1)} + \frac{A_2}{(x - r_2)} + \cdots + \frac{A_n}{(x - r_n)}.$$

Step 3. **Clear denominators** Multiply both sides of the equation in Step 2 by $q(x) = (x - r_1)(x - r_2) \cdots (x - r_n)$, which produces conditions for $A_1, \ldots, A_n$.

Step 4. **Solve for coefficients** Equate like powers of x in Step 3 to solve for the undetermined coefficients $A_1, \ldots, A_n$.

QUICK CHECK 2 If the denominator of a reduced proper rational function is $(x - 1)(x + 5)(x - 10)$, what is the general form of its partial fraction decomposition? ◀

EXAMPLE 1   Integrating with partial fractions

a. Find the partial fraction decomposition for $f(x) = \dfrac{3x^2 + 7x - 2}{x^3 - x^2 - 2x}$.

b. Evaluate $\displaystyle\int f(x)\,dx$.

SOLUTION

a. The partial fraction decomposition is done in four steps.

Step 1: Factoring the denominator, we find that

$$x^3 - x^2 - 2x = x(x + 1)(x - 2),$$

in which only simple linear factors appear.

Step 2: The partial fraction decomposition has one term for each factor in the denominator:

> You can call the undetermined coefficients $A_1, A_2, A_3, \ldots$ or $A, B, C, \ldots$. The latter choice avoids subscripts.

$$\frac{3x^2 + 7x - 2}{x(x + 1)(x - 2)} = \frac{A}{x} + \frac{B}{x + 1} + \frac{C}{x - 2}. \qquad (3)$$

The goal is to find the undetermined coefficients A, B, and C.

Step 3: We multiply both sides of equation (3) by $x(x + 1)(x - 2)$:

$$3x^2 + 7x - 2 = A(x + 1)(x - 2) + Bx(x - 2) + Cx(x + 1)$$
$$= (A + B + C)x^2 + (-A - 2B + C)x - 2A.$$

Step 4: We now equate coefficients of x^2, x^1, and x^0 on both sides of the equation in Step 3.

Equate coefficients of x^2: $A + B + C = 3$

Equate coefficients of x^1: $-A - 2B + C = 7$

Equate coefficients of x^0: $-2A = -2$

The third equation implies that $A = 1$, which is substituted into the first two equations to give

$$B + C = 2 \quad \text{and} \quad -2B + C = 8.$$

Solving for B and C, we conclude that $A = 1, B = -2$, and $C = 4$. Substituting the values of A, B, and C into equation (3), the partial fraction decomposition is

$$f(x) = \frac{1}{x} - \frac{2}{x + 1} + \frac{4}{x - 2}.$$

b. Integration is now straightforward:

$$\int \frac{3x^2 + 7x - 2}{x^3 - x^2 - 2x}\,dx = \int \left(\frac{1}{x} - \frac{2}{x + 1} + \frac{4}{x - 2} \right) dx \qquad \text{Partial fractions}$$

$$= \ln|x| - 2\ln|x + 1| + 4\ln|x - 2| + K \qquad \text{Integrate; arbitrary constant } K.$$

$$= \ln \frac{|x|(x - 2)^4}{(x + 1)^2} + K. \qquad \text{Properties of logarithms}$$

Related Exercises 5–26 ◄

A Shortcut (Convenient Values)   Solving for more than three unknown coefficients in a partial fraction decomposition may be difficult. In the case of simple linear factors, a shortcut saves work. In Example 1, Step 3 led to the equation

$$3x^2 + 7x - 2 = A(x + 1)(x - 2) + Bx(x - 2) + Cx(x + 1).$$

➤ In cases other than simple linear factors, the shortcut can be used to determine some, but not all the coefficients, which reduces the work required to find the remaining coefficients. A modified shortcut can be utilized to find all the coefficients; see the margin note next to Example 3.

Because this equation holds for *all* values of x, it must hold for any particular value of x. By choosing values of x judiciously, it is easy to solve for A, B, and C. For example, setting $x = 0$ in this equation results in $-2 = -2A$, or $A = 1$. Setting $x = -1$ results in $-6 = 3B$, or $B = -2$, and setting $x = 2$ results in $24 = 6C$, or $C = 4$. In each case, we choose a value of x that eliminates all but one term on the right side of the equation.

EXAMPLE 2   Using the shortcut

a. Find the partial fraction decomposition for $f(x) = \dfrac{3x^2 + 2x + 5}{(x - 1)(x^2 - x - 20)}$.

b. Evaluate $\displaystyle\int_2^4 f(x)\,dx$.

SOLUTION

a. We use four steps to obtain the partial fraction decomposition.

Step 1: Factoring the denominator of f results in $(x - 1)(x - 5)(x + 4)$, so the integrand has three simple linear factors.

Step 2: We form the partial fraction decomposition with one term for each factor in the denominator:

$$\frac{3x^2 + 2x + 5}{(x - 1)(x - 5)(x + 4)} = \frac{A}{x - 1} + \frac{B}{x - 5} + \frac{C}{x + 4}. \tag{4}$$

The goal is to find the undetermined coefficients A, B, and C.

Step 3: We now multiply both sides of equation (4) by $(x - 1)(x - 5)(x + 4)$:

$$3x^2 + 2x + 5 = A(x - 5)(x + 4) + B(x - 1)(x + 4) + C(x - 1)(x - 5). \tag{5}$$

Step 4: The shortcut is now used to determine A, B, and C. Substituting $x = 1, 5$, and -4 in equation (5) allows us to solve directly for the coefficients:

$$\text{Letting } x = 1 \Rightarrow 10 = -20A + 0 \cdot B + 0 \cdot C \Rightarrow A = -\frac{1}{2};$$

$$\text{Letting } x = 5 \Rightarrow 90 = 0 \cdot A + 36B + 0 \cdot C \Rightarrow B = \frac{5}{2};$$

$$\text{Letting } x = -4 \Rightarrow 45 = 0 \cdot A + 0 \cdot B + 45C \Rightarrow C = 1.$$

Substituting the values of A, B, and C into equation (4) gives the partial fraction decomposition

$$f(x) = -\frac{1/2}{x - 1} + \frac{5/2}{x - 5} + \frac{1}{x + 4}.$$

b. We now carry out the integration.

$$\int_2^4 f(x)\,dx = \int_2^4 \left(-\frac{1/2}{x - 1} + \frac{5/2}{x - 5} + \frac{1}{x + 4} \right) dx \qquad \text{Partial fractions}$$

$$= \left(-\frac{1}{2}\ln|x - 1| + \frac{5}{2}\ln|x - 5| + \ln|x + 4| \right)\Big|_2^4 \qquad \text{Integrate.}$$

$$= -\frac{1}{2}\ln 3 + \frac{5}{2}\underbrace{\ln 1}_{0} + \ln 8 - \left(-\frac{1}{2}\underbrace{\ln 1}_{0} + \frac{5}{2}\ln 3 + \ln 6 \right) \qquad \text{Evaluate.}$$

$$= -3\ln 3 + \ln 8 - \ln 6 \qquad \text{Simplify.}$$

$$= \ln\frac{4}{81} \approx -3.008 \qquad \text{Log properties}$$

Related Exercises 5–26 ◄

Repeated Linear Factors

> *Simple* means the factor is raised to the first power; *repeated* means the factor is raised to an integer power greater than 1.

The preceding discussion relies on the assumption that the denominator of the rational function can be factored into simple linear factors of the form $(x - r)$. But what about denominators such as $x^2(x - 3)$ or $(x + 2)^2(x - 4)^3$, in which linear factors are raised to integer powers greater than 1? In these cases we have *repeated linear factors*, and a modification to the previous procedure must be made.

Here is the modification: Suppose the factor $(x - r)^m$ appears in the denominator, where $m > 1$ is an integer. Then there must be a partial fraction for each power of $(x - r)$ up to and including the mth power. For example, if $x^2(x - 3)^4$ appears in the denominator, then the partial fraction decomposition includes the terms

> Think of x^2 as the repeated linear factor $(x - 0)^2$.

$$\frac{A}{x} + \frac{B}{x^2} + \frac{C}{(x - 3)} + \frac{D}{(x - 3)^2} + \frac{E}{(x - 3)^3} + \frac{F}{(x - 3)^4}.$$

The rest of the partial fraction procedure remains the same, although the amount of work increases as the number of coefficients increases.

PROCEDURE   **Partial Fractions for Repeated Linear Factors**

Suppose the repeated linear factor $(x - r)^m$ appears in the denominator of a proper rational function in reduced form. The partial fraction decomposition has a partial fraction for each power of $(x - r)$ up to and including the mth power; that is, the partial fraction decomposition contains the sum

$$\frac{A_1}{(x - r)} + \frac{A_2}{(x - r)^2} + \frac{A_3}{(x - r)^3} + \cdots + \frac{A_m}{(x - r)^m},$$

where $A_1, \ldots, A_m$ are constants to be determined.

EXAMPLE 3   **Integrating with repeated linear factors**   Evaluate $\int f(x)\, dx$, where
$$f(x) = \frac{5x^2 - 3x + 2}{x^3 - 2x^2}.$$

SOLUTION   The denominator factors as $x^3 - 2x^2 = x^2(x - 2)$, so it has one simple linear factor $(x - 2)$ and one repeated linear factor x^2. The partial fraction decomposition has the form

$$\frac{5x^2 - 3x + 2}{x^2(x - 2)} = \frac{A}{x} + \frac{B}{x^2} + \frac{C}{(x - 2)}.$$

Multiplying both sides of the partial fraction decomposition by $x^2(x - 2)$, we find

$$5x^2 - 3x + 2 = Ax(x - 2) + B(x - 2) + Cx^2$$
$$= (A + C)x^2 + (-2A + B)x - 2B.$$

The coefficients A, B, and C are determined by equating the coefficients of x^2, x^1, and x^0.

> The shortcut can be used to obtain two of the three coefficients easily. Choosing $x = 0$ allows B to be determined. Choosing $x = 2$ determines C. To find A, any other value of x may be substituted.

Equate coefficients of x^2:	$A + C = 5$
Equate coefficients of x^1:	$-2A + B = -3$
Equate coefficients of x^0:	$-2B = 2$

Solving these three equations in three unknowns results in the solution $A = 1$, $B = -1$, and $C = 4$. When A, B, and C are substituted, the partial fraction decomposition is

$$f(x) = \frac{1}{x} - \frac{1}{x^2} + \frac{4}{x - 2}.$$

Integration is now straightforward:

$$\int \frac{5x^2 - 3x + 2}{x^3 - 2x^2}\, dx = \int \left(\frac{1}{x} - \frac{1}{x^2} + \frac{4}{x - 2} \right) dx \qquad \text{Partial fractions}$$

$$= \ln |x| + \frac{1}{x} + 4 \ln |x - 2| + K \qquad \text{Integrate; arbitrary constant } K.$$

$$= \frac{1}{x} + \ln \left(|x|(x - 2)^4 \right) + K. \qquad \text{Properties of logarithms}$$

Related Exercises 27–37 ◄

QUICK CHECK 3 State the form of the partial fraction decomposition of the reduced proper rational function $p(x)/q(x)$ if $q(x) = x^2(x - 3)^2(x - 1)$. ◄

Irreducible Quadratic Factors

By the Fundamental Theorem of Algebra, we know that a polynomial with real-valued coefficients can be written as the product of linear factors of the form $x - r$ and *irreducible quadratic factors* of the form $ax^2 + bx + c$, where $r, a, b,$ and c are real numbers. By irreducible, we mean that $ax^2 + bx + c$ cannot be factored over the real numbers. For example, the polynomial

> The quadratic $ax^2 + bx + c$ has no real roots and cannot be factored over the real numbers if $b^2 - 4ac < 0$.

$$x^9 + 4x^8 + 6x^7 + 34x^6 + 64x^5 - 84x^4 - 287x^3 - 500x^2 - 354x - 180$$

factors as

$$\underbrace{(x - 2)}_{\substack{\text{linear} \\ \text{factor}}}\underbrace{(x + 3)^2}_{\substack{\text{repeated} \\ \text{linear} \\ \text{factor}}}\underbrace{(x^2 - 2x + 10)}_{\substack{\text{irreducible} \\ \text{quadratic} \\ \text{factor}}}\underbrace{(x^2 + x + 1)^2}_{\substack{\text{repeated} \\ \text{irreducible} \\ \text{quadratic factor}}}.$$

In this factored form, we see linear factors (simple and repeated) and irreducible quadratic factors (simple and repeated).

With irreducible quadratic factors, two cases must be considered: simple and repeated factors. Simple quadratic factors are examined in the following examples, and repeated quadratic factors (which generally involve long computations) are explored in the exercises.

PROCEDURE   Partial Fractions with Simple Irreducible Quadratic Factors

Suppose a simple irreducible factor $ax^2 + bx + c$ appears in the denominator of a proper rational function in reduced form. The partial fraction decomposition contains a term of the form

$$\frac{Ax + B}{ax^2 + bx + c},$$

where A and B are unknown coefficients to be determined.

EXAMPLE 4   Setting up partial fractions Give the appropriate form of the partial fraction decomposition for the following functions.

a. $\dfrac{x^2 + 1}{x^4 - 4x^3 - 32x^2}$ **b.** $\dfrac{10}{(x - 2)^2(x^2 + 2x + 2)}$

SOLUTION

a. The denominator factors as $x^2(x^2 - 4x - 32) = x^2(x - 8)(x + 4)$. Therefore, x is a repeated linear factor, and $(x - 8)$ and $(x + 4)$ are simple linear factors. The required form of the decomposition is

$$\frac{A}{x} + \frac{B}{x^2} + \frac{C}{x - 8} + \frac{D}{x + 4}.$$

We see that the factor $x^2 - 4x - 32$ is quadratic, but it can be factored as $(x - 8)(x + 4)$, so it is not irreducible.

> In Example 4b, the factor $(x - 2)^2$ cannot be treated as an irreducible quadratic factor; it is a repeated linear factor.

b. The denominator is already fully factored. The quadratic factor $x^2 + 2x + 2$ cannot be factored using real numbers; therefore, it is irreducible. The form of the decomposition is

$$\frac{A}{x - 2} + \frac{B}{(x - 2)^2} + \frac{Cx + D}{x^2 + 2x + 2}.$$

Related Exercises 38–41 ◄

EXAMPLE 5 Integrating with partial fractions Evaluate

$$\int \frac{7x^2 - 13x + 13}{(x - 2)(x^2 - 2x + 3)}\, dx.$$

SOLUTION The appropriate form of the partial fraction decomposition is

$$\frac{7x^2 - 13x + 13}{(x - 2)(x^2 - 2x + 3)} = \frac{A}{x - 2} + \frac{Bx + C}{x^2 - 2x + 3}.$$

Note that the irreducible quadratic factor requires $Bx + C$ in the numerator of the second fraction. Multiplying both sides of this equation by $(x - 2)(x^2 - 2x + 3)$ leads to

$$7x^2 - 13x + 13 = A(x^2 - 2x + 3) + (Bx + C)(x - 2)$$
$$= (A + B)x^2 + (-2A - 2B + C)x + (3A - 2C).$$

Equating coefficients of equal powers of x results in the equations

$$A + B = 7, \quad -2A - 2B + C = -13, \quad \text{and} \quad 3A - 2C = 13.$$

Solving this system of equations gives $A = 5, B = 2$, and $C = 1$; therefore, the original integral can be written as

$$\int \frac{7x^2 - 13x + 13}{(x - 2)(x^2 - 2x + 3)}\, dx = \int \frac{5}{x - 2}\, dx + \int \frac{2x + 1}{x^2 - 2x + 3}\, dx.$$

Let's work on the second (more difficult) integral. The substitution $u = x^2 - 2x + 3$ would work if $du = (2x - 2)\, dx$ appeared in the numerator. For this reason, we write the numerator as $2x + 1 = (2x - 2) + 3$ and split the integral:

$$\int \frac{2x + 1}{x^2 - 2x + 3}\, dx = \int \frac{2x - 2}{x^2 - 2x + 3}\, dx + \int \frac{3}{x^2 - 2x + 3}\, dx.$$

Assembling all the pieces, we have

$$\int \frac{7x^2 - 13x + 13}{(x - 2)(x^2 - 2x + 3)}\, dx$$

$$= \int \frac{5}{x - 2}\, dx + \underbrace{\int \frac{2x - 2}{x^2 - 2x + 3}\, dx}_{\text{let } u = x^2 - 2x + 3} + \int \frac{3}{\underbrace{x^2 - 2x + 3}_{(x - 1)^2 + 2}}\, dx$$

$$= 5 \ln |x - 2| + \ln |x^2 - 2x + 3| + \frac{3}{\sqrt{2}} \tan^{-1}\left(\frac{x - 1}{\sqrt{2}}\right) + K \quad \text{Integrate.}$$

$$= \ln |(x - 2)^5(x^2 - 2x + 3)| + \frac{3}{\sqrt{2}} \tan^{-1}\left(\frac{x - 1}{\sqrt{2}}\right) + K. \quad \text{Property of logarithms}$$

To evaluate the last integral $\int \frac{3}{x^2 - 2x + 3}\, dx$, we completed the square in the denominator and used the substitution $u = x - 1$ to produce $3 \int \frac{du}{u^2 + 2}$, which is a standard form.

Related Exercises 42–50 ◄

Long Division   The preceding discussion of partial fraction decomposition assumes that $f(x) = p(x)/q(x)$ is a proper rational function. If this is not the case and we are faced with an improper rational function f, we divide the denominator into the numerator and express f in two parts. One part will be a polynomial, and the other will be a proper rational function. For example, given the function

$$f(x) = \frac{2x^3 + 11x^2 + 28x + 33}{x^2 - x - 6},$$

we perform long division.

$$
\begin{array}{r}
2x\ \ + 13 \\
x^2 - x - 6\overline{)\,2x^3 + 11x^2 + 28x +\ \ 33} \\
\underline{2x^3 -\ \ 2x^2 - 12x\quad\quad\ } \\
13x^2 + 40x +\ \ 33 \\
\underline{13x^2 - 13x -\ \ 78} \\
53x + 111
\end{array}
$$

QUICK CHECK 4 What is the result of simplifying $\dfrac{x}{x + 1}$ by long division? ◀

It follows that

$$f(x) = \underbrace{2x + 13}_{\substack{\text{polynomial;} \\ \text{easy to} \\ \text{integrate}}} + \underbrace{\frac{53x + 111}{x^2 - x - 6}}_{\substack{\text{apply partial fraction} \\ \text{decomposition}}}.$$

The first piece is easily integrated, and the second piece now qualifies for the methods described in this section.

SUMMARY   **Partial Fraction Decompositions**

Let $f(x) = p(x)/q(x)$ be a proper rational function in reduced form. Assume the denominator q has been factored completely over the real numbers and m is a positive integer.

1. **Simple linear factor** A factor $x - r$ in the denominator requires the partial fraction $\dfrac{A}{x - r}$.

2. **Repeated linear factor** A factor $(x - r)^m$ with $m > 1$ in the denominator requires the partial fractions

$$\frac{A_1}{(x - r)} + \frac{A_2}{(x - r)^2} + \frac{A_3}{(x - r)^3} + \cdots + \frac{A_m}{(x - r)^m}.$$

3. **Simple irreducible quadratic factor** An irreducible factor $ax^2 + bx + c$ in the denominator requires the partial fraction

$$\frac{Ax + B}{ax^2 + bx + c}.$$

4. **Repeated irreducible quadratic factor** (See Exercises 83–86.) An irreducible factor $(ax^2 + bx + c)^m$ with $m > 1$ in the denominator requires the partial fractions

$$\frac{A_1 x + B_1}{ax^2 + bx + c} + \frac{A_2 x + B_2}{(ax^2 + bx + c)^2} + \cdots + \frac{A_m x + B_m}{(ax^2 + bx + c)^m}.$$

SECTION 7.5 EXERCISES

Review Questions

1. What kinds of functions can be integrated using partial fraction decomposition?

2. Give an example of each of the following.
   a. A simple linear factor
   b. A repeated linear factor
   c. A simple irreducible quadratic factor
   d. A repeated irreducible quadratic factor

3. What term(s) should appear in the partial fraction decomposition of a proper rational function with each of the following?
   a. A factor of $x - 3$ in the denominator
   b. A factor of $(x - 4)^3$ in the denominator
   c. A factor of $x^2 + 2x + 6$ in the denominator

4. What is the first step in integrating $\dfrac{x^2 + 2x - 3}{x + 1}$?

Basic Skills

5–12. Setting up partial fraction decomposition *Give the partial fraction decomposition for the following functions.*

5. $\dfrac{2}{x^2 - 2x - 8}$

6. $\dfrac{x - 9}{x^2 - 3x - 18}$

7. $\dfrac{5x - 7}{x^2 - 3x + 2}$

8. $\dfrac{11x - 10}{x^2 - x}$

9. $\dfrac{x^2}{x^3 - 16x}, \ x \neq 0$

10. $\dfrac{x^2 - 3x}{x^3 - 3x^2 - 4x}, \ x \neq 0$

11. $\dfrac{x + 2}{x^3 - 3x^2 + 2x}$

12. $\dfrac{x^2 - 4x + 11}{(x - 3)(x - 1)(x + 1)}$

13–26. Simple linear factors *Evaluate the following integrals.*

13. $\displaystyle\int \dfrac{3}{(x - 1)(x + 2)}\, dx$

14. $\displaystyle\int \dfrac{8}{(x - 2)(x + 6)}\, dx$

15. $\displaystyle\int \dfrac{6}{x^2 - 1}\, dx$

16. $\displaystyle\int_0^1 \dfrac{dt}{t^2 - 9}$

17. $\displaystyle\int_{-1}^{2} \dfrac{5x}{x^2 - x - 6}\, dx$

18. $\displaystyle\int \dfrac{21x^2}{x^3 - x^2 - 12x}\, dx$

19. $\displaystyle\int \dfrac{10x}{x^2 - 2x - 24}\, dx$

20. $\displaystyle\int \dfrac{y + 1}{y^3 + 3y^2 - 18y}\, dy$

21. $\displaystyle\int \dfrac{6x^2}{x^4 - 5x^2 + 4}\, dx$

22. $\displaystyle\int \dfrac{4x - 2}{x^3 - x}\, dx$

23. $\displaystyle\int \dfrac{x^2 + 12x - 4}{x^3 - 4x}\, dx$

24. $\displaystyle\int \dfrac{z^2 + 20z - 15}{z^3 + 4z^2 - 5z}\, dz$

25. $\displaystyle\int \dfrac{dx}{x^4 - 10x^2 + 9}$

26. $\displaystyle\int_0^5 \dfrac{2}{x^2 - 4x - 32}\, dx$

27–37. Repeated linear factors *Evaluate the following integrals.*

27. $\displaystyle\int \dfrac{81}{x^3 - 9x^2}\, dx$

28. $\displaystyle\int \dfrac{16x^2}{(x - 6)(x + 2)^2}\, dx$

29. $\displaystyle\int_{-1}^{1} \dfrac{x}{(x + 3)^2}\, dx$

30. $\displaystyle\int \dfrac{dx}{x^3 - 2x^2 - 4x + 8}$

31. $\displaystyle\int \dfrac{2}{x^3 + x^2}\, dx$

32. $\displaystyle\int_1^2 \dfrac{2}{t^3(t + 1)}\, dt$

33. $\displaystyle\int \dfrac{x - 5}{x^2(x + 1)}\, dx$

34. $\displaystyle\int \dfrac{x^2}{(x - 2)^3}\, dx$

35. $\displaystyle\int \dfrac{x^2 - x}{(x - 2)(x - 3)^2}\, dx$

36. $\displaystyle\int \dfrac{12y - 8}{y^4 - 2y^2 + 1}\, dy$

37. $\displaystyle\int \dfrac{x^2 - 4}{x^3 - 2x^2 + x}\, dx$

38–41. Setting up partial fraction decompositions *Give the appropriate form of the partial fraction decomposition for the following functions.*

38. $\dfrac{2}{x(x^2 - 6x + 9)}$

39. $\dfrac{20x}{(x - 1)^2(x^2 + 1)}$

40. $\dfrac{x^2}{x^3(x^2 + 1)}$

41. $\dfrac{2x^2 + 3}{(x^2 - 8x + 16)(x^2 + 3x + 4)}$

42–50. Simple irreducible quadratic factors *Evaluate the following integrals.*

42. $\displaystyle\int \dfrac{8(x^2 + 4)}{x(x^2 + 8)}\, dx$

43. $\displaystyle\int \dfrac{x^2 + x + 2}{(x + 1)(x^2 + 1)}\, dx$

44. $\displaystyle\int \dfrac{x^2 + 3x + 2}{x(x^2 + 2x + 2)}\, dx$

45. $\displaystyle\int \dfrac{2x^2 + 5x + 5}{(x + 1)(x^2 + 2x + 2)}\, dx$

46. $\displaystyle\int \dfrac{z + 1}{z(z^2 + 4)}\, dz$

47. $\displaystyle\int \dfrac{20x}{(x - 1)(x^2 + 4x + 5)}\, dx$

48. $\displaystyle\int \dfrac{2x + 1}{x^2 + 4}\, dx$

49. $\displaystyle\int \dfrac{x^2}{x^3 - x^2 + 4x - 4}\, dx$

50. $\displaystyle\int \dfrac{dy}{(y^2 + 1)(y^2 + 2)}$

Further Explorations

51. **Explain why or why not** Determine whether the following statements are true and give an explanation or counterexample.

   a. To evaluate $\displaystyle\int \dfrac{4x^6}{x^4 + 3x^2}\, dx$, the first step is to find the partial fraction decomposition of the integrand.

   b. The easiest way to evaluate $\displaystyle\int \dfrac{6x + 1}{3x^2 + x}\, dx$ is with a partial fraction decomposition of the integrand.

   c. The rational function $f(x) = \dfrac{1}{x^2 - 13x + 42}$ has an irreducible quadratic denominator.

   d. The rational function $f(x) = \dfrac{1}{x^2 - 13x + 43}$ has an irreducible quadratic denominator.

T 52–55. Areas of regions *Find the area of the following regions.*

52. The region bounded by the curve $y = x/(1 + x)$, the x-axis, and the line $x = 4$

53. The region bounded by the curve $y = 10/(x^2 - 2x - 24)$, the x-axis, and the lines $x = -2$ and $x = 2$

54. The region bounded by the curves $y = 1/x$, $y = x/(3x + 4)$, and the line $x = 10$

55. The region bounded by the curve $y = \dfrac{x^2 - 4x - 4}{x^2 - 4x - 5}$ and the x-axis

56–61. Volumes of solids *Find the volume of the following solids.*

56. The region bounded by $y = 1/(x + 1)$, $y = 0$, $x = 0$, and $x = 2$ is revolved about the y-axis.

57. The region bounded by $y = x/(x + 1)$, the x-axis, and $x = 4$ is revolved about the x-axis.

58. The region bounded by $y = (1 - x^2)^{-1/2}$ and $y = 4$ is revolved about the x-axis.

59. The region bounded by $y = \dfrac{1}{\sqrt{x(3 - x)}}$, $y = 0$, $x = 1$, and $x = 2$ is revolved about the x-axis.

60. The region bounded by $y = \dfrac{1}{\sqrt{4 - x^2}}$, $y = 0$, $x = -1$, and $x = 1$ is revolved about the x-axis.

61. The region bounded by $y = 1/(x + 2)$, $y = 0$, $x = 0$, and $x = 3$ is revolved about the line $x = -1$.

62. What's wrong? Why are there no constants A and B satisfying

$$\frac{x^2}{(x - 4)(x + 5)} = \frac{A}{x - 4} + \frac{B}{x + 5}?$$

63–74. Preliminary steps *The following integrals require a preliminary step such as long division or a change of variables before using the method of partial fractions. Evaluate these integrals.*

63. $\displaystyle \int \frac{dx}{1 + e^x}$

64. $\displaystyle \int \frac{x^4 + 1}{x^3 + 9x} \, dx$

65. $\displaystyle \int \frac{3x^2 + 4x - 6}{x^2 - 3x + 2} \, dx$

66. $\displaystyle \int \frac{2z^3 + z^2 - 6z + 7}{z^2 + z - 6} \, dz$

67. $\displaystyle \int \frac{dt}{2 + e^t}$

68. $\displaystyle \int \frac{dx}{e^x + e^{2x}}$

69. $\displaystyle \int \frac{\sec t}{1 + \sin t} \, dt$

70. $\displaystyle \int \sqrt{e^x + 1} \, dx$ (*Hint: Let $u = \sqrt{e^x + 1}$.*)

71. $\displaystyle \int \frac{e^x}{(e^x - 1)(e^x + 2)} \, dx$

72. $\displaystyle \int \frac{\cos \theta}{(\sin^3 \theta - 4 \sin \theta)} \, d\theta$

73. $\displaystyle \int \frac{dx}{(e^x + e^{-x})^2}$

74. $\displaystyle \int \frac{dy}{y(\sqrt{a} - \sqrt{y})}$, for $a > 0$. (*Hint: Let $u = \sqrt{y}$.*)

75. Another form of $\displaystyle \int \sec x \, dx.$

a. Verify the identity $\sec x = \dfrac{\cos x}{1 - \sin^2 x}$.

b. Use the identity in part (a) to verify that
$$\int \sec x \, dx = \frac{1}{2} \ln \left| \frac{1 + \sin x}{1 - \sin x} \right| + C.$$
(*Source: The College Mathematics Journal 32, 5, Nov 2001*)

76–81. Fractional powers *Use the indicated substitution to convert the given integral to an integral of a rational function. Evaluate the resulting integral.*

76. $\displaystyle \int \frac{dx}{x - \sqrt[3]{x}}$; $x = u^3$

77. $\displaystyle \int \frac{dx}{\sqrt[4]{x + 2} + 1}$; $x + 2 = u^4$

78. $\displaystyle \int \frac{dx}{x\sqrt{1 + 2x}}$; $1 + 2x = u^2$

79. $\displaystyle \int \frac{dx}{\sqrt{x} + \sqrt[3]{x}}$; $x = u^6$

80. $\displaystyle \int \frac{dx}{x - \sqrt[4]{x}}$; $x = u^4$

81. $\displaystyle \int \frac{dx}{\sqrt{1 + \sqrt{x}}}$; $x = (u^2 - 1)^2$

T 82. Arc length of the natural logarithm Consider the curve $y = \ln x$.

a. Find the length of the curve from $x = 1$ to $x = a$ and call it $L(a)$. (*Hint: The change of variables $u = \sqrt{x^2 + 1}$ allows evaluation by partial fractions.*)

b. Graph $L(a)$.

c. As a increases, $L(a)$ increases as what power of a?

83–86. Repeated quadratic factors *Refer to the summary box (Partial Fraction Decompositions) and evaluate the following integrals.*

83. $\displaystyle \int \frac{2}{x(x^2 + 1)^2} \, dx$

84. $\displaystyle \int \frac{dx}{(x + 1)(x^2 + 2x + 2)^2}$

85. $\displaystyle \int \frac{x}{(x - 1)(x^2 + 2x + 2)^2} \, dx$

86. $\displaystyle \int \frac{x^3 + 1}{x(x^2 + x + 1)^2} \, dx$

87. Two methods Evaluate $\displaystyle \int \frac{dx}{x^2 - 1}$, for $x > 1$, in two ways: using partial fractions and a trigonometric substitution. Reconcile your two answers.

88–94. Rational functions of trigonometric functions *An integrand with trigonometric functions in the numerator and denominator can often be converted to a rational integrand using the substitution* $u = \tan(x/2)$ *or equivalently* $x = 2\tan^{-1} u$. *The following relations are used in making this change of variables.*

$$A:\ dx = \frac{2}{1 + u^2}\,du \quad B:\ \sin x = \frac{2u}{1 + u^2} \quad C:\ \cos x = \frac{1 - u^2}{1 + u^2}$$

88. Verify relation A by differentiating $x = 2\tan^{-1} u$. Verify relations B and C using a right-triangle diagram and the double-angle formulas

$$\sin x = 2\sin\frac{x}{2}\cos\frac{x}{2} \quad \text{and} \quad \cos x = 2\cos^2\frac{x}{2} - 1.$$

89. Evaluate $\displaystyle\int \frac{dx}{1 + \sin x}$.

90. Evaluate $\displaystyle\int \frac{dx}{2 + \cos x}$.

91. Evaluate $\displaystyle\int \frac{dx}{1 - \cos x}$.

92. Evaluate $\displaystyle\int \frac{dx}{1 + \sin x + \cos x}$.

93. Evaluate $\displaystyle\int_0^{\pi/2} \frac{d\theta}{\cos\theta + \sin\theta}$.

94. Evaluate $\displaystyle\int_0^{\pi/3} \frac{\sin\theta}{1 - \sin\theta}\,d\theta$.

Applications

95. Three start-ups Three cars, A, B, and C, start from rest and accelerate along a line according to the following velocity functions:

$$v_A(t) = \frac{88t}{t + 1}, \quad v_B(t) = \frac{88t^2}{(t + 1)^2}, \quad \text{and} \quad v_C(t) = \frac{88t^2}{t^2 + 1}.$$

a. Which car travels farthest on the interval $0 \le t \le 1$?
b. Which car travels farthest on the interval $0 \le t \le 5$?
c. Find the position functions for each car assuming that each car starts at the origin.
d. Which car ultimately gains the lead and remains in front?

■ 96. Skydiving A skydiver has a downward velocity given by

$$v(t) = V_T\left(\frac{1 - e^{-2gt/V_T}}{1 + e^{-2gt/V_T}}\right),$$

where $t = 0$ is the instant the skydiver starts falling, $g \approx 9.8\ \text{m/s}^2$ is the acceleration due to gravity, and V_T is the terminal velocity of the skydiver.

a. Evaluate $v(0)$ and $\displaystyle\lim_{t\to\infty} v(t)$ and interpret these results.
b. Graph the velocity function.
c. Verify by integration that the position function is given by

$$s(t) = V_T t + \frac{V_T^2}{g}\ln\left(\frac{1 + e^{-2gt/V_T}}{2}\right),$$

where $s'(t) = v(t)$ and $s(0) = 0$.
d. Graph the position function.
   (See the Guided Project *Terminal velocity* for more details on free fall and terminal velocity.)

Additional Exercises

97. $\pi < \dfrac{22}{7}$ One of the earliest approximations to π is $\dfrac{22}{7}$. Verify that $0 < \displaystyle\int_0^1 \frac{x^4(1 - x)^4}{1 + x^2}\,dx = \frac{22}{7} - \pi$. Why can you conclude that $\pi < \dfrac{22}{7}$?

98. Challenge Show that with the change of variables $u = \sqrt{\tan x}$, the integral $\int\sqrt{\tan x}\,dx$ can be converted to an integral amenable to partial fractions. Evaluate $\int_0^{\pi/4}\sqrt{\tan x}\,dx$.

QUICK CHECK ANSWERS

1. $\ln|x - 2| + 2\ln|x + 4| = \ln|(x - 2)(x + 4)^2|$
2. $A/(x - 1) + B/(x + 5) + C/(x - 10)$
3. $A/x + B/x^2 + C/(x - 3) + D/(x - 3)^2 + E/(x - 1)$
4. $1 - \dfrac{1}{x + 1}$ ◀

7.6 Other Integration Strategies

The integration methods studied so far—various substitutions, integration by parts, and partial fractions—are examples of *analytical methods*; they are done with pencil and paper, and they give exact results. While many important integrals can be evaluated with analytical methods, many more integrals lie beyond their reach. For example, the following integrals cannot be evaluated in terms of familiar functions:

$$\int e^{x^2}\,dx, \quad \int \sin x^2\,dx, \quad \int \frac{\sin x}{x}\,dx, \quad \int \frac{e^{-x}}{x}\,dx, \quad \text{and} \quad \int \ln(\ln x)\,dx.$$

The next two sections survey alternative strategies for evaluating integrals when standard analytical methods do not work. These strategies fall into three categories.

1. **Tables of integrals** The endpapers of this text contain a table of many standard integrals. Because these integrals were evaluated analytically, using tables is considered an analytical method. Tables of integrals also contain reduction formulas like those discussed in Sections 7.2 and 7.3.

2. **Symbolic methods** Computer algebra systems have sophisticated algorithms to evaluate difficult integrals. Many definite and indefinite integrals can be evaluated exactly using these symbolic methods.

3. Numerical methods The value of a definite integral can be approximated accurately using numerical methods introduced in the next section. *Numerical* means that these methods compute numbers rather than manipulate symbols. Computers and calculators often have built-in functions to carry out numerical calculations.

Figure 7.10 is a chart of the various integration strategies and how they are related.

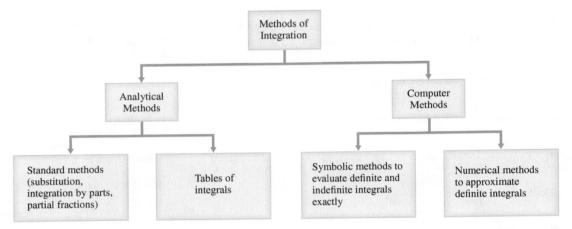

Figure 7.10

> A short table of integrals is found at the end of the book. Longer tables of integrals are found online and in venerable collections such as the *CRC Mathematical Tables* and *Handbook of Mathematical Functions*, by Abramowitz and Stegun.

Using Tables of Integrals

Given a specific integral, you *may* be able to find the identical integral in a table of integrals. More likely, some preliminary work is needed to convert the given integral into one that appears in a table. Most tables give only indefinite integrals, although some tables include special definite integrals. The following examples illustrate various ways in which tables of integrals are used.

EXAMPLE 1   Using tables of integrals Evaluate the integral $\displaystyle\int \frac{dx}{x\sqrt{2x-9}}$.

SOLUTION It is worth noting that this integral may be evaluated with the change of variables $u^2 = 2x - 9$. Alternatively, a table of integrals includes the integral

$$\int \frac{dx}{x\sqrt{ax - b}} = \frac{2}{\sqrt{b}} \tan^{-1} \sqrt{\frac{ax - b}{b}} + C, \quad \text{where} \quad b > 0,$$

which matches the given integral. Letting $a = 2$ and $b = 9$, we find that

> Letting $u^2 = 2x - 9$, we have $u\,du = dx$ and $x = \frac{1}{2}(u^2 + 9)$. Therefore,
>
> $$\int \frac{dx}{x\sqrt{2x-9}} = 2 \int \frac{du}{u^2 + 9}.$$

$$\int \frac{dx}{x\sqrt{2x - 9}} = \frac{2}{\sqrt{9}} \tan^{-1} \sqrt{\frac{2x - 9}{9}} + C = \frac{2}{3} \tan^{-1} \frac{\sqrt{2x - 9}}{3} + C.$$

Related Exercises 5–22 ◄

EXAMPLE 2   Preliminary work Evaluate $\int \sqrt{x^2 + 6x}\, dx$.

SOLUTION Most tables of integrals do not include this integral. The nearest integral you are likely to find is $\int \sqrt{x^2 \pm a^2}\, dx$. The given integral can be put into this form by completing the square and using a substitution:

$$x^2 + 6x = x^2 + 6x + 9 - 9 = (x + 3)^2 - 9.$$

With the change of variables $u = x + 3$, the evaluation appears as follows:

$$\int \sqrt{x^2 + 6x}\, dx = \int \sqrt{(x + 3)^2 - 9}\, dx \qquad \text{Complete the square.}$$

$$= \int \sqrt{u^2 - 9}\, du \qquad u = x + 3, du = dx$$

$$= \frac{u}{2} \sqrt{u^2 - 9} - \frac{9}{2} \ln |u + \sqrt{u^2 - 9}| + C \quad \text{Table of integrals}$$

$$= \frac{x + 3}{2} \sqrt{(x + 3)^2 - 9} - \frac{9}{2} \ln |x + 3 + \sqrt{(x + 3)^2 - 9}| + C$$
$$\text{Replace } u \text{ with } x + 3.$$

$$= \frac{x + 3}{2} \sqrt{x^2 + 6x} - \frac{9}{2} \ln |x + 3 + \sqrt{x^2 + 6x}| + C. \quad \text{Simplify.}$$

Related Exercises 23–38 ◄

EXAMPLE 3   Using tables of integrals for area Find the area of the region bounded by the curve $y = \dfrac{1}{1 + \sin x}$ and the x-axis between $x = 0$ and $x = \pi$.

SOLUTION The region in question (Figure 7.11) lies entirely above the x-axis, so its area is $\displaystyle\int_0^{\pi} \frac{dx}{1 + \sin x}$. A matching integral in a table of integrals is

$$\int \frac{dx}{1 + \sin ax} = -\frac{1}{a} \tan \left(\frac{\pi}{4} - \frac{ax}{2} \right) + C.$$

Evaluating the definite integral with $a = 1$, we have

$$\int_0^{\pi} \frac{dx}{1 + \sin x} = -\tan \left(\frac{\pi}{4} - \frac{x}{2} \right) \Big|_0^{\pi} = -\tan \left(-\frac{\pi}{4} \right) - \left(-\tan \frac{\pi}{4} \right) = 2.$$

Related Exercises 39–46 ◄

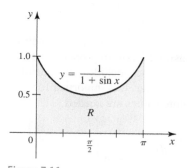

Figure 7.11

QUICK CHECK 1 Use the result of Example 3 to evaluate $\displaystyle\int_0^{\pi/2} \frac{dx}{1 + \sin x}$. ◄

Symbolic Methods

Computer algebra systems evaluate many integrals exactly using symbolic methods, and they approximate many definite integrals using numerical methods. Different software packages may produce different results for the same indefinite integral, but ultimately, they must agree. The discussion that follows does not rely on one particular computer algebra system. Rather, it illustrates results from different systems and shows some of the idiosyncrasies of using a computer algebra system.

QUICK CHECK 2 Using one computer algebra system, it was found that $\int \sin x \cos x\, dx = \frac{1}{2} \sin^2 x + C$; using another computer algebra system, it was found that $\int \sin x \cos x\, dx = -\frac{1}{2} \cos^2 x + C$. Reconcile the two answers. ◄

➤ Most computer algebra systems do not include the constant of integration after evaluating an indefinite integral. But it should always be included when reporting a result.

EXAMPLE 4   Apparent discrepancies Evaluate $\displaystyle\int \frac{dx}{\sqrt{e^x + 1}}$ using tables and a computer algebra system.

> Recall that the *hyperbolic tangent* is defined as
>
> $$\tanh x = \frac{e^x - e^{-x}}{e^x + e^{-x}}.$$
>
> Its inverse is the *inverse hyperbolic tangent*, written $\tanh^{-1} x$.

SOLUTION Using one particular computer algebra system, we find that

$$\int \frac{dx}{\sqrt{e^x + 1}} = -2 \tanh^{-1} \sqrt{e^x + 1} + C,$$

where $\tanh^{-1}$ is the *inverse hyperbolic tangent* function (Section 6.10). However, we can obtain a result in terms of more familiar functions by first using the substitution $u = e^x$, which implies that $du = e^x \, dx$ or $dx = du/e^x = du/u$. The integral becomes

$$\int \frac{dx}{\sqrt{e^x + 1}} = \int \frac{du}{u\sqrt{u + 1}}.$$

Using a computer algebra system again, we obtain

$$\int \frac{dx}{\sqrt{e^x + 1}} = \int \frac{du}{u\sqrt{u + 1}} = \ln\left(\sqrt{1 + u} - 1\right) - \ln\left(\sqrt{1 + u} + 1\right)$$

$$= \ln\left(\sqrt{1 + e^x} - 1\right) - \ln\left(\sqrt{1 + e^x} + 1\right).$$

> Some computer algebra systems use $\log x$ for $\ln x$.

A table of integrals leads to a third equivalent form of the integral:

$$\int \frac{dx}{\sqrt{e^x + 1}} = \int \frac{du}{u\sqrt{u + 1}} = \ln\left(\frac{\sqrt{u + 1} - 1}{\sqrt{u + 1} + 1}\right) + C$$

$$= \ln\left(\frac{\sqrt{e^x + 1} - 1}{\sqrt{e^x + 1} + 1}\right) + C.$$

Often the difference between two results is a few steps of algebra or a trigonometric identity. In this case, the final two results are reconciled using logarithm properties. This example illustrates that computer algebra systems generally do not include constants of integration and may omit absolute values when logarithms appear. It is important for the user to determine whether integration constants and absolute values are needed.

Related Exercises 47–62 ◄

QUICK CHECK 3 Using partial fractions, we know that $\displaystyle\int \frac{dx}{x(x + 1)} = \ln\left|\frac{x}{x + 1}\right| + C.$ Using a computer algebra system, we find that $\displaystyle\int \frac{dx}{x(x + 1)} = \ln x - \ln(x + 1)$. What is wrong with the result from the computer algebra system? ◄

EXAMPLE 5 **Symbolic versus numerical integration** Use a computer algebra system to evaluate $\displaystyle\int_0^1 \sin x^2 \, dx$.

SOLUTION Sometimes a computer algebra system gives the exact value of an integral in terms of an unfamiliar function, or it may not be able to evaluate the integral exactly. For example, one particular computer algebra system returns the result

$$\int_0^1 \sin x^2 \, dx = \sqrt{\frac{\pi}{2}} \, S\left(\sqrt{\frac{2}{\pi}}\right),$$

where S is known as the *Fresnel integral function* $\left(S(x) = \displaystyle\int_0^x \sin\left(\frac{\pi t^2}{2}\right) dt\right)$. However, if the computer algebra system is instructed to approximate the integral, the result is

$$\int_0^1 \sin x^2 \, dx \approx 0.3102683017,$$

which is an excellent approximation.

Related Exercises 47–62 ◄

SECTION 7.6 EXERCISES

Review Questions

1. Give some examples of analytical methods for evaluating integrals.

2. Does a computer algebra system give an exact result for an indefinite integral? Explain.

3. Why might an integral found in a table differ from the same integral evaluated by a computer algebra system?

4. Is a reduction formula an analytical method or a numerical method? Explain.

Basic Skills

5–22. Table lookup integrals *Use a table of integrals to determine the following indefinite integrals.*

5. $\displaystyle\int \cos^{-1} x \, dx$

6. $\displaystyle\int \sin 3x \cos 2x \, dx$

7. $\displaystyle\int \frac{dx}{\sqrt{x^2 + 16}}$

8. $\displaystyle\int \frac{dx}{\sqrt{x^2 - 25}}$

9. $\displaystyle\int \frac{3u}{2u + 7} \, du$

10. $\displaystyle\int \frac{dy}{y(2y + 9)}$

11. $\displaystyle\int \frac{dx}{1 - \cos 4x}$

12. $\displaystyle\int \frac{dx}{x\sqrt{81 - x^2}}$

13. $\displaystyle\int \frac{x}{\sqrt{4x + 1}} \, dx$

14. $\displaystyle\int t\sqrt{4t + 12} \, dt$

15. $\displaystyle\int \frac{dx}{\sqrt{9x^2 - 100}}, x > \frac{10}{3}$

16. $\displaystyle\int \frac{dx}{225 - 16x^2}$

17. $\displaystyle\int \frac{dx}{(16 + 9x^2)^{3/2}}$

18. $\displaystyle\int \sqrt{4x^2 - 9} \, dx, x > \frac{3}{2}$

19. $\displaystyle\int \frac{dx}{x\sqrt{144 - x^2}}$

20. $\displaystyle\int \frac{dv}{v(v^2 + 8)}$

21. $\displaystyle\int \ln^2 x \, dx$

22. $\displaystyle\int x^2 e^{5x} \, dx$

23–38. Preliminary work *Use a table of integrals to determine the following indefinite integrals. These integrals require preliminary work, such as completing the square or changing variables, before they can be found in a table.*

23. $\displaystyle\int \sqrt{x^2 + 10x} \, dx, x > 0$

24. $\displaystyle\int \sqrt{x^2 - 8x} \, dx, x > 8$

25. $\displaystyle\int \frac{dx}{x^2 + 2x + 10}$

26. $\displaystyle\int \sqrt{x^2 - 4x + 8} \, dx$

27. $\displaystyle\int \frac{dx}{x(x^{10} + 1)}$

28. $\displaystyle\int \frac{dt}{t(t^8 - 256)}$

29. $\displaystyle\int \frac{dx}{\sqrt{x^2 - 6x}}, x > 6$

30. $\displaystyle\int \frac{dx}{\sqrt{x^2 + 10x}}, x > 0$

31. $\displaystyle\int \frac{e^x}{\sqrt{e^{2x} + 4}} \, dx$

32. $\displaystyle\int \frac{\sqrt{\ln^2 x + 4}}{x} \, dx$

33. $\displaystyle\int \frac{\cos x}{\sin^2 x + 2 \sin x} \, dx$

34. $\displaystyle\int \frac{\cos^{-1} \sqrt{x}}{\sqrt{x}} \, dx$

35. $\displaystyle\int \frac{\tan^{-1} x^3}{x^4} \, dx$

36. $\displaystyle\int \frac{e^{3t}}{\sqrt{4 + e^{2t}}} \, dt$

37. $\displaystyle\int \frac{(\ln x) \sin^{-1} (\ln x)}{x} \, dx$

38. $\displaystyle\int \frac{dt}{\sqrt{1 + 4e^t}}$

39–46. Geometry problems *Use a table of integrals to solve the following problems.*

39. Find the length of the curve $y = x^2/4$ on the interval $[0, 8]$.

40. Find the length of the curve $y = x^{3/2} + 8$ on the interval $[0, 2]$.

41. Find the length of the curve $y = e^x$ on the interval $[0, \ln 2]$.

42. The region bounded by the graph of $y = x^2\sqrt{\ln x}$ and the x-axis on the interval $[1, e]$ is revolved about the x-axis. What is the volume of the solid that is formed?

43. The region bounded by the graph of $y = \dfrac{1}{\sqrt{x} + 4}$ and the x-axis on the interval $[0, 12]$ is revolved about the y-axis. What is the volume of the solid that is formed?

44. Find the area of the region bounded by the graph of $y = \dfrac{1}{\sqrt{x^2 - 2x + 2}}$ and the x-axis between $x = 0$ and $x = 3$.

45. The region bounded by the graphs of $y = \pi/2, y = \sin^{-1} x$, and the y-axis is revolved about the y-axis. What is the volume of the solid that is formed?

46. The graphs of $f(x) = \dfrac{2}{x^2 + 1}$ and $g(x) = \dfrac{7}{4\sqrt{x^2 + 1}}$ are shown in the figure. Which is greater, the average value of f or that of g on the interval $[-1, 1]$?

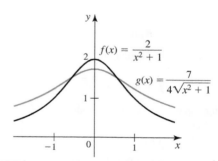

47–54. Indefinite integrals *Use a computer algebra system to evaluate the following indefinite integrals. Assume that a is a positive real number.*

47. $\displaystyle\int \frac{x}{\sqrt{2x + 3}} \, dx$

48. $\displaystyle\int \sqrt{4x^2 + 36} \, dx$

49. $\displaystyle\int \tan^2 3x \, dx$

50. $\displaystyle\int (a^2 - t^2)^{-2} \, dt$

51. $\displaystyle\int \frac{(x^2 - a^2)^{3/2}}{x} \, dx$

52. $\displaystyle\int \frac{dx}{x(a^2 - x^2)^2}$

53. $\displaystyle\int (a^2 - x^2)^{3/2} \, dx$

54. $\displaystyle\int (y^2 + a^2)^{-5/2} \, dy$

55–62. Definite integrals *Use a computer algebra system to evaluate the following definite integrals. In each case, find an exact value of the integral (obtained by a symbolic method) and find an approximate value (obtained by a numerical method). Compare the results.*

55. $\displaystyle\int_{2/3}^{4/5} x^8 \, dx$

56. $\displaystyle\int_0^{\pi/2} \cos^6 x \, dx$

57. $\displaystyle\int_0^4 (9 + x^2)^{3/2} \, dx$

58. $\displaystyle\int_{1/2}^1 \frac{\sin^{-1} x}{x} \, dx$

59. $\displaystyle\int_0^{\pi/2} \frac{dt}{1 + \tan^2 t}$

60. $\displaystyle\int_0^{2\pi} \frac{dt}{(4 + 2\sin t)^2}$

61. $\displaystyle\int_0^1 (\ln x) \ln (1 + x) \, dx$

62. $\displaystyle\int_0^{\pi/4} \ln (1 + \tan x) \, dx$

Further Explorations

63. Explain why or why not Determine whether the following statements are true and give an explanation or counterexample.

   a. It is possible that a computer algebra system says

$$\int \frac{dx}{x(x - 1)} = \ln (x - 1) - \ln x \text{ and a table of integrals}$$

   says $\displaystyle\int \frac{dx}{x(x - 1)} = \ln \left| \frac{x - 1}{x} \right| + C.$

   b. A computer algebra system working in symbolic mode could give the result $\int_0^1 x^8 \, dx = \frac{1}{9}$, and a computer algebra system working in approximate (numerical) mode could give the result $\int_0^1 x^8 \, dx = 0.11111111.$

64. Apparent discrepancy Three different computer algebra systems give the following results:

$$\int \frac{dx}{x\sqrt{x^4 - 1}} = \frac{1}{2} \cos^{-1} \sqrt{x^{-4}} = \frac{1}{2} \cos^{-1} x^{-2} = \frac{1}{2} \tan^{-1} \sqrt{x^4 - 1}.$$

Explain how they can all be correct.

65. Reconciling results Using one computer algebra system,

it was found that $\displaystyle\int \frac{dx}{1 + \sin x} = \frac{\sin x - 1}{\cos x}$, and using another

computer algebra system, it was found that $\displaystyle\int \frac{dx}{1 + \sin x} =$

$\dfrac{2 \sin (x/2)}{\cos (x/2) + \sin (x/2)}$. Reconcile the two answers.

66. Apparent discrepancy Resolve the apparent discrepancy between

$$\int \frac{dx}{x(x - 1)(x + 2)} = \frac{1}{6} \ln \frac{(x - 1)^2 |x + 2|}{|x|^3} + C \quad \text{and}$$

$$\int \frac{dx}{x(x - 1)(x + 2)} = \frac{\ln |x - 1|}{3} + \frac{\ln |x + 2|}{6} - \frac{\ln |x|}{2} + C.$$

67–70. Reduction formulas *Use the reduction formulas in a table of integrals to evaluate the following integrals.*

67. $\displaystyle\int x^3 e^{2x} \, dx$

68. $\displaystyle\int p^2 e^{-3p} \, dp$

69. $\displaystyle\int \tan^4 3y \, dy$

70. $\displaystyle\int \sec^4 4t \, dt$

71–74. Double table lookup *The following integrals may require more than one table lookup. Evaluate the integrals using a table of integrals; then check your answer with a computer algebra system.*

71. $\displaystyle\int x \sin^{-1} 2x \, dx$

72. $\displaystyle\int 4x \cos^{-1} 10x \, dx$

73. $\displaystyle\int \frac{\tan^{-1} x}{x^2} \, dx$

74. $\displaystyle\int \frac{\sin^{-1} ax}{x^2} \, dx, a > 0$

75. Evaluating an integral without the Fundamental Theorem of Calculus Evaluate $\int_0^{\pi/4} \ln (1 + \tan x) \, dx$ using the following steps.

   a. If f is integrable on $[0, b]$, use substitution to show that

$$\int_0^b f(x) \, dx = \int_0^{b/2} (f(x) + f(b - x)) \, dx.$$

   b. Use part (a) and the identity $\tan (\alpha + \beta) = \dfrac{\tan \alpha + \tan \beta}{1 - \tan \alpha \tan \beta}$

   to evaluate $\int_0^{\pi/4} \ln (1 + \tan x) \, dx.$
   (*Source: The College Mathematics Journal* 33, 4, Sep 2004)

76. Two integration approaches Evaluate $\int \cos (\ln x) \, dx$ two different ways:

   a. Use tables after first using the substitution $u = \ln x$.
   b. Use integration by parts twice to verify your answer to part (a).

Applications

77. Period of a pendulum Consider a pendulum of length L meters swinging only under the influence of gravity. Suppose the pendulum starts swinging with an initial displacement of θ_0 radians (see figure). The period (time to complete one full cycle) is given by

$$T = \frac{4}{\omega} \int_0^{\pi/2} \frac{d\varphi}{\sqrt{1 - k^2 \sin^2 \varphi}},$$

where $\omega^2 = g/L$, $g \approx 9.8$ m/s^2 is the acceleration due to gravity, and $k^2 = \sin^2 (\theta_0/2)$. Assume $L = 9.8$ m, which means $\omega = 1$ s^{-1}.

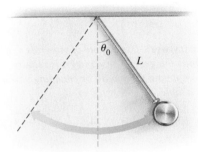

   a. Use a computer algebra system to find the period of the pendulum for $\theta_0 = 0.1, 0.2, \ldots, 0.9, 1.0$ rad.
   b. For small values of θ_0, the period should be approximately 2π seconds. For what values of θ_0 are your computed values within 10% of 2π (relative error less than 0.1)?

Additional Exercises

T **78. Arc length of a parabola** Let $L(c)$ be the length of the parabola $f(x) = x^2$ from $x = 0$ to $x = c$, where $c \geq 0$ is a constant.

a. Find an expression for L and graph the function.

b. Is L concave up or concave down on $[0, \infty)$?

c. Show that as c becomes large and positive, the arc length function increases as c^2; that is, $L(c) \approx kc^2$, where k is a constant.

79–82. Deriving formulas *Evaluate the following integrals. Assume a and b are real numbers and n is an integer.*

79. $\displaystyle\int \frac{x}{ax + b}\, dx$ (Use $u = ax + b$.)

80. $\displaystyle\int \frac{x}{\sqrt{ax + b}}\, dx$ (Use $u^2 = ax + b$.)

81. $\int x(ax + b)^n\, dx$ (Use $u = ax + b$.)

82. $\int x^n \sin^{-1} x\, dx$ (Use integration by parts.)

T **83. Powers of sine and cosine** It can be shown that

$$\int_0^{\pi/2} \sin^n x\, dx = \int_0^{\pi/2} \cos^n x\, dx =$$

$$\begin{cases} \dfrac{1 \cdot 3 \cdot 5 \cdots (n-1)}{2 \cdot 4 \cdot 6 \cdots n} \cdot \dfrac{\pi}{2} & \text{if } n \geq 2 \text{ is an even integer} \\[2ex] \dfrac{2 \cdot 4 \cdot 6 \cdots (n-1)}{3 \cdot 5 \cdot 7 \cdots n} & \text{if } n \geq 3 \text{ is an odd integer.} \end{cases}$$

a. Use a computer algebra system to confirm this result for $n = 2, 3, 4,$ and 5.

b. Evaluate the integrals with $n = 10$ and confirm the result.

c. Using graphing and/or symbolic computation, determine whether the values of the integrals increase or decrease as n increases.

T **84. A remarkable integral** It is a fact that $\displaystyle\int_0^{\pi/2} \frac{dx}{1 + \tan^m x} = \frac{\pi}{4}$ for *all* real numbers m.

a. Graph the integrand for $m = -2, -3/2, -1, -1/2, 0, 1/2, 1, 3/2,$ and 2, and explain geometrically how the area under the curve on the interval $[0, \pi/2]$ remains constant as m varies.

b. Use a computer algebra system to confirm that the integral is constant for all m.

QUICK CHECK ANSWERS

1. 1   **2.** Because $\sin^2 x = 1 - \cos^2 x$, the two results differ by a constant, which can be absorbed in the arbitrary constant C.   **3.** The second result agrees with the first for $x > 0$ after using $\ln a - \ln b = \ln(a/b)$. The second result should have absolute values and an arbitrary constant. ◄

7.7 Numerical Integration

Situations arise in which the analytical methods we have developed so far cannot be used to evaluate a definite integral. For example, an integrand may not have an obvious antiderivative (such as $\cos x^2$ and $1/\ln x$), or perhaps the value of the integrand is known only at a finite set of points, which makes finding an antiderivative impossible.

When analytical methods fail, we often turn to *numerical methods*, which are typically done on a calculator or computer. These methods do not produce exact values of definite integrals, but they provide approximations that are generally quite accurate. Many calculators, software packages, and computer algebra systems have built-in numerical integration methods. In this section, we explore some of these methods.

Absolute and Relative Error

Because numerical methods do not typically produce exact results, we should be concerned about the accuracy of approximations, which leads to the ideas of *absolute* and *relative error.*

> **DEFINITION Absolute and Relative Error**
>
> Suppose c is a computed numerical solution to a problem having an exact solution x. There are two common measures of the error in c as an approximation to x:
>
> $$\text{absolute error} = |c - x|$$
>
> and
>
> $$\text{relative error} = \frac{|c - x|}{|x|} \quad (\text{if } x \neq 0).$$

➤ Because the exact solution is usually not known, the goal in practice is to estimate the maximum size of the error.

EXAMPLE 1 **Absolute and relative error** The ancient Greeks used $\frac{22}{7}$ to approximate the value of π. Determine the absolute and relative error in this approximation to π.

SOLUTION Letting $c = \frac{22}{7}$ be the approximate value of $x = \pi$, we find that

$$\text{absolute error} = \left| \frac{22}{7} - \pi \right| \approx 0.00126$$

and

$$\text{relative error} = \frac{|22/7 - \pi|}{|\pi|} \approx 0.000402 \approx 0.04\%.$$

Related Exercises 7–10 ◀

Midpoint Rule

Many numerical integration methods are based on the ideas that underlie Riemann sums; these methods approximate the net area of regions bounded by curves. A typical problem is shown in Figure 7.12, where we see a function f defined on an interval $[a, b]$. The goal is to approximate the value of $\int_a^b f(x)\, dx$. As with Riemann sums, we first partition the interval $[a, b]$ into n subintervals of equal length $\Delta x = (b - a)/n$. This partition establishes $n + 1$ grid points

$$x_0 = a, \quad x_1 = a + \Delta x, \quad x_2 = a + 2\Delta x, \ldots, \quad x_k = a + k\Delta x, \ldots, \quad x_n = b.$$

The kth subinterval is $[x_{k-1}, x_k]$, for $k = 1, 2, \ldots, n$.

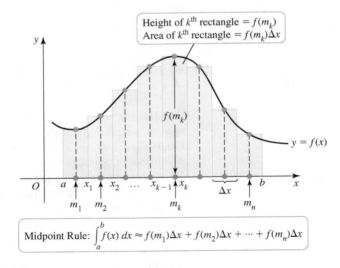

Midpoint Rule: $\int_a^b f(x)\, dx \approx f(m_1)\Delta x + f(m_2)\Delta x + \cdots + f(m_n)\Delta x$

Figure 7.12

The Midpoint Rule approximates the region under the curve using rectangles. The bases of the rectangles have width Δx. The height of the kth rectangle is $f(m_k)$, where $m_k = (x_{k-1} + x_k)/2$ is the midpoint of the kth subinterval (Figure 7.12). Therefore, the net area of the kth rectangle is $f(m_k)\Delta x$.

Let $M(n)$ be the Midpoint Rule approximation to the integral using n rectangles. Summing the net areas of the rectangles, we have

> ➤ If $f(m_k) < 0$ for some k, then the net area of the corresponding rectangle is negative, which makes a negative contribution to the approximation (Section 5.2).

$$\int_a^b f(x)\, dx \approx M(n)$$

$$= f(m_1)\Delta x + f(m_2)\Delta x + \cdots + f(m_n)\Delta x$$

$$= \sum_{k=1}^{n} f\left(\frac{x_{k-1} + x_k}{2} \right) \Delta x.$$

Just as with Riemann sums, the Midpoint Rule approximations to $\int_a^b f(x)\, dx$ generally improve as n increases.

▶ The Midpoint Rule is a midpoint
Riemann sum, introduced in Section 5.1.

DEFINITION Midpoint Rule

Suppose f is defined and integrable on $[a, b]$. The **Midpoint Rule approximation** to $\int_a^b f(x)\, dx$ using n equally spaced subintervals on $[a, b]$ is

$$M(n) = f(m_1)\Delta x + f(m_2)\Delta x + \cdots + f(m_n)\Delta x$$

$$= \sum_{k=1}^{n} f\left(\frac{x_{k-1} + x_k}{2}\right)\Delta x,$$

where $\Delta x = (b - a)/n$, $x_k = a + k\Delta x$, and $m_k = (x_{k-1} + x_k)/2$ is the midpoint of $[x_{k-1}, x_k]$, for $k = 1, \ldots, n$.

QUICK CHECK 1 To apply the Midpoint Rule on the interval $[3, 11]$ with $n = 4$, at what points must the integrand be evaluated? ◀

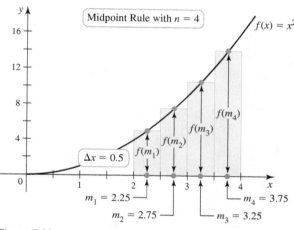

Midpoint Rule with $n = 4$

$\Delta x = 0.5$

$f(m_1)$ $f(m_2)$ $f(m_3)$ $f(m_4)$

$f(x) = x^2$

$m_1 = 2.25$ $m_4 = 3.75$

$m_2 = 2.75$ $m_3 = 3.25$

Figure 7.13

EXAMPLE 2 **Applying the Midpoint Rule** Approximate $\int_2^4 x^2\, dx$ using the Midpoint Rule with $n = 4$ and $n = 8$ subintervals.

SOLUTION With $a = 2$, $b = 4$, and $n = 4$ subintervals, the length of each subinterval is $\Delta x = (b - a)/n = 2/4 = 0.5$. The grid points are

$$x_0 = 2, \quad x_1 = 2.5, \quad x_2 = 3, \quad x_3 = 3.5, \quad \text{and} \quad x_4 = 4.$$

The integrand must be evaluated at the midpoints (Figure 7.13)

$$m_1 = 2.25, \quad m_2 = 2.75, \quad m_3 = 3.25, \quad \text{and} \quad m_4 = 3.75.$$

With $f(x) = x^2$ and $n = 4$, the Midpoint Rule approximation is

$$M(4) = f(m_1)\Delta x + f(m_2)\Delta x + f(m_3)\Delta x + f(m_4)\Delta x$$
$$= (m_1^2 + m_2^2 + m_3^2 + m_4^2)\Delta x$$
$$= (2.25^2 + 2.75^2 + 3.25^2 + 3.75^2) \cdot 0.5$$
$$= 18.625.$$

The exact area of the region is $\frac{56}{3}$, so this Midpoint Rule approximation has an absolute error of

$$|18.625 - 56/3| \approx 0.0417$$

and a relative error of

$$\left|\frac{18.625 - 56/3}{56/3}\right| \approx 0.00223 = 0.223\%.$$

Using $n = 8$ subintervals, the midpoint approximation is

$$M(8) = \sum_{k=1}^{8} f(m_k)\Delta x = 18.65625,$$

which has an absolute error of about 0.0104 and a relative error of about 0.0558%. We see that increasing n and using more rectangles decreases the error in the approximations.

Related Exercises 11–14 ◀

The Trapezoid Rule

Another numerical method for estimating $\int_a^b f(x)\, dx$ is the Trapezoid Rule, which uses the same partition of the interval $[a, b]$ described for the Midpoint Rule. Instead of approximating the region under the curve by rectangles, the Trapezoid Rule uses (what else?) trapezoids. The bases of the trapezoids have length Δx. The sides of the kth

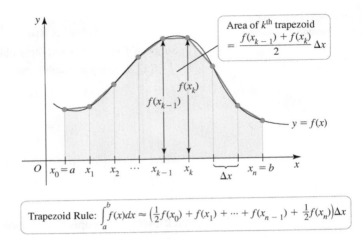

Figure 7.14

> This derivation of the Trapezoid Rule assumes that f is nonnegative on $[a, b]$. However, the same argument can be used if f is negative on all or part of $[a, b]$. In fact, the argument illustrates how negative contributions to the net area arise when f is negative.

Trapezoid Rule: $\int_a^b f(x)\,dx \approx \left(\frac{1}{2}f(x_0) + f(x_1) + \cdots + f(x_{n-1}) + \frac{1}{2}f(x_n)\right)\Delta x$

Area of a trapezoid

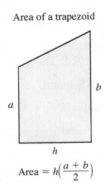

Area $= h\left(\dfrac{a+b}{2}\right)$

trapezoid have lengths $f(x_{k-1})$ and $f(x_k)$, for $k = 1, 2, \ldots, n$ (Figure 7.14). Therefore, the net area of the kth trapezoid is $\left(\dfrac{f(x_{k-1}) + f(x_k)}{2}\right)\Delta x$.

Letting $T(n)$ be the Trapezoid Rule approximation to the integral using n subintervals, we have

$$\int_a^b f(x)\,dx \approx T(n)$$

$$= \underbrace{\left(\frac{f(x_0) + f(x_1)}{2}\right)\Delta x}_{\text{area of first trapezoid}} + \underbrace{\left(\frac{f(x_1) + f(x_2)}{2}\right)\Delta x}_{\text{area of second trapezoid}} + \cdots + \underbrace{\left(\frac{f(x_{n-1}) + f(x_n)}{2}\right)\Delta x}_{\text{area of } n\text{th trapezoid}}$$

$$= \left(\frac{f(x_0)}{2} + \underbrace{\frac{f(x_1)}{2} + \frac{f(x_1)}{2}}_{f(x_1)} + \cdots + \underbrace{\frac{f(x_{n-1})}{2} + \frac{f(x_{n-1})}{2}}_{f(x_{n-1})} + \frac{f(x_n)}{2}\right)\Delta x$$

$$= \left(\frac{f(x_0)}{2} + \underbrace{f(x_1) + \cdots + f(x_{n-1})}_{\sum_{k=1}^{n-1} f(x_k)} + \frac{f(x_n)}{2}\right)\Delta x.$$

As with the Midpoint Rule, the Trapezoid Rule approximations generally improve as n increases.

QUICK CHECK 2 Does the Trapezoid Rule underestimate or overestimate the value of $\int_0^4 x^2\,dx$? ◄

DEFINITION Trapezoid Rule

Suppose f is defined and integrable on $[a, b]$. The **Trapezoid Rule approximation** to $\int_a^b f(x)\,dx$ using n equally spaced subintervals on $[a, b]$ is

$$T(n) = \left(\frac{1}{2}f(x_0) + \sum_{k=1}^{n-1} f(x_k) + \frac{1}{2}f(x_n)\right)\Delta x,$$

where $\Delta x = (b - a)/n$ and $x_k = a + k\Delta x$, for $k = 0, 1, \ldots, n$.

EXAMPLE 3 **Applying the Trapezoid Rule** Approximate $\int_2^4 x^2\, dx$ using the Trapezoid Rule with $n = 4$ subintervals.

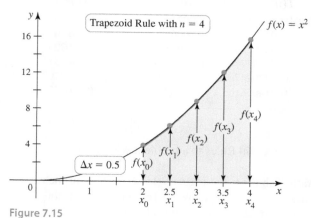

Trapezoid Rule with $n = 4$

$f(x) = x^2$

$\Delta x = 0.5$ $f(x_0)$

$f(x_1)$

$f(x_2)$

$f(x_3)$

$f(x_4)$

x_0 x_1 x_2 x_3 x_4

Figure 7.15

SOLUTION As in Example 2, the grid points are

$$x_0 = 2, \quad x_1 = 2.5, \quad x_2 = 3, \quad x_3 = 3.5, \quad \text{and} \quad x_4 = 4.$$

With $f(x) = x^2$ and $n = 4$, the Trapezoid Rule approximation is

$$
\begin{aligned}
T(4) &= \tfrac{1}{2}f(x_0)\Delta x + f(x_1)\Delta x + f(x_2)\Delta x + f(x_3)\Delta x + \tfrac{1}{2}f(x_4)\Delta x \\
&= \left(\tfrac{1}{2}x_0^2 + x_1^2 + x_2^2 + x_3^2 + \tfrac{1}{2}x_4^2\right)\Delta x \\
&= \left(\tfrac{1}{2}\cdot 2^2 + 2.5^2 + 3^2 + 3.5^2 + \tfrac{1}{2}\cdot 4^2\right)\cdot 0.5 \\
&= 18.75.
\end{aligned}
$$

Figure 7.15 shows the approximation with $n = 4$ trapezoids. The exact area of the region is $56/3$, so the Trapezoid Rule approximation has an absolute error of about 0.0833 and a relative error of approximately 0.00446, or 0.446%. Increasing n decreases this error.

Related Exercises 15–18 ◄

EXAMPLE 4 **Errors in the Midpoint and Trapezoid Rules** Given that

$$\int_0^1 xe^{-x}\, dx = 1 - 2e^{-1},$$

find the absolute errors in the Midpoint Rule and Trapezoid Rule approximations to the integral with $n = 4, 8, 16, 32, 64,$ and 128 subintervals.

SOLUTION Because the exact value of the integral is known (which does *not* happen in practice), we can compute the error in various approximations. For example, if $n = 16$, then

$$\Delta x = \frac{1}{16} \quad \text{and} \quad x_k = \frac{k}{16}, \quad \text{for } k = 0, 1, \ldots, n.$$

Using sigma notation and a calculator, we have

$$M(16) = \sum_{k=1}^{16} f\!\left(\overbrace{\frac{(k-1)/16}{2}}^{x_{k-1}} \overbrace{+ k/16}^{x_k}\right)\overbrace{\frac{1}{16}}^{\Delta x} = \sum_{k=1}^{16} f\!\left(\frac{2k-1}{32}\right)\frac{1}{16} \approx 0.26440383609318$$

and

$$T(16) = \left(\frac{1}{2}f(0) + \sum_{k=1}^{15} f(k/16) + \frac{1}{2}f(1)\right)\frac{1}{16} \approx 0.26391564480235.$$

$x_0 = a$ x_k $x_{16} = b$

The absolute error in the Midpoint Rule approximation with $n = 16$ is $|M(16) - (1 - 2e^{-1})| \approx 0.000163$. The absolute error in the Trapezoid Rule approximation with $n = 16$ is $|T(16) - (1 - 2e^{-1})| \approx 0.000325$.

The Midpoint Rule and Trapezoid Rule approximations to the integral, together with the associated absolute errors, are shown in Table 7.5 for various values of n. Notice that as n increases, the errors in both methods decrease, as expected. With $n = 128$ subintervals, the approximations $M(128)$ and $T(128)$ agree to four decimal places. Based on these approximations, a good approximation to the integral is 0.2642. The way in which the errors decrease is also worth noting. If you look carefully at both error columns in Table 7.5, you will see that each time n is doubled (or Δx is halved), the error decreases by a factor of approximately 4.

Table 7.5

n	M(n)	T(n)	Error in M(n)	Error in T(n)
4	0.26683456310319	0.25904504019141	0.00259	0.00520
8	0.26489148795740	0.26293980164730	0.000650	0.00130
16	0.26440383609318	0.26391564480235	0.000163	0.000325
32	0.26428180513718	0.26415974044777	0.0000407	0.0000814
64	0.26425129001915	0.26422077279247	0.0000102	0.0000203
128	0.26424366077837	0.26423603140581	0.00000254	0.00000509

Related Exercises 19–26 ◄

QUICK CHECK 3 Compute the approximate factor by which the error decreases in Table 7.5 between $T(16)$ and $T(32)$, and between $T(32)$ and $T(64)$. ◄

We now apply the Midpoint and Trapezoid Rules to a problem with real data.

EXAMPLE 5   World oil production Table 7.6 and Figure 7.16 show data for the rate of world crude oil production (in billions of barrels/yr) over a 16-year period. If the rate of oil production is given by the (assumed to be integrable) function R, then the total amount of oil produced in billions of barrels over the time period $a \le t \le b$ is $Q = \int_a^b R(t)\, dt$ (Section 6.1). Use the Midpoint and Trapezoid Rules to approximate the total oil produced between 1995 and 2011.

SOLUTION For convenience, let $t = 0$ represent 1995 and $t = 16$ represent 2011. We let $R(t)$ be the rate of oil production in the year corresponding to t (for example, $R(6) = 25.2$ is the rate in 2001). The goal is to approximate $Q = \int_0^{16} R(t)\, dt$. If we use $n = 4$ subintervals, then $\Delta t = 4$ yr. The resulting Midpoint and Trapezoid Rule approximations (in billions of barrels) are

$$Q \approx M(4) = (R(2) + R(6) + R(10) + R(14))\Delta t$$
$$= (23.0 + 25.2 + 25.9 + 26.4)4$$
$$= 402.0$$

and

$$Q \approx T(4) = \left(\frac{1}{2}R(0) + R(4) + R(8) + R(12) + \frac{1}{2}R(16)\right)\Delta t$$
$$= \left(\frac{1}{2}\cdot 21.9 + 24.5 + 24.5 + 27.0 + \frac{1}{2}\cdot 27.0\right)4$$
$$= 401.8.$$

The two methods give reasonable agreement. Using $n = 8$ subintervals, with $\Delta t = 2$ yr, similar calculations give the approximations

$$Q \approx M(8) = 399.8 \quad\text{and}\quad Q \approx T(8) = 401.9.$$

The given data do not allow us to compute the next Midpoint Rule approximation $M(16)$. However, we can compute the next Trapezoid Rule approximation $T(16)$, and here is a good way to do it. If $T(n)$ and $M(n)$ are known, then the next Trapezoid Rule approximation is (Exercise 62)

$$T(2n) = \frac{T(n) + M(n)}{2}.$$

Using this identity, we find that

$$T(16) = \frac{T(8) + M(8)}{2} = \frac{401.9 + 399.8}{2} \approx 400.9.$$

Based on these calculations, the best approximation to the total oil produced between 1995 and 2011 is 400.9 billion barrels.

Related Exercises 27–30 ◄

Table 7.6

Year	World Crude Oil Production (billions barrels/yr)
1995	21.9
1996	22.3
1997	23.0
1998	23.7
1999	24.5
2000	23.7
2001	25.2
2002	24.8
2003	24.5
2004	25.2
2005	25.9
2006	26.3
2007	27.0
2008	26.9
2009	26.4
2010	27.0
2011	27.0

(*Source*: U.S. Energy Information Administration)

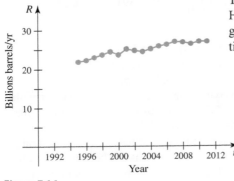

Figure 7.16
(*Source*: U.S. Energy Information Administration)

The Midpoint and Trapezoid Rules, as well as left and right Riemann sums, can be applied to problems in which data are given on a nonuniform grid (that is, the lengths of the sub-intervals vary). In the case of the Trapezoid Rule, the net areas of the approximating trapezoids must be computed individually and then summed, as shown in the next example.

EXAMPLE 6 **Net change in sea level** Table 7.7 lists rates of change $s'(t)$ in global sea level $s(t)$ in various years from 1995 ($t = 0$) to 2011 ($t = 16$), with rates of change reported in mm/yr.

Table 7.7

t (years from 1995)	0 (1995)	3 (1998)	5 (2000)	7 (2002)	8 (2003)	12 (2007)	14 (2009)	16 (2011)
$s'(t)$ (mm/yr)	0.51	5.19	4.39	2.21	5.24	0.63	4.19	2.38

(*Source:* Collecte Localisation Satellites/Centre national d'études spatiales/Legos)

> The rate of change in sea level varies from one location on Earth to the next; sea level also varies seasonally and is influenced by ocean currents. The data in Table 7.7 reflect approximate rates of change at the beginning of each year listed, averaged over the entire globe.

a. Assuming s' is continuous on $[0, 16]$, explain how a definite integral can be used to find the net change in sea level from 1995 to 2011; then write the definite integral.

b. Use the data in Table 7.7 and generalize the Trapezoid Rule to estimate the value of the integral from part (a).

SOLUTION

a. The net change in any quantity Q over the interval $[a, b]$ is $Q(b) - Q(a)$ (Section 6.1). When the rate of change Q' is known, the net change in Q is found by integrating Q' over the same interval; that is,

$$\text{net change in } Q = Q(b) - Q(a) = \int_a^b Q'(t)\,dt. \quad \text{Fundamental Theorem}$$

Therefore, the net change in sea level from 1995 to 2011 is $\int_0^{16} s'(t)\,dt$.

b. The values from Table 7.7 are plotted in Figure 7.17, accompanied by seven trapezoids whose area approximates $\int_0^{16} s'(t)\,dt$. Notice that the grid points (the t-values in Table 7.7) do not form a regular partition of the interval $[0, 16]$. Therefore, we must generalize the standard Trapezoid Rule and compute the area of each trapezoid separately.

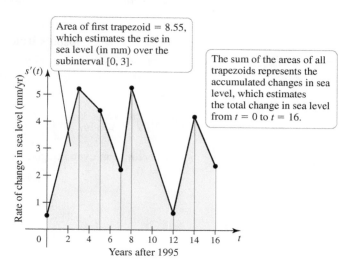

Figure 7.17

Focusing on the first trapezoid over the subinterval $[0, 3]$, we find that its area is

$$\underbrace{\text{area of first trapezoid}}_{\substack{\\ A = \frac{1}{2}(b_1 + b_2)h}} = \frac{1}{2} \cdot \underbrace{(s'(0) + s'(3))}_{\text{measured in mm/yr}} \cdot \underbrace{3}_{\text{yr}} = \frac{1}{2} \cdot (0.51 + 5.19) \cdot 3 = 8.55.$$

Because s' is measured in mm/yr and t is measured in yr, the area of this trapezoid (8.55) is interpreted as the approximate net change in sea level from 1995 to 1998, measured in mm.

As we add new trapezoid areas to the ongoing sum that approximates $\int_0^{16} s'(t)\,dt$, the changes in sea level accumulate, resulting in the total change in sea level on $[0, 16]$. The sum of the areas of all seven trapezoids is

$$\underbrace{\frac{1}{2}(s'(0) + s'(3)) \cdot 3}_{\text{first trapezoid}} + \underbrace{\frac{1}{2}(s'(3) + s'(5)) \cdot 2}_{\text{second trapezoid...}} + \frac{1}{2}(s'(5) + s'(7)) \cdot 2 + \frac{1}{2}(s'(7) + s'(8)) \cdot 1$$

$$+ \frac{1}{2}(s'(8) + s'(12)) \cdot 4 + \frac{1}{2}(s'(12) + s'(14)) \cdot 2 + \underbrace{\frac{1}{2}(s'(14) + s'(16)) \cdot 2}_{\text{...last trapezoid}} = 51.585.$$

We conclude that an estimate of the rise in sea level from 1995 to 2011 is 51.585 mm.

Related Exercises 31–34 ◀

Simpson's Rule

An improvement over the Midpoint Rule and the Trapezoid Rule results when the graph of f is approximated with curves rather than line segments. Let's return to the partition used by the Midpoint and Trapezoid Rules, but now suppose we work with three neighboring points on the curve $y = f(x)$, say $(x_0, f(x_0))$, $(x_1, f(x_1))$, and $(x_2, f(x_2))$. These three points determine a *parabola*, and it is easy to find the net area bounded by the parabola on the interval $[x_0, x_2]$. When this idea is applied to every group of three consecutive points along the interval of integration, the result is *Simpson's Rule*. With n subintervals, Simpson's Rule is denoted $S(n)$ and is given by

$$\int_a^b f(x)\,dx \approx S(n)$$

$$= (f(x_0) + 4f(x_1) + 2f(x_2) + 4f(x_3) + \cdots + 2f(x_{n-2}) + 4f(x_{n-1}) + f(x_n))\frac{\Delta x}{3}.$$

Notice that apart from the first and last terms, the coefficients alternate between 4 and 2; *n must be an even integer* for this rule to apply.

DEFINITION Simpson's Rule

Suppose f is defined and integrable on $[a, b]$ and $n \geq 2$ is an even integer. The **Simpson's Rule approximation** to $\int_a^b f(x)\,dx$ using n equally spaced subintervals on $[a, b]$ is

$$S(n) = (f(x_0) + 4f(x_1) + 2f(x_2) + 4f(x_3) + \cdots + 4f(x_{n-1}) + f(x_n))\frac{\Delta x}{3},$$

where n is an even integer, $\Delta x = (b - a)/n$, and $x_k = a + k\Delta x$, for $k = 0, 1, \ldots, n$.

You can use the formula for Simpson's Rule given above; but here is an easier way. If you already have the Trapezoid Rule approximations $T(n)$ and $T(2n)$, the next Simpson's Rule approximation follows immediately with a simple calculation (Exercise 64):

$$S(2n) = \frac{4T(2n) - T(n)}{3}.$$

EXAMPLE 7   Errors in the Trapezoid Rule and Simpson's Rule Given that $\int_0^1 xe^{-x}\,dx = 1 - 2e^{-1}$, find the absolute errors in the Trapezoid Rule and Simpson's Rule approximations to the integral with $n = 8, 16, 32, 64,$ and 128 subintervals.

SOLUTION Because the shortcut formula for Simpson's Rule is based on values generated by the Trapezoid Rule, it is best to calculate the Trapezoid Rule approximations first. The second column of Table 7.8 shows the Trapezoid Rule approximations computed in Example 4. Having a column of Trapezoid Rule approximations, the corresponding Simpson's Rule approximations are easily found. For example, if $n = 4$, we have

$$S(8) = \frac{4T(8) - T(4)}{3} \approx 0.26423805546593.$$

The table also shows the absolute errors in the approximations. The Simpson's Rule errors decrease more rapidly than the Trapezoid Rule errors. By careful inspection, you will see that the Simpson's Rule errors decrease with a clear pattern: Each time n is doubled (or Δx is halved), the errors decrease by a factor of approximately 16, which makes Simpson's Rule a more accurate method.

QUICK CHECK 4 Compute the approximate factor by which the error decreases in Table 7.8 between $S(16)$ and $S(32)$ and between $S(32)$ and $S(64)$.

Table 7.8

n	$T(n)$	$S(n)$	Error in $T(n)$	Error in $S(n)$
4	0.25904504019141		0.00520	
8	0.26293980164730	0.26423805546593	0.00130	0.00000306
16	0.26391564480235	0.26424092585404	0.000325	0.000000192
32	0.26415974044777	0.26424110566291	0.0000814	0.0000000120
64	0.26422077279247	0.26424111690738	0.0000203	0.000000000750
128	0.26423603140581	0.26424111761026	0.00000509	0.0000000000469

Related Exercises 35–42 ◀

Errors in Numerical Integration

A detailed analysis of the errors in the three methods we have discussed goes beyond the scope of the book. We state without proof the standard error theorems for the methods and note that Examples 3, 4, and 6 are consistent with these results.

➤ Because $\Delta x = \dfrac{b - a}{n}$, the error bounds in Theorem 7.2 can also be written as

$$E_M \le \frac{k(b - a)^3}{24n^2},$$

$$E_T \le \frac{k(b - a)^3}{12n^2}, \text{ and}$$

$$E_S \le \frac{K(b - a)^5}{180n^4}.$$

THEOREM 7.2   Errors in Numerical Integration
Assume that f'' is continuous on the interval $[a, b]$ and that k is a real number such that $|f''(x)| \le k$, for all x in $[a, b]$. The absolute errors in approximating the integral $\int_a^b f(x)\,dx$ by the Midpoint Rule and Trapezoid Rule with n subintervals satisfy the inequalities

$$E_M \le \frac{k(b - a)}{24}(\Delta x)^2 \quad \text{and} \quad E_T \le \frac{k(b - a)}{12}(\Delta x)^2,$$

respectively, where $\Delta x = (b - a)/n$.

Assume that $f^{(4)}$ is continuous on the interval $[a, b]$ and that K is a real number such that $|f^{(4)}(x)| \le K$ on $[a, b]$. The absolute error in approximating the integral $\int_a^b f(x)\,dx$ by Simpson's Rule with n subintervals satisfies the inequality

$$E_S \le \frac{K(b - a)}{180}(\Delta x)^4.$$

The absolute errors associated with the Midpoint Rule and Trapezoid Rule are proportional to $(\Delta x)^2$. So if Δx is reduced by a factor of 2, the errors decrease roughly by a factor of 4, as shown in Example 4. Simpson's Rule is a more accurate method; its error is proportional to $(\Delta x)^4$, which means that if Δx is reduced by a factor of 2, the errors decrease roughly by a factor of 16, as shown in Example 6. Computing both the Trapezoid Rule and Simpson's Rule together, as shown in Example 6, is a powerful method that produces accurate approximations with relatively little work.

SECTION 7.7 EXERCISES

Review Questions

1. If the interval $[4, 18]$ is partitioned into $n = 28$ subintervals of equal length, what is Δx?

2. Explain geometrically how the Midpoint Rule is used to approximate a definite integral.

3. Explain geometrically how the Trapezoid Rule is used to approximate a definite integral.

4. If the Midpoint Rule is used on the interval $[-1, 11]$ with $n = 3$ subintervals, at what x-coordinates is the integrand evaluated?

5. If the Trapezoid Rule is used on the interval $[-1, 9]$ with $n = 5$ subintervals, at what x-coordinates is the integrand evaluated?

6. State how to compute the Simpson's Rule approximation $S(2n)$ if the Trapezoid Rule approximations $T(2n)$ and $T(n)$ are known.

Basic Skills

7–10. Absolute and relative error *Compute the absolute and relative errors in using c to approximate x.*

7. $x = \pi$; $c = 3.14$

8. $x = \sqrt{2}$; $c = 1.414$

9. $x = e$; $c = 2.72$

10. $x = e$; $c = 2.718$

11–14. Midpoint Rule approximations *Find the indicated Midpoint Rule approximations to the following integrals.*

11. $\int_{2}^{10} 2x^2 \, dx$ using $n = 1, 2,$ and 4 subintervals

12. $\int_{1}^{9} x^3 \, dx$ using $n = 1, 2,$ and 4 subintervals

13. $\int_{0}^{1} \sin \pi x \, dx$ using $n = 6$ subintervals

14. $\int_{0}^{1} e^{-x} \, dx$ using $n = 8$ subintervals

15–18. Trapezoid Rule approximations *Find the indicated Trapezoid Rule approximations to the following integrals.*

15. $\int_{2}^{10} 2x^2 \, dx$ using $n = 2, 4,$ and 8 subintervals

16. $\int_{1}^{9} x^3 \, dx$ using $n = 2, 4,$ and 8 subintervals

17. $\int_{0}^{1} \sin \pi x \, dx$ using $n = 6$ subintervals

18. $\int_{0}^{1} e^{-x} \, dx$ using $n = 8$ subintervals

19. **Midpoint Rule, Trapezoid Rule, and relative error** Find the Midpoint and Trapezoid Rule approximations to $\int_{0}^{1} \sin \pi x \, dx$ using $n = 25$ subintervals. Compute the relative error of each approximation.

20. **Midpoint Rule, Trapezoid Rule, and relative error** Find the Midpoint and Trapezoid Rule approximations to $\int_{0}^{1} e^{-x} \, dx$ using $n = 50$ subintervals. Compute the relative error of each approximation.

21–26. Comparing the Midpoint and Trapezoid Rules *Apply the Midpoint and Trapezoid Rules to the following integrals. Make a table similar to Table 7.5 showing the approximations and errors for $n = 4, 8, 16,$ and 32. The exact values of the integrals are given for computing the error.*

21. $\int_{1}^{5} (3x^2 - 2x) \, dx = 100$

22. $\int_{-2}^{6} \left(\frac{x^3}{16} - x \right) dx = 4$

23. $\int_{0}^{\pi/4} 3 \sin 2x \, dx = \frac{3}{2}$

24. $\int_{1}^{e} \ln x \, dx = 1$

25. $\int_{0}^{\pi} \sin x \cos 3x \, dx = 0$

26. $\int_{0}^{8} e^{-2x} \, dx = \frac{1 - e^{-16}}{2}$

27–30. Temperature data *Hourly temperature data for Boulder, Colorado, San Francisco, California, Nantucket, Massachusetts, and Duluth, Minnesota, over a 12 hr period on the same day of January are shown in the figure. Assume that these data are taken from a continuous temperature function $T(t)$. The average temperature over the 12-hr period is $\bar{T} = \dfrac{1}{12} \int_{0}^{12} T(t) \, dt.$*

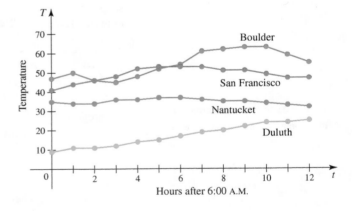

t	0	1	2	3	4	5	6	7	8	9	10	11	12
B	47	50	46	45	48	52	54	61	62	63	63	59	55
SF	41	44	46	48	52	53	53	53	51	51	49	47	47
N	35	34	34	36	36	37	37	36	35	35	34	33	32
D	9	11	11	12	14	15	17	19	20	22	24	24	25

27. Find an accurate approximation to the average temperature over the 12-hr period for Boulder. State your method.

28. Find an accurate approximation to the average temperature over the 12-hr period for San Francisco. State your method.

29. Find an accurate approximation to the average temperature over the 12-hr period for Nantucket. State your method.

30. Find an accurate approximation to the average temperature over the 12-hr period for Duluth. State your method.

31–34. Nonuniform grids *Use the indicated methods to solve the following problems with nonuniform grids.*

31. A curling iron is plugged into an outlet at time $t = 0$. Its temperature T in degrees Fahrenheit, assumed to be a continuous function that is strictly increasing and concave down on $0 \le t \le 120$, is given at various times (in seconds) in the table.

t (seconds)	0	20	45	60	90	110	120
T(t) (°F)	70	130	200	239	311	355	375

a. Approximate $\dfrac{1}{120}\displaystyle\int_0^{120} T(t)\, dt$ in three ways: using a left Riemann sum, a right Riemann sum, and the Trapezoid Rule. Interpret the value of $\dfrac{1}{120}\displaystyle\int_0^{120} T(t)\, dt$ in the context of this problem.

b. Which of the estimates made in part (a) overestimates the value of $\dfrac{1}{120}\displaystyle\int_0^{120} T(t)\, dt$? Underestimates? Justify your answers with a simple sketch of the sums you computed.

c. Evaluate and interpret $\displaystyle\int_0^{120} T'(t)\, dt$ in the context of this problem.

32. Approximating integrals The function f is twice differentiable on $(-\infty, \infty)$. Values of f at various points on $[0, 20]$ are given in the table.

x	0	4	7	12	14	18	20
f(x)	3	0	-2	-1	2	4	7

a. Approximate $\displaystyle\int_0^{20} f(x)\, dx$ in three ways: using a left Riemann sum, a right Riemann sum, and the Trapezoid Rule.

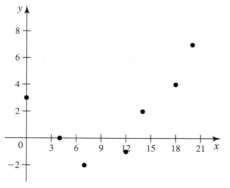

b. A scatterplot of the data in the table is provided in the figure. Use the scatterplot to illustrate each of the approximations in part (a) by sketching appropriate rectangles for the Riemann sums and by sketching trapezoids for the Trapezoid Rule approximation.

c. Evaluate $\displaystyle\int_4^{12} (3f'(x) + 2)\, dx$.

33. A hot-air balloon is launched from an elevation of 5400 ft above sea level. As it rises, its vertical velocity is computed using a device (called a *variometer*) that measures the change in atmospheric pressure. The vertical velocities at selected times are shown in the table (with units of ft/min).

t (min)	0	1	1.5	3	3.5	4	5
Velocity (ft/min)	0	100	120	150	110	90	80

a. Use the Trapezoid Rule to estimate the elevation of the balloon after five minutes. Remember that the balloon starts at an elevation of 5400 ft.

b. Use a right Riemann sum to estimate the elevation of the balloon after five minutes.

c. A polynomial that fits the data reasonably well is

$$g(t) = 3.49t^3 - 43.21t^2 + 142.43t - 1.75.$$

Estimate the elevation of the balloon after five minutes using this polynomial.

34. A piece of wood paneling must be cut in the shape shown in the figure. The coordinates of several points on its curved surface are also shown (with units of inches).

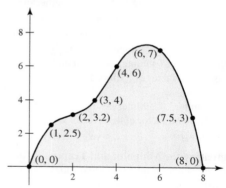

a. Estimate the surface area of the paneling using the Trapezoid Rule.

b. Estimate the surface area of the paneling using a left Riemann sum.

c. Could two identical pieces be cut from a 9-in by 9-in piece of wood? Answer carefully.

T 35–38. Trapezoid Rule and Simpson's Rule *Consider the following integrals and the given values of n.*

a. *Find the Trapezoid Rule approximations to the integral using n and 2n subintervals.*

b. *Find the Simpson's Rule approximation to the integral using 2n subintervals. It is easiest to obtain Simpson's Rule approximations from the Trapezoid Rule approximations, as in Example 7.*

c. *Compute the absolute errors in the Trapezoid Rule and Simpson's Rule with 2n subintervals.*

35. $\int_0^1 e^{2x}\,dx;\ n = 25$

36. $\int_0^2 x^4\,dx;\ n = 30$

37. $\int_1^e \dfrac{dx}{x};\ n = 50$

38. $\int_0^{\pi/4} \dfrac{dx}{1 + x^2};\ n = 64$

T 39–42. Simpson's Rule *Apply Simpson's Rule to the following integrals. It is easiest to obtain the Simpson's Rule approximations from the Trapezoid Rule approximations, as in Example 7. Make a table similar to Table 7.8 showing the approximations and errors for* n = 4, 8, 16, *and* 32. *The exact values of the integrals are given for computing the error.*

39. $\int_0^4 (3x^5 - 8x^3)\,dx = 1536$

40. $\int_1^e \ln x\,dx = 1$

41. $\int_0^\pi e^{-t}\sin t\,dt = \dfrac{1}{2}\left(e^{-\pi} + 1\right)$

42. $\int_0^6 3e^{-3x}\,dx = 1 - e^{-18} \approx 1.000000$

Further Explorations

43. Explain why or why not Determine whether the following statements are true and give an explanation or counterexample.

  a. The Trapezoid Rule is exact when used to approximate the definite integral of a linear function.

  b. If the number of subintervals used in the Midpoint Rule is increased by a factor of 3, the error is expected to decrease by a factor of 8.

  c. If the number of subintervals used in the Trapezoid Rule is increased by a factor of 4, the error is expected to decrease by a factor of 16.

T 44–47. Comparing the Midpoint and Trapezoid Rules *Compare the errors in the Midpoint and Trapezoid Rules with* n = 4, 8, 16, *and* 32 *subintervals when they are applied to the following integrals (with their exact values given).*

44. $\int_0^{\pi/2} \sin^6 x\,dx = \dfrac{5\pi}{32}$

45. $\int_0^{\pi/2} \cos^9 x\,dx = \dfrac{128}{315}$

46. $\int_0^1 (8x^7 - 7x^8)\,dx = \dfrac{2}{9}$

47. $\int_0^\pi \ln (5 + 3\cos x)\,dx = \pi \ln \dfrac{9}{2}$

T 48–51. Using Simpson's Rule *Approximate the following integrals using Simpson's Rule. Experiment with values of n to ensure that the error is less than* 10^{-3}.

48. $\int_0^{2\pi} \dfrac{dx}{(5 + 3\sin x)^2} = \dfrac{5\pi}{32}$

49. $\int_0^\pi \dfrac{4\cos x}{5 - 4\cos x}\,dx = \dfrac{2\pi}{3}$

50. $\int_0^\pi \ln (2 + \cos x)\,dx = \pi \ln\left(\dfrac{2 + \sqrt{3}}{2}\right)$

51. $\int_0^\pi \sin 6x \cos 3x\,dx = \dfrac{4}{9}$

Applications

T 52. Period of a pendulum A standard pendulum of length L swinging under only the influence of gravity (no resistance) has a period of

$$T = \frac{4}{\omega}\int_0^{\pi/2} \frac{d\varphi}{\sqrt{1 - k^2 \sin^2 \varphi}},$$

where $\omega^2 = g/L$, $k^2 = \sin^2(\theta_0/2)$, $g \approx 9.8$ m/s^2 is the acceleration due to gravity, and θ_0 is the initial angle from which the pendulum is released (in radians). Use numerical integration to approximate the period of a pendulum with $L = 1$ m that is released from an angle of $\theta_0 = \pi/4$ rad.

T 53. Arc length of an ellipse The length of an ellipse with axes of length $2a$ and $2b$ is

$$\int_0^{2\pi} \sqrt{a^2 \cos^2 t + b^2 \sin^2 t}\,dt.$$

Use numerical integration and experiment with different values of n to approximate the length of an ellipse with $a = 4$ and $b = 8$.

T 54. Sine integral The theory of diffraction produces the sine integral function $\text{Si}(x) = \displaystyle\int_0^x \frac{\sin t}{t}\,dt$. Use the Midpoint Rule to approximate $\text{Si}(1)$ and $\text{Si}(10)$. (Recall that $\lim_{x\to 0}(\sin x)/x = 1$.) Experiment with the number of subintervals until you obtain approximations that have an error less than 10^{-3}. A rule of thumb is that if two successive approximations differ by less than 10^{-3}, then the error is usually less than 10^{-3}.

T 55. Normal distribution of heights The heights of U.S. men are normally distributed with a mean of 69 inches and a standard deviation of 3 inches. This means that the fraction of men with a height between a and b (with $a < b$) inches is given by the integral

$$\frac{1}{3\sqrt{2\pi}} \int_a^b e^{-((x-69)/3)^2/2}\,dx.$$

What percentage of American men are between 66 and 72 inches tall? Use the method of your choice and experiment with the number of subintervals until you obtain successive approximations that differ by less than 10^{-3}.

T 56. Normal distribution of movie lengths A recent study revealed that the lengths of U.S. movies are normally distributed with a mean of 110 minutes and a standard deviation of 22 minutes. This means that the fraction of movies with lengths between a and b minutes (with $a < b$) is given by the integral

$$\frac{1}{22\sqrt{2\pi}}\int_a^b e^{-((x-110)/22)^2/2}\,dx.$$

What percentage of U.S. movies are between 1 hr and 1.5 hr long (60–90 min)?

T 57. U.S. oil produced and imported The figure shows the rate at which U.S. oil was produced and imported between 1920 and 2005 in units of millions of barrels per day. The total amount of oil produced or imported is given by the area of the region under the corresponding curve. Be careful with units because both days and years are used in this data set.

  a. Use numerical integration to estimate the amount of U.S. oil produced between 1940 and 2000. Use the method of your choice and experiment with values of n.

  b. Use numerical integration to estimate the amount of oil imported between 1940 and 2000. Use the method of your choice and experiment with values of n.

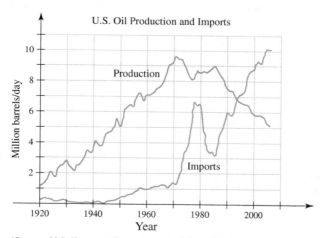

(*Source:* U.S. Energy Information Administration)

Additional Exercises

T 58. Estimating error Refer to Theorem 7.2 and let $f(x) = e^{x^2}$.

  a. Find a Trapezoid Rule approximation to $\int_0^1 e^{x^2}\,dx$ using $n = 50$ subintervals.

  b. Calculate $f''(x)$.

  c. Explain why $|f''(x)| < 18$ on $[0, 1]$, given that $e < 3$.

  d. Use Theorem 7.2 to find an upper bound on the absolute error in the estimate found in part (a).

T 59. Estimating error Refer to Theorem 7.2 and let $f(x) = \sin e^x$.

  a. Find a Trapezoid Rule approximation to $\int_0^1 \sin e^x\,dx$ using $n = 40$ subintervals.

  b. Calculate $f''(x)$.

  c. Explain why $|f''(x)| < 6$ on $[0, 1]$, given that $e < 3$. (*Hint:* Graph f''.)

  d. Find an upper bound on the absolute error in the estimate found in part (a) using Theorem 7.2.

60. Exact Trapezoid Rule Prove that the Trapezoid Rule is exact (no error) when approximating the definite integral of a linear function.

61. Exact Simpson's Rule

  a. Use Simpson's Rule to approximate $\int_0^4 x^3\,dx$ using two subintervals ($n = 2$); compare the approximation to the value of the integral.

  b. Use Simpson's Rule to approximate $\int_0^4 x^3\,dx$ using four subintervals ($n = 4$); compare the approximation to the value of the integral.

  c. Use the error bound associated with Simpson's Rule given in Theorem 7.2 to explain why the approximations in parts (a) and (b) give the exact value of the integral.

  d. Use Theorem 7.2 to explain why a Simpson's Rule approximation using any (even) number of subintervals gives the exact value of $\int_a^b f(x)\,dx$, where $f(x)$ is a polynomial of degree 3 or less.

62. Shortcut for the Trapezoid Rule Given a Midpoint Rule approximation $M(n)$ and a Trapezoid Rule approximation $T(n)$ for a continuous function on $[a, b]$ with n subintervals, show that $T(2n) = (T(n) + M(n))/2$.

63. Trapezoid Rule and concavity Suppose f is positive and its first two derivatives are continuous on $[a, b]$. If f'' is positive on $[a, b]$, then is a Trapezoid Rule estimate of $\int_a^b f(x)\,dx$ an underestimate or overestimate of the integral? Justify your answer using Theorem 7.2 and an illustration.

64. Shortcut for Simpson's Rule Using the notation of the text, prove that $S(2n) = \dfrac{4T(2n) - T(n)}{3}$, for $n \geq 1$.

T 65. Another Simpson's Rule formula Another Simpson's Rule formula is $S(2n) = \dfrac{2M(n) + T(n)}{3}$, for $n \geq 1$. Use this rule to estimate $\int_1^e 1/x\,dx$ using $n = 10$ subintervals.

QUICK CHECK ANSWERS

1. 4, 6, 8, 10 **2.** Overestimates **3.** 4 and 4 **4.** 16 and 16 ◄

7.8 Improper Integrals

The definite integrals we have encountered so far involve finite-valued functions and finite intervals of integration. In this section, you will see that definite integrals can sometimes be evaluated when these conditions are not met. Here is an example. The energy required to launch a rocket from the surface of Earth ($R = 6370$ km from the center of Earth) to an altitude H is given by an integral of the form $\int_R^{R+H} k/x^2 \, dx$, where k is a constant that includes the mass of the rocket, the mass of Earth, and the gravitational constant. This integral may be evaluated for any finite altitude $H > 0$. Now suppose that the aim is to launch the rocket to an arbitrarily large altitude H so that it escapes Earth's gravitational field. The energy required is given by the preceding integral as $H \to \infty$, which we write $\int_R^\infty k/x^2 \, dx$. This integral is an example of an *improper integral*, and it has a finite value (which explains why it is possible to launch rockets to outer space). For historical reasons, the term *improper integral* is used for cases in which

- the interval of integration is infinite, or
- the integrand is unbounded on the interval of integration.

In this section, we explore improper integrals and their many uses.

Infinite Intervals

A simple example illustrates what can happen when integrating a function over an infinite interval. Consider the integral $\displaystyle\int_1^b \frac{1}{x^2} \, dx$, for any real number $b > 1$. As shown in Figure 7.18, this integral gives the area of the region bounded by the curve $y = x^{-2}$ and the x-axis between $x = 1$ and $x = b$. In fact, the value of the integral is

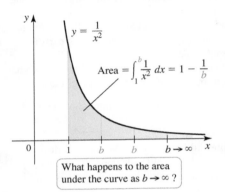

$y = \dfrac{1}{x^2}$

Area $= \displaystyle\int_1^b \frac{1}{x^2} \, dx = 1 - \frac{1}{b}$

What happens to the area under the curve as $b \to \infty$?

Figure 7.18

$$\int_1^b \frac{1}{x^2} \, dx = -\frac{1}{x}\bigg|_1^b = 1 - \frac{1}{b}.$$

For example, if $b = 2$, the area under the curve is $\frac{1}{2}$; if $b = 3$, the area under the curve is $\frac{2}{3}$. In general, as b increases, the area under the curve increases.

Now let's ask what happens to the area as b becomes arbitrarily large. Letting $b \to \infty$, the area of the region under the curve is

$$\lim_{b \to \infty} \left(1 - \frac{1}{b}\right) = 1.$$

We have discovered, surprising as it may seem, a curve of *infinite* length that bounds a region with *finite* area (1 square unit).

We express this result as

$$\int_1^\infty \frac{1}{x^2} \, dx = 1,$$

which is an improper integral because ∞ appears in the upper limit. In general, to evaluate $\int_a^\infty f(x) \, dx$, we first integrate over a finite interval $[a, b]$ and then let $b \to \infty$. Similar procedures are used to evaluate $\int_{-\infty}^b f(x) \, dx$ and $\int_{-\infty}^\infty f(x) \, dx$.

DEFINITION **Improper Integrals over Infinite Intervals**

1. If f is continuous on $[a, \infty)$, then

$$\int_a^\infty f(x)\,dx = \lim_{b \to \infty} \int_a^b f(x)\,dx.$$

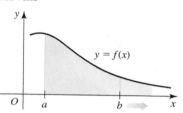

2. If f is continuous on $(-\infty, b]$, then

$$\int_{-\infty}^b f(x)\,dx = \lim_{a \to -\infty} \int_a^b f(x)\,dx.$$

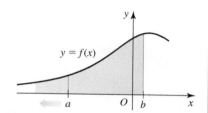

3. If f is continuous on $(-\infty, \infty)$, then

$$\int_{-\infty}^\infty f(x)\,dx = \lim_{a \to -\infty} \int_a^c f(x)\,dx$$

$$+ \lim_{b \to \infty} \int_c^b f(x)\,dx,$$

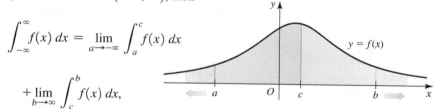

where c is any real number.

If the limits in cases 1–3 exist, then the improper integrals **converge**; otherwise, they **diverge**.

> ▶ Doubly infinite integrals (Case 3 in the definition) must be evaluated as two independent limits and not as
> $$\int_{-\infty}^\infty f(x)\,dx = \lim_{b \to \infty} \int_{-b}^b f(x)\,dx.$$

EXAMPLE 1 **Infinite intervals** Evaluate each integral.

a. $\displaystyle\int_0^\infty e^{-3x}\,dx$ **b.** $\displaystyle\int_{-\infty}^\infty \frac{dx}{1 + x^2}$

SOLUTION

a. Using the definition of the improper integral, we have

$$\int_0^\infty e^{-3x}\,dx = \lim_{b \to \infty} \int_0^b e^{-3x}\,dx \qquad \text{Definition of improper integral}$$

$$= \lim_{b \to \infty} \left(-\frac{1}{3} e^{-3x} \right)\Bigg|_0^b \qquad \text{Evaluate the integral.}$$

$$= \lim_{b \to \infty} \frac{1}{3}\left(1 - e^{-3b}\right) \qquad \text{Simplify.}$$

$$= \frac{1}{3}\left(1 - \underbrace{\lim_{b \to \infty} \frac{1}{e^{3b}}}_{\text{equals } 0}\right) = \frac{1}{3}. \qquad \text{Evaluate the limit; } e^{-3b} = \frac{1}{e^{3b}}.$$

In this case, the limit exists, so the integral converges and the region under the curve has a finite area of $\frac{1}{3}$ (Figure 7.19).

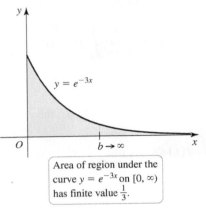

Area of region under the curve $y = e^{-3x}$ on $[0, \infty)$ has finite value $\frac{1}{3}$.

Figure 7.19

Area of region under the curve $y = \dfrac{1}{1 + x^2}$ on $(-\infty, \infty)$ has finite value π.

Figure 7.20

▶ Recall that

$$\int \frac{dx}{a^2 + x^2} = \frac{1}{a}\tan^{-1}\frac{x}{a} + C.$$

The graph of $y = \tan^{-1} x$ shows that

$$\lim_{x \to \infty} \tan^{-1} x = \frac{\pi}{2} \text{ and } \lim_{x \to -\infty} \tan^{-1} x = -\frac{\pi}{2}.$$

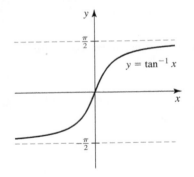

b. Using the definition of the improper integral, we choose $c = 0$ and write

$$\int_{-\infty}^{\infty} \frac{dx}{1 + x^2} = \lim_{a \to -\infty} \int_{a}^{c} \frac{dx}{1 + x^2} + \lim_{b \to \infty} \int_{c}^{b} \frac{dx}{1 + x^2} \qquad \text{Definition of improper integral}$$

$$= \lim_{a \to -\infty} \tan^{-1} x \Big|_{a}^{0} + \lim_{b \to \infty} \tan^{-1} x \Big|_{0}^{b} \qquad \text{Evaluate integral; } c = 0.$$

$$= \lim_{a \to -\infty} (0 - \tan^{-1} a) + \lim_{b \to \infty} (\tan^{-1} b - 0) \qquad \text{Simplify.}$$

$$= \frac{\pi}{2} + \frac{\pi}{2} = \pi. \qquad \text{Evaluate limits.}$$

The same result is obtained with any value of the intermediate point c; therefore, the value of the integral is π (Figure 7.20).

Related Exercises 5–28 ◀

QUICK CHECK 1 The function $f(x) = 1 + x^{-1}$ decreases to 1 as $x \to \infty$. Does $\int_1^{\infty} f(x)\, dx$ exist? ◀

EXAMPLE 2   The family $f(x) = 1/x^p$ Consider the family of functions $f(x) = 1/x^p$, where p is a real number. For what values of p does $\int_1^{\infty} f(x)\, dx$ converge?

SOLUTION For $p > 0$, the functions $f(x) = 1/x^p$ approach zero as $x \to \infty$, with larger values of p giving greater rates of decrease (Figure 7.21). Assuming $p \neq 1$, the integral is evaluated as follows:

▶ Recall that for $p \neq 1$,

$$\int \frac{1}{x^p}\, dx = \int x^{-p}\, dx$$

$$= \frac{x^{-p+1}}{-p + 1} + C$$

$$= \frac{x^{1-p}}{1 - p} + C.$$

$$\int_1^{\infty} \frac{1}{x^p}\, dx = \lim_{b \to \infty} \int_1^{b} x^{-p}\, dx \qquad \text{Definition of improper integral}$$

$$= \frac{1}{1 - p} \lim_{b \to \infty} \left(x^{1-p} \Big|_1^{b} \right) \qquad \text{Evaluate the integral on a finite interval.}$$

$$= \frac{1}{1 - p} \lim_{b \to \infty} (b^{1-p} - 1). \qquad \text{Simplify.}$$

It is easiest to consider three cases.

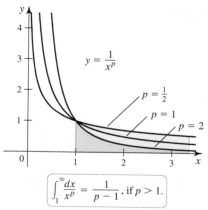

$$\int_1^\infty \frac{dx}{x^p} = \frac{1}{p-1}, \text{ if } p > 1.$$

Figure 7.21

▶ Example 2 is important in the study of infinite series in Chapter 8. It shows that a continuous function f must do more than simply decrease to zero for its integral on $[a, \infty)$ to converge; it must decrease to zero *sufficiently fast*.

Case 1: If $p > 1$, then $p - 1 > 0$, and $b^{1-p} = 1/b^{p-1}$ approaches 0 as $b \to \infty$. Therefore, the integral converges and its value is

$$\int_1^\infty \frac{1}{x^p}\,dx = \frac{1}{1-p}\lim_{b\to\infty}\underbrace{(b^{1-p}-1)}_{\substack{\text{approaches}\\ 0}} = \frac{1}{p-1}.$$

Case 2: If $p < 1$, then $1 - p > 0$, and the integral diverges:

$$\int_1^\infty \frac{1}{x^p}\,dx = \frac{1}{1-p}\lim_{b\to\infty}\underbrace{(b^{1-p}-1)}_{\substack{\text{arbitrarily}\\ \text{large}}} = \infty.$$

Case 3: If $p = 1$, then $\int_1^\infty \frac{1}{x}\,dx = \lim_{b\to\infty} \ln b = \infty$, so the integral diverges.

In summary, $\int_1^\infty \frac{1}{x^p}\,dx = \frac{1}{p-1}$ if $p > 1$, and the integral diverges if $p \le 1$.

Related Exercises 5–28 ◀

QUICK CHECK 2 Use the result of Example 2 to evaluate $\int_1^\infty \frac{1}{x^4}\,dx.$ ◀

EXAMPLE 3 Solids of revolution Let R be the region bounded by the graph of $y = x^{-1}$ and the x-axis, for $x \ge 1$.

a. What is the volume of the solid generated when R is revolved about the x-axis?
b. What is the surface area of the solid generated when R is revolved about the x-axis?
c. What is the volume of the solid generated when R is revolved about the y-axis?

SOLUTION

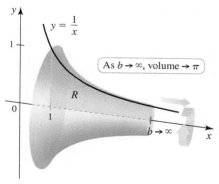

Figure 7.22

a. The region in question and the corresponding solid of revolution are shown in Figure 7.22. We use the disk method (Section 6.3) over the interval $[1, b]$ and then let $b \to \infty$:

$$\text{Volume} = \int_1^\infty \pi(f(x))^2\,dx \qquad \text{Disk method}$$

$$= \pi \lim_{b\to\infty} \int_1^b \frac{1}{x^2}\,dx \qquad \text{Definition of improper integral}$$

$$= \pi \lim_{b\to\infty}\left(1 - \frac{1}{b}\right) = \pi. \qquad \text{Evaluate the integral.}$$

The improper integral exists, and the solid has a volume of π cubic units.

b. Using the results of Section 6.6, the area of the surface generated on the interval $[1, b]$, where $b > 1$, is

$$\int_1^b 2\pi f(x)\sqrt{1 + f'(x)^2}\,dx.$$

The area of the surface generated on the interval $[1, \infty)$ is found by letting $b \to \infty$:

$$\text{surface area} = 2\pi \lim_{b \to \infty} \int_1^b f(x) \sqrt{1 + f'(x)^2}\, dx \quad \text{Surface area formula; let } b \to \infty.$$

$$= 2\pi \lim_{b \to \infty} \int_1^b \frac{1}{x} \sqrt{1 + \left(-\frac{1}{x^2}\right)^2}\, dx \quad \text{Substitute } f \text{ and } f'.$$

$$= 2\pi \lim_{b \to \infty} \int_1^b \frac{1}{x^3} \sqrt{1 + x^4}\, dx. \quad \text{Simplify.}$$

▶ The integral in Example 3b can be evaluated directly by using the substitution $u = x^2$ and then consulting a table of integrals.

Notice that on the interval of integration $x \geq 1$, we have $\sqrt{1 + x^4} > \sqrt{x^4} = x^2$, which means that

$$\frac{1}{x^3} \sqrt{1 + x^4} > \frac{x^2}{x^3} = \frac{1}{x}.$$

Therefore, for all b with $1 < b < \infty$,

$$\text{surface area} = 2\pi \int_1^b \frac{1}{x^3} \sqrt{1 + x^4}\, dx > 2\pi \int_1^b \frac{1}{x}\, dx.$$

▶ The solid in Examples 3a and 3b is called *Gabriel's horn* or *Torricelli's trumpet*. We have shown—quite remarkably—that it has finite volume and infinite surface area.

Because $2\pi \lim\limits_{b \to \infty} \int_1^b \frac{1}{x}\, dx = \infty$ (by Example 2), the preceding inequality implies

that $2\pi \lim\limits_{b \to \infty} \int_1^b \frac{1}{x^3} \sqrt{1 + x^4}\, dx = \infty$. Therefore, the integral diverges and the

surface area of the solid is infinite.

▶ Recall that if $f(x) > 0$ on $[a, b]$ and the region bounded by the graph of f and the x-axis on $[a, b]$ is revolved about the y-axis, the volume of the solid generated is

$$V = \int_a^b 2\pi x f(x)\, dx.$$

c. The region in question and the corresponding solid of revolution are shown in Figure 7.23. Using the shell method (Section 6.4) on the interval $[1, b)$ and letting $b \to \infty$, the volume is given by

$$\text{Volume} = \int_1^\infty 2\pi x f(x)\, dx \quad \text{Shell method}$$

$$= 2\pi \int_1^\infty 1\, dx \quad f(x) = x^{-1}$$

$$= 2\pi \lim_{b \to \infty} \int_1^b 1\, dx \quad \text{Definition of improper integral}$$

$$= 2\pi \lim_{b \to \infty} (b - 1) \quad \text{Evaluate the integral over a finite interval.}$$

$$= \infty. \quad \text{The improper integral diverges.}$$

Revolving the region R about the y-axis, the volume of the solid is infinite.

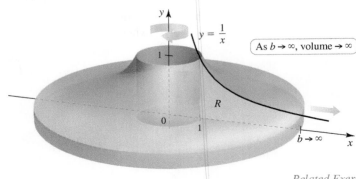

Figure 7.23

Related Exercises 29–34 ◀

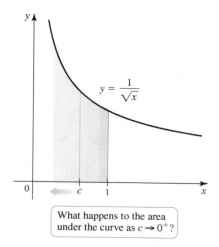

$y = \dfrac{1}{\sqrt{x}}$

What happens to the area under the curve as $c \to 0^+$?

Figure 7.24

> The functions $f(x) = 1/x^p$ are unbounded at $x = 0$, for $p > 0$. It can be shown (Exercise 74) that
>
> $$\int_0^1 \frac{dx}{x^p} = \frac{1}{1-p},$$
>
> provided $p < 1$. Otherwise, the integral diverges.

Unbounded Integrands

Improper integrals also occur when the integrand becomes infinite somewhere on the interval of integration. Consider the function $f(x) = 1/\sqrt{x}$ (Figure 7.24). Let's examine the area of the region bounded by the graph of f between $x = 0$ and $x = 1$. Notice that f is not defined at $x = 0$, and it increases without bound as $x \to 0^+$.

The idea here is to replace the lower limit 0 with a nearby positive number c and then consider the integral $\displaystyle\int_c^1 \frac{dx}{\sqrt{x}}$, where $0 < c < 1$. We find that

$$\int_c^1 \frac{dx}{\sqrt{x}} = 2\sqrt{x}\,\Big|_c^1 = 2(1 - \sqrt{c}).$$

To find the area of the region under the curve over the interval $(0, 1]$, we let $c \to 0^+$. The resulting area, which we denote $\displaystyle\int_0^1 \frac{dx}{\sqrt{x}}$, is

$$\lim_{c \to 0^+} \int_c^1 \frac{dx}{\sqrt{x}} = \lim_{c \to 0^+} 2(1 - \sqrt{c}) = 2.$$

Once again, we have a surprising result: Although the region in question has a boundary curve with infinite length, the area of the region is finite.

QUICK CHECK 3 Explain why the one-sided limit $c \to 0^+$ (instead of a two-sided limit) must be used in the previous calculation. ◄

The preceding example shows that if a function is unbounded at a point c, it may be possible to integrate that function over an interval that contains c. The point c may occur at either endpoint or at an interior point of the interval of integration.

DEFINITIONS Improper Integrals with an Unbounded Integrand

1. Suppose f is continuous on $(a, b]$ with $\displaystyle\lim_{x \to a^+} f(x) = \pm\infty$. Then

$$\int_a^b f(x)\, dx = \lim_{c \to a^+} \int_c^b f(x)\, dx.$$

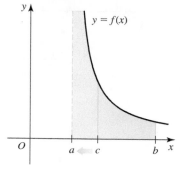

2. Suppose f is continuous on $[a, b)$ with $\displaystyle\lim_{x \to b^-} f(x) = \pm\infty$. Then

$$\int_a^b f(x)\, dx = \lim_{c \to b^-} \int_a^c f(x)\, dx.$$

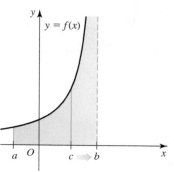

3. Suppose f is continuous on $[a, b]$ except at the interior point p where f is unbounded. Then

$$\int_a^b f(x)\, dx = \lim_{c \to p^-} \int_a^c f(x)\, dx + \lim_{d \to p^+} \int_d^b f(x)\, dx.$$

If the limits in cases 1–3 exist, then the improper integrals **converge**; otherwise, they **diverge**.

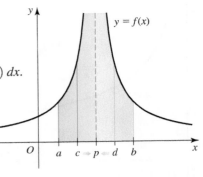

EXAMPLE 4 Infinite integrand Find the area of the region R between the graph of $f(x) = \dfrac{1}{\sqrt{9 - x^2}}$ and the x-axis on the interval $(-3, 3)$ (if it exists).

SOLUTION The integrand is even and has vertical asymptotes at $x = \pm 3$ (Figure 7.25). By symmetry, the area of R is given by

$$\int_{-3}^{3} \frac{1}{\sqrt{9 - x^2}}\, dx = 2\int_{0}^{3} \frac{1}{\sqrt{9 - x^2}}\, dx,$$

assuming these improper integrals exist. Because the integrand is unbounded at $x = 3$, we replace the upper limit with c, evaluate the resulting integral, and then let $c \to 3^-$:

> ▶ Recall that
> $$\int \frac{dx}{\sqrt{a^2 - x^2}} = \sin^{-1}\frac{x}{a} + C.$$

$$2\int_{0}^{3} \frac{dx}{\sqrt{9 - x^2}} = 2\lim_{c \to 3^-} \int_{0}^{c} \frac{dx}{\sqrt{9 - x^2}} \qquad \text{Definition of improper integral}$$

$$= 2\lim_{c \to 3^-} \sin^{-1}\frac{x}{3}\Big|_0^c \qquad \text{Evaluate the integral.}$$

$$= 2\lim_{c \to 3^-} \left(\underbrace{\sin^{-1}\frac{c}{3}}_{\text{approaches } \pi/2} - \underbrace{\sin^{-1} 0}_{\text{equals } 0} \right). \qquad \text{Simplify.}$$

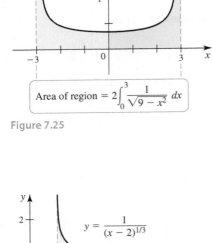

Area of region $= 2\displaystyle\int_0^3 \frac{1}{\sqrt{9 - x^2}}\, dx$

Figure 7.25

Note that as $c \to 3^-$, $\sin^{-1}(c/3) \to \sin^{-1} 1 = \pi/2$. Therefore, the area of R is

$$2\int_{0}^{3} \frac{1}{\sqrt{9 - x^2}}\, dx = 2\left(\frac{\pi}{2} - 0 \right) = \pi.$$

Related Exercises 35–56 ◀

EXAMPLE 5 Infinite integrand at an interior point Evaluate $\displaystyle\int_1^{10} \frac{dx}{(x - 2)^{1/3}}$.

SOLUTION The integrand is unbounded at $x = 2$, which is an interior point of the interval of integration (Figure 7.26). We split the interval into two subintervals and evaluate an improper integral on each subinterval:

$$\int_1^{10} \frac{dx}{(x - 2)^{1/3}} = \lim_{a \to 2^-} \int_1^a \frac{dx}{(x - 2)^{1/3}} + \lim_{b \to 2^+} \int_b^{10} \frac{dx}{(x - 2)^{1/3}} \qquad \begin{array}{l}\text{Definition of improper}\\ \text{integral}\end{array}$$

$$= \lim_{a \to 2^-} \frac{3}{2}(x - 2)^{2/3}\Big|_1^a + \lim_{b \to 2^+} \frac{3}{2}(x - 2)^{2/3}\Big|_b^{10} \qquad \text{Evaluate integrals.}$$

Figure 7.26

> We interpret the result of 9/2 from Example 5 as the net area bounded by the curve $y = 1/(x-2)^{1/3}$ over the interval $[1, 10]$.

$$= \frac{3}{2} \left(\lim_{a \to 2^-} (a-2)^{2/3} - (1-2)^{2/3} \right)$$

$$+ \frac{3}{2} \left((10-2)^{2/3} - \lim_{b \to 2^+} (b-2)^{2/3} \right) \quad \text{Simplify.}$$

$$= \frac{3}{2} \left(0 - (-1)^{2/3} + 8^{2/3} - 0 \right) = \frac{9}{2}. \quad \text{Evaluate limits.}$$

Related Exercises 35–56 ◄

We close with one of many practical uses of improper integrals.

EXAMPLE 6 Bioavailability The most efficient way to deliver a drug to its intended target site is to administer it intravenously (directly into the blood). If a drug is administered any other way (for example, by injection, orally, by nasal inhalant, or by skin patch), then some of the drug is typically lost due to absorption before it gets to the blood. By definition, the bioavailability of a drug measures the effectiveness of a nonintravenous method compared to the intravenous method. The bioavailability of intravenous dosing is 100%.

Let the functions $C_i(t)$ and $C_o(t)$ give the concentration of a drug in the blood, for times $t \geq 0$, using intravenous and oral dosing, respectively. (These functions can be determined through clinical experiments.) Assuming the same amount of drug is initially administered by both methods, the bioavailability for an oral dose is defined to be

$$F = \frac{\text{AUC}_o}{\text{AUC}_i} = \frac{\displaystyle\int_0^\infty C_o(t)\, dt}{\displaystyle\int_0^\infty C_i(t)\, dt},$$

where AUC is used in the pharmacology literature to mean *area under the curve*.

Suppose the concentration of a certain drug in the blood in mg/L when given intravenously is $C_i(t) = 100e^{-0.3t}$, where $t \geq 0$ is measured in hours. Suppose also that the concentration of the same drug when delivered orally is $C_o(t) = 90(e^{-0.3t} - e^{-2.5t})$ (Figure 7.27). Find the bioavailability of the drug.

SOLUTION Evaluating the integrals of the concentration functions, we find that

$$\text{AUC}_i = \int_0^\infty C_i(t)\, dt = \int_0^\infty 100e^{-0.3t}\, dt$$

$$= \lim_{b \to \infty} \int_0^b 100e^{-0.3t}\, dt \qquad \text{Improper integral}$$

$$= \lim_{b \to \infty} \frac{1000}{3} \left(1 - \underbrace{e^{-0.3b}}_{\substack{\text{approaches} \\ \text{zero}}} \right) \qquad \text{Evaluate the integral.}$$

$$= \frac{1000}{3}. \qquad \text{Evaluate the limit.}$$

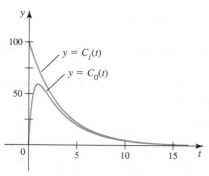

Figure 7.27

Similarly,

$$\text{AUC}_o = \int_0^\infty C_o(t)\, dt = \int_0^\infty 90(e^{-0.3t} - e^{-2.5t})\, dt$$

$$= \lim_{b \to \infty} \int_0^b 90(e^{-0.3t} - e^{-2.5t})\, dt \qquad \text{Improper integral}$$

$$= \lim_{b \to \infty} \left(300(1 - \underbrace{e^{-0.3b}}_{\substack{\text{approaches} \\ \text{zero}}}) - 36(1 - \underbrace{e^{-2.5b}}_{\substack{\text{approaches} \\ \text{zero}}}) \right) \qquad \text{Evaluate the integral.}$$

$$= 264. \qquad\qquad\qquad\qquad\qquad \text{Evaluate the limit.}$$

Therefore, the bioavailability is $F = 264/(1000/3) = 0.792$, which means oral administration of the drug is roughly 80% as effective as intravenous dosing. Notice that F is the ratio of the areas under the two curves on the interval $[0, \infty)$.

Related Exercises 57–60 ◄

SECTION 7.8 EXERCISES

Review Questions

1. What are the two general ways in which an improper integral may occur?

2. Explain how to evaluate $\int_a^\infty f(x)\, dx$.

3. Explain how to evaluate $\int_0^1 x^{-1/2}\, dx$.

4. For what values of p does $\int_1^\infty x^{-p}\, dx$ converge?

Basic Skills

5–28. Infinite intervals of integration *Evaluate the following integrals or state that they diverge.*

5. $\displaystyle\int_1^\infty x^{-2}\, dx$

6. $\displaystyle\int_0^\infty \frac{dx}{(x+1)^3}$

7. $\displaystyle\int_{-\infty}^0 e^x\, dx$

8. $\displaystyle\int_1^\infty 2^{-x}\, dx$

9. $\displaystyle\int_2^\infty \frac{dx}{\sqrt{x}}$

10. $\displaystyle\int_{-\infty}^0 \frac{dx}{\sqrt[3]{2-x}}$

11. $\displaystyle\int_0^\infty e^{-2x}\, dx$

12. $\displaystyle\int_{4/\pi}^\infty \frac{1}{x^2} \sec^2\left(\frac{1}{x}\right) dx$

13. $\displaystyle\int_0^\infty e^{-ax}\, dx, a > 0$

14. $\displaystyle\int_2^\infty \frac{dy}{y \ln y}$

15. $\displaystyle\int_{e^2}^\infty \frac{dx}{x \ln^p x}, p > 1$

16. $\displaystyle\int_0^\infty \frac{p}{\sqrt[5]{p^2+1}}\, dp$

17. $\displaystyle\int_{-\infty}^\infty x e^{-x^2}\, dx$

18. $\displaystyle\int_0^\infty \cos x\, dx$

19. $\displaystyle\int_2^\infty \frac{\cos(\pi/x)}{x^2}\, dx$

20. $\displaystyle\int_{-\infty}^\infty \frac{dx}{x^2 + 2x + 5}$

21. $\displaystyle\int_0^\infty \frac{e^u}{e^{2u}+1}\, du$

22. $\displaystyle\int_{-\infty}^a \sqrt{e^x}\, dx, a$ real

23. $\displaystyle\int_1^\infty \frac{dv}{v(v+1)}$

24. $\displaystyle\int_1^\infty \frac{dx}{x^2(x+1)}$

25. $\displaystyle\int_1^\infty \frac{3x^2+1}{x^3+x}\, dx$

26. $\displaystyle\int_1^\infty \frac{1}{z^2} \sin\frac{\pi}{z}\, dz$

27. $\displaystyle\int_2^\infty \frac{dx}{(x+2)^2}$

28. $\displaystyle\int_1^\infty \frac{\tan^{-1} s}{s^2+1}\, ds$

29–34. Volumes on infinite intervals *Find the volume of the described solid of revolution or state that it does not exist.*

29. The region bounded by $f(x) = x^{-2}$ and the x-axis on the interval $[1, \infty)$ is revolved about the x-axis.

30. The region bounded by $f(x) = (x^2 + 1)^{-1/2}$ and the x-axis on the interval $[2, \infty)$ is revolved about the x-axis.

31. The region bounded by $f(x) = \sqrt{\dfrac{x+1}{x^3}}$ and the x-axis on the interval $[1, \infty)$ is revolved about the x-axis.

32. The region bounded by $f(x) = (x+1)^{-3}$ and the x-axis on the interval $[0, \infty)$ is revolved about the y-axis.

33. The region bounded by $f(x) = \dfrac{1}{\sqrt{x} \ln x}$ and the x-axis on the interval $[2, \infty)$ is revolved about the x-axis.

34. The region bounded by $f(x) = \dfrac{\sqrt{x}}{\sqrt[3]{x^2+1}}$ and the x-axis on the interval $[0, \infty)$ is revolved about the x-axis.

35–50. Integrals with unbounded integrands *Evaluate the following integrals or state that they diverge.*

35. $\displaystyle\int_0^8 \frac{dx}{\sqrt[3]{x}}$

36. $\displaystyle\int_0^{\pi/2} \tan \theta\, d\theta$

37. $\displaystyle\int_1^2 \frac{dx}{\sqrt{x-1}}$

38. $\displaystyle\int_{-3}^1 \frac{dx}{(2x+6)^{2/3}}$

39. $\displaystyle\int_0^{\pi/2} \sec x \tan x\, dx$

40. $\displaystyle\int_3^4 \frac{dz}{(z-3)^{3/2}}$

41. $\displaystyle\int_0^1 \frac{e^{\sqrt{x}}}{\sqrt{x}}\, dx$

42. $\displaystyle\int_0^{\ln 3} \frac{e^y}{(e^y-1)^{2/3}}\, dy$

43. $\int_0^1 \frac{x^3}{x^4 - 1}\, dx$

44. $\int_1^\infty \frac{dx}{\sqrt[3]{x - 1}}$

45. $\int_0^{10} \frac{dx}{\sqrt[4]{10 - x}}$

46. $\int_1^{11} \frac{dx}{(x - 3)^{2/3}}$

47. $\int_{-1}^1 \ln y^2\, dy$

48. $\int_{-2}^6 \frac{dx}{\sqrt{|x - 2|}}$

49. $\int_{-2}^2 \frac{dp}{\sqrt{4 - p^2}}$

50. $\int_0^9 \frac{dx}{(x - 1)^{1/3}}$

51–56. Volumes with infinite integrands *Find the volume of the described solid of revolution or state that it does not exist.*

51. The region bounded by $f(x) = (x - 1)^{-1/4}$ and the x-axis on the interval $(1, 2]$ is revolved about the x-axis.

52. The region bounded by $f(x) = (x^2 - 1)^{-1/4}$ and the x-axis on the interval $(1, 2]$ is revolved about the y-axis.

53. The region bounded by $f(x) = (4 - x)^{-1/3}$ and the x-axis on the interval $[0, 4)$ is revolved about the y-axis.

54. The region bounded by $f(x) = (x + 1)^{-3/2}$ and the x-axis on the interval $(-1, 1]$ is revolved about the line $y = -1$.

55. The region bounded by $f(x) = \tan x$ and the x-axis on the interval $[0, \pi/2)$ is revolved about the x-axis.

56. The region bounded by $f(x) = -\ln x$ and the x-axis on the interval $(0, 1]$ is revolved about the x-axis.

57. Bioavailability When a drug is given intravenously, the concentration of the drug in the blood is $C_i(t) = 250e^{-0.08t}$, for $t \geq 0$. When the same drug is given orally, the concentration of the drug in the blood is $C_o(t) = 200(e^{-0.08t} - e^{-1.8t})$, for $t \geq 0$. Compute the bioavailability of the drug.

58. Draining a pool Water is drained from a swimming pool at a rate given by $R(t) = 100\, e^{-0.05t}$ gal/hr. If the drain is left open indefinitely, how much water drains from the pool?

59. Maximum distance An object moves on a line with velocity $v(t) = 10/(t + 1)^2$ mi/hr, for $t \geq 0$. What is the maximum distance the object can travel?

60. Depletion of oil reserves Suppose that the rate at which a company extracts oil is given by $r(t) = r_0 e^{-kt}$, where $r_0 = 10^7$ barrels/yr and $k = 0.005$ yr^{-1}. Suppose also the estimate of the total oil reserve is 2×10^9 barrels. If the extraction continues indefinitely, will the reserve be exhausted?

Further Explorations

61. Explain why or why not Determine whether the following statements are true and give an explanation or counterexample.

a. If f is continuous and $0 < f(x) < g(x)$ on the interval $[0, \infty)$, and $\int_0^\infty g(x)\, dx = M < \infty$, then $\int_0^\infty f(x)\, dx$ exists.

b. If $\lim_{x \to \infty} f(x) = 1$, then $\int_0^\infty f(x)\, dx$ exists.

c. If $\int_0^1 x^{-p}\, dx$ exists, then $\int_0^1 x^{-q}\, dx$ exists, where $q > p$.

d. If $\int_1^\infty x^{-p}\, dx$ exists, then $\int_1^\infty x^{-q}\, dx$ exists, where $q > p$.

e. $\int_1^\infty \frac{dx}{x^{3p+2}}$ exists, for $p > -\frac{1}{3}$.

62. Incorrect calculation What is wrong with this calculation?
$$\int_{-1}^1 \frac{dx}{x} = \ln|x| \Big|_{-1}^1 = \ln 1 - \ln 1 = 0$$

63. Using symmetry Use symmetry to evaluate the following integrals.

a. $\int_{-\infty}^\infty e^{-|x|}\, dx$ **b.** $\int_{-\infty}^\infty \frac{x^3}{1 + x^8}\, dx$

64. Integral with a parameter For what values of p does the integral $\int_2^\infty \frac{dx}{x \ln^p x}$ exist and what is its value (in terms of p)?

T 65. Improper integrals by numerical methods Use the Trapezoid Rule (Section 7.7) to approximate $\int_0^R e^{-x^2}\, dx$ with $R = 2, 4$, and 8. For each value of R, take $n = 4, 8, 16$, and 32, and compare approximations with successive values of n. Use these approximations to approximate $I = \int_0^\infty e^{-x^2}\, dx$.

66–68. Integration by parts *Use integration by parts to evaluate the following integrals.*

66. $\int_0^\infty xe^{-x}\, dx$ **67.** $\int_0^1 x \ln x\, dx$ **68.** $\int_1^\infty \frac{\ln x}{x^2}\, dx$

T 69. A close comparison Graph the integrands and then evaluate and compare the values of $\int_0^\infty xe^{-x^2}\, dx$ and $\int_0^\infty x^2 e^{-x^2}\, dx$.

70. Area between curves Let R be the region bounded by the graphs of $y = x^{-p}$ and $y = x^{-q}$, for $x \geq 1$, where $q > p > 1$. Find the area of R.

71. Area between curves Let R be the region bounded by the graphs of $y = e^{-ax}$ and $y = e^{-bx}$, for $x \geq 0$, where $a > b > 0$. Find the area of R.

72. An area function Let $A(a)$ denote the area of the region bounded by $y = e^{-ax}$ and the x-axis on the interval $[0, \infty)$. Graph the function $A(a)$, for $0 < a < \infty$. Describe how the area of the region decreases as the parameter a increases.

T 73. Regions bounded by exponentials Let $a > 0$ and let R be the region bounded by the graph of $y = e^{-ax}$ and the x-axis on the interval $[b, \infty)$.

a. Find $A(a, b)$, the area of R as a function of a and b.

b. Find the relationship $b = g(a)$ such that $A(a, b) = 2$.

c. What is the minimum value of b (call it b^*) such that when $b > b^*$, $A(a, b) = 2$ for some value of $a > 0$?

74. The family $f(x) = 1/x^p$ revisited Consider the family of functions $f(x) = 1/x^p$, where p is a real number. For what values of p does the integral $\int_0^1 f(x)\, dx$ exist? What is its value?

75. When is the volume finite? Let R be the region bounded by the graph of $f(x) = x^{-p}$ and the x-axis, for $0 < x \leq 1$.

a. Let S be the solid generated when R is revolved about the x-axis. For what values of p is the volume of S finite?

b. Let S be the solid generated when R is revolved about the y-axis. For what values of p is the volume of S finite?

76. When is the volume finite? Let R be the region bounded by the graph of $f(x) = x^{-p}$ and the x-axis, for $x \geq 1$.

a. Let S be the solid generated when R is revolved about the x-axis. For what values of p is the volume of S finite?

b. Let S be the solid generated when R is revolved about the y-axis. For what values of p is the volume of S finite?

77–80. Numerical methods *Use numerical methods or a calculator to approximate the following integrals as closely as possible. The exact value of each integral is given.*

77. $\displaystyle\int_0^{\pi/2} \ln(\sin x)\,dx = \int_0^{\pi/2} \ln(\cos x)\,dx = -\frac{\pi \ln 2}{2}$

78. $\displaystyle\int_0^{\infty} \frac{\sin^2 x}{x^2}\,dx = \frac{\pi}{2}$

79. $\displaystyle\int_0^{\infty} \ln\left(\frac{e^x + 1}{e^x - 1}\right) dx = \frac{\pi^2}{4}$

80. $\displaystyle\int_0^1 \frac{\ln x}{1 + x}\,dx = -\frac{\pi^2}{12}$

Applications

81. Perpetual annuity Imagine that today you deposit $B in a savings account that earns interest at a rate of $p\%$ per year compounded continuously (Section 6.9). The goal is to draw an income of $I per year from the account forever. The amount of money that must be deposited is $B = I\int_0^{\infty} e^{-rt}\,dt$, where $r = p/100$. Suppose you find an account that earns 12% interest annually and you wish to have an income from the account of $5000 per year. How much must you deposit today?

82. Draining a tank Water is drained from a 3000-gal tank at a rate that starts at 100 gal/hr and decreases continuously by 5%/hr. If the drain is left open indefinitely, how much water drains from the tank? Can a full tank be emptied at this rate?

83. Decaying oscillations Let $a > 0$ and b be real numbers. Use integration to confirm the following identities. (See Exercise 68 of Section 7.2)

    a. $\displaystyle\int_0^{\infty} e^{-ax} \cos bx\,dx = \frac{a}{a^2 + b^2}$

    b. $\displaystyle\int_0^{\infty} e^{-ax} \sin bx\,dx = \frac{b}{a^2 + b^2}$

84. Electronic chips Suppose the probability that a particular computer chip fails after a hours of operation is $0.00005 \int_a^{\infty} e^{-0.00005t}\,dt$.

    a. Find the probability that the computer chip fails after 15,000 hr of operation.

    b. Of the chips that are still operating after 15,000 hr, what fraction of these will operate for at least another 15,000 hr?

    c. Evaluate $0.00005 \int_0^{\infty} e^{-0.00005t}\,dt$ and interpret its meaning.

85. Average lifetime The average time until a computer chip fails (see Exercise 84) is $0.00005 \int_0^{\infty} te^{-0.00005t}\,dt$. Find this value.

86. The Eiffel Tower property Let R be the region between the curves $y = e^{-cx}$ and $y = -e^{-cx}$ on the interval $[a, \infty)$, where $a \geq 0$ and $c > 0$. The center of mass of R is located at $(\bar{x}, 0)$, where $\bar{x} = \dfrac{\int_a^{\infty} xe^{-cx}\,dx}{\int_a^{\infty} e^{-cx}\,dx}$. (The profile of the Eiffel Tower is modeled by the two exponential curves; see the Guided Project *The exponential Eiffel Tower.*)

    a. For $a = 0$ and $c = 2$, sketch the curves that define R and find the center of mass of R. Indicate the location of the center of mass.

    b. With $a = 0$ and $c = 2$, find equations of the lines tangent to the curves at the points corresponding to $x = 0$.

    c. Show that the tangent lines intersect at the center of mass.

    d. Show that this same property holds for any $a \geq 0$ and any $c > 0$; that is, the tangent lines to the curves $y = \pm e^{-cx}$ at $x = a$ intersect at the center of mass of R.

    (*Source:* P. Weidman and I. Pinelis, *Comptes Rendu Mechanique,* 332, 571–584, 2004)

87. Escape velocity and black holes The work required to launch an object from the surface of Earth to outer space is given by $W = \int_R^{\infty} F(x)\,dx$, where $R = 6370$ km is the approximate radius of Earth, $F(x) = GMm/x^2$ is the gravitational force between Earth and the object, G is the gravitational constant, M is the mass of Earth, m is the mass of the object, and $GM = 4 \times 10^{14}$ m^3/s^2.

    a. Find the work required to launch an object in terms of m.

    b. What escape velocity v_e is required to give the object a kinetic energy $\frac{1}{2}mv_e^2$ equal to W?

    c. The French scientist Laplace anticipated the existence of black holes in the 18th century with the following argument: If a body has an escape velocity that equals or exceeds the speed of light, $c = 300{,}000$ km/s, then light cannot escape the body and it cannot be seen. Show that such a body has a radius $R \leq 2GM/c^2$. For Earth to be a black hole, what would its radius need to be?

88. Adding a proton to a nucleus The nucleus of an atom is positively charged because it consists of positively charged protons and uncharged neutrons. To bring a free proton toward a nucleus, a repulsive force $F(r) = kqQ/r^2$ must be overcome, where $q = 1.6 \times 10^{-19}$ C (coulombs) is the charge on the proton, $k = 9 \times 10^9$ N-m^2/C^2, Q is the charge on the nucleus, and r is the distance between the center of the nucleus and the proton. Find the work required to bring a free proton (assumed to be a point mass) from a large distance $(r \to \infty)$ to the edge of a nucleus that has a charge $Q = 50q$ and a radius of 6×10^{-11} m.

89. Gaussians An important function in statistics is the Gaussian (or normal distribution, or bell-shaped curve), $f(x) = e^{-ax^2}$.

    a. Graph the Gaussian for $a = 0.5, 1,$ and 2.

    b. Given that $\displaystyle\int_{-\infty}^{\infty} e^{-ax^2}\,dx = \sqrt{\frac{\pi}{a}}$, compute the area under the curves in part (a).

    c. Complete the square to evaluate $\int_{-\infty}^{\infty} e^{-(ax^2+bx+c)}\,dx$, where $a > 0, b,$ and c are real numbers.

90–94. Laplace transforms *A powerful tool in solving problems in engineering and physics is the Laplace transform. Given a function $f(t)$, the Laplace transform is a new function $F(s)$ defined by*

$$F(s) = \int_0^{\infty} e^{-st}f(t)\,dt,$$

where we assume that s is a positive real number. For example, to find the Laplace transform of $f(t) = e^{-t}$, the following improper integral is evaluated:

$$F(s) = \int_0^{\infty} e^{-st}e^{-t}\,dt = \int_0^{\infty} e^{-(s+1)t}\,dt = \frac{1}{s+1}.$$

Verify the following Laplace transforms, where a is a real number.

90. $f(t) = 1 \longrightarrow F(s) = \dfrac{1}{s}$

91. $f(t) = e^{at} \longrightarrow F(s) = \dfrac{1}{s-a}$

92. $f(t) = t \longrightarrow F(s) = \dfrac{1}{s^2}$

93. $f(t) = \sin at \longrightarrow F(s) = \dfrac{a}{s^2 + a^2}$

94. $f(t) = \cos at \longrightarrow F(s) = \dfrac{s}{s^2 + a^2}$

Additional Exercises

95. Improper integrals Evaluate the following improper integrals (Putnam Exam, 1939).

a. $\displaystyle\int_1^3 \frac{dx}{\sqrt{(x-1)(3-x)}}$

b. $\displaystyle\int_1^\infty \frac{dx}{e^{x+1} + e^{3-x}}$

96. A better way Compute $\int_0^1 \ln x \, dx$ using integration by parts. Then explain why $-\int_0^\infty e^{-x} dx$ (an easier integral) gives the same result.

97. Competing powers For what values of $p > 0$ is
$$\int_0^\infty \frac{dx}{x^p + x^{-p}} < \infty?$$

98. Gamma function The gamma function is defined by $\Gamma(p) = \int_0^\infty x^{p-1} e^{-x} dx$, for p not equal to zero or a negative integer.

a. Use the reduction formula
$$\int_0^\infty x^p e^{-x} dx = p \int_0^\infty x^{p-1} e^{-x} dx, \text{ for } p = 1, 2, 3, \ldots$$
to show that $\Gamma(p+1) = p!$ (p factorial).

b. Use the substitution $x = u^2$ and the fact that
$$\int_0^\infty e^{-u^2} du = \frac{\sqrt{\pi}}{2} \text{ to show that } \Gamma\left(\frac{1}{2}\right) = \sqrt{\pi}.$$

99. Many methods needed Show that $\displaystyle\int_0^\infty \frac{\sqrt{x}\ln x}{(1+x)^2} dx = \pi$ in the following steps.

a. Integrate by parts with $u = \sqrt{x}\ln x$.
b. Change variables by letting $y = 1/x$.

c. Show that $\displaystyle\int_0^1 \frac{\ln x}{\sqrt{x}(1+x)} dx = -\int_1^\infty \frac{\ln x}{\sqrt{x}(1+x)} dx$ (and that both integrals converge). Conclude that
$$\int_0^\infty \frac{\ln x}{\sqrt{x}(1+x)} dx = 0.$$

d. Evaluate the remaining integral using the change of variables $z = \sqrt{x}$.

(*Source: Mathematics Magazine* 59, 1, Feb 1986)

100. Riemann sums to integrals Show that
$$L = \lim_{n\to\infty}\left(\frac{1}{n}\ln n! - \ln n\right) = -1 \text{ in the following steps.}$$

a. Note that $n! = n(n-1)(n-2)\cdots 1$ and use $\ln(ab) = \ln a + \ln b$ to show that
$$L = \lim_{n\to\infty}\left(\left(\frac{1}{n}\sum_{k=1}^n \ln k\right) - \ln n\right)$$
$$= \lim_{n\to\infty}\frac{1}{n}\sum_{k=1}^n \ln\frac{k}{n}.$$

b. Identify the limit of this sum as a Riemann sum for $\int_0^1 \ln x \, dx$. Integrate this improper integral by parts and reach the desired conclusion.

101–102. Improper integrals and l'Hôpital's Rule *Evaluate the following integrals.*

101. $\displaystyle\int_0^a x^x(\ln x + 1) \, dx, a > 0$

102. $\displaystyle\int_0^\infty x^{-x}(\ln x + 1) \, dx$

QUICK CHECK ANSWERS

1. The integral diverges. $\lim_{b\to\infty}\int_1^b (1+x^{-1}) dx = \lim_{b\to\infty}(x + \ln x)\Big|_1^b$ does not exist. **2.** $\frac{1}{3}$ **3.** c must approach 0 through values in the interval of integration $(0, 1)$. Therefore, $c \to 0^+$. ◄

7.9 Introduction to Differential Equations

If you had to demonstrate the utility of mathematics to a skeptic, a convincing way would be to cite *differential equations*. This vast subject lies at the heart of mathematical modeling and is used in engineering, the natural and biological sciences, economics, management, and finance. Differential equations rely heavily on calculus, and they are usually studied in advanced courses that follow calculus. Nevertheless, you have now seen enough calculus to understand a brief survey of differential equations and appreciate their power.

An Overview

If you studied Section 4.9 or 6.1, then you saw a preview of differential equations. Given the *derivative* of a function (for example, a velocity or some other rate of change), these two sections show how to find the function itself by integration. This process amounts to solving a differential equation.

More generally, a differential equation involves an unknown function and its derivatives. The unknown in a differential equation is not a number (as in an algebraic equation), but rather *a function.* Examples of differential equations are

$$(A)\ y''(x) + 16y = 0, \quad (B)\ \frac{dy}{dx} + 4y = \cos x, \quad (C)\ y'(t) = 0.1y(100 - y).$$

In each case, the goal is to find solutions of the equation—that is, functions y that satisfy the equation. Just to be clear about what we mean by a solution, consider equation (A). If we substitute $y = \cos 4x$ and $y'' = -16 \cos 4x$ into this equation, we find that

$$\underbrace{-16 \cos 4x}_{y''} + \underbrace{16 \cos 4x}_{16y} = 0,$$

which implies that $y = \cos 4x$ is a solution of the equation. You should verify that $y = C \cos 4x$ is also a solution for any real number C (as is $y = C \sin 4x$). Let's begin by verifying that given functions are solutions of a differential equation.

EXAMPLE 1   Verifying solutions Consider the exponential growth equation $y'(t) = 2.5y$.

a. Show by substitution that the exponential function $y = 10e^{2.5t}$ is a solution of the differential equation.

b. Show by substitution that the function $y = Ce^{2.5t}$ is a solution of the same differential equation, for *any* constant C.

SOLUTION

a. We differentiate $y = 10e^{2.5t}$ to obtain $y'(t) = 2.5 \cdot 10e^{2.5t}$. Now observe that

$$y'(t) = \underbrace{2.5 \cdot 10e^{2.5t}}_{y'(t)} = 2.5 \cdot \underbrace{10e^{2.5t}}_{y(t)} = 2.5y.$$

Therefore, the function $y = 10e^{2.5t}$ satisfies the equation $y'(t) = 2.5y$.

b. Duplicating the calculation of part (a) with 10 replaced with an arbitrary constant C, we find that

$$y'(t) = \underbrace{2.5 \cdot Ce^{2.5t}}_{y'(t)} = 2.5 \cdot \underbrace{Ce^{2.5t}}_{y(t)} = 2.5y.$$

The functions $y = Ce^{2.5t}$ also satisfy the equation, where C is an arbitrary constant.

Related Exercises 9–12 ◄

The basic terminology associated with differential equations is helpful. The **order** of a differential equation is the highest order appearing on a derivative in the equation. For example, the equations $y' + 4y = \cos x$ and $y' = 0.1y(100 - y)$ are first order, and $y'' + 16y = 0$ is second order.

> ➤ A *linear* differential equation cannot have terms such as y^2, yy', or $\sin y$, where y is the unknown function.

Linear differential equations (first- and second-order) have the form

$$\underbrace{y'(x) + p(x)y(x) = f(x)}_{\text{first-order}} \quad \text{and} \quad \underbrace{y''(x) + p(x)y'(x) + q(x)y(x) = f(x),}_{\text{second-order}}$$

where p, q, and f are given functions that depend only on the independent variable x. Of the equations on p. 581, (A) and (B) are linear, but (C) is **nonlinear** (because the right side contains y^2).

> ➤ The term *initial condition* originates with equations in which the independent variable is *time*. In such problems, the initial state of the system (for example, position and velocity) is specified at some initial time (often $t = 0$). We use the term *initial condition* whenever information about the solution is given at a single point.

A differential equation is often accompanied by **initial conditions** that specify the values of y, and possibly its derivatives, at a particular point. In general, an nth-order equation requires n initial conditions. A differential equation, together with the appropriate number of initial conditions, is called an **initial value problem.** A typical first-order initial value problem has the form

$$y'(t) = f(t, y) \quad \text{Differential equation}$$
$$y(0) = A, \quad \quad \text{Initial condition}$$

where A is given and f is a given expression that involves t and/or y.

EXAMPLE 2 **Solution of an initial value problem** Consider the differential equation in Example 1. Find the solution of the initial value problem

$$y'(t) = 2.5y \quad \text{Differential equation}$$

$$y(0) = 3.2. \quad \text{Initial condition}$$

SOLUTION By Example 1b, functions of the form $y = Ce^{2.5t}$ satisfy the differential equation $y'(t) = 2.5y$, where C is an arbitrary constant. We now use the initial condition $y(0) = 3.2$ to determine the arbitrary constant C. Noting that $y(0) = Ce^{2.5 \cdot 0} = C$, the condition $y(0) = 3.2$ implies that $C = 3.2$.

Therefore, $y = 3.2e^{2.5t}$ is the solution of the initial value problem. Figure 7.28 shows the family of curves $y = Ce^{2.5t}$ for several different values of the constant C. It also shows the function $y = 3.2e^{2.5t}$ highlighted in red, which is the solution of the initial value problem.

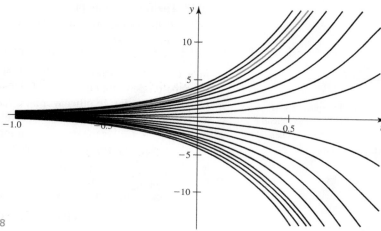

Figure 7.28

Related Exercises 13–16 ◄

▶ A technicality: To keep matters simple, we use *general solution* to refer to the largest family of solutions of a differential equation. Some nonlinear equations have isolated solutions that are not included in this family of solutions. For example, you can check that for real numbers C, the functions $y = 1/(C - t)$ satisfy the equation $y'(t) = y^2$. Therefore, we call $y = 1/(C - t)$ the general solution, even though it does not include $y = 0$, which is also a solution.

▶ The two integrals in the calculation of Example 3 both produce an arbitrary constant of integration. These two constants may be combined as one arbitrary constant.

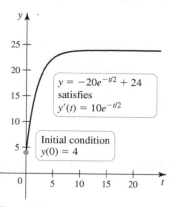

Figure 7.29

Solving a first-order differential equation requires integration—you must "undo" the derivative $y'(t)$ to find $y(t)$. One integration introduces one arbitrary constant, which generates an entire family of solutions. Solving an nth-order differential equation typically requires n integrations, each of which introduces an arbitrary constant; again, the result is a family of solutions. For any differential equation, the largest family of solutions, generated by arbitrary constants, is called the **general solution.** For instance, in Example 1, we found the general solution $y = Ce^{2.5t}$.

EXAMPLE 3 **An initial value problem** Solve the initial value problem

$$y'(t) = 10e^{-t/2}, \quad y(0) = 4.$$

SOLUTION Notice that the right side of the equation depends only on t. The solution is found by integrating both sides of the differential equation with respect to t:

$$\underbrace{\int y'(t) \, dt}_{y(t)} = \int 10e^{-t/2} \, dt \quad \text{Integrate both sides with respect to } t.$$

$$y = -20e^{-t/2} + C. \quad \text{Evaluate integrals; } y(t) \text{ is an antiderivative of } y'(t).$$

We have found the general solution, which involves one arbitrary constant. To determine its value, we use the initial condition by substituting $t = 0$ and $y = 4$ into the general solution:

$$y(0) = (-20e^{-t/2} + C)|_{t=0} = -20 + C = 4 \Rightarrow C = 24.$$

Therefore, the solution of the initial value problem is $y = -20e^{-t/2} + 24$ (Figure 7.29). You should check that this function satisfies both the differential equation and the initial condition.

Related Exercises 17–20 ◄

QUICK CHECK 1 What is the order of the equation in Example 3? Is it linear or nonlinear? ◄

In Examples 2 and 3, we found solutions to initial value problems without worrying about whether there might be other solutions. Once we find a solution to an initial value problem, how can we be sure there aren't other solutions? More generally, given a particular initial value problem, how do we know whether a solution exists and whether it is unique?

These theoretical questions are handled by powerful *existence and uniqueness theorems* whose proofs are presented in advanced courses. Here is an informal statement of an existence and uniqueness theorem for the type of initial value problems encountered in this section:

The solution of the general first-order initial value problem

$$y'(t) = f(t, y), y(a) = A$$

exists and is unique in some region that contains the point (a, A) provided f is a "well-behaved" function in that region.

The technical challenges arise in defining *well-behaved* in the most general way possible. The initial value problems we consider in this section satisfy the conditions of this theorem and can be assumed to have unique solutions.

A First-Order Linear Differential Equation

In Section 6.9, we studied functions that exhibit exponential growth or decay. Such functions have the property that their rate of change at a particular point is proportional to the function value at that point. In other words, these functions satisfy a first-order differential equation of the form $y'(t) = ky$, where k is a real number. You should verify by substitution that the function $y = Ce^{kt}$ is the general solution of this equation, where C is an arbitrary constant.

> ➤ The solution of the equation $y'(t) = ky$ is $y = Ce^{kt}$, so it models exponential growth when $k > 0$ and exponential decay when $k < 0$.

Now let's generalize and consider the first-order linear equation $y'(t) = ky + b$, where k and b are real numbers. Solutions of this equation have a wide range of behavior (depending on the values of k and b), and the equation itself has many modeling applications. Specifically, the terms of the equation have the following meaning:

$$\underbrace{y'(t)}_{\substack{\text{rate of change} \\ \text{of } y}} = \underbrace{ky}_{\substack{\text{natural growth or} \\ \text{decay rate of } y}} + \underbrace{b.}_{\substack{\text{growth of decay} \\ \text{rate due to external} \\ \text{effects}}}$$

For example, if y represents the number of fish in a hatchery, then ky (with $k > 0$) models exponential growth in the fish population, in the absence of other factors, and $b < 0$ is the harvesting rate at which the population is depleted. As another example, if y represents the amount of a drug in the blood, then ky (with $k < 0$) models exponential decay of the drug through the kidneys, and $b > 0$ is the rate at which the drug is added to the blood intravenously. We can give an explicit solution for the equation $y'(t) = ky + b$.

We begin by dividing both sides of the equation $y'(t) = ky + b$ by $ky + b$, which gives

$$\frac{y'(t)}{ky + b} = 1.$$

Because the goal is to determine y from $y'(t)$, we integrate both sides of this equation with respect to t:

$$\int \frac{y'(t)}{ky + b} dt = \int dt.$$

The factor $y'(t) dt$ on the left side is simply dy. Making this substitution and evaluating the integrals, we have

> ➤ The arbitrary constant of integration needs to be included in only one of the integrals.

$$\int \frac{dy}{ky + b} = \int dt \quad \text{or} \quad \frac{1}{k}\ln|ky + b| = t + C.$$

For the moment, we assume that $ky + b \geq 0$, or equivalently $y \geq -b/k$, so the absolute value may be removed. Multiplying through by k, exponentiating both sides of the equation, and solving for y gives the solution $y = Ce^{kt} - b/k$. In the process of solving for y, we have successively redefined C; for example, if C is arbitrary, then kC and e^C are also arbitrary. You can also show that if $ky + b < 0$, or $y < -b/k$, then the same solution results.

> The equation $y'(t) = ky + b$ is one of many first-order linear differential equations. If k and b are functions of t, the equation is still first-order linear.

Solution of a First-Order Linear Differential Equation

The general solution of the first-order linear equation $y'(t) = ky + b$, where k and b are specified real numbers, is $y = Ce^{kt} - b/k$, where C is an arbitrary constant. Given an initial condition, the value of C may be determined.

QUICK CHECK 2 Verify by substitution that $y = Ce^{kt} - b/k$ is a solution of $y'(t) = ky + b$. ◄

EXAMPLE 4   An initial value problem for drug dosing A drug is administered to a patient through an intravenous line at a rate of 6 mg/hr. The drug has a half-life that corresponds to a rate constant of 0.03/hr (Section 6.9). Let $y(t)$ be the amount of drug in the blood for $t \geq 0$. Solve the following initial value problem and interpret the solution.

$$\text{Differential equation:} \quad y'(t) = -0.03y + 6$$
$$\text{Initial condition:} \quad\quad y(0) = 0$$

SOLUTION The equation has the form $y'(t) = ky + b$, where $k = -0.03$ and $b = 6$. Therefore, the general solution is $y(t) = Ce^{-0.03t} + 200$. To determine the value of C for this particular problem, we substitute $y(0) = 0$ into the general solution. We find that $y(0) = C + 200 = 0$, which implies that $C = -200$. Therefore, the solution of the initial value problem is

$$y = -200e^{-0.03t} + 200 = 200(1 - e^{-0.03t}).$$

The graph of the solution (Figure 7.30) reveals an important fact: Though the amount of drug in the blood increases, it approaches a steady-state level of

$$\lim_{t \to \infty} y(t) = \lim_{t \to \infty} (200(1 - e^{-0.03t})) = 200 \text{ mg}.$$

Related Exercises 21–30 ◄

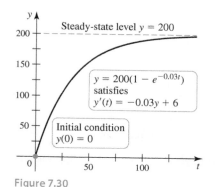

Figure 7.30

QUICK CHECK 3 What is the solution of $y'(t) = 3y(t) + 6$ with the initial condition $y(0) = 14$? ◄

Separable First-Order Differential Equations

The most general first-order differential equation has the form $y'(t) = F(t, y)$, where F is an expression that involves t and/or y. We have a *chance* of solving such an equation if it can be written in the form

$$g(y) y'(t) = h(t),$$

in which the terms that involve y appear on one side of the equation *separated* from the terms that involve t. An equation that can be written in this form is said to be **separable**.

The solution of the linear equation $y'(t) = ky + b$ presented above is a specific example of the method for solving separable differential equations. In general, we solve the separable equation $g(y) y'(t) = h(t)$ by integrating both sides of the equation with respect to t.

> The result of this change of variables is that the left side of the equation is integrated with respect to y and the right side is integrated with respect to t. With this justification, this shortcut is permissible and is often taken.

$$\int g(y) \underbrace{y'(t) \, dt}_{dy} = \int h(t) \, dt \quad \text{Integrate both sides.}$$

$$\int g(y) \, dy = \int h(t) \, dt \quad \text{Change of variables on the left side}$$

QUICK CHECK 4 Write $y'(t) = (t^2 + 1)/y^3$ in separated form. ◄

A change of variables on the left side of the equation leaves us with two integrals to evaluate, one with respect to y and one with respect to t. Finding a solution depends on evaluating these integrals.

EXAMPLE 5   A separable equation Find the function that satisfies the initial value problem

$$\frac{dy}{dx} = y^2 e^{-x}, \qquad y(0) = \frac{1}{2}.$$

SOLUTION The equation can be written in separable form by dividing both sides of the equation by y^2 to give $y'(x)/y^2 = e^{-x}$. We now integrate both sides of the equation with respect to x and evaluate the resulting integrals.

$$\int \underbrace{\frac{1}{y^2} y'(x)\, dx}_{dy} = \int e^{-x}\, dx$$

$$\int \frac{dy}{y^2} = \int e^{-x}\, dx \qquad \text{Change of variables on the left side}$$

$$-\frac{1}{y} = -e^{-x} + C \qquad \text{Evaluate the integrals.}$$

Solving for y gives the general solution

$$y = \frac{1}{e^{-x} - C}.$$

The initial condition $y(0) = \frac{1}{2}$ implies that

$$y(0) = \frac{1}{e^0 - C} = \frac{1}{1 - C} = \frac{1}{2}.$$

Solving for C gives $C = -1$, so the solution of the initial value problem is $y = \dfrac{1}{e^{-x} + 1}$. The solution (Figure 7.31) has a graph that passes through $(0, \frac{1}{2})$ and rises to approach the asymptote $y = 1$ (because $\displaystyle\lim_{x \to \infty} \frac{1}{e^{-x} + 1} = 1$).

Related Exercises 31–40 ◄

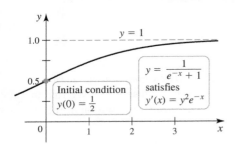

Figure 7.31

➤ The logistic equation is used to describe the population of many different species as well as the spread of rumors and epidemics (Exercises 41–42).

EXAMPLE 6   Logistic population growth Fifty fruit flies are in a large container at the beginning of an experiment. Let $P(t)$ be the number of fruit flies in the container t days later. At first, the population grows exponentially, but due to limited space and food supply, the growth rate decreases and the population is prevented from growing without bound. This experiment can be modeled by the *logistic equation*

$$\frac{dP}{dt} = 0.1P\left(1 - \frac{P}{300}\right)$$

together with the initial condition $P(0) = 50$. Solve this initial value problem.

SOLUTION We see that the equation is separable by writing it in the form

$$\frac{1}{P\left(1 - \dfrac{P}{300}\right)} \cdot \frac{dP}{dt} = 0.1.$$

Integrating both sides with respect to t leads to the equation

$$\int \frac{1}{P\left(1 - \dfrac{P}{300}\right)}\, dP = \underbrace{\int 0.1\, dt}_{0.1t + C}. \tag{1}$$

The integral on the right side of equation (1) is $\int 0.1\, dt = 0.1t + C$. Because the integrand on the left side is a rational function in P, we use partial fractions. You should verify that

$$\frac{1}{P\left(1 - \dfrac{P}{300}\right)} = \frac{300}{P(300 - P)} = \frac{1}{P} + \frac{1}{300 - P},$$

and therefore,

$$\int \frac{1}{P\left(1 - \dfrac{P}{300}\right)}\, dP = \int \left(\frac{1}{P} + \frac{1}{300 - P}\right) dP = \ln \left| \frac{P}{300 - P} \right| + C.$$

> Notice again that two constants of integration have been combined into one.

Equation (1) now becomes

$$\ln \left| \frac{P}{300 - P} \right| = 0.1t + C. \tag{2}$$

The final step is to solve for P, which is tangled up inside the logarithm. To simplify matters, we assume that if the initial population $P(0)$ is between 0 and 300, then $0 < P(t) < 300$ for all $t > 0$. This assumption (which can be verified independently) allows us to remove the absolute value on the left side of equation (2).

> It is always a good idea to check that the final solution satisfies the initial condition. In this case, $P(0) = 50$.

Using the initial condition $P(0) = 50$ and solving for C (Exercise 68), we find that $C = -\ln 5$. Solving for P, the solution of the initial value problem is

$$P = \frac{300}{1 + 5e^{-0.1t}}.$$

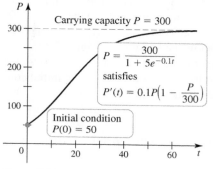

Figure 7.32

The graph of the solution shows that the population increases, but not without bound (Figure 7.32). Instead, it approaches a steady state value of

$$\lim_{t \to \infty} P(t) = \lim_{t \to \infty} \frac{300}{1 + 5e^{-0.1t}} = 300,$$

which is the maximum population that the environment (space and food supply) can sustain. This steady-state population is called the **carrying capacity**.

Related Exercises 41–42 ◄

Direction Fields

The geometry of first-order differential equations is beautifully displayed using *direction fields*. Consider the general first-order differential equation $y'(t) = F(t, y)$, where F is a given expression involving t and/or y. A solution of this equation has the property that at each point (t, y) of the solution curve, the slope of the curve is $F(t, y)$. A **direction field** is simply a picture that shows the slope of the solution at selected points of the ty-plane.

> Drawing direction fields by hand can be tedious. It's best to use a calculator or software.

For example, consider the equation $y'(t) = y^2 e^{-t}$. We choose a regular grid of points in the ty-plane, and at each point (t, y), we make a small line segment with slope $y^2 e^{-t}$. The line segment at a point P gives the slope of the solution curve that passes through P (Figure 7.33). For example, along the t-axis ($y = 0$), the slopes of the line segments are $F(t, 0) = 0$. And along the y-axis ($t = 0$), the slopes of the line segments are $F(0, y) = y^2$.

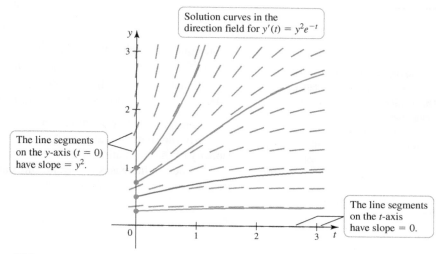

Figure 7.33

Now suppose an initial condition $y(a) = A$ is given. We start at the point (a, A) in the direction field and sketch a curve in the positive t-direction that follows the flow of the direction field. At each point of the solution curve, the slope matches the direction field. A different initial condition gives a different solution curve (Figure 7.33). The collection of solution curves for several different initial conditions is a representation of the general solution of the equation.

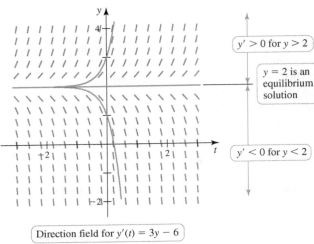

Direction field for $y'(t) = 3y - 6$

Figure 7.34

EXAMPLE 7 Direction field for a linear equation Sketch the direction field for the first-order linear equation $y'(t) = 3y - 6$. For what initial conditions at $t = 0$ are the solutions increasing? Decreasing?

SOLUTION Notice that $y'(t) = 0$ when $y = 2$. Therefore, the direction field has horizontal line segments when $y = 2$. The line $y = 2$ corresponds to an *equilibrium solution*, a solution that is constant in time: If the initial condition is $y(0) = 2$, then the solution is $y = 2$ for $t \geq 0$.

We also see that $y'(t) > 0$ when $y > 2$. Therefore, the direction field has small line segments with positive slopes above the line $y = 2$. When $y < 2$, $y'(t) < 0$, which means the direction field has small line segments with negative slopes below the line $y = 2$ (Figure 7.34).

The direction field shows that if the initial condition satisfies $y(0) > 2$, the resulting solution increases for $t \geq 0$. If the initial condition satisfies $y(0) < 2$, the resulting solution decreases for $t \geq 0$.

Related Exercises 43–48 ◄

QUICK CHECK 5 In Example 7, describe the behavior of the solution that results from the initial condition (a) $y(-1) = 3$ and (b) $y(-2) = 0$. ◄

EXAMPLE 8 Direction field for the logistic equation Consider the logistic equation of Example 6,

$$\frac{dP}{dt} = 0.1P\left(1 - \frac{P}{300}\right) \quad \text{for} \quad t \geq 0,$$

and its direction field (Figure 7.35). Sketch the solution curves corresponding to each of the initial conditions $y(0) = 50$, $y(0) = 150$, and $y(0) = 350$.

SOLUTION A few preliminary observations are useful. Because P represents a population, we assume that $P \geq 0$.

- Notice that $\frac{dP}{dt} = 0$ when $P = 0$ or $P = 300$. Therefore, if the initial population is $P = 0$ or $P = 300$, then $\frac{dP}{dt} = 0$ for all $t \geq 0$, and the solution is constant. For this reason, the direction field has horizontal line segments when $P = 0$ and $P = 300$.
- The equation implies that $dP/dt > 0$ when $0 < P < 300$. Therefore, the direction field has positive slopes, and the solutions are increasing for $t \geq 0$ and $0 < P < 300$.
- The equation also implies that $dP/dt < 0$ when $P > 300$. Therefore, the direction field has negative slopes, and the solutions are decreasing for $t \geq 0$ and $P > 300$.

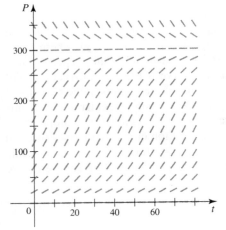

Figure 7.35

➤ The constant solutions $P = 0$ and $P = 300$ are equilibrium solutions. The solution $P = 0$ is an *unstable* equilibrium because nearby solution curves move away from $P = 0$. By contrast, the solution $P = 300$ is a stable equilibrium because nearby solution curves are attracted to $P = 300$.

Figure 7.36 shows the direction field with three solution curves corresponding to three different initial conditions. The horizontal line $P = 300$ corresponds to the carrying capacity of the population. We see that if the initial population is less than 300, the resulting solution increases to the carrying capacity from below. If the initial population is greater than 300, the resulting solution decreases to the carrying capacity from above.

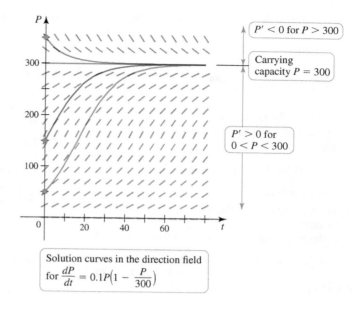

Figure 7.36

Related Exercises 43–48 ◄

Direction fields are useful for at least two reasons. As shown in Example 7, a direction field provides valuable qualitative information about the solutions of a differential equation *without solving the equation*. In addition, it turns out that direction fields are the basis for many computer-based methods for approximating solutions of a differential equation. The computer begins with the initial condition and advances the solution in small steps, always following the direction field at each time step.

SECTION 7.9 EXERCISES

Review Questions

1. What is the order of $y''(t) + 9y(t) = 10$?

2. Is $y''(t) + 9y(t) = 10$ linear or nonlinear?

3. How many arbitrary constants appear in the general solution of $y''(t) + 9y(t) = 10$?

4. If the general solution of a differential equation is $y = Ce^{-3t} + 10$, what is the solution that satisfies the initial condition $y(0) = 5$?

5. What is a separable first-order differential equation?

6. Is the equation $t^2 y'(t) = (t + 4)/y^2$ separable?

7. Explain how to solve a separable differential equation of the form $g(y) y'(t) = h(t)$.

8. Explain how to sketch the direction field of the equation $y'(t) = F(t, y)$, where F is given.

Basic Skills

9–12. Verifying general solutions *Verify that the given function y is a solution of the differential equation that follows it. Assume that C, C_1, and C_2 are arbitrary constants.*

9. $y = Ce^{-5t}; y'(t) + 5y = 0$

10. $y = Ct^{-3}; ty'(t) + 3y = 0$

11. $y = C_1 \sin 4t + C_2 \cos 4t; y''(t) + 16y = 0$

12. $y = C_1 e^{-x} + C_2 e^x; y''(x) - y = 0$

13–16. Verifying solutions of initial value problems *Verify that the given function y is a solution of the initial value problem that follows it.*

13. $y = 16e^{2t} - 10; y'(t) - 2y = 20, y(0) = 6$

14. $y = 8t^6 - 3; ty'(t) - 6y = 18, y(1) = 5$

15. $y = -3 \cos 3t; y''(t) + 9y = 0, y(0) = -3, y'(0) = 0$

16. $y = \frac{1}{4}(e^{2x} - e^{-2x}); y''(x) - 4y = 0, y(0) = 0, y'(0) = 1$

17–20. Warm-up initial value problems *Solve the following problems.*

17. $y'(t) = 3t^2 - 4t + 10, y(0) = 20$

18. $\dfrac{dy}{dt} = 8e^{-4t} + 1, y(0) = 5$

19. $y'(t) = (2t^2 + 4)/t, y(1) = 2$

20. $\dfrac{dy}{dx} = 3 \cos 2x + 2 \sin 3x, y(\pi/2) = 8$

21–24. First-order linear equations *Find the general solution of the following equations.*

21. $y'(t) = 3y - 4$

22. $\dfrac{dy}{dx} = -y + 2$

23. $y'(x) = -2y - 4$

24. $\dfrac{dy}{dt} = 2y + 6$

25–28. Initial value problems *Solve the following problems.*

25. $y'(t) = 3y - 6$, $y(0) = 9$ **26.** $\dfrac{dy}{dx} = -y + 2$, $y(0) = -2$

27. $y'(t) = -2y - 4$, $y(0) = 0$ **28.** $\dfrac{du}{dx} = 2u + 6$, $u(1) = 6$

T 29. Intravenous drug dosing The amount of drug in the blood of a patient (in mg) due to an intravenous line is governed by the initial value problem

$$y'(t) = -0.02y + 3, \quad y(0) = 0 \qquad \text{for } t \geq 0,$$

where t is measured in hours.

a. Find and graph the solution of the initial value problem.
b. What is the steady-state level of the drug?
c. When does the drug level reach 90% of the steady-state value?

T 30. Fish harvesting A fish hatchery has 500 fish at time $t = 0$, when harvesting begins at a rate of b fish/yr, where $b > 0$. The fish population is modeled by the initial value problem

$$y'(t) = 0.1y - b, \quad y(0) = 500 \qquad \text{for } t \geq 0,$$

where t is measured in years.

a. Find the fish population for $t \geq 0$ in terms of the harvesting rate b.
b. Graph the solution in the case that $b = 40$ fish/yr. Describe the solution.
c. Graph the solution in the case that $b = 60$ fish/yr. Describe the solution.

31–34. Separable differential equations *Find the general solution of the following equations.*

31. $\dfrac{dy}{dt} = \dfrac{3t^2}{y}$

32. $\dfrac{dy}{dx} = y(x^2 + 1)$, where $y > 0$

33. $y'(t) = e^{y/2} \sin t$

34. $x^2 \dfrac{dw}{dx} = \sqrt{w}(3x + 1)$

35–40. Separable differential equations *Determine whether the following equations are separable. If so, solve the given initial value problem.*

35. $\dfrac{dy}{dt} = ty + 2$, $y(1) = 2$

36. $y'(t) = y(4t^3 + 1)$, $y(0) = 4$

37. $y'(t) = \dfrac{e^t}{2y}$, $y(\ln 2) = 1$

38. $(\sec x)\, y'(x) = y^3$, $y(0) = 3$

39. $\dfrac{dy}{dx} = e^{x-y}$, $y(0) = \ln 3$

40. $y'(t) = 2e^{3y-t}$, $y(0) = 0$

T 41. Logistic equation for a population A community of hares on an island has a population of 50 when observations begin at $t = 0$. The population for $t \geq 0$ is modeled by the initial value problem

$$\frac{dP}{dt} = 0.08P\left(1 - \frac{P}{200}\right), \qquad P(0) = 50.$$

a. Find and graph the solution of the initial value problem.
b. What is the steady-state population?

T 42. Logistic equation for an epidemic When an infected person is introduced into a closed and otherwise healthy community, the number of people who become infected with the disease (in the absence of any intervention) may be modeled by the logistic equation

$$\frac{dP}{dt} = kP\left(1 - \frac{P}{A}\right), \qquad P(0) = P_0,$$

where k is a positive infection rate, A is the number of people in the community, and P_0 is the number of infected people at $t = 0$. The model assumes no recovery or intervention.

a. Find the solution of the initial value problem in terms of k, A, and P_0.
b. Graph the solution in the case that $k = 0.025$, $A = 300$, and $P_0 = 1$.
c. For fixed values of k and A, describe the long-term behavior of the solutions for any P_0 with $0 < P_0 < A$.

43–44. Direction fields *A differential equation and its direction field are given. Sketch a graph of the solution that results with each initial condition.*

43. $y'(t) = \dfrac{t^2}{y^2 + 1}$,
$y(0) = -2$ and
$y(-2) = 0$

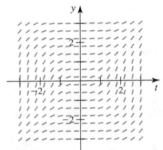

44. $y'(t) = \dfrac{\sin t}{y}$,
$y(-2) = -2$ and
$y(-2) = 2$

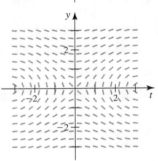

45. Matching direction fields Match equations a–d with the direction fields A–D.

a. $y'(t) = t/2$
b. $y'(t) = y/2$
c. $y'(t) = (t^2 + y^2)/2$
d. $y'(t) = y/t$

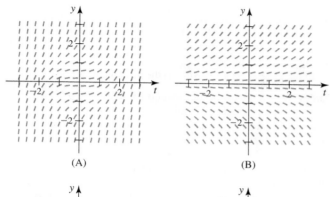

(A)   (B)

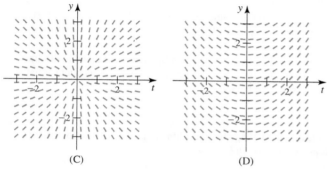

(C)   (D)

46–48. Sketching direction fields *Use the window* $[-2, 2] \times [-2, 2]$ *to sketch a direction field for the following equations. Then sketch the solution curve that corresponds to the given initial condition.*

46. $y'(t) = y - 3, \ y(0) = 1$ **47.** $y'(x) = \sin x, \ y(-2) = 2$

48. $y'(t) = \sin y, \ y(-2) = \frac{1}{2}$

Further Explorations

49. Explain why or why not Determine whether the following statements are true and give an explanation or counterexample.

a. The general solution of $y'(t) = 20y$ is $y = e^{20t}$.
b. The functions $y = 2e^{-2t}$ and $y = 10e^{-2t}$ do not both satisfy the differential equation $y' + 2y = 0$.
c. The equation $y'(t) = ty + 2y + 2t + 4$ is not separable.
d. A solution of $y'(t) = 2\sqrt{y}$ is $y = (t + 1)^2$.

50–55. Equilibrium solutions *A differential equation of the form* $y'(t) = F(y)$ *is said to be* **autonomous** *(the function F depends only on y). The constant function* $y = y_0$ *is an equilibrium solution of the equation provided* $F(y_0) = 0$ *(because then* $y'(t) = 0$, *and the solution remains constant for all t). Note that equilibrium solutions correspond to horizontal line segments in the direction field. Note also that for autonomous equations, the direction field is independent of t. Consider the following equations.*

a. *Find all equilibrium solutions.*
b. *Sketch the direction field on either side of the equilibrium solutions for* $t \geq 0$.
c. *Sketch the solution curve that corresponds to the initial condition* $y(0) = 1$.

50. $y'(t) = 2y + 4$ **51.** $y'(t) = y^2$

52. $y'(t) = y(2 - y)$ **53.** $y'(t) = y(y - 3)$

54. $y'(t) = \sin y$ **55.** $y'(t) = y(y - 3)(y + 2)$

56–59. Solving initial value problems *Solve the following problems using the method of your choice.*

56. $u'(t) = 4u - 2, \ u(0) = 4$ **57.** $\dfrac{dp}{dt} = \dfrac{p + 1}{t^2}, \ p(1) = 3$

58. $\dfrac{dz}{dx} = \dfrac{z^2}{1 + x^2}, \ z(0) = \dfrac{1}{6}$

59. $w'(t) = 2t \cos^2 w, \ w(0) = \pi/4$

60. Optimal harvesting rate Let $y(t)$ be the population of a species that is being harvested. Consider the harvesting model $y'(t) = 0.008y - h, y(0) = y_0$, where $h > 0$ is the annual harvesting rate and y_0 is the initial population of the species.

a. If $y_0 = 2000$, what harvesting rate should be used to maintain a constant population of $y = 2000$ for $t \geq 0$?
b. If the harvesting rate is $h = 200/\text{year}$, what initial population ensures a constant population for $t \geq 0$?

Applications

61. Logistic equation for spread of rumors Sociologists model the spread of rumors using logistic equations. The key assumption is that at any given time, a fraction y of the population, where $0 \leq y \leq 1$, knows the rumor, while the remaining fraction $1 - y$ does not. Furthermore, the rumor spreads by interactions between those who know the rumor and those who do not. The number of such interactions is proportional to $y(1 - y)$. Therefore, the equation that models the spread of the rumor is $y'(t) = ky(1 - y)$, where k is a positive real number. The fraction of people who initially know the rumor is $y(0) = y_0$, where $0 < y_0 < 1$.

a. Solve this initial value problem and give the solution in terms of k and y_0.
b. Assume $k = 0.3$ weeks^{-1} and graph the solution for $y_0 = 0.1$ and $y_0 = 0.7$.
c. Describe and interpret the long-term behavior of the rumor function for any $0 < y_0 < 1$.

62. Free fall An object in free fall may be modeled by assuming that the only forces at work are the gravitational force and resistance (friction due to the medium in which the object falls). By Newton's second law (mass × acceleration = the sum of the external forces), the velocity of the object satisfies the differential equation

$$\underbrace{m}_{\text{mass}} \cdot \underbrace{v'(t)}_{\text{acceleration}} = \underbrace{mg + f(v)}_{\text{external forces}},$$

where f is a function that models the resistance and the positive direction is downward. One common assumption (often used for motion in air) is that $f(v) = -kv^2$, where $k > 0$ is a drag coefficient.

a. Show that the equation can be written in the form $v'(t) = g - av^2$, where $a = k/m$.
b. For what (positive) value of v is $v'(t) = 0$? (This equilibrium solution is called the **terminal velocity**.)
c. Find the solution of this separable equation assuming $v(0) = 0$ and $0 < v(t)^2 < g/a$, for $t \geq 0$.
d. Graph the solution found in part (c) with $g = 9.8$ m/s^2, $m = 1$ kg, and $k = 0.1$ kg/m, and verify that the terminal velocity agrees with the value found in part (b).

63. Free fall Using the background given in Exercise 62, assume the resistance is given by $f(v) = -Rv$, where $R > 0$ is a drag coefficient (an assumption often made for a heavy medium such as water or oil).

  a. Show that the equation can be written in the form
  $v'(t) = g - bv$, where $b = R/m$.

  b. For what (positive) value of v is $v'(t) = 0$? (This equilibrium solution is called the **terminal velocity**.)

  c. Find the solution of this separable equation assuming $v(0) = 0$ and $0 < v < g/b$.

  d. Graph the solution found in part (c) with $g = 9.8 \text{ m/s}^2$, $m = 1 \text{ kg}$, and $R = 0.1 \text{ kg/s}$, and verify that the terminal velocity agrees with the value found in part (b).

64. Torricelli's Law An open cylindrical tank initially filled with water drains through a hole in the bottom of the tank according to Torricelli's Law (see figure). If $h(t)$ is the depth of water in the tank for $t \geq 0$, then Torricelli's Law implies $h'(t) = 2k\sqrt{h}$, where k is a constant that includes the acceleration due to gravity, the radius of the tank, and the radius of the drain. Assume that the initial depth of the water is $h(0) = H$.

  a. Find the general solution of the equation.
  b. Find the solution in the case that $k = 0.1$ and $H = 0.5$ m.
  c. In general, how long does it take the tank to drain in terms of k and H?

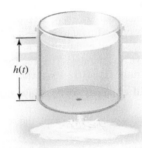

$h(t)$

65. Chemical rate equations The reaction of chemical compounds can often be modeled by differential equations. Let $y(t)$ be the concentration of a substance in reaction for $t \geq 0$ (typical units of y are moles/L). The change in the concentration of the substance, under appropriate conditions, is $\dfrac{dy}{dt} = -ky^n$, where $k > 0$ is a rate constant and the positive integer n is the order of the reaction.

  a. Show that for a first-order reaction $(n = 1)$, the concentration obeys an exponential decay law.
  b. Solve the initial value problem for a second-order reaction $(n = 2)$ assuming $y(0) = y_0$.
  c. Graph and compare the concentration for a first-order and second-order reaction with $k = 0.1$ and $y_0 = 1$.

66. Tumor growth The growth of cancer tumors may be modeled by the Gompertz growth equation. Let $M(t)$ be the mass of the tumor for $t \geq 0$. The relevant initial value problem is

$$\frac{dM}{dt} = -aM \ln\frac{M}{K}, \qquad M(0) = M_0,$$

where a and K are positive constants and $0 < M_0 < K$.

  a. Graph the growth rate function $R(M) = -aM \ln\dfrac{M}{K}$ assuming $a = 1$ and $K = 4$. For what values of M is the growth rate positive? For what value of M is the growth rate a maximum?

  b. Solve the initial value problem and graph the solution for $a = 1$, $K = 4$, and $M_0 = 1$. Describe the growth pattern of the tumor. Is the growth unbounded? If not, what is the limiting size of the tumor?

  c. In the general equation, what is the meaning of K?

67. Endowment model An endowment is an investment account in which the balance ideally remains constant and withdrawals are made on the interest earned by the account. Such an account may be modeled by the initial value problem $B'(t) = aB - m$ for $t \geq 0$, with $B(0) = B_0$. The constant a reflects the annual interest rate, m is the annual rate of withdrawal, and B_0 is the initial balance in the account.

  a. Solve the initial value problem with $a = 0.05$, $m = \$1000/\text{yr}$, and $B_0 = \$15,000$. Does the balance in the account increase or decrease?

  b. If $a = 0.05$ and $B_0 = \$50,000$, what is the annual withdrawal rate m that ensures a constant balance in the account? What is the constant balance?

Additional Exercises

68. Solution of the logistic equation Consider the solution of the logistic equation in Example 6.

  a. From the general solution $\ln\left|\dfrac{P}{300 - P}\right| = 0.1t + C$, show that the initial condition $P(0) = 50$ implies that $C = -\ln 5$.

  b. Solve for P and show that $P = \dfrac{300}{1 + 5e^{-0.1t}}$.

69. Direction field analysis Consider the general first-order initial value problem $y'(t) = ay + b$, $y(0) = y_0$, for $t \geq 0$, where a, b, and y_0 are real numbers.

  a. Explain why $y = -b/a$ is an equilibrium solution and corresponds to horizontal line segments in the direction field.

  b. Draw a representative direction field in the case that $a > 0$. Show that if $y_0 > -b/a$, then the solution increases for $t \geq 0$ and if $y_0 < -b/a$, then the solution decreases for $t \geq 0$.

  c. Draw a representative direction field in the case that $a < 0$. Show that if $y_0 > -b/a$, then the solution decreases for $t \geq 0$ and if $y_0 < -b/a$, then the solution increases for $t \geq 0$.

70. Concavity of solutions Consider the logistic equation

$$P'(t) = 0.1P\left(1 - \frac{P}{300}\right), \text{ for } t \geq 0,$$

with $P(0) > 0$. Show that the solution curve is concave down for $150 < P < 300$ and concave up for $0 < P < 150$ and $P > 300$.

QUICK CHECK ANSWERS
1. The equation is first order and linear. 3. The solution is $y(t) = 16e^{3t} - 2$. 4. $y^3 y'(t) = t^2 + 1$ 5. a. Solution increases for $t \geq -1$. b. Solution decreases for $t \geq -2$. ◄

CHAPTER 7   REVIEW EXERCISES

1. **Explain why or why not** Determine whether the following statements are true and give an explanation or counterexample.

   a. The integral $\int x^2 e^{2x}\, dx$ can be evaluated using integration by parts.

   b. To evaluate the integral $\int \dfrac{dx}{\sqrt{x^2 - 100}}$ analytically, it is best to use partial fractions.

   c. One computer algebra system produces $\int 2\sin x \cos x\, dx = \sin^2 x$. Another computer algebra system produces $\int 2\sin x \cos x\, dx = -\cos^2 x$. One computer algebra system is wrong (apart from a missing constant of integration).

   d. $\int 2\sin x \cos x\, dx = -\dfrac{1}{2}\cos 2x + C.$

   e. The best approach to evaluating $\int \dfrac{x^3 + 1}{3x^2}\, dx$ is to use the change of variables $u = x^3 + 1$.

2–7. Basic integration techniques *Use the methods introduced in Section 7.1 to evaluate the following integrals.*

2. $\displaystyle\int \cos\left(\tfrac{x}{2} + \tfrac{\pi}{3}\right) dx$

3. $\displaystyle\int \dfrac{3x}{\sqrt{x} + 4}\, dx$

4. $\displaystyle\int \dfrac{2 - \sin 2\theta}{\cos^2 2\theta}\, d\theta$

5. $\displaystyle\int_{-2}^{1} \dfrac{3}{x^2 + 4x + 13}\, dx$

6. $\displaystyle\int \dfrac{x^3 + 3x^2 + 1}{x^3 + 1}\, dx$

7. $\displaystyle\int \dfrac{\sqrt{t} - 1}{2t}\, dt$ (Hint: Let $u = \sqrt{t} - 1$.)

8–11. Integration by parts *Use integration by parts to evaluate the following integrals.*

8. $\displaystyle\int_{-1}^{\ln 2} \dfrac{3t}{e^t}\, dt$

9. $\displaystyle\int \dfrac{x}{2\sqrt{x + 2}}\, dx$

10. $\displaystyle\int x \tan^{-1} x\, dx$

11. $\displaystyle\int x \sinh x\, dx$

12–17. Trigonometric integrals *Evaluate the following trigonometric integrals.*

12. $\displaystyle\int_{\pi}^{2\pi} \cot \dfrac{x}{3}\, dx$

13. $\displaystyle\int_{0}^{\pi/4} \cos^5 2x \sin^2 2x\, dx$

14. $\displaystyle\int \tan^3 \theta\, d\theta$

15. $\displaystyle\int \dfrac{\sin^4 t}{\cos^6 t}\, dt$

16. $\displaystyle\int \csc^2 x \cot x\, dx$

17. $\displaystyle\int \tan^3 \theta \sec^3 \theta\, d\theta$

18–21. Trigonometric substitutions *Evaluate the following integrals using a trigonometric substitution.*

18. $\displaystyle\int \dfrac{\sqrt{1 - x^2}}{x}\, dx$

19. $\displaystyle\int_{\sqrt{2}}^{2} \dfrac{\sqrt{x^2 - 1}}{x}\, dx$

20. $\displaystyle\int \dfrac{w^3}{\sqrt{4 - w^2}}\, dw$

21. $\displaystyle\int \dfrac{x^3}{\sqrt{x^2 + 4}}\, dx$

22–25. Partial fractions *Use partial fractions to evaluate the following integrals.*

22. $\displaystyle\int \dfrac{8x + 5}{2x^2 + 3x + 1}\, dx$

23. $\displaystyle\int \dfrac{2x^2 + 7x + 4}{x^3 + 2x^2 + 2x}\, dx$

24. $\displaystyle\int_{-1/2}^{1/2} \dfrac{u^2 + 1}{u^2 - 1}\, du$

25. $\displaystyle\int \dfrac{3x^3 + 4x^2 + 6x}{(x + 1)^2(x^2 + 4)}\, dx$

26–29. Table of integrals *Use a table of integrals to evaluate the following integrals.*

26. $\displaystyle\int x(2x + 3)^5\, dx$

27. $\displaystyle\int \dfrac{dx}{x\sqrt{4x - 6}}$

28. $\displaystyle\int_{0}^{\pi/2} \dfrac{d\theta}{1 + \sin 2\theta}$

29. $\displaystyle\int \sec^5 x\, dx$

30–31. Approximations *Use a computer algebra system to approximate the value of the following integrals.*

30. $\displaystyle\int_{1}^{\sqrt{e}} x^3 \ln^3 x\, dx$

31. $\displaystyle\int_{-1}^{1} e^{-2x^2}\, dx$

T **32. Errors in numerical integration** Let $I = \int_{-1}^{2}(x^7 - 3x^5 - x^2 + \tfrac{7}{8})\, dx$ and note that $I = 0$.

   a. Complete the following table with Trapezoid Rule ($T(n)$) and Midpoint Rule ($M(n)$) approximations to I for various values of n.

   b. Fill in the error columns with the absolute errors in the approximations in part (a).

   c. How do the errors in $T(n)$ decrease as n doubles in size?

   d. How do the errors in $M(n)$ decrease as n doubles in size?

n	$T(n)$	$M(n)$	Abs error in $T(n)$	Abs error in $M(n)$
4				
8				
16				
32				
64				

T **33. Numerical integration methods** Let $I = \int_{0}^{3} x^2\, dx = 9$ and consider the Trapezoid Rule ($T(n)$) and the Midpoint Rule ($M(n)$) approximations to I.

   a. Compute $T(6)$ and $M(6)$.

   b. Compute $T(12)$ and $M(12)$.

34–37. Improper integrals *Evaluate the following integrals.*

34. $\displaystyle\int_{-\infty}^{-1} \dfrac{dx}{(x - 1)^4}$

35. $\displaystyle\int_{0}^{\infty} x e^{-x}\, dx$

36. $\displaystyle\int_{0}^{\pi} \sec^2 x\, dx$

37. $\displaystyle\int_{0}^{3} \dfrac{dx}{\sqrt{9 - x^2}}$

38–63. Miscellaneous Integrals *Evaluate the following integrals analytically.*

38. $\displaystyle\int \frac{x^2 - 4}{x + 4}\, dx$

39. $\displaystyle\int \frac{d\theta}{1 + \cos\theta}$

40. $\displaystyle\int x^2 \cos x\, dx$

41. $\displaystyle\int e^x \sin x\, dx$

42. $\displaystyle\int_1^e x^2 \ln x\, dx$

43. $\displaystyle\int \cos^2 4\theta\, d\theta$

44. $\displaystyle\int \sin 3x \cos^6 3x\, dx$

45. $\displaystyle\int \sec^5 z \tan z\, dz$

46. $\displaystyle\int_0^{\pi/2} \cos^4 x\, dx$

47. $\displaystyle\int_0^{\pi/6} \sin^5 \theta\, d\theta$

48. $\displaystyle\int \tan^4 u\, du$

49. $\displaystyle\int \frac{dx}{\sqrt{4 - x^2}}$

50. $\displaystyle\int \frac{dx}{\sqrt{9x^2 - 25}}, x > \frac{5}{3}$

51. $\displaystyle\int \frac{dy}{y^2\sqrt{9 - y^2}}$

52. $\displaystyle\int_0^{\sqrt{3}/2} \frac{x^2}{(1 - x^2)^{3/2}}\, dx$

53. $\displaystyle\int_0^{\sqrt{3}/2} \frac{4}{9 + 4x^2}\, dx$

54. $\displaystyle\int \frac{(1 - u^2)^{5/2}}{u^8}\, du$

55. $\displaystyle\int \operatorname{sech}^2 x \sinh x\, dx$

56. $\displaystyle\int x^2 \cosh x\, dx$

57. $\displaystyle\int_0^{\ln(\sqrt{3}+2)} \frac{\cosh x}{\sqrt{4 - \sinh^2 x}}\, dx$

58. $\displaystyle\int \sinh^{-1} x\, dx$

59. $\displaystyle\int \frac{dx}{x^2 - 2x - 15}$

60. $\displaystyle\int \frac{dx}{x^3 - 2x^2}$

61. $\displaystyle\int_0^1 \frac{dy}{(y + 1)(y^2 + 1)}$

62. $\displaystyle\int_0^{\infty} \frac{6x}{1 + x^6}\, dx$

63. $\displaystyle\int_0^2 \frac{dx}{\sqrt[3]{|x - 1|}}$

64–69. Preliminary work *Make a change of variables or use an algebra step before evaluating the following integrals.*

64. $\displaystyle\int_{-1}^1 \frac{dx}{x^2 + 2x + 5}$

65. $\displaystyle\int \frac{dx}{x^2 - x - 2}$

66. $\displaystyle\int \frac{3x^2 + x - 3}{x^2 - 1}\, dx$

67. $\displaystyle\int \frac{2x^2 - 4x}{x^2 - 4}\, dx$

68. $\displaystyle\int_{1/12}^{1/4} \frac{dx}{\sqrt{x}(1 + 4x)}$

69. $\displaystyle\int \frac{e^{2t}}{(1 + e^{4t})^{3/2}}\, dt$

70. Three ways Evaluate $\displaystyle\int \frac{dx}{4 - x^2}$ using (i) partial fractions, (ii) a trigonometric substitution, and (iii) Theorem 6.12 (Section 6.10). Then show that the results are consistent.

71–74. Volumes *The region R is bounded by the curve $y = \ln x$ and the x-axis on the interval $[1, e]$. Find the volume of the solid that is generated when R is revolved in the following ways.*

71. About the x-axis

72. About the y-axis

73. About the line $x = 1$

74. About the line $y = 1$

75. Comparing volumes Let R be the region bounded by the graph of $y = \sin x$ and the x-axis on the interval $[0, \pi]$. Which is greater, the volume of the solid generated when R is revolved about the x-axis or the y-axis?

76. Comparing areas Show that the area of the region bounded by the graph of $y = ae^{-ax}$ and the x-axis on the interval $[0, \infty)$ is the same for all values of $a > 0$.

T 77. Zero log integral It is evident from the graph of $y = \ln x$ that for every real number a with $0 < a < 1$, there is a unique real number $b = g(a)$ with $b > 1$, such that $\int_a^b \ln x\, dx = 0$ (the net area bounded by the graph of $y = \ln x$ on $[a, b]$ is 0).

a. Approximate $b = g(\frac{1}{2})$.

b. Approximate $b = g(\frac{1}{3})$.

c. Find the equation satisfied by all pairs of numbers (a, b) such that $b = g(a)$.

d. Is g an increasing or decreasing function of a? Explain.

78. Arc length Find the length of the curve $y = \ln x$ on the interval $[1, e^2]$.

79. Average velocity Find the average velocity of a projectile whose velocity over the interval $0 \le t \le \pi$ is given by $v(t) = 10 \sin 3t$.

80. Comparing distances Starting at the same time and place $(t = 0$ and $s = 0)$, the velocity of car A (in mi/hr) is given by $u(t) = 40/(t + 1)$ and the velocity of car B (in mi/hr) is given by $v(t) = 40e^{-t/2}$.

a. After $t = 2$ hr, which car has traveled farther?

b. After $t = 3$ hr, which car has traveled farther?

c. If allowed to travel indefinitely $(t \to \infty)$, which car will travel a finite distance?

81. Traffic flow When data from a traffic study are fitted to a curve, the flow rate of cars past a point on a highway is approximated by $R(t) = 800te^{-t/2}$ cars/hr. How many cars pass the measuring site during the time interval $0 \le t \le 4$?

T 82. Comparing integrals Graph the functions $f(x) = \pm 1/x^2$, $g(x) = (\cos x)/x^2$, and $h(x) = (\cos^2 x)/x^2$. Without evaluating integrals and knowing that $\int_1^{\infty} f(x)\, dx$ has a finite value, determine whether $\int_1^{\infty} g(x)\, dx$ and $\int_1^{\infty} h(x)\, dx$ have finite values.

83. A family of logarithm integrals Let $I(p) = \displaystyle\int_1^e \frac{\ln x}{x^p}\, dx$, where p is a real number.

a. Find an expression for $I(p)$, for all real values of p.

b. Evaluate $\lim\limits_{p \to \infty} I(p)$ and $\lim\limits_{p \to -\infty} I(p)$.

c. For what value of p is $I(p) = 1$?

84. Arc length Find the length of the curve
$$y = \frac{x}{2}\sqrt{3 - x^2} + \frac{3}{2}\sin^{-1}\frac{x}{\sqrt{3}} \text{ from } x = 0 \text{ to } x = 1.$$

T 85. Best approximation Let $I = \displaystyle\int_0^1 \frac{x^2 - x}{\ln x}\, dx$. Use any method you choose to find a good approximation to I. You may use the facts that $\lim\limits_{x \to 0^+} \frac{x^2 - x}{\ln x} = 0$ and $\lim\limits_{x \to 1} \frac{x^2 - x}{\ln x} = 1$.

T 86. Numerical integration Use a calculator to determine the integer n that satisfies $\displaystyle\int_0^{1/2} \frac{\ln(1 + 2x)}{x}\, dx = \frac{\pi^2}{n}$.

T 87. Numerical integration Use a calculator to determine the integer n that satisfies $\int_0^1 \dfrac{\sin^{-1}x}{x}\,dx = \dfrac{\pi \ln 2}{n}$.

88. Two worthy integrals

a. Let $I(a) = \displaystyle\int_0^\infty \dfrac{dx}{(1 + x^a)(1 + x^2)}$, where a is a real number. Evaluate $I(a)$ and show that its value is independent of a. (*Hint:* Split the integral into two integrals over $[0, 1]$ and $[1, \infty)$; then use a change of variables to convert the second integral into an integral over $[0, 1]$.)

b. Let f be any positive continuous function on $[0, \pi/2]$.

Evaluate $\displaystyle\int_0^{\pi/2} \dfrac{f(\cos x)}{f(\cos x) + f(\sin x)}\,dx$.

(*Hint:* Use the identity $\cos(\pi/2 - x) = \sin x$.)

(*Source: Mathematics Magazine* 81, 2, Apr 2008)

T 89. Comparing volumes Let R be the region bounded by $y = \ln x$, the x-axis, and the line $x = a$, where $a > 1$.

a. Find the volume $V_1(a)$ of the solid generated when R is revolved about the x-axis (as a function of a).

b. Find the volume $V_2(a)$ of the solid generated when R is revolved about the y-axis (as a function of a).

c. Graph V_1 and V_2. For what values of $a > 1$ is $V_1(a) > V_2(a)$?

90. Equal volumes

a. Let R be the region bounded by the graph of $f(x) = x^{-p}$ and the x-axis, for $x \geq 1$. Let V_1 and V_2 be the volumes of the solids generated when R is revolved about the x-axis and the y-axis, respectively, if they exist. For what values of p (if any) is $V_1 = V_2$?

b. Repeat part (a) on the interval $(0, 1]$.

91. Equal volumes Let R_1 be the region bounded by the graph of $y = e^{-ax}$ and the x-axis on the interval $[0, b]$ where $a > 0$ and $b > 0$. Let R_2 be the region bounded by the graph of $y = e^{-ax}$ and the x-axis on the interval $[b, \infty)$. Let V_1 and V_2 be the volumes of the solids generated when R_1 and R_2 are revolved about the x-axis. Find and graph the relationship between a and b for which $V_1 = V_2$.

92–96. Initial value problems *Solve the following initial value problems.*

92. $y'(t) + 3y = 0,\ y(0) = 6$ **93.** $y'(t) = 2y + 4,\ y(0) = 8$

94. $\dfrac{dy}{dt} = \dfrac{2ty}{\ln y},\ y(2) = e$ **95.** $y'(t) = \dfrac{t + 1}{2ty},\ y(1) = 4$

96. $\dfrac{dy}{dt} = \sqrt{y}\,\sin t,\ y(0) = 4$

97. Limit of a solution Evaluate $\lim\limits_{t \to \infty} y(t)$, where y is the solution of the initial value problem $y'(t) = \dfrac{\sec y}{t^2},\ y(1) = 0$.

98–100. Sketching direction fields *Use the window* $[-2, 2] \times [-2, 2]$ *to sketch a direction field for the given differential equation. Then sketch the solution curve that corresponds to the given initial condition.*

98. $y'(t) = 3y - 6,\ y(0) = 1$ **99.** $y'(t) = t^2,\ y(-1) = -1$

100. $y'(t) = y - t,\ y(-2) = \frac{1}{2}$

T 101. Enzyme kinetics The consumption of a substrate in a reaction involving an enzyme is often modeled using Michaelis-Menton kinetics, which involves the initial value problem $\dfrac{ds}{dt} = -\dfrac{Qs}{K + s}$, $s(0) = s_0$, where $s(t)$ is the amount of substrate present at time $t \geq 0$, and Q and K are positive constants. Solve the initial value problem with $Q = 10$, $K = 5$, and $s_0 = 50$. Notice that the solution can be expressed explicitly only with t as a function of s. Graph the solution and describe how s behaves as $t \to \infty$. (See the Guided Project *Enzyme kinetics*.)

102. Investment model An investment account, which earns interest and has regular deposits, can be modeled by the initial value problem $B'(t) = aB + m$ for $t \geq 0$, with $B(0) = B_0$. The constant a reflects the monthly interest rate, m is the rate of monthly deposits, and B_0 is the initial balance in the account. Solve the initial value problem with $a = 0.005$, $m = \$100/\text{month}$, and $B_0 = \$100$. After how many months does the account have a balance of \$7500?

Chapter 7 Guided Projects

Applications of the material in this chapter and related topics can be found in the following Guided Projects. For additional information, see the Preface.

- Cooling coffee
- Euler's method for differential equations
- Terminal velocity
- A pursuit problem
- How long will your iPod last?

- Simpson's rule
- Predator-prey models
- Period of the pendulum
- Logistic growth
- Mercator projections

8

Sequences and Infinite Series

▶ Keeping with common practice, the terms *series* and *infinite series* are used interchangeably throughout this chapter.

▶ The dots (..., an ellipsis) after the last number of a sequence mean that the list continues indefinitely.

Chapter Preview This chapter covers topics that lie at the foundation of calculus—indeed, at the foundation of mathematics. The first task is to make a clear distinction between a *sequence* and an *infinite series*. A sequence is an ordered *list* of numbers, $a_1, a_2, \ldots$, while an infinite series is a *sum* of numbers, $a_1 + a_2 + \cdots$. The idea of convergence to a limit is important for both sequences and series, but convergence is analyzed differently in the two cases. To determine limits of sequences, we use the same tools used for limits of functions at infinity. Convergence of infinite series is a different matter, and we develop the required methods in this chapter. The study of infinite series begins with *geometric series*, which have theoretical importance and are used to answer many practical questions (When is your auto loan paid off? How much antibiotic is in your blood if you take three pills per day?). We then present several tests that are used to determine whether series with positive terms converge. Finally, alternating series, whose terms alternate in sign, are discussed in anticipation of power series in the next chapter.

8.1 An Overview

To understand sequences and series, you must understand how they differ and how they are related. The purposes of this opening section are to introduce sequences and series in concrete terms, and to illustrate both their differences and their relationships with each other.

Examples of Sequences

Consider the following *list* of numbers:

$$\{1, 4, 7, 10, 13, 16, \ldots\}.$$

Each number in the list is obtained by adding 3 to the previous number in the list. With this rule, we could extend the list indefinitely.

This list is an example of a *sequence*, where each number in the sequence is called a **term** of the sequence. We denote sequences in any of the following forms:

$$\{a_1, a_2, a_3, \ldots, a_n, \ldots\}, \qquad \{a_n\}_{n=1}^{\infty}, \quad \text{or} \quad \{a_n\}.$$

The subscript n that appears in a_n is called an **index**, and it indicates the order of terms in the sequence. The choice of a starting index is arbitrary, but sequences usually begin with $n = 0$ or $n = 1$.

The sequence $\{1, 4, 7, 10, \dots\}$ can be defined in two ways. First, we have the rule that each term of the sequence is 3 more than the previous term; that is, $a_2 = a_1 + 3$, $a_3 = a_2 + 3$, $a_4 = a_3 + 3$, and so forth. In general, we see that

$$a_1 = 1 \quad \text{and} \quad a_{n+1} = a_n + 3, \quad \text{for } n = 1, 2, 3, \dots.$$

This way of defining a sequence is called a *recurrence relation* (or an *implicit formula*). It specifies the initial term of the sequence (in this case, $a_1 = 1$) and gives a general rule for computing the next term of the sequence from previous terms. For example, if you know a_{100}, the recurrence relation can be used to find a_{101}.

Suppose instead you want to find a_{147} directly without computing the first 146 terms of the sequence. The first four terms of the sequence can be written

$$a_1 = 1 + (3 \cdot 0), \qquad a_2 = 1 + (3 \cdot 1), \qquad a_3 = 1 + (3 \cdot 2), \qquad a_4 = 1 + (3 \cdot 3).$$

Observe the pattern: The nth term of the sequence is 1 plus 3 multiplied by $n - 1$, or

$$a_n = 1 + 3(n - 1) = 3n - 2, \quad \text{for } n = 1, 2, 3, \dots.$$

With this *explicit formula*, the nth term of the sequence is determined directly from the value of n. For example, with $n = 147$,

$$a_{147} = 3 \cdot \underset{n}{\underbrace{147}} - 2 = 439.$$

QUICK CHECK 1 Find a_{10} for the sequence $\{1, 4, 7, 10, \dots\}$ using the recurrence relation and then again using the explicit formula for the nth term. ◄

> When defined by an explicit formula $a_n = f(n)$, it is evident that sequences are functions. The domain is generally a subset of the nonnegative integers, and one real number a_n is assigned to each integer n in the domain.

DEFINITION Sequence

A **sequence** $\{a_n\}$ is an ordered list of numbers of the form

$$\{a_1, a_2, a_3, \dots, a_n, \dots\}.$$

A sequence may be generated by a **recurrence relation** of the form $a_{n+1} = f(a_n)$, for $n = 1, 2, 3, \dots$, where a_1 is given. A sequence may also be defined with an **explicit formula** of the form $a_n = f(n)$, for $n = 1, 2, 3, \dots.$

EXAMPLE 1   Explicit formulas Use the explicit formula for $\{a_n\}_{n=1}^{\infty}$ to write the first four terms of each sequence. Sketch a graph of the sequence.

a. $a_n = \dfrac{1}{2^n}$ **b.** $a_n = \dfrac{(-1)^n n}{n^2 + 1}$

SOLUTION

a. Substituting $n = 1, 2, 3, 4, \dots$ into the explicit formula $a_n = \dfrac{1}{2^n}$, we find that the terms of the sequence are

$$\left\{ \frac{1}{2}, \frac{1}{2^2}, \frac{1}{2^3}, \frac{1}{2^4}, \dots \right\} = \left\{ \frac{1}{2}, \frac{1}{4}, \frac{1}{8}, \frac{1}{16}, \dots \right\}.$$

The graph of a sequence is the graph of a function that is defined only on a set of integers. In this case, we plot the coordinate pairs (n, a_n), for $n = 1, 2, 3, \dots$, resulting in a graph consisting of individual points. The graph of the sequence $a_n = \dfrac{1}{2^n}$ suggests that the terms of this sequence approach 0 as n increases (Figure 8.1).

b. Substituting $n = 1, 2, 3, 4, \dots$ into the explicit formula, the terms of the sequence are

$$\left\{ \frac{(-1)^1 (1)}{1^2 + 1}, \frac{(-1)^2 2}{2^2 + 1}, \frac{(-1)^3 3}{3^2 + 1}, \frac{(-1)^4 4}{4^2 + 1}, \dots \right\} = \left\{ -\frac{1}{2}, \frac{2}{5}, -\frac{3}{10}, \frac{4}{17}, \dots \right\}.$$

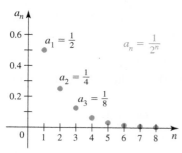

Figure 8.1

> The "switch" $(-1)^n$ is used frequently to alternate the signs of the terms of sequences and series.

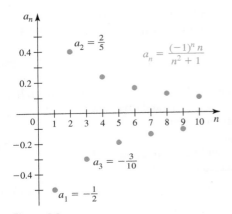

Figure 8.2

From the graph (Figure 8.2), we see that the terms of the sequence alternate in sign and appear to approach 0 as n increases.

Related Exercises 9–16 ◄

EXAMPLE 2   Recurrence relations Use the recurrence relation for $\{a_n\}_{n=1}^{\infty}$ to write the first four terms of the sequences

$$a_{n+1} = 2a_n + 1, a_1 = 1 \quad \text{and} \quad a_{n+1} = 2a_n + 1, a_1 = -1.$$

SOLUTION Notice that the recurrence relation is the same for the two sequences; only the first term differs. The first four terms of each of the sequences are as follows.

n	a_n with $a_1 = 1$	a_n with $a_1 = -1$
1	$a_1 = 1$ (given)	$a_1 = -1$ (given)
2	$a_2 = 2a_1 + 1 = 2 \cdot 1 + 1 = 3$	$a_2 = 2a_1 + 1 = 2(-1) + 1 = -1$
3	$a_3 = 2a_2 + 1 = 2 \cdot 3 + 1 = 7$	$a_3 = 2a_2 + 1 = 2(-1) + 1 = -1$
4	$a_4 = 2a_3 + 1 = 2 \cdot 7 + 1 = 15$	$a_4 = 2a_3 + 1 = 2(-1) + 1 = -1$

We see that the terms of the first sequence increase without bound, while all terms of the second sequence are -1. Clearly, the initial term of the sequence may determine the behavior of the entire sequence.

Related Exercises 17–22 ◄

QUICK CHECK 2 Find an explicit formula for the sequence $\{1, 3, 7, 15, \dots\}$ (Example 2). ◄

EXAMPLE 3   Working with sequences Consider the following sequences.

a. $\{a_n\} = \{-2, 5, 12, 19, \dots\}$ **b.** $\{b_n\} = \{3, 6, 12, 24, 48, \dots\}$

(i)   Find the next two terms of the sequence.

(ii) Find a recurrence relation that generates the sequence.

(iii) Find an explicit formula for the nth term of the sequence.

SOLUTION

a. (i)   Each term is obtained by adding 7 to its predecessor. The next two terms are $19 + 7 = 26$ and $26 + 7 = 33$.

> ➤ In Example 3, we chose the starting index $n = 0$. Other choices are possible.

(ii) Because each term is seven more than its predecessor, a recurrence relation is

$$a_{n+1} = a_n + 7, a_0 = -2, \quad \text{for } n = 0, 1, 2, \dots.$$

(iii) Notice that $a_0 = -2, a_1 = -2 + (1 \cdot 7)$, and $a_2 = -2 + (2 \cdot 7)$, so an explicit formula is

$$a_n = 7n - 2, \quad \text{for } n = 0, 1, 2, \dots.$$

b. (i)   Each term is obtained by multiplying its predecessor by 2. The next two terms are $48 \cdot 2 = 96$ and $96 \cdot 2 = 192$.

(ii) Because each term is two times its predecessor, a recurrence relation is

$$a_{n+1} = 2a_n, a_0 = 3, \quad \text{for } n = 0, 1, 2, \dots.$$

(iii) To obtain an explicit formula, note that $a_0 = 3, a_1 = 3(2^1)$, and $a_2 = 3(2^2)$. In general,

$$a_n = 3(2^n), \quad \text{for } n = 0, 1, 2, \dots.$$

Related Exercises 23–30 ◄

Limit of a Sequence

Perhaps the most important question about a sequence is this: If you go farther and farther out in the sequence, $a_{100}, \ldots, a_{10,000}, \ldots, a_{100,000}, \ldots$, how do the terms of the sequence behave? Do they approach a specific number, and if so, what is that number? Or do they grow in magnitude without bound? Or do they wander around with or without a pattern?

The long-term behavior of a sequence is described by its **limit**. The limit of a sequence is defined rigorously in the next section. For now, we work with an informal definition.

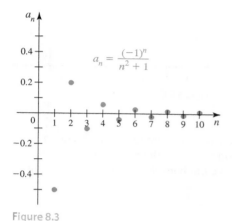

$a_n = \dfrac{(-1)^n}{n^2 + 1}$

Figure 8.3

> **DEFINITION Limit of a Sequence**
>
> If the terms of a sequence $\{a_n\}$ approach a unique number L as n increases—that is, if a_n can be made arbitrarily close to L by taking n sufficiently large—then we say $\lim\limits_{n \to \infty} a_n = L$ exists, and the sequence **converges** to L. If the terms of the sequence do not approach a single number as n increases, the sequence has no limit, and the sequence **diverges**.

EXAMPLE 4 Limits of sequences Write the first four terms of each sequence. If you believe the sequence converges, make a conjecture about its limit. If the sequence appears to diverge, explain why.

a. $\left\{\dfrac{(-1)^n}{n^2 + 1}\right\}_{n=1}^{\infty}$ Explicit formula

b. $\{\cos n\pi\}_{n=1}^{\infty}$ Explicit formula

c. $\{a_n\}_{n=1}^{\infty}$, where $a_{n+1} = -2a_n, a_1 = 1$ Recurrence relation

SOLUTION

a. Beginning with $n = 1$, the first four terms of the sequence are

$$\left\{\frac{(-1)^1}{1^2 + 1}, \frac{(-1)^2}{2^2 + 1}, \frac{(-1)^3}{3^2 + 1}, \frac{(-1)^4}{4^2 + 1}, \ldots\right\} = \left\{-\frac{1}{2}, \frac{1}{5}, -\frac{1}{10}, \frac{1}{17}, \ldots\right\}.$$

The terms decrease in magnitude and approach zero with alternating signs. The limit appears to be 0 (Figure 8.3).

b. The first four terms of the sequence are

$$\{\cos \pi, \cos 2\pi, \cos 3\pi, \cos 4\pi, \ldots\} = \{-1, 1, -1, 1, \ldots\}.$$

In this case, the terms of the sequence alternate between -1 and $+1$, and never approach a single value. Therefore, the sequence diverges (Figure 8.4).

c. The first four terms of the sequence are

$$\{1, -2a_1, -2a_2, -2a_3, \ldots\} = \{1, -2, 4, -8, \ldots\}.$$

Because the magnitudes of the terms increase without bound, the sequence diverges (Figure 8.5).

Related Exercises 31–40 ◄

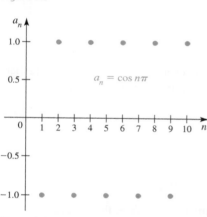

$a_n = \cos n\pi$

Figure 8.4

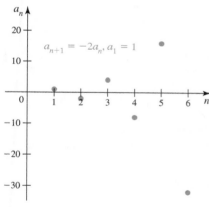

$a_{n+1} = -2a_n, a_1 = 1$

Figure 8.5

EXAMPLE 5 Limit of a sequence Enumerate and graph the terms of the following sequence, and make a conjecture about its limit.

$$a_n = \frac{4n^3}{n^3 + 1}, \qquad \text{for } n = 1, 2, 3, \ldots. \quad \text{Explicit formula}$$

SOLUTION The first 14 terms of the sequence $\{a_n\}$ are tabulated in Table 8.1 and graphed in Figure 8.6. The terms appear to approach 4.

Table 8.1

n	a_n	n	a_n
1	2.000	8	3.992
2	3.556	9	3.995
3	3.857	10	3.996
4	3.938	11	3.997
5	3.968	12	3.998
6	3.982	13	3.998
7	3.988	14	3.999

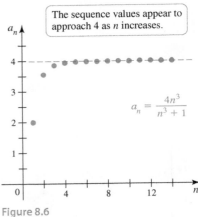

The sequence values appear to approach 4 as n increases.

$$a_n = \frac{4n^3}{n^3 + 1}$$

Figure 8.6

Related Exercises 41–54 ◀

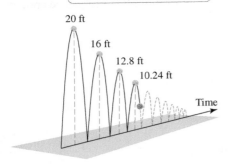

The height of each bounce of the basketball is 0.8 of the height of the previous bounce.

20 ft
16 ft
12.8 ft
10.24 ft
Time

Figure 8.7

EXAMPLE 6   A bouncing ball A basketball tossed straight up in the air reaches a high point and falls to the floor. Each time the ball bounces on the floor it rebounds to 0.8 of its previous height. Let h_n be the high point after the nth bounce, with the initial height being $h_0 = 20$ ft.

a. Find a recurrence relation and an explicit formula for the sequence $\{h_n\}$.

b. What is the high point after the 10th bounce? after the 20th bounce?

c. Speculate on the limit of the sequence $\{h_n\}$.

SOLUTION

a. We first write and graph the heights of the ball for several bounces using the rule that each height is 0.8 of the previous height (Figure 8.7). For example, we have

$$h_0 = 20 \text{ ft,}$$
$$h_1 = 0.8\, h_0 = 16 \text{ ft,}$$
$$h_2 = 0.8\, h_1 = 0.8^2\, h_0 = 12.80 \text{ ft,}$$
$$h_3 = 0.8\, h_2 = 0.8^3\, h_0 = 10.24 \text{ ft, and}$$
$$h_4 = 0.8\, h_3 = 0.8^4\, h_0 \approx 8.19 \text{ ft.}$$

Each number in the list is 0.8 of the previous number. Therefore, the recurrence relation for the sequence of heights is

$$h_{n+1} = 0.8\, h_n, \quad h_0 = 20, \quad \text{for } n = 0, 1, 2, 3, \ldots.$$

To find an explicit formula for the nth term, note that

$$h_1 = h_0 \cdot 0.8, \quad h_2 = h_0 \cdot 0.8^2, \quad h_3 = h_0 \cdot 0.8^3, \quad \text{and} \quad h_4 = h_0 \cdot 0.8^4.$$

In general, we have

$$h_n = h_0 \cdot 0.8^n = 20 \cdot 0.8^n, \quad \text{for } n = 0, 1, 2, 3, \ldots,$$

which is an explicit formula for the terms of the sequence.

b. Using the explicit formula for the sequence, we see that after $n = 10$ bounces, the next height is

$$h_{10} = 20 \cdot 0.8^{10} \approx 2.15 \text{ ft.}$$

After $n = 20$ bounces, the next height is

$$h_{20} = 20 \cdot 0.8^{20} \approx 0.23 \text{ ft.}$$

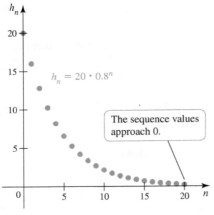

$h_n = 20 \cdot 0.8^n$

The sequence values approach 0.

Figure 8.8

c. The terms of the sequence (Figure 8.8) appear to decrease and approach 0. A reasonable conjecture is that $\lim_{n \to \infty} h_n = 0$.

Related Exercises 55–58 ◀

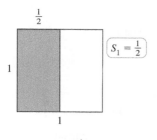

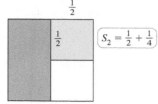

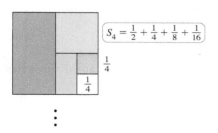

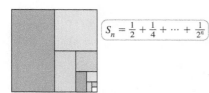

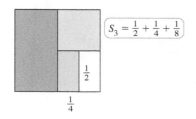

Figure 8.9

Infinite Series and the Sequence of Partial Sums

An infinite series can be viewed as a *sum* of an infinite set of numbers; it has the form

$$a_1 + a_2 + \cdots + a_n + \cdots,$$

where the terms of the series, $a_1, a_2, \ldots,$ are real numbers. We first answer the question: How is it possible to sum an infinite set of numbers and produce a finite number? Here is an informative example.

Consider a unit square (sides of length 1) that is subdivided as shown in Figure 8.9. We let S_n be the area of the colored region in the nth figure of the progression. The area of the colored region in the first figure is

$$S_1 = \frac{1}{2} \cdot 1 = \frac{1}{2}. \qquad \frac{1}{2} = \frac{2^1 - 1}{2^1}$$

The area of the colored region in the second figure is S_1 plus the area of the smaller blue square, which is $\frac{1}{2} \cdot \frac{1}{2} = \frac{1}{4}$. Therefore,

$$S_2 = \frac{1}{2} + \frac{1}{4} = \frac{3}{4}. \qquad \frac{3}{4} = \frac{2^2 - 1}{2^2}$$

The area of the colored region in the third figure is S_2 plus the area of the smaller green rectangle, which is $\frac{1}{2} \cdot \frac{1}{4} = \frac{1}{8}$. Therefore,

$$S_3 = \frac{1}{2} + \frac{1}{4} + \frac{1}{8} = \frac{7}{8}. \qquad \frac{7}{8} = \frac{2^3 - 1}{2^3}$$

Continuing in this manner, we find that

$$S_n = \frac{1}{2} + \frac{1}{4} + \frac{1}{8} + \cdots + \frac{1}{2^n} = \frac{2^n - 1}{2^n}.$$

If this process is continued indefinitely, the area of the colored region S_n approaches the area of the unit square, which is 1. So it is plausible that

$$\lim_{n \to \infty} S_n = \underbrace{\frac{1}{2} + \frac{1}{4} + \frac{1}{8} + \cdots}_{\text{sum continues indefinitely}} = 1.$$

The explicit formula $S_n = \dfrac{2^n - 1}{2^n}$ can be analyzed to verify our assertion that $\lim_{n \to \infty} S_n = 1$; we turn to that task in Section 8.2.

This example shows that it is possible to sum an infinite set of numbers and obtain a finite number—in this case, the sum is 1. The sequence $\{S_n\}$ generated in this example is extremely important. It is called a *sequence of partial sums*, and its limit is the value of the infinite series $\frac{1}{2} + \frac{1}{4} + \frac{1}{8} + \cdots$. The idea of a sequence of partial sums is illustrated by the decimal expansion of 1.

EXAMPLE 7 **Working with series** Consider the infinite series

$$0.9 + 0.09 + 0.009 + 0.0009 + \cdots,$$

where each term of the sum is $\frac{1}{10}$ of the previous term.

a. Find the sum of the first one, two, three, and four terms of the series.

b. What value would you assign to the infinite series $0.9 + 0.09 + 0.009 + \cdots$?

SOLUTION

a. Let S_n denote the sum of the first n terms of the given series. Then

$$S_1 = 0.9,$$
$$S_2 = 0.9 + 0.09 = 0.99,$$
$$S_3 = 0.9 + 0.09 + 0.009 = 0.999, \text{ and}$$
$$S_4 = 0.9 + 0.09 + 0.009 + 0.0009 = 0.9999.$$

b. The sums $S_1, S_2, \ldots, S_n$ form a sequence $\{S_n\}$, which is a sequence of partial sums. As more and more terms are included, the values of S_n approach 1. Therefore, a reasonable conjecture for the value of the series is 1:

$$\underbrace{\underbrace{\underbrace{0.9}_{S_1 = 0.9} + 0.09}_{S_2 = 0.99} + 0.009}_{S_3 = 0.999} + 0.0009 + \cdots = 1.$$

Related Exercises 59–62 ◄

QUICK CHECK 3 Reasoning as in Example 7, what is the value of $0.3 + 0.03 + 0.003 + \cdots$? ◄

▶ Recall the summation notation introduced in Chapter 5: $\sum_{k=1}^{n} a_k$ means $a_1 + a_2 + \cdots + a_n$.

The nth term of the sequence is

$$S_n = \underbrace{0.9 + 0.09 + 0.009 + \cdots + 0.0\ldots09}_{n \text{ terms}} = \sum_{k=1}^{n} 9 \cdot 0.1^k.$$

We observed that $\lim_{n \to \infty} S_n = 1$. For this reason, we write

$$\lim_{n \to \infty} S_n = \lim_{n \to \infty} \underbrace{\sum_{k=1}^{n} 9 \cdot 0.1^k}_{S_n} = \underbrace{\sum_{k=1}^{\infty} 9 \cdot 0.1^k}_{\text{new object}} = 1.$$

By letting $n \to \infty$, a new mathematical object $\sum_{k=1}^{\infty} 9 \cdot 0.1^k$ is created. It is an infinite series, and its value is the *limit* of the sequence of partial sums.

▶ The term *series* is used for historical reasons. When you see *series*, you should think *sum*.

DEFINITION Infinite Series

Given a sequence $\{a_1, a_2, a_3, \ldots\}$, the sum of its terms

$$a_1 + a_2 + a_3 + \cdots = \sum_{k=1}^{\infty} a_k$$

is called an **infinite series**. The **sequence of partial sums** $\{S_n\}$ associated with this series has the terms

$$S_1 = a_1$$
$$S_2 = a_1 + a_2$$
$$S_3 = a_1 + a_2 + a_3$$
$$\vdots$$
$$S_n = a_1 + a_2 + a_3 + \cdots + a_n = \sum_{k=1}^{n} a_k, \quad \text{for } n = 1, 2, 3, \ldots.$$

If the sequence of partial sums $\{S_n\}$ has a limit L, the infinite series **converges** to that limit, and we write

$$\sum_{k=1}^{\infty} a_k = \lim_{n \to \infty} \underbrace{\sum_{k=1}^{n} a_k}_{S_n} = \lim_{n \to \infty} S_n = L.$$

QUICK CHECK 4 Do the series $\sum_{k=1}^{\infty} 1$ and $\sum_{k=1}^{\infty} k$ converge or diverge? ◄

If the sequence of partial sums diverges, the infinite series also **diverges**.

EXAMPLE 8 Sequence of partial sums Consider the infinite series

$$\sum_{k=1}^{\infty} \frac{1}{k(k+1)}.$$

a. Find the first four terms of the sequence of partial sums.
b. Find an expression for S_n and make a conjecture about the value of the series.

SOLUTION

a. The sequence of partial sums can be evaluated explicitly:

$$S_1 = \sum_{k=1}^{1} \frac{1}{k(k+1)} = \frac{1}{2},$$

$$S_2 = \sum_{k=1}^{2} \frac{1}{k(k+1)} = \frac{1}{2} + \frac{1}{6} = \frac{2}{3},$$

$$S_3 = \sum_{k=1}^{3} \frac{1}{k(k+1)} = \frac{1}{2} + \frac{1}{6} + \frac{1}{12} = \frac{3}{4}, \text{ and}$$

$$S_4 = \sum_{k=1}^{4} \frac{1}{k(k+1)} = \frac{1}{2} + \frac{1}{6} + \frac{1}{12} + \frac{1}{20} = \frac{4}{5}.$$

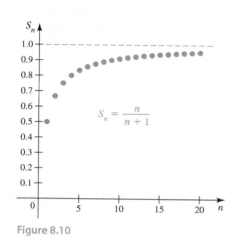

$$S_n = \frac{n}{n+1}$$

Figure 8.10

b. Based on the pattern in the sequence of partial sums, a reasonable conjecture is that $S_n = \dfrac{n}{n+1}$, for $n = 1, 2, 3, \ldots$, which produces the sequence $\left\{ \dfrac{1}{2}, \dfrac{2}{3}, \dfrac{3}{4}, \dfrac{4}{5}, \dfrac{5}{6}, \ldots \right\}$ (Figure 8.10). Because $\displaystyle\lim_{n\to\infty} \frac{n}{n+1} = 1$, we claim that

$$\sum_{k=1}^{\infty} \frac{1}{k(k+1)} = \lim_{n\to\infty} S_n = 1.$$

Related Exercises 63–66 ◄

QUICK CHECK 5 Find the first four terms of the sequence of partial sums for the series $\displaystyle\sum_{k=1}^{\infty} (-1)^k k$. Does the series converge or diverge? ◄

Summary

This section features three key ideas to keep in mind.

- A *sequence* $\{a_1, a_2, \ldots, a_n, \ldots\}$ is an ordered *list* of numbers.

- An *infinite series* $\displaystyle\sum_{k=1}^{\infty} a_k = a_1 + a_2 + a_3 + \cdots$ is a *sum* of numbers.

- A *sequence of partial sums* $\{S_1, S_2, S_3, \ldots\}$, where $S_n = a_1 + a_2 + \cdots + a_n$, is used to evaluate the series $\displaystyle\sum_{k=1}^{\infty} a_k$.

For sequences, we ask about the behavior of the individual terms as we go out farther and farther in the list; that is, we ask about $\lim_{n \to \infty} a_n$. For infinite series, we examine the sequence of partial sums related to the series. If the sequence of partial sums $\{S_n\}$ has a limit, then the infinite series $\sum_{k=1}^{\infty} a_k$ converges to that limit. If the sequence of partial sums does not have a limit, the infinite series diverges.

Table 8.2 shows the correspondences between sequences/series and functions, and between summation and integration. For a sequence, the index n plays the role of the independent variable and takes on integer values; the terms of the sequence $\{a_n\}$ correspond to the dependent variable.

With sequences $\{a_n\}$, the idea of accumulation corresponds to summation, whereas with functions, accumulation corresponds to integration. A finite sum is analogous to integrating a function over a finite interval. An infinite series is analogous to integrating a function over an infinite interval.

Table 8.2

	Sequences/Series	Functions
Independent variable	n	x
Dependent variable	a_n	$f(x)$
Domain	Integers	Real numbers
	e.g., $n = 1, 2, 3, \ldots$	e.g., $\{x: x \geq 1\}$
Accumulation	Sums	Integrals
Accumulation over a finite interval	$\sum_{k=1}^{n} a_k$	$\int_{1}^{n} f(x)\, dx$
Accumulation over an infinite interval	$\sum_{k=1}^{\infty} a_k$	$\int_{1}^{\infty} f(x)\, dx$

SECTION 8.1 EXERCISES

Review Questions

1. Define *sequence* and give an example.

2. Suppose the sequence $\{a_n\}$ is defined by the explicit formula $a_n = 1/n$, for $n = 1, 2, 3, \ldots$. Write out the first five terms of the sequence.

3. Suppose the sequence $\{a_n\}$ is defined by the recurrence relation $a_{n+1} = na_n$, for $n = 1, 2, 3, \ldots$, where $a_1 = 1$. Write out the first five terms of the sequence.

4. Define *finite sum* and give an example.

5. Define *infinite series* and give an example.

6. Given the series $\sum_{k=1}^{\infty} k$, evaluate the first four terms of its sequence of partial sums $S_n = \sum_{k=1}^{n} k$.

7. The terms of a sequence of partial sums are defined by $S_n = \sum_{k=1}^{n} k^2$, for $n = 1, 2, 3, \ldots$. Evaluate the first four terms of the sequence.

8. Consider the infinite series $\sum_{k=1}^{\infty} \frac{1}{k}$. Evaluate the first four terms of the sequence of partial sums.

Basic Skills

9–16. Explicit formulas *Write the first four terms of the sequence* $\{a_n\}_{n=1}^{\infty}$.

9. $a_n = 1/10^n$

10. $a_n = 3n + 1$

11. $a_n = \dfrac{(-1)^n}{2^n}$

12. $a_n = 2 + (-1)^n$

13. $a_n = \dfrac{2^{n+1}}{2^n + 1}$

14. $a_n = n + 1/n$

15. $a_n = 1 + \sin(\pi n/2)$

16. $a_n = 2n^2 - 3n + 1$

17–22. Recurrence relations *Write the first four terms of the sequence* $\{a_n\}$ *defined by the following recurrence relations.*

17. $a_{n+1} = 2a_n; \quad a_1 = 2$

18. $a_{n+1} = a_n/2; \quad a_1 = 32$

19. $a_{n+1} = 3a_n - 12; \quad a_1 = 10$

20. $a_{n+1} = a_n^2 - 1; \quad a_1 = 1$

21. $a_{n+1} = 3a_n^2 + n + 1; \quad a_1 = 0$

22. $a_{n+1} = a_n + a_{n-1}; \quad a_1 = 1, a_0 = 1$

23–30. Working with sequences *Several terms of a sequence* $\{a_n\}_{n=1}^{\infty}$ *are given.*

a. *Find the next two terms of the sequence.*

b. *Find a recurrence relation that generates the sequence (supply the initial value of the index and the first term of the sequence).*

c. *Find an explicit formula for the nth term of the sequence.*

23. $\left\{1, \dfrac{1}{2}, \dfrac{1}{4}, \dfrac{1}{8}, \dfrac{1}{16}, \ldots\right\}$ **24.** $\{1, -2, 3, -4, 5, \ldots\}$

25. $\{-5, 5, -5, 5, \ldots\}$ **26.** $\{2, 5, 8, 11, \ldots\}$

27. $\{1, 2, 4, 8, 16, \ldots\}$ **28.** $\{1, 4, 9, 16, 25, \ldots\}$

29. $\{1, 3, 9, 27, 81, \ldots\}$ **30.** $\{64, 32, 16, 8, 4, \ldots\}$

31–40. Limits of sequences *Write the terms* $a_1, a_2, a_3,$ *and* a_4 *of the following sequences. If the sequence appears to converge, make a conjecture about its limit. If the sequence diverges, explain why.*

31. $a_n = 10^n - 1;\ n = 1, 2, 3, \ldots$

32. $a_n = n^4 + 1;\ n = 1, 2, 3, \ldots$

33. $a_n = \dfrac{1}{10^n};\ n = 1, 2, 3, \ldots$

34. $a_{n+1} = \dfrac{a_n}{10};\ a_0 = 1$

35. $a_n = \dfrac{(-1)^n}{2^n};\ n = 1, 2, 3, \ldots$

36. $a_n = 1 - 10^{-n};\ n = 1, 2, 3, \ldots$

37. $a_{n+1} = 1 + \dfrac{a_n}{2};\ a_0 = 2$

38. $a_{n+1} = 1 - \dfrac{a_n}{2};\ a_0 = \dfrac{2}{3}$

T 39. $a_{n+1} = \dfrac{a_n}{11} + 50;\ a_0 = 50$

40. $a_{n+1} = 10a_n - 1;\ a_0 = 0$

T 41–46. Explicit formulas for sequences *Consider the formulas for the following sequences. Using a calculator, make a table with at least ten terms and determine a plausible value for the limit of the sequence or state that the sequence diverges.*

41. $a_n = \cot^{-1} 2^n;\ n = 1, 2, 3, \ldots$

42. $a_n = 2 \tan^{-1}(1000n);\ n = 1, 2, 3, \ldots$

43. $a_n = n^2 - n;\ n = 1, 2, 3, \ldots$

44. $a_n = \dfrac{100n - 1}{10n};\ n = 1, 2, 3, \ldots$

45. $a_n = \dfrac{5^n}{5^n + 1};\ n = 1, 2, 3, \ldots$

46. $a_n = 2^n \sin(2^{-n});\ n = 1, 2, 3, \ldots$

47–48. Limits from graphs *Consider the following sequences.*

a. *Find the first four terms of the sequence.*

b. *Based on part (a) and the figure, determine a plausible limit of the sequence.*

47. $a_n = 2 + 2^{-n};\ n = 1, 2, 3, \ldots$

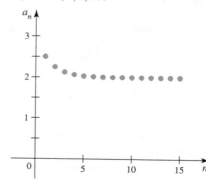

48. $a_n = \dfrac{n^2}{n^2 - 1};\ n = 2, 3, 4, \ldots$

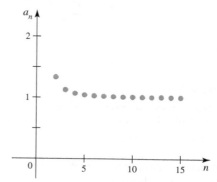

T 49–54. Recurrence relations *Consider the following recurrence relations. Using a calculator, make a table with at least ten terms and determine a plausible limit of the sequence or state that the sequence diverges.*

49. $a_{n+1} = \dfrac{1}{2}a_n + 2;\ a_0 = 3$

50. $a_n = \dfrac{1}{4}a_{n-1} - 3;\ a_0 = 1$

51. $a_{n+1} = 2a_n + 1;\ a_0 = 0$

52. $a_{n+1} = \dfrac{a_n}{10} + 3;\ a_0 = 10$

53. $a_{n+1} = \dfrac{1}{2}\sqrt{a_n} + 3;\ a_0 = 1000$

54. $a_{n+1} = \sqrt{1 + a_n};\ a_0 = 1$

55–58. Heights of bouncing balls *A ball is thrown upward to a height of* h_0 *meters. After each bounce, the ball rebounds to a fraction r of its previous height. Let* h_n *be the height after the nth bounce. Consider the following values of* h_0 *and r.*

a. *Find the first four terms of the sequence of heights* $\{h_n\}$.

b. *Find an explicit formula for the nth term of the sequence* $\{h_n\}$.

55. $h_0 = 20,\ r = 0.5$ **56.** $h_0 = 10,\ r = 0.9$

57. $h_0 = 30,\ r = 0.25$ **58.** $h_0 = 20,\ r = 0.75$

59–62. Sequences of partial sums *For the following infinite series, find the first four terms of the sequence of partial sums. Then make a conjecture about the value of the infinite series.*

59. $0.3 + 0.03 + 0.003 + \cdots$

60. $0.6 + 0.06 + 0.006 + \cdots$

61. $4 + 0.9 + 0.09 + 0.009 + \cdots$

62. $1 + \frac{1}{2} + \frac{1}{4} + \frac{1}{8} + \cdots$

63–66. Formulas for sequences of partial sums *Consider the following infinite series.*

a. *Find the first four terms of the sequence of partial sums.*
b. *Use the results of part (a) to find a formula for S_n.*
c. *Find the value of the series.*

63. $\displaystyle\sum_{k=1}^{\infty} \frac{2}{(2k-1)(2k+1)}$

64. $\displaystyle\sum_{k=1}^{\infty} \frac{1}{2^k}$

65. $\displaystyle\sum_{k=1}^{\infty} \frac{1}{4k^2-1}$

66. $\displaystyle\sum_{k=1}^{\infty} \frac{2}{3^k}$

Further Explorations

67. Explain why or why not Determine whether the following statements are true and give an explanation or counterexample.

   a. The sequence of partial sums for the series $1 + 2 + 3 + \cdots$ is $\{1, 3, 6, 10, \ldots\}$.

   b. If a sequence of positive numbers converges, then the terms of the sequence must decrease in size.

   c. If the terms of the sequence $\{a_n\}$ are positive and increasing, then the sequence of partial sums for the series $\displaystyle\sum_{k=1}^{\infty} a_k$ diverges.

68–69. Distance traveled by bouncing balls *A ball is thrown upward to a height of h_0 meters. After each bounce, the ball rebounds to a fraction r of its previous height. Let h_n be the height after the nth bounce and let S_n be the total distance the ball has traveled at the moment of the nth bounce.*

a. *Find the first four terms of the sequence $\{S_n\}$.*
b. *Make a table of 20 terms of the sequence $\{S_n\}$ and determine a plausible value for the limit of $\{S_n\}$.*

68. $h_0 = 20,\ r = 0.5$

69. $h_0 = 20,\ r = 0.75$

70–77. Sequences of partial sums *Consider the following infinite series.*

a. *Write out the first four terms of the sequence of partial sums.*
b. *Estimate the limit of $\{S_n\}$ or state that it does not exist.*

70. $\displaystyle\sum_{k=1}^{\infty} \cos \pi k$

71. $\displaystyle\sum_{k=1}^{\infty} 9(0.1)^k$

72. $\displaystyle\sum_{k=1}^{\infty} 1.5^k$

73. $\displaystyle\sum_{k=1}^{\infty} 3^{-k}$

74. $\displaystyle\sum_{k=1}^{\infty} k$

75. $\displaystyle\sum_{k=1}^{\infty} (-1)^k$

76. $\displaystyle\sum_{k=1}^{\infty} (-1)^k k$

77. $\displaystyle\sum_{k=1}^{\infty} \frac{3}{10^k}$

Applications

78–81. Practical sequences *Consider the following situations that generate a sequence.*

a. *Write out the first five terms of the sequence.*
b. *Find an explicit formula for the terms of the sequence.*
c. *Find a recurrence relation that generates the sequence.*
d. *Using a calculator or a graphing utility, estimate the limit of the sequence or state that it does not exist.*

78. Population growth When a biologist begins a study, a colony of prairie dogs has a population of 250. Regular measurements reveal that each month the prairie dog population increases by 3%. Let p_n be the population (rounded to whole numbers) at the end of the nth month, where the initial population is $p_0 = 250$.

79. Radioactive decay A material transmutes 50% of its mass to another element every 10 years due to radioactive decay. Let M_n be the mass of the radioactive material at the end of the nth decade, where the initial mass of the material is $M_0 = 20$ g.

80. Consumer Price Index The Consumer Price Index (the CPI is a measure of the U.S. cost of living) is given a base value of 100 in the year 1984. Assume the CPI has increased by an average of 3% per year since 1984. Let c_n be the CPI n years after 1984, where $c_0 = 100$.

81. Drug elimination Jack took a 200-mg dose of a painkiller at midnight. Every hour, 5% of the drug is washed out of his bloodstream. Let d_n be the amount of drug in Jack's blood n hours after the drug was taken, where $d_0 = 200$ mg.

82. A square root finder A well-known method for approximating $\sqrt{c}$ for a positive real number c consists of the following recurrence relation (based on Newton's method; see Section 4.8). Let $a_0 = c$ and

$$a_{n+1} = \frac{1}{2}\left(a_n + \frac{c}{a_n}\right), \qquad \text{for } n = 0, 1, 2, 3, \ldots.$$

a. Use this recurrence relation to approximate $\sqrt{10}$. How many terms of the sequence are needed to approximate $\sqrt{10}$ with an error less than 0.01? How many terms of the sequence are needed to approximate $\sqrt{10}$ with an error less than 0.0001? (To compute the error, assume a calculator gives the exact value.)
b. Use this recurrence relation to approximate $\sqrt{c}$, for $c = 2, 3, \ldots, 10$. Make a table showing the number of terms of the sequence needed to approximate $\sqrt{c}$ with an error less than 0.01.

QUICK CHECK ANSWERS

1. $a_{10} = 28$ **2.** $a_n = 2^n - 1,\ n = 1, 2, 3, \ldots$
3. $0.33333\ldots = \frac{1}{3}$ **4.** Both diverge. **5.** $S_1 = -1, S_2 = 1,$
$S_3 = -2, S_4 = 2$; the series diverges. ◄

8.2 Sequences

The previous section sets the stage for an in-depth investigation of sequences and infinite series. This section is devoted to sequences, and the remainder of the chapter deals with series.

Limit of a Sequence and Limit Laws

A fundamental question about sequences concerns the behavior of the terms as we go out farther and farther in the sequence. For example, in the sequence

$$\{a_n\}_{n=0}^{\infty} = \left\{\frac{1}{n^2 + 1}\right\}_{n=0}^{\infty} = \left\{1, \frac{1}{2}, \frac{1}{5}, \frac{1}{10}, \dots\right\},$$

the terms remain positive and decrease to 0. We say that this sequence converges and its limit is 0, written $\lim\limits_{n\to\infty} a_n = 0$. Similarly, the terms of the sequence

$$\{b_n\}_{n=1}^{\infty} = \left\{(-1)^n \frac{n(n+1)}{2}\right\}_{n=1}^{\infty} = \{-1, 3, -6, 10, \dots\}$$

increase in magnitude and do not approach a unique value as n increases. In this case, we say that the sequence diverges.

Limits of sequences are really no different from limits at infinity of functions except that the variable n assumes only integer values as $n \to \infty$. This idea works as follows.

Given a sequence $\{a_n\}$, we define a function f such that $f(n) = a_n$ for all indices n. For example, if $a_n = n/(n+1)$, then we let $f(x) = x/(x+1)$. By the methods of Section 2.5, we know that $\lim\limits_{x\to\infty} f(x) = 1$; because the terms of the sequence lie on the graph of f, it follows that $\lim\limits_{n\to\infty} a_n = 1$ (Figure 8.11). This reasoning is the basis of the following theorem.

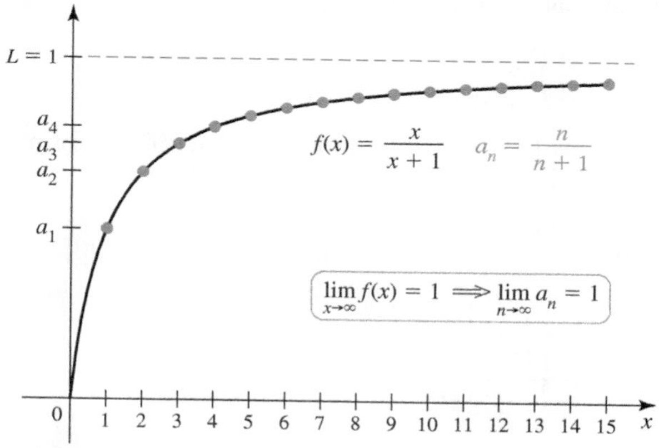

$$f(x) = \frac{x}{x+1} \qquad a_n = \frac{n}{n+1}$$

$$\lim_{x\to\infty} f(x) = 1 \implies \lim_{n\to\infty} a_n = 1$$

Figure 8.11

> The converse of Theorem 8.1 is not true. For example, if $a_n = \cos 2\pi n$, then $\lim\limits_{n\to\infty} a_n = 1$, but $\lim\limits_{x\to\infty} \cos 2\pi x$ does not exist.

THEOREM 8.1   Limits of Sequences from Limits of Functions

Suppose f is a function such that $f(n) = a_n$ for all positive integers n. If $\lim\limits_{x\to\infty} f(x) = L$, then the limit of the sequence $\{a_n\}$ is also L.

Because of the correspondence between limits of sequences and limits of functions at infinity, we have the following properties that are analogous to those for functions given in Theorem 2.3.

> The limit of a sequence $\{a_n\}$ is determined by the terms in the *tail* of the sequence—the terms with large values of n. If the sequences $\{a_n\}$ and $\{b_n\}$ differ in their first 100 terms but have identical terms for $n > 100$, then they have the same limit. For this reason, the initial index of a sequence (for example, $n = 0$ or $n = 1$) is often not specified.

THEOREM 8.2   Limit Laws for Sequences

Assume that the sequences $\{a_n\}$ and $\{b_n\}$ have limits A and B, respectively. Then

1. $\lim\limits_{n\to\infty} (a_n \pm b_n) = A \pm B$

2. $\lim\limits_{n\to\infty} ca_n = cA$, where c is a real number

3. $\lim\limits_{n\to\infty} a_n b_n = AB$

4. $\lim\limits_{n\to\infty} \dfrac{a_n}{b_n} = \dfrac{A}{B}$, provided $B \neq 0$.

EXAMPLE 1   Limits of sequences Determine the limits of the following sequences.

a. $a_n = \dfrac{3n^3}{n^3 + 1}$ **b.** $b_n = \left(\dfrac{n + 5}{n}\right)^n$ **c.** $c_n = n^{1/n}$

SOLUTION

a. A function with the property that $f(n) = a_n$ is $f(x) = \dfrac{3x^3}{x^3 + 1}$. Dividing numerator and denominator by x^3 (or appealing to Theorem 2.7), we find that $\lim\limits_{x \to \infty} f(x) = 3$. (Alternatively, we can apply l'Hôpital's Rule and obtain the same result.) We conclude that $\lim\limits_{n \to \infty} a_n = 3$.

b. The limit

$$\lim_{n \to \infty} b_n = \lim_{n \to \infty} \left(\frac{n + 5}{n}\right)^n = \lim_{n \to \infty} \left(1 + \frac{5}{n}\right)^n$$

has the indeterminate form 1^∞. Recall that for this limit (Section 4.7), we first evaluate

$$L = \lim_{n \to \infty} \ln\left(1 + \frac{5}{n}\right)^n = \lim_{n \to \infty} n \ln\left(1 + \frac{5}{n}\right),$$

> When using l'Hôpital's Rule, it is customary to treat n as a continuous variable and differentiate with respect to n, rather than write the sequence as a function of x, as was done in Example 1a.

and then, if L exists, $\lim\limits_{n \to \infty} b_n = e^L$. Using l'Hôpital's Rule for the indeterminate form $0/0$, we have

$$L = \lim_{n \to \infty} n \ln\left(1 + \frac{5}{n}\right) = \lim_{n \to \infty} \frac{\ln\left(1 + (5/n)\right)}{1/n} \qquad \text{Indeterminate form } 0/0$$

$$= \lim_{n \to \infty} \frac{\dfrac{1}{1 + (5/n)}\left(-\dfrac{5}{n^2}\right)}{-1/n^2} \qquad \text{L'Hôpital's Rule}$$

$$= \lim_{n \to \infty} \frac{5}{1 + (5/n)} = 5. \qquad \text{Simplify; } 5/n \to 0 \text{ as } n \to \infty.$$

> For a review of l'Hôpital's Rule, see Section 4.7, where we showed that
> $$\lim_{x \to \infty} \left(1 + \frac{a}{x}\right)^x = e^a.$$

Because $\lim\limits_{n \to \infty} b_n = e^L = e^5$, we have $\lim\limits_{n \to \infty} \left(\dfrac{5 + n}{n}\right)^n = e^5$.

c. The limit has the indeterminate form ∞^0, so we first evaluate $L = \lim\limits_{n \to \infty} \ln n^{1/n} = \lim\limits_{n \to \infty} \dfrac{\ln n}{n}$; if L exists, then $\lim\limits_{n \to \infty} c_n = e^L$. Using either l'Hôpital's Rule or the relative growth rates in Section 4.7, we find that $L = 0$. Therefore, $\lim\limits_{n \to \infty} c_n = e^0 = 1$.

Related Exercises 9–34 ◄

Terminology for Sequences

We now introduce some terminology for sequences that is similar to that used for functions. The following terms are used to describe sequences $\{a_n\}$.

> Because an increasing sequence is, by definition, nondecreasing, it is also monotonic. Similarly, a decreasing sequence is monotonic.

DEFINITIONS   Terminology for Sequences

$\{a_n\}$ is **increasing** if $a_{n+1} > a_n$; for example, $\{0, 1, 2, 3, \dots\}$.

$\{a_n\}$ is **nondecreasing** if $a_{n+1} \ge a_n$; for example, $\{1, 1, 2, 2, 3, 3, \dots\}$.

$\{a_n\}$ is **decreasing** if $a_{n+1} < a_n$; for example, $\{2, 1, 0, -1, \dots\}$.

$\{a_n\}$ is **nonincreasing** if $a_{n+1} \le a_n$; for example, $\{0, -1, -1, -2, -2, -3, -3, \dots\}$.

$\{a_n\}$ is **monotonic** if it is either nonincreasing or nondecreasing (it moves in one direction).

$\{a_n\}$ is **bounded** if there is number M such that $|a_n| \le M$, for all relevant values of n.

For example, the sequence

$$\{a_n\} = \left\{1 - \frac{1}{n}\right\}_{n=1}^{\infty} = \left\{0, \frac{1}{2}, \frac{2}{3}, \frac{3}{4}, \ldots\right\}$$

satisfies $|a_n| \leq 1$, for $n \geq 1$, and it terms are increasing in size. Therefore, the sequence is bounded and increasing; it is also monotonic (Figure 8.12). The sequence

$$\{a_n\} = \left\{1 + \frac{1}{n}\right\}_{n=1}^{\infty} = \left\{2, \frac{3}{2}, \frac{4}{3}, \frac{5}{4}, \ldots\right\}$$

satisfies $|a_n| \leq 2$, for $n \geq 1$, and it terms are decreasing in size. Therefore, the sequence is bounded and decreasing; it is also monotonic (Figure 8.12).

QUICK CHECK 1 Classify the following sequences as bounded, monotonic, or neither.

a. $\left\{\frac{1}{2}, \frac{3}{4}, \frac{7}{8}, \frac{15}{16}, \ldots\right\}$

b. $\left\{1, -\frac{1}{2}, \frac{1}{4}, -\frac{1}{8}, \frac{1}{16}, \ldots\right\}$

c. $\{1, -2, 3, -4, 5, \ldots\}$

d. $\{1, 1, 1, 1, \ldots\}$ ◄

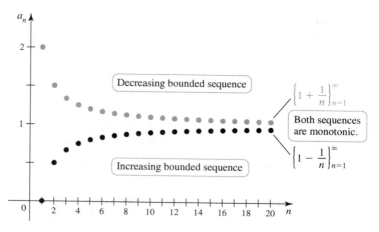

Figure 8.12

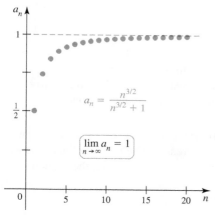

Figure 8.13

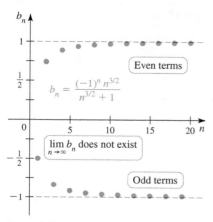

Figure 8.14

EXAMPLE 2 **Limits of sequences and graphing** Compare and contrast the behavior of $\{a_n\}$ and $\{b_n\}$ as $n \to \infty$.

a. $a_n = \dfrac{n^{3/2}}{n^{3/2} + 1}$ **b.** $b_n = \dfrac{(-1)^n n^{3/2}}{n^{3/2} + 1}$

SOLUTION

a. The terms of $\{a_n\}$ are positive, increasing, and bounded (Figure 8.13). Dividing the numerator and denominator of a_n by $n^{3/2}$, we see that

$$\lim_{n \to \infty} a_n = \lim_{n \to \infty} \frac{n^{3/2}}{n^{3/2} + 1} = \lim_{n \to \infty} \frac{1}{1 + \underbrace{\frac{1}{n^{3/2}}}_{\text{approaches 0 as } n \to \infty}} = 1.$$

b. The terms of the bounded sequence $\{b_n\}$ alternate in sign. Using the result of part (a), it follows that the even terms form an increasing sequence that approaches 1 and the odd terms form a decreasing sequence that approaches -1 (Figure 8.14). Therefore, the sequence diverges, illustrating the fact that the presence of $(-1)^n$ may significantly alter the behavior of a sequence.

Related Exercises 35–44 ◄

Geometric Sequences

Geometric sequences have the property that each term is obtained by multiplying the previous term by a fixed constant, called the **ratio**. They have the form $\{r^n\}$ or $\{ar^n\}$, where the ratio r and $a \neq 0$ are real numbers.

EXAMPLE 3   **Geometric sequences**   Graph the following sequences and discuss their behavior.

a. $\{0.75^n\}$ **b.** $\{(-0.75)^n\}$ **c.** $\{1.15^n\}$ **d.** $\{(-1.15)^n\}$

SOLUTION

a. When a number less than 1 in magnitude is raised to increasing powers, the resulting numbers decrease to zero. The sequence $\{0.75^n\}$ converges to zero and is monotonic (Figure 8.15).

b. Note that $\{(-0.75)^n\} = \{(-1)^n 0.75^n\}$. Observe also that the factor $(-1)^n$ oscillates between 1 and -1, while 0.75^n decreases to zero as n increases. Therefore, the sequence oscillates and converges to zero (Figure 8.16).

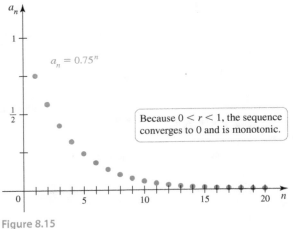

Because $0 < r < 1$, the sequence converges to 0 and is monotonic.

$a_n = 0.75^n$

Figure 8.15

Because $(-r)^n = (-1)^n r^n$ and $0 < r < 1$, the sequence oscillates *and* converges to 0.

$a_n = (-0.75)^n$

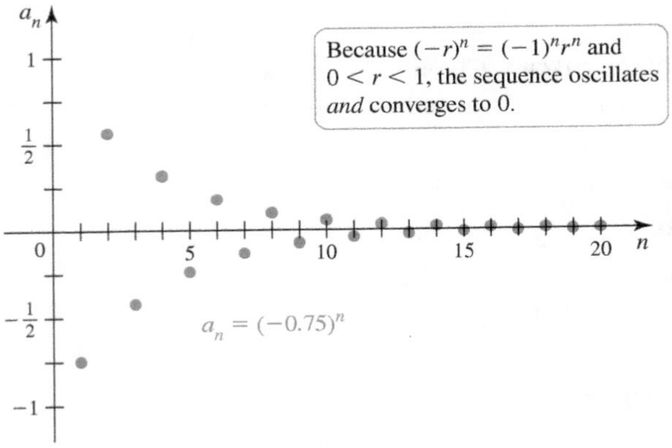

Figure 8.16

c. When a number greater than 1 in magnitude is raised to increasing powers, the resulting numbers increase in magnitude. The terms of the sequence $\{1.15^n\}$ are positive and increase without bound. In this case, the sequence diverges and is monotonic (Figure 8.17).

d. We write $\{(-1.15)^n\} = \{(-1)^n 1.15^n\}$ and observe that $(-1)^n$ oscillates between 1 and -1, while 1.15^n increases without bound as n increases. The terms of the sequence increase in magnitude without bound and alternate in sign. In this case, the sequence oscillates and diverges (Figure 8.18).

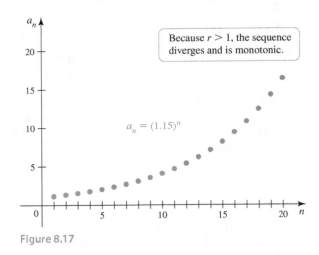

Because $r > 1$, the sequence diverges and is monotonic.

$a_n = (1.15)^n$

Figure 8.17

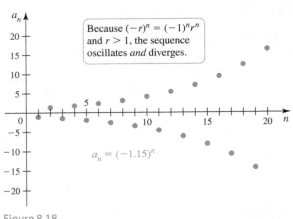

Because $(-r)^n = (-1)^n r^n$ and $r > 1$, the sequence oscillates *and* diverges.

$a_n = (-1.15)^n$

Figure 8.18

Related Exercises 45–52 ◄

QUICK CHECK 2   Describe the behavior of $\{r^n\}$ in the cases $r = -1$ and $r = 1$. ◄

The results of Example 3 and Quick Check 2 are summarized in the following theorem.

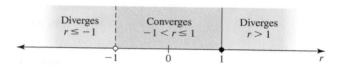

> **THEOREM 8.3   Geometric Sequences**
> Let r be a real number. Then
> $$\lim_{n \to \infty} r^n = \begin{cases} 0 & \text{if } |r| < 1 \\ 1 & \text{if } r = 1 \\ \text{does not exist} & \text{if } r \le -1 \text{ or } r > 1. \end{cases}$$
> If $r > 0$, then $\{r^n\}$ is a monotonic sequence. If $r < 0$, then $\{r^n\}$ oscillates.
>
> | Diverges $r \le -1$ | Converges $-1 < r \le 1$ | Diverges $r > 1$ |

The previous examples show that a sequence may display any of the following behaviors:

- It may converge to a single value, which is the limit of the sequence.
- Its terms may increase in magnitude without bound (either with one sign or with mixed signs), in which case the sequence diverges.
- Its terms may remain bounded but settle into an oscillating pattern in which the terms approach two or more values; in this case, the sequence diverges.

Not illustrated in the preceding examples is one other type of behavior: The terms of a sequence may remain bounded, but wander chaotically forever without a pattern. In this case, the sequence also diverges (see the Guided Project *Chaos!*)

The Squeeze Theorem

We cite two theorems that are used to evaluate limits and to establish that limits exist. The first theorem is a direct analog of the Squeeze Theorem from Section 2.3.

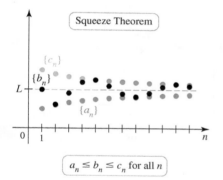

Figure 8.19

> **THEOREM 8.4   Squeeze Theorem for Sequences**
> Let $\{a_n\}$, $\{b_n\}$, and $\{c_n\}$ be sequences with $a_n \le b_n \le c_n$ for all integers n greater than some index N. If $\lim_{n \to \infty} a_n = \lim_{n \to \infty} c_n = L$, then $\lim_{n \to \infty} b_n = L$ (Figure 8.19).

EXAMPLE 4   Squeeze Theorem Find the limit of the sequence $b_n = \dfrac{\cos n}{n^2 + 1}$.

SOLUTION The goal is to find two sequences $\{a_n\}$ and $\{c_n\}$ whose terms lie below and above the terms of the given sequence $\{b_n\}$. Note that $-1 \le \cos n \le 1$, for all n. Therefore,

$$\underbrace{-\frac{1}{n^2 + 1}}_{a_n} \le \underbrace{\frac{\cos n}{n^2 + 1}}_{b_n} \le \underbrace{\frac{1}{n^2 + 1}}_{c_n}.$$

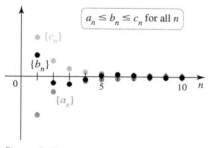

Figure 8.20

Letting $a_n = -\dfrac{1}{n^2 + 1}$ and $c_n = \dfrac{1}{n^2 + 1}$, we have $a_n \le b_n \le c_n$, for $n \ge 1$. Furthermore, $\lim_{n \to \infty} a_n = \lim_{n \to \infty} c_n = 0$. By the Squeeze Theorem, $\lim_{n \to \infty} b_n = 0$ (Figure 8.20).

Related Exercises 53–58 ◄

Bounded Monotonic Sequence Theorem

Suppose you pour a cup of hot coffee and put it on your desk to cool. Assume that every minute you measure the temperature of the coffee to create a sequence of temperature readings $\{T_1, T_2, T_3, \ldots\}$. This sequence has two notable properties: First, the terms of the sequence are decreasing (because the coffee is cooling); and second, the sequence is bounded below (because the temperature of the coffee cannot be less than the temperature of the surrounding room). In fact, if the measurements continue indefinitely, the sequence of temperatures converges to the temperature of the room. This example illustrates an important theorem that characterizes convergent sequences in terms of boundedness and monotonicity. The theorem is easy to believe, but its proof is beyond the scope of this text.

THEOREM 8.5   Bounded Monotonic Sequences

A bounded monotonic sequence converges.

> **Some optional terminology** M is called an *upper bound* of the first sequence in Figure 8.21a, and N is a *lower bound* of the second sequence in Figure 8.21b. The number M^* is the *least upper bound* of a sequence (or a set) if it is the smallest of all the upper bounds. It is a fundamental property of the real numbers that if a sequence (or a nonempty set) is bounded above, then it has a least upper bound. It can be shown that an increasing sequence that is bounded above converges to its least upper bound. Similarly, a decreasing sequence that is bounded below converges to its greatest lower bound.

Figure 8.21 shows the two cases of this theorem. In the first case, we see a nondecreasing sequence, all of whose terms are less than M. It must converge to a limit less than or equal to M. Similarly, a nonincreasing sequence, all of whose terms are greater than N, must converge to a limit greater than or equal to N.

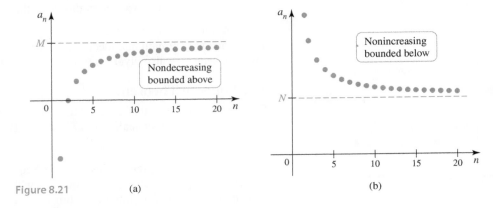

Figure 8.21   (a)   (b)

An Application: Recurrence Relations

> Most drugs decay exponentially in the bloodstream and have a characteristic half-life assuming that the drug absorbs quickly into the blood.

EXAMPLE 5   Sequences for drug doses Suppose your doctor prescribes a 100-mg dose of an antibiotic to be taken every 12 hours. Furthermore, the drug is known to have a half-life of 12 hours; that is, every 12 hours half of the drug in your blood is eliminated.

a. Find the sequence that gives the amount of drug in your blood immediately after each dose.

b. Use a graph to propose the limit of this sequence; that is, in the long run, how much drug do you have in your blood?

c. Find the limit of the sequence directly.

SOLUTION

a. Let d_n be the amount of drug in the blood immediately following the nth dose, where $n = 1, 2, 3, \ldots$ and $d_1 = 100$ mg. We want to write a recurrence relation that gives the amount of drug in the blood after the $(n + 1)$st dose (d_{n+1}) in terms of the amount of drug after the nth dose (d_n). In the 12 hours between the nth dose and the $(n + 1)$st dose, half of the drug in the blood is eliminated *and* another 100 mg of drug is added. So we have

$$d_{n+1} = 0.5\,d_n + 100, \qquad \text{for } n = 1, 2, 3, \ldots, \text{ with } d_1 = 100,$$

which is the recurrence relation for the sequence $\{d_n\}$.

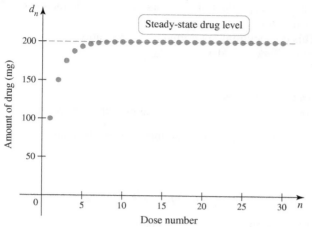

Figure 8.22

b. We see from Figure 8.22 that after about 10 doses (5 days) the amount of antibiotic in the blood is close to 200 mg, and—importantly for your body—it never exceeds 200 mg.

c. The graph of part (b) gives evidence that the terms of the sequence are increasing and bounded (Exercise 96). By the Bounded Monotonic Sequence Theorem, the sequence has a limit; therefore, $\lim_{n \to \infty} d_n = L$ and $\lim_{n \to \infty} d_{n+1} = L$. We now take the limit of both sides of the recurrence relation:

$$d_{n+1} = 0.5\, d_n + 100 \qquad \text{Recurrence relation}$$

$$\underbrace{\lim_{n \to \infty} d_{n+1}}_{L} = 0.5 \underbrace{\lim_{n \to \infty} d_n}_{L} + \lim_{n \to \infty} 100 \qquad \text{Limits of both sides}$$

$$L = 0.5L + 100. \qquad \text{Substitute } L.$$

Solving for L, the steady-state drug level is $L = 200$.

Related Exercises 59–62 ◀

QUICK CHECK 3 If a drug has the same half-life as in Example 5, (i) how would the steady-state level of drug in the blood change if the regular dose were 150 mg instead of 100 mg? (ii) How would the steady-state level change if the dosing interval were 6 hr instead of 12 hr? ◀

Growth Rates of Sequences

All the hard work we did in Section 4.7 to establish the relative growth rates of functions is now applied to sequences. Here is the question: Given two nondecreasing sequences of positive terms $\{a_n\}$ and $\{b_n\}$, which sequence grows faster as $n \to \infty$? As with functions, to compare growth rates, we evaluate $\lim_{n \to \infty} a_n/b_n$. If $\lim_{n \to \infty} a_n/b_n = 0$, then $\{b_n\}$ grows faster than $\{a_n\}$. If $\lim_{n \to \infty} a_n/b_n = \infty$, then $\{a_n\}$ grows faster than $\{b_n\}$.

Using the results of Section 4.7, we immediately arrive at the following ranking of growth rates of sequences as $n \to \infty$, with positive real numbers p, q, r, s, and $b > 1$:

$$\{\ln^q n\} \ll \{n^p\} \ll \{n^p \ln^r n\} \ll \{n^{p+s}\} \ll \{b^n\} \ll \{n^n\}.$$

➤ 0! = 1 (by definition)

1! = 1

2! = 2 · 1! = 2

3! = 3 · 2! = 6

4! = 4 · 3! = 24

5! = 5 · 4! = 120

6! = 6 · 5! = 720

As before, the notation $\{a_n\} \ll \{b_n\}$ means $\{b_n\}$ *grows faster than* $\{a_n\}$ as $n \to \infty$. Another important sequence that should be added to the list is the **factorial sequence** $\{n!\}$, where $n! = n(n-1)(n-2)\cdots 2 \cdot 1$. Where does the factorial sequence $\{n!\}$ appear in the list? The following argument provides some intuition. Notice that

$$n^n = \underbrace{n \cdot n \cdot n \cdots n,}_{n \text{ factors}} \qquad \text{whereas}$$

$$n! = \underbrace{n \cdot (n-1) \cdot (n-2) \cdots 2 \cdot 1.}_{n \text{ factors}}$$

The nth term of both sequences involves the product of n factors; however, the factors of $n!$ decrease, while the factors of n^n are the same. Based on this observation, we claim that $\{n^n\}$ grows faster than $\{n!\}$, and we have the ordering $\{n!\} \ll \{n^n\}$. But where does $\{n!\}$ appear in the list relative to $\{b^n\}$? Again, some intuition is gained by noting that

$$b^n = \underbrace{b \cdot b \cdot b \cdots b,}_{n \text{ factors}} \qquad \text{whereas}$$

$$n! = \underbrace{n \cdot (n-1) \cdot (n-2) \cdots 2 \cdot 1.}_{n \text{ factors}}$$

The nth term of both sequences involves a product of n factors; however, the factors of b^n remain constant as n increases, while the factors of $n!$ increase with n. So we claim that $\{n!\}$ grows faster than $\{b^n\}$. This conjecture is supported by computation, although the outcome of the race may not be immediately evident if b is large (Exercise 91).

THEOREM 8.6   Growth Rates of Sequences

The following sequences are ordered according to increasing growth rates as $n \to \infty$; that is, if $\{a_n\}$ appears before $\{b_n\}$ in the list, then $\lim\limits_{n\to\infty} \dfrac{a_n}{b_n} = 0$ and

$$\lim_{n\to\infty} \frac{b_n}{a_n} = \infty:$$

$$\{\ln^q n\} \ll \{n^p\} \ll \{n^p \ln^r n\} \ll \{n^{p+s}\} \ll \{b^n\} \ll \{n!\} \ll \{n^n\}.$$

The ordering applies for positive real numbers p, q, r, s, and $b > 1$.

QUICK CHECK 4 Which sequence grows faster: $\{\ln n\}$ or $\{n^{1.1}\}$? What is

$$\lim_{n\to\infty} \frac{n^{1,000,000}}{e^n}?$$ ◄

It is worth noting that the rankings in Theorem 8.6 do not change if a sequence is multiplied by a positive constant (Exercise 104).

EXAMPLE 6   Convergence and growth rates Compare growth rates of sequences to determine whether the following sequences converge.

a. $\left\{\dfrac{\ln n^{10}}{0.00001n}\right\}$ b. $\left\{\dfrac{n^8 \ln n}{n^{8.001}}\right\}$ c. $\left\{\dfrac{n!}{10^n}\right\}$

SOLUTION

a. Because $\ln n^{10} = 10 \ln n$, the sequence in the numerator is a constant multiple of the sequence $\{\ln n\}$. Similarly, the sequence in the denominator is a constant multiple of the sequence $\{n\}$. By Theorem 8.6, $\{n\}$ grows faster than $\{\ln n\}$ as $n \to \infty$; therefore, the sequence $\left\{\dfrac{\ln n^{10}}{0.00001n}\right\}$ converges to zero.

b. The sequence in the numerator is $\{n^p \ln^r n\}$ of Theorem 8.6 with $p = 8$ and $r = 1$. The sequence in the denominator is $\{n^{p+s}\}$ of Theorem 8.6 with $p = 8$ and $s = 0.001$. Because $\{n^{p+s}\}$ grows faster than $\{n^p \ln^r n\}$ as $n \to \infty$, we conclude that $\left\{\dfrac{n^8 \ln n}{n^{8.001}}\right\}$ converges to zero.

c. Using Theorem 8.6, we see that $n!$ grows faster than any exponential function as $n \to \infty$. Therefore, $\lim\limits_{n\to\infty} \dfrac{n!}{10^n} = \infty$, and the sequence diverges. Figure 8.23 gives a visual comparison of the growth rates of $\{n!\}$ and $\{10^n\}$. Because these sequences grow so quickly, we plot the logarithm of the terms. The exponential sequence $\{10^n\}$ dominates the factorial sequence $\{n!\}$ until $n = 25$ terms. At that point, the factorial sequence overtakes the exponential sequence.

Related Exercises 63–68 ◄

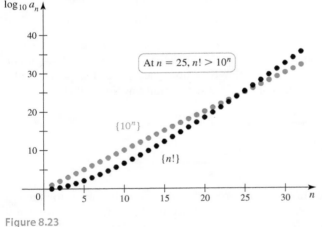

Figure 8.23

Formal Definition of a Limit of a Sequence

As with limits of functions, there is a formal definition of the limit of a sequence.

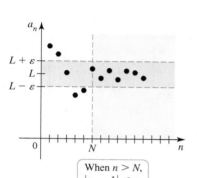

$L + \varepsilon$
L
$L - \varepsilon$

When $n > N$,
$|a_n - L| < \varepsilon$

Figure 8.24

DEFINITION Limit of a Sequence

The sequence $\{a_n\}$ converges to L provided the terms of a_n can be made arbitrarily close to L by taking n sufficiently large. More precisely, $\{a_n\}$ has the unique limit L if given any $\varepsilon > 0$, it is possible to find a positive integer N (depending only on ε) such that

$$|a_n - L| < \varepsilon \qquad \text{whenever } n > N.$$

If the **limit of a sequence** is L, we say the sequence **converges** to L, written

$$\lim_{n \to \infty} a_n = L.$$

A sequence that does not converge is said to **diverge**.

The formal definition of the limit of a convergent sequence is interpreted in much the same way as the limit at infinity of a function. Given a small tolerance $\varepsilon > 0$, how far out in the sequence must you go so that all succeeding terms are within ε of the limit L (Figure 8.24)? Given *any* value of $\varepsilon > 0$ (no matter how small), you must find a value of N such that all terms beyond a_N are within ε of L.

EXAMPLE 7 Limits using the formal definition Consider the claim that
$$\lim_{n \to \infty} a_n = \lim_{n \to \infty} \frac{n}{n-1} = 1.$$

a. Given $\varepsilon = 0.01$, find a value of N that satisfies the conditions of the limit definition.
b. Prove that $\lim_{n \to \infty} a_n = 1$.

SOLUTION

a. We must find an integer N such that $|a_n - 1| < \varepsilon = 0.01$ whenever $n > N$. This condition can be written

$$|a_n - 1| = \left| \frac{n}{n-1} - 1 \right| = \left| \frac{1}{n-1} \right| < 0.01.$$

Noting that $n > 1$, the absolute value can be removed. The condition on n becomes $n - 1 > 1/0.01 = 100$, or $n > 101$. Therefore, we take $N = 101$ or any larger number. This means that $|a_n - 1| < 0.01$ whenever $n > 101$.

b. Given *any* $\varepsilon > 0$, we must find a value of N (depending on ε) that guarantees $|a_n - 1| = \left| \dfrac{n}{n-1} - 1 \right| < \varepsilon$ whenever $n > N$. For $n > 1$, the inequality $\left| \dfrac{n}{n-1} - 1 \right| < \varepsilon$ implies that

$$\left| \frac{n}{n-1} - 1 \right| = \frac{1}{n-1} < \varepsilon.$$

Solving for n, we find that $\dfrac{1}{n-1} < \varepsilon$ or $n - 1 > \dfrac{1}{\varepsilon}$ or $n > \dfrac{1}{\varepsilon} + 1$. Therefore, given a tolerance $\varepsilon > 0$, we must look beyond a_N in the sequence, where $N \geq \dfrac{1}{\varepsilon} + 1$, to be sure that the terms of the sequence are within ε of the limit 1. Because we can provide a value of N for *any* $\varepsilon > 0$, the limit exists and equals 1.

Related Exercises 69–74 ◄

➤ In general, $1/\varepsilon + 1$ is not an integer, so N should be the least integer greater than $1/\varepsilon + 1$ or any larger integer.

SECTION 8.2 EXERCISES

Review Questions

1. Give an example of a nonincreasing sequence with a limit.

2. Give an example of a nondecreasing sequence without a limit.

3. Give an example of a bounded sequence that has a limit.

4. Give an example of a bounded sequence without a limit.

5. For what values of r does the sequence $\{r^n\}$ converge? Diverge?

6. Explain how the methods used to find the limit of a function as $x \to \infty$ are used to find the limit of a sequence.

7. Compare the growth rates of $\{n^{100}\}$ and $\{e^{n/100}\}$ as $n \to \infty$.

8. Explain how two sequences that differ only in their first ten terms can have the same limit.

Basic Skills

9–34. Limits of sequences *Find the limit of the following sequences or determine that the limit does not exist.*

9. $\left\{\dfrac{n^3}{n^4 + 1}\right\}$

10. $\left\{\dfrac{n^{12}}{3n^{12} + 4}\right\}$

11. $\left\{\dfrac{3n^3 - 1}{2n^3 + 1}\right\}$

12. $\left\{\dfrac{2e^n + 1}{e^n}\right\}$

13. $\left\{\dfrac{3^{n+1} + 3}{3^n}\right\}$

14. $\left\{\dfrac{k}{\sqrt{9k^2 + 1}}\right\}$

15. $\{\tan^{-1} n\}$

16. $\{\sqrt{n^2 + 1} - n\}$

17. $\left\{\dfrac{\tan^{-1} n}{n}\right\}$

18. $\{n^{2/n}\}$

19. $\left\{\left(1 + \dfrac{2}{n}\right)^n\right\}$

20. $\left\{\left(\dfrac{n}{n + 5}\right)^n\right\}$

21. $\left\{\sqrt{\left(1 + \dfrac{1}{2n}\right)^n}\right\}$

22. $\left\{\left(1 + \dfrac{4}{n}\right)^{3n}\right\}$

23. $\left\{\dfrac{n}{e^n + 3n}\right\}$

24. $\left\{\dfrac{\ln (1/n)}{n}\right\}$

25. $\left\{\left(\dfrac{1}{n}\right)^{1/n}\right\}$

26. $\left\{\left(1 - \dfrac{4}{n}\right)^n\right\}$

27. $\{b_n\}$, where $b_n = \begin{cases} n/(n + 1) & \text{if } n \le 5000 \\ ne^{-n} & \text{if } n > 5000 \end{cases}$

28. $\{\ln (n^3 + 1) - \ln (3n^3 + 10n)\}$

29. $\{\ln \sin (1/n) + \ln n\}$

30. $\{n(1 - \cos(1/n))\}$

31. $\left\{n \sin \dfrac{6}{n}\right\}$

32. $\left\{\dfrac{(-1)^n}{n}\right\}$

33. $\left\{\dfrac{(-1)^n n}{n + 1}\right\}$

34. $\left\{\dfrac{(-1)^{n+1} n^2}{2n^3 + n}\right\}$

[T] 35–44. Limits of sequences and graphing *Find the limit of the following sequences or determine that the limit does not exist. Verify your result with a graphing utility.*

35. $a_n = \sin \dfrac{n\pi}{2}$

36. $a_n = \dfrac{(-1)^n n}{n + 1}$

37. $a_n = \dfrac{\sin (n\pi/3)}{\sqrt{n}}$

38. $a_n = \dfrac{3^n}{3^n + 4^n}$

39. $a_n = 1 + \cos \dfrac{1}{n}$

40. $a_n = \dfrac{e^{-n}}{2 \sin(e^{-n})}$

41. $a_n = e^{-n} \cos n$

42. $a_n = \dfrac{\ln n}{n^{1.1}}$

43. $a_n = (-1)^n \sqrt[n]{n}$

44. $a_n = \cot\left(\dfrac{n\pi}{2n + 2}\right)$

45–52. Geometric sequences *Determine whether the following sequences converge or diverge, and state whether they are monotonic or whether they oscillate. Give the limit when the sequence converges.*

45. $\{0.2^n\}$

46. $\{1.2^n\}$

47. $\{(-0.7)^n\}$

48. $\{5(-1.01)^n\}$

49. $\{1.00001^n\}$

50. $\{2^{n+1} 3^{-n}\}$

51. $\{(-2.5)^n\}$

52. $\{100(-0.003)^n\}$

53–58. Squeeze Theorem *Find the limit of the following sequences or state that they diverge.*

53. $\left\{\dfrac{\cos n}{n}\right\}$

54. $\left\{\dfrac{\sin 6n}{5n}\right\}$

55. $\left\{\dfrac{\sin n}{2^n}\right\}$

56. $\left\{\dfrac{\cos (n\pi/2)}{\sqrt{n}}\right\}$

57. $\left\{\dfrac{2 \tan^{-1} n}{n^3 + 4}\right\}$

58. $\left\{\dfrac{n \sin^3 (n\pi/2)}{n + 1}\right\}$

[T] 59. Periodic dosing Many people take aspirin on a regular basis as a preventive measure for heart disease. Suppose a person takes 80 mg of aspirin every 24 hours. Assume also that aspirin has a half-life of 24 hours; that is, every 24 hours, half of the drug in the blood is eliminated.

a. Find a recurrence relation for the sequence $\{d_n\}$ that gives the amount of drug in the blood after the nth dose, where $d_1 = 80$.

b. Using a calculator, determine the limit of the sequence. In the long run, how much drug is in the person's blood?

c. Confirm the result of part (b) by finding the limit of $\{d_n\}$ directly.

[T] 60. A car loan Marie takes out a $20,000 loan for a new car. The loan has an annual interest rate of 6% or, equivalently, a monthly interest rate of 0.5%. Each month, the bank adds interest to the loan balance (the interest is always 0.5% of the current balance), and then Marie makes a $200 payment to reduce the loan balance. Let B_n be the loan balance immediately after the nth payment, where $B_0 = $20,000$.

a. Write the first five terms of the sequence $\{B_n\}$.

b. Find a recurrence relation that generates the sequence $\{B_n\}$.

c. Determine how many months are needed to reduce the loan balance to zero.

[T] 61. A savings plan James begins a savings plan in which he deposits $100 at the beginning of each month into an account that earns 9% interest annually or, equivalently, 0.75% per month. To be clear, on the first day of each month, the bank adds 0.75% of the current balance as interest, and then James deposits $100. Let B_n be the balance in the account after the nth deposit, where $B_0 = 0.

a. Write the first five terms of the sequence $\{B_n\}$.

b. Find a recurrence relation that generates the sequence $\{B_n\}$.

c. How many months are needed to reach a balance of $5000?

T 62. Diluting a solution A tank is filled with 100 L of a 40% alcohol solution (by volume). You repeatedly perform the following operation: Remove 2 L of the solution from the tank and replace them with 2 L of 10% alcohol solution.

a. Let C_n be the concentration of the solution in the tank after the nth replacement, where $C_0 = 40\%$. Write the first five terms of the sequence $\{C_n\}$.

b. After how many replacements does the alcohol concentration reach 15%?

c. Determine the limiting (steady-state) concentration of the solution that is approached after many replacements.

63–68. Growth rates of sequences *Use Theorem 8.6 to find the limit of the following sequences or state that they diverge.*

63. $\left\{\dfrac{n!}{n^n}\right\}$

64. $\left\{\dfrac{3^n}{n!}\right\}$

65. $\left\{\dfrac{n^{10}}{\ln^{20} n}\right\}$

66. $\left\{\dfrac{n^{10}}{\ln^{1000} n}\right\}$

67. $\left\{\dfrac{n^{1000}}{2^n}\right\}$

68. $\left\{\dfrac{e^{n/10}}{2^n}\right\}$

69–74. Formal proofs of limits *Use the formal definition of the limit of a sequence to prove the following limits.*

69. $\lim\limits_{n\to\infty} \dfrac{1}{n} = 0$

70. $\lim\limits_{n\to\infty} \dfrac{1}{n^2} = 0$

71. $\lim\limits_{n\to\infty} \dfrac{3n^2}{4n^2+1} = \dfrac{3}{4}$

72. $\lim\limits_{n\to\infty} b^{-n} = 0$, for $b > 1$

73. $\lim\limits_{n\to\infty} \dfrac{cn}{bn+1} = \dfrac{c}{b}$, for real numbers $b > 0$ and $c > 0$

74. $\lim\limits_{n\to\infty} \dfrac{n}{n^2+1} = 0$

Further Explorations

75. **Explain why or why not** Determine whether the following statements are true and give an explanation or counterexample.

a. If $\lim\limits_{n\to\infty} a_n = 1$ and $\lim\limits_{n\to\infty} b_n = 3$, then $\lim\limits_{n\to\infty} \dfrac{b_n}{a_n} = 3$.

b. If $\lim\limits_{n\to\infty} a_n = 0$ and $\lim\limits_{n\to\infty} b_n = \infty$, then $\lim\limits_{n\to\infty} a_n b_n = 0$.

c. The convergent sequences $\{a_n\}$ and $\{b_n\}$ differ in their first 100 terms, but $a_n = b_n$, for $n > 100$. It follows that $\lim\limits_{n\to\infty} a_n = \lim\limits_{n\to\infty} b_n$.

d. If $\{a_n\} = \left\{1, \frac{1}{2}, \frac{1}{3}, \frac{1}{4}, \frac{1}{5}, \ldots\right\}$ and $\{b_n\} = \left\{1, 0, \frac{1}{2}, 0, \frac{1}{3}, 0, \frac{1}{4}, 0, \ldots\right\}$, then $\lim\limits_{n\to\infty} a_n = \lim\limits_{n\to\infty} b_n$.

e. If the sequence $\{a_n\}$ converges, then the sequence $\{(-1)^n a_n\}$ converges.

f. If the sequence $\{a_n\}$ diverges, then the sequence $\{0.000001 a_n\}$ diverges.

76–77. Reindexing *Express each sequence $\{a_n\}_{n=1}^{\infty}$ as an equivalent sequence of the form $\{b_n\}_{n=3}^{\infty}$.*

76. $\{2n + 1\}_{n=1}^{\infty}$

77. $\{n^2 + 6n - 9\}_{n=1}^{\infty}$

78–85. More sequences *Evaluate the limit of the following sequences or state that the limit does not exist.*

78. $a_n = \displaystyle\int_1^n x^{-2}\, dx$

79. $a_n = \dfrac{75^{n-1}}{99^n} + \dfrac{5^n \sin n}{8^n}$

80. $a_n = \tan^{-1}\left(\dfrac{10n}{10n+4}\right)$

81. $a_n = \cos(0.99^n) + \dfrac{7^n + 9^n}{63^n}$

82. $a_n = \dfrac{4^n + 5n!}{n! + 2^n}$

83. $a_n = \dfrac{6^n + 3^n}{6^n + n^{100}}$

84. $a_n = \dfrac{n^8 + n^7}{n^7 + n^8 \ln n}$

85. $a_n = \dfrac{7^n}{n^7 5^n}$

T 86–90. Sequences by recurrence relations *Consider the following sequences defined by a recurrence relation. Use a calculator, analytical methods, and/or graphing to make a conjecture about the limit of the sequence or state that the sequence diverges.*

86. $a_{n+1} = \frac{1}{2}a_n + 2;\ a_0 = 5$

87. $a_{n+1} = 2a_n(1 - a_n);\ a_0 = 0.3$

88. $a_{n+1} = \frac{1}{2}(a_n + 2/a_n);\ a_0 = 2$

89. $a_{n+1} = 4a_n(1 - a_n);\ a_0 = 0.5$

90. $a_{n+1} = \sqrt{2 + a_n};\ a_0 = 1$

T 91. Crossover point The sequence $\{n!\}$ ultimately grows faster than the sequence $\{b^n\}$, for any $b > 1$, as $n \to \infty$. However, b^n is generally greater than $n!$ for small values of n. Use a calculator to determine the smallest value of n such that $n! > b^n$ for each of the cases $b = 2$, $b = e$, and $b = 10$.

Applications

T 92. Fish harvesting A fishery manager knows that her fish population naturally increases at a rate of 1.5% per month, while 80 fish are harvested each month. Let F_n be the fish population after the nth month, where $F_0 = 4000$ fish.

a. Write out the first five terms of the sequence $\{F_n\}$.

b. Find a recurrence relation that generates the sequence $\{F_n\}$.

c. Does the fish population decrease or increase in the long run?

d. Determine whether the fish population decreases or increases in the long run if the initial population is 5500 fish.

e. Determine the initial fish population F_0 below which the population decreases.

T 93. The hungry heifer A heifer weighing 200 lb today gains 5 lb per day with a food cost of 45¢/day. The price for heifers is 65¢/lb today but is falling 1¢/day.

a. Let h_n be the profit in selling the heifer on the nth day, where $h_0 = (200\text{ lb}) \cdot (\$0.65/\text{lb}) = \$130$. Write out the first 10 terms of the sequence $\{h_n\}$.

b. How many days after today should the heifer be sold to maximize the profit?

T 94. Sleep model After many nights of observation, you notice that if you oversleep one night, you tend to undersleep the following night, and vice versa. This pattern of compensation is described by the relationship

$$x_{n+1} = \frac{1}{2}(x_n + x_{n-1}), \quad \text{for } n = 1, 2, 3, \ldots,$$

where x_n is the number of hours of sleep you get on the nth night and $x_0 = 7$ and $x_1 = 6$ are the number of hours of sleep on the first two nights, respectively.

a. Write out the first six terms of the sequence $\{x_n\}$ and confirm that the terms alternately increase and decrease.

b. Show that the explicit formula

$$x_n = \frac{19}{3} + \frac{2}{3}\left(-\frac{1}{2}\right)^n, \quad \text{for } n \geq 0,$$

generates the terms of the sequence in part (a).

c. What is the limit of the sequence?

T 95. Calculator algorithm The CORDIC (COordinate Rotation DIgital Calculation) algorithm is used by most calculators to evaluate trigonometric and logarithmic functions. An important number in the CORDIC algorithm, called the *aggregate constant*, is given by the infinite product $\prod_{n=0}^{\infty} \frac{2^n}{\sqrt{1 + 2^{2n}}}$, where $\prod_{n=0}^{N} a_n$ represents the product $a_0 \cdot a_1 \cdots a_N$.

This infinite product is the limit of the sequence

$$\left\{ \prod_{n=0}^{0} \frac{2^n}{\sqrt{1 + 2^{2n}}}, \prod_{n=0}^{1} \frac{2^n}{\sqrt{1 + 2^{2n}}}, \prod_{n=0}^{2} \frac{2^n}{\sqrt{1 + 2^{2n}}}, \dots \right\}.$$

Estimate the value of the aggregate constant. (See the Guided Project *CORDIC algorithms: How your calculator works.*)

Additional Exercises

96. Bounded monotonic proof Use mathematical induction to prove that the drug dose sequence in Example 5,

$$d_{n+1} = 0.5d_n + 100, d_1 = 100, \quad \text{for } n = 1, 2, 3, \dots,$$

is bounded and monotonic.

T 97. Repeated square roots Consider the expression

$$\sqrt{1 + \sqrt{1 + \sqrt{1 + \sqrt{1 + \cdots}}}}, \text{where the process continues}$$
indefinitely.

a. Show that this expression can be built in steps using the recurrence relation $a_0 = 1, a_{n+1} = \sqrt{1 + a_n}$, for $n = 0, 1, 2, 3, \dots$. Explain why the value of the expression can be interpreted as $\lim_{n \to \infty} a_n$, provided the limit exists.

b. Evaluate the first five terms of the sequence $\{a_n\}$.

c. Estimate the limit of the sequence. Compare your estimate with $(1 + \sqrt{5})/2$, a number known as the *golden mean*.

d. Assuming the limit exists, use the method of Example 5 to determine the limit exactly.

e. Repeat the preceding analysis for the expression

$$\sqrt{p + \sqrt{p + \sqrt{p + \sqrt{p + \cdots}}}}, \text{where } p > 0. \text{ Make a}$$
table showing the approximate value of this expression for various values of p. Does the expression seem to have a limit for all positive values of p?

T 98. A sequence of products Find the limit of the sequence

$$\{a_n\}_{n=2}^{\infty} = \left\{ \left(1 - \frac{1}{2}\right)\left(1 - \frac{1}{3}\right) \cdots \left(1 - \frac{1}{n}\right) \right\}_{n=2}^{\infty}.$$

T 99. Continued fractions The expression

$$1 + \cfrac{1}{1 + \cfrac{1}{1 + \cfrac{1}{1 + \cfrac{1}{1 + \cdots}}}},$$

where the process continues indefinitely, is called a *continued fraction*.

a. Show that this expression can be built in steps using the recurrence relation $a_0 = 1, a_{n+1} = 1 + 1/a_n$, for $n = 0, 1, 2, 3, \dots$. Explain why the value of the expression can be interpreted as $\lim_{n \to \infty} a_n$, provided the limit exists.

b. Evaluate the first five terms of the sequence $\{a_n\}$.

c. Using computation and/or graphing, estimate the limit of the sequence.

d. Assuming the limit exists, use the method of Example 5 to determine the limit exactly. Compare your estimate with $(1 + \sqrt{5})/2$, a number known as the *golden mean*.

e. Assuming the limit exists, use the same ideas to determine the value of

$$a + \cfrac{b}{a + \cfrac{b}{a + \cfrac{b}{a + \cfrac{b}{a + \cdots}}}},$$

where a and b are positive real numbers.

T 100. Tower of powers For a positive real number p, the tower of exponents $p^{p^{p^{\cdot^{\cdot^{\cdot}}}}}$ continues indefinitely and the expression is ambiguous. The tower could be built from the top as the limit of the sequence $\{p^p, (p^p)^p, ((p^p)^p)^p, \dots\}$, in which case the sequence is defined recursively as

$$a_{n+1} = a_n^p \text{ (building from the top),} \quad (1)$$

where $a_1 = p^p$. The tower could also be built from the bottom as the limit of the sequence $\{p^p, p^{(p^p)}, p^{(p^{(p^p)})}, \dots\}$, in which case the sequence is defined recursively as

$$a_{n+1} = p^{a_n} \text{ (building from the bottom),} \quad (2)$$

where again $a_1 = p^p$.

a. Estimate the value of the tower with $p = 0.5$ by building from the top. That is, use tables to estimate the limit of the sequence defined recursively by (1) with $p = 0.5$. Estimate the maximum value of $p > 0$ for which the sequence has a limit.

b. Estimate the value of the tower with $p = 1.2$ by building from the bottom. That is, use tables to estimate the limit of the sequence defined recursively by (2) with $p = 1.2$. Estimate the maximum value of $p > 1$ for which the sequence has a limit.

T 101. Fibonacci sequence The famous Fibonacci sequence was proposed by Leonardo Pisano, also known as Fibonacci, in about A.D. 1200 as a model for the growth of rabbit populations. It is given by the recurrence relation $f_{n+1} = f_n + f_{n-1}$, for $n = 1, 2, 3, \dots$, where $f_0 = 1, f_1 = 1$. Each term of the sequence is the sum of its two predecessors.

a. Write out the first ten terms of the sequence.

b. Is the sequence bounded?

c. Estimate or determine $\varphi = \lim_{n \to \infty} \dfrac{f_{n+1}}{f_n}$, the ratio of the successive terms of the sequence. Provide evidence that $\varphi = (1 + \sqrt{5})/2$, a number known as the *golden mean*.

d. Use induction to verify the remarkable result that

$$f_n = \frac{1}{\sqrt{5}} \left(\varphi^n - (-1)^n \varphi^{-n} \right).$$

102. Arithmetic-geometric mean Pick two positive numbers a_0 and b_0 with $a_0 > b_0$, and write out the first few terms of the two sequences $\{a_n\}$ and $\{b_n\}$:

$$a_{n+1} = \frac{a_n + b_n}{2}, \quad b_{n+1} = \sqrt{a_n b_n}, \quad \text{for } n = 0, 1, 2. \dots$$

(Recall that the arithmetic mean $A = (p + q)/2$ and the geometric mean $G = \sqrt{pq}$ of two positive numbers p and q satisfy $A \geq G$.)

a. Show that $a_n > b_n$ for all n.

b. Show that $\{a_n\}$ is a decreasing sequence and $\{b_n\}$ is an increasing sequence.

c. Conclude that $\{a_n\}$ and $\{b_n\}$ converge.

d. Show that $a_{n+1} - b_{n+1} < (a_n - b_n)/2$ and conclude that $\lim_{n\to\infty} a_n = \lim_{n\to\infty} b_n$. The common value of these limits is called the arithmetic-geometric mean of a_0 and b_0, denoted $\text{AGM}(a_0, b_0)$.

e. Estimate $\text{AGM}(12, 20)$. Estimate Gauss' constant $1/\text{AGM}(1, \sqrt{2})$.

103. The hailstone sequence Here is a fascinating (unsolved) problem known as the hailstone problem (or the Ulam Conjecture or the Collatz Conjecture). It involves sequences in two different ways. First, choose a positive integer N and call it a_0. This is the *seed* of a sequence. The rest of the sequence is generated as follows: For $n = 0, 1, 2, \ldots$

$$a_{n+1} = \begin{cases} a_n/2 & \text{if } a_n \text{ is even} \\ 3a_n + 1 & \text{if } a_n \text{ is odd.} \end{cases}$$

However, if $a_n = 1$ for any n, then the sequence terminates.

a. Compute the sequence that results from the seeds $N = 2, 3, 4, \ldots, 10$. You should verify that in all these cases, the sequence eventually terminates. The hailstone conjecture (still unproved) states that for all positive integers N, the sequence terminates after a finite number of terms.

b. Now define the hailstone sequence $\{H_k\}$, which is the number of terms needed for the sequence $\{a_n\}$ to terminate starting with a seed of k. Verify that $H_2 = 1, H_3 = 7$, and $H_4 = 2$.

c. Plot as many terms of the hailstone sequence as is feasible. How did the sequence get its name? Does the conjecture appear to be true?

104. Prove that if $\{a_n\} \ll \{b_n\}$ (as used in Theorem 8.6), then $\{ca_n\} \ll \{db_n\}$, where c and d are positive real numbers.

105. Convergence proof Consider the sequence defined by
$$a_{n+1} = \sqrt{3a_n}, a_1 = \sqrt{3}, \text{ for } n \geq 1.$$

a. Show that $\{a_n\}$ is increasing.

b. Show that $\{a_n\}$ is bounded between 0 and 3.

c. Explain why $\lim_{n\to\infty} a_n$ exists.

d. Find $\lim_{n\to\infty} a_n$.

106–110. Comparing sequences *In the following exercises, two sequences are given, one of which initially has smaller values, but eventually "overtakes" the other sequence. Find the sequence with the larger growth rate and the value of n at which it overtakes the other sequence.*

106. $a_n = \sqrt{n}$ and $b_n = 2 \ln n, n \geq 3$

107. $a_n = e^{n/2}$ and $b_n = n^5, n \geq 2$

108. $a_n = n^{1.001}$ and $b_n = \ln n^{10}, n \geq 1$

109. $a_n = n!$ and $b_n = n^{0.7n}, n \geq 2$

110. $a_n = n^{10}$ and $b_n = n^9 \ln^3 n, n \geq 7$

111. Comparing sequences with a parameter For what values of a does the sequence $\{n!\}$ grow faster than the sequence $\{n^{an}\}$? (*Hint:* Stirling's formula is useful: $n! \approx \sqrt{2\pi n}\, n^n e^{-n}$, for large values of n.)

QUICK CHECK ANSWERS

1. a. Bounded, monotonic;   **b.** Bounded, not monotonic;   **c.** Not bounded, not monotonic;   **d.** Bounded, monotonic (both nonincreasing and nondecreasing)   **2.** If $r = -1$, the sequence is $\{-1, 1, -1, 1, \ldots\}$, the terms alternate in sign, and the sequence diverges. If $r = 1$, the sequence is $\{1, 1, 1, 1, \ldots\}$, the terms are constant, and the sequence converges to 1.   **3.** Both changes would increase the steady-state level of drug.   **4.** $\{n^{1.1}\}$ grows faster; the limit is 0. ◀

8.3 Infinite Series

> The sequence of partial sums may be visualized nicely as follows:

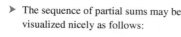

We begin our discussion of infinite series with *geometric series*. These series arise more frequently than any other infinite series, they are used in many practical problems, and they illustrate all the essential features of infinite series in general. First let's summarize some important ideas from Section 8.1.

Recall that every infinite series $\sum_{k=1}^{\infty} a_k$ has a sequence of partial sums:

$$S_1 = a_1, \qquad S_2 = a_1 + a_2, \qquad S_3 = a_1 + a_2 + a_3,$$

and in general, $S_n = \sum_{k=1}^{n} a_k$, for $n = 1, 2, 3, \ldots$.

If the sequence of partial sums $\{S_n\}$ converges—that is, if $\lim_{n\to\infty} S_n = L$—then the value of the infinite series is also L. If the sequence of partial sums diverges, then the infinite series also diverges.

In summary, to evaluate an infinite series, it is necessary to determine a formula for the sequence of partial sums $\{S_n\}$ and then find its limit. This procedure can be carried out with the series that we discuss in this section: geometric series and telescoping series.

Geometric Sums and Series

> Geometric *sequences* have the form $\{r^k\}$ or $\{ar^k\}$. Geometric *sums* and *series* have the form $\sum r^k$ or $\sum ar^k$.

As a preliminary step to geometric series, we study geometric sums, which are *finite sums* in which each term in the sum is a constant multiple of the previous term. A **geometric sum** with n terms has the form

$$S_n = a + ar + ar^2 + \cdots + ar^{n-1} = \sum_{k=0}^{n-1} ar^k,$$

where $a \neq 0$ and r are real numbers; r is called the **ratio** of the sum and a is its first term. For example, the geometric sum with $r = 0.1$, $a = 0.9$, and $n = 4$ is

$$0.9 + 0.09 + 0.009 + 0.0009 = 0.9(1 + 0.1 + 0.01 + 0.001)$$

$$= \sum_{k=0}^{3} 0.9(0.1^k).$$

QUICK CHECK 1 Which of the following sums are not geometric sums?

a. $\displaystyle\sum_{k=0}^{10} \left(\tfrac{1}{2}\right)^k$ **b.** $\displaystyle\sum_{k=0}^{20} \frac{1}{k}$

c. $\displaystyle\sum_{k=0}^{30} (2k + 1)$ ◄

Our goal is to find a formula for the value of the geometric sum

$$S_n = a + ar + ar^2 + \cdots + ar^{n-1}, \tag{1}$$

for any values of $a \neq 0$, r, and the positive integer n. Doing so requires a clever maneuver. The first step is to multiply both sides of equation (1) by the ratio r:

$$rS_n = r(a + ar + ar^2 + ar^3 + \cdots + ar^{n-1})$$
$$= ar + ar^2 + ar^3 + \cdots + ar^{n-1} + ar^n. \tag{2}$$

> The notation $\displaystyle\sum_{k=0}^{\infty} ar^k$ appears to have an undefined first term when $r = 0$. The notation is understood to mean $a + ar + ar^2 + \cdots$ and therefore, the series has a value of a when $r = 0$.

We now subtract equation (2) from equation (1). Notice how most of the terms on the right sides of these equations cancel, leaving

$$S_n - rS_n = a - ar^n.$$

Assuming $r \neq 1$ and solving for S_n results in a general formula for the value of a geometric sum:

$$S_n = a\frac{1 - r^n}{1 - r}. \tag{3}$$

Having dealt with geometric sums, it is a short step to *geometric series*. We simply note that the geometric sums $S_n = \displaystyle\sum_{k=0}^{n-1} ar^k$ form the sequence of partial sums for the geometric series $\displaystyle\sum_{k=0}^{\infty} ar^k$. The value of the geometric series is the limit of its sequence of partial sums (provided it exists). Using equation (3), we have

QUICK CHECK 2 Verify that the geometric sum formula gives the correct result for the sums $1 + \frac{1}{2}$ and $\frac{1}{2} + \frac{1}{4} + \frac{1}{8}$. ◄

$$\underbrace{\sum_{k=0}^{\infty} ar^k}_{\text{geometric series}} = \lim_{n \to \infty} \underbrace{\sum_{k=0}^{n-1} ar^k}_{\text{geometric sum } S_n} = \lim_{n \to \infty} a\frac{1 - r^n}{1 - r}.$$

To compute this limit, we must examine the behavior of r^n as $n \to \infty$. Recall from our work with geometric sequences (Section 8.2) that

$$\lim_{n \to \infty} r^n = \begin{cases} 0 & \text{if } |r| < 1 \\ 1 & \text{if } r = 1 \\ \text{does not exist} & \text{if } r \leq -1 \text{ or } r > 1. \end{cases}$$

Case 1: $|r| < 1$ Because $\displaystyle\lim_{n \to \infty} r^n = 0$, we have

$$\lim_{n \to \infty} S_n = \lim_{n \to \infty} a\frac{1 - r^n}{1 - r} = a\frac{1 - \overbrace{\lim_{n \to \infty} r^n}^{0}}{1 - r} = \frac{a}{1 - r}.$$

In the case that $|r| < 1$, the geometric series *converges* to $\dfrac{a}{1 - r}$.

Case 2: $|r| > 1$ In this case, $\lim_{n\to\infty} r^n$ does not exist, so $\lim_{n\to\infty} S_n$ does not exist and the series diverges.

Case 3: $|r| = 1$ If $r = 1$, then the geometric series is $\displaystyle\sum_{k=0}^{\infty} a = a + a + a + \cdots$, which diverges. If $r = -1$, the geometric series is $\displaystyle a\sum_{k=0}^{\infty}(-1)^k = a - a + a - \cdots$, which also diverges (because the sequence of partial sums oscillates between 0 and a). We summarize these results in Theorem 8.7.

QUICK CHECK 3 Evaluate $\frac{1}{2} + \frac{1}{4} + \frac{1}{8} + \frac{1}{16} + \cdots$. ◄

THEOREM 8.7   Geometric Series

Let $a \neq 0$ and r be real numbers. If $|r| < 1$, then $\displaystyle\sum_{k=0}^{\infty} ar^k = \frac{a}{1-r}$. If $|r| \geq 1$, then the series diverges.

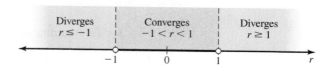

QUICK CHECK 4 Explain why $\displaystyle\sum_{k=0}^{\infty} 0.2^k$ converges and why $\displaystyle\sum_{k=0}^{\infty} 2^k$ diverges. ◄

EXAMPLE 1   Geometric series Evaluate the following geometric series or state that the series diverges.

a. $\displaystyle\sum_{k=0}^{\infty} 1.1^k$ **b.** $\displaystyle\sum_{k=0}^{\infty} e^{-k}$ **c.** $\displaystyle\sum_{k=2}^{\infty} 3(-0.75)^k$

SOLUTION

a. The ratio of this geometric series is $r = 1.1$. Because $|r| \geq 1$, the series diverges.

b. Note that $e^{-k} = \dfrac{1}{e^k} = \left(\dfrac{1}{e}\right)^k$. Therefore, the ratio of the series is $r = \dfrac{1}{e}$, and its first term is $a = 1$. Because $|r| < 1$, the series converges and its value is

$$\sum_{k=0}^{\infty} e^{-k} = \sum_{k=0}^{\infty}\left(\frac{1}{e}\right)^k = \frac{1}{1 - (1/e)} = \frac{e}{e-1} \approx 1.582.$$

c. Writing out the first few terms of the series is helpful:

> The series in Example 1c is called an *alternating series* because the terms alternate in sign. Such series are discussed in detail in Section 8.6.

$$\sum_{k=2}^{\infty} 3(-0.75)^k = \underbrace{3(-0.75)^2}_{a} + \underbrace{3(-0.75)^3}_{ar} + \underbrace{3(-0.75)^4}_{ar^2} + \cdots.$$

We see that the first term of the series is $a = 3(-0.75)^2$ and that the ratio of the series is $r = -0.75$. Because $|r| < 1$, the series converges, and its value is

$$\sum_{k=2}^{\infty} 3(-0.75)^k = \underbrace{\frac{3(-0.75)^2}{1 - (-0.75)}}_{\frac{a}{1-r}} = \frac{27}{28}.$$

Related Exercises 7–40 ◄

EXAMPLE 2   **Decimal expansions as geometric series** Write $1.0\overline{35} = 1.0353535\ldots$ as a geometric series and express its value as a fraction.

SOLUTION Notice that the decimal part of this number is a convergent geometric series with $a = 0.035$ and $r = 0.01$:

$$1.0353535\ldots = 1 + \underbrace{0.035 + 0.00035 + 0.0000035 + \cdots}_{\text{geometric series with } a = 0.035 \text{ and } r = 0.01}.$$

Evaluating the series, we have

$$1.0353535\ldots = 1 + \frac{a}{1-r} = 1 + \frac{0.035}{1-0.01} = 1 + \frac{35}{990} = \frac{205}{198}.$$

Related Exercises 41–54 ◄

Telescoping Series

With geometric series, we carried out the entire evaluation process by finding a formula for the sequence of partial sums and evaluating the limit of the sequence. Not many infinite series can be subjected to this sort of analysis. With another class of series, called **telescoping series**, it can also be done. Here is an example.

EXAMPLE 3   **Telescoping series** Evaluate the following series.

a. $\displaystyle\sum_{k=1}^{\infty}\left(\frac{1}{3^k} - \frac{1}{3^{k+1}}\right)$ **b.** $\displaystyle\sum_{k=1}^{\infty}\frac{1}{k(k+1)}$

SOLUTION

a. The nth term of the sequence of partial sums is

$$S_n = \sum_{k=1}^{n}\left(\frac{1}{3^k} - \frac{1}{3^{k+1}}\right) = \left(\frac{1}{3} - \frac{1}{3^2}\right) + \left(\frac{1}{3^2} - \frac{1}{3^3}\right) + \cdots + \left(\frac{1}{3^n} - \frac{1}{3^{n+1}}\right)$$

$$= \frac{1}{3} + \underbrace{\left(-\frac{1}{3^2} + \frac{1}{3^2}\right)}_{0} + \cdots + \underbrace{\left(-\frac{1}{3^n} + \frac{1}{3^n}\right)}_{0} - \frac{1}{3^{n+1}} \qquad \text{Regroup terms.}$$

$$= \frac{1}{3} - \frac{1}{3^{n+1}}. \qquad\qquad\qquad\qquad\qquad\qquad \text{Simplify.}$$

Observe that the interior terms of the sum cancel (or telescope), leaving a simple expression for S_n. Taking the limit, we find that

$$\sum_{k=1}^{\infty}\left(\frac{1}{3^k} - \frac{1}{3^{k+1}}\right) = \lim_{n\to\infty} S_n = \lim_{n\to\infty}\left(\frac{1}{3} - \underbrace{\frac{1}{3^{n+1}}}_{\to 0}\right) = \frac{1}{3}.$$

► See Section 7.5 for a review of partial fractions.

b. Using the method of partial fractions, the sequence of partial sums is

$$S_n = \sum_{k=1}^{n}\frac{1}{k(k+1)} = \sum_{k=1}^{n}\left(\frac{1}{k} - \frac{1}{k+1}\right).$$

Writing out this sum, we see that

$$S_n = \left(1 - \frac{1}{2}\right) + \left(\frac{1}{2} - \frac{1}{3}\right) + \left(\frac{1}{3} - \frac{1}{4}\right) + \cdots + \left(\frac{1}{n} - \frac{1}{n+1}\right)$$

$$= 1 + \underbrace{\left(-\frac{1}{2} + \frac{1}{2}\right)}_{0} + \underbrace{\left(-\frac{1}{3} + \frac{1}{3}\right)}_{0} + \cdots + \underbrace{\left(-\frac{1}{n} + \frac{1}{n}\right)}_{0} - \frac{1}{n+1}$$

$$= 1 - \frac{1}{n+1}.$$

Again, the sum telescopes and all the interior terms cancel. The result is a simple formula for the nth term of the sequence of partial sums. The value of the series is

$$\sum_{k=1}^{\infty} \frac{1}{k(k+1)} = \lim_{n \to \infty} S_n = \lim_{n \to \infty} \left(1 - \frac{1}{n+1}\right) = 1.$$

Related Exercises 55–68 ◄

SECTION 8.3 EXERCISES

Review Questions

1. What is the defining characteristic of a geometric series? Give an example.

2. What is the difference between a geometric sum and a geometric series?

3. What is meant by the *ratio* of a geometric series?

4. Does a geometric sum always have a finite value?

5. Does a geometric series always have a finite value?

6. What is the condition for convergence of the geometric series $\sum_{k=0}^{\infty} ar^k$?

Basic Skills

7–18. Geometric sums *Evaluate each geometric sum.*

7. $\sum_{k=0}^{8} 3^k$

T 8. $\sum_{k=0}^{10} \left(\frac{1}{4}\right)^k$

T 9. $\sum_{k=0}^{20} \left(\frac{2}{5}\right)^{2k}$

10. $\sum_{k=4}^{12} 2^k$

T 11. $\sum_{k=0}^{9} \left(-\frac{3}{4}\right)^k$

T 12. $\sum_{k=1}^{5} (-2.5)^k$

13. $\sum_{k=0}^{6} \pi^k$

T 14. $\sum_{k=1}^{10} \left(\frac{4}{7}\right)^k$

15. $\sum_{k=0}^{20} (-1)^k$

16. $1 + \frac{2}{3} + \frac{4}{9} + \frac{8}{27}$

T 17. $\frac{1}{4} + \frac{1}{12} + \frac{1}{36} + \frac{1}{108} + \cdots + \frac{1}{2916}$

T 18. $\frac{1}{5} + \frac{3}{25} + \frac{9}{125} + \cdots + \frac{243}{15,625}$

19–34. Geometric series *Evaluate each geometric series or state that it diverges.*

19. $\sum_{k=0}^{\infty} \left(\frac{1}{4}\right)^k$

20. $\sum_{k=0}^{\infty} \left(\frac{3}{5}\right)^k$

21. $\sum_{k=0}^{\infty} 0.9^k$

22. $1 + \frac{2}{7} + \frac{2^2}{7^2} + \frac{2^3}{7^3} + \cdots$

23. $1 + 1.01 + 1.01^2 + 1.01^3 + \cdots$

24. $1 + \frac{1}{\pi} + \frac{1}{\pi^2} + \frac{1}{\pi^3} + \cdots$

25. $\sum_{k=1}^{\infty} e^{-2k}$

26. $\sum_{m=2}^{\infty} \frac{5}{2^m}$

27. $\sum_{k=1}^{\infty} 2^{-3k}$

28. $\sum_{k=3}^{\infty} \frac{3 \cdot 4^k}{7^k}$

29. $\sum_{k=4}^{\infty} \frac{1}{5^k}$

30. $\sum_{k=0}^{\infty} \left(\frac{4}{3}\right)^{-k}$

31. $1 + \frac{e}{\pi} + \frac{e^2}{\pi^2} + \frac{e^3}{\pi^3} + \cdots$

32. $\frac{1}{16} + \frac{3}{64} + \frac{9}{256} + \frac{27}{1024} + \cdots$

33. $\sum_{k=0}^{\infty} \left(\frac{1}{4}\right)^k 5^{3-k}$

T 34. $\sum_{k=2}^{\infty} \left(\frac{3}{8}\right)^{3k}$

35–40. Geometric series with alternating signs *Evaluate each geometric series or state that it diverges.*

35. $\sum_{k=0}^{\infty} \left(-\frac{9}{10}\right)^k$

36. $\sum_{k=1}^{\infty} \left(-\frac{2}{3}\right)^k$

37. $3 \sum_{k=0}^{\infty} (-\pi)^{-k}$

38. $\sum_{k=1}^{\infty} (-e)^{-k}$

39. $\sum_{k=2}^{\infty} (-0.15)^k$

40. $\sum_{k=1}^{\infty} 3 \left(-\frac{1}{8}\right)^{3k}$

41–54. Decimal expansions *Write each repeating decimal first as a geometric series and then as a fraction (a ratio of two integers).*

41. $0.\overline{3} = 0.333\ldots$

42. $0.\overline{6} = 0.666\ldots$

43. $0.\overline{1} = 0.111\ldots$

44. $0.\overline{5} = 0.555\ldots$

45. $0.\overline{09} = 0.090909\ldots$

46. $0.\overline{27} = 0.272727\ldots$

47. $0.\overline{037} = 0.037037\ldots$

48. $0.\overline{027} = 0.027027\ldots$

49. $0.\overline{12} = 0.121212\ldots$

50. $1.\overline{25} = 1.252525\ldots$

51. $0.\overline{456} = 0.456456456\ldots$

52. $1.00\overline{39} = 1.00393939\ldots$

53. $0.00\overline{952} = 0.00952952\ldots$

54. $5.12\overline{83} = 5.12838383\ldots$

55–68. Telescoping series *For the following telescoping series, find a formula for the nth term of the sequence of partial sums $\{S_n\}$. Then evaluate $\lim_{n \to \infty} S_n$ to obtain the value of the series or state that the series diverges.*

55. $\sum_{k=1}^{\infty} \left(\frac{1}{k+1} - \frac{1}{k+2}\right)$

56. $\sum_{k=1}^{\infty} \left(\frac{1}{k+2} - \frac{1}{k+3}\right)$

57. $\sum_{k=1}^{\infty} \frac{1}{(k+6)(k+7)}$

58. $\sum_{k=0}^{\infty} \frac{1}{(3k+1)(3k+4)}$

59. $\sum_{k=3}^{\infty} \frac{4}{(4k-3)(4k+1)}$

60. $\sum_{k=3}^{\infty} \frac{2}{(2k-1)(2k+1)}$

61. $\sum_{k=1}^{\infty} \ln \frac{k+1}{k}$

62. $\sum_{k=1}^{\infty} (\sqrt{k+1} - \sqrt{k})$

63. $\displaystyle\sum_{k=1}^{\infty} \frac{1}{(k + p)(k + p + 1)}$, where p is a positive integer

64. $\displaystyle\sum_{k=1}^{\infty} \frac{1}{(ak + 1)(ak + a + 1)}$, where a is a positive integer

65. $\displaystyle\sum_{k=1}^{\infty} \left(\frac{1}{\sqrt{k + 1}} - \frac{1}{\sqrt{k + 3}} \right)$

66. $\displaystyle\sum_{k=0}^{\infty} \left(\sin\left(\frac{(k + 1)\pi}{2k + 1} \right) - \sin\left(\frac{k\pi}{2k - 1} \right) \right)$

67. $\displaystyle\sum_{k=0}^{\infty} \frac{1}{16k^2 + 8k - 3}$

68. $\displaystyle\sum_{k=1}^{\infty} \left(\tan^{-1}(k + 1) - \tan^{-1} k \right)$

Further Explorations

69. **Explain why or why not** Determine whether the following statements are true and give an explanation or counterexample.

    a. $\displaystyle\sum_{k=1}^{\infty} \left(\frac{\pi}{e} \right)^{-k}$ is a convergent geometric series.

    b. If a is a real number and $\displaystyle\sum_{k=12}^{\infty} a^k$ converges, then $\displaystyle\sum_{k=1}^{\infty} a^k$ converges.

    c. If the series $\displaystyle\sum_{k=1}^{\infty} a^k$ converges and $|a| < |b|$, then the series $\displaystyle\sum_{k=1}^{\infty} b^k$ converges.

    d. Viewed as a function of r, the series $1 + r^2 + r^3 + \cdots$ takes on all values in the interval $\left(\frac{1}{2}, \infty \right)$.

    e. Viewed as a function of r, the series $\displaystyle\sum_{k=1}^{\infty} r^k$ takes on all values in the interval $\left(-\frac{1}{2}, \infty \right)$.

70–73. Evaluating series *Evaluate each series or state that it diverges.*

70. $\displaystyle\sum_{k=1}^{\infty} \left(\sin^{-1}(1/k) - \sin^{-1}(1/(k + 1)) \right)$

71. $\displaystyle\sum_{k=1}^{\infty} \frac{(-2)^k}{3^{k+1}}$

72. $\displaystyle\sum_{k=1}^{\infty} \frac{\pi^k}{e^{k+1}}$

73. $\displaystyle\sum_{k=2}^{\infty} \frac{\ln((k + 1)k^{-1})}{(\ln k) \ln (k + 1)}$

74. **Evaluating an infinite series two ways** Evaluate the series $\displaystyle\sum_{k=1}^{\infty} \left(\frac{1}{2^k} - \frac{1}{2^{k+1}} \right)$ two ways.

    a. Use a telescoping series argument.

    b. Use a geometric series argument after first simplifying $\dfrac{1}{2^k} - \dfrac{1}{2^{k+1}}$.

75. **Evaluating an infinite series two ways** Evaluate the series $\displaystyle\sum_{k=1}^{\infty} \left(\frac{4}{3^k} - \frac{4}{3^{k+1}} \right)$ two ways.

    a. Use a telescoping series argument.

    b. Use a geometric series argument after first simplifying $\dfrac{4}{3^k} - \dfrac{4}{3^{k+1}}$.

76. **Zeno's paradox** The Greek philosopher Zeno of Elea (who lived about 450 B.C.) invented many paradoxes, the most famous of which tells of a race between the swift warrior Achilles and a tortoise. Zeno argued

> *The slower when running will never be overtaken by the quicker; for that which is pursuing must first reach the point from which that which is fleeing started, so that the slower must necessarily always be some distance ahead.*

In other words, by giving the tortoise a head start, Achilles will never overtake the tortoise because every time Achilles reaches the point where the tortoise was, the tortoise has moved ahead. Resolve this paradox by assuming that Achilles gives the tortoise a 1-mi head start and runs 5 mi/hr to the tortoise's 1 mi/hr. How far does Achilles run before he overtakes the tortoise, and how long does it take?

77. **Archimedes' quadrature of the parabola** The Greeks solved several calculus problems almost 2000 years before the discovery of calculus. One example is Archimedes' calculation of the area of the region R bounded by a segment of a parabola, which he did using the "method of exhaustion." As shown in the figure, the idea was to fill R with an infinite sequence of triangles. Archimedes began with an isosceles triangle inscribed in the parabola, with area A_1, and proceeded in stages, with the number of new triangles doubling at each stage. He was able to show (the key to the solution) that at each stage, the area of a new triangle is $\frac{1}{8}$ of the area of a triangle at the previous stage; for example, $A_2 = \frac{1}{8} A_1$, and so forth. Show, as Archimedes did, that the area of R is $\frac{4}{3}$ times the area of A_1.

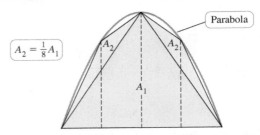

$A_2 = \frac{1}{8}A_1$

Parabola

78. **Value of a series**

    a. Evaluate the series

$$\sum_{k=1}^{\infty} \frac{3^k}{(3^{k+1} - 1)(3^k - 1)}.$$

    b. For what values of a does the series

$$\sum_{k=1}^{\infty} \frac{a^k}{(a^{k+1} - 1)(a^k - 1)}$$

converge, and in those cases, what is its value?

Applications

T 79. House loan Suppose you take out a home mortgage for $180,000 at a monthly interest rate of 0.5%. If you make payments of $1000/month, after how many months will the loan balance be zero? Estimate the answer by graphing the sequence of loan balances and then obtain an exact answer using infinite series.

T 80. Car loan Suppose you borrow $20,000 for a new car at a monthly interest rate of 0.75%. If you make payments of $600/month, after how many months will the loan balance be zero? Estimate the answer by graphing the sequence of loan balances and then obtain an exact answer using infinite series.

81. Fish harvesting A fishery manager knows that her fish population naturally increases at a rate of 1.5% per month. At the end of each month, 120 fish are harvested. Let F_n be the fish population after the nth month, where $F_0 = 4000$ fish. Assume that this process continues indefinitely. Use infinite series to find the long-term (steady-state) population of the fish.

82. Periodic doses Suppose that you take 200 mg of an antibiotic every 6 hr. The half-life of the drug is 6 hr (the time it takes for half of the drug to be eliminated from your blood). Use infinite series to find the long-term (steady-state) amount of antibiotic in your blood.

83. China's one-son policy In 1978, in an effort to reduce population growth, China instituted a policy that allows only one child per family. One unintended consequence has been that, because of a cultural bias toward sons, China now has many more young boys than girls. To solve this problem, some people have suggested replacing the one-child policy with a one-son policy: A family may have children until a boy is born. Suppose that the one-son policy were implemented and that natural birth rates remained the same (half boys and half girls). Using geometric series, compare the total number of children under the two policies.

84. Double glass An insulated window consists of two parallel panes of glass with a small spacing between them. Suppose that each pane reflects a fraction p of the incoming light and transmits the remaining light. Considering all reflections of light between the panes, what fraction of the incoming light is ultimately transmitted by the window? Assume the amount of incoming light is 1.

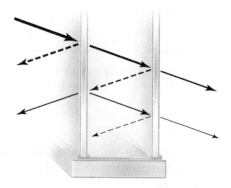

85. Bouncing ball for time Suppose a rubber ball, when dropped from a given height, returns to a fraction p of that height. In the absence of air resistance, a ball dropped from a height h requires $\sqrt{2h/g}$ seconds to fall to the ground, where $g \approx 9.8 \text{ m/s}^2$ is the acceleration due to gravity. The time taken to bounce *up* to a given height equals the time to fall from that height to the ground. How long does it take a ball dropped from 10 m to come to rest?

86. Multiplier effect Imagine that the government of a small community decides to give a total of W, distributed equally, to all its citizens. Suppose that each month each citizen saves a fraction p of his or her new wealth and spends the remaining $1 - p$ in the community. Assume no money leaves or enters the community, and all the spent money is redistributed throughout the community.

a. If this cycle of saving and spending continues for many months, how much money is ultimately spent? Specifically, by what factor is the initial investment of W increased (in terms of p)? Economists refer to this increase in the investment as the *multiplier effect*.

b. Evaluate the limits $p \to 0$ and $p \to 1$, and interpret their meanings.

(See the Guided Project *Economic stimulus packages* for more on stimulus packages.)

87. Snowflake island fractal The fractal called the *snowflake island* (or *Koch island*) is constructed as follows: Let I_0 be an equilateral triangle with sides of length 1. The figure I_1 is obtained by replacing the middle third of each side of I_0 with a new outward equilateral triangle with sides of length $1/3$ (see figure). The process is repeated where I_{n+1} is obtained by replacing the middle third of each side of I_n with a new outward equilateral triangle with sides of length $1/3^{n+1}$. The limiting figure as $n \to \infty$ is called the snowflake island.

a. Let L_n be the perimeter of I_n. Show that $\lim_{n \to \infty} L_n = \infty$.

b. Let A_n be the area of I_n. Find $\lim_{n \to \infty} A_n$. It exists!

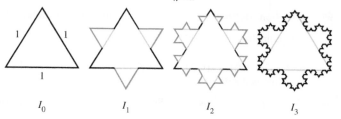

I_0 I_1 I_2 I_3

Additional Exercises

88. Decimal expansions

a. Consider the number $0.555555\ldots$, which can be viewed as the series $5 \sum_{k=1}^{\infty} 10^{-k}$. Evaluate the geometric series to obtain a rational value of $0.555555\ldots$.

b. Consider the number $0.54545454\ldots$, which can be represented by the series $54 \sum_{k=1}^{\infty} 10^{-2k}$. Evaluate the geometric series to obtain a rational value of the number.

c. Now generalize parts (a) and (b). Suppose you are given a number with a decimal expansion that repeats in cycles of length p, say, $n_1, n_2. \ldots, n_p$, where $n_1, \ldots, n_p$ are integers between 0 and 9. Explain how to use geometric series to obtain a rational form for $0.\overline{n_1 n_2 \cdots n_p}$.

d. Try the method of part (c) on the number $0.\overline{123456789} = 0.123456789123456789\ldots$.

e. Prove that $0.\overline{9} = 1$.

89. Remainder term Consider the geometric series $S = \sum\limits_{k=0}^{\infty} r^k$,

which has the value $1/(1 - r)$ provided $|r| < 1$. Let

$$S_n = \sum_{k=0}^{n-1} r^k = \frac{1 - r^n}{1 - r}$$ be the sum of the first n terms.

The magnitude of the remainder R_n is the error in approximating S by S_n. Show that

$$R_n = S - S_n = \frac{r^n}{1 - r}.$$

90–93. Comparing remainder terms *Use Exercise 89 to determine how many terms of each series are needed so that the partial sum is within 10^{-6} of the value of the series (that is, to ensure $|R_n| < 10^{-6}$).*

90. a. $\sum\limits_{k=0}^{\infty} 0.6^k$ **b.** $\sum\limits_{k=0}^{\infty} 0.15^k$

91. a. $\sum\limits_{k=0}^{\infty} (-0.8)^k$ **b.** $\sum\limits_{k=0}^{\infty} 0.2^k$

92. a. $\sum\limits_{k=0}^{\infty} 0.72^k$ **b.** $\sum\limits_{k=0}^{\infty} (-0.25)^k$

93. a. $\sum\limits_{k=0}^{\infty} \left(\dfrac{1}{\pi}\right)^k$ **b.** $\sum\limits_{k=0}^{\infty} \left(\dfrac{1}{e}\right)^k$

94. Functions defined as series Suppose a function f is defined by the geometric series $f(x) = \sum\limits_{k=0}^{\infty} x^k$.

a. Evaluate $f(0), f(0.2), f(0.5), f(1)$, and $f(1.5)$, if possible.
b. What is the domain of f?

95. Functions defined as series Suppose a function f is defined by the geometric series $f(x) = \sum\limits_{k=0}^{\infty} (-1)^k x^k$.

a. Evaluate $f(0), f(0.2), f(0.5), f(1)$, and $f(1.5)$, if possible.
b. What is the domain of f?

96. Functions defined as series Suppose a function f is defined by the geometric series $f(x) = \sum\limits_{k=0}^{\infty} x^{2k}$.

a. Evaluate $f(0), f(0.2), f(0.5), f(1)$, and $f(1.5)$, if possible.
b. What is the domain of f?

97. Series in an equation For what values of x does the geometric series

$$f(x) = \sum_{k=0}^{\infty} \left(\frac{1}{1+x}\right)^k$$

converge? Solve $f(x) = 3$.

98. Bubbles Imagine a stack of hemispherical soap bubbles with decreasing radii $r_1 = 1, r_2, r_3, \ldots$ (see figure). Let h_n be the distance between the diameters of bubble n and bubble $n + 1$, and let H_n be the total height of the stack with n bubbles.

a. Use the Pythagorean theorem to show that in a stack with n bubbles, $h_1^2 = r_1^2 - r_2^2, h_2^2 = r_2^2 - r_3^2$, and so forth. Note that for the last bubble $h_n = r_n$.
b. Use part (a) to show that the height of a stack with n bubbles is

$$H_n = \sqrt{r_1^2 - r_2^2} + \sqrt{r_2^2 - r_3^2} + \cdots + \sqrt{r_{n-1}^2 - r_n^2} + r_n.$$

c. The height of a stack of bubbles depends on how the radii decrease. Suppose that $r_1 = 1, r_2 = a, r_3 = a^2, \ldots, r_n = a^{n-1}$, where $0 < a < 1$ is a fixed real number. In terms of a, find the height H_n of a stack with n bubbles.
d. Suppose the stack in part (c) is extended indefinitely $(n \to \infty)$. In terms of a, how high would the stack be?
e. Challenge problem: Fix n and determine the sequence of radii $r_1, r_2, r_3, \ldots, r_n$ that maximizes H_n, the height of the stack with n bubbles.

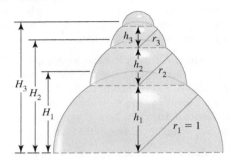

T 99. Values of the geometric series Consider the geometric series $f(r) = \sum\limits_{k=0}^{\infty} r^k$, where $|r| < 1$.

a. Fill in the following table that shows the value of the series $f(r)$ for various values of r.

r	−0.9	−0.7	−0.5	−0.2	0	0.2	0.5	0.7	0.9
$f(r)$									

b. Graph f, for $|r| < 1$.
c. Evaluate $\lim\limits_{r \to 1^-} f(r)$ and $\lim\limits_{r \to -1^+} f(r)$.

T 100. Convergence rates Consider series $S = \sum\limits_{k=0}^{\infty} r^k$, where $|r| < 1$,

and its sequence of partial sums $S_n = \sum\limits_{k=0}^{n} r^k$.

a. Complete the following table showing the smallest value of n, calling it $N(r)$, such that $|S - S_n| < 10^{-4}$, for various values of r. For example, with $r = 0.5$ and $S = 2$, we find that $|S - S_{13}| = 1.2 \times 10^{-4}$ and $|S - S_{14}| = 6.1 \times 10^{-5}$. Therefore, $N(0.5) = 14$.

r	−0.9	−0.7	−0.5	−0.2	0	0.2	0.5	0.7	0.9
$N(r)$							14		

b. Make a graph of $N(r)$ for the values of r in part (a).
c. How does the rate of convergence of the geometric series depend on r?

QUICK CHECK ANSWERS

1. b and c   **2.** Using the formula, the values are $\frac{3}{2}$ and $\frac{7}{8}$.
3. 1   **4.** The first converges because $|r| = 0.2 < 1$; the second diverges because $|r| = 2 > 1$. ◀

8.4 The Divergence and Integral Tests

With geometric series and telescoping series, the sequence of partial sums can be found and its limit can be evaluated (when it exists). Unfortunately, it is difficult or impossible to find an explicit formula for the sequence of partial sums for most infinite series. Therefore, it is difficult to obtain the exact value of most convergent series.

In light of these observations, we now shift our focus and ask a simple *yes* or *no* question: Given an infinite series, does it converge? If the answer is *no*, the series diverges and there are no more questions to ask. If the answer is *yes*, the series converges and it may be possible to estimate its value.

The Divergence Test

One of the simplest and most useful tests determines whether an infinite series *diverges*. Though our focus in this section and the next is on series with positive terms, the Divergence Test applies to series with arbitrary terms.

> **THEOREM 8.8   Divergence Test**
> If Σa_k converges, then $\lim_{k \to \infty} a_k = 0$. Equivalently, if $\lim_{k \to \infty} a_k \neq 0$, then the series diverges.

Important note: Theorem 8.8 cannot be used to conclude that a series converges.

Proof: Let $\{S_n\}$ be the sequence of partial sums for the series Σa_k. Assuming the series converges, it has a finite value, call it S, where

$$S = \lim_{n \to \infty} S_n = \lim_{n \to n} S_{n-1}.$$

Note that $S_n - S_{n-1} = a_n$. Therefore,

$$\lim_{n \to \infty} a_n = \lim_{n \to \infty} (S_n - S_{n-1}) = S - S = 0;$$

> ► If the statement *if p, then q* is true, then its contrapositive, *if (not q), then (not p)*, is also true. However its converse, *if q, then p*, is not necessarily true. Try it out on the true statement, *if I live in Paris, then I live in France.*

that is, $\lim_{n \to \infty} a_n = 0$ (which implies $\lim_{k \to \infty} a_k = 0$; Figure 8.25). The second part of the test follows immediately because it is the *contrapositive* of the first part (see margin note). ◄

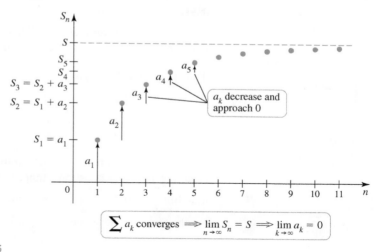

Figure 8.25

EXAMPLE 1   Using the Divergence Test Determine whether the following series diverge or state that the Divergence Test is inconclusive.

a. $\displaystyle\sum_{k=0}^{\infty} \frac{k}{k+1}$ **b.** $\displaystyle\sum_{k=1}^{\infty} \frac{1+3^k}{2^k}$ **c.** $\displaystyle\sum_{k=1}^{\infty} \frac{1}{k}$ **d.** $\displaystyle\sum_{k=1}^{\infty} \frac{1}{k^2}$

SOLUTION By the Divergence Test, if $\lim\limits_{k\to\infty} a_k \neq 0$, then the series $\sum a_k$ diverges.

a. $\displaystyle\lim_{k\to\infty} a_k = \lim_{k\to\infty} \frac{k}{k+1} = 1 \neq 0$

The terms of the series do not approach zero, so the series diverges by the Divergence Test.

b. $\displaystyle\lim_{k\to\infty} a_k = \lim_{k\to\infty} \frac{1+3^k}{2^k}$

$\displaystyle = \lim_{k\to\infty} \left(\underbrace{2^{-k}}_{\to\,0} + \underbrace{\left(\frac{3}{2}\right)^k}_{\to\,\infty} \right)$ Simplify.

$= \infty$

In this case, $\lim\limits_{k\to\infty} a_k \neq 0$, so the corresponding series $\displaystyle\sum_{k=1}^{\infty} \frac{1+3^k}{2^k}$ diverges by the Divergence Test.

c. $\displaystyle\lim_{k\to\infty} a_k = \lim_{k\to\infty} \frac{1}{k} = 0$

In this case, the terms of the series approach zero, so the Divergence Test is inconclusive. Remember, the Divergence Test cannot be used to prove that a series converges.

d. $\displaystyle\lim_{k\to\infty} a_k = \lim_{k\to\infty} \frac{1}{k^2} = 0$

As in part (c), the terms of the series approach 0, so the Divergence Test is inconclusive.

Related Exercises 9–18 ◀

QUICK CHECK 1 Apply the Divergence Test to the geometric series $\sum r^k$. For what values of r does the series diverge? ◀

To summarize: If the terms a_k of a given series do *not* approach zero as $k \to \infty$, then the series diverges. Unfortunately, the test is easy to misuse. It's tempting to conclude that if the terms of the series approach zero, then the series converges. However, look again at the series in Examples 1(c) and 1(d). Although it is true that $\lim\limits_{k\to\infty} a_k = 0$ for both series, we will soon discover that one of them converges while the other diverges. We cannot tell which behavior to expect based only on the observation that $\lim\limits_{k\to\infty} a_k = 0$.

The Harmonic Series

We now look at an example with a surprising result. Consider the infinite series

$$\sum_{k=1}^{\infty} \frac{1}{k} = 1 + \frac{1}{2} + \frac{1}{3} + \frac{1}{4} + \frac{1}{5} + \cdots,$$

a famous series known as the **harmonic series**. Does it converge? As explained in Example 1(c), this question cannot be answered by the Divergence Test, despite the fact that $\lim\limits_{k\to\infty} \frac{1}{k} = 0$. Suppose instead you try to answer the convergence question by writing out the terms of the sequence of partial sums:

$$S_1 = 1, \qquad\qquad S_2 = 1 + \frac{1}{2} = \frac{3}{2},$$

$$S_3 = 1 + \frac{1}{2} + \frac{1}{3} = \frac{11}{6}, \qquad S_4 = 1 + \frac{1}{2} + \frac{1}{3} + \frac{1}{4} = \frac{25}{12},$$

and in general,

$$S_n = \sum_{k=1}^{n} \frac{1}{k} = 1 + \frac{1}{2} + \frac{1}{3} + \frac{1}{4} + \cdots + \frac{1}{n}.$$

There is no obvious pattern in this sequence, and in fact, no simple explicit formula for S_n exists; so we analyze the sequence numerically. Have a look at the first 200 terms of the sequence of partial sums shown in Figure 8.26. What do you think—does the series converge? The terms of the sequence of partial sums increase, but at a decreasing rate. They could approach a limit or they could increase without bound.

Computing additional terms of the sequence of partial sums does not provide conclusive evidence. Table 8.3 shows that the sum of the first million terms is less than 15; the sum of the first 10^{40} terms—an unimaginably large number of terms—is less than 100. This is a case in which computation alone is not sufficient to determine whether a series converges. We need another way to determine whether the series converges.

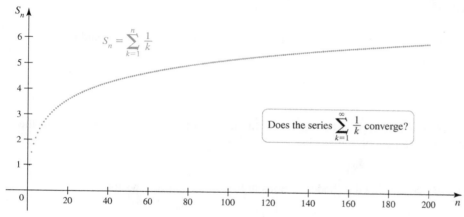

Figure 8.26

Table 8.3

n	S_n	n	S_n
10^3	≈ 7.49	10^{10}	≈ 23.60
10^4	≈ 9.79	10^{20}	≈ 46.63
10^5	≈ 12.09	10^{30}	≈ 69.65
10^6	≈ 14.39	10^{40}	≈ 92.68

Does the series $\sum_{k=1}^{\infty} \frac{1}{k}$ converge?

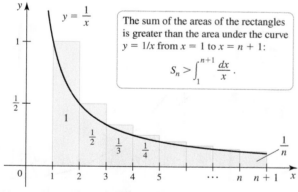

Figure 8.27

The sum of the areas of the rectangles is greater than the area under the curve $y = 1/x$ from $x = 1$ to $x = n + 1$:

$$S_n > \int_1^{n+1} \frac{dx}{x}.$$

▶ Recall that $\int \frac{dx}{x} = \ln |x| + C$. In Section 7.8, we showed that $\int_1^{\infty} \frac{dx}{x^p}$ diverges for $p \le 1$. Therefore, $\int_1^{\infty} \frac{dx}{x}$ diverges.

Observe that the nth term of the sequence of partial sums,

$$S_n = \sum_{k=1}^{n} \frac{1}{k} = 1 + \frac{1}{2} + \frac{1}{3} + \frac{1}{4} + \cdots + \frac{1}{n},$$

is represented geometrically by a left Riemann sum of the function $y = \frac{1}{x}$ on the interval $[1, n + 1]$ (Figure 8.27). This fact follows by noticing that the areas of the rectangles, from left to right, are $1, \frac{1}{2}, \ldots,$ and $\frac{1}{n}$. Comparing the sum of the areas of these n rectangles with the area under the curve, we see that $S_n > \int_1^{n+1} \frac{dx}{x}$. We know that $\int_1^{n+1} \frac{dx}{x} = \ln(n + 1)$ increases without bound as n increases. Because S_n exceeds $\int_1^{n+1} \frac{dx}{x}$, S_n also increases without bound; therefore, $\lim_{n \to \infty} S_n = \infty$ and the harmonic series $\sum_{k=1}^{\infty} \frac{1}{k}$ diverges. This argument justifies the following theorem.

THEOREM 8.9   Harmonic Series

The harmonic series $\displaystyle\sum_{k=1}^{\infty} \frac{1}{k} = 1 + \frac{1}{2} + \frac{1}{3} + \frac{1}{4} + \frac{1}{5} + \cdots$ diverges—even though the terms of the series approach zero.

The ideas used to demonstrate that the harmonic series diverges are now used to prove a new and powerful convergence test. This test and those presented in Section 8.5 apply only to series with positive terms.

The Integral Test

The fact that infinite series are sums and that integrals are limits of sums suggests a connection between series and integrals. The Integral Test exploits this connection.

THEOREM 8.10   Integral Test

Suppose f is a continuous, positive, decreasing function, for $x \geq 1$, and let $a_k = f(k)$, for $k = 1, 2, 3, \ldots$. Then

$$\sum_{k=1}^{\infty} a_k \quad \text{and} \quad \int_1^{\infty} f(x)\, dx$$

either both converge or both diverge. In the case of convergence, the value of the integral is *not* equal to the value of the series.

➤ The Integral Test also applies if the terms of the series a_k are decreasing for $k > N$ for some finite number $N > 1$. The proof can be modified to account for this situation.

Proof: By comparing the shaded regions in Figure 8.28, it follows that

$$\sum_{k=2}^{n} a_k < \int_1^{n} f(x)\, dx < \sum_{k=1}^{n-1} a_k. \tag{1}$$

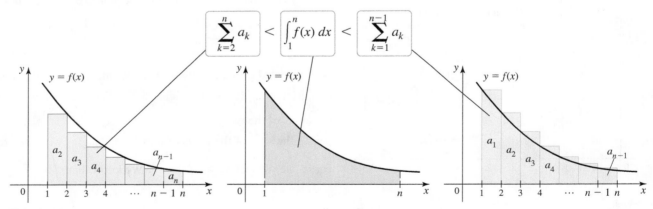

Figure 8.28

The proof must demonstrate two results: If the improper integral $\int_1^{\infty} f(x)\, dx$ has a finite value, then the infinite series converges, *and* if the infinite series converges, then the improper integral has a finite value. First suppose that the improper integral $\int_1^\infty f(x)\,dx$ has a finite value, say I. We have

$$\sum_{k=1}^{n} a_k = a_1 + \sum_{k=2}^{n} a_k \qquad \text{Separate the first term of the series.}$$

$$< a_1 + \int_1^n f(x)\,dx \qquad \text{Left inequality in expression (1)}$$

$$< a_1 + \int_1^\infty f(x)\,dx \qquad f \text{ is positive, so } \int_1^n f(x)\,dx < \int_1^\infty f(x)\,dx.$$

$$= a_1 + I.$$

> In this proof, we rely twice on the Bounded Monotonic Sequence Theorem of Section 8.2: A bounded monotonic sequence converges.

This argument implies that the terms of the sequence of partial sums $S_n = \sum_{k=1}^{n} a_k$ are bounded above by $a_1 + I$. Because $\{S_n\}$ is also increasing (the series consists of positive terms), the sequence of partial sums converges, which means the series $\sum_{k=1}^{\infty} a_k$ converges (to a value less than or equal to $a_1 + I$).

Now suppose the infinite series $\sum_{k=1}^{\infty} a_k$ converges and has a value S. We have

$$\int_1^n f(x)\,dx < \sum_{k=1}^{n-1} a_k \qquad \text{Right inequality in expression (1)}$$

$$< \sum_{k=1}^{\infty} a_k \qquad \text{Terms } a_k \text{ are positive.}$$

$$= S. \qquad \text{Value of infinite series}$$

> An extended version of this proof can be used to show that, in fact,
> $$\int_1^\infty f(x)\,dx < \sum_{k=1}^{\infty} a_k \text{ (strict inequality)}$$
> in all cases.

We see that the sequence $\left\{ \int_1^n f(x)\,dx \right\}$ is increasing (because $f(x) > 0$) and bounded above by a fixed number S. Therefore, the improper integral $\int_1^\infty f(x)\,dx = \lim_{n\to\infty} \int_1^n f(x)\,dx$ has a finite value (less than or equal to S).

We have shown that if $\int_1^\infty f(x)\,dx$ is finite, then $\sum a_k$ converges and vice versa. The same inequalities imply that $\int_1^\infty f(x)\,dx$ and $\sum a_k$ also diverge together. ◄

The Integral Test is used to determine *whether* a series converges or diverges. For this reason, adding or subtracting a few terms in the series *or* changing the lower limit of integration to another finite point does not change the outcome of the test. Therefore, the test depends on neither the lower index of the series nor the lower limit of the integral.

EXAMPLE 2 Applying the Integral Test Determine whether the following series converge.

a. $\displaystyle\sum_{k=1}^{\infty} \frac{k}{k^2 + 1}$ **b.** $\displaystyle\sum_{k=3}^{\infty} \frac{1}{\sqrt{2k - 5}}$ **c.** $\displaystyle\sum_{k=0}^{\infty} \frac{1}{k^2 + 4}$

SOLUTION

a. The function associated with this series is $f(x) = x/(x^2 + 1)$, which is positive, for $x \geq 1$. We must also show that the terms of the series are decreasing beyond some fixed term of the series. The first few terms of the series are $\left\{ \frac{1}{2}, \frac{2}{5}, \frac{3}{10}, \frac{4}{17}, \ldots \right\}$, and it appears that the terms are decreasing. When the decreasing property is difficult to confirm, one approach is to use derivatives to show that the associated function is decreasing. In this case, we have

$$f'(x) = \frac{d}{dx}\left(\frac{x}{x^2 + 1} \right) = \underbrace{\frac{x^2 + 1 - 2x^2}{(x^2 + 1)^2}}_{\text{Quotient Rule}} = \frac{1 - x^2}{(x^2 + 1)^2}.$$

For $x > 1, f'(x) < 0$, which implies that the function and the terms of the series are decreasing. The integral that determines convergence is

$$\int_1^\infty \frac{x}{x^2 + 1}\,dx = \lim_{b\to\infty} \int_1^b \frac{x}{x^2 + 1}\,dx \qquad \text{Definition of improper integral}$$

$$= \lim_{b\to\infty} \frac{1}{2} \ln (x^2 + 1)\Big|_1^b \qquad \text{Evaluate integral.}$$

$$= \frac{1}{2} \lim_{b\to\infty} \left(\ln (b^2 + 1) - \ln 2\right) \qquad \text{Simplify.}$$

$$= \infty. \qquad \lim_{b\to\infty} \ln (b^2 + 1) = \infty$$

Because the integral diverges, the series diverges.

b. The Integral Test may be modified to accommodate initial indices other than $k = 1$. The terms of this series decrease, for $k \geq 3$. In this case, the relevant integral is

$$\int_3^\infty \frac{dx}{\sqrt{2x - 5}} = \lim_{b\to\infty} \int_3^b \frac{dx}{\sqrt{2x - 5}} \qquad \text{Definition of improper integral}$$

$$= \lim_{b\to\infty} \sqrt{2x - 5}\Big|_3^b \qquad \text{Evaluate integral.}$$

$$= \infty. \qquad \lim_{b\to\infty} \sqrt{2b - 5} = \infty$$

Because the integral diverges, the series also diverges.

c. The terms of the series are positive and decrease, for $k \geq 0$. The relevant integral is

$$\int_0^\infty \frac{dx}{x^2 + 4} = \lim_{b\to\infty} \int_0^b \frac{dx}{x^2 + 4} \qquad \text{Definition of improper integral}$$

$$= \lim_{b\to\infty} \frac{1}{2} \tan^{-1} \frac{x}{2}\Big|_0^b \qquad \text{Evaluate integral.}$$

$$= \frac{1}{2} \underbrace{\lim_{b\to\infty} \tan^{-1} \frac{b}{2}}_{\frac{\pi}{2}} - \tan^{-1} 0 \qquad \text{Simplify.}$$

$$= \frac{\pi}{4}. \qquad \tan^{-1} x \to \frac{\pi}{2}, \text{ as } x \to \infty.$$

Because the integral is finite (equivalently, it converges), the infinite series also converges $\left(\text{but not to } \dfrac{\pi}{4}\right)$.

Related Exercises 19–28 ◄

The *p*-Series

The Integral Test is used to prove Theorem 8.11, which addresses the convergence of an entire family of infinite series known as the *p-series*.

THEOREM 8.11 **Convergence of the *p*-Series**

The *p*-series $\displaystyle\sum_{k=1}^\infty \frac{1}{k^p}$ converges for $p > 1$ and diverges for $p \leq 1$.

Proof: To apply the Integral Test, observe that the terms of the given series are positive and decreasing, for $p > 0$. The function associated with the series is $f(x) = \dfrac{1}{x^p}$. The relevant integral is $\displaystyle\int_1^\infty \dfrac{dx}{x^p}$. Appealing to Example 2 in Section 7.8, recall that this improper integral converges for $p > 1$ and diverges for $p \leq 1$. Therefore, by the Integral Test, the p-series $\displaystyle\sum_{k=1}^\infty \dfrac{1}{k^p}$ converges for $p > 1$ and diverges for $0 < p \leq 1$. For $p \leq 0$, the series diverges by the Divergence Test.

EXAMPLE 3 Using the p-series test Determine whether the following series converge or diverge.

a. $\displaystyle\sum_{k=1}^\infty k^{-3}$ **b.** $\displaystyle\sum_{k=1}^\infty \dfrac{1}{\sqrt[4]{k^3}}$ **c.** $\displaystyle\sum_{k=4}^\infty \dfrac{1}{(k-1)^2}$

SOLUTION

a. Because $\displaystyle\sum_{k=1}^\infty k^{-3} = \sum_{k=1}^\infty \dfrac{1}{k^3}$ is a p-series with $p = 3$, it converges by Theorem 8.11.

b. This series is a p-series with $p = \frac{3}{4}$. By Theorem 8.11, it diverges.

c. The series

$$\sum_{k=4}^\infty \dfrac{1}{(k-1)^2} = \sum_{k=3}^\infty \dfrac{1}{k^2} = \dfrac{1}{3^2} + \dfrac{1}{4^2} + \dfrac{1}{5^2} + \cdots$$

is a convergent p-series ($p = 2$) without the first two terms. As we prove shortly, adding or removing a finite number of terms does not affect the convergence of a series. Therefore, the given series converges.

Related Exercises 29–34 ◀

Estimating the Value of Infinite Series

The Integral Test is powerful in its own right, but it comes with an added bonus. It can be used to estimate the value of a convergent series with positive terms. We define the **remainder** to be the error in approximating a convergent series by the sum of its first n terms; that is,

$$R_n = \underbrace{\sum_{k=1}^\infty a_k}_{\substack{\text{value of} \\ \text{series}}} - \underbrace{\sum_{k=1}^n a_k}_{\substack{\text{approximation based} \\ \text{on first } n \text{ terms}}} = a_{n+1} + a_{n+2} + a_{n+3} + \cdots.$$

The remainder consists of the *tail* of the series—those terms beyond a_n. For series with positive terms, the remainder is positive.

QUICK CHECK 3 If Σa_k is a convergent series of positive terms, why is $R_n > 0$? ◀

We now argue much as we did in the proof of the Integral Test. Let f be a continuous, positive, decreasing function such that $f(k) = a_k$, for all relevant k. From Figure 8.29, we see that $\int_{n+1}^\infty f(x)\,dx < R_n$.

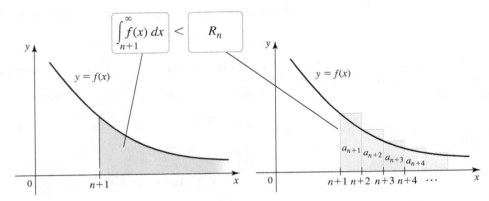

Figure 8.29

Similarly, Figure 8.30 shows that $R_n < \int_n^\infty f(x)\, dx$.

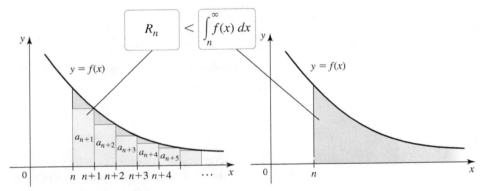

Figure 8.30

Combining these two inequalities, the remainder is squeezed between two integrals:

$$\int_{n+1}^\infty f(x)\, dx < R_n < \int_n^\infty f(x)\, dx. \tag{2}$$

If the integrals can be evaluated, this result provides an estimate of the remainder.

    There is, however, another equally useful way to express this result. Notice that the value of the series is

$$S = \sum_{k=1}^\infty a_k = \underbrace{\sum_{k=1}^n a_k}_{S_n} + R_n,$$

which is the sum of the first n terms S_n and the remainder R_n. Adding S_n to each term of (2), we have

$$\underbrace{S_n + \int_{n+1}^\infty f(x)\, dx}_{L_n} < \underbrace{\sum_{k=1}^\infty a_k}_{S_n + R_n = S} < \underbrace{S_n + \int_n^\infty f(x)\, dx}_{U_n}.$$

These inequalities can be abbreviated as $L_n < S < U_n$, where S is the exact value of the series, and L_n and U_n are lower and upper bounds for S, respectively. If the integrals in these bounds can be evaluated, it is straightforward to compute S_n (by summing the first n terms of the series) and to compute both L_n and U_n.

> **THEOREM 8.12   Estimating Series with Positive Terms**
> Let f be a continuous, positive, decreasing function, for $x \geq 1$, and let $a_k = f(k)$,
> for $k = 1, 2, 3, \ldots$. Let $S = \sum_{k=1}^{\infty} a_k$ be a convergent series and let $S_n = \sum_{k=1}^{n} a_k$ be
> the sum of the first n terms of the series. The remainder $R_n = S - S_n$ satisfies
>
> $$R_n < \int_{n}^{\infty} f(x)\, dx.$$
>
> Furthermore, the exact value of the series is bounded as follows:
>
> $$S_n + \int_{n+1}^{\infty} f(x)\, dx < \sum_{k=1}^{\infty} a_k < S_n + \int_{n}^{\infty} f(x)\, dx.$$

EXAMPLE 4   Approximating a p-series

a. How many terms of the convergent p-series $\sum_{k=1}^{\infty} \dfrac{1}{k^2}$ must be summed to obtain an approximation that is within 10^{-3} of the exact value of the series?

b. Find an approximation to the series using 50 terms of the series.

SOLUTION The function associated with this series is $f(x) = 1/x^2$.

a. Using the bound on the remainder, we have

$$R_n < \int_{n}^{\infty} f(x)\, dx = \int_{n}^{\infty} \frac{dx}{x^2} = \frac{1}{n}.$$

To ensure that $R_n < 10^{-3}$, we must choose n so that $1/n < 10^{-3}$, which implies that $n > 1000$. In other words, we must sum at least 1001 terms of the series to be sure that the remainder is less than 10^{-3}.

b. Using the bounds on the series, we have $L_n < S < U_n$, where S is the exact value of the series, and

$$L_n = S_n + \int_{n+1}^{\infty} \frac{dx}{x^2} = S_n + \frac{1}{n+1} \quad \text{and} \quad U_n = S_n + \int_{n}^{\infty} \frac{dx}{x^2} = S_n + \frac{1}{n}.$$

> The values of p-series with even values of p are generally known. For example, with $p = 2$, the series converges to $\pi^2/6$ (a proof is outlined in Exercise 66); with $p = 4$, the series converges to $\pi^4/90$. The values of p-series with odd values of p are not known.

Therefore, the series is bounded as follows:

$$S_n + \frac{1}{n+1} < S < S_n + \frac{1}{n},$$

where S_n is the sum of the first n terms. Using a calculator to sum the first 50 terms of the series, we find that $S_{50} \approx 1.625133$. The exact value of the series is in the interval

$$S_{50} + \frac{1}{50+1} < S < S_{50} + \frac{1}{50},$$

or $1.644741 < S < 1.645133$. Taking the average of these two bounds as our approximation of S, we find that $S \approx 1.644937$. This estimate is better than simply using S_{50}. Figure 8.31a shows the lower and upper bounds, L_n and U_n, respectively, for $n = 1, 2, \ldots, 50$. Figure 8.31b shows these bounds on an enlarged scale for $n = 50, 51, \ldots, 100$. These figures illustrate how the exact value of the series is squeezed into a narrowing interval as n increases.

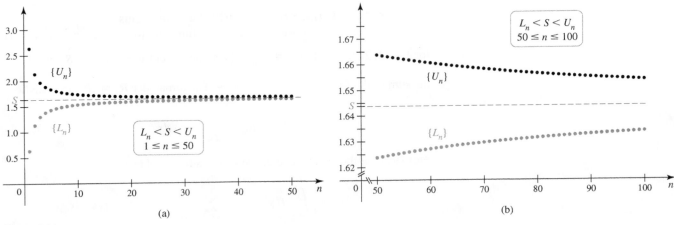

Figure 8.31

Related Exercises 35–42 ◄

Properties of Convergent Series

We close this section with several properties that are useful in upcoming work. The notation $\sum a_k$, without initial and final values of k, is used to refer to a general infinite series whose terms may be positive or negative (or both).

> ➤ The **leading terms** of an infinite series are those at the beginning with a small index. The **tail** of an infinite series consists of the terms at the "end" of the series with a large and increasing index. The convergence or divergence of an infinite series depends on the tail of the series, while the value of a convergent series is determined primarily by the leading terms.

> **THEOREM 8.13 Properties of Convergent Series**
>
> **1.** Suppose $\sum a_k$ converges to A and c is a real number. The series $\sum ca_k$ converges, and $\sum ca_k = c\sum a_k = cA$.
>
> **2.** Suppose $\sum a_k$ converges to A and $\sum b_k$ converges to B. The series $\sum (a_k \pm b_k)$ converges, and $\sum (a_k \pm b_k) = \sum a_k \pm \sum b_k = A \pm B$.
>
> **3.** If M is a positive integer, then $\displaystyle\sum_{k=1}^{\infty} a_k$ and $\displaystyle\sum_{k=M}^{\infty} a_k$ either both converge or both diverge. In general, *whether* a series converges does not depend on a finite number of terms added to or removed from the series. However, the *value* of a convergent series does change if nonzero terms are added or removed.

Proof: These properties are proved using properties of finite sums and limits of sequences. To prove Property 1, assume that $\displaystyle\sum_{k=1}^{\infty} a_k$ converges to A and note that

$$\sum_{k=1}^{\infty} ca_k = \lim_{n\to\infty} \sum_{k=1}^{n} ca_k \qquad \text{Definition of infinite series}$$

$$= \lim_{n\to\infty} c\sum_{k=1}^{n} a_k \qquad \text{Property of finite sums}$$

$$= c\lim_{n\to\infty} \sum_{k=1}^{n} a_k \qquad \text{Property of limits}$$

$$= c\sum_{k=1}^{\infty} a_k \qquad \text{Definition of infinite series}$$

$$= cA. \qquad \text{Value of the series}$$

Property 2 is proved in a similar way (Exercise 62).

Property 3 follows by noting that for finite sums with $1 < M < n$,

$$\sum_{k=M}^{n} a_k = \sum_{k=1}^{n} a_k - \sum_{k=1}^{M-1} a_k.$$

Letting $n \to \infty$ in this equation and assuming that $\sum_{k=1}^{\infty} a_k = A$, it follows that

$$\sum_{k=M}^{\infty} a_k = \underbrace{\sum_{k=1}^{\infty} a_k}_{A} - \underbrace{\sum_{k=1}^{M-1} a_k}_{\text{finite number}}.$$

QUICK CHECK 4 Explain why if $\sum_{k=1}^{\infty} a_k$ converges, then the series $\sum_{k=5}^{\infty} a_k$ (with a different starting index) also converges. Do the two series have the same value? ◄

Because the right side has a finite value, $\sum_{k=M}^{\infty} a_k$ converges. Similarly, if $\sum_{k=M}^{\infty} a_k$ converges, then $\sum_{k=1}^{\infty} a_k$ converges. By an analogous argument, if one of these series diverges, then the other series diverges. ◄

Use caution when applying Theorem 8.13. For example, you can write

$$\sum_{k=2}^{\infty} \frac{1}{k(k-1)} = \sum_{k=2}^{\infty} \left(\frac{1}{k-1} - \frac{1}{k} \right)$$

and then recognize a telescoping series (that converges to 1). An *incorrect* application of Theorem 8.13 would be to write

$$\sum_{k=2}^{\infty} \left(\frac{1}{k-1} - \frac{1}{k} \right) = \underbrace{\sum_{k=2}^{\infty} \frac{1}{k-1}}_{\text{diverges}} - \underbrace{\sum_{k=2}^{\infty} \frac{1}{k}}_{\text{diverges}} \quad \text{This is } incorrect!$$

and then conclude that the original series diverges. Neither $\sum_{k=2}^{\infty} \frac{1}{k-1}$ nor $\sum_{k=2}^{\infty} \frac{1}{k}$ converges; therefore, Property 2 of Theorem 8.13 does not apply.

EXAMPLE 5 Using properties of series Evaluate the infinite series

$$S = \sum_{k=1}^{\infty} \left(5\left(\frac{2}{3}\right)^k - \frac{2^{k-1}}{7^k} \right).$$

SOLUTION We examine the two series $\sum_{k=1}^{\infty} 5\left(\frac{2}{3}\right)^k$ and $\sum_{k=1}^{\infty} \frac{2^{k-1}}{7^k}$ individually. The first series is a geometric series and is evaluated using the methods of Section 8.3. Its first few terms are

$$\sum_{k=1}^{\infty} 5\left(\frac{2}{3}\right)^k = 5\left(\frac{2}{3}\right) + 5\left(\frac{2}{3}\right)^2 + 5\left(\frac{2}{3}\right)^3 + \cdots.$$

The first term of the series is $a = 5\left(\frac{2}{3}\right)$ and the ratio is $r = \frac{2}{3} < 1$; therefore,

$$\sum_{k=1}^{\infty} 5\left(\frac{2}{3}\right)^k = \frac{a}{1-r} = \frac{5\left(\frac{2}{3}\right)}{1 - \frac{2}{3}} = 10.$$

Writing out the first few terms of the second series, we see that it, too, is a geometric series:

$$\sum_{k=1}^{\infty} \frac{2^{k-1}}{7^k} = \frac{1}{7} + \frac{2}{7^2} + \frac{2^2}{7^3} + \cdots.$$

The first term is $a = \frac{1}{7}$ and the ratio is $r = \frac{2}{7} < 1$; therefore,

$$\sum_{k=1}^{\infty} \frac{2^{k-1}}{7^k} = \frac{a}{1-r} = \frac{\frac{1}{7}}{1-\frac{2}{7}} = \frac{1}{5}.$$

Both series converge. By Property 2 of Theorem 8.13, we combine the two series and have $S = 10 - \frac{1}{5} = \frac{49}{5}$.

Related Exercises 43–50 ◄

QUICK CHECK 5 For a series with positive terms, explain why the sequence of partial sums $\{S_n\}$ is an increasing sequence. ◄

SECTION 8.4 EXERCISES

Review Questions

1. If we know that $\lim_{k\to\infty} a_k = 1$, then what can we say about $\sum_{k=1}^{\infty} a_k$?

2. Is it true that if the terms of a series of positive terms decrease to zero, then the series converges? Explain using an example.

3. Can the Integral Test be used to determine whether a series diverges?

4. For what values of p does the series $\sum_{k=1}^{\infty} \frac{1}{k^p}$ converge? For what values of p does it diverge?

5. For what values of p does the series $\sum_{k=10}^{\infty} \frac{1}{k^p}$ converge (initial index is 10)? For what values of p does it diverge?

6. Explain why the sequence of partial sums for a series with positive terms is an increasing sequence.

7. Define the remainder of an infinite series.

8. If a series of positive terms converges, does it follow that the remainder R_n must decrease to zero as $n \to \infty$? Explain.

Basic Skills

9–18. Divergence Test *Use the Divergence Test to determine whether the following series diverge or state that the test is inconclusive.*

9. $\sum_{k=0}^{\infty} \frac{k}{2k+1}$

10. $\sum_{k=1}^{\infty} \frac{k}{k^2+1}$

11. $\sum_{k=2}^{\infty} \frac{k}{\ln k}$

12. $\sum_{k=1}^{\infty} \frac{k^2}{2^k}$

13. $\sum_{k=0}^{\infty} \frac{1}{1000+k}$

14. $\sum_{k=1}^{\infty} \frac{k^3}{k^3+1}$

15. $\sum_{k=2}^{\infty} \frac{\sqrt{k}}{\ln^{10} k}$

16. $\sum_{k=1}^{\infty} \frac{\sqrt{k^2+1}}{k}$

17. $\sum_{k=1}^{\infty} k^{1/k}$

18. $\sum_{k=1}^{\infty} \frac{k^3}{k!}$

19–28. Integral Test *Use the Integral Test to determine the convergence or divergence of the following series, or state that the test does not apply.*

19. $\sum_{k=2}^{\infty} \frac{1}{e^k}$

20. $\sum_{k=1}^{\infty} \frac{k}{\sqrt{k^2+4}}$

21. $\sum_{k=1}^{\infty} ke^{-2k^2}$

22. $\sum_{k=1}^{\infty} \frac{1}{\sqrt[3]{k+10}}$

23. $\sum_{k=0}^{\infty} \frac{1}{\sqrt{k+8}}$

24. $\sum_{k=2}^{\infty} \frac{1}{k(\ln k)^2}$

25. $\sum_{k=1}^{\infty} \frac{k}{e^k}$

26. $\sum_{k=3}^{\infty} \frac{1}{k(\ln k)\ln\ln k}$

27. $\sum_{k=1}^{\infty} \frac{|\sin k|}{k^2}$

28. $\sum_{k=1}^{\infty} \frac{k}{(k^2+1)^3}$

29–34. p-series *Determine the convergence or divergence of the following series.*

29. $\sum_{k=1}^{\infty} \frac{1}{k^{10}}$

30. $\sum_{k=2}^{\infty} \frac{k^e}{k^\pi}$

31. $\sum_{k=3}^{\infty} \frac{1}{(k-2)^4}$

32. $\sum_{k=1}^{\infty} 2k^{-3/2}$

33. $\sum_{k=1}^{\infty} \frac{1}{\sqrt[3]{k}}$

34. $\sum_{k=1}^{\infty} \frac{1}{\sqrt[3]{27k^2}}$

T **35–42. Remainders and estimates** *Consider the following convergent series.*

a. *Find an upper bound for the remainder in terms of n.*
b. *Find how many terms are needed to ensure that the remainder is less than 10^{-3}.*
c. *Find lower and upper bounds (L_n and U_n, respectively) on the exact value of the series.*
d. *Find an interval in which the value of the series must lie if you approximate it using ten terms of the series.*

35. $\sum_{k=1}^{\infty} \frac{1}{k^6}$

36. $\sum_{k=1}^{\infty} \frac{1}{k^8}$

37. $\sum_{k=1}^{\infty} \frac{1}{3^k}$

38. $\sum_{k=2}^{\infty} \frac{1}{k(\ln k)^2}$

39. $\sum_{k=1}^{\infty} \frac{1}{k^{3/2}}$

40. $\sum_{k=1}^{\infty} e^{-k}$

41. $\sum_{k=1}^{\infty} \frac{1}{k^3}$

42. $\sum_{k=1}^{\infty} ke^{-k^2}$

43–50. Properties of series *Use the properties of infinite series to evaluate the following series.*

43. $\sum_{k=1}^{\infty} \frac{4}{12^k}$

44. $\sum_{k=2}^{\infty} 3e^{-k}$

45. $\sum_{k=0}^{\infty} \left(3\left(\frac{2}{5}\right)^k - 2\left(\frac{5}{7}\right)^k\right)$

46. $\sum_{k=1}^{\infty} \left(2\left(\frac{3}{5}\right)^k + 3\left(\frac{4}{9}\right)^k\right)$

47. $\sum_{k=1}^{\infty} \left(\frac{1}{3}\left(\frac{5}{6}\right)^k + \frac{3}{5}\left(\frac{7}{9}\right)^k\right)$

48. $\sum_{k=0}^{\infty} \left(\frac{1}{2}(0.2)^k + \frac{3}{2}(0.8)^k\right)$

49. $\sum_{k=1}^{\infty} \left(\left(\frac{1}{6}\right)^k + \left(\frac{1}{3}\right)^{k-1}\right)$

50. $\sum_{k=0}^{\infty} \frac{2-3^k}{6^k}$

Further Explorations

51. Explain why or why not Determine whether the following statements are true and give an explanation or counterexample.

a. If $\sum_{k=1}^{\infty} a_k$ converges, then $\sum_{k=10}^{\infty} a_k$ converges.

b. If $\sum_{k=1}^{\infty} a_k$ diverges, then $\sum_{k=10}^{\infty} a_k$ diverges.

c. If $\sum a_k$ converges, then $\sum (a_k + 0.0001)$ also converges.

d. If $\sum p^k$ diverges, then $\sum (p + 0.001)^k$ diverges, for a fixed real number p.

e. If $\sum k^{-p}$ converges, then $\sum k^{-p+0.001}$ converges.

f. If $\lim_{k \to \infty} a_k = 0$, then $\sum a_k$ converges.

52–57. Choose your test *Determine whether the following series converge or diverge.*

52. $\displaystyle\sum_{k=1}^{\infty} \sqrt{\frac{k+1}{k}}$

53. $\displaystyle\sum_{k=1}^{\infty} \frac{1}{(3k+1)(3k+4)}$

54. $\displaystyle\sum_{k=0}^{\infty} \frac{10}{k^2 + 9}$

55. $\displaystyle\sum_{k=1}^{\infty} \frac{k}{\sqrt{k^2 + 1}}$

56. $\displaystyle\sum_{k=1}^{\infty} \frac{2^k + 3^k}{4^k}$

57. $\displaystyle\sum_{k=1}^{\infty} \frac{4}{k (\ln k)^2}$

58. Log p-series Consider the series $\displaystyle\sum_{k=2}^{\infty} \frac{1}{k(\ln k)^p}$, where p is a real number.

a. Use the Integral Test to determine the values of p for which this series converges.

b. Does this series converge faster for $p = 2$ or $p = 3$? Explain.

59. Loglog p-series Consider the series $\displaystyle\sum_{k=3}^{\infty} \frac{1}{k (\ln k)(\ln \ln k)^p}$, where p is a real number.

a. For what values of p does this series converge?

b. Which of the following series converges faster? Explain.

$$\sum_{k=2}^{\infty} \frac{1}{k(\ln k)^2} \quad \text{or} \quad \sum_{k=3}^{\infty} \frac{1}{k (\ln k)(\ln \ln k)^2}?$$

60. Find a series Find a series that

a. converges faster than $\displaystyle\sum \frac{1}{k^2}$ but slower than $\displaystyle\sum \frac{1}{k^3}$.

b. Diverges faster than $\displaystyle\sum \frac{1}{k}$ but slower than $\displaystyle\sum \frac{1}{\sqrt{k}}$.

c. Converges faster than $\displaystyle\sum \frac{1}{k \ln^2 k}$ but slower than $\displaystyle\sum \frac{1}{k^2}$.

Additional Exercises

61. A divergence proof Give an argument similar to that given in the text for the harmonic series to show that $\displaystyle\sum_{k=1}^{\infty} \frac{1}{\sqrt{k}}$ diverges.

62. Properties proof Use the ideas in the proof of Property 1 of Theorem 8.13 to prove Property 2 of Theorem 8.13.

63. Property of divergent series Prove that if $\sum a_k$ diverges, then $\sum c a_k$ also diverges, where $c \neq 0$ is a constant.

64. Prime numbers The prime numbers are those positive integers that are divisible by only 1 and themselves (for example, 2, 3, 5, 7, 11, 13, ...). A celebrated theorem states that the sequence of prime numbers $\{p_k\}$ satisfies $\lim_{k \to \infty} p_k/(k \ln k) = 1$. Show that $\displaystyle\sum_{k=2}^{\infty} \frac{1}{k \ln k}$ diverges, which implies that the series $\displaystyle\sum_{k=1}^{\infty} \frac{1}{p_k}$ diverges.

T 65. The zeta function The Riemann zeta function is the subject of extensive research and is associated with several renowned unsolved problems. It is defined by $\zeta(x) = \displaystyle\sum_{k=1}^{\infty} \frac{1}{k^x}$. When x is a real number, the zeta function becomes a p-series. For even positive integers p, the value of $\zeta(p)$ is known exactly. For example,

$$\sum_{k=1}^{\infty} \frac{1}{k^2} = \frac{\pi^2}{6}, \quad \sum_{k=1}^{\infty} \frac{1}{k^4} = \frac{\pi^4}{90}, \quad \text{and} \quad \sum_{k=1}^{\infty} \frac{1}{k^6} = \frac{\pi^6}{945}, \ldots$$

Use the estimation techniques described in the text to approximate $\zeta(3)$ and $\zeta(5)$ (whose values are not known exactly) with a remainder less than 10^{-3}.

66. Showing that $\displaystyle\sum_{k=1}^{\infty} \frac{1}{k^2} = \frac{\pi^2}{6}$ In 1734, Leonhard Euler informally proved that $\displaystyle\sum_{k=1}^{\infty} \frac{1}{k^2} = \frac{\pi^2}{6}$. An elegant proof is outlined here that uses the inequality

$$\cot^2 x < \frac{1}{x^2} < 1 + \cot^2 x \left(\text{provided that } 0 < x < \frac{\pi}{2} \right)$$

and the identity

$$\sum_{k=1}^{n} \cot^2 k\theta = \frac{n(2n-1)}{3}, \text{ for } n = 1, 2, 3, \ldots, \text{where } \theta = \frac{\pi}{2n+1}.$$

a. Show that $\displaystyle\sum_{k=1}^{n} \cot^2 k\theta < \frac{1}{\theta^2} \sum_{k=1}^{n} \frac{1}{k^2} < n + \sum_{k=1}^{n} \cot^2 k\theta$.

b. Use the inequality in part (a) to show that

$$\frac{n(2n-1)\pi^2}{3(2n+1)^2} < \sum_{k=1}^{n} \frac{1}{k^2} < \frac{n(2n+2)\pi^2}{3(2n+1)^2}.$$

c. Use the Squeeze Theorem to conclude that $\displaystyle\sum_{k=1}^{\infty} \frac{1}{k^2} = \frac{\pi^2}{6}$.

(Source: The College Mathematics Journal, 24, 5, Nov 1993)

67. Reciprocals of odd squares Assume that $\displaystyle\sum_{k=1}^{\infty} \frac{1}{k^2} = \frac{\pi^2}{6}$ (Exercises 65 and 66) and that the terms of this series may be rearranged without changing the value of the series. Determine the sum of the reciprocals of the squares of the odd positive integers.

T 68. Shifted p-series Consider the sequence $\{F_n\}$ defined by

$$F_n = \sum_{k=1}^{\infty} \frac{1}{k(k+n)},$$

for $n = 0, 1, 2, \ldots$. When $n = 0$, the series is a p-series, and we have $F_0 = \pi^2/6$ (Exercises 65 and 66).

a. Explain why $\{F_n\}$ is a decreasing sequence.

b. Plot $\{F_n\}$, for $n = 1, 2, \ldots, 20$.

c. Based on your experiments, make a conjecture about $\lim_{n \to \infty} F_n$.

69. A sequence of sums Consider the sequence $\{x_n\}$ defined for $n = 1, 2, 3, \ldots$ by

$$x_n = \sum_{k=n+1}^{2n} \frac{1}{k} = \frac{1}{n+1} + \frac{1}{n+2} + \cdots + \frac{1}{2n}.$$

a. Write out the terms x_1, x_2, x_3.

b. Show that $\frac{1}{2} \leq x_n < 1$, for $n = 1, 2, 3, \ldots$.

c. Show that x_n is the right Riemann sum for $\displaystyle\int_1^2 \frac{dx}{x}$ using n subintervals.

d. Conclude that $\lim_{n \to \infty} x_n = \ln 2$.

T 70. The harmonic series and Euler's constant

   a. Sketch the function $f(x) = 1/x$ on the interval $[1, n + 1]$, where n is a positive integer. Use this graph to verify that

$$\ln(n+1) < 1 + \frac{1}{2} + \frac{1}{3} + \cdots + \frac{1}{n} < 1 + \ln n.$$

   b. Let S_n be the sum of the first n terms of the harmonic series, so part (a) says $\ln(n+1) < S_n < 1 + \ln n$. Define the new sequence $\{E_n\}$ by

$$E_n = S_n - \ln(n+1), \quad \text{for } n = 1, 2, 3, \ldots.$$

   Show that $E_n > 0$, for $n = 1, 2, 3, \ldots.$

   c. Using a figure similar to that used in part (a), show that

$$\frac{1}{n+1} > \ln(n+2) - \ln(n+1).$$

   d. Use parts (a) and (c) to show that $\{E_n\}$ is an increasing sequence ($E_{n+1} > E_n$).

   e. Use part (a) to show that $\{E_n\}$ is bounded above by 1.

   f. Conclude from parts (d) and (e) that $\{E_n\}$ has a limit less than or equal to 1. This limit is known as **Euler's constant** and is denoted γ (the Greek lowercase gamma).

   g. By computing terms of $\{E_n\}$, estimate the value of γ and compare it to the value $\gamma \approx 0.5772$. (It has been conjectured that γ is irrational.)

   h. The preceding arguments show that the sum of the first n terms of the harmonic series satisfy $S_n \approx 0.5772 + \ln(n+1)$. How many terms must be summed for the sum to exceed 10?

71. Stacking dominoes Consider a set of identical dominoes that are 2 inches long. The dominoes are stacked on top of each other with their long edges aligned so that each domino overhangs the one beneath it *as far as possible* (see figure).

   a. If there are n dominoes in the stack, what is the *greatest* distance that the top domino can be made to overhang the bottom domino? (*Hint:* Put the nth domino beneath the previous $n - 1$ dominoes.)

   b. If we allow for infinitely many dominoes in the stack, what is the greatest distance that the top domino can be made to overhang the bottom domino?

72. Gabriel's wedding cake Consider a wedding cake of infinite height, each layer of which is a right circular cylinder of height 1. The bottom layer of the cake has a radius of 1, the second layer has a radius of $1/2$, the third layer has a radius of $1/3$, and the nth layer has a radius of $1/n$ (see figure).

   a. To determine how much frosting is needed to cover the cake, find the area of the lateral (vertical) sides of the wedding cake. What is the area of the horizontal surfaces of the cake?

   b. Determine the volume of the cake. (*Hint:* Use the result of Exercise 66.)

   c. Comment on your answers to parts (a) and (b).

(*Source: The College Mathematics Journal*, 30, 1, Jan 1999)

73. The harmonic series and the Fibonacci sequence The Fibonacci sequence $\{1, 1, 2, 3, 5, 8, 13, \ldots\}$ is generated by the recurrence relation

$$f_{n+1} = f_n + f_{n-1}, \text{ for } n = 1, 2, 3, \ldots, \text{ where } f_0 = 1, f_1 = 1.$$

   a. It can be shown that the sequence of ratios of successive terms of the sequence $\left\{\dfrac{f_{n+1}}{f_n}\right\}$ has a limit φ. Divide both sides of the recurrence relation by f_n, take the limit as $n \to \infty$, and show that $\varphi = \lim\limits_{n \to \infty} \dfrac{f_{n+1}}{f_n} = \dfrac{1 + \sqrt{5}}{2} \approx 1.618$.

   b. Show that $\lim\limits_{n \to \infty} \dfrac{f_{n-1}}{f_{n+1}} = 1 - \dfrac{1}{\varphi} \approx 0.382$.

   c. Now consider the harmonic series and group terms as follows:

$$\sum_{k=1}^{\infty} \frac{1}{k} = 1 + \frac{1}{2} + \frac{1}{3} + \underbrace{\left(\frac{1}{4} + \frac{1}{5}\right)}_{2 \text{ terms}} + \underbrace{\left(\frac{1}{6} + \frac{1}{7} + \frac{1}{8}\right)}_{3 \text{ terms}}$$

$$+ \underbrace{\left(\frac{1}{9} + \cdots + \frac{1}{13}\right)}_{5 \text{ terms}} + \cdots.$$

   With the Fibonacci sequence in mind, show that

$$\sum_{k=1}^{\infty} \frac{1}{k} \geq 1 + \frac{1}{2} + \frac{1}{3} + \frac{2}{5} + \frac{3}{8} + \frac{5}{13} + \cdots = 1 + \sum_{k=1}^{\infty} \frac{f_{k-1}}{f_{k+1}}.$$

   d. Use part (b) to conclude that the harmonic series diverges.

   (*Source: The College Mathematics Journal*, 43, May 2012)

QUICK CHECK ANSWERS

1. The series diverges for $|r| \geq 1$. **2. a.** Divergent p-series **b.** Convergent geometric series **c.** Convergent p-series **3.** The remainder is $R_n = a_{n+1} + a_{n+2} + \cdots$, which consists of positive numbers. **4.** Removing a finite number of terms does not change whether the series converges. It generally changes the value of the series. **5.** Given the nth term of the sequence of partial sums S_n, the next term is obtained by adding a positive number. So $S_{n+1} > S_n$, which means the sequence is increasing. ◄

8.5 The Ratio, Root, and Comparison Tests

We now consider several additional convergence tests for series with positive terms: the Ratio Test, the Root Test, and two comparison tests. The Ratio Test is used frequently throughout the next chapter, and comparison tests are valuable when no other test works. As in Section 8.4, these tests determine *whether* an infinite series converges, but they do not establish the value of the series.

The Ratio Test

The Integral Test is powerful, but limited, because it requires evaluating integrals. For example, the series $\sum 1/k!$, with a factorial term, cannot be handled by the Integral Test. The next test significantly enlarges the set of infinite series that we can analyze.

> ▶ In words, the Ratio Test says the limit of the ratio of successive terms of the series must be less than 1 for convergence of the series.

THEOREM 8.14   Ratio Test

Let $\sum a_k$ be an infinite series with positive terms and let $r = \lim\limits_{k \to \infty} \dfrac{a_{k+1}}{a_k}$.

1. If $0 \leq r < 1$, the series converges.
2. If $r > 1$ (including $r = \infty$), the series diverges.
3. If $r = 1$, the test is inconclusive.

> ▶ See Appendix B for a formal proof of Theorem 8.14.

Proof (outline): The idea behind the proof provides insight. Let's assume that the limit r exists. Then as k gets large and the ratio a_{k+1}/a_k approaches r, we have $a_{k+1} \approx ra_k$. Therefore, as one goes farther and farther out in the series, it behaves like

$$a_k + a_{k+1} + a_{k+2} + \cdots \approx a_k + ra_k + r^2 a_k + r^3 a_k + \cdots$$
$$= a_k \left(1 + r + r^2 + r^3 + \cdots \right).$$

The tail of the series, which determines whether the series converges, behaves like a geometric series with ratio r. We know that if $0 \leq r < 1$, the geometric series converges, and if $r > 1$, the series diverges, which is the conclusion of the Ratio Test.   ◄

EXAMPLE 1   Using the Ratio Test Use the Ratio Test to determine whether the following series converge.

a. $\displaystyle\sum_{k=1}^{\infty} \frac{10^k}{k!}$ **b.** $\displaystyle\sum_{k=1}^{\infty} \frac{k^k}{k!}$ **c.** $\displaystyle\sum_{k=1}^{\infty} e^{-k}\left(k^2 + 4\right)$

SOLUTION In each case, the limit of the ratio of successive terms is determined.

> ▶ Recall that
> $$k! = k \cdot (k-1) \cdots 2 \cdot 1.$$
> Therefore,
> $$(k+1)! = (k+1)\underbrace{k\,(k-1)\cdots 1}_{k!}$$
> $$= (k+1)k!.$$

a. $r = \lim\limits_{k \to \infty} \dfrac{a_{k+1}}{a_k} = \lim\limits_{k \to \infty} \dfrac{10^{k+1}/(k+1)!}{10^k/k!}$ Substitute a_{k+1} and a_k.

$\qquad = \lim\limits_{k \to \infty} \dfrac{10^{k+1}}{10^k} \cdot \dfrac{k!}{(k+1)k!}$ Invert and multiply.

$\qquad = \lim\limits_{k \to \infty} \dfrac{10}{k+1} = 0$ Simplify and evaluate the limit.

Because $r = 0 < 1$, the series converges by the Ratio Test.

▶ Recall from Section 4.7 that
$$\lim_{k \to \infty} \left(1 + \frac{1}{k}\right)^k = e \approx 2.718.$$

b. $r = \lim\limits_{k \to \infty} \dfrac{a_{k+1}}{a_k} = \lim\limits_{k \to \infty} \dfrac{(k+1)^{k+1}/(k+1)!}{k^k/k!}$ Substitute a_{k+1} and a_k.

$\qquad\qquad = \lim\limits_{k \to \infty} \left(\dfrac{k+1}{k}\right)^k$ Simplify.

$\qquad\qquad = \lim\limits_{k \to \infty} \left(1 + \dfrac{1}{k}\right)^k = e$ Simplify and evaluate the limit.

Because $r = e > 1$, the series diverges by the Ratio Test. Alternatively, we could have noted that $\lim\limits_{k \to \infty} k^k/k! = \infty$ (Theorem 8.6) and used the Divergence Test to reach the same conclusion.

c. $r = \lim\limits_{k \to \infty} \dfrac{a_{k+1}}{a_k} = \lim\limits_{k \to \infty} \dfrac{e^{-(k+1)}((k+1)^2 + 4)}{e^{-k}(k^2 + 4)}$ Substitute a_{k+1} and a_k.

$\qquad\qquad = \lim\limits_{k \to \infty} \dfrac{e^{-k}e^{-1}(k^2 + 2k + 5)}{e^{-k}(k^2 + 4)}$ Simplify.

$\qquad\qquad = e^{-1} \underbrace{\lim\limits_{k \to \infty} \dfrac{k^2 + 2k + 5}{k^2 + 1}}_{1}$ Simplify.

$\qquad\qquad = e^{-1}$

Because $e^{-1} = \dfrac{1}{e} < 1$, the series converges by the Ratio Test.

Related Exercises 9–18 ◀

QUICK CHECK 1 Evaluate $10!/9!$, $(k+2)!/k!$, and $k!/(k+1)!$ ◀

The Ratio Test is conclusive for many series. Nevertheless, observe what happens when the Ratio Test is applied to the harmonic series $\sum\limits_{k=1}^{\infty} \dfrac{1}{k}$:

$$r = \lim_{k \to \infty} \frac{a_{k+1}}{a_k} = \lim_{k \to \infty} \frac{1/(k+1)}{1/k} = \lim_{k \to \infty} \frac{k}{k+1} = 1,$$

▶ At the end of this section, we offer guidelines to help you to decide which convergence test is best suited for a given series.

which means the test is inconclusive. We know the harmonic series diverges, yet the Ratio Test cannot be used to establish this fact. Like all the convergence tests presented so far, the Ratio Test works only for certain classes of series. For this reason, it is useful to present a few additional convergence tests.

QUICK CHECK 2 Verify that the Ratio Test is inconclusive for $\sum\limits_{k=1}^{\infty} \dfrac{1}{k^2}$. What test could be applied to show that $\sum\limits_{k=1}^{\infty} \dfrac{1}{k^2}$ converges? ◀

The Root Test

Occasionally a series arises for which the preceding tests are difficult to apply. In these situations, the Root Test may be the tool that is needed.

THEOREM 8.15   Root Test

Let Σa_k be an infinite series with nonnegative terms and let $\rho = \lim\limits_{k \to \infty} \sqrt[k]{a_k}$.

1. If $0 \le \rho < 1$, the series converges.

2. If $\rho > 1$ (including $\rho = \infty$), the series diverges.

3. If $\rho = 1$, the test is inconclusive.

Proof (outline): Assume that the limit ρ exists. If k is large, we have $\rho \approx \sqrt[k]{a_k}$ or $a_k \approx \rho^k$. For large values of k, the tail of the series, which determines whether a series converges, behaves like

$$a_k + a_{k+1} + a_{k+2} + \cdots \approx \rho^k + \rho^{k+1} + \rho^{k+2} + \cdots.$$

> See Appendix B for a formal proof of Theorem 8.15.

Therefore, the tail of the series is approximately a geometric series with ratio ρ. If $0 \leq \rho < 1$, the geometric series converges, and if $\rho > 1$, the series diverges, which is the conclusion of the Root Test. ◄

EXAMPLE 2 **Using the Root Test** Use the Root Test to determine whether the following series converge.

a. $\displaystyle\sum_{k=1}^{\infty} \left(\frac{4k^2 - 3}{7k^2 + 6} \right)^k$ **b.** $\displaystyle\sum_{k=1}^{\infty} \frac{2^k}{k^{10}}$

SOLUTION

a. The required limit is

$$\rho = \lim_{k \to \infty} \sqrt[k]{\left(\frac{4k^2 - 3}{7k^2 + 6} \right)^k} = \lim_{k \to \infty} \frac{4k^2 - 3}{7k^2 + 6} = \frac{4}{7}.$$

Because $0 \leq \rho < 1$, the series converges by the Root Test.

b. In this case,

$$\rho = \lim_{k \to \infty} \sqrt[k]{\frac{2^k}{k^{10}}} = \lim_{k \to \infty} \frac{2}{k^{10/k}} = \lim_{k \to \infty} \frac{2}{\left(k^{1/k}\right)^{10}} = 2. \quad \lim_{k \to \infty} k^{1/k} = 1$$

Because $\rho > 1$, the series diverges by the Root Test.

We could have used the Ratio Test for both series in this example, but the Root Test is easier to apply in each case. In part (b), the Divergence Test leads to the same conclusion.

Related Exercises 19–26 ◄

The Comparison Test

Tests that use known series to test unknown series are called *comparison tests*. The first test is the Basic Comparison Test or simply the Comparison Test.

> Whether a series converges depends on the behavior of terms in the tail (large values of the index). So the inequalities $0 < a_k \leq b_k$ and $0 < b_k \leq a_k$ need not hold for all terms of the series. They must hold for all $k > N$ for some positive integer N.

THEOREM 8.16 **Comparison Test**

Let Σa_k and Σb_k be series with positive terms.

1. If $0 < a_k \leq b_k$ and Σb_k converges, then Σa_k converges.

2. If $0 < b_k \leq a_k$ and Σb_k diverges, then Σa_k diverges.

Proof: Assume that Σb_k converges, which means that Σb_k has a finite value B. The sequence of partial sums for Σa_k satisfies

$$S_n = \sum_{k=1}^{n} a_k \leq \sum_{k=1}^{n} b_k \quad a_k \leq b_k$$

$$< \sum_{k=1}^{\infty} b_k \qquad \text{Positive terms are added to a finite sum.}$$

$$= B. \qquad \text{Value of series}$$

Therefore, the sequence of partial sums for Σa_k is increasing and bounded above by B. By the Bounded Monotonic Sequence Theorem (Theorem 8.5), the sequence of partial sums of Σa_k has a limit, which implies that Σa_k converges. The second case of the theorem is proved in a similar way. ◄

The Comparison Test can be illustrated with graphs of sequences of partial sums. Consider the series

$$\sum_{k=1}^{\infty} a_k = \sum_{k=1}^{\infty} \frac{1}{k^2 + 10} \quad \text{and} \quad \sum_{k=1}^{\infty} b_k = \sum_{k=1}^{\infty} \frac{1}{k^2}.$$

Because $\frac{1}{k^2 + 10} < \frac{1}{k^2}$, it follows that $a_k < b_k$, for $k \geq 1$. Furthermore, $\sum b_k$ is a convergent p-series. By the Comparison Test, we conclude that $\sum a_k$ also converges (Figure 8.32). The second case of the Comparison Test is illustrated with the series

$$\sum_{k=4}^{\infty} a_k = \sum_{k=4}^{\infty} \frac{1}{\sqrt{k} - 3} \quad \text{and} \quad \sum_{k=4}^{\infty} b_k = \sum_{k=4}^{\infty} \frac{1}{\sqrt{k}}.$$

Now $\frac{1}{\sqrt{k}} < \frac{1}{\sqrt{k} - 3}$, for $k \geq 4$. Therefore, $b_k < a_k$, for $k \geq 4$. Because $\sum b_k$ is a divergent p-series, by the Comparison Test, $\sum a_k$ also diverges. Figure 8.33 shows that the sequence of partial sums for $\sum a_k$ lies above the sequence of partial sums for $\sum b_k$. Because the sequence of partial sums for $\sum b_k$ diverges, the sequence of partial sums for $\sum a_k$ also diverges.

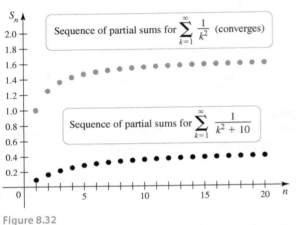

Figure 8.32

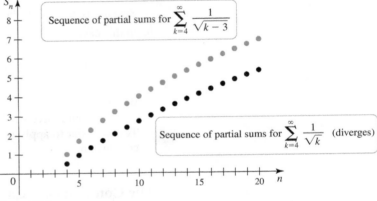

Figure 8.33

The key in using the Comparison Test is finding an appropriate comparison series. Plenty of practice will enable you to spot patterns and choose good comparison series.

EXAMPLE 3   Using the Comparison Test Determine whether the following series converge.

a. $\displaystyle\sum_{k=1}^{\infty} \frac{k^3}{2k^4 - 1}$ **b.** $\displaystyle\sum_{k=2}^{\infty} \frac{\ln k}{k^3}$

SOLUTION In using comparison tests, it's helpful to get a feel for how the terms of the given series are decreasing. If they are not decreasing, the series diverges.

> If $\sum a_k$ diverges, then $\sum c a_k$ also diverges for any constant $c \neq 0$ (Exercise 63 of Section 8.4).

a. As we go farther and farther out in this series ($k \to \infty$), the terms behave like

$$\frac{k^3}{2k^4 - 1} \approx \frac{k^3}{2k^4} = \frac{1}{2k}.$$

So a reasonable choice for a comparison series is the divergent series $\sum \dfrac{1}{2k}$. We must now show that the terms of the given series are *greater* than the terms of the comparison series. It is done by noting that $2k^4 - 1 < 2k^4$. Inverting both sides, we have

$$\frac{1}{2k^4 - 1} > \frac{1}{2k^4}, \quad \text{which implies that} \quad \frac{k^3}{2k^4 - 1} > \frac{k^3}{2k^4} = \frac{1}{2k}.$$

Because $\sum \dfrac{1}{2k}$ diverges, case (2) of the Comparison Test implies that the given series also diverges.

b. We note that $\ln k < k$, for $k \geq 2$, and then divide by k^3:

$$\frac{\ln k}{k^3} < \frac{k}{k^3} = \frac{1}{k^2}.$$

QUICK CHECK 3 Explain why it is difficult to use the divergent series $\sum 1/k$ as a comparison series to test $\sum 1/(k+1)$. ◄

Therefore, an appropriate comparison series is the convergent *p*-series $\sum \dfrac{1}{k^2}$. Because $\sum \dfrac{1}{k^2}$ converges, the given series converges.

Related Exercises 27–38 ◄

The Limit Comparison Test

The Comparison Test should be tried if there is an obvious comparison series and the necessary inequality is easily established. Notice, however, that if the series in Example 3a were $\displaystyle\sum_{k=1}^{\infty} \dfrac{k^3}{2k^4 + 10}$ instead of $\displaystyle\sum_{k=1}^{\infty} \dfrac{k^3}{2k^4 - 1}$, then the comparison to the series $\sum \dfrac{1}{2k}$ would not work. Rather than fiddling with inequalities, it is often easier to use a more refined test called the *Limit Comparison Test*.

QUICK CHECK 4 For case (1) of the Limit Comparison Test, we must have $0 < L < \infty$. Why can either a_k or b_k be chosen as the known comparison series? That is, why can L be the limit of a_k/b_k or b_k/a_k? ◄

> **THEOREM 8.17 Limit Comparison Test**
> Let $\sum a_k$ and $\sum b_k$ be series with positive terms and let
>
> $$\lim_{k \to \infty} \frac{a_k}{b_k} = L.$$
>
> **1.** If $0 < L < \infty$ (that is, L is a finite positive number), then $\sum a_k$ and $\sum b_k$ either both converge or both diverge.
>
> **2.** If $L = 0$ and $\sum b_k$ converges, then $\sum a_k$ converges.
>
> **3.** If $L = \infty$ and $\sum b_k$ diverges, then $\sum a_k$ diverges.

> ► Recall that $|x| < a$ is equivalent to $-a < x < a$.

Proof (Case 1): Recall the definition of $\displaystyle\lim_{k \to \infty} \dfrac{a_k}{b_k} = L$: Given any $\varepsilon > 0$, $\left| \dfrac{a_k}{b_k} - L \right| < \varepsilon$ provided k is sufficiently large. In this case, let's take $\varepsilon = L/2$. It then follows that for sufficiently large k, $\left| \dfrac{a_k}{b_k} - L \right| < \dfrac{L}{2}$, or (removing the absolute value) $-\dfrac{L}{2} < \dfrac{a_k}{b_k} - L < \dfrac{L}{2}$. Adding L to all terms in these inequalities, we have

$$\frac{L}{2} < \frac{a_k}{b_k} < \frac{3L}{2}.$$

These inequalities imply that for sufficiently large k,

$$\frac{Lb_k}{2} < a_k < \frac{3Lb_k}{2}.$$

We see that the terms of $\sum a_k$ are sandwiched between multiples of the terms of $\sum b_k$. By the Comparison Test, it follows that the two series converge or diverge together. Cases (2) and (3) ($L = 0$ and $L = \infty$, respectively) are treated in Exercise 81. ◄

EXAMPLE 4   Using the Limit Comparison Test Determine whether the following series converge.

a. $\displaystyle\sum_{k=1}^{\infty} \frac{5k^4 - 2k^2 + 3}{2k^6 - k + 5}$ **b.** $\displaystyle\sum_{k=1}^{\infty} \frac{\ln k}{k^2}.$

SOLUTION In both cases, we must find a comparison series whose terms behave like the terms of the given series as $k \to \infty$.

a. As $k \to \infty$, a rational function behaves like the ratio of the leading (highest-power) terms. In this case, as $k \to \infty$,

$$\frac{5k^4 - 2k^2 + 3}{2k^6 - k + 5} \approx \frac{5k^4}{2k^6} = \frac{5}{2k^2}.$$

Therefore, a reasonable comparison series is the convergent p-series $\displaystyle\sum_{k=1}^{\infty} \frac{1}{k^2}$ (the factor of $5/2$ does not affect whether the given series converges). Having chosen a comparison series, we compute the limit L:

$$L = \lim_{k \to \infty} \frac{(5k^4 - 2k^2 + 3)/(2k^6 - k + 5)}{1/k^2} \qquad \text{Ratio of terms of series}$$

$$= \lim_{k \to \infty} \frac{k^2(5k^4 - 2k^2 + 3)}{2k^6 - k + 5} \qquad \text{Simplify.}$$

$$= \lim_{k \to \infty} \frac{5k^6 - 2k^4 + 3k^2}{2k^6 - k + 5} = \frac{5}{2}. \qquad \text{Simplify and evaluate the limit.}$$

We see that $0 < L < \infty$; therefore, the given series converges.

b. Why is this series interesting? We know that $\displaystyle\sum_{k=1}^{\infty} \frac{1}{k^2}$ converges and that $\displaystyle\sum_{k=1}^{\infty} \frac{1}{k}$ diverges. The given series $\displaystyle\sum_{k=1}^{\infty} \frac{\ln k}{k^2}$ is "between" these two series. This observation suggests that we use either $\displaystyle\sum_{k=1}^{\infty} \frac{1}{k^2}$ or $\displaystyle\sum_{k=1}^{\infty} \frac{1}{k}$ as a comparison series. In the first case, letting $a_k = \ln k/k^2$ and $b_k = 1/k^2$, we find that

$$L = \lim_{k \to \infty} \frac{a_k}{b_k} = \lim_{k \to \infty} \frac{\ln k/k^2}{1/k^2} = \lim_{k \to \infty} \ln k = \infty.$$

Case (3) of the Limit Comparison Test does not apply here because the comparison series $\displaystyle\sum_{k=1}^{\infty} \frac{1}{k^2}$ converges; we can reach the conclusion of case (3) only when the comparison series *diverges*.

If, instead, we use the comparison series $\displaystyle\sum b_k = \sum \frac{1}{k}$, then

$$L = \lim_{k \to \infty} \frac{a_k}{b_k} = \lim_{k \to \infty} \frac{\ln k/k^2}{1/k} = \lim_{k \to \infty} \frac{\ln k}{k} = 0.$$

Case (2) of the Limit Comparison Test does not apply here because the comparison series $\displaystyle\sum_{k=1}^{\infty} \frac{1}{k}$ diverges; case (2) is conclusive only when the comparison series *converges*.

With a bit more cunning, the Limit Comparison Test becomes conclusive. A series that lies "between" $\sum\limits_{k=1}^{\infty} \dfrac{1}{k^2}$ and $\sum\limits_{k=1}^{\infty} \dfrac{1}{k}$ is the convergent p-series $\sum\limits_{k=1}^{\infty} \dfrac{1}{k^{3/2}}$; we try it as a comparison series. Letting $a_k = \ln k/k^2$ and $b_k = 1/k^{3/2}$, we find that

$$L = \lim_{k\to\infty} \frac{a_k}{b_k} = \lim_{k\to\infty} \frac{\ln k/k^2}{1/k^{3/2}} = \lim_{k\to\infty} \frac{\ln k}{\sqrt{k}} = 0.$$

(This limit is evaluated using l'Hôpital's Rule or by recalling that $\ln k$ grows more slowly than any positive power of k.) Now case (2) of the Limit Comparison Test applies; the comparison series $\sum \dfrac{1}{k^{3/2}}$ converges, so the given series converges.

Related Exercises 27–38 ◀

Guidelines for Choosing a Test

We close by outlining a procedure that puts the various convergence tests in perspective. Here is a reasonable course of action when testing a series of positive terms $\sum a_k$ for convergence.

1. Begin with the Divergence Test. If you show that $\lim\limits_{k\to\infty} a_k \neq 0$, then the series diverges and your work is finished. The order of growth rates of sequences given in Section 8.2 is useful for evaluating $\lim\limits_{k\to\infty} a_k$. (Recall that the Divergence Test also applies to series with arbitrary terms.)

2. Is the series a special series? Recall the convergence properties for the following series.
   - Geometric series: $\sum ar^k$ converges for $|r| < 1$ and diverges for $|r| \geq 1$ $(a \neq 0)$.
   - p-series: $\sum \dfrac{1}{k^p}$ converges for $p > 1$ and diverges for $p \leq 1$.
   - Check also for a telescoping series.

3. If the general kth term of the series looks like a function you can integrate, then try the Integral Test.

4. If the general kth term of the series involves $k!$, k^k, or a^k, where a is a constant, the Ratio Test is advisable. Series with k in an exponent may yield to the Root Test.

5. If the general kth term of the series is a rational function of k (or a root of a rational function), use the Comparison or the Limit Comparison Test with the families of series given in Step 2 as comparison series.

These guidelines will help, but in the end, convergence tests are mastered through practice. It's your turn.

SECTION 8.5 EXERCISES

Review Questions

1. Explain how the Ratio Test works.

2. Explain how the Root Test works.

3. Explain how the Limit Comparison Test works.

4. What is the first test you should use in analyzing the convergence of a series?

5. What test is advisable if a series of positive terms involves a factorial term?

6. What tests are best for the series $\sum a_k$ when a_k is a rational function of k?

7. Explain why, with a series of positive terms, the sequence of partial sums is an increasing sequence.

8. Do the tests discussed in this section tell you the value of the series? Explain.

Basic Skills

9–18. The Ratio Test *Use the Ratio Test to determine whether the following series converge.*

9. $\sum\limits_{k=1}^{\infty} \dfrac{1}{k!}$

10. $\sum\limits_{k=1}^{\infty} \dfrac{2^k}{k!}$

11. $\sum\limits_{k=1}^{\infty} \dfrac{k^2}{4^k}$

12. $\sum\limits_{k=1}^{\infty} \dfrac{k^k}{2^k}$

13. $\sum\limits_{k=1}^{\infty} ke^{-k}$

14. $\sum\limits_{k=1}^{\infty} \dfrac{k^k}{k!}$

15. $\sum\limits_{k=1}^{\infty} \dfrac{2^k}{k^{99}}$

16. $\sum\limits_{k=1}^{\infty} \dfrac{k^6}{k!}$

17. $\sum\limits_{k=1}^{\infty} \dfrac{(k!)^2}{(2k)!}$

18. $2 + \dfrac{4}{16} + \dfrac{8}{81} + \dfrac{16}{256} + \cdots$

19–26. The Root Test *Use the Root Test to determine whether the following series converge.*

19. $\displaystyle\sum_{k=1}^{\infty}\left(\frac{10k^3+k}{9k^3+k+1}\right)^k$ 20. $\displaystyle\sum_{k=1}^{\infty}\left(\frac{2k}{k+1}\right)^k$

21. $\displaystyle\sum_{k=1}^{\infty}\frac{k^2}{2^k}$ 22. $\displaystyle\sum_{k=1}^{\infty}\left(1+\frac{3}{k}\right)^{k^2}$

23. $\displaystyle\sum_{k=1}^{\infty}\left(\frac{k}{k+1}\right)^{2k^2}$ 24. $\displaystyle\sum_{k=1}^{\infty}\left(\frac{1}{\ln(k+1)}\right)^k$

25. $1+\left(\dfrac{1}{2}\right)^2+\left(\dfrac{1}{3}\right)^3+\left(\dfrac{1}{4}\right)^4+\cdots$

26. $\displaystyle\sum_{k=1}^{\infty}\frac{k}{e^k}$

27–38. Comparison tests *Use the Comparison Test or Limit Comparison Test to determine whether the following series converge.*

27. $\displaystyle\sum_{k=1}^{\infty}\frac{1}{k^2+4}$ 28. $\displaystyle\sum_{k=1}^{\infty}\frac{k^2+k-1}{k^4+4k^2-3}$

29. $\displaystyle\sum_{k=1}^{\infty}\frac{k^2-1}{k^3+4}$ 30. $\displaystyle\sum_{k=1}^{\infty}\frac{0.0001}{k+4}$

31. $\displaystyle\sum_{k=1}^{\infty}\frac{1}{k^{3/2}+1}$ 32. $\displaystyle\sum_{k=1}^{\infty}\sqrt{\frac{k}{k^3+1}}$

33. $\displaystyle\sum_{k=1}^{\infty}\frac{\sin(1/k)}{k^2}$ 34. $\displaystyle\sum_{k=1}^{\infty}\frac{1}{3^k-2^k}$

35. $\displaystyle\sum_{k=1}^{\infty}\frac{1}{2k-\sqrt{k}}$ 36. $\displaystyle\sum_{k=1}^{\infty}\frac{1}{k\sqrt{k+2}}$

37. $\displaystyle\sum_{k=1}^{\infty}\frac{\sqrt[3]{k^2+1}}{\sqrt{k^3+2}}$ 38. $\displaystyle\sum_{k=2}^{\infty}\frac{1}{(k\ln k)^2}$

Further Explorations

39. **Explain why or why not** Determine whether the following statements are true and give an explanation or counterexample.

  a. Suppose that $0<a_k<b_k$. If $\sum a_k$ converges, then $\sum b_k$ converges.
  b. Suppose that $0<a_k<b_k$. If $\sum a_k$ diverges, then $\sum b_k$ diverges.
  c. Suppose $0<b_k<c_k<a_k$. If $\sum a_k$ converges, then $\sum b_k$ and $\sum c_k$ converge.
  d. The Ratio Test is always inconclusive when applied to $\sum a_k$, where a_k is a rational function of k.

40–69. Choose your test *Use the test of your choice to determine whether the following series converge.*

40. $\left(\dfrac{1}{2}\right)^2+\left(\dfrac{2}{3}\right)^3+\left(\dfrac{3}{4}\right)^4+\cdots$

41. $\displaystyle\sum_{k=1}^{\infty}\left(1+\frac{2}{k}\right)^k$ 42. $\displaystyle\sum_{k=1}^{\infty}\left(\frac{k^2}{2k^2+1}\right)^k$ 43. $\displaystyle\sum_{k=1}^{\infty}\frac{k^{100}}{(k+1)!}$

44. $\displaystyle\sum_{k=1}^{\infty}\frac{\sin^2 k}{k^2}$ 45. $\displaystyle\sum_{k=1}^{\infty}(\sqrt[k]{k}-1)^{2k}$ 46. $\displaystyle\sum_{k=1}^{\infty}\frac{2^k}{e^k-1}$

47. $\displaystyle\sum_{k=1}^{\infty}\frac{k^2+2k+1}{3k^2+1}$ 48. $\displaystyle\sum_{k=1}^{\infty}\frac{1}{5^k-1}$

49. $\displaystyle\sum_{k=3}^{\infty}\frac{1}{\ln k}$ 50. $\displaystyle\sum_{k=3}^{\infty}\frac{1}{5^k-3^k}$ 51. $\displaystyle\sum_{k=1}^{\infty}\frac{1}{\sqrt{k^3-k+1}}$

52. $\displaystyle\sum_{k=1}^{\infty}\frac{(k!)^3}{(3k)!}$ 53. $\displaystyle\sum_{k=1}^{\infty}\left(\frac{1}{k}+2^{-k}\right)$ 54. $\displaystyle\sum_{k=2}^{\infty}\frac{5\ln k}{k}$

55. $\displaystyle\sum_{k=1}^{\infty}\frac{2^k k!}{k^k}$ 56. $\displaystyle\sum_{k=1}^{\infty}\left(1-\frac{1}{k}\right)^{k^2}$ 57. $\displaystyle\sum_{k=1}^{\infty}\frac{k^8}{k^{11}+3}$

58. $\displaystyle\sum_{k=1}^{\infty}\frac{1}{(1+p)^k},\ p>0$ 59. $\displaystyle\sum_{k=1}^{\infty}\frac{1}{k^{1+p}},\ p>0$

60. $\displaystyle\sum_{k=2}^{\infty}\frac{1}{k^2\ln k}$ 61. $\displaystyle\sum_{k=1}^{\infty}\ln\left(\frac{k+2}{k+1}\right)$ 62. $\displaystyle\sum_{k=1}^{\infty}k^{-1/k}$

63. $\displaystyle\sum_{k=2}^{\infty}\frac{1}{k\ln k}$ 64. $\displaystyle\sum_{k=1}^{\infty}\sin^2\frac{1}{k}$ 65. $\displaystyle\sum_{k=1}^{\infty}\tan\frac{1}{k}$

66. $\displaystyle\sum_{k=2}^{\infty}100k^{-k}$ 67. $\dfrac{1}{1\cdot3}+\dfrac{1}{3\cdot5}+\dfrac{1}{5\cdot7}+\cdots$

68. $\dfrac{1}{2^2}+\dfrac{2}{3^2}+\dfrac{3}{4^2}+\cdots$ 69. $\dfrac{1}{1!}+\dfrac{4}{2!}+\dfrac{9}{3!}+\dfrac{16}{4!}+\cdots$

70–77. Convergence parameter *Find the values of the parameter $p>0$ for which the following series converge.*

70. $\displaystyle\sum_{k=2}^{\infty}\frac{1}{(\ln k)^p}$ 71. $\displaystyle\sum_{k=2}^{\infty}\frac{\ln k}{k^p}$

72. $\displaystyle\sum_{k=2}^{\infty}\frac{1}{k(\ln k)(\ln\ln k)^p}$ 73. $\displaystyle\sum_{k=2}^{\infty}\left(\frac{\ln k}{k}\right)^p$

74. $\displaystyle\sum_{k=0}^{\infty}\frac{k!\,p^k}{(k+1)^k}$ (*Hint:* Stirling's formula is useful: $k!\approx\sqrt{2\pi k}\,k^k e^{-k}$ for large k.)

75. $\displaystyle\sum_{k=1}^{\infty}\frac{kp^k}{k+1}$ 76. $\displaystyle\sum_{k=1}^{\infty}\ln\left(\frac{k}{k+1}\right)^p$

77. $\displaystyle\sum_{k=1}^{\infty}\left(1-\frac{p}{k}\right)^k$

78. **Series of squares** Prove that if $\sum a_k$ is a convergent series of positive terms, then the series $\sum a_k^2$ also converges.

79. **Geometric series revisited** We know from Section 8.3 that the geometric series $\sum ar^k\ (a\neq0)$ converges if $0<r<1$ and diverges if $r>1$. Prove these facts using the Integral Test, the Ratio Test, and the Root Test. Now consider all values of r. What can be determined about the geometric series using the Divergence Test?

80. **Two sine series** Determine whether the following series converge.

  a. $\displaystyle\sum_{k=1}^{\infty}\sin\frac{1}{k}$ b. $\displaystyle\sum_{k=1}^{\infty}\frac{1}{k}\sin\frac{1}{k}$

Additional Exercises

81. **Limit Comparison Test proof** Use the proof of case (1) of the Limit Comparison Test (Theorem 8.17) to prove cases (2) and (3).

82–87. A glimpse ahead to power series *Use the Ratio Test to determine the values of $x\geq0$ for which each series converges.*

82. $\displaystyle\sum_{k=1}^{\infty}\frac{x^k}{k!}$ 83. $\displaystyle\sum_{k=1}^{\infty}x^k$ 84. $\displaystyle\sum_{k=1}^{\infty}\frac{x^k}{k}$

85. $\sum_{k=1}^{\infty} \dfrac{x^k}{k^2}$ **86.** $\sum_{k=1}^{\infty} \dfrac{x^{2k}}{k^2}$ **87.** $\sum_{k=1}^{\infty} \dfrac{x^k}{2^k}$

88. Infinite products An infinite product $P = a_1 a_2 a_3 \ldots$, which is denoted $\prod_{k=1}^{\infty} a_k$, is the limit of the *sequence of partial products* $\{a_1, a_1 a_2, a_1 a_2 a_3, \ldots \}$. Assume that $a_k > 0$ for all k.

   a. Show that the infinite product converges (which means its sequence of partial products converges) provided the series $\sum_{k=1}^{\infty} \ln a_k$ converges.

   b. Consider the infinite product

$$P = \prod_{k=2}^{\infty}\left(1 - \frac{1}{k^2}\right) = \frac{3}{4}\cdot\frac{8}{9}\cdot\frac{15}{16}\cdot\frac{24}{25}\cdots.$$

   Write out the first few terms of the sequence of partial products,

$$P_n = \prod_{k=2}^{n}\left(1 - \frac{1}{k^2}\right)$$

   (for example, $P_2 = \frac{3}{4}, P_3 = \frac{2}{3}$). Write out enough terms to determine the value of $P = \lim_{n\to\infty} P_n$.

   c. Use the results of parts (a) and (b) to evaluate the series

$$\sum_{k=2}^{\infty} \ln\left(1 - \frac{1}{k^2}\right).$$

89. Infinite products *Use the ideas of Exercise 88 to evaluate the following infinite products.*

   a. $\displaystyle\prod_{k=0}^{\infty} e^{1/2^k} = e \cdot e^{1/2} \cdot e^{1/4} \cdot e^{1/8} \ldots$

   b. $\displaystyle\prod_{k=2}^{\infty}\left(1 - \frac{1}{k}\right) = \frac{1}{2}\cdot\frac{2}{3}\cdot\frac{3}{4}\cdot\frac{4}{5}\ldots$

90. An early limit Working in the early 1600s, the mathematicians Wallis, Pascal, and Fermat were calculating the area of the region under the curve $y = x^p$ between $x = 0$ and $x = 1$, where p is a positive integer. Using arguments that predated the Fundamental Theorem of Calculus, they were able to prove that

$$\lim_{n\to\infty} \frac{1}{n} \sum_{k=0}^{n-1}\left(\frac{k}{n}\right)^p = \frac{1}{p+1}.$$

Use what you know about Riemann sums and integrals to verify this limit.

91. Stirling's formula Complete the following steps to find the values of $p > 0$ for which the series $\sum_{k=1}^{\infty} \dfrac{1 \cdot 3 \cdot 5 \cdots (2k-1)}{p^k k!}$ converges.

   a. Use the Ratio Test to show that $\sum_{k=1}^{\infty} \dfrac{1 \cdot 3 \cdot 5 \cdots (2k-1)}{p^k k!}$ converges for $p > 2$.

   b. Use Stirling's formula, $k! \approx \sqrt{2\pi k}\, k^k e^{-k}$ for large k, to determine whether the series converges when $p = 2$. (*Hint:*
$$1 \cdot 3 \cdot 5 \cdots (2k-1) = \frac{1\cdot 2\cdot 3\cdot 4\cdot 5\cdot 6\cdots(2k-1)2k}{2\cdot 4\cdot 6\cdots 2k}.)$$
(See the Guided Project *Stirling's formula and n!* for more on this topic.)

QUICK CHECK ANSWERS

1. 10; $(k+2)(k+1)$; $1/(k+1)$ **2.** The Integral Test or p-series with $p = 2$ **3.** To use the Comparison Test, we would need to show that $1/(k+1) > 1/k$, which is not true.

4. If $\lim\limits_{k\to\infty} \dfrac{a_k}{b_k} = L$ for $0 < L < \infty$, then $\lim\limits_{k\to\infty} \dfrac{b_k}{a_k} = \dfrac{1}{L}$, where $0 < 1/L < \infty$. ◄

8.6 Alternating Series

Our previous discussion focused on infinite series with positive terms, which is certainly an important part of the entire subject. But there are many interesting series with terms of mixed sign. For example, the series

$$1 + \frac{1}{2} - \frac{1}{3} - \frac{1}{4} + \frac{1}{5} + \frac{1}{6} - \frac{1}{7} - \frac{1}{8} + \cdots$$

has the pattern that two positive terms are followed by two negative terms and vice versa. Clearly, infinite series could have endless sign patterns, so we need to restrict our attention.

Fortunately, the simplest sign pattern is also the most important. We consider **alternating series** in which the signs strictly alternate, as in the series

$$\sum_{k=1}^{\infty} \frac{(-1)^{k+1}}{k} = 1 - \frac{1}{2} + \frac{1}{3} - \frac{1}{4} + \frac{1}{5} - \frac{1}{6} + \frac{1}{7} - \frac{1}{8} + \cdots.$$

The factor $(-1)^{k+1}$ (or $(-1)^k$) has the pattern $\{\ldots, 1, -1, 1, -1, \ldots \}$ and provides the alternating signs.

Alternating Harmonic Series

Let's see what is different about alternating series by working with the series $\sum_{k=1}^{\infty} \frac{(-1)^{k+1}}{k}$, which is called the **alternating harmonic series**. Recall that this series *without* the alternating signs, $\sum_{k=1}^{\infty} \frac{1}{k}$, is the *divergent* harmonic series. So an immediate question is whether the presence of alternating signs affects the convergence of a series.

We investigate this question by looking at the sequence of partial sums for the series. In this case, the first four terms of the sequence of partial sums are

$$S_1 = 1$$

$$S_2 = 1 - \frac{1}{2} = \frac{1}{2}$$

$$S_3 = 1 - \frac{1}{2} + \frac{1}{3} = \frac{5}{6}$$

$$S_4 = 1 - \frac{1}{2} + \frac{1}{3} - \frac{1}{4} = \frac{7}{12}.$$

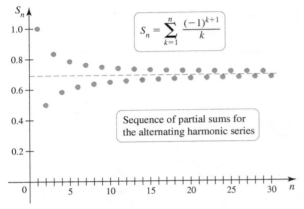

$$S_n = \sum_{k=1}^{n} \frac{(-1)^{k+1}}{k}$$

Sequence of partial sums for the alternating harmonic series

Figure 8.34

Plotting the first 30 terms of the sequence of partial sums results in Figure 8.34, which has several noteworthy features.

- The terms of the sequence of partial sums appear to converge to a limit; if they do, it means that, while the harmonic series diverges, the *alternating* harmonic series converges. We will soon learn that taking a divergent series with positive terms and making it an alternating series *may* turn it into a convergent series.

- For series with *positive* terms, the sequence of partial sums is necessarily an increasing sequence. Because the terms of an alternating series alternate in sign, the sequence of partial sums is not increasing (Figure 8.34).

- For the alternating harmonic series, the odd terms of the sequence of partial sums form a decreasing sequence and the even terms form an increasing sequence. As a result, the limit of the sequence of partial sums lies between any two consecutive terms of the sequence.

QUICK CHECK 1 Write out the first few terms of the sequence of partial sums for the alternating series $1 - 2 + 3 - 4 + 5 - 6 + \cdots$. Does this series appear to converge or diverge? ◄

Alternating Series Test

We now consider alternating series in general, which are written $\sum(-1)^{k+1}a_k$, where $a_k > 0$. With the exception of the Divergence Test, none of the convergence tests for series with positive terms applies to alternating series. The fortunate news is that one test works for most alternating series—and it is easy to use.

▶ Depending on the sign of the first term of the series, an alternating series may be written with $(-1)^k$ or $(-1)^{k+1}$.

▶ Recall that the Divergence Test of Section 8.4 applies to all series: If the terms of *any* series (including an alternating series) do not tend to zero, then the series diverges.

THEOREM 8.18 Alternating Series Test

The alternating series $\sum(-1)^{k+1}a_k$ converges provided

1. the terms of the series are nonincreasing in magnitude ($0 < a_{k+1} \leq a_k$, for k greater than some index N) and

2. $\lim_{k\to\infty} a_k = 0$.

There is potential for confusion here. *For series of positive terms,* $\lim_{k\to\infty} a_k = 0$ *does not imply convergence. For alternating series with nonincreasing terms,* $\lim_{k\to\infty} a_k = 0$ *does imply convergence.*

Proof: The proof is short and instructive; it relies on Figure 8.35. We consider an alternating series in the form

$$\sum_{k=1}^{\infty}(-1)^{k+1}a_k = a_1 - a_2 + a_3 - a_4 + \cdots.$$

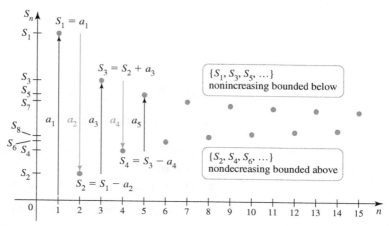

Figure 8.35

Because the terms of the series are nonincreasing in magnitude, the even terms of the sequence of partial sums $\{S_{2k}\} = \{S_2, S_4, \ldots\}$ form a nondecreasing sequence that is bounded above by S_1. By the Bounded Monotonic Sequence Theorem (Section 8.2), this sequence has a limit; call it L. Similarly, the odd terms of the sequence of partial sums $\{S_{2k-1}\} = \{S_1, S_3, \ldots\}$ form a nonincreasing sequence that is bounded below by S_2. By the Bounded Monotonic Sequence Theorem, this sequence also has a limit; call it L'. At the moment, we cannot conclude that $L = L'$. However, notice that $S_{2k} = S_{2k-1} - a_{2k}$. By the condition that $\lim_{k \to \infty} a_k = 0$, it follows that

$$\underbrace{\lim_{k\to\infty} S_{2k}}_{L} = \underbrace{\lim_{k\to\infty} S_{2k-1}}_{L'} - \underbrace{\lim_{k\to\infty} a_{2k}}_{0},$$

or $L = L'$. Therefore, the sequence of partial sums converges to a (unique) limit and the corresponding alternating series converges to that limit. ◄

Now we can confirm that the alternating harmonic series $\sum_{k=1}^{\infty} \dfrac{(-1)^{k+1}}{k}$ converges.

This fact follows immediately from the Alternating Series Test because the terms $a_k = \dfrac{1}{k}$ decrease and $\lim_{k \to \infty} a_k = 0$.

▶ $\sum_{k=1}^{\infty} \dfrac{1}{k}$
- Diverges
- Partial sums increase.

$\sum_{k=1}^{\infty} \dfrac{(-1)^{k+1}}{k}$
- Converges
- Partial sums bound the series above and below.

THEOREM 8.19   Alternating Harmonic Series

The alternating harmonic series $\displaystyle\sum_{k=1}^{\infty} \frac{(-1)^{k+1}}{k} = 1 - \frac{1}{2} + \frac{1}{3} - \frac{1}{4} + \frac{1}{5} - \cdots$

converges (even though the harmonic series $\displaystyle\sum_{k=1}^{\infty} \frac{1}{k} = 1 + \frac{1}{2} + \frac{1}{3} + \frac{1}{4} + \frac{1}{5} + \cdots$

diverges).

QUICK CHECK 2 Explain why the value of a convergent alternating series, with terms that are nonincreasing in magnitude, is trapped between successive terms of the sequence of partial sums. ◄

EXAMPLE 1   Alternating Series Test Determine whether the following series converge or diverge.

a. $\displaystyle\sum_{k=1}^{\infty} \frac{(-1)^{k+1}}{k^2}$ **b.** $2 - \dfrac{3}{2} + \dfrac{4}{3} - \dfrac{5}{4} + \cdots$ **c.** $\displaystyle\sum_{k=2}^{\infty} \frac{(-1)^k \ln k}{k}$

SOLUTION

a. The terms of this series decrease in magnitude, for $k \geq 1$. Furthermore,

$$\lim_{k\to\infty} a_k = \lim_{k\to\infty} \frac{1}{k^2} = 0.$$

Therefore, the series converges.

b. The magnitudes of the terms of this series are $a_k = \dfrac{k+1}{k} = 1 + \dfrac{1}{k}$. While these terms decrease, they approach 1, not 0, as $k \to \infty$. By the Divergence Test, the series diverges.

c. The first step is to show that the terms decrease in magnitude after some fixed term of the series. One way to proceed is to look at the function $f(x) = \dfrac{\ln x}{x}$, which generates the terms of the series. By the Quotient Rule, $f'(x) = \dfrac{1 - \ln x}{x^2}$. The fact that $f'(x) < 0$, for $x > e$, implies that the terms $\dfrac{\ln k}{k}$ decrease, for $k \geq 3$. As long as the terms of the series decrease for all k greater than some fixed integer, the first condition of the test is met. Furthermore, using l'Hôpital's Rule or the fact that $\{\ln k\}$ increases more slowly than $\{k\}$ (Section 8.2), we see that

$$\lim_{k\to\infty} a_k = \lim_{k\to\infty} \frac{\ln k}{k} = 0.$$

The conditions of the Alternating Series Test are met and the series converges.

Related Exercises 11–28 ◄

Remainders in Alternating Series

Recall that if a series converges to a value S, then the remainder is $R_n = S - S_n$, where S_n is the sum of the first n terms of the series. The magnitude of the remainder is the *absolute error* in approximating S by S_n.

An upper bound on the magnitude of the remainder in an alternating series arises from the following observation: When the terms are nonincreasing in magnitude, the value of the series is always trapped between successive terms of the sequence of partial sums. Therefore, as shown in Figure 8.36,

$$|R_n| = |S - S_n| \leq |S_{n+1} - S_n| = a_{n+1}.$$

This argument justifies the following theorem.

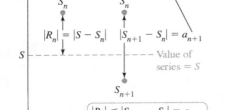

Figure 8.36

THEOREM 8.20   Remainder in Alternating Series

Let $\displaystyle\sum_{k=1}^{\infty} (-1)^{k+1} a_k$ be a convergent alternating series with terms that are nonincreasing in magnitude. Let $R_n = S - S_n$ be the remainder in approximating the value of that series by the sum of its first n terms. Then $|R_n| \leq a_{n+1}$. In other words, the magnitude of the remainder is less than or equal to the magnitude of the first neglected term.

EXAMPLE 2   **Remainder in an alternating series**

a. In turns out that $\ln 2 = 1 - \dfrac{1}{2} + \dfrac{1}{3} - \dfrac{1}{4} + \cdots = \displaystyle\sum_{k=1}^{\infty} \dfrac{(-1)^{k+1}}{k}$. How many terms of the series are required to approximate $\ln 2$ with an error less than 10^{-6}? The exact value of the series is given but is not needed to answer the question.

b. Consider the series $-1 + \dfrac{1}{2!} - \dfrac{1}{3!} + \dfrac{1}{4!} - \cdots = \displaystyle\sum_{k=1}^{\infty} \dfrac{(-1)^k}{k!}$. Find an upper bound for the magnitude of the error in approximating the value of the series (which is $e^{-1} - 1$) with $n = 9$ terms.

SOLUTION   Notice that both series meet the conditions of Theorem 8.20.

a. The series is expressed as the sum of the first n terms plus the remainder:

$$\sum_{k=1}^{\infty} \frac{(-1)^{k+1}}{k} = \underbrace{1 - \frac{1}{2} + \frac{1}{3} - \frac{1}{4} + \cdots + \frac{(-1)^{n+1}}{n}}_{S_n \,=\, \text{the sum of the first } n \text{ terms}} + \underbrace{\frac{(-1)^{n+2}}{n+1}}_{\substack{|R_n| \,=\, |S - S_n| \text{ is less} \\ \text{than the magnitude} \\ \text{of this term}}} + \cdots.$$

In magnitude, the remainder is less than or equal to the magnitude of the $(n + 1)$st term:

$$|R_n| = |S - S_n| \le a_{n+1} = \frac{1}{n+1}.$$

To ensure that the error is less than 10^{-6}, we require that

$$a_{n+1} = \frac{1}{n+1} < 10^{-6}, \quad \text{or} \quad n + 1 > 10^6.$$

Therefore, it takes 1 million terms of the series to approximate $\ln 2$ with an error less than 10^{-6}.

b. The series may be expressed as the sum of the first nine terms plus the remainder:

$$\sum_{k=1}^{\infty} \frac{(-1)^k}{k!} = \underbrace{-1 + \frac{1}{2!} - \frac{1}{3!} + \cdots - \frac{1}{9!}}_{S_9 \,=\, \text{sum of first 9 terms}} + \underbrace{\frac{1}{10!}}_{\substack{|R_9| \,=\, |S - S_9| \\ \text{is less than} \\ \text{this term}}} - \cdots.$$

The error committed when using the first nine terms to approximate the value of the series satisfies

$$|R_9| = |S - S_9| \le a_{10} = \frac{1}{10!} \approx 2.8 \times 10^{-7}.$$

Therefore, the error is no greater than 2.8×10^{-7}. As a check, the difference between the sum of the first nine terms, $\displaystyle\sum_{k=1}^{9} \frac{(-1)^k}{k!} \approx -0.632120811$, and the exact value, $S = e^{-1} - 1 \approx -0.632120559$, is approximately 2.5×10^{-7}. Therefore, the actual error satisfies the bound given by Theorem 8.20.

Related Exercises 29–44 ◄

QUICK CHECK 3 Compare and comment on the speed of convergence of the two series in the previous example. Why does one series converge more rapidly than the other? ◄

Absolute and Conditional Convergence

In this final segment, some terminology is introduced that is needed in Chapter 9. We now let the notation $\sum a_k$ denote any series—a series of positive terms, an alternating series, or even a more general infinite series.

Look again at the convergent alternating harmonic series $\sum (-1)^{k+1}/k$. The corresponding series of positive terms, $\sum 1/k$, is the divergent harmonic series. In contrast, we saw in Example 1a that the alternating series $\sum (-1)^{k+1}/k^2$ converges, and the corresponding p-series of positive terms $\sum 1/k^2$ also converges. These examples illustrate that removing the alternating signs in a convergent series *may* or *may not* result in a convergent series. The terminology that we now introduce distinguishes these cases.

> **DEFINITION   Absolute and Conditional Convergence**
>
> If $\sum |a_k|$ converges, then $\sum a_k$ **converges absolutely**. If $\sum |a_k|$ diverges and $\sum a_k$ converges, then $\sum a_k$ **converges conditionally**.

The series $\sum (-1)^{k+1}/k^2$ is an example of an absolutely convergent series because the series of absolute values,

$$\sum_{k=1}^{\infty} \left| \frac{(-1)^{k+1}}{k^2} \right| = \sum_{k=1}^{\infty} \frac{1}{k^2},$$

is a convergent p-series. In this case, removing the alternating signs in the series does *not* affect its convergence.

On the other hand, the convergent alternating harmonic series $\sum (-1)^{k+1}/k$ has the property that the corresponding series of absolute values,

$$\sum_{k=1}^{\infty} \left| \frac{(-1)^{k+1}}{k} \right| = \sum_{k=1}^{\infty} \frac{1}{k},$$

does *not* converge. In this case, removing the alternating signs in the series *does* affect convergence, so this series does not converge absolutely. Instead, we say it *converges conditionally*. A convergent series (such as $\sum (-1)^{k+1}/k$) may not converge absolutely. However, if a series converges absolutely, then it converges.

> **THEOREM 8.21   Absolute Convergence Implies Convergence**
>
> If $\sum |a_k|$ converges, then $\sum a_k$ converges (absolute convergence implies convergence). Equivalently, if $\sum a_k$ diverges, then $\sum |a_k|$ diverges.

Proof: Because $|a_k| = a_k$ or $|a_k| = -a_k$, it follows that $0 \le a_k + |a_k| \le 2|a_k|$. By assumption, $\sum |a_k|$ converges, which, in turn, implies that $2\sum |a_k|$ converges. Using the Comparison Test and the inequality $0 \le a_k + |a_k| \le 2|a_k|$, it follows that $\sum (a_k + |a_k|)$ converges. Now note that

$$\sum a_k = \sum (a_k + |a_k| - |a_k|) = \underbrace{\sum (a_k + |a_k|)}_{\text{converges}} - \underbrace{\sum |a_k|}_{\text{converges}}.$$

We see that $\sum a_k$ is the sum of two convergent series, so it also converges. The second statement of the theorem is logically equivalent to the first statement.   ◀

Figure 8.37 gives an overview of absolute and conditional convergence. It shows the universe of all infinite series, split first according to whether they converge or diverge. Convergent series are further divided between absolutely and conditionally convergent series.

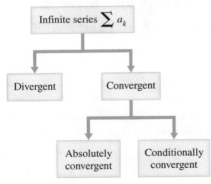

Figure 8.37

Here are a few more consequences of these definitions.

QUICK CHECK 4 Explain why a convergent series of positive terms converges absolutely. ◄

- The distinction between absolute and conditional convergence is relevant only for series of mixed sign, which includes alternating series. If a series of positive terms converges, it converges absolutely; conditional convergence does not apply.

- To test for absolute convergence, we test the series $\sum |a_k|$, which is a series of positive terms. Therefore, the convergence tests of Sections 8.4 and 8.5 (for positive-term series) are used to determine absolute convergence.

EXAMPLE 3   Absolute and conditional convergence Determine whether the following series diverge, converge absolutely, or converge conditionally.

a. $\displaystyle\sum_{k=1}^{\infty} \frac{(-1)^{k+1}}{\sqrt{k}}$ **b.** $\displaystyle\sum_{k=1}^{\infty} \frac{(-1)^{k+1}}{\sqrt{k^3}}$ **c.** $\displaystyle\sum_{k=1}^{\infty} \frac{\sin k}{k^2}$ **d.** $\displaystyle\sum_{k=1}^{\infty} \frac{(-1)^k k}{k+1}$

SOLUTION

a. We examine the series of absolute values,

$$\sum_{k=1}^{\infty} \left| \frac{(-1)^{k+1}}{\sqrt{k}} \right| = \sum_{k=1}^{\infty} \frac{1}{\sqrt{k}},$$

which is a divergent p-series (with $p = \frac{1}{2} < 1$). Therefore, the given alternating series does not converge absolutely. To determine whether the series converges conditionally, we look at the original series—with alternating signs. The magnitude of the terms of this series decrease with $\lim_{k \to \infty} 1/\sqrt{k} = 0$, so by the Alternating Series Test, the series converges. Because this series converges, but not absolutely, it converges conditionally.

b. To assess absolute convergence, we look at the series of absolute values,

$$\sum_{k=1}^{\infty} \left| \frac{(-1)^{k+1}}{\sqrt{k^3}} \right| = \sum_{k=1}^{\infty} \frac{1}{k^{3/2}},$$

which is a convergent p-series (with $p = \frac{3}{2} > 1$). Therefore, the original alternating series converges absolutely (and by Theorem 8.21 it converges).

c. The terms of this series do not strictly alternate sign (the first few signs are $+++--$), so the Alternating Series Test does not apply. Because $|\sin k| \leq 1$, the terms of the series of absolute values satisfy

$$\left| \frac{\sin k}{k^2} \right| = \frac{|\sin k|}{k^2} \leq \frac{1}{k^2}.$$

The series $\sum \dfrac{1}{k^2}$ is a convergent p-series. Therefore, by the Comparison Test, the series $\sum \left| \dfrac{\sin k}{k^2} \right|$ converges, which implies that the series $\sum \dfrac{\sin k}{k^2}$ converges absolutely (and by Theorem 8.21 it converges).

d. Notice that $\lim_{k \to \infty} k/(k+1) = 1$. The terms of the series do not tend to zero, and by the Divergence Test, the series diverges.

Related Exercises 45–56 ◄

We close the chapter with the summary of tests and series shown in Table 8.4.

Table 8.4 **Special Series and Convergence Tests**

Series or Test	Form of Series	Condition for Convergence	Condition for Divergence	Comments
Geometric series	$\sum_{k=0}^{\infty} ar^k, a \neq 0$	$|r| < 1$	$|r| \geq 1$	If $|r| < 1$, then $\sum_{k=0}^{\infty} ar^k = \dfrac{a}{1-r}$.
Divergence Test	$\sum_{k=1}^{\infty} a_k$	Does not apply	$\lim_{k \to \infty} a_k \neq 0$	Cannot be used to prove convergence
Integral Test	$\sum_{k=1}^{\infty} a_k$, where $a_k = f(k)$ and f is continuous, positive, and decreasing	$\int_1^{\infty} f(x)\, dx$ converges.	$\int_1^{\infty} f(x)\, dx$ diverges.	The value of the integral is not the value of the series.
p-series	$\sum_{k=1}^{\infty} \dfrac{1}{k^p}$	$p > 1$	$p \leq 1$	Useful for comparison tests
Ratio Test	$\sum_{k=1}^{\infty} a_k$, where $a_k > 0$	$\lim_{k \to \infty} \dfrac{a_{k+1}}{a_k} < 1$	$\lim_{k \to \infty} \dfrac{a_{k+1}}{a_k} > 1$	Inconclusive if $\lim_{k \to \infty} \dfrac{a_{k+1}}{a_k} = 1$
Root Test	$\sum_{k=1}^{\infty} a_k$, where $a_k \geq 0$	$\lim_{k \to \infty} \sqrt[k]{a_k} < 1$	$\lim_{k \to \infty} \sqrt[k]{a_k} > 1$	Inconclusive if $\lim_{k \to \infty} \sqrt[k]{a_k} = 1$
Comparison Test	$\sum_{k=1}^{\infty} a_k$, where $a_k > 0$	$0 < a_k \leq b_k$ and $\sum_{k=1}^{\infty} b_k$ converges.	$0 < b_k \leq a_k$ and $\sum_{k=1}^{\infty} b_k$ diverges	$\sum_{k=1}^{\infty} a_k$ is given; you supply $\sum_{k=1}^{\infty} b_k$.
Limit Comparison Test	$\sum_{k=1}^{\infty} a_k$, where $a_k > 0, b_k > 0$	$0 \leq \lim_{k \to \infty} \dfrac{a_k}{b_k} < \infty$ and $\sum_{k=1}^{\infty} b_k$ converges.	$\lim_{k \to \infty} \dfrac{a_k}{b_k} > 0$ and $\sum_{k=1}^{\infty} b_k$ diverges.	$\sum_{k=1}^{\infty} a_k$ is given; you supply $\sum_{k=1}^{\infty} b_k$.
Alternating Series Test	$\sum_{k=1}^{\infty} (-1)^k a_k$, where $a_k > 0, 0 < a_{k+1} \leq a_k$	$\lim_{k \to \infty} a_k = 0$	$\lim_{k \to \infty} a_k \neq 0$	Remainder R_n satisfies $|R_n| \leq a_{n+1}$
Absolute Convergence	$\sum_{k=1}^{\infty} a_k$, a_k arbitrary	$\sum_{k=1}^{\infty} |a_k|$ converges		Applies to arbitrary series

SECTION 8.6 EXERCISES

Review Questions

1. Explain why the sequence of partial sums for an alternating series is not an increasing sequence.

2. Describe how to apply the Alternating Series Test.

3. Why does the value of a converging alternating series with terms that are nonincreasing in magnitude lie between any two consecutive terms of its sequence of partial sums?

4. Suppose an alternating series with terms that are nonincreasing in magnitude converges to a value L. Explain how to estimate the remainder that occurs when the series is terminated after n terms.

5. Explain why the magnitude of the remainder in an alternating series (with terms that are nonincreasing in magnitude) is less than or equal to the magnitude of the first neglected term.

6. Give an example of a convergent alternating series that fails to converge absolutely.

7. Is it possible for a series of positive terms to converge conditionally? Explain.

8. Why does absolute convergence imply convergence?

9. Is it possible for an alternating series to converge absolutely but not conditionally?

10. Give an example of a series that converges conditionally but not absolutely.

Basic Skills

11–28. Alternating Series Test *Determine whether the following series converge.*

11. $\displaystyle\sum_{k=0}^{\infty} \frac{(-1)^k}{2k+1}$

12. $\displaystyle\sum_{k=1}^{\infty} \frac{(-1)^k}{\sqrt{k}}$

13. $\displaystyle\sum_{k=1}^{\infty} \frac{(-1)^k k}{3k+2}$

14. $\displaystyle\sum_{k=1}^{\infty} (-1)^k \left(1 + \frac{1}{k}\right)^k$

15. $\displaystyle\sum_{k=1}^{\infty} \frac{(-1)^{k+1}}{k^3}$

16. $\displaystyle\sum_{k=0}^{\infty} \frac{(-1)^k}{k^2 + 10}$

17. $\displaystyle\sum_{k=1}^{\infty} (-1)^{k+1} \frac{k^2}{k^3 + 1}$

18. $\displaystyle\sum_{k=2}^{\infty} (-1)^k \frac{\ln k}{k^2}$

19. $\displaystyle\sum_{k=2}^{\infty} (-1)^k \frac{k^2 - 1}{k^2 + 3}$

20. $\displaystyle\sum_{k=0}^{\infty} \left(-\frac{1}{5}\right)^k$

21. $\displaystyle\sum_{k=2}^{\infty} (-1)^k \left(1 + \frac{1}{k}\right)$

22. $\displaystyle\sum_{k=1}^{\infty} \frac{\cos \pi k}{k^2}$

23. $\displaystyle\sum_{k=1}^{\infty} (-1)^{k+1} \frac{k^{10} + 2k^5 + 1}{k(k^{10} + 1)}$

24. $\displaystyle\sum_{k=2}^{\infty} \frac{(-1)^k}{k \ln^2 k}$

25. $\displaystyle\sum_{k=1}^{\infty} (-1)^{k+1} k^{1/k}$

26. $\displaystyle\sum_{k=1}^{\infty} (-1)^{k+1} \frac{k!}{k^k}$

27. $\displaystyle\sum_{k=0}^{\infty} \frac{(-1)^k}{\sqrt{k^2 + 4}}$

28. $\displaystyle\sum_{k=1}^{\infty} (-1)^k k \sin \frac{1}{k}$

T 29–38. Remainders in alternating series *Determine how many terms of the following convergent series must be summed to be sure that the remainder is less than 10^{-4} in magnitude. Although you do not need it, the exact value of the series is given in each case.*

29. $\ln 2 = \displaystyle\sum_{k=1}^{\infty} \frac{(-1)^{k+1}}{k}$

30. $\dfrac{1}{e} = \displaystyle\sum_{k=0}^{\infty} \frac{(-1)^k}{k!}$

31. $\dfrac{\pi}{4} = \displaystyle\sum_{k=0}^{\infty} \frac{(-1)^k}{2k+1}$

32. $\dfrac{\pi^2}{12} = \displaystyle\sum_{k=1}^{\infty} \frac{(-1)^{k+1}}{k^2}$

33. $\dfrac{7\pi^4}{720} = \displaystyle\sum_{k=1}^{\infty} \frac{(-1)^{k+1}}{k^4}$

34. $\dfrac{\pi^3}{32} = \displaystyle\sum_{k=0}^{\infty} \frac{(-1)^k}{(2k+1)^3}$

35. $\dfrac{\pi\sqrt{3}}{9} + \dfrac{\ln 2}{3} = \displaystyle\sum_{k=0}^{\infty} \frac{(-1)^k}{3k+1}$

36. $\dfrac{31\pi^6}{30{,}240} = \displaystyle\sum_{k=1}^{\infty} \frac{(-1)^{k+1}}{k^6}$

37. $\pi = \displaystyle\sum_{k=0}^{\infty} \frac{(-1)^k}{4^k} \left(\frac{2}{4k+1} + \frac{2}{4k+2} + \frac{1}{4k+3}\right)$

38. $\dfrac{\pi\sqrt{3}}{9} - \dfrac{\ln 2}{3} = \displaystyle\sum_{k=0}^{\infty} \frac{(-1)^k}{3k+2}$

T 39–44. Estimating infinite series *Estimate the value of the following convergent series with an absolute error less than 10^{-3}.*

39. $\displaystyle\sum_{k=1}^{\infty} \frac{(-1)^k}{k^5}$

40. $\displaystyle\sum_{k=1}^{\infty} \frac{(-1)^k}{(2k+1)^3}$

41. $\displaystyle\sum_{k=1}^{\infty} \frac{(-1)^k k}{k^2 + 1}$

42. $\displaystyle\sum_{k=1}^{\infty} \frac{(-1)^k k}{k^4 + 1}$

43. $\displaystyle\sum_{k=1}^{\infty} \frac{(-1)^k}{k^k}$

44. $\displaystyle\sum_{k=1}^{\infty} \frac{(-1)^{k+1}}{(2k+1)!}$

45–56. Absolute and conditional convergence *Determine whether the following series converge absolutely, converge conditionally, or diverge.*

45. $\displaystyle\sum_{k=1}^{\infty} \frac{(-1)^k}{k^{2/3}}$

46. $\displaystyle\sum_{k=1}^{\infty} \frac{(-1)^k}{\sqrt{k}}$

47. $\displaystyle\sum_{k=1}^{\infty} \frac{(-1)^{k+1}}{k^{3/2}}$

48. $\displaystyle\sum_{k=1}^{\infty} \left(-\frac{1}{3}\right)^k$

49. $\displaystyle\sum_{k=1}^{\infty} \frac{\cos k}{k^3}$

50. $\displaystyle\sum_{k=1}^{\infty} \frac{(-1)^k k^2}{\sqrt{k^6 + 1}}$

51. $\displaystyle\sum_{k=1}^{\infty} (-1)^k \tan^{-1} k$

52. $\displaystyle\sum_{k=1}^{\infty} (-1)^k e^{-k}$

53. $\displaystyle\sum_{k=1}^{\infty} \frac{(-1)^k k}{2k+1}$

54. $\displaystyle\sum_{k=2}^{\infty} \frac{(-1)^k}{\ln k}$

55. $\displaystyle\sum_{k=1}^{\infty} \frac{(-1)^k \tan^{-1} k}{k^3}$

56. $\displaystyle\sum_{k=1}^{\infty} \frac{(-1)^{k+1} e^k}{(k+1)!}$

Further Explorations

57. **Explain why or why not** Determine whether the following statements are true and give an explanation or counterexample.

   a. A series that converges must converge absolutely.
   b. A series that converges absolutely must converge.
   c. A series that converges conditionally must converge.
   d. If Σa_k diverges, then $\Sigma |a_k|$ diverges.
   e. If Σa_k^2 converges, then Σa_k converges.
   f. If $a_k > 0$ and Σa_k converges, then Σa_k^2 converges.
   g. If Σa_k converges conditionally, then $\Sigma |a_k|$ diverges.

58. **Alternating Series Test** Show that the series

$$\frac{1}{3} - \frac{2}{5} + \frac{3}{7} - \frac{4}{9} + \cdots = \sum_{k=1}^{\infty} (-1)^{k+1} \frac{k}{2k+1}$$

   diverges. Which condition of the Alternating Series Test is not satisfied?

59. **Alternating p-series** Given that $\displaystyle\sum_{k=1}^{\infty} \frac{1}{k^2} = \frac{\pi^2}{6}$, show that

$$\sum_{k=1}^{\infty} \frac{(-1)^{k+1}}{k^2} = \frac{\pi^2}{12}. \text{ (Assume the result of Exercise 63.)}$$

60. **Alternating p-series** Given that $\displaystyle\sum_{k=1}^{\infty} \frac{1}{k^4} = \frac{\pi^4}{90}$, show that

$$\sum_{k=1}^{\infty} \frac{(-1)^{k+1}}{k^4} = \frac{7\pi^4}{720}. \text{ (Assume the result of Exercise 63.)}$$

61. **Geometric series** In Section 8.3, we established that the geometric series Σr^k converges provided $|r| < 1$. Notice that if $-1 < r < 0$, the geometric series is also an alternating series. Use the Alternating Series Test to show that for $-1 < r < 0$, the series Σr^k converges.

T 62. Remainders in alternating series Given any infinite series Σa_k, let $N(r)$ be the number of terms of the series that must be summed to guarantee that the remainder is less than 10^{-r} in magnitude, where r is a positive integer.

   a. Graph the function $N(r)$ for the three alternating p-series $\displaystyle\sum_{k=1}^{\infty} \frac{(-1)^{k+1}}{k^p}$, for $p = 1, 2,$ and 3. Compare the three graphs and discuss what they mean about the rates of convergence of the three series.

   b. Carry out the procedure of part (a) for the series $\displaystyle\sum_{k=1}^{\infty} \frac{(-1)^{k+1}}{k!}$ and compare the rates of convergence of all four series.

Additional Exercises

63. Rearranging series It can be proved that if a series converges absolutely, then its terms may be summed in any order without changing the value of the series. However, if a series converges conditionally, then the value of the series depends on the order of summation. For example, the (conditionally convergent) alternating harmonic series has the value

$$1 - \frac{1}{2} + \frac{1}{3} - \frac{1}{4} + \cdots = \ln 2.$$

Show that by rearranging the terms (so the sign pattern is $++-$),

$$1 + \frac{1}{3} - \frac{1}{2} + \frac{1}{5} + \frac{1}{7} - \frac{1}{4} + \cdots = \frac{3}{2}\ln 2.$$

64. A better remainder Suppose an alternating series $\sum (-1)^k a_k$, with terms that are nonincreasing in magnitude, converges to S and the sum of the first n terms of the series is S_n. Suppose also that the difference between the magnitudes of consecutive terms decreases with k. It can be shown that for $n \geq 1$,

$$\left| S - \left(S_n + \frac{(-1)^{n+1}a_{n+1}}{2} \right) \right| \leq \frac{1}{2}|a_{n+1} - a_{n+2}|.$$

a. Interpret this inequality and explain why it is a better approximation to S than S_n.

b. For the following series, determine how many terms of the series are needed to approximate its exact value with an error less than 10^{-6} using both S_n and the method explained in part (a).

(i) $\displaystyle\sum_{k=1}^{\infty} \frac{(-1)^k}{k}$ **(ii)** $\displaystyle\sum_{k=2}^{\infty} \frac{(-1)^k}{k \ln k}$ **(iii)** $\displaystyle\sum_{k=2}^{\infty} \frac{(-1)^k}{\sqrt{k}}$

65. A fallacy Explain the fallacy in the following argument.

Let $x = 1 + \dfrac{1}{3} + \dfrac{1}{5} + \dfrac{1}{7} + \cdots$ and

$y = \dfrac{1}{2} + \dfrac{1}{4} + \dfrac{1}{6} + \dfrac{1}{8} + \cdots$. It follows that $2y = x + y$,

which implies that $x = y$. On the other hand,

$$x - y = \underbrace{\left(1 - \frac{1}{2}\right)}_{>0} + \underbrace{\left(\frac{1}{3} - \frac{1}{4}\right)}_{>0} + \underbrace{\left(\frac{1}{5} - \frac{1}{6}\right)}_{>0} + \cdots > 0$$

is a sum of positive terms, so $x > y$. Therefore, we have shown that $x = y$ and $x > y$.

66. Conditions of the Alternating Series Test Consider the alternating series

$$\sum_{k=1}^{\infty} (-1)^{k+1}a_k, \text{ where } a_k = \begin{cases} \dfrac{4}{k+1}, & \text{if } k \text{ is odd} \\[2mm] \dfrac{2}{k}, & \text{if } k \text{ is even} \end{cases}$$

a. Write out the first ten terms of the series, group them in pairs, and show that the even partial sums of the series form the (divergent) harmonic series.

b. Show that $\displaystyle\lim_{k\to\infty} a_k = 0$.

c. Explain why the series diverges even though the terms of the series approach zero.

QUICK CHECK ANSWERS

1. $1, -1, 2, -2, 3, -3, \ldots$; series diverges.   **2.** The even terms of the sequence of partial sums approach the value of the series from one side; the odd terms of the sequence of partial sums approach the value of the series from the other side.   **3.** The second series with $k!$ in the denominators converges much more quickly than the first series because $k!$ increases much faster than k as $k \to \infty$.   **4.** If a series has positive terms, the series of absolute values is the same as the series itself. ◄

CHAPTER 8   REVIEW EXERCISES

1. Explain why or why not Determine whether the following statements are true and give an explanation or counterexample.

a. The terms of the sequence $\{a_n\}$ increase in magnitude, so the limit of the sequence does not exist.

b. The terms of the series $\sum 1/\sqrt{k}$ approach zero, so the series converges.

c. The terms of the sequence of partial sums of the series $\sum a_k$ approach $\frac{5}{2}$, so the infinite series converges to $\frac{5}{2}$.

d. An alternating series that converges absolutely must converge conditionally.

e. The sequence $a_n = \dfrac{n^2}{n^2 + 1}$ converges.

f. The sequence $a_n = \dfrac{(-1)^n n^2}{n^2 + 1}$ converges.

g. The series $\displaystyle\sum_{k=1}^{\infty} \frac{k^2}{k^2 + 1}$ converges.

h. The sequence of partial sums associated with the series $\displaystyle\sum_{k=1}^{\infty} \frac{1}{k^2 + 1}$ converges.

2–10. Limits of sequences *Evaluate the limit of the sequence or state that it does not exist.*

2. $a_n = \dfrac{n^2 + 4}{\sqrt{4n^4 + 1}}$ **3.** $a_n = \dfrac{8^n}{n!}$

4. $a_n = \left(1 + \dfrac{3}{n}\right)^{2n}$ **5.** $a_n = \sqrt[n]{n}$

6. $a_n = n - \sqrt{n^2 - 1}$ **7.** $a_n = \left(\dfrac{1}{n}\right)^{1/\ln n}$

8. $a_n = \sin\dfrac{\pi n}{6}$ **9.** $a_n = \dfrac{(-1)^n}{0.9^n}$

10. $a_n = \tan^{-1} n$

11. Sequence of partial sums Consider the series

$$\sum_{k=1}^{\infty} \frac{1}{k(k+2)} = \frac{1}{2}\sum_{k=1}^{\infty} \left(\frac{1}{k} - \frac{1}{k+2}\right).$$

a. Write the first four terms of the sequence of partial sums $S_1, \ldots, S_4$.

b. Write the nth term of the sequence of partial sums S_n.

c. Find $\displaystyle\lim_{n\to\infty} S_n$ and evaluate the series.

12–20. Evaluating series *Evaluate the following infinite series or state that the series diverges.*

12. $\displaystyle\sum_{k=1}^{\infty}\left(\frac{9}{10}\right)^{k}$

13. $\displaystyle\sum_{k=1}^{\infty}3(1.001)^{k}$

14. $\displaystyle\sum_{k=0}^{\infty}\left(-\frac{1}{5}\right)^{k}$

15. $\displaystyle\sum_{k=1}^{\infty}\frac{1}{k(k+1)}$

16. $\displaystyle\sum_{k=2}^{\infty}\left(\frac{1}{\sqrt{k}}-\frac{1}{\sqrt{k-1}}\right)$

17. $\displaystyle\sum_{k=1}^{\infty}\left(\frac{3}{3k-2}-\frac{3}{3k+1}\right)$

18. $\displaystyle\sum_{k=1}^{\infty}4^{-3k}$

19. $\displaystyle\sum_{k=1}^{\infty}\frac{2^{k}}{3^{k+2}}$

20. $\displaystyle\sum_{k=0}^{\infty}\left(\left(\frac{1}{3}\right)^{k}-\left(\frac{2}{3}\right)^{k+1}\right)$

21. Sequences of partial sums The sequences of partial sums for three series are shown in the figures. Assume that the pattern in the sequences continues as $n\to\infty$.

   a. Does it appear that series A converges? If so, what is its (approximate) value?

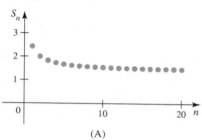

(A)

   b. What can you conclude about the convergence or divergence of series B?

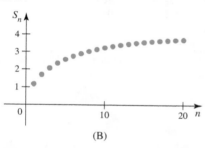

(B)

   c. Does it appear that series C converges? If so, what is its (approximate) value?

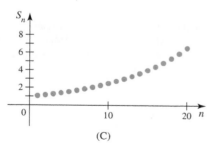

(C)

22–42. Convergence or divergence *Use a convergence test of your choice to determine whether the following series converge or diverge.*

22. $\displaystyle\sum_{k=1}^{\infty}\frac{2}{k^{3/2}}$

23. $\displaystyle\sum_{k=1}^{\infty}k^{-2/3}$

24. $\displaystyle\sum_{k=1}^{\infty}\frac{2k^{2}+1}{\sqrt{k^{3}+2}}$

25. $\displaystyle\sum_{k=1}^{\infty}\frac{2^{k}}{e^{k}}$

26. $\displaystyle\sum_{k=1}^{\infty}\left(\frac{k}{k+3}\right)^{2k}$

27. $\displaystyle\sum_{k=1}^{\infty}\frac{2^{k}k!}{k^{k}}$

28. $\displaystyle\sum_{k=1}^{\infty}\frac{1}{\sqrt{k}\sqrt{k+1}}$

29. $\displaystyle\sum_{k=1}^{\infty}\frac{3}{2+e^{k}}$

30. $\displaystyle\sum_{k=1}^{\infty}k\sin\frac{1}{k}$

31. $\displaystyle\sum_{k=1}^{\infty}\frac{\sqrt[3]{k}}{k^{3}}$

32. $\displaystyle\sum_{k=1}^{\infty}\frac{1}{1+\ln k}$

33. $\displaystyle\sum_{k=1}^{\infty}k^{5}e^{-k}$

34. $\displaystyle\sum_{k=4}^{\infty}\frac{2}{k^{2}-10}$

35. $\displaystyle\sum_{k=1}^{\infty}\frac{\ln k^{2}}{k^{2}}$

36. $\displaystyle\sum_{k=1}^{\infty}ke^{-k}$

37. $\displaystyle\sum_{k=0}^{\infty}\frac{2\cdot 4^{k}}{(2k+1)!}$

38. $\displaystyle\sum_{k=0}^{\infty}\frac{9^{k}}{(2k)!}$

39. $\displaystyle\sum_{k=1}^{\infty}\frac{\coth k}{k}$

40. $\displaystyle\sum_{k=1}^{\infty}\frac{1}{\sinh k}$

41. $\displaystyle\sum_{k=1}^{\infty}\tanh k$

42. $\displaystyle\sum_{k=0}^{\infty}\operatorname{sech}k$

43–50. Alternating series *Determine whether the following series converge or diverge. In the case of convergence, state whether the convergence is conditional or absolute.*

43. $\displaystyle\sum_{k=2}^{\infty}\frac{(-1)^{k}}{k^{2}-1}$

44. $\displaystyle\sum_{k=1}^{\infty}\frac{(-1)^{k+1}(k^{2}+4)}{2k^{2}+1}$

45. $\displaystyle\sum_{k=1}^{\infty}(-1)^{k}ke^{-k}$

46. $\displaystyle\sum_{k=1}^{\infty}\frac{(-1)^{k}}{\sqrt{k^{2}+1}}$

47. $\displaystyle\sum_{k=1}^{\infty}\frac{(-1)^{k+1}10^{k}}{k!}$

48. $\displaystyle\sum_{k=2}^{\infty}\frac{(-1)^{k}}{k\ln k}$

49. $\displaystyle\sum_{k=1}^{\infty}\frac{(-2)^{k+1}}{k^{2}}$

50. $\displaystyle\sum_{k=0}^{\infty}\frac{(-1)^{k}}{e^{k}+e^{-k}}$

51. Sequences versus series

   a. Find the limit of the sequence $\left\{\left(-\frac{4}{5}\right)^{k}\right\}$.

   b. Evaluate $\displaystyle\sum_{k=0}^{\infty}\left(-\frac{4}{5}\right)^{k}$.

52. Sequences versus series

   a. Find the limit of the sequence $\left\{\frac{1}{k}-\frac{1}{k+1}\right\}$.

   b. Evaluate $\displaystyle\sum_{k=1}^{\infty}\left(\frac{1}{k}-\frac{1}{k+1}\right)$.

53–56. Sequences versus series

53. Give an example (if possible) of a sequence $\{a_{k}\}$ that converges, while the series $\displaystyle\sum_{k=1}^{\infty}a_{k}$ diverges.

54. Give an example (if possible) of a series $\displaystyle\sum_{k=1}^{\infty}a_{k}$ that converges, while the sequence $\{a_{k}\}$ diverges.

55. **a.** Does the sequence $\left\{\frac{k}{k+1}\right\}$ converge? Why or why not?

   b. Does the series $\displaystyle\sum_{k=1}^{\infty}\frac{k}{k+1}$ converge? Why or why not?

56. Is it true that the geometric sequence $\{r^{k}\}$ converges if and only if the geometric series $\displaystyle\sum_{k=1}^{\infty}r^{k}$ converges?

57. Partial sums Let S_{n} be the nth partial sum of $\displaystyle\sum_{k=1}^{\infty}a_{k}=8$. Find $\displaystyle\lim_{k\to\infty}a_{k}$ and $\displaystyle\lim_{n\to\infty}S_{n}$.

T 58. Remainder term Let R_n be the remainder associated with $\sum_{k=1}^{\infty} \dfrac{1}{k^5}$. Find an upper bound for R_n (in terms of n). How many terms of the series must be summed to approximate the series with an error less than 10^{-4}?

59. Conditional p-series Find the values of p for which $\sum_{k=1}^{\infty} \dfrac{(-1)^k}{k^p}$ converges conditionally.

60. Logarithmic p-series Show that the series $\sum_{k=2}^{\infty} \dfrac{1}{k(\ln k)^p}$ converges provided $p > 1$.

T 61. Error in a finite sum Approximate the series $\sum_{k=1}^{\infty} \dfrac{1}{5^k}$ by evaluating the first 20 terms. Compute an upper bound for the error in the approximation.

T 62. Error in a finite sum Approximate the series $\sum_{k=1}^{\infty} \dfrac{1}{k^5}$ by evaluating the first 20 terms. Compute an upper bound for the error in the approximation.

T 63. Error in a finite alternating sum How many terms of the series $\sum_{k=1}^{\infty} \dfrac{(-1)^{k+1}}{k^4}$ must be summed to ensure that the error is less than 10^{-8}?

64. Equations involving series Solve the following equations for x.

a. $\sum_{k=0}^{\infty} e^{kx} = 2$ **b.** $\sum_{k=0}^{\infty} (3x)^k = 4$

c. $\sum_{k=1}^{\infty} \left(\dfrac{x}{kx - \frac{x}{2}} - \dfrac{x}{kx + \frac{x}{2}} \right) = 6$

65. Building a tunnel—first scenario A crew of workers is constructing a tunnel through a mountain. Understandably, the rate of construction decreases because rocks and earth must be removed a greater distance as the tunnel gets longer. Suppose that each week the crew digs 0.95 of the distance it dug the previous week. In the first week, the crew constructed 100 m of tunnel.

a. How far does the crew dig in 10 weeks? 20 weeks? N weeks?
b. What is the longest tunnel the crew can build at this rate?

66. Building a tunnel—second scenario As in Exercise 65, a crew of workers is constructing a tunnel. The time required to dig 100 m increases by 10% each week, starting with 1 week to dig the first 100 m. Can the crew complete a 1.5-km (1500-m) tunnel in 30 weeks? Explain.

67. Pages of circles On page 1 of a book, there is one circle of radius 1. On page 2, there are two circles of radius $\frac{1}{2}$. On page n, there are 2^{n-1} circles of radius 2^{-n+1}.

a. What is the sum of the areas of the circles on page n of the book?
b. Assuming the book continues indefinitely $(n \to \infty)$, what is the sum of the areas of all the circles in the book?

T 68. Sequence on a calculator Let $\{x_n\}$ be generated by the recurrence relation $x_0 = 1$ and $x_{n+1} = x_n + \cos x_n$, for $n = 0, 1, 2, \ldots$. Use a calculator (in radian mode) to generate as many terms of the sequence $\{x_n\}$ needed to find the integer p such that $\lim\limits_{n \to \infty} x_n = \pi/p$.

69. A savings plan Suppose that you open a savings account by depositing $100. The account earns interest at an annual rate of 3% per year (0.25% per month). At the end of each month, you earn interest on the current balance, and then you deposit $100. Let B_n be the balance at the beginning of the nth month, where $B_0 = \$100$.

a. Find a recurrence relation for the sequence $\{B_n\}$.
b. Find an explicit formula that gives B_n, for $n = 0, 1, 2, 3, \ldots$.

70. Sequences of integrals Find the limits of the sequences $\{a_n\}$ and $\{b_n\}$.

a. $a_n = \int_0^1 x^n \, dx, \ n \geq 1$ **b.** $b_n = \int_1^n \dfrac{dx}{x^p}, \ p > 1, n \geq 1$

71. Sierpinski triangle The fractal called the *Sierpinski triangle* is the limit of a sequence of figures. Starting with the equilateral triangle with sides of length 1, an inverted equilateral triangle with sides of length $\frac{1}{2}$ is removed. Then, three inverted equilateral triangles with sides of length $\frac{1}{4}$ are removed from this figure (see figure). The process continues in this way. Let T_n be the total area of the removed triangles after stage n of the process. The area of an equilateral triangle with side length L is $A = \sqrt{3}L^2/4$.

a. Find T_1 and T_2, the total area of the removed triangles after stages 1 and 2, respectively.
b. Find T_n, for $n = 1, 2, 3, \ldots$.
c. Find $\lim\limits_{n \to \infty} T_n$.
d. What is the area of the original triangle that remains as $n \to \infty$?

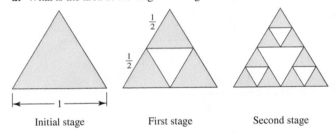

Initial stage   First stage   Second stage

72. Max sine sequence Let $a_n = \max\{\sin 1, \sin 2, \ldots, \sin n\}$, for $n = 1, 2, 3, \ldots$, where $\max\{\ldots\}$ denotes the maximum element of the set. Does $\{a_n\}$ converge? If so, make a conjecture about the limit.

Chapter 8 Guided Projects

Applications of the material in this chapter and related topics can be found in the following Guided Projects. For additional information, see the Preface.

- Chaos!
- Financial matters
- Periodic drug dosing
- Economic stimulus packages
- The mathematics of loans
- Archimedes' approximation to π
- Exact values of infinite series
- Conditional convergence in a crystal lattice

9

Power Series

Chapter Preview Until now, you have worked with infinite series consisting of real numbers. In this chapter, we make a seemingly small, but significant, change by considering infinite series whose terms include powers of a variable. With this change, an infinite series becomes a *power series*. One of the most fundamental ideas in all of calculus is that functions can be represented by power series. As a first step toward this result, we look at approximating functions using polynomials. The transition from polynomials to power series is then straightforward, and we learn how to represent the familiar functions of mathematics in terms of power series called *Taylor series*. The remainder of the chapter is devoted to the properties and many uses of Taylor series.

9.1 Approximating Functions with Polynomials

Power series provide a way to represent familiar functions and to define new functions. For this reason, power series—like sets and functions—are among the most fundamental entities in mathematics.

What Is a Power Series?

A *power series* is an infinite series of the form

$$\sum_{k=0}^{\infty} c_k x^k = \underbrace{c_0 + c_1 x + c_2 x^2 + \cdots + c_n x^n}_{n\text{th-degree polynomial}} + \underbrace{c_{n+1} x^{n+1} + \cdots}_{\text{terms continue}},$$

or, more generally,

$$\sum_{k=0}^{\infty} c_k (x-a)^k = \underbrace{c_0 + c_1 (x-a) + \cdots + c_n (x-a)^n}_{n\text{th-degree polynomial}} + \underbrace{c_{n+1}(x-a)^{n+1} + \cdots}_{\text{terms continue}},$$

where the *center* of the series a and the coefficients c_k are constants. This type of series is called a power series because it consists of powers of x or $(x-a)$.

Viewed another way, a power series is built up from polynomials of increasing degree, as shown in the following progression.

$$\left.\begin{array}{l} \text{Degree 0: } c_0 \\ \text{Degree 1: } c_0 + c_1 x \\ \text{Degree 2: } c_0 + c_1 x + c_2 x^2 \\ \quad \vdots \qquad \vdots \qquad \vdots \\ \text{Degree } n: c_0 + c_1 x + c_2 x^2 + \cdots + c_n x^n = \displaystyle\sum_{k=0}^{n} c_k x^k \end{array}\right\} \text{Polynomials}$$

$$\quad \vdots \qquad \vdots \qquad \vdots$$

$$\left.c_0 + c_1 x + c_2 x^2 + \cdots + c_n x^n + \cdots = \displaystyle\sum_{k=0}^{\infty} c_k x^k \right\} \text{Power series}$$

According to this perspective, a power series is a "super-polynomial." Therefore, we begin our exploration of power series by using polynomials to approximate functions.

Polynomial Approximation

An important observation motivates our work. To evaluate a polynomial $\big($say, $f(x) = x^8 - 4x^5 + \frac{1}{2}\big)$, all we need is arithmetic—addition, subtraction, multiplication, and division. However, algebraic functions $\big($say, $f(x) = \sqrt[3]{x^4 - 1}\big)$ and the trigonometric, logarithmic, and exponential functions usually cannot be evaluated exactly using arithmetic. Therefore, it makes practical sense to use the simplest of functions, polynomials, to approximate more complicated functions.

Linear and Quadratic Approximation

In Section 4.5, you learned that if a function f is differentiable at a point a, then it can be approximated near a by its tangent line, which is the linear approximation to f at the point a. The linear approximation at a is given by

$$y - f(a) = f'(a)(x - a) \quad \text{or} \quad y = f(a) + f'(a)(x - a).$$

Because the linear approximation is a first-degree polynomial, we name it p_1:

$$p_1(x) = f(a) + f'(a)(x - a).$$

This polynomial has some important properties: It matches f in *value* and in *slope* at a. In other words (Figure 9.1),

$$p_1(a) = f(a) \quad \text{and} \quad p_1'(a) = f'(a).$$

Linear approximation works well if f has a fairly constant slope near a. However, if f has a lot of curvature near a, then the tangent line may not provide an accurate approximation. To remedy this situation, we create a quadratic approximating polynomial by adding one new term to the linear polynomial. Denoting this new polynomial p_2, we let

$$p_2(x) = \underbrace{f(a) + f'(a)(x - a)}_{p_1(x)} + \underbrace{c_2(x - a)^2}_{\text{quadratic term}}.$$

The new term consists of a coefficient c_2 that must be determined and a quadratic factor $(x - a)^2$.

To determine c_2 and to ensure that p_2 is a good approximation to f near the point a, we require that p_2 agree with f in value, slope, and concavity at a; that is, p_2 must satisfy the matching conditions

$$p_2(a) = f(a), \quad p_2'(a) = f'(a), \quad \text{and} \quad p_2''(a) = f''(a),$$

where we assume that f and its first and second derivatives exist at a (Figure 9.2).

Substituting $x = a$ into p_2, we see immediately that $p_2(a) = f(a)$, so the first matching condition is met. Differentiating p_2 once, we have

$$p_2'(x) = f'(a) + 2c_2(x - a).$$

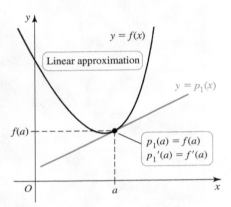

Figure 9.1

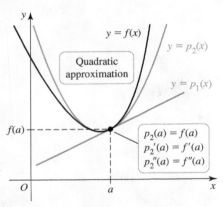

Figure 9.2

▶ Matching concavity (second derivatives) ensures that the graph of p_2 bends in the same direction as the graph of f at a.

So $p_2'(a) = f'(a)$, and the second matching condition is also met. Because $p_2''(a) = 2c_2$, the third matching condition is

$$p_2''(a) = 2c_2 = f''(a).$$

It follows that $c_2 = \frac{1}{2}f''(a)$; therefore, the quadratic approximating polynomial is

$$p_2(x) = \underbrace{f(a) + f'(a)(x - a)}_{p_1(x)} + \frac{f''(a)}{2}(x - a)^2.$$

EXAMPLE 1   Linear and quadratic approximations for ln x

a. Find the linear approximation to $f(x) = \ln x$ at $x = 1$.

b. Find the quadratic approximation to $f(x) = \ln x$ at $x = 1$.

c. Use these approximations to estimate $\ln 1.05$.

SOLUTION

a. Note that $f(1) = 0$, $f'(x) = 1/x$, and $f'(1) = 1$. Therefore, the linear approximation to $f(x) = \ln x$ at $x = 1$ is

$$p_1(x) = f(1) + f'(1)(x - 1) = 0 + 1(x - 1) = x - 1.$$

As shown in Figure 9.3, p_1 matches f in value ($p_1(1) = f(1)$) and in slope ($p_1'(1) = f'(1)$) at $x = 1$.

b. We first compute $f''(x) = -1/x^2$ and $f''(1) = -1$. Building on the linear approximation found in part (a), the quadratic approximation is

$$p_2(x) = \underbrace{x - 1}_{p_1(x)} + \underbrace{\frac{1}{2}f''(1)}_{c_2}(x - 1)^2$$

$$= (x - 1) - \frac{1}{2}(x - 1)^2.$$

Because p_2 matches f in value, slope, and concavity at $x = 1$, it provides a better approximation to f near $x = 1$ (Figure 9.3).

c. To approximate $\ln 1.05$, we substitute $x = 1.05$ into each polynomial approximation:

$$p_1(1.05) = 1.05 - 1 = 0.05 \text{ and} \qquad \text{Linear approximation}$$

$$p_2(1.05) = (1.05 - 1) - \frac{1}{2}(1.05 - 1)^2 = 0.04875. \quad \text{Quadratic approximation}$$

The value of $\ln 1.05$ given by a calculator, rounded to five decimal places, is 0.04879, showing the improvement in quadratic approximation over linear approximation.

Related Exercises 7–14 ◄

We now extend the idea of linear and quadratic approximation to obtain higher-degree polynomials that generally provide better approximations.

Taylor Polynomials

Assume that f and its first n derivatives exist at a; our goal is to find an nth-degree polynomial that approximates the values of f near a. The first step is to use p_2 to obtain a cubic polynomial p_3 of the form

$$p_3(x) = p_2(x) + c_3(x - a)^3$$

that satisfies the four matching conditions

$$p_3(a) = f(a), \quad p_3'(a) = f'(a), \quad p_3''(a) = f''(a), \quad \text{and} \quad p_3'''(a) = f'''(a).$$

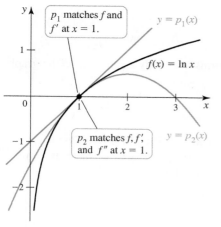

p_1 matches f and f' at $x = 1$.

$y = p_1(x)$

$f(x) = \ln x$

p_2 matches $f, f',$ and f'' at $x = 1$.

$y = p_2(x)$

Figure 9.3

▶ Building on ideas that were already circulating in the early 18th century, Brook Taylor (1685–1731) published Taylor's Theorem in 1715. He is also credited with discovering integration by parts.

Because p_3 is built "on top of " p_2, the first three matching conditions are met. The last condition, $p_3'''(a) = f'''(a)$, is used to determine c_3. A short calculation shows that $p_3'''(x) = 3 \cdot 2c_3 = 3!c_3$, so the last matching condition is $p_3'''(a) = 3!c_3 = f'''(a)$. Solving for c_3, we have $c_3 = \dfrac{f'''(a)}{3!}$. Therefore, the cubic approximating polynomial is

$$p_3(x) = \underbrace{f(a) + f'(a)(x - a) + \frac{f''(a)}{2!}(x - a)^2}_{p_2(x)} + \frac{f'''(a)}{3!}(x - a)^3.$$

▶ Recall that $2! = 2 \cdot 1$, $3! = 3 \cdot 2 \cdot 1$, $k! = k \cdot (k - 1)!$, and by definition, $0! = 1$.

QUICK CHECK 1 Verify that p_3 satisfies $p_3{}^{(k)}(a) = f^{(k)}(a)$, for $k = 0, 1, 2,$ and 3. ◀

Continuing in this fashion (Exercise 74), building each new polynomial on the previous polynomial, the nth approximating polynomial for f at a is

$$p_n(x) = f(a) + f'(a)(x - a) + \frac{f''(a)}{2!}(x - a)^2 + \cdots + \frac{f^{(n)}(a)}{n!}(x - a)^n.$$

It satisfies the $n + 1$ matching conditions

$$p_n(a) = f(a), \quad p_n'(a) = f'(a), \quad p_n''(a) = f''(a), \ldots, p_n^{(n)}(a) = f^{(n)}(a).$$

These conditions ensure that the graph of p_n conforms as closely as possible to the graph of f near a (Figure 9.4).

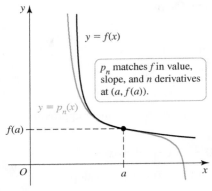

p_n matches f in value, slope, and n derivatives at $(a, f(a))$.

Figure 9.4

▶ Recall that $f^{(n)}$ denotes the nth derivative of f. By convention, the zeroth derivative $f^{(0)}$ is f itself.

DEFINITION Taylor Polynomials

Let f be a function with f', f'', $\ldots$, and $f^{(n)}$ defined at a. The **nth-order Taylor polynomial** for f with its **center** at a, denoted p_n, has the property that it matches f in value, slope, and all derivatives up to the nth derivative at a; that is,

$$p_n(a) = f(a), p_n'(a) = f'(a), \ldots, \text{and } p_n^{(n)}(a) = f^{(n)}(a).$$

The nth-order Taylor polynomial centered at a is

$$p_n(x) = f(a) + f'(a)(x - a) + \frac{f''(a)}{2!}(x - a)^2 + \cdots + \frac{f^{(n)}(a)}{n!}(x - a)^n.$$

More compactly, $p_n(x) = \displaystyle\sum_{k=0}^{n} c_k(x - a)^k$, where the **coefficients** are

$$c_k = \frac{f^{(k)}(a)}{k!}, \qquad \text{for } k = 0, 1, 2, \ldots, n.$$

EXAMPLE 2 Taylor polynomials for $\sin x$ Find the Taylor polynomials $p_1, \ldots, p_7$ centered at $x = 0$ for $f(x) = \sin x$.

SOLUTION We begin by differentiating f repeatedly and evaluating the derivatives at 0; these calculations allow us to compute c_k, for $k = 0, 1, \ldots, 7$. Notice that a pattern emerges:

$$\begin{aligned}
f(x) &= \sin x \Rightarrow f(0) = 0 \\
f'(x) &= \cos x \Rightarrow f'(0) = 1 \\
f''(x) &= -\sin x \Rightarrow f''(0) = 0 \\
f'''(x) &= -\cos x \Rightarrow f'''(0) = -1 \\
f^{(4)}(x) &= \sin x \Rightarrow f^{(4)}(0) = 0.
\end{aligned}$$

The derivatives of $\sin x$ at 0 cycle through the values $\{0, 1, 0, -1\}$. Therefore, $f^{(5)}(0) = 1$, $f^{(6)}(0) = 0$, and $f^{(7)}(0) = -1$.

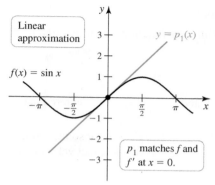

Figure 9.5

▶ It is worth repeating that the next polynomial in the sequence is obtained by adding one new term to the previous polynomial. For example,

$$p_3(x) = p_2(x) + \frac{f'''(a)}{3!}(x-a)^3.$$

QUICK CHECK 2 Verify the following properties for $f(x) = \sin x$ and $p_3(x) = x - x^3/6$:

$$f(0) = p_3(0),$$
$$f'(0) = p_3'(0),$$
$$f''(0) = p_3''(0), \text{ and}$$
$$f'''(0) = p_3'''(0).$$ ◀

We now construct the Taylor polynomials that approximate $f(x) = \sin x$ near 0, beginning with the linear polynomial. The polynomial of order $n = 1$ is

$$p_1(x) = f(0) + f'(0)(x - 0) = x,$$

whose graph is the line through the origin with slope 1 (Figure 9.5). Notice that f and p_1 agree in value ($f(0) = p_1(0) = 0$) and in slope ($f'(0) = p_1'(0) = 1$) at 0. We see that p_1 provides a good fit to f near 0, but the graphs diverge visibly for $|x| > 0.5$.

The polynomial of order $n = 2$ is

$$p_2(x) = \underbrace{f(0)}_{0} + \underbrace{f'(0)x}_{1} + \underbrace{\frac{f''(0)}{2!}x^2}_{0} = x,$$

so p_2 is the same as p_1.

The polynomial of order $n = 3$ is

$$p_3(x) = \underbrace{f(0) + f'(0)x + \frac{f''(0)}{2!}x^2}_{p_2(x)\,=\,x} + \underbrace{\frac{f'''(0)}{3!}x^3}_{-1/3!} = x - \frac{x^3}{6}.$$

We have designed p_3 to agree with f in value, slope, concavity, and third derivative at 0 (Figure 9.6). Consequently, p_3 provides a better approximation to f over a larger interval than p_1.

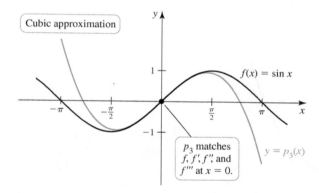

Figure 9.6

The procedure for finding Taylor polynomials may be extended to polynomials of any order. Because the even derivatives of $f(x) = \sin x$ are zero at $x = 0$, $p_4(x) = p_3(x)$. For the same reason, $p_6(x) = p_5(x)$:

$$p_6(x) = p_5(x) = x - \frac{x^3}{3!} + \frac{x^5}{5!}, \qquad c_5 = \frac{f^{(5)}(0)}{5!} = \frac{1}{5!}$$

Finally, the Taylor polynomial of order $n = 7$ is

$$p_7(x) = x - \frac{x^3}{3!} + \frac{x^5}{5!} - \frac{x^7}{7!}, \qquad c_7 = \frac{f^{(7)}(0)}{7!} = -\frac{1}{7!}$$

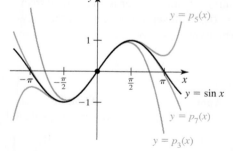

Figure 9.7

From Figure 9.7 we see that as the order of the Taylor polynomials increases, more accurate approximations to $f(x) = \sin x$ are obtained over larger intervals centered at 0. For example, p_7 is a good fit to $f(x) = \sin x$ over the interval $[-\pi, \pi]$. Notice that $\sin x$ and its Taylor polynomials (centered at 0) are all odd functions.

Related Exercises 15–22 ◀

QUICK CHECK 3 Why do the Taylor polynomials for $\sin x$ centered at 0 consist only of odd powers of x? ◀

Approximations with Taylor Polynomials

Taylor polynomials find widespread use in approximating functions, as illustrated in the following examples.

EXAMPLE 3   Taylor polynomials for e^x

a. Find the Taylor polynomials of order $n = 0, 1, 2,$ and 3 for $f(x) = e^x$ centered at 0. Graph f and the polynomials.

> Recall that if c is an approximation to x, the absolute error in c is $|x - c|$ and the relative error in c is $|x - c|/|x|$. We use *error* to refer to *absolute error*.

b. Use the polynomials in part (a) to approximate $e^{0.1}$ and $e^{-0.25}$. Find the absolute errors, $|f(x) - p_n(x)|$, in the approximations. Use calculator values for the exact values of f.

SOLUTION

a. Recall that the coefficients for the Taylor polynomials centered at 0 are

$$c_k = \frac{f^{(k)}(0)}{k!}, \qquad \text{for } k = 0, 1, 2, \ldots, n.$$

With $f(x) = e^x$, we have $f^{(k)}(x) = e^x$, $f^{(k)}(0) = 1$, and $c_k = 1/k!$, for $k = 0, 1, 2, 3 \ldots$. The first four polynomials are

$$p_0(x) = f(0) = 1,$$
$$p_1(x) = f(0) + f'(0)x = 1 + x,$$
$$\underbrace{p_1(x) = 1}_{} \quad \underbrace{1}_{}$$

$$p_2(x) = \underbrace{f(0) + f'(0)x}_{p_1(x) = 1 + x} + \underbrace{\frac{f''(0)}{2!}}_{1/2}x^2 = 1 + x + \frac{x^2}{2}, \text{ and}$$

$$p_3(x) = \underbrace{f(0) + f'(0)x + \frac{f''(0)}{2!}x^2}_{p_2(x) = 1 + x + x^2/2} + \underbrace{\frac{f^{(3)}(0)}{3!}}_{1/6}x^3 = 1 + x + \frac{x^2}{2} + \frac{x^3}{6}.$$

Notice that each successive polynomial provides a better fit to $f(x) = e^x$ near 0 (Figure 9.8). Continuing the pattern in these polynomials, the nth-order Taylor polynomial for e^x centered at 0 is

$$p_n(x) = 1 + x + \frac{x^2}{2!} + \frac{x^3}{3!} + \cdots + \frac{x^n}{n!} = \sum_{k=0}^{n} \frac{x^k}{k!}.$$

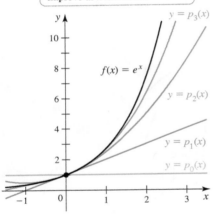

Taylor polynomials for $f(x) = e^x$ centered at 0. Approximations improve as n increases.

Figure 9.8

b. We evaluate $p_n(0.1)$ and $p_n(-0.25)$, for $n = 0, 1, 2,$ and 3, and compare these values to the calculator values of $e^{0.1} \approx 1.1051709$ and $e^{-0.25} \approx 0.77880078$. The results are shown in Table 9.1. Observe that the errors in the approximations decrease as n increases. In addition, the errors in approximating $e^{0.1}$ are smaller in magnitude than the errors in approximating $e^{-0.25}$ because $x = 0.1$ is closer to the center of the polynomials than $x = -0.25$. Reasonable approximations based on these calculations are $e^{0.1} \approx 1.105$ and $e^{-0.25} \approx 0.78$.

> A rule of thumb in finding estimates based on several approximations: Keep all the digits that are common to the last two approximations after rounding.

QUICK CHECK 4 Write out the next two Taylor polynomials p_4 and p_5 for $f(x) = e^x$ in Example 3. ◄

Table 9.1

n	Approximation $p_n(0.1)$	Absolute Error $\lvert e^{0.1} - p_n(0.1) \rvert$	Approximation $p_n(-0.25)$	Absolute Error $\lvert e^{-0.25} - p_n(-0.25) \rvert$
0	1	1.1×10^{-1}	1	2.2×10^{-1}
1	1.1	5.2×10^{-3}	0.75	2.9×10^{-2}
2	1.105	1.7×10^{-4}	0.78125	2.4×10^{-3}
3	1.105167	4.3×10^{-6}	0.778646	1.5×10^{-4}

Related Exercises 23–28 ◄

EXAMPLE 4 Approximating a real number using Taylor polynomials Use polynomials of order $n = 0, 1, 2,$ and 3 to approximate $\sqrt{18}$.

SOLUTION Letting $f(x) = \sqrt{x}$, we choose the center $a = 16$ because it is near 18, and f and its derivatives are easy to evaluate at 16. The Taylor polynomials have the form

$$p_n(x) = f(16) + f'(16)(x - 16) + \frac{f''(16)}{2!}(x - 16)^2 + \cdots + \frac{f^{(n)}(16)}{n!}(x - 16)^n.$$

We now evaluate the required derivatives:

$$f(x) = \sqrt{x} \Rightarrow f(16) = 4,$$

$$f'(x) = \frac{1}{2}x^{-1/2} \Rightarrow f'(16) = \frac{1}{8},$$

$$f''(x) = -\frac{1}{4}x^{-3/2} \Rightarrow f''(16) = -\frac{1}{256}, \text{ and}$$

$$f'''(x) = \frac{3}{8}x^{-5/2} \Rightarrow f'''(16) = \frac{3}{8192}.$$

Therefore, the polynomial p_3 (which includes p_0, p_1, and p_2) is

$$p_3(x) = \underbrace{\underbrace{\underbrace{4}_{p_0(x)} + \frac{1}{8}(x - 16)}_{p_1(x)} - \frac{1}{512}(x - 16)^2}_{p_2(x)} + \frac{1}{16{,}384}(x - 16)^3.$$

The Taylor polynomials (Figure 9.9) give better approximations to f as the order of the approximation increases.

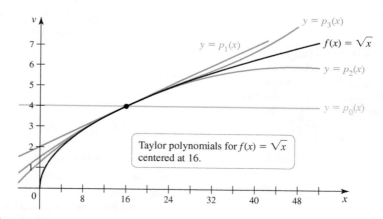

Figure 9.9

Letting $x = 18$, we obtain the approximations to $\sqrt{18}$ and the associated absolute errors shown in Table 9.2. (A calculator is used for the value of $\sqrt{18}$.) As expected, the errors decrease as n increases. Based on these calculations, a reasonable approximation is $\sqrt{18} \approx 4.24$.

QUICK CHECK 5 At what point would you center the Taylor polynomials for $\sqrt{x}$ and $\sqrt[4]{x}$ to approximate $\sqrt{51}$ and $\sqrt[4]{15}$, respectively? ◄

Table 9.2

n	Approximation $p_n(18)$	Absolute Error $|\sqrt{18} - p_n(18)|$
0	4	2.4×10^{-1}
1	4.25	7.4×10^{-3}
2	4.242188	4.5×10^{-4}
3	4.242676	3.5×10^{-5}

Related Exercises 29–48 ◄

Remainder in a Taylor Polynomial

Taylor polynomials provide good approximations to functions near a specific point. But how accurate are the approximations? To answer this question we define the *remainder* in a Taylor polynomial. If p_n is the Taylor polynomial for f of order n, then the remainder at the point x is

$$R_n(x) = f(x) - p_n(x).$$

The absolute value of the remainder is the error made in approximating $f(x)$ by $p_n(x)$. Equivalently, we have $f(x) = p_n(x) + R_n(x)$, which says that f consists of two components: the polynomial approximation and the associated remainder.

DEFINITION Remainder in a Taylor Polynomial

Let p_n be the Taylor polynomial of order n for f. The **remainder** in using p_n to approximate f at the point x is

$$R_n(x) = f(x) - p_n(x).$$

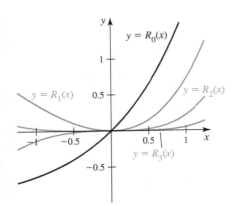

The idea of a remainder is illustrated in Figure 9.10, where we see the remainders associated with various Taylor polynomials for $f(x) = e^x$ centered at 0 (Example 3). For fixed order n, the remainders tend to increase in magnitude as x moves farther from the center of the polynomials (in this case 0). And for fixed x, remainders decrease in magnitude to zero with increasing n.

Remainders increase in magnitude as $|x|$ increases. Remainders decrease in magnitude to zero as n increases.

Figure 9.10

The remainder for a Taylor polynomial may be written quite concisely, which enables us to estimate remainders. The following result is known as *Taylor's Theorem* (or the *Remainder Theorem*).

▶ The remainder R_n for a Taylor polynomial can be expressed in several different forms. The form stated in Theorem 9.1 is called the *Lagrange form* of the remainder.

THEOREM 9.1   Taylor's Theorem (Remainder Theorem)

Let f have continuous derivatives up to $f^{(n+1)}$ on an open interval I containing a. For all x in I,

$$f(x) = p_n(x) + R_n(x),$$

where p_n is the nth-order Taylor polynomial for f centered at a and the remainder is

$$R_n(x) = \frac{f^{(n+1)}(c)}{(n+1)!}(x-a)^{n+1},$$

for some point c between x and a.

Discussion: We make two observations about Theorem 9.1 and outline a proof in Exercise 92. First, the case $n = 0$ is the Mean Value Theorem (Section 4.6), which states that

$$\frac{f(x) - f(a)}{x - a} = f'(c),$$

where c is a point between x and a. Rearranging this expression, we have

$$f(x) = \underbrace{f(a)}_{p_0(x)} + \underbrace{f'(c)(x-a)}_{R_0(x)}$$

$$= p_0(x) + R_0(x),$$

which is Taylor's Theorem with $n = 0$. Not surprisingly, the term $f^{(n+1)}(c)$ in Taylor's Theorem comes from a Mean Value Theorem argument.

The second observation makes the remainder easier to remember. If you write the $(n+1)$st Taylor polynomial p_{n+1}, the highest-degree term is $\dfrac{f^{(n+1)}(a)}{(n+1)!}(x-a)^{n+1}$. Replacing $f^{(n+1)}(a)$ with $f^{(n+1)}(c)$ results in the remainder for p_n.

Estimating the Remainder

The remainder has both practical and theoretical importance. We deal with practical matters now and theoretical matters in Section 9.3. The remainder is used to estimate errors in approximations and to determine the number of terms of a Taylor polynomial needed to achieve a prescribed accuracy.

Because c is generally unknown, the difficulty in estimating the remainder is finding a bound for $|f^{(n+1)}(c)|$. Assuming this can be done, the following theorem gives a standard estimate for the remainder term.

THEOREM 9.2 Estimate of the Remainder

Let n be a fixed positive integer. Suppose there exists a number M such that $|f^{(n+1)}(c)| \le M$, for all c between a and x inclusive. The remainder in the nth-order Taylor polynomial for f centered at a satisfies

$$|R_n(x)| = |f(x) - p_n(x)| \le M \frac{|x - a|^{n+1}}{(n+1)!}.$$

Proof: The proof requires taking the absolute value of the remainder in Theorem 9.1, replacing $|f^{(n+1)}(c)|$ with a larger quantity M, and forming an inequality. ◄

We now give three examples that demonstrate how the remainder is computed and used in different ways.

EXAMPLE 5 Estimating the remainder for $\cos x$ Find a bound for the magnitude of the remainder for the Taylor polynomials of $f(x) = \cos x$ centered at 0.

SOLUTION According to Theorem 9.1 with $a = 0$, we have

$$R_n(x) = \frac{f^{(n+1)}(c)}{(n+1)!} x^{n+1},$$

where c is a point between 0 and x. Notice that $f^{(n+1)}(c) = \pm \sin c$ or $f^{(n+1)}(c) = \pm \cos c$ depending on the value of n. In all cases, $|f^{(n+1)}(c)| \le 1$. Therefore, we take $M = 1$ in Theorem 9.2, and the absolute value of the remainder can be bounded as

$$|R_n(x)| = \left| \frac{f^{(n+1)}(c)}{(n+1)!} x^{n+1} \right| \le \frac{|x|^{n+1}}{(n+1)!}.$$

For example, if we approximate $\cos 0.1$ using the Taylor polynomial p_{10}, the remainder satisfies

$$|R_{10}(0.1)| \le \frac{0.1^{11}}{11!} \approx 2.5 \times 10^{-19}.$$

Related Exercises 49–54 ◄

EXAMPLE 6 Estimating a remainder Consider again Example 4 in which we approximated $\sqrt{18}$ using the Taylor polynomial

$$p_3(x) = 4 + \frac{1}{8}(x - 16) - \frac{1}{512}(x - 16)^2 + \frac{1}{16{,}384}(x - 16)^3.$$

In that example, we computed the error in the approximation knowing the exact value of $\sqrt{18}$ (obtained with a calculator). In the more realistic case in which we do not know the exact value, Theorem 9.2 allows us to estimate remainders (or errors). Applying this theorem with $n = 3$, $a = 16$, and $x = 18$, we find that the remainder in approximating $\sqrt{18}$ by $p_3(18)$ satisfies the bound

$$|R_3(18)| \le M \frac{(18 - 16)^4}{4!} = \frac{2}{3} M,$$

where M is a number that satisfies $|f^{(4)}(c)| \le M$, for all c between 16 and 18 inclusive. In this particular problem, we find that $f^{(4)}(c) = -\dfrac{15}{16}c^{-7/2}$, so M must be chosen (as small as possible) such that $|f^{(4)}(c)| = \dfrac{15}{16}c^{-7/2} = \dfrac{15}{16c^{7/2}} \le M$, for $16 \le c \le 18$.

You can verify that $\dfrac{15}{16c^{7/2}}$ is a decreasing function of c on $[16, 18]$ and has a maximum value of approximately 5.7×10^{-5} at $c = 16$ (Figure 9.11). Therefore, a bound on the remainder is

$$|R_3(18)| \le \frac{2}{3}M \approx \frac{2}{3} \cdot 5.7 \times 10^{-5} \approx 3.8 \times 10^{-5}.$$

Notice that the actual error computed in Example 4 (Table 9.2) is 3.5×10^{-5}, which is less than the bound on the remainder—as it should be.

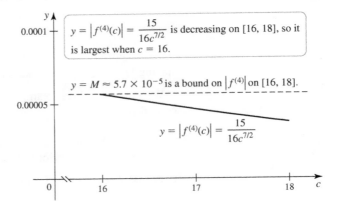

$y = |f^{(4)}(c)| = \dfrac{15}{16c^{7/2}}$ is decreasing on $[16, 18]$, so it is largest when $c = 16$.

$y = M \approx 5.7 \times 10^{-5}$ is a bound on $|f^{(4)}|$ on $[16, 18]$.

$y = |f^{(4)}(c)| = \dfrac{15}{16c^{7/2}}$

Figure 9.11

Related Exercises 55–60 ◀

EXAMPLE 7 Estimating the remainder for e^x Find a bound on the remainder in approximating $e^{0.45}$ using the Taylor polynomial of order $n = 6$ for $f(x) = e^x$ centered at 0.

SOLUTION Using Theorem 9.2, a bound on the remainder is given by

$$|R_n(x)| \le M\frac{|x - a|^{n+1}}{(n + 1)!},$$

where M is chosen such that $|f^{(n+1)}(c)| \le M$, for all c between a and x inclusive. Notice that $f(x) = e^x$ implies that $f^{(k)}(x) = e^x$, for $k = 0, 1, 2, \ldots$. In this particular problem, we have $n = 6$, $a = 0$, and $x = 0.45$, so the bound on the remainder takes the form

$$|R_6(0.45)| \le M\frac{|0.45 - 0|^7}{7!} \approx 7.4 \times 10^{-7}\,M,$$

where M is chosen such that $|f^{(7)}(c)| = e^c \le M$, for all c in the interval $[0, 0.45]$. Because e^c is an increasing function of c, its maximum value on the interval $[0, 0.45]$ occurs at $c = 0.45$ and is $e^{0.45}$. However, $e^{0.45}$ cannot be evaluated exactly (it is the number we are approximating), so we must find a number M such that $e^{0.45} \le M$. Here is one of many ways to obtain a bound: We observe that $e^{0.45} < e^{1/2} < 4^{1/2} = 2$ and take $M = 2$ (Figure 9.12). Therefore, a bound on the remainder is

$$|R_6(0.45)| \le 7.4 \times 10^{-7}\,M \approx 1.5 \times 10^{-6}.$$

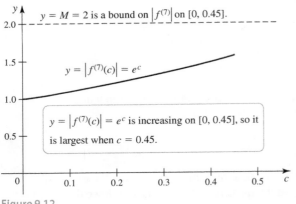

$y = M = 2$ is a bound on $|f^{(7)}|$ on $[0, 0.45]$.

$y = |f^{(7)}(c)| = e^c$

$y = |f^{(7)}(c)| = e^c$ is increasing on $[0, 0.45]$, so it is largest when $c = 0.45$.

Figure 9.12

> Recall that if $f(x) = e^x$, then
>
> $$p_n(x) = \sum_{k=0}^{n} \frac{x^k}{k!}.$$

QUICK CHECK 6 In Example 7, find an approximate upper bound for $R_7(0.45)$. ◄

Using the Taylor polynomial derived in Example 3 with $n = 6$, the resulting approximation to $e^{0.45}$ is

$$p_6(0.45) = \sum_{k=0}^{6} \frac{0.45^k}{k!} \approx 1.5683114;$$

it has an error that does not exceed 1.5×10^{-6}.

Related Exercises 55–60 ◄

EXAMPLE 8 Working with the remainder The nth-order Taylor polynomial for $f(x) = \ln(1 - x)$ centered at 0 is

$$p_n(x) = -\sum_{k=1}^{n} \frac{x^k}{k} = -x - \frac{x^2}{2} - \frac{x^3}{3} - \cdots - \frac{x^n}{n}.$$

a. Find a bound on the error in approximating $\ln(1 - x)$ by $p_3(x)$ for values of x in the interval $\left[-\frac{1}{2}, \frac{1}{2}\right]$.

b. How many terms of the Taylor polynomial are needed to approximate values of $f(x) = \ln(1 - x)$ with an error less than 10^{-3} on the interval $\left[-\frac{1}{2}, \frac{1}{2}\right]$?

SOLUTION

a. The remainder for the Taylor polynomial p_3 is $R_3(x) = \dfrac{f^{(4)}(c)}{4!} x^4$, where c is between 0 and x. Computing four derivatives of f, we find that $f^{(4)}(x) = -\dfrac{6}{(1 - x)^4}$.

On the interval $\left[-\frac{1}{2}, \frac{1}{2}\right]$, the maximum magnitude of this derivative occurs at $x = \frac{1}{2}$ (because the denominator is smallest at $x = \frac{1}{2}$) and is $6/\left(\frac{1}{2}\right)^4 = 96$. Similarly, the factor x^4 has its maximum magnitude at $x = \pm\frac{1}{2}$ and it is $\left(\frac{1}{2}\right)^4 = \frac{1}{16}$. Therefore, $|R_3(x)| \leq \dfrac{96}{4!}\left(\frac{1}{16}\right) = 0.25$ on the interval $\left[-\frac{1}{2}, \frac{1}{2}\right]$. The error in approximating $f(x)$ by $p_3(x)$, for $-\frac{1}{2} \leq x \leq \frac{1}{2}$, does not exceed 0.25.

b. For any positive integer n, the remainder is $R_n(x) = \dfrac{f^{(n+1)}(c)}{(n + 1)!} x^{n+1}$. Differentiating f several times reveals that

$$f^{(n+1)}(x) = -\frac{n!}{(1 - x)^{n+1}}.$$

On the interval $\left[-\frac{1}{2}, \frac{1}{2}\right]$, the maximum magnitude of this derivative occurs at $x = \frac{1}{2}$ and is $n!/\left(\frac{1}{2}\right)^{n+1}$. Similarly, x^{n+1} has its maximum magnitude at $x = \pm\frac{1}{2}$, and it is $\left(\frac{1}{2}\right)^{n+1}$. Therefore, a bound on the remainder is

$$|R_n(x)| = \frac{1}{(n + 1)!} \cdot \underbrace{|f^{(n+1)}(c)|}_{\leq\, n!2^{n+1}} \cdot \underbrace{|x|^{n+1}}_{\leq\, \left(\frac{1}{2}\right)^{n+1}}$$

$$\leq \frac{1}{(n + 1)!} \cdot n!2^{n+1} \cdot \frac{1}{2^{n+1}}$$

$$= \frac{1}{n + 1}. \qquad\qquad \frac{n!}{n + 1!} = \frac{1}{n + 1}$$

To ensure that the error is less than 10^{-3} on the entire interval $\left[-\frac{1}{2}, \frac{1}{2}\right]$, n must satisfy $|R_n| \leq \dfrac{1}{n + 1} < 10^{-3}$ or $n > 999$. The error is likely to be significantly less than 10^{-3} if x is near 0.

Related Exercises 61–72 ◄

SECTION 9.1 EXERCISES

Review Questions

1. Suppose you use a second-order Taylor polynomial centered at 0 to approximate a function f. What matching conditions are satisfied by the polynomial?

2. Does the accuracy of an approximation given by a Taylor polynomial generally increase or decrease with the order of the approximation? Explain.

3. The first three Taylor polynomials for $f(x) = \sqrt{1 + x}$ centered at 0 are $p_0(x) = 1$, $p_1(x) = 1 + \dfrac{x}{2}$, and $p_2(x) = 1 + \dfrac{x}{2} - \dfrac{x^2}{8}$. Find three approximations to $\sqrt{1.1}$.

4. In general, how many terms do the Taylor polynomials p_2 and p_3 have in common?

5. How is the remainder $R_n(x)$ in a Taylor polynomial defined?

6. Explain how to estimate the remainder in an approximation given by a Taylor polynomial.

Basic Skills

7–14. Linear and quadratic approximation

a. Find the linear approximating polynomial for the following functions centered at the given point a.
b. Find the quadratic approximating polynomial for the following functions centered at the given point a.
c. Use the polynomials obtained in parts (a) and (b) to approximate the given quantity.

7. $f(x) = 8x^{3/2}$, $a = 1$; approximate $8 \cdot 1.1^{3/2}$.

8. $f(x) = \dfrac{1}{x}$, $a = 1$; approximate $\dfrac{1}{1.05}$.

9. $f(x) = e^{-x}$, $a = 0$; approximate $e^{-0.2}$.

10. $f(x) = \sqrt{x}$, $a = 4$; approximate $\sqrt{3.9}$.

11. $f(x) = (1 + x)^{-1}$, $a = 0$; approximate $\dfrac{1}{1.05}$.

12. $f(x) = \cos x$, $a = \pi/4$; approximate $\cos(0.24\pi)$.

13. $f(x) = x^{1/3}$, $a = 8$; approximate $7.5^{1/3}$.

14. $f(x) = \tan^{-1} x$, $a = 0$; approximate $\tan^{-1} 0.1$.

15–22. Taylor polynomials

a. Find the nth-order Taylor polynomials of the given function centered at 0, for $n = 0, 1,$ and 2.
b. Graph the Taylor polynomials and the function.

15. $f(x) = \cos x$

16. $f(x) = e^{-x}$

17. $f(x) = \ln(1 - x)$

18. $f(x) = (1 + x)^{-1/2}$

19. $f(x) = \tan x$

20. $f(x) = (1 + x)^{-2}$

21. $f(x) = (1 + x)^{-3}$

22. $f(x) = \sin^{-1} x$

23–28. Approximations with Taylor polynomials

a. Use the given Taylor polynomial p_2 to approximate the given quantity.
b. Compute the absolute error in the approximation assuming the exact value is given by a calculator.

23. Approximate $\sqrt{1.05}$ using $f(x) = \sqrt{1 + x}$ and $p_2(x) = 1 + x/2 - x^2/8$.

24. Approximate $\sqrt[3]{1.1}$ using $f(x) = \sqrt[3]{1 + x}$ and $p_2(x) = 1 + x/3 - x^2/9$.

25. Approximate $\dfrac{1}{\sqrt{1.08}}$ using $f(x) = \dfrac{1}{\sqrt{1 + x}}$ and $p_2(x) = 1 - x/2 + 3x^2/8$.

26. Approximate $\ln 1.06$ using $f(x) = \ln(1 + x)$ and $p_2(x) = x - x^2/2$.

27. Approximate $e^{-0.15}$ using $f(x) = e^{-x}$ and $p_2(x) = 1 - x + x^2/2$.

28. Approximate $\dfrac{1}{1.12^3}$ using $f(x) = \dfrac{1}{(1 + x)^3}$ and $p_2(x) = 1 - 3x + 6x^2$.

29–38. Taylor polynomials centered at $a \neq 0$

a. Find the nth-order Taylor polynomials for the following functions centered at the given point a, for $n = 0, 1,$ and 2.
b. Graph the Taylor polynomials and the function.

29. $f(x) = x^3$, $a = 1$

30. $f(x) = 8\sqrt{x}$, $a = 1$

31. $f(x) = \sin x$, $a = \pi/4$

32. $f(x) = \cos x$, $a = \pi/6$

33. $f(x) = \sqrt{x}$, $a = 9$

34. $f(x) = \sqrt[3]{x}$, $a = 8$

35. $f(x) = \ln x$, $a = e$

36. $f(x) = \sqrt[4]{x}$, $a = 16$

37. $f(x) = \tan^{-1} x + x^2 + 1$, $a = 1$

38. $f(x) = e^x$, $a = \ln 2$

39–48. Approximations with Taylor polynomials

a. Approximate the given quantities using Taylor polynomials with $n = 3$.
b. Compute the absolute error in the approximation assuming the exact value is given by a calculator.

39. $e^{0.12}$

40. $\cos(-0.2)$

41. $\tan(-0.1)$

42. $\ln 1.05$

43. $\sqrt{1.06}$

44. $\sqrt[4]{79}$

45. $\sqrt{101}$

46. $\sqrt[3]{126}$

47. $\sinh 0.5$

48. $\tanh 0.5$

49–54. Remainders Find the remainder R_n for the nth-order Taylor polynomial centered at a for the given functions. Express the result for a general value of n.

49. $f(x) = \sin x$, $a = 0$

50. $f(x) = \cos 2x$, $a = 0$

51. $f(x) = e^{-x}$, $a = 0$

52. $f(x) = \cos x$, $a = \pi/2$

53. $f(x) = \sin x$, $a = \pi/2$

54. $f(x) = 1/(1 - x)$, $a = 0$

55–60. Estimating errors Use the remainder to find a bound on the error in approximating the following quantities with the nth-order Taylor polynomial centered at 0. Estimates are not unique.

55. $\sin 0.3$, $n = 4$

56. $\cos 0.45$, $n = 3$

57. $e^{0.25}$, $n = 4$

58. $\tan 0.3$, $n = 2$

59. $e^{-0.5}$, $n = 4$

60. $\ln 1.04$, $n = 3$

T 61–66. Error bounds *Use the remainder to find a bound on the error in the following approximations on the given interval. Error bounds are not unique.*

61. $\sin x \approx x - x^3/6$ on $[-\pi/4, \pi/4]$

62. $\cos x \approx 1 - x^2/2$ on $[-\pi/4, \pi/4]$

63. $e^x \approx 1 + x + x^2/2$ on $\left[-\frac{1}{2}, \frac{1}{2}\right]$

64. $\tan x \approx x$ on $[-\pi/6, \pi/6]$

65. $\ln(1 + x) \approx x - x^2/2$ on $[-0.2, 0.2]$

66. $\sqrt{1 + x} \approx 1 + x/2$ on $[-0.1, 0.1]$

67–72. Number of terms *What is the minimum order of the Taylor polynomial required to approximate the following quantities with an absolute error no greater than 10^{-3}? (The answer depends on your choice of a center.)*

67. $e^{-0.5}$ **68.** $\sin 0.2$ **69.** $\cos(-0.25)$

70. $\ln 0.85$ **71.** $\sqrt{1.06}$ **72.** $1/\sqrt{0.85}$

Further Explorations

73. Explain why or why not Determine whether the following statements are true and give an explanation or counterexample.

  a. Only even powers of x appear in the Taylor polynomials for $f(x) = e^{-2x}$ centered at 0.

  b. Let $f(x) = x^5 - 1$. The Taylor polynomial for f of order 10 centered at 0 is f itself.

  c. Only even powers of x appear in the nth-order Taylor polynomial for $f(x) = \sqrt{1 + x^2}$ centered at 0.

  d. Suppose f'' is continuous on an interval that contains a, where f has an inflection point at a. Then the second-order Taylor polynomial for f at a is linear.

74. Taylor coefficients for $x = a$ Follow the procedure in the text to show that the nth-order Taylor polynomial that matches f and its derivatives up to order n at a has coefficients

$$c_k = \frac{f^{(k)}(a)}{k!}, \text{ for } k = 0, 1, 2, \ldots, n.$$

75. Matching functions with polynomials Match functions a–f with Taylor polynomials A–F (all centered at 0). Give reasons for your choices.

  a. $\sqrt{1 + 2x}$ **A.** $p_2(x) = 1 + 2x + 2x^2$

  b. $\dfrac{1}{\sqrt{1 + 2x}}$ **B.** $p_2(x) = 1 - 6x + 24x^2$

  c. e^{2x} **C.** $p_2(x) = 1 + x - \dfrac{x^2}{2}$

  d. $\dfrac{1}{1 + 2x}$ **D.** $p_2(x) = 1 - 2x + 4x^2$

  e. $\dfrac{1}{(1 + 2x)^3}$ **E.** $p_2(x) = 1 - x + \dfrac{3}{2}x^2$

  f. e^{-2x} **F.** $p_2(x) = 1 - 2x + 2x^2$

T 76. Dependence of errors on x Consider $f(x) = \ln(1 - x)$ and its Taylor polynomials given in Example 8.

  a. Graph $y = |f(x) - p_2(x)|$ and $y = |f(x) - p_3(x)|$ on the interval $\left[-\frac{1}{2}, \frac{1}{2}\right]$ (two curves).

  b. At what points of $\left[-\frac{1}{2}, \frac{1}{2}\right]$ is the error largest? Smallest?

  c. Are these results consistent with the theoretical error bounds obtained in Example 8?

Applications

T 77–84. Small argument approximations *Consider the following common approximations when x is near zero.*

  a. *Estimate $f(0.1)$ and give a bound on the error in the approximation.*

  b. *Estimate $f(0.2)$ and give a bound on the error in the approximation.*

77. $f(x) = \sin x \approx x$ **78.** $f(x) = \tan x \approx x$

79. $f(x) = \cos x \approx 1 - x^2/2$ **80.** $f(x) = \tan^{-1}x \approx x$

81. $f(x) = \sqrt{1 + x} \approx 1 + x/2$

82. $f(x) = \ln(1 + x) \approx x - x^2/2$

83. $f(x) = e^x \approx 1 + x$ **84.** $f(x) = \sin^{-1}x \approx x$

T 85. Errors in approximations Suppose you approximate $f(x) = \sec x$ at the points $x = -0.2, -0.1, 0.0, 0.1,$ and 0.2 using the Taylor polynomials $p_2(x) = 1 + x^2/2$ and $p_4(x) = 1 + x^2/2 + 5x^4/24$. Assume that the exact value of $\sec x$ is given by a calculator.

  a. Complete the table showing the absolute errors in the approximations at each point. Show two significant digits.

x	$|\sec x - p_2(x)|$	$|\sec x - p_4(x)|$
-0.2		
-0.1		
0.0		
0.1		
0.2		

  b. In each error column, how do the errors vary with x? For what values of x are the errors largest and smallest in magnitude?

T 86–89. Errors in approximations *Carry out the procedure described in Exercise 85 with the following functions and Taylor polynomials.*

86. $f(x) = \cos x$, $p_2(x) = 1 - \dfrac{x^2}{2}$, $p_4(x) = 1 - \dfrac{x^2}{2} + \dfrac{x^4}{24}$

87. $f(x) = e^{-x}$, $p_1(x) = 1 - x$, $p_2(x) = 1 - x + \dfrac{x^2}{2}$

88. $f(x) = \ln(1 + x)$, $p_1(x) = x$, $p_2(x) = x - \dfrac{x^2}{2}$

89. $f(x) = \tan x$, $p_1(x) = x$, $p_3(x) = x + \dfrac{x^3}{3}$

T 90. Best expansion point Suppose you wish to approximate $\cos(\pi/12)$ using Taylor polynomials. Is the approximation more accurate if you use Taylor polynomials centered at 0 or $\pi/6$? Use a calculator for numerical experiments and check for consistency with Theorem 9.2. Does the answer depend on the order of the polynomial?

T 91. Best expansion point Suppose you wish to approximate $e^{0.35}$ using Taylor polynomials. Is the approximation more accurate if you use Taylor polynomials centered at 0 or $\ln 2$? Use a calculator for numerical experiments and check for consistency with Theorem 9.2. Does the answer depend on the order of the polynomial?

Additional Exercises

92. Proof of Taylor's Theorem There are several proofs of Taylor's Theorem, which lead to various forms of the remainder. The following proof is instructive because it leads to two different forms of the remainder and it relies on the Fundamental Theorem of Calculus, integration by parts, and the Mean Value Theorem for Integrals. Assume that f has at least $n + 1$ continuous derivatives on an interval containing a.

a. Show that the Fundamental Theorem of Calculus can be written in the form

$$f(x) = f(a) + \int_a^x f'(t)\, dt.$$

b. Use integration by parts ($u = f'(t)$, $dv = dt$) to show that

$$f(x) = f(a) + (x - a)f'(a) + \int_a^x (x - t)f''(t)\, dt.$$

c. Show that n integrations by parts gives

$$f(x) = f(a) + \frac{f'(a)}{1!}(x - a) + \frac{f''(a)}{2!}(x - a)^2 + \cdots$$
$$+ \frac{f^{(n)}(a)}{n!}(x - a)^n + \underbrace{\int_a^x \frac{f^{(n+1)}(t)}{n!}(x - t)^n\, dt.}_{R_n(x)}$$

d. *Challenge:* The result in part (c) looks like $f(x) = p_n(x) + R_n(x)$, where p_n is the nth-order Taylor polynomial and R_n is a new form of the remainder, known as the integral form of the remainder. Use the Mean Value Theorem for Integrals (Section 5.4) to show that R_n can be expressed in the form

$$R_n(x) = \frac{f^{(n+1)}(c)}{(n + 1)!}(x - a)^{n+1},$$

where c is between a and x.

93. Tangent line is p_1 Let f be differentiable at $x = a$.

a. Find the equation of the line tangent to the curve $y = f(x)$ at $(a, f(a))$.
b. Verify that the Taylor polynomial p_1 centered at a describes the tangent line found in part (a).

94. Local extreme points and inflection points Suppose f has continuous first and second derivatives at a.

a. Show that if f has a local maximum at a, then the Taylor polynomial p_2 centered at a also has a local maximum at a.
b. Show that if f has a local minimum at a, then the Taylor polynomial p_2 centered at a also has a local minimum at a.
c. Is it true that if f has an inflection point at a, then the Taylor polynomial p_2 centered at a also has an inflection point at a?
d. Are the converses in parts (a) and (b) true? If p_2 has a local extreme point at a, does f have the same type of point at a?

T 95. Approximating $\sin x$ Let $f(x) = \sin x$ and let p_n and q_n be nth-order Taylor polynomials for f centered at 0 and π, respectively.

a. Find p_5 and q_5.
b. Graph f, p_5, and q_5 on the interval $[-\pi, 2\pi]$. On what interval is p_5 a better approximation to f than q_5? On what interval is q_5 a better approximation to f than p_5?
c. Complete the following table showing the errors in the approximations given by p_5 and q_5 at selected points.

x	$|\sin x - p_5(x)|$	$|\sin x - q_5(x)|$
$\pi/4$		
$\pi/2$		
$3\pi/4$		
$5\pi/4$		
$7\pi/4$		

d. At which points in the table is p_5 a better approximation to f than q_5? At which points do p_5 and q_5 give comparable approximations to f? Explain your observations.

T 96. Approximating $\ln x$ Let $f(x) = \ln x$ and let p_n and q_n be the nth-order Taylor polynomials for f centered at 1 and e, respectively.

a. Find p_3 and q_3.
b. Graph f, p_3, and q_3 on the interval $(0, 4]$.
c. Complete the following table showing the errors in the approximations given by p_3 and q_3 at selected points.

x	$|\ln x - p_3(x)|$	$|\ln x - q_3(x)|$
0.5		
1.0		
1.5		
2		
2.5		
3		
3.5		

d. At which points in the table is p_3 a better approximation to f than q_3? Explain your observations.

T 97. Approximating square roots Let p_1 and q_1 be the first-order Taylor polynomials for $f(x) = \sqrt{x}$ centered at 36 and 49, respectively.

a. Find p_1 and q_1.
b. Complete the following table showing the errors when using p_1 and q_1 to approximate $f(x)$ at $x = 37, 39, 41, 43, 45,$ and 47. Use a calculator to obtain an exact value of $f(x)$.

x	$|\sqrt{x} - p_1(x)|$	$|\sqrt{x} - q_1(x)|$
37		
39		
41		
43		
45		
47		

c. At which points in the table is p_1 a better approximation to f than q_1? Explain this result.

T 98. A different kind of approximation When approximating a function f using a Taylor polynomial, we use information about f and its derivatives at one point. An alternative approach (called *interpolation*) uses information about f at several different points. Suppose we wish to approximate $f(x) = \sin x$ on the interval $[0, \pi]$.

a. Write the (quadratic) Taylor polynomial p_2 for f centered at $\frac{\pi}{2}$.

b. Now consider a quadratic interpolating polynomial
$q(x) = ax^2 + bx + c$. The coefficients a, b, and c are chosen
such that the following conditions are satisfied:

$$q(0) = f(0), q\left(\frac{\pi}{2}\right) = f\left(\frac{\pi}{2}\right), \text{ and } q(\pi) = f(\pi).$$

Show that $q(x) = -\frac{4}{\pi^2}x^2 + \frac{4}{\pi}x$.

c. Graph f, p_2, and q on $[0, \pi]$.
d. Find the error in approximating $f(x) = \sin x$ at the points
$\frac{\pi}{4}, \frac{\pi}{2}, \frac{3\pi}{4}$, and π using p_2 and q.
e. Which function, p_2 or q, is a better approximation to f on
$[0, \pi]$? Explain.

9.2 Properties of Power Series

The preceding section demonstrated that Taylor polynomials provide accurate approximations to many functions and that, in general, the approximations improve as the degree of the polynomials increases. In this section, we take the next step and let the degree of the Taylor polynomials increase without bound to produce a *power series*.

Geometric Series as Power Series

A good way to become familiar with power series is to return to *geometric series*, first encountered in Section 8.3. Recall that for a fixed number r,

$$\sum_{k=0}^{\infty} r^k = 1 + r + r^2 + \cdots = \frac{1}{1-r}, \qquad \text{provided } |r| < 1.$$

It's a small change to replace the real number r with the variable x. In doing so, the geometric series becomes a new representation of a familiar function:

$$\sum_{k=0}^{\infty} x^k = 1 + x + x^2 + \cdots = \frac{1}{1-x}, \qquad \text{provided } |x| < 1.$$

This infinite series is a power series and it is a representation of the function $1/(1 - x)$ that is valid on the interval $|x| < 1$.

In general, power series are used to represent familiar functions such as trigonometric, exponential, and logarithmic functions. They are also used to define new functions. For example, consider the function defined by

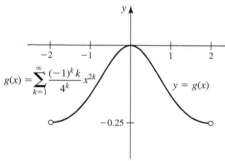

$g(x) = \sum_{k=1}^{\infty} \frac{(-1)^k k}{4^k} x^{2k}$

$y = g(x)$

$$g(x) = \sum_{k=1}^{\infty} \frac{(-1)^k k}{4^k} x^{2k}.$$

The term *function* is used advisedly because it's not yet clear whether g really is a function. If so, is it continuous? Does it have a derivative? Judging by its graph (Figure 9.13), g appears to be an ordinary continuous and differentiable function on $(-2, 2)$ (which is identified at the end of the chapter). In fact, power series satisfy the defining property of all functions: For each admissible value of x, a power series has at most one value. For this reason, we refer to a power series as a function, although the domain, properties, and identity of the function may need to be discovered.

Figure 9.13

➤ Figure 9.13 shows an approximation to the graph of g made by summing the first 500 terms of the power series at selected values of x on the interval $(-2, 2)$.

QUICK CHECK 1 By substituting $x = 0$ in the power series for g, evaluate $g(0)$ for the function in Figure 9.13. ◄

Convergence of Power Series

First let's establish some terminology associated with power series.

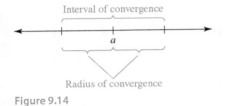

Interval of convergence

a

Radius of convergence

Figure 9.14

> **DEFINITION** **Power Series**
>
> A **power series** has the general form
>
> $$\sum_{k=0}^{\infty} c_k (x - a)^k,$$
>
> where a and c_k are real numbers, and x is a variable. The c_k's are the **coefficients** of the power series and a is the **center** of the power series. The set of values of x for which the series converges is its **interval of convergence**. The **radius of convergence** of the power series, denoted R, is the distance from the center of the series to the boundary of the interval of convergence (Figure 9.14).

How do we determine the interval of convergence for a given power series? The presence of the terms x^k or $(x - a)^k$ in a power series suggests using the Ratio Test or the Root Test. Because these terms could be positive or negative, we test a power series for absolute convergence (remember that the Ratio and Root Tests apply only to series with positive terms). By Theorem 8.21, if we determine the values of x for which the series converges absolutely, we have a set of values for which the series converges.

Before turning to examples, we point out some important facts. Suppose we test the series $\sum a_k$ for absolute convergence using the Ratio Test. If

$$r = \lim_{k \to \infty} \left| \frac{a_{k+1}}{a_k} \right| < 1,$$

it follows that $\sum |a_k|$ converges, which in turn implies that $\sum a_k$ converges (Theorem 8.21). On the other hand, if $r > 1$, then for large k we have $|a_{k+1}| > |a_k|$, which means the terms of the sequence $\{a_k\}$ grow in magnitude as $k \to \infty$. Therefore, $\lim_{k \to \infty} a_k \neq 0$, and we conclude that $\sum a_k$ diverges by the Divergence Test (recall that the Divergence Test applies to *arbitrary* series). If $r = 1$, the Ratio Test is inconclusive, and we use other tests to determine convergence.

A similar argument can be made when using the Root Test to determine the interval of convergence. We first test the series for absolute convergence. When $\rho < 1$, the series converges absolutely (and therefore converges), but when $\rho > 1$, the terms of the series do not tend to 0, so the series diverges by the Divergence Test. If $\rho = 1$, the test is inconclusive, and other tests must be used.

The following examples illustrate how the Ratio and Root Tests are used to determine the interval and radius of convergence.

EXAMPLE 1 Interval and radius of convergence Find the interval and radius of convergence for each power series.

a. $\displaystyle\sum_{k=0}^{\infty} \frac{x^k}{k!}$ **b.** $\displaystyle\sum_{k=0}^{\infty} \frac{(-1)^k (x - 2)^k}{4^k}$ **c.** $\displaystyle\sum_{k=1}^{\infty} k! \, x^k$

SOLUTION

a. The center of the power series is 0 and the terms of the series are $x^k/k!$. Due to the presence of the factor $k!$, we test the series for absolute convergence using the Ratio Test:

$$r = \lim_{k \to \infty} \frac{|x^{k+1}/(k + 1)!|}{|x^k/k!|} \qquad \text{Ratio Test for absolute convergence}$$

$$= \lim_{k \to \infty} \frac{|x|^{k+1}}{|x|^k} \cdot \frac{k!}{(k + 1)!} \qquad \text{Invert and multiply.}$$

$$= |x| \lim_{k \to \infty} \frac{1}{k + 1} = 0. \qquad \text{Simplify and take the limit with } x \text{ fixed.}$$

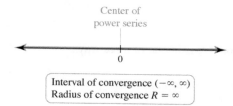

Figure 9.15

Notice that in taking the limit as $k \to \infty$, x is held fixed. Because $r = 0$ for all real numbers x, the series converges absolutely for all x. Using Theorem 8.21, we conclude that the series converges for all x. Therefore, the interval of convergence is $(-\infty, \infty)$ (Figure 9.15) and the radius of convergence is $R = \infty$.

b. We test for absolute convergence using the Root Test:

$$\rho = \lim_{k \to \infty} \sqrt[k]{\left| \frac{(-1)^k (x-2)^k}{4^k} \right|} = \frac{|x-2|}{4}.$$

In this case, ρ depends on the value of x. For absolute convergence, x must satisfy

$$\rho = \frac{|x-2|}{4} < 1,$$

which implies that $|x - 2| < 4$. Using standard techniques for solving inequalities, the solution set is $-4 < x - 2 < 4$, or $-2 < x < 6$. We conclude that the series converges on $(-2, 6)$ (by Theorem 8.21, absolute convergence implies convergence). When $-\infty < x < -2$ or $6 < x < \infty$, we have $\rho > 1$, so the series diverges on these intervals (the terms of the series do not approach 0 as $k \to \infty$ and the Divergence Test applies).

➤ Either the Ratio Test or the Root Test works for the power series in Example 1b.

The Root Test does not give information about convergence at the endpoints $x = -2$ and $x = 6$, because at these points, the Root Test results in $\rho = 1$. To test for convergence at the endpoints, we substitute each endpoint into the series and carry out separate tests. At $x = -2$, the power series becomes

$$\sum_{k=0}^{\infty} \frac{(-1)^k (x-2)^k}{4^k} = \sum_{k=0}^{\infty} \frac{4^k}{4^k} \quad \text{Substitute } x = -2 \text{ and simplify.}$$

$$= \sum_{k=0}^{\infty} 1. \quad \text{Diverges by Divergence Test}$$

➤ The Ratio and Root Tests determine the radius of convergence conclusively. However, the interval of convergence is not determined until the endpoints are tested.

The series clearly diverges at the left endpoint. At $x = 6$, the power series is

$$\sum_{k=0}^{\infty} \frac{(-1)^k (x-2)^k}{4^k} = \sum_{k=0}^{\infty} (-1)^k \frac{4^k}{4^k} \quad \text{Substitute } x = 6 \text{ and simplify.}$$

$$= \sum_{k=0}^{\infty} (-1)^k. \quad \text{Diverges by Divergence Test}$$

This series also diverges at the right endpoint. Therefore, the interval of convergence is $(-2, 6)$, excluding the endpoints (Figure 9.16), and the radius of convergence is $R = 4$.

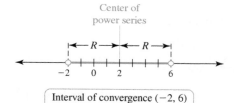

Figure 9.16

c. In this case, the Ratio Test is preferable:

$$r = \lim_{k \to \infty} \frac{|(k+1)! \, x^{k+1}|}{|k! \, x^k|} \quad \text{Ratio Test for absolute convergence}$$

$$= |x| \lim_{k \to \infty} \frac{(k+1)!}{k!} \quad \text{Simplify.}$$

$$= |x| \lim_{k \to \infty} (k+1) \quad \text{Simplify.}$$

$$= \infty. \quad \text{If } x \ne 0$$

We see that $r > 1$ for all $x \ne 0$, so the series diverges on $(-\infty, 0)$ and $(0, \infty)$.

The only way to satisfy $r < 1$ is to take $x = 0$, in which case the power series has a value of 0. The interval of convergence of the power series consists of the single point $x = 0$ (Figure 9.17), and the radius of convergence is $R = 0$.

Related Exercises 9–28 ◄

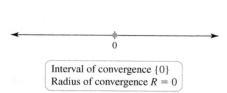

Figure 9.17

Example 1 illustrates the three common types of intervals of convergence, which are summarized in the following theorem (see Appendix B for a proof).

➤ Theorem 9.3 implies that the interval of convergence is symmetric about the center of the series; the radius of convergence R is determined by analyzing r from the Ratio Test (or ρ from the Root Test). The theorem says nothing about convergence at the endpoints. For example, the intervals of convergence $(2, 6)$, $(2, 6]$, $[2, 6)$, and $[2, 6]$ all have a radius of convergence of $R = 2$.

THEOREM 9.3   Convergence of Power Series

A power series $\sum_{k=0}^{\infty} c_k(x - a)^k$ centered at a converges in one of three ways:

1. The series converges for all x, in which case the interval of convergence is $(-\infty, \infty)$ and the radius of convergence is $R = \infty$.

2. There is a real number $R > 0$ such that the series converges for $|x - a| < R$ and diverges for $|x - a| > R$, in which case the radius of convergence is R.

3. The series converges only at a, in which case the radius of convergence is $R = 0$.

QUICK CHECK 2 What are the interval and radius of convergence of the geometric series $\sum x^k$? ◄

EXAMPLE 2   Interval and radius of convergence Use the Ratio Test to find the radius and interval of convergence of $\displaystyle\sum_{k=1}^{\infty} \frac{(x - 2)^k}{\sqrt{k}}$.

➤ The power series in Example 2 could also be analyzed using the Root Test.

SOLUTION

$$r = \lim_{k\to\infty} \frac{|(x - 2)^{k+1}/\sqrt{k + 1}|}{|(x - 2)^k/\sqrt{k}|} \qquad \text{Ratio Test for absolute convergence}$$

$$= |x - 2| \lim_{k\to\infty} \sqrt{\frac{k}{k + 1}} \qquad \text{Simplify.}$$

$$= |x - 2| \sqrt{\underbrace{\lim_{k\to\infty} \frac{k}{k + 1}}_{1}} \qquad \text{Limit Law}$$

$$= |x - 2| \qquad \text{Limit equals 1.}$$

The series converges absolutely (and therefore converges) for all x such that $r < 1$, which implies $|x - 2| < 1$, or $1 < x < 3$. On the intervals $-\infty < x < 1$ and $3 < x < \infty$, we have $r > 1$ and the series diverges.

We now test the endpoints. Substituting $x = 1$ gives the series

$$\sum_{k=1}^{\infty} \frac{(x - 2)^k}{\sqrt{k}} = \sum_{k=1}^{\infty} \frac{(-1)^k}{\sqrt{k}}.$$

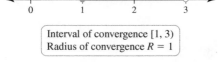

Center of
power series

$\vdash\!\!-R\!-\!\!\vdash\!\!-R\!-\!\!\dashv$

0   1   2   3

Interval of convergence $[1, 3)$
Radius of convergence $R = 1$

Figure 9.18

This series converges by the Alternating Series Test (the terms of the series decrease in magnitude and approach 0 as $k \to \infty$). Substituting $x = 3$ gives the series

$$\sum_{k=1}^{\infty} \frac{(x - 2)^k}{\sqrt{k}} = \sum_{k=1}^{\infty} \frac{1}{\sqrt{k}},$$

which is a divergent p-series. We conclude that the interval of convergence is $1 \le x < 3$ and the radius of convergence is $R = 1$ (Figure 9.18).

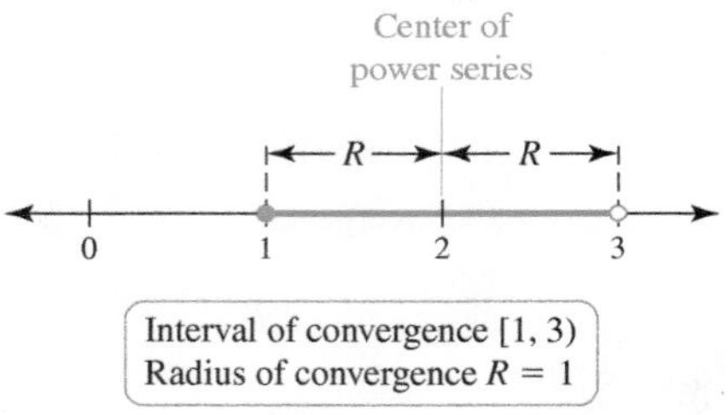

Related Exercises 9–28 ◄

Combining Power Series

A power series defines a function on its interval of convergence. When power series are combined algebraically, new functions are defined. The following theorem, stated without proof, gives three common ways to combine power series.

> New power series can also be defined as the product and quotient of power series. The calculation of the coefficients of such series is more challenging (Exercise 75).

> Theorem 9.4 also applies to power series centered at points other than $x = 0$. Property 1 applies directly; Properties 2 and 3 apply with slight modifications.

THEOREM 9.4 Combining Power Series

Suppose the power series $\sum c_k x^k$ and $\sum d_k x^k$ converge to $f(x)$ and $g(x)$, respectively, on an interval I.

1. **Sum and difference:** The power series $\sum (c_k \pm d_k)x^k$ converges to $f(x) \pm g(x)$ on I.

2. **Multiplication by a power:** Suppose m is an integer such that $k + m \geq 0$ for all terms of the power series $x^m \sum c_k x^k = \sum c_k x^{k+m}$. This series converges to $x^m f(x)$ for all $x \neq 0$ in I. When $x = 0$, the series converges to $\lim_{x \to 0} x^m f(x)$.

3. **Composition:** If $h(x) = bx^m$, where m is a positive integer and b is a nonzero real number, the power series $\sum c_k (h(x))^k$ converges to the composite function $f(h(x))$, for all x such that $h(x)$ is in I.

EXAMPLE 3   Combining power series Given the geometric series

$$\frac{1}{1 - x} = \sum_{k=0}^{\infty} x^k = 1 + x + x^2 + x^3 + \cdots, \qquad \text{for } |x| < 1,$$

find the power series and interval of convergence for the following functions.

a. $\dfrac{x^5}{1 - x}$ **b.** $\dfrac{1}{1 - 2x}$ **c.** $\dfrac{1}{1 + x^2}$

SOLUTION

a.
$$\frac{x^5}{1 - x} = x^5 (1 + x + x^2 + \cdots) \quad \text{Theorem 9.4, Property 2}$$

$$= x^5 + x^6 + x^7 + \cdots$$

$$= \sum_{k=0}^{\infty} x^{k+5}$$

This geometric series has a ratio $r = x$ and converges when $|r| = |x| < 1$. The interval of convergence is $|x| < 1$.

b. We substitute $2x$ for x in the power series for $\dfrac{1}{1 - x}$:

$$\frac{1}{1 - 2x} = 1 + (2x) + (2x)^2 + \cdots \quad \text{Theorem 9.4, Property 3}$$

$$= \sum_{k=0}^{\infty} (2x)^k.$$

This geometric series has a ratio $r = 2x$ and converges provided $|r| = |2x| < 1$ or $|x| < \frac{1}{2}$. The interval of convergence is $|x| < \frac{1}{2}$.

c. We substitute $-x^2$ for x in the power series for $\dfrac{1}{1 - x}$:

$$\frac{1}{1 + x^2} = 1 + (-x^2) + (-x^2)^2 + \cdots \quad \text{Theorem 9.4, Property 3}$$

$$= 1 - x^2 + x^4 - \cdots$$

$$= \sum_{k=0}^{\infty} (-1)^k x^{2k}.$$

This geometric series has a ratio of $r = -x^2$ and converges provided $|r| = |-x^2| = |x^2| < 1$ or $|x| < 1$.

Related Exercises 29–40 ◄

Differentiating and Integrating Power Series

Some properties of polynomials carry over to power series, but others do not. For example, a polynomial is defined for all values of x, whereas a power series is defined only on its interval of convergence. In general, the properties of polynomials carry over to power series when the power series is restricted to its interval of convergence. The following result illustrates this principle.

> Theorem 9.5 makes no claim about the convergence of the differentiated or integrated series at the endpoints of the interval of convergence.

THEOREM 9.5   Differentiating and Integrating Power Series

Suppose the power series $\sum c_k(x - a)^k$ converges for $|x - a| < R$ and defines a function f on that interval.

1. Then f is differentiable (which implies continuous) for $|x - a| < R$, and f' is found by differentiating the power series for f term by term; that is,

$$f'(x) = \sum kc_k(x - a)^{k-1},$$

   for $|x - a| < R$.

2. The indefinite integral of f is found by integrating the power series for f term by term; that is,

$$\int f(x)dx = \sum c_k \frac{(x - a)^{k+1}}{k + 1} + C,$$

   for $|x - a| < R$, where C is an arbitrary constant.

The proof of this theorem requires advanced ideas and is omitted. However, some discussion is in order before turning to examples. The statements in Theorem 9.5 about term-by-term differentiation and integration say two things. First, the differentiated and integrated power series converge, provided x belongs to the interior of the interval of convergence. But the theorem claims more than convergence. According to the theorem, the differentiated and integrated power series converge to the derivative and indefinite integral of f, respectively, on the interior of the interval of convergence. Let's use this theorem to develop new power series.

EXAMPLE 4   Differentiating and integrating power series Consider the geometric series

$$f(x) = \frac{1}{1 - x} = \sum_{k=0}^{\infty} x^k = 1 + x + x^2 + x^3 + \cdots, \quad \text{for } |x| < 1.$$

a. Differentiate this series term by term to find the power series for f' and identify the function it represents.

b. Integrate this series term by term and identify the function it represents.

SOLUTION

a. We know that $f'(x) = (1 - x)^{-2}$. Differentiating the series, we find that

$$f'(x) = \frac{d}{dx}(1 + x + x^2 + x^3 + \cdots) \qquad \text{Differentiate the power series for } f.$$

$$= 1 + 2x + 3x^2 + \cdots \qquad \text{Differentiate term by term.}$$

$$= \sum_{k=0}^{\infty} (k + 1)\, x^k. \qquad \text{Summation notation}$$

Therefore, on the interval $|x| < 1$,

$$f'(x) = (1 - x)^{-2} = \sum_{k=0}^{\infty} (k + 1)\, x^k.$$

Theorem 9.5 makes no claim about convergence of the differentiated series to f' at the endpoints. In this case, substituting $x = \pm 1$ into the power series for f' reveals that the series diverges at both endpoints.

b. Integrating f and integrating the power series term by term, we have

$$\int \frac{dx}{1 - x} = \int (1 + x + x^2 + x^3 + \cdots)\, dx,$$

which implies that

$$-\ln |1 - x| = x + \frac{x^2}{2} + \frac{x^3}{3} + \frac{x^4}{4} + \cdots + C,$$

where C is an arbitrary constant. Notice that the left side is 0 when $x = 0$. The right side is 0 when $x = 0$ provided we choose $C = 0$. Because $|x| < 1$, the absolute value sign on the left side may be removed. Multiplying both sides by -1, we have a series representation for $\ln (1 - x)$:

$$\ln (1 - x) = -x - \frac{x^2}{2} - \frac{x^3}{3} - \frac{x^4}{4} - \cdots = -\sum_{k=1}^{\infty} \frac{x^k}{k}.$$

It is interesting to test the endpoints of the interval $|x| < 1$. When $x = 1$, the series is (a multiple of) the divergent harmonic series, and when $x = -1$, the series is the convergent alternating harmonic series (Section 8.6). So the interval of convergence is $-1 \le x < 1$. Although we know the series converges at $x = -1$, Theorem 9.5 guarantees convergence to $\ln (1 - x)$ only at the interior points. We cannot use Theorem 9.5 to claim that the series converges to $\ln 2$ at $x = -1$. In fact, it does, as shown in Section 9.3.

Related Exercises 41–46 ◄

QUICK CHECK 3 Use the result of Example 4 to write a series representation for $\ln \frac{1}{2} = -\ln 2$. ◄

EXAMPLE 5   Functions to power series Find power series representations centered at 0 for the following functions and give their intervals of convergence.

a. $\tan^{-1} x$ **b.** $\ln \left(\dfrac{1 + x}{1 - x} \right)$

SOLUTION In both cases, we work with known power series and use differentiation, integration, and other combinations.

a. The key is to recall that

$$\int \frac{dx}{1 + x^2} = \tan^{-1} x + C$$

and that, by Example 3c,

$$\frac{1}{1 + x^2} = 1 - x^2 + x^4 - \cdots, \qquad \text{provided } |x| < 1.$$

We now integrate both sides of this last expression:

$$\int \frac{dx}{1 + x^2} = \int (1 - x^2 + x^4 - \cdots)\, dx,$$

which implies that

$$\tan^{-1} x = x - \frac{x^3}{3} + \frac{x^5}{5} - \cdots + C.$$

Substituting $x = 0$ and noting that $\tan^{-1} 0 = 0$, the two sides of this equation agree provided we choose $C = 0$. Therefore,

$$\tan^{-1} x = x - \frac{x^3}{3} + \frac{x^5}{5} - \cdots = \sum_{k=0}^{\infty} \frac{(-1)^k x^{2k+1}}{2k + 1}.$$

> Again, Theorem 9.5 does not guarantee that the power series in Example 5a converges to $\tan^{-1} x$ at $x = \pm 1$. In fact, it does.

By Theorem 9.5, this power series converges to $\tan^{-1} x$ for $|x| < 1$. Testing the endpoints separately, we find that it also converges at $x = \pm 1$. Therefore, the interval of convergence is $[-1, 1]$.

b. We have already seen (Example 4) that

$$\ln (1 - x) = -x - \frac{x^2}{2} - \frac{x^3}{3} - \cdots.$$

> Nicolaus Mercator (1620–1687) and Sir Isaac Newton (1642–1727) independently derived the power series for $\ln (1 + x)$, which is called the *Mercator series*.

Replacing x with $-x$ (Property 3 of Theorem 9.4), we have

$$\ln (1 - (-x)) = \ln (1 + x) = x - \frac{x^2}{2} + \frac{x^3}{3} - \cdots.$$

Subtracting these two power series gives

$$\ln \left(\frac{1 + x}{1 - x} \right) = \ln (1 + x) - \ln (1 - x) \quad \text{Properties of logarithms}$$

$$= \underbrace{\left(x - \frac{x^2}{2} + \frac{x^3}{3} - \cdots \right)}_{\ln (1 + x)} - \underbrace{\left(-x - \frac{x^2}{2} - \frac{x^3}{3} - \cdots \right)}_{\ln (1 - x)}, \quad \text{for } |x| < 1$$

$$= 2 \left(x + \frac{x^3}{3} + \frac{x^5}{5} + \cdots \right) \quad \text{Combine; use Property 1 of Theorem 9.4.}$$

$$= 2 \sum_{k=0}^{\infty} \frac{x^{2k+1}}{2k + 1}. \quad \text{Summation notation}$$

This power series is the difference of two power series, both of which converge on the interval $|x| < 1$. Therefore, by Theorem 9.4, the new series also converges on $|x| < 1$.

Related Exercises 47–52 ◀

QUICK CHECK 4 Verify that the power series in Example 5b does not converge at the endpoints $x = \pm 1$. ◀

If you look carefully, every example in this section is ultimately based on the geometric series. Using this single series, we were able to develop power series for many other functions. Imagine what we could do with a few more basic power series. The following section accomplishes precisely that end. There, we discover power series for many of the standard functions of calculus.

SECTION 9.2 EXERCISES

Review Questions

1. Write the first four terms of a power series with coefficients c_0, c_1, c_2, and c_3 centered at 0.

2. Write the first four terms of a power series with coefficients c_0, c_1, c_2, and c_3 centered at 3.

3. What tests are used to determine the radius of convergence of a power series?

4. Explain why a power series is tested for *absolute* convergence.

5. Do the interval and radius of convergence of a power series change when the series is differentiated or integrated? Explain.

6. What is the radius of convergence of the power series $\Sigma c_k (x/2)^k$ if the radius of convergence of $\Sigma c_k x^k$ is R?

7. What is the interval of convergence of the power series $\Sigma (4x)^k$?

8. How are the radii of convergence of the power series $\Sigma c_k x^k$ and $\Sigma (-1)^k c_k x^k$ related?

Basic Skills

9–28. Interval and radius of convergence *Determine the radius of convergence of the following power series. Then test the endpoints to determine the interval of convergence.*

9. $\sum (2x)^k$

10. $\sum \dfrac{(2x)^k}{k!}$

11. $\sum \dfrac{(x-1)^k}{k}$

12. $\sum \dfrac{(x-1)^k}{k!}$

13. $\sum (kx)^k$

14. $\sum k!\,(x-10)^k$

15. $\sum \sin^k\!\left(\dfrac{1}{k}\right) x^k$

16. $\sum \dfrac{2^k (x-3)^k}{k}$

17. $\sum \left(\dfrac{x}{3}\right)^k$

18. $\sum (-1)^k \dfrac{x^k}{5^k}$

19. $\sum \dfrac{x^k}{k^k}$

20. $\sum (-1)^k \dfrac{k(x-4)^k}{2^k}$

21. $\sum \dfrac{k^2 x^{2k}}{k!}$

22. $\sum k\,(x-1)^k$

23. $\sum \dfrac{x^{2k+1}}{3^{k-1}}$

24. $\sum \left(-\dfrac{x}{10}\right)^{2k}$

25. $\sum \dfrac{(x-1)^k k^k}{(k+1)^k}$

26. $\sum \dfrac{(-2)^k (x+3)^k}{3^{k+1}}$

27. $\sum \dfrac{k^{20} x^k}{(2k+1)!}$

28. $\sum (-1)^k \dfrac{x^{3k}}{27^k}$

29–34. Combining power series *Use the geometric series*

$$f(x) = \dfrac{1}{1-x} = \sum_{k=0}^{\infty} x^k, \quad \text{for } |x| < 1,$$

to find the power series representation for the following functions (centered at 0). Give the interval of convergence of the new series.

29. $f(3x) = \dfrac{1}{1-3x}$

30. $g(x) = \dfrac{x^3}{1-x}$

31. $h(x) = \dfrac{2x^3}{1-x}$

32. $f(x^3) = \dfrac{1}{1-x^3}$

33. $p(x) = \dfrac{4x^{12}}{1-x}$

34. $f(-4x) = \dfrac{1}{1+4x}$

35–40. Combining power series *Use the power series representation*

$$f(x) = \ln(1-x) = -\sum_{k=1}^{\infty} \dfrac{x^k}{k}, \quad \text{for } -1 \le x < 1,$$

to find the power series for the following functions (centered at 0). Give the interval of convergence of the new series.

35. $f(3x) = \ln(1-3x)$

36. $g(x) = x^3 \ln(1-x)$

37. $h(x) = x \ln(1-x)$

38. $f(x^3) = \ln(1-x^3)$

39. $p(x) = 2x^6 \ln(1-x)$

40. $f(-4x) = \ln(1+4x)$

41–46. Differentiating and integrating power series *Find the power series representation for g centered at 0 by differentiating or integrating the power series for f (perhaps more than once). Give the interval of convergence for the resulting series.*

41. $g(x) = \dfrac{2}{(1-2x)^2}$ using $f(x) = \dfrac{1}{1-2x}$

42. $g(x) = \dfrac{1}{(1-x)^3}$ using $f(x) = \dfrac{1}{1-x}$

43. $g(x) = \dfrac{1}{(1-x)^4}$ using $f(x) = \dfrac{1}{1-x}$

44. $g(x) = \dfrac{x}{(1+x^2)^2}$ using $f(x) = \dfrac{1}{1+x^2}$

45. $g(x) = \ln(1-3x)$ using $f(x) = \dfrac{1}{1-3x}$

46. $g(x) = \ln(1+x^2)$ using $f(x) = \dfrac{x}{1+x^2}$

47–52. Functions to power series *Find power series representations centered at 0 for the following functions using known power series. Give the interval of convergence for the resulting series.*

47. $f(x) = \dfrac{1}{1+x^2}$

48. $f(x) = \dfrac{1}{1-x^4}$

49. $f(x) = \dfrac{3}{3+x}$

50. $f(x) = \ln\sqrt{1-x^2}$

51. $f(x) = \ln\sqrt{4-x^2}$

52. $f(x) = \tan^{-1}(4x^2)$

Further Explorations

53. **Explain why or why not** Determine whether the following statements are true and give an explanation or counterexample.

   a. The interval of convergence of the power series $\sum c_k (x-3)^k$ could be $(-2, 8)$.

   b. The series $\sum (-2x)^k$ converges on the interval $-\frac{1}{2} < x < \frac{1}{2}$.

   c. If $f(x) = \sum c_k x^k$ on the interval $|x| < 1$, then $f(x^2) = \sum c_k x^{2k}$ on the interval $|x| < 1$.

   d. If $f(x) = \sum c_k x^k = 0$, for all x on an interval $(-a, a)$, then $c_k = 0$, for all k.

54. **Radius of convergence** Find the radius of convergence of

$$\sum \left(1 + \dfrac{1}{k}\right)^{k^2} x^k.$$

55. **Radius of convergence** Find the radius of convergence of

$$\sum \dfrac{k!\,x^k}{k^k}.$$

56–59. Summation notation *Write the following power series in summation (sigma) notation.*

56. $1 + \dfrac{x}{2} + \dfrac{x^2}{4} + \dfrac{x^3}{6} + \cdots$

57. $1 - \dfrac{x}{2} + \dfrac{x^2}{3} - \dfrac{x^3}{4} + \cdots$

58. $x - \dfrac{x^3}{4} + \dfrac{x^5}{9} - \dfrac{x^7}{16} + \cdots$

59. $-\dfrac{x^2}{1!} + \dfrac{x^4}{2!} - \dfrac{x^6}{3!} + \dfrac{x^8}{4!} - \cdots$

60. **Scaling power series** If the power series $f(x) = \sum c_k x^k$ has an interval of convergence of $|x| < R$, what is the interval of convergence of the power series for $f(ax)$, where $a \ne 0$ is a real number?

61. **Shifting power series** If the power series $f(x) = \sum c_k x^k$ has an interval of convergence of $|x| < R$, what is the interval of convergence of the power series for $f(x-a)$, where $a \ne 0$ is a real number?

62–67. Series to functions *Find the function represented by the following series and find the interval of convergence of the series. (Not all these series are power series.)*

62. $\sum_{k=0}^{\infty} (x^2 + 1)^{2k}$

63. $\sum_{k=0}^{\infty} (\sqrt{x} - 2)^k$

64. $\sum_{k=1}^{\infty} \dfrac{x^{2k}}{4k}$

65. $\sum_{k=0}^{\infty} e^{-kx}$

66. $\sum_{k=1}^{\infty} \dfrac{(x-2)^k}{3^{2k}}$

67. $\sum_{k=0}^{\infty} \left(\dfrac{x^2-1}{3}\right)^k$

68. A useful substitution Replace x with $x - 1$ in the series

$$\ln(1 + x) = \sum_{k=1}^{\infty} \frac{(-1)^{k+1} x^k}{k}$$ to obtain a power series for $\ln x$

centered at $x = 1$. What is the interval of convergence for the new power series?

69–72. Exponential function *In Section 9.3, we show that the power series for the exponential function centered at 0 is*

$$e^x = \sum_{k=0}^{\infty} \frac{x^k}{k!}, \quad \text{for } -\infty < x < \infty.$$

Use the methods of this section to find the power series for the following functions. Give the interval of convergence for the resulting series.

69. $f(x) = e^{-x}$
70. $f(x) = e^{2x}$
71. $f(x) = e^{-3x}$
72. $f(x) = x^2 e^x$

Additional Exercises

73. Powers of x multiplied by a power series Prove that if

$$f(x) = \sum_{k=0}^{\infty} c_k x^k \text{ converges with radius of convergence } R, \text{ then}$$

the power series for $x^m f(x)$ also converges with radius of convergence R, for positive integers m.

74. Remainders Let

$$f(x) = \sum_{k=0}^{\infty} x^k = \frac{1}{1-x} \quad \text{and} \quad S_n(x) = \sum_{k=0}^{n-1} x^k.$$

The remainder in truncating the power series after n terms is $R_n(x) = f(x) - S_n(x)$, which depends on x.

a. Show that $R_n(x) = x^n/(1-x)$.
b. Graph the remainder function on the interval $|x| < 1$ for $n = 1, 2, 3$. Discuss and interpret the graph. Where on the interval is $|R_n(x)|$ largest? Smallest?
c. For fixed n, minimize $|R_n(x)|$ with respect to x. Does the result agree with the observations in part (b)?
d. Let $N(x)$ be the number of terms required to reduce $|R_n(x)|$ to less than 10^{-6}. Graph the function $N(x)$ on the interval $|x| < 1$. Discuss and interpret the graph.

75. Product of power series Let

$$f(x) = \sum_{k=0}^{\infty} c_k x^k \quad \text{and} \quad g(x) = \sum_{k=0}^{\infty} d_k x^k.$$

a. Multiply the power series together as if they were polynomials, collecting all terms that are multiples of 1, x, and x^2. Write the first three terms of the product $f(x)g(x)$.
b. Find a general expression for the coefficient of x^n in the product series, for $n = 0, 1, 2, \ldots$.

76. Inverse sine Given the power series

$$\frac{1}{\sqrt{1 - x^2}} = 1 + \frac{1}{2} x^2 + \frac{1 \cdot 3}{2 \cdot 4} x^4 + \frac{1 \cdot 3 \cdot 5}{2 \cdot 4 \cdot 6} x^6 + \cdots,$$

for $-1 < x < 1$, find the power series for $f(x) = \sin^{-1} x$ centered at 0.

77. Computing with power series Consider the following function and its power series:

$$f(x) = \frac{1}{(1 - x)^2} = \sum_{k=1}^{\infty} k x^{k-1}, \quad \text{for } -1 < x < 1.$$

a. Let $S_n(x)$ be the sum of the first n terms of the series. With $n = 5$ and $n = 10$, graph $f(x)$ and $S_n(x)$ at the sample points $x = -0.9, -0.8, \ldots, -0.1, 0, 0.1, \ldots, 0.8, 0.9$ (two graphs). Where is the difference in the graphs the greatest?
b. What value of n is needed to guarantee that $|f(x) - S_n(x)| < 0.01$ at all of the sample points?

QUICK CHECK ANSWERS

1. $g(0) = 0$ **2.** $|x| < 1, R = 1$ **3.** Substituting
$$x = 1/2, \ln(1/2) = -\ln 2 = -\sum_{k=1}^{\infty} \frac{1}{2^k k} \blacktriangleleft$$

9.3 Taylor Series

In the preceding section, we saw that a power series represents a function on its interval of convergence. This section explores the opposite question: Given a function, what is its power series representation? We have already made significant progress in answering this question because we know how Taylor polynomials are used to approximate functions. We now extend Taylor polynomials to produce power series—called *Taylor series*—that provide series representations for functions.

Taylor Series for a Function

Suppose a function f has derivatives $f^{(k)}(a)$ of *all* orders at the point a. If we write the nth-order Taylor polynomial for f centered at a and allow n to increase indefinitely, a power series is obtained:

$$\underbrace{c_0 + c_1(x - a) + c_2(x - a)^2 + \cdots + c_n(x - a)^n}_{\text{Taylor polynomial of order } n} + \cdots \xrightarrow{n \to \infty} \sum_{k=0}^{\infty} c_k(x - a)^k.$$

The coefficients of the Taylor polynomial are given by

$$c_k = \frac{f^{(k)}(a)}{k!}, \quad \text{for } k = 0, 1, 2, \ldots.$$

These coefficients are also the coefficients of the power series, which is called the *Taylor series for f centered at a*. It is the natural extension of the set of Taylor polynomials for f at a. The special case of a Taylor series centered at 0 is called a *Maclaurin series*.

> ▶ Maclaurin series are named after the Scottish mathematician Colin Maclaurin (1698–1746), who described them (with credit to Taylor) in a textbook in 1742.

DEFINITION Taylor/Maclaurin Series for a Function

Suppose the function f has derivatives of all orders on an interval centered at the point a. The **Taylor series for f centered at a** is

$$f(a) + f'(a)(x - a) + \frac{f'(a)}{2!}(x - a)^2 + \frac{f^{(3)}(a)}{3!}(x - a)^3 + \cdots$$

$$= \sum_{k=0}^{\infty} \frac{f^{(k)}(a)}{k!}(x - a)^k.$$

A Taylor series centered at 0 is called a **Maclaurin series**.

For the Taylor series to be useful, we need to know two things:

- the values of x for which the Taylor series converges, and
- the values of x for which the Taylor series for f *equals* f.

> ▶ There are unusual cases in which the Taylor series for a function converges to a different function (Exercise 90).

The second question is subtle and is postponed for a few pages. For now, we find the Taylor series for f centered at a point, but we refrain from saying $f(x)$ equals the power series.

QUICK CHECK 1 Verify that if the Taylor series for f centered at a is evaluated at $x = a$, then the Taylor series equals $f(a)$. ◀

EXAMPLE 1 Maclaurin series and convergence Find the Maclaurin series (which is the Taylor series centered at 0) for the following functions. Find the interval of convergence.

a. $f(x) = \cos x$ **b.** $f(x) = \dfrac{1}{1 - x}$

SOLUTION The procedure for finding the coefficients of a Taylor series is the same as for Taylor polynomials; most of the work is computing the derivatives of f.

a. The Maclaurin series has the form

$$\sum_{k=0}^{\infty} c_k x^k, \quad \text{where } c_k = \frac{f^{(k)}(0)}{k!}, \quad \text{for } k = 0, 1, 2, \ldots.$$

We evaluate derivatives of $f(x) = \cos x$ at $x = 0$.

$$f(x) = \cos x \implies f(0) = 1$$
$$f'(x) = -\sin x \implies f'(0) = 0$$
$$f''(x) = -\cos x \implies f''(0) = -1$$
$$f'''(x) = \sin x \implies f'''(0) = 0$$
$$f^{(4)}(x) = \cos x \implies f^{(4)}(0) = 1$$
$$\vdots \qquad\qquad \vdots$$

> In Example 1a, we note that both $\cos x$ and its Maclaurin series are even functions. Be cautions with this observation. A Taylor series for an even function centered at a point different from 0 may be even, odd, or neither. A similar behavior occurs with odd functions.

Because the odd-order derivatives are zero, $c_k = \dfrac{f^{(k)}(0)}{k!} = 0$ when k is odd. Using the even-order derivatives, we have

$$c_0 = f(0) = 1, \qquad c_2 = \frac{f^{(2)}(0)}{2!} = -\frac{1}{2!},$$

$$c_4 = \frac{f^{(4)}(0)}{4!} = \frac{1}{4!}, \qquad c_6 = \frac{f^{(6)}(0)}{6!} = -\frac{1}{6!},$$

and in general, $c_{2k} = \dfrac{(-1)^k}{(2k)!}$. Therefore, the Maclaurin series for f is

$$1 - \frac{x^2}{2!} + \frac{x^4}{4!} - \frac{x^6}{6!} + \cdots = \sum_{k=0}^{\infty} \frac{(-1)^k}{(2k)!} x^{2k}.$$

Notice that this series contains all the Taylor polynomials. In this case, it consists only of even powers of x, reflecting the fact that $\cos x$ is an even function.

For what values of x does the series converge? As discussed in Section 9.2, we apply the Ratio Test to $\displaystyle\sum_{k=0}^{\infty} \left| \frac{(-1)^k}{(2k)!} x^{2k} \right|$ to test for absolute convergence:

$$r = \lim_{k \to \infty} \left| \frac{(-1)^{k+1} x^{2(k+1)} / (2(k+1))!}{(-1)^k x^{2k} / (2k)!} \right| \qquad r = \lim_{k \to \infty} \left| \frac{a_{k+1}}{a_k} \right|$$

$$= \lim_{k \to \infty} \left| \frac{x^2}{(2k+2)(2k+1)} \right| = 0. \qquad \text{Simplify and take the limit with } x \text{ fixed.}$$

> Recall that
> $$(2k+2)! = (2k+2)(2k+1)(2k)!.$$
> Therefore, $\dfrac{(2k)!}{(2k+2)!} = \dfrac{1}{(2k+2)(2k+1)}.$

In this case, $r < 1$ for all x, so the Maclaurin series converges absolutely for all x, which implies (by Theorem 8.21) that the series converges for all x. We conclude that the interval of convergence is $-\infty < x < \infty$.

b. We proceed in a similar way with $f(x) = 1/(1-x)$ by evaluating the derivatives of f at 0:

$$f(x) = \frac{1}{1-x} \implies f(0) = 1,$$

$$f'(x) = \frac{1}{(1-x)^2} \implies f'(0) = 1,$$

$$f''(x) = \frac{2}{(1-x)^3} \implies f''(0) = 2!,$$

$$f'''(x) = \frac{3 \cdot 2}{(1-x)^4} \implies f'''(0) = 3!,$$

$$f^{(4)}(x) = \frac{4 \cdot 3 \cdot 2}{(1-x)^5} \implies f^{(4)}(0) = 4!,$$

and in general, $f^{(k)}(0) = k!$. Therefore, the Maclaurin series coefficients are

$$c_k = \frac{f^{(k)}(0)}{k!} = \frac{k!}{k!} = 1, \text{ for } k = 0, 1, 2, \ldots. \text{ The series for } f \text{ centered at 0 is}$$

$$1 + x + x^2 + x^3 + \cdots = \sum_{k=0}^{\infty} x^k.$$

This power series is familiar! The Maclaurin series for $f(x) = 1/(1-x)$ is a geometric series. We could apply the Ratio Test, but we have already demonstrated that this series converges for $|x| < 1$.

Related Exercises 9–20 ◀

QUICK CHECK 2 Based on Example 1b, what is the Taylor series for $f(x) = (1+x)^{-1}$? ◀

The preceding example has an important lesson. *There is only one power series representation for a given function about a given point; however, there may be several ways to find it.*

EXAMPLE 2   **Center other than 0** Find the first four nonzero terms of the Taylor series for $f(x) = \sqrt[3]{x}$ centered at 8.

SOLUTION Notice that f has derivatives of all orders at $x = 8$. The Taylor series centered at 8 has the form

$$\sum_{k=0}^{\infty} c_k(x - 8)^k, \quad \text{where } c_k = \frac{f^{(k)}(8)}{k!}.$$

Next, we evaluate derivatives:

$$f(x) = x^{1/3} \Rightarrow f(8) = 2,$$

$$f'(x) = \frac{1}{3}x^{-2/3} \Rightarrow f'(8) = \frac{1}{12},$$

$$f''(x) = -\frac{2}{9}x^{-5/3} \Rightarrow f''(8) = -\frac{1}{144}, \text{ and}$$

$$f'''(x) = \frac{10}{27}x^{-8/3} \Rightarrow f'''(8) = \frac{5}{3456}.$$

We now assemble the power series:

$$2 + \frac{1}{12}(x - 8) + \frac{1}{2!}\left(-\frac{1}{144}\right)(x - 8)^2 + \frac{1}{3!}\left(\frac{5}{3456}\right)(x - 8)^3 + \cdots$$

$$= 2 + \frac{1}{12}(x - 8) - \frac{1}{288}(x - 8)^2 + \frac{5}{20{,}736}(x - 8)^3 + \cdots.$$

Related Exercises 21–28 ◄

EXAMPLE 3   **Manipulating Maclaurin series** Let $f(x) = e^x$.

a. Find the Maclaurin series for f.

b. Find its interval of convergence.

c. Use the Maclaurin series for e^x to find the Maclaurin series for the functions $x^4 e^x$, e^{-2x}, and e^{-x^2}.

SOLUTION

a. The coefficients of the Taylor polynomials for $f(x) = e^x$ centered at 0 are $c_k = 1/k!$ (Example 3, Section 9.1). They are also the coefficients of the Maclaurin series. Therefore, the Maclaurin series for e^x is

$$1 + \frac{x}{1!} + \frac{x^2}{2!} + \cdots + \frac{x^n}{n!} + \cdots = \sum_{k=0}^{\infty} \frac{x^k}{k!}.$$

b. By the Ratio Test,

$$r = \lim_{k \to \infty} \left| \frac{x^{k+1}/(k + 1)!}{x^k/k!} \right| \qquad \text{Substitute } (k + 1)\text{st and } k\text{th terms.}$$

$$= \lim_{k \to \infty} \left| \frac{x}{k + 1} \right| = 0. \qquad \text{Simplify; take the limit with } x \text{ fixed.}$$

Because $r < 1$ for all x, the interval of convergence is $-\infty < x < \infty$.

c. As stated in Theorem 9.4, power series may be added, multiplied by powers of x, or composed with functions on their intervals of convergence. Therefore, the Maclaurin series for $x^4 e^x$ is

$$x^4 \sum_{k=0}^{\infty} \frac{x^k}{k!} = \sum_{k=0}^{\infty} \frac{x^{k+4}}{k!} = x^4 + \frac{x^5}{1!} + \frac{x^6}{2!} + \cdots + \frac{x^{k+4}}{k!} + \cdots.$$

Similarly, e^{-2x} is the composition $f(-2x)$. Replacing x with $-2x$ in the Maclaurin series for f, the series representation for e^{-2x} is

$$\sum_{k=0}^{\infty} \frac{(-2x)^k}{k!} = \sum_{k=0}^{\infty} \frac{(-1)^k (2x)^k}{k!} = 1 - 2x + 2x^2 - \frac{4}{3}x^3 + \cdots.$$

The Maclaurin series for e^{-x^2} is obtained by replacing x with $-x^2$ in the power series for f. The resulting series is

$$\sum_{k=0}^{\infty} \frac{(-x^2)^k}{k!} = \sum_{k=0}^{\infty} \frac{(-1)^k x^{2k}}{k!} = 1 - x^2 + \frac{x^4}{2!} - \frac{x^6}{3!} + \cdots.$$

QUICK CHECK 3 Find the first three terms of the Maclaurin series for $2xe^x$ and e^{-x}. ◄

Because the interval of convergence of $f(x) = e^x$ is $-\infty < x < \infty$, the manipulations used to obtain the series for $x^4 e^x$, e^{-2x}, or e^{-x^2} do not change the interval of convergence. If in doubt about the interval of convergence of a new series, apply the Ratio Test.

Related Exercises 29–38 ◄

The Binomial Series

We know from algebra that if p is a positive integer, then $(1 + x)^p$ is a polynomial of degree p. In fact,

$$(1 + x)^p = \binom{p}{0} + \binom{p}{1} x + \binom{p}{2} x^2 + \cdots + \binom{p}{p} x^p,$$

where the binomial coefficients $\binom{p}{k}$ are defined as follows.

> ➤ For nonnegative integers p and k with $0 \le k \le p$, the binomial coefficients may also be defined as
> $$\binom{p}{k} = \frac{p!}{k!(p-k)!}, \text{ where } 0! = 1.$$
> The coefficients form the rows of Pascal's triangle. The coefficients of $(1 + x)^5$ form the sixth row of the triangle.
>
> ```
>           1
>         1   1
>       1   2   1
>     1   3   3   1
>   1   4   6   4   1
> 1   5   10   10   5   1
> ```

DEFINITION Binomial Coefficients

For real numbers p and integers $k \ge 1$,

$$\binom{p}{k} = \frac{p(p-1)(p-2)\cdots(p-k+1)}{k!}, \qquad \binom{p}{0} = 1.$$

For example,

$$(1 + x)^5 = \underbrace{\binom{5}{0}}_{1} + \underbrace{\binom{5}{1}}_{5} x + \underbrace{\binom{5}{2}}_{10} x^2 + \underbrace{\binom{5}{3}}_{10} x^3 + \underbrace{\binom{5}{4}}_{5} x^4 + \underbrace{\binom{5}{5}}_{1} x^5$$

$$= 1 + 5x + 10x^2 + 10x^3 + 5x^4 + x^5.$$

QUICK CHECK 4 Evaluate the binomial coefficients $\binom{-3}{2}$ and $\binom{\frac{1}{2}}{3}$. ◄

Our goal is to extend this idea to the functions $f(x) = (1 + x)^p$, where $p \ne 0$ is a real number. The result is a Taylor series called the *binomial series*.

> **THEOREM 9.6 Binomial Series**
> For real numbers $p \neq 0$, the Taylor series for $f(x) = (1 + x)^p$ centered at 0 is the **binomial series**
>
> $$\sum_{k=0}^{\infty} \binom{p}{k} x^k = 1 + \sum_{k=1}^{\infty} \frac{p(p-1)(p-2) \cdots (p-k+1)}{k!} x^k$$
>
> $$= 1 + px + \frac{p(p-1)}{2!} x^2 + \frac{p(p-1)(p-2)}{3!} x^3 + \cdots.$$
>
> The series converges for $|x| < 1$ (and possibly at the endpoints, depending on p). If p is a nonnegative integer, the series terminates and results in a polynomial of degree p.

> To evaluate $\binom{p}{k}$, start with p and successively subtract 1 until k factors are obtained; then take the product of these k factors and divide by $k!$. Recall that
> $$\binom{p}{0} = 1.$$

Proof: We seek a power series centered at 0 of the form

$$\sum_{k=0}^{\infty} c_k x^k, \quad \text{where } c_k = \frac{f^{(k)}(0)}{k!}, \quad \text{for } k = 0, 1, 2, \ldots.$$

The job is to evaluate the derivatives of f at 0:

$$f(x) = (1 + x)^p \Rightarrow f(0) = 1,$$
$$f'(x) = p(1 + x)^{p-1} \Rightarrow f'(0) = p,$$
$$f''(x) = p(p-1)(1 + x)^{p-2} \Rightarrow f''(0) = p(p-1), \text{ and}$$
$$f'''(x) = p(p-1)(p-2)(1+x)^{p-3} \Rightarrow f'''(0) = p(p-1)(p-2).$$

A pattern emerges: The kth derivative $f^{(k)}(0)$ involves the k factors $p(p-1)(p-2) \cdots (p-k+1)$. In general, we have

$$f^{(k)}(0) = p(p-1)(p-2) \cdots (p-k+1).$$

Therefore,

$$c_k = \frac{f^{(k)}(0)}{k!} = \frac{p(p-1)(p-2) \cdots (p-k+1)}{k!} = \binom{p}{k}, \quad \text{for } k = 0, 1, 2, \ldots.$$

The Taylor series for $f(x) = (1 + x)^p$ centered at 0 is

$$\binom{p}{0} + \binom{p}{1}x + \binom{p}{2}x^2 + \binom{p}{3}x^3 + \cdots = \sum_{k=0}^{\infty} \binom{p}{k} x^k.$$

This series has the same general form for all values of p. When p is a nonnegative integer, the series terminates and it is a polynomial of degree p.

The interval of convergence for the binomial series is determined by the Ratio Test. Holding p and x fixed, the relevant limit is

$$r = \lim_{k \to \infty} \left| \frac{x^{k+1} p(p-1) \cdots (p-k+1)(p-k)/(k+1)!}{x^k p(p-1) \cdots (p-k+1)/k!} \right| \quad \text{Ratio of } (k+1)\text{st to } k\text{th term}$$

$$= |x| \lim_{k \to \infty} \underbrace{\left| \frac{p-k}{k+1} \right|}_{\text{approaches 1}} \quad \text{Cancel factors and simplify.}$$

> In Theorem 9.6, it can be shown that the interval of convergence for the binomial series is
> - $(-1, 1)$ if $p \leq -1$,
> - $(-1, 1]$ if $-1 < p < 0$, and
> - $[-1, 1]$ if $p > 0$ and not an integer.

$$= |x|.$$

With p fixed,
$$\lim_{k \to \infty} \left| \frac{(p-k)}{k+1} \right| = 1.$$

Absolute convergence requires that $r = |x| < 1$. Therefore, the series converges for $|x| < 1$. Depending on the value of p, the interval of convergence may include the endpoints; see margin note. ◄

> A binomial series is a Taylor series. Because the series in Example 4 is centered at 0, it is also a Maclaurin series.

EXAMPLE 4 Binomial series Consider the function $f(x) = \sqrt{1 + x}$.

a. Find the first four terms of the binomial series for f centered at 0.

b. Approximate $\sqrt{1.15}$ to three decimal places. Assume the series for f converges to f on its interval of convergence, which is $[-1, 1]$.

SOLUTION

a. We use the formula for the binomial coefficients with $p = \frac{1}{2}$ to compute the first four coefficients:

$$c_0 = 1, \qquad c_1 = \binom{\frac{1}{2}}{1} = \frac{\left(\frac{1}{2}\right)}{1!} = \frac{1}{2},$$

$$c_2 = \binom{\frac{1}{2}}{2} = \frac{\frac{1}{2}\left(-\frac{1}{2}\right)}{2!} = -\frac{1}{8}, \qquad c_3 = \binom{\frac{1}{2}}{3} = \frac{\frac{1}{2}\left(-\frac{1}{2}\right)\left(-\frac{3}{2}\right)}{3!} = \frac{1}{16}.$$

The leading terms of the binomial series are

$$1 + \frac{1}{2}x - \frac{1}{8}x^2 + \frac{1}{16}x^3 - \cdots.$$

Table 9.3

n	Approximation $p_n(0.15)$
0	1.0
1	1.075
2	1.0721875
3	1.072398438

> The remainder theorem for alternating series (Section 8.6) could be used in Example 4 to estimate the number of terms of the Maclaurin series needed to achieve a desired accuracy.

b. Truncating the binomial series in part (a) produces Taylor polynomials p_n that may be used to approximate $f(0.15) = \sqrt{1.15}$. With $x = 0.15$, we find the polynomial approximations shown in Table 9.3. Four terms of the power series $(n = 3)$ give $\sqrt{1.15} \approx 1.072$. Because the approximations with $n = 2$ and $n = 3$ agree to three decimal places, when rounded, the approximation 1.072 is accurate to three decimal places.

Related Exercises 39–44 ◄

QUICK CHECK 5 Use two and three terms of the binomial series in Example 4 to approximate $\sqrt{1.1}$. ◄

EXAMPLE 5 Working with binomial series Consider the functions

$$f(x) = \sqrt[3]{1 + x} \quad \text{and} \quad g(x) = \sqrt[3]{c + x}, \text{ where } c > 0 \text{ is a constant.}$$

a. Find the first four terms of the binomial series for f centered at 0.

b. Use part (a) to find the first four terms of the binomial series for g centered at 0.

c. Use part (b) to approximate $\sqrt[3]{23}, \sqrt[3]{24}, \ldots, \sqrt[3]{31}$. Assume the series for g converges to g on its interval of convergence.

SOLUTION

a. Because $f(x) = (1 + x)^{1/3}$, we find the binomial coefficients with $p = \frac{1}{3}$.

$$c_0 = \binom{\frac{1}{3}}{0} = 1, \qquad c_1 = \binom{\frac{1}{3}}{1} = \frac{\left(\frac{1}{3}\right)}{1!} = \frac{1}{3},$$

$$c_2 = \binom{\frac{1}{3}}{2} = \frac{\left(\frac{1}{3}\right)\left(\frac{1}{3} - 1\right)}{2!} = -\frac{1}{9}, \qquad c_3 = \binom{\frac{1}{3}}{3} = \frac{\left(\frac{1}{3}\right)\left(\frac{1}{3} - 1\right)\left(\frac{1}{3} - 2\right)}{3!} = \frac{5}{81} \cdots$$

The first four terms of the binomial series are

$$1 + \frac{1}{3}x - \frac{1}{9}x^2 + \frac{5}{81}x^3 - \cdots.$$

b. To avoid deriving a new series for $g(x) = \sqrt[3]{c + x}$, a few steps of algebra allow us to use part (a). Note that

$$g(x) = \sqrt[3]{c + x} = \sqrt[3]{c\left(1 + \frac{x}{c}\right)} = \sqrt[3]{c} \cdot \sqrt[3]{1 + \frac{x}{c}} = \sqrt[3]{c} \cdot f\left(\frac{x}{c}\right).$$

In other words, g can be expressed in terms of f, for which we already have a binomial series. The binomial series for g is obtained by substituting x/c into the binomial series for f and multiplying by $\sqrt[3]{c}$:

$$g(x) = \sqrt[3]{c}\underbrace{\left(1 + \frac{1}{3}\left(\frac{x}{c}\right) - \frac{1}{9}\left(\frac{x}{c}\right)^2 + \frac{5}{81}\left(\frac{x}{c}\right)^3 - \cdots\right)}_{f(x/c)}.$$

It can be shown that the series for f in part (a) converges to $f(x)$ for $|x| \le 1$. Therefore, the series for $f(x/c)$ converges to $f(x/c)$ provided $|x/c| \le 1$, or, equivalently, for $|x| \le c$.

c. The series of part (b) may be truncated after four terms to approximate cube roots. For example, note that $\sqrt[3]{29} = \sqrt[3]{\underset{c}{27} + \underset{x}{2}}$, so we take $c = 27$ and $x = 2$.

The choice $c = 27$ is made because 29 is near 27 and $\sqrt[3]{c} = \sqrt[3]{27} = 3$ is easy to evaluate. Substituting $c = 27$ and $x = 2$, we find that

$$\sqrt[3]{29} \approx \sqrt[3]{27}\left(1 + \frac{1}{3}\left(\frac{2}{27}\right) - \frac{1}{9}\left(\frac{2}{27}\right)^2 + \frac{5}{81}\left(\frac{2}{27}\right)^3\right) \approx 3.0723.$$

The same method is used to approximate the cube roots of $23, 24, \ldots, 30, 31$ (Table 9.4). The absolute error is the difference between the approximation and the value given by a calculator. Notice that the errors increase as we move away from 27.

Table 9.4

	Approximation	Absolute Error
$\sqrt[3]{23}$	2.8439	6.7×10^{-5}
$\sqrt[3]{24}$	2.8845	2.0×10^{-5}
$\sqrt[3]{25}$	2.9240	3.9×10^{-6}
$\sqrt[3]{26}$	2.9625	2.4×10^{-7}
$\sqrt[3]{27}$	3	0
$\sqrt[3]{28}$	3.0366	2.3×10^{-7}
$\sqrt[3]{29}$	3.0723	3.5×10^{-6}
$\sqrt[3]{30}$	3.1072	1.7×10^{-5}
$\sqrt[3]{31}$	3.1414	5.4×10^{-5}

Related Exercises 45–56 ◄

Convergence of Taylor Series

It may seem that the story of Taylor series is over. But there is a technical point that is easily overlooked. Given a function f, we know how to write its Taylor series centered at a point a, and we know how to find its interval of convergence. We still do not know that the series actually converges to f. The remaining task is to determine when the Taylor series for f actually converges to f on its interval of convergence. Fortunately, the necessary tools have already been presented in Taylor's Theorem (Theorem 9.1), which gives the remainder for Taylor polynomials.

Assume f has derivatives of *all* orders on an open interval containing the point a. Taylor's Theorem tells us that

$$f(x) = p_n(x) + R_n(x),$$

where p_n is the nth-order Taylor polynomial for f centered at a,

$$R_n(x) = \frac{f^{(n+1)}(c)}{(n+1)!}(x - a)^{n+1}$$

is the remainder, and c is a point between x and a. We see that the remainder, $R_n(x) = f(x) - p_n(x)$, measures the difference between f and the approximating polynomial p_n.

When we say the Taylor series converges to f at a point x, we mean the value of the Taylor series at x equals $f(x)$; that is, $\lim\limits_{n\to\infty} p_n(x) = f(x)$. The following theorem makes these ideas precise.

THEOREM 9.7   Convergence of Taylor Series

Let f have derivatives of all orders on an open interval I containing a. The Taylor series for f centered at a converges to f, for all x in I, if and only if $\lim\limits_{n\to\infty} R_n(x) = 0$, for all x in I, where

$$R_n(x) = \frac{f^{(n+1)}(c)}{(n+1)!}(x-a)^{n+1}$$

is the remainder at x (with c between x and a).

Proof: The theorem requires derivatives of *all* orders. Therefore, by Taylor's Theorem (Theorem 9.1), the remainder exists in the given form for all n. Let p_n denote the nth-order Taylor polynomial and note that $\lim\limits_{n\to\infty} p_n(x)$ is the Taylor series for f centered at a, evaluated at a point x in I.

First, assume that $\lim\limits_{n\to\infty} R_n(x) = 0$ on the interval I and recall that $p_n(x) = f(x) - R_n(x)$. Taking limits of both sides, we have

$$\underbrace{\lim_{n\to\infty} p_n(x)}_{\text{Taylor series}} = \lim_{n\to\infty} (f(x) - R_n(x)) = \underbrace{\lim_{n\to\infty} f(x)}_{f(x)} - \underbrace{\lim_{n\to\infty} R_n(x)}_{0} = f(x).$$

We conclude that the Taylor series $\lim\limits_{n\to\infty} p_n(x)$ equals $f(x)$, for all x in I.

Conversely, if the Taylor series converges to f, then $f(x) = \lim\limits_{n\to\infty} p_n(x)$ and

$$0 = f(x) - \lim_{n\to\infty} p_n(x) = \lim_{n\to\infty} \underbrace{(f(x) - p_n(x))}_{R_n(x)} = \lim_{n\to\infty} R_n(x).$$

It follows that $\lim\limits_{n\to\infty} R_n(x) = 0$, for all x in I.   ◄

Even with an expression for the remainder, it may be difficult to show that $\lim\limits_{n\to\infty} R_n(x) = 0$. The following examples illustrate cases in which it is possible.

EXAMPLE 6   Remainder in the Maclaurin series for e^x Show that the Maclaurin series for $f(x) = e^x$ converges to $f(x)$, for $-\infty < x < \infty$.

SOLUTION As shown in Example 3, the Maclaurin series for $f(x) = e^x$ is

$$\sum_{k=0}^{\infty} \frac{x^k}{k!} = 1 + x + \frac{x^2}{2!} + \cdots + \frac{x^n}{n!} + \cdots,$$

which converges for $-\infty < x < \infty$. In Example 7 of Section 9.1 it was shown that the remainder is

$$R_n(x) = \frac{e^c}{(n+1)!} x^{n+1},$$

where c is between 0 and x. Notice that the intermediate point c varies with n, but it is always between 0 and x. Therefore, e^c is between $e^0 = 1$ and e^x; in fact, $e^c \le e^{|x|}$, for all n. It follows that

$$|R_n(x)| \le \frac{e^{|x|}}{(n+1)!} |x|^{n+1}.$$

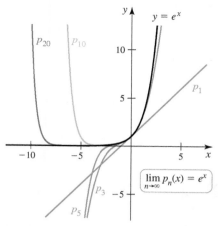

Figure 9.19

Holding x fixed, we have

$$\lim_{n \to \infty} |R_n(x)| = \lim_{n \to \infty} \frac{e^{|x|}}{(n+1)!}|x|^{n+1} = e^{|x|} \lim_{n \to \infty} \frac{|x|^{n+1}}{(n+1)!} = 0,$$

where we used the fact that $\lim_{n \to \infty} x^n/n! = 0$, for $-\infty < x < \infty$ (Section 8.2). Because $\lim_{n \to \infty} |R_n(x)| = 0$, it follows that for all real numbers x, the Taylor series converges to e^x, or

$$e^x = \sum_{k=0}^{\infty} \frac{x^k}{k!} = 1 + x + \frac{x^2}{2!} + \cdots + \frac{x^n}{n!} + \cdots.$$

The convergence of the Taylor series to e^x is illustrated in Figure 9.19, where Taylor polynomials of increasing degree are graphed together with e^x.

Related Exercises 57–60 ◄

EXAMPLE 7 **Maclaurin series convergence for $\cos x$** Show that the Maclaurin series for $\cos x$,

$$1 - \frac{x^2}{2!} + \frac{x^4}{4!} - \frac{x^6}{6!} + \cdots = \sum_{k=0}^{\infty} (-1)^k \frac{x^{2k}}{(2k)!},$$

converges to $f(x) = \cos x$, for $-\infty < x < \infty$.

SOLUTION To show that the power series converges to f, we must show that $\lim_{n \to \infty} |R_n(x)| = 0$, for $-\infty < x < \infty$. According to Taylor's Theorem with $a = 0$,

$$R_n(x) = \frac{f^{(n+1)}(c)}{(n+1)!} x^{n+1},$$

where c is between 0 and x. Notice that $f^{(n+1)}(c) = \pm \sin c$ or $f^{(n+1)}(c) = \pm \cos c$. In all cases, $|f^{(n+1)}(c)| \leq 1$. Therefore, the absolute value of the remainder term is bounded as

$$|R_n(x)| = \left| \frac{f^{(n+1)}(c)}{(n+1)!} x^{n+1} \right| \leq \frac{|x|^{n+1}}{(n+1)!}.$$

Holding x fixed and using $\lim_{n \to \infty} x^n/n! = 0$, we see that $\lim_{n \to \infty} R_n(x) = 0$ for all x. Therefore, the given power series converges to $f(x) = \cos x$, for all x; that is, $\cos x = \sum_{k=0}^{\infty} \frac{(-1)^k x^{2k}}{(2k)!}$. The convergence of the Taylor series to $\cos x$ is illustrated in Figure 9.20.

Related Exercises 57–60 ◄

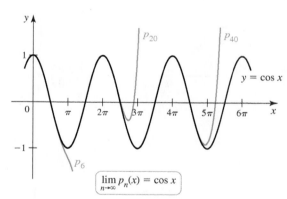

Figure 9.20

The procedure used in Examples 6 and 7 can be carried out for all the Taylor series we have worked with so far (with varying degrees of difficulty). In each case, the Taylor series converges to the function it represents on the interval of convergence. Table 9.5 summarizes commonly used Taylor series centered at 0 and the functions to which they converge.

▶ Table 9.5 asserts, without proof, that in several cases, the Taylor series for f converges to f at the endpoints of the interval of convergence. Proving convergence at the endpoints generally requires advanced techniques. It may also be done using the following theorem:

Suppose the Taylor series for f centered at 0 converges to f on the interval $(-R, R)$. If the series converges at $x = R$, then it converges to $\lim_{x \to R^-} f(x)$. If the series converges at $x = -R$, then it converges to $\lim_{x \to -R^+} f(x)$.

For example, this theorem would allow us to conclude that the series for $\ln(1 + x)$ converges to $\ln 2$ at $x = 1$.

Table 9.5

$$\frac{1}{1 - x} = 1 + x + x^2 + \cdots + x^k + \cdots = \sum_{k=0}^{\infty} x^k, \quad \text{for } |x| < 1$$

$$\frac{1}{1 + x} = 1 - x + x^2 - \cdots + (-1)^k x^k + \cdots = \sum_{k=0}^{\infty} (-1)^k x^k, \quad \text{for } |x| < 1$$

$$e^x = 1 + x + \frac{x^2}{2!} + \cdots + \frac{x^k}{k!} + \cdots = \sum_{k=0}^{\infty} \frac{x^k}{k!}, \quad \text{for } |x| < \infty$$

$$\sin x = x - \frac{x^3}{3!} + \frac{x^5}{5!} - \cdots + \frac{(-1)^k x^{2k+1}}{(2k + 1)!} + \cdots = \sum_{k=0}^{\infty} \frac{(-1)^k x^{2k+1}}{(2k + 1)!}, \quad \text{for } |x| < \infty$$

$$\cos x = 1 - \frac{x^2}{2!} + \frac{x^4}{4!} - \cdots + \frac{(-1)^k x^{2k}}{(2k)!} + \cdots = \sum_{k=0}^{\infty} \frac{(-1)^k x^{2k}}{(2k)!}, \quad \text{for } |x| < \infty$$

$$\ln(1 + x) = x - \frac{x^2}{2} + \frac{x^3}{3} - \cdots + \frac{(-1)^{k+1} x^k}{k} + \cdots = \sum_{k=1}^{\infty} \frac{(-1)^{k+1} x^k}{k}, \quad \text{for } -1 < x \le 1$$

$$-\ln(1 - x) = x + \frac{x^2}{2} + \frac{x^3}{3} + \cdots + \frac{x^k}{k} + \cdots = \sum_{k=1}^{\infty} \frac{x^k}{k}, \quad \text{for } -1 \le x < 1$$

$$\tan^{-1} x = x - \frac{x^3}{3} + \frac{x^5}{5} - \cdots + \frac{(-1)^k x^{2k+1}}{2k + 1} + \cdots = \sum_{k=0}^{\infty} \frac{(-1)^k x^{2k+1}}{2k + 1}, \quad \text{for } |x| \le 1$$

$$\sinh x = x + \frac{x^3}{3!} + \frac{x^5}{5!} + \cdots + \frac{x^{2k+1}}{(2k + 1)!} + \cdots = \sum_{k=0}^{\infty} \frac{x^{2k+1}}{(2k + 1)!}, \quad \text{for } |x| < \infty$$

$$\cosh x = 1 + \frac{x^2}{2!} + \frac{x^4}{4!} + \cdots + \frac{x^{2k}}{(2k)!} + \cdots = \sum_{k=0}^{\infty} \frac{x^{2k}}{(2k)!}, \quad \text{for } |x| < \infty$$

▶ As noted on p. 689, the binomial series may converge to $(1 + x)^p$ at $x = \pm 1$, depending on the value of p.

$$(1 + x)^p = \sum_{k=0}^{\infty} \binom{p}{k} x^k, \text{ for } |x| < 1 \text{ and } \binom{p}{k} = \frac{p(p - 1)(p - 2) \cdots (p - k + 1)}{k!}, \binom{p}{0} = 1$$

SECTION 9.3 EXERCISES

Review Questions

1. How are the Taylor polynomials for a function f centered at a related to the Taylor series for the function f centered at a?

2. What conditions must be satisfied by a function f to have a Taylor series centered at a?

3. How do you find the coefficients of the Taylor series for f centered at a?

4. How do you find the interval of convergence of a Taylor series?

5. Suppose you know the Maclaurin series for f and it converges for $|x| < 1$. How do you find the Maclaurin series for $f(x^2)$ and where does it converge?

6. For what values of p does the Taylor series for $f(x) = (1 + x)^p$ centered at 0 terminate?

7. In terms of the remainder, what does it mean for a Taylor series for a function f to converge to f?

8. Write the Maclaurin series for e^{2x}.

Basic Skills

9–20. Maclaurin series

a. Find the first four nonzero terms of the Maclaurin series for the given function.

b. Write the power series using summation notation.

c. Determine the interval of convergence of the series.

9. $f(x) = e^{-x}$

10. $f(x) = \cos 2x$

11. $f(x) = (1 + x^2)^{-1}$

12. $f(x) = \ln(1 + 4x)$

13. $f(x) = e^{2x}$

14. $f(x) = (1 + 2x)^{-1}$

15. $f(x) = \tan^{-1} \frac{x}{2}$

16. $f(x) = \sin 3x$

17. $f(x) = 3^x$

18. $f(x) = \log_3(x + 1)$

19. $f(x) = \cosh 3x$

20. $f(x) = \sinh 2x$

21–28. Taylor series centered at $a \neq 0$

a. Find the first four nonzero terms of the Taylor series for the given function centered at a.

b. Write the power series using summation notation.

21. $f(x) = \sin x, a = \pi/2$

22. $f(x) = \cos x, a = \pi$

23. $f(x) = 1/x, a = 1$

24. $f(x) = 1/x, a = 2$

25. $f(x) = \ln x, a = 3$

26. $f(x) = e^x, a = \ln 2$

27. $f(x) = 2^x, a = 1$

28. $f(x) = 10^x, a = 2$

29–38. Manipulating Taylor series *Use the Taylor series in Table 9.5 to find the first four nonzero terms of the Taylor series for the following functions centered at 0.*

29. $\ln(1 + x^2)$

30. $\sin x^2$

31. $\dfrac{1}{1 - 2x}$

32. $\ln(1 + 2x)$

33. $\begin{cases} \dfrac{e^x - 1}{x} & \text{if } x \neq 0 \\ 1 & \text{if } x = 0 \end{cases}$

34. $\cos x^3$

35. $(1 + x^4)^{-1}$

36. $x \tan^{-1} x^2$

37. $\sinh x^2$

38. $\cosh 3x$

T 39–44. Binomial series

a. Find the first four nonzero terms of the binomial series centered at 0 for the given function.

b. Use the first four nonzero terms of the series to approximate the given quantity.

39. $f(x) = (1 + x)^{-2}$; approximate $1/1.21 = 1/1.1^2$.

40. $f(x) = \sqrt{1 + x}$; approximate $\sqrt{1.06}$.

41. $f(x) = \sqrt[4]{1 + x}$; approximate $\sqrt[4]{1.12}$.

42. $f(x) = (1 + x)^{-3}$; approximate $1/1.331 = 1/1.1^3$.

43. $f(x) = (1 + x)^{-2/3}$; approximate $1.18^{-2/3}$.

44. $f(x) = (1 + x)^{2/3}$; approximate $1.02^{2/3}$.

45–50. Working with binomial series *Use properties of power series, substitution, and factoring to find the first four nonzero terms of the Maclaurin series for the following functions. Give the interval of convergence for the new series (Theorem 9.4 is useful). Use the Maclaurin series*

$$\sqrt{1 + x} = 1 + \frac{x}{2} - \frac{x^2}{8} + \frac{x^3}{16} - \cdots, \quad \text{for } -1 \leq x \leq 1.$$

45. $\sqrt{1 + x^2}$

46. $\sqrt{4 + x}$

47. $\sqrt{9 - 9x}$

48. $\sqrt{1 - 4x}$

49. $\sqrt{a^2 + x^2}, a > 0$

50. $\sqrt{4 - 16x^2}$

51–56. Working with binomial series *Use properties of power series, substitution, and factoring of constants to find the first four nonzero terms of the Maclaurin series for the following functions. Use the Maclaurin series*

$$(1 + x)^{-2} = 1 - 2x + 3x^2 - 4x^3 + \cdots, \quad \text{for } -1 < x < 1.$$

51. $(1 + 4x)^{-2}$

52. $\dfrac{1}{(1 - 4x)^2}$

53. $\dfrac{1}{(4 + x^2)^2}$

54. $(x^2 - 4x + 5)^{-2}$

55. $\dfrac{1}{(3 + 4x)^2}$

56. $\dfrac{1}{(1 + 4x^2)^2}$

57–60. Remainders *Find the remainder in the Taylor series centered at the point a for the following functions. Then show that $\lim\limits_{n \to \infty} R_n(x) = 0$ for all x in the interval of convergence.*

57. $f(x) = \sin x, a = 0$

58. $f(x) = \cos 2x, a = 0$

59. $f(x) = e^{-x}, a = 0$

60. $f(x) = \cos x, a = \pi/2$

Further Explorations

61. Explain why or why not Determine whether the following statements are true and give an explanation or counterexample.

a. The function $f(x) = \sqrt{x}$ has a Taylor series centered at 0.

b. The function $f(x) = \csc x$ has a Taylor series centered at $\pi/2$.

c. If f has a Taylor series that converges only on $(-2, 2)$, then $f(x^2)$ has a Taylor series that also converges only on $(-2, 2)$.

d. If $p(x)$ is the Taylor series for f centered at 0, then $p(x - 1)$ is the Taylor series for f centered at 1.

e. The Taylor series for an even function about 0 has only even powers of x.

62–69. Any method

a. Use any analytical method to find the first four nonzero terms of the Taylor series centered at 0 for the following functions. You do not need to use the definition of the Taylor series coefficients.

b. Determine the radius of convergence of the series.

62. $f(x) = \cos 2x + 2 \sin x$

63. $f(x) = \dfrac{e^x + e^{-x}}{2}$

64. $f(x) = \begin{cases} \dfrac{\sin x}{x} & \text{if } x \neq 0 \\ 1 & \text{if } x = 0 \end{cases}$

65. $f(x) = (1 + x^2)^{-2/3}$

66. $f(x) = x^2 \cos x^2$

67. $f(x) = \sqrt{1 - x^2}$

68. $f(x) = b^x$, for $b > 0, b \neq 1$

69. $f(x) = \dfrac{1}{x^4 + 2x^2 + 1}$

T 70–73. Approximating powers *Compute the coefficients for the Taylor series for the following functions about the given point a and then use the first four terms of the series to approximate the given number.*

70. $f(x) = \sqrt{x}$ with $a = 36$; approximate $\sqrt{39}$.

71. $f(x) = \sqrt[3]{x}$ with $a = 64$; approximate $\sqrt[3]{60}$.

72. $f(x) = 1/\sqrt{x}$ with $a = 4$; approximate $1/\sqrt{3}$.

73. $f(x) = \sqrt[4]{x}$ with $a = 16$; approximate $\sqrt[4]{13}$.

74. Geometric/binomial series Recall that the Taylor series for $f(x) = 1/(1 - x)$ about 0 is the geometric series $\sum\limits_{k=0}^{\infty} x^k$. Show that this series can also be found as a binomial series.

75. Integer coefficients Show that the first five nonzero coefficients of the Taylor series (binomial series) for $f(x) = \sqrt{1 + 4x}$ about 0 are integers. (In fact, *all* the coefficients are integers.)

76. Choosing a good center Suppose you want to approximate $\sqrt{72}$ using four terms of a Taylor series. Compare the accuracy of the approximations obtained using Taylor series for $\sqrt{x}$ centered at 64 and 81.

77. Alternative means By comparing the first four terms, show that the Maclaurin series for $\sin^2 x$ can be found (a) by squaring the Maclaurin series for $\sin x$, (b) by using the identity $\sin^2 x = (1 - \cos 2x)/2$, or (c) by computing the coefficients using the definition.

78. Alternative means By comparing the first four terms, show that the Maclaurin series for $\cos^2 x$ can be found (a) by squaring the Maclaurin series for $\cos x$, (b) by using the identity $\cos^2 x = (1 + \cos 2x)/2$, or (c) by computing the coefficients using the definition.

79. Designer series Find a power series that has $(2, 6)$ as an interval of convergence.

80–81. Patterns in coefficients *Find the next two terms of the following Taylor series.*

80. $\sqrt{1 + x}$: $1 + \dfrac{1}{2}x - \dfrac{1}{2 \cdot 4}x^2 + \dfrac{1 \cdot 3}{2 \cdot 4 \cdot 6}x^3 - \cdots$.

81. $\dfrac{1}{\sqrt{1 + x}}$: $1 - \dfrac{1}{2}x + \dfrac{1 \cdot 3}{2 \cdot 4}x^2 - \dfrac{1 \cdot 3 \cdot 5}{2 \cdot 4 \cdot 6}x^3 + \cdots$.

82. Composition of series Use composition of series to find the first three terms of the Maclaurin series for the following functions.

    a. $e^{\sin x}$ **b.** $e^{\tan x}$ **c.** $\sqrt{1 + \sin^2 x}$

Applications

🖥 **83–86. Approximations** *Choose a Taylor series and center point to approximate the following quantities with an error of 10^{-4} or less.*

83. $\cos 40°$ **84.** $\sin (0.98\pi)$

85. $\sqrt[3]{83}$ **86.** $1/\sqrt[4]{17}$

87. Different approximation strategies Suppose you want to approximate $\sqrt[3]{128}$ to within 10^{-4} of the exact value.

    a. Use a Taylor polynomial for $f(x) = (125 + x)^{1/3}$ centered at 0.

    b. Use a Taylor polynomial for $f(x) = x^{1/3}$ centered at 125.

    c. Compare the two approaches. Are they equivalent?

Additional Exercises

88. Mean Value Theorem Explain why the Mean Value Theorem (Theorem 4.9 of Section 4.6) is a special case of Taylor's Theorem.

89. Version of the Second Derivative Test Assume that f has at least two continuous derivatives on an interval containing a with $f'(a) = 0$. Use Taylor's Theorem to prove the following version of the Second Derivative Test.

    a. If $f''(x) > 0$ on some interval containing a, then f has a local minimum at a.

    b. If $f''(x) < 0$ on some interval containing a, then f has a local maximum at a.

90. Nonconvergence to f Consider the function

$$f(x) = \begin{cases} e^{-1/x^2} & \text{if } x \neq 0 \\ 0 & \text{if } x = 0. \end{cases}$$

    a. Use the definition of the derivative to show that $f'(0) = 0$.

    b. Assume the fact that $f^{(k)}(0) = 0$, for $k = 1, 2, 3, \ldots$. (You can write a proof using the definition of the derivative.) Write the Taylor series for f centered at 0.

    c. Explain why the Taylor series for f does not converge to f for $x \neq 0$.

QUICK CHECK ANSWERS

1. When evaluated at $x = a$, all terms of the series are zero except the first term, which is $f(a)$. Therefore, the series equals $f(a)$ at this point.   **2.** $1 - x + x^2 - x^3 + x^4 - \cdots$ **3.** $2x + 2x^2 + x^3$; $1 - x + x^2/2$ **4.** $6, 1/16$ **5.** $1.05, 1.04875$ ◄

9.4 Working with Taylor Series

We now know the Taylor series for many familiar functions, and we have tools for working with power series. The goal of this final section is to illustrate additional techniques associated with power series. As you will see, power series cover the entire landscape of calculus from limits and derivatives to integrals and approximation. We present five different topics that you can explore selectively.

Limits by Taylor Series

An important use of Taylor series is evaluating limits. Two examples illustrate the essential ideas.

EXAMPLE 1   A limit by Taylor series Evaluate $\lim\limits_{x \to 0} \dfrac{x^2 + 2\cos x - 2}{3x^4}$.

> ▶ L'Hôpital's Rule may be impractical when it must be used more than once on the same limit or when derivatives are difficult to compute.

SOLUTION Because the limit has the indeterminate form $0/0$, l'Hôpital's Rule can be used, which requires four applications of the rule. Alternatively, because the limit involves values of x near 0, we substitute the Maclaurin series for $\cos x$. Recalling that

$$\cos x = 1 - \frac{x^2}{2} + \frac{x^4}{24} - \frac{x^6}{720} + \cdots, \quad \text{Table 9.5, page 694}$$

we have

> ▶ In using series to evaluate limits, it is often not obvious how many terms of the Taylor series to use. When in doubt, include extra (higher-order) terms. The dots in the calculation stand for powers of x greater than the last power that appears.

$$\lim_{x \to 0} \frac{x^2 + 2\cos x - 2}{3x^4} = \lim_{x \to 0} \frac{x^2 + 2\left(1 - \dfrac{x^2}{2} + \dfrac{x^4}{24} - \dfrac{x^6}{720} + \cdots\right) - 2}{3x^4} \qquad \text{Substitute for } \cos x.$$

$$= \lim_{x \to 0} \frac{x^2 + \left(2 - x^2 + \dfrac{x^4}{12} - \dfrac{x^6}{360} + \cdots\right) - 2}{3x^4} \qquad \text{Simplify.}$$

$$= \lim_{x \to 0} \frac{\dfrac{x^4}{12} - \dfrac{x^6}{360} + \cdots}{3x^4} \qquad \text{Simplify.}$$

$$= \lim_{x \to 0} \left(\frac{1}{36} - \frac{x^2}{1080} + \cdots\right) = \frac{1}{36}. \qquad \begin{array}{l}\text{Use Theorem 9.4,}\\ \text{Property 2;}\\ \text{evaluate limit.}\end{array}$$

Related Exercises 7–24 ◀

QUICK CHECK 1 Use the Taylor series $\sin x = x - x^3/6 + \cdots$ to verify that $\lim\limits_{x \to 0} (\sin x)/x = 1.$ ◀

EXAMPLE 2   A limit by Taylor series Evaluate

$$\lim_{x \to \infty} \left(6x^5 \sin \frac{1}{x} - 6x^4 + x^2\right).$$

SOLUTION A Taylor series may be centered at any finite point in the domain of the function, but we don't have the tools needed to expand a function about $x = \infty$. Using a technique introduced earlier, we replace x with $1/t$ and note that as $x \to \infty$, $t \to 0^+$. The new limit becomes

$$\lim_{x \to \infty} \left(6x^5 \sin \frac{1}{x} - 6x^4 + x^2\right) = \lim_{t \to 0^+} \left(\frac{6 \sin t}{t^5} - \frac{6}{t^4} + \frac{1}{t^2}\right) \qquad \text{Replace } x \text{ with } 1/t.$$

$$= \lim_{t \to 0^+} \left(\frac{6 \sin t - 6t + t^3}{t^5}\right). \qquad \text{Common denominator}$$

This limit has the indeterminate form $0/0$. We now expand $\sin t$ in a Taylor series centered at $t = 0$. Because

$$\sin t = t - \frac{t^3}{6} + \frac{t^5}{120} - \frac{t^7}{5040} + \cdots, \qquad \text{Table 9.5, page 694}$$

the value of the original limit is

$$\lim_{t \to 0^+} \left(\frac{6 \sin t - 6t + t^3}{t^5} \right)$$

$$= \lim_{t \to 0^+} \left(\frac{6\left(t - \dfrac{t^3}{6} + \dfrac{t^5}{120} - \dfrac{t^7}{5040} + \cdots \right) - 6t + t^3}{t^5} \right) \qquad \text{Substitute for } \sin t.$$

$$= \lim_{t \to 0^+} \left(\frac{\dfrac{t^5}{20} - \dfrac{t^7}{840} + \cdots}{t^5} \right) \qquad \text{Simplify.}$$

$$= \lim_{t \to 0^+} \left(\frac{1}{20} - \frac{t^2}{840} + \cdots \right) = \frac{1}{20}. \qquad \begin{array}{l}\text{Use Theorem 9.4,}\\ \text{Property 2; evaluate limit.}\end{array}$$

Related Exercises 7–24 ◄

Differentiating Power Series

The following examples illustrate ways in which term-by-term differentiation (Theorem 9.5) may be used.

EXAMPLE 3   **Power series for derivatives** Differentiate the Maclaurin series for $f(x) = \sin x$ to verify that $\dfrac{d}{dx}(\sin x) = \cos x$.

SOLUTION The Maclaurin series for $f(x) = \sin x$ is

$$\sin x = x - \frac{x^3}{3!} + \frac{x^5}{5!} - \frac{x^7}{7!} + \cdots,$$

and it converges for $-\infty < x < \infty$. By Theorem 9.5, the differentiated series also converges for $-\infty < x < \infty$ and it converges to $f'(x)$. Differentiating, we have

$$\frac{d}{dx}\left(x - \frac{x^3}{3!} + \frac{x^5}{5!} - \frac{x^7}{7!} + \cdots \right) = 1 - \frac{x^2}{2!} + \frac{x^4}{4!} - \frac{x^6}{6!} + \cdots = \cos x.$$

QUICK CHECK 2 Differentiate the power series for $\cos x$ (given in Example 3) and identify the result. ◄

The differentiated series is the Maclaurin series for $\cos x$, confirming that $f'(x) = \cos x$.

Related Exercises 25–32 ◄

EXAMPLE 4   **A differential equation** Find a power series solution of the differential equation $y'(t) = y + 2$, subject to the initial condition $y(0) = 6$. Identify the function represented by the power series.

SOLUTION Because the initial condition is given at $t = 0$, we assume the solution has a Taylor series centered at 0 of the form $y(t) = \displaystyle\sum_{k=0}^{\infty} c_k t^k$, where the coefficients c_k must be determined. Recall that the coefficients of the Taylor series are given by

$$c_k = \frac{y^{(k)}(0)}{k!}, \quad \text{for } k = 0, 1, 2, \ldots.$$

If we can determine $y^{(k)}(0)$, for $k = 0, 1, 2, \ldots$, the coefficients of the series are also determined.

Substituting the initial condition $t = 0$ and $y = 6$ into the power series

$$y(t) = c_0 + c_1 t + c_2 t^2 + \cdots,$$

we find that

$$6 = c_0 + c_1(0) + c_2(0)^2 + \cdots.$$

It follows that $c_0 = 6$. To determine $y'(0)$, we substitute $t = 0$ into the differential equation; the result is $y'(0) = y(0) + 2 = 6 + 2 = 8$. Therefore, $c_1 = y'(0)/1! = 8$.

The remaining derivatives are obtained by successively differentiating the differential equation and substituting $t = 0$. We find that $y''(0) = y'(0) = 8$, $y'''(0) = y''(0) = 8$, and in general, $y^{(k)}(0) = 8$, for $k = 2, 3, 4, \ldots$. Therefore,

$$c_k = \frac{y^{(k)}(0)}{k!} = \frac{8}{k!}, \quad \text{for } k = 1, 2, 3, \ldots,$$

and the Taylor series for the solution is

$$y(t) = c_0 + c_1 t + c_2 t^2 + \cdots$$

$$= 6 + \frac{8}{1!} t + \frac{8}{2!} t^2 + \frac{8}{3!} t^3 + \cdots.$$

To identify the function represented by this series, we write

$$y(t) = \underbrace{-2 + 8}_{6} + \frac{8}{1!} t + \frac{8}{2!} t^2 + \frac{8}{3!} t^3 + \cdots$$

$$= -2 + 8 \underbrace{\left(1 + t + \frac{t^2}{2!} + \frac{t^3}{3!} + \cdots \right)}_{e^t}.$$

> You should check that $y(t) = -2 + 8e^t$ satisfies $y'(t) = y + 2$ and $y(0) = 6$.

The power series that appears is the Taylor series for e^t. Therefore, the solution is $y = -2 + 8e^t$.

Related Exercises 33–36 ◄

Integrating Power Series

The following example illustrates the use of power series in approximating integrals that cannot be evaluated by analytical methods.

EXAMPLE 5   Approximating a definite integral Approximate the value of the integral $\int_0^1 e^{-x^2}\, dx$ with an error no greater than 5×10^{-4}.

SOLUTION The antiderivative of e^{-x^2} cannot be expressed in terms of familiar functions. The strategy is to write the Maclaurin series for e^{-x^2} and integrate it term by term. Recall that integration of a power series is valid within its interval of convergence (Theorem 9.5). Beginning with the Maclaurin series

$$e^x = 1 + x + \frac{x^2}{2!} + \frac{x^3}{3!} + \cdots + \frac{x^n}{n!} + \cdots,$$

which converges for $-\infty < x < \infty$, we replace x with $-x^2$ to obtain

$$e^{-x^2} = 1 - x^2 + \frac{x^4}{2!} - \frac{x^6}{3!} + \cdots + \frac{(-1)^n x^{2n}}{n!} + \cdots,$$

which also converges for $-\infty < x < \infty$. By the Fundamental Theorem of Calculus,

$$\int_0^1 e^{-x^2}\, dx = \left(x - \frac{x^3}{3} + \frac{x^5}{5 \cdot 2!} - \frac{x^7}{7 \cdot 3!} + \cdots + \frac{(-1)^n x^{2n+1}}{(2n+1)n!} + \cdots \right)\Bigg|_0^1$$

$$= 1 - \frac{1}{3} + \frac{1}{5 \cdot 2!} - \frac{1}{7 \cdot 3!} + \cdots + \frac{(-1)^n}{(2n+1)n!} + \cdots.$$

> The integral in Example 5 is important in statistics and probability theory because of its relationship to the *normal distribution*.

Because the definite integral is expressed as an alternating series, the magnitude of the remainder in truncating the series after n terms is less than the magnitude of the first neglected term, which is $\left| \dfrac{(-1)^{n+1}}{(2n+3)(n+1)!} \right|$. By trial and error, we find that the magnitude of this term is less than 5×10^{-4} if $n \geq 5$ (with $n = 5$, we have $\dfrac{1}{13 \cdot 6!} \approx 1.07 \times 10^{-4}$).

The sum of the terms of the series up to $n = 5$ gives the approximation

$$\int_0^1 e^{-x^2}\, dx \approx 1 - \frac{1}{3} + \frac{1}{5 \cdot 2!} - \frac{1}{7 \cdot 3!} + \frac{1}{9 \cdot 4!} - \frac{1}{11 \cdot 5!} \approx 0.747.$$

Related Exercises 37–44 ◀

Representing Real Numbers

When values of x are substituted into a convergent power series, the result may be a series representation of a familiar real number. The following example illustrates some techniques.

EXAMPLE 6   Evaluating infinite series

a. Use the Maclaurin series for $f(x) = \tan^{-1} x$ to evaluate

$$1 - \frac{1}{3} + \frac{1}{5} - \cdots = \sum_{k=0}^{\infty} \frac{(-1)^k}{2k + 1}.$$

b. Let $f(x) = (e^x - 1)/x$, for $x \neq 0$, and $f(0) = 1$. Use the Maclaurin series for f to evaluate $f'(1)$ and $\displaystyle\sum_{k=1}^{\infty} \frac{k}{(k + 1)!}$.

SOLUTION

> The series in Example 6a (known as the *Gregory series*) is one of a multitude of series representations of π. Because this series converges slowly, it does not provide an efficient way to approximate π.

a. From Table 9.5 (page 694), we see that for $|x| \leq 1$,

$$\tan^{-1} x = x - \frac{x^3}{3} + \frac{x^5}{5} - \cdots + \frac{(-1)^k x^{2k+1}}{2k + 1} + \cdots = \sum_{k=0}^{\infty} \frac{(-1)^k x^{2k+1}}{2k + 1}.$$

Substituting $x = 1$, we have

$$\tan^{-1} 1 = 1 - \frac{1^3}{3} + \frac{1^5}{5} - \cdots = \sum_{k=0}^{\infty} \frac{(-1)^k}{2k + 1}.$$

Because $\tan^{-1} 1 = \pi/4$, the value of the series is $\pi/4$.

b. Using the Maclaurin series for e^x, the series for $f(x) = (e^x - 1)/x$ is

$$f(x) = \frac{e^x - 1}{x} = \frac{1}{x}\left(\left(1 + x + \frac{x^2}{2!} + \frac{x^3}{3!} + \cdots\right) - 1\right) \quad \text{Substitute series for } e^x.$$

$$= 1 + \frac{x}{2!} + \frac{x^2}{3!} + \frac{x^3}{4!} + \cdots = \sum_{k=1}^{\infty} \frac{x^{k-1}}{k!}, \quad \text{Theorem 9.4, Property 2}$$

which converges for $-\infty < x < \infty$. By the Quotient Rule,

$$f'(x) = \frac{xe^x - (e^x - 1)}{x^2}.$$

Differentiating the series for f term by term (Theorem 9.5), we find that

$$f'(x) = \frac{d}{dx}\left(1 + \frac{x}{2!} + \frac{x^2}{3!} + \frac{x^3}{4!} + \cdots\right)$$

$$= \frac{1}{2!} + \frac{2x}{3!} + \frac{3x^2}{4!} + \cdots = \sum_{k=1}^{\infty} \frac{kx^{k-1}}{(k + 1)!}.$$

We now have two expressions for f'; they are evaluated at $x = 1$ to show that

QUICK CHECK 3 What value of x would you substitute into the Maclaurin series for $\tan^{-1} x$ to obtain a series representation for $\pi/6$? ◀

$$f'(1) = 1 = \sum_{k=1}^{\infty} \frac{k}{(k + 1)!}.$$

Related Exercises 45–54 ◀

Representing Functions as Power Series

Power series have a fundamental role in mathematics in defining functions and providing alternative representations of familiar functions. As an overall review, we close this chapter with two examples that use many techniques for working with power series.

EXAMPLE 7 **Identify the series** Identify the function represented by the power series $\sum_{k=0}^{\infty} \dfrac{(1-2x)^k}{k!}$ and give its interval of convergence.

SOLUTION The Maclaurin series for the exponential function,

$$e^x = \sum_{k=0}^{\infty} \frac{x^k}{k!},$$

converges for $-\infty < x < \infty$. Replacing x with $1 - 2x$ produces the given series:

$$\sum_{k=0}^{\infty} \frac{(1-2x)^k}{k!} = e^{1-2x}.$$

This replacement is allowed because $1 - 2x$ is within the interval of convergence of the series for e^x; that is, $-\infty < 1 - 2x < \infty$, for all x. Therefore, the given series represents e^{1-2x}, for $-\infty < x < \infty$.   *Related Exercises 55–64* ◄

EXAMPLE 8 **Mystery series** The power series $\sum_{k=1}^{\infty} \dfrac{(-1)^k k}{4^k} x^{2k}$ appeared in the opening of Section 9.2. Determine the interval of convergence of the power series and find the function it represents on this interval.

SOLUTION Applying the Ratio Test to the series, we determine that it converges when $|x^2/4| < 1$, which implies that $|x| < 2$. A quick check of the endpoints of the original series confirms that it diverges at $x = \pm 2$. Therefore, the interval of convergence is $|x| < 2$.

To find the function represented by the series, we apply several maneuvers until we obtain a geometric series. First note that

$$\sum_{k=1}^{\infty} \frac{(-1)^k k}{4^k} x^{2k} = \sum_{k=1}^{\infty} k\left(-\frac{1}{4}\right)^k x^{2k}.$$

The series on the right is not a geometric series because of the presence of the factor k. The key is to realize that k could appear in this way through differentiation; specifically, something like $\dfrac{d}{dx}(x^{2k}) = 2kx^{2k-1}$. To achieve terms of this form, we write

$$\underbrace{\sum_{k=1}^{\infty} \frac{(-1)^k k}{4^k} x^{2k}}_{\text{original series}} = \sum_{k=1}^{\infty} k\left(-\frac{1}{4}\right)^k x^{2k}$$

$$= \frac{1}{2}\sum_{k=1}^{\infty} 2k\left(-\frac{1}{4}\right)^k x^{2k} \qquad \text{Multiply and divide by 2.}$$

$$= \frac{x}{2}\sum_{k=1}^{\infty} 2k\left(-\frac{1}{4}\right)^k x^{2k-1}. \qquad \text{Remove } x \text{ from the series.}$$

Now we identify the last series as the derivative of another series:

$$\underbrace{\sum_{k=1}^{\infty} \frac{(-1)^k k}{4^k} x^{2k}}_{\text{original series}} = \frac{x}{2}\sum_{k=1}^{\infty} \left(-\frac{1}{4}\right)^k \underbrace{2kx^{2k-1}}_{\frac{d}{dx}(x^{2k})}$$

$$= \frac{x}{2}\sum_{k=1}^{\infty} \left(-\frac{1}{4}\right)^k \frac{d}{dx}(x^{2k}) \qquad \text{Identify a derivative.}$$

$$= \frac{x}{2}\frac{d}{dx}\left(\sum_{k=1}^{\infty} \left(-\frac{x^2}{4}\right)^k\right). \qquad \text{Combine factors; differentiate term by term.}$$

This last series is a geometric series with a ratio $r = -x^2/4$ and first term $-x^2/4$; therefore, its value is $\dfrac{-x^2/4}{1 + (x^2/4)}$, provided $\left|\dfrac{x^2}{4}\right| < 1$, or $|x| < 2$. We now have

$$\underbrace{\sum_{k=1}^{\infty} \frac{(-1)^k k}{4^k} x^{2k}}_{\text{original series}} = \frac{x}{2} \frac{d}{dx}\left(\sum_{k=1}^{\infty}\left(-\frac{x^2}{4}\right)^k\right)$$

$$= \frac{x}{2} \frac{d}{dx}\left(\frac{-x^2/4}{1 + (x^2/4)}\right) \qquad \text{Sum of geometric series}$$

$$= \frac{x}{2} \frac{d}{dx}\left(\frac{-x^2}{4 + x^2}\right) \qquad \text{Simplify.}$$

$$= -\frac{4x^2}{(4 + x^2)^2}. \qquad \text{Differentiate and simplify.}$$

Therefore, the function represented by the power series on $(-2, 2)$ has been uncovered; it is

$$f(x) = -\frac{4x^2}{(4 + x^2)^2}.$$

Notice that f is defined for $-\infty < x < \infty$ (Figure 9.21), but its power series centered at 0 converges to f only on $(-2, 2)$.

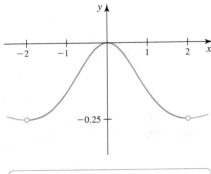

$$\sum_{k=1}^{\infty} \frac{(-1)^k k}{4^k} x^{2k} = -\frac{4x^2}{(4 + x^2)^2} \text{ on } (-2, 2)$$

Figure 9.21

Related Exercises 55–64 ◄

SECTION 9.4 EXERCISES

Review Questions

1. Explain the strategy presented in this section for evaluating a limit of the form $\lim\limits_{x\to a} f(x)/g(x)$, where f and g have Taylor series centered at a.

2. Explain the method presented in this section for approximating $\int_a^b f(x)\, dx$, where f has a Taylor series with an interval of convergence centered at a that includes b.

3. How would you approximate $e^{-0.6}$ using the Taylor series for e^x?

4. Suggest a Taylor series and a method for approximating π.

5. If $f(x) = \sum\limits_{k=0}^{\infty} c_k x^k$ and the series converges for $|x| < b$, what is the power series for $f'(x)$?

6. What condition must be met by a function f for it to have a Taylor series centered at a?

Basic Skills

7–24. Limits *Evaluate the following limits using Taylor series.*

7. $\lim\limits_{x\to 0} \dfrac{e^x - 1}{x}$

8. $\lim\limits_{x\to 0} \dfrac{\tan^{-1} x - x}{x^3}$

9. $\lim\limits_{x\to 0} \dfrac{-x - \ln(1 - x)}{x^2}$

10. $\lim\limits_{x\to 0} \dfrac{\sin 2x}{x}$

11. $\lim\limits_{x\to 0} \dfrac{e^x - e^{-x}}{x}$

12. $\lim\limits_{x\to 0} \dfrac{1 + x - e^x}{4x^2}$

13. $\lim\limits_{x\to 0} \dfrac{2 \cos 2x - 2 + 4x^2}{2x^4}$

14. $\lim\limits_{x\to\infty} x \sin\dfrac{1}{x}$

15. $\lim\limits_{x\to 0} \dfrac{\ln(1 + x) - x + x^2/2}{x^3}$

16. $\lim\limits_{x\to 4} \dfrac{x^2 - 16}{\ln(x - 3)}$

17. $\lim\limits_{x\to 0} \dfrac{3 \tan^{-1} x - 3x + x^3}{x^5}$

18. $\lim\limits_{x\to 0} \dfrac{\sqrt{1 + x} - 1 - (x/2)}{4x^2}$

19. $\lim\limits_{x\to 0} \dfrac{12x - 8x^3 - 6 \sin 2x}{x^5}$

20. $\lim\limits_{x\to 1} \dfrac{x - 1}{\ln x}$

21. $\lim\limits_{x\to 2} \dfrac{x - 2}{\ln(x - 1)}$

22. $\lim\limits_{x\to\infty} x(e^{1/x} - 1)$

23. $\lim\limits_{x\to 0} \dfrac{e^{-2x} - 4 e^{-x/2} + 3}{2x^2}$

24. $\lim\limits_{x\to 0} \dfrac{(1 - 2x)^{-1/2} - e^x}{8x^2}$

25–32. Power series for derivatives

a. *Differentiate the Taylor series about 0 for the following functions.*
b. *Identify the function represented by the differentiated series.*
c. *Give the interval of convergence of the power series for the derivative.*

25. $f(x) = e^x$

26. $f(x) = \cos x$

27. $f(x) = \ln(1 + x)$

28. $f(x) = \sin x^2$

29. $f(x) = e^{-2x}$

30. $f(x) = (1 - x)^{-1}$

31. $f(x) = \tan^{-1} x$

32. $f(x) = -\ln(1 - x)$

33–36. Differential equations

a. *Find a power series for the solution of the following differential equations, subject to the given initial condition.*
b. *Identify the function represented by the power series.*

33. $y'(t) - y = 0, y(0) = 2$

34. $y'(t) + 4y = 8, y(0) = 0$

35. $y'(t) - 3y = 10, y(0) = 2$

36. $y'(t) = 6y + 9, y(0) = 2$

T 37–44. Approximating definite integrals *Use a Taylor series to approximate the following definite integrals. Retain as many terms as needed to ensure the error is less than* 10^{-4}.

37. $\displaystyle\int_0^{0.25} e^{-x^2}\, dx$

38. $\displaystyle\int_0^{0.2} \sin x^2\, dx$

39. $\displaystyle\int_{-0.35}^{0.35} \cos 2x^2\, dx$

40. $\displaystyle\int_0^{0.2} \sqrt{1 + x^4}\, dx$

41. $\displaystyle\int_0^{0.35} \tan^{-1} x\, dx$

42. $\displaystyle\int_0^{0.4} \ln\left(1 + x^2\right) dx$

43. $\displaystyle\int_0^{0.5} \frac{dx}{\sqrt{1 + x^6}}$

44. $\displaystyle\int_0^{0.2} \frac{\ln(1 + t)}{t}\, dt$

45–50. Approximating real numbers *Use an appropriate Taylor series to find the first four nonzero terms of an infinite series that is equal to the following numbers.*

45. e^2

46. $\sqrt{e}$

47. $\cos 2$

48. $\sin 1$

49. $\ln \frac{3}{2}$

50. $\tan^{-1} \frac{1}{2}$

51. Evaluating an infinite series Let $f(x) = (e^x - 1)/x$, for $x \neq 0$, and $f(0) = 1$. Use the Taylor series for f about 0 and evaluate $f(1)$ to find the value of $\displaystyle\sum_{k=0}^{\infty} \frac{1}{(k + 1)!}$.

52. Evaluating an infinite series Let $f(x) = (e^x - 1)/x$, for $x \neq 0$, and $f(0) = 1$. Use the Taylor series for f and f' about 0 to evaluate $f'(2)$ to find the value of $\displaystyle\sum_{k=1}^{\infty} \frac{k\, 2^{k-1}}{(k + 1)!}$.

53. Evaluating an infinite series Write the Taylor series for $f(x) = \ln(1 + x)$ about 0 and find its interval of convergence. Assume the Taylor series converges to f on the interval of convergence. Evaluate $f(1)$ to find the value of $\displaystyle\sum_{k=1}^{\infty} \frac{(-1)^{k+1}}{k}$ (the alternating harmonic series).

54. Evaluating an infinite series Write the Maclaurin series for $f(x) = \ln(1 + x)$ and find the interval of convergence. Evaluate $f(-\frac{1}{2})$ to find the value of $\displaystyle\sum_{k=1}^{\infty} \frac{1}{k \cdot 2^k}$.

55–64. Representing functions by power series *Identify the functions represented by the following power series.*

55. $\displaystyle\sum_{k=0}^{\infty} \frac{x^k}{2^k}$

56. $\displaystyle\sum_{k=0}^{\infty} (-1)^k \frac{x^k}{3^k}$

57. $\displaystyle\sum_{k=0}^{\infty} (-1)^k \frac{x^{2k}}{4^k}$

58. $\displaystyle\sum_{k=0}^{\infty} 2^k x^{2k+1}$

59. $\displaystyle\sum_{k=1}^{\infty} \frac{x^k}{k}$

60. $\displaystyle\sum_{k=0}^{\infty} \frac{(-1)^k x^{k+1}}{4^k}$

61. $\displaystyle\sum_{k=1}^{\infty} (-1)^k \frac{kx^{k+1}}{3^k}$

62. $\displaystyle\sum_{k=1}^{\infty} \frac{x^{2k}}{k}$

63. $\displaystyle\sum_{k=2}^{\infty} \frac{k(k-1)x^k}{3^k}$

64. $\displaystyle\sum_{k=2}^{\infty} \frac{x^k}{k(k-1)}$

Further Explorations

65. Explain why or why not Determine whether the following statements are true and give an explanation or counterexample.

   a. To evaluate $\displaystyle\int_0^2 \frac{dx}{1 - x}$, one could expand the integrand in a Taylor series and integrate term by term.

   b. To approximate $\pi/3$, one could substitute $x = \sqrt{3}$ into the Taylor series for $\tan^{-1} x$.

   c. $\displaystyle\sum_{k=0}^{\infty} \frac{(\ln 2)^k}{k!} = 2$.

66–68. Limits with a parameter *Use Taylor series to evaluate the following limits. Express the result in terms of the parameter(s).*

66. $\displaystyle\lim_{x \to 0} \frac{e^{ax} - 1}{x}$

67. $\displaystyle\lim_{x \to 0} \frac{\sin ax}{\sin bx}$

68. $\displaystyle\lim_{x \to 0} \frac{\sin ax - \tan^{-1} ax}{bx^3}$

69. A limit by Taylor series Use Taylor series to evaluate $\displaystyle\lim_{x \to 0} \left(\frac{\sin x}{x}\right)^{1/x^2}$.

70. Inverse hyperbolic sine The *inverse hyperbolic sine* is defined in several ways; among them are

$$\sinh^{-1} x = \ln\left(x + \sqrt{x^2 + 1}\right) = \int_0^x \frac{dt}{\sqrt{1 + t^2}}.$$

Find the first four terms of the Taylor series for $\sinh^{-1} x$ using these two definitions (and be sure they agree).

71–74. Derivative trick *Here is an alternative way to evaluate higher derivatives of a function f that may save time. Suppose you can find the Taylor series for f centered at the point a without evaluating derivatives (for example, from a known series). Explain why $f^{(k)}(a) = k!$ multiplied by the coefficient of $(x - a)^k$. Use this idea to evaluate $f^{(3)}(0)$ and $f^{(4)}(0)$ for the following functions. Use known series and do not evaluate derivatives.*

71. $f(x) = e^{\cos x}$

72. $f(x) = \dfrac{x^2 + 1}{\sqrt[3]{1 + x}}$

73. $f(x) = \displaystyle\int_0^x \sin t^2\, dt$

74. $f(x) = \displaystyle\int_0^x \frac{1}{1 + t^4}\, dt$

Applications

75. Probability: tossing for a head The expected (average) number of tosses of a fair coin required to obtain the first head is $\displaystyle\sum_{k=1}^{\infty} k\left(\frac{1}{2}\right)^k$. Evaluate this series and determine the expected number of tosses. (*Hint:* Differentiate a geometric series.)

76. Probability: sudden death playoff Teams A and B go into sudden death overtime after playing to a tie. The teams alternate possession of the ball, and the first team to score wins. Each team has a $\frac{1}{6}$ chance of scoring when it has the ball, with Team A having the ball first.

   a. The probability that Team A ultimately wins is $\displaystyle\sum_{k=0}^{\infty} \frac{1}{6}\left(\frac{5}{6}\right)^{2k}$. Evaluate this series.

   b. The expected number of rounds (possessions by either team) required for the overtime to end is $\displaystyle\frac{1}{6}\sum_{k=1}^{\infty} k\left(\frac{5}{6}\right)^{k-1}$. Evaluate this series.

T 77. Elliptic integrals The period of a pendulum is given by

$$T = 4\sqrt{\frac{\ell}{g}} \int_0^{\pi/2} \frac{d\theta}{\sqrt{1 - k^2 \sin^2 \theta}} = 4\sqrt{\frac{\ell}{g}}\, F(k),$$

where ℓ is the length of the pendulum, $g \approx 9.8 \text{ m/s}^2$ is the acceleration due to gravity, $k = \sin(\theta_0/2)$, and θ_0 is the initial angular displacement of the pendulum (in radians). The integral in this formula $F(k)$ is called an *elliptic integral*, and it cannot be evaluated analytically.

a. Approximate $F(0.1)$ by expanding the integrand in a Taylor (binomial) series and integrating term by term.

b. How many terms of the Taylor series do you suggest using to obtain an approximation to $F(0.1)$ with an error less than 10^{-3}?

c. Would you expect to use fewer or more terms (than in part (b)) to approximate $F(0.2)$ to the same accuracy? Explain.

78. Sine integral function The function $\text{Si}(x) = \int_0^x \frac{\sin t}{t}\, dt$ is called the *sine integral function*.

a. Expand the integrand in a Taylor series about 0.

b. Integrate the series to find a Taylor series for Si.

c. Approximate $\text{Si}(0.5)$ and $\text{Si}(1)$. Use enough terms of the series so the error in the approximation does not exceed 10^{-3}.

T 79. Fresnel integrals The theory of optics gives rise to the two *Fresnel integrals*

$$S(x) = \int_0^x \sin t^2\, dt \quad \text{and} \quad C(x) = \int_0^x \cos t^2\, dt.$$

a. Compute $S'(x)$ and $C'(x)$.

b. Expand $\sin t^2$ and $\cos t^2$ in a Maclaurin series and then integrate to find the first four nonzero terms of the Maclaurin series for S and C.

c. Use the polynomials in part (b) to approximate $S(0.05)$ and $C(-0.25)$.

d. How many terms of the Maclaurin series are required to approximate $S(0.05)$ with an error no greater than 10^{-4}?

e. How many terms of the Maclaurin series are required to approximate $C(-0.25)$ with an error no greater than 10^{-6}?

T 80. Error function An essential function in statistics and the study of the normal distribution is the *error function*

$$\text{erf}(x) = \frac{2}{\sqrt{\pi}} \int_0^x e^{-t^2}\, dt.$$

a. Compute the derivative of $\text{erf}(x)$.

b. Expand e^{-t^2} in a Maclaurin series; then integrate to find the first four nonzero terms of the Maclaurin series for erf.

c. Use the polynomial in part (b) to approximate $\text{erf}(0.15)$ and $\text{erf}(-0.09)$.

d. Estimate the error in the approximations of part (c).

T 81. Bessel functions Bessel functions arise in the study of wave propagation in circular geometries (for example, waves on a circular drum head). They are conveniently defined as power series. One of an infinite family of Bessel functions is

$$J_0(x) = \sum_{k=0}^{\infty} \frac{(-1)^k}{2^{2k}(k!)^2} x^{2k}.$$

a. Write out the first four terms of J_0.

b. Find the radius and interval of convergence of the power series for J_0.

c. Differentiate J_0 twice and show (by keeping terms through x^6) that J_0 satisfies the equation $x^2 y''(x) + xy'(x) + x^2 y(x) = 0$.

Additional Exercises

82. Power series for sec x Use the identity $\sec x = \frac{1}{\cos x}$ and long division to find the first three terms of the Maclaurin series for sec x.

83. Symmetry

a. Use infinite series to show that $\cos x$ is an even function. That is, show $\cos(-x) = \cos x$.

b. Use infinite series to show that $\sin x$ is an odd function. That is, show $\sin(-x) = -\sin x$.

84. Behavior of csc x We know that $\lim_{x \to 0^+} \csc x = \infty$. Use long division to determine exactly how csc x grows as $x \to 0^+$. Specifically, find a, b, and c (all positive) in the following sentence: As $x \to 0^+$, $\csc x \approx \dfrac{a}{x^b} + cx$.

85. L'Hôpital's Rule by Taylor series Suppose f and g have Taylor series about the point a.

a. If $f(a) = g(a) = 0$ and $g'(a) \neq 0$, evaluate $\lim_{x \to a} f(x)/g(x)$ by expanding f and g in their Taylor series. Show that the result is consistent with l'Hôpital's Rule.

b. If $f(a) = g(a) = f'(a) = g'(a) = 0$ and $g''(a) \neq 0$, evaluate $\lim_{x \to a} \dfrac{f(x)}{g(x)}$ by expanding f and g in their Taylor series. Show that the result is consistent with two applications of l'Hôpital's Rule.

T 86. Newton's derivation of the sine and arcsine series Newton discovered the binomial series and then used it ingeniously to obtain many more results. Here is a case in point.

a. Referring to the figure, show that $x = \sin s$ or $s = \sin^{-1} x$.

b. The area of a circular sector of radius r subtended by an angle θ is $\frac{1}{2} r^2 \theta$. Show that the area of the circular sector APE is $s/2$, which implies that

$$s = 2 \int_0^x \sqrt{1 - t^2}\, dt - x\sqrt{1 - x^2}.$$

c. Use the binomial series for $f(x) = \sqrt{1 - x^2}$ to obtain the first few terms of the Taylor series for $s = \sin^{-1} x$.

d. Newton next inverted the series in part (c) to obtain the Taylor series for $x = \sin s$. He did this by assuming that $\sin s = \sum a_k s^k$ and solving $x = \sin(\sin^{-1} x)$ for the coefficients a_k. Find the first few terms of the Taylor series for $\sin s$ using this idea (a computer algebra system might be helpful as well).

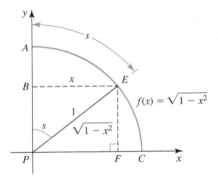

QUICK CHECK ANSWERS

1. $\dfrac{\sin x}{x} = \dfrac{x - x^3/3! + \cdots}{x} = 1 - \dfrac{x^2}{3!} + \cdots \to 1$ as $x \to 0$

2. The result is the power series for $-\sin x$. **3.** $x = 1/\sqrt{3}$ (which lies in the interval of convergence) ◄

CHAPTER 9   REVIEW EXERCISES

1. Explain why or why not Determine whether the following statements are true and give an explanation or counterexample.

a. Let p_n be the nth-order Taylor polynomial for f centered at 2. The approximation $p_3(2.1) \approx f(2.1)$ is likely to be more accurate than the approximation $p_2(2.2) \approx f(2.2)$.

b. If the Taylor series for f centered at 3 has a radius of convergence of 6, then the interval of convergence is $[-3, 9]$.

c. The interval of convergence of the power series $\sum c_k x^k$ could be $\left(-\frac{7}{3}, \frac{7}{3}\right)$.

d. The Maclaurin series for $f(x) = (1 + x)^{12}$ has a finite number of nonzero terms.

2–9. Taylor polynomials *Find the nth-order Taylor polynomial for the following functions centered at the given point a.*

2. $f(x) = \sin 2x, n = 3, a = 0$

3. $f(x) = \cos x^2, n = 2, a = 0$

4. $f(x) = e^{-x}, n = 2, a = 0$

5. $f(x) = \ln(1 + x), n = 3, a = 0$

6. $f(x) = \cos x, n = 2, a = \pi/4$

7. $f(x) = \ln x, n = 2, a = 1$

8. $f(x) = \sinh 2x, n = 4, a = 0$

9. $f(x) = \cosh x, n = 3, a = \ln 2$

⊤ 10–13. Approximations

a. Find the Taylor polynomials of order $n = 0, 1,$ and 2 for the given functions centered at the given point a.

b. Make a table showing the approximations and the absolute error in these approximations using a calculator for the exact function value.

10. $f(x) = \cos x, a = 0$; approximate $\cos(-0.08)$.

11. $f(x) = e^x, a = 0$; approximate $e^{-0.08}$.

12. $f(x) = \sqrt{1 + x}, a = 0$; approximate $\sqrt{1.08}$.

13. $f(x) = \sin x, a = \pi/4$; approximate $\sin(\pi/5)$.

14–16. Estimating remainders *Find the remainder term $R_n(x)$ for the Taylor series centered at 0 for the following functions. Find an upper bound for the magnitude of the remainder on the given interval for the given value of n. (The bound is not unique.)*

14. $f(x) = e^x$; bound $R_3(x)$, for $|x| < 1$.

15. $f(x) = \sin x$; bound $R_3(x)$, for $|x| < \pi$.

16. $f(x) = \ln(1 - x)$; bound $R_3(x)$, for $|x| < 1/2$.

17–24. Radius and interval of convergence *Use the Ratio or Root Test to determine the radius of convergence of the following power series. Test the endpoints to determine the interval of convergence, when appropriate.*

17. $\sum \dfrac{k^2 x^k}{k!}$

18. $\sum \dfrac{x^{4k}}{k^2}$

19. $\sum (-1)^k \dfrac{(x + 1)^{2k}}{k!}$

20. $\sum \dfrac{(x - 1)^k}{k \cdot 5^k}$

21. $\sum \left(\dfrac{x}{9}\right)^{3k}$

22. $\sum \dfrac{(x + 2)^k}{\sqrt{k}}$

23. $\sum \dfrac{(x + 2)^k}{2^k \ln k}$

24. $x + \dfrac{x^3}{3} + \dfrac{x^5}{5} + \dfrac{x^7}{7} + \cdots$

25–30. Power series from the geometric series *Use the geometric series $\sum_{k=0}^{\infty} x^k = \dfrac{1}{1 - x}$, for $|x| < 1$, to determine the Maclaurin series and the interval of convergence for the following functions.*

25. $f(x) = \dfrac{1}{1 - x^2}$

26. $f(x) = \dfrac{1}{1 + x^3}$

27. $f(x) = \dfrac{1}{1 + 5x}$

28. $f(x) = \dfrac{10x}{1 + x}$

29. $f(x) = \dfrac{1}{(1 - 10x)^2}$

30. $f(x) = \ln(1 - 4x)$

31–38. Taylor series *Write out the first three nonzero terms of the Taylor series for the following functions centered at the given point a. Then write the series using summation notation.*

31. $f(x) = e^{3x}, a = 0$

32. $f(x) = 1/x, a = 1$

33. $f(x) = \cos x, a = \pi/2$

34. $f(x) = \dfrac{x^2}{1 + x}, a = 0$

35. $f(x) = \tan^{-1} 4x, a = 0$

36. $f(x) = \sin 2x, a = -\pi/2$

37. $f(x) = \cosh 3x, a = 0$

38. $f(x) = \dfrac{1}{4 + x^2}, a = 0$

39–42. Binomial series *Write out the first three terms of the Maclaurin series for the following functions.*

39. $f(x) = (1 + x)^{1/3}$

40. $f(x) = (1 + x)^{-1/2}$

41. $f(x) = (1 + x/2)^{-3}$

42. $f(x) = (1 + 2x)^{-5}$

43–46. Convergence *Write the remainder term $R_n(x)$ for the Taylor series for the following functions centered at the given point a. Then show that $\lim_{n\to\infty} |R_n(x)| = 0$, for all x in the given interval.*

43. $f(x) = e^{-x}, a = 0, -\infty < x < \infty$

44. $f(x) = \sin x, a = 0, -\infty < x < \infty$

45. $f(x) = \ln(1 + x), a = 0, -\frac{1}{2} \le x \le \frac{1}{2}$

46. $f(x) = \sqrt{1 + x}, a = 0, -\frac{1}{2} \le x \le \frac{1}{2}$

47–52. Limits by power series *Use Taylor series to evaluate the following limits.*

47. $\lim_{x\to 0} \dfrac{x^2/2 - 1 + \cos x}{x^4}$

48. $\lim_{x\to 0} \dfrac{2 \sin x - \tan^{-1} x - x}{2x^5}$

49. $\lim_{x\to 4} \dfrac{\ln(x - 3)}{x^2 - 16}$

50. $\lim\limits_{x \to 0} \dfrac{\sqrt{1 + 2x} - 1 - x}{x^2}$

51. $\lim\limits_{x \to 0} \dfrac{\sec x - \cos x - x^2}{x^4}$ $\left(\text{\textit{Hint:} The Maclaurin series for sec } x \text{ is}\right.$
$\left.1 + \dfrac{x^2}{2} + \dfrac{5x^4}{24} + \dfrac{61x^6}{720} + \cdots .\right)$

52. $\lim\limits_{x \to 0} \dfrac{(1 + x)^{-2} - \sqrt[3]{1 - 6x}}{2x^2}$

T **53–56. Definite integrals by power series** *Use a Taylor series to approximate the following definite integrals. Retain as many terms as necessary to ensure the error is less than 10^{-3}.*

53. $\displaystyle\int_0^{1/2} e^{-x^2}\, dx$

54. $\displaystyle\int_0^{1/2} \tan^{-1} x\, dx$

55. $\displaystyle\int_0^1 x \cos x\, dx$

56. $\displaystyle\int_0^{1/2} x^2 \tan^{-1} x\, dx$

T **57–60. Approximating real numbers** *Use an appropriate Taylor series to find the first four nonzero terms of an infinite series that is equal to the following numbers. There is more than one way to choose the center of the series.*

57. $\sqrt{119}$

58. $\sin 20°$

59. $\tan^{-1}\left(-\tfrac{1}{3}\right)$

60. $\sinh(-1)$

61. A differential equation Find a power series solution of the differential equation $y'(x) - 4y + 12 = 0$, subject to the condition $y(0) = 4$. Identify the solution in terms of known functions.

T **62. Rejected quarters** The probability that a random quarter is *not* rejected by a vending machine is given by the integral

$11.4 \int_0^{0.14} e^{-102x^2}\, dx$ (assuming that the weights of quarters are normally distributed with a mean of 5.670 g and a standard deviation of 0.07 g). Expand the integrand in $n = 2$ and $n = 3$ terms of a Taylor series and integrate to find two estimates of the probability. Check for agreement between the two estimates.

T **63. Approximating ln 2** Consider the following three ways to approximate ln 2.

  a. Use the Taylor series for $\ln(1 + x)$ centered at 0 and evaluate it at $x = 1$ (convergence was asserted in Table 9.5). Write the resulting infinite series.

  b. Use the Taylor series for $\ln(1 - x)$ centered at 0 and the identity $\ln 2 = -\ln\dfrac{1}{2}$. Write the resulting infinite series.

  c. Use the property $\ln(a/b) = \ln a - \ln b$ and the series of parts (a) and (b) to find the Taylor series for $f(x) = \ln\left(\dfrac{1 + x}{1 - x}\right)$ centered at 0.

  d. At what value of x should the series in part (c) be evaluated to approximate ln 2? Write the resulting infinite series for ln 2.

  e. Using four terms of the series, which of the three series derived in parts (a)–(d) gives the best approximation to ln 2? Can you explain why?

T **64. Graphing Taylor polynomials** Consider the function $f(x) = (1 + x)^{-4}$.

  a. Find the Taylor polynomials p_0, p_1, p_2, and p_3 centered at 0.

  b. Use a graphing utility to plot the Taylor polynomials and f, for $-1 < x < 1$.

  c. For each Taylor polynomial, give the interval on which its graph appears indistinguishable from the graph of f.

Chapter 9 Guided Projects

Applications of the material in this chapter and related topics can be found in the following Guided Projects. For additional information, see the Preface.

- Series approximations to π
- Euler's formula (Taylor series with complex numbers)
- Stirling's formula and $n!$
- Three-sigma quality control
- Fourier series

10

Parametric and Polar Curves

Chapter Preview Until now, all our work has involved in the Cartesian coordinate system with functions of the form $y = f(x)$. There are, however, alternative ways to generate curves and represent functions. We begin by introducing parametric equations, which are featured prominently in Chapter 11 to represent curves and trajectories in three-dimensional space. When working with objects that have circular, cylindrical, or spherical shapes, other coordinate systems are often advantageous. In this chapter, we introduce the polar coordinate system for circular geometries. Cylindrical and spherical coordinate systems appear in Chapter 13. After working with parametric equations and polar coordinates, the next step is to investigate calculus in these settings. How do we find slopes of tangent lines and rates of change? How are areas of regions bounded by curves in polar coordinates computed? The chapter ends with the related topic of *conic sections*. Ellipses, parabolas, and hyperbolas (all of which are conic sections) can be represented in both Cartesian and polar coordinates. These important families of curves have many fascinating properties and they appear throughout the remainder of the book.

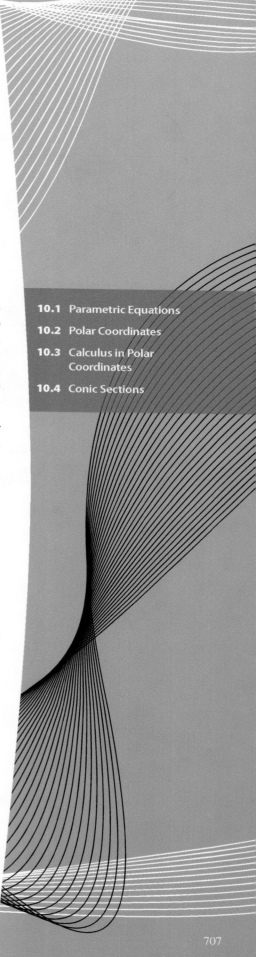

10.1 Parametric Equations

So far, we have used functions of the form $y = F(x)$ to describe curves in the xy-plane. In this section, we look at another way to define curves, known as *parametric equations*. As you will see, parametric curves enable us to describe both common and exotic curves; they are also indispensable for modeling the trajectories of moving objects.

Basic Ideas

A motor boat travels counterclockwise around a circular course with a radius of 4 miles, completing one lap every 2π hours at a constant speed. Suppose we wish to describe the points on the path of the boat $(x(t), y(t))$ at any time $t \geq 0$, where t is measured in hours. We assume that the boat starts on the positive x-axis at the point $(4, 0)$ (Figure 10.1). Note that the angle θ corresponding to the position of the boat increases by 2π radians every 2π hours beginning with $\theta = 0$ when $t = 0$; therefore, $\theta = t$, for $t \geq 0$. It follows that the x- and y-coordinates of the boat are

$$x = 4 \cos \theta = 4 \cos t \quad \text{and} \quad y = 4 \sin \theta = 4 \sin t,$$

where $t \geq 0$. You can confirm that when $t = 0$, the boat is at the starting point $(4, 0)$; when $t = 2\pi$, it returns to the starting point.

The equations $x = 4 \cos t$ and $y = 4 \sin t$ are examples of **parametric equations**. They specify x and y in terms of a third variable t called a **parameter**, which often represents time.

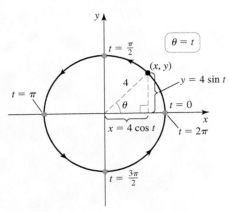

Figure 10.1

▶ The parameter t is the independent variable. There are two dependent variables, x and y.

In general, parametric equations have the form

$$x = f(t), \quad y = g(t),$$

where f and g are given functions and the parameter t typically varies over a specified interval $a \le t \le b$ (Figure 10.2). The **parametric curve** described by these equations consists of the points in the plane

$$(x, y) = (f(t), g(t)), \quad \text{for } a \le t \le b.$$

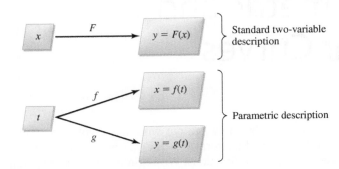

Figure 10.2

EXAMPLE 1 Parametric parabola Graph and analyze the parametric equations

$$x = f(t) = 2t, \quad y = g(t) = \frac{1}{2}t^2 - 4, \quad \text{for } 0 \le t \le 8.$$

SOLUTION Plotting individual points often helps in visualizing a parametric curve. Table 10.1 shows the values of x and y corresponding to several values of t on the interval $[0, 8]$. By plotting the (x, y) pairs in Table 10.1 and connecting them with a smooth curve, we obtain the graph shown in Figure 10.3. As t increases from its initial value of $t = 0$ to its final value of $t = 8$, the curve is generated from the initial point $(0, -4)$ to the final point $(16, 28)$. Notice that the values of the parameter do not appear in the graph. The only signature of the parameter is the direction in which the curve is generated: In this case, it unfolds upward and to the right, as indicated by the arrows on the curve.

Table 10.1

t	x	y	(x, y)
0	0	-4	$(0, -4)$
1	2	$-\frac{7}{2}$	$(2, -\frac{7}{2})$
2	4	-2	$(4, -2)$
3	6	$\frac{1}{2}$	$(6, \frac{1}{2})$
4	8	4	$(8, 4)$
5	10	$\frac{17}{2}$	$(10, \frac{17}{2})$
6	12	14	$(12, 14)$
7	14	$\frac{41}{2}$	$(14, \frac{41}{2})$
8	16	28	$(16, 28)$

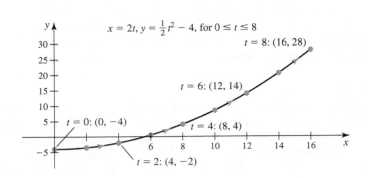

Figure 10.3

Sometimes it is possible to eliminate the parameter from a set of parametric equations and obtain a description of the curve in terms of x and y. In this case, from the x-equation, we have $t = x/2$, which may be substituted into the y-equation to give

$$y = \frac{1}{2}t^2 - 4 = \frac{1}{2}\left(\frac{x}{2}\right)^2 - 4 = \frac{x^2}{8} - 4.$$

Expressed in this form, we identify the graph as part of a parabola. Because t lies in the interval $0 \leq t \leq 8$ and $x = 2t$, it follows that x lies in the interval $0 \leq x \leq 16$. Therefore, the parametric equations generate the segment of the parabola for $0 \leq x \leq 16$.

Related Exercises 11–20 ◄

QUICK CHECK 1 Identify the graph generated by the parametric equations $x = t^2$, $y = t$, for $-10 \leq t \leq 10$. ◄

Given a set of parametric equations, the preceding example shows that as the parameter increases, the corresponding curve unfolds in a particular direction. The following definition captures this fact and is important in upcoming work.

DEFINITION Positive Orientation

The direction in which a parametric curve is generated as the parameter increases is called the **positive orientation** of the curve (and is indicated by arrows on the curve).

The question of orientation is particularly important for closed curves such as circles.

EXAMPLE 2   Parametric circle Graph and analyze the parametric equations

$$x = 4 \cos 2\pi t, \quad y = 4 \sin 2\pi t, \quad \text{for } 0 \leq t \leq 1.$$

SOLUTION For each value of t in Table 10.2, the corresponding ordered pairs (x, y) are recorded. Plotting these points as t increases from $t = 0$ to $t = 1$ results in a graph that appears to be a circle of radius 4; it is generated with positive orientation in the counterclockwise direction, beginning and ending at $(4, 0)$ (Figure 10.4). Letting t increase beyond $t = 1$ would simply retrace the same curve.

Table 10.2

t	(x, y)
0	$(4, 0)$
$\frac{1}{8}$	$(2\sqrt{2}, 2\sqrt{2})$
$\frac{1}{4}$	$(0, 4)$
$\frac{3}{8}$	$(-2\sqrt{2}, 2\sqrt{2})$
$\frac{1}{2}$	$(-4, 0)$
$\frac{3}{4}$	$(0, -4)$
1	$(4, 0)$

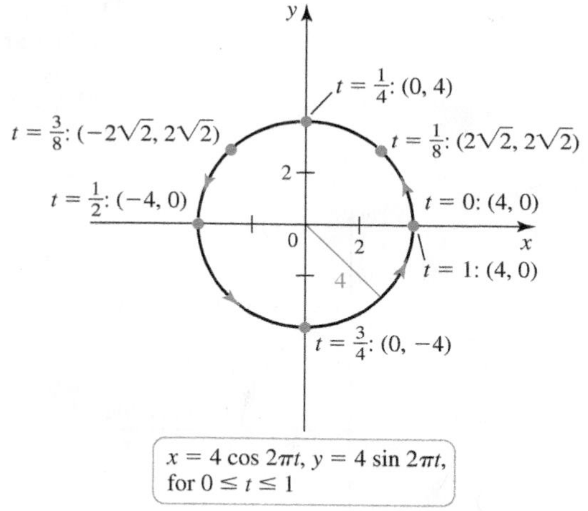

Figure 10.4

To identify the curve conclusively, the parameter t is eliminated by observing that

$$x^2 + y^2 = (4 \cos 2\pi t)^2 + (4 \sin 2\pi t)^2$$
$$= 16\underbrace{(\cos^2 2\pi t + \sin^2 2\pi t)}_{1} = 16. \quad \cos^2 \theta + \sin^2 \theta = 1$$

The graph of the parametric equations is the circle $x^2 + y^2 = 16$, whose positive orientation is in the counterclockwise direction.

Related Exercises 21–32 ◄

Generalizing Example 2 for nonzero real numbers a and b in the parametric equations $x = a \cos bt$, $y = a \sin bt$, notice that

$$x^2 + y^2 = (a \cos bt)^2 + (a \sin bt)^2$$
$$= a^2 \underbrace{(\cos^2 bt + \sin^2 bt)}_{1} = a^2.$$

> For a nonzero constant b, the functions $\sin bt$ and $\cos bt$ have period $2\pi/|b|$. The equations $x = a \cos bt$, $y = -a \sin bt$ also describe a circle of radius $|a|$, as do the equations $x = \pm a \sin bt$, $y = \pm a \cos bt$, as t varies over an interval of length $2\pi/|b|$.

Therefore, the parametric equations $x = a \cos bt$, $y = a \sin bt$ describe all or part of the circle $x^2 + y^2 = a^2$, centered at the origin with radius $|a|$, for any nonzero value of b. The circle is traversed once as t varies over any interval of length $2\pi/|b|$. If t represents time, the circle is traversed once in $2\pi/|b|$ time units, which means we can vary the speed at which the curve unfolds by varying b. If $b > 0$, the positive orientation is in the counterclockwise direction. If $b < 0$, the curve is generated in the clockwise direction.

More generally, the parametric equations

$$x = x_0 + a \cos bt, \quad y = y_0 + a \sin bt$$

describe all or part of the circle $(x - x_0)^2 + (y - y_0)^2 = a^2$, centered at (x_0, y_0) with radius $|a|$. If $b > 0$, then the circle is generated in the counterclockwise direction. Example 3 shows that a single curve—for example, a circle of radius 4—may be parameterized in many different ways.

> In Example 3, the constant $|b|$ is called the *angular frequency* because it is the number of radians the object moves per unit time. The turtle travels 2π rad every 30 min, so the angular frequency is $2\pi/30 = \pi/15$ rad/min. Because radians have no units, the angular frequency in this case has units *per minute*, written min^{-1}.

EXAMPLE 3 Circular path A turtle walks with constant speed in the counterclockwise direction on a circular track of radius 4 ft centered at the origin. Starting from the point $(4, 0)$, the turtle completes one lap in 30 minutes. Find a parametric description of the path of the turtle at any time $t \geq 0$, where t is measured in minutes.

SOLUTION Example 2 showed that a circle of radius of 4, generated in the counterclockwise direction, may be described by the parametric equations

$$x = 4 \cos bt, \quad y = 4 \sin bt, \quad \text{where} \quad b > 0.$$

The *angular frequency* b must be chosen so that as t varies from 0 to 30, the product bt varies from 0 to 2π. Specifically, when $t = 30$, we must have $30b = 2\pi$, or $b = \dfrac{\pi}{15}$ rad/min. Therefore, the parametric equations for the turtle's motion are

$$x = 4 \cos \frac{\pi t}{15}, \quad y = 4 \sin \frac{\pi t}{15}, \quad \text{for } 0 \leq t \leq 30.$$

You should check that as t varies from 0 to 30, the points (x, y) make one complete circuit of a circle of radius 4 (Figure 10.5).

Related Exercises 33–36 ◄

QUICK CHECK 2 Give the center and radius of the circle generated by the equations $x = 3 \sin t$, $y = -3 \cos t$, for $0 \leq t \leq 2\pi$. Specify the direction of positive orientation. ◄

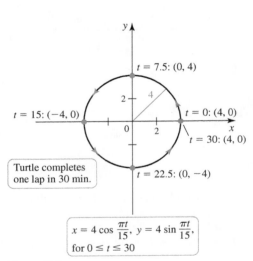

$x = 4 \cos \dfrac{\pi t}{15}$, $y = 4 \sin \dfrac{\pi t}{15}$, for $0 \leq t \leq 30$

Figure 10.5

Among the most important of all parametric equations are

$$x = x_0 + at, \quad y = y_0 + bt, \quad \text{for } -\infty < t < \infty,$$

where x_0, y_0, a, and b are constants with $a \neq 0$. The curve described by these equations is found by eliminating the parameter. The first step is to solve the x-equation for t, which gives us $t = \dfrac{x - x_0}{a}$. When t is substituted into the y-equation, the result is an equation for y in terms of x:

$$y = y_0 + bt = y_0 + b\left(\frac{x - x_0}{a}\right) \quad \text{or} \quad y - y_0 = \frac{b}{a}(x - x_0).$$

This equation describes a line with slope $\dfrac{b}{a}$ passing through the point (x_0, y_0).

SUMMARY   **Parametric Equation of a Line**

The equations

$$x = x_0 + at, \, y = y_0 + bt, \quad \text{for } -\infty < t < \infty,$$

where $x_0, y_0, a,$ and b are constants with $a \neq 0$, describe a line with slope $\dfrac{b}{a}$ passing through the point (x_0, y_0). If $a = 0$ and $b \neq 0$, the line is vertical.

Notice that the parametric description of a given line is not unique: For example, if k is any nonzero constant, the numbers a and b may be replaced with ka and kb, respectively, and the resulting equations describe the same line (although it may be generated in the opposite direction and at a different speed).

EXAMPLE 4   **Parametric equations of lines**

a. Consider the parametric equations $x = -2 + 3t, y = 4 - 6t$, for $-\infty < t < \infty$, which describe a line. Find the slope-intercept form of the line.

b. Find two pairs of parametric equations for the line with slope $\dfrac{1}{3}$ that passes through the point $(2, 1)$.

c. Find parametric equations for the line segment starting at $P(4, 7)$ and ending at $Q(2, -3)$.

SOLUTION

a. To eliminate the parameter, first solve the x-equation for t to find that $t = \dfrac{x + 2}{3}$.

Replacing t in the y-equation yields

$$y = 4 - 6\left(\frac{x + 2}{3}\right) = 4 - 2x - 4 = -2x.$$

The line $y = -2x$ passes through the origin with slope -2.

b. We use the general parametric equations of a line given in the Summary box. Because the slope of the line is $\dfrac{1}{3}$, we choose $a = 3$ and $b = 1$. Letting $x_0 = 2$ and $y_0 = 1$, parametric equations for the line are $x = 2 + 3t, y = 1 + t$, for $-\infty < t < \infty$. The line passes through $(2, 1)$ when $t = 0$ and rises to the right as t increases (Figure 10.6). Notice that other choices for a and b also work. For example, with $a = -6$ and $b = -2$, the equations are $x = 2 - 6t, y = 1 - 2t$, for $-\infty < t < \infty$. These equations describe the same line, but now, as t increases, the line is generated in the opposite direction (descending to the left).

c. The slope of this line is $\dfrac{7 - (-3)}{4 - 2} = 5$. However, notice that when the line segment is traversed from P to Q, both x and y are decreasing (Figure 10.7). To account for the direction in which the line segment is generated, we let $a = -1$ and $b = -5$. Because $P(4, 7)$ is the starting point of the line segment, we choose $x_0 = 4$ and $y_0 = 7$. The resulting equations are $x = 4 - t, y = 7 - 5t$. Notice that $t = 0$ corresponds to the starting point $(4, 7)$. Because the equations describe a line *segment*, the interval for t must be restricted. What value of t corresponds to the endpoint of the line segment $Q(2, -3)$? Setting $x = 4 - t = 2$, we find that $t = 2$. As a check, we set $y = 7 - 5t = -3$, which also implies that $t = 2$. (If these two calculations do not give the same value of t, it probably means the slope was not computed correctly.) Therefore, the equations for the line segment are $x = 4 - t, y = 7 - 5t$, for $0 \le t \le 2$.

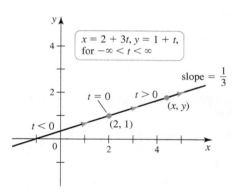

$x = 2 + 3t, y = 1 + t,$
for $-\infty < t < \infty$

slope $= \dfrac{1}{3}$

$t = 0$ $t > 0$

(x, y)

$t < 0$

$(2, 1)$

Figure 10.6

➤ The choices $a = -1$ and $b = -5$ result in a slope of $b/a = 5$. These choices also imply that as we move from P to Q, a decrease in x corresponds to a decrease in y.

➤ Lines and line segments may have unexpected parametric representations. For example, the equations $x = \sin t, y = 2 \sin t$ represent the line segment $y = 2x$, where $-1 \le x \le 1$ (recall that the range of $x = \sin t$ is $[-1, 1]$).

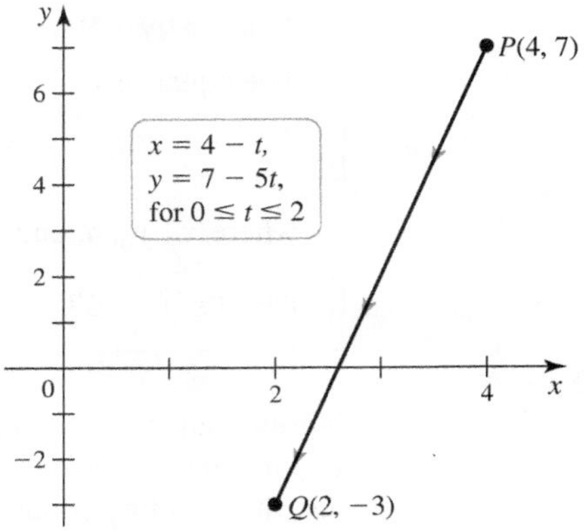

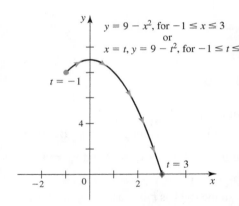

Figure 10.7 is referenced by the graph at top right showing $x = 4 - t$, $y = 7 - 5t$, for $0 \le t \le 2$, with points $P(4, 7)$ and $Q(2, -3)$.

QUICK CHECK 3 Describe the curve generated by $x = 3 + 2t$, $y = -12 - 6t$, for $-\infty < t < \infty$. ◄

Figure 10.7

Related Exercises 37–44 ◄

EXAMPLE 5 **Parametric equations of curves** A common task (particularly in upcoming chapters) is to parameterize curves given either by Cartesian equations or by graphs. Find a parametric representation of the following curves.

a. The segment of the parabola $y = 9 - x^2$, for $-1 \le x \le 3$

b. The complete curve $x = (y - 5)^2 + \sqrt{y}$

c. The piecewise linear path connecting $P(-2, 0)$ to $Q(0, 3)$ to $R(4, 0)$ (in that order), where the parameter varies over the interval $0 \le t \le 2$

SOLUTION

a. The simplest way to represent a curve $y = f(x)$ parametrically is to let $x = t$ and $y = f(t)$, where t is the parameter. We must then find the appropriate interval for the parameter. Using this approach, the curve $y = 9 - x^2$ has the parametric representation

$$x = t, \quad y = 9 - t^2, \quad \text{for} \quad -1 \le t \le 3.$$

This representation is not unique. For example, you can verify that the parametric equations

$$x = 1 - t, \quad y = 9 - (1 - t)^2, \quad \text{for} \quad -2 \le t \le 2$$

also do the job, although these equations trace the parabola from right to left, while the original equations trace the curve from left to right (Figure 10.8).

b. In this case, it is easier to let $y = t$. Then a parametric description of the curve is

$$x = (t - 5)^2 + \sqrt{t}, \quad y = t.$$

Notice that t can take values only in the interval $[0, \infty)$. As $t \to \infty$, we see that $x \to \infty$ and $y \to \infty$ (Figure 10.9).

c. The path consists of two line segments (Figure 10.10) that can be parameterized separately in the form $x = x_0 + at$ and $y = y_0 + bt$. The line segment PQ originates

The graph at left labeled Figure 10.8 shows $y = 9 - x^2$, for $-1 \le x \le 3$ or $x = t$, $y = 9 - t^2$, for $-1 \le t \le 3$, with $t = -1$ and $t = 3$ marked.

Figure 10.8

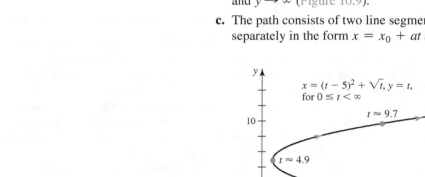

Figure 10.9

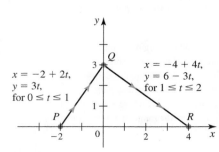

Figure 10.10

at $P(-2, 0)$ and unfolds in the positive x-direction with slope $\frac{3}{2}$. It can be represented as

$$x = -2 + 2t, \quad y = 3t, \quad \text{for } 0 \le t \le 1.$$

Finding the parametric equations for the line segment QR requires some ingenuity. We want the line segment to originate at $Q(0, 3)$ when $t = 1$ and end at $R(4, 0)$ when $t = 2$. Observe that when $t = 1, x = 0$ and when $t = 2, x = 4$. Substituting these pairs of values into the general x-equation $x = x_0 + at$, we obtain the equations

$$x_0 + a = 0 \quad \text{\small $x = 0$ when $t = 1$}$$
$$x_0 + 2a = 4. \quad \text{\small $x = 4$ when $t = 2$}$$

Solving for x_0 and a, we find that $x_0 = -4$ and $a = 4$. Applying a similar procedure to the general y-equation $y = y_0 + bt$, the relevant conditions are

$$y_0 + b = 3 \quad \text{\small $y = 3$ when $t = 1$}$$
$$y_0 + 2b = 0. \quad \text{\small $y = 0$ when $t = 2$}$$

Solving for y_0 and b, we find that $y_0 = 6$ and $b = -3$. Putting it all together, the equations for the line segment QR are

$$x = -4 + 4t, y = 6 - 3t, \quad \text{for } 1 \le t \le 2.$$

You can verify that the points $Q(0, 3)$ and $R(4, 0)$ correspond to $t = 1$ and $t = 2$, respectively. Furthermore, the slope of the line is $\dfrac{b}{a} = -\dfrac{3}{4}$, which is correct.

Related Exercises 45–48 ◄

QUICK CHECK 4 Find parametric equations for the line segment that goes from $Q(0, 3)$ to $P(-2, 0)$. ◄

Many fascinating curves are generated by points on rolling wheels; Examples 6 and 7 investigate two such curves.

EXAMPLE 6 Rolling wheels The path of a light on the rim of a wheel rolling on a flat surface (Figure 10.11a) is a **cycloid**, which has the parametric equations

$$x = a(t - \sin t), \quad y = a(1 - \cos t), \quad \text{for } t \ge 0,$$

where $a > 0$. Use a graphing utility to graph the cycloid with $a = 1$. On what interval does the parameter generate the first arch of the cycloid?

SOLUTION The graph of the cycloid, for $0 \le t \le 3\pi$, is shown in Figure 10.11b. The wheel completes one full revolution on the interval $0 \le t \le 2\pi$, which gives one arch of the cycloid.

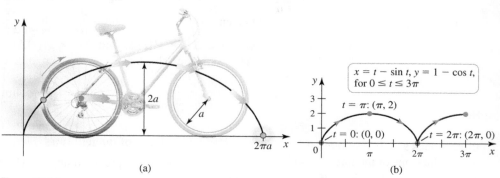

Figure 10.11

(a)

(b)

Related Exercises 49–58 ◄

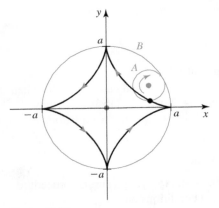

Figure 10.12

EXAMPLE 7 More rolling wheels The path of a point on circle A with radius $a/4$ that rolls on the inside of circle B with radius a (Figure 10.12) is an **astroid** or a **hypocycloid**. Its parametric equations are

$$x = a\cos^3 t, \quad y = a\sin^3 t, \quad \text{for } 0 \le t \le 2\pi.$$

Graph the astroid with $a = 1$ and find its equation in terms of x and y.

SOLUTION Because both $\cos^3 t$ and $\sin^3 t$ have a period of 2π, the complete curve is generated on the interval $0 \le t \le 2\pi$ (Figure 10.13). To eliminate t from the parametric equations, note that $x^{2/3} = \cos^2 t$ and $y^{2/3} = \sin^2 t$. Therefore,

$$x^{2/3} + y^{2/3} = \cos^2 t + \sin^2 t = 1,$$

where the Pythagorean identity has been used. We see that an alternative description of the astroid is $x^{2/3} + y^{2/3} = 1$.

Related Exercises 49–58 ◄

Derivatives and Parametric Equations

Parametric equations express a relationship between the variables x and y. Therefore, it makes sense to ask about dy/dx, the rate of change of y with respect to x at a point on a parametric curve. Once we know how to compute dy/dx, it can be used to determine slopes of lines tangent to parametric curves.

Consider the parametric equations $x = f(t)$, $y = g(t)$ on an interval on which both f and g are differentiable. The Chain Rule relates the derivatives $\dfrac{dy}{dt}$, $\dfrac{dx}{dt}$, and $\dfrac{dy}{dx}$:

$$\frac{dy}{dt} = \frac{dy}{dx}\frac{dx}{dt}.$$

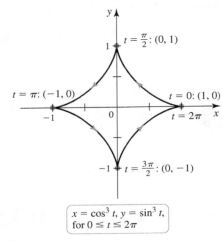

$x = \cos^3 t, \ y = \sin^3 t,$
for $0 \le t \le 2\pi$

Figure 10.13

Provided that $\dfrac{dx}{dt} \ne 0$, we divide both sides of this equation by $\dfrac{dx}{dt}$ and solve for $\dfrac{dy}{dx}$ to obtain the following result.

THEOREM 10.1 Derivative for Parametric Curves
Let $x = f(t)$ and $y = g(t)$, where f and g are differentiable on an interval $[a, b]$. Then the slope of the line tangent to the curve at the point corresponding to t is

$$\frac{dy}{dx} = \frac{dy/dt}{dx/dt} = \frac{g'(t)}{f'(t)},$$

provided $f'(t) \ne 0$.

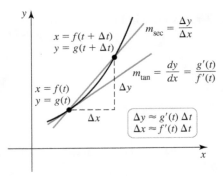

Figure 10.14

QUICK CHECK 5 Use Theorem 10.1 to find the slope of the line $x = 4t$, $y = 2t$, for $-\infty < t < \infty$. ◄

Figure 10.14 gives a geometric explanation of Theorem 10.1. The slope of the line tangent to a curve at a point is $\dfrac{dy}{dx} = \lim\limits_{\Delta x \to 0} \dfrac{\Delta y}{\Delta x}$. Using linear approximation (Section 4.5), we have $\Delta x \approx f'(t)\Delta t$ and $\Delta y \approx g'(t)\Delta t$, with these approximations improving as $\Delta t \to 0$. Notice also that $\Delta t \to 0$ as $\Delta x \to 0$. Therefore, the slope of the tangent line is

$$\frac{dy}{dx} = \lim_{\Delta x \to 0} \frac{\Delta y}{\Delta x} = \lim_{\Delta t \to 0} \frac{g'(t)\Delta t}{f'(t)\Delta t} = \frac{g'(t)}{f'(t)}.$$

EXAMPLE 8 Slopes of tangent lines Find $\dfrac{dy}{dx}$ for the following curves. Interpret the result and determine the points (if any) at which the curve has a horizontal or a vertical tangent line.

a. $x = f(t) = t$, $y = g(t) = 2\sqrt{t}$, for $t \ge 0$

b. $x = f(t) = 4\cos t$, $y = g(t) = 16\sin t$, for $0 \le t \le 2\pi$

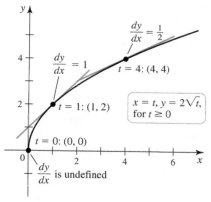

Figure 10.15

> In general, the equations $x = a \cos t$, $y = b \sin t$, for $0 \le t \le 2\pi$, describe an ellipse. The constants a and b can be seen as horizontal and vertical scalings of the unit circle $x = \cos t$, $y = \sin t$. Ellipses are explored in Exercises 75–80 and in Section 10.4.

SOLUTION

a. We find that $f'(t) = 1$ and $g'(t) = 1/\sqrt{t}$. Therefore,

$$\frac{dy}{dx} = \frac{g'(t)}{f'(t)} = \frac{1/\sqrt{t}}{1} = \frac{1}{\sqrt{t}},$$

provided $t \ne 0$. Notice that $dy/dx \ne 0$ for $t > 0$, so the curve has no horizontal tangent lines. On the other hand, as $t \to 0^+$, we see that $dy/dx \to \infty$. Therefore, the curve has a vertical tangent line at the point $(0, 0)$. To eliminate t from the parametric equations, we substitute $t = x$ into the y-equation to find that $y = 2\sqrt{x}$. Because $y \ge 0$, the curve is the upper half of a parabola (Figure 10.15). Slopes of tangent lines at other points on the curve are found by substituting the corresponding values of t. For example, the point $(4, 4)$ corresponds to $t = 4$ and the slope of the tangent line at that point is $1/\sqrt{4} = \frac{1}{2}$.

b. These parametric equations describe an **ellipse** (Exercises 75–76) with a major axis of length 32 on the y-axis and a minor axis of length 8 on the x-axis (Figure 10.16). In this case, $f'(t) = -4 \sin t$ and $g'(t) = 16 \cos t$. Therefore,

$$\frac{dy}{dx} = \frac{g'(t)}{f'(t)} = \frac{16 \cos t}{-4 \sin t} = -4 \cot t.$$

At $t = 0$ and $t = \pi$, $\cot t$ is undefined. Notice that

$$\lim_{t \to 0^+} \frac{dy}{dx} = \lim_{t \to 0^+} (-4 \cot t) = -\infty \quad \text{and} \quad \lim_{t \to 0^-} \frac{dy}{dx} = \lim_{t \to 0^-} (-4 \cot t) = \infty.$$

Consequently, a vertical tangent line occurs at the point corresponding to $t = 0$, which is $(4, 0)$ (Figure 10.16). A similar argument shows that a vertical tangent line occurs at the point corresponding to $t = \pi$, which is $(-4, 0)$.

At $t = \pi/2$ and $t = 3\pi/2$, $\cot t = 0$ and the curve has horizontal tangent lines at the corresponding points $(0, \pm 16)$. Slopes of tangent lines at other points on the curve may be found. For example, the point $(2\sqrt{2}, 8\sqrt{2})$ corresponds to $t = \pi/4$; the slope of the tangent line at that point is $-4 \cot \pi/4 = -4$.

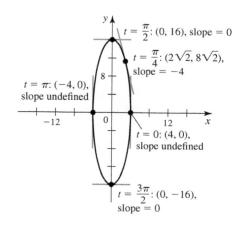

Figure 10.16

Related Exercises 59–64 ◄

SECTION 10.1 EXERCISES

Review Questions

1. Explain how a pair of parametric equations generates a curve in the xy-plane.

2. Give two pairs of parametric equations that generate a circle centered at the origin with radius 6.

3. Give parametric equations that describe a full circle of radius R, centered at the origin with clockwise orientation, where the parameter varies over the interval $[0, 10]$.

4. Give parametric equations that generate the line with slope -2 passing through $(1, 3)$.

5. Find parametric equations for the parabola $y = x^2$.

6. Describe the similarities and differences between the parametric equations $x = t, y = t^2$ and $x = -t, y = t^2$, where $t \geq 0$ in each case.

7. Find a function $y = f(x)$ that describes the parametric curve $x = -2t + 1, y = 3t^2$, for $-\infty < t < \infty$.

8. In which direction is the curve $x = -2 \sin t, y = 2 \cos t$, for $0 < t < 2\pi$, generated?

9. Explain how to find the slope of the line tangent to the curve $x = f(t), y = g(t)$ at the point $(f(a), g(a))$.

10. Explain how to find points on the curve $x = f(t), y = g(t)$ at which there is a horizontal tangent line.

Basic Skills

11–14. Working with parametric equations *Consider the following parametric equations.*

a. *Make a brief table of values of t, x, and y.*
b. *Plot the (x, y) pairs in the table and the complete parametric curve, indicating the positive orientation (the direction of increasing t).*
c. *Eliminate the parameter to obtain an equation in x and y.*
d. *Describe the curve.*

11. $x = 2t, y = 3t - 4; \ -10 \leq t \leq 10$

12. $x = t^2 + 2, y = 4t; \ -4 \leq t \leq 4$

13. $x = -t + 6, y = 3t - 3; \ -5 \leq t \leq 5$

14. $x = t^3 - 1, y = 5t + 1; \ -3 \leq t \leq 3$

15–20. Working with parametric equations *Consider the following parametric equations.*

a. *Eliminate the parameter to obtain an equation in x and y.*
b. *Describe the curve and indicate the positive orientation.*

15. $x = \sqrt{t} + 4, y = 3\sqrt{t}; \ 0 \leq t \leq 16$

16. $x = (t + 1)^2, y = t + 2; \ -10 \leq t \leq 10$

17. $x = \cos t, y = \sin^2 t; \ 0 \leq t \leq \pi$

18. $x = 1 - \sin^2 s, y = \cos s; \ \pi \leq s \leq 2\pi$

19. $x = r - 1, y = r^3; \ -4 \leq r \leq 4$

20. $x = e^{2t}, y = e^t + 1; \ 0 \leq t \leq 25$

21–26. Circles and arcs *Eliminate the parameter to find a description of the following circles or circular arcs in terms of x and y. Give the center and radius, and indicate the positive orientation.*

21. $x = 3 \cos t, y = 3 \sin t; \ \pi \leq t \leq 2\pi$

22. $x = 3 \cos t, y = 3 \sin t; \ 0 \leq t \leq \pi/2$

23. $x = \cos t, y = 1 + \sin t; \ 0 \leq t \leq 2\pi$

24. $x = 2 \sin t - 3, y = 2 \cos t + 5; \ 0 \leq t \leq 2\pi$

25. $x = -7 \cos 2t, y = -7 \sin 2t; \ 0 \leq t \leq \pi$

26. $x = 1 - 3 \sin 4\pi t, y = 2 + 3 \cos 4\pi t; \ 0 \leq t \leq \frac{1}{2}$

27–32. Parametric equations of circles *Find parametric equations for the following circles and give an interval for the parameter values. Graph the circle and find a description in terms of x and y. Answers are not unique.*

27. A circle centered at the origin with radius 4, generated counterclockwise

28. A circle centered at the origin with radius 12, generated clockwise with initial point $(0, 12)$

29. A circle centered at $(2, 3)$ with radius 1, generated counterclockwise

30. A circle centered at $(2, 0)$ with radius 3, generated clockwise

31. A circle centered at $(-2, -3)$ with radius 8, generated clockwise

32. A circle centered at $(2, -4)$ with radius $\frac{3}{2}$, generated counterclockwise with initial point $(\frac{7}{2}, -4)$

33–36. Circular motion *Find parametric equations that describe the circular path of the following objects. For Exercises 33–35, assume (x, y) denotes the position of the object relative to the origin at the center of the circle. Use the units of time specified in the problem. There is more than one way to describe any circle.*

33. A go-cart moves counterclockwise with constant speed around a circular track of radius 400 m, completing a lap in 1.5 min.

34. The tip of the 15-inch second hand of a clock completes one revolution in 60 seconds.

35. A bicyclist rides counterclockwise with constant speed around a circular velodrome track with a radius of 50 m, completing one lap in 24 seconds.

36. A Ferris wheel has a radius of 20 m and completes a revolution in the clockwise direction at constant speed in 3 min. Assume that x and y measure the horizontal and vertical positions of a seat on the Ferris wheel relative to a coordinate system whose origin is at the low point of the wheel. Assume the seat begins moving at the origin.

37–40. Parametric lines *Find the slope of each line and a point on the line. Then graph the line.*

37. $x = 3 + t, y = 1 - t$

38. $x = 4 - 3t, y = -2 + 6t$

39. $x = 8 + 2t, y = 1$

40. $x = 1 + 2t/3, y = -4 - 5t/2$

41–44. Line segments *Find a parametric description of the line segment from the point P to the point Q. Solutions are not unique.*

41. $P(0, 0), Q(2, 8)$

42. $P(1, 3), Q(-2, 6)$

43. $P(-1, -3), Q(6, -16)$

44. $P(8, 2), Q(-2, -3)$

45–48. Curves to parametric equations *Give a set of parametric equations that describes the following curves. Graph the curve and indicate the positive orientation. If not given, specify the interval over which the parameter varies.*

45. The segment of the parabola $y = 2x^2 - 4$, where $-1 \leq x \leq 5$

46. The complete curve $x = y^3 - 3y$

47. The piecewise linear path from $P(-2, 3)$ to $Q(2, -3)$ to $R(3, 5)$, using parameter values $0 \leq t \leq 2$

48. The path consisting of the line segment from $(-4, 4)$ to $(0, 8)$, followed by the segment of the parabola $y = 8 - 2x^2$ from $(0, 8)$ to $(2, 0)$, using parameter values $0 \leq t \leq 3$

T 49–54. More parametric curves *Use a graphing utility to graph the following curves. Be sure to choose an interval for the parameter that generates all features of interest.*

49. Spiral $x = t \cos t, y = t \sin t; \ t \geq 0$

50. Witch of Agnesi $x = 2 \cot t, y = 1 - \cos 2t$

51. Folium of Descartes $x = \dfrac{3t}{1 + t^3}, y = \dfrac{3t^2}{1 + t^3}$

52. Involute of a circle $x = \cos t + t \sin t, y = \sin t - t \cos t$

53. Evolute of an ellipse $x = \dfrac{a^2 - b^2}{a} \cos^3 t, y = \dfrac{a^2 - b^2}{b} \sin^3 t$; $a = 4$ and $b = 3$

54. Cissoid of Diocles $x = 2 \sin 2t, y = \dfrac{2 \sin^3 t}{\cos t}$

T 55–58. Beautiful curves *Consider the family of curves*

$$x = \left(2 + \frac{1}{2} \sin at\right) \cos \left(t + \frac{\sin bt}{c}\right),$$

$$y = \left(2 + \frac{1}{2} \sin at\right) \sin \left(t + \frac{\sin bt}{c}\right).$$

Plot the curve for the given values of a, b, and c with $0 \le t \le 2\pi$. (*Source: Mathematica in Action,* Stan Wagon, Springer, 2010; created by Norton Starr, Amherst College)

55. $a = b = 5, c = 2$

56. $a = 6, b = 12, c = 3$

57. $a = 18, b = 18, c = 7$

58. $a = 7, b = 4, c = 1$

59–64. Derivatives *Consider the following parametric curves.*

a. *Determine dy/dx in terms of t and evaluate it at the given value of t.*

b. *Make a sketch of the curve showing the tangent line at the point corresponding to the given value of t.*

59. $x = 2 + 4t, y = 4 - 8t; t = 2$

60. $x = 3 \sin t, y = 3 \cos t; t = \pi/2$

61. $x = \cos t, y = 8 \sin t; t = \pi/2$

62. $x = 2t, y = t^3; t = -1$

T 63. $x = t + 1/t, y = t - 1/t; t = 1$

64. $x = \sqrt{t}, y = 2t; t = 4$

Further Explorations

65. Explain why or why not Determine whether the following statements are true and give an explanation or counterexample.

a. The equations $x = -\cos t, y = -\sin t$, for $0 \le t \le 2\pi$, generate a circle in the clockwise direction.

b. An object following the parametric curve $x = 2 \cos 2\pi t$, $y = 2 \sin 2\pi t$ circles the origin once every 1 time unit.

c. The parametric equations $x = t, y = t^2$, for $t \ge 0$, describe the complete parabola $y = x^2$.

d. The parametric equations $x = \cos t, y = \sin t$, for $-\pi/2 \le t \le \pi/2$, describe a semicircle.

e. There are two points on the curve $x = -4 \cos t, y = \sin t$, for $0 \le t \le 2\pi$, at which there is a vertical tangent line.

66–69. Tangent lines *Find an equation of the line tangent to the curve at the point corresponding to the given value of t.*

66. $x = \sin t, y = \cos t; t = \pi/4$

67. $x = t^2 - 1, y = t^3 + t; t = 2$

68. $x = e^t, y = \ln(t + 1); t = 0$

69. $x = \cos t + t \sin t, y = \sin t - t \cos t; t = \pi/4$

70–73. Words to curves *Find parametric equations for the following curves. Include an interval for the parameter values. Answers are not unique.*

70. The left half of the parabola $y = x^2 + 1$, originating at $(0, 1)$

71. The line that passes through the points $(1, 1)$ and $(3, 5)$, oriented in the direction of increasing x

72. The lower half of the circle centered at $(-2, 2)$ with radius 6, oriented in the counterclockwise direction

73. The upper half of the parabola $x = y^2$, originating at $(0, 0)$

74. Matching curves and equations Match equations a–d with graphs A–D. Explain your reasoning.

a. $x = t^2 - 2, y = t^3 - t$

b. $x = \cos(t + \sin 50t), y = \sin(t + \cos 50t)$

c. $x = t + \cos 2t, y = t - \sin 4t$

d. $x = 2 \cos t + \cos 20t, y = 2 \sin t + \sin 20t$

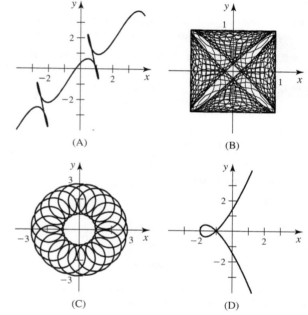

(A)   (B)

(C)   (D)

75–76. Ellipses *An ellipse (discussed in detail in Section 10.4) is generated by the parametric equations $x = a \cos t, y = b \sin t$. If $0 < a < b$, then the long axis (or **major axis**) lies on the y-axis and the short axis (or **minor axis**) lies on the x-axis. If $0 < b < a$, the axes are reversed. The lengths of the axes in the x- and y-directions are 2a and 2b, respectively. Sketch the graph of the following ellipses. Specify an interval in t over which the entire curve is generated.*

75. $x = 4 \cos t, y = 9 \sin t$

76. $x = 12 \sin 2t, y = 3 \cos 2t$

77–80. Parametric equations of ellipses *Find parametric equations (not unique) of the following ellipses (see Exercises 75–76). Graph the ellipse and find a description in terms of x and y.*

77. An ellipse centered at the origin with major axis of length 6 on the x-axis and minor axis of length 3 on the y-axis, generated counterclockwise

78. An ellipse centered at the origin with major and minor axes of lengths 12 and 2, on the x- and y-axes, respectively, generated clockwise

79. An ellipse centered at $(-2, -3)$ with major and minor axes of lengths 30 and 20, parallel to the x- and y-axes, respectively, generated counterclockwise (*Hint:* Shift the parametric equations.)

80. An ellipse centered at $(0, -4)$ with major and minor axes of lengths 10 and 3, parallel to the *x*- and *y*-axes, respectively, generated clockwise (*Hint:* Shift the parametric equations.)

81. Intersecting lines Consider the following pairs of lines. Determine whether the lines are parallel or intersecting. If the lines intersect, then determine the point of intersection.

a. $x = 1 + s, y = 2s$ and $x = 1 + 2t, y = 3t$
b. $x = 2 + 5s, y = 1 + s$ and $x = 4 + 10t, y = 3 + 2t$
c. $x = 1 + 3s, y = 4 + 2s$ and $x = 4 - 3t, y = 6 + 4t$

82. Multiple descriptions Which of the following parametric equations describe the same curve?

a. $x = 2t^2, y = 4 + t; \ -4 \le t \le 4$
b. $x = 2t^4, y = 4 + t^2; \ -2 \le t \le 2$
c. $x = 2t^{2/3}, y = 4 + t^{1/3}; \ -64 \le t \le 64$

83–87. Eliminating the parameter *Eliminate the parameter to express the following parametric equations as a single equation in x and y.*

83. $x = 2 \sin 8t, y = 2 \cos 8t$ **84.** $x = \sin 8t, y = 2 \cos 8t$

85. $x = t, y = \sqrt{4 - t^2}$ **86.** $x = \sqrt{t + 1}, y = \dfrac{1}{t + 1}$

87. $x = \tan t, y = \sec^2 t - 1$

88. $x = a \sin^n t, y = b \cos^n t$, where *a* and *b* are real numbers and *n* is a positive integer

89–92. Slopes of tangent lines *Find all the points at which the following curves have the given slope.*

89. $x = 4 \cos t, y = 4 \sin t$; slope $= \frac{1}{2}$

90. $x = 2 \cos t, y = 8 \sin t$; slope $= -1$

91. $x = t + 1/t, y = t - 1/t$; slope $= 1$

92. $x = 2 + \sqrt{t}, y = 2 - 4t$; slope $= -8$

93–94. Equivalent descriptions *Find real numbers a and b such that equations A and B describe the same curve.*

93. A: $x = 10 \sin t, y = 10 \cos t; \ 0 \le t \le 2\pi$
     B: $x = 10 \sin 3t, y = 10 \cos 3t; \ a \le t \le b$

94. A: $x = t + t^3, y = 3 + t^2; \ -2 \le t \le 2$
     B: $x = t^{1/3} + t, y = 3 + t^{2/3}; \ a \le t \le b$

T 95–96. Lissajous curves *Consider the following Lissajous curves. Graph the curve and estimate the coordinates of the points on the curve at which there is (a) a horizontal tangent line and (b) a vertical tangent line. (See the Guided Project Parametric art for more on Lissajous curves.)*

95. $x = \sin 2t, y = 2 \sin t;$
$0 \le t \le 2\pi$

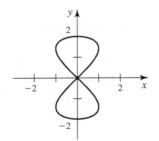

96. $x = \sin 4t, y = \sin 3t;$
$0 \le t \le 2\pi$

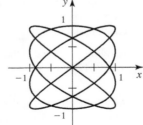

T 97. Lamé curves The *Lamé curve* described by $\left|\dfrac{x}{a}\right|^n + \left|\dfrac{y}{b}\right|^n = 1$, where *a*, *b*, and *n* are positive real numbers, is a generalization of an ellipse.

a. Express this equation in parametric form (four pairs of equations are needed).
b. Graph the curve for $a = 4$ and $b = 2$, for various values of *n*.
c. Describe how the curves change as *n* increases.

T 98. Hyperbolas A family of curves called *hyperbolas* (discussed in Section 10.4) has the parametric equations $x = a \tan t$, $y = b \sec t$, for $-\pi < t < \pi$ and $|t| \ne \pi/2$, where *a* and *b* are nonzero real numbers. Graph the hyperbola with $a = b = 1$. Indicate clearly the direction in which the curve is generated as *t* increases from $t = -\pi$ to $t = \pi$.

T 99. Trochoid explorations A *trochoid* is the path followed by a point *b* units from the center of a wheel of radius *a* as the wheel rolls along the *x*-axis. Its parametric description is $x = at - b \sin t, y = a - b \cos t$. Choose specific values of *a* and *b*, and use a graphing utility to plot different trochoids. In particular, explore the difference between the cases $a > b$ and $a < b$.

T 100. Epitrochoid An *epitrochoid* is the path of a point on a circle of radius *b* as it rolls on the outside of a circle of radius *a*. It is described by the equations

$$x = (a + b) \cos t - c \cos\left(\frac{(a + b)t}{b}\right)$$

$$y = (a + b) \sin t - c \sin\left(\frac{(a + b)t}{b}\right).$$

Use a graphing utility to explore the dependence of the curve on the parameters *a*, *b*, and *c*.

T 101. Hypocycloid A general *hypocycloid* is described by the equations

$$x = (a - b) \cos t + b \cos\left(\frac{(a - b)t}{b}\right)$$

$$y = (a - b) \sin t - b \sin\left(\frac{(a - b)t}{b}\right).$$

Use a graphing utility to explore the dependence of the curve on the parameters *a* and *b*.

Applications

T 102. Paths of moons An idealized model of the path of a moon (relative to the Sun) moving with constant speed in a circular orbit around a planet, where the planet in turn revolves around the Sun, is given by the parametric equations

$$x(\theta) = a \cos \theta + \cos n\theta, y(\theta) = a \sin \theta + \sin n\theta.$$

The distance from the moon to the planet is taken to be 1, the distance from the planet to the Sun is *a*, and *n* is the number of times the moon orbits the planet for every 1 revolution of the planet around the Sun. Plot the graph of the path of a moon for the given constants; then conjecture which values of *n* produce loops for a fixed value of *a*.

a. $a = 4, n = 3$ **b.** $a = 4, n = 4$ **c.** $a = 4, n = 5$

T 103. Paths of the moons of Earth and Jupiter Use the equations in Exercise 102 to plot the paths of the following moons in our solar system.

　a. Each year our moon revolves around Earth about $n = 13.4$ times, and the distance from the Sun to Earth is approximately $a = 389.2$ times the distance from Earth to our moon.

　b. Plot a graph of the path of Callisto (one of Jupiter's moons) that corresponds to values of $a = 727.5$ and $n = 259.6$. Plot a small portion of the graph to see the detailed behavior of the orbit.

　c. Plot a graph of the path of Io (another of Jupiter's moons) that corresponds to values of $a = 1846.2$ and $n = 2448.8$. Plot a small portion of the path of Io to see the loops in its orbit. (*Source* for Exercises 102–103: *The Sun, the Moon, and Convexity, The College Mathematics Journal*, 32, Sep 2001)

104. Air drop A plane traveling horizontally at 80 m/s over flat ground at an elevation of 3000 m releases an emergency packet. The trajectory of the packet is given by

$$x = 80t, \quad y = -4.9t^2 + 3000, \quad \text{for } t \geq 0,$$

where the origin is the point on the ground directly beneath the plane at the moment of the release. Graph the trajectory of the packet and find the coordinates of the point where the packet lands.

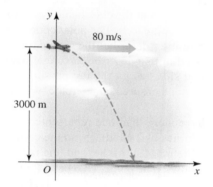

105. Air drop—inverse problem A plane traveling horizontally at 100 m/s over flat ground at an elevation of 4000 m must drop an emergency packet on a target on the ground. The trajectory of the packet is given by

$$x = 100t, \quad y = -4.9t^2 + 4000, \quad \text{for } t \geq 0,$$

where the origin is the point on the ground directly beneath the plane at the moment of the release. How many horizontal meters before the target should the packet be released in order to hit the target?

106. Projectile explorations A projectile launched from the ground with an initial speed of 20 m/s and a launch angle θ follows a trajectory approximated by

$$x = (20 \cos \theta)t, \quad y = -4.9t^2 + (20 \sin \theta)t,$$

where x and y are the horizontal and vertical positions of the projectile relative to the launch point $(0, 0)$.

　a. Graph the trajectory for various values of θ in the range $0 < \theta < \pi/2$.

　b. Based on your observations, what value of θ gives the greatest range (the horizontal distance between the launch and landing points)?

Additional Exercises

T 107. Implicit function graph Explain and carry out a method for graphing the curve $x = 1 + \cos^2 y - \sin^2 y$ using parametric equations and a graphing utility.

108. Second derivative Assume a curve is given by the parametric equations $x = f(t)$ and $y = g(t)$, where f and g are twice differentiable. Use the Chain Rule to show that

$$y''(x) = \frac{f'(t)g''(t) - g'(t)f''(t)}{(f'(t))^3}.$$

109. General equations for a circle Prove that the equations

$$x = a \cos t + b \sin t, \quad y = c \cos t + d \sin t,$$

where a, b, c, and d are real numbers, describe a circle of radius R provided $a^2 + c^2 = b^2 + d^2 = R^2$ and $ab + cd = 0$.

110. x^y versus y^x Consider positive real numbers x and y. Notice that $4^3 < 3^4$, while $3^2 > 2^3$, and $4^2 = 2^4$. Describe the regions in the first quadrant of the xy-plane in which $x^y > y^x$ and $x^y < y^x$. (*Hint:* Find a parametric description of the curve that separates the two regions.)

QUICK CHECK ANSWERS

1. A segment of the parabola $x = y^2$ opening to the right with vertex at the origin　**2.** The circle has center $(0, 0)$ and radius 3; it is generated in the counterclockwise direction (positive orientation) starting at $(0, -3)$.　**3.** The line $y = -3x - 3$ with slope -3 passing through $(3, -12)$ (when $t = 0$)　**4.** One possibility is $x = -2t, y = 3 - 3t$, for $0 \leq t \leq 1$.　**5.** $\frac{1}{2}$ ◄

10.2 Polar Coordinates

> Recall that the terms *Cartesian* coordinate system and *rectangular* coordinate system both describe the usual *xy*-coordinate system.

Suppose you work for a company that designs heat shields for space vehicles. The shields are thin plates that are either rectangular or circular in shape. To solve the heat transfer equations for these two shields, you must choose a coordinate system that best fits the geometry of the problem. A Cartesian (rectangular) coordinate system is a natural choice for the rectangular shields (Figure 10.17a). However, it does not provide a good fit for the circular shields (Figure 10.17b). On the other hand, a **polar coordinate** system, in which the coordinates are constant on circles and rays, is better suited for the circular shields (Figure 10.17c).

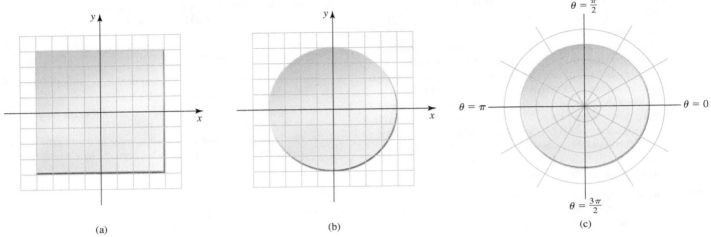

Figure 10.17

➤ Polar points and curves are plotted on a rectangular coordinate system, with standard "x" and "y" labels attached to the axes. However, plotting polar points and curves is often easier using polar graph paper, which has concentric circles centered at the origin and rays emanating from the origin (Figure 10.17c).

QUICK CHECK 1 Which of the following coordinates represent the same point: $(3, \pi/2)$, $(3, 3\pi/2)$, $(3, 5\pi/2)$, $(-3, -\pi/2)$, and $(-3, 3\pi/2)$? ◄

Defining Polar Coordinates

Like Cartesian coordinates, polar coordinates are used to locate points in the plane. When working in polar coordinates, the origin of the coordinate system is also called the **pole**, and the positive x-axis is called the **polar axis**. The polar coordinates for a point P have the form (r, θ). **The radial coordinate** r describes the *signed* (or *directed*) distance from the origin to P. The **angular coordinate** θ describes an angle whose initial side is the positive x-axis and whose terminal side lies on the ray passing through the origin and P (Figure 10.18a). Positive angles are measured counterclockwise from the positive x-axis.

With polar coordinates, points have more than one representation for two reasons. First, angles are determined up to multiples of 2π radians, so the coordinates (r, θ) and $(r, \theta \pm 2\pi)$ refer to the same point (Figure 10.18b). Second, the radial coordinate may be negative, which is interpreted as follows: The points (r, θ) and $(-r, \theta)$ are reflections of each other through the origin (Figure 10.18c). This means that (r, θ), $(-r, \theta + \pi)$, and $(-r, \theta - \pi)$ all refer to the same point. The origin is specified as $(0, \theta)$ in polar coordinates, where θ is any angle.

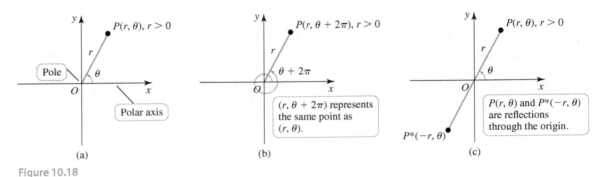

Figure 10.18

EXAMPLE 1   Points in polar coordinates Graph the following points in polar coordinates: $Q\left(1, \frac{5\pi}{4}\right)$, $R\left(-1, \frac{7\pi}{4}\right)$, and $S\left(2, -\frac{3\pi}{2}\right)$. Give two alternative representations for each point.

SOLUTION The point $Q\left(1, \frac{5\pi}{4}\right)$ is one unit from the origin O on a line OQ that makes an angle of $\frac{5\pi}{4}$ with the positive x-axis (Figure 10.19a). Subtracting 2π from the angle, the point Q can be represented as $\left(1, -\frac{3\pi}{4}\right)$. Subtracting π from the angle and negating the radial coordinate implies Q also has the coordinates $\left(-1, \frac{\pi}{4}\right)$.

To locate the point $R\left(-1, \frac{7\pi}{4}\right)$, it is easiest first to find the point $R^*\left(1, \frac{7\pi}{4}\right)$ in the fourth quadrant. Then $R\left(-1, \frac{7\pi}{4}\right)$ is the reflection of R^* through the origin (Figure 10.19b). Other representations of R include $\left(-1, -\frac{\pi}{4}\right)$ and $\left(1, \frac{3\pi}{4}\right)$.

The point $S\left(2, -\frac{3\pi}{2}\right)$ is two units from the origin, found by rotating *clockwise* through an angle of $\frac{3\pi}{2}$ (Figure 10.19c). The point S can also be represented as $\left(2, \frac{\pi}{2}\right)$ or $\left(-2, -\frac{\pi}{2}\right)$.

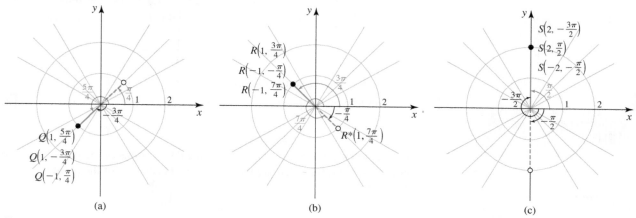

(a)   (b)   (c)

Figure 10.19

Related Exercises 9–14 ◀

Converting Between Cartesian and Polar Coordinates

We often need to convert between Cartesian and polar coordinates. The conversion equations emerge when we look at a right triangle (Figure 10.20) in which

$$\cos \theta = \frac{x}{r} \quad \text{and} \quad \sin \theta = \frac{y}{r}.$$

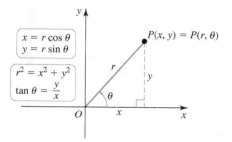

Figure 10.20

Given a point with polar coordinates (r, θ), we see that its Cartesian coordinates are $x = r \cos \theta$ and $y = r \sin \theta$. Conversely, given a point with Cartesian coordinates (x, y), its radial polar coordinate satisfies $r^2 = x^2 + y^2$. The coordinate θ is determined using the relation $\tan \theta = y/x$, where the quadrant in which θ lies is determined by the signs of x and y. Figure 10.20 illustrates the conversion formulas for a point P in the first quadrant. The same relationships hold if P is in any of the other three quadrants.

QUICK CHECK 2 Draw versions of Figure 10.20 with P in the second, third, and fourth quadrants. Verify that the same conversion formulas hold in all cases.◀

➤ To determine θ, you may also use the relationships $\cos \theta = x/r$ and $\sin \theta = y/r$. Either method requires checking the signs of x and y to verify that θ is in the correct quadrant.

PROCEDURE   Converting Coordinates

A point with polar coordinates (r, θ) has Cartesian coordinates (x, y), where

$$x = r \cos \theta \quad \text{and} \quad y = r \sin \theta.$$

A point with Cartesian coordinates (x, y) has polar coordinates (r, θ), where

$$r^2 = x^2 + y^2 \quad \text{and} \quad \tan \theta = \frac{y}{x}.$$

EXAMPLE 2   Converting coordinates

a. Express the point with polar coordinates $P\left(2, \frac{3\pi}{4}\right)$ in Cartesian coordinates.

b. Express the point with Cartesian coordinates $Q(1, -1)$ in polar coordinates.

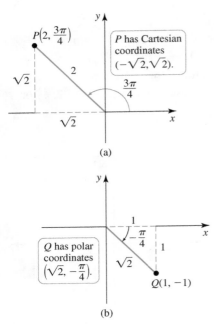

(a)

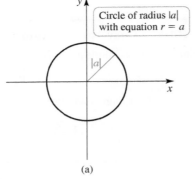

(b)

Figure 10.21

SOLUTION

a. The point $P(2, \frac{3\pi}{4})$ has Cartesian coordinates

$$x = r \cos \theta = 2 \cos \tfrac{3\pi}{4} = -\sqrt{2} \quad \text{and}$$
$$y = r \sin \theta = 2 \sin \tfrac{3\pi}{4} = \sqrt{2}.$$

As shown in Figure 10.21a, P is in the second quadrant.

b. It's best to locate this point first to be sure that the angle θ is chosen correctly. As shown in Figure 10.21b, the point $Q(1, -1)$ is in the fourth quadrant at a distance $r = \sqrt{1^2 + (-1)^2} = \sqrt{2}$ from the origin. The coordinate θ satisfies

$$\tan \theta = \frac{y}{x} = \frac{-1}{1} = -1.$$

The angle in the fourth quadrant with $\tan \theta = -1$ is $\theta = -\frac{\pi}{4}$ or $\frac{7\pi}{4}$. Therefore, two (of infinitely many) polar representations of Q are $\left(\sqrt{2}, -\frac{\pi}{4}\right)$ and $\left(\sqrt{2}, \frac{7\pi}{4}\right)$.

Related Exercises 15–26 ◀

QUICK CHECK 3 Give two polar coordinate descriptions of the point with Cartesian coordinates $(1, 0)$. What are the Cartesian coordinates of the point with polar coordinates $\left(2, \frac{\pi}{2}\right)$? ◀

Basic Curves in Polar Coordinates

A curve in polar coordinates is the set of points that satisfy an equation in r and θ. Some sets of points are easier to describe in polar coordinates than in Cartesian coordinates. Let's begin by examining polar equations of circles, lines and spirals.

The polar equation $r = 3$ is satisfied by the set of points whose distance from the origin is 3. The angle θ is arbitrary because it is not specified by the equation, so the graph of $r = 3$ is the circle of radius 3 centered at the origin. In general, the equation $r = a$ describes a circle of radius $|a|$ centered at the origin (Figure 10.22a).

The equation $\theta = \pi/3$ is satisfied by the points whose angle with respect to the positive x-axis is $\pi/3$. Because r is unspecified, it is arbitrary (and can be positive or negative). Therefore, $\theta = \pi/3$ describes the line through the origin making an angle of $\pi/3$ with the positive x-axis. More generally, $\theta = \theta_0$ describes the line through the origin making an angle of θ_0 with the positive x-axis (Figure 10.22b).

➤ If the equation $\theta = \theta_0$ is accompanied by the condition $r \geq 0$, the resulting set of points is a *ray* emanating from the origin.

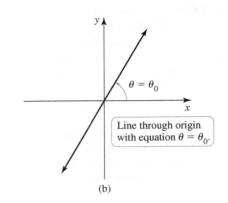

(a)   (b)

Figure 10.22

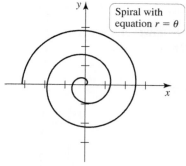

Figure 10.23

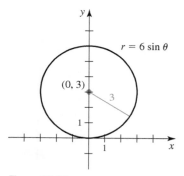

Figure 10.24

The simplest polar equation that involves both r and θ is $r = \theta$. Restricting θ to the interval $\theta \geq 0$, we see that as θ increases, r increases. Therefore, as θ increases, the points on the curve move away from the origin as they circle the origin in a counterclockwise direction, generating a spiral (Figure 10.23).

QUICK CHECK 4 Describe the polar curves $r = 12$, $r = 6\theta$, and $r \sin \theta = 10$. ◄

EXAMPLE 3 **Polar to Cartesian coordinates** Convert the polar equation $r = 6 \sin \theta$ to Cartesian coordinates and describe the corresponding graph.

SOLUTION Multiplying both sides of the equation by r produces the equation $r^2 = 6r \sin \theta$. Using the conversion relations $r^2 = x^2 + y^2$ and $y = r \sin \theta$, the equation

$$\underbrace{r^2}_{x^2 + y^2} = \underbrace{6r \sin \theta}_{6y}$$

becomes $x^2 + y^2 - 6y = 0$. Completing the square gives the equation

$$x^2 + \underbrace{y^2 - 6y + 9}_{(y - 3)^2} - 9 = x^2 + (y - 3)^2 - 9 = 0.$$

We recognize $x^2 + (y - 3)^2 = 9$ as the equation of a circle of radius 3 centered at $(0, 3)$ (Figure 10.24).

Related Exercises 27–36 ◄

Calculations similar to those in Example 3 lead to the following equations of circles in polar coordinates.

SUMMARY **Circles in Polar Coordinates**

The equation $r = a$ describes a circle of radius $|a|$ centered at $(0, 0)$.

The equation $r = 2a \sin \theta$ describes a circle of radius $|a|$ centered at $(0, a)$.

The equation $r = 2a \cos \theta$ describes a circle of radius $|a|$ centered at $(a, 0)$.

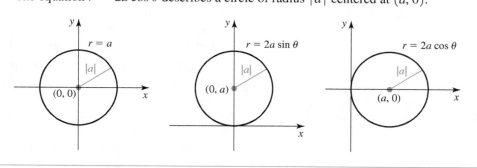

Graphing in Polar Coordinates

Equations in polar coordinates often describe curves that are difficult to represent in Cartesian coordinates. Partly for this reason, curve-sketching methods for polar coordinates differ from those used for curves in Cartesian coordinates. Conceptually, the easiest graphing method is to choose several values of θ, calculate the corresponding r-values, and tabulate the coordinates. The points are then plotted and connected with a smooth curve.

> When a curve is described as $r = f(\theta)$, it is natural to tabulate points in θ-r format, just as we list points in x-y format for $y = f(x)$. Despite this fact, the standard form for writing an ordered pair in polar coordinates is (r, θ).

Table 10.3

θ	$r = 1 + \sin \theta$
0	1
$\pi/6$	$3/2$
$\pi/2$	2
$5\pi/6$	$3/2$
π	1
$7\pi/6$	$1/2$
$3\pi/2$	0
$11\pi/6$	$1/2$
2π	1

EXAMPLE 4   Plotting a polar curve Graph the polar equation $r = f(\theta) = 1 + \sin \theta$.

SOLUTION The domain of f consists of all real values of θ; however, the complete curve is generated by letting θ vary over any interval of length 2π. Table 10.3 shows several (r, θ) pairs, which are plotted in Figure 10.25. The resulting curve, called a **cardioid**, is symmetric about the y-axis.

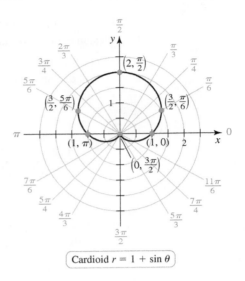

Cardioid $r = 1 + \sin \theta$

Figure 10.25

Related Exercises 37–48 ◄

Cartesian-to-Polar Method Plotting polar curves point by point is time-consuming, and important details may not be revealed. Here is an alternative procedure for graphing polar curves that is usually quicker and more reliable.

PROCEDURE   Cartesian-to-Polar Method for Graphing $r = f(\theta)$

1. Graph $r = f(\theta)$ *as if r and θ were Cartesian coordinates* with θ on the horizontal axis and r on the vertical axis. Be sure to choose an interval for θ on which the entire polar curve is produced.

2. Use the Cartesian graph in Step 1 as a guide to sketch the points (r, θ) on the final *polar* curve.

EXAMPLE 5   Plotting polar graphs Use the Cartesian-to-polar method to graph the polar equation $r = 1 + \sin \theta$ (Example 4).

SOLUTION Viewing r and θ as Cartesian coordinates, the graph of $r = 1 + \sin \theta$ on the interval $[0, 2\pi]$ is a standard sine curve with amplitude 1 shifted up 1 unit (Figure 10.26). Notice that the graph begins with $r = 1$ at $\theta = 0$, increases to $r = 2$ at $\theta = \pi/2$, decreases to $r = 0$ at $\theta = 3\pi/2$ (which indicates an intersection with the origin on the polar graph), and increases to $r = 1$ at $\theta = 2\pi$. The second row of Figure 10.26 shows the final polar curve (a cardioid) as it is transferred from the Cartesian curve.

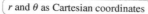

r and θ as Cartesian coordinates

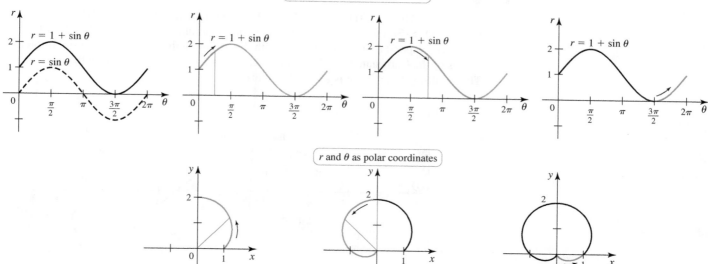

Figure 10.26

Related Exercises 37–48 ◄

Symmetry Given a polar equation in r and θ, three types of symmetry are easy to spot (Figure 10.27).

> ► Any two of these three symmetries implies the third. For example, if a graph is symmetric about both the x- and y-axes, then it is symmetric about the origin.

SUMMARY **Symmetry in Polar Equations**

Symmetry about the x-axis occurs if the point (r, θ) is on the graph whenever $(r, -\theta)$ is on the graph.

Symmetry about the y-axis occurs if the point (r, θ) is on the graph whenever $(r, \pi - \theta) = (-r, -\theta)$ is on the graph.

Symmetry about the origin occurs if the point (r, θ) is on the graph whenever $(-r, \theta) = (r, \theta + \pi)$ is on the graph.

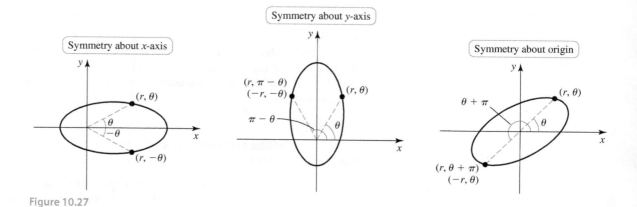

Figure 10.27

QUICK CHECK 5 Identify the symmetry in the graph of (a) $r = 4 + 4\cos\theta$ and (b) $r = 4\sin\theta$. ◄

For instance, consider the polar equation $r = 1 + \sin\theta$ in Example 5. If (r, θ) satisfies the equation, then $(r, \pi - \theta)$ also satisfies the equation because $\sin\theta = \sin(\pi - \theta)$. Therefore, the graph is symmetric about the y-axis, as shown in Figure 10.27. Testing for symmetry produces a more accurate graph and often simplifies the task of graphing polar equations.

EXAMPLE 6 Plotting polar graphs Graph the polar equation $r = 3 \sin 2\theta$.

SOLUTION The Cartesian graph of $r = 3 \sin 2\theta$ on the interval $[0, 2\pi]$ has amplitude 3 and period π (Figure 10.28a). The θ-intercepts occur at $\theta = 0, \pi/2, \pi, 3\pi/2$, and 2π, which correspond to the intersections with the origin on the polar graph. Furthermore, the arches of the Cartesian curve between θ-intercepts correspond to loops in the polar curve. The resulting polar curve is a **four-leaf rose** (Figure 10.28b).

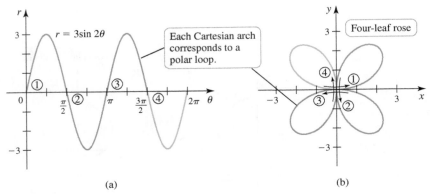

(a)   (b)

Figure 10.28

The graph is symmetric about the x-axis, the y-axis, and the origin. It is instructive to see how these symmetries are justified. To prove symmetry about the y-axis, notice that

$$(r, \theta) \text{ on the graph} \Rightarrow r = 3 \sin 2\theta$$
$$\Rightarrow r = -3 \sin 2(-\theta) \qquad \sin(-\theta) = -\sin\theta$$
$$\Rightarrow -r = 3 \sin 2(-\theta) \qquad \text{Simplify.}$$
$$\Rightarrow (-r, -\theta) \text{ on the graph.}$$

We see that if (r, θ) is on the graph, then $(-r, -\theta)$ is also on the graph, which implies symmetry about the y-axis. Similarly, to prove symmetry about the origin, notice that

$$(r, \theta) \text{ on the graph} \Rightarrow r = 3 \sin 2\theta$$
$$\Rightarrow r = 3 \sin(2\theta + 2\pi) \qquad \sin(\theta + 2\pi) = \sin\theta$$
$$\Rightarrow r = 3 \sin(2(\theta + \pi)) \qquad \text{Simplify.}$$
$$\Rightarrow (r, \theta + \pi) \text{ on the graph.}$$

We have shown that if (r, θ) is on the graph, then $(r, \theta + \pi)$ is also on the graph, which implies symmetry about the origin. Symmetry about the y-axis and the origin imply symmetry about the x-axis. Had we proved these symmetries in advance, we could have graphed the curve only in the first quadrant—reflections about the x- and y-axes would produce the full curve.

Related Exercises 37–48 ◄

> **Subtle Point**
>
> The fact that one point has infinitely many representations in polar coordinates presents potential pitfalls. In Example 6, you can show that $(-r, \theta)$ does *not* satisfy the equation $r = 3 \sin 2\theta$ when (r, θ) satisfies the equation. And yet, as shown, the graph is symmetric about the origin because $(r, \theta + \pi)$ satisfies the equation whenever (r, θ) satisfies the equation. Note that $(-r, \theta)$ and $(r, \theta + \pi)$ are the same point.

EXAMPLE 7 Plotting polar graphs Graph the polar equation $r^2 = 9 \cos \theta$. Use a graphing utility to check your work.

SOLUTION The graph of this equation has symmetry about the origin (because of the r^2) and about the x-axis (because of $\cos \theta$). These two symmetries imply symmetry about the y-axis.

A preliminary step is required before using the Cartesian-to-polar method for graphing the curve. Solving the given equation for r, we find that $r = \pm 3\sqrt{\cos \theta}$. Notice that $\cos \theta < 0$, for $\pi/2 < \theta < 3\pi/2$, so the curve does not exist on that interval. Therefore, we plot the curve on the intervals $0 \le \theta \le \pi/2$ and $3\pi/2 \le \theta \le 2\pi$ (the interval $[-\frac{\pi}{2}, \frac{\pi}{2}]$ would also work). Both the positive and negative values of r are included in the Cartesian graph (Figure 10.29a).

Now we are ready to transfer points from the Cartesian graph to the final polar graph (Figure 10.29b). The resulting curve is called a **lemniscate**.

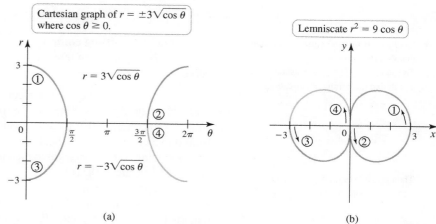

Cartesian graph of $r = \pm 3\sqrt{\cos\theta}$ where $\cos\theta \geq 0$.

$r = 3\sqrt{\cos\theta}$

$r = -3\sqrt{\cos\theta}$

(a)

Lemniscate $r^2 = 9\cos\theta$

(b)

Figure 10.29

Related Exercises 37–48 ◄

EXAMPLE 8 Matching polar and Cartesian graphs The butterfly curve is described by the equation

$$r = e^{\sin\theta} - 2\cos 4\theta, \quad \text{for } 0 \leq \theta \leq 2\pi,$$

which is plotted in Cartesian and polar coordinates in Figure 10.30. Follow the Cartesian graph through the points $A, B, C, \ldots, N, O$ and mark the corresponding points on the polar curve

> ➤ See Exercise 107 for a spectacular enhancement of the butterfly curve.

SOLUTION Point A in Figure 10.30a has the Cartesian coordinates $(\theta = 0, r = -1)$. The corresponding point in the polar plot (Figure 10.30b) with polar coordinates $(-1, 0)$ is marked A. Point B in the Cartesian plot is on the θ-axis; therefore, $r = 0$. The corresponding point in the polar plot is the origin. The same argument used to locate B applies to $F, H, J, L,$ and N, all of which appear at the origin in the polar plot. In general, the local and endpoint maxima and minima in the Cartesian graph ($A, C, D, E, G, I, K, M,$ and O) correspond to the extreme points of the loops of the polar plot and are marked accordingly in Figure 10.30b.

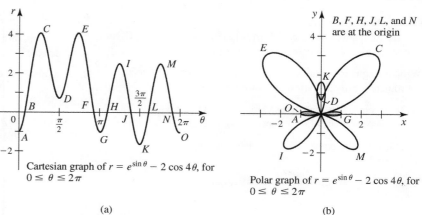

Cartesian graph of $r = e^{\sin\theta} - 2\cos 4\theta$, for $0 \leq \theta \leq 2\pi$

(a)

$B, F, H, J, L,$ and N are at the origin

Polar graph of $r = e^{\sin\theta} - 2\cos 4\theta$, for $0 \leq \theta \leq 2\pi$

(b)

Figure 10.30

(*Source:* T. H. Fay, *Amer. Math. Monthly* 96, 1989, revived in Wagon and Packel, *Animating Calculus*, Freeman, 1994)

Related Exercises 49–52 ◄

Using Graphing Utilities

When graphing polar curves that eventually close on themselves, it is necessary to specify an interval in θ that generates the entire curve. In some cases, this problem is a challenge in itself.

EXAMPLE 9   Plotting complete curves Consider the closed curve described by $r = \cos(2\theta/5)$. Give an interval in θ that generates the entire curve and then graph the curve.

SOLUTION Recall that $\cos\theta$ has a period of 2π. Therefore, $\cos(2\theta/5)$ completes one cycle when $2\theta/5$ varies from 0 to 2π, or when θ varies from 0 to 5π. Therefore, it is tempting to conclude that the complete curve $r = \cos(2\theta/5)$ is generated as θ varies from 0 to 5π. But you can check that the point corresponding to $\theta = 0$ is *not* the point corresponding to $\theta = 5\pi$, which means the curve does not close on itself over the interval $[0, 5\pi]$ (Figure 10.31a).

To graph the *complete* curve $r = \cos(2\theta/5)$, we must find an interval $[0, P]$, where P is an integer multiple of 5π (so that $f(0) = f(P)$) and an integer multiple of 2π (so that the points $(0, f(0))$ and $(P, f(P)$ are the same). The smallest number satisfying these conditions is 10π. Graphing $r = \cos(2\theta/5)$ over the interval $[0, 10\pi]$ produces the complete curve (Figure 10.31b).

> ▶ **Using a parametric equation plotter to graph polar curves**
> To graph $r = f(\theta)$, treat θ as a parameter and define the parametric equations
> $$x = r\cos\theta = \underbrace{f(\theta)}_{r}\cos\theta$$
> $$y = r\sin\theta = \underbrace{f(\theta)}_{r}\sin\theta$$
> Then graph $(x(\theta), y(\theta))$ as a parametric curve with θ as the parameter.

> ▶ The prescription given in Example 9 for finding P when working with functions of the form $f(\theta) = \sin\dfrac{p\theta}{q}$ or $f(\theta) = \cos\dfrac{p\theta}{q}$ ensures that the complete curve is generated. Smaller values of P work in some cases.

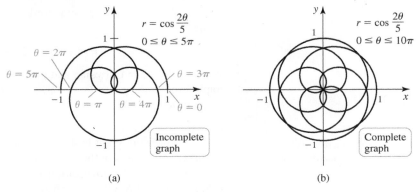

Figure 10.31

Related Exercises 53–60 ◀

SECTION 10.2 EXERCISES

Review Questions

1. Plot the points with polar coordinates $(2, \frac{\pi}{6})$ and $(-3, -\frac{\pi}{2})$. Give two alternative sets of coordinate pairs for both points.

2. Write the equations that are used to express a point with polar coordinates (r, θ) in Cartesian coordinates.

3. Write the equations that are used to express a point with Cartesian coordinates (x, y) in polar coordinates.

4. What is the polar equation of a circle of radius $|a|$ centered at the origin?

5. What is the polar equation of the vertical line $x = 5$?

6. What is the polar equation of the horizontal line $y = 5$?

7. Explain three symmetries in polar graphs and how they are detected in equations.

8. Explain the Cartesian-to-polar method for graphing polar curves.

Basic Skills

9–13. *Graph the points with the following polar coordinates. Give two alternative representations of the points in polar coordinates.*

9. $(2, \frac{\pi}{4})$

10. $(3, \frac{2\pi}{3})$

11. $(-1, -\frac{\pi}{3})$

12. $(2, \frac{7\pi}{4})$

13. $(-4, \frac{3\pi}{2})$

14. Points in polar coordinates *Give two sets of polar coordinates for each of the points A–F in the figure.*

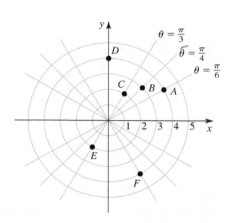

15–20. Converting coordinates *Express the following polar coordinates in Cartesian coordinates.*

15. $(3, \frac{\pi}{4})$ **16.** $(1, \frac{2\pi}{3})$ **17.** $(1, -\frac{\pi}{3})$

18. $(2, \frac{7\pi}{4})$ **19.** $(-4, \frac{3\pi}{4})$ **20.** $(4, 5\pi)$

21–26. Converting coordinates *Express the following Cartesian coordinates in polar coordinates in at least two different ways.*

21. $(2, 2)$ **22.** $(-1, 0)$

23. $(1, \sqrt{3})$ **24.** $(-9, 0)$

25. $(-4, 4\sqrt{3})$ **26.** $(4, 4\sqrt{3})$

27–36. Polar-to-Cartesian coordinates *Convert the following equations to Cartesian coordinates. Describe the resulting curve.*

27. $r \cos \theta = -4$ **28.** $r = \cot \theta \csc \theta$

29. $r = 2$ **30.** $r = 3 \csc \theta$

31. $r = 2 \sin \theta + 2 \cos \theta$ **32.** $\sin \theta = |\cos \theta|$

33. $r \cos \theta = \sin 2\theta$ **34.** $r = \sin \theta \sec^2 \theta$

35. $r = 8 \sin \theta$ **36.** $r = \dfrac{1}{2 \cos \theta + 3 \sin \theta}$

37–40. Simple curves *Tabulate and plot enough points to sketch a graph of the following equations.*

37. $r = 8 \cos \theta$ **38.** $r = 4 + 4 \cos \theta$

39. $r(\sin \theta - 2 \cos \theta) = 0$ **40.** $r = 1 - \cos \theta$

41–48. Graphing polar curves *Graph the following equations. Use a graphing utility to check your work and produce a final graph.*

41. $r = 1 - \sin \theta$ **42.** $r = 2 - 2 \sin \theta$

43. $r = \sin^2(\theta/2)$ **44.** $r^2 = 4 \sin \theta$

45. $r^2 = 16 \cos \theta$ **46.** $r^2 = 16 \sin 2\theta$

47. $r = \sin 3\theta$ **48.** $r = 2 \sin 5\theta$

49–52. Matching polar and Cartesian curves *A Cartesian and a polar graph of $r = f(\theta)$ are given in the figures. Mark the points on the polar graph that correspond to the points shown on the Cartesian graph.*

49. $r = 1 - 2 \sin 3\theta$

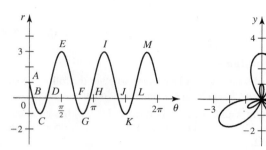

50. $r = \sin(1 + 3 \cos \theta)$

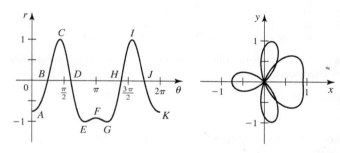

51. $r = \dfrac{1}{4} - \cos 4\theta$

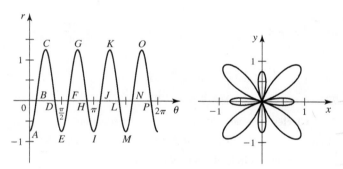

52. $r = \cos \theta + \sin 2\theta$

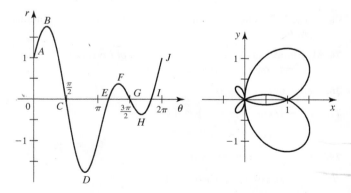

53–60. Using a graphing utility *Use a graphing utility to graph the following equations. In each case, give the smallest interval $[0, P]$ that generates the entire curve.*

53. $r = \sin \dfrac{\theta}{4}$ **54.** $r = 2 - 4 \cos 5\theta$

55. $r = \cos 3\theta + \cos^2 2\theta$ **56.** $r = 2 \sin \dfrac{2\theta}{3}$

57. $r = \cos \dfrac{3\theta}{5}$ **58.** $r = \sin \dfrac{3\theta}{7}$

59. $r = 1 - 3 \cos 2\theta$ **60.** $r = 1 - 2 \sin 5\theta$

Further Explorations

61. Explain why or why not Determine whether the following statements are true and give an explanation or counterexample.

    a. The point with Cartesian coordinates $(-2, 2)$ has polar coordinates $(2\sqrt{2}, 3\pi/4)$, $(2\sqrt{2}, 11\pi/4)$, $(2\sqrt{2}, -5\pi/4)$, and $(-2\sqrt{2}, -\pi/4)$.

    b. The graphs of $r \cos \theta = 4$ and $r \sin \theta = -2$ intersect exactly once.

    c. The graphs of $r = 2$ and $\theta = \pi/4$ intersect exactly once.

    d. The point $(3, \pi/2)$ lies on the graph of $r = 3 \cos 2\theta$.

    e. The graphs of $r = 2 \sec \theta$ and $r = 3 \csc \theta$ are lines.

62–65. Cartesian-to-polar coordinates *Convert the following equations to polar coordinates.*

62. $y = 3$ **63.** $y = x^2$

64. $(x - 1)^2 + y^2 = 1$ **65.** $y = 1/x$

66–73. Sets in polar coordinates *Sketch the following sets of points* (r, θ).

66. $r = 3$ **67.** $\theta = \dfrac{2\pi}{3}$

68. $2 \le r \le 8$ **69.** $\dfrac{\pi}{2} \le \theta \le \dfrac{3\pi}{4}$

70. $1 < r < 2$ and $\dfrac{\pi}{6} \le \theta \le \dfrac{\pi}{3}$ **71.** $|\theta| \le \dfrac{\pi}{3}$

72. $0 < r < 3$ and $0 \le \theta \le \pi$ **73.** $r \ge 2$

74. Circles in general Show that the polar equation

$$r^2 - 2r (a \cos \theta + b \sin \theta) = R^2 - a^2 - b^2$$

describes a circle of radius R centered at (a, b).

75. Circles in general Show that the polar equation

$$r^2 - 2rr_0 \cos (\theta - \theta_0) = R^2 - r_0^{\,2}$$

describes a circle of radius R whose center has polar coordinates (r_0, θ_0).

76–81. Equations of circles *Use the results of Exercises 74–75 to describe and graph the following circles.*

76. $r^2 - 6r \cos \theta = 16$

77. $r^2 - 4r \cos (\theta - \pi/3) = 12$

78. $r^2 - 8r \cos (\theta - \pi/2) = 9$

79. $r^2 - 2r(2 \cos \theta + 3 \sin \theta) = 3$

80. $r^2 + 2r(\cos \theta - 3 \sin \theta) = 4$

81. $r^2 - 2r(-\cos \theta + 2 \sin \theta) = 4$

82. Equations of circles Find equations of the circles in the figure. Determine whether the combined area of the circles is greater than or less than the area of the region inside the square but outside the circles.

83. Vertical lines Consider the polar curve $r = 2 \sec \theta$.

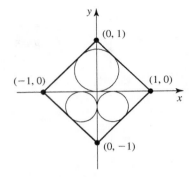

    a. Graph the curve on the intervals $(\pi/2, 3\pi/2)$, $(3\pi/2, 5\pi/2)$, and $(5\pi/2, 7\pi/2)$. In each case, state the direction in which the curve is generated as θ increases.

    b. Show that on any interval $(n\pi/2, (n + 2)\pi/2)$, where n is an odd integer, the graph is the vertical line $x = 2$.

84. Lines in polar coordinates

    a. Show that an equation of the line $y = mx + b$ in polar coordinates is $r = \dfrac{b}{\sin \theta - m \cos \theta}$.

    b. Use the figure to find an alternative polar equation of a line, $r \cos (\theta_0 - \theta) = r_0$. Note that $Q(r_0, \theta_0)$ is a fixed point on the line such that OQ is perpendicular to the line and $r_0 \ge 0$; $P(r, \theta)$ is an arbitrary point on the line.

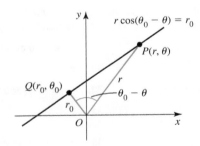

85–88. Equations of lines *Use the result of Exercise 84 to describe and graph the following lines.*

85. $r \cos \left(\dfrac{\pi}{3} - \theta \right) = 3$ **86.** $r \cos \left(\theta + \dfrac{\pi}{6} \right) = 4$

87. $r(\sin \theta - 4 \cos \theta) - 3 = 0$ **88.** $r(4 \sin \theta - 3 \cos \theta) = 6$

89. The limaçon family The equations $r = a + b \cos \theta$ and $r = a + b \sin \theta$ describe curves known as *limaçons* (from Latin for *snail*). We have already encountered cardioids, which occur when $|a| = |b|$. The limaçon has an inner loop if $|a| < |b|$. The limaçon has a dent or dimple if $|b| < |a| < 2|b|$. And the limaçon is oval-shaped if $|a| > 2|b|$. Match equations a–f with the limaçons in the figures A–F.

    a. $r = -1 + \sin \theta$ **b.** $r = -1 + 2 \cos \theta$

    c. $r = 2 + \sin \theta$ **d.** $r = 1 - 2 \cos \theta$

    e. $r = 1 + 2 \sin \theta$ **f.** $r = 1 + \dfrac{2}{3} \sin \theta$

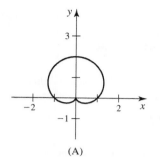

(A)

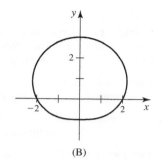

(B)

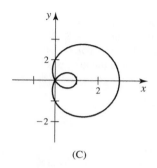

(C)

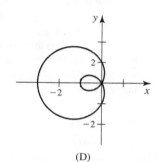

(D)

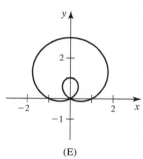

(E)

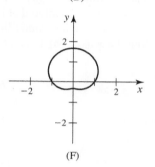

(F)

90. Limiting limaçon Consider the family of limaçons $r = 1 + b \cos \theta$. Describe how the curves change as $b \to \infty$.

91–94. The lemniscate family *Equations of the form $r^2 = a \sin 2\theta$ and $r^2 = a \cos 2\theta$ describe lemniscates (see Example 7). Graph the following lemniscates.*

91. $r^2 = \cos 2\theta$

92. $r^2 = 4 \sin 2\theta$

93. $r^2 = -2 \sin 2\theta$

94. $r^2 = -8 \cos 2\theta$

95–98. The rose family *Equations of the form $r = a \sin m\theta$ or $r = a \cos m\theta$, where a is a real number and m is a positive integer, have graphs known as roses (see Example 6). Graph the following roses.*

95. $r = \sin 2\theta$

96. $r = 4 \cos 3\theta$

97. $r = 2 \sin 4\theta$

98. $r = 6 \sin 5\theta$

99. Number of rose petals Show that the graph of $r = a \sin m\theta$ or $r = a \cos m\theta$ is a rose with m leaves if m is an odd integer and a rose with $2m$ leaves if m is an even integer.

100–102. Spirals *Graph the following spirals. Indicate the direction in which the spiral is generated as θ increases, where $\theta > 0$. Let $a = 1$ and $a = -1$.*

100. Spiral of Archimedes: $r = a\theta$

101. Logarithmic spiral: $r = e^{a\theta}$

102. Hyperbolic spiral: $r = a/\theta$

103–106. Intersection points *Points at which the graphs of $r = f(\theta)$ and $r = g(\theta)$ intersect must be determined carefully. Solving $f(\theta) = g(\theta)$ identifies some—but perhaps not all—intersection points. The reason is that the curves may pass through the same point for different values of θ. Use analytical methods and a graphing utility to find all the intersection points of the following curves.*

103. $r = 2 \cos \theta$ and $r = 1 + \cos \theta$

104. $r^2 = 4 \cos \theta$ and $r = 1 + \cos \theta$

105. $r = 1 - \sin \theta$ and $r = 1 + \cos \theta$

106. $r^2 = \cos 2\theta$ and $r^2 = \sin 2\theta$

107. Enhanced butterfly curve The butterfly curve of Example 8 is enhanced by adding a term:

$$r = e^{\sin \theta} - 2 \cos 4\theta + \sin^5 (\theta/12), \quad \text{for } 0 \le \theta \le 24\pi.$$

a. Graph the curve.

b. Explain why the new term produces the observed effect.

(*Source:* S. Wagon and E. Packel, *Animating Calculus,* Freeman, 1994)

108. Finger curves Consider the curve $r = f(\theta) = \cos a^\theta - 1.5$, where $a = (1 + 12\pi)^{1/(2\pi)} \approx 1.78933$ (see figure).

a. Show that $f(0) = f(2\pi)$ and find the point on the curve that corresponds to $\theta = 0$ and $\theta = 2\pi$.

b. Is the same curve produced over the intervals $[-\pi, \pi]$ and $[0, 2\pi]$?

c. Let $f(\theta) = \cos a^\theta - b$, where $a = (1 + 2k\pi)^{1/(2\pi)}$, k is an integer, and b is a real number. Show that $f(0) = f(2\pi)$ and that the curve closes on itself.

d. Plot the curve with various values of k. How many fingers can you produce?

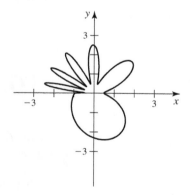

Applications

109. Earth–Mars system A simplified model assumes that the orbits of Earth and Mars are circular with radii of 2 and 3, respectively, and that Earth completes one orbit in one year while Mars takes two years. When $t = 0$, Earth is at $(2, 0)$ and Mars is at $(3, 0)$; both orbit the Sun (at $(0, 0)$) in the counterclockwise direction.

The position of Mars relative to Earth is given by the parametric equations

$$x = (3 - 4 \cos \pi t) \cos \pi t + 2, \quad y = (3 - 4 \cos \pi t) \sin \pi t.$$

a. Graph the parametric equations, for $0 \le t \le 2$.

b. Letting $r = (3 - 4 \cos \pi t)$, explain why the path of Mars relative to Earth is a limaçon (Exercise 89).

110. Channel flow Water flows in a shallow semicircular channel with inner and outer radii of 1 m and 2 m (see figure). At a point $P(r, \theta)$ in the channel, the flow is in the tangential direction (counterclockwise along circles), and it depends only on r, the distance from the center of the semicircles.

a. Express the region formed by the channel as a set in polar coordinates.

b. Express the inflow and outflow regions of the channel as sets in polar coordinates.

c. Suppose the tangential velocity of the water in m/s is given by $v(r) = 10r$, for $1 \le r \le 2$. Is the velocity greater at $(1.5, \frac{\pi}{4})$ or $(1.2, \frac{3\pi}{4})$? Explain.

d. Suppose the tangential velocity of the water is given by

$$v(r) = \frac{20}{r}, \text{ for } 1 \le r \le 2. \text{ Is the velocity greater at } (1.8, \frac{\pi}{6})$$

or $(1.3, \frac{2\pi}{3})$? Explain.

e. The total amount of water that flows through the channel (across a cross section of the channel $\theta = \theta_0$) is proportional to $\int_1^2 v(r)\, dr$. Is the total flow through the channel greater for the flow in part (c) or (d)?

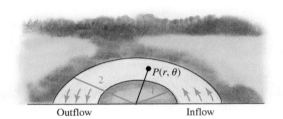

Outflow   Inflow

Additional Exercises

111. Special circles Show that the equation $r = a \cos \theta + b \sin \theta$, where a and b are real numbers, describes a circle. Find the center and radius of the circle.

112. Cartesian lemniscate Find the equation in Cartesian coordinates of the lemniscate $r^2 = a^2 \cos 2\theta$, where a is a real number.

113. Subtle symmetry Without using a graphing utility, determine the symmetries (if any) of the curve $r = 4 - \sin(\theta/2)$.

T 114. Complete curves Consider the polar curve $r = \cos(n\theta/m)$, where n and m are integers.

a. Graph the complete curve when $n = 2$ and $m = 3$.

b. Graph the complete curve when $n = 3$ and $m = 7$.

c. Find a general rule in terms of m and n (where m and n have no common factors) for determining the least positive number P such that the complete curve is generated over the interval $[0, P]$.

QUICK CHECK ANSWERS

1. All the points are the same except $(3, 3\pi/2)$.
3. Polar coordinates: $(1, 0)$, $(1, 2\pi)$; Cartesian coordinates: $(0, 2)$ **4.** A circle centered at the origin with radius 12; a double spiral; the horizontal line $y = 10$ **5.** (a) Symmetric about the x-axis; (b) symmetric about the y-axis ◄

10.3 Calculus in Polar Coordinates

Having learned about the *geometry* of polar coordinates, we now have the tools needed to explore *calculus* in polar coordinates. Familiar topics, such as slopes of tangent lines and areas bounded by curves, are now revisited in a different setting.

Slopes of Tangent Lines

Given a function $y = f(x)$, the slope of the line tangent to the graph at a given point is $\frac{dy}{dx}$ or $f'(x)$. So it is tempting to conclude that the slope of a curve described by the polar equation $r = f(\theta)$ is $\frac{dr}{d\theta} = f'(\theta)$. Unfortunately, it's not that simple.

The key observation is that the slope of a tangent line—in any coordinate system—is the rate of change of the vertical coordinate y with respect to the horizontal coordinate x, which is $\frac{dy}{dx}$. We begin by writing the polar equation $r = f(\theta)$ in parametric form with θ as a parameter:

$$x = r \cos \theta = f(\theta) \cos \theta \quad \text{and} \quad y = r \sin \theta = f(\theta) \sin \theta. \tag{1}$$

> ➤ The slope is the change in the vertical coordinate divided by the change in the horizontal coordinate, independent of the coordinate system. In polar coordinates, neither r nor θ corresponds to a vertical or horizontal coordinate.

From Section 10.1, when x and y are defined parametrically as differentiable functions of θ, the derivative is $\dfrac{dy}{dx} = \dfrac{dy/d\theta}{dx/d\theta}$. Using the Product Rule to compute $\dfrac{dy}{d\theta}$ and $\dfrac{dx}{d\theta}$ in equation (1), we have

$$\frac{dy}{dx} = \overbrace{\frac{f'(\theta)\sin\theta + f(\theta)\cos\theta}{\underbrace{f'(\theta)\cos\theta - f(\theta)\sin\theta}_{dx/d\theta}}}^{dy/d\theta}. \tag{2}$$

If the graph passes through the origin for some angle θ_0, then $f(\theta_0) = 0$, and equation (2) simplifies to

$$\frac{dy}{dx} = \frac{\sin\theta_0}{\cos\theta_0} = \tan\theta_0,$$

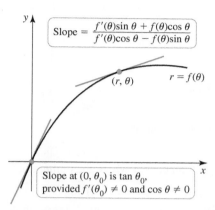

Figure 10.32

provided $f'(\theta_0) \neq 0$. Assuming $\cos\theta_0 \neq 0$, $\tan\theta_0$ is the slope of the line $\theta = \theta_0$, which also passes through the origin. In this case, we conclude that if $f(\theta_0) = 0$, then the tangent line at $(0, \theta_0)$ is simply $\theta = \theta_0$ (Figure 10.32). If $f(\theta_0) = 0$, $f'(\theta_0) \neq 0$, and $\cos\theta_0 = 0$, the graph has a vertical tangent line at the origin.

QUICK CHECK 1 Verify that if $y = f(\theta)\sin\theta$, then $y'(\theta) = f'(\theta)\sin\theta + f(\theta)\cos\theta$ (which was used earlier to find dy/dx). ◄

THEOREM 10.2 Slope of a Tangent Line
Let f be a differentiable function at θ_0. The slope of the line tangent to the curve $r = f(\theta)$ at the point $(f(\theta_0), \theta_0)$ is

$$\frac{dy}{dx} = \frac{f'(\theta_0)\sin\theta_0 + f(\theta_0)\cos\theta_0}{f'(\theta_0)\cos\theta_0 - f(\theta_0)\sin\theta_0},$$

provided the denominator is nonzero at the point. At angles θ_0 for which $f(\theta_0) = 0$, $f'(\theta_0) \neq 0$, and $\cos\theta_0 \neq 0$, the tangent line is $\theta = \theta_0$ with slope $\tan\theta_0$.

EXAMPLE 1   Slopes on a circle Find the slopes of the lines tangent to the circle $r = f(\theta) = 10$.

SOLUTION In this case, $f(\theta)$ is constant (independent of θ). Therefore, $f'(\theta) = 0$, $f(\theta) \neq 0$, and the slope formula becomes

$$\frac{dy}{dx} = \frac{f'(\theta)\sin\theta + f(\theta)\cos\theta}{f'(\theta)\cos\theta - f(\theta)\sin\theta} = -\frac{\cos\theta}{\sin\theta} = -\cot\theta.$$

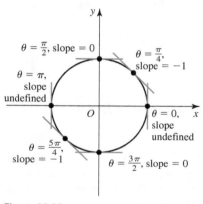

Figure 10.33

We can check a few points to see that this result makes sense. With $\theta = 0$ and $\theta = \pi$, the slope $\dfrac{dy}{dx} = -\cot\theta$ is undefined, which implies the tangent lines are vertical at these points (Figure 10.33). With $\theta = \pi/2$ and $\theta = 3\pi/2$, the slope is zero; with $\theta = 3\pi/4$ and $\theta = 7\pi/4$, the slope is 1; and with $\theta = \pi/4$ and $\theta = 5\pi/4$, the slope is -1. At all points $P(r, \theta)$ on the circle, the slope of the line OP from the origin to P is $\tan\theta$, which is the negative reciprocal of $-\cot\theta$. Therefore, OP is perpendicular to the tangent line at all points P on the circle.

Related Exercises 5–14 ◄

EXAMPLE 2   Vertical and horizontal tangent lines Find the points on the interval $-\pi \leq \theta \leq \pi$ at which the cardioid $r = f(\theta) = 1 - \cos\theta$ has a vertical or horizontal tangent line.

SOLUTION Applying Theorem 10.2, we find that

$$\frac{dy}{dx} = \frac{f'(\theta)\sin\theta + f(\theta)\cos\theta}{f'(\theta)\cos\theta - f(\theta)\sin\theta}$$

$$= \frac{\overbrace{\sin\theta\sin\theta}^{\sin^2\theta\,=\,1\,-\,\cos^2\theta} + (1-\cos\theta)\cos\theta}{\underbrace{\sin\theta\cos\theta - (1-\cos\theta)\sin\theta}_{\sin\theta(2\cos\theta - 1)}} \quad \text{Substitute for } f(\theta) \text{ and } f'(\theta).$$

$$= -\frac{(2\cos^2\theta - \cos\theta - 1)}{\sin\theta(2\cos\theta - 1)} \quad \text{Simplify.}$$

$$= -\frac{(2\cos\theta + 1)(\cos\theta - 1)}{\sin\theta(2\cos\theta - 1)}. \quad \text{Factor the numerator.}$$

The points with a horizontal tangent line satisfy $\frac{dy}{dx} = 0$ and occur where the numerator is zero and the denominator is nonzero. The numerator is zero when $\theta = 0$ and $\pm 2\pi/3$. Because the denominator is *not* zero when $\theta = \pm 2\pi/3$, horizontal tangent lines occur at $\theta = \pm 2\pi/3$ (Figure 10.34).

Vertical tangent lines occur where the numerator of $\frac{dy}{dx}$ is nonzero and the denominator is zero. The denominator is zero when $\theta = 0$, $\pm\pi$, and $\pm\pi/3$, and the numerator is not zero at $\theta = \pm\pi$ and $\pm\pi/3$. Therefore, vertical tangent lines occur at $\theta = \pm\pi$ and $\pm\pi/3$.

The point $(0, 0)$ on the curve must be handled carefully because both the numerator and denominator of $\frac{dy}{dx}$ equal 0 at $\theta = 0$. Notice that with $f(\theta) = 1 - \cos\theta$, we have $f(0) = f'(0) = 0$. Therefore, $\frac{dy}{dx}$ may be computed as a limit using l'Hôpital's Rule. As $\theta \to 0^+$, we find that

$$\frac{dy}{dx} = \lim_{\theta \to 0^+}\left(-\frac{(2\cos\theta + 1)(\cos\theta - 1)}{\sin\theta(2\cos\theta - 1)}\right)$$

$$= \lim_{\theta \to 0^+}\frac{4\cos\theta\sin\theta - \sin\theta}{-2\sin^2\theta + 2\cos^2\theta - \cos\theta} \quad \text{L'Hôpital's Rule}$$

$$= \frac{0}{1} = 0. \quad \text{Evaluate the limit.}$$

A similar calculation using l'Hôpital's Rule shows that as $\theta \to 0^-$, $\frac{dy}{dx} \to 0$. Therefore, the curve has a slope of 0 at $(0, 0)$.

Related Exercises 15–20 ◄

QUICK CHECK 2 What is the slope of the line tangent to the cardioid in Example 2 at the point corresponding to $\theta = \pi/4$? ◄

Area of Regions Bounded by Polar Curves

The problem of finding the area of a region bounded by polar curves brings us back to the slice-and-sum strategy used extensively in Chapters 5 and 6. The objective is to find the area of the region R bounded by the graph of $r = f(\theta)$ between the two rays $\theta = \alpha$ and $\theta = \beta$ (Figure 10.35a). We assume that f is continuous and nonnegative on $[\alpha, \beta]$.

The area of R is found by slicing the region in the radial direction, creating wedge-shaped slices. The interval $[\alpha, \beta]$ is partitioned into n subintervals by choosing the grid points

$$\alpha = \theta_0 < \theta_1 < \theta_2 < \cdots < \theta_k < \cdots < \theta_n = \beta.$$

We let $\Delta\theta_k = \theta_k - \theta_{k-1}$, for $k = 1, 2, \ldots, n$, and we let θ_k^* be any point of the interval $[\theta_{k-1}, \theta_k]$. The kth slice is approximated by the sector of a circle swept out by an angle $\Delta\theta_k^*$

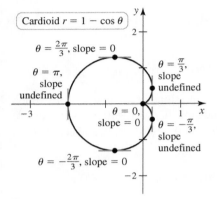

Cardioid $r = 1 - \cos\theta$

$\theta = \frac{2\pi}{3}$, slope $= 0$

$\theta = \pi$, slope undefined

$\theta = \frac{\pi}{3}$, slope undefined

$\theta = 0$, slope $= 0$

$\theta = -\frac{\pi}{3}$, slope undefined

$\theta = -\frac{2\pi}{3}$, slope $= 0$

Figure 10.34

Area of circle $= \pi r^2$

Area of $\Delta\theta/(2\pi)$ of a circle

$= \left(\frac{\Delta\theta}{2\pi}\right)\pi r^2 = \frac{1}{2}r^2\Delta\theta$

with radius $f(\theta_k^*)$ (Figure 10.35b). Therefore, the area of the kth slice is approximately $\frac{1}{2}f(\theta_k^*)^2\Delta\theta_k$, for $k = 1, 2, \ldots, n$ (Figure 10.35c). To find the approximate area of R, we sum the areas of these slices:

$$\text{area} \approx \sum_{k=1}^{n}\frac{1}{2}f(\theta_k^*)^2\,\Delta\theta_k.$$

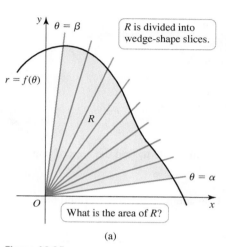

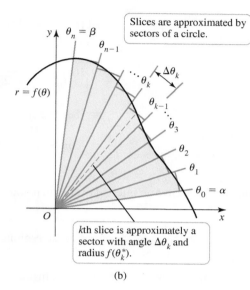

Slices are approximated by sectors of a circle.

R is divided into wedge-shape slices.

What is the area of R?

kth slice is approximately a sector with angle $\Delta\theta_k$ and radius $f(\theta_k^*)$.

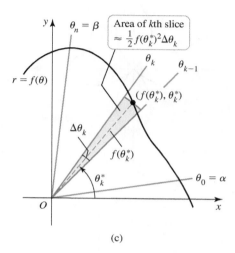

Area of kth slice $\approx \frac{1}{2}f(\theta_k^*)^2\Delta\theta_k$

(a)   (b)   (c)

Figure 10.35

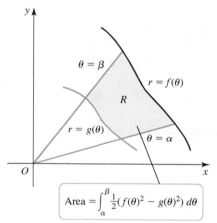

$$\text{Area} = \int_{\alpha}^{\beta}\frac{1}{2}(f(\theta)^2 - g(\theta)^2)\,d\theta$$

Figure 10.36

> If R is bounded by the graph of $r = f(\theta)$ between $\theta = \alpha$ and $\theta = \beta$, then $g(\theta) = 0$ and the area of R is $\int_{\alpha}^{\beta}\frac{1}{2}f(\theta)^2\,d\theta$.

> Though we assume $r = f(\theta) \geq 0$ when deriving the formula for the area of a region bounded by a polar curve, the formula is valid when $r < 0$ (see, for example, Exercise 48).

This approximation is a Riemann sum, and the approximation improves as we take more sectors ($n \to \infty$) and let $\Delta\theta_k \to 0$, for all k. The exact area is given by $\lim_{n\to\infty}\sum_{k=1}^{n}\frac{1}{2}f(\theta_k^*)^2\,\Delta\theta_k$, which we identify as the definite integral $\int_{\alpha}^{\beta}\frac{1}{2}f(\theta)^2\,d\theta$.

With a slight modification, a more general result is obtained for the area of a region R bounded by two curves, $r = f(\theta)$ and $r = g(\theta)$, between the rays $\theta = \alpha$ and $\theta = \beta$ (Figure 10.36). We assume that f and g are continuous and $f(\theta) \geq g(\theta) \geq 0$ on $[\alpha, \beta]$. To find the area of R, we subtract the area of the region bounded by $r = g(\theta)$ from the area of the entire region bounded by $r = f(\theta)$ (all between $\theta = \alpha$ and $\theta = \beta$); that is,

$$\text{area} = \int_{\alpha}^{\beta}\frac{1}{2}f(\theta)^2\,d\theta - \int_{\alpha}^{\beta}\frac{1}{2}g(\theta)^2\,d\theta = \int_{\alpha}^{\beta}\frac{1}{2}(f(\theta)^2 - g(\theta)^2)\,d\theta.$$

DEFINITION Area of Regions in Polar Coordinates

Let R be the region bounded by the graphs of $r = f(\theta)$ and $r = g(\theta)$, between $\theta = \alpha$ and $\theta = \beta$, where f and g are continuous and $f(\theta) \geq g(\theta) \geq 0$ on $[\alpha, \beta]$. The area of R is

$$\int_{\alpha}^{\beta}\frac{1}{2}(f(\theta)^2 - g(\theta)^2)\,d\theta.$$

QUICK CHECK 3 Use integration to find the area of the circle $r = f(\theta) = 8$, for $0 \leq \theta \leq 2\pi$. ◄

EXAMPLE 3 Area of a polar region Find the area of the four-leaf rose $r = f(\theta) = 2\cos 2\theta$.

SOLUTION The graph of the rose (Figure 10.37) *appears* to be symmetric about the x- and y-axes; in fact, these symmetries can be proved. Appealing to this symmetry, we

▶ The equation $r = 2 \cos 2\theta$ is unchanged when θ is replaced with $-\theta$ (symmetry about the x-axis) and when θ is replaced with $\pi - \theta$ (symmetry about the y-axis).

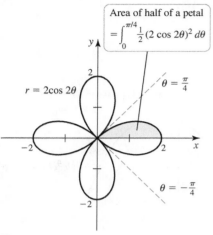

Area of half of a petal
$$= \int_0^{\pi/4} \frac{1}{2}(2 \cos 2\theta)^2 \, d\theta$$

$r = 2\cos 2\theta$

$\theta = \frac{\pi}{4}$

$\theta = -\frac{\pi}{4}$

Figure 10.37

find the area of one-half of a leaf and then multiply the result by 8 to obtain the area of the full rose. The upper half of the rightmost leaf is generated as θ increases from $\theta = 0$ (when $r = 2$) to $\theta = \pi/4$ (when $r = 0$). Therefore, the area of the entire rose is

$$8 \int_0^{\pi/4} \frac{1}{2} f(\theta)^2 \, d\theta = 4 \int_0^{\pi/4} (2 \cos 2\theta)^2 \, d\theta \qquad f(\theta) = 2 \cos 2\theta$$

$$= 16 \int_0^{\pi/4} \cos^2 2\theta \, d\theta \qquad \text{Simplify.}$$

$$= 16 \int_0^{\pi/4} \frac{1 + \cos 4\theta}{2} \, d\theta \qquad \text{Half-angle formula}$$

$$= (8\theta + 2 \sin 4\theta) \Big|_0^{\pi/4} \qquad \text{Fundamental Theorem}$$

$$= (2\pi + 0) - (0 + 0) = 2\pi. \qquad \text{Simplify.}$$

Related Exercises 21–36 ◀

QUICK CHECK 4 Give an interval over which you could integrate to find the area of one leaf of the rose $r = 2 \sin 3\theta$. ◀

EXAMPLE 4   Areas of polar regions Consider the circle $r = 1$ and the cardioid $r = 1 + \cos \theta$ (Figure 10.38).

a. Find the area of the region inside the circle and inside the cardioid.

b. Find the area of the region inside the circle and outside the cardioid.

SOLUTION

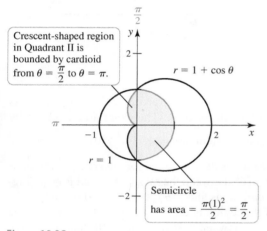

Crescent-shaped region in Quadrant II is bounded by cardioid from $\theta = \frac{\pi}{2}$ to $\theta = \pi$.

$r = 1 + \cos \theta$

$r = 1$

Semicircle has area $= \dfrac{\pi(1)^2}{2} = \dfrac{\pi}{2}$.

Figure 10.38

a. The points of intersection of the two curves can be found by solving $1 + \cos \theta = 1$, or $\cos \theta = 0$. The solutions are $\theta = \pm \pi/2$. The region inside the circle and inside the cardioid consists of two subregions (Figure 10.38):

• a semicircle with radius 1 in the first and fourth quadrants bounded by the circle $r = 1$, and

• two crescent-shaped regions in the second and third quadrants bounded by the cardioid $r = 1 + \cos \theta$ and the y-axis.

The area of the semicircle is $\pi/2$. To find the area of the upper crescent-shaped region in the second quadrant, notice that it is bounded by $r = 1 + \cos \theta$, as θ varies from $\pi/2$ to π. Therefore, its area is

$$\int_{\pi/2}^{\pi} \frac{1}{2}(1 + \cos \theta)^2 \, d\theta = \int_{\pi/2}^{\pi} \frac{1}{2}(1 + 2 \cos \theta + \cos^2 \theta) \, d\theta \qquad \text{Expand.}$$

$$= \frac{1}{2} \int_{\pi/2}^{\pi} \left(1 + 2 \cos \theta + \frac{1 + \cos 2\theta}{2}\right) d\theta \qquad \begin{array}{l}\text{Half-angle}\\\text{formula}\end{array}$$

$$= \frac{1}{2}\left(\theta + 2 \sin \theta + \frac{\theta}{2} + \frac{\sin 2\theta}{4}\right)\Big|_{\pi/2}^{\pi} \qquad \begin{array}{l}\text{Evaluate}\\\text{integral.}\end{array}$$

$$= \frac{3\pi}{8} - 1. \qquad \text{Simplify.}$$

The area of the entire region (two crescents and a semicircle) is

$$2\left(\frac{3\pi}{8} - 1\right) + \frac{\pi}{2} = \frac{5\pi}{4} - 2.$$

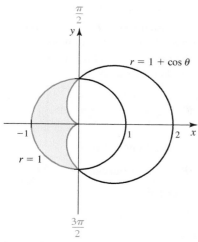

$$\frac{\pi}{2}$$

$r = 1 + \cos\theta$

$r = 1$

$$\frac{3\pi}{2}$$

Figure 10.39

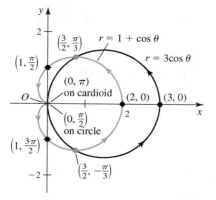

Figure 10.40

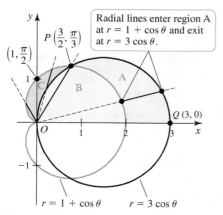

Radial lines enter region A at $r = 1 + \cos\theta$ and exit at $r = 3\cos\theta$.

$r = 1 + \cos\theta$ $r = 3\cos\theta$

Figure 10.41

▶ One way to verify that the inner and outer boundaries of a region have been correctly identified is to draw a ray from the origin through the region—the ray should enter the region at the inner boundary and exit the region at the outer boundary. In Example 6a, this is the case for every ray through region A, for $0 \le \theta \le \pi/3$.

b. The region inside the circle and outside the cardioid is bounded by the outer curve $r = 1$ and the inner curve $r = 1 + \cos\theta$ on the interval $[\pi/2, 3\pi/2]$ (Figure 10.39). Using the symmetry about the x-axis, the area of the region is

$$2\int_{\pi/2}^{\pi} \frac{1}{2}\left(1^2 - (1 + \cos\theta)^2\right) d\theta = \int_{\pi/2}^{\pi} (-2\cos\theta - \cos^2\theta)\, d\theta \quad \text{Simplify the integrand.}$$

$$= 2 - \frac{\pi}{4}. \quad \text{Evaluate the integral.}$$

Note that the regions in parts (a) and (b) comprise the interior of a circle of radius 1; indeed, their areas have a sum of π.

Related Exercises 21–36 ◀

Part of the challenge in setting up area integrals in polar coordinates is finding the points of intersection of two polar curves. The following example shows some of the subtleties of this process.

EXAMPLE 5 Points of intersection Find the points of intersection of the circle $r = 3\cos\theta$ and the cardioid $r = 1 + \cos\theta$ (Figure 10.40).

SOLUTION The fact that a point has multiple representations in polar coordinates may lead to subtle difficulties in finding intersection points. We first proceed algebraically. Equating the two expressions for r and solving for θ, we have

$$3\cos\theta = 1 + \cos\theta \quad \text{or} \quad \cos\theta = \frac{1}{2},$$

which has roots $\theta = \pm\pi/3$. Therefore, two intersection points are $(3/2, \pi/3)$ and $(3/2, -\pi/3)$ (Figure 10.40). Without examining graphs of the curves, we might be tempted to stop here. Yet the figure shows another intersection point at the origin O that has not been detected. To find the third intersection point, we must investigate the way in which the two curves are generated. As θ increases from 0 to 2π, the cardioid is generated counterclockwise, beginning at $(2, 0)$. The cardioid passes through O when $\theta = \pi$. As θ increases from 0 to π, the circle is generated counterclockwise, beginning at $(3, 0)$. The circle passes through O when $\theta = \pi/2$. Therefore, the intersection point O is $(0, \pi)$ on the cardioid (and these coordinates do not satisfy the equation of the circle), while O is $(0, \pi/2)$ on the circle (and these coordinates do not satisfy the equation of the cardioid). There is no foolproof rule for detecting such "hidden" intersection points. Care must be used.

Related Exercises 37–40 ◀

EXAMPLE 6 Computing areas Example 5 discussed the points of intersection of the curves $r = 3\cos\theta$ (a circle) and $r = 1 + \cos\theta$ (a cardioid). Use those results to compute the areas of the following non-overlapping regions in Figure 10.41.

a. region A   **b.** region B   **c.** region C

SOLUTION

a. It is evident that region A is bounded on the inside by the cardioid and on the outside by the circle between the points $Q(\theta = 0)$ and $P(\theta = \pi/3)$. Therefore, the area of region A is

$$\frac{1}{2}\int_0^{\pi/3} \left((3\cos\theta)^2 - (1 + \cos\theta)^2\right) d\theta$$

$$= \frac{1}{2}\int_0^{\pi/3} (8\cos^2\theta - 1 - 2\cos\theta)\, d\theta \quad \text{Simplify.}$$

$$= \frac{1}{2}\int_0^{\pi/3} (3 + 4\cos 2\theta - 2\cos\theta)\, d\theta \quad \cos^2\theta = \frac{1 + \cos 2\theta}{2}$$

$$= \frac{1}{2}(3\theta + 2\sin 2\theta - 2\sin\theta)\Big|_0^{\pi/3} = \frac{\pi}{2}. \quad \text{Evaluate integral.}$$

b. Examining region B, notice that a ray drawn from the origin enters the region immediately. There is no inner boundary, and the outer boundary is $r = 1 + \cos\theta$ on $0 \le \theta \le \pi/3$ and $r = 3\cos\theta$ on $\pi/3 \le \theta \le \pi/2$ (recall from Example 5 that $\theta = \pi/2$ is the angle at which the circle intersects the origin). Therefore, we slice the region into two parts at $\theta = \pi/3$ and write two integrals for its area:

$$\text{area of region B} = \frac{1}{2}\int_0^{\pi/3} (1 + \cos\theta)^2\, d\theta + \frac{1}{2}\int_{\pi/3}^{\pi/2} (3\cos\theta)^2\, d\theta.$$

While these integrals may be evaluated directly, it's easier to notice that

$$\text{area of region B} = \text{area of semicircle } OPQ - \text{area of region A}.$$

Because $r = 3\cos\theta$ is a circle with a radius of $3/2$, we have

$$\text{area of region B} = \frac{1}{2}\cdot\pi\left(\frac{3}{2}\right)^2 - \frac{\pi}{2} = \frac{5\pi}{8}.$$

c. It's easy to *incorrectly* identify the inner boundary of region C as the circle and the outer boundary as the cardioid. While these identifications are true when $\pi/3 \le \theta \le \pi/2$ (notice again the radial lines in Figure 10.41), there is only one boundary curve (the cardioid) when $\pi/2 \le \theta \le \pi$. We conclude that the area of region C is

$$\frac{1}{2}\int_{\pi/3}^{\pi/2} ((1 + \cos\theta)^2 - (3\cos\theta)^2)\, d\theta + \frac{1}{2}\int_{\pi/2}^{\pi} (1 + \cos\theta)^2\, d\theta = \frac{\pi}{8}.$$

Related Exercises 41–44 ◄

SECTION 10.3 EXERCISES

Review Questions

1. Express the polar equation $r = f(\theta)$ in parametric form in Cartesian coordinates, where θ is the parameter.

2. How do you find the slope of the line tangent to the polar graph of $r = f(\theta)$ at a point?

3. Explain why the slope of the line tangent to the polar graph of $r = f(\theta)$ is not $\dfrac{dr}{d\theta}$.

4. What integral must be evaluated to find the area of the region bounded by the polar graphs of $r = f(\theta)$ and $r = g(\theta)$ on the interval $\alpha \le \theta \le \beta$, where $f(\theta) \ge g(\theta) \ge 0$?

Basic Skills

5–14. Slopes of tangent lines *Find the slope of the line tangent to the following polar curves at the given points. At the points where the curve intersects the origin (when this occurs), find the equation of the tangent line in polar coordinates.*

5. $r = 1 - \sin\theta;\ (\frac{1}{2}, \frac{\pi}{6})$

6. $r = 4\cos\theta;\ (2, \frac{\pi}{3})$

7. $r = 8\sin\theta;\ (4, \frac{5\pi}{6})$

8. $r = 4 + \sin\theta;\ (4, 0)$ and $(3, \frac{3\pi}{2})$

9. $r = 6 + 3\cos\theta;\ (3, \pi)$ and $(9, 0)$

10. $r = 2\sin 3\theta$; at the tips of the leaves

11. $r = 4\cos 2\theta$; at the tips of the leaves

12. $r = 1 + 2\sin 2\theta;\ (3, \frac{\pi}{4})$

13. $r^2 = 4\cos 2\theta;\ (0, \pm\frac{\pi}{4})$

14. $r = 2\theta;\ (\frac{\pi}{2}, \frac{\pi}{4})$

15–20. Horizontal and vertical tangents *Find the points at which the following polar curves have a horizontal or a vertical tangent line.*

15. $r = 4\cos\theta$

16. $r = 2 + 2\sin\theta$

17. $r = \sin 2\theta$

18. $r = 3 + 6\sin\theta$

19. $r = 1 - \sin\theta$

20. $r = \sec\theta$

21–36. Areas of regions *Make a sketch of the region and its bounding curves. Find the area of the region.*

21. The region inside the curve $r = \sqrt{\cos\theta}$

22. The region inside the right lobe of $r = \sqrt{\cos 2\theta}$

23. The region inside the circle $r = 8\sin\theta$

24. The region inside the cardioid $r = 4 + 4\sin\theta$

25. The region inside the limaçon $r = 2 + \cos\theta$

26. The region inside all the leaves of the rose $r = 3\sin 2\theta$

27. The region inside one leaf of $r = \cos 3\theta$

28. The region inside the inner loop of $r = \cos \theta - \frac{1}{2}$

29. The region outside the circle $r = \frac{1}{2}$ and inside the circle $r = \cos \theta$

30. The region inside the curve $r = \sqrt{\cos \theta}$ and outside the circle $r = 1/\sqrt{2}$

31. The region inside the curve $r = \sqrt{\cos \theta}$ and inside the circle $r = 1/\sqrt{2}$ in the first quadrant

32. The region inside the right lobe of $r = \sqrt{\cos 2\theta}$ and inside the circle $r = 1/\sqrt{2}$ in the first quadrant

33. The region inside one leaf of the rose $r = \cos 5\theta$

34. The region inside the rose $r = 4 \cos 2\theta$ and outside the circle $r = 2$

35. The region inside the rose $r = 4 \sin 2\theta$ and inside the circle $r = 2$

36. The region inside the lemniscate $r^2 = 2 \sin 2\theta$ and outside the circle $r = 1$

☐ 37–40. Intersection points *Use algebraic methods to find as many intersection points of the following curves as possible. Use graphical methods to identify the remaining intersection points.*

37. $r = 3 \sin \theta$ and $r = 3 \cos \theta$

38. $r = 2 + 2 \sin \theta$ and $r = 2 - 2 \sin \theta$

39. $r = 1 + \sin \theta$ and $r = 1 + \cos \theta$

40. $r = 1$ and $r = \sqrt{2} \cos 2\theta$

41–44. Finding areas *In Exercises 37–40, you found the intersection points of pairs of curves. Find the area of the entire region that lies within both of the following pairs of curves.*

41. $r = 3 \sin \theta$ and $r = 3 \cos \theta$

42. $r = 2 + 2 \sin \theta$ and $r = 2 - 2 \sin \theta$

43. $r = 1 + \sin \theta$ and $r = 1 + \cos \theta$

44. $r = 1$ and $r = \sqrt{2} \cos 2\theta$

Further Explorations

45. Explain why or why not Determine whether the following statements are true and give an explanation or counterexample.

  a. The area of the region bounded by the polar graph of $r = f(\theta)$ on the interval $[\alpha, \beta]$ is $\int_{\alpha}^{\beta} f(\theta)\, d\theta$.

  b. The slope of the line tangent to the polar curve $r = f(\theta)$ at a point (r, θ) is $f'(\theta)$.

46. Multiple identities Explain why the point $(-1, 3\pi/2)$ is on the polar graph of $r = 1 + \cos \theta$ even though it does not satisfy the equation $r = 1 + \cos \theta$.

47–50. Area of plane regions *Find the areas of the following regions.*

47. The region common to the circles $r = 2 \sin \theta$ and $r = 1$

48. The region inside the inner loop of the limaçon $r = 2 + 4 \cos \theta$

49. The region inside the outer loop but outside the inner loop of the limaçon $r = 3 - 6 \sin \theta$

50. The region common to the circle $r = 3 \cos \theta$ and the cardioid $r = 1 + \cos \theta$

☐ 51. Spiral tangent lines Use a graphing utility to determine the first three points with $\theta \geq 0$ at which the spiral $r = 2\theta$ has a horizontal tangent line. Find the first three points with $\theta \geq 0$ at which the spiral $r = 2\theta$ has a vertical tangent line.

52. Area of roses Assume m is a positive integer.

  a. *Even number of leaves*: What is the relationship between the total area enclosed by the $4m$-leaf rose $r = \cos(2m\theta)$ and m?

  b. *Odd number of leaves*: What is the relationship between the total area enclosed by the $(2m + 1)$-leaf rose $r = \cos((2m + 1)\theta)$ and m?

53. Regions bounded by a spiral Let R_n be the region bounded by the nth turn and the $(n + 1)$st turn of the spiral $r = e^{-\theta}$ in the first and second quadrants, for $\theta \geq 0$ (see figure).

  a. Find the area A_n of R_n.
  b. Evaluate $\lim_{n \to \infty} A_n$.
  c. Evaluate $\lim_{n \to \infty} A_{n+1}/A_n$.

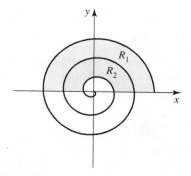

54–57. Area of polar regions *Find the area of the regions bounded by the following curves.*

54. The complete three-leaf rose $r = 2 \cos 3\theta$

55. The lemniscate $r^2 = 6 \sin 2\theta$

56. The limaçon $r = 2 - 4 \sin \theta$

57. The limaçon $r = 4 - 2 \cos \theta$

Applications

58. Blood vessel flow A blood vessel with a circular cross section of constant radius R carries blood that flows parallel to the axis of the vessel with a velocity of $v(r) = V(1 - r^2/R^2)$, where V is a constant and r is the distance from the axis of the vessel.

  a. Where is the velocity a maximum? A minimum?
  b. Find the average velocity of the blood over a cross section of the vessel.
  c. Suppose the velocity in the vessel is given by $v(r) = V(1 - r^2/R^2)^{1/p}$, where $p \geq 1$. Graph the velocity profiles for $p = 1, 2$, and 6 on the interval $0 \leq r \leq R$. Find the average velocity in the vessel as a function of p. How does the average velocity behave as $p \to \infty$?

59–61. Grazing goat problems *Consider the following sequence of problems related to grazing goats tied to a rope. (See the Guided Project Grazing goat problems.)*

59. A circular corral of unit radius is enclosed by a fence. A goat inside the corral is tied to the fence with a rope of length $0 \leq a \leq 2$ (see figure). What is the area of the region (inside the corral) that the goat can graze? Check your answer with the special cases $a = 0$ and $a = 2$.

60. A circular concrete slab of unit radius is surrounded by grass. A goat is tied to the edge of the slab with a rope of length $0 \leq a \leq 2$ (see figure). What is the area of the grassy region that the goat can graze? Note that the rope can extend over the concrete slab. Check your answer with the special cases $a = 0$ and $a = 2$.

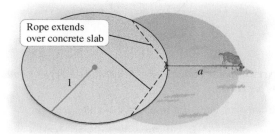

Rope extends over concrete slab

61. A circular corral of unit radius is enclosed by a fence. A goat is outside the corral and tied to the fence with a rope of length $0 \leq a \leq \pi$ (see figure). What is the area of the region (outside the corral) that the goat can reach?

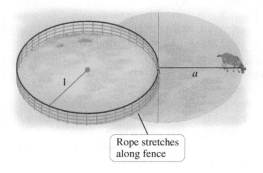

Rope stretches along fence

Additional Exercises

62. Tangents and normals Let a polar curve be described by $r = f(\theta)$ and let ℓ be the line tangent to the curve at the point $P(x, y) = P(r, \theta)$ (see figure).

a. Explain why $\tan \alpha = \dfrac{dy}{dx}$.

b. Explain why $\tan \theta = y/x$.

c. Let φ be the angle between ℓ and the line through O and P. Prove that $\tan \varphi = f(\theta)/f'(\theta)$.

d. Prove that the values of θ for which ℓ is parallel to the x-axis satisfy $\tan \theta = -f(\theta)/f'(\theta)$.

e. Prove that the values of θ for which ℓ is parallel to the y-axis satisfy $\tan \theta = f'(\theta)/f(\theta)$.

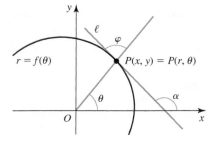

63. Isogonal curves Let a curve be described by $r = f(\theta)$, where $f(\theta) > 0$ on its domain. Referring to the figure of Exercise 62, a curve is **isogonal** provided the angle φ is constant for all θ.

a. Prove that φ is constant for all θ provided $\cot \varphi = f'(\theta)/f(\theta)$ is constant, which implies that $\dfrac{d}{d\theta}(\ln f(\theta)) = k$, where k is a constant.

b. Use part (a) to prove that the family of logarithmic spirals $r = Ce^{k\theta}$ consists of isogonal curves, where C and k are constants.

c. Graph the curve $r = 2e^{2\theta}$ and confirm the result of part (b).

QUICK CHECK ANSWERS

1. Apply the Product Rule.   **2.** $\sqrt{2} + 1$

3. Area $= \displaystyle\int_0^{2\pi} \tfrac{1}{2}(8)^2 \, d\theta = 64\pi$ **4.** $\left[0, \frac{\pi}{3}\right]$ or $\left[\frac{\pi}{3}, \frac{2\pi}{3}\right]$

(among others) ◄

10.4 Conic Sections

Conic sections are best visualized as the Greeks did over 2000 years ago by slicing a double cone with a plane (Figure 10.42). Three of the seven different sets of points that arise in this way are *ellipses*, *parabolas*, and *hyperbolas*. These curves have practical applications and broad theoretical importance. For example, celestial bodies travel in orbits that are modeled by ellipses and hyperbolas. Mirrors for telescopes are designed using the properties of conic sections. And architectural structures, such as domes and arches, are sometimes based on these curves.

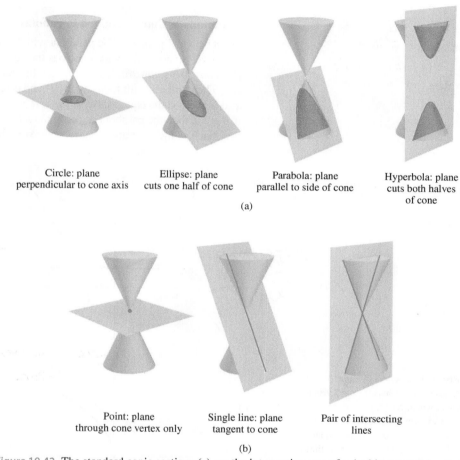

Circle: plane perpendicular to cone axis

Ellipse: plane cuts one half of cone

Parabola: plane parallel to side of cone

Hyperbola: plane cuts both halves of cone

(a)

Point: plane through cone vertex only

Single line: plane tangent to cone

Pair of intersecting lines

(b)

Figure 10.42 The standard conic sections (a) are the intersection sets of a double cone and a plane that does not pass through the vertex of the cone. Degenerate conic sections (lines and points) are produced when a plane passes through the vertex of the cone (b).

Parabolas

A **parabola** is the set of points in a plane that are equidistant from a fixed point F (called the **focus**) and a fixed line (called the **directrix**). In the four standard orientations, a parabola may open upward, downward, to the right, or to the left. We derive the equation of the parabola that opens upward.

Suppose the focus F is on the y-axis at $(0, p)$ and the directrix is the horizontal line $y = -p$, where $p > 0$. The parabola is the set of points P that satisfy the defining property $|PF| = |PL|$, where $L(x, -p)$ is the point on the directrix closest to P

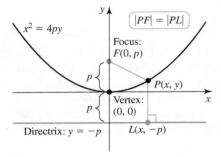

Figure 10.43

QUICK CHECK 1 Verify that $\sqrt{x^2 + (y - p)^2} = y + p$ is equivalent to $x^2 = 4py$. ◄

(Figure 10.43). Consider an arbitrary point $P(x, y)$ that satisfies this condition. Applying the distance formula, we have

$$\underbrace{\sqrt{x^2 + (y - p)^2}}_{|PF|} = \underbrace{y + p}_{|PL|}.$$

Squaring both sides of this equation and simplifying gives the equation $x^2 = 4py$. This is the equation of a parabola that is symmetric about the y-axis and opens upward. The **vertex** of the parabola is the point closest to the directrix; in this case, it is $(0, 0)$ (which satisfies $|PF| = |PL| = p$).

The equations of the other three standard parabolas are derived in a similar way.

Equations of Four Standard Parabolas

Let p be a real number. The parabola with focus at $(0, p)$ and directrix $y = -p$ is symmetric about the y-axis and has the equation $x^2 = 4py$. If $p > 0$, then the parabola opens *upward*; if $p < 0$, then the parabola opens *downward*.

The parabola with focus at $(p, 0)$ and directrix $x = -p$ is symmetric about the x-axis and has the equation $y^2 = 4px$. If $p > 0$, then the parabola opens *to the right*; if $p < 0$, then the parabola opens *to the left*.

Each of these parabolas has its vertex at the origin (Figure 10.44).

➤ Recall that a curve is symmetric with respect to the x-axis if $(x, -y)$ is on the curve whenever (x, y) is on the curve. So a y^2-term indicates symmetry with respect to the x-axis. Similarly, an x^2-term indicates symmetry with respect to the y-axis.

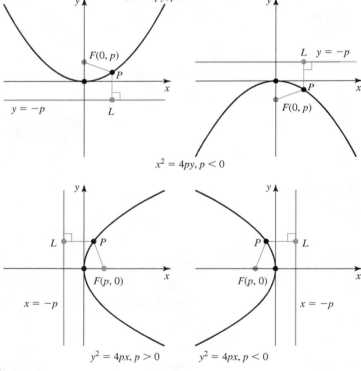

Figure 10.44

QUICK CHECK 2 In which direction do the following parabolas open?

a. $y^2 = -4x$ **b.** $x^2 = 4y$ ◄

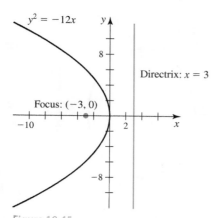

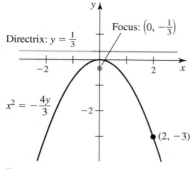

Figure 10.45

EXAMPLE 1 **Graphing parabolas** Find the focus and directrix of the parabola $y^2 = -12x$. Sketch its graph.

SOLUTION The y^2-term indicates that the parabola is symmetric with respect to the x-axis. Rewriting the equation as $x = -y^2/12$, we see that $x \leq 0$ for all y, implying that the parabola opens to the left. Comparing $y^2 = -12x$ to the standard form $y^2 = 4px$, we see that $p = -3$; therefore, the focus is $(-3, 0)$, and the directrix is $x = 3$ (Figure 10.45).

Related Exercises 13–18 ◄

EXAMPLE 2 **Equations of parabolas** Find the equation of the parabola with vertex $(0, 0)$ that opens downward and passes through the point $(2, -3)$.

SOLUTION The standard parabola that opens downward has the equation $x^2 = 4py$. The point $(2, -3)$ must satisfy this equation. Substituting $x = 2$ and $y = -3$ into $x^2 = 4py$, we find that $p = -\frac{1}{3}$. Therefore, the focus is at $(0, -\frac{1}{3})$, the directrix is $y = \frac{1}{3}$, and the equation of the parabola is $x^2 = -4y/3$, or $y = -3x^2/4$ (Figure 10.46).

Related Exercises 19–26 ◄

Reflection Property Parabolas have a property that makes them useful in the design of reflectors and transmitters. A particle approaching a parabola on any line parallel to the axis of the parabola is reflected on a line that passes through the focus (Figure 10.47); this property is used to focus incoming light by a parabolic mirror on a telescope. Alternatively, signals emanating from the focus are reflected on lines parallel to the axis, a property used to design radio transmitters and headlights (Exercise 83).

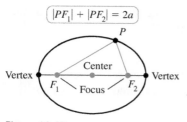

Figure 10.46

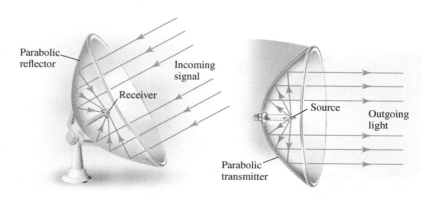

Figure 10.47

Ellipses

An **ellipse** is the set of points in a plane whose distances from two fixed points have a constant sum that we denote $2a$ (Figure 10.48). Each of the two fixed points is a **focus** (plural **foci**). The equation of an ellipse is simplest if the foci are on the x-axis at $(\pm c, 0)$ or on the y-axis at $(0, \pm c)$. In either case, the **center** of the ellipse is $(0, 0)$. If the foci are on the x-axis, the points $(\pm a, 0)$ lie on the ellipse and are called **vertices**. If the foci are on the y-axis, the vertices are $(0, \pm a)$ (Figure 10.49). A short calculation (Exercise 85) using the definition of the ellipse results in the following equations for an ellipse.

$$\boxed{|PF_1| + |PF_2| = 2a}$$

Figure 10.48

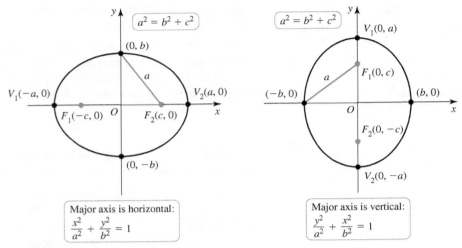

Figure 10.49

> When necessary, we distinguish between the *major-axis vertices* $(\pm a, 0)$ or $(0, \pm a)$, and the *minor-axis vertices* $(\pm b, 0)$ or $(0, \pm b)$. The word *vertices* (without further description) is understood to mean *major-axis vertices*.

QUICK CHECK 3 In the case that the vertices and foci are on the x-axis, show that the length of the minor axis of an ellipse is $2b$. ◄

Equations of Standard Ellipses

An ellipse centered at the origin with foci F_1 and F_2 at $(\pm c, 0)$ and vertices V_1 and V_2 at $(\pm a, 0)$ has the equation

$$\frac{x^2}{a^2} + \frac{y^2}{b^2} = 1, \quad \text{where } a^2 = b^2 + c^2.$$

An ellipse centered at the origin with foci at $(0, \pm c)$ and vertices at $(0, \pm a)$ has the equation

$$\frac{y^2}{a^2} + \frac{x^2}{b^2} = 1, \quad \text{where } a^2 = b^2 + c^2.$$

In both cases, $a > b > 0$ and $a > c > 0$, the length of the long axis (called the **major axis**) is $2a$, and the length of the short axis (called the **minor axis**) is $2b$.

EXAMPLE 3 Graphing ellipses Find the vertices, foci, and length of the major and minor axes of the ellipse $\dfrac{x^2}{9} + \dfrac{y^2}{4} = 1$. Graph the ellipse.

SOLUTION Because $9 > 4$, we identify $a^2 = 9$ and $b^2 = 4$. Therefore, $a = 3$ and $b = 2$. The lengths of the major and minor axes are $2a = 6$ and $2b = 4$, respectively. The vertices V_1 and V_2 are at $(\pm 3, 0)$ and lie on the x-axis, as do the foci. The relationship $c^2 = a^2 - b^2$ implies that $c^2 = 5$, or $c = \sqrt{5}$. Therefore, the foci F_1 and F_2 are at $(\pm\sqrt{5}, 0)$. The graph of the ellipse is shown in Figure 10.50.

Related Exercises 27–32 ◄

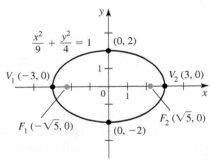

Figure 10.50

EXAMPLE 4 Equation of an ellipse Find the equation of the ellipse centered at the origin with its foci on the y-axis, a major axis of length 8, and a minor axis of length 4. Graph the ellipse.

SOLUTION Because the length of the major axis is 8, the vertices V_1 and V_2 are located at $(0, \pm 4)$, and $a = 4$. Because the length of the minor axis is 4, we have $b = 2$. Therefore, the equation of the ellipse is

$$\frac{y^2}{16} + \frac{x^2}{4} = 1.$$

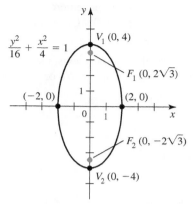

$$\frac{y^2}{16} + \frac{x^2}{4} = 1$$

Figure 10.51

Using the relation $c^2 = a^2 - b^2$, we find that $c = 2\sqrt{3}$ and the foci F_1 and F_2 are at $(0, \pm 2\sqrt{3})$. The ellipse is shown in Figure 10.51.

Related Exercises 33–38 ◄

Hyperbolas

A **hyperbola** is the set of points in a plane whose distances from two fixed points have a constant difference, either $2a$ or $-2a$ (Figure 10.52). As with ellipses, the two fixed points are called **foci**. We consider the case in which the foci are on either the x-axis at $(\pm c, 0)$ or on the y-axis at $(0, \pm c)$. If the foci are on the x-axis, the points $(\pm a, 0)$ on the hyperbola are called the **vertices**. In this case, the hyperbola has no y-intercepts, but it has the **asymptotes** $y = \pm bx/a$, where $b^2 = c^2 - a^2$. Similarly, if the foci are on the y-axis, the vertices are $(0, \pm a)$, the hyperbola has no x-intercepts, and it has the asymptotes $y = \pm ax/b$ (Figure 10.53). A short calculation (Exercise 86) using the definition of the hyperbola results in the following equations for standard hyperbolas.

➤ Asymptotes that are not parallel to one of the coordinate axes, as in the case of the standard hyperbolas, are called **oblique**, or **slant, asymptotes**.

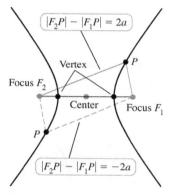

Figure 10.52

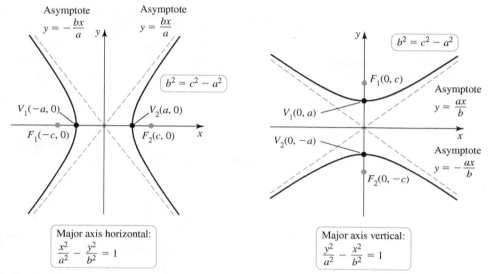

Figure 10.53

➤ Notice that the asymptotes for hyperbolas are $y = \pm bx/a$ when the vertices are on the x-axis and $y = \pm ax/b$ when the vertices are on the y-axis (the roles of a and b are reversed).

Equations of Standard Hyperbolas

A hyperbola centered at the origin with foci F_1 and F_2 at $(\pm c, 0)$ and vertices V_1 and V_2 at $(\pm a, 0)$ has the equation

$$\frac{x^2}{a^2} - \frac{y^2}{b^2} = 1, \quad \text{where} \quad b^2 = c^2 - a^2.$$

The hyperbola has **asymptotes** $y = \pm bx/a$.

A hyperbola centered at the origin with foci at $(0, \pm c)$ and vertices at $(0, \pm a)$ has the equation

$$\frac{y^2}{a^2} - \frac{x^2}{b^2} = 1, \quad \text{where} \quad b^2 = c^2 - a^2.$$

The hyperbola has **asymptotes** $y = \pm ax/b$.

In both cases, $c > a > 0$ and $c > b > 0$.

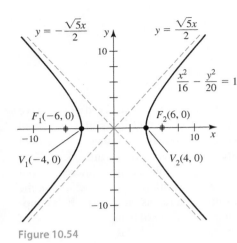

Figure 10.54

> ▶ The conic section lies in the plane formed by the directrix and the focus.

EXAMPLE 5   Graphing hyperbolas Find the equation of the hyperbola centered at the origin with vertices V_1 and V_2 at $(\pm 4, 0)$ and foci F_1 and F_2 at $(\pm 6, 0)$. Graph the hyperbola.

SOLUTION Because the foci are on the x-axis, the vertices are also on the x-axis, and there are no y-intercepts. With $a = 4$ and $c = 6$, we have $b^2 = c^2 - a^2 = 20$, or $b = 2\sqrt{5}$. Therefore, the equation of the hyperbola is

$$\frac{x^2}{16} - \frac{y^2}{20} = 1.$$

The asymptotes are $y = \pm bx/a = \pm \sqrt{5}x/2$ (Figure 10.54).

Related Exercises 39–50 ◀

QUICK CHECK 4 Identify the vertices and foci of the hyperbola $y^2 - x^2/4 = 1$. ◀

Eccentricity and Directrix

Parabolas, ellipses, and hyperbolas may also be developed in a single unified way called the *eccentricity-directrix* approach. We let ℓ be a line called the **directrix** and F be a point not on ℓ called a **focus**. The **eccentricity** is a real number $e > 0$. Consider the set C of points P in a plane with the property that the distance $|PF|$ equals e multiplied by the perpendicular distance $|PL|$ from P to ℓ (Figure 10.55); that is,

$$|PF| = e|PL| \quad \text{or} \quad \frac{|PF|}{|PL|} = e = \text{constant}.$$

Depending on the value of e, the set C is one of the three standard conic sections, as described in the following theorem.

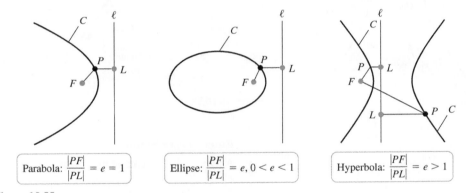

Figure 10.55

> ▶ Theorem 10.3 for ellipses and hyperbolas describes how the entire curve is generated using just one focus and one directrix. Nevertheless, every ellipse and every hyperbola has two foci and two directrices.

THEOREM 10.3   Eccentricity-Directrix Theorem

Suppose ℓ is a line, F is a point not on ℓ, and e is a positive real number. Let C be the set of points P in a plane with the property that $\dfrac{|PF|}{|PL|} = e$, where $|PL|$ is the perpendicular distance from P to ℓ.

1. If $e = 1$, C is a **parabola**.
2. If $0 < e < 1$, C is an **ellipse**.
3. If $e > 1$, C is a **hyperbola**.

The proof of this theorem is straightforward; it requires an algebraic calculation that is found in Appendix B. The proof establishes relationships between five parameters a, b, c, d, and e that are characteristic of any ellipse or hyperbola. The relationships are given in the following summary.

SUMMARY   Properties of Ellipses and Hyperbolas

An ellipse or a hyperbola centered at the origin has the following properties.

	Foci on x-axis	Foci on y-axis
Major-axis vertices:	$(\pm a, 0)$	$(0, \pm a)$
Minor-axis vertices (for ellipses):	$(0, \pm b)$	$(\pm b, 0)$
Foci:	$(\pm c, 0)$	$(0, \pm c)$
Directrices:	$x = \pm d$	$y = \pm d$

Eccentricity: $0 < e < 1$ for ellipses, $e > 1$ for hyperbolas.

Given any two of the five parameters $a, b, c, d,$ and e, the other three are found using the relations

$$c = ae, \quad d = \frac{a}{e},$$

$$b^2 = a^2 - c^2 \quad \text{(for ellipses)}, \qquad b^2 = c^2 - a^2 \quad \text{(for hyperbolas)}.$$

QUICK CHECK 5 Given an ellipse with $a = 3$ and $e = \frac{1}{2}$, what are the values of $b, c,$ and d? ◄

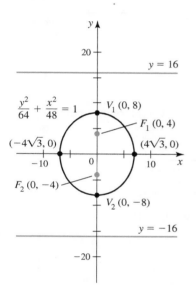

Figure 10.56

EXAMPLE 6   Equations of ellipses Find the equation of the ellipse centered at the origin with foci F_1 and F_2 at $(0, \pm 4)$ and eccentricity $e = \frac{1}{2}$. Give the length of the major and minor axes, the location of the vertices, and the directrices. Graph the ellipse.

SOLUTION An ellipse with its major axis along the y-axis has the equation

$$\frac{y^2}{a^2} + \frac{x^2}{b^2} = 1,$$

where a and b must be determined (with $a > b$). Because the foci are at $(0, \pm 4)$, we have $c = 4$. Using $e = \frac{1}{2}$ and the relation $c = ae$, it follows that $a = c/e = 8$. So the length of the major axis is $2a = 16$, and the major-axis vertices V_1 and V_2 are $(0, \pm 8)$. Also, $d = a/e = 16$, so the directrices are $y = \pm 16$. Finally, $b^2 = a^2 - c^2 = 48$, or $b = 4\sqrt{3}$. So the length of the minor axis is $2b = 8\sqrt{3}$, and the minor-axis vertices are $(\pm 4\sqrt{3}, 0)$ (Figure 10.56). The equation of the ellipse is

$$\frac{y^2}{64} + \frac{x^2}{48} = 1.$$

Related Exercises 51–54 ◄

Polar Equations of Conic Sections

It turns out that conic sections have a natural representation in polar coordinates, provided we use the eccentricity-directrix approach given in Theorem 10.3. Furthermore, a single polar equation covers parabolas, ellipses, and hyperbolas.

When working in polar equations, the key is to place a focus of the conic section at the origin of the coordinate system. We begin by placing one focus F at the origin and taking a directrix perpendicular to the x-axis through $(d, 0)$, where $d > 0$ (Figure 10.57). We now use the definition $\dfrac{|PF|}{|PL|} = e$, where $P(r, \theta)$ is an arbitrary point on the conic.

As shown in Figure 10.57, $|PF| = r$ and $|PL| = d - r\cos\theta$. The condition $\dfrac{|PF|}{|PL|} = e$ implies that $r = e(d - r\cos\theta)$. Solving for r, we have

$$r = \frac{ed}{1 + e\cos\theta}.$$

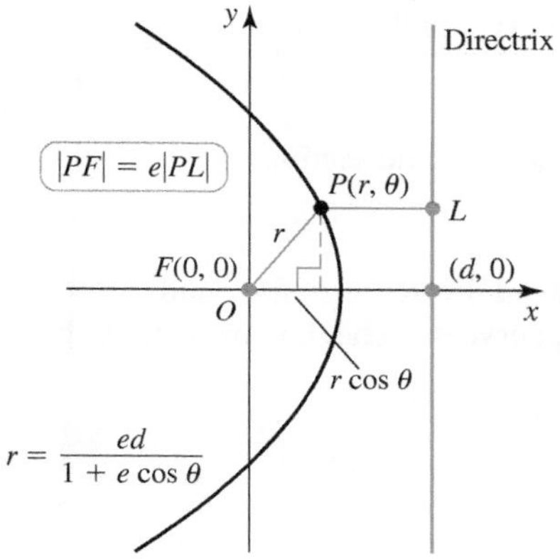

$|PF| = e|PL|$

$$r = \frac{ed}{1 + e\cos\theta}$$

Figure 10.57

A similar derivation (Exercise 74) with the directrix at $x = -d$, where $d > 0$, results in the equation

$$r = \frac{ed}{1 - e \cos \theta}.$$

For horizontal directrices at $y = \pm d$ (Figure 10.58), a similar argument (Exercise 74) leads to the equations

$$r = \frac{ed}{1 \pm e \sin \theta}.$$

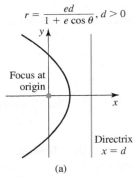

$$r = \frac{ed}{1 + e \cos \theta}, d > 0$$

(a)

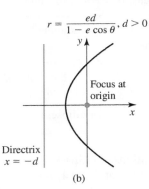

$$r = \frac{ed}{1 - e \cos \theta}, d > 0$$

(b)

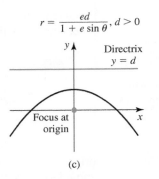

$$r = \frac{ed}{1 + e \sin \theta}, d > 0$$

(c)

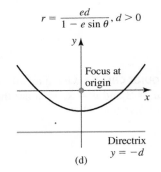

$$r = \frac{ed}{1 - e \sin \theta}, d > 0$$

(d)

Figure 10.58

THEOREM 10.4   Polar Equations of Conic Sections

Let $d > 0$. The conic section with a focus at the origin and eccentricity e has the polar equation

$$r = \frac{ed}{1 + e \cos \theta} \quad \text{or} \quad r = \frac{ed}{1 - e \cos \theta}.$$

if one directrix is $x = d$ if one directrix is $x = -d$

The conic section with a focus at the origin and eccentricity e has the polar equation

$$r = \frac{ed}{1 + e \sin \theta} \quad \text{or} \quad r = \frac{ed}{1 - e \sin \theta}.$$

if one directrix is $y = d$ if one directrix is $y = -d$

If $0 < e < 1$, the conic section is an ellipse; if $e = 1$, it is a parabola; and if $e > 1$, it is a hyperbola. The curves are defined over any interval in θ of length 2π.

QUICK CHECK 6 On which axis do the vertices and foci of the conic section $r = 2/(1 - 2 \sin \theta)$ lie? ◄

EXAMPLE 7   Conic sections in polar coordinates Find the vertices, foci, and directrices of the following conic sections. Graph each curve and check your work with a graphing utility.

a. $r = \dfrac{8}{2 + 3 \cos \theta}$ **b.** $r = \dfrac{2}{1 + \sin \theta}$

SOLUTION

a. The equation must be expressed in standard polar form for a conic section. Dividing numerator and denominator by 2, we have

$$r = \frac{4}{1 + \frac{3}{2}\cos\theta},$$

which allows us to identify $e = \frac{3}{2}$. Therefore, the equation describes a hyperbola (because $e > 1$) with one focus at the origin.

    The directrices are vertical (because $\cos\theta$ appears in the equation). Knowing that $ed = 4$, we have $d = 4/e = \frac{8}{3}$, and one directrix is $x = \frac{8}{3}$. Letting $\theta = 0$ and $\theta = \pi$, the polar coordinates of the vertices are $\left(\frac{8}{5}, 0\right)$ and $(-8, \pi)$; equivalently, the vertices are $\left(\frac{8}{5}, 0\right)$ and $(8, 0)$ in Cartesian coordinates (Figure 10.59). The center of the hyperbola is halfway between the vertices; therefore, its Cartesian coordinates are $\left(\frac{24}{5}, 0\right)$. The distance between the focus at $(0, 0)$ and the nearest vertex $\left(\frac{8}{5}, 0\right)$ is $\frac{8}{5}$. Therefore, the other focus is $\frac{8}{5}$ units to the right of the vertex $(8, 0)$. So the Cartesian coordinates of the foci are $\left(\frac{48}{5}, 0\right)$ and $(0, 0)$. Because the directrices are symmetric about the center and the left directrix is $x = \frac{8}{3}$, the right directrix is $x = \frac{104}{15} \approx 6.9$. The graph of the hyperbola (Figure 10.59) is generated as θ varies from 0 to 2π (with $\theta \neq \pm\cos^{-1}\left(-\frac{2}{3}\right)$).

b. The equation is in standard form, and it describes a parabola because $e = 1$. The sole focus is at the origin. The directrix is horizontal (because of the $\sin\theta$ term); $ed = 2$ implies that $d = 2$, and the directrix is $y = 2$. The parabola opens downward because of the plus sign in the denominator. The vertex corresponds to $\theta = \frac{\pi}{2}$ and has polar coordinates $\left(1, \frac{\pi}{2}\right)$, or Cartesian coordinates $(0, 1)$. Setting $\theta = 0$ and $\theta = \pi$, the parabola crosses the x-axis at $(2, 0)$ and $(2, \pi)$ in polar coordinates, or $(\pm 2, 0)$ in Cartesian coordinates. As θ increases from $-\frac{\pi}{2}$ to $\frac{\pi}{2}$, the right branch of the parabola is generated, and as θ increases from $\frac{\pi}{2}$ to $\frac{3\pi}{2}$, the left branch of the parabola is generated (Figure 10.60).

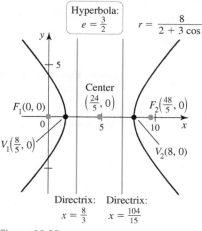

Figure 10.59

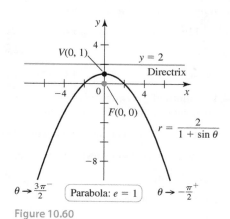

Figure 10.60

Related Exercises 55–64 ◄

EXAMPLE 8 **Conics in polar coordinates** Use a graphing utility to plot the curves

$$r = \frac{e}{1 + e\cos\theta},$$ with $e = 0.2, 0.4, 0.6,$ and 0.8. Comment on the effect of varying the eccentricity, e.

SOLUTION Because $0 < e < 1$ for each value of e, all the curves are ellipses. Notice that the equation is in standard form with $d = 1$; therefore, the curves have the same directrix, $x = d = 1$. As the eccentricity increases, the ellipses becomes more elongated. Small values of e correspond to more circular ellipses (Figure 10.61).

Related Exercises 65–66 ◄

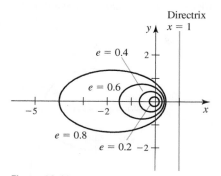

Figure 10.61

SECTION 10.4 EXERCISES

Review Questions

1. Give the property that defines all parabolas.

2. Give the property that defines all ellipses.

3. Give the property that defines all hyperbolas.

4. Sketch the three basic conic sections in standard position with vertices and foci on the x-axis.

5. Sketch the three basic conic sections in standard position with vertices and foci on the y-axis.

6. What is the equation of the standard parabola with its vertex at the origin that opens downward?

7. What is the equation of the standard ellipse with vertices at $(\pm a, 0)$ and foci at $(\pm c, 0)$?

8. What is the equation of the standard hyperbola with vertices at $(0, \pm a)$ and foci at $(0, \pm c)$?

9. Given vertices $(\pm a, 0)$ and eccentricity e, what are the coordinates of the foci of an ellipse and a hyperbola?

10. Give the equation in polar coordinates of a conic section with a focus at the origin, eccentricity e, and a directrix $x = d$, where $d > 0$.

11. What are the equations of the asymptotes of a standard hyperbola with vertices on the x-axis?

12. How does the eccentricity determine the type of conic section?

Basic Skills

13–18. Graphing parabolas *Sketch a graph of the following parabolas. Specify the location of the focus and the equation of the directrix. Use a graphing utility to check your work.*

13. $x^2 = 12y$

14. $y^2 = 20x$

15. $x = -y^2/16$

16. $4x = -y^2$

17. $8y = -3x^2$

18. $12x = 5y^2$

19–24. Equations of parabolas *Find an equation of the following parabolas, assuming the vertex is at the origin.*

19. A parabola that opens to the right with directrix $x = -4$

20. A parabola that opens downward with directrix $y = 6$

21. A parabola with focus at $(3, 0)$

22. A parabola with focus at $(-4, 0)$

23. A parabola symmetric about the y-axis that passes through the point $(2, -6)$

24. A parabola symmetric about the x-axis that passes through the point $(1, -4)$

25–26. From graphs to equations *Write an equation of the following parabolas.*

25.

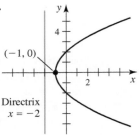

26.

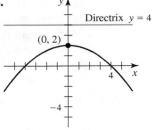

27–32. Graphing ellipses *Sketch a graph of the following ellipses. Plot and label the coordinates of the vertices and foci, and find the lengths of the major and minor axes. Use a graphing utility to check your work.*

27. $\dfrac{x^2}{4} + y^2 = 1$

28. $\dfrac{x^2}{9} + \dfrac{y^2}{4} = 1$

29. $\dfrac{x^2}{4} + \dfrac{y^2}{16} = 1$

30. $x^2 + \dfrac{y^2}{9} = 1$

31. $\dfrac{x^2}{5} + \dfrac{y^2}{7} = 1$

32. $12x^2 + 5y^2 = 60$

33–36. Equations of ellipses *Find an equation of the following ellipses, assuming the center is at the origin. Sketch a graph labeling the vertices and foci.*

33. An ellipse whose major axis is on the x-axis with length 8 and whose minor axis has length 6

34. An ellipse with vertices $(\pm 6, 0)$ and foci $(\pm 4, 0)$

35. An ellipse with vertices $(\pm 5, 0)$, passing through the point $(4, \frac{3}{5})$

36. An ellipse with vertices $(0, \pm 10)$, passing through the point $(\sqrt{3}/2, 5)$

37–38. From graphs to equations *Write an equation of the following ellipses.*

37.

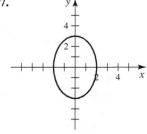

38.

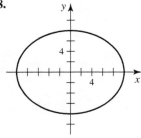

39–44. Graphing hyperbolas *Sketch a graph of the following hyperbolas. Specify the coordinates of the vertices and foci, and find the equations of the asymptotes. Use a graphing utility to check your work.*

39. $\dfrac{x^2}{4} - y^2 = 1$ **40.** $\dfrac{y^2}{16} - \dfrac{x^2}{9} = 1$

41. $4x^2 - y^2 = 16$ **42.** $25y^2 - 4x^2 = 100$

43. $\dfrac{x^2}{3} - \dfrac{y^2}{5} = 1$ **44.** $10x^2 - 7y^2 = 140$

45–48. Equations of hyperbolas *Find an equation of the following hyperbolas, assuming the center is at the origin. Sketch a graph labeling the vertices, foci, and asymptotes. Use a graphing utility to check your work.*

45. A hyperbola with vertices $(\pm 4, 0)$ and foci $(\pm 6, 0)$

46. A hyperbola with vertices $(\pm 1, 0)$ that passes through $\left(\frac{5}{3}, 8\right)$

47. A hyperbola with vertices $(\pm 2, 0)$ and asymptotes $y = \pm 3x/2$

48. A hyperbola with vertices $(0, \pm 4)$ and asymptotes $y = \pm 2x$

49–50. From graphs to equations *Write an equation of the following hyperbolas.*

49.

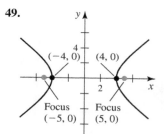

50.

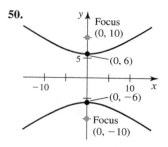

51–54. Eccentricity–directrix approach *Find an equation of the following curves, assuming the center is at the origin. Sketch a graph labeling the vertices, foci, asymptotes (if they exist), and directrices. Use a graphing utility to check your work.*

51. An ellipse with vertices $(\pm 9, 0)$ and eccentricity $\frac{1}{3}$

52. An ellipse with vertices $(0, \pm 9)$ and eccentricity $\frac{1}{4}$

53. A hyperbola with vertices $(\pm 1, 0)$ and eccentricity 3

54. A hyperbola with vertices $(0, \pm 4)$ and eccentricity 2

55–60. Polar equations for conic sections *Graph the following conic sections, labeling the vertices, foci, directrices, and asymptotes (if they exist). Use a graphing utility to check your work.*

55. $r = \dfrac{4}{1 + \cos\theta}$ **56.** $r = \dfrac{4}{2 + \cos\theta}$ **57.** $r = \dfrac{1}{2 - \cos\theta}$

58. $r = \dfrac{6}{3 + 2\sin\theta}$ **59.** $r = \dfrac{1}{2 - 2\sin\theta}$ **60.** $r = \dfrac{12}{3 - \cos\theta}$

61–64. Tracing hyperbolas and parabolas *Graph the following equations. Then use arrows and labeled points to indicate how the curve is generated as θ increases from 0 to 2π.*

61. $r = \dfrac{1}{1 + \sin\theta}$ **62.** $r = \dfrac{1}{1 + 2\cos\theta}$

63. $r = \dfrac{3}{1 - \cos\theta}$ **64.** $r = \dfrac{1}{1 - 2\cos\theta}$

T 65. Parabolas with a graphing utility Use a graphing utility to graph the parabolas $y^2 = 4px$, for $p = -5, -2, -1, 1, 2$, and 5 on the same set of axes. Explain how the shapes of the curves vary as p changes.

T 66. Hyperbolas with a graphing utility Use a graphing utility to graph the hyperbolas $r = \dfrac{e}{1 + e\cos\theta}$, for $e = 1.1, 1.3, 1.5, 1.7,$ and 2 on the same set of axes. Explain how the shapes of the curves vary as e changes.

Further Explorations

67. Explain why or why not Determine whether the following statements are true and give an explanation or counterexample.

  a. The hyperbola $x^2/4 - y^2/9 = 1$ has no y-intercepts.

  b. On every ellipse, there are exactly two points at which the curve has slope s, where s is any real number.

  c. Given the directrices and foci of a standard hyperbola, it is possible to find its vertices, eccentricity, and asymptotes.

  d. The point on a parabola closest to the focus is the vertex.

68–71. Tangent lines *Find an equation of the line tangent to the following curves at the given point.*

68. $y^2 = 8x;\ (8, -8)$ **69.** $x^2 = -6y;\ (-6, -6)$

70. $r = \dfrac{1}{1 + \sin\theta};\ \left(\dfrac{2}{3}, \dfrac{\pi}{6}\right)$ **71.** $y^2 - \dfrac{x^2}{64} = 1;\ \left(6, -\dfrac{5}{4}\right)$

72–73. Graphs to polar equations *Find a polar equation for each conic section. Assume one focus is at the origin.*

72.

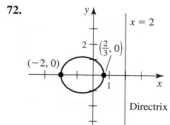

73.

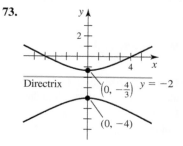

74. Deriving polar equations for conics Modify Figure 10.57 to derive the polar equation of a conic section with a focus at the origin in the following three cases.

  a. Vertical directrix at $x = -d$, where $d > 0$

  b. Horizontal directrix at $y = d$, where $d > 0$

  c. Horizontal directrix at $y = -d$, where $d > 0$

75. Another construction for a hyperbola Suppose two circles, whose centers are at least $2a$ units apart (see figure), are centered at F_1 and F_2, respectively. The radius of one circle is $2a + r$ and the radius of the other circle is r, where $r \geq 0$. Show that as r increases, the intersection point P of the two circles describes one branch of a hyperbola with foci at F_1 and F_2.

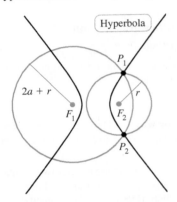

76. The ellipse and the parabola Let R be the region bounded by the upper half of the ellipse $x^2/2 + y^2 = 1$ and the parabola $y = x^2/\sqrt{2}$.

a. Find the area of R.
b. Which is greater, the volume of the solid generated when R is revolved about the x-axis or the volume of the solid generated when R is revolved about the y-axis?

77. Tangent lines for an ellipse Show that an equation of the line tangent to the ellipse $x^2/a^2 + y^2/b^2 = 1$ at the point (x_0, y_0) is

$$\frac{xx_0}{a^2} + \frac{yy_0}{b^2} = 1.$$

78. Tangent lines for a hyperbola Find an equation of the line tangent to the hyperbola $x^2/a^2 - y^2/b^2 = 1$ at the point (x_0, y_0).

79. Volume of an ellipsoid Suppose that the ellipse $x^2/a^2 + y^2/b^2 = 1$ is revolved about the x-axis. What is the volume of the solid enclosed by the *ellipsoid* that is generated? Is the volume different if the same ellipse is revolved about the y-axis?

80. Area of a sector of a hyperbola Consider the region R bounded by the right branch of the hyperbola $x^2/a^2 - y^2/b^2 = 1$ and the vertical line through the right focus.

a. What is the area of R?
b. Sketch a graph that shows how the area of R varies with the eccentricity e, for $e > 1$.

81. Volume of a hyperbolic cap Consider the region R bounded by the right branch of the hyperbola $x^2/a^2 - y^2/b^2 = 1$ and the vertical line through the right focus.

a. What is the volume of the solid that is generated when R is revolved about the x-axis?
b. What is the volume of the solid that is generated when R is revolved about the y-axis?

82. Volume of a paraboloid (Archimedes) The region bounded by the parabola $y = ax^2$ and the horizontal line $y = h$ is revolved about the y-axis to generate a solid bounded by a surface called

a *paraboloid* (where $a > 0$ and $h > 0$). Show that the volume of the solid is $\frac{2}{3}$ the volume of the cone with the same base and vertex.

Applications

(See the Guided Project Properties of Conic sections for additional applications of conic sections.)

83. Reflection property of parabolas Consider the parabola $y = x^2/4p$ with its focus at $F(0, p)$ (see figure). The goal is to show that the angle of incidence between the ray ℓ and the tangent line L (α in the figure) equals the angle of reflection between the line PF and L (β in the figure). If these two angles are equal, then the reflection property is proved because ℓ is reflected through F.

a. Let $P(x_0, y_0)$ be a point on the parabola. Show that the slope of the line tangent to the curve at P is $\tan \theta = x_0/(2p)$.
b. Show that $\tan \varphi = (p - y_0)/x_0$.
c. Show that $\alpha = \pi/2 - \theta$; therefore, $\tan \alpha = \cot \theta$.
d. Note that $\beta = \theta + \varphi$. Use the tangent addition formula $\tan (\theta + \varphi) = \dfrac{\tan \theta + \tan \varphi}{1 - \tan \theta \tan \varphi}$ to show that $\tan \alpha = \tan \beta = 2p/x_0$.
e. Conclude that because α and β are acute angles, $\alpha = \beta$.

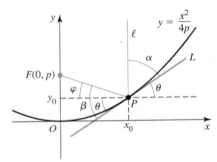

84. Golden Gate Bridge Completed in 1937, San Francisco's Golden Gate Bridge is 2.7 km long and weighs about 890,000 tons. The length of the span between the two central towers is 1280 m; the towers themselves extend 152 m above the roadway. The cables that support the deck of the bridge between the two towers hang in a parabola (see figure). Assuming the origin is midway between the towers on the deck of the bridge, find an equation that describes the cables. How long is a guy wire that hangs vertically from the cables to the roadway 500 m from the center of the bridge?

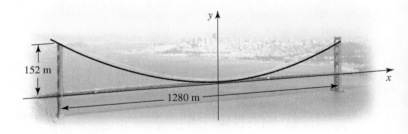

Additional Exercises

85. Equation of an ellipse Consider an ellipse to be the set of points in a plane whose distances from two fixed points have a constant sum $2a$. Derive the equation of an ellipse. Assume the two fixed points are on the x-axis equidistant from the origin.

86. Equation of a hyperbola Consider a hyperbola to be the set of points in a plane whose distances from two fixed points have a constant difference of $2a$ or $-2a$. Derive the equation of a hyperbola. Assume the two fixed points are on the x-axis equidistant from the origin.

87. Equidistant set Show that the set of points equidistant from a circle and a line not passing through the circle is a parabola. Assume the circle, line, and parabola lie in the same plane.

88. Polar equation of a conic Show that the polar equation of an ellipse or a hyperbola with one focus at the origin, major axis of length $2a$ on the x-axis, and eccentricity e is

$$r = \frac{a(1 - e^2)}{1 + e \cos \theta}.$$

89. Shared asymptotes Suppose that two hyperbolas with eccentricities e and E have perpendicular major axes and share a set of asymptotes. Show that $e^{-2} + E^{-2} = 1$.

90–94. Focal chords *A **focal chord** of a conic section is a line through a focus joining two points of the curve. The **latus rectum** is the focal chord perpendicular to the major axis of the conic. Prove the following properties.*

90. The lines tangent to the endpoints of any focal chord of a parabola $y^2 = 4px$ intersect on the directrix and are perpendicular.

91. Let L be the latus rectum of the parabola $y^2 = 4px$, for $p > 0$. Let F be the focus of the parabola, P be any point on the parabola to the left of L, and D be the (shortest) distance between P and L. Show that for all P, $D + |FP|$ is a constant. Find the constant.

92. The length of the latus rectum of the parabola $y^2 = 4px$ or $x^2 = 4py$ is $4|p|$.

93. The length of the latus rectum of an ellipse centered at the origin is $2b^2/a = 2b\sqrt{1 - e^2}$.

94. The length of the latus rectum of a hyperbola centered at the origin is $2b^2/a = 2b\sqrt{e^2 - 1}$.

95. Confocal ellipse and hyperbola Show that an ellipse and a hyperbola that have the same two foci intersect at right angles.

96. Approach to asymptotes Show that the vertical distance between a hyperbola $x^2/a^2 - y^2/b^2 = 1$ and its asymptote $y = bx/a$ approaches zero as $x \to \infty$, where $0 < b < a$.

97. Sector of a hyperbola Let H be the right branch of the hyperbola $x^2 - y^2 = 1$ and let ℓ be the line $y = m(x - 2)$ that passes through the point $(2, 0)$ with slope m, where $-\infty < m < \infty$. Let R be the region in the first quadrant bounded by H and ℓ (see figure). Let $A(m)$ be the area of R. Note that for some values of m, $A(m)$ is not defined.

    a. Find the x-coordinates of the intersection points between H and ℓ as functions of m; call them $u(m)$ and $v(m)$, where $v(m) > u(m) > 1$. For what values of m are there two intersection points?

    b. Evaluate $\lim\limits_{m \to 1^+} u(m)$ and $\lim\limits_{m \to 1^+} v(m)$.

    c. Evaluate $\lim\limits_{m \to \infty} u(m)$ and $\lim\limits_{m \to \infty} v(m)$.

    d. Evaluate and interpret $\lim\limits_{m \to \infty} A(m)$.

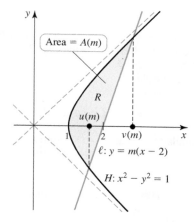

T 98. The anvil of a hyperbola Let H be the hyperbola $x^2 - y^2 = 1$ and let S be the 2-by-2 square bisected by the asymptotes of H. Let R be the anvil-shaped region bounded by the hyperbola and the horizontal lines $y = \pm p$ (see figure).

    a. For what value of p is the area of R equal to the area of S?

    b. For what value of p is the area of R twice the area of S?

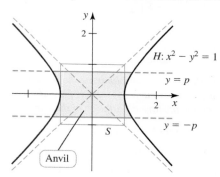

99. Parametric equations for an ellipse Consider the parametric equations

$$x = a \cos t + b \sin t, \quad y = c \cos t + d \sin t,$$

where a, b, c, and d are real numbers.

    a. Show that (apart from a set of special cases) the equations describe an ellipse of the form $Ax^2 + Bxy + Cy^2 = K$, where A, B, C, and K are constants.

    b. Show that (apart from a set of special cases), the equations describe an ellipse with its axes aligned with the x- and y-axes provided $ab + cd = 0$.

    c. Show that the equations describe a circle provided $ab + cd = 0$ and $c^2 + d^2 = a^2 + b^2 \neq 0$.

QUICK CHECK ANSWERS

2. a. Left   **b.** Up   **3.** The minor-axis vertices are $(0, \pm b)$. The distance between them is $2b$, which is the length of the minor axis.   **4.** Vertices: $(0, \pm 1)$; foci: $(0, \pm\sqrt{5})$ **5.** $b = 3\sqrt{3}/2$, $c = 3/2$, $d = 6$ **6.** y-axis ◄

CHAPTER 10   REVIEW EXERCISES

1. **Explain why or why not** Determine whether the following statements are true and give an explanation or counterexample.

   a. A set of parametric equations for a given curve is always unique.

   b. The equations $x = e^t, y = 2e^t$, for $-\infty < t < \infty$, describe a line passing through the origin with slope 2.

   c. The polar coordinates $(3, -3\pi/4)$ and $(-3, \pi/4)$ describe the same point in the plane.

   d. The area of the region between the inner and outer loops of the limaçon $r = f(\theta) = 1 - 4\cos\theta$ is $\dfrac{1}{2}\displaystyle\int_0^{2\pi} f(\theta)^2\, d\theta$.

   e. The hyperbola $y^2/2 - x^2/4 = 1$ has no x-intercepts.

   f. The equation $x^2 + 4y^2 - 2x = 3$ describes an ellipse.

2–5. Parametric curves

   a. Plot the following curves, indicating the positive orientation.
   b. Eliminate the parameter to obtain an equation in x and y.
   c. Identify or briefly describe the curve.
   d. Evaluate dy/dx at the specified point.

2. $x = t^2 + 4, y = 6 - t$, for $-\infty < t < \infty$; $(5, 5)$

3. $x = e^t, y = 3e^{-2t}$, for $-\infty < t < \infty$; $(1, 3)$

4. $x = 10\sin 2t, y = 16\cos 2t$, for $0 \le t \le \pi$; $(5\sqrt{3}, 8)$

5. $x = \ln t, y = 8\ln t^2$, for $1 \le t \le e^2$; $(1, 16)$

6. **Circles** What is the relationship among a, b, c, and d such that the equations $x = a\cos t + b\sin t, y = c\cos t + d\sin t$ describe a circle? What is the radius of the circle?

7–9. Eliminating the parameter Eliminate the parameter to find a description of the following curves in terms of x and y. Give a geometric description and the positive orientation of the curve.

7. $x = 4\cos t, y = 3\sin t$; $0 \le t \le 2\pi$

8. $x = 4\cos t - 1, y = 4\sin t + 2$; $0 \le t \le 2\pi$

9. $x = \sin t - 3, y = \cos t + 6$; $0 \le t \le \pi$

10. **Parametric to polar equations** Find a description of the following curve in polar coordinates and describe the curve.

$$x = (1 + \cos t)\cos t, \ y = (1 + \cos t)\sin t + 6; \ 0 \le t \le 2\pi$$

11–16. Parametric description Write parametric equations for the following curves. Solutions are not unique.

11. The circle $x^2 + y^2 = 9$, generated clockwise

12. The upper half of the ellipse $\dfrac{x^2}{9} + \dfrac{y^2}{4} = 1$, generated counterclockwise

13. The right side of the ellipse $\dfrac{x^2}{9} + \dfrac{y^2}{4} = 1$, generated counterclockwise

14. The line $y - 3 = 4(x + 2)$

15. The line segment from $P(-1, 0)$ to $Q(1, 1)$ and the line segment from Q to P

16. The segment of the curve $f(x) = x^3 + 2x$ from $(0, 0)$ to $(2, 12)$

T 17. **Tangent lines** Find an equation of the line tangent to the cycloid $x = t - \sin t, y = 1 - \cos t$ at the points corresponding to $t = \pi/6$ and $t = 2\pi/3$.

18–19. Sets in polar coordinates Sketch the following sets of points.

18. $\{(r, \theta): 4 \le r^2 \le 9\}$

19. $\{(r, \theta): 0 \le r \le 4, -\pi/2 \le \theta \le -\pi/3\}$

20. **Matching polar curves** Match equations a–f with graphs A–F.

   a. $r = 3\sin 4\theta$ **b.** $r^2 = 4\cos\theta$
   c. $r = 2 - 3\sin\theta$ **d.** $r = 1 + 2\cos\theta$
   e. $r = 3\cos 3\theta$ **f.** $r = e^{-\theta/6}$

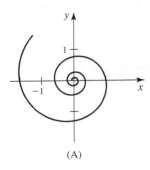

(A)

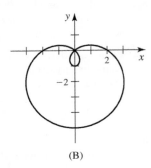

(B)

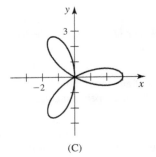

(C)

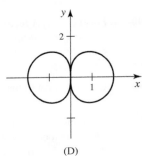

(D)

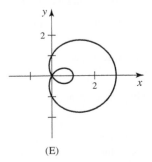

(E)

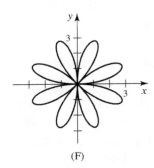

(F)

21. **Polar valentine** Liz wants to show her love for Jake by passing him a valentine on her graphing calculator. Sketch each of the following curves and determine which one Liz should use to get a heart-shaped curve.

   a. $r = 5\cos\theta$ **b.** $r = 1 - \sin\theta$ **c.** $r = \cos 3\theta$

22. **Jake's response** Jake responds to Liz (Exercise 21) with a graph that shows that his love for her is infinite. Sketch each of the following curves. Which one should Jake send to Liz to get an infinity symbol?

   a. $r = \theta$, for $\theta \ge 0$ **b.** $r = \frac{1}{2} + \sin\theta$ **c.** $r^2 = \cos 2\theta$

23. **Polar conversion** Write the equation

$$r^2 + r(2\sin\theta - 6\cos\theta) = 0$$

in Cartesian coordinates and identify the corresponding curve.

24. Polar conversion Consider the equation $r = 4/(\sin\theta + \cos\theta)$.

    a. Convert the equation to Cartesian coordinates and identify the curve it describes.

    b. Graph the curve and indicate the points that correspond to $\theta = 0, \pi/2$, and 2π.

    c. Give an interval in θ on which the entire curve is generated.

25. Cartesian conversion Write the equation $(x - 4)^2 + y^2 = 16$ in polar coordinates and state values of θ that produce the entire graph of the circle.

26. Cartesian conversion Write the equation $x = y^2$ in polar coordinates and state values of θ that produce the entire graph of the parabola.

T 27. Intersection points Consider the polar equations $r = 1$ and $r = 2 - 4\cos\theta$.

    a. Graph the curves. How many intersection points do you observe?

    b. Give approximate polar coordinates of the intersection points.

T 28–31. Slopes of tangent lines

    a. Find all points where the following curves have vertical and horizontal tangent lines.

    b. Find the slope of the lines tangent to the curve at the origin (when relevant).

    c. Sketch the curve and all the tangent lines identified in parts (a) and (b).

28. $r = 2\cos 2\theta$ **29.** $r = 4 + 2\sin\theta$

30. $r = 3 - 6\cos\theta$ **31.** $r^2 = 2\cos 2\theta$

32–37. Areas of regions *Find the area of the following regions. In each case, graph the curve(s) and shade the region in question.*

32. The region enclosed by all the leaves of the rose $r = 3\sin 4\theta$

33. The region enclosed by the limaçon $r = 3 - \cos\theta$

34. The region inside the limaçon $r = 2 + \cos\theta$ and outside the circle $r = 2$

T 35. The region inside the lemniscate $r^2 = 4\cos 2\theta$ and outside the circle $r = \frac{1}{2}$

36. The area that is inside both the cardioids $r = 1 - \cos\theta$ and $r = 1 + \cos\theta$

37. The area that is inside the cardioid $r = 1 + \cos\theta$ and outside the cardioid $r = 1 - \cos\theta$

38–43. Conic sections

    a. Determine whether the following equations describe a parabola, an ellipse, or a hyperbola.

    b. Use analytical methods to determine the location of the foci, vertices, and directrices.

    c. Find the eccentricity of the curve.

    d. Make an accurate graph of the curve.

38. $x = 16y^2$ **39.** $x^2 - y^2/2 = 1$

40. $x^2/4 + y^2/25 = 1$ **41.** $y^2 - 4x^2 = 16$

42. $y = 8x^2 + 16x + 8$ **43.** $4x^2 + 8y^2 = 16$

44. Matching equations and curves Match equations a–f with graphs A–F.

    a. $x^2 - y^2 = 4$ **b.** $x^2 + 4y^2 = 4$

    c. $y^2 - 3x = 0$ **d.** $x^2 + 3y = 1$

    e. $x^2/4 + y^2/8 = 1$ **f.** $y^2/8 - x^2/2 = 1$

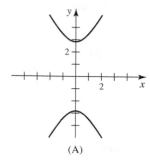

(A)

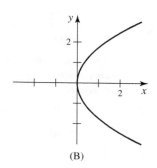

(B)

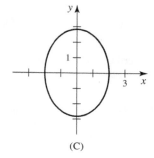

(C)

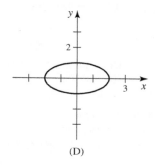

(D)

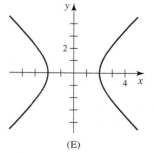

(E)

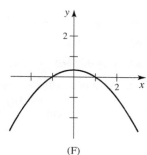

(F)

45–48. Tangent lines *Find an equation of the line tangent to the following curves at the given point. Check your work with a graphing utility.*

45. $y^2 = -12x; \left(-\dfrac{4}{3}, -4\right)$ **46.** $x^2 = 5y; \left(-2, \dfrac{4}{5}\right)$

47. $\dfrac{x^2}{100} + \dfrac{y^2}{64} = 1; \left(-6, -\dfrac{32}{5}\right)$ **48.** $\dfrac{x^2}{16} - \dfrac{y^2}{9} = 1; \left(\dfrac{20}{3}, -4\right)$

49–52. Polar equations for conic sections *Graph the following conic sections, labeling vertices, foci, directrices, and asymptotes (if they exist). Give the eccentricity of the curve. Use a graphing utility to check your work.*

49. $r = \dfrac{2}{1 + \sin\theta}$ **50.** $r = \dfrac{3}{1 - 2\cos\theta}$

51. $r = \dfrac{4}{2 + \cos\theta}$ **52.** $r = \dfrac{10}{5 + 2\cos\theta}$

53. A polar conic section Consider the equation $r^2 = \sec 2\theta$.

    a. Convert the equation to Cartesian coordinates and identify the curve.

    b. Find the vertices, foci, directrices, and eccentricity of the curve.

    c. Graph the curve. Explain why the polar equation does not have the form given in the text for conic sections in polar coordinates.

54–57. Eccentricity-directrix approach *Find an equation of the following curves, assuming the center is at the origin. Graph the curve, labeling vertices, foci, asymptotes (if they exist), and directrices.*

54. An ellipse with foci $(\pm 4, 0)$ and directrices $x = \pm 8$

55. An ellipse with vertices $(0, \pm 4)$ and directrices $y = \pm 10$

56. A hyperbola with vertices $(\pm 4, 0)$ and directrices $x = \pm 2$

57. A hyperbola with vertices $(0, \pm 2)$ and directrices $y = \pm 1$

58. Conic parameters A hyperbola has eccentricity $e = 2$ and foci $(0, \pm 2)$. Find the location of the vertices and directrices.

59. Conic parameters An ellipse has vertices $(0, \pm 6)$ and foci $(0, \pm 4)$. Find the eccentricity, the directrices, and the minor-axis vertices.

T **60–63. Intersection points** *Use analytical methods to find as many intersection points of the following curves as possible. Use methods of your choice to find the remaining intersection points.*

60. $r = 1 - \cos\theta$ and $r = \theta$

61. $r^2 = \sin 2\theta$ and $r = \theta$

62. $r^2 = \sin 2\theta$ and $r = 1 - 2\sin\theta$

63. $r = \theta/2$ and $r = -\theta$, for $\theta \geq 0$

64. Area of an ellipse Consider the polar equation of an ellipse $r = ed/(1 \pm e\cos\theta)$, where $0 < e < 1$. Evaluate an integral in polar coordinates to show that the area of the region enclosed by the ellipse is πab, where $2a$ and $2b$ are the lengths of the major and minor axes, respectively.

65. Maximizing area Among all rectangles centered at the origin with vertices on the ellipse $x^2/a^2 + y^2/b^2 = 1$, what are the dimensions of the rectangle with the maximum area (in terms of a and b)? What is that area?

66. Equidistant set Let S be the square centered at the origin with vertices $(\pm a, \pm a)$. Describe and sketch the set of points that are equidistant from the square and the origin.

67. Bisecting an ellipse Let R be the region in the first quadrant bounded by the ellipse $x^2/a^2 + y^2/b^2 = 1$. Find the value of m (in terms of a and b) such that the line $y = mx$ divides R into two subregions of equal area.

68. Parabola-hyperbola tangency Let P be the parabola $y = px^2$ and H be the right half of the hyperbola $x^2 - y^2 = 1$.

    a. For what value of p is P tangent to H?

    b. At what point does the tangency occur?

    c. Generalize your results for the hyperbola $x^2/a^2 - y^2/b^2 = 1$.

69. Another ellipse construction Start with two circles centered at the origin with radii $0 < a < b$ (see figure). Assume the line ℓ through the origin intersects the smaller circle at Q and the larger circle at R. Let $P(x, y)$ have the y-coordinate of Q and the x-coordinate of R. Show that the set of points $P(x, y)$ generated in this way for all lines ℓ through the origin is an ellipse.

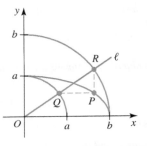

70–71. Graphs to polar equations *Find a polar equation for the conic sections in the figures.*

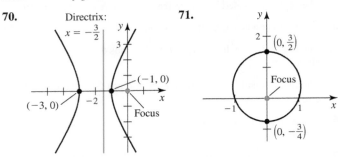

Chapter 10 Guided Projects

Applications of the material in this chapter and related topics can be found in the following Guided Projects. For additional information, see the Preface.

- The amazing cycloid
- Parametric art
- Polar art
- Grazing goat problems
- Translations and rotations of axes
- Celestial orbits
- Properties of conic sections

11

Vectors and Vector-Valued Functions

Chapter Preview We now make a significant departure from previous chapters by stepping out of the xy-plane ($\mathbb{R}^2$) into three-dimensional space ($\mathbb{R}^3$). The fundamental concept of a *vector*—a quantity with magnitude and direction—is introduced in two and three dimensions. We then put vectors in motion by introducing *vector-valued functions*, or simply *vector functions*. The calculus of vector functions is a direct extension of everything you already know about limits, derivatives, and integrals. Also, with the calculus of vector functions, we can solve a wealth of practical problems involving the motion of objects in space. The chapter closes with an exploration of arc length, curvature, and tangent and normal vectors, all important features of space curves.

11.1 Vectors in the Plane

Imagine a raft drifting down a river, carried by the current. The speed and direction of the raft at a point may be represented by an arrow (Figure 11.1). The length of the arrow represents the speed of the raft at that point; longer arrows correspond to greater speeds. The orientation of the arrow gives the direction in which the raft is headed at that point. The arrows at points A and C in Figure 11.1 have the same length and direction, indicating that the raft has the same speed and heading at these locations. The arrow at B is shorter and points to the left of the rock, indicating that the raft slows down as it nears the rock.

Figure 11.1

Basic Vector Operations

The arrows that describe the raft's motion are examples of *vectors*—quantities that have both *length* (or *magnitude*) and *direction*. Vectors arise naturally in many situations. For example, electric and magnetic fields, the flow of air over an airplane wing, and the velocity and acceleration of elementary particles are described by vectors (Figure 11.2). In this section, we examine vectors in the xy-plane and then extend the concept to three dimensions in Section 11.2.

The vector whose *tail* is at the point P and whose *head* is at the point Q is denoted $\overrightarrow{PQ}$ (Figure 11.3). The vector $\overrightarrow{QP}$ has its tail at Q and its head at P. We also label vectors with single boldfaced characters such as **u** and **v**.

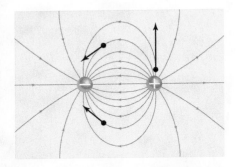

Electric field vectors due to two charges

Figure 11.2

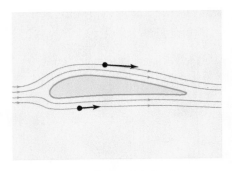

Velocity vectors of air flowing
over an airplane wing

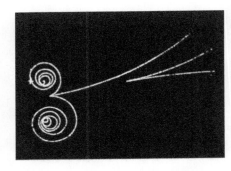

Tracks of elementary particles in a cloud chamber
are aligned with the velocity vectors of the particles.

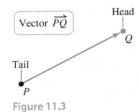

Figure 11.3

Figure 11.4

Two vectors **u** and **v** are *equal*, written **u** = **v**, if they have equal length and point in the same direction (Figure 11.4). An important fact is that equal vectors do not necessarily have the same location. *Any* two vectors with the same length and direction are equal.

Not all quantities are represented by vectors. For example, mass, temperature, and price have magnitude, but no direction. Such quantities are described by real numbers and are called *scalars*.

> ➤ In this book, *scalar* is another word for *real number*.

> ➤ The vector **v** is commonly handwritten as $\vec{v}$. The zero vector is handwritten as $\vec{0}$.

Vectors, Equal Vectors, Scalars, Zero Vector

Vectors are quantities that have both length (or magnitude) and direction. Two vectors are **equal** if they have the same magnitude and direction. Quantities having magnitude but no direction are called **scalars**. One exception is the **zero vector**, denoted **0**: It has length 0 and no direction.

Scalar Multiplication

A scalar c and a vector **v** can be combined using scalar-vector multiplication, or simply *scalar multiplication*. The resulting vector, denoted $c\mathbf{v}$, is called a *scalar multiple* of **v**. The magnitude of $c\mathbf{v}$ is $|c|$ multiplied by the magnitude of **v**. The vector $c\mathbf{v}$ has the same direction as **v** if $c > 0$. If $c < 0$, then $c\mathbf{v}$ and **v** point in opposite directions. If $c = 0$, then the product $0\mathbf{v} = \mathbf{0}$ (the zero vector).

For example, the vector $3\mathbf{v}$ is three times as long as **v** and has the same direction as **v**. The vector $-2\mathbf{v}$ is twice as long as **v**, but it points in the opposite direction. The vector $\frac{1}{2}\mathbf{v}$ points in the same direction as **v** and has half the length of **v** (Figure 11.5). The vectors **v**, $3\mathbf{v}$, $-2\mathbf{v}$, and $\frac{1}{2}\mathbf{v}$ are examples of *parallel vectors*: Each one is a scalar multiple of the others.

Same direction
as **v** and half
as long as **v**.

$\frac{1}{2}\mathbf{v}$

$-2\mathbf{v}$

Twice as long as
v, pointing in the
opposite direction.

$3\mathbf{v}$

v

Same direction as **v**
and three times
as long as **v**.

Figure 11.5

DEFINITION Scalar Multiples and Parallel Vectors

Given a scalar c and a vector **v**, the **scalar multiple** $c\mathbf{v}$ is a vector whose magnitude is $|c|$ multiplied by the magnitude of **v**. If $c > 0$, then $c\mathbf{v}$ has the same direction as **v**. If $c < 0$, then $c\mathbf{v}$ and **v** point in opposite directions. Two vectors are **parallel** if they are scalar multiples of each other.

> For convenience, we write $-\mathbf{u}$ for $(-1)\mathbf{u}$, $-c\mathbf{u}$ for $(-c)\mathbf{u}$, and $\mathbf{u}/c$ for $\frac{1}{c}\mathbf{u}$.

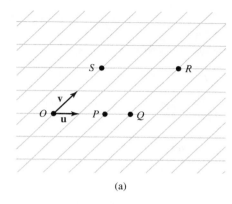

(a)

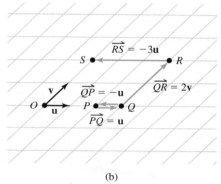

(b)

Figure 11.6

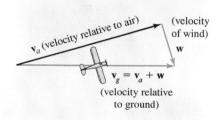

Figure 11.7

QUICK CHECK 3 Use the Triangle Rule to show that the vectors in Figure 11.8 satisfy $\mathbf{u} + \mathbf{v} = \mathbf{v} + \mathbf{u}$. ◄

Notice that $0\mathbf{v} = \mathbf{0}$ for all vectors $\mathbf{v}$. It follows that *the zero vector is parallel to all vectors*. While it may seem counterintuitive, this result turns out to be a useful convention.

QUICK CHECK 1 Describe the magnitude and direction of the vector $-5\mathbf{v}$ relative to $\mathbf{v}$. ◄

EXAMPLE 1 Parallel vectors Using Figure 11.6a, write the following vectors in terms of $\mathbf{u}$ or $\mathbf{v}$.

a. $\overrightarrow{PQ}$ **b.** $\overrightarrow{QP}$ **c.** $\overrightarrow{QR}$ **d.** $\overrightarrow{RS}$

SOLUTION

a. The vector $\overrightarrow{PQ}$ has the same direction and length as $\mathbf{u}$; therefore, $\overrightarrow{PQ} = \mathbf{u}$. These two vectors are equal even though they have different locations (Figure 11.6b).

b. Because $\overrightarrow{QP}$ and $\mathbf{u}$ have equal length but opposite directions, $\overrightarrow{QP} = (-1)\mathbf{u} = -\mathbf{u}$.

c. $\overrightarrow{QR}$ points in the same direction as $\mathbf{v}$ and is twice as long as $\mathbf{v}$, so $\overrightarrow{QR} = 2\mathbf{v}$.

d. $\overrightarrow{RS}$ points in the direction opposite that of $\mathbf{u}$ with three times the length of $\mathbf{u}$. Consequently, $\overrightarrow{RS} = -3\mathbf{u}$.

Related Exercises 17–20 ◄

Vector Addition and Subtraction

To illustrate the idea of vector addition, consider a plane flying horizontally at a constant speed in a crosswind (Figure 11.7). The length of vector $\mathbf{v}_a$ represents the plane's *airspeed*, which is the speed the plane would have in still air; $\mathbf{v}_a$ points in the direction of the nose of the plane. The wind vector $\mathbf{w}$ points in the direction of the crosswind and has a length equal to the speed of the crosswind. The combined effect of the motion of the plane and the wind is the *vector sum* $\mathbf{v}_g = \mathbf{v}_a + \mathbf{w}$, which is the velocity of the plane relative to the ground.

QUICK CHECK 2 Sketch the sum $\mathbf{v}_a + \mathbf{w}$ in Figure 11.7 if the direction of $\mathbf{w}$ is reversed. ◄

Figure 11.8 illustrates two ways to form the vector sum of two nonzero vectors $\mathbf{u}$ and $\mathbf{v}$ geometrically. The first method, called the **Triangle Rule**, places the tail of $\mathbf{v}$ at the head of $\mathbf{u}$. The sum $\mathbf{u} + \mathbf{v}$ is the vector that extends from the tail of $\mathbf{u}$ to the head of $\mathbf{v}$ (Figure 11.8b).

When $\mathbf{u}$ and $\mathbf{v}$ are not parallel, another way to form $\mathbf{u} + \mathbf{v}$ is to use the **Parallelogram Rule**. The *tails* of $\mathbf{u}$ and $\mathbf{v}$ are connected to form adjacent sides of a parallelogram; then the remaining two sides of the parallelogram are sketched. The sum $\mathbf{u} + \mathbf{v}$ is the vector that coincides with the diagonal of the parallelogram, beginning at the tails of $\mathbf{u}$ and $\mathbf{v}$ (Figure 11.8c). The Triangle Rule and Parallelogram Rule each produce the same vector sum $\mathbf{u} + \mathbf{v}$.

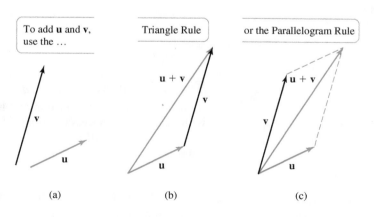

Figure 11.8

The difference $\mathbf{u} - \mathbf{v}$ is defined to be the sum $\mathbf{u} + (-\mathbf{v})$. By the Triangle Rule, the tail of $-\mathbf{v}$ is placed at the head of $\mathbf{u}$; then $\mathbf{u} - \mathbf{v}$ extends from the tail of $\mathbf{u}$ to the head of $-\mathbf{v}$ (Figure 11.9a). Equivalently, when the tails of $\mathbf{u}$ and $\mathbf{v}$ coincide, $\mathbf{u} - \mathbf{v}$ has its tail at the head of $\mathbf{v}$ and its head at the head of $\mathbf{u}$ (Figure 11.9b).

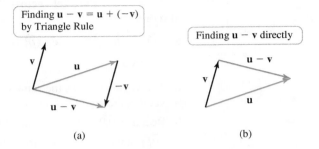

(a)   (b)

Figure 11.9

EXAMPLE 2   Vector operations Use Figure 11.10 to write the following vectors as sums of scalar multiples of $\mathbf{v}$ and $\mathbf{w}$.

a. $\overrightarrow{OP}$ **b.** $\overrightarrow{OQ}$ **c.** $\overrightarrow{QR}$

SOLUTION

a. Using the Triangle Rule, we start at O, move three lengths of $\mathbf{v}$ in the direction of $\mathbf{v}$ and then two lengths of $\mathbf{w}$ in the direction of $\mathbf{w}$ to reach P. Therefore, $\overrightarrow{OP} = 3\mathbf{v} + 2\mathbf{w}$ (Figure 11.11a).

b. The vector $\overrightarrow{OQ}$ coincides with the diagonal of a parallelogram having adjacent sides equal to $3\mathbf{v}$ and $-\mathbf{w}$. By the Parallelogram Rule, $\overrightarrow{OQ} = 3\mathbf{v} - \mathbf{w}$ (Figure 11.11b).

c. The vector $\overrightarrow{QR}$ lies on the diagonal of a parallelogram having adjacent sides equal to $\mathbf{v}$ and $2\mathbf{w}$. Therefore, $\overrightarrow{QR} = \mathbf{v} + 2\mathbf{w}$ (Figure 11.11c).

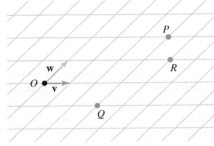

Figure 11.10

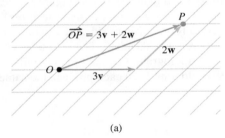

(a)

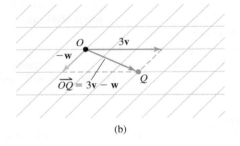

(b)

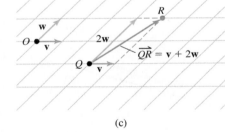

(c)

Figure 11.11

Related Exercises 21–22 ◄

Vector Components

So far, vectors have been examined from a geometric point of view. To do calculations with vectors, it is necessary to introduce a coordinate system. We begin by considering a vector $\mathbf{v}$ whose tail is at the origin in the Cartesian plane and whose head is at the point (v_1, v_2) (Figure 11.12a).

► Round brackets (a, b) enclose the *coordinates* of a point, while angle brackets $\langle a, b \rangle$ enclose the *components* of a vector. Note that in component form, the zero vector is $\mathbf{0} = \langle 0, 0 \rangle$.

DEFINITION   Position Vectors and Vector Components

A vector $\mathbf{v}$ with its tail at the origin and head at the point (v_1, v_2) is called a **position vector** (or is said to be in **standard position**) and is written $\langle v_1, v_2 \rangle$. The real numbers v_1 and v_2 are the x- and y-**components** of $\mathbf{v}$, respectively. The position vectors $\mathbf{u} = \langle u_1, u_2 \rangle$ and $\mathbf{v} = \langle v_1, v_2 \rangle$ are **equal** if and only if $u_1 = v_1$ and $u_2 = v_2$.

There are infinitely many vectors equal to the position vector **v**, all with the same length and direction (Figure 11.12b). It is important to abide by the convention that **v** $= \langle v_1, v_2 \rangle$ refers to the position vector **v** *or to any other vector equal to* **v**.

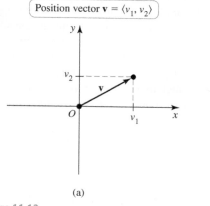

Position vector **v** $= \langle v_1, v_2 \rangle$

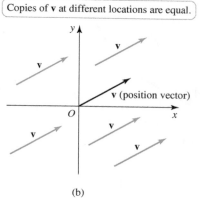

Copies of **v** at different locations are equal.

(a)   (b)

Figure 11.12

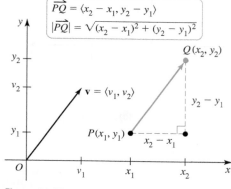

$$\overrightarrow{PQ} = \langle x_2 - x_1, y_2 - y_1 \rangle$$
$$|\overrightarrow{PQ}| = \sqrt{(x_2 - x_1)^2 + (y_2 - y_1)^2}$$

Figure 11.13

Now consider the vector $\overrightarrow{PQ}$ equal to **v**, but not in standard position, with its tail at the point $P(x_1, y_1)$ and its head at the point $Q(x_2, y_2)$. The x-component of $\overrightarrow{PQ}$ is the difference in the x-coordinates of Q and P, or $x_2 - x_1$. The y-component of $\overrightarrow{PQ}$ is the difference in the y-coordinates, $y_2 - y_1$ (Figure 11.13). Therefore, $\overrightarrow{PQ}$ has the same length and direction as the position vector $\langle v_1, v_2 \rangle = \langle x_2 - x_1, y_2 - y_1 \rangle$, and we write $\overrightarrow{PQ} = \langle x_2 - x_1, y_2 - y_1 \rangle$.

QUICK CHECK 4 Given the points $P(2, 3)$ and $Q(-4, 1)$, find the components of $\overrightarrow{PQ}$. ◄

As already noted, there are infinitely many vectors equal to a given position vector. All these vectors have the same length and direction; therefore, they are all equal. In other words, two arbitrary vectors are **equal** if they are equal to the same position vector. For example, the vector $\overrightarrow{PQ}$ from $P(2, 5)$ to $Q(6, 3)$ and the vector $\overrightarrow{AB}$ from $A(7, 12)$ to $B(11, 10)$ are equal because they both equal the position vector $\langle 4, -2 \rangle$.

Magnitude

The magnitude of a vector is simply its length. By the Pythagorean Theorem and Figure 11.13, we have the following definition.

► Just as the absolute value $|p - q|$ gives the distance between the points p and q on the number line, the magnitude $|\overrightarrow{PQ}|$ is the distance between the points P and Q. The magnitude of a vector is also called its **norm**.

DEFINITION Magnitude of a Vector

Given the points $P(x_1, y_1)$ and $Q(x_2, y_2)$, the **magnitude**, or **length**, of $\overrightarrow{PQ} = \langle x_2 - x_1, y_2 - y_1 \rangle$, denoted $|\overrightarrow{PQ}|$, is the distance between P and Q:

$$|\overrightarrow{PQ}| = \sqrt{(x_2 - x_1)^2 + (y_2 - y_1)^2}.$$

The magnitude of the position vector **v** $= \langle v_1, v_2 \rangle$ is $|\mathbf{v}| = \sqrt{v_1^2 + v_2^2}$.

EXAMPLE 3   Calculating components and magnitude Given the points $O(0, 0)$, $P(-3, 4)$, and $Q(6, 5)$, find the components and magnitude of the following vectors.

a. $\overrightarrow{OP}$ **b.** $\overrightarrow{PQ}$

SOLUTION

a. The vector $\overrightarrow{OP}$ is the position vector whose head is located at $P(-3, 4)$. Therefore, $\overrightarrow{OP} = \langle -3, 4 \rangle$ and its magnitude is $|\overrightarrow{OP}| = \sqrt{(-3)^2 + 4^2} = 5$.

b. $\overrightarrow{PQ} = \langle 6 - (-3), 5 - 4 \rangle = \langle 9, 1 \rangle$ and $|\overrightarrow{PQ}| = \sqrt{9^2 + 1^2} = \sqrt{82}$.

Related Exercises 23–27 ◄

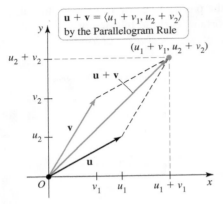

Figure 11.14

Vector Operations in Terms of Components

We now show how vector addition, vector subtraction, and scalar multiplication are performed using components. Suppose $\mathbf{u} = \langle u_1, u_2 \rangle$ and $\mathbf{v} = \langle v_1, v_2 \rangle$. The vector sum of $\mathbf{u}$ and $\mathbf{v}$ is $\mathbf{u} + \mathbf{v} = \langle u_1 + v_1, u_2 + v_2 \rangle$. This definition of a vector sum is consistent with the Parallelogram Rule given earlier (Figure 11.14).

For a scalar c and a vector $\mathbf{u}$, the scalar multiple $c\mathbf{u}$ is $c\mathbf{u} = \langle cu_1, cu_2 \rangle$; that is, the scalar c multiplies each component of $\mathbf{u}$. If $c > 0$, $\mathbf{u}$ and $c\mathbf{u}$ have the same direction (Figure 11.15a). If $c < 0$, $\mathbf{u}$ and $c\mathbf{u}$ have opposite directions (Figure 11.15b). In either case, $|c\mathbf{u}| = |c| |\mathbf{u}|$ (Exercise 87).

Notice that $\mathbf{u} - \mathbf{v} = \mathbf{u} + (-\mathbf{v})$, where $-\mathbf{v} = \langle -v_1, -v_2 \rangle$. Therefore, the vector difference of $\mathbf{u}$ and $\mathbf{v}$ is $\mathbf{u} - \mathbf{v} = \langle u_1 - v_1, u_2 - v_2 \rangle$.

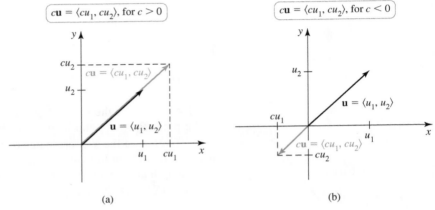

Figure 11.15

> Recall that $\mathbb{R}^2$ (pronounced *R-two*) stands for the *xy*-plane or the set of all ordered pairs of real numbers.

DEFINITION Vector Operations in $\mathbb{R}^2$

Suppose c is a scalar, $\mathbf{u} = \langle u_1, u_2 \rangle$, and $\mathbf{v} = \langle v_1, v_2 \rangle$.

$$\mathbf{u} + \mathbf{v} = \langle u_1 + v_1, u_2 + v_2 \rangle \quad \text{Vector addition}$$
$$\mathbf{u} - \mathbf{v} = \langle u_1 - v_1, u_2 - v_2 \rangle \quad \text{Vector subtraction}$$
$$c\mathbf{u} = \langle cu_1, cu_2 \rangle \quad \text{Scalar multiplication}$$

EXAMPLE 4 Vector operations Let $\mathbf{u} = \langle -1, 2 \rangle$ and $\mathbf{v} = \langle 2, 3 \rangle$.

a. Evaluate $|\mathbf{u} + \mathbf{v}|$.

b. Simplify $2\mathbf{u} - 3\mathbf{v}$.

c. Find two vectors half as long as $\mathbf{u}$ and parallel to $\mathbf{u}$.

SOLUTION

a. Because $\mathbf{u} + \mathbf{v} = \langle -1, 2 \rangle + \langle 2, 3 \rangle = \langle 1, 5 \rangle$, we have
$|\mathbf{u} + \mathbf{v}| = \sqrt{1^2 + 5^2} = \sqrt{26}$.

b. $2\mathbf{u} - 3\mathbf{v} = 2\langle -1, 2 \rangle - 3\langle 2, 3 \rangle = \langle -2, 4 \rangle - \langle 6, 9 \rangle = \langle -8, -5 \rangle$

c. The vectors $\frac{1}{2}\mathbf{u} = \frac{1}{2}\langle -1, 2 \rangle = \langle -\frac{1}{2}, 1 \rangle$ and $-\frac{1}{2}\mathbf{u} = -\frac{1}{2}\langle -1, 2 \rangle = \langle \frac{1}{2}, -1 \rangle$ have half the length of $\mathbf{u}$ and are parallel to $\mathbf{u}$.

Related Exercises 28–41 ◄

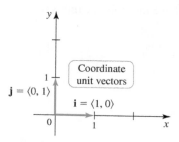

Figure 11.16

Unit Vectors

A **unit vector** is any vector with length 1. Two useful unit vectors are the **coordinate unit vectors** $\mathbf{i} = \langle 1, 0 \rangle$ and $\mathbf{j} = \langle 0, 1 \rangle$ (Figure 11.16). These vectors are directed along the coordinate axes and allow us to express all vectors in an alternative form. For example, by the Triangle Rule (Figure 11.17a),

$$\langle 3, 4 \rangle = 3\langle 1, 0 \rangle + 4\langle 0, 1 \rangle = 3\mathbf{i} + 4\mathbf{j}.$$

In general, the vector $\mathbf{v} = \langle v_1, v_2 \rangle$ (Figure 11.17b) is also written

$$\mathbf{v} = v_1\langle 1, 0 \rangle + v_2\langle 0, 1 \rangle = v_1\mathbf{i} + v_2\mathbf{j}.$$

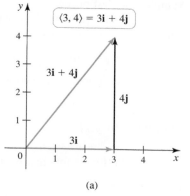
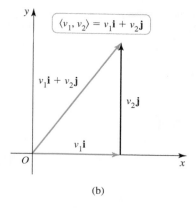

(a)

(b)

Figure 11.17

➤ Coordinate unit vectors are also called **standard basis vectors**.

$\mathbf{u} = \dfrac{\mathbf{v}}{|\mathbf{v}|}$ and $-\mathbf{u} = -\dfrac{\mathbf{v}}{|\mathbf{v}|}$ have length 1.

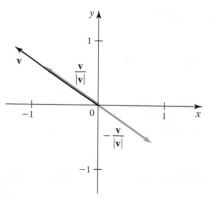

Figure 11.18

Given a nonzero vector $\mathbf{v}$, we sometimes need to construct a new vector parallel to $\mathbf{v}$ of a specified length. Dividing $\mathbf{v}$ by its length, we obtain the vector $\mathbf{u} = \dfrac{\mathbf{v}}{|\mathbf{v}|}$. Because $\mathbf{u}$ is a positive scalar multiple of $\mathbf{v}$, it follows that $\mathbf{u}$ has the same direction as $\mathbf{v}$. Furthermore, $\mathbf{u}$ is a unit vector because $|\mathbf{u}| = \dfrac{|\mathbf{v}|}{|\mathbf{v}|} = 1$. The vector $-\mathbf{u} = -\dfrac{\mathbf{v}}{|\mathbf{v}|}$ is also a unit vector (Figure 11.18). Therefore, $\pm\dfrac{\mathbf{v}}{|\mathbf{v}|}$ are unit vectors parallel to $\mathbf{v}$ that point in opposite directions.

To construct a vector that points in the direction of $\mathbf{v}$ and has a specified length $c > 0$, we form the vector $\dfrac{c\mathbf{v}}{|\mathbf{v}|}$. It is a positive scalar multiple of $\mathbf{v}$, so it points in the direction of $\mathbf{v}$, and its length is $\left|\dfrac{c\mathbf{v}}{|\mathbf{v}|}\right| = |c|\dfrac{|\mathbf{v}|}{|\mathbf{v}|} = c$. The vector $-\dfrac{c\mathbf{v}}{|\mathbf{v}|}$ points in the opposite direction and also has length c.

QUICK CHECK 5 Find vectors of length 10 parallel to the unit vector $\mathbf{u} = \left\langle \dfrac{3}{5}, \dfrac{4}{5} \right\rangle$. ◄

EXAMPLE 5 **Magnitude and unit vectors** Consider the points $P(1, -2)$ and $Q(6, 10)$.

a. Find $\overrightarrow{PQ}$ and two unit vectors parallel to $\overrightarrow{PQ}$.

b. Find two vectors of length 2 parallel to $\overrightarrow{PQ}$.

SOLUTION

a. $\overrightarrow{PQ} = \langle 6 - 1, 10 - (-2) \rangle = \langle 5, 12 \rangle$, or $5\mathbf{i} + 12\mathbf{j}$. Because $|\overrightarrow{PQ}| = \sqrt{5^2 + 12^2} = \sqrt{169} = 13$, a unit vector parallel to $\overrightarrow{PQ}$ is

$$\frac{\overrightarrow{PQ}}{|\overrightarrow{PQ}|} = \frac{\langle 5, 12 \rangle}{13} = \left\langle \frac{5}{13}, \frac{12}{13} \right\rangle = \frac{5}{13}\mathbf{i} + \frac{12}{13}\mathbf{j}.$$

The unit vector parallel to $\overrightarrow{PQ}$ with the opposite direction is $\left\langle -\frac{5}{13}, -\frac{12}{13} \right\rangle$.

b. To obtain two vectors of length 2 that are parallel to $\vec{PQ}$, we multiply the unit vector $\frac{5}{13}\mathbf{i} + \frac{12}{13}\mathbf{j}$ by ± 2:

$$2\left(\frac{5}{13}\mathbf{i} + \frac{12}{13}\mathbf{j}\right) = \frac{10}{13}\mathbf{i} + \frac{24}{13}\mathbf{j} \quad \text{and} \quad -2\left(\frac{5}{13}\mathbf{i} + \frac{12}{13}\mathbf{j}\right) = -\frac{10}{13}\mathbf{i} - \frac{24}{13}\mathbf{j}.$$

Related Exercises 42–47 ◄

QUICK CHECK 6 Verify that the vector $\left(\frac{5}{13}, \frac{12}{13}\right)$ has length 1. ◄

Properties of Vector Operations

> ➤ The Parallelogram Rule illustrates the commutative property $\mathbf{u} + \mathbf{v} = \mathbf{v} + \mathbf{u}$.

When we stand back and look at vector operations, ten general properties emerge. For example, the first property says that vector addition is commutative, which means $\mathbf{u} + \mathbf{v} = \mathbf{v} + \mathbf{u}$. This property is proved by letting $\mathbf{u} = \langle u_1, u_2 \rangle$ and $\mathbf{v} = \langle v_1, v_2 \rangle$. By the commutative property of addition for real numbers,

$$\mathbf{u} + \mathbf{v} = \langle u_1 + v_1, u_2 + v_2 \rangle = \langle v_1 + u_1, v_2 + u_2 \rangle = \mathbf{v} + \mathbf{u}.$$

The proofs of other properties are outlined in Exercises 82–85.

SUMMARY   Properties of Vector Operations

Suppose $\mathbf{u}$, $\mathbf{v}$, and $\mathbf{w}$ are vectors and a and c are scalars. Then the following properties hold (for vectors in any number of dimensions).

1. $\mathbf{u} + \mathbf{v} = \mathbf{v} + \mathbf{u}$	Commutative property of addition
2. $(\mathbf{u} + \mathbf{v}) + \mathbf{w} = \mathbf{u} + (\mathbf{v} + \mathbf{w})$	Associative property of addition
3. $\mathbf{v} + \mathbf{0} = \mathbf{v}$	Additive identity
4. $\mathbf{v} + (-\mathbf{v}) = \mathbf{0}$	Additive inverse
5. $c(\mathbf{u} + \mathbf{v}) = c\mathbf{u} + c\mathbf{v}$	Distributive property 1
6. $(a + c)\mathbf{v} = a\mathbf{v} + c\mathbf{v}$	Distributive property 2
7. $0\mathbf{v} = \mathbf{0}$	Multiplication by zero scalar
8. $c\mathbf{0} = \mathbf{0}$	Multiplication by zero vector
9. $1\mathbf{v} = \mathbf{v}$	Multiplicative identity
10. $a(c\mathbf{v}) = (ac)\mathbf{v}$	Associative property of scalar multiplication

---

These properties allow us to solve vector equations. For example, to solve the equation $\mathbf{u} + \mathbf{v} = \mathbf{w}$ for $\mathbf{u}$, we proceed as follows:

$$(\mathbf{u} + \mathbf{v}) + (-\mathbf{v}) = \mathbf{w} + (-\mathbf{v}) \quad \text{Add } -\mathbf{v} \text{ to both sides.}$$
$$\mathbf{u} + \underbrace{(\mathbf{v} + (-\mathbf{v}))}_{0} = \mathbf{w} + (-\mathbf{v}) \quad \text{Property 2}$$
$$\mathbf{u} + \mathbf{0} = \mathbf{w} - \mathbf{v} \quad \text{Property 4}$$
$$\mathbf{u} = \mathbf{w} - \mathbf{v}. \quad \text{Property 3}$$

QUICK CHECK 7 Solve $3\mathbf{u} + 4\mathbf{v} = 12\mathbf{w}$ for $\mathbf{u}$. ◄

Applications of Vectors

Vectors have countless practical applications, particularly in the physical sciences and engineering. These applications are explored throughout the remainder of the book. For now, we present two common uses of vectors: to describe velocities and forces.

> *Velocity of the boat relative to the water* means the velocity (direction and speed) the boat would have in still water (or relative to someone traveling with the current).

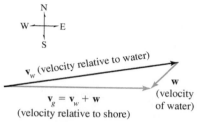

Figure 11.19

Velocity Vectors Consider a motorboat crossing a river whose current is everywhere represented by the constant vector **w** (Figure 11.19); this means that $|\mathbf{w}|$ is the speed of the moving water and **w** points in the direction of the moving water. Assume that the vector $\mathbf{v}_w$ gives the velocity of the boat relative to the water. The combined effect of **w** and $\mathbf{v}_w$ is the sum $\mathbf{v}_g = \mathbf{v}_w + \mathbf{w}$, which is velocity of the boat that would be observed by someone on the shore (or on the ground).

EXAMPLE 6 **Speed of a boat in a current** Suppose the water in a river moves southwest (45° west of south) at 4 mi/hr and a motorboat travels due east at 15 mi/hr relative to the shore. Determine the speed of the boat and its heading relative to the moving water (Figure 11.19).

SOLUTION To solve this problem, the vectors are placed in a coordinate system (Figure 11.20). Because the boat moves east at 15 mi/hr, the velocity relative to the shore is $\mathbf{v}_g = \langle 15, 0 \rangle$. To obtain the components of $\mathbf{w} = \langle w_x, w_y \rangle$, observe that $|\mathbf{w}| = 4$ and the lengths of the sides of the 45–45–90 triangle in Figure 11.20 are

$$|w_x| = |w_y| = |\mathbf{w}| \cos 45° = \frac{4}{\sqrt{2}} = 2\sqrt{2}.$$

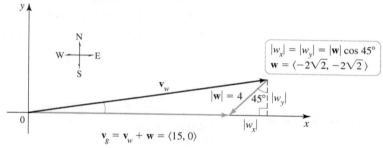

Figure 11.20

Given the orientation of **w** (southwest), $\mathbf{w} = \langle -2\sqrt{2}, -2\sqrt{2} \rangle$. Because $\mathbf{v}_g = \mathbf{v}_w + \mathbf{w}$ (Figure 11.20),

$$\mathbf{v}_w = \mathbf{v}_g - \mathbf{w} = \langle 15, 0 \rangle - \langle -2\sqrt{2}, -2\sqrt{2} \rangle$$
$$= \langle 15 + 2\sqrt{2}, 2\sqrt{2} \rangle.$$

The magnitude of $\mathbf{v}_w$ is

$$|\mathbf{v}_w| = \sqrt{(15 + 2\sqrt{2})^2 + (2\sqrt{2})^2} \approx 18.$$

Therefore, the speed of the boat relative to the water is approximately 18 mi/hr.

The heading of the boat is given by the angle θ between $\mathbf{v}_w$ and the positive x-axis. The x-component of $\mathbf{v}_w$ is $15 + 2\sqrt{2}$ and the y-component is $2\sqrt{2}$. Therefore,

$$\theta = \tan^{-1}\left(\frac{2\sqrt{2}}{15 + 2\sqrt{2}}\right) \approx 9°.$$

The heading of the boat is approximately 9° north of east, and its speed relative to the water is approximately 18 mi/hr.

Related Exercises 48–53 ◄

> Recall that the lengths of the legs of a 45–45–90 triangle are equal and are $1/\sqrt{2}$ times the length of the hypotenuse.

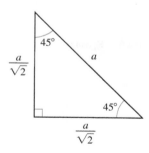

> The magnitude of **F** is typically measured in pounds (lb) or newtons (N), where $1 \text{ N} = 1 \text{ kg-m/s}^2$.

> The vector $\langle \cos\theta, \sin\theta \rangle$ is a unit vector. Therefore, any position vector **v** may be written $\mathbf{v} = \langle |\mathbf{v}| \cos\theta, |\mathbf{v}| \sin\theta \rangle$, where θ is the angle that **v** makes with the positive x-axis.

Force Vectors Suppose a child pulls on the handle of a wagon at an angle of θ with the horizontal (Figure 11.21a). The vector **F** represents the force exerted on the wagon; it has a magnitude $|\mathbf{F}|$ and a direction given by θ. We denote the horizontal and vertical components of **F** by F_x and F_y, respectively. From Figure 11.21b, we see that $F_x = |\mathbf{F}| \cos\theta$, $F_y = |\mathbf{F}| \sin\theta$, and the force vector is $\mathbf{F} = \langle |\mathbf{F}| \cos\theta, |\mathbf{F}| \sin\theta \rangle$.

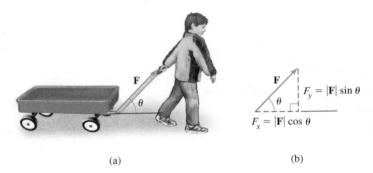

(a)   (b)

Figure 11.21

EXAMPLE 7   Finding force vectors A child pulls a wagon (Figure 11.21) with a force of $|\mathbf{F}| = 20$ lb at an angle of $\theta = 30°$ to the horizontal. Find the force vector **F**.

SOLUTION The force vector (Figure 11.22) is

$$\mathbf{F} = \langle |\mathbf{F}| \cos\theta, |\mathbf{F}| \sin\theta \rangle = \langle 20 \cos 30°, 20 \sin 30° \rangle = \langle 10\sqrt{3}, 10 \rangle.$$

Related Exercises 54–58 ◄

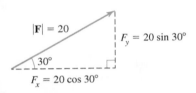

Figure 11.22

EXAMPLE 8   Balancing forces A 400-lb engine is suspended from two chains that form 60° angles with a horizontal ceiling (Figure 11.23). How much weight does each chain support?

SOLUTION Let $\mathbf{F}_1$ and $\mathbf{F}_2$ denote the forces exerted by the chains on the engine and let $\mathbf{F}_3$ be the downward force due to the weight of the engine (Figure 11.23). Placing the vectors in a standard coordinate system (Figure 11.24), we find that $\mathbf{F}_1 = \langle |\mathbf{F}_1| \cos 60°, |\mathbf{F}_1| \sin 60° \rangle$, $\mathbf{F}_2 = \langle -|\mathbf{F}_2| \cos 60°, |\mathbf{F}_2| \sin 60° \rangle$, and $\mathbf{F}_3 = \langle 0, -400 \rangle$.

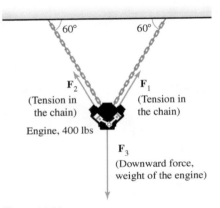

Figure 11.23

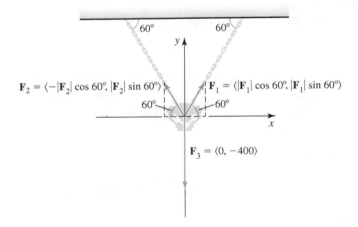

Figure 11.24

> The components of $\mathbf{F}_2$ in Example 8 can also be computed using an angle of 120°. That is, $\mathbf{F}_2 = \langle |\mathbf{F}_2| \cos 120°, |\mathbf{F}_2| \sin 120° \rangle$.

If the engine is in equilibrium (so the chains and engine are stationary), the sum of the forces is zero; that is, $\mathbf{F}_1 + \mathbf{F}_2 + \mathbf{F}_3 = \mathbf{0}$ or $\mathbf{F}_1 + \mathbf{F}_2 = -\mathbf{F}_3$. Therefore,

$$\langle |\mathbf{F}_1| \cos 60° - |\mathbf{F}_2| \cos 60°, |\mathbf{F}_1| \sin 60° + |\mathbf{F}_2| \sin 60° \rangle = \langle 0, 400 \rangle.$$

Equating corresponding components, we obtain two equations to be solved for $|\mathbf{F}_1|$ and $|\mathbf{F}_2|$:

$$|\mathbf{F}_1| \cos 60° - |\mathbf{F}_2| \cos 60° = 0 \text{ and}$$
$$|\mathbf{F}_1| \sin 60° + |\mathbf{F}_2| \sin 60° = 400.$$

Factoring the first equation, we find that $(|\mathbf{F}_1| - |\mathbf{F}_2|) \cos 60° = 0$, which implies that $|\mathbf{F}_1| = |\mathbf{F}_2|$. Replacing $|\mathbf{F}_2|$ with $|\mathbf{F}_1|$ in the second equation gives $2|\mathbf{F}_1| \sin 60° = 400$. Noting that $\sin 60° = \sqrt{3}/2$ and solving for $|\mathbf{F}_1|$, we find that $|\mathbf{F}_1| = 400/\sqrt{3} \approx 231$. Each chain must be able to support a weight of approximately 231 lb.

Related Exercises 54–58 ◄

SECTION 11.1 EXERCISES

Review Questions

1. Interpret the following statement: Points have a location, but no size or direction; nonzero vectors have a size and direction, but no location.

2. What is a position vector?

3. Draw x- and y-axes on a page and mark two points P and Q. Then draw $\vec{PQ}$ and $\vec{QP}$.

4. On the diagram of Exercise 3, draw the position vector that is equal to $\vec{PQ}$.

5. Given a position vector $\mathbf{v}$, why are there infinitely many vectors equal to $\mathbf{v}$?

6. Explain how to add two vectors geometrically.

7. Explain how to find a scalar multiple of a vector geometrically.

8. Given two points P and Q, how are the components of $\vec{PQ}$ determined?

9. If $\mathbf{u} = \langle u_1, u_2 \rangle$ and $\mathbf{v} = \langle v_1, v_2 \rangle$, how do you find $\mathbf{u} + \mathbf{v}$?

10. If $\mathbf{v} = \langle v_1, v_2 \rangle$ and c is a scalar, how do you find $c\mathbf{v}$?

11. How do you compute the magnitude of $\mathbf{v} = \langle v_1, v_2 \rangle$?

12. Express the vector $\mathbf{v} = \langle v_1, v_2 \rangle$ in terms of the unit vectors $\mathbf{i}$ and $\mathbf{j}$.

13. How do you compute $|\vec{PQ}|$ from the coordinates of the points P and Q?

14. Explain how to find two unit vectors parallel to a vector $\mathbf{v}$.

15. How do you find a vector of length 10 in the direction of $\mathbf{v} = \langle 3, -2 \rangle$?

16. If a force of magnitude 100 is directed 45° south of east, what are its components?

Basic Skills

17–22. Vector operations *Refer to the figure and carry out the following vector operations.*

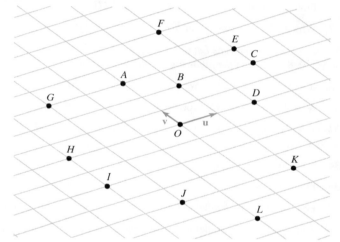

17. **Scalar multiples** Which of the following vectors equals $\vec{CE}$? (There may be more than one correct answer.)
    - a. $\mathbf{v}$
    - b. $\frac{1}{2}\vec{HI}$
    - c. $\frac{1}{3}\vec{OA}$
    - d. $\mathbf{u}$
    - e. $\frac{1}{2}\vec{IH}$

18. **Scalar multiples** Which of the following vectors equals $\vec{BK}$? (There may be more than one correct answer.)
    - a. $6\mathbf{v}$
    - b. $-6\mathbf{v}$
    - c. $3\vec{HI}$
    - d. $3\vec{IH}$
    - e. $2\vec{AO}$

19. **Scalar multiples** Write the following vectors as scalar multiples of $\mathbf{u}$ or $\mathbf{v}$.
    - a. $\vec{OA}$
    - b. $\vec{OD}$
    - c. $\vec{OH}$
    - d. $\vec{AG}$
    - e. $\vec{CE}$

20. **Scalar multiples** Write the following vectors as scalar multiples of $\mathbf{u}$ or $\mathbf{v}$.
    - a. $\vec{IH}$
    - b. $\vec{HI}$
    - c. $\vec{JK}$
    - d. $\vec{FD}$
    - e. $\vec{EA}$

21. Vector addition Write the following vectors as sums of scalar multiples of **u** and **v**.

a. $\overrightarrow{OE}$ b. $\overrightarrow{OB}$ c. $\overrightarrow{OF}$ d. $\overrightarrow{OG}$ e. $\overrightarrow{OC}$
f. $\overrightarrow{OI}$ g. $\overrightarrow{OJ}$ h. $\overrightarrow{OK}$ i. $\overrightarrow{OL}$

22. Vector addition Write the following vectors as sums of scalar multiples of **u** and **v**.

a. $\overrightarrow{BF}$ b. $\overrightarrow{DE}$ c. $\overrightarrow{AF}$ d. $\overrightarrow{AD}$ e. $\overrightarrow{CD}$
f. $\overrightarrow{JD}$ g. $\overrightarrow{JI}$ h. $\overrightarrow{DB}$ i. $\overrightarrow{IL}$

23. Components and magnitudes Define the points $O(0, 0)$, $P(3, 2)$, $Q(4, 2)$, and $R(-6, -1)$. For each vector, do the following.

(i) Sketch the vector in an xy-coordinate system.
(ii) Compute the magnitude of the vector.

a. $\overrightarrow{OP}$ b. $\overrightarrow{QP}$ c. $\overrightarrow{RQ}$

24–27. Components and equality *Define the points $P(-3, -1)$, $Q(-1, 2)$, $R(1, 2)$, $S(3, 5)$, $T(4, 2)$, and $U(6, 4)$.*

24. Sketch $\overrightarrow{PU}$, $\overrightarrow{TR}$, and $\overrightarrow{SQ}$ and the corresponding position vectors.

25. Sketch $\overrightarrow{QU}$, $\overrightarrow{PT}$, and $\overrightarrow{RS}$ and the corresponding position vectors.

26. Find the equal vectors among $\overrightarrow{PQ}$, $\overrightarrow{RS}$, and $\overrightarrow{TU}$.

27. Which of the vectors $\overrightarrow{QT}$ or $\overrightarrow{SU}$ is equal to $\langle 5, 0 \rangle$?

28–33. Vector operations *Let $\mathbf{u} = \langle 4, -2 \rangle$, $\mathbf{v} = \langle -4, 6 \rangle$, and $\mathbf{w} = \langle 0, 8 \rangle$. Express the following vectors in the form $\langle a, b \rangle$.*

28. $\mathbf{u} + \mathbf{v}$ **29.** $\mathbf{w} - \mathbf{u}$ **30.** $2\mathbf{u} + 3\mathbf{v}$

31. $\mathbf{w} - 3\mathbf{v}$ **32.** $10\mathbf{u} - 3\mathbf{v} + \mathbf{w}$ **33.** $8\mathbf{w} + \mathbf{v} - 6\mathbf{u}$

34–41. Vector operations *Let $\mathbf{u} = \langle 3, -4 \rangle$, $\mathbf{v} = \langle 1, 1 \rangle$, and $\mathbf{w} = \langle -1, 0 \rangle$.*

34. Find $|\mathbf{u} + \mathbf{v}|$.   **35.** Find $|-2\mathbf{v}|$.

36. Find $|\mathbf{u} + \mathbf{v} + \mathbf{w}|$.   **37.** Find $|2\mathbf{u} + 3\mathbf{v} - 4\mathbf{w}|$.

38. Find two vectors parallel to **u** with four times the magnitude of **u**.

39. Find two vectors parallel to **v** with three times the magnitude of **v**.

40. Which has the greater magnitude, $2\mathbf{u}$ or $7\mathbf{v}$?

41. Which has the greater magnitude, $\mathbf{u} - \mathbf{v}$ or $\mathbf{w} - \mathbf{u}$?

42–47. Unit vectors *Define the points $P(-4, 1)$, $Q(3, -4)$, and $R(2, 6)$.*

42. Express $\overrightarrow{PQ}$ in the form $a\mathbf{i} + b\mathbf{j}$.

43. Express $\overrightarrow{QR}$ in the form $a\mathbf{i} + b\mathbf{j}$.

44. Find the unit vector with the same direction as $\overrightarrow{QR}$.

45. Find two unit vectors parallel to $\overrightarrow{PR}$.

46. Find two vectors parallel to $\overrightarrow{RP}$ with length 4.

47. Find two vectors parallel to $\overrightarrow{QP}$ with length 4.

48. A boat in a current The water in a river moves south at 10 mi/hr. A motorboat travels due east at a speed of 20 mi/hr relative to the shore. Determine the speed and direction of the boat relative to the moving water.

49. Another boat in a current The water in a river moves south at 5 km/hr. A motorboat travels due east at a speed of 40 km/hr relative to the water. Determine the speed of the boat relative to the shore.

50. Parachute in the wind In still air, a parachute with a payload falls vertically at a terminal speed of 4 m/s. Find the direction and magnitude of its terminal velocity relative to the ground if it falls in a steady wind blowing horizontally from west to east at 10 m/s.

51. Airplane in a wind An airplane flies horizontally from east to west at 320 mi/hr relative to the air. If it flies in a steady 40 mi/hr wind that blows horizontally toward the southwest (45° south of west), find the speed and direction of the airplane relative to the ground.

52. Canoe in a current A woman in a canoe paddles due west at 4 mi/hr relative to the water in a current that flows northwest at 2 mi/hr. Find the speed and direction of the canoe relative to the shore.

53. Boat in a wind A sailboat floats in a current that flows due east at 1 m/s. Due to a wind, the boat's actual speed relative to the shore is $\sqrt{3}$ m/s in a direction 30° north of east. Find the speed and direction of the wind.

54. Towing a boat A boat is towed with a force of 150 lb with a rope that makes an angle of 30° to the horizontal. Find the horizontal and vertical components of the force.

55. Pulling a suitcase Suppose you pull a suitcase with a strap that makes a 60° angle with the horizontal. The magnitude of the force you exert on the suitcase is 40 lb.

a. Find the horizontal and vertical components of the force.
b. Is the horizontal component of the force greater if the angle of the strap is 45° instead of 60°?
c. Is the vertical component of the force greater if the angle of the strap is 45° instead of 60°?

56. Which is greater? Which has a greater horizontal component, a 100-N force directed at an angle of 60° above the horizontal or a 60-N force directed at an angle of 30° above the horizontal?

57. Suspended load If a 500-lb load is suspended by two chains (see figure), what is the magnitude of the force each chain must be able to support?

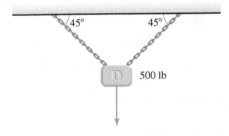

58. Net force Three forces are applied to an object, as shown in the figure. Find the magnitude and direction of the sum of the forces.

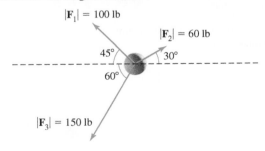

Further Explorations

59. Explain why or why not Determine whether the following statements are true and give an explanation or counterexample.

    a. José travels from point A to point B in the plane by following vector **u**, then vector **v**, and then vector **w**. If he starts at A and follows **w**, then **v**, and then **u**, he still arrives at B.

    b. Maria travels from A to B in the plane by following the vector **u**. By following $-\mathbf{u}$, she returns from B to A.

    c. $|\mathbf{u} + \mathbf{v}| \geq |\mathbf{u}|$, for all vectors **u** and **v**.

    d. $|\mathbf{u} + \mathbf{v}| \geq |\mathbf{u}| + |\mathbf{v}|$, for all vectors **u** and **v**.

    e. Parallel vectors have the same length.

    f. If $\overrightarrow{AB} = \overrightarrow{CD}$, then $A = C$ and $B = D$.

    g. If **u** and **v** are perpendicular, then $|\mathbf{u} + \mathbf{v}| = |\mathbf{u}| + |\mathbf{v}|$.

    h. If **u** and **v** are parallel and have the same direction, then $|\mathbf{u} + \mathbf{v}| = |\mathbf{u}| + |\mathbf{v}|$.

60. Finding vectors from two points Given the points $A(-2, 0)$, $B(6, 16)$, $C(1, 4)$, $D(5, 4)$, $E(\sqrt{2}, \sqrt{2})$, and $F(3\sqrt{2}, -4\sqrt{2})$, find the position vector equal to the following vectors.

    a. $\overrightarrow{AB}$ **b.** $\overrightarrow{AC}$ **c.** $\overrightarrow{EF}$ **d.** $\overrightarrow{CD}$

61. Unit vectors

    a. Find two unit vectors parallel to $\mathbf{v} = 6\mathbf{i} - 8\mathbf{j}$.

    b. Find b if $\mathbf{v} = \langle \frac{1}{3}, b \rangle$ is a unit vector.

    c. Find all values of a such that $\mathbf{w} = a\mathbf{i} - \dfrac{a}{3}\mathbf{j}$ is a unit vector.

62. Equal vectors For the points $A(3, 4)$, $B(6, 10)$, $C(a + 2, b + 5)$, and $D(b + 4, a - 2)$, find the values of a and b such that $\overrightarrow{AB} = \overrightarrow{CD}$.

63–66. Vector equations *Use the properties of vectors to solve the following equations for the unknown vector* $\mathbf{x} = \langle a, b \rangle$. *Let* $\mathbf{u} = \langle 2, -3 \rangle$ *and* $\mathbf{v} = \langle -4, 1 \rangle$.

63. $10\mathbf{x} = \mathbf{u}$

64. $2\mathbf{x} + \mathbf{u} = \mathbf{v}$

65. $3\mathbf{x} - 4\mathbf{u} = \mathbf{v}$

66. $-4\mathbf{x} = \mathbf{u} - 8\mathbf{v}$

67–69. Linear combinations *A sum of scalar multiples of two or more vectors (such as* $c_1\mathbf{u} + c_2\mathbf{v} + c_3\mathbf{w}$, *where* c_i *are scalars) is called a* **linear combination** *of the vectors. Let* $\mathbf{i} = \langle 1, 0 \rangle$, $\mathbf{j} = \langle 0, 1 \rangle$, $\mathbf{u} = \langle 1, 1 \rangle$, *and* $\mathbf{v} = \langle -1, 1 \rangle$.

67. Express $\langle 4, -8 \rangle$ as a linear combination of **i** and **j** (that is, find scalars c_1 and c_2 such that $\langle 4, -8 \rangle = c_1\mathbf{i} + c_2\mathbf{j}$).

68. Express $\langle 4, -8 \rangle$ as a linear combination of **u** and **v**.

69. For arbitrary real numbers a and b, express $\langle a, b \rangle$ as a linear combination of **u** and **v**.

70–71. Solving vector equations *Solve the following pairs of equations for the vectors* **u** *and* **v**. *Assume* $\mathbf{i} = \langle 1, 0 \rangle$ *and* $\mathbf{j} = \langle 0, 1 \rangle$.

70. $2\mathbf{u} = \mathbf{i}, \mathbf{u} - 4\mathbf{v} = \mathbf{j}$

71. $2\mathbf{u} + 3\mathbf{v} = \mathbf{i}, \mathbf{u} - \mathbf{v} = \mathbf{j}$

72–75. Designer vectors *Find the following vectors.*

72. The vector that is 3 times $\langle 3, -5 \rangle$ plus -9 times $\langle 6, 0 \rangle$

73. The vector in the direction of $\langle 5, -12 \rangle$ with length 3

74. The vector in the direction opposite that of $\langle 6, -8 \rangle$ with length 10

75. The position vector for your final location if you start at the origin and walk along $\langle 4, -6 \rangle$ followed by $\langle 5, 9 \rangle$

Applications

76. Ant on a page An ant walks due east at a constant speed of 2 mi/hr on a sheet of paper that rests on a table. Suddenly, the sheet of paper starts moving southeast at $\sqrt{2}$ mi/hr. Describe the motion of the ant relative to the table.

77. Clock vectors Consider the 12 vectors that have their tails at the center of a (circular) clock and their heads at the numbers on the edge of the clock.

    a. What is the sum of these 12 vectors?

    b. If the 12:00 vector is removed, what is the sum of the remaining 11 vectors?

    c. By removing one or more of these 12 clock vectors, explain how to make the sum of the remaining vectors as large as possible in magnitude.

    d. Consider the 11 vectors that originate at the number 12 at the top of the clock and point to the other 11 numbers. What is the sum of the vectors?

(*Source: Calculus*, Gilbert Strang, Wellesley-Cambridge Press, 1991)

78. Three-way tug-of-war Three people located at A, B, and C pull on ropes tied to a ring. Find the magnitude and direction of the force with which the person at C must pull so that no one moves (the system is in equilibrium).

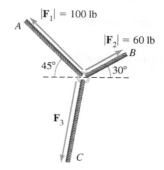

79. Net force Jack pulls east on a rope attached to a camel with a force of 40 lb. Jill pulls north on a rope attached to the same camel with a force of 30 lb. What is the magnitude and direction of the force on the camel? Assume the vectors lie in a horizontal plane.

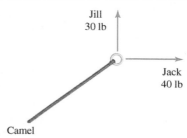

80. Mass on a plane A 100-kg object rests on an inclined plane at an angle of 30° to the floor. Find the components of the force perpendicular to and parallel to the plane. (The vertical component of the force exerted by an object of mass m is its weight, which is mg, where $g = 9.8 \text{ m/s}^2$ is the acceleration due to gravity.)

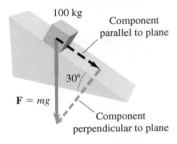

Additional Exercises

81–85. Vector properties *Prove the following vector properties using components. Then make a sketch to illustrate the property geometrically. Suppose* **u**, **v**, *and* **w** *are vectors in the xy-plane and a and c are scalars.*

81. $\mathbf{u} + \mathbf{v} = \mathbf{v} + \mathbf{u}$ Commutative property

82. $(\mathbf{u} + \mathbf{v}) + \mathbf{w} = \mathbf{u} + (\mathbf{v} + \mathbf{w})$ Associative property

83. $a(c\mathbf{v}) = (ac)\mathbf{v}$ Associative property

84. $a(\mathbf{u} + \mathbf{v}) = a\mathbf{u} + a\mathbf{v}$ Distributive property 1

85. $(a + c)\mathbf{v} = a\mathbf{v} + c\mathbf{v}$ Distributive property 2

86. Midpoint of a line segment Use vectors to show that the midpoint of the line segment joining $P(x_1, y_1)$ and $Q(x_2, y_2)$ is the point $\left(\dfrac{x_1 + x_2}{2}, \dfrac{y_1 + y_2}{2}\right)$ (*Hint:* Let O be the origin and let M be the midpoint of PQ. Draw a picture and show that $\overrightarrow{OM} = \overrightarrow{OP} + \frac{1}{2}\overrightarrow{PQ} = \overrightarrow{OP} + \frac{1}{2}(\overrightarrow{OQ} - \overrightarrow{OP})$.)

87. Magnitude of scalar multiple Prove that $|c\mathbf{v}| = |c||\mathbf{v}|$, where c is a scalar and **v** is a vector.

88. Equality of vectors Assume $\overrightarrow{PQ}$ equals $\overrightarrow{RS}$. Does it follow that $\overrightarrow{PR}$ is equal to $\overrightarrow{QS}$? Explain your answer.

89. Linear independence A pair of nonzero vectors in the plane is *linearly dependent* if one vector is a scalar multiple of the other. Otherwise, the pair is *linearly independent*.

   a. Which pairs of the following vectors are linearly dependent and which are linearly independent: $\mathbf{u} = \langle 2, -3\rangle$, $\mathbf{v} = \langle -12, 18\rangle$, and $\mathbf{w} = \langle 4, 6\rangle$?

   b. Geometrically, what does it mean for a pair of nonzero vectors in the plane to be linearly dependent? Linearly independent?

   c. Prove that if a pair of vectors **u** and **v** is linearly independent, then given any vector **w**, there are constants c_1 and c_2 such that $\mathbf{w} = c_1\mathbf{u} + c_2\mathbf{v}$.

90. Perpendicular vectors Show that two nonzero vectors $\mathbf{u} = \langle u_1, u_2\rangle$ and $\mathbf{v} = \langle v_1, v_2\rangle$ are perpendicular to each other if $u_1 v_1 + u_2 v_2 = 0$.

91. Parallel and perpendicular vectors Let $\mathbf{u} = \langle a, 5\rangle$ and $\mathbf{v} = \langle 2, 6\rangle$.

   a. Find the value of a such that **u** is parallel to **v**.

   b. Find the value of a such that **u** is perpendicular to **v**.

92. The Triangle Inequality Suppose **u** and **v** are vectors in the plane.

   a. Use the Triangle Rule for adding vectors to explain why $|\mathbf{u} + \mathbf{v}| \leq |\mathbf{u}| + |\mathbf{v}|$. This result is known as the *Triangle Inequality*.

   b. Under what conditions is $|\mathbf{u} + \mathbf{v}| = |\mathbf{u}| + |\mathbf{v}|$?

QUICK CHECK ANSWERS

1. The vector $-5\mathbf{v}$ is five times as long as **v** and points in the opposite direction.   **2.** $\mathbf{v}_a + \mathbf{w}$ points in a northeasterly direction.   **3.** Constructing $\mathbf{u} + \mathbf{v}$ and $\mathbf{v} + \mathbf{u}$ using the Triangle Rule produces vectors having the same direction and magnitude.   **4.** $\overrightarrow{PQ} = \langle -6, -2\rangle$ **5.** $10\mathbf{u} = \langle 6, 8\rangle$ and $-10\mathbf{u} = \langle -6, -8\rangle$ **6.** $\left|\left\langle \dfrac{5}{13}, \dfrac{12}{13}\right\rangle\right| = \sqrt{\dfrac{25 + 144}{169}} = \sqrt{\dfrac{169}{169}} = 1$ **7.** $\mathbf{u} = -\frac{4}{3}\mathbf{v} + 4\mathbf{w}$ ◄

11.2 Vectors in Three Dimensions

Up to this point, our study of calculus has been limited to functions, curves, and vectors that can be plotted in the two-dimensional xy-plane. However, a two-dimensional coordinate system is insufficient for modeling many physical phenomena. For example, to describe the trajectory of a jet gaining altitude, we need two coordinates, say x and y, to measure east–west and north–south distances. In addition, another coordinate, say z, is needed to measure the altitude of the jet. By adding a third coordinate and creating an ordered triple (x, y, z), the location of the jet can be described. The set of all points described by the triples (x, y, z) is called *three-dimensional space*, xyz-space, or $\mathbb{R}^3$. Many of the properties of xyz-space are extensions of familiar ideas you have seen in the xy-plane.

The *xyz*-Coordinate System

▶ The notation $\mathbb{R}^3$ (pronounced *R-three*) stands for the set of all ordered triples of real numbers.

A three-dimensional coordinate system is created by adding a new axis, called the **z-axis**, to the familiar *xy*-coordinate system. The new *z*-axis is inserted through the origin perpendicular to the *x*- and *y*-axes (Figure 11.25). The result is a new coordinate system called the **three-dimensional rectangular coordinate system** or the ***xyz*-coordinate system**.

The coordinate system described here is a conventional **right-handed coordinate system**: If the curled fingers of the right hand are rotated from the positive *x*-axis to the positive *y*-axis, the thumb points in the direction of the positive *z*-axis (Figure 11.25).

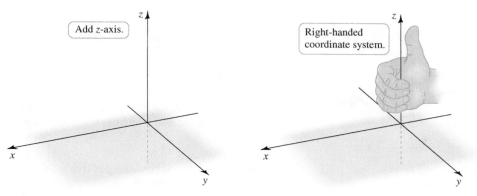

Figure 11.25

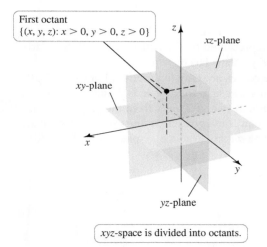

Figure 11.26

The coordinate plane containing the *x*-axis and *y*-axis is still called the *xy*-plane. We now have two new coordinate planes: the ***xz*-plane** containing the *x*-axis and the *z*-axis, and the ***yz*-plane** containing the *y*-axis and the *z*-axis. Taken together, these three coordinate planes divide *xyz*-space into eight regions called **octants** (Figure 11.26).

The point where all three axes intersect is the **origin**, which has coordinates $(0, 0, 0)$. An ordered triple (a, b, c) refers to the point in *xyz*-space that is found by starting at the origin, moving *a* units in the *x*-direction, *b* units in the *y*-direction, and *c* units in the *z*-direction. With a negative coordinate, you move in the negative direction along the corresponding coordinate axis. To visualize this point, it's helpful to construct a rectangular box with one vertex at the origin and the opposite vertex at the point (a, b, c) (Figure 11.27).

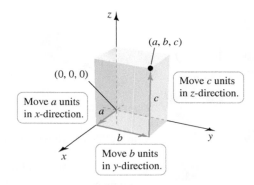

Figure 11.27

EXAMPLE 1   Plotting points in *xyz*-space Plot the following points.

a. $(3, 4, 5)$ **b.** $(-2, -3, 5)$

SOLUTION

a. Starting at $(0, 0, 0)$, we move 3 units in the *x*-direction to the point $(3, 0, 0)$, then 4 units in the *y*-direction to the point $(3, 4, 0)$, and finally, 5 units in the *z*-direction to reach the point $(3, 4, 5)$ (Figure 11.28).

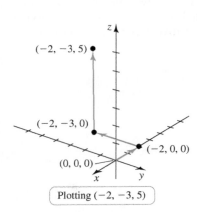

Plotting $(-2, -3, 5)$

Figure 11.29

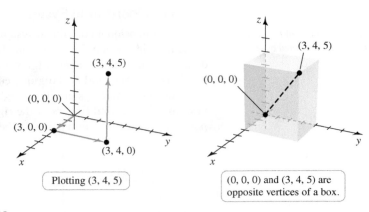

Plotting (3, 4, 5)

(0, 0, 0) and (3, 4, 5) are opposite vertices of a box.

Figure 11.28

b. We move -2 units in the x-direction to $(-2, 0, 0)$, -3 units in the y-direction to $(-2, -3, 0)$, and 5 units in the z-direction to reach $(-2, -3, 5)$ (Figure 11.29).

Related Exercises 9–14 ◄

QUICK CHECK 1 Suppose the positive x-, y-, and z-axes point east, north, and upward, respectively. Describe the location of the points $(-1, -1, 0)$, $(1, 0, 1)$, and $(-1, -1, -1)$ relative to the origin. ◄

Equations of Simple Planes

The xy-plane consists of all points in xyz-space that have a z-coordinate of 0. Therefore, the xy-plane is the set $\{(x, y, z) : z = 0\}$; it is represented by the equation $z = 0$. Similarly, the xz-plane has the equation $y = 0$, and the yz-plane has the equation $x = 0$.

> Planes that are not parallel to the coordinate planes are discussed in Section 12.1.

Planes parallel to one of the coordinate planes are easy to describe. For example, the equation $x = 2$ describes the set of all points whose x-coordinate is 2 and whose y- and z-coordinates are arbitrary; this plane is parallel to and 2 units from the yz-plane. Similarly, the equation $y = a$ describes a plane that is everywhere a units from the xz-plane, and $z = a$ is the equation of a horizontal plane a units from the xy-plane (Figure 11.30).

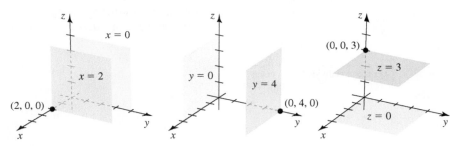

Figure 11.30

Plane is parallel to the xz-plane and passes through $(2, -3, 7)$.

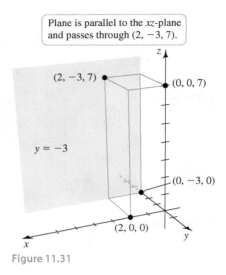

Figure 11.31

QUICK CHECK 2 To which coordinate planes are the planes $x = -2$ and $z = 16$ parallel? ◄

EXAMPLE 2   Parallel planes Determine the equation of the plane parallel to the xz-plane passing through the point $(2, -3, 7)$.

SOLUTION Points on a plane parallel to the xz-plane have the same y-coordinate. Therefore, the plane passing through the point $(2, -3, 7)$ with a y-coordinate of -3 has the equation $y = -3$ (Figure 11.31).

Related Exercises 15–22 ◄

Distances in xyz-Space

Recall that the distance between two points (x_1, y_1) and (x_2, y_2) in the xy-plane is $\sqrt{(x_2 - x_1)^2 + (y_2 - y_1)^2}$. This distance formula is useful in deriving a similar formula for the distance between two points $P(x_1, y_1, z_1)$ and $Q(x_2, y_2, z_2)$ in xyz-space.

Figure 11.32 shows the points P and Q, together with the auxiliary point $R(x_2, y_2, z_1)$, which has the same z-coordinate as P and the same x- and y-coordinates as Q. The line segment PR has length $|PR| = \sqrt{(x_2 - x_1)^2 + (y_2 - y_1)^2}$ and is one leg of the right triangle $\triangle PRQ$. The length of the hypotenuse of that triangle is the distance between P and Q:

$$\sqrt{|PR|^2 + |RQ|^2} = \sqrt{\underbrace{(x_2 - x_1)^2 + (y_2 - y_1)^2}_{|PR|^2} + \underbrace{(z_2 - z_1)^2}_{|RQ|^2}}.$$

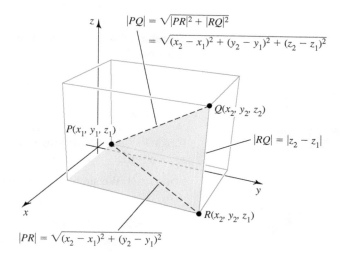

$|PQ| = \sqrt{|PR|^2 + |RQ|^2}$

$= \sqrt{(x_2 - x_1)^2 + (y_2 - y_1)^2 + (z_2 - z_1)^2}$

$Q(x_2, y_2, z_2)$

$P(x_1, y_1, z_1)$

$|RQ| = |z_2 - z_1|$

$R(x_2, y_2, z_1)$

$|PR| = \sqrt{(x_2 - x_1)^2 + (y_2 - y_1)^2}$

Figure 11.32

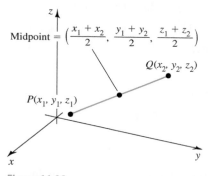

$\text{Midpoint} = \left(\dfrac{x_1 + x_2}{2}, \dfrac{y_1 + y_2}{2}, \dfrac{z_1 + z_2}{2} \right)$

$Q(x_2, y_2, z_2)$

$P(x_1, y_1, z_1)$

Figure 11.33

Distance Formula in xyz-Space

The distance between the points $P(x_1, y_1, z_1)$ and $Q(x_2, y_2, z_2)$ is

$$\sqrt{(x_2 - x_1)^2 + (y_2 - y_1)^2 + (z_2 - z_1)^2}.$$

By using the distance formula, we can derive the formula (Exercise 79) for the **midpoint** of the line segment joining $P(x_1, y_1, z_1)$ and $Q(x_2, y_2, z_2)$, which is found by averaging the x-, y-, and z-coordinates (Figure 11.33):

$$\text{Midpoint} = \left(\frac{x_1 + x_2}{2}, \frac{y_1 + y_2}{2}, \frac{z_1 + z_2}{2} \right).$$

Equation of a Sphere

A *sphere* is the set of all points that are a constant distance r from a point (a, b, c); r is the *radius* of the sphere and (a, b, c) is the *center* of the sphere. A *ball* centered at (a, b, c) with radius r consists of all the points inside and on the sphere centered at (a, b, c) with radius r (Figure 11.34). We now use the distance formula to translate these statements.

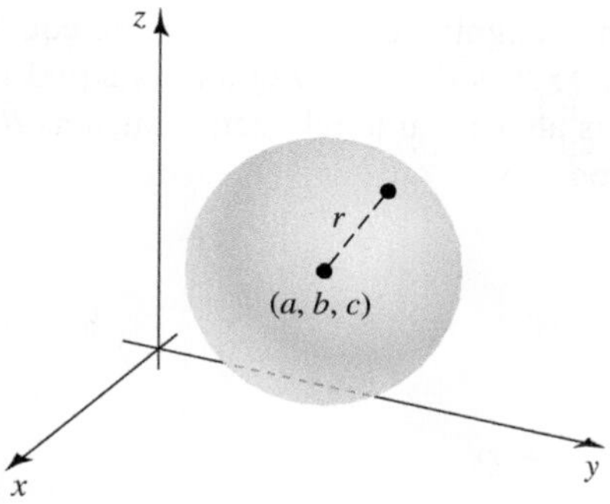

Figure 11.34

Sphere: $(x - a)^2 + (y - b)^2 + (z - c)^2 = r^2$

Ball: $(x - a)^2 + (y - b)^2 + (z - c)^2 \le r^2$

> Just as a circle is the boundary of a disk in two dimensions, a *sphere* is the boundary of a *ball* in three dimensions. We have defined a *closed ball*, which includes its boundary. An *open ball* does not contain its boundary.

Spheres and Balls

A **sphere** centered at (a, b, c) with radius r is the set of points satisfying the equation

$$(x - a)^2 + (y - b)^2 + (z - c)^2 = r^2.$$

A **ball** centered at (a, b, c) with radius r is the set of points satisfying the inequality

$$(x - a)^2 + (y - b)^2 + (z - c)^2 \le r^2.$$

EXAMPLE 3   Equation of a sphere   Consider the points $P(1, -2, 5)$ and $Q(3, 4, -6)$. Find an equation of the sphere for which the line segment PQ is a diameter.

SOLUTION   The center of the sphere is the midpoint of PQ:

$$\left(\frac{1+3}{2}, \frac{-2+4}{2}, \frac{5-6}{2}\right) = \left(2, 1, -\frac{1}{2}\right).$$

The diameter of the sphere is the distance $|PQ|$, which is

$$\sqrt{(3-1)^2 + (4+2)^2 + (-6-5)^2} = \sqrt{161}.$$

Therefore, the sphere's radius is $\frac{1}{2}\sqrt{161}$, its center is $(2, 1, -\frac{1}{2})$, and it is described by the equation

$$(x-2)^2 + (y-1)^2 + \left(z + \frac{1}{2}\right)^2 = \left(\frac{1}{2}\sqrt{161}\right)^2 = \frac{161}{4}.$$

Related Exercises 23–28 ◄

EXAMPLE 4   Identifying equations   Describe the set of points that satisfy the equation $x^2 + y^2 + z^2 - 2x + 6y - 8z = -1$.

SOLUTION   We simplify the equation by completing the square and factoring:

$$(x^2 - 2x) + (y^2 + 6y) + (z^2 - 8z) = -1 \quad \text{Group terms.}$$
$$(x^2 - 2x + 1) + (y^2 + 6y + 9) + (z^2 - 8z + 16) = 25 \quad \text{Complete the square.}$$
$$(x-1)^2 + (y+3)^2 + (z-4)^2 = 25. \quad \text{Factor.}$$

The equation describes a sphere of radius 5 with center $(1, -3, 4)$.

Related Exercises 29–38 ◄

QUICK CHECK 3   Describe the solution set of the equation

$$(x-1)^2 + y^2 + (z+1)^2 + 4 = 0. ◄$$

Vectors in $\mathbb{R}^3$

Vectors in $\mathbb{R}^3$ are straightforward extensions of vectors in the xy-plane; we simply include a third component. The position vector $\mathbf{v} = \langle v_1, v_2, v_3 \rangle$ has its tail at the origin and its head at the point (v_1, v_2, v_3). Vectors having the same magnitude and direction are equal. Therefore, the vector from $P(x_1, y_1, z_1)$ to $Q(x_2, y_2, z_2)$ is denoted $\overrightarrow{PQ}$ and is equal to the position vector $\langle x_2 - x_1, y_2 - y_1, z_2 - z_1 \rangle$. It is also equal to all vectors such as $\overrightarrow{RS}$ (Figure 11.35) that have the same length and direction as $\mathbf{v}$.

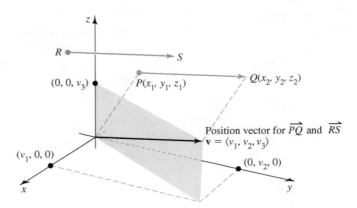

Figure 11.35

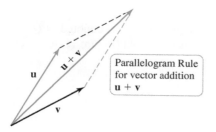

Parallelogram Rule for vector addition
$\mathbf{u} + \mathbf{v}$

The operations of vector addition and scalar multiplication in $\mathbb{R}^2$ generalize in a natural way to three dimensions. For example, the sum of two vectors is found geometrically using the Triangle Rule or the Parallelogram Rule (Section 11.1). The sum is found analytically by adding the respective components of the two vectors. As with two-dimensional vectors, scalar multiplication corresponds to stretching or compressing a vector, possibly with a reversal of direction. Two nonzero vectors are parallel if one is a scalar multiple of the other (Figure 11.36).

QUICK CHECK 4 Which of the following vectors are parallel to each other?

a. $\mathbf{u} = \langle -2, 4, -6 \rangle$ **b.** $\mathbf{v} = \langle 4, -8, 12 \rangle$ **c.** $\mathbf{w} = \langle -1, 2, 3 \rangle$ ◄

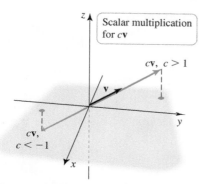

Scalar multiplication for $c\mathbf{v}$

Figure 11.36

DEFINITION **Vector Operations in $\mathbb{R}^3$**

Let c be a scalar, $\mathbf{u} = \langle u_1, u_2, u_3 \rangle$, and $\mathbf{v} = \langle v_1, v_2, v_3 \rangle$.

$$\mathbf{u} + \mathbf{v} = \langle u_1 + v_1, u_2 + v_2, u_3 + v_3 \rangle \quad \text{Vector addition}$$
$$\mathbf{u} - \mathbf{v} = \langle u_1 - v_1, u_2 - v_2, u_3 - v_3 \rangle \quad \text{Vector subtraction}$$
$$c\mathbf{u} = \langle cu_1, cu_2, cu_3 \rangle \quad \text{Scalar multiplication}$$

EXAMPLE 5 **Vectors in $\mathbb{R}^3$** Let $\mathbf{u} = \langle 2, -4, 1 \rangle$ and $\mathbf{v} = \langle 3, 0, -1 \rangle$. Find the components of the following vectors and draw them in $\mathbb{R}^3$.

a. $\dfrac{1}{2}\mathbf{u}$ **b.** $-2\mathbf{v}$ **c.** $\mathbf{u} + 2\mathbf{v}$

SOLUTION

a. Using the definition of scalar multiplication, $\dfrac{1}{2}\mathbf{u} = \dfrac{1}{2}\langle 2, -4, 1 \rangle = \left\langle 1, -2, \dfrac{1}{2} \right\rangle$. The vector $\dfrac{1}{2}\mathbf{u}$ has the same direction as $\mathbf{u}$ with half the magnitude of $\mathbf{u}$ (Figure 11.37).

b. Using scalar multiplication, $-2\mathbf{v} = -2\langle 3, 0, -1 \rangle = \langle -6, 0, 2 \rangle$. The vector $-2\mathbf{v}$ has the opposite direction as $\mathbf{v}$ and twice the magnitude of $\mathbf{v}$ (Figure 11.38).

c. Using vector addition and scalar multiplication,

$$\mathbf{u} + 2\mathbf{v} = \langle 2, -4, 1 \rangle + 2\langle 3, 0, -1 \rangle = \langle 8, -4, -1 \rangle.$$

The vector $\mathbf{u} + 2\mathbf{v}$ is drawn by applying the Parallelogram Rule to $\mathbf{u}$ and $2\mathbf{v}$ (Figure 11.39).

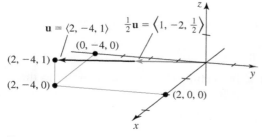

Figure 11.37

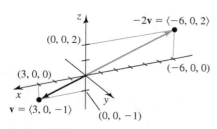

Figure 11.38

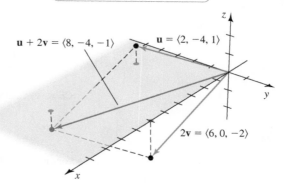

$\mathbf{u} + 2\mathbf{v}$ by the Parallelogram Rule

Figure 11.39

Related Exercises 39–44 ◄

Magnitude and Unit Vectors

The magnitude of the vector $\overrightarrow{PQ}$ from $P(x_1, y_1, z_1)$ to $Q(x_2, y_2, z_2)$ is denoted $|\overrightarrow{PQ}|$; it is the distance between P and Q and is given by the distance formula (Figure 11.40).

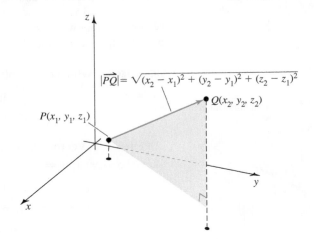

$$|\overrightarrow{PQ}| = \sqrt{(x_2 - x_1)^2 + (y_2 - y_1)^2 + (z_2 - z_1)^2}$$

$Q(x_2, y_2, z_2)$

$P(x_1, y_1, z_1)$

Figure 11.40

DEFINITION   Magnitude of a Vector

The **magnitude** (or **length**) of the vector $\overrightarrow{PQ} = \langle x_2 - x_1, y_2 - y_1, z_2 - z_1 \rangle$ is the distance from $P(x_1, y_1, z_1)$ to $Q(x_2, y_2, z_2)$:

$$|\overrightarrow{PQ}| = \sqrt{(x_2 - x_1)^2 + (y_2 - y_1)^2 + (z_2 - z_1)^2}.$$

The coordinate unit vectors introduced in Section 11.1 extend naturally to three dimensions. The three coordinate unit vectors in $\mathbb{R}^3$ (Figure 11.41) are

$$\mathbf{i} = \langle 1, 0, 0 \rangle, \quad \mathbf{j} = \langle 0, 1, 0 \rangle, \quad \text{and} \quad \mathbf{k} = \langle 0, 0, 1 \rangle.$$

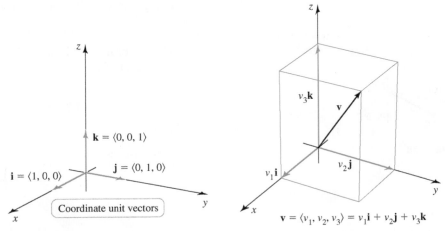

$\mathbf{k} = \langle 0, 0, 1 \rangle$

$\mathbf{i} = \langle 1, 0, 0 \rangle$ $\mathbf{j} = \langle 0, 1, 0 \rangle$

Coordinate unit vectors

$v_3\mathbf{k}$ $\mathbf{v}$

$v_1\mathbf{i}$ $v_2\mathbf{j}$

$\mathbf{v} = \langle v_1, v_2, v_3 \rangle = v_1\mathbf{i} + v_2\mathbf{j} + v_3\mathbf{k}$

Figure 11.41

These unit vectors give an alternative way of expressing position vectors. If $\mathbf{v} = \langle v_1, v_2, v_3 \rangle$, then we have

$$\mathbf{v} = v_1\langle 1, 0, 0 \rangle + v_2\langle 0, 1, 0 \rangle + v_3\langle 0, 0, 1 \rangle = v_1\mathbf{i} + v_2\mathbf{j} + v_3\mathbf{k}.$$

EXAMPLE 6 **Magnitudes and unit vectors** Consider the points $P(5, 3, 1)$ and $Q(-7, 8, 1)$.

a. Express $\vec{PQ}$ in terms of the unit vectors $\mathbf{i}$, $\mathbf{j}$, and $\mathbf{k}$.

b. Find the magnitude of $\vec{PQ}$.

c. Find the position vector of magnitude 10 in the direction of $\vec{PQ}$.

SOLUTION

a. $\vec{PQ}$ is equal to the position vector $\langle -7 - 5, 8 - 3, 1 - 1 \rangle = \langle -12, 5, 0 \rangle$. Therefore, $\vec{PQ} = -12\mathbf{i} + 5\mathbf{j}$.

b. $|\vec{PQ}| = |-12\mathbf{i} + 5\mathbf{j}| = \sqrt{12^2 + 5^2} = \sqrt{169} = 13$

c. The unit vector in the direction of $\vec{PQ}$ is $\mathbf{u} = \dfrac{\vec{PQ}}{|\vec{PQ}|} = \dfrac{1}{13}\langle -12, 5, 0 \rangle$. Therefore,

the vector in the direction of $\mathbf{u}$ with a magnitude of 10 is $10\mathbf{u} = \dfrac{10}{13}\langle -12, 5, 0 \rangle$.

Related Exercises 45–50 ◀

QUICK CHECK 5 Which vector has the smaller magnitude: $\mathbf{u} = 3\mathbf{i} - \mathbf{j} - \mathbf{k}$ or $\mathbf{v} = 2(\mathbf{i} + \mathbf{j} + \mathbf{k})$? ◀

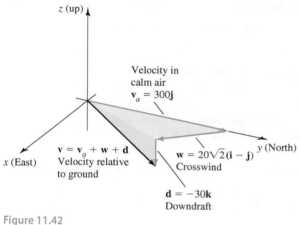

z (up)

Velocity in calm air
$\mathbf{v}_a = 300\mathbf{j}$

$\mathbf{v} = \mathbf{v}_a + \mathbf{w} + \mathbf{d}$
Velocity relative to ground

x (East)

$\mathbf{w} = 20\sqrt{2}(\mathbf{i} - \mathbf{j})$
Crosswind

y (North)

$\mathbf{d} = -30\mathbf{k}$
Downdraft

Figure 11.42

EXAMPLE 7 **Flight in crosswinds** A plane is flying horizontally due north in calm air at 300 mi/hr when it encounters a horizontal crosswind blowing southeast at 40 mi/hr and a downdraft blowing vertically downward at 30 mi/hr. What are the resulting speed and direction of the plane relative to the ground?

SOLUTION Let the unit vectors $\mathbf{i}$, $\mathbf{j}$, and $\mathbf{k}$ point east, north, and upward, respectively (Figure 11.42). The velocity of the plane relative to the air (300 mi/hr due north) is $\mathbf{v}_a = 300\mathbf{j}$. The crosswind blows 45° south of east, so its component to the east is $40 \cos 45° = 20\sqrt{2}$ (in the $\mathbf{i}$ direction) and its component to the south is $40 \cos 45° = 20\sqrt{2}$ (in the $-\mathbf{j}$ direction). Therefore, the crosswind may be expressed as $\mathbf{w} = 20\sqrt{2}\mathbf{i} - 20\sqrt{2}\mathbf{j}$. Finally, the downdraft in the negative $\mathbf{k}$ direction is $\mathbf{d} = -30\mathbf{k}$. The velocity of the plane relative to the ground is the sum of $\mathbf{v}_a$, $\mathbf{w}$, and $\mathbf{d}$:

$$\begin{aligned}\mathbf{v} &= \mathbf{v}_a + \mathbf{w} + \mathbf{d} \\ &= 300\mathbf{j} + (20\sqrt{2}\mathbf{i} - 20\sqrt{2}\mathbf{j}) - 30\mathbf{k} \\ &= 20\sqrt{2}\mathbf{i} + (300 - 20\sqrt{2})\mathbf{j} - 30\mathbf{k}.\end{aligned}$$

Figure 11.42 shows the velocity vector of the plane. A quick calculation shows that the speed is $|\mathbf{v}| \approx 275$ mi/hr. The direction of the plane is slightly east of north and downward. In the next section, we present methods for precisely determining the direction of a vector.

Related Exercises 51–56 ◀

SECTION 11.2 EXERCISES

Review Questions

1. Explain how to plot the point $(3, -2, 1)$ in $\mathbb{R}^3$.

2. What is the y-coordinate of all points in the xz-plane?

3. Describe the plane $x = 4$.

4. What position vector is equal to the vector from $(3, 5, -2)$ to $(0, -6, 3)$?

5. Let $\mathbf{u} = \langle 3, 5, -7 \rangle$ and $\mathbf{v} = \langle 6, -5, 1 \rangle$. Evaluate $\mathbf{u} + \mathbf{v}$ and $3\mathbf{u} - \mathbf{v}$.

6. What is the magnitude of a vector joining two points $P(x_1, y_1, z_1)$ and $Q(x_2, y_2, z_2)$?

7. Which point is farther from the origin, $(3, -1, 2)$ or $(0, 0, -4)$?

8. Express the vector from $P(-1, -4, 6)$ to $Q(1, 3, -6)$ as a position vector in terms of $\mathbf{i}$, $\mathbf{j}$, and $\mathbf{k}$.

Basic Skills

9–12. Points in $\mathbb{R}^3$ *Find the coordinates of the vertices A, B, and C of the following rectangular boxes.*

9.

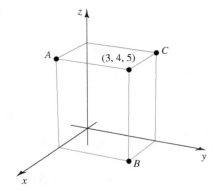

10.

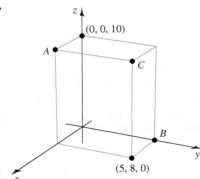

11.

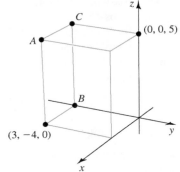

12. Assume all the edges have the same length.

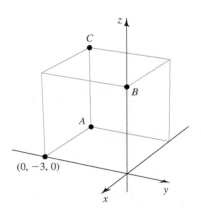

13–14. Plotting points in $\mathbb{R}^3$ *For each point $P(x, y, z)$ given below, let $A(x, y, 0)$, $B(x, 0, z)$, and $C(0, y, z)$ be points in the xy-, xz-, and yz-planes, respectively. Plot and label the points A, B, C, and P in $\mathbb{R}^3$.*

13. a. $P(2, 2, 4)$ **b.** $P(1, 2, 5)$ **c.** $P(-2, 0, 5)$

14. a. $P(-3, 2, 4)$ **b.** $P(4, -2, -3)$ **c.** $P(-2, -4, -3)$

15–20. Sketching planes *Sketch the following planes in the window* $[0, 5] \times [0, 5] \times [0, 5]$.

15. $x = 2$ **16.** $z = 3$ **17.** $y = 2$ **18.** $z = y$

19. The plane that passes through $(2, 0, 0)$, $(0, 3, 0)$, and $(0, 0, 4)$.

20. The plane parallel to the *xz*-plane containing the point $(1, 2, 3)$.

21. Planes Sketch the plane parallel to the *xy*-plane through $(2, 4, 2)$ and find its equation.

22. Planes Sketch the plane parallel to the *yz*-plane through $(2, 4, 2)$ and find its equation.

23–26. Spheres and balls *Find an equation or inequality that describes the following objects.*

23. A sphere with center $(1, 2, 3)$ and radius 4

24. A sphere with center $(1, 2, 0)$ passing through the point $(3, 4, 5)$

25. A ball with center $(-2, 0, 4)$ and radius 1

26. A ball with center $(0, -2, 6)$ with the point $(1, 4, 8)$ on its boundary

27. Midpoints and spheres Find an equation of the sphere passing through $P(1, 0, 5)$ and $Q(2, 3, 9)$ with its center at the midpoint of PQ.

28. Midpoints and spheres Find an equation of the sphere passing through $P(-4, 2, 3)$ and $Q(0, 2, 7)$ with its center at the midpoint of PQ.

29–38. Identifying sets *Give a geometric description of the following sets of points.*

29. $(x - 1)^2 + y^2 + z^2 - 9 = 0$

30. $(x + 1)^2 + y^2 + z^2 - 2y - 24 = 0$

31. $x^2 + y^2 + z^2 - 2y - 4z - 4 = 0$

32. $x^2 + y^2 + z^2 - 6x + 6y - 8z - 2 = 0$

33. $x^2 + y^2 - 14y + z^2 \geq -13$

34. $x^2 + y^2 - 14y + z^2 \leq -13$

35. $x^2 + y^2 + z^2 - 8x - 14y - 18z \leq 79$

36. $x^2 + y^2 + z^2 - 8x + 14y - 18z \geq 65$

37. $x^2 - 2x + y^2 + 6y + z^2 + 10 = 0$

38. $x^2 - 4x + y^2 + 6y + z^2 + 14 = 0$

39–44. Vector operations *For the given vectors* **u** *and* **v**, *evaluate the following expressions.*

    a. $3\mathbf{u} + 2\mathbf{v}$ **b.** $4\mathbf{u} - \mathbf{v}$ **c.** $|\mathbf{u} + 3\mathbf{v}|$

39. $\mathbf{u} = \langle 4, -3, 0 \rangle$, $\mathbf{v} = \langle 0, 1, 1 \rangle$

40. $\mathbf{u} = \langle -2, -3, 0 \rangle$, $\mathbf{v} = \langle 1, 2, 1 \rangle$

41. $\mathbf{u} = \langle -2, 1, -2 \rangle$, $\mathbf{v} = \langle 1, 1, 1 \rangle$

42. $\mathbf{u} = \langle -5, 0, 2 \rangle$, $\mathbf{v} = \langle 3, 1, 1 \rangle$

43. $\mathbf{u} = \langle -7, 11, 8 \rangle$, $\mathbf{v} = \langle 3, -5, -1 \rangle$

44. $\mathbf{u} = \langle -4, -8\sqrt{3}, 2\sqrt{2} \rangle$, $\mathbf{v} = \langle 2, 3\sqrt{3}, -\sqrt{2} \rangle$

45–50. Unit vectors and magnitude *Consider the following points P and Q.*

a. *Find* $\overrightarrow{PQ}$ *and state your answer in two forms:* $\langle a, b, c \rangle$ *and* $a\mathbf{i} + b\mathbf{j} + c\mathbf{k}$.

b. *Find the magnitude of* $\overrightarrow{PQ}$.

c. *Find two unit vectors parallel to* $\overrightarrow{PQ}$.

45. $P(1, 5, 0), Q(3, 11, 2)$

46. $P(5, 11, 12), Q(1, 14, 13)$

47. $P(-3, 1, 0), Q(-3, -4, 1)$

48. $P(3, 8, 12), Q(3, 9, 11)$

49. $P(0, 0, 2), Q(-2, 4, 0)$

50. $P(a, b, c), Q(1, 1, -1)$ *(a, b,* and *c* are real numbers*)*

51. Flight in crosswinds A model airplane is flying horizontally due north at 20 mi/hr when it encounters a horizontal crosswind blowing east at 20 mi/hr and a downdraft blowing vertically downward at 10 mi/hr.

 a. Find the position vector that represents the velocity of the plane relative to the ground.

 b. Find the speed of the plane relative to the ground.

52. Another crosswind flight A model airplane is flying horizontally due east at 10 mi/hr when it encounters a horizontal crosswind blowing south at 5 mi/hr and an updraft blowing vertically upward at 5 mi/hr.

 a. Find the position vector that represents the velocity of the plane relative to the ground.

 b. Find the speed of the plane relative to the ground.

53. Crosswinds A small plane is flying horizontally due east in calm air at 250 mi/hr when it is hit by a horizontal crosswind blowing southwest at 50 mi/hr and a 30-mi/hr updraft. Find the resulting speed of the plane and describe with a sketch the approximate direction of the velocity relative to the ground.

54. Combined force An object at the origin is acted on by the forces $\mathbf{F}_1 = 20\mathbf{i} - 10\mathbf{j}$, $\mathbf{F}_2 = 30\mathbf{j} + 10\mathbf{k}$, and $\mathbf{F}_3 = 40\mathbf{i} + 20\mathbf{k}$. Find the magnitude of the combined force and describe the approximate direction of the force.

55. Submarine course A submarine climbs at an angle of 30° above the horizontal with a heading to the northeast. If its speed is 20 knots, find the components of the velocity in the east, north, and vertical directions.

56. Maintaining equilibrium An object is acted upon by the forces $\mathbf{F}_1 = \langle 10, 6, 3 \rangle$ and $\mathbf{F}_2 = \langle 0, 4, 9 \rangle$. Find the force $\mathbf{F}_3$ that must act on the object so that the sum of the forces is zero.

Further Explorations

57. Explain why or why not Determine whether the following statements are true and give an explanation or counterexample.

 a. Suppose $\mathbf{u}$ and $\mathbf{v}$ both make a 45° angle with $\mathbf{w}$ in $\mathbb{R}^3$. Then $\mathbf{u} + \mathbf{v}$ makes a 45° angle with $\mathbf{w}$.

 b. Suppose $\mathbf{u}$ and $\mathbf{v}$ both make a 90° angle with $\mathbf{w}$ in $\mathbb{R}^3$. Then $\mathbf{u} + \mathbf{v}$ can never make a 90° angle with $\mathbf{w}$.

 c. $\mathbf{i} + \mathbf{j} + \mathbf{k} = \mathbf{0}$.

 d. The intersection of the planes $x = 1$, $y = 1$, and $z = 1$ is a point.

58–60. Sets of points *Describe with a sketch the sets of points* (x, y, z) *satisfying the following equations.*

58. $(x + 1)(y - 3) = 0$ **59.** $x^2 y^2 z^2 > 0$

60. $y - z = 0$

61–64. Sets of points

61. Give a geometric description of the set of points (x, y, z) satisfying the pair of equations $z = 0$ and $x^2 + y^2 = 1$. Sketch a figure of this set of points.

62. Give a geometric description of the set of points (x, y, z) satisfying the pair of equations $z = x^2$ and $y = 0$. Sketch a figure of this set of points.

63. Give a geometric description of the set of points (x, y, z) that lie on the intersection of the sphere $x^2 + y^2 + z^2 = 5$ and the plane $z = 1$.

64. Give a geometric description of the set of points (x, y, z) that lie on the intersection of the sphere $x^2 + y^2 + z^2 = 36$ and the plane $z = 6$.

65. Describing a circle Find a pair of equations describing a circle of radius 3 centered at $(2, 4, 1)$ that lies in a plane parallel to the *xz*-plane.

66. Describing a line Find a pair of equations describing a line passing through the point $(-2, -5, 1)$ that is parallel to the *x*-axis.

67–70. Parallel vectors of varying lengths *Find vectors parallel to* $\mathbf{v}$ *of the given length.*

67. $\mathbf{v} = \langle 6, -8, 0 \rangle$; length = 20

68. $\mathbf{v} = \langle 3, -2, 6 \rangle$; length = 10

69. $\mathbf{v} = \overrightarrow{PQ}$ with $P(3, 4, 0)$ and $Q(2, 3, 1)$; length = 3

70. $\mathbf{v} = \overrightarrow{PQ}$ with $P(1, 0, 1)$ and $Q(2, -1, 1)$; length = 3

71. Collinear points Determine whether the points P, Q, and R are collinear (lie on a line) by comparing $\overrightarrow{PQ}$ and $\overrightarrow{PR}$. If the points are collinear, determine which point lies between the other two points.

 a. $P(1, 6, -5), Q(2, 5, -3), R(4, 3, 1)$

 b. $P(1, 5, 7), Q(5, 13, -1), R(0, 3, 9)$

 c. $P(1, 2, 3), Q(2, -3, 6), R(3, -1, 9)$

 d. $P(9, 5, 1), Q(11, 18, 4), R(6, 3, 0)$

72. Collinear points Determine the values of x and y such that the points $(1, 2, 3)$, $(4, 7, 1)$, and $(x, y, 2)$ are collinear (lie on a line).

73. Lengths of the diagonals of a box What is the longest diagonal of a rectangular 2 ft × 3 ft × 4 ft box?

Applications

74. Forces on an inclined plane An object on an inclined plane does not slide provided the component of the object's weight parallel to the plane $|\mathbf{W}_{par}|$ is less than or equal to the magnitude of the opposing frictional force $|\mathbf{F}_r|$. The magnitude of the frictional force, in turn, is proportional to the component of the object's weight perpendicular to the plane $|\mathbf{W}_{perp}|$ (see figure). The constant of proportionality is the coefficient of static friction $\mu > 0$.

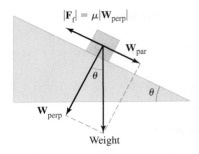

$$|\mathbf{F}_f| = \mu|\mathbf{W}_{perp}|$$

Weight

a. Suppose a 100-lb block rests on a plane that is tilted at an angle of $\theta = 20°$ to the horizontal. Find $|\mathbf{W}_{par}|$ and $|\mathbf{W}_{perp}|$.
b. The condition for the block not sliding is $|\mathbf{W}_{par}| \le \mu|\mathbf{W}_{perp}|$. If $\mu = 0.65$, does the block slide?
c. What is the critical angle above which the block slides with $\mu = 0.65$?

75. Three-cable load A 500-kg load hangs from three cables of equal length that are anchored at the points $(-2, 0, 0)$, $(1, \sqrt{3}, 0)$, and $(1, -\sqrt{3}, 0)$. The load is located at $(0, 0, -2\sqrt{3})$. Find the vectors describing the forces on the cables due to the load.

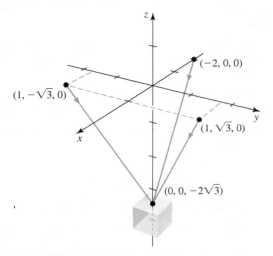

76. Four-cable load A 500-lb load hangs from four cables of equal length that are anchored at the points $(\pm 2, 0, 0)$ and $(0, \pm 2, 0)$. The load is located at $(0, 0, -4)$. Find the vectors describing the forces on the cables due to the load.

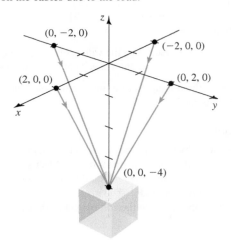

Additional Exercises

77. Possible parallelograms The points $O(0, 0, 0)$, $P(1, 4, 6)$, and $Q(2, 4, 3)$ lie at three vertices of a parallelogram. Find all possible locations of the fourth vertex.

78. Diagonals of parallelograms Two sides of a parallelogram are formed by the vectors $\mathbf{u}$ and $\mathbf{v}$. Prove that the diagonals of the parallelogram are $\mathbf{u} + \mathbf{v}$ and $\mathbf{u} - \mathbf{v}$.

79. Midpoint formula Prove that the midpoint of the line segment joining $P(x_1, y_1, z_1)$ and $Q(x_2, y_2, z_2)$ is

$$\left(\frac{x_1 + x_2}{2}, \frac{y_1 + y_2}{2}, \frac{z_1 + z_2}{2}\right).$$

80. Equation of a sphere For constants a, b, c, and d, show that the equation

$$x^2 + y^2 + z^2 - 2ax - 2by - 2cz = d$$

describes a sphere centered at (a, b, c) with radius r, where $r^2 = d + a^2 + b^2 + c^2$, provided $d + a^2 + b^2 + c^2 > 0$.

81. Medians of a triangle—coordinate free Assume that $\mathbf{u}$, $\mathbf{v}$, and $\mathbf{w}$ are vectors in $\mathbb{R}^3$ that form the sides of a triangle (see figure). Use the following steps to prove that the medians intersect at a point that divides each median in a 2:1 ratio. The proof does not use a coordinate system.

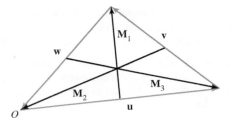

a. Show that $\mathbf{u} + \mathbf{v} + \mathbf{w} = \mathbf{0}$.
b. Let $\mathbf{M}_1$ be the median vector from the midpoint of $\mathbf{u}$ to the opposite vertex. Define $\mathbf{M}_2$ and $\mathbf{M}_3$ similarly. Using the geometry of vector addition show that $\mathbf{M}_1 = \mathbf{u}/2 + \mathbf{v}$. Find analogous expressions for $\mathbf{M}_2$ and $\mathbf{M}_3$.
c. Let $\mathbf{a}$, $\mathbf{b}$, and $\mathbf{c}$ be the vectors from O to the points one-third of the way along $\mathbf{M}_1$, $\mathbf{M}_2$, and $\mathbf{M}_3$, respectively. Show that $\mathbf{a} = \mathbf{b} = \mathbf{c} = (\mathbf{u} - \mathbf{w})/3$.
d. Conclude that the medians intersect at a point that divides each median in a 2:1 ratio.

82. Medians of a triangle—with coordinates In contrast to the proof in Exercise 81, we now use coordinates and position vectors to prove the same result. Without loss of generality, let $P(x_1, y_1, 0)$ and $Q(x_2, y_2, 0)$ be two points in the xy-plane and let $R(x_3, y_3, z_3)$ be a third point, such that P, Q, and R do not lie on a line. Consider $\triangle PQR$.

a. Let M_1 be the midpoint of the side PQ. Find the coordinates of M_1 and the components of the vector $\vec{RM_1}$.
b. Find the vector $\vec{OZ_1}$ from the origin to the point Z_1 two-thirds of the way along $\vec{RM_1}$.
c. Repeat the calculation of part (b) with the midpoint M_2 of RQ and the vector $\vec{PM_2}$ to obtain the vector $\vec{OZ_2}$.
d. Repeat the calculation of part (b) with the midpoint M_3 of PR and the vector $\vec{QM_3}$ to obtain the vector $\vec{OZ_3}$.
e. Conclude that the medians of $\triangle PQR$ intersect at a point. Give the coordinates of the point.
f. With $P(2, 4, 0)$, $Q(4, 1, 0)$, and $R(6, 3, 4)$, find the point at which the medians of $\triangle PQR$ intersect.

83. The amazing quadrilateral property—coordinate free The points P, Q, R, and S, joined by the vectors **u**, **v**, **w**, and **x**, are the vertices of a quadrilateral in $\mathbb{R}^3$. *The four points needn't lie in a plane* (see figure). Use the following steps to prove that the line segments joining the midpoints of the sides of the quadrilateral form a parallelogram. The proof does not use a coordinate system.

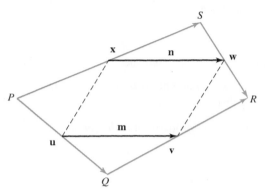

a. Use vector addition to show that $\mathbf{u} + \mathbf{v} = \mathbf{w} + \mathbf{x}$.
b. Let **m** be the vector that joins the midpoints of PQ and QR. Show that $\mathbf{m} = (\mathbf{u} + \mathbf{v})/2$.

c. Let **n** be the vector that joins the midpoints of PS and SR. Show that $\mathbf{n} = (\mathbf{x} + \mathbf{w})/2$.
d. Combine parts (a), (b), and (c) to conclude that $\mathbf{m} = \mathbf{n}$.
e. Explain why part (d) implies that the line segments joining the midpoints of the sides of the quadrilateral form a parallelogram.

84. The amazing quadrilateral property—with coordinates Prove the quadrilateral property in Exercise 83, assuming the coordinates of P, Q, R, and S are $P(x_1, y_1, 0)$, $Q(x_2, y_2, 0)$, $R(x_3, y_3, 0)$, and $S(x_4, y_4, z_4)$, where we assume that P, Q, and R lie in the xy-plane without loss of generality.

QUICK CHECK ANSWERS

1. Southwest; due east and upward; southwest and downward **2.** yz-plane; xy-plane **3.** No solution **4.** **u** and **v** are parallel. **5.** $|\mathbf{u}| = \sqrt{11}$ and $|\mathbf{v}| = \sqrt{12} = 2\sqrt{3}$; **u** has the smaller magnitude. ◄

11.3 Dot Products

> The dot product is also called the *scalar product*, a term we do not use in order to avoid confusion with *scalar multiplication*.

The *dot product* is used to determine the angle between two vectors. It is also a tool for calculating *projections*—the measure of how much of a given vector lies in the direction of another vector.

To see the usefulness of the dot product, consider an example. Recall that the work done by a constant force F in moving an object a distance d is $W = Fd$ (Section 6.7). This rule is valid provided the force acts in the direction of motion (Figure 11.43a). Now assume the force is a vector **F** applied at an angle θ to the direction of motion; the resulting displacement of the object is a vector **d**. In this case, the work done by the force is the component of the force in the direction of motion multiplied by the distance moved by the object, which is $W = (|\mathbf{F}| \cos \theta)|\mathbf{d}|$ (Figure 11.43b). We call this product of the magnitudes of two vectors and the cosine of the angle between them the dot product.

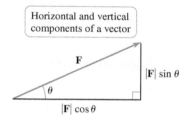

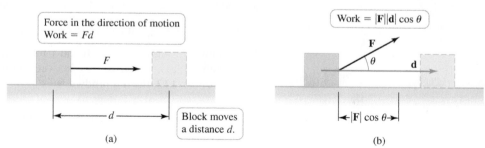

Figure 11.43

Two Forms of the Dot Product

The example of work done by a force leads to our first definition of the dot product. We then give an equivalent formula that is often better suited for computation.

DEFINITION Dot Product

Given two nonzero vectors **u** and **v** in two or three dimensions, their **dot product** is

$$\mathbf{u} \cdot \mathbf{v} = |\mathbf{u}||\mathbf{v}| \cos \theta,$$

where θ is the angle between **u** and **v** with $0 \leq \theta \leq \pi$ (Figure 11.44). If $\mathbf{u} = \mathbf{0}$ or $\mathbf{v} = \mathbf{0}$, then $\mathbf{u} \cdot \mathbf{v} = 0$, and θ is undefined.

The dot product of two vectors is itself a scalar. Two special cases immediately arise:

- **u** and **v** are parallel ($\theta = 0$ or $\theta = \pi$) if and only if $\mathbf{u} \cdot \mathbf{v} = \pm|\mathbf{u}||\mathbf{v}|$.
- **u** and **v** are perpendicular ($\theta = \pi/2$) if and only if $\mathbf{u} \cdot \mathbf{v} = 0$.

The second case gives rise to the important property of *orthogonality*.

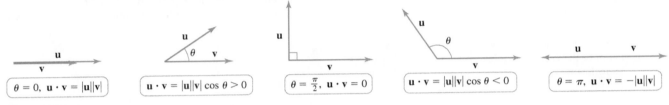

$\theta = 0, \ \mathbf{u} \cdot \mathbf{v} = |\mathbf{u}||\mathbf{v}|$ $\mathbf{u} \cdot \mathbf{v} = |\mathbf{u}||\mathbf{v}| \cos \theta > 0$ $\theta = \frac{\pi}{2}, \ \mathbf{u} \cdot \mathbf{v} = 0$ $\mathbf{u} \cdot \mathbf{v} = |\mathbf{u}||\mathbf{v}| \cos \theta < 0$ $\theta = \pi, \ \mathbf{u} \cdot \mathbf{v} = -|\mathbf{u}||\mathbf{v}|$

Figure 11.44

> ➤ In two and three dimensions, *orthogonal* and *perpendicular* are used interchangeably. *Orthogonal* is a more general term that also applies in more than three dimensions.

DEFINITION Orthogonal Vectors

Two vectors **u** and **v** are **orthogonal** if and only if $\mathbf{u} \cdot \mathbf{v} = 0$. The zero vector is orthogonal to all vectors. In two or three dimensions, two nonzero orthogonal vectors are perpendicular to each other.

QUICK CHECK 1 Sketch two nonzero vectors **u** and **v** with $\theta = 0$. Sketch two nonzero vectors **u** and **v** with $\theta = \pi$. ◄

EXAMPLE 1 Dot products Compute the dot products of the following vectors.

a. $\mathbf{u} = 2\mathbf{i} - 6\mathbf{j}$ and $\mathbf{v} = 12\mathbf{k}$

b. $\mathbf{u} = \langle \sqrt{3}, 1 \rangle$ and $\mathbf{v} = \langle 0, 1 \rangle$

SOLUTION

a. The vector **u** lies in the *xy*-plane and the vector **v** is perpendicular to the *xy*-plane. Therefore, $\theta = \dfrac{\pi}{2}$, **u** and **v** are orthogonal, and $\mathbf{u} \cdot \mathbf{v} = 0$ (Figure 11.45a).

b. As shown in Figure 11.45b, **u** and **v** form two sides of a 30–60–90 triangle in the *xy*-plane, with an angle of $\pi/3$ between them. Because $|\mathbf{u}| = 2$, $|\mathbf{v}| = 1$, and $\cos \pi/3 = 1/2$, the dot product is

$$\mathbf{u} \cdot \mathbf{v} = |\mathbf{u}||\mathbf{v}| \cos \theta = 2 \cdot 1 \cdot \frac{1}{2} = 1.$$

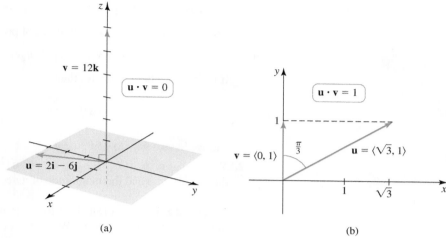

Figure 11.45

(a)   (b)

Related Exercises 9–14 ◄

The definition of the dot product requires knowing the angle θ between the vectors. Often the angle is not known; in fact, it may be exactly what we seek. For this reason, we present another method for computing the dot product that does not require knowing θ.

➤ In $\mathbb{R}^2$ with $\mathbf{u} = \langle u_1, u_2 \rangle$ and $\mathbf{v} = \langle v_1, v_2 \rangle$, $\mathbf{u} \cdot \mathbf{v} = u_1 v_1 + u_2 v_2$.

> **THEOREM 11.1 Dot Product**
> Given two vectors $\mathbf{u} = \langle u_1, u_2, u_3 \rangle$ and $\mathbf{v} = \langle v_1, v_2, v_3 \rangle$,
> $$\mathbf{u} \cdot \mathbf{v} = u_1 v_1 + u_2 v_2 + u_3 v_3.$$

Proof: Consider two position vectors $\mathbf{u} = \langle u_1, u_2, u_3 \rangle$ and $\mathbf{v} = \langle v_1, v_2, v_3 \rangle$, and suppose θ is the angle between them. The vector $\mathbf{u} - \mathbf{v}$ forms the third side of a triangle (Figure 11.46). By the Law of Cosines,

$$|\mathbf{u} - \mathbf{v}|^2 = |\mathbf{u}|^2 + |\mathbf{v}|^2 - \underbrace{2|\mathbf{u}||\mathbf{v}| \cos \theta}_{\mathbf{u} \cdot \mathbf{v}}.$$

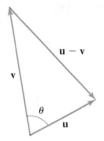

Figure 11.46

The definition of the dot product, $\mathbf{u} \cdot \mathbf{v} = |\mathbf{u}||\mathbf{v}| \cos \theta$, allows us to write

$$\mathbf{u} \cdot \mathbf{v} = |\mathbf{u}||\mathbf{v}| \cos \theta = \frac{1}{2} \left(|\mathbf{u}|^2 + |\mathbf{v}|^2 - |\mathbf{u} - \mathbf{v}|^2 \right). \tag{1}$$

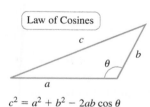

Law of Cosines

$$c^2 = a^2 + b^2 - 2ab \cos \theta$$

Using the definition of magnitude, we find that

$$|\mathbf{u}|^2 = u_1^2 + u_2^2 + u_3^2, \quad |\mathbf{v}|^2 = v_1^2 + v_2^2 + v_3^2,$$

and

$$|\mathbf{u} - \mathbf{v}|^2 = (u_1 - v_1)^2 + (u_2 - v_2)^2 + (u_3 - v_3)^2.$$

Expanding the terms in $|\mathbf{u} - \mathbf{v}|^2$ and simplifying yields

$$|\mathbf{u}|^2 + |\mathbf{v}|^2 - |\mathbf{u} - \mathbf{v}|^2 = 2(u_1 v_1 + u_2 v_2 + u_3 v_3).$$

Substituting into expression (1) gives a compact expression for the dot product:

$$\mathbf{u} \cdot \mathbf{v} = u_1 v_1 + u_2 v_2 + u_3 v_3.$$

◄

This new representation of $\mathbf{u} \cdot \mathbf{v}$ has two immediate consequences.

1. Combining it with the definition of dot product gives

$$\mathbf{u} \cdot \mathbf{v} = u_1 v_1 + u_2 v_2 + u_3 v_3 = |\mathbf{u}||\mathbf{v}| \cos \theta.$$

If $\mathbf{u}$ and $\mathbf{v}$ are both nonzero, then

$$\cos \theta = \frac{u_1 v_1 + u_2 v_2 + u_3 v_3}{|\mathbf{u}||\mathbf{v}|} = \frac{\mathbf{u} \cdot \mathbf{v}}{|\mathbf{u}||\mathbf{v}|},$$

and we have a way to compute θ.

2. Notice that $\mathbf{u} \cdot \mathbf{u} = u_1^2 + u_2^2 + u_3^2 = |\mathbf{u}|^2$. Therefore, we have a relationship between the dot product and the magnitude of a vector: $|\mathbf{u}| = \sqrt{\mathbf{u} \cdot \mathbf{u}}$ or $|\mathbf{u}|^2 = \mathbf{u} \cdot \mathbf{u}$.

QUICK CHECK 2 Use Theorem 11.1 to compute the dot products $\mathbf{i} \cdot \mathbf{j}$, $\mathbf{i} \cdot \mathbf{k}$, and $\mathbf{j} \cdot \mathbf{k}$ for the unit coordinate vectors. What do you conclude about the angles between these vectors? ◄

EXAMPLE 2 Dot products and angles Let $\mathbf{u} = \langle \sqrt{3}, 1, 0 \rangle$, $\mathbf{v} = \langle 1, \sqrt{3}, 0 \rangle$, and $\mathbf{w} = \langle 1, \sqrt{3}, 2\sqrt{3} \rangle$.

a. Compute $\mathbf{u} \cdot \mathbf{v}$.

b. Find the angle between $\mathbf{u}$ and $\mathbf{v}$.

c. Find the angle between $\mathbf{u}$ and $\mathbf{w}$.

SOLUTION

a. $\mathbf{u} \cdot \mathbf{v} = \langle \sqrt{3}, 1, 0 \rangle \cdot \langle 1, \sqrt{3}, 0 \rangle = \sqrt{3} + \sqrt{3} + 0 = 2\sqrt{3}$

b. Note that $|\mathbf{u}| = \sqrt{\mathbf{u} \cdot \mathbf{u}} = \sqrt{\langle \sqrt{3}, 1, 0 \rangle \cdot \langle \sqrt{3}, 1, 0 \rangle} = 2$ and similarly $|\mathbf{v}| = 2$. Therefore,

$$\cos \theta = \frac{\mathbf{u} \cdot \mathbf{v}}{|\mathbf{u}||\mathbf{v}|} = \frac{2\sqrt{3}}{2 \cdot 2} = \frac{\sqrt{3}}{2}.$$

Because $0 \le \theta \le \pi$, it follows that $\theta = \cos^{-1} \frac{\sqrt{3}}{2} = \frac{\pi}{6}$.

c. $\cos \theta = \frac{\mathbf{u} \cdot \mathbf{w}}{|\mathbf{u}||\mathbf{w}|} = \frac{\langle \sqrt{3}, 1, 0 \rangle \cdot \langle 1, \sqrt{3}, 2\sqrt{3} \rangle}{|\langle \sqrt{3}, 1, 0 \rangle||\langle 1, \sqrt{3}, 2\sqrt{3} \rangle|} = \frac{2\sqrt{3}}{2 \cdot 4} = \frac{\sqrt{3}}{4}$

It follows that

$$\theta = \cos^{-1} \frac{\sqrt{3}}{4} \approx 1.12 \, \text{rad} \approx 64.3°.$$

Related Exercises 15–24 ◄

Properties of Dot Products

The properties of the dot product in the following theorem are easily proved using vector components (Exercises 76–80).

➤ Theorem 11.1 extends to vectors with any number of components. If $\mathbf{u} = \langle u_1, \ldots, u_n \rangle$ and $\mathbf{v} = \langle v_1, \ldots, v_n \rangle$, then

$$\mathbf{u} \cdot \mathbf{v} = u_1 v_1 + \cdots + u_n v_n.$$

The properties in Theorem 11.2 also apply in two or more dimensions.

THEOREM 11.2 Properties of the Dot Product
Suppose $\mathbf{u}$, $\mathbf{v}$, and $\mathbf{w}$ are vectors and let c be a scalar.

1. $\mathbf{u} \cdot \mathbf{v} = \mathbf{v} \cdot \mathbf{u}$ Commutative property

2. $c(\mathbf{u} \cdot \mathbf{v}) = (c\mathbf{u}) \cdot \mathbf{v} = \mathbf{u} \cdot (c\mathbf{v})$ Associative property

3. $\mathbf{u} \cdot (\mathbf{v} + \mathbf{w}) = \mathbf{u} \cdot \mathbf{v} + \mathbf{u} \cdot \mathbf{w}$ Distributive property

Orthogonal Projections

Given vectors **u** and **v**, how closely aligned are they? That is, how much of **u** points in the direction of **v**? This question is answered using *projections*. As shown in Figure 11.47a, the projection of the vector **u** onto a nonzero vector **v**, denoted proj$_v$**u**, is the "shadow" cast by **u** onto the line through **v**. The projection of **u** onto **v** is itself a vector; it points in the same direction as **v** if the angle between **u** and **v** lies in the interval $0 \le \theta < \pi/2$ (Figure 11.47b); it points in the direction opposite that of **v** if the angle between **u** and **v** lies in the interval $\pi/2 < \theta \le \pi$ (Figure 11.47c). If $\theta = \dfrac{\pi}{2}$, **u** and **v** are orthogonal, and there is no shadow.

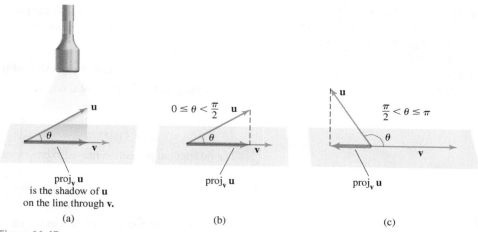

proj$_v$**u**
is the shadow of **u**
on the line through **v**.

(a)   (b)   (c)

Figure 11.47

To find the projection of **u** onto **v**, we proceed as follows: With the tails of **u** and **v** together, we drop a perpendicular line segment from the head of **u** to the point P on the line through **v** (Figure 11.48). The vector $\overrightarrow{OP}$ is the *orthogonal projection of* **u** *onto* **v**. An expression for proj$_v$**u** is found using two observations.

- If $0 \le \theta < \pi/2$, then proj$_v$**u** has length $|\mathbf{u}| \cos \theta$ and points in the direction of the unit vector $\mathbf{v}/|\mathbf{v}|$ (Figure 11.48a). Therefore,

$$\text{proj}_v\mathbf{u} = \underbrace{|\mathbf{u}| \cos \theta}_{\text{length}} \underbrace{\left(\frac{\mathbf{v}}{|\mathbf{v}|} \right)}_{\text{direction}}.$$

We define the *scalar component of* **u** *in the direction of* **v** to be scal$_v$**u** $= |\mathbf{u}| \cos \theta$. In this case, scal$_v$**u** is the length of proj$_v$**u**.

- If $\pi/2 < \theta \le \pi$, then proj$_v$**u** has length $-|\mathbf{u}| \cos \theta$ (which is positive) and points in the direction of $-\mathbf{v}/|\mathbf{v}|$ (Figure 11.48b). Therefore,

$$\text{proj}_v\mathbf{u} = \underbrace{-|\mathbf{u}| \cos \theta}_{\text{length}} \underbrace{\left(-\frac{\mathbf{v}}{|\mathbf{v}|} \right)}_{\text{direction}} = |\mathbf{u}| \cos \theta \left(\frac{\mathbf{v}}{|\mathbf{v}|} \right).$$

In this case, scal$_v$**u** $= |\mathbf{u}| \cos \theta < 0$.

We see that in both cases, the expression for proj$_v$**u** is the same:

$$\text{proj}_v\mathbf{u} = \underbrace{|\mathbf{u}| \cos \theta}_{\text{scal}_v\mathbf{u}} \left(\frac{\mathbf{v}}{|\mathbf{v}|} \right) = \text{scal}_v\mathbf{u}\left(\frac{\mathbf{v}}{|\mathbf{v}|} \right).$$

Note that if $\theta = \dfrac{\pi}{2}$, proj$_v$**u** $= \mathbf{0}$ and scal$_v$**u** $= 0$.

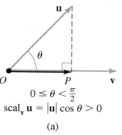

$0 \le \theta < \dfrac{\pi}{2}$

scal$_v$**u** $= |\mathbf{u}| \cos \theta > 0$

(a)

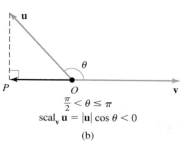

$\dfrac{\pi}{2} < \theta \le \pi$

scal$_v$**u** $= |\mathbf{u}| \cos \theta < 0$

(b)

Figure 11.48

➤ Notice that scal$_v$**u** may be positive, negative, or zero. However, $|$scal$_v$**u**$|$ is the length of proj$_v$**u**. The projection proj$_v$**u** is defined for all vectors **u**, but only for nonzero vectors **v**.

Using properties of the dot product, $\text{proj}_{\mathbf{v}}\mathbf{u}$ may be written in different ways:

$$\text{proj}_{\mathbf{v}}\mathbf{u} = |\mathbf{u}|\cos\theta\left(\frac{\mathbf{v}}{|\mathbf{v}|}\right)$$

$$= \frac{\mathbf{u}\cdot\mathbf{v}}{|\mathbf{v}|}\left(\frac{\mathbf{v}}{|\mathbf{v}|}\right) \qquad |\mathbf{u}|\cos\theta = \frac{|\mathbf{u}||\mathbf{v}|\cos\theta}{|\mathbf{v}|} = \frac{\mathbf{u}\cdot\mathbf{v}}{|\mathbf{v}|}$$

$$= \underbrace{\left(\frac{\mathbf{u}\cdot\mathbf{v}}{\mathbf{v}\cdot\mathbf{v}}\right)}_{\text{scalar}}\mathbf{v}. \qquad \text{Regroup terms; } |\mathbf{v}|^2 = \mathbf{v}\cdot\mathbf{v}$$

QUICK CHECK 3 Let $\mathbf{u} = 4\mathbf{i} - 3\mathbf{j}$. By inspection (not calculations), find the orthogonal projection of $\mathbf{u}$ onto $\mathbf{i}$ and onto $\mathbf{j}$. Find the scalar component of $\mathbf{u}$ in the direction of $\mathbf{i}$ and in the direction of $\mathbf{j}$. ◄

The first two expressions show that $\text{proj}_{\mathbf{v}}\mathbf{u}$ is a scalar multiple of the unit vector $\dfrac{\mathbf{v}}{|\mathbf{v}|}$, whereas the last expression shows that $\text{proj}_{\mathbf{v}}\mathbf{u}$ is a scalar multiple of $\mathbf{v}$.

DEFINITION (Orthogonal) Projection of u onto v

The **orthogonal projection of u onto v**, denoted $\text{proj}_{\mathbf{v}}\mathbf{u}$, where $\mathbf{v} \neq \mathbf{0}$, is

$$\text{proj}_{\mathbf{v}}\mathbf{u} = |\mathbf{u}|\cos\theta\left(\frac{\mathbf{v}}{|\mathbf{v}|}\right).$$

The orthogonal projection may also be computed with the formulas

$$\text{proj}_{\mathbf{v}}\mathbf{u} = \text{scal}_{\mathbf{v}}\mathbf{u}\left(\frac{\mathbf{v}}{|\mathbf{v}|}\right) = \left(\frac{\mathbf{u}\cdot\mathbf{v}}{\mathbf{v}\cdot\mathbf{v}}\right)\mathbf{v},$$

where the **scalar component of u in the direction of v** is

$$\text{scal}_{\mathbf{v}}\mathbf{u} = |\mathbf{u}|\cos\theta = \frac{\mathbf{u}\cdot\mathbf{v}}{|\mathbf{v}|}.$$

EXAMPLE 3   Orthogonal projections Find $\text{proj}_{\mathbf{v}}\mathbf{u}$ and $\text{scal}_{\mathbf{v}}\mathbf{u}$ for the following vectors and illustrate each result.

a. $\mathbf{u} = \langle 4, 1\rangle$, $\mathbf{v} = \langle 3, 4\rangle$

b. $\mathbf{u} = \langle -4, -3\rangle$, $\mathbf{v} = \langle 1, -1\rangle$

SOLUTION

a. The scalar component of $\mathbf{u}$ in the direction of $\mathbf{v}$ (Figure 11.49) is

$$\text{scal}_{\mathbf{v}}\mathbf{u} = \frac{\mathbf{u}\cdot\mathbf{v}}{|\mathbf{v}|} = \frac{\langle 4, 1\rangle\cdot\langle 3, 4\rangle}{|\langle 3, 4\rangle|} = \frac{16}{5}.$$

Because $\dfrac{\mathbf{v}}{|\mathbf{v}|} = \left\langle \dfrac{3}{5}, \dfrac{4}{5}\right\rangle$, we have

$$\text{proj}_{\mathbf{v}}\mathbf{u} = \text{scal}_{\mathbf{v}}\mathbf{u}\left(\frac{\mathbf{v}}{|\mathbf{v}|}\right) = \frac{16}{5}\left\langle\frac{3}{5}, \frac{4}{5}\right\rangle = \frac{16}{25}\langle 3, 4\rangle.$$

b. Using another formula for $\text{proj}_{\mathbf{v}}\mathbf{u}$, we have

$$\text{proj}_{\mathbf{v}}\mathbf{u} = \left(\frac{\mathbf{u}\cdot\mathbf{v}}{\mathbf{v}\cdot\mathbf{v}}\right)\mathbf{v} = \left(\frac{\langle -4, -3\rangle\cdot\langle 1, -1\rangle}{\langle 1, -1\rangle\cdot\langle 1, -1\rangle}\right)\langle 1, -1\rangle = -\frac{1}{2}\langle 1, -1\rangle.$$

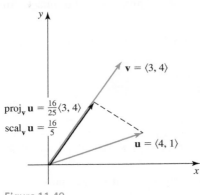

$\mathbf{v} = \langle 3, 4\rangle$

$\text{proj}_{\mathbf{v}}\mathbf{u} = \frac{16}{25}\langle 3, 4\rangle$

$\text{scal}_{\mathbf{v}}\mathbf{u} = \frac{16}{5}$

$\mathbf{u} = \langle 4, 1\rangle$

Figure 11.49

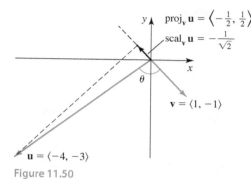

Figure 11.50

The vectors $\mathbf{v}$ and $\text{proj}_\mathbf{v}\mathbf{u}$ point in opposite directions because $\pi/2 < \theta \leq \pi$ (Figure 11.50). This fact is reflected in the scalar component of $\mathbf{u}$ in the direction of $\mathbf{v}$, which is negative:

$$\text{scal}_\mathbf{v}\mathbf{u} = \frac{\langle -4, -3 \rangle \cdot \langle 1, -1 \rangle}{|\langle 1, -1 \rangle|} = -\frac{1}{\sqrt{2}}.$$

Related Exercises 25–36 ◄

Applications of Dot Products

Work and Force   In the opening of this section, we observed that if a constant force $\mathbf{F}$ acts at an angle θ to the direction of motion of an object (Figure 11.51), the work done by the force is

$$W = |\mathbf{F}| \cos\theta \, |\mathbf{d}| = \mathbf{F} \cdot \mathbf{d}.$$

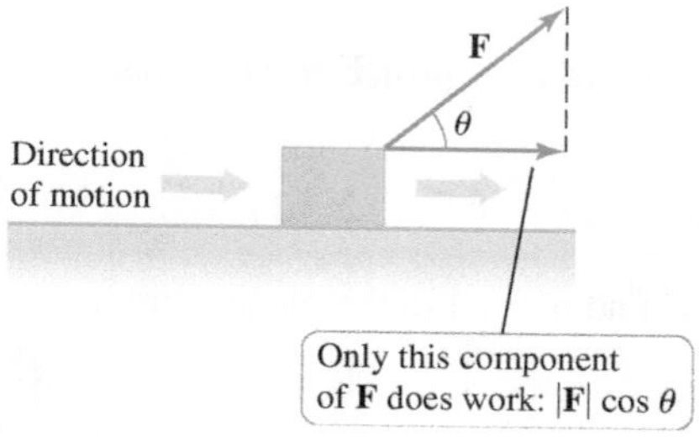

Notice that the work is a scalar, and if the force acts in a direction orthogonal to the motion, then $\theta = \pi/2$, $\mathbf{F} \cdot \mathbf{d} = 0$, and no work is done by the force.

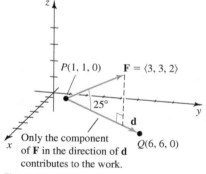

Figure 11.51

> If the unit of force is newtons (N) and the distance is measured in meters, then the unit of work is joules (J), where 1 J = 1 N-m. If force is measured in lb and distance is measured in ft, then work has units of ft-lb.

DEFINITION   **Work**

Let a constant force $\mathbf{F}$ be applied to an object, producing a displacement $\mathbf{d}$. If the angle between $\mathbf{F}$ and $\mathbf{d}$ is θ, then the **work** done by the force is

$$W = |\mathbf{F}||\mathbf{d}| \cos\theta = \mathbf{F} \cdot \mathbf{d}.$$

EXAMPLE 4   **Calculating work**   A force $\mathbf{F} = \langle 3, 3, 2 \rangle$ (in newtons) moves an object along a line segment from $P(1, 1, 0)$ to $Q(6, 6, 0)$ (in meters). What is the work done by the force? Interpret the result.

SOLUTION   The displacement of the object is $\mathbf{d} = \overrightarrow{PQ} = \langle 6 - 1, 6 - 1, 0 - 0 \rangle = \langle 5, 5, 0 \rangle$. Therefore, the work done by the force is

$$W = \mathbf{F} \cdot \mathbf{d} = \langle 3, 3, 2 \rangle \cdot \langle 5, 5, 0 \rangle = 30 \text{ J}.$$

To interpret this result, notice that the angle between the force and the displacement vector satisfies

$$\cos\theta = \frac{\mathbf{F} \cdot \mathbf{d}}{|\mathbf{F}||\mathbf{d}|} = \frac{\langle 3, 3, 2 \rangle \cdot \langle 5, 5, 0 \rangle}{|\langle 3, 3, 2 \rangle||\langle 5, 5, 0 \rangle|} = \frac{30}{\sqrt{22}\sqrt{50}} \approx 0.905.$$

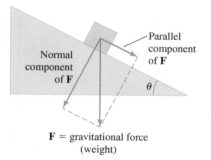

Figure 11.52

Therefore, $\theta \approx 0.44$ rad $\approx 25°$. The magnitude of the force is $|\mathbf{F}| = \sqrt{22} \approx 4.7$ N, but only the component of that force in the direction of motion, $|\mathbf{F}| \cos\theta \approx \sqrt{22} \cos 0.44 \approx 4.2$ N, contributes to the work (Figure 11.52).

Related Exercises 37–42 ◄

Parallel and Normal Forces   Projections find frequent use in expressing a force in terms of orthogonal components. A common situation arises when an object rests on an inclined plane (Figure 11.53). The gravitational force on the object equals its weight, which is directed vertically downward. The projections of the gravitational force in the directions **parallel** to and **normal** (or perpendicular) to the plane are of interest. Specifically, the projection of the force parallel to the plane determines the tendency of the object to slide down the plane, while the projection of the force normal to the plane determines its tendency to "stick" to the plane.

Figure 11.53

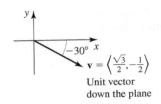

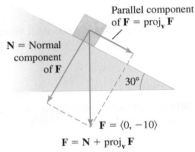

Unit vector
down the plane

Parallel component
of $\mathbf{F} = \text{proj}_{\mathbf{v}} \mathbf{F}$

$\mathbf{N}$ = Normal
component
of $\mathbf{F}$

$30°$

$\mathbf{F} = \langle 0, -10 \rangle$

$\mathbf{F} = \mathbf{N} + \text{proj}_{\mathbf{v}} \mathbf{F}$

Figure 11.54

EXAMPLE 5   Components of a force A 10-lb block rests on a plane that is inclined at 30° below the horizontal. Find the components of the gravitational force parallel and normal (perpendicular) to the plane.

SOLUTION The gravitational force $\mathbf{F}$ acting on the block equals the weight of the block (10 lb), which we regard as a point mass. Using the coordinate system shown in Figure 11.54, the force acts in the negative y-direction; therefore, $\mathbf{F} = \langle 0, -10 \rangle$. The direction *down* the plane is given by the unit vector $\mathbf{v} = \langle \cos(-30°), \sin(-30°) \rangle = \langle \frac{\sqrt{3}}{2}, -\frac{1}{2} \rangle$ (check that $|\mathbf{v}| = 1$). The component of the gravitational force parallel to the plane is

$$\text{proj}_{\mathbf{v}} \mathbf{F} = \left(\frac{\mathbf{F} \cdot \mathbf{v}}{\mathbf{v} \cdot \mathbf{v}} \right) \mathbf{v} = \left(\underbrace{\langle 0, -10 \rangle}_{F} \cdot \underbrace{\langle \frac{\sqrt{3}}{2}, -\frac{1}{2} \rangle}_{v} \right) \underbrace{\langle \frac{\sqrt{3}}{2}, -\frac{1}{2} \rangle}_{v} = 5 \langle \frac{\sqrt{3}}{2}, -\frac{1}{2} \rangle.$$

Let the component of $\mathbf{F}$ normal to the plane be $\mathbf{N}$. Note that $\mathbf{F} = \text{proj}_{\mathbf{v}} \mathbf{F} + \mathbf{N}$ so that

$$\mathbf{N} = \mathbf{F} - \text{proj}_{\mathbf{v}} \mathbf{F} = \langle 0, -10 \rangle - 5 \langle \frac{\sqrt{3}}{2}, -\frac{1}{2} \rangle = -5 \langle \frac{\sqrt{3}}{2}, \frac{3}{2} \rangle.$$

Figure 11.54 shows how the components of $\mathbf{F}$ parallel and normal to the plane combine to form the total force $\mathbf{F}$.

Related Exercises 43–46 ◄

SECTION 11.3 EXERCISES

Review Questions

1. Express the dot product of $\mathbf{u}$ and $\mathbf{v}$ in terms of their magnitudes and the angle between them.

2. Express the dot product of $\mathbf{u}$ and $\mathbf{v}$ in terms of the components of the vectors.

3. Compute $\langle 2, 3, -6 \rangle \cdot \langle 1, -8, 3 \rangle$.

4. What is the dot product of two orthogonal vectors?

5. Explain how to find the angle between two nonzero vectors.

6. Use a sketch to illustrate the projection of $\mathbf{u}$ onto $\mathbf{v}$.

7. Use a sketch to illustrate the scalar component of $\mathbf{u}$ in the direction of $\mathbf{v}$.

8. Explain how the work done by a force in moving an object is computed using dot products.

Basic Skills

9–12. Dot product from the definition *Consider the following vectors $\mathbf{u}$ and $\mathbf{v}$. Sketch the vectors, find the angle between the vectors, and compute the dot product using the definition $\mathbf{u} \cdot \mathbf{v} = |\mathbf{u}||\mathbf{v}| \cos \theta$.*

9. $\mathbf{u} = 4\mathbf{i}$ and $\mathbf{v} = 6\mathbf{j}$

10. $\mathbf{u} = \langle -3, 2, 0 \rangle$ and $\mathbf{v} = \langle 0, 0, 6 \rangle$

11. $\mathbf{u} = \langle 10, 0 \rangle$ and $\mathbf{v} = \langle 10, 10 \rangle$

12. $\mathbf{u} = \langle -\sqrt{3}, 1 \rangle$ and $\mathbf{v} = \langle \sqrt{3}, 1 \rangle$

13. **Dot product from the definition** Compute $\mathbf{u} \cdot \mathbf{v}$ if $\mathbf{u}$ and $\mathbf{v}$ are unit vectors and the angle between them is $\pi/3$.

14. **Dot product from the definition** Compute $\mathbf{u} \cdot \mathbf{v}$ if $\mathbf{u}$ is a unit vector, $|\mathbf{v}| = 2$, and the angle between them is $3\pi/4$.

⊤ **15–24. Dot products and angles** *Compute the dot product of the vectors $\mathbf{u}$ and $\mathbf{v}$, and find the angle between the vectors.*

15. $\mathbf{u} = \mathbf{i} + \mathbf{j}$ and $\mathbf{v} = \mathbf{i} - \mathbf{j}$

16. $\mathbf{u} = \langle 10, 0 \rangle$ and $\mathbf{v} = \langle -5, 5 \rangle$

17. $\mathbf{u} = \mathbf{i}$ and $\mathbf{v} = \mathbf{i} + \sqrt{3}\mathbf{j}$

18. $\mathbf{u} = \sqrt{2}\mathbf{i} + \sqrt{2}\mathbf{j}$ and $\mathbf{v} = -\sqrt{2}\mathbf{i} - \sqrt{2}\mathbf{j}$

19. $\mathbf{u} = 4\mathbf{i} + 3\mathbf{j}$ and $\mathbf{v} = 4\mathbf{i} - 6\mathbf{j}$

20. $\mathbf{u} = \langle 3, 4, 0 \rangle$ and $\mathbf{v} = \langle 0, 4, 5 \rangle$

21. $\mathbf{u} = \langle -10, 0, 4 \rangle$ and $\mathbf{v} = \langle 1, 2, 3 \rangle$

22. $\mathbf{u} = \langle 3, -5, 2 \rangle$ and $\mathbf{v} = \langle -9, 5, 1 \rangle$

23. $\mathbf{u} = 2\mathbf{i} - 3\mathbf{k}$ and $\mathbf{v} = \mathbf{i} + 4\mathbf{j} + 2\mathbf{k}$

24. $\mathbf{u} = \mathbf{i} - 4\mathbf{j} - 6\mathbf{k}$ and $\mathbf{v} = 2\mathbf{i} - 4\mathbf{j} + 2\mathbf{k}$

25–28. Sketching orthogonal projections *Find $\text{proj}_{\mathbf{v}}\mathbf{u}$ and $\text{scal}_{\mathbf{v}}\mathbf{u}$ by inspection without using formulas.*

25.

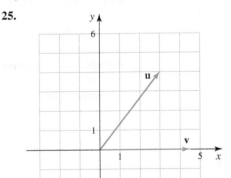

26.

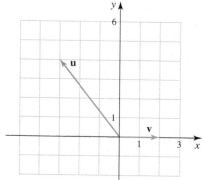

27.

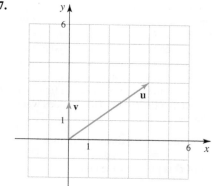

28.

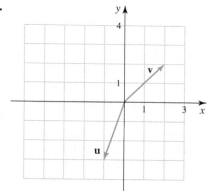

29–36. Calculating orthogonal projections *For the given vectors* **u** *and* **v**, *calculate* proj$_\mathbf{v}$**u** *and* scal$_\mathbf{v}$**u**.

29. $\mathbf{u} = \langle -1, 4 \rangle$ and $\mathbf{v} = \langle -4, 2 \rangle$

30. $\mathbf{u} = \langle 10, 5 \rangle$ and $\mathbf{v} = \langle 2, 6 \rangle$

31. $\mathbf{u} = \langle 3, 3, -3 \rangle$ and $\mathbf{v} = \langle 1, -1, 2 \rangle$

32. $\mathbf{u} = \langle 13, 0, 26 \rangle$ and $\mathbf{v} = \langle 4, -1, -3 \rangle$

33. $\mathbf{u} = \langle -8, 0, 2 \rangle$ and $\mathbf{v} = \langle 1, 3, -3 \rangle$

34. $\mathbf{u} = \langle 5, 0, 15 \rangle$ and $\mathbf{v} = \langle 0, 4, -2 \rangle$

35. $\mathbf{u} = 5\mathbf{i} + \mathbf{j} - 5\mathbf{k}$ and $\mathbf{v} = -\mathbf{i} + \mathbf{j} - 2\mathbf{k}$

36. $\mathbf{u} = \mathbf{i} + 4\mathbf{j} + 7\mathbf{k}$ and $\mathbf{v} = 2\mathbf{i} - 4\mathbf{j} + 2\mathbf{k}$

37–42. Computing work *Calculate the work done in the following situations.*

37. A suitcase is pulled 50 ft along a horizontal sidewalk with a constant force of 30 lb at an angle of 30° above the horizontal.

38. A stroller is pushed 20 m with a constant force of 10 N at an angle of 15° below the horizontal.

39. A sled is pulled 10 m along horizontal ground with a constant force of 5 N at an angle of 45° above the horizontal.

40. A constant force $\mathbf{F} = \langle 4, 3, 2 \rangle$ (in newtons) moves an object from $(0, 0, 0)$ to $(8, 6, 0)$. (Distance is measured in meters.)

41. A constant force $\mathbf{F} = \langle 40, 30 \rangle$ (in newtons) is used to move a sled horizontally 10 m.

42. A constant force $\mathbf{F} = \langle 2, 4, 1 \rangle$ (in newtons) moves an object from $(0, 0, 0)$ to $(2, 4, 6)$. (Distance is measured in meters.)

43–46. Parallel and normal forces *Find the components of the vertical force* $\mathbf{F} = \langle 0, -10 \rangle$ *in the directions parallel to and normal to the following inclined planes. Show that the total force is the sum of the two component forces.*

43. A plane that makes an angle of $\pi/4$ with the positive x-axis

44. A plane that makes an angle of $\pi/6$ with the positive x-axis

45. A plane that makes an angle of $\pi/3$ with the positive x-axis

46. A plane that makes an angle of $\theta = \tan^{-1} \frac{4}{5}$ with the positive x-axis

Further Explorations

47. **Explain why or why not** Determine whether the following statements are true and give an explanation or counterexample.

    a. proj$_\mathbf{v}$**u** = proj$_\mathbf{u}$**v**.
    b. If nonzero vectors **u** and **v** have the same magnitude, they make equal angles with $\mathbf{u} + \mathbf{v}$.
    c. $(\mathbf{u} \cdot \mathbf{i})^2 + (\mathbf{u} \cdot \mathbf{j})^2 + (\mathbf{u} \cdot \mathbf{k})^2 = |\mathbf{u}|^2$.
    d. If **u** is orthogonal to **v** and **v** is orthogonal to **w**, then **u** is orthogonal to **w**.
    e. The vectors orthogonal to $\langle 1, 1, 1 \rangle$ lie on the same line.
    f. If proj$_\mathbf{v}$**u** = **0**, then vectors **u** and **v** (both nonzero) are orthogonal.

48–52. Orthogonal vectors *Let a and b be real numbers.*

48. Find all unit vectors orthogonal to $\mathbf{v} = \langle 3, 4, 0 \rangle$.

49. Find all vectors $\langle 1, a, b \rangle$ orthogonal to $\langle 4, -8, 2 \rangle$.

50. Describe all unit vectors orthogonal to $\mathbf{v} = \mathbf{i} + \mathbf{j} + \mathbf{k}$.

51. Find three mutually orthogonal unit vectors in $\mathbb{R}^3$ besides $\pm\mathbf{i}, \pm\mathbf{j}$, and $\pm\mathbf{k}$.

52. Find two vectors that are orthogonal to $\langle 0, 1, 1 \rangle$ and to each other.

53. **Equal angles** Consider the set of all unit position vectors **u** in $\mathbb{R}^3$ that make a 60° angle with the unit vector **k** in $\mathbb{R}^3$.

    a. Prove that proj$_\mathbf{k}$**u** is the same for all vectors in this set.
    b. Is scal$_\mathbf{k}$**u** the same for all vectors in this set?

54–57. Vectors with equal projections *Given a fixed vector* **v**, *there is an infinite set of vectors* **u** *with the same value of* proj$_\mathbf{v}$**u**.

54. Find another vector that has the same projection onto $\mathbf{v} = \langle 1, 1 \rangle$ as $\mathbf{u} = \langle 1, 2 \rangle$. Draw a picture.

55. Let $\mathbf{v} = \langle 1, 1 \rangle$. Give a description of the position vectors **u** such that proj$_\mathbf{v}$**u** = proj$_\mathbf{v}\langle 1, 2 \rangle$.

56. Find another vector that has the same projection onto $\mathbf{v} = \langle 1, 1, 1 \rangle$ as $\mathbf{u} = \langle 1, 2, 3 \rangle$.

57. Let $\mathbf{v} = \langle 0, 0, 1 \rangle$. Give a description of all position vectors $\mathbf{u}$ such that $\text{proj}_\mathbf{v}\mathbf{u} = \text{proj}_\mathbf{v}\langle 1, 2, 3 \rangle$.

58–61. Decomposing vectors *For the following vectors* $\mathbf{u}$ *and* $\mathbf{v}$, *express* $\mathbf{u}$ *as the sum* $\mathbf{u} = \mathbf{p} + \mathbf{n}$, *where* $\mathbf{p}$ *is parallel to* $\mathbf{v}$ *and* $\mathbf{n}$ *is orthogonal to* $\mathbf{v}$.

58. $\mathbf{u} = \langle 4, 3 \rangle, \mathbf{v} = \langle 1, 1 \rangle$

59. $\mathbf{u} = \langle -2, 2 \rangle, \mathbf{v} = \langle 2, 1 \rangle$

60. $\mathbf{u} = \langle 4, 3, 0 \rangle, \mathbf{v} = \langle 1, 1, 1 \rangle$

61. $\mathbf{u} = \langle -1, 2, 3 \rangle, \mathbf{v} = \langle 2, 1, 1 \rangle$

62–65. Distance between a point and a line *Carry out the following steps to determine the (least) distance between the point P and the line* ℓ *through the origin.*

a. *Find any vector* $\mathbf{v}$ *in the direction of* ℓ.
b. *Find the position vector* $\mathbf{u}$ *corresponding to P.*
c. *Find* $\text{proj}_\mathbf{v}\mathbf{u}$.
d. *Show that* $\mathbf{w} = \mathbf{u} - \text{proj}_\mathbf{v}\mathbf{u}$ *is a vector orthogonal to* $\mathbf{v}$ *whose length is the distance between P and the line* ℓ.
e. *Find* $\mathbf{w}$ *and* $|\mathbf{w}|$. *Explain why* $|\mathbf{w}|$ *is the least distance between P and* ℓ.

62. $P(2, -5); \ell: y = 3x$

63. $P(-12, 4); \ell: y = 2x$

64. $P(0, 2, 6); \ell$ is parallel to $\langle 3, 0, -4 \rangle$.

65. $P(1, 1, -1); \ell$ is parallel to $\langle -6, 8, 3 \rangle$.

66–68. Orthogonal unit vectors in $\mathbb{R}^2$ Consider the vectors $\mathbf{I} = \langle 1/\sqrt{2}, 1/\sqrt{2} \rangle$ and $\mathbf{J} = \langle -1/\sqrt{2}, 1/\sqrt{2} \rangle$.

66. Show that $\mathbf{I}$ and $\mathbf{J}$ are orthogonal unit vectors.

67. Express $\mathbf{I}$ and $\mathbf{J}$ in terms of the usual unit coordinate vectors $\mathbf{i}$ and $\mathbf{j}$. Then write $\mathbf{i}$ and $\mathbf{j}$ in terms of $\mathbf{I}$ and $\mathbf{J}$.

68. Write the vector $\langle 2, -6 \rangle$ in terms of $\mathbf{I}$ and $\mathbf{J}$.

69. Orthogonal unit vectors in $\mathbb{R}^3$ Consider the vectors $\mathbf{I} = \langle 1/2, 1/2, 1/\sqrt{2} \rangle$, $\mathbf{J} = \langle -1/\sqrt{2}, 1/\sqrt{2}, 0 \rangle$, and $\mathbf{K} = \langle 1/2, 1/2, -1/\sqrt{2} \rangle$.

a. Sketch $\mathbf{I}$, $\mathbf{J}$, and $\mathbf{K}$ and show that they are unit vectors.
b. Show that $\mathbf{I}$, $\mathbf{J}$, and $\mathbf{K}$ are pairwise orthogonal.
c. Express the vector $\langle 1, 0, 0 \rangle$ in terms of $\mathbf{I}$, $\mathbf{J}$, and $\mathbf{K}$.

70–71. Angles of a triangle *For the given points P, Q, and R, find the approximate measurements of the angles of* $\triangle PQR$.

70. $P(1, -4), Q(2, 7), R(-2, 2)$

71. $P(0, -1, 3), Q(2, 2, 1), R(-2, 2, 4)$

Applications

72. Flow through a circle Suppose water flows in a thin sheet over the xy-plane with a uniform velocity given by the vector $\mathbf{v} = \langle 1, 2 \rangle$; this means that at all points of the plane, the velocity of the water has components 1 m/s in the x-direction and 2 m/s in the y-direction (see figure). Let C be an imaginary unit circle (that does not interfere with the flow).

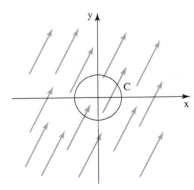

a. Show that at the point (x, y) on the circle C, the outward-pointing unit vector normal to C is $\mathbf{n} = \langle x, y \rangle$.
b. Show that at the point $(\cos \theta, \sin \theta)$ on the circle C, the outward-pointing unit vector normal to C is also $\mathbf{n} = \langle \cos \theta, \sin \theta \rangle$.
c. Find all points on C at which the velocity is normal to C.
d. Find all points on C at which the velocity is tangential to C.
e. At each point on C, find the component of $\mathbf{v}$ normal to C. Express the answer as a function of (x, y) and as a function of θ.
f. What is the net flow through the circle? That is, does water accumulate inside the circle?

73. Heat flux Let D be a solid heat-conducting cube formed by the planes $x = 0$, $x = 1$, $y = 0$, $y = 1$, $z = 0$, and $z = 1$. The heat flow at every point of D is given by the constant vector $\mathbf{Q} = \langle 0, 2, 1 \rangle$.

a. Through which faces of D does $\mathbf{Q}$ point into D?
b. Through which faces of D does $\mathbf{Q}$ point out of D?
c. On which faces of D is $\mathbf{Q}$ tangential to D (pointing neither in nor out of D)?
d. Find the scalar component of $\mathbf{Q}$ normal to the face $x = 0$.
e. Find the scalar component of $\mathbf{Q}$ normal to the face $z = 1$.
f. Find the scalar component of $\mathbf{Q}$ normal to the face $y = 0$.

74. Hexagonal circle packing The German mathematician Gauss proved that the densest way to pack circles with the same radius in the plane is to place the centers of the circles on a hexagonal grid (see figure). Some molecular structures use this packing or its three-dimensional analog. Assume all circles have a radius of 1 and let $\mathbf{r}_{ij}$ be the vector that extends from the center of circle i to the center of circle j, for $i, j = 0, 1, \ldots, 6$.

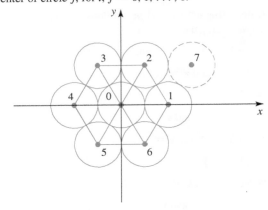

a. Find $\mathbf{r}_{0j}$, for $j = 1, 2, \ldots, 6$.
b. Find $\mathbf{r}_{12}$, $\mathbf{r}_{34}$, and $\mathbf{r}_{61}$.
c. Imagine circle 7 is added to the arrangement as shown in the figure. Find $\mathbf{r}_{07}$, $\mathbf{r}_{17}$, $\mathbf{r}_{47}$, and $\mathbf{r}_{75}$.

75. Hexagonal sphere packing Imagine three unit spheres (radius equal to 1) with centers at $O(0, 0, 0)$, $P(\sqrt{3}, -1, 0)$, and $Q(\sqrt{3}, 1, 0)$. Now place another unit sphere symmetrically on top of these spheres with its center at R (see figure).

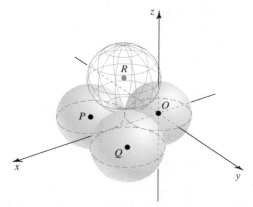

a. Find the coordinates of R. (*Hint:* The distance between the centers of any two spheres is 2.)
b. Let $\mathbf{r}_{IJ}$ be the vector from the center of sphere I to the center of sphere J. Find $\mathbf{r}_{OP}$, $\mathbf{r}_{OQ}$, $\mathbf{r}_{PQ}$, $\mathbf{r}_{OR}$, and $\mathbf{r}_{PR}$.

Additional Exercises

76–80. Properties of dot products *Let* $\mathbf{u} = \langle u_1, u_2, u_3 \rangle$, $\mathbf{v} = \langle v_1, v_2, v_3 \rangle$, *and* $\mathbf{w} = \langle w_1, w_2, w_3 \rangle$. *Prove the following vector properties, where c is a scalar.*

76. $|\mathbf{u} \cdot \mathbf{v}| \le |\mathbf{u}||\mathbf{v}|$

77. $\mathbf{u} \cdot \mathbf{v} = \mathbf{v} \cdot \mathbf{u}$ Commutative property

78. $c(\mathbf{u} \cdot \mathbf{v}) = (c\mathbf{u}) \cdot \mathbf{v} = \mathbf{u} \cdot (c\mathbf{v})$ Associative property

79. $\mathbf{u} \cdot (\mathbf{v} + \mathbf{w}) = \mathbf{u} \cdot \mathbf{v} + \mathbf{u} \cdot \mathbf{w}$ Distributive property

80. Distributive properties
a. Show that $(\mathbf{u} + \mathbf{v}) \cdot (\mathbf{u} + \mathbf{v}) = |\mathbf{u}|^2 + 2\mathbf{u} \cdot \mathbf{v} + |\mathbf{v}|^2$.
b. Show that $(\mathbf{u} + \mathbf{v}) \cdot (\mathbf{u} + \mathbf{v}) = |\mathbf{u}|^2 + |\mathbf{v}|^2$ if $\mathbf{u}$ is orthogonal to $\mathbf{v}$.
c. Show that $(\mathbf{u} + \mathbf{v}) \cdot (\mathbf{u} - \mathbf{v}) = |\mathbf{u}|^2 - |\mathbf{v}|^2$.

81. Prove or disprove For fixed values of a, b, c, and d, the value of $\text{proj}_{\langle ka, kb \rangle} \langle c, d \rangle$ is constant for all nonzero values of k, for $\langle a, b \rangle \ne \langle 0, 0 \rangle$.

82. Orthogonal lines Recall that two lines $y = mx + b$ and $y = nx + c$ are orthogonal provided $mn = -1$ (the slopes are negative reciprocals of each other). Prove that the condition $mn = -1$ is equivalent to the orthogonality condition $\mathbf{u} \cdot \mathbf{v} = 0$, where $\mathbf{u}$ points in the direction of one line and $\mathbf{v}$ points in the direction of the other line.

83. Direction angles and cosines Let $\mathbf{v} = \langle a, b, c \rangle$ and let α, β, and γ be the angles between $\mathbf{v}$ and the positive x-axis, the positive y-axis, and the positive z-axis, respectively (see figure).

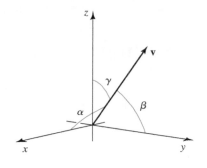

a. Prove that $\cos^2 \alpha + \cos^2 \beta + \cos^2 \gamma = 1$.
b. Find a vector that makes a $45°$ angle with $\mathbf{i}$ and $\mathbf{j}$. What angle does it make with $\mathbf{k}$?
c. Find a vector that makes a $60°$ angle with $\mathbf{i}$ and $\mathbf{j}$. What angle does it make with $\mathbf{k}$?
d. Is there a vector that makes a $30°$ angle with $\mathbf{i}$ and $\mathbf{j}$? Explain.
e. Find a vector $\mathbf{v}$ such that $\alpha = \beta = \gamma$. What is the angle?

84–88. Cauchy–Schwarz Inequality *The definition* $\mathbf{u} \cdot \mathbf{v} = |\mathbf{u}||\mathbf{v}| \cos \theta$ *implies that* $|\mathbf{u} \cdot \mathbf{v}| \le |\mathbf{u}||\mathbf{v}|$ *(because* $|\cos \theta| \le 1$*). This inequality, known as the Cauchy–Schwarz Inequality, holds in any number of dimensions and has many consequences.*

84. What conditions on $\mathbf{u}$ and $\mathbf{v}$ lead to equality in the Cauchy–Schwarz Inequality?

85. Verify that the Cauchy–Schwarz Inequality holds for $\mathbf{u} = \langle 3, -5, 6 \rangle$ and $\mathbf{v} = \langle -8, 3, 1 \rangle$.

86. Geometric-arithmetic mean Use the vectors $\mathbf{u} = \langle \sqrt{a}, \sqrt{b} \rangle$ and $\mathbf{v} = \langle \sqrt{b}, \sqrt{a} \rangle$ to show that $\sqrt{ab} \le (a + b)/2$, where $a \ge 0$ and $b \ge 0$.

87. Triangle Inequality Consider the vectors $\mathbf{u}$, $\mathbf{v}$, and $\mathbf{u} + \mathbf{v}$ (in any number of dimensions). Use the following steps to prove that $|\mathbf{u} + \mathbf{v}| \le |\mathbf{u}| + |\mathbf{v}|$.
a. Show that $|\mathbf{u} + \mathbf{v}|^2 = (\mathbf{u} + \mathbf{v}) \cdot (\mathbf{u} + \mathbf{v}) = |\mathbf{u}|^2 + 2\mathbf{u} \cdot \mathbf{v} + |\mathbf{v}|^2$.
b. Use the Cauchy–Schwarz Inequality to show that $|\mathbf{u} + \mathbf{v}|^2 \le (|\mathbf{u}| + |\mathbf{v}|)^2$.
c. Conclude that $|\mathbf{u} + \mathbf{v}| \le |\mathbf{u}| + |\mathbf{v}|$.
d. Interpret the Triangle Inequality geometrically in $\mathbb{R}^2$ or $\mathbb{R}^3$.

88. Algebra inequality Show that
$$(u_1 + u_2 + u_3)^2 \le 3(u_1^2 + u_2^2 + u_3^2),$$
for any real numbers u_1, u_2, and u_3. (*Hint:* Use the Cauchy–Schwarz Inequality in three dimensions with $\mathbf{u} = \langle u_1, u_2, u_3 \rangle$ and choose $\mathbf{v}$ in the right way.)

89. Diagonals of a parallelogram Consider the parallelogram with adjacent sides $\mathbf{u}$ and $\mathbf{v}$.
a. Show that the diagonals of the parallelogram are $\mathbf{u} + \mathbf{v}$ and $\mathbf{u} - \mathbf{v}$.
b. Prove that the diagonals have the same length if and only if $\mathbf{u} \cdot \mathbf{v} = 0$.
c. Show that the sum of the squares of the lengths of the diagonals equals the sum of the squares of the lengths of the sides.

90. Distance between a point and a line in the plane Use projections to find a general formula for the (least) distance between the point $P(x_0, y_0)$ and the line $ax + by = c$. (See Exercises 62–65.)

QUICK CHECK ANSWERS

1. If $\theta = 0$, $\mathbf{u}$ and $\mathbf{v}$ are parallel and point in the same direction. If $\theta = \pi$, $\mathbf{u}$ and $\mathbf{v}$ are parallel and point in opposite directions. **2.** All these dot products are zero, and the unit vectors are mutually orthogonal. The angle between two different unit vectors is $\pi/2$. **3.** $\text{proj}_\mathbf{i}\mathbf{u} = 4\mathbf{i}$, $\text{proj}_\mathbf{j}\mathbf{u} = -3\mathbf{j}$, $\text{scal}_\mathbf{i}\mathbf{u} = 4$, $\text{scal}_\mathbf{j}\mathbf{u} = -3$ ◄

11.4 Cross Products

The dot product combines two vectors to produce a *scalar* result. There is an equally fundamental way to combine two vectors in $\mathbb{R}^3$ and obtain a *vector* result. This operation, known as the *cross product* (or *vector product*), may be motivated by a physical application.

Suppose you want to loosen a bolt with a wrench. As you apply force to the end of the wrench in the plane perpendicular to the bolt, the "twisting power" you generate depends on three variables:

- the magnitude of the force **F** applied to the wrench;
- the length $|\mathbf{r}|$ of the wrench;
- the angle at which the force is applied to the wrench.

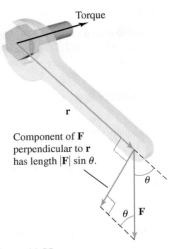

Torque

r

Component of **F**
perpendicular to **r**
has length $|\mathbf{F}|\sin\theta$.

θ

θ **F**

Figure 11.55

The twisting generated by a force acting at a distance from a pivot point is called **torque** (from the Latin *to twist*). The torque is a vector whose magnitude is proportional to $|\mathbf{F}|$, $|\mathbf{r}|$, and $\sin\theta$, where θ is the angle between **F** and **r** (Figure 11.55). If the force is applied parallel to the wrench—for example, if you pull the wrench ($\theta = 0$) or push the wrench ($\theta = \pi$)—there is no twisting effect; if the force is applied perpendicular to the wrench ($\theta = \pi/2$), the twisting effect is maximized. The direction of the torque vector is defined to be orthogonal to both **F** and **r**. As we will see shortly, the torque is expressed in terms of the cross product of **F** and **r**.

The Cross Product

The preceding physical example leads to the following definition of the cross product.

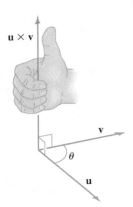

$\mathbf{u} \times \mathbf{v}$

v

θ

u

Figure 11.56

> **DEFINITION Cross Product**
>
> Given two nonzero vectors **u** and **v** in $\mathbb{R}^3$, the **cross product** $\mathbf{u} \times \mathbf{v}$ is a vector with magnitude
>
> $$|\mathbf{u} \times \mathbf{v}| = |\mathbf{u}||\mathbf{v}|\sin\theta,$$
>
> where $0 \le \theta \le \pi$ is the angle between **u** and **v**. The direction of $\mathbf{u} \times \mathbf{v}$ is given by the **right-hand rule**: When you put the vectors tail to tail and let the fingers of your right hand curl from **u** to **v**, the direction of $\mathbf{u} \times \mathbf{v}$ is the direction of your thumb, orthogonal to both **u** and **v** (Figure 11.56). When $\mathbf{u} \times \mathbf{v} = \mathbf{0}$, the direction of $\mathbf{u} \times \mathbf{v}$ is undefined.

The following theorem is a consequence of the definition of the cross product.

QUICK CHECK 1 Sketch the vectors $\mathbf{u} = \langle 1, 2, 0 \rangle$ and $\mathbf{v} = \langle -1, 2, 0 \rangle$. Which way does $\mathbf{u} \times \mathbf{v}$ point? Which way does $\mathbf{v} \times \mathbf{u}$ point? ◄

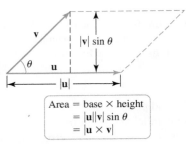

v

$|\mathbf{v}|\sin\theta$

θ **u**

$|\mathbf{u}|$

Area = base × height
   = $|\mathbf{u}||\mathbf{v}|\sin\theta$
   = $|\mathbf{u} \times \mathbf{v}|$

Figure 11.57

> **THEOREM 11.3 Geometry of the Cross Product**
> Let **u** and **v** be two nonzero vectors in $\mathbb{R}^3$.
>
> 1. The vectors **u** and **v** are parallel ($\theta = 0$ or $\theta = \pi$) if and only if $\mathbf{u} \times \mathbf{v} = \mathbf{0}$.
> 2. If **u** and **v** are two sides of a parallelogram (Figure 11.57), then the area of the parallelogram is
>
> $$|\mathbf{u} \times \mathbf{v}| = |\mathbf{u}||\mathbf{v}|\sin\theta.$$

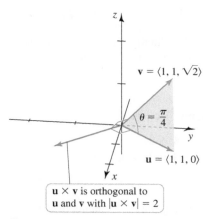

$\mathbf{v} = \langle 1, 1, \sqrt{2} \rangle$

$\theta = \dfrac{\pi}{4}$

$\mathbf{u} = \langle 1, 1, 0 \rangle$

$\mathbf{u} \times \mathbf{v}$ is orthogonal to $\mathbf{u}$ and $\mathbf{v}$ with $|\mathbf{u} \times \mathbf{v}| = 2$

Figure 11.58

EXAMPLE 1   A cross product Find the magnitude and direction of $\mathbf{u} \times \mathbf{v}$, where $\mathbf{u} = \langle 1, 1, 0 \rangle$ and $\mathbf{v} = \langle 1, 1, \sqrt{2} \rangle$.

SOLUTION Because $\mathbf{u}$ is one side of a 45–45–90 triangle and $\mathbf{v}$ is the hypotenuse (Figure 11.58), we have $\theta = \pi/4$ and $\sin \theta = \frac{1}{\sqrt{2}}$. Also, $|\mathbf{u}| = \sqrt{2}$ and $|\mathbf{v}| = 2$, so the magnitude of $\mathbf{u} \times \mathbf{v}$ is

$$|\mathbf{u} \times \mathbf{v}| = |\mathbf{u}||\mathbf{v}| \sin \theta = \sqrt{2} \cdot 2 \cdot \frac{1}{\sqrt{2}} = 2.$$

The direction of $\mathbf{u} \times \mathbf{v}$ is given by the right-hand rule: $\mathbf{u} \times \mathbf{v}$ is orthogonal to $\mathbf{u}$ and $\mathbf{v}$ (Figure 11.58).

Related Exercises 7–14 ◄

Properties of the Cross Product

The cross product has several algebraic properties that simplify calculations. For example, scalars factor out of a cross product; that is, if a and b are scalars, then (Exercise 69)

$$(a\mathbf{u}) \times (b\mathbf{v}) = ab(\mathbf{u} \times \mathbf{v}).$$

The order in which the cross product is performed is important. The magnitudes of $\mathbf{u} \times \mathbf{v}$ and $\mathbf{v} \times \mathbf{u}$ are equal. However, applying the right-hand rule shows that $\mathbf{u} \times \mathbf{v}$ and $\mathbf{v} \times \mathbf{u}$ point in opposite directions. Therefore, $\mathbf{u} \times \mathbf{v} = -(\mathbf{v} \times \mathbf{u})$. There are two distributive properties for the cross product, whose proofs are omitted.

THEOREM 11.4   Properties of the Cross Product
Let $\mathbf{u}$, $\mathbf{v}$, and $\mathbf{w}$ be nonzero vectors in $\mathbb{R}^3$, and let a and b be scalars.

1. $\mathbf{u} \times \mathbf{v} = -(\mathbf{v} \times \mathbf{u})$ Anticommutative property
2. $(a\mathbf{u}) \times (b\mathbf{v}) = ab(\mathbf{u} \times \mathbf{v})$ Associative property
3. $\mathbf{u} \times (\mathbf{v} + \mathbf{w}) = (\mathbf{u} \times \mathbf{v}) + (\mathbf{u} \times \mathbf{w})$ Distributive property
4. $(\mathbf{u} + \mathbf{v}) \times \mathbf{w} = (\mathbf{u} \times \mathbf{w}) + (\mathbf{v} \times \mathbf{w})$ Distributive property

---

QUICK CHECK 2 Explain why the vector $2\mathbf{u} \times 3\mathbf{v}$ points in the same direction as $\mathbf{u} \times \mathbf{v}$. ◄

EXAMPLE 2   Cross products of unit vectors Evaluate all the cross products among the coordinate unit vectors $\mathbf{i}$, $\mathbf{j}$, and $\mathbf{k}$.

SOLUTION These vectors are mutually orthogonal, which means the angle between any two distinct vectors is $\theta = \pi/2$ and $\sin \theta = 1$. Furthermore, $|\mathbf{i}| = |\mathbf{j}| = |\mathbf{k}| = 1$. Therefore, the cross product of any two distinct vectors has magnitude 1. By the right-hand rule, when the fingers of the right hand curl from $\mathbf{i}$ to $\mathbf{j}$, the thumb points in the direction of the positive z-axis (Figure 11.59). The unit vector in the positive z-direction is $\mathbf{k}$, so $\mathbf{i} \times \mathbf{j} = \mathbf{k}$. Similar calculations show that $\mathbf{j} \times \mathbf{k} = \mathbf{i}$ and $\mathbf{k} \times \mathbf{i} = \mathbf{j}$.

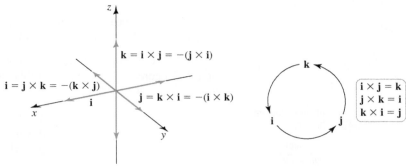

$\mathbf{k} = \mathbf{i} \times \mathbf{j} = -(\mathbf{j} \times \mathbf{i})$

$\mathbf{i} = \mathbf{j} \times \mathbf{k} = -(\mathbf{k} \times \mathbf{j})$

$\mathbf{j} = \mathbf{k} \times \mathbf{i} = -(\mathbf{i} \times \mathbf{k})$

$\mathbf{i} \times \mathbf{j} = \mathbf{k}$
$\mathbf{j} \times \mathbf{k} = \mathbf{i}$
$\mathbf{k} \times \mathbf{i} = \mathbf{j}$

Figure 11.59

By property 1 of Theorem 11.4, $\mathbf{j} \times \mathbf{i} = -(\mathbf{i} \times \mathbf{j}) = -\mathbf{k}$, so $\mathbf{j} \times \mathbf{i}$ and $\mathbf{i} \times \mathbf{j}$ point in opposite directions. Similarly, $\mathbf{k} \times \mathbf{j} = -\mathbf{i}$ and $\mathbf{i} \times \mathbf{k} = -\mathbf{j}$. These relationships are easily remembered with the circle diagram in Figure 11.59. Finally, the angle between any unit vector and itself is $\theta = 0$. Therefore, $\mathbf{i} \times \mathbf{i} = \mathbf{j} \times \mathbf{j} = \mathbf{k} \times \mathbf{k} = \mathbf{0}$.

Related Exercises 15–20 ◄

> **THEOREM 11.5   Cross Products of Coordinate Unit Vectors**
> $$\mathbf{i} \times \mathbf{j} = -(\mathbf{j} \times \mathbf{i}) = \mathbf{k} \qquad \mathbf{j} \times \mathbf{k} = -(\mathbf{k} \times \mathbf{j}) = \mathbf{i}$$
> $$\mathbf{k} \times \mathbf{i} = -(\mathbf{i} \times \mathbf{k}) = \mathbf{j} \qquad \mathbf{i} \times \mathbf{i} = \mathbf{j} \times \mathbf{j} = \mathbf{k} \times \mathbf{k} = \mathbf{0}$$

What is missing so far is an efficient method for finding the components of the cross product of two vectors in $\mathbb{R}^3$. Let $\mathbf{u} = u_1\mathbf{i} + u_2\mathbf{j} + u_3\mathbf{k}$ and $\mathbf{v} = v_1\mathbf{i} + v_2\mathbf{j} + v_3\mathbf{k}$. Using the distributive properties of the cross product (Theorem 11.4), we have

$$
\begin{aligned}
\mathbf{u} \times \mathbf{v} &= (u_1\mathbf{i} + u_2\mathbf{j} + u_3\mathbf{k}) \times (v_1\mathbf{i} + v_2\mathbf{j} + v_3\mathbf{k}) \\
&= u_1v_1 \underbrace{(\mathbf{i} \times \mathbf{i})}_{0} + u_1v_2 \underbrace{(\mathbf{i} \times \mathbf{j})}_{\mathbf{k}} + u_1v_3 \underbrace{(\mathbf{i} \times \mathbf{k})}_{-\mathbf{j}} \\
&\quad + u_2v_1 \underbrace{(\mathbf{j} \times \mathbf{i})}_{-\mathbf{k}} + u_2v_2 \underbrace{(\mathbf{j} \times \mathbf{j})}_{0} + u_2v_3 \underbrace{(\mathbf{j} \times \mathbf{k})}_{\mathbf{i}} \\
&\quad + u_3v_1 \underbrace{(\mathbf{k} \times \mathbf{i})}_{\mathbf{j}} + u_3v_2 \underbrace{(\mathbf{k} \times \mathbf{j})}_{-\mathbf{i}} + u_3v_3 \underbrace{(\mathbf{k} \times \mathbf{k})}_{0}.
\end{aligned}
$$

> ► The determinant of the matrix A is denoted both $|A|$ and det A. The formula for the determinant of a 3×3 matrix A is
>
> $$\begin{vmatrix} a_1 & a_2 & a_3 \\ b_1 & b_2 & b_3 \\ c_1 & c_2 & c_3 \end{vmatrix} = a_1 \begin{vmatrix} b_2 & b_3 \\ c_2 & c_3 \end{vmatrix} - a_2 \begin{vmatrix} b_1 & b_3 \\ c_1 & c_3 \end{vmatrix}$$
> $$+ a_3 \begin{vmatrix} b_1 & b_2 \\ c_1 & c_2 \end{vmatrix},$$
>
> where
>
> $$\begin{vmatrix} a & b \\ c & d \end{vmatrix} = ad - bc.$$

This formula looks impossible to remember until we see that it fits the pattern used to evaluate 3×3 determinants. Specifically, if we compute the determinant of the matrix

$$
\begin{array}{ll}
\text{Unit vectors} & \rightarrow \\
\text{Components of } \mathbf{u} & \rightarrow \\
\text{Components of } \mathbf{v} & \rightarrow
\end{array}
\begin{pmatrix} \mathbf{i} & \mathbf{j} & \mathbf{k} \\ u_1 & u_2 & u_3 \\ v_1 & v_2 & v_3 \end{pmatrix}
$$

(expanding about the first row), the following formula for the cross product emerges (see margin note).

> **THEOREM 11.6   Evaluating the Cross Product**
> Let $\mathbf{u} = u_1\mathbf{i} + u_2\mathbf{j} + u_3\mathbf{k}$ and $\mathbf{v} = v_1\mathbf{i} + v_2\mathbf{j} + v_3\mathbf{k}$. Then
>
> $$\mathbf{u} \times \mathbf{v} = \begin{vmatrix} \mathbf{i} & \mathbf{j} & \mathbf{k} \\ u_1 & u_2 & u_3 \\ v_1 & v_2 & v_3 \end{vmatrix} = \begin{vmatrix} u_2 & u_3 \\ v_2 & v_3 \end{vmatrix}\mathbf{i} - \begin{vmatrix} u_1 & u_3 \\ v_1 & v_3 \end{vmatrix}\mathbf{j} + \begin{vmatrix} u_1 & u_2 \\ v_1 & v_2 \end{vmatrix}\mathbf{k}.$$

EXAMPLE 3   Area of a triangle Find the area of the triangle with vertices $O(0, 0, 0)$, $P(2, 3, 4)$, and $Q(3, 2, 0)$ (Figure 11.60).

SOLUTION First consider the parallelogram, two of whose sides are the vectors $\overrightarrow{OP}$ and $\overrightarrow{OQ}$. By Theorem 11.3, the area of this parallelogram is $|\overrightarrow{OP} \times \overrightarrow{OQ}|$. Computing the cross product, we find that

$$
\overrightarrow{OP} \times \overrightarrow{OQ} = \begin{vmatrix} \mathbf{i} & \mathbf{j} & \mathbf{k} \\ 2 & 3 & 4 \\ 3 & 2 & 0 \end{vmatrix} = \begin{vmatrix} 3 & 4 \\ 2 & 0 \end{vmatrix}\mathbf{i} - \begin{vmatrix} 2 & 4 \\ 3 & 0 \end{vmatrix}\mathbf{j} + \begin{vmatrix} 2 & 3 \\ 3 & 2 \end{vmatrix}\mathbf{k}
$$

$$
= -8\mathbf{i} + 12\mathbf{j} - 5\mathbf{k}.
$$

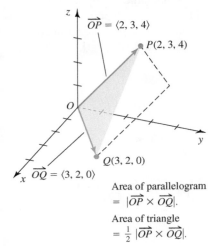

$\overrightarrow{OP} = \langle 2, 3, 4 \rangle$

$P(2, 3, 4)$

$Q(3, 2, 0)$

$\overrightarrow{OQ} = \langle 3, 2, 0 \rangle$

Area of parallelogram
$= |\overrightarrow{OP} \times \overrightarrow{OQ}|$.

Area of triangle
$= \frac{1}{2}|\overrightarrow{OP} \times \overrightarrow{OQ}|$.

Figure 11.60

Therefore, the area of the parallelogram is

$$|\vec{OP} \times \vec{OQ}| = |-8\mathbf{i} + 12\mathbf{j} - 5\mathbf{k}| = \sqrt{233} \approx 15.26.$$

The triangle with vertices O, P, and Q comprises half of the parallelogram, so its area is $\sqrt{233}/2 \approx 7.63$.

Related Exercises 21–34 ◄

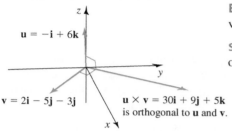

$\mathbf{u} = -\mathbf{i} + 6\mathbf{k}$

$\mathbf{v} = 2\mathbf{i} - 5\mathbf{j} - 3\mathbf{j}$ $\mathbf{u} \times \mathbf{v} = 30\mathbf{i} + 9\mathbf{j} + 5\mathbf{k}$ is orthogonal to $\mathbf{u}$ and $\mathbf{v}$.

Figure 11.61

QUICK CHECK 3 A good check on a cross product calculation is to verify that $\mathbf{u}$ and $\mathbf{v}$ are orthogonal to the computed $\mathbf{u} \times \mathbf{v}$. In Example 4, verify that $\mathbf{u} \cdot (\mathbf{u} \times \mathbf{v}) = 0$ and $\mathbf{v} \cdot (\mathbf{u} \times \mathbf{v}) = 0$. ◄

EXAMPLE 4 **Vector orthogonal to two vectors** Find a vector orthogonal to the two vectors $\mathbf{u} = -\mathbf{i} + 6\mathbf{k}$ and $\mathbf{v} = 2\mathbf{i} - 5\mathbf{j} - 3\mathbf{k}$.

SOLUTION A vector orthogonal to $\mathbf{u}$ and $\mathbf{v}$ is parallel to $\mathbf{u} \times \mathbf{v}$ (Figure 11.61). One such orthogonal vector is

$$\mathbf{u} \times \mathbf{v} = \begin{vmatrix} \mathbf{i} & \mathbf{j} & \mathbf{k} \\ -1 & 0 & 6 \\ 2 & -5 & -3 \end{vmatrix}$$

$$= (0 + 30)\mathbf{i} - (3 - 12)\mathbf{j} + (5 - 0)\mathbf{k}$$

$$= 30\mathbf{i} + 9\mathbf{j} + 5\mathbf{k}.$$

Any scalar multiple of this vector is also orthogonal to $\mathbf{u}$ and $\mathbf{v}$.

Related Exercises 35–38 ◄

Applications of the Cross Product

We now investigate two physical applications of the cross product.

Torque Returning to the example of applying a force to a wrench, suppose a force $\mathbf{F}$ is applied to the point P at the head of a vector $\mathbf{r} = \vec{OP}$ (Figure 11.62). The **torque**, or twisting effect, produced by the force about the point O is given by $\boldsymbol{\tau} = \mathbf{r} \times \mathbf{F}$. The torque vector has a magnitude of

$$|\boldsymbol{\tau}| = |\mathbf{r} \times \mathbf{F}| = |\mathbf{r}||\mathbf{F}| \sin \theta,$$

where θ is the angle between $\mathbf{r}$ and $\mathbf{F}$. The direction of the torque is given by the right-hand rule; it is orthogonal to both $\mathbf{r}$ and $\mathbf{F}$. As noted earlier, if $\mathbf{r}$ and $\mathbf{F}$ are parallel, then $\sin \theta = 0$ and the torque is zero. For a given $\mathbf{r}$ and $\mathbf{F}$, the maximum torque occurs when $\mathbf{F}$ is applied in a direction orthogonal to $\mathbf{r}$ ($\theta = \pi/2$).

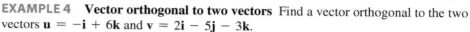

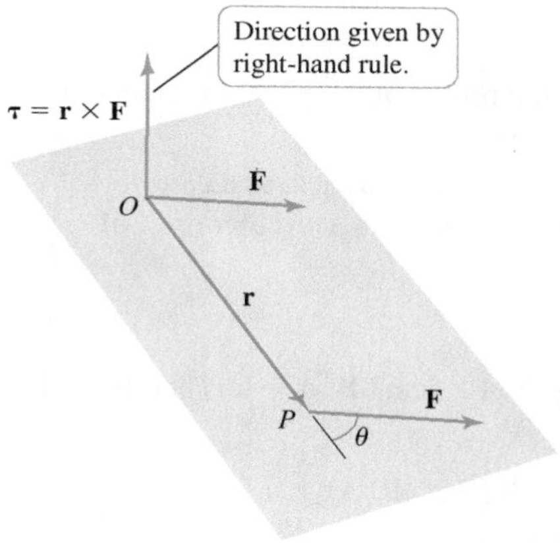

Direction given by right-hand rule.

$\boldsymbol{\tau} = \mathbf{r} \times \mathbf{F}$

O

$\mathbf{F}$

$\mathbf{r}$

P θ $\mathbf{F}$

Figure 11.62

EXAMPLE 5 **Tightening a bolt** A force of 20 N is applied to a wrench attached to a bolt in a direction perpendicular to the bolt (Figure 11.63). Which produces more torque: applying the force at an angle of 60° on a wrench that is 0.15 m long or applying the force at an angle of 135° on a wrench that is 0.25 m long? In each case, what is the direction of the torque?

➤ When standard threads are added to the bolt in Figure 11.63, the forces used in Example 5 cause the bolt to move upward into a nut—in the direction of the torque.

nut $\boldsymbol{\tau}$

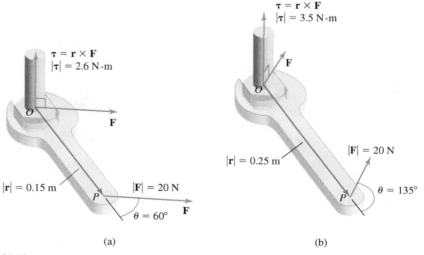

$\boldsymbol{\tau} = \mathbf{r} \times \mathbf{F}$
$|\boldsymbol{\tau}| = 2.6$ N-m

O $\mathbf{F}$

$|\mathbf{r}| = 0.15$ m P $|\mathbf{F}| = 20$ N

$\theta = 60°$ $\mathbf{F}$

(a)

$\boldsymbol{\tau} = \mathbf{r} \times \mathbf{F}$
$|\boldsymbol{\tau}| = 3.5$ N-m

$\mathbf{F}$

O

$|\mathbf{r}| = 0.25$ m $|\mathbf{F}| = 20$ N

P $\theta = 135°$

(b)

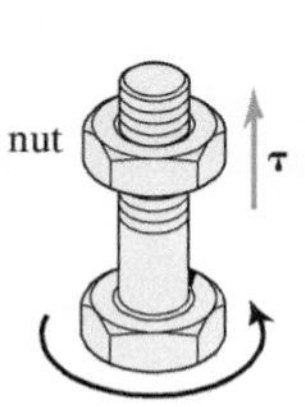

Figure 11.63

SOLUTION The magnitude of the torque in the first case is

$$|\boldsymbol{\tau}| = |\mathbf{r}||\mathbf{F}| \sin \theta = (0.15 \text{ m})(20 \text{ N}) \sin 60° \approx 2.6 \text{ N-m}.$$

In the second case, the magnitude of the torque is

$$|\boldsymbol{\tau}| = |\mathbf{r}||\mathbf{F}| \sin \theta = (0.25 \text{ m})(20 \text{ N}) \sin 135° \approx 3.5 \text{ N-m}.$$

The second instance gives the greater torque. In both cases, the torque is orthogonal to **r** and **F**, parallel to the shaft of the bolt (Figure 11.63).

Related Exercises 39–44 ◄

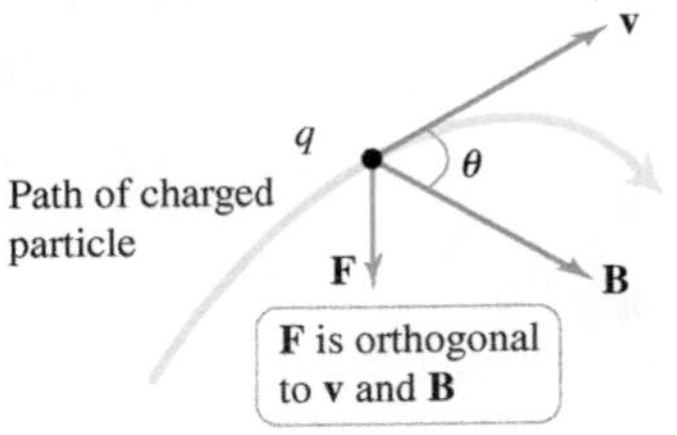

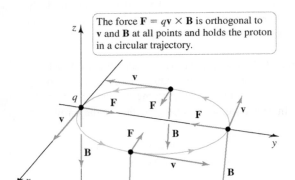

Path of charged particle

F is orthogonal to **v** and **B**

Figure 11.64

Magnetic Force on a Moving Charge Moving electric charges (either an isolated charge or a current in a wire) experience a force when they pass through a magnetic field. For an isolated charge q, the force is given by $\mathbf{F} = q(\mathbf{v} \times \mathbf{B})$, where **v** is the velocity of the charge and **B** is the magnetic field. The magnitude of the force is

$$|\mathbf{F}| = |q||\mathbf{v} \times \mathbf{B}| = |q||\mathbf{v}||\mathbf{B}| \sin \theta,$$

where θ is the angle between **v** and **B** (Figure 11.64). Note that the sign of the charge also determines the direction of the force. If the velocity vector is parallel to the magnetic field, the charge experiences no force. The maximum force occurs when the velocity is orthogonal to the magnetic field.

> The standard unit of magnetic field strength is the tesla (T, named after Nicola Tesla). A typical strong bar magnet has a strength of about 1 T. In terms of other units, $1 \text{ T} = 1 \text{ kg}/(\text{C-s})$, where C is the unit of charge called the *coulomb*.

EXAMPLE 6 **Force on a proton** A proton with a mass of 1.7×10^{-27} kg and a charge of $q = +1.6 \times 10^{-19}$ coulombs (C) moves along the x-axis with a speed of $|\mathbf{v}| = 9 \times 10^{5}$ m/s. When it reaches $(0, 0, 0)$, a uniform magnetic field is turned on. The field has a constant strength of 1 tesla (1 T) and is directed along the negative z-axis (Figure 11.65).

a. Find the magnitude and direction of the force on the proton at the instant it enters the magnetic field.

b. Assume that the proton loses no energy and the force in part (a) acts as a *centripetal force* with magnitude $|\mathbf{F}| = m|\mathbf{v}|^2/R$ that keeps the proton in a circular orbit of radius R. Find the radius of the orbit.

The force $\mathbf{F} = q\mathbf{v} \times \mathbf{B}$ is orthogonal to **v** and **B** at all points and holds the proton in a circular trajectory.

Figure 11.65

SOLUTION

a. Expressed as vectors, we have $\mathbf{v} = 9 \times 10^{5}\,\mathbf{i}$ and $\mathbf{B} = -\mathbf{k}$. Therefore, the force on the proton in newtons is

$$\mathbf{F} = q(\mathbf{v} \times \mathbf{B}) = 1.6 \times 10^{-19}\big((9 \times 10^{5}\,\mathbf{i}) \times (-\mathbf{k})\big)$$
$$= 1.44 \times 10^{-13}\mathbf{j}.$$

As shown in Figure 11.65, when the proton enters the magnetic field in the positive x-direction, the force acts in the positive y-direction, which changes the path of the proton.

b. The magnitude of the force acting on the proton remains 1.44×10^{-13} N at all times (from part (a)). Equating this force to the centripetal force $|\mathbf{F}| = m|\mathbf{v}|^2/R$, we find that

$$R = \frac{m|\mathbf{v}|^2}{|\mathbf{F}|} = \frac{(1.7 \times 10^{-27} \text{ kg})(9 \times 10^{5} \text{ m/s})^2}{1.44 \times 10^{-13} \text{ N}} \approx 0.01 \text{ m}.$$

Assuming no energy loss, the proton moves in a circular orbit of radius 0.01 m.

Related Exercises 45–48 ◄

SECTION 11.4 EXERCISES

Review Questions

1. Explain how to find the magnitude of the cross product $\mathbf{u} \times \mathbf{v}$.

2. Explain how to find the direction of the cross product $\mathbf{u} \times \mathbf{v}$.

3. What is the magnitude of the cross product of two parallel vectors?

4. If $\mathbf{u}$ and $\mathbf{v}$ are orthogonal, what is the magnitude of $\mathbf{u} \times \mathbf{v}$?

5. Explain how to use a determinant to compute $\mathbf{u} \times \mathbf{v}$.

6. Explain how to find the torque produced by a force using cross products.

Basic Skills

7–8. Cross products from the definition *Find the cross product* $\mathbf{u} \times \mathbf{v}$ *in each figure.*

7.

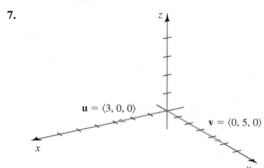

$\mathbf{u} = \langle 3, 0, 0 \rangle$
$\mathbf{v} = \langle 0, 5, 0 \rangle$

8.

$\mathbf{v} = \langle 0, 0, 2 \rangle$
$\mathbf{u} = \langle -4, 0, 0 \rangle$

9–12. Cross products from the definition *Sketch the following vectors* $\mathbf{u}$ *and* $\mathbf{v}$. *Then compute* $|\mathbf{u} \times \mathbf{v}|$ *and show the cross product on your sketch.*

9. $\mathbf{u} = \langle 0, -2, 0 \rangle, \mathbf{v} = \langle 0, 1, 0 \rangle$

10. $\mathbf{u} = \langle 0, 4, 0 \rangle, \mathbf{v} = \langle 0, 0, -8 \rangle$

11. $\mathbf{u} = \langle 3, 3, 0 \rangle, \mathbf{v} = \langle 3, 3, 3\sqrt{2} \rangle$

12. $\mathbf{u} = \langle 0, -2, -2 \rangle, \mathbf{v} = \langle 0, 2, -2 \rangle$

13. **Magnitude of a cross product** Compute $|\mathbf{u} \times \mathbf{v}|$ if $\mathbf{u}$ and $\mathbf{v}$ are unit vectors and the angle between $\mathbf{u}$ and $\mathbf{v}$ is $\pi/4$.

14. **Magnitude of a cross product** Compute $|\mathbf{u} \times \mathbf{v}|$ if $|\mathbf{u}| = 3$ and $|\mathbf{v}| = 4$ and the angle between $\mathbf{u}$ and $\mathbf{v}$ is $2\pi/3$.

15–20. Coordinate unit vectors *Compute the following cross products. Then make a sketch showing the two vectors and their cross product.*

15. $\mathbf{j} \times \mathbf{k}$ 16. $\mathbf{i} \times \mathbf{k}$ 17. $-\mathbf{j} \times \mathbf{k}$

18. $3\mathbf{j} \times \mathbf{i}$ 19. $-2\mathbf{i} \times 3\mathbf{k}$ 20. $2\mathbf{j} \times (-5)\mathbf{i}$

21–24. Area of a parallelogram *Find the area of the parallelogram that has two adjacent sides* $\mathbf{u}$ *and* $\mathbf{v}$.

21. $\mathbf{u} = 3\mathbf{i} - \mathbf{j}, \mathbf{v} = 3\mathbf{j} + 2\mathbf{k}$

22. $\mathbf{u} = -3\mathbf{i} + 2\mathbf{k}, \mathbf{v} = \mathbf{i} + \mathbf{j} + \mathbf{k}$

23. $\mathbf{u} = 2\mathbf{i} - \mathbf{j} - 2\mathbf{k}, \mathbf{v} = 3\mathbf{i} + 2\mathbf{j} - \mathbf{k}$

24. $\mathbf{u} = 8\mathbf{i} + 2\mathbf{j} - 3\mathbf{k}, \mathbf{v} = 2\mathbf{i} + 4\mathbf{j} - 4\mathbf{k}$

25–28. Area of a triangle *For the given points A, B, and C, find the area of the triangle with vertices A, B, and C.*

25. $A(0, 0, 0), B(3, 0, 1), C(1, 1, 0)$

26. $A(1, 2, 3), B(5, 1, 5), C(2, 3, 3)$

27. $A(5, 6, 2), B(7, 16, 4), C(6, 7, 3)$

28. $A(-1, -5, -3), B(-3, -2, -1), C(0, -5, -1)$

29–34. Computing cross products *Find the cross products* $\mathbf{u} \times \mathbf{v}$ *and* $\mathbf{v} \times \mathbf{u}$ *for the following vectors* $\mathbf{u}$ *and* $\mathbf{v}$.

29. $\mathbf{u} = \langle 3, 5, 0 \rangle, \mathbf{v} = \langle 0, 3, -6 \rangle$

30. $\mathbf{u} = \langle -4, 1, 1 \rangle, \mathbf{v} = \langle 0, 1, -1 \rangle$

31. $\mathbf{u} = \langle 2, 3, -9 \rangle, \mathbf{v} = \langle -1, 1, -1 \rangle$

32. $\mathbf{u} = \langle 3, -4, 6 \rangle, \mathbf{v} = \langle 1, 2, -1 \rangle$

33. $\mathbf{u} = 3\mathbf{i} - \mathbf{j} - 2\mathbf{k}, \mathbf{v} = \mathbf{i} + 3\mathbf{j} - 2\mathbf{k}$

34. $\mathbf{u} = 2\mathbf{i} - 10\mathbf{j} + 15\mathbf{k}, \mathbf{v} = 0.5\mathbf{i} + \mathbf{j} - 0.6\mathbf{k}$

35–38. Orthogonal vectors *Find a vector orthogonal to the given vectors.*

35. $\langle 0, 1, 2 \rangle$ and $\langle -2, 0, 3 \rangle$

36. $\langle 1, 2, 3 \rangle$ and $\langle -2, 4, -1 \rangle$

37. $\langle 8, 0, 4 \rangle$ and $\langle -8, 2, 1 \rangle$

38. $\langle 6, -2, 4 \rangle$ and $\langle 1, 2, 3 \rangle$

39. **Tightening a bolt** Suppose you apply a force of 20 N to a 0.25-meter-long wrench attached to a bolt in a direction perpendicular to the bolt. Determine the magnitude of the torque when the force is applied at an angle of 45° to the wrench.

40. **Opening a laptop** A force of 1.5 lb is applied in a direction perpendicular to the screen of a laptop at a distance of 10 in from the hinge of the screen. Find the magnitude of the torque (in ft-lb) that is applied.

41–44. Computing torque *Answer the following questions about torque.*

41. Let $\mathbf{r} = \overrightarrow{OP} = \mathbf{i} + \mathbf{j} + \mathbf{k}$. A force $\mathbf{F} = \langle 20, 0, 0 \rangle$ is applied at P. Find the torque about O that is produced.

42. Let $\mathbf{r} = \overrightarrow{OP} = \mathbf{i} - \mathbf{j} + 2\mathbf{k}$. A force $\mathbf{F} = \langle 10, 10, 0 \rangle$ is applied at P. Find the torque about O that is produced.

43. Let $\mathbf{r} = \overrightarrow{OP} = 10\mathbf{i}$. Which is greater (in magnitude): the torque about O when a force $\mathbf{F} = 5\mathbf{i} - 5\mathbf{k}$ is applied at P or the torque about O when a force $\mathbf{F} = 4\mathbf{i} - 3\mathbf{j}$ is applied at P?

44. A pump handle has a pivot at $(0, 0, 0)$ and extends to $P(5, 0, -5)$. A force $\mathbf{F} = \langle 1, 0, -10 \rangle$ is applied at P. Find the magnitude and direction of the torque about the pivot.

45–48. Force on a moving charge *Answer the following questions about force on a moving charge.*

45. A particle with a positive unit charge ($q = 1$) enters a constant magnetic field $\mathbf{B} = \mathbf{i} + \mathbf{j}$ with a velocity $\mathbf{v} = 20\mathbf{k}$. Find the magnitude and direction of the force on the particle. Make a sketch of the magnetic field, the velocity, and the force.

46. A particle with a unit negative charge ($q = -1$) enters a constant magnetic field $\mathbf{B} = 5\mathbf{k}$ with a velocity $\mathbf{v} = \mathbf{i} + 2\mathbf{j}$. Find the magnitude and direction of the force on the particle. Make a sketch of the magnetic field, the velocity, and the force.

47. An electron ($q = -1.6 \times 10^{-19}\,\text{C}$) enters a constant 2-T magnetic field at an angle of $45°$ to the field with a speed of $2 \times 10^5\,\text{m/s}$. Find the magnitude of the force on the electron.

48. A proton ($q = 1.6 \times 10^{-19}\,\text{C}$) with velocity $2 \times 10^6\,\mathbf{j}\,\text{m/s}$ experiences a force in newtons of $\mathbf{F} = 5 \times 10^{-12}\,\mathbf{k}$ as it passes through the origin. Find the magnitude and direction of the magnetic field at that instant.

Further Explorations

49. Explain why or why not Determine whether the following statements are true and give an explanation or counterexample.

   a. The cross product of two nonzero vectors is a nonzero vector.

   b. $|\mathbf{u} \times \mathbf{v}|$ is less than both $|\mathbf{u}|$ and $|\mathbf{v}|$.

   c. If $\mathbf{u}$ points east and $\mathbf{v}$ points south, then $\mathbf{u} \times \mathbf{v}$ points west.

   d. If $\mathbf{u} \times \mathbf{v} = \mathbf{0}$ and $\mathbf{u} \cdot \mathbf{v} = 0$, then either $\mathbf{u} = \mathbf{0}$ or $\mathbf{v} = \mathbf{0}$.

   e. Law of Cancellation? If $\mathbf{u} \times \mathbf{v} = \mathbf{u} \times \mathbf{w}$, then $\mathbf{v} = \mathbf{w}$.

50–51. Collinear points *Use cross products to determine whether the points A, B, and C are collinear.*

50. $A(3, 2, 1)$, $B(5, 4, 7)$, and $C(9, 8, 19)$

51. $A(-3, -2, 1)$, $B(1, 4, 7)$, and $C(4, 10, 14)$

52. Finding an unknown Find the value of a such that $\langle a, a, 2 \rangle \times \langle 1, a, 3 \rangle = \langle 2, -4, 2 \rangle$.

53. Parallel vectors Evaluate $\langle a, b, a \rangle \times \langle b, a, b \rangle$. For what nonzero values of a and b are the vectors $\langle a, b, a \rangle$ and $\langle b, a, b \rangle$ parallel?

54–57. Areas of triangles *Find the area of the following triangles T.*

54. The sides of T are $\mathbf{u} = \langle 0, 6, 0 \rangle$, $\mathbf{v} = \langle 4, 4, 4 \rangle$, and $\mathbf{u} - \mathbf{v}$.

55. The sides of T are $\mathbf{u} = \langle 3, 3, 3 \rangle$, $\mathbf{v} = \langle 6, 0, 6 \rangle$, and $\mathbf{u} - \mathbf{v}$.

56. The vertices of T are $O(0, 0, 0)$, $P(2, 4, 6)$, and $Q(3, 5, 7)$.

57. The vertices of T are $O(0, 0, 0)$, $P(1, 2, 3)$, and $Q(6, 5, 4)$.

58. A unit cross product Under what conditions is $\mathbf{u} \times \mathbf{v}$ a unit vector?

59. Vector equation Find all vectors $\mathbf{u}$ that satisfy the equation

$$\langle 1, 1, 1 \rangle \times \mathbf{u} = \langle -1, -1, 2 \rangle.$$

60. Vector equation Find all vectors $\mathbf{u}$ that satisfy the equation

$$\langle 1, 1, 1 \rangle \times \mathbf{u} = \langle 0, 0, 1 \rangle.$$

61. Area of a triangle Find the area of the triangle with vertices on the coordinate axes at the points $(a, 0, 0)$, $(0, b, 0)$, and $(0, 0, c)$, in terms of a, b, and c.

62–64. Scalar triple product *Another operation with vectors is the scalar triple product, defined to be $\mathbf{u} \cdot (\mathbf{v} \times \mathbf{w})$, for vectors $\mathbf{u}$, $\mathbf{v}$, and $\mathbf{w}$ in $\mathbb{R}^3$.*

62. Express $\mathbf{u}$, $\mathbf{v}$, and $\mathbf{w}$ in terms of their components and show that $\mathbf{u} \cdot (\mathbf{v} \times \mathbf{w})$ equals the determinant

$$\begin{vmatrix} u_1 & u_2 & u_3 \\ v_1 & v_2 & v_3 \\ w_1 & w_2 & w_3 \end{vmatrix}.$$

63. a. Consider the *parallelepiped* (slanted box) determined by the position vectors $\mathbf{u}$, $\mathbf{v}$, and $\mathbf{w}$ (see figure). Show that the volume of the parallelepiped is the absolute value of the scalar triple product $|\mathbf{u} \cdot (\mathbf{v} \times \mathbf{w})|$.

   b. Use the scalar triple product to find the volume of the parallelepiped determined by the vectors $\mathbf{u} = \langle 3, 1, 0 \rangle$, $\mathbf{v} = \langle 2, 4, 1 \rangle$, and $\mathbf{w} = \langle 1, 1, 5 \rangle$.

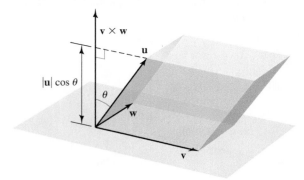

64. Prove that $\mathbf{u} \cdot (\mathbf{v} \times \mathbf{w}) = (\mathbf{u} \times \mathbf{v}) \cdot \mathbf{w}$.

Applications

65. Bicycle brakes A set of caliper brakes exerts a force on the rim of a bicycle wheel that creates a frictional force $\mathbf{F}$ of 40 N perpendicular to the radius of the wheel (see figure). Assuming the wheel has a radius of 66 cm, find the magnitude and direction of the torque about the axle of the wheel.

66. Arm torque A horizontally outstretched arm supports a weight of 20 lb in a hand (see figure). If the distance from the shoulder to the elbow is 1 ft and the distance from the elbow to the hand is 1 ft, find the magnitude and describe the direction of the torque about (a) the shoulder and (b) the elbow. (The units of torque in this case are ft-lb.)

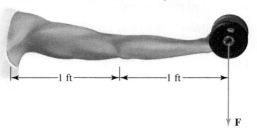

67. Electron speed An electron with a mass of 9.1×10^{-31} kg and a charge of -1.6×10^{-19} C travels in a circular path with no loss of energy in a magnetic field of 0.05 T that is orthogonal to the path of the electron (see figure). If the radius of the path is 0.002 m, what is the speed of the electron?

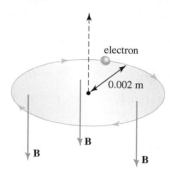

Additional Exercises

68. Three proofs Prove that $\mathbf{u} \times \mathbf{u} = \mathbf{0}$ in three ways.

   a. Use the definition of the cross product.
   b. Use the determinant formulation of the cross product.
   c. Use the property that $\mathbf{u} \times \mathbf{v} = -(\mathbf{v} \times \mathbf{u})$.

69. Associative property Prove in two ways that for scalars a and b, $(a\mathbf{u}) \times (b\mathbf{v}) = ab(\mathbf{u} \times \mathbf{v})$. Use the definition of the cross product and the determinant formula.

70–72. Possible identities *Determine whether the following statements are true using a proof or counterexample. Assume that* $\mathbf{u}$, $\mathbf{v}$, *and* $\mathbf{w}$ *are nonzero vectors in* $\mathbb{R}^3$.

70. $\mathbf{u} \times (\mathbf{u} \times \mathbf{v}) = \mathbf{0}$

71. $(\mathbf{u} - \mathbf{v}) \times (\mathbf{u} + \mathbf{v}) = 2\mathbf{u} \times \mathbf{v}$

72. $\mathbf{u} \cdot (\mathbf{v} \times \mathbf{w}) = \mathbf{w} \cdot (\mathbf{u} \times \mathbf{v})$

73–74. Identities *Prove the following identities. Assume that* $\mathbf{u}$, $\mathbf{v}$, $\mathbf{w}$, *and* $\mathbf{x}$ *are nonzero vectors in* $\mathbb{R}^3$.

73. $\mathbf{u} \times (\mathbf{v} \times \mathbf{w}) = (\mathbf{u} \cdot \mathbf{w})\mathbf{v} - (\mathbf{u} \cdot \mathbf{v})\mathbf{w}$ Vector triple product

74. $(\mathbf{u} \times \mathbf{v}) \cdot (\mathbf{w} \times \mathbf{x}) = (\mathbf{u} \cdot \mathbf{w})(\mathbf{v} \cdot \mathbf{x}) - (\mathbf{u} \cdot \mathbf{x})(\mathbf{v} \cdot \mathbf{w})$

75. Cross product equations Suppose $\mathbf{u}$ and $\mathbf{v}$ are known nonzero vectors in $\mathbb{R}^3$.

   a. Prove that the equation $\mathbf{u} \times \mathbf{z} = \mathbf{v}$ has a nonzero solution $\mathbf{z}$ if and only if $\mathbf{u} \cdot \mathbf{v} = 0$. (*Hint:* Take the dot product of both sides with $\mathbf{v}$.)
   b. Explain this result geometrically.

QUICK CHECK ANSWERS

1. $\mathbf{u} \times \mathbf{v}$ points in the positive z-direction; $\mathbf{v} \times \mathbf{u}$ points in the negative z-direction.   **2.** The vector $2\mathbf{u}$ points in the same direction as $\mathbf{u}$ and the vector $3\mathbf{v}$ points in the same direction as $\mathbf{v}$. So the right-hand rule gives the same direction for $2\mathbf{u} \times 3\mathbf{v}$ as it does for $\mathbf{u} \times \mathbf{v}$.   **3.** $\mathbf{u} \cdot (\mathbf{u} \times \mathbf{v}) = \langle -1, 0, 6 \rangle \cdot \langle 30, 9, 5 \rangle = -30 + 0 + 30 = 0$. A similar calculation shows that $\mathbf{v} \cdot (\mathbf{u} \times \mathbf{v}) = 0$. ◄

11.5 Lines and Curves in Space

Imagine a projectile moving along a path in three-dimensional space; it could be an electron or a comet, a soccer ball or a rocket. If you take a snapshot of the object, its position is described by a static position vector $\mathbf{r} = \langle x, y, z \rangle$. However, if you want to describe the full trajectory of the object as it unfolds in time, you must represent the object's position with a *vector-valued function* such as $\mathbf{r}(t) = \langle x(t), y(t), z(t) \rangle$ whose components change in time (Figure 11.66). The goal of this section is to describe continuous motion by using vector-valued functions.

Vector-Valued Functions

A function of the form $\mathbf{r}(t) = \langle x(t), y(t), z(t) \rangle$ may be viewed in two ways.

- It is a set of three parametric equations that describe a curve in space.

- It is also a **vector-valued function**, which means that the three dependent variables (x, y, and z) are the components of $\mathbf{r}$, and each component varies with respect to a single independent variable t (that often represents time).

Here is the connection between these perspectives: As t varies, a point $(x(t), y(t), z(t))$ on a parametric curve is also the head of the position vector $\mathbf{r}(t) = \langle x(t), y(t), z(t) \rangle$. In other words, a vector-valued function is a set of parametric equations written in vector form. It is useful to keep both of these interpretations in mind as you work with vector-valued functions.

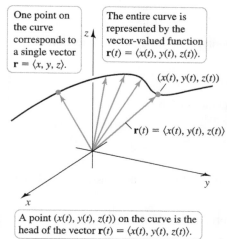

Figure 11.66

Lines in Space

Two distinct points in $\mathbb{R}^3$ determine a unique line. Alternatively, one point and a direction also determine a unique line. We use both of these properties to derive parametric equations for lines in space. The result is an example of a vector-valued function in $\mathbb{R}^3$.

Let ℓ be the line passing through the point $P_0(x_0, y_0, z_0)$ parallel to the nonzero vector $\mathbf{v} = \langle a, b, c \rangle$, where P_0 and $\mathbf{v}$ are given. The fixed point P_0 is associated with the position vector $\mathbf{r}_0 = \overrightarrow{OP_0} = \langle x_0, y_0, z_0 \rangle$. We let $P(x, y, z)$ be a variable point on ℓ and let $\mathbf{r} = \overrightarrow{OP} = \langle x, y, z \rangle$ be the position vector associated with P (Figure 11.67). Because ℓ is parallel to $\mathbf{v}$, the vector $\overrightarrow{P_0P}$ is also parallel to $\mathbf{v}$; therefore, $\overrightarrow{P_0P} = t\mathbf{v}$, where t is a real number. By vector addition, we see that $\overrightarrow{OP} = \overrightarrow{OP_0} + \overrightarrow{P_0P}$, or $\overrightarrow{OP} = \overrightarrow{OP_0} + t\mathbf{v}$. It follows that

$$\underbrace{\langle x, y, z \rangle}_{\mathbf{r} = \overrightarrow{OP}} = \underbrace{\langle x_0, y_0, z_0 \rangle}_{\mathbf{r}_0 = \overrightarrow{OP_0}} + t\underbrace{\langle a, b, c \rangle}_{\mathbf{v}} \quad \text{or} \quad \mathbf{r} = \mathbf{r}_0 + t\mathbf{v}.$$

Equating components, the line is described by the parametric equations

$$x = x_0 + at, \qquad y = y_0 + bt, \qquad z = z_0 + ct, \quad \text{for } -\infty < t < \infty.$$

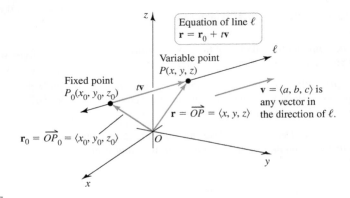

Figure 11.67

QUICK CHECK 1 Describe the line $\mathbf{r}(t) = t\mathbf{k}$, for $-\infty < t < \infty$. Describe the line $\mathbf{r}(t) = t(\mathbf{i} + \mathbf{j} + 0\mathbf{k})$, for $-\infty < t < \infty$. ◀

➤ There are infinitely many equations for the same line. The direction vector is determined only up to a scalar multiple.

The parameter t determines the location of points on the line, where $t = 0$ corresponds to P_0. If t increases from 0, we move along the line in the direction of $\mathbf{v}$, and if t decreases from 0, we move along the line in the direction of $-\mathbf{v}$. As t varies over all real numbers ($-\infty < t < \infty$), the vector $\mathbf{r}$ sweeps out the entire line ℓ. If, instead of knowing the direction $\mathbf{v}$ of the line, we are given two points $P_0(x_0, y_0, z_0)$ and $P_1(x_1, y_1, z_1)$, then the direction of the line is $\mathbf{v} = \overrightarrow{P_0P_1} = \langle x_1 - x_0, y_1 - y_0, z_1 - z_0 \rangle$.

Equation of a Line

An **equation of the line** passing through the point $P_0(x_0, y_0, z_0)$ in the direction of the vector $\mathbf{v} = \langle a, b, c \rangle$ is $\mathbf{r} = \mathbf{r}_0 + t\mathbf{v}$, or

$$\langle x, y, z \rangle = \langle x_0, y_0, z_0 \rangle + t\langle a, b, c \rangle, \quad \text{for } -\infty < t < \infty.$$

Equivalently, the corresponding parametric equations of the line are

$$x = x_0 + at, \quad y = y_0 + bt, \quad z = z_0 + ct, \quad \text{for } -\infty < t < \infty.$$

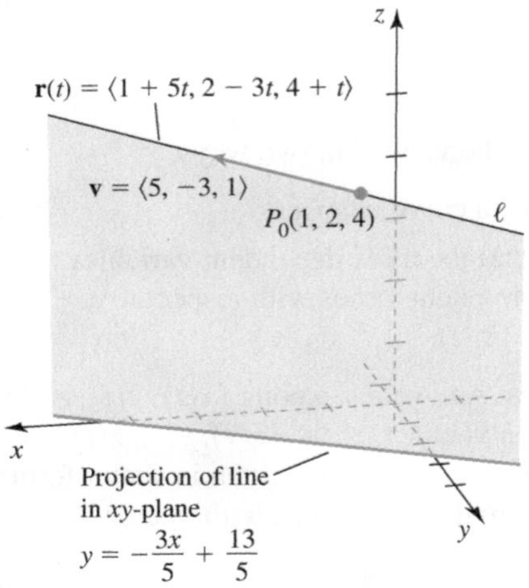

EXAMPLE 1   Equations of lines Find an equation of the line ℓ that passes through the point $P_0(1, 2, 4)$ in the direction of $\mathbf{v} = \langle 5, -3, 1 \rangle$.

SOLUTION We are given $\mathbf{r}_0 = \langle 1, 2, 4 \rangle$. Therefore, an equation of the line is

$$\mathbf{r}(t) = \mathbf{r}_0 + t\mathbf{v} = \langle 1, 2, 4 \rangle + t\langle 5, -3, 1 \rangle = \langle 1 + 5t, 2 - 3t, 4 + t \rangle,$$

for $-\infty < t < \infty$ (Figure 11.68). The corresponding parametric equations are

$$x = 1 + 5t, \qquad y = 2 - 3t, \qquad z = 4 + t, \quad \text{for } -\infty < t < \infty.$$

$\mathbf{r}(t) = \langle 1 + 5t, 2 - 3t, 4 + t \rangle$

$\mathbf{v} = \langle 5, -3, 1 \rangle$

$P_0(1, 2, 4)$

Projection of line in xy-plane

$y = -\dfrac{3x}{5} + \dfrac{13}{5}$

Figure 11.68

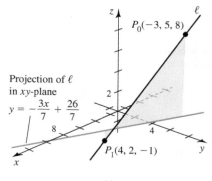

Projection of ℓ
in xy-plane
$y = -\dfrac{3x}{7} + \dfrac{26}{7}$

$P_0(-3, 5, 8)$

$P_1(4, 2, -1)$

(a)

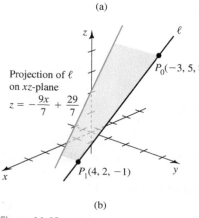

Projection of ℓ
on xz-plane
$z = -\dfrac{9x}{7} + \dfrac{29}{7}$

$P_0(-3, 5, 8)$

$P_1(4, 2, -1)$

(b)

Figure 11.69

> A related problem: To find the point at which the line in Example 2 intersects the xy-plane, we set $z = 0$, solve for t, and find the corresponding x- and y-coordinates: $z = 0$ implies $t = \frac{8}{9}$, which implies $x = \frac{29}{9}$ and $y = \frac{7}{3}$.

The line is easier to visualize if it is plotted together with its projection in the xy-plane. Setting $z = 0$ (the equation of the xy-plane), parametric equations of the projection line are $x = 1 + 5t, y = 2 - 3t$, and $z = 0$. Eliminating t from these equations, an equation of the projection line is $y = -\frac{3}{5}x + \frac{13}{5}$ (Figure 11.68).

Related Exercises 9–24 ◄

EXAMPLE 2 Equations of lines Let ℓ be the line that passes through the points $P_0(-3, 5, 8)$ and $P_1(4, 2, -1)$.

a. Find an equation of ℓ.

b. Find equations of the projections of ℓ on the xy- and xz-planes. Then graph those projection lines.

SOLUTION

a. The direction of the line is

$$\mathbf{v} = \overrightarrow{P_0P_1} = \langle 4 - (-3), 2 - 5, -1 - 8 \rangle = \langle 7, -3, -9 \rangle.$$

Therefore, with $\mathbf{r}_0 = \langle -3, 5, 8 \rangle$, an equation of ℓ is

$$\begin{aligned} \mathbf{r}(t) &= \mathbf{r}_0 + t\mathbf{v} \\ &= \langle -3, 5, 8 \rangle + t\langle 7, -3, -9 \rangle \\ &= \langle -3 + 7t, 5 - 3t, 8 - 9t \rangle. \end{aligned}$$

b. Setting the z-component of the equation of ℓ equal to zero, parametric equations of the projection of ℓ on the xy-plane are $x = -3 + 7t, y = 5 - 3t$. Eliminating t from these equations gives the equation $y = -\frac{3}{7}x + \frac{26}{7}$ (Figure 11.69a) in the xy-plane. Parametric equations of the projection of ℓ on the xz-plane (setting $y = 0$) are $x = -3 + 7t, z = 8 - 9t$. Eliminating t gives the equation $z = -\frac{9}{7}x + \frac{29}{7}$ (Figure 11.69b) in the xz-plane.

Related Exercises 9–24 ◄

QUICK CHECK 2 In the equation of the line

$$\mathbf{r}(t) = \langle x_0, y_0, z_0 \rangle + t\langle x_1 - x_0, y_1 - y_0, z_1 - z_0 \rangle,$$

what value of t corresponds to the point $P_0(x_0, y_0, z_0)$? What value of t corresponds to the point $P_1(x_1, y_1, z_1)$? ◄

EXAMPLE 3 Equation of a line segment Find an equation of the line segment that extends from $P_0(3, -1, 4)$ to $P_1(0, 5, 2)$.

SOLUTION The same ideas used to find an equation of an entire line work here. We just restrict the values of the parameter t, so that only the given line segment is generated. The direction of the line segment is

$$\mathbf{v} = \overrightarrow{P_0P_1} = \langle 0 - 3, 5 - (-1), 2 - 4 \rangle = \langle -3, 6, -2 \rangle.$$

Letting $\mathbf{r}_0 = \langle 3, -1, 4 \rangle$, an equation of the line through P_0 and P_1 is

$$\mathbf{r}(t) = \mathbf{r}_0 + t\mathbf{v} = \langle 3 - 3t, -1 + 6t, 4 - 2t \rangle.$$

Notice that if $t = 0$, then $\mathbf{r}(0) = \langle 3, -1, 4 \rangle$, which is a vector with endpoint P_0. If $t = 1$, then $\mathbf{r}(1) = \langle 0, 5, 2 \rangle$, which is a vector with endpoint P_1. Letting t vary from 0 to 1 generates the line segment from P_0 to P_1 (Figure 11.70). Therefore, an equation of the line segment is

$$\mathbf{r}(t) = \langle 3 - 3t, -1 + 6t, 4 - 2t \rangle, \quad \text{for } 0 \leq t \leq 1.$$

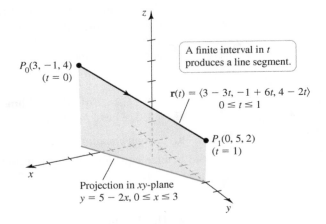

Figure 11.70

Related Exercises 25–28 ◀

Curves in Space

We now explore general vector-valued functions of the form

$$\mathbf{r}(t) = \langle f(t), g(t), h(t) \rangle = f(t)\mathbf{i} + g(t)\mathbf{j} + h(t)\mathbf{k},$$

where f, g, and h are defined on an interval $a \leq t \leq b$. The **domain** of $\mathbf{r}$ is the largest set of values of t on which all of f, g, and h are defined.

> ➤ When f, g, and h are linear functions of t, the resulting curve is a line or line segment.

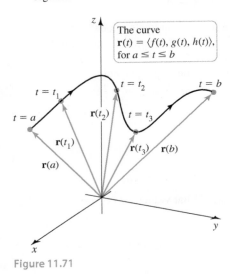

Figure 11.71

Figure 11.71 illustrates how a parameterized curve is generated by such a function. As the parameter t varies over the interval $a \leq t \leq b$, each value of t produces a position vector that corresponds to a point on the curve, starting at the initial vector $\mathbf{r}(a)$ and ending at the terminal vector $\mathbf{r}(b)$. The resulting parameterized curve can either have finite length or extend indefinitely. The curve may also cross itself or close and retrace itself.

Orientation of Curves   If a smooth curve C is viewed only as a set of points, then at any point of C, it is possible to draw tangent vectors in two directions (Figure 11.72a). On the other hand, a parameterized curve described by the function $\mathbf{r}(t)$, where $a \leq t \leq b$, has a natural direction, or **orientation**. The *positive* orientation is the direction in which the curve is generated as the parameter increases from a to b. For example, the positive orientation of the circle $\mathbf{r}(t) = \langle \cos t, \sin t \rangle$, for $0 \leq t \leq 2\pi$, is counterclockwise (Figure 11.72b). The orientation of a parameterized curve and its tangent vectors are consistent: The positive orientation of the curve is the direction in which the tangent vectors point along the curve. A precise definition of the tangent vector is given in Section 11.6.

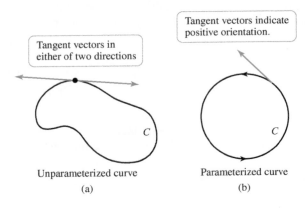

Figure 11.72

EXAMPLE 4   **A helix** Graph the curve described by the equation

$$\mathbf{r}(t) = 4 \cos t\,\mathbf{i} + \sin t\,\mathbf{j} + \tfrac{t}{2\pi}\,\mathbf{k},$$

where (a) $0 \le t \le 2\pi$ and (b) $-\infty < t < \infty$.

SOLUTION

a. We begin by setting $z = 0$ to determine the projection of the curve in the xy-plane. The resulting function $\mathbf{r}(t) = 4 \cos t\,\mathbf{i} + \sin t\,\mathbf{j}$ implies that $x = 4 \cos t$ and $y = \sin t$; these equations describe an ellipse in the xy-plane whose positive direction is counterclockwise (Figure 11.73a). Because $z = \tfrac{t}{2\pi}$, the value of z increases from 0 to 1 as t increases from 0 to 2π. Therefore, the curve rises out of the xy-plane to create a helix (or coil). Over the interval $[0, 2\pi]$, the helix begins at $(4, 0, 0)$, circles the z-axis once, and ends at $(4, 0, 1)$ (Figure 11.73b).

b. Letting the parameter vary over the interval $-\infty < t < \infty$ generates a helix that winds around the z-axis endlessly in both directions (Figure 11.73c). The positive orientation is in the upward direction (increasing z-direction).

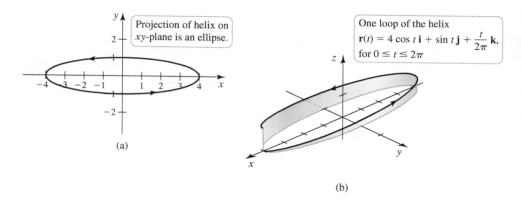

Projection of helix on xy-plane is an ellipse.

(a)

One loop of the helix
$\mathbf{r}(t) = 4 \cos t\,\mathbf{i} + \sin t\,\mathbf{j} + \dfrac{t}{2\pi}\,\mathbf{k}$,
for $0 \le t \le 2\pi$

(b)

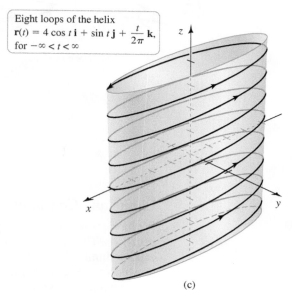

Eight loops of the helix
$\mathbf{r}(t) = 4 \cos t\,\mathbf{i} + \sin t\,\mathbf{j} + \dfrac{t}{2\pi}\,\mathbf{k}$,
for $-\infty < t < \infty$

(c)

Figure 11.73

▶ Recall that the functions $\sin at$ and $\cos at$ oscillate a times over the interval $[0, 2\pi]$. Therefore, their period is $2\pi/a$.

Related Exercises 29–36 ◀

EXAMPLE 5   **Roller coaster curve** Graph the curve

$$\mathbf{r}(t) = \cos t\,\mathbf{i} + \sin t\,\mathbf{j} + 0.4 \sin 2t\,\mathbf{k}, \quad \text{for } 0 \le t \le 2\pi.$$

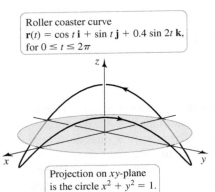

Roller coaster curve
$\mathbf{r}(t) = \cos t\,\mathbf{i} + \sin t\,\mathbf{j} + 0.4 \sin 2t\,\mathbf{k}$,
for $0 \le t \le 2\pi$

Projection on xy-plane
is the circle $x^2 + y^2 = 1$.

Figure 11.74

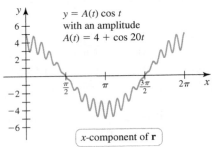

$y = A(t) \cos t$
with an amplitude
$A(t) = 4 + \cos 20t$

x-component of $\mathbf{r}$

Figure 11.75

SOLUTION Without the z-component, the resulting function $\mathbf{r}(t) = \cos t\,\mathbf{i} + \sin t\,\mathbf{j}$ describes a circle of radius 1 in the xy-plane. The z-component of the function varies between -0.4 and 0.4 with a period of π units. Therefore, on the interval $[0, 2\pi]$, the z-coordinates of points on the curve oscillate twice between -0.4 and 0.4, while the x- and y-coordinates describe a circle. The result is a curve that circles the z-axis once in the counterclockwise direction with two peaks and two valleys (Figure 11.74).

Related Exercises 37–40 ◄

EXAMPLE 6   Slinky curve   Graph the curve

$$\mathbf{r}(t) = (4 + \cos 20t) \cos t\,\mathbf{i} + (4 + \cos 20t) \sin t\,\mathbf{j} + 0.4 \sin 20t\,\mathbf{k},$$

for $0 \le t \le 2\pi$.

SOLUTION The factor $A(t) = 4 + \cos 20t$ that appears in the x- and y-components is a varying amplitude for $\cos t\,\mathbf{i}$ and $\sin t\,\mathbf{j}$. Its effect is seen in the graph of the x-component $A(t) \cos t$ (Figure 11.75). For $0 \le t \le 2\pi$, the curve consists of one period of $4 \cos t$ with 20 small oscillations superimposed on it. As a result, the x-component of $\mathbf{r}$ varies from -5 to 5 with 20 small oscillations along the way. A similar behavior is seen in the y-component of $\mathbf{r}$. Finally, the z-component of $\mathbf{r}$, which is $0.4 \sin 20t$, oscillates between -0.4 and 0.4 twenty times over $[0, 2\pi]$. Combining these effects, we discover a coil-shaped curve that circles the z-axis in the counterclockwise direction and closes on itself. Figure 11.76 shows two views, one looking along the xy-plane and the other from overhead on the z-axis.

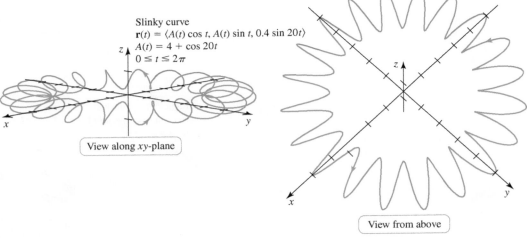

Slinky curve
$\mathbf{r}(t) = \langle A(t) \cos t, A(t) \sin t, 0.4 \sin 20t \rangle$
$A(t) = 4 + \cos 20t$
$0 \le t \le 2\pi$

View along xy-plane

View from above

Figure 11.76

Related Exercises 37–40 ◄

Limits and Continuity for Vector-Valued Functions

We have presented vector-valued functions and established their relationship to parametric equations. The next step is to investigate the calculus of vector-valued functions. The concepts of limits, derivatives, and integrals of vector-valued functions are direct extensions of what you have already learned.

The limit of a vector-valued function $\mathbf{r}(t) = f(t)\mathbf{i} + g(t)\mathbf{j} + h(t)\mathbf{k}$ is defined much as it is for scalar-valued functions. If there is a vector $\mathbf{L}$ such that the scalar function $|\mathbf{r}(t) - \mathbf{L}|$ can be made arbitrarily small by taking t sufficiently close to a, then we write $\lim_{t \to a} \mathbf{r}(t) = \mathbf{L}$ and say the limit of $\mathbf{r}$ as t approaches a is $\mathbf{L}$.

DEFINITION   Limit of a Vector-Valued Function

A vector-valued function $\mathbf{r}$ approaches the limit $\mathbf{L}$ as t approaches a, written $\lim_{t \to a} \mathbf{r}(t) = \mathbf{L}$, provided $\lim_{t \to a} |\mathbf{r}(t) - \mathbf{L}| = 0$.

Notice that while $\mathbf{r}$ is vector valued, $|\mathbf{r}(t) - \mathbf{L}|$ is a function of the single variable t, to which our familiar limit theorems apply. Therefore, this definition and a short calculation (Exercise 78) lead to a straightforward method for computing limits of the vector-valued function $\mathbf{r} = \langle f, g, h \rangle$. Suppose that

$$\lim_{t \to a} f(t) = L_1, \qquad \lim_{t \to a} g(t) = L_2, \qquad \text{and} \qquad \lim_{t \to a} h(t) = L_3.$$

Then

$$\lim_{t \to a} \mathbf{r}(t) = \left\langle \lim_{t \to a} f(t), \lim_{t \to a} g(t), \lim_{t \to a} h(t) \right\rangle = \langle L_1, L_2, L_3 \rangle.$$

In other words, the limit of $\mathbf{r}$ is determined by computing the limits of its components.

The limits laws in Chapter 2 have analogs for vector-valued functions. For example, if $\lim_{t \to a} \mathbf{r}(t)$ and $\lim_{t \to a} \mathbf{s}(t)$ exist and c is a scalar, then

$$\lim_{t \to a} (\mathbf{r}(t) + \mathbf{s}(t)) = \lim_{t \to a} \mathbf{r}(t) + \lim_{t \to a} \mathbf{s}(t) \quad \text{and} \quad \lim_{t \to a} c\mathbf{r}(t) = c\lim_{t \to a} \mathbf{r}(t).$$

The idea of continuity also extends directly to vector-valued functions. A function $\mathbf{r}(t) = f(t)\mathbf{i} + g(t)\mathbf{j} + h(t)\mathbf{k}$ is continuous at a provided $\lim_{t \to a} \mathbf{r}(t) = \mathbf{r}(a)$. Specifically, if the component functions f, g, and h are continuous at a, then $\mathbf{r}$ is also continuous at a and vice versa. The function $\mathbf{r}$ is continuous on an interval I if it is continuous for all t in I.

➤ Continuity is often taken as part of the definition of a parameterized curve.

Continuity has the same intuitive meaning in this setting as it does for scalar-valued functions. If $\mathbf{r}$ is continuous on an interval, the curve it describes has no breaks or gaps, which is an important property when $\mathbf{r}$ describes the trajectory of an object.

EXAMPLE 7 **Limits and continuity** Consider the function

$$\mathbf{r}(t) = \cos \pi t\, \mathbf{i} + \sin \pi t\, \mathbf{j} + e^{-t}\mathbf{k}, \quad \text{for } t \geq 0.$$

a. Evaluate $\lim_{t \to 2} \mathbf{r}(t)$.

b. Evaluate $\lim_{t \to \infty} \mathbf{r}(t)$.

c. At what points is $\mathbf{r}$ continuous?

SOLUTION

a. We evaluate the limit of each component of $\mathbf{r}$:

$$\lim_{t \to 2} \mathbf{r}(t) = \lim_{t \to 2} (\underbrace{\cos \pi t\, \mathbf{i}}_{\to 1} + \underbrace{\sin \pi t\, \mathbf{j}}_{\to 0} + \underbrace{e^{-t}\mathbf{k}}_{\to e^{-2}}) = \mathbf{i} + e^{-2}\mathbf{k}.$$

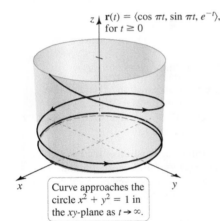

$\mathbf{r}(t) = \langle \cos \pi t, \sin \pi t, e^{-t} \rangle$, for $t \geq 0$

Curve approaches the circle $x^2 + y^2 = 1$ in the xy-plane as $t \to \infty$.

Figure 11.77

b. Note that although $\lim_{t \to \infty} e^{-t} = 0$, $\lim_{t \to \infty} \cos t$ and $\lim_{t \to \infty} \sin t$ do not exist. Therefore, $\lim_{t \to \infty} \mathbf{r}(t)$ does not exist. As shown in Figure 11.77, the curve is a coil that approaches the unit circle in the xy-plane.

c. Because the components of $\mathbf{r}$ are continuous for all t, $\mathbf{r}$ is also continuous for all t.

Related Exercises 41–46 ◄

SECTION 11.5 EXERCISES

Review Questions

1. How many independent variables does the function $\mathbf{r}(t) = \langle f(t), g(t), h(t) \rangle$ have?

2. How many dependent scalar variables does the function $\mathbf{r}(t) = \langle f(t), g(t), h(t) \rangle$ have?

3. Why is $\mathbf{r}(t) = \langle f(t), g(t), h(t) \rangle$ called a vector-valued function?

4. Explain how to find a vector in the direction of the line segment from $P_0(x_0, y_0, z_0)$ to $P_1(x_1, y_1, z_1)$.

5. What is an equation of the line through the points $P_0(x_0, y_0, z_0)$ and $P_1(x_1, y_1, z_1)$?

6. In what plane does the curve $\mathbf{r}(t) = t\mathbf{i} + t^2\mathbf{k}$ lie?

7. How do you evaluate $\lim_{t \to a} \mathbf{r}(t)$, where $\mathbf{r}(t) = \langle f(t), g(t), h(t) \rangle$?

8. How do you determine whether $\mathbf{r}(t) = f(t)\mathbf{i} + g(t)\mathbf{j} + h(t)\mathbf{k}$ is continuous at $t = a$?

Basic Skills

9–24. Equations of lines *Find equations of the following lines.*

9. The line through $(0, 0, 1)$ in the direction of the vector $\mathbf{v} = \langle 4, 7, 0 \rangle$

10. The line through $(-3, 2, -1)$ in the direction of the vector
$\mathbf{v} = \langle 1, -2, 0 \rangle$

11. The line through $(0, 0, 1)$ parallel to the y-axis

12. The line through $(0, 0, 1)$ parallel to the x-axis

13. The line through $(0, 0, 0)$ and $(1, 2, 3)$

14. The line through $(1, 0, 1)$ and $(3, -3, 3)$

15. The line through $(-3, 4, 6)$ and $(5, -1, 0)$

16. The line through $(0, 4, 8)$ and $(10, -5, -4)$

17. The line through $(0, 0, 0)$ that is parallel to the line
$\mathbf{r}(t) = \langle 3 - 2t, 5 + 8t, 7 - 4t \rangle$

18. The line through $(1, -3, 4)$ that is parallel to the line
$\mathbf{r}(t) = \langle 3 + 4t, 5 - t, 7 \rangle$

19. The line through $(0, 0, 0)$ that is perpendicular to both
$\mathbf{u} = \langle 1, 0, 2 \rangle$ and $\mathbf{v} = \langle 0, 1, 1 \rangle$

20. The line through $(-3, 4, 2)$ that is perpendicular to both
$\mathbf{u} = \langle 1, 1, -5 \rangle$ and $\mathbf{v} = \langle 0, 4, 0 \rangle$

21. The line through $(-2, 5, 3)$ that is perpendicular to both
$\mathbf{u} = \langle 1, 1, 2 \rangle$ and the x-axis

22. The line through $(0, 2, 1)$ that is perpendicular to both
$\mathbf{u} = \langle 4, 3, -5 \rangle$ and the z-axis

23. The line through $(1, 2, 3)$ that is perpendicular to
the lines $\mathbf{r}_1(t) = \langle 3 - 2t, 5 + 8t, 7 - 4t \rangle$ and
$\mathbf{r}_2(t) = \langle -2t, 5 + t, 7 - t \rangle$

24. The line through $(1, 0, -1)$ that is perpendicular to the lines
$\mathbf{r}_1(t) = \langle 3 + 2t, 3t, -4t \rangle$ and $\mathbf{r}_2(t) = \langle t, t, -t \rangle$

25–28. Line segments *Find an equation of the line segment joining the first point to the second point.*

25. $(0, 0, 0)$ and $(1, 2, 3)$

26. $(1, 0, 1)$ and $(0, -2, 1)$

27. $(2, 4, 8)$ and $(7, 5, 3)$

28. $(-1, -8, 4)$ and $(-9, 5, -3)$

29–36. Curves in space *Graph the curves described by the following functions, indicating the positive orientation.*

29. $\mathbf{r}(t) = \langle \cos t, 0, \sin t \rangle$ for $0 \le t \le 2\pi$

30. $\mathbf{r}(t) = \langle 0, 4 \cos t, 16 \sin t \rangle$ for $0 \le t \le 2\pi$

31. $\mathbf{r}(t) = \cos t \, \mathbf{i} + \mathbf{j} + \sin t \, \mathbf{k}$, for $0 \le t \le 2\pi$

32. $\mathbf{r}(t) = 2 \cos t \, \mathbf{i} + 2 \sin t \, \mathbf{j} + 2 \, \mathbf{k}$, for $0 \le t \le 2\pi$

▣ 33. $\mathbf{r}(t) = t \cos t \, \mathbf{i} + t \sin t \, \mathbf{j} + t \, \mathbf{k}$, for $0 \le t \le 6\pi$

▣ 34. $\mathbf{r}(t) = 4 \sin t \, \mathbf{i} + 4 \cos t \, \mathbf{j} + e^{-t/10} \, \mathbf{k}$, for $0 \le t < \infty$

▣ 35. $\mathbf{r}(t) = e^{-t/20} \sin t \, \mathbf{i} + e^{-t/20} \cos t \, \mathbf{j} + t \, \mathbf{k}$, for $0 \le t < \infty$

▣ 36. $\mathbf{r}(t) = e^{-t/10} \mathbf{i} + 3 \cos t \, \mathbf{j} + 3 \sin t \, \mathbf{k}$, for $0 \le t < \infty$

▣ 37–40. Exotic curves *Graph the curves described by the following functions. Use analysis to anticipate the shape of the curve before using a graphing utility.*

37. $\mathbf{r}(t) = 0.5 \cos 15t \, \mathbf{i} + (8 + \sin 15t) \cos t \, \mathbf{j} + (8 + \sin 15t) \sin t \, \mathbf{k}$,
for $0 \le t \le 2\pi$

38. $\mathbf{r}(t) = 2 \cos t \, \mathbf{i} + 4 \sin t \, \mathbf{j} + \cos 10t \, \mathbf{k}$, for $0 \le t \le 2\pi$

39. $\mathbf{r}(t) = \sin t \, \mathbf{i} + \sin^2 t \, \mathbf{j} + t/(5\pi) \, \mathbf{k}$, for $0 \le t \le 10\pi$

40. $\mathbf{r}(t) = \cos t \sin 3t \, \mathbf{i} + \sin t \sin 3t \, \mathbf{j} + \sqrt{t} \, \mathbf{k}$, for $0 \le t \le 9$

41–46. Limits *Evaluate the following limits.*

41. $\displaystyle\lim_{t \to \pi/2} \left(\cos 2t \, \mathbf{i} - 4 \sin t \, \mathbf{j} + \frac{2t}{\pi} \, \mathbf{k} \right)$

42. $\displaystyle\lim_{t \to \ln 2} (2e^t \mathbf{i} + 6e^{-t} \mathbf{j} - 4e^{-2t} \mathbf{k})$

43. $\displaystyle\lim_{t \to \infty} \left(e^{-t} \mathbf{i} - \frac{2t}{t + 1} \mathbf{j} + \tan^{-1} t \, \mathbf{k} \right)$

44. $\displaystyle\lim_{t \to 2} \left(\frac{t}{t^2 + 1} \mathbf{i} - 4e^{-t} \sin \pi t \, \mathbf{j} + \frac{1}{\sqrt{4t + 1}} \mathbf{k} \right)$

45. $\displaystyle\lim_{t \to 0} \left(\frac{\sin t}{t} \mathbf{i} - \frac{e^t - t - 1}{t} \mathbf{j} + \frac{\cos t + t^2/2 - 1}{t^2} \mathbf{k} \right)$

46. $\displaystyle\lim_{t \to 0} \left(\frac{\tan t}{t} \mathbf{i} - \frac{3t}{\sin t} \mathbf{j} + \sqrt{t + 1} \, \mathbf{k} \right)$

Further Explorations

47. Explain why or why not Determine whether the following statements are true and give an explanation or counterexample.

  a. The line $\mathbf{r}(t) = \langle 3, -1, 4 \rangle + t \langle 6, -2, 8 \rangle$ passes through the origin.

  b. Any two nonparallel lines in $\mathbb{R}^3$ intersect.

  c. The curve $\mathbf{r}(t) = \langle e^{-t}, \sin t, -\cos t \rangle$ approaches a circle as $t \to \infty$.

  d. If $\mathbf{r}(t) = e^{-t^2} \langle 1, 1, 1 \rangle$ then $\displaystyle\lim_{t \to \infty} \mathbf{r}(t) = \lim_{t \to -\infty} \mathbf{r}(t)$.

48. Point of intersection Determine an equation of the line that is perpendicular to the lines $\mathbf{r}(t) = \langle -2 + 3t, 2t, 3t \rangle$ and $\mathbf{R}(s) = \langle -6 + s, -8 + 2s, -12 + 3s \rangle$ and passes through the point of intersection of the lines $\mathbf{r}$ and $\mathbf{R}$.

49. Point of intersection Determine an equation of the line that is perpendicular to the lines $\mathbf{r}(t) = \langle 4t, 1 + 2t, 3t \rangle$ and $\mathbf{R}(s) = \langle -1 + s, -7 + 2s, -12 + 3s \rangle$ and passes through the point of intersection of the lines $\mathbf{r}$ and $\mathbf{R}$.

50–55. Skew lines *A pair of lines in $\mathbb{R}^3$ are said to be **skew** if they are neither parallel nor intersecting. Determine whether the following pairs of lines are parallel, intersecting, or skew. If the lines intersect, determine the point(s) of intersection.*

50. $\mathbf{r}(t) = \langle 3 + 4t, 1 - 6t, 4t \rangle$;
$\mathbf{R}(s) = \langle -2s, 5 + 3s, 4 - 2s \rangle$

51. $\mathbf{r}(t) = \langle 1 + 6t, 3 - 7t, 2 + t \rangle$;
$\mathbf{R}(s) = \langle 10 + 3s, 6 + s, 14 + 4s \rangle$

52. $\mathbf{r}(t) = \langle 4 + 5t, -2t, 1 + 3t \rangle$;
$\mathbf{R}(s) = \langle 10s, 6 + 4s, 4 + 6s \rangle$

53. $\mathbf{r}(t) = \langle 4, 6 - t, 1 + t \rangle$;
$\mathbf{R}(s) = \langle -3 - 7s, 1 + 4s, 4 - s \rangle$

54. $\mathbf{r}(t) = \langle 4 + t, -2t, 1 + 3t \rangle$;
$\mathbf{R}(s) = \langle 1 - 7s, 6 + 14s, 4 - 21s \rangle$

55. $\mathbf{r}(t) = \langle 1 + 2t, 7 - 3t, 6 + t \rangle$;
$\mathbf{R}(s) = \langle -9 + 6s, 22 - 9s, 1 + 3s \rangle$

56–59. Domains *Find the domain of the following vector-valued functions.*

56. $\mathbf{r}(t) = \dfrac{2}{t-1}\mathbf{i} + \dfrac{3}{t+2}\mathbf{j}$

57. $\mathbf{r}(t) = \sqrt{t+2}\,\mathbf{i} + \sqrt{2-t}\,\mathbf{j}$

58. $\mathbf{r}(t) = \cos 2t\,\mathbf{i} + e^{\sqrt{t}}\mathbf{j} + \dfrac{12}{t}\mathbf{k}$

59. $\mathbf{r}(t) = \sqrt{4-t^2}\,\mathbf{i} + \sqrt{t}\,\mathbf{j} - \dfrac{2}{\sqrt{1+t}}\mathbf{k}$

60–63. Line-plane intersections *Find the point (if it exists) at which the following planes and lines intersect.*

60. $x = 3$; $\mathbf{r}(t) = \langle t, t, t \rangle$

61. $z = 4$; $\mathbf{r}(t) = \langle 2t+1, -t+4, t-6 \rangle$

62. $y = -2$; $\mathbf{r}(t) = \langle 2t+1, -t+4, t-6 \rangle$

63. $z = -8$; $\mathbf{r}(t) = \langle 3t-2, t-6, -2t+4 \rangle$

64–66. Curve-plane intersections *Find the points (if they exist) at which the following planes and curves intersect.*

64. $y = 1$; $\mathbf{r}(t) = \langle 10\cos t, 2\sin t, 1 \rangle$, for $0 \le t \le 2\pi$

65. $z = 16$; $\mathbf{r}(t) = \langle t, 2t, 4+3t \rangle$, for $-\infty < t < \infty$

66. $y + x = 0$; $\mathbf{r}(t) = \langle \cos t, \sin t, t \rangle$, for $0 \le t \le 4\pi$

67. Matching functions with graphs Match functions a–f with the appropriate graphs A–F.

a. $\mathbf{r}(t) = \langle t, -t, t \rangle$
b. $\mathbf{r}(t) = \langle t^2, t, t \rangle$
c. $\mathbf{r}(t) = \langle 4\cos t, 4\sin t, 2 \rangle$
d. $\mathbf{r}(t) = \langle 2t, \sin t, \cos t \rangle$
e. $\mathbf{r}(t) = \langle \sin t, \cos t, \sin 2t \rangle$
f. $\mathbf{r}(t) = \langle \sin t, 2t, \cos t \rangle$

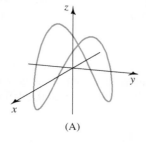
(A)

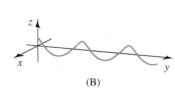
(B)

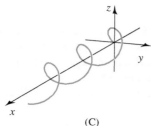
(C)

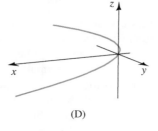
(D)

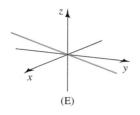
(E)

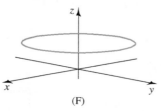
(F)

68. Intersecting lines and colliding particles Consider the lines

$$\mathbf{r}(t) = \langle 2 + 2t, 8 + t, 10 + 3t \rangle \text{ and}$$
$$\mathbf{R}(s) = \langle 6 + s, 10 - 2s, 16 - s \rangle.$$

a. Determine whether the lines intersect (have a common point) and if so, find the coordinates of that point.
b. If $\mathbf{r}$ and $\mathbf{R}$ describe the paths of two particles, do the particles collide? Assume that $t \ge 0$ and $s \ge 0$ measure time in seconds, and that motion starts at $s = t = 0$.

69. Upward path Consider the curve described by the vector function $\mathbf{r}(t) = (50e^{-t}\cos t)\mathbf{i} + (50e^{-t}\sin t)\mathbf{j} + (5 - 5e^{-t})\mathbf{k}$, for $t \ge 0$.

a. What is the initial point of the path corresponding to $\mathbf{r}(0)$?
b. What is $\lim_{t\to\infty} \mathbf{r}(t)$?
c. Sketch the curve.
d. Eliminate the parameter t to show that $z = 5 - r/10$, where $r^2 = x^2 + y^2$.

70–73. Closed plane curves *Consider the curve*
$\mathbf{r}(t) = (a\cos t + b\sin t)\mathbf{i} + (c\cos t + d\sin t)\mathbf{j} + (e\cos t + f\sin t)\mathbf{k}$,
where a, b, c, d, e, and f are real numbers. It can be shown that this curve lies in a plane.

70. Assuming the curve lies in a plane, show that it is a circle centered at the origin with radius R provided $a^2 + c^2 + e^2 = b^2 + d^2 + f^2 = R^2$ and $ab + cd + ef = 0$.

71. Graph the following curve and describe it.

$$\mathbf{r}(t) = \left(\frac{1}{\sqrt{2}}\cos t + \frac{1}{\sqrt{3}}\sin t\right)\mathbf{i} + \left(-\frac{1}{\sqrt{2}}\cos t + \frac{1}{\sqrt{3}}\sin t\right)\mathbf{j}$$
$$+ \left(\frac{1}{\sqrt{3}}\sin t\right)\mathbf{k}$$

72. Graph the following curve and describe it.

$$\mathbf{r}(t) = (2\cos t + 2\sin t)\mathbf{i} + (-\cos t + 2\sin t)\mathbf{j}$$
$$+ (\cos t - 2\sin t)\mathbf{k}$$

73. Find a general expression for a nonzero vector orthogonal to the plane containing the curve.

$$\mathbf{r}(t) = (a\cos t + b\sin t)\mathbf{i} + (c\cos t + d\sin t)\mathbf{j}$$
$$+ (e\cos t + f\sin t)\mathbf{k},$$

where $\langle a, c, e \rangle \times \langle b, d, f \rangle \ne \mathbf{0}$.

Applications

Applications of parametric curves are considered in detail in Section 11.7.

74. Golf slice A golfer launches a tee shot down a horizontal fairway; it follows a path given by $\mathbf{r}(t) = \langle at, (75 - 0.1a)t, -5t^2 + 80t \rangle$, where $t \ge 0$ measures time in seconds and $\mathbf{r}$ has units of feet. The y-axis points straight down the fairway and the z-axis points vertically upward. The parameter a is the slice factor that determines how much the shot deviates from a straight path down the fairway.

a. With no slice ($a = 0$), sketch and describe the shot. How far does the ball travel horizontally (the distance between the point the ball leaves the ground and the point where it first strikes the ground)?
b. With a slice ($a = 0.2$), sketch and describe the shot. How far does the ball travel horizontally?
c. How far does the ball travel horizontally with $a = 2.5$?

Additional Exercises

75–77. Curves on spheres

📵 **75.** Graph the curve $\mathbf{r}(t) = \left\langle \frac{1}{2} \sin 2t, \frac{1}{2}(1 - \cos 2t), \cos t \right\rangle$ and prove that it lies on the surface of a sphere centered at the origin.

76. Prove that for integers m and n, the curve

$$\mathbf{r}(t) = \langle a \sin mt \cos nt, b \sin mt \sin nt, c \cos mt \rangle$$

lies on the surface of a sphere provided $a^2 + b^2 = c^2$.

77. Find the period of the function in Exercise 76; that is, in terms of m and n, find the smallest positive real number T such that $\mathbf{r}(t + T) = \mathbf{r}(t)$ for all t.

78. Limits of vector functions Let $\mathbf{r}(t) = \langle f(t), g(t), h(t) \rangle$.

  a. Assume that $\lim\limits_{t \to a} \mathbf{r}(t) = \mathbf{L} = \langle L_1, L_2, L_3 \rangle$, which means that $\lim\limits_{t \to a} |\mathbf{r}(t) - \mathbf{L}| = 0$. Prove that

  $$\lim_{t \to a} f(t) = L_1, \quad \lim_{t \to a} g(t) = L_2, \quad \text{and} \quad \lim_{t \to a} h(t) = L_3.$$

  b. Assume that $\lim\limits_{t \to a} f(t) = L_1$, $\lim\limits_{t \to a} g(t) = L_2$, and $\lim\limits_{t \to a} h(t) = L_3$. Prove that $\lim\limits_{t \to a} \mathbf{r}(t) = \mathbf{L} = \langle L_1, L_2, L_3 \rangle$, which means that $\lim\limits_{t \to a} |\mathbf{r}(t) - \mathbf{L}| = 0$.

79. Distance between a point and a line Show that the (least) distance d between a point Q and a line $\mathbf{r} = \mathbf{r}_0 + t\mathbf{v}$ (both in $\mathbb{R}^3$)

is $d = \dfrac{|\overrightarrow{PQ} \times \mathbf{v}|}{|\mathbf{v}|}$, where P is a point on the line.

80–82. Calculating the distance from a point to a line *Use the formula in Exercise 79 to find the (least) distance between the given point Q and line $\mathbf{r}$.*

80. $Q(5, 6, 1); \mathbf{r}(t) = \langle 1 + 3t, 3 - 4t, t + 1 \rangle$

81. $Q(-5, 2, 9); \mathbf{r}(t) = \langle 5t + 7, 2 - t, 12t + 4 \rangle$

82. $Q(6, 6, 7), \mathbf{r}(t) = \langle 3t, -3t, 4 \rangle$

QUICK CHECK ANSWERS

1. The z-axis; the line $y = x$ in the xy-plane   **2.** When $t = 0$, the point on the line is P_0; when $t = 1$, the point on the line is P_1. ◄

11.6 Calculus of Vector-Valued Functions

We now turn to the topic of ultimate interest in this chapter: the calculus of vector-valued functions. Everything you learned about differentiating and integrating functions of the form $y = f(x)$ carries over to vector-valued functions $\mathbf{r}(t)$; you simply apply the rules of differentiation and integration to the individual components of $\mathbf{r}$.

The Derivative and Tangent Vector

Consider the function $\mathbf{r}(t) = f(t)\mathbf{i} + g(t)\mathbf{j} + h(t)\mathbf{k}$, where f, g, and h are differentiable functions on an interval $a < t < b$. The first task is to explain the meaning of the *derivative* of a vector-valued function and to show how to compute it. We begin with the definition of the derivative—now with a vector perspective:

$$\mathbf{r}'(t) = \lim_{\Delta t \to 0} \frac{\Delta \mathbf{r}}{\Delta t} = \lim_{\Delta t \to 0} \frac{\mathbf{r}(t + \Delta t) - \mathbf{r}(t)}{\Delta t}.$$

Before computing this limit, we look at its geometry. The function $\mathbf{r}(t) = f(t)\mathbf{i} + g(t)\mathbf{j} + h(t)\mathbf{k}$ describes a parameterized curve in space. Let P be a point on that curve associated with the position vector $\mathbf{r}(t)$ and let Q be a nearby point associated with the position vector $\mathbf{r}(t + \Delta t)$, where $\Delta t > 0$ is a small increment in t (Figure 11.78a). The difference $\Delta \mathbf{r} = \mathbf{r}(t + \Delta t) - \mathbf{r}(t)$ is the vector $\overrightarrow{PQ}$, where we assume $\Delta \mathbf{r} \neq \mathbf{0}$. Because Δt is a scalar, the direction of $\Delta \mathbf{r}/\Delta t$ is the same as the direction of $\overrightarrow{PQ}$.

As Δt approaches 0, Q approaches P and the vector $\Delta \mathbf{r}/\Delta t$ approaches a limiting vector that we denote $\mathbf{r}'(t)$ (Figure 11.78b). This new vector $\mathbf{r}'(t)$ has two important interpretations.

> ➤ An analogous argument can be given for $\Delta t < 0$, with the same result. Figure 11.78 illustrates the tangent vector $\mathbf{r}'$ for $\Delta t > 0$.

• The vector $\mathbf{r}'(t)$ points in the direction of the curve at P. For this reason, $\mathbf{r}'(t)$ is a *tangent vector* at P (provided it is not the zero vector).

• The vector $\mathbf{r}'(t)$ is the *derivative* of $\mathbf{r}$ with respect to t; it gives the rate of change of the function $\mathbf{r}(t)$ at the point P. In fact, if $\mathbf{r}(t)$ is the position function of a moving object, then $\mathbf{r}'(t)$ is the velocity vector of the object, which always points in the direction of motion, and $|\mathbf{r}'(t)|$ is the speed of the object.

> ➤ Section 11.7 is devoted to problems of motion in two and three dimensions.

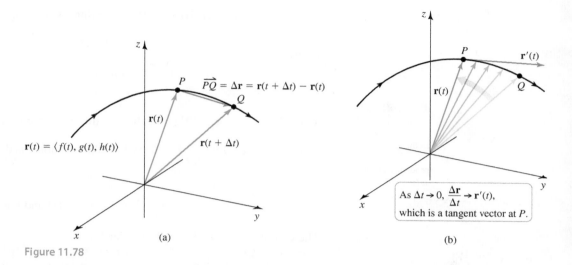

Figure 11.78

We now evaluate the limit that defines $\mathbf{r}'(t)$ by expressing $\mathbf{r}$ in terms of its components and using the properties of limits.

$$
\begin{aligned}
\mathbf{r}'(t) &= \lim_{\Delta t \to 0} \frac{\mathbf{r}(t + \Delta t) - \mathbf{r}(t)}{\Delta t} \\[2mm]
&= \lim_{\Delta t \to 0} \frac{(f(t + \Delta t)\,\mathbf{i} + g(t + \Delta t)\,\mathbf{j} + h(t + \Delta t)\,\mathbf{k}) - (f(t)\,\mathbf{i} + g(t)\,\mathbf{j} + h(t)\,\mathbf{k})}{\Delta t}
\end{aligned}
$$

Substitute components of $\mathbf{r}$.

$$
= \lim_{\Delta t \to 0} \left(\frac{f(t + \Delta t) - f(t)}{\Delta t}\,\mathbf{i} + \frac{g(t + \Delta t) - g(t)}{\Delta t}\,\mathbf{j} + \frac{h(t + \Delta t) - h(t)}{\Delta t}\,\mathbf{k} \right)
$$

Rearrange terms inside of limit.

$$
= \underbrace{\lim_{\Delta t \to 0} \frac{f(t + \Delta t) - f(t)}{\Delta t}}_{f'(t)}\,\mathbf{i} + \underbrace{\lim_{\Delta t \to 0} \frac{g(t + \Delta t) - g(t)}{\Delta t}}_{g'(t)}\,\mathbf{j} + \underbrace{\lim_{\Delta t \to 0} \frac{h(t + \Delta t) - h(t)}{\Delta t}}_{h'(t)}\,\mathbf{k}
$$

Limit of sum equals sum of limits.

Because f, g, and h are differentiable scalar-valued functions of the variable t, the three limits in the last step are identified as the derivatives of f, g, and h, respectively. Therefore, there are no surprises:

$$
\mathbf{r}'(t) = f'(t)\,\mathbf{i} + g'(t)\,\mathbf{j} + h'(t)\,\mathbf{k}.
$$

In other words, to differentiate the vector-valued function $\mathbf{r}(t)$, we simply differentiate each of its components with respect to t.

DEFINITION Derivative and Tangent Vector

Let $\mathbf{r}(t) = f(t)\,\mathbf{i} + g(t)\,\mathbf{j} + h(t)\,\mathbf{k}$, where f, g, and h are differentiable functions on (a, b). Then $\mathbf{r}$ has a **derivative** (or is **differentiable**) on (a, b) and

$$
\mathbf{r}'(t) = f'(t)\,\mathbf{i} + g'(t)\,\mathbf{j} + h'(t)\,\mathbf{k}.
$$

Provided $\mathbf{r}'(t) \neq \mathbf{0}$, $\mathbf{r}'(t)$ is a **tangent vector** at the point corresponding to $\mathbf{r}(t)$.

EXAMPLE 1 **Derivative of vector functions** Compute the derivative of the following functions.

a. $\mathbf{r}(t) = \langle t^3, 3t^2, t^3/6 \rangle$

b. $\mathbf{r}(t) = e^{-t}\mathbf{i} + 10\sqrt{t}\,\mathbf{j} + 2\cos 3t\,\mathbf{k}$

SOLUTION

a. $\mathbf{r}'(t) = \langle 3t^2, 6t, t^2/2 \rangle$; note that $\mathbf{r}$ is differentiable for all t and $\mathbf{r}'(0) = \mathbf{0}$.

b. $\mathbf{r}'(t) = -e^{-t}\mathbf{i} + \dfrac{5}{\sqrt{t}}\mathbf{j} - 6\sin 3t\,\mathbf{k}$; the function $\mathbf{r}$ is differentiable for $t > 0$.

Related Exercises 7–20 ◄

QUICK CHECK 1 Let $\mathbf{r}(t) = \langle t, t, t \rangle$. Compute $\mathbf{r}'(t)$ and interpret the result. ◄

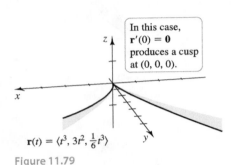

In this case, $\mathbf{r}'(0) = \mathbf{0}$ produces a cusp at $(0, 0, 0)$.

$\mathbf{r}(t) = \langle t^3, 3t^2, \frac{1}{6}t^3 \rangle$

Figure 11.79

▶ If a curve has a cusp at a point, then $\mathbf{r}'(t) = \mathbf{0}$ at that point. However, the converse is not true; it may happen that $\mathbf{r}'(t) = \mathbf{0}$ at a point that is not a cusp (Exercise 89).

The condition that $\mathbf{r}'(t) \neq \mathbf{0}$ in order for the tangent vector to be defined requires explanation. Consider the function $\mathbf{r}(t) = \langle t^3, 3t^2, t^3/6 \rangle$. As shown in Example 1a, $\mathbf{r}'(0) = \mathbf{0}$; that is, all three components of $\mathbf{r}'(t)$ are zero simultaneously when $t = 0$. We see in Figure 11.79 that this otherwise smooth curve has a *cusp*, or a sharp point, at the origin. If $\mathbf{r}$ describes the motion of an object, then $\mathbf{r}'(t) = \mathbf{0}$ means that the velocity (and speed) of the object is zero at a point. At such a stationary point, the object *may* change direction abruptly, creating a cusp in its trajectory. For this reason, we say a function $\mathbf{r}(t) = \langle f(t), g(t), h(t) \rangle$ is **smooth** on an interval if f, g, and h are differentiable *and* $\mathbf{r}'(t) \neq \mathbf{0}$ on that interval. Smooth curves have no cusps or corners.

Unit Tangent Vector In situations in which only the direction (but not the length) of the tangent vector is of interest, we work with the *unit tangent vector*. It is the vector with magnitude 1, formed by dividing $\mathbf{r}'(t)$ by its length.

DEFINITION **Unit Tangent Vector**

Let $\mathbf{r}(t) = f(t)\,\mathbf{i} + g(t)\,\mathbf{j} + h(t)\,\mathbf{k}$ be a smooth parameterized curve, for $a \leq t \leq b$. The **unit tangent vector** for a particular value of t is

$$\mathbf{T}(t) = \frac{\mathbf{r}'(t)}{|\mathbf{r}'(t)|}.$$

QUICK CHECK 2 Suppose $\mathbf{r}'(t)$ has units m/s. Explain why $\mathbf{T}(t) = \mathbf{r}'(t)/|\mathbf{r}'(t)|$ is dimensionless (has no units) and carries information only about direction. ◄

EXAMPLE 2 **Unit tangent vectors** Find the unit tangent vectors for the following parameterized curves.

a. $\mathbf{r}(t) = \langle t^2, 4t, 4\ln t \rangle$, for $t > 0$

b. $\mathbf{r}(t) = \langle 10, 3\cos t, 3\sin t \rangle$, for $0 \leq t \leq 2\pi$

SOLUTION

a. A tangent vector is $\mathbf{r}'(t) = \langle 2t, 4, 4/t \rangle$, which has a magnitude of

$$|\mathbf{r}'(t)| = \sqrt{(2t)^2 + 4^2 + \left(\frac{4}{t}\right)^2} \qquad \text{Definition of magnitude}$$

$$= \sqrt{4t^2 + 16 + \frac{16}{t^2}} \qquad \text{Expand.}$$

$$= \sqrt{\left(2t + \frac{4}{t}\right)^2} \qquad \text{Factor.}$$

$$= 2t + \frac{4}{t}. \qquad \text{Simplify.}$$

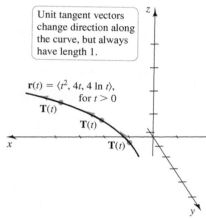

Unit tangent vectors change direction along the curve, but always have length 1.

$\mathbf{r}(t) = \langle t^2, 4t, 4 \ln t \rangle,$
for $t > 0$

$\mathbf{T}(t)$

$\mathbf{T}(t)$

$\mathbf{T}(t)$

Figure 11.80

Therefore, the unit tangent vector for a particular value of t is

$$\mathbf{T}(t) = \frac{\langle 2t, 4, 4/t \rangle}{2t + 4/t}.$$

As shown in Figure 11.80, the unit tangent vectors change direction along the curve but maintain unit length.

b. In this case, $\mathbf{r}'(t) = \langle 0, -3 \sin t, 3 \cos t \rangle$ and

$$|\mathbf{r}'(t)| = \sqrt{0^2 + (-3 \sin t)^2 + (3 \cos t)^2} = \sqrt{9\underbrace{(\sin^2 t + \cos^2 t)}_{1}} = 3.$$

Therefore, the unit tangent vector for a particular value of t is

$$\mathbf{T}(t) = \frac{1}{3} \langle 0, -3 \sin t, 3 \cos t \rangle = \langle 0, -\sin t, \cos t \rangle.$$

The direction of $\mathbf{T}$ changes along the curve, but its length remains 1.

Related Exercises 21–30 ◄

Derivative Rules The rules for derivatives for single-variable functions either carry over directly to vector-valued functions or have close analogs. These rules are generally proved by working on the individual components of the vector function.

> With the exception of the Cross Product Rule, these rules apply to vector-valued functions with any number of components. Notice that we have three new product rules, all of which mimic the original Product Rule. In Rule 4, $\mathbf{u}$ must be differentiable at $f(t)$.

THEOREM 11.7 Derivative Rules

Let $\mathbf{u}$ and $\mathbf{v}$ be differentiable vector-valued functions and let f be a differentiable scalar-valued function, all at a point t. Let $\mathbf{c}$ be a constant vector. The following rules apply.

1. $\dfrac{d}{dt}(\mathbf{c}) = \mathbf{0}$ Constant Rule

2. $\dfrac{d}{dt}(\mathbf{u}(t) + \mathbf{v}(t)) = \mathbf{u}'(t) + \mathbf{v}'(t)$ Sum Rule

3. $\dfrac{d}{dt}(f(t)\mathbf{u}(t)) = f'(t)\mathbf{u}(t) + f(t)\mathbf{u}'(t)$ Product Rule

4. $\dfrac{d}{dt}(\mathbf{u}(f(t))) = \mathbf{u}'(f(t))f'(t)$ Chain Rule

5. $\dfrac{d}{dt}(\mathbf{u}(t) \cdot \mathbf{v}(t)) = \mathbf{u}'(t) \cdot \mathbf{v}(t) + \mathbf{u}(t) \cdot \mathbf{v}'(t)$ Dot Product Rule

6. $\dfrac{d}{dt}(\mathbf{u}(t) \times \mathbf{v}(t)) = \mathbf{u}'(t) \times \mathbf{v}(t) + \mathbf{u}(t) \times \mathbf{v}'(t)$ Cross Product Rule

---

QUICK CHECK 3 Let $\mathbf{u}(t) = \langle t, t, t \rangle$ and $\mathbf{v}(t) = \langle 1, 1, 1 \rangle$. Compute $\dfrac{d}{dt}(\mathbf{u}(t) \cdot \mathbf{v}(t))$ using Derivative Rule 5 and show that it agrees with the result obtained by first computing the dot product and differentiating directly. ◄

The proofs of these rules are assigned in Exercises 86–88 with the exception of the following representative proofs.

Proof of the Chain Rule: Let $\mathbf{u}(t) = \langle u_1(t), u_2(t), u_3(t) \rangle$, which implies that

$$\mathbf{u}(f(t)) = u_1(f(t))\,\mathbf{i} + u_2(f(t))\,\mathbf{j} + u_3(f(t))\,\mathbf{k}.$$

We now apply the ordinary Chain Rule componentwise:

$$\frac{d}{dt}\left(\mathbf{u}(f(t))\right) = \frac{d}{dt}\left(u_1(f(t))\,\mathbf{i} + u_2(f(t))\,\mathbf{j} + u_3(f(t))\,\mathbf{k}\right) \qquad \text{Components of } \mathbf{u}$$

$$= \frac{d}{dt}\left(u_1(f(t))\right)\mathbf{i} + \frac{d}{dt}\left(u_2(f(t))\right)\mathbf{j} + \frac{d}{dt}\left(u_3(f(t))\right)\mathbf{k} \qquad \text{Derivative of a sum}$$

$$= u_1'(f(t))f'(t)\,\mathbf{i} + u_2'(f(t))f'(t)\,\mathbf{j} + u_3'(f(t))f'(t)\,\mathbf{k} \qquad \text{Chain Rule}$$

$$= \left(u_1'(f(t))\,\mathbf{i} + u_2'(f(t))\,\mathbf{j} + u_3'(f(t))\,\mathbf{k}\right)f'(t) \qquad \text{Factor } f'(t).$$

$$= \mathbf{u}'(f(t))f'(t). \qquad \text{Definition of } \mathbf{u}'$$

◄

Proof of the Dot Product Rule: One proof of the Dot Product Rule uses the standard Product Rule on each component. Let $\mathbf{u}(t) = \langle u_1(t), u_2(t), u_3(t) \rangle$ and $\mathbf{v}(t) = \langle v_1(t), v_2(t), v_3(t) \rangle$. Then

$$\frac{d}{dt}(\mathbf{u} \cdot \mathbf{v}) = \frac{d}{dt}(u_1 v_1 + u_2 v_2 + u_3 v_3) \qquad \text{Definition of dot product}$$

$$= u_1' v_1 + u_1 v_1' + u_2' v_2 + u_2 v_2' + u_3' v_3 + u_3 v_3' \qquad \text{Product Rule}$$

$$= \underbrace{u_1' v_1 + u_2' v_2 + u_3' v_3}_{\mathbf{u}' \cdot \mathbf{v}} + \underbrace{u_1 v_1' + u_2 v_2' + u_3 v_3'}_{\mathbf{u} \cdot \mathbf{v}'} \qquad \text{Rearrange.}$$

$$= \mathbf{u}' \cdot \mathbf{v} + \mathbf{u} \cdot \mathbf{v}'.$$

◄

EXAMPLE 3   Derivative rules Compute the following derivatives, where

$$\mathbf{u}(t) = t\,\mathbf{i} + t^2\,\mathbf{j} - t^3\,\mathbf{k} \quad \text{and} \quad \mathbf{v}(t) = \sin t\,\mathbf{i} + 2\cos t\,\mathbf{j} + \cos t\,\mathbf{k}.$$

a. $\dfrac{d}{dt}\left(\mathbf{v}(t^2)\right)$ **b.** $\dfrac{d}{dt}\left(t^2\,\mathbf{v}(t)\right)$ **c.** $\dfrac{d}{dt}\left(\mathbf{u}(t) \cdot \mathbf{v}(t)\right)$

SOLUTION

a. Note that $\mathbf{v}'(t) = \cos t\,\mathbf{i} - 2\sin t\,\mathbf{j} - \sin t\,\mathbf{k}$. Using the Chain Rule, we have

$$\frac{d}{dt}\left(\mathbf{v}(t^2)\right) = \mathbf{v}'(t^2)\frac{d}{dt}(t^2) = \underbrace{(\cos t^2\,\mathbf{i} - 2\sin t^2\,\mathbf{j} - \sin t^2\,\mathbf{k})}_{\mathbf{v}'(t^2)}(2t).$$

b. $\dfrac{d}{dt}\left(t^2\,\mathbf{v}(t)\right) = \dfrac{d}{dt}(t^2)\mathbf{v}(t) + t^2\dfrac{d}{dt}\left(\mathbf{v}(t)\right) \qquad \text{Product Rule}$

$$= 2t\,\mathbf{v}(t) + t^2\,\mathbf{v}'(t)$$

$$= 2t\,\underbrace{(\sin t\,\mathbf{i} + 2\cos t\,\mathbf{j} + \cos t\,\mathbf{k})}_{\mathbf{v}(t)} + t^2\underbrace{(\cos t\,\mathbf{i} - 2\sin t\,\mathbf{j} - \sin t\,\mathbf{k})}_{\mathbf{v}'(t)}$$

Differentiate.

$$= (2t\sin t + t^2\cos t)\,\mathbf{i} + (4t\cos t - 2t^2\sin t)\,\mathbf{j} + (2t\cos t - t^2\sin t)\,\mathbf{k}$$

Collect terms.

c. $\dfrac{d}{dt}\left(\mathbf{u}(t) \cdot \mathbf{v}(t)\right) = \mathbf{u}'(t) \cdot \mathbf{v}(t) + \mathbf{u}(t) \cdot \mathbf{v}'(t) \qquad \text{Dot Product Rule}$

$$= (\mathbf{i} + 2t\,\mathbf{j} - 3t^2\,\mathbf{k}) \cdot (\sin t\,\mathbf{i} + 2\cos t\,\mathbf{j} + \cos t\,\mathbf{k})$$
$$+ (t\,\mathbf{i} + t^2\,\mathbf{j} - t^3\,\mathbf{k}) \cdot (\cos t\,\mathbf{i} - 2\sin t\,\mathbf{j} - \sin t\,\mathbf{k}) \qquad \text{Differentiate.}$$

$$= (\sin t + 4t\cos t - 3t^2\cos t) + (t\cos t - 2t^2\sin t + t^3\sin t) \qquad \text{Dot products}$$

$$= (1 - 2t^2 + t^3)\sin t + (5t - 3t^2)\cos t \qquad \text{Simplify.}$$

Note that the result is a scalar. The same result is obtained if you first compute $\mathbf{u} \cdot \mathbf{v}$ and then differentiate.   *Related Exercises 31–40* ◄

Higher-Order Derivatives   Higher-order derivatives of vector-valued functions are computed in the expected way: We simply differentiate each component multiple times. Second derivatives feature prominently in the next section, playing the role of acceleration.

EXAMPLE 4   Higher-order derivatives Compute the first, second, and third derivative of $\mathbf{r}(t) = \langle t^2, 8 \ln t, 3e^{-2t} \rangle$.

SOLUTION Differentiating once, we have $\mathbf{r}'(t) = \langle 2t, 8/t, -6e^{-2t} \rangle$. Differentiating again produces $\mathbf{r}''(t) = \langle 2, -8/t^2, 12e^{-2t} \rangle$. Differentiating once more, we have $\mathbf{r}'''(t) = \langle 0, 16/t^3, -24e^{-2t} \rangle$.

Related Exercises 41–46 ◄

Integrals of Vector-Valued Functions

An **antiderivative** of the vector function $\mathbf{r}$ is a function $\mathbf{R}$ such that $\mathbf{R}' = \mathbf{r}$. If

$$\mathbf{r}(t) = f(t)\mathbf{i} + g(t)\mathbf{j} + h(t)\mathbf{k},$$

then an antiderivative of $\mathbf{r}$ is

$$\mathbf{R}(t) = F(t)\mathbf{i} + G(t)\mathbf{j} + H(t)\mathbf{k},$$

where F, G, and H are antiderivatives of f, g, and h, respectively. This fact follows by differentiating the components of $\mathbf{R}$ and verifying that $\mathbf{R}' = \mathbf{r}$. The collection of all antiderivatives of $\mathbf{r}$ is the *indefinite integral* of $\mathbf{r}$.

DEFINITION   Indefinite Integral of a Vector-Valued Function

Let $\mathbf{r}(t) = f(t)\mathbf{i} + g(t)\mathbf{j} + h(t)\mathbf{k}$ be a vector function and let $\mathbf{R}(t) = F(t)\mathbf{i} + G(t)\mathbf{j} + H(t)\mathbf{k}$, where F, G, and H are antiderivatives of f, g, and h, respectively. The **indefinite integral** of $\mathbf{r}$ is

$$\int \mathbf{r}(t)\, dt = \mathbf{R}(t) + \mathbf{C},$$

where $\mathbf{C}$ is an arbitrary constant vector. Alternatively, in component form,

$$\int \langle f(t), g(t), h(t) \rangle\, dt = \langle F(t), G(t), H(t) \rangle + \langle C_1, C_2, C_3 \rangle.$$

EXAMPLE 5   Indefinite integrals Compute

$$\int \left(\frac{t}{\sqrt{t^2 + 2}}\mathbf{i} + e^{-3t}\mathbf{j} + (\sin 4t + 1)\mathbf{k} \right) dt.$$

> The substitution $u = t^2 + 2$ is used to evaluate the **i**-component of the integral.

SOLUTION We compute the indefinite integral of each component:

$$\int \left(\frac{t}{\sqrt{t^2 + 2}}\mathbf{i} + e^{-3t}\mathbf{j} + (\sin 4t + 1)\mathbf{k} \right) dt$$

$$= (\sqrt{t^2 + 2} + C_1)\mathbf{i} + \left(-\frac{1}{3}e^{-3t} + C_2 \right)\mathbf{j} + \left(-\frac{1}{4}\cos 4t + t + C_3 \right)\mathbf{k}$$

$$= \sqrt{t^2 + 2}\,\mathbf{i} - \frac{1}{3}e^{-3t}\mathbf{j} + \left(t - \frac{1}{4}\cos 4t \right)\mathbf{k} + \mathbf{C}. \quad \text{Let } \mathbf{C} = C_1\mathbf{i} + C_2\mathbf{j} + C_3\mathbf{k}.$$

The constants C_1, C_2, and C_3 are combined to form one vector constant $\mathbf{C}$ at the end of the calculation.

Related Exercises 47–52 ◄

QUICK CHECK 4 Let $\mathbf{r}(t) = \langle 1, 2t, 3t^2 \rangle$. Compute $\int \mathbf{r}(t)\, dt$. ◄

EXAMPLE 6   Finding one antiderivative Find $\mathbf{r}(t)$ such that $\mathbf{r}'(t) = \langle 10, \sin t, t \rangle$ and $\mathbf{r}(0) = \mathbf{j}$.

SOLUTION The required function $\mathbf{r}$ is an antiderivative of $\langle 10, \sin t, t \rangle$:

$$\mathbf{r}(t) = \int \langle 10, \sin t, t \rangle \, dt = \left\langle 10t, -\cos t, \frac{t^2}{2} \right\rangle + \mathbf{C},$$

where $\mathbf{C}$ is an arbitrary constant vector. The condition $\mathbf{r}(0) = \mathbf{j}$ allows us to determine $\mathbf{C}$; substituting $t = 0$ implies that $\mathbf{r}(0) = \langle 0, -1, 0 \rangle + \mathbf{C} = \mathbf{j}$, where $\mathbf{j} = \langle 0, 1, 0 \rangle$. Solving for $\mathbf{C}$, we have $\mathbf{C} = \langle 0, 1, 0 \rangle - \langle 0, -1, 0 \rangle = \langle 0, 2, 0 \rangle$. Therefore,

$$\mathbf{r}(t) = \left\langle 10t, 2 - \cos t, \frac{t^2}{2} \right\rangle.$$

Related Exercises 53–58 ◄

Definite integrals are evaluated by applying the Fundamental Theorem of Calculus to each component of a vector-valued function.

DEFINITION Definite Integral of a Vector-Valued Function

Let $\mathbf{r}(t) = f(t) \, \mathbf{i} + g(t) \, \mathbf{j} + h(t) \, \mathbf{k}$, where f, g, and h are integrable on the interval $[a, b]$. The **definite integral** of $\mathbf{r}$ on $[a, b]$ is

$$\int_a^b \mathbf{r}(t) \, dt = \left(\int_a^b f(t) \, dt \right) \mathbf{i} + \left(\int_a^b g(t) \, dt \right) \mathbf{j} + \left(\int_a^b h(t) \, dt \right) \mathbf{k}$$

EXAMPLE 7   Definite integrals Evaluate

$$\int_0^\pi \left(\mathbf{i} + 3 \cos \frac{t}{2} \mathbf{j} - 4t \, \mathbf{k} \right) dt.$$

SOLUTION

$$\int_0^\pi \left(\mathbf{i} + 3 \cos \frac{t}{2} \mathbf{j} - 4t \, \mathbf{k} \right) dt = t \, \mathbf{i} \Big|_0^\pi + 6 \sin \frac{t}{2} \mathbf{j} \Big|_0^\pi - 2t^2 \, \mathbf{k} \Big|_0^\pi \qquad \text{Evaluate integrals for each component.}$$

$$= \pi \, \mathbf{i} + 6\mathbf{j} - 2\pi^2 \, \mathbf{k} \qquad \text{Simplify.}$$

Related Exercises 59–66 ◄

With the tools of differentiation and integration in hand, we are prepared to tackle some practical problems, notably the motion of objects in space.

SECTION 11.6 EXERCISES

Review Questions

1. What is the derivative of $\mathbf{r}(t) = \langle f(t), g(t), h(t) \rangle$?

2. Explain the geometric meaning of $\mathbf{r}'(t)$.

3. Given a tangent vector on an oriented curve, how do you find the unit tangent vector?

4. Compute $\mathbf{r}''(t)$ when $\mathbf{r}(t) = \langle t^{10}, 8t, \cos t \rangle$.

5. How do you find the indefinite integral of $\mathbf{r}(t) = \langle f(t), g(t), h(t) \rangle$?

6. How do you evaluate $\int_a^b \mathbf{r}(t) \, dt$?

Basic Skills

7–14. Derivatives of vector-valued functions *Differentiate the following functions.*

7. $\mathbf{r}(t) = \langle \cos t, t^2, \sin t \rangle$

8. $\mathbf{r}(t) = 4e^t \mathbf{i} + 5\mathbf{j} + \ln t \, \mathbf{k}$

9. $\mathbf{r}(t) = \langle 2t^3, 6\sqrt{t}, 3/t \rangle$

10. $\mathbf{r}(t) = \langle 4, 3 \cos 2t, 2 \sin 3t \rangle$

11. $\mathbf{r}(t) = e^t \mathbf{i} + 2e^{-t} \mathbf{j} - 4e^{2t} \mathbf{k}$

12. $\mathbf{r}(t) = \tan t \, \mathbf{i} + \sec t \, \mathbf{j} + \cos^2 t \, \mathbf{k}$

13. $\mathbf{r}(t) = \langle te^{-t}, t \ln t, t \cos t \rangle$

14. $\mathbf{r}(t) = \langle (t + 1)^{-1}, \tan^{-1} t, \ln (t + 1) \rangle$

15–20. Tangent vectors *Find a tangent vector at the given value of t for the following parameterized curves.*

15. $\mathbf{r}(t) = \langle t, 3t^2, t^3 \rangle$, $t = 1$

16. $\mathbf{r}(t) = \langle e^t, e^{3t}, e^{5t} \rangle$, $t = 0$

17. $\mathbf{r}(t) = \langle t, \cos 2t, 2 \sin t \rangle$, $t = \pi/2$

18. $\mathbf{r}(t) = \langle 2 \sin t, 3 \cos t, \sin (t/2) \rangle$, $t = \pi$

19. $\mathbf{r}(t) = 2t^4 \mathbf{i} + 6t^{3/2} \mathbf{j} + \dfrac{10}{t} \mathbf{k}$, $t = 1$

20. $\mathbf{r}(t) = 2e^t \mathbf{i} + e^{-2t} \mathbf{j} + 4e^{2t} \mathbf{k}$, $t = \ln 3$

21–26. Unit tangent vectors *Find the unit tangent vector for the following parameterized curves.*

21. $\mathbf{r}(t) = \langle 2t, 2t, t \rangle$, for $0 \le t \le 1$

22. $\mathbf{r}(t) = \langle \cos t, \sin t, 2 \rangle$, for $0 \le t \le 2\pi$

23. $\mathbf{r}(t) = \langle 8, \cos 2t, 2 \sin 2t \rangle$, for $0 \le t \le 2\pi$

24. $\mathbf{r}(t) = \langle \sin t, \cos t, \cos t \rangle$, for $0 \le t \le 2\pi$

25. $\mathbf{r}(t) = \langle t, 2, 2/t \rangle$, for $t \ge 1$

26. $\mathbf{r}(t) = \langle e^{2t}, 2e^{2t}, 2e^{-3t} \rangle$, for $t \ge 0$

27–30. Unit tangent vectors at a point *Find the unit tangent vector at the given value of t for the following parameterized curves.*

27. $\mathbf{r}(t) = \langle \cos 2t, 4, 3 \sin 2t \rangle$, for $0 \le t \le \pi$; $t = \pi/2$

28. $\mathbf{r}(t) = \langle \sin t, \cos t, e^{-t} \rangle$, for $0 \le t \le \pi$; $t = 0$

29. $\mathbf{r}(t) = \langle 6t, 6, 3/t \rangle$, for $0 < t < 2$; $t = 1$

30. $\mathbf{r}(t) = \langle \sqrt{7}e^t, 3e^t, 3e^t \rangle$, for $0 \le t \le 1$; $t = \ln 2$

31–36. Derivative rules *Let*

$$\mathbf{u}(t) = 2t^3 \mathbf{i} + (t^2 - 1)\mathbf{j} - 8\mathbf{k} \ \text{and} \ \mathbf{v}(t) = e^t \mathbf{i} + 2e^{-t} \mathbf{j} - e^{2t} \mathbf{k}.$$

Compute the derivative of the following functions.

31. $(t^{12} + 3t)\mathbf{u}(t)$ **32.** $(4t^8 - 6t^3)\mathbf{v}(t)$

33. $\mathbf{u}(t^4 - 2t)$ **34.** $\mathbf{v}(\sqrt{t})$

35. $\mathbf{u}(t) \cdot \mathbf{v}(t)$ **36.** $\mathbf{u}(t) \times \mathbf{v}(t)$

37–40. Derivative rules *Compute the following derivatives.*

37. $\dfrac{d}{dt}(t^2(\mathbf{i} + 2\mathbf{j} - 2t\mathbf{k}) \cdot (e^t \mathbf{i} + 2e^t \mathbf{j} - 3e^{-t} \mathbf{k}))$

38. $\dfrac{d}{dt}((t^3 \mathbf{i} - 2t\mathbf{j} - 2\mathbf{k}) \times (t\mathbf{i} - t^2 \mathbf{j} - t^3 \mathbf{k}))$

39. $\dfrac{d}{dt}((3t^2 \mathbf{i} + \sqrt{t}\mathbf{j} - 2t^{-1} \mathbf{k}) \cdot (\cos t \mathbf{i} + \sin 2t \mathbf{j} - 3t \mathbf{k}))$

40. $\dfrac{d}{dt}((t^3 \mathbf{i} + 6\mathbf{j} - 2\sqrt{t}\mathbf{k}) \times (3t\mathbf{i} - 12t^2 \mathbf{j} - 6t^{-2} \mathbf{k}))$

41–46. Higher-order derivatives *Compute $\mathbf{r}''(t)$ and $\mathbf{r}'''(t)$ for the following functions.*

41. $\mathbf{r}(t) = \langle t^2 + 1, t + 1, 1 \rangle$

42. $\mathbf{r}(t) = \langle 3t^{12} - t^2, t^8 + t^3, t^{-4} - 2 \rangle$

43. $\mathbf{r}(t) = \langle \cos 3t, \sin 4t, \cos 6t \rangle$

44. $\mathbf{r}(t) = \langle e^{4t}, 2e^{-4t} + 1, 2e^{-t} \rangle$

45. $\mathbf{r}(t) = \sqrt{t + 4}\, \mathbf{i} + \dfrac{t}{t + 1}\mathbf{j} - e^{-t^2} \mathbf{k}$

46. $\mathbf{r}(t) = \tan t\, \mathbf{i} + \left(t + \dfrac{1}{t}\right)\mathbf{j} - \ln (t + 1)\, \mathbf{k}$

47–52. Indefinite integrals *Compute the indefinite integral of the following functions.*

47. $\mathbf{r}(t) = \langle t^4 - 3t, 2t - 1, 10 \rangle$

48. $\mathbf{r}(t) = \langle 5t^{-4} - t^2, t^6 - 4t^3, 2/t \rangle$

49. $\mathbf{r}(t) = \langle 2 \cos t, 2 \sin 3t, 4 \cos 8t \rangle$

50. $\mathbf{r}(t) = te^t \mathbf{i} + t \sin t^2 \mathbf{j} - \dfrac{2t}{\sqrt{t^2 + 4}} \mathbf{k}$

51. $\mathbf{r}(t) = e^{3t} \mathbf{i} + \dfrac{1}{1 + t^2}\mathbf{j} - \dfrac{1}{\sqrt{2t}} \mathbf{k}$

52. $\mathbf{r}(t) = 2^t \mathbf{i} + \dfrac{1}{1 + 2t}\mathbf{j} + \ln t\, \mathbf{k}$

53–58. Finding r from r′ *Find the function $\mathbf{r}$ that satisfies the given conditions.*

53. $\mathbf{r}'(t) = \langle e^t, \sin t, \sec^2 t \rangle$; $\mathbf{r}(0) = \langle 2, 2, 2 \rangle$

54. $\mathbf{r}'(t) = \langle 0, 2, 2t \rangle$; $\mathbf{r}(1) = \langle 4, 3, -5 \rangle$

55. $\mathbf{r}'(t) = \langle 1, 2t, 3t^2 \rangle$; $\mathbf{r}(1) = \langle 4, 3, -5 \rangle$

56. $\mathbf{r}'(t) = \langle \sqrt{t}, \cos \pi t, 4/t \rangle$; $\mathbf{r}(1) = \langle 2, 3, 4 \rangle$

57. $\mathbf{r}'(t) = \langle e^{2t}, 1 - 2e^{-t}, 1 - 2e^t \rangle$; $\mathbf{r}(0) = \langle 1, 1, 1 \rangle$

58. $\mathbf{r}'(t) = \dfrac{t}{t^2 + 1}\mathbf{i} + te^{-t^2} \mathbf{j} - \dfrac{2t}{\sqrt{t^2 + 4}} \mathbf{k}$; $\mathbf{r}(0) = \mathbf{i} + \dfrac{3}{2}\mathbf{j} - 3\mathbf{k}$

59–66. Definite integrals *Evaluate the following definite integrals.*

59. $\displaystyle\int_{-1}^{1} (\mathbf{i} + t\mathbf{j} + 3t^2 \mathbf{k})\, dt$

60. $\displaystyle\int_{1}^{4} (6t^2 \mathbf{i} + 8t^3 \mathbf{j} + 9t^2 \mathbf{k})\, dt$

61. $\displaystyle\int_{0}^{\ln 2} (e^t \mathbf{i} + e^t \cos(\pi e^t)\mathbf{j})\, dt$

62. $\displaystyle\int_{1/2}^{1} \left(\dfrac{3}{1 + 2t}\mathbf{i} - \pi \csc^2\left(\dfrac{\pi}{2}t\right)\mathbf{k}\right) dt$

63. $\displaystyle\int_{-\pi}^{\pi} (\sin t\, \mathbf{i} + \cos t\, \mathbf{j} + 2t\, \mathbf{k})\, dt$

64. $\displaystyle\int_{0}^{\ln 2} (e^{-t} \mathbf{i} + 2e^{2t} \mathbf{j} - 4e^t \mathbf{k})\, dt$

65. $\displaystyle\int_{0}^{2} te^t(\mathbf{i} + 2\mathbf{j} - \mathbf{k})\, dt$

66. $\displaystyle\int_{0}^{\pi/4} (\sec^2 t\, \mathbf{i} - 2 \cos t\, \mathbf{j} - \mathbf{k})\, dt$

Further Explorations

67. Explain why or why not Determine whether the following statements are true and give an explanation or counterexample.

  a. The vectors $\mathbf{r}(t)$ and $\mathbf{r}'(t)$ are parallel for all values of t in the domain.

  b. The curve described by the function $\mathbf{r}(t) = \langle t, t^2 - 2t, \cos \pi t \rangle$ is smooth, for $-\infty < t < \infty$.

  c. If f, g, and h are odd integrable functions and a is a real number, then

$$\int_{-a}^{a} (f(t)\,\mathbf{i} + g(t)\,\mathbf{j} + h(t)\,\mathbf{k})\, dt = \mathbf{0}.$$

68–71. Tangent lines *Suppose the vector-valued function* $\mathbf{r}(t) = \langle f(t), g(t), h(t) \rangle$ *is smooth on an interval containing the point* t_0. *The line tangent to* $\mathbf{r}(t)$ *at* $t = t_0$ *is the line parallel to the tangent vector* $\mathbf{r}'(t_0)$ *that passes through* $(f(t_0), g(t_0), h(t_0))$. *For each of the following functions, find an equation of the line tangent to the curve at* $t = t_0$. *Choose an orientation for the line that is the same as the direction of* $\mathbf{r}'$.

68. $\mathbf{r}(t) = \langle e^t, e^{2t}, e^{3t} \rangle$; $t_0 = 0$

69. $\mathbf{r}(t) = \langle 2 + \cos t, 3 + \sin 2t, t \rangle$; $t_0 = \pi/2$

70. $\mathbf{r}(t) = \langle \sqrt{2t + 1}, \sin \pi t, 4 \rangle$; $t_0 = 4$

71. $\mathbf{r}(t) = \langle 3t - 1, 7t + 2, t^2 \rangle$; $t_0 = 1$

72–77. Derivative rules *Let* $\mathbf{u}(t) = \langle 1, t, t^2 \rangle$, $\mathbf{v}(t) = \langle t^2, -2t, 1 \rangle$, *and* $g(t) = 2\sqrt{t}$. *Compute the derivatives of the following functions.*

72. $\mathbf{u}(t^3)$ **73.** $\mathbf{v}(e^t)$ **74.** $g(t)\mathbf{v}(t)$

75. $\mathbf{v}(g(t))$ **76.** $\mathbf{u}(t) \cdot \mathbf{v}(t)$ **77.** $\mathbf{u}(t) \times \mathbf{v}(t)$

78–83. Relationship between r and r′

78. Consider the circle $\mathbf{r}(t) = \langle a \cos t, a \sin t \rangle$, for $0 \le t \le 2\pi$, where a is a positive real number. Compute $\mathbf{r}'$ and show that it is orthogonal to $\mathbf{r}$ for all t.

79. Consider the parabola $\mathbf{r}(t) = \langle at^2 + 1, t \rangle$, for $-\infty < t < \infty$, where a is a positive real number. Find all points on the parabola at which $\mathbf{r}$ and $\mathbf{r}'$ are orthogonal.

80. Consider the curve $\mathbf{r}(t) = \langle \sqrt{t}, 1, t \rangle$, for $t > 0$. Find all points on the curve at which $\mathbf{r}$ and $\mathbf{r}'$ are orthogonal.

81. Consider the helix $\mathbf{r}(t) = \langle \cos t, \sin t, t \rangle$, for $-\infty < t < \infty$. Find all points on the helix at which $\mathbf{r}$ and $\mathbf{r}'$ are orthogonal.

82. Consider the ellipse $\mathbf{r}(t) = \langle 2 \cos t, 8 \sin t, 0 \rangle$, for $0 \le t \le 2\pi$. Find all points on the ellipse at which $\mathbf{r}$ and $\mathbf{r}'$ are orthogonal.

83. Give two families of curves in $\mathbb{R}^3$ for which $\mathbf{r}$ and $\mathbf{r}'$ are parallel for all t in the domain.

84. Derivative rules Suppose $\mathbf{u}$ and $\mathbf{v}$ are differentiable functions at $t = 0$ with $\mathbf{u}(0) = \langle 0, 1, 1 \rangle$, $\mathbf{u}'(0) = \langle 0, 7, 1 \rangle$, $\mathbf{v}(0) = \langle 0, 1, 1 \rangle$, and $\mathbf{v}'(0) = \langle 1, 1, 2 \rangle$. Evaluate the following expressions.

  a. $\dfrac{d}{dt}(\mathbf{u} \cdot \mathbf{v})\Big|_{t=0}$ b. $\dfrac{d}{dt}(\mathbf{u} \times \mathbf{v})\Big|_{t=0}$

  c. $\dfrac{d}{dt}(\cos t\, \mathbf{u}(t))\Big|_{t=0}$

Additional Exercises

85. Vectors r and r′ for lines

  a. If $\mathbf{r}(t) = \langle at, bt, ct \rangle$ with $\langle a, b, c \rangle \ne \langle 0, 0, 0 \rangle$, show that the angle between $\mathbf{r}$ and $\mathbf{r}'$ is constant for all $t > 0$.

  b. If $\mathbf{r}(t) = \langle x_0 + at, y_0 + bt, z_0 + ct \rangle$, where x_0, y_0, and z_0 are not all zero, show that the angle between $\mathbf{r}$ and $\mathbf{r}'$ varies with t.

  c. Explain the results of parts (a) and (b) geometrically.

86. Proof of Sum Rule By expressing $\mathbf{u}$ and $\mathbf{v}$ in terms of their components, prove that

$$\frac{d}{dt}(\mathbf{u}(t) + \mathbf{v}(t)) = \mathbf{u}'(t) + \mathbf{v}'(t).$$

87. Proof of Product Rule By expressing $\mathbf{u}$ in terms of its components, prove that

$$\frac{d}{dt}(f(t)\mathbf{u}(t)) = f'(t)\mathbf{u}(t) + f(t)\mathbf{u}'(t).$$

88. Proof of Cross Product Rule Prove that

$$\frac{d}{dt}(\mathbf{u}(t) \times \mathbf{v}(t)) = \mathbf{u}'(t) \times \mathbf{v}(t) + \mathbf{u}(t) \times \mathbf{v}'(t).$$

There are two ways to proceed: Either express $\mathbf{u}$ and $\mathbf{v}$ in terms of their three components or use the definition of the derivative.

⊤ 89. Cusps and noncusps

  a. Graph the curve $\mathbf{r}(t) = \langle t^3, t^3 \rangle$. Show that $\mathbf{r}'(0) = \mathbf{0}$ and the curve does not have a cusp at $t = 0$. Explain.

  b. Graph the curve $\mathbf{r}(t) = \langle t^3, t^2 \rangle$. Show that $\mathbf{r}'(0) = \mathbf{0}$ and the curve has a cusp at $t = 0$. Explain.

  c. The functions $\mathbf{r}(t) = \langle t, t^2 \rangle$ and $\mathbf{p}(t) = \langle t^2, t^4 \rangle$ both satisfy $y = x^2$. Explain how the curves they parameterize are different.

  d. Consider the curve $\mathbf{r}(t) = \langle t^m, t^n \rangle$, where $m > 1$ and $n > 1$ are integers with no common factors. Is it true that the curve has a cusp at $t = 0$ if one (not both) of m and n is even? Explain.

90. Motion on a sphere Prove that $\mathbf{r}$ describes a curve that lies on the surface of a sphere centered at the origin ($x^2 + y^2 + z^2 = a^2$ with $a \ge 0$) if and only if $\mathbf{r}$ and $\mathbf{r}'$ are orthogonal at all points of the curve.

QUICK CHECK ANSWERS

1. $\mathbf{r}(t)$ describes a line, so its tangent vector $\mathbf{r}'(t) = \langle 1, 1, 1 \rangle$ has constant direction and magnitude.
2. Both $\mathbf{r}'$ and $|\mathbf{r}'|$ have units of m/s. In forming $\mathbf{r}'/|\mathbf{r}'|$, the units cancel and $\mathbf{T}(t)$ is without units. **3.** $\dfrac{d}{dt}(\mathbf{u}(t) \cdot \mathbf{v}(t)) = \langle 1, 1, 1 \rangle \cdot \langle 1, 1, 1 \rangle + \langle t, t, t \rangle \cdot \langle 0, 0, 0 \rangle = 3$.
$\dfrac{d}{dt}(\langle t, t, t \rangle \cdot \langle 1, 1, 1 \rangle) = \dfrac{d}{dt}(3t) = 3$. **4.** $\langle t, t^2, t^3 \rangle + \mathbf{C}$, where $\mathbf{C} = \langle a, b, c \rangle$, and a, b, and c are real numbers ◄

11.7 Motion in Space

It is a remarkable fact that given the forces acting on an object and its initial position and velocity, the motion of the object in three-dimensional space can be modeled for all future times. To be sure, the accuracy of the results depends on how well the various forces on the object are described. For example, it may be more difficult to predict the trajectory of a spinning soccer ball than the path of a space station orbiting Earth. Nevertheless, as shown in this section, by combining Newton's Second Law of Motion with everything we have learned about vectors, it is possible to solve a variety of moving body problems.

Position, Velocity, Speed, Acceleration

Until now, we have studied objects that move in one dimension (along a line). The next step is to consider the motion of objects in two dimensions (in a plane) and three dimensions (in space). We work in a three-dimensional coordinate system and let the vector-valued function $\mathbf{r}(t) = \langle x(t), y(t), z(t) \rangle$ describe the *position* of a moving object at times $t \geq 0$. The curve described by $\mathbf{r}$ is the *path* or *trajectory* of the object (Figure 11.81). Just as with one-dimensional motion, the rate of change of the position function with respect to time is the *instantaneous velocity* of the object—a vector with three components corresponding to the velocity in the x-, y-, and z-directions:

$$\mathbf{v}(t) = \mathbf{r}'(t) = \langle x'(t), y'(t), z'(t) \rangle.$$

This expression should look familiar. The velocity vectors of a moving object are simply tangent vectors; that is, at any point, the velocity vector is tangent to the trajectory (Figure 11.81).

As with one-dimensional motion, the *speed* of an object moving in three dimensions is the magnitude of its velocity vector:

$$|\mathbf{v}(t)| = |\langle x'(t), y'(t), z'(t) \rangle| = \sqrt{x'(t)^2 + y'(t)^2 + z'(t)^2}.$$

The speed is a nonnegative scalar-valued function.

Finally, the *acceleration* of a moving object is the rate of change of the velocity:

$$\mathbf{a}(t) = \mathbf{v}'(t) = \mathbf{r}''(t).$$

While the position vector gives the path of a moving object and the velocity vector is always tangent to the path, the acceleration vector is more difficult to visualize. Figure 11.82 shows one particular instance of two-dimensional motion. The trajectory is a segment of a parabola and is traced out by the position vectors (shown at $t = 0$ and $t = 1$). As expected, the velocity vectors are tangent to the trajectory. In this case, the acceleration is $\mathbf{a} = \langle -2, 0 \rangle$; it is constant in magnitude and direction for all times. The relationships among $\mathbf{r}$, $\mathbf{v}$, and $\mathbf{a}$ are explored in the coming examples.

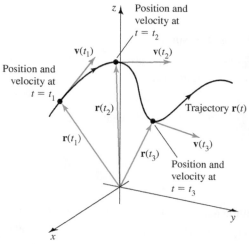

Figure 11.81

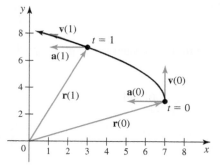

Figure 11.82

▶ In the case of two-dimensional motion, $\mathbf{r}(t) = \langle x(t), y(t) \rangle$, $\mathbf{v}(t) = \mathbf{r}'(t)$, and $\mathbf{a}(t) = \mathbf{r}''(t)$.

DEFINITION **Position, Velocity, Speed, Acceleration**

Let the **position** of an object moving in three-dimensional space be given by $\mathbf{r}(t) = \langle x(t), y(t), z(t) \rangle$, for $t \geq 0$. The **velocity** of the object is

$$\mathbf{v}(t) = \mathbf{r}'(t) = \langle x'(t), y'(t), z'(t) \rangle.$$

The **speed** of the object is the scalar function

$$|\mathbf{v}(t)| = \sqrt{x'(t)^2 + y'(t)^2 + z'(t)^2}.$$

The **acceleration** of the object is $\mathbf{a}(t) = \mathbf{v}'(t) = \mathbf{r}''(t)$.

QUICK CHECK 1 Given $\mathbf{r}(t) = \langle t, t^2, t^3 \rangle$, find $\mathbf{v}(t)$ and $\mathbf{a}(t)$. ◀

EXAMPLE 1   Velocity and acceleration for circular motion Consider the two-dimensional motion given by the position vector

$$\mathbf{r}(t) = \langle x(t), y(t) \rangle = \langle 3\cos t, 3\sin t \rangle, \quad \text{for } 0 \le t \le 2\pi.$$

a. Sketch the trajectory of the object.

b. Find the velocity and speed of the object.

c. Find the acceleration of the object.

d. Sketch the position, velocity, and acceleration vectors, for $t = 0, \pi/2, \pi$, and $3\pi/2$.

SOLUTION

a. Notice that

$$x(t)^2 + y(t)^2 = 9(\cos^2 t + \sin^2 t) = 9,$$

which is an equation of a circle centered at the origin with radius 3. The object moves on this circle in the counterclockwise direction (Figure 11.83).

b. $\mathbf{v}(t) = \langle x'(t), y'(t) \rangle = \langle -3\sin t, 3\cos t \rangle$ Velocity vector

$$|\mathbf{v}(t)| = \sqrt{x'(t)^2 + y'(t)^2} \qquad\qquad \text{Definition of speed}$$

$$= \sqrt{(-3\sin t)^2 + (3\cos t)^2}$$

$$= \sqrt{9\underbrace{(\sin^2 t + \cos^2 t)}_{1}} = 3$$

v(π/2)   t = π/2

v(0)

r(π/2) a(π/2)

t = π   a(π)   r(0)   t = 0

r(π)   a(0)

a(3π/2) r(3π/2)

v(π)

t = 3π/2   v(3π/2)

Circular motion: At all times $\mathbf{a}(t) = -\mathbf{r}(t)$ and $\mathbf{v}(t)$ is orthogonal to $\mathbf{r}(t)$ and $\mathbf{a}(t)$.

Figure 11.83

The velocity vector has a constant magnitude and a continuously changing direction.

c. Differentiating the velocity, we find that $\mathbf{a}(t) = \mathbf{v}'(t) = \langle -3\cos t, -3\sin t \rangle = -\mathbf{r}(t)$. In this case, the acceleration vector is the negative of the position vector at all times.

d. The relationships among $\mathbf{r}, \mathbf{v}$, and $\mathbf{a}$ at four points in time are shown in Figure 11.83. The velocity vector is always tangent to the trajectory and has length 3, while the acceleration vector and position vector each have length 3 and point in opposite directions. At all times, $\mathbf{v}$ is orthogonal to $\mathbf{r}$ and $\mathbf{a}$.

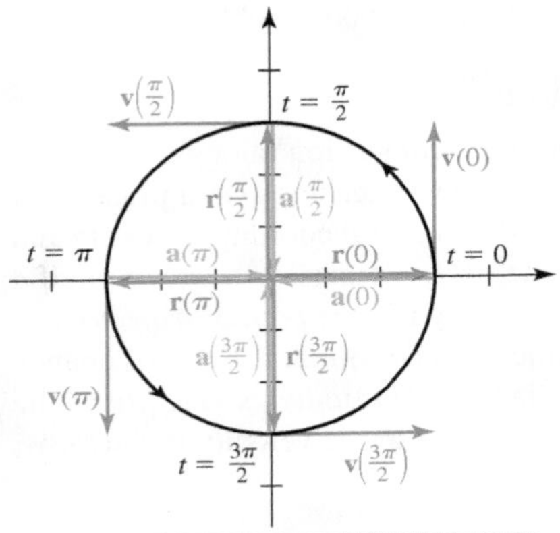

Related Exercises 7–18 ◄

EXAMPLE 2   Comparing trajectories Consider the trajectories described by the position functions

$$\mathbf{r}(t) = \left\langle t, t^2 - 4, \frac{t^3}{4} - 8 \right\rangle, \quad \text{for } t \ge 0, \text{ and}$$

$$\mathbf{R}(t) = \left\langle t^2, t^4 - 4, \frac{t^6}{4} - 8 \right\rangle, \quad \text{for } t \ge 0,$$

where t is measured in the same time units for both functions.

a. Graph and compare the trajectories using a graphing utility.

b. Find the velocity vectors associated with the position functions.

SOLUTION

a. Plotting the position functions at selected values of t results in the trajectories shown in Figure 11.84. Because $\mathbf{r}(0) = \mathbf{R}(0) = \langle 0, -4, -8 \rangle$, both curves have the same initial point. For $t \ge 0$, the two curves consist of the same points, but they are traced out differently. For example, both curves pass through the point $(4, 12, 8)$, but that point corresponds to $\mathbf{r}(4)$ on the first curve and $\mathbf{R}(2)$ on the second curve. In general, $\mathbf{r}(t^2) = \mathbf{R}(t)$, for $t \ge 0$.

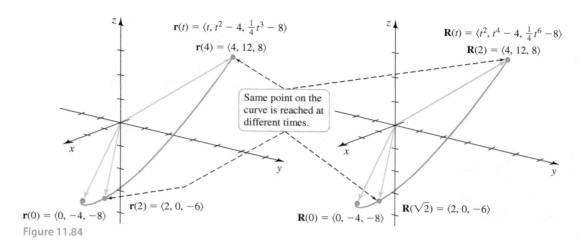

Same point on the curve is reached at different times.

$\mathbf{r}(t) = \langle t, t^2 - 4, \frac{1}{4}t^3 - 8 \rangle$

$\mathbf{r}(4) = \langle 4, 12, 8 \rangle$

$\mathbf{r}(0) = \langle 0, -4, -8 \rangle$

$\mathbf{r}(2) = \langle 2, 0, -6 \rangle$

$\mathbf{R}(t) = \langle t^2, t^4 - 4, \frac{1}{4}t^6 - 8 \rangle$

$\mathbf{R}(2) = \langle 4, 12, 8 \rangle$

$\mathbf{R}(0) = \langle 0, -4, -8 \rangle$

$\mathbf{R}(\sqrt{2}) = \langle 2, 0, -6 \rangle$

Figure 11.84

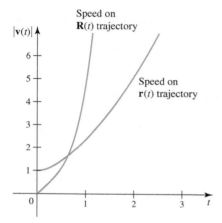

Figure 11.85

> See Exercise 61 for a discussion of nonuniform straight-line motion.

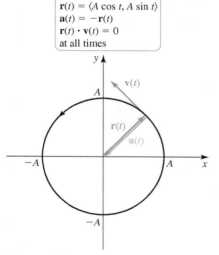

Circular trajectory
$\mathbf{r}(t) = \langle A \cos t, A \sin t \rangle$
$\mathbf{a}(t) = -\mathbf{r}(t)$
$\mathbf{r}(t) \cdot \mathbf{v}(t) = 0$
at all times

Figure 11.86

b. The velocity vectors are

$$\mathbf{r}'(t) = \left\langle 1, 2t, \frac{3t^2}{4} \right\rangle \quad \text{and} \quad \mathbf{R}'(t) = \left\langle 2t, 4t^3, \frac{3}{2}t^5 \right\rangle.$$

The difference in the motion on the two curves is revealed by the graphs of the speeds associated with the trajectories (Figure 11.85). The object on the first trajectory reaches the point $(4, 12, 8)$ at $t = 4$, where its speed is $|\mathbf{r}'(4)| = |\langle 1, 8, 12 \rangle| \approx 14.5$. The object on the second trajectory reaches the same point $(4, 12, 8)$ at $t = 2$, where its speed is $|\mathbf{R}'(2)| = |\langle 4, 32, 48 \rangle| \approx 57.8$.

Related Exercises 19–24 ◄

QUICK CHECK 2 Find the functions that give the speed of the two objects in Example 2, for $t \geq 0$ (corresponding to the graphs in Figure 11.85). ◄

Straight-Line and Circular Motion

Two types of motion in space arise frequently and deserve to be singled out. First consider a trajectory described by the vector function

$$\mathbf{r}(t) = \langle x_0 + at, y_0 + bt, z_0 + ct \rangle, \quad \text{for } t \geq 0,$$

where $x_0, y_0, z_0, a, b,$ and c are constants. This function describes a straight-line trajectory with an initial point $\langle x_0, y_0, z_0 \rangle$ and a direction given by the vector $\langle a, b, c \rangle$ (Section 11.5). The velocity on this trajectory is the constant $\mathbf{v}(t) = \mathbf{r}'(t) = \langle a, b, c \rangle$ in the direction of the trajectory, and the acceleration is $\mathbf{a} = \langle 0, 0, 0 \rangle$. The motion associated with this function is **uniform** (constant velocity) **straight-line motion**.

A different situation is **circular motion** (Example 1). Consider the two-dimensional circular path

$$\mathbf{r}(t) = \langle A \cos t, A \sin t \rangle, \quad \text{for } 0 \leq t \leq 2\pi,$$

where A is a nonzero constant (Figure 11.86). The velocity and acceleration vectors are

$$\mathbf{v}(t) = \langle -A \sin t, A \cos t \rangle \quad \text{and}$$
$$\mathbf{a}(t) = \langle -A \cos t, -A \sin t \rangle = -\mathbf{r}(t).$$

Notice that $\mathbf{r}$ and $\mathbf{a}$ are parallel, but point in opposite directions. Furthermore, $\mathbf{r} \cdot \mathbf{v} = \mathbf{a} \cdot \mathbf{v} = 0$; therefore, the position and acceleration vectors are both orthogonal to the velocity vectors at any given point (Figure 11.86). Finally, $\mathbf{r}, \mathbf{v},$ and $\mathbf{a}$ have constant magnitude A and variable directions. The conclusion that $\mathbf{r} \cdot \mathbf{v} = 0$ applies to any motion for which $|\mathbf{r}|$ is constant; that is, motion on a circle or a sphere (Figure 11.87).

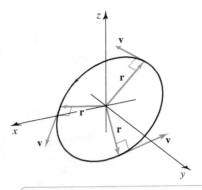

On a trajectory on which $|\mathbf{r}|$ is constant, $\mathbf{v}$ is orthogonal to $\mathbf{r}$ at all points.

Figure 11.87

> **THEOREM 11.8   Motion with Constant $|\mathbf{r}|$**
> Let $\mathbf{r}$ describe a path on which $|\mathbf{r}|$ is constant (motion on a circle or sphere centered at the origin). Then $\mathbf{r} \cdot \mathbf{v} = 0$, which means the position vector and the velocity vector are orthogonal at all times for which the functions are defined.

Proof: If $\mathbf{r}$ has constant magnitude, then $|\mathbf{r}(t)|^2 = \mathbf{r}(t) \cdot \mathbf{r}(t) = c$ for some constant c. Differentiating the equation $\mathbf{r}(t) \cdot \mathbf{r}(t) = c$, we have

$$0 = \frac{d}{dt}(\mathbf{r}(t) \cdot \mathbf{r}(t)) \qquad \text{Differentiate both sides of } |\mathbf{r}(t)|^2 = c$$
$$= \mathbf{r}'(t) \cdot \mathbf{r}(t) + \mathbf{r}(t) \cdot \mathbf{r}'(t) \qquad \text{Derivative of dot product (Theorem 11.7)}$$
$$= 2\mathbf{r}'(t) \cdot \mathbf{r}(t) \qquad \text{Simplify.}$$
$$= 2\mathbf{v}(t) \cdot \mathbf{r}(t). \qquad \mathbf{r}'(t) = \mathbf{v}(t)$$

Because $\mathbf{r}(t) \cdot \mathbf{v}(t) = 0$ for all t, it follows that $\mathbf{r}$ and $\mathbf{v}$ are orthogonal for all t. ◄

EXAMPLE 3   Path on a sphere An object moves on a trajectory described by

$$\mathbf{r}(t) = \langle x(t), y(t), z(t) \rangle = \langle 3\cos t, 5\sin t, 4\cos t \rangle, \quad \text{for } 0 \le t \le 2\pi.$$

a. Show that the object moves on a sphere and find the radius of the sphere.

b. Find the velocity and speed of the object.

> ➤ For generalizations of this example and explorations of trajectories that lie on spheres and ellipses, see Exercises 79, 82, and 83.

SOLUTION

a. $|\mathbf{r}(t)|^2 = x(t)^2 + y(t)^2 + z(t)^2$ Square of the distance from the origin
$$= (3\cos t)^2 + (5\sin t)^2 + (4\cos t)^2 \quad \text{Substitute.}$$
$$= 25\cos^2 t + 25\sin^2 t \quad \text{Simplify.}$$
$$= 25\underbrace{(\cos^2 t + \sin^2 t)}_{1} = 25 \quad \text{Factor.}$$

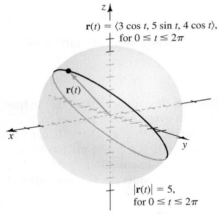

$\mathbf{r}(t) = \langle 3\cos t, 5\sin t, 4\cos t \rangle$, for $0 \le t \le 2\pi$

$|\mathbf{r}(t)| = 5$, for $0 \le t \le 2\pi$

Figure 11.88

Therefore, $|\mathbf{r}(t)| = 5$, for $0 \le t \le 2\pi$, and the trajectory lies on a sphere of radius 5 centered at the origin (Figure 11.88).

b. $\mathbf{v}(t) = \mathbf{r}'(t) = \langle -3\sin t, 5\cos t, -4\sin t \rangle$ Velocity vector
$$|\mathbf{v}(t)| = \sqrt{\mathbf{v}(t) \cdot \mathbf{v}(t)} \qquad \text{Speed of the object}$$
$$= \sqrt{9\sin^2 t + 25\cos^2 t + 16\sin^2 t} \qquad \text{Evaluate the dot product.}$$
$$= \sqrt{25\underbrace{(\sin^2 t + \cos^2 t)}_{1}} \qquad \text{Simplify.}$$
$$= 5 \qquad \text{Simplify.}$$

The speed of the object is always 5. You should verify that $\mathbf{r}(t) \cdot \mathbf{v}(t) = 0$, for all t, implying that $\mathbf{r}$ and $\mathbf{v}$ are always orthogonal.

Related Exercises 25–30 ◄

QUICK CHECK 3 Verify that $\mathbf{r}(t) \cdot \mathbf{v}(t) = 0$ in Example 3. ◄

Two-Dimensional Motion in a Gravitational Field

Newton's Second Law of Motion, which is used to model the motion of most objects, states that

$$\underbrace{\text{mass}}_{m} \cdot \underbrace{\text{acceleration}}_{\mathbf{a}(t)\, =\, \mathbf{r}''(t)} = \underbrace{\text{sum of all forces.}}_{\sum \mathbf{F}_k}$$

The governing law says something about the *acceleration* of an object, and in order to describe the motion fully, we must find the velocity and position from the acceleration.

Finding Velocity and Position from Acceleration

We begin with the case of two-dimensional projectile motion in which the only force acting on the object is the gravitational force; for the moment, air resistance and other possible external forces are neglected.

A convenient coordinate system uses a y-axis that points vertically upward and an x-axis that points in the direction of horizontal motion. The gravitational force is in the negative y-direction and is given by $\mathbf{F} = \langle 0, -mg \rangle$, where m is the mass of the object and $g \approx 9.8 \text{ m/s}^2 \approx 32 \text{ ft/s}^2$ is the acceleration due to gravity (Figure 11.89).

With these observations, Newton's Second Law takes the form

$$m\mathbf{a}(t) = \mathbf{F} = \langle 0, -mg \rangle.$$

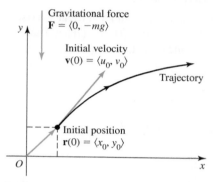

Gravitational force
$\mathbf{F} = \langle 0, -mg \rangle$

Initial velocity
$\mathbf{v}(0) = \langle u_0, v_0 \rangle$

Trajectory

Initial position
$\mathbf{r}(0) = \langle x_0, y_0 \rangle$

Figure 11.89

Significantly, the mass of the object cancels, leaving the vector equation

$$\mathbf{a}(t) = \langle 0, -g \rangle. \tag{1}$$

In order to find the velocity $\mathbf{v}(t) = \langle x'(t), y'(t) \rangle$ and the position $\mathbf{r}(t) = \langle x(t), y(t) \rangle$ from this equation, we must be given the following **initial conditions**:

$$\text{Initial velocity at } t = 0\text{: } \mathbf{v}(0) = \langle u_0, v_0 \rangle \text{ and}$$
$$\text{Initial position at } t = 0\text{: } \mathbf{r}(0) = \langle x_0, y_0 \rangle.$$

We proceed in two steps.

> ➤ Recall that an antiderivative of 0 is a constant C and an antiderivative of $-g$ is $-gt + C$.

1. **Solve for the velocity** The velocity is an antiderivative of the acceleration in equation (1). Integrating the acceleration, we have

$$\mathbf{v}(t) = \int \mathbf{a}(t)\, dt = \int \langle 0, -g \rangle\, dt = \langle 0, -gt \rangle + \mathbf{C},$$

> ➤ You have a choice. You may do these calculations in vector notation as we have done here, or you may work with individual components.

where $\mathbf{C}$ is an arbitrary constant vector. The arbitrary constant is determined by substituting $t = 0$ and using the initial condition $\mathbf{v}(0) = \langle u_0, v_0 \rangle$. We find that $\mathbf{v}(0) = \langle 0, 0 \rangle + \mathbf{C} = \langle u_0, v_0 \rangle$, or $\mathbf{C} = \langle u_0, v_0 \rangle$. Therefore, the velocity is

$$\mathbf{v}(t) = \langle 0, -gt \rangle + \langle u_0, v_0 \rangle = \langle u_0, -gt + v_0 \rangle. \tag{2}$$

Notice that the horizontal component of velocity is simply the initial horizontal velocity u_0 for all time. The vertical component of velocity decreases linearly from its initial value of v_0.

2. **Solve for the position** The position is an antiderivative of the velocity given by equation (2):

$$\mathbf{r}(t) = \int \mathbf{v}(t)\, dt = \int \langle u_0, -gt + v_0 \rangle\, dt = \left\langle u_0 t, -\frac{1}{2} gt^2 + v_0 t \right\rangle + \mathbf{C},$$

where $\mathbf{C}$ is an arbitrary constant vector. Substituting $t = 0$, we have $\mathbf{r}(0) = \langle 0, 0 \rangle + \mathbf{C} = \langle x_0, y_0 \rangle$, which implies that $\mathbf{C} = \langle x_0, y_0 \rangle$. Therefore, the position of the object, for $t \geq 0$, is

$$\mathbf{r}(t) = \left\langle u_0 t, -\frac{1}{2} g t^2 + v_0 t \right\rangle + \langle x_0, y_0 \rangle = \Big\langle \underbrace{u_0 t + x_0}_{x(t)}, \underbrace{-\frac{1}{2} g t^2 + v_0 t + y_0}_{y(t)} \Big\rangle.$$

SUMMARY Two-Dimensional Motion in a Gravitational Field

Consider an object moving in a plane with a horizontal x-axis and a vertical y-axis, subject only to the force of gravity. Given the initial velocity $\mathbf{v}(0) = \langle u_0, v_0 \rangle$ and the initial position $\mathbf{r}(0) = \langle x_0, y_0 \rangle$, the velocity of the object, for $t \geq 0$, is

$$\mathbf{v}(t) = \langle x'(t), y'(t) \rangle = \langle u_0, -gt + v_0 \rangle$$

and the position is

$$\mathbf{r}(t) = \langle x(t), y(t) \rangle = \left\langle u_0 t + x_0, -\frac{1}{2} g t^2 + v_0 t + y_0 \right\rangle.$$

EXAMPLE 4   Flight of a baseball A baseball is hit from 3 ft above home plate with an initial velocity in ft/s of $\mathbf{v}(0) = \langle u_0, v_0 \rangle = \langle 80, 80 \rangle$. Neglect all forces other than gravity.

a. Find the position and velocity of the ball between the time it is hit and the time it first hits the ground.

b. Show that the trajectory of the ball is a segment of a parabola.

c. Assuming a flat playing field, how far does the ball travel horizontally? Plot the trajectory of the ball.

d. What is the maximum height of the ball?

e. Does the ball clear a 20-ft fence that is 380 ft from home plate (directly under the path of the ball)?

SOLUTION Assume the origin is located at home plate. Because distances are measured in feet, we use $g = 32$ ft/s^2.

a. Substituting $x_0 = 0$ and $y_0 = 3$ into the equation for $\mathbf{r}$, the position of the ball is

$$\mathbf{r}(t) = \langle x(t), y(t) \rangle = \langle 80t, -16t^2 + 80t + 3 \rangle, \quad \text{for } t \geq 0. \qquad (3)$$

We then compute $\mathbf{v}(t) = \mathbf{r}'(t) = \langle 80, -32t + 80 \rangle$.

b. Equation (3) says that the horizontal position is $x = 80t$ and the vertical position is $y = -16t^2 + 80t + 3$. Substituting $t = x/80$ into the equation for y gives

$$y = -16\left(\frac{x}{80}\right)^2 + x + 3 = -\frac{x^2}{400} + x + 3,$$

which is an equation of a parabola.

c. The ball lands on the ground at the value of $t > 0$ at which $y = 0$. Solving $y(t) = -16t^2 + 80t + 3 = 0$, we find that $t \approx -0.04$ and $t \approx 5.04$ s. The first root is not relevant for the problem at hand, so we conclude that the ball lands when $t \approx 5.04$ s. The horizontal distance traveled by the ball is $x(5.04) \approx 403$ ft. The path of the ball in the xy-coordinate system on the time interval $[0, 5.04]$ is shown in Figure 11.90.

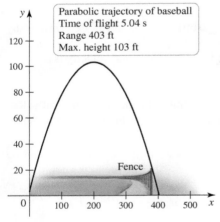

Parabolic trajectory of baseball
Time of flight 5.04 s
Range 403 ft
Max. height 103 ft

Fence

Figure 11.90

▶ The equation in part (c) can be solved using the quadratic formula or a root-finder on a calculator.

d. The ball reaches its maximum height at the time its vertical velocity is zero. Solving $y'(t) = -32t + 80 = 0$, we find that $t = 2.5$ s. The height at that time is $y(2.5) = 103$ ft.

e. The ball reaches a horizontal distance of 380 ft (the distance to the fence) when $x(t) = 80t = 380$. Solving for t, we find that $t = 4.75$ s. The height of the ball at that time is $y(4.75) = 22$ ft. So, indeed, the ball clears a 20-ft fence.

Related Exercises 31–36 ◄

QUICK CHECK 4 Write the functions $x(t)$ and $y(t)$ in Example 4 in the case that $x_0 = 0$, $y_0 = 2$, $u_0 = 100$, and $v_0 = 60$. ◄

Range, Time of Flight, Maximum Height   Having solved one specific motion problem, we can make some general observations about two-dimensional projectile motion in a gravitational field. Assume that the motion of an object begins at the origin; that is, $x_0 = y_0 = 0$. Assume also that the object is launched at an angle of α ($0 \le \alpha \le \pi/2$) above the horizontal with an initial speed $|\mathbf{v}_0|$ (Figure 11.91). This means that the initial velocity is

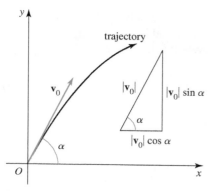

Figure 11.91

$$\langle u_0, v_0 \rangle = \langle |\mathbf{v}_0| \cos \alpha, |\mathbf{v}_0| \sin \alpha \rangle.$$

Substituting these values into the general expressions for the velocity and position, we find that the velocity of the object is

$$\mathbf{v}(t) = \langle u_0, -gt + v_0 \rangle = \langle |\mathbf{v}_0| \cos \alpha, -gt + |\mathbf{v}_0| \sin \alpha \rangle.$$

The position of the object (with $x_0 = y_0 = 0$) is

$$\mathbf{r}(t) = \langle x(t), y(t) \rangle = \langle (|\mathbf{v}_0| \cos \alpha)t, -gt^2/2 + (|\mathbf{v}_0| \sin \alpha)t \rangle.$$

Notice that the motion is determined entirely by the parameters $|\mathbf{v}_0|$ and α. Several general conclusions now follow.

▶ The other root of the equation $y(t) = 0$ is $t = 0$, the time the object leaves the ground.

1. Assuming the object is launched from the origin over horizontal ground, it returns to the ground when $y(t) = -gt^2/2 + (|\mathbf{v}_0| \sin \alpha)t = 0$. Solving for t, the **time of flight** is $T = 2|\mathbf{v}_0| \sin \alpha / g$.

2. The **range** of the object, which is the horizontal distance it travels, is the x-coordinate of the trajectory when $t = T$:

$$x(T) = (|\mathbf{v}_0| \cos \alpha)T$$

$$= (|\mathbf{v}_0| \cos \alpha)\frac{2|\mathbf{v}_0| \sin \alpha}{g} \qquad \text{Substitute for } T.$$

$$= \frac{2|\mathbf{v}_0|^2 \sin \alpha \cos \alpha}{g} \qquad \text{Simplify.}$$

$$= \frac{|\mathbf{v}_0|^2 \sin 2\alpha}{g}. \qquad 2 \sin \alpha \cos \alpha = \sin 2\alpha$$

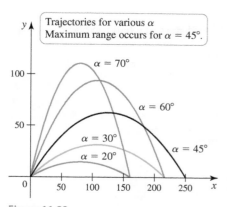

Figure 11.92

Note that on the interval $0 \le \alpha \le \pi/2$, $\sin 2\alpha$ has a maximum value of 1 when $\alpha = \pi/4$, so the maximum range is $|\mathbf{v}_0|^2/g$. In other words, in an ideal world, firing an object from the ground at an angle of $\pi/4$ (45°) maximizes its range. Notice that the ranges obtained with the angles α and $\pi/2 - \alpha$ are equal (Figure 11.92).

QUICK CHECK 5 Show that the range attained with an angle α equals the range attained with the angle $\pi/2 - \alpha$. ◄

3. The maximum height of the object is reached when the vertical velocity is zero, or when $y'(t) = -gt + |\mathbf{v_0}| \sin \alpha = 0$. Solving for t, the maximum height is reached at $t = |\mathbf{v_0}|(\sin \alpha)/g = T/2$, which is half the time of flight. The object spends equal amounts of time ascending and descending. The maximum height is

$$y\left(\frac{T}{2}\right) = \frac{(|\mathbf{v_0}| \sin \alpha)^2}{2g}.$$

4. Finally, by eliminating t from the equations for $x(t)$ and $y(t)$, it can be shown (Exercise 78) that the trajectory of the object is a segment of a parabola.

> ➤ Use caution with the formulas in the summary box: They are applicable only when the initial position of the object is the origin.

SUMMARY   Two-Dimensional Motion

Assume an object traveling over horizontal ground, acted on only by the gravitational force, has an initial position $\langle x_0, y_0 \rangle = \langle 0, 0 \rangle$ and initial velocity $\langle u_0, v_0 \rangle = \langle |\mathbf{v_0}| \cos \alpha, |\mathbf{v_0}| \sin \alpha \rangle$. The trajectory, which is a segment of a parabola, has the following properties.

$$\text{time of flight} = T = \frac{2|\mathbf{v_0}| \sin \alpha}{g}$$

$$\text{range} = \frac{|\mathbf{v_0}|^2 \sin 2\alpha}{g}$$

$$\text{maximum height} = y\left(\frac{T}{2}\right) = \frac{(|\mathbf{v_0}| \sin \alpha)^2}{2g}$$

EXAMPLE 5   Flight of a golf ball A golf ball is driven down a horizontal fairway with an initial speed of 55 m/s at an initial angle of 25° (from a tee with negligible height). Neglect all forces except gravity and assume that the ball's trajectory lies in a plane.

a. How far does the ball travel horizontally and when does it land?

b. What is the maximum height of the ball?

c. At what angles should the ball be hit to reach a green that is 300 m from the tee?

SOLUTION

a. Using the range formula with $\alpha = 25°$ and $|\mathbf{v_0}| = 55$ m/s, the ball travels

$$\frac{|\mathbf{v_0}|^2 \sin 2\alpha}{g} = \frac{(55 \text{ m/s})^2 \sin 50°}{9.8 \text{ m/s}^2} \approx 236 \text{ m}.$$

The time of the flight is

$$T = \frac{2|\mathbf{v_0}| \sin \alpha}{g} = \frac{2(55 \text{ m/s}) \sin 25°}{9.8 \text{ m/s}^2} \approx 4.7 \text{ s}.$$

b. The maximum height of the ball is

$$\frac{(|\mathbf{v_0}| \sin \alpha)^2}{2g} = \frac{((55 \text{ m/s}) (\sin 25°))^2}{2(9.8 \text{ m/s}^2)} \approx 27.6 \text{ m}.$$

c. Letting R denote the range and solving the range formula for $\sin 2\alpha$, we find that $\sin 2\alpha = Rg/|\mathbf{v_0}|^2$. For a range of $R = 300$ m and an initial speed of $|\mathbf{v_0}| = 55$ m/s, the required angle satisfies

$$\sin 2\alpha = \frac{Rg}{|\mathbf{v_0}|^2} = \frac{(300 \text{ m}) (9.8 \text{ m/s}^2)}{(55 \text{ m/s})^2} \approx 0.972.$$

To travel a horizontal distance of exactly 300 m, the required angles are $\alpha = \frac{1}{2} \sin^{-1} 0.972 \approx 38.2°$ or 51.8°.

Related Exercises 37–42 ◄

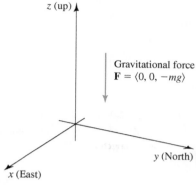

Gravitational force
$\mathbf{F} = \langle 0, 0, -mg \rangle$

z (up)

y (North)

x (East)

Figure 11.93

Three-Dimensional Motion

To solve three-dimensional motion problems, we adopt a coordinate system in which the x- and y-axes point in two perpendicular horizontal directions (for example, east and north), while the positive z-axis points vertically upward (Figure 11.93). Newton's Second Law now has three components and appears in the form

$$m\mathbf{a}(t) = \langle mx''(t), my''(t), mz''(t) \rangle = \mathbf{F}.$$

If only the gravitational force is present (now in the negative z-direction), then the force vector is $\mathbf{F} = \langle 0, 0, -mg \rangle$; the equation of motion is then $\mathbf{a}(t) = \langle 0, 0, -g \rangle$. Other effects, such as crosswinds, spins, or slices, can be modeled by including other force components.

EXAMPLE 6   Projectile motion   A small projectile is fired over horizontal ground in an easterly direction with an initial speed of $|\mathbf{v}_0| = 300$ m/s at an angle of $\alpha = 30°$ above the horizontal. A crosswind blows from south to north, producing an acceleration of the projectile of 0.36 m/s² to the north.

a. Where does the projectile land? How far does it land from its launch site?

b. In order to correct for the crosswind and make the projectile land due east of the launch site, at what angle from due east must the projectile be fired? Assume the initial speed $|\mathbf{v}_0| = 300$ m/s and the angle of elevation $\alpha = 30°$ are the same as in part (a).

SOLUTION

a. Letting $g = 9.8$ m/s², the equations of motion are $\mathbf{a}(t) = \mathbf{v}'(t) = \langle 0, 0.36, -9.8 \rangle$. Proceeding as in the two-dimensional case, the indefinite integral of the acceleration is the velocity function

$$\mathbf{v}(t) = \langle 0, 0.36t, -9.8t \rangle + \mathbf{C},$$

where $\mathbf{C}$ is an arbitrary constant. With an initial speed $|\mathbf{v}_0| = 300$ m/s and an angle of elevation of $\alpha = 30°$ (Figure 11.94a), the initial velocity is

$$\mathbf{v}(0) = \langle 300 \cos 30°, 0, 300 \sin 30° \rangle = \langle 150\sqrt{3}, 0, 150 \rangle.$$

Substituting $t = 0$ and using the initial condition, we find that $\mathbf{C} = \langle 150\sqrt{3}, 0, 150 \rangle$. Therefore, the velocity function is

$$\mathbf{v}(t) = \langle 150\sqrt{3}, 0.36t, -9.8t + 150 \rangle.$$

Integrating the velocity function produces the position function

$$\mathbf{r}(t) = \langle 150\sqrt{3}t, 0.18t^2, -4.9t^2 + 150t \rangle + \mathbf{C}.$$

Using the initial condition $\mathbf{r}(0) = \langle 0, 0, 0 \rangle$, we find that $\mathbf{C} = \langle 0, 0, 0 \rangle$, and the position function is

$$\mathbf{r}(t) = \langle x(t), y(t), z(t) \rangle = \langle 150\sqrt{3}t, 0.18t^2, -4.9t^2 + 150t \rangle.$$

The projectile lands when $z(t) = -4.9t^2 + 150t = 0$. Solving for t, the positive root, which gives the time of flight, is $T = 150/4.9 \approx 30.6$ s. The x- and y-coordinates at that time are

$$x(T) \approx 7953 \text{ m} \quad \text{and} \quad y(T) \approx 169 \text{ m}.$$

Therefore, the projectile lands approximately 7953 m east and 169 m north of the firing site. Because the projectile started at $(0, 0, 0)$, it traveled a horizontal distance of $\sqrt{7953^2 + 169^2} \approx 7955$ m (Figure 11.94a).

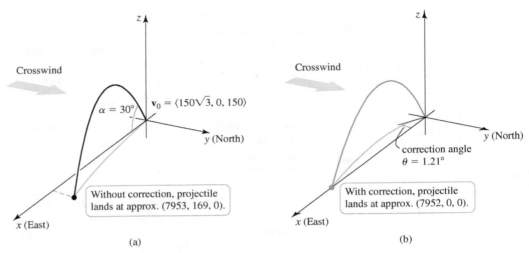

Figure 11.94

b. Keeping the initial speed of the projectile equal to $|\mathbf{v}_0| = 300$ m/s, we decompose the horizontal component of the speed, $150\sqrt{3}$ m/s, into an east component, $u_0 = 150\sqrt{3} \cos \theta$, and a north component, $v_0 = 150\sqrt{3} \sin \theta$, where θ is the angle relative to due east; we must determine the correction angle θ (Figure 11.94b). The x- and y-components of the position are

$$x(t) = (150\sqrt{3} \cos \theta)t \quad \text{and} \quad y(t) = 0.18t^2 + (150\sqrt{3} \sin \theta)t.$$

These changes in the initial velocity affect the x- and y-equations, but not the z-equation. Therefore, the time of flight is still $T = 150/4.9 \approx 30.6$ s. The aim is to choose θ so that the projectile lands on the x-axis (due east from the launch site), which means $y(T) = 0$. Solving

$$y(T) = 0.18T^2 + (150\sqrt{3} \sin \theta)T = 0,$$

with $T = 150/4.9$, we find that $\sin \theta \approx -0.0212$; therefore, $\theta \approx -0.0212$ rad $\approx -1.21°$. In other words, the projectile must be fired at a horizontal angle of $1.21°$ to the *south* of east to correct for the northerly crosswind (Figure 11.94b). The landing location of the projectile is $x(T) \approx 7952$ m and $y(T) = 0$.

Related Exercises 43–52 ◀

SECTION 11.7 EXERCISES

Review Questions

1. Given the position function **r** of a moving object, explain how to find the velocity, speed, and acceleration of the object.

2. What is the relationship between the position and velocity vectors for motion on a circle?

3. Write Newton's Second Law of Motion in vector form.

4. Write Newton's Second Law of Motion for three-dimensional motion with only the gravitational force (acting in the z-direction).

5. Given the acceleration of an object and its initial velocity, how do you find the velocity of the object, for $t \geq 0$?

6. Given the velocity of an object and its initial position, how do you find the position of the object, for $t \geq 0$?

Basic Skills

7–18. Velocity and acceleration from position *Consider the following position functions.*

a. Find the velocity and speed of the object.
b. Find the acceleration of the object.

7. $\mathbf{r}(t) = \langle 3t^2 + 1, 4t^2 + 3 \rangle$, for $t \geq 0$

8. $\mathbf{r}(t) = \left\langle \dfrac{5}{2}t^2 + 3, 6t^2 + 10 \right\rangle$, for $t \geq 0$

9. $\mathbf{r}(t) = \langle 2 + 2t, 1 - 4t \rangle$, for $t \geq 0$

10. $\mathbf{r}(t) = \langle 1 - t^2, 3 + 2t^3 \rangle$, for $t \geq 0$

11. $\mathbf{r}(t) = \langle 8 \sin t, 8 \cos t \rangle$, for $0 \leq t \leq 2\pi$

12. $\mathbf{r}(t) = \langle 3 \cos t, 4 \sin t \rangle$, for $0 \leq t \leq 2\pi$

13. $\mathbf{r}(t) = \left\langle t^2 + 3, t^2 + 10, \frac{1}{2}t^2 \right\rangle$, for $t \geq 0$

14. $\mathbf{r}(t) = \langle 2e^{2t} + 1, e^{2t} - 1, 2e^{2t} - 10 \rangle$, for $t \geq 0$

15. $\mathbf{r}(t) = \langle 3 + t, 2 - 4t, 1 + 6t \rangle$, for $t \geq 0$

16. $\mathbf{r}(t) = \langle 3 \sin t, 5 \cos t, 4 \sin t \rangle$, for $0 \leq t \leq 2\pi$

17. $\mathbf{r}(t) = \langle 1, t^2, e^{-t} \rangle$, for $t \geq 0$

18. $\mathbf{r}(t) = \langle 13 \cos 2t, 12 \sin 2t, 5 \sin 2t \rangle$, for $0 \leq t \leq \pi$

T **19–24. Comparing trajectories** *Consider the following position functions* $\mathbf{r}$ *and* $\mathbf{R}$ *for two objects.*

a. *Find the interval* $[c, d]$ *over which the* $\mathbf{R}$ *trajectory is the same as the* $\mathbf{r}$ *trajectory over* $[a, b]$.
b. *Find the velocity for both objects.*
c. *Graph the speed of the two objects over the intervals* $[a, b]$ *and* $[c, d]$, *respectively.*

19. $\mathbf{r}(t) = \langle t, t^2 \rangle, [a, b] = [0, 2]$,
    $\mathbf{R}(t) = \langle 2t, 4t^2 \rangle$ on $[c, d]$

20. $\mathbf{r}(t) = \langle 1 + 3t, 2 + 4t \rangle, [a, b] = [0, 6]$,
    $\mathbf{R}(t) = \langle 1 + 9t, 2 + 12t \rangle$ on $[c, d]$

21. $\mathbf{r}(t) = \langle \cos t, 4 \sin t \rangle, [a, b] = [0, 2\pi]$,
    $\mathbf{R}(t) = \langle \cos 3t, 4 \sin 3t \rangle$ on $[c, d]$

22. $\mathbf{r}(t) = \langle 2 - e^t, 4 - e^{-t} \rangle, [a, b] = [0, \ln 10]$,
    $\mathbf{R}(t) = \langle 2 - t, 4 - 1/t \rangle$ on $[c, d]$

23. $\mathbf{r}(t) = \langle 4 + t^2, 3 - 2t^4, 1 + 3t^6 \rangle, [a, b] = [0, 6]$,
    $\mathbf{R}(t) = \langle 4 + \ln t, 3 - 2 \ln^2 t, 1 + 3 \ln^3 t \rangle$ on $[c, d]$
    For graphing, let $c = 1$ and $d = 20$.

24. $\mathbf{r}(t) = \langle 2 \cos 2t, \sqrt{2} \sin 2t, \sqrt{2} \sin 2t \rangle, [a, b] = [0, \pi]$,
    $\mathbf{R}(t) = \langle 2 \cos 4t, \sqrt{2} \sin 4t, \sqrt{2} \sin 4t \rangle$ on $[c, d]$

25–30. Trajectories on circles and spheres *Determine whether the following trajectories lie on a circle in* $\mathbb{R}^2$ *or sphere in* $\mathbb{R}^3$ *centered at the origin. If so, find the radius of the circle or sphere and show that the position vector and the velocity vector are everywhere orthogonal.*

25. $\mathbf{r}(t) = \langle 8 \cos 2t, 8 \sin 2t \rangle$, for $0 \leq t \leq \pi$

26. $\mathbf{r}(t) = \langle 4 \sin t, 2 \cos t \rangle$, for $0 \leq t \leq 2\pi$

27. $\mathbf{r}(t) = \langle \sin t + \sqrt{3} \cos t, \sqrt{3} \sin t - \cos t \rangle$, for $0 \leq t \leq 2\pi$

28. $\mathbf{r}(t) = \langle 3 \sin t, 5 \cos t, 4 \sin t \rangle$, for $0 \leq t \leq 2\pi$

29. $\mathbf{r}(t) = \langle \sin t, \cos t, \cos t \rangle$, for $0 \leq t \leq 2\pi$

30. $\mathbf{r}(t) = \langle \sqrt{3} \cos t + \sqrt{2} \sin t, -\sqrt{3} \cos t + \sqrt{2} \sin t, \sqrt{2} \sin t \rangle$, for $0 \leq t \leq 2\pi$

31–36. Solving equations of motion *Given an acceleration vector, initial velocity* $\langle u_0, v_0 \rangle$, *and initial position* $\langle x_0, y_0 \rangle$, *find the velocity and position vectors, for* $t \geq 0$.

31. $\mathbf{a}(t) = \langle 0, 1 \rangle, \langle u_0, v_0 \rangle = \langle 2, 3 \rangle, \langle x_0, y_0 \rangle = \langle 0, 0 \rangle$

32. $\mathbf{a}(t) = \langle 1, 2 \rangle, \langle u_0, v_0 \rangle = \langle 1, 1 \rangle, \langle x_0, y_0 \rangle = \langle 2, 3 \rangle$

33. $\mathbf{a}(t) = \langle 0, 10 \rangle, \langle u_0, v_0 \rangle = \langle 0, 5 \rangle, \langle x_0, y_0 \rangle = \langle 1, -1 \rangle$

34. $\mathbf{a}(t) = \langle 1, t \rangle, \langle u_0, v_0 \rangle = \langle 2, -1 \rangle, \langle x_0, y_0 \rangle = \langle 0, 8 \rangle$

35. $\mathbf{a}(t) = \langle \cos t, 2 \sin t \rangle, \langle u_0, v_0 \rangle = \langle 0, 1 \rangle, \langle x_0, y_0 \rangle = \langle 1, 0 \rangle$

36. $\mathbf{a}(t) = \langle e^{-t}, 1 \rangle, \langle u_0, v_0 \rangle = \langle 1, 0 \rangle, \langle x_0, y_0 \rangle = \langle 0, 0 \rangle$

T **37–42. Two-dimensional motion** *Consider the motion of the following objects. Assume the x-axis is horizontal, the positive y-axis is vertical, the ground is horizontal, and only the gravitational force acts on the object.*

a. *Find the velocity and position vectors, for* $t \geq 0$.
b. *Graph the trajectory.*
c. *Determine the time of flight and range of the object.*
d. *Determine the maximum height of the object.*

37. A soccer ball has an initial position $\langle x_0, y_0 \rangle = \langle 0, 0 \rangle$ when it is kicked with an initial velocity of $\langle u_0, v_0 \rangle = \langle 30, 6 \rangle$ m/s.

38. A golf ball has an initial position $\langle x_0, y_0 \rangle = \langle 0, 0 \rangle$ when it is hit at an angle of $30°$ with an initial speed of 150 ft/s.

39. A baseball has an initial position (in feet) of $\langle x_0, y_0 \rangle = \langle 0, 6 \rangle$ when it is thrown with an initial velocity of $\langle u_0, v_0 \rangle = \langle 80, 10 \rangle$ ft/s.

40. A baseball is thrown horizontally from a height of 10 ft above the ground with a speed of 132 ft/s.

41. A projectile is launched from a platform 20 ft above the ground at an angle of $60°$ above the horizontal with a speed of 250 ft/s. Assume the origin is at the base of the platform.

42. A rock is thrown from the edge of a vertical cliff 40 m above the ground at an angle of $45°$ above the horizontal with a speed of $10\sqrt{2}$ m/s. Assume the origin is at the foot of the cliff.

43–46. Solving equations of motion *Given an acceleration vector, initial velocity* $\langle u_0, v_0, w_0 \rangle$, *and initial position* $\langle x_0, y_0, z_0 \rangle$, *find the velocity and position vectors, for* $t \geq 0$.

43. $\mathbf{a}(t) = \langle 0, 0, 10 \rangle, \langle u_0, v_0, w_0 \rangle = \langle 1, 5, 0 \rangle$,
    $\langle x_0, y_0, z_0 \rangle = \langle 0, 5, 0 \rangle$

44. $\mathbf{a}(t) = \langle 1, t, 4t \rangle, \langle u_0, v_0, w_0 \rangle = \langle 20, 0, 0 \rangle$,
    $\langle x_0, y_0, z_0 \rangle = \langle 0, 0, 0 \rangle$

45. $\mathbf{a}(t) = \langle \sin t, \cos t, 1 \rangle, \langle u_0, v_0, w_0 \rangle = \langle 0, 2, 0 \rangle$,
    $\langle x_0, y_0, z_0 \rangle = \langle 0, 0, 0 \rangle$

46. $\mathbf{a}(t) = \langle t, e^{-t}, 1 \rangle, \langle u_0, v_0, w_0 \rangle = \langle 0, 0, 1 \rangle$,
    $\langle x_0, y_0, z_0 \rangle = \langle 4, 0, 0 \rangle$

T **47–52. Three-dimensional motion** *Consider the motion of the following objects. Assume the x-axis points east, the y-axis points north, the positive z-axis is vertical and opposite g, the ground is horizontal, and only the gravitational force acts on the object unless otherwise stated.*

a. *Find the velocity and position vectors, for* $t \geq 0$.
b. *Make a sketch of the trajectory.*
c. *Determine the time of flight and range of the object.*
d. *Determine the maximum height of the object.*

47. A bullet is fired from a rifle 1 m above the ground in a northeast direction. The initial velocity of the bullet is $\langle 200, 200, 0 \rangle$ m/s.

48. A golf ball is hit east down a fairway with an initial velocity of $\langle 50, 0, 30 \rangle$ m/s. A crosswind blowing to the south produces an acceleration of the ball of -0.8 m/s^2.

49. A baseball is hit 3 ft above home plate with an initial velocity of $\langle 60, 80, 80 \rangle$ ft/s. The spin on the baseball produces a horizontal acceleration of the ball of 10 ft/s^2 in the eastward direction.

50. A baseball is hit 3 ft above home plate with an initial velocity of $\langle 30, 30, 80 \rangle$ ft/s. The spin on the baseball produces a horizontal acceleration of the ball of 5 ft/s^2 in the northward direction.

51. A small rocket is fired from a launch pad 10 m above the ground with an initial velocity, in m/s, of $\langle 300, 400, 500 \rangle$. A crosswind blowing to the north produces an acceleration of the rocket of 2.5 m/s^2.

52. A soccer ball is kicked from the point $\langle 0, 0, 0 \rangle$ with an initial velocity of $\langle 0, 80, 80 \rangle$ ft/s. The spin on the ball produces an acceleration of $\langle 1.2, 0, 0 \rangle \text{ ft/s}^2$.

Further Explorations

53. Explain why or why not Determine whether the following statements are true and give an explanation or counterexample.

    a. If the speed of an object is constant, then its velocity components are constant.

    b. The functions $\mathbf{r}(t) = \langle \cos t, \sin t \rangle$ and $\mathbf{R}(t) = \langle \sin t^2, \cos t^2 \rangle$ generate the same set of points, for $t \geq 0$.

    c. A velocity vector of variable magnitude cannot have a constant direction.

    d. If the acceleration of an object is $\mathbf{a}(t) = \mathbf{0}$, for all $t \geq 0$, then the velocity of the object is constant.

    e. If you double the initial speed of a projectile, its range also doubles (assume no forces other than gravity act on the projectile).

    f. If you double the initial speed of a projectile, its time of flight also doubles (assume no forces other than gravity).

    g. A trajectory with $\mathbf{v}(t) = \mathbf{a}(t) \neq \mathbf{0}$, for all t, is possible.

⊤ 54–57. Trajectory properties *Find the time of flight, range, and maximum height of the following two-dimensional trajectories, assuming no forces other than gravity. In each case, the initial position is $\langle 0, 0 \rangle$ and the initial velocity is $\mathbf{v}_0 = \langle u_0, v_0 \rangle$.*

54. $\langle u_0, v_0 \rangle = \langle 10, 20 \rangle$ ft/s

55. Initial speed $|\mathbf{v}_0| = 150$ m/s, launch angle $\alpha = 30°$

56. $\langle u_0, v_0 \rangle = \langle 40, 80 \rangle$ m/s

57. Initial speed $|\mathbf{v}_0| = 400$ ft/s, launch angle $\alpha = 60°$

58. Motion on the moon The acceleration due to gravity on the moon is approximately $g/6$ (one-sixth its value on Earth). Compare the time of flight, range, and maximum height of a projectile on the moon with the corresponding values on Earth.

59. Firing angles A projectile is fired over horizontal ground from the origin with an initial speed of 60 m/s. What firing angles produce a range of 300 m?

⊤ 60. Firing strategies Suppose you wish to fire a projectile over horizontal ground from the origin and attain a range of 1000 m.

    a. Sketch a graph of the initial speed required for all firing angles $0 < \alpha < \pi/2$.

    b. What firing angle requires the least initial speed?

61. Nonuniform straight-line motion Consider the motion of an object given by the position function

$$\mathbf{r}(t) = f(t)\langle a, b, c \rangle + \langle x_0, y_0, z_0 \rangle, \quad \text{for } t \geq 0,$$

where a, b, c, x_0, y_0, and z_0 are constants, and f is a differentiable scalar function, for $t \geq 0$.

    a. Explain why this function describes motion along a line.

    b. Find the velocity function. In general, is the velocity constant in magnitude or direction along the path?

62. A race Two people travel from $P(4, 0)$ to $Q(-4, 0)$ along the paths given by

$$\mathbf{r}(t) = \langle 4 \cos (\pi t/8), 4 \sin (\pi t/8) \rangle \quad \text{and}$$
$$\mathbf{R}(t) = \langle 4 - t, (4 - t)^2 - 16 \rangle.$$

    a. Graph both paths between P and Q.

    b. Graph the speeds of both people between P and Q.

    c. Who arrives at Q first?

63. Circular motion Consider an object moving along the circular trajectory $\mathbf{r}(t) = \langle A \cos \omega t, A \sin \omega t \rangle$, where A and ω are constants.

    a. Over what time interval $[0, T]$ does the object traverse the circle once?

    b. Find the velocity and speed of the object. Is the velocity constant in either direction or magnitude? Is the speed constant?

    c. Find the acceleration of the object.

    d. How are the position and velocity related? How are the position and acceleration related?

    e. Sketch the position, velocity, and acceleration vectors at four different points on the trajectory with $A = \omega = 1$.

64. A linear trajectory An object moves along a straight line from the point $P(1, 2, 4)$ to the point $Q(-6, 8, 10)$.

    a. Find a position function $\mathbf{r}$ that describes the motion if it occurs with a constant speed over the time interval $[0, 5]$.

    b. Find a position function $\mathbf{r}$ that describes the motion if it occurs with speed e^t.

65. A circular trajectory An object moves clockwise around a circle centered at the origin with radius 5 m beginning at the point $(0, 5)$.

    a. Find a position function $\mathbf{r}$ that describes the motion if the object moves with a constant speed, completing 1 lap every 12 s.

    b. Find a position function $\mathbf{r}$ that describes the motion if it occurs with speed e^{-t}.

66. A helical trajectory An object moves on the helix $\langle \cos t, \sin t, t \rangle$, for $t \geq 0$.

    a. Find a position function $\mathbf{r}$ that describes the motion if it occurs with a constant speed of 10.

    b. Find a position function $\mathbf{r}$ that describes the motion if it occurs with speed t.

⊤ 67. Speed on an ellipse An object moves along an ellipse given by the function $\mathbf{r}(t) = \langle a \cos t, b \sin t \rangle$, for $0 \leq t \leq 2\pi$, where $a > 0$ and $b > 0$.

    a. Find the velocity and speed of the object in terms of a and b, for $0 \leq t \leq 2\pi$.

    b. With $a = 1$ and $b = 6$, graph the speed function, for $0 \leq t \leq 2\pi$. Mark the points on the trajectory at which the speed is a minimum and a maximum.

    c. Is it true that the object speeds up along the flattest (straightest) parts of the trajectory and slows down where the curves are sharpest?

    d. For general a and b, find the ratio of the maximum speed to the minimum speed on the ellipse (in terms of a and b).

⊤ 68. Travel on a cycloid Consider an object moving on a cycloid with the position function $\mathbf{r}(t) = \langle t - \sin t, 1 - \cos t \rangle$, for $0 \leq t \leq 4\pi$.

    a. Graph the trajectory.

    b. Find the velocity and speed of the object. At what point(s) on the trajectory does the object move fastest? Slowest?

c. Find the acceleration of the object and show that $|\mathbf{a}(t)|$ is constant.

d. Explain why the trajectory has a cusp at $t = 2\pi$.

69. Analyzing a trajectory Consider the trajectory given by the position function

$$\mathbf{r}(t) = \langle 50e^{-t} \cos t, 50e^{-t} \sin t, 5(1 - e^{-t}) \rangle, \quad \text{for } t \geq 0.$$

a. Find the initial point ($t = 0$) and the "terminal" point ($\lim_{t \to \infty} \mathbf{r}(t)$) of the trajectory.

b. At what point on the trajectory is the speed the greatest?

c. Graph the trajectory.

Applications

T 70. Golf shot A golfer stands 390 ft (130 yd) horizontally from the hole and 40 ft below the hole (see figure). Assuming the ball is hit with an initial speed of 150 ft/s, at what angle(s) should it be hit to land in the hole? Assume that the path of the ball lies in a plane.

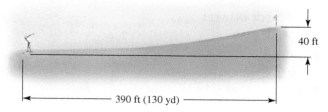

390 ft (130 yd)

40 ft

T 71. Another golf shot A golfer stands 420 ft (140 yd) horizontally from the hole and 50 ft above the hole (see figure). Assuming the ball is hit with an initial speed of 120 ft/s, at what angle(s) should it be hit to land in the hole? Assume that the path of the ball lies in a plane.

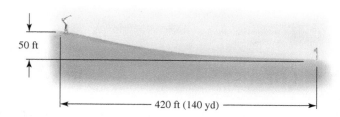

50 ft

420 ft (140 yd)

T 72. Initial velocity of a golf shot A golfer stands 390 ft horizontally from the hole and 40 ft below the hole (see figure for Exercise 70). If the ball leaves the ground at an initial angle of 45° with the horizontal, with what initial velocity should it be hit to land in the hole?

T 73. Initial velocity of a golf shot A golfer stands 420 ft horizontally from the hole and 50 ft above the hole (see figure for Exercise 71). If the ball leaves the ground at an initial angle of 30° with the horizontal, with what initial velocity should it be hit to land in the hole?

T 74. Ski jump The lip of a ski jump is 8 m above the outrun that is sloped at an angle of 30° to the horizontal (see figure).

a. If the initial velocity of a ski jumper at the lip of the jump is $\langle 40, 0 \rangle$ m/s, what is the length of the jump (distance from the origin to the landing point)? Assume only gravity affects the motion.

b. Assume that air resistance produces a constant horizontal acceleration of 0.15 m/s² opposing the motion. What is the length of the jump?

c. Suppose that the takeoff ramp is tilted upward at an angle of θ, so that the skier's initial velocity is $40\langle \cos\theta, \sin\theta \rangle$ m/s. What value of θ maximizes the length of the jump? Express your answer in degrees and neglect air resistance.

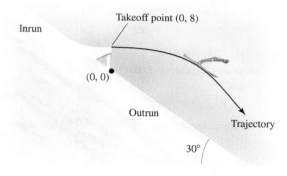

Inrun

Takeoff point (0, 8)

(0, 0)

Outrun

Trajectory

30°

75. Designing a baseball pitch A baseball leaves the hand of a pitcher 6 vertical feet above and 60 horizontal feet from home plate. Assume that the coordinate axes are oriented as shown in the figure.

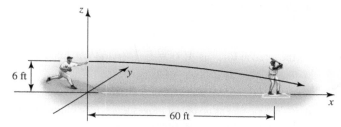

6 ft

60 ft

a. In the absence of all forces except gravity, assume that a pitch is thrown with an initial velocity of $\langle 130, 0, -3 \rangle$ ft/s (about 90 mi/hr). How far above the ground is the ball when it crosses home plate and how long does it take the pitch to arrive?

b. What vertical velocity component should the pitcher use so that the pitch crosses home plate exactly 3 ft above the ground?

c. A simple model to describe the curve of a baseball assumes that the spin of the ball produces a constant sideways acceleration (in the y-direction) of c ft/s². Assume a pitcher throws a curve ball with $c = 8$ ft/s² (one-fourth the acceleration of gravity). How far does the ball move in the y-direction by the time it reaches home plate, assuming an initial velocity of $\langle 130, 0, -3 \rangle$ ft/s?

d. In part (c), does the ball curve more in the first half of its trip to the plate or in the second half? How does this fact affect the batter?

e. Suppose the pitcher releases the ball from an initial position of $\langle 0, -3, 6 \rangle$ with initial velocity $\langle 130, 0, -3 \rangle$. What value of the spin parameter c is needed to put the ball over home plate passing through the point $(60, 0, 3)$?

76. Trajectory with a sloped landing Assume an object is launched from the origin with an initial speed $|\mathbf{v}_0|$ at an angle α to the horizontal, where $0 < \alpha < \dfrac{\pi}{2}$.

a. Find the time of flight, range, and maximum height (relative to the launch point) of the trajectory if the ground slopes *downward* at a constant angle of θ from the launch site, where $0 < \theta < \dfrac{\pi}{2}$.

b. Find the time of flight, range, and maximum height of the trajectory if the ground slopes *upward* at a constant angle of θ from the launch site. Assume $\tan \theta < \dfrac{1}{2} \tan \alpha$.

77. Time of flight, range, height Derive the formulas for time of flight, range, and maximum height in the case that an object is launched from the initial position $\langle 0, y_0 \rangle$ above horizontal ground with initial velocity $|\mathbf{v}_0| \langle \cos \alpha, \sin \alpha \rangle$.

Additional Exercises

78. Parabolic trajectories Show that the two-dimensional trajectory

$$x(t) = u_0 t + x_0 \quad \text{and} \quad y(t) = -\frac{gt^2}{2} + v_0 t + y_0, \quad \text{for } 0 \le t \le T,$$

of an object moving in a gravitational field is a segment of a parabola for some value of $T > 0$. Find T such that $y(T) = 0$.

79. Tilted ellipse Consider the curve $\mathbf{r}(t) = \langle \cos t, \sin t, c \sin t \rangle$, for $0 \le t \le 2\pi$, where c is a real number. Assuming the curve lies in a plane, prove that the curve is an ellipse in that plane.

80. Equal area property Consider the ellipse $\mathbf{r}(t) = \langle a \cos t, b \sin t \rangle$, for $0 \le t \le 2\pi$, where a and b are real numbers. Let θ be the angle between the position vector and the x-axis.

    a. Show that $\tan \theta = (b/a) \tan t$.
    b. Find $\theta'(t)$.
    c. Recall that the area bounded by the polar curve $r = f(\theta)$ on the interval $[0, \theta]$ is $A(\theta) = \dfrac{1}{2} \displaystyle\int_0^\theta (f(u))^2 \, du$. Letting $f(\theta(t)) = |\mathbf{r}(\theta(t))|$, show that $A'(t) = \dfrac{1}{2} ab$.
    d. Conclude that as an object moves around the ellipse, it sweeps out equal areas in equal times.

81. Another property of constant $|\mathbf{r}|$ motion Suppose an object moves on the surface of a sphere with $|\mathbf{r}(t)|$ constant for all t. Show that $\mathbf{r}(t)$ and $\mathbf{a}(t) = \mathbf{r}''(t)$ satisfy $\mathbf{r}(t) \cdot \mathbf{a}(t) = -|\mathbf{v}(t)|^2$.

82. Conditions for a circular/elliptical trajectory in the plane An object moves along a path given by

$$\mathbf{r}(t) = \langle a \cos t + b \sin t, c \cos t + d \sin t \rangle, \quad \text{for } 0 \le t \le 2\pi.$$

    a. What conditions on a, b, c, and d guarantee that the path is a circle?
    b. What conditions on a, b, c, and d guarantee that the path is an ellipse?

83. Conditions for a circular/elliptical trajectory in space An object moves along a path given by

$$\mathbf{r}(t) = \langle a \cos t + b \sin t, c \cos t + d \sin t, e \cos t + f \sin t \rangle,$$
$$\text{for } 0 \le t \le 2\pi.$$

    a. Show that the curve described by $\mathbf{r}$ lies in a plane.
    b. What conditions on a, b, c, d, e, and f guarantee that the curve described by $\mathbf{r}$ is a circle?

QUICK CHECK ANSWERS

1. $\mathbf{v}(t) = \langle 1, 2t, 3t^2 \rangle$, $\mathbf{a}(t) = \langle 0, 2, 6t \rangle$
2. $|\mathbf{r}'(t)| = \sqrt{1 + 4t^2 + 9t^4/16}$
   $|\mathbf{R}'(t)| = \sqrt{4t^2 + 16t^6 + 9t^{10}/4}$
3. $\mathbf{r} \cdot \mathbf{v} = \langle 3 \cos t, 5 \sin t, 4 \cos t \rangle$
   $\cdot \langle -3 \sin t, 5 \cos t, -4 \sin t \rangle = 0$
4. $x(t) = 100t, y(t) = -16t^2 + 60t + 2$
5. $\sin(2(\pi/2 - \alpha)) = \sin(\pi - 2\alpha) = \sin 2\alpha$ ◄

11.8 Length of Curves

With the methods of Section 11.7, it is possible to model the trajectory of an object moving in three-dimensional space. Although we can predict the position of the object at all times, we still don't have the tools needed to answer a simple question: How far does the object travel along its flight path over a given interval of time? In this section, we answer this question of *arc length*.

Arc Length

> Arc length for curves of the form $y = f(x)$ was discussed in Section 6.5. You should look for the parallels between that discussion and the one in this section.

Suppose that a parameterized curve C is given by the vector-valued function $\mathbf{r}(t) = \langle f(t), g(t), h(t) \rangle$, for $a \le t \le b$, where f', g', and h' are continuous on $[a, b]$. We first show how to find the length of the two-dimensional curve $\mathbf{r}(t) = \langle f(t), g(t) \rangle$, for $a \le t \le b$. The modification for three-dimensional curves then follows.

To find the length of the curve between $(f(a), g(a))$ and $(f(b), g(b))$, we first subdivide the interval $[a, b]$ into n subintervals using the grid points

$$a = t_0 < t_1 < t_2 < \cdots < t_n = b.$$

The next step is to connect consecutive points on the curve,

$$(f(t_0), g(t_0)), \ldots, (f(t_k), g(t_k)), \ldots, (f(t_n), g(t_n)),$$

with line segments (Figure 11.95a).

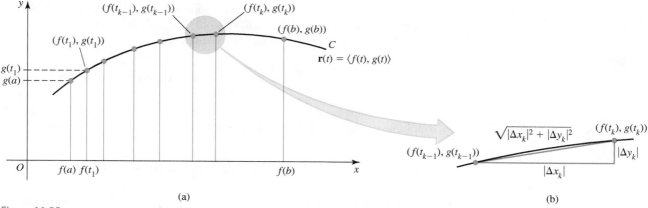

Figure 11.95

The kth line segment is the hypotenuse of a right triangle, whose legs have lengths $|\Delta x_k|$ and $|\Delta y_k|$, where

$$\Delta x_k = f(t_k) - f(t_{k-1}) \quad \text{and} \quad \Delta y_k = g(t_k) - g(t_{k-1}),$$

for $k = 1, 2, \ldots, n$ (Figure 11.95b). Therefore, the length of the kth line segment is

$$\sqrt{|\Delta x_k|^2 + |\Delta y_k|^2}.$$

The length of the entire curve L is approximated by the sum of the lengths of the line segments:

$$L \approx \sum_{k=1}^{n} \sqrt{|\Delta x_k|^2 + |\Delta y_k|^2} = \sum_{k=1}^{n} \sqrt{(\Delta x_k)^2 + (\Delta y_k)^2}. \tag{1}$$

The goal is to express this sum as a Riemann sum.

The change in $x = f(t)$ over the kth subinterval is $\Delta x_k = f(t_k) - f(t_{k-1})$. By the Mean Value Theorem, there is a point t_k^* in (t_{k-1}, t_k) such that

$$\underbrace{\overbrace{\frac{f(t_k) - f(t_{k-1})}{t_k - t_{k-1}}}^{\Delta x_k}}_{\Delta t_k} = f'(t_k^*).$$

So the change in x as t changes by $\Delta t_k = t_k - t_{k-1}$ is

$$\Delta x_k = f(t_k) - f(t_{k-1}) = f'(t_k^*)\Delta t_k.$$

Similarly, the change in y over the kth subinterval is

$$\Delta y_k = g(t_k) - g(t_{k-1}) = g'(\hat{t}_k)\Delta t_k,$$

where $\hat{t}_k$ is also a point in (t_{k-1}, t_k). We substitute these expressions for Δx_k and Δy_k into equation (1):

$$L \approx \sum_{k=1}^{n} \sqrt{(\Delta x_k)^2 + (\Delta y_k)^2}$$

$$= \sum_{k=1}^{n} \sqrt{(f'(t_k^*)\Delta t_k)^2 + (g'(\hat{t}_k)\Delta t_k)^2} \quad \text{Substitute for } \Delta x_k \text{ and } \Delta y_k.$$

$$= \sum_{k=1}^{n} \sqrt{f'(t_k^*)^2 + g'(\hat{t}_k)^2}\,\Delta t_k. \quad \text{Factor } \Delta t_k \text{ out of square root.}$$

The intermediate points t_k^* and $\hat{t}_k$ both approach t_k as n increases and as Δt_k approaches zero. Therefore, given the conditions on f' and g', the limit of this sum as $n \to \infty$ and $\Delta t_k \to 0$, for all k, exists and equals a definite integral:

$$L = \lim_{n \to \infty} \sum_{k=1}^{n} \sqrt{f'(t_k^*)^2 + g'(\hat{t}_k)^2} \, \Delta t_k = \int_a^b \sqrt{f'(t)^2 + g'(t)^2} \, dt.$$

An analogous arc length formula for three-dimensional curves follows using a similar argument. The length of the curve $\mathbf{r}(t) = \langle f(t), g(t), h(t) \rangle$ on the interval $[a, b]$ is

$$L = \int_a^b \sqrt{f'(t)^2 + g'(t)^2 + h'(t)^2} \, dt.$$

Noting that $\mathbf{r}'(t) = \langle f'(t), g'(t), h'(t) \rangle$, we state the following definition.

> ➤ Arc length integrals are usually difficult to evaluate exactly. The few easily evaluated integrals appear in the examples and exercises. Often numerical methods must be used to approximate the more challenging integrals (see Example 4).

> ➤ For curves in the xy-plane, we set $h(t) = 0$ in the definition of arc length.

DEFINITION Arc Length for Vector Functions

Consider the parameterized curve $\mathbf{r}(t) = \langle f(t), g(t), h(t) \rangle$, where f', g', and h' are continuous, and the curve is traversed once for $a \leq t \leq b$. The **arc length** of the curve between $(f(a), g(a), h(a))$ and $(f(b), g(b), h(b))$ is

$$L = \int_a^b \sqrt{f'(t)^2 + g'(t)^2 + h'(t)^2} \, dt = \int_a^b |\mathbf{r}'(t)| \, dt.$$

QUICK CHECK 1 Use the arc length formula to find the length of the line $\mathbf{r}(t) = \langle t, t \rangle$, for $0 \leq t \leq 1$. ◄

Let's use the arc length integral to derive the formula for the circumference of a circle.

EXAMPLE 1 Circumference of a circle Prove that the circumference of a circle of radius $a > 0$ is $2\pi a$.

SOLUTION A circle of radius a is described by

$$\mathbf{r}(t) = \langle f(t), g(t) \rangle = \langle a \cos t, a \sin t \rangle, \text{ for } 0 \leq t \leq 2\pi.$$

> ➤ An important fact is that the arc length of a smooth parameterized curve is independent of the choice of parameter (Exercise 70).

Note that $f'(t) = -a \sin t$ and $g'(t) = a \cos t$. The circumference is

$$L = \int_0^{2\pi} \sqrt{f'(t)^2 + g'(t)^2} \, dt \qquad \text{Arc length formula}$$

$$= \int_0^{2\pi} \sqrt{(-a \sin t)^2 + (a \cos t)^2} \, dt \qquad \text{Substitute for } f' \text{ and } g'.$$

$$= a \int_0^{2\pi} \sqrt{\sin^2 t + \cos^2 t} \, dt \qquad \text{Factor } a > 0 \text{ out of square root.}$$

QUICK CHECK 2 What does the arc length formula give for the length of the line $\mathbf{r}(t) = \langle t, t, t \rangle$, for $0 \leq t \leq 1$? ◄

$$= a \int_0^{2\pi} 1 \, dt \qquad \sin^2 t + \cos^2 t = 1$$

$$= 2\pi a. \qquad \text{Integrate a constant.}$$

Related Exercises 9–22 ◄

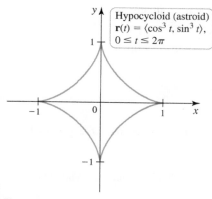

Hypocycloid (astroid)
$\mathbf{r}(t) = \langle \cos^3 t, \sin^3 t \rangle$,
$0 \le t \le 2\pi$

Figure 11.96

EXAMPLE 2   Length of a hypocycloid (or astroid) Find the length of the complete hypocycloid given by $\mathbf{r}(t) = \langle \cos^3 t, \sin^3 t \rangle$, where $0 \le t \le 2\pi$ (Figure 11.96).

SOLUTION The length of the entire curve is four times the length of the curve in the first quadrant. You should verify that the curve in the first quadrant is generated as the parameter varies from $t = 0$ (corresponding to $(1, 0)$) to $t = \pi/2$ (corresponding to $(0, 1)$). Letting $f(t) = \cos^3 t$ and $g(t) = \sin^3 t$, we have

$$f'(t) = -3 \cos^2 t \sin t \quad \text{and} \quad g'(t) = 3 \sin^2 t \cos t.$$

The arc length of the full curve is

$$L = 4 \int_0^{\pi/2} \sqrt{f'(t)^2 + g'(t)^2}\, dt \qquad \text{Factor of 4 by symmetry}$$

$$= 4 \int_0^{\pi/2} \sqrt{(-3 \cos^2 t \sin t)^2 + (3 \sin^2 t \cos t)^2}\, dt \quad \text{Substitute for } f' \text{ and } g'.$$

$$= 4 \int_0^{\pi/2} \sqrt{9 \cos^4 t \sin^2 t + 9 \cos^2 t \sin^4 t}\, dt \qquad \text{Simplify terms.}$$

$$= 4 \int_0^{\pi/2} 3\sqrt{\cos^2 t \sin^2 t \underbrace{(\cos^2 t + \sin^2 t)}_{1}}\, dt \qquad \text{Factor.}$$

$$= 12 \int_0^{\pi/2} \cos t \sin t\, dt. \qquad \cos t \sin t \ge 0, \text{ for } 0 \le t \le \frac{\pi}{2}$$

Letting $u = \sin t$ with $du = \cos t\, dt$, we have

$$L = 12 \int_0^{\pi/2} \cos t \sin t\, dt = 12 \int_0^1 u\, du = 6.$$

The length of the entire hypocycloid is 6 units.

Related Exercises 9–22 ◄

▶ Recall from Chapter 6 that the distance traveled by an object in one dimension is $\int_a^b |\mathbf{v}(t)|\, dt$. The arc length formula generalizes this formula to three dimensions.

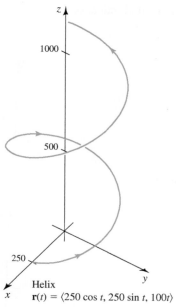

Helix
$\mathbf{r}(t) = \langle 250 \cos t, 250 \sin t, 100t \rangle$

Figure 11.97

Paths and Trajectories If the function $\mathbf{r}(t) = \langle x(t), y(t), z(t) \rangle$ is the position function for a moving object, then the arc length formula has a natural interpretation. Recall that $\mathbf{v}(t) = \mathbf{r}'(t)$ is the velocity of the object and $|\mathbf{v}(t)| = |\mathbf{r}'(t)|$ is the speed of the object. Therefore, the arc length formula becomes

$$L = \int_a^b |\mathbf{r}'(t)|\, dt = \int_a^b |\mathbf{v}(t)|\, dt.$$

This formula is an analog of the familiar *distance = speed × elapsed time* formula.

EXAMPLE 3   Flight of an eagle An eagle rises at a rate of 100 vertical ft/min on a helical path given by

$$\mathbf{r}(t) = \langle 250 \cos t, 250 \sin t, 100t \rangle$$

(Figure 11.97), where $\mathbf{r}$ is measured in feet and t is measured in minutes. How far does it travel in 10 min?

SOLUTION The speed of the eagle is

$$|\mathbf{v}(t)| = \sqrt{x'(t)^2 + y'(t)^2 + z'(t)^2}$$

$$= \sqrt{(-250 \sin t)^2 + (250 \cos t)^2 + 100^2} \quad \text{Substitute derivatives.}$$

$$= \sqrt{250^2 (\sin^2 t + \cos^2 t) + 100^2} \qquad \text{Combine terms.}$$

$$= \sqrt{250^2 + 100^2} \approx 269. \qquad \sin^2 t + \cos^2 t = 1$$

The constant speed makes the arc length integral easy to evaluate:

$$L = \int_0^{10} |\mathbf{v}(t)| \, dt \approx \int_0^{10} 269 \, dt = 2690.$$

The eagle travels approximately 2690 ft in 10 min.

Related Exercises 23–26 ◄

QUICK CHECK 3 If the speed of an object is a constant S (as in Example 3), explain why the arc length on the interval $[a, b]$ is $S(b - a)$. ◄

The following application of arc length leads to an integral that is difficult to evaluate exactly.

EXAMPLE 4 Lengths of planetary orbits According to Kepler's first law, the planets revolve about the sun in elliptical orbits. A vector function that describes an ellipse in the xy-plane is

$$\mathbf{r}(t) = \langle a \cos t, b \sin t \rangle, \qquad \text{where } 0 \le t \le 2\pi.$$

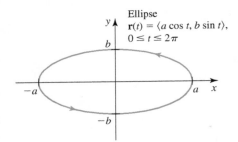

Ellipse
$\mathbf{r}(t) = \langle a \cos t, b \sin t \rangle,$
$0 \le t \le 2\pi$

If $a > b > 0$, then $2a$ is the length of the major axis and $2b$ is the length of the minor axis (Figure 11.98). Verify the lengths of the planetary orbits given in Table 11.1. Distances are given in terms of the astronomical unit (AU), which is the length of the semimajor axis of Earth's orbit, or about 93 million miles.

Figure 11.98

▶ The German astronomer and mathematician Johannes Kepler (1571–1630) worked with the meticulously gathered data of Tycho Brahe to formulate three empirical laws obeyed by planets and comets orbiting the sun. The work of Kepler formed the foundation for Newton's laws of gravitation developed 50 years later.

▶ In September 2006, Pluto joined the ranks of Ceres, Haumea, Makemake, and Eris as one of five dwarf planets in our solar system.

Table 11.1

Planet	Semimajor axis, a (AU)	Semiminor axis, b (AU)	$\alpha = b/a$	Orbit length (AU)
Mercury	0.387	0.379	0.979	2.407
Venus	0.723	0.723	1.000	4.543
Earth	1.000	0.999	0.999	6.280
Mars	1.524	1.517	0.995	9.554
Jupiter	5.203	5.179	0.995	32.616
Saturn	9.539	9.524	0.998	59.888
Uranus	19.182	19.161	0.999	120.458
Neptune	30.058	30.057	1.000	188.857

SOLUTION Using the arc length formula, the length of a general elliptical orbit is

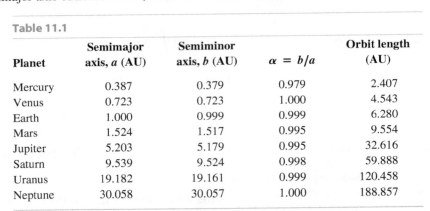

$$L = \int_0^{2\pi} \sqrt{x'(t)^2 + y'(t)^2} \, dt$$

$$= \int_0^{2\pi} \sqrt{(-a \sin t)^2 + (b \cos t)^2} \, dt \quad \text{Substitute for } x'(t) \text{ and } y'(t).$$

$$= \int_0^{2\pi} \sqrt{a^2 \sin^2 t + b^2 \cos^2 t} \, dt. \quad \text{Simplify.}$$

Factoring a^2 out of the square root and letting $\alpha = b/a$, we have

$$L = \int_0^{2\pi} \sqrt{a^2 \left(\sin^2 t + (b/a)^2 \cos^2 t\right)} \, dt \quad \text{Factor out } a^2.$$

$$= a \int_0^{2\pi} \sqrt{\sin^2 t + \alpha^2 \cos^2 t} \, dt \quad \text{Let } \alpha = b/a.$$

$$= 4a \int_0^{\pi/2} \sqrt{\sin^2 t + \alpha^2 \cos^2 t} \, dt. \quad \text{Use symmetry; quarter orbit on } [0, \pi/2].$$

▶ The integral that gives the length of an ellipse is a *complete elliptic integral of the second kind.* Many reference books and software packages provide approximate values of this integral.

Unfortunately, an antiderivative for this integrand cannot be found in terms of elementary functions, so we have two options: This integral is well known and values have been tabulated for various values of α. Alternatively, we may use a calculator to approximate the integral numerically (see Section 7.7). Using numerical integration, the orbit lengths in Table 11.1 are obtained. For example, the length of Mercury's orbit with $a = 0.387$ and $\alpha = 0.979$ is

$$L = 4a \int_0^{\pi/2} \sqrt{\sin^2 t + \alpha^2 \cos^2 t}\, dt$$

$$= 1.548 \int_0^{\pi/2} \sqrt{\sin^2 t + 0.959 \cos^2 t}\, dt \quad \text{Simplify.}$$

$$\approx 2.407. \qquad\qquad\qquad\qquad\qquad \text{Approximate using calculator.}$$

▶ Though rounded values for α appear in Table 11.1, the calculations in Example 4 were done in full precision and rounded to three decimal places only in the final step.

The fact that α is close to 1 for all the planets means that their orbits are nearly circular. For this reason, the lengths of the orbits shown in the table are nearly equal to $2\pi a$, which is the length of a circular orbit with radius a.

Related Exercises 27–30 ◀

Arc Length of a Polar Curve

▶ Recall from Section 10.2 that to convert from polar to Cartesian coordinates we use the relations

$$x = r \cos \theta \quad \text{and} \quad y = r \sin \theta.$$

We now return to polar coordinates and answer the arc length question for polar curves: Given the polar equation $r = f(\theta)$, what is the length of the corresponding curve for $\alpha \le \theta \le \beta$? The key idea is to express the polar equation as a set of parametric equations in Cartesian coordinates and then use the arc length formula derived above. Letting θ play the role of a parameter and using $r = f(\theta)$, parametric equations for the polar curve are

$$x = r \cos \theta = f(\theta) \cos \theta \quad \text{and} \quad y = r \sin \theta = f(\theta) \sin \theta,$$

where $\alpha \le \theta \le \beta$. The arc length formula in terms of the parameter θ is

$$L = \int_\alpha^\beta \sqrt{\left(\frac{dx}{d\theta}\right)^2 + \left(\frac{dy}{d\theta}\right)^2}\, d\theta,$$

where

$$\frac{dx}{d\theta} = f'(\theta) \cos \theta - f(\theta) \sin \theta \quad \text{and} \quad \frac{dy}{d\theta} = f'(\theta) \sin \theta + f(\theta) \cos \theta.$$

When substituted into the arc length formula and simplified, the result is a new arc length integral (Exercise 68).

Spiral
$r = \theta$,
$0 \le \theta \le 2\pi$

Figure 11.99

> ### Arc Length of a Polar Curve
>
> Let f have a continuous derivative on the interval $[\alpha, \beta]$. The **arc length** of the polar curve $r = f(\theta)$ on $[\alpha, \beta]$ is
>
> $$L = \int_\alpha^\beta \sqrt{f(\theta)^2 + f'(\theta)^2}\, d\theta.$$

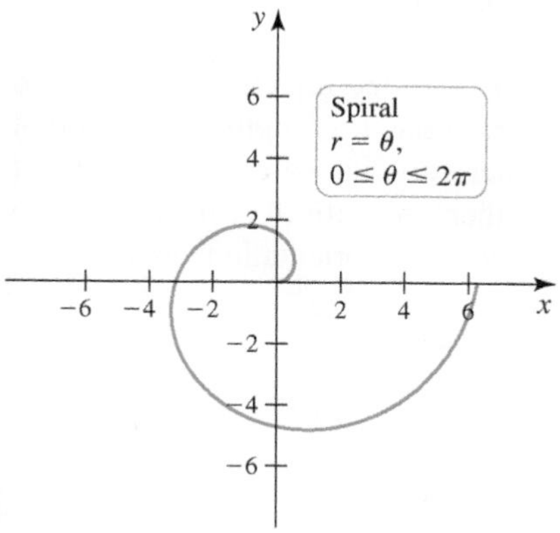

QUICK CHECK 4 Use the arc length formula to verify that the circumference of the circle $r = f(\theta) = 1$, for $0 \le \theta \le 2\pi$, is 2π. ◀

EXAMPLE 5 **Arc length of polar curves**

a. Find the arc length of the spiral $r = f(\theta) = \theta$, for $0 \le \theta \le 2\pi$ (Figure 11.99).

b. Find the arc length of the cardioid $r = 1 + \cos \theta$ (Figure 11.100).

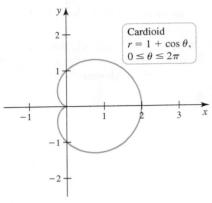

Figure 11.100

SOLUTION

a. $L = \int_0^{2\pi} \sqrt{\theta^2 + 1} \, d\theta$ 　　　　　　　　　$f(\theta) = \theta$ and $f'(\theta) = 1$

$\quad = \left(\dfrac{\theta}{2} \sqrt{\theta^2 + 1} + \dfrac{1}{2} \ln \left(\theta + \sqrt{\theta^2 + 1} \right) \right) \Big|_0^{2\pi}$ 　　Table of integrals or trigonometric substitution

$\quad = \pi \sqrt{4\pi^2 + 1} + \dfrac{1}{2} \ln \left(2\pi + \sqrt{4\pi^2 + 1} \right)$ 　　Substitute limits of integration.

$\quad \approx 21.26$ 　　　　　　　　　　　　　　　Evaluate.

b. The cardioid is symmetric about the x-axis and its upper half is generated for $0 \le \theta \le \pi$. The length of the full curve is twice the length of its upper half:

$L = 2 \int_0^{\pi} \sqrt{(1 + \cos \theta)^2 + (-\sin \theta)^2} \, d\theta$ 　　$f(\theta) = 1 + \cos \theta; f'(\theta) = -\sin \theta$

$\quad = 2 \int_0^{\pi} \sqrt{2 + 2 \cos \theta} \, d\theta$ 　　　　　　Simplify.

$\quad = 2 \int_0^{\pi} \sqrt{4 \cos^2 (\theta/2)} \, d\theta$ 　　　　　$1 + \cos \theta = 2 \cos^2 (\theta/2)$

$\quad = 4 \int_0^{\pi} \cos (\theta/2) \, d\theta$ 　　　　　　　$\cos (\theta/2) \ge 0$, for $0 \le \theta \le \pi$

$\quad = 8 \sin (\theta/2) \Big|_0^{\pi} = 8.$ 　　　　　　　Integrate and simplify.

Related Exercises 31–40 ◄

Arc Length as a Parameter

Until now, the parameter t used to describe a curve $\mathbf{r}(t) = \langle f(t), g(t), h(t) \rangle$ has been chosen either for convenience or because it represents time in some specified unit. We now introduce the most natural parameter for describing curves; that parameter is *arc length*. Let's see what it means for a curve to be *parameterized by arc length*.

Consider the following two characterizations of the unit circle centered at the origin:

- $\langle \cos t, \sin t \rangle$, for $0 \le t \le 2\pi$
- $\langle \cos 2t, \sin 2t \rangle$, for $0 \le t \le \pi$

In the first description, as the parameter t increases from $t = 0$ to $t = 2\pi$, the full circle is generated and the arc length s of the curve also increases from $s = 0$ to $s = 2\pi$. In other words, as the parameter t increases, it measures the arc length of the curve that is generated (Figure 11.101a).

In the second description, as t varies from $t = 0$ to $t = \pi$, the full circle is generated and the arc length increases from $s = 0$ to $s = 2\pi$. In this case, the length of the interval in t does not equal the length of the curve generated; therefore, the parameter t does not correspond to arc length (Figure 11.101b). In general, there are infinitely many ways to parameterize a given curve; however, for a given initial point and orientation, arc length is the parameter for only one of them.

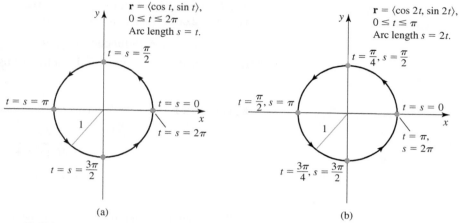

Figure 11.101

QUICK CHECK 5 Consider the portion of a circle $\mathbf{r}(t) = \langle \cos t, \sin t \rangle$, for $a \le t \le b$. Show that the arc length of the curve is $b - a$. ◄

➤ Notice that t is the independent variable of the function $s(t)$, so a different symbol u is used for the variable of integration. It is common to use s as the arc length function.

The Arc Length Function Suppose that a smooth curve is represented by the function $\mathbf{r}(t) = \langle f(t), g(t), h(t) \rangle$, for $t \ge a$, where t is a parameter. Notice that as t increases, the length of the curve also increases. Using the arc length formula, the length of the curve from $\mathbf{r}(a)$ to $\mathbf{r}(t)$ is

$$s(t) = \int_a^t \sqrt{f'(u)^2 + g'(u)^2 + h'(u)^2}\, du = \int_a^t |\mathbf{v}(u)|\, du.$$

This equation gives the relationship between the arc length of a curve and any parameter t used to describe the curve.

An important consequence of this relationship arises if we differentiate both sides with respect to t using the Fundamental Theorem of Calculus:

$$\frac{ds}{dt} = \frac{d}{dt}\left(\int_a^t |\mathbf{v}(u)|\, du \right) = |\mathbf{v}(t)|.$$

Specifically, if t represents time and $\mathbf{r}$ is the position of an object moving on the curve, then the rate of change of the arc length with respect to time is the speed of the object. Notice that if $\mathbf{r}(t)$ describes a smooth curve, then $|\mathbf{v}(t)| \ne 0$; hence $ds/dt > 0$, and s is an increasing function of t—as t increases, the arc length also increases. If $\mathbf{r}(t)$ is a curve on which $|\mathbf{v}(t)| = 1$, then

$$s(t) = \int_a^t |\mathbf{v}(u)|\, du = \int_a^t 1\, du = t - a,$$

which means the parameter t corresponds to arc length. These observations are summarized in the following theorem.

THEOREM 11.9 Arc Length as a Function of a Parameter

Let $\mathbf{r}(t)$ describe a smooth curve, for $t \ge a$. The arc length is given by

$$s(t) = \int_a^t |\mathbf{v}(u)|\, du,$$

where $|\mathbf{v}| = |\mathbf{r}'|$. Equivalently, $\dfrac{ds}{dt} = |\mathbf{v}(t)|$. If $|\mathbf{v}(t)| = 1$, for all $t \ge a$, then the parameter t corresponds to arc length.

EXAMPLE 6   Arc length parameterization Consider the helix
$\mathbf{r}(t) = \langle 2 \cos t, 2 \sin t, 4t \rangle$, for $t \geq 0$.

a. Find the arc length function $s(t)$.

b. Find another description of the helix that uses arc length as the parameter.

SOLUTION

a. Note that $\mathbf{r}'(t) = \langle -2 \sin t, 2 \cos t, 4 \rangle$ and

$$
\begin{aligned}
|\mathbf{v}(t)| = |\mathbf{r}'(t)| &= \sqrt{(-2 \sin t)^2 + (2 \cos t)^2 + 4^2} \\
&= \sqrt{4(\sin^2 t + \cos^2 t) + 4^2} \qquad \text{Simplify.} \\
&= \sqrt{4 + 4^2} \qquad\qquad\qquad \sin^2 t + \cos^2 t = 1 \\
&= \sqrt{20} = 2\sqrt{5}. \qquad\qquad\quad \text{Simplify.}
\end{aligned}
$$

Therefore, the relationship between the arc length s and the parameter t is

$$
s(t) = \int_a^t |\mathbf{v}(u)| \, du = \int_0^t 2\sqrt{5} \, du = 2\sqrt{5} \, t.
$$

An increase of $1/(2\sqrt{5})$ in the parameter t corresponds to an increase of 1 in the arc length. Therefore, the curve is not parameterized by arc length.

b. Substituting $t = s/(2\sqrt{5})$ into the original parametric description of the helix, we find that the description with arc length as a parameter is (using a different function name)

$$
\mathbf{r}_1(s) = \left\langle 2 \cos \left(\frac{s}{2\sqrt{5}} \right), 2 \sin \left(\frac{s}{2\sqrt{5}} \right), \frac{2s}{\sqrt{5}} \right\rangle, \quad \text{for } s \geq 0.
$$

This description has the property that an increment of Δs in the parameter corresponds to an increment of exactly Δs in the arc length.

Related Exercises 41–50 ◄

QUICK CHECK 6 Does the line $\mathbf{r}(t) = \langle t, t, t \rangle$ have arc length as a parameter? Explain. ◄

As you will see in Section 11.9, using arc length as a parameter—when it can be done—generally leads to simplified calculations.

SECTION 11.8 EXERCISES

Review Questions

1. Find the length of the line given by $\mathbf{r}(t) = \langle t, 2t \rangle$, for $a \leq t \leq b$.

2. Explain how to find the length of the curve $\mathbf{r}(t) = \langle f(t), g(t), h(t) \rangle$, for $a \leq t \leq b$.

3. Express the arc length of a curve in terms of the speed of an object moving along the curve.

4. Suppose an object moves in space with the position function $\mathbf{r}(t) = \langle x(t), y(t), z(t) \rangle$. Write the integral that gives the distance it travels between $t = a$ and $t = b$.

5. An object moves on a trajectory given by $\mathbf{r}(t) = \langle 10 \cos 2t, 10 \sin 2t \rangle$, for $0 \leq t \leq \pi$. How far does it travel?

6. How do you find the arc length of the polar curve $r = f(\theta)$, for $\alpha \leq \theta \leq \beta$, assuming f' is continuous on $[\alpha, \beta]$?

7. Explain what it means for a curve to be parameterized by its arc length.

8. Is the curve $\mathbf{r}(t) = \langle \cos t, \sin t \rangle$ parameterized by its arc length? Explain.

Basic Skills

9–22. Arc length calculations *Find the length of the following two- and three-dimensional curves.*

9. $\mathbf{r}(t) = \langle 3t^2 - 1, 4t^2 + 5 \rangle$, for $0 \leq t \leq 1$

10. $\mathbf{r}(t) = \langle 3t - 1, 4t + 5, t \rangle$, for $0 \leq t \leq 1$

11. $\mathbf{r}(t) = \langle 3 \cos t, 3 \sin t \rangle$, for $0 \leq t \leq \pi$

12. $\mathbf{r}(t) = \langle 4 \cos 3t, 4 \sin 3t \rangle$, for $0 \leq t \leq 2\pi/3$

13. $\mathbf{r}(t) = \langle \cos t + t \sin t, \sin t - t \cos t \rangle$, for $0 \leq t \leq \pi/2$

14. $\mathbf{r}(t) = \langle \cos t + \sin t, \cos t - \sin t \rangle$, for $0 \leq t \leq 2\pi$

15. $\mathbf{r}(t) = \langle 2 + 3t, 1 - 4t, -4 + 3t \rangle$, for $1 \leq t \leq 6$

16. $\mathbf{r}(t) = \langle 4 \cos t, 4 \sin t, 3t \rangle$, for $0 \leq t \leq 6\pi$

17. $\mathbf{r}(t) = \langle t, 8 \sin t, 8 \cos t \rangle$, for $0 \le t \le 4\pi$

18. $\mathbf{r}(t) = \langle t^2/2, (2t+1)^{3/2}/3 \rangle$, for $0 \le t \le 2$

19. $\mathbf{r}(t) = \langle e^{2t}, 2e^{2t} + 5, 2e^{2t} - 20 \rangle$, for $0 \le t \le \ln 2$

20. $\mathbf{r}(t) = \langle t^2, t^3 \rangle$, for $0 \le t \le 4$

21. $\mathbf{r}(t) = \langle \cos^3 t, \sin^3 t \rangle$, for $0 \le t \le \pi/2$

22. $\mathbf{r}(t) = \langle 3 \cos t, 4 \cos t, 5 \sin t \rangle$, for $0 \le t \le 2\pi$

23–26. Speed and arc length *For the following trajectories, find the speed associated with the trajectory and then find the length of the trajectory on the given interval.*

23. $\mathbf{r}(t) = \langle 2t^3, -t^3, 5t^3 \rangle$, for $0 \le t \le 4$

24. $\mathbf{r}(t) = \langle 5 \cos t^2, 5 \sin t^2, 12t^2 \rangle$, for $0 \le t \le 2$

25. $\mathbf{r}(t) = \langle 13 \sin 2t, 12 \cos 2t, 5 \cos 2t \rangle$, for $0 \le t \le \pi$

26. $\mathbf{r}(t) = \langle e^t \sin t, e^t \cos t, e^t \rangle$, for $0 \le t \le \ln 2$

T 27–30. Arc length approximations *Use a calculator to approximate the length of the following curves. In each case, simplify the arc length integral as much as possible before finding an approximation.*

27. $\mathbf{r}(t) = \langle 2 \cos t, 4 \sin t \rangle$, for $0 \le t \le 2\pi$

28. $\mathbf{r}(t) = \langle 2 \cos t, 4 \sin t, 6 \cos t \rangle$, for $0 \le t \le 2\pi$

29. $\mathbf{r}(t) = \langle t, 4t^2, 10 \rangle$, for $-2 \le t \le 2$

30. $\mathbf{r}(t) = \langle e^t, 2e^{-t}, t \rangle$, for $0 \le t \le \ln 3$

31–40. Arc length of polar curves *Find the length of the following polar curves.*

31. The complete circle $r = a \sin \theta$, where $a > 0$

32. The complete cardioid $r = 2 - 2 \sin \theta$

33. The spiral $r = \theta^2$, where $0 \le \theta \le 2\pi$

34. The spiral $r = e^\theta$, where $0 \le \theta \le 2\pi n$, for a positive integer n

35. The complete cardioid $r = 4 + 4 \sin \theta$

36. The spiral $r = 4\theta^2$, for $0 \le \theta \le 6$

37. The spiral $r = 2e^{2\theta}$, for $0 \le \theta \le \ln 8$

38. The curve $r = \sin^2(\theta/2)$, for $0 \le \theta \le \pi$

39. The curve $r = \sin^3(\theta/3)$, for $0 \le \theta \le \pi/2$

40. The parabola $r = \sqrt{2}/(1 + \cos \theta)$, for $0 \le \theta \le \pi/2$

41–50. Arc length parameterization *Determine whether the following curves use arc length as a parameter. If not, find a description that uses arc length as a parameter.*

41. $\mathbf{r}(t) = \langle 1, \sin t, \cos t \rangle$, for $t \ge 1$

42. $\mathbf{r}(t) = \left\langle \dfrac{t}{\sqrt{3}}, \dfrac{t}{\sqrt{3}}, \dfrac{t}{\sqrt{3}} \right\rangle$, for $0 \le t \le 10$

43. $\mathbf{r}(t) = \langle t, 2t \rangle$, for $0 \le t \le 3$

44. $\mathbf{r}(t) = \langle t + 1, 2t - 3, 6t \rangle$, for $0 \le t \le 10$

45. $\mathbf{r}(t) = \langle 2 \cos t, 2 \sin t \rangle$, for $0 \le t \le 2\pi$

46. $\mathbf{r}(t) = \langle 5 \cos t, 3 \sin t, 4 \sin t \rangle$, for $0 \le t \le \pi$

47. $\mathbf{r}(t) = \langle \cos t^2, \sin t^2 \rangle$, for $0 \le t \le \sqrt{\pi}$

48. $\mathbf{r}(t) = \langle t^2, 2t^2, 4t^2 \rangle$, for $1 \le t \le 4$

49. $\mathbf{r}(t) = \langle e^t, e^t, e^t \rangle$, for $t \ge 0$

50. $\mathbf{r}(t) = \left\langle \dfrac{\cos t}{\sqrt{2}}, \dfrac{\cos t}{\sqrt{2}}, \sin t \right\rangle$, for $0 \le t \le 10$

Further Explorations

51. **Explain why or why not** Determine whether the following statements are true and give an explanation or counterexample.

    a. If an object moves on a trajectory with constant speed S over a time interval $a \le t \le b$, then the length of the trajectory is $S(b - a)$.

    b. The curves defined by $\mathbf{r}(t) = \langle f(t), g(t) \rangle$ and $\mathbf{R}(t) = \langle g(t), f(t) \rangle$ have the same length over the interval $[a, b]$.

    c. The curve $\mathbf{r}(t) = \langle f(t), g(t) \rangle$, for $0 \le a \le t \le b$, and the curve $\mathbf{R}(t) = \langle f(t^2), g(t^2) \rangle$, for $\sqrt{a} \le t \le \sqrt{b}$, have the same length.

    d. The curve $\mathbf{r}(t) = \langle t, t^2, 3t^2 \rangle$, for $1 \le t \le 4$, is parameterized by arc length.

52. **Length of a line segment** Consider the line segment joining the points $P(x_0, y_0, z_0)$ and $Q(x_1, y_1, z_1)$.

    a. Find a parametric description of the line segment PQ.

    b. Use the arc length formula to find the length of PQ.

    c. Use geometry (distance formula) to verify the result of part (b).

53. **Tilted circles** Let the curve C be described by $\mathbf{r}(t) = \langle a \cos t, b \sin t, c \sin t \rangle$, where a, b, and c are real positive numbers.

    a. Assume that C lies in a plane. Show that C is a circle centered at the origin provided $a^2 = b^2 + c^2$.

    b. Find the arc length of the circle.

    c. Assuming that the curve lies in a plane, find the conditions for which $\mathbf{r}(t) = \langle a \cos t + b \sin t, c \cos t + d \sin t, e \cos t + f \sin t \rangle$ describes a circle. Then find its arc length.

54. **A family of arc length integrals** Find the length of the curve $\mathbf{r}(t) = \langle t^m, t^m, t^{3m/2} \rangle$, for $0 \le a \le t \le b$, where m is a real number. Express the result in terms of m, a, and b.

55. **A special case** Suppose a curve is described by $\mathbf{r}(t) = \langle A h(t), B h(t) \rangle$, for $a \le t \le b$, where A and B are constants and h has a continuous derivative.

    a. Show that the length of the curve is

$$\sqrt{A^2 + B^2} \int_a^b |h'(t)| \, dt.$$

    b. Use part (a) to find the length of the curve $x = 2t^3$, $y = 5t^3$, for $0 \le t \le 4$.

    c. Use part (a) to find the length of the curve $x = 4/t$, $y = 10/t$, for $1 \le t \le 8$.

56. **Spiral arc length** Consider the spiral $r = 4\theta$, for $\theta \ge 0$.

    a. Use a trigonometric substitution to find the length of the spiral, for $0 \le \theta \le \sqrt{8}$.

    b. Find $L(\theta)$, the length of the spiral on the interval $[0, \theta]$, for any $\theta \ge 0$.

    c. Show that $L'(\theta) > 0$. Is $L''(\theta)$ positive or negative? Interpret your answer.

57. **Spiral arc length** Find the length of the entire spiral $r = e^{-a\theta}$, for $\theta \ge 0$ and $a > 0$.

▣ 58–61. Arc length using technology *Use a calculator to find the approximate length of the following curves.*

58. The three-leaf rose $r = 2 \cos 3\theta$

59. The lemniscate $r^2 = 6 \sin 2\theta$

60. The limaçon $r = 2 - 4 \sin \theta$

61. The limaçon $r = 4 - 2 \cos \theta$

Applications

62. **A cycloid** A cycloid is the path traced by a point on a circle rolling on a flat surface (think of a light on the rim of a moving bicycle wheel). The cycloid generated by a circle of radius a is given by the parametric equations

$$x = a(t - \sin t), \quad y = a(1 - \cos t);$$

the parameter range $0 \le t \le 2\pi$ produces one arch of the cycloid (see figure). Show that the length of one arch of a cycloid is $8a$.

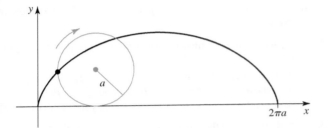

▣ 63. **Projectile trajectories** A projectile (such as a baseball or a cannonball) launched from the origin with an initial horizontal velocity u_0 and an initial vertical velocity v_0 moves in a parabolic trajectory given by

$$x = u_0 t, \quad y = -\tfrac{1}{2} g t^2 + v_0 t, \quad \text{for } t \ge 0,$$

where air resistance is neglected and $g \approx 9.8 \text{ m/s}^2$ is the acceleration due to gravity (see Section 11.7).

a. Let $u_0 = 20$ m/s and $v_0 = 25$ m/s. Assuming the projectile is launched over horizontal ground, at what time does it return to Earth?

b. Find the integral that gives the length of the trajectory from launch to landing.

c. Evaluate the integral in part (b) by first making the change of variables $u = -gt + v_0$. The resulting integral is evaluated either by making a second change of variables or by using a calculator. What is the length of the trajectory?

d. How far does the projectile land from its launch site?

64. **Variable speed on a circle** Consider a particle that moves in a plane according to the equations $x = \sin t^2$ and $y = \cos t^2$ with a starting position $(0, 1)$ at $t = 0$.

a. Describe the path of the particle, including the time required to return to the starting position.

b. What is the length of the path in part (a)?

c. Describe how the motion of this particle differs from the motion described by the equations $x = \sin t$ and $y = \cos t$.

d. Consider the motion described by $x = \sin t^n$ and $y = \cos t^n$, where n is a positive integer. Describe the path of the particle, including the time required to return to the starting position.

e. What is the length of the path in part (d) for any positive integer n?

f. If you were watching a race on a circular path between two runners, one moving according to $x = \sin t$ and $y = \cos t$ and one according to $x = \sin t^2$ and $y = \cos t^2$, who would win and when would one runner pass the other?

Additional Exercises

65. **Arc length parameterization** Prove that the line $\mathbf{r}(t) = \langle x_0 + at, y_0 + bt, z_0 + ct \rangle$ is parameterized by arc length provided $a^2 + b^2 + c^2 = 1$.

66. **Arc length parameterization** Prove that the curve $\mathbf{r}(t) = \langle a \cos t, b \sin t, c \sin t \rangle$ is parameterized by arc length provided $a^2 = b^2 + c^2 = 1$.

67. **Lengths of related curves** Suppose a curve is given by $\mathbf{r}(t) = \langle f(t), g(t) \rangle$, where f' and g' are continuous, for $a \le t \le b$. Assume the curve is traversed once, for $a \le t \le b$, and the length of the curve between $(f(a), g(a))$ and $(f(b), g(b))$ is L. Prove that for any nonzero constant c the length of the curve defined by $\mathbf{r}(t) = \langle cf(t), cg(t) \rangle$, for $a \le t \le b$, is $|c|L$.

68. **Arc length for polar curves** Prove that the length of the curve $r = f(\theta)$, for $\alpha \le \theta \le \beta$, is

$$L = \int_{\alpha}^{\beta} \sqrt{f(\theta)^2 + f'(\theta)^2} \, d\theta.$$

69. **Arc length for $y = f(x)$** The arc length formula for functions of the form $y = f(x)$ on $[a, b]$ found in Section 6.5 is

$$L = \int_{a}^{b} \sqrt{1 + f'(x)^2} \, dx.$$

Derive this formula from the arc length formula for vector curves. (*Hint:* Let $x = t$ be the parameter.)

70. **Change of variables** Consider the parameterized curves $\mathbf{r}(t) = \langle f(t), g(t), h(t) \rangle$ and $\mathbf{R}(t) = \langle f(u(t)), g(u(t)), h(u(t)) \rangle$, where f, g, h, and u are continuously differentiable functions and u has an inverse on $[a, b]$.

a. Show that the curve generated by $\mathbf{r}$ on the interval $a \le t \le b$ is the same as the curve generated by $\mathbf{R}$ on $u^{-1}(a) \le t \le u^{-1}(b)$ (or $u^{-1}(b) \le t \le u^{-1}(a)$).

b. Show that the lengths of the two curves are equal. (*Hint:* Use the Chain Rule and a change of variables in the arc length integral for the curve generated by $\mathbf{R}$.)

QUICK CHECK ANSWERS

1. $\sqrt{2}$ **2.** $\sqrt{3}$

3. $L = \int_{a}^{b} |\mathbf{v}(t)| \, dt = \int_{a}^{b} S \, dt = S(b - a)$ **4.** 2π

5. For $a \le t \le b$, the curve C generated is $(b - a)/2\pi$ of a full circle. Because the full circle has a length of 2π, the curve C has a length of $b - a$.   **6.** No. If t increases by 1 unit, the length of the curve increases by $\sqrt{3}$ units. ◄

11.9 Curvature and Normal Vectors

We know how to find tangent vectors and lengths of curves in space, but much more can be said about the shape of such curves. In this section, we introduce several new concepts. *Curvature* measures how *fast* a curve turns at a point, the *normal vector* gives the *direction* in which a curve turns, and the *binormal vector* and the *torsion* describe the twisting of a curve.

Curvature

Imagine driving a car along a winding mountain road. There are two ways to change the velocity of the car (that is, to accelerate). You can change the *speed* of the car or you can change the *direction* of the car. A change of speed is relatively easy to describe, so we postpone that discussion and focus on the change of direction. The rate at which the car changes direction is related to the notion of *curvature*.

Unit Tangent Vector   Recall from Section 11.6 that if $\mathbf{r}(t) = \langle x(t), y(t), z(t) \rangle$ is a smooth oriented curve, then the unit tangent vector at a point is the unit vector that points in the direction of the tangent vector $\mathbf{r}'(t)$; that is,

$$\mathbf{T}(t) = \frac{\mathbf{r}'(t)}{|\mathbf{r}'(t)|} = \frac{\mathbf{v}(t)}{|\mathbf{v}(t)|}.$$

Because $\mathbf{T}$ is a unit vector, its length does not change along the curve. The only way $\mathbf{T}$ can change is through a change in direction.

How quickly does $\mathbf{T}$ change (in direction) as we move along the curve? If a small increment in arc length Δs along the curve results in a large change in the direction of $\mathbf{T}$, the curve is turning quickly over that interval and we say it has a large *curvature* (Figure 11.102a). If a small increment Δs in arc length results in a small change in the direction of $\mathbf{T}$, the curve is turning slowly over that interval and it has a small curvature (Figure 11.102b). The magnitude of the rate at which the direction of $\mathbf{T}$ changes with respect to arc length is the curvature of the curve.

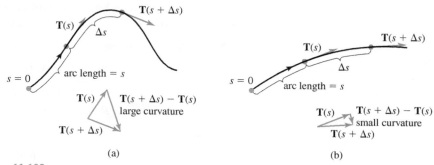

(a)   (b)

Figure 11.102

▶ Recall that the unit tangent vector at a point depends on the orientation of the curve. The curvature does not depend on the orientation of the curve, but it does depend on the shape of the curve. The Greek letter κ (kappa) is used to denote curvature.

DEFINITION Curvature

Let $\mathbf{r}$ describe a smooth parameterized curve. If s denotes arc length and $\mathbf{T} = \mathbf{r}'/|\mathbf{r}'|$ is the unit tangent vector, the **curvature** is $\kappa(s) = \left| \dfrac{d\mathbf{T}}{ds} \right|$.

Note that κ is a nonnegative scalar-valued function. A large value of κ at a point indicates a tight curve that changes direction quickly. If κ is small, then the curve is relatively flat and its direction changes slowly. The minimum curvature (zero) occurs on a straight line where the tangent vector never changes direction along the curve.

In order to evaluate $d\mathbf{T}/ds$, a description of the curve in terms of the arc length appears to be needed, but it may be difficult to obtain. A short calculation leads to the first of two practical curvature formulas.

Letting t be an arbitrary parameter, we begin with the Chain Rule and write $\dfrac{d\mathbf{T}}{dt} = \dfrac{d\mathbf{T}}{ds} \cdot \dfrac{ds}{dt}$. Dividing by $ds/dt = |\mathbf{v}|$ and taking absolute values leads to

$$\kappa = \left| \frac{d\mathbf{T}}{ds} \right| = \frac{|d\mathbf{T}/dt|}{|ds/dt|} = \frac{1}{|\mathbf{v}|} \left| \frac{d\mathbf{T}}{dt} \right|.$$

This derivation is a proof of the following theorem.

THEOREM 11.10   Curvature Formula
Let $\mathbf{r}(t)$ describe a smooth parameterized curve, where t is any parameter. If $\mathbf{v} = \mathbf{r}'$ is the velocity and $\mathbf{T}$ is the unit tangent vector, then the curvature is

$$\kappa(t) = \frac{1}{|\mathbf{v}|} \left| \frac{d\mathbf{T}}{dt} \right| = \frac{|\mathbf{T}'(t)|}{|\mathbf{r}'(t)|}.$$

EXAMPLE 1   Lines have zero curvature Consider the line $\mathbf{r}(t) = \langle x_0 + at, y_0 + bt, z_0 + ct \rangle$, for $-\infty < t < \infty$. Show that $\kappa = 0$ at all points on the line.

SOLUTION Note that $\mathbf{r}'(t) = \langle a, b, c \rangle$ and $|\mathbf{r}'(t)| = |\mathbf{v}(t)| = \sqrt{a^2 + b^2 + c^2}$. Therefore,

$$\mathbf{T}(t) = \frac{\mathbf{r}'(t)}{|\mathbf{r}'(t)|} = \frac{\langle a, b, c \rangle}{\sqrt{a^2 + b^2 + c^2}}.$$

Because $\mathbf{T}$ is a constant, $\dfrac{d\mathbf{T}}{dt} = \mathbf{0}$; therefore, $\kappa = 0$ at all points of the line.

Related Exercises 11–20 ◄

EXAMPLE 2   Circles have constant curvature Consider the circle $\mathbf{r}(t) = \langle R \cos t, R \sin t \rangle$, for $0 \le t \le 2\pi$, where $R > 0$. Show that $\kappa = 1/R$.

SOLUTION We compute $\mathbf{r}'(t) = \langle -R \sin t, R \cos t \rangle$ and

$$\begin{aligned}
|\mathbf{v}(t)| = |\mathbf{r}'(t)| &= \sqrt{(-R \sin t)^2 + (R \cos t)^2} \\
&= \sqrt{R^2 (\sin^2 t + \cos^2 t)} && \text{Simplify.} \\
&= R. && \sin^2 t + \cos^2 t = 1, R > 0
\end{aligned}$$

Therefore,

$$\mathbf{T}(t) = \frac{\mathbf{r}'(t)}{|\mathbf{r}'(t)|} = \frac{\langle -R \sin t, R \cos t \rangle}{R} = \langle -\sin t, \cos t \rangle, \text{ and}$$

$$\frac{d\mathbf{T}}{dt} = \langle -\cos t, -\sin t \rangle.$$

> The curvature of a curve at a point can also be visualized in terms of a **circle of curvature**, which is a circle of radius R that is tangent to the curve at that point. The curvature at the point is $\kappa = 1/R$. See Exercises 70–74.

Combining these observations, the curvature is

$$\kappa = \frac{1}{|\mathbf{v}|} \left| \frac{d\mathbf{T}}{dt} \right| = \frac{1}{R} |\langle -\cos t, -\sin t \rangle| = \frac{1}{R} \underbrace{\sqrt{\cos^2 t + \sin^2 t}}_{1} = \frac{1}{R}.$$

The curvature of a circle is constant; a circle with a small radius has a large curvature and vice versa.

Related Exercises 11–20 ◄

QUICK CHECK 1 What is the curvature of the circle $\mathbf{r}(t) = \langle 3 \sin t, 3 \cos t \rangle$? ◄

An Alternative Curvature Formula A second curvature formula, which pertains specifically to trajectories of moving objects, is easier to use in some cases. The calculation is instructive because it relies on many properties of vector functions. In the end, a remarkably simple formula emerges.

Again consider a smooth curve $\mathbf{r}(t) = \langle x(t), y(t), z(t) \rangle$, where $\mathbf{v}(t) = \mathbf{r}'(t)$ and $\mathbf{a}(t) = \mathbf{v}'(t)$ are the velocity and acceleration of an object moving along that curve, respectively. We assume that $\mathbf{v}(t) \neq \mathbf{0}$ and $\mathbf{a}(t) \neq \mathbf{0}$. Because $\mathbf{T} = \mathbf{v}/|\mathbf{v}|$, we begin by writing $\mathbf{v} = |\mathbf{v}|\,\mathbf{T}$ and differentiating both sides with respect to t:

$$\mathbf{a} = \frac{d\mathbf{v}}{dt} = \frac{d}{dt}\left(|\mathbf{v}(t)|\,\mathbf{T}(t)\right) = \frac{d}{dt}\left(|\mathbf{v}(t)|\right)\mathbf{T}(t) + |\mathbf{v}(t)|\frac{d\mathbf{T}}{dt}. \qquad \text{Product Rule (1)}$$

We now form $\mathbf{v} \times \mathbf{a}$:

▶ Distributive law for cross products:

$\mathbf{w} \times (\mathbf{u} + \mathbf{v}) = (\mathbf{w} \times \mathbf{u}) + (\mathbf{w} \times \mathbf{v})$

$(\mathbf{u} + \mathbf{v}) \times \mathbf{w} = (\mathbf{u} \times \mathbf{w}) + (\mathbf{v} \times \mathbf{w})$

$$\mathbf{v} \times \mathbf{a} = \underbrace{|\mathbf{v}|\mathbf{T}}_{v} \times \underbrace{\left[\frac{d}{dt}(|\mathbf{v}|)\mathbf{T} + |\mathbf{v}|\frac{d\mathbf{T}}{dt}\right]}_{a}$$

$$= \underbrace{|\mathbf{v}|\mathbf{T} \times \left(\frac{d}{dt}(|\mathbf{v}|)\right)\mathbf{T}}_{0} + |\mathbf{v}|\mathbf{T} \times |\mathbf{v}|\frac{d\mathbf{T}}{dt} \qquad \text{Distributive law for cross products}$$

The first term in this expression has the form $a\mathbf{T} \times b\mathbf{T}$, where a and b are scalars. Therefore, $a\mathbf{T}$ and $b\mathbf{T}$ are parallel vectors and $a\mathbf{T} \times b\mathbf{T} = \mathbf{0}$. To simplify the second term, recall that a vector $\mathbf{u}(t)$ of constant length has the property that $\mathbf{u}$ and $d\mathbf{u}/dt$ are orthogonal (Section 11.7). Because $\mathbf{T}$ is a unit vector, it has constant length, and $\mathbf{T}$ and $d\mathbf{T}/dt$ are orthogonal. Furthermore, scalar multiples of $\mathbf{T}$ and $d\mathbf{T}/dt$ are also orthogonal. Therefore, the magnitude of the second term simplifies as follows:

▶ Recall that the magnitude of the cross product of nonzero vectors is $|\mathbf{u} \times \mathbf{v}| = |\mathbf{u}||\mathbf{v}| \sin\theta$, where θ is the angle between the vectors. If the vectors are orthogonal, $\sin\theta = 1$ and $|\mathbf{u} \times \mathbf{v}| = |\mathbf{u}||\mathbf{v}|$.

$$\left||\mathbf{v}|\mathbf{T} \times |\mathbf{v}|\frac{d\mathbf{T}}{dt}\right| = |\mathbf{v}||\mathbf{T}|\left||\mathbf{v}|\frac{d\mathbf{T}}{dt}\right|\underbrace{\sin\theta}_{1} \qquad |\mathbf{u} \times \mathbf{v}| = |\mathbf{u}||\mathbf{v}|\sin\theta$$

$$= |\mathbf{v}|^2\left|\frac{d\mathbf{T}}{dt}\right|\underbrace{|\mathbf{T}|}_{1} \qquad \text{Simplify, } \theta = \pi/2.$$

$$= |\mathbf{v}|^2\left|\frac{d\mathbf{T}}{dt}\right|. \qquad |\mathbf{T}| = 1$$

The final step is to use Theorem 11.10 and substitute $\left|\dfrac{d\mathbf{T}}{dt}\right| = \kappa|\mathbf{v}|$. Putting these results together, we find that

$$|\mathbf{v} \times \mathbf{a}| = |\mathbf{v}|^2\left|\frac{d\mathbf{T}}{dt}\right| = |\mathbf{v}|^2\kappa|\mathbf{v}| = \kappa|\mathbf{v}|^3.$$

▶ Note that $\mathbf{a}(t) = \mathbf{0}$ corresponds to straight-line motion and $\kappa = 0$. If $\mathbf{v}(t) = \mathbf{0}$, the object is at rest and κ is undefined.

Solving for the curvature gives $\kappa = \dfrac{|\mathbf{v} \times \mathbf{a}|}{|\mathbf{v}|^3}$.

THEOREM 11.11 Alternative Curvature Formula
Let $\mathbf{r}$ be the position of an object moving on a smooth curve. The **curvature** at a point on the curve is

$$\kappa = \frac{|\mathbf{v} \times \mathbf{a}|}{|\mathbf{v}|^3},$$

where $\mathbf{v} = \mathbf{r}'$ is the velocity and $\mathbf{a} = \mathbf{v}'$ is the acceleration.

QUICK CHECK 2 Use the alternative curvature formula to compute the curvature of the curve $\mathbf{r}(t) = \langle t^2, 10, -10 \rangle$. ◀

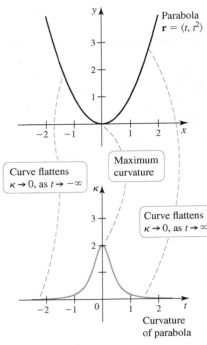

Figure 11.103

EXAMPLE 3   Curvature of a parabola Find the curvature of the parabola $\mathbf{r}(t) = \langle t, at^2 \rangle$, for $-\infty < t < \infty$, where $a > 0$ is a real number.

SOLUTION The alternative formula works well in this case. We find that $\mathbf{v}(t) = \mathbf{r}'(t) = \langle 1, 2at \rangle$ and $\mathbf{a}(t) = \mathbf{v}'(t) = \langle 0, 2a \rangle$. To compute the cross product $\mathbf{v} \times \mathbf{a}$, we append a third component of 0 to each vector:

$$\mathbf{v} \times \mathbf{a} = \begin{vmatrix} \mathbf{i} & \mathbf{j} & \mathbf{k} \\ 1 & 2at & 0 \\ 0 & 2a & 0 \end{vmatrix} = 2a\,\mathbf{k}.$$

Therefore, the curvature is

$$\kappa(t) = \frac{|\mathbf{v} \times \mathbf{a}|}{|\mathbf{v}|^3} = \frac{|2a\,\mathbf{k}|}{|\langle 1, 2at \rangle|^3} = \frac{2a}{(1 + 4a^2 t^2)^{3/2}}.$$

The curvature is a maximum at the vertex of the parabola where $t = 0$ and $\kappa = 2a$. The curvature decreases as one moves along the curve away from the vertex, as shown in Figure 11.103 with $a = 1$.

Related Exercises 21–26 ◄

EXAMPLE 4   Curvature of a helix Find the curvature of the helix $\mathbf{r}(t) = \langle a \cos t, a \sin t, bt \rangle$, for $-\infty < t < \infty$, where $a > 0$ and $b > 0$ are real numbers.

SOLUTION We use the alternative curvature formula, with

$$\mathbf{v}(t) = \mathbf{r}'(t) = \langle -a \sin t, a \cos t, b \rangle \quad \text{and}$$
$$\mathbf{a}(t) = \mathbf{v}'(t) = \langle -a \cos t, -a \sin t, 0 \rangle.$$

The cross product $\mathbf{v} \times \mathbf{a}$ is

$$\mathbf{v} \times \mathbf{a} = \begin{vmatrix} \mathbf{i} & \mathbf{j} & \mathbf{k} \\ -a \sin t & a \cos t & b \\ -a \cos t & -a \sin t & 0 \end{vmatrix} = ab \sin t\,\mathbf{i} - ab \cos t\,\mathbf{j} + a^2\,\mathbf{k}.$$

Therefore,

$$|\mathbf{v} \times \mathbf{a}| = |ab \sin t\,\mathbf{i} - ab \cos t\,\mathbf{j} + a^2\,\mathbf{k}|$$
$$= \sqrt{a^2 b^2 \underbrace{(\sin^2 t + \cos^2 t)}_{1} + a^4}$$
$$= a\sqrt{a^2 + b^2}.$$

By a familiar calculation, $|\mathbf{v}| = |\langle -a \sin t, a \cos t, b \rangle| = \sqrt{a^2 + b^2}$. Therefore,

$$\kappa = \frac{|\mathbf{v} \times \mathbf{a}|}{|\mathbf{v}|^3} = \frac{a\sqrt{a^2 + b^2}}{(\sqrt{a^2 + b^2})^3} = \frac{a}{a^2 + b^2}.$$

A similar calculation shows that all helices of this form have constant curvature.

Related Exercises 21–26 ◄

> In the curvature formula for the helix, if $b = 0$, the helix becomes a circle of radius a with $\kappa = \dfrac{1}{a}$. At the other extreme, holding a fixed and letting $b \to \infty$ stretches and straightens the helix so that $\kappa \to 0$.

Principal Unit Normal Vector

The curvature answers the question of how *fast* a curve turns. The *principal unit normal* vector determines the *direction* in which a curve turns. Specifically, the magnitude of $d\mathbf{T}/ds$ is the curvature: $\kappa = |d\mathbf{T}/ds|$. What about the direction of $d\mathbf{T}/ds$? If only the direction, but not the magnitude, of a vector is of interest, it is convenient to work with a unit vector that has the same direction as the original vector. We apply this idea to $d\mathbf{T}/ds$. The unit vector that points in the direction of $d\mathbf{T}/ds$ is the *principal unit normal vector*.

▶ The principal unit normal vector depends on the shape of the curve but not on the orientation of the curve.

> **DEFINITION Principal Unit Normal Vector**
>
> Let $\mathbf{r}$ describe a smooth curve parameterized by arc length. The **principal unit normal vector** at a point P on the curve at which $\kappa \neq 0$ is
>
> $$\mathbf{N}(s) = \frac{d\mathbf{T}/ds}{|d\mathbf{T}/ds|} = \frac{1}{\kappa}\frac{d\mathbf{T}}{ds}.$$
>
> For other parameters, we use the equivalent formula
>
> $$\mathbf{N}(t) = \frac{d\mathbf{T}/dt}{|d\mathbf{T}/dt|},$$
>
> evaluated at the value of t corresponding to P.

The practical formula $\mathbf{N} = \dfrac{d\mathbf{T}/dt}{|d\mathbf{T}/dt|}$ follows from the definition by using the Chain Rule to write $\dfrac{d\mathbf{T}}{ds} = \dfrac{d\mathbf{T}}{dt} \cdot \dfrac{dt}{ds}$ (Exercise 80). Two important properties of the principal unit normal vector follow from the definition.

> **THEOREM 11.12   Properties of the Principal Unit Normal Vector**
>
> Let $\mathbf{r}$ describe a smooth parameterized curve with unit tangent vector $\mathbf{T}$ and principal unit normal vector $\mathbf{N}$.
>
> 1. $\mathbf{T}$ and $\mathbf{N}$ are orthogonal at all points of the curve; that is, $\mathbf{T} \cdot \mathbf{N} = 0$ at all points where $\mathbf{N}$ is defined.
> 2. The principal unit normal vector points to the inside of the curve—in the direction that the curve is turning.

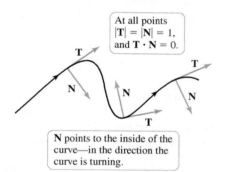

At all points $|\mathbf{T}| = |\mathbf{N}| = 1$, and $\mathbf{T} \cdot \mathbf{N} = 0$.

N points to the inside of the curve—in the direction the curve is turning.

Figure 11.104

Proof:

1. As a unit vector, $\mathbf{T}$ has constant length. Therefore, by Theorem 11.8, $\mathbf{T}$ and $d\mathbf{T}/dt$ (or $\mathbf{T}$ and $d\mathbf{T}/ds$) are orthogonal. Because $\mathbf{N}$ is a scalar multiple of $d\mathbf{T}/ds$, $\mathbf{T}$ and $\mathbf{N}$ are orthogonal (Figure 11.104).

2. We motivate—but do not prove—this fact, by recalling that

$$\frac{d\mathbf{T}}{ds} = \lim_{\Delta s \to 0} \frac{\mathbf{T}(s + \Delta s) - \mathbf{T}(s)}{\Delta s}.$$

Therefore, $d\mathbf{T}/ds$ points in the approximate direction of $\mathbf{T}(s + \Delta s) - \mathbf{T}(s)$ when Δs is small. As shown in Figure 11.105, this difference points in the direction in which the curve is turning. Because $\mathbf{N}$ is a positive scalar multiple of $d\mathbf{T}/ds$, it points in the same direction. ◀

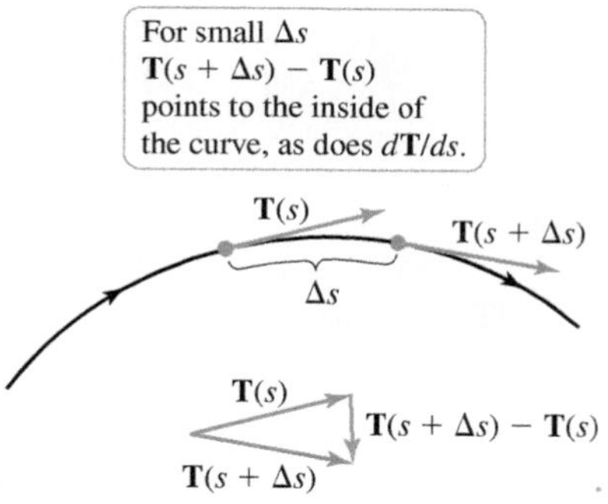

For small Δs
$\mathbf{T}(s + \Delta s) - \mathbf{T}(s)$ points to the inside of the curve, as does $d\mathbf{T}/ds$.

$\mathbf{T}(s)$ $\mathbf{T}(s + \Delta s)$
Δs

$\mathbf{T}(s)$
$\mathbf{T}(s + \Delta s) - \mathbf{T}(s)$
$\mathbf{T}(s + \Delta s)$

Figure 11.105

QUICK CHECK 3 Consider the parabola $\mathbf{r}(t) = \langle t, -t^2 \rangle$. Does the principal unit normal vector point in the positive y-direction or negative y-direction along the curve? ◀

EXAMPLE 5   Principal unit normal vector for a helix Find the principal unit normal vector for the helix $\mathbf{r}(t) = \langle a \cos t, a \sin t, bt \rangle$, for $-\infty < t < \infty$, where $a > 0$ and $b > 0$ are real numbers.

SOLUTION Several preliminary calculations are needed. First, we have $\mathbf{v}(t) = \mathbf{r}'(t) = \langle -a \sin t, a \cos t, b \rangle$. Therefore,

$$
\begin{aligned}
|\mathbf{v}(t)| = |\mathbf{r}'(t)| &= \sqrt{(-a \sin t)^2 + (a \cos t)^2 + b^2} \\
&= \sqrt{a^2 (\sin^2 t + \cos^2 t) + b^2} \qquad \text{Simplify.} \\
&= \sqrt{a^2 + b^2}. \qquad\qquad\qquad \sin^2 t + \cos^2 t = 1
\end{aligned}
$$

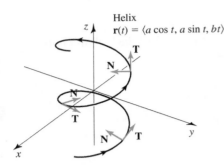

Helix
$\mathbf{r}(t) = \langle a \cos t, a \sin t, bt \rangle$

T · N = 0 at all points of the curve.
T points in the direction of the curve.
N points to the inside of the curve.

Figure 11.106

QUICK CHECK 4 Why is the principal unit normal vector for a straight line undefined? ◄

➤ Recall that the speed is $|\mathbf{v}| = ds/dt$, where s is arc length.

The unit tangent vector is

$$\mathbf{T}(t) = \frac{\mathbf{r}'(t)}{|\mathbf{r}'(t)|} = \frac{\langle -a \sin t, a \cos t, b \rangle}{\sqrt{a^2 + b^2}}.$$

Notice that **T** points along the curve in an upward direction (at an angle to the horizontal that satisfies the equation $\tan \theta = b/a$) (Figure 11.106). We can now calculate the principal unit normal vector. First, we determine that

$$\frac{d\mathbf{T}}{dt} = \frac{d}{dt} \left(\frac{\langle -a \sin t, a \cos t, b \rangle}{\sqrt{a^2 + b^2}} \right) = \frac{\langle -a \cos t, -a \sin t, 0 \rangle}{\sqrt{a^2 + b^2}}$$

and

$$\left| \frac{d\mathbf{T}}{dt} \right| = \frac{a}{\sqrt{a^2 + b^2}}.$$

The principal unit normal vector now follows:

$$\mathbf{N} = \frac{d\mathbf{T}/dt}{|d\mathbf{T}/dt|} = \frac{\dfrac{\langle -a \cos t, -a \sin t, 0 \rangle}{\sqrt{a^2 + b^2}}}{\dfrac{a}{\sqrt{a^2 + b^2}}} = \langle -\cos t, -\sin t, 0 \rangle.$$

Several important checks should be made. First note that **N** is a unit vector; that is, $|\mathbf{N}| = 1$. It should also be confirmed that $\mathbf{T} \cdot \mathbf{N} = 0$; that is, the unit tangent vector and the principal unit normal vector are everywhere orthogonal. Finally, **N** is parallel to the xy-plane and points inward toward the z-axis, in the direction the curve turns (Figure 11.106). Notice that in the special case $b = 0$, the trajectory is a circle, but the normal vector is still $\mathbf{N} = \langle -\cos t, -\sin t, 0 \rangle$.

Related Exercises 27–34 ◄

Components of the Acceleration

The vectors **T** and **N** may be used to gain insight into how moving objects accelerate. Recall the observation made earlier that the two ways to change the velocity of an object (to accelerate) are to change its *speed* and change its *direction* of motion. We show that changing the speed produces acceleration in the direction of **T** and changing the direction produces acceleration in the direction of **N**.

We begin with the fact that $\mathbf{T} = \dfrac{\mathbf{v}}{|\mathbf{v}|}$ or $\mathbf{v} = \mathbf{T}|\mathbf{v}| = \mathbf{T}\dfrac{ds}{dt}$. Differentiating both sides of $\mathbf{v} = \mathbf{T}\dfrac{ds}{dt}$ with respect to t gives

$$\mathbf{a} = \frac{d\mathbf{v}}{dt} = \frac{d}{dt} \left(\mathbf{T}\frac{ds}{dt} \right)$$

$$= \frac{d\mathbf{T}}{dt}\frac{ds}{dt} + \mathbf{T}\frac{d^2s}{dt^2} \qquad \text{Product Rule}$$

$$= \underbrace{\frac{d\mathbf{T}}{ds}\underbrace{\frac{ds}{dt}}_{|\mathbf{v}|}\frac{ds}{dt}}_{k\mathbf{N}} + \mathbf{T}\frac{d^2s}{dt^2} \qquad \text{Chain Rule: } \frac{d\mathbf{T}}{dt} = \frac{d\mathbf{T}}{ds}\frac{ds}{dt}$$

$$= k\mathbf{N}|\mathbf{v}|^2 + \mathbf{T}\frac{d^2s}{dt^2}. \qquad \text{Substitute.}$$

We now identify the normal and tangential components of the acceleration.

▶ Note that a_N and a_T are defined even at points where $\kappa = 0$ and $\mathbf{N}$ is undefined.

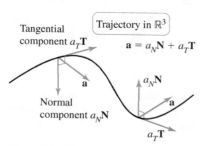

Tangential component $a_T\mathbf{T}$

Normal component $a_N\mathbf{N}$

Trajectory in $\mathbb{R}^3$

$\mathbf{a} = a_N\mathbf{N} + a_T\mathbf{T}$

$a_N\mathbf{N}$

$a_T\mathbf{T}$

Figure 11.107

THEOREM 11.13   Tangential and Normal Components of the Acceleration
The acceleration vector of an object moving in space along a smooth curve has the following representation in terms of its **tangential component** a_T (in the direction of $\mathbf{T}$) and its **normal component** a_N (in the direction of $\mathbf{N}$):

$$\mathbf{a} = a_N\mathbf{N} + a_T\mathbf{T},$$

where $a_N = \kappa|\mathbf{v}|^2 = \dfrac{|\mathbf{v} \times \mathbf{a}|}{|\mathbf{v}|}$ and $a_T = \dfrac{d^2s}{dt^2}$.

The tangential component of the acceleration, in the direction of $\mathbf{T}$, is the usual acceleration $a_T = d^2s/dt^2$ of an object moving along a straight line (Figure 11.107). The normal component, in the direction of $\mathbf{N}$, increases with the speed $|\mathbf{v}|$ and with the curvature. Higher speeds on tighter curves produce greater normal accelerations.

EXAMPLE 6   Acceleration on a circular path Find the components of the acceleration on the circular trajectory

$$\mathbf{r}(t) = \langle R\cos\omega t, R\sin\omega t\rangle,$$

where R and ω are positive real numbers.

SOLUTION We find that $\mathbf{r}'(t) = \langle -R\omega\sin\omega t, R\omega\cos\omega t\rangle$, $|\mathbf{v}(t)| = |\mathbf{r}'(t)| = R\omega$, and, by Example 2, $\kappa = 1/R$. Recall that $ds/dt = |\mathbf{v}(t)|$, which is constant; therefore, $d^2s/dt^2 = 0$ and the tangential component of the acceleration is zero. The acceleration is

$$\mathbf{a} = \kappa|\mathbf{v}|^2\mathbf{N} + \underbrace{\frac{d^2s}{dt^2}}_{0}\mathbf{T} = \frac{1}{R}(R\omega)^2\mathbf{N} = R\omega^2\mathbf{N}.$$

On a circular path (traversed at constant speed), the acceleration is entirely in the normal direction, orthogonal to the tangent vectors. The acceleration increases with the radius of the circle R and with the frequency of the motion ω.

Related Exercises 35–40 ◀

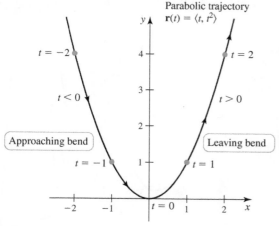

Parabolic trajectory
$\mathbf{r}(t) = \langle t, t^2\rangle$

$t = -2$

$t < 0$

Approaching bend

$t = -1$

$t = 2$

$t > 0$

Leaving bend

$t = 1$

$t = 0$

Figure 11.108

▶ Using the fact that $|\mathbf{T}| = |\mathbf{N}| = 1$, we have, from Section 11.3,

$$a_N = \text{scal}_{\mathbf{N}}\mathbf{a} = \frac{\mathbf{a} \cdot \mathbf{N}}{|\mathbf{N}|} = \mathbf{a} \cdot \mathbf{N}$$

and

$$a_T = \text{scal}_{\mathbf{T}}\mathbf{a} = \frac{\mathbf{a} \cdot \mathbf{T}}{|\mathbf{T}|} = \mathbf{a} \cdot \mathbf{T} = \frac{\mathbf{v} \cdot \mathbf{a}}{|\mathbf{v}|}.$$

EXAMPLE 7   A bend in the road The driver of a car follows the parabolic trajectory $\mathbf{r}(t) = \langle t, t^2\rangle$, for $-2 \le t \le 2$, through a sharp bend (Figure 11.108). Find the tangential and normal components of the acceleration of the car.

SOLUTION The velocity and acceleration vectors are easily computed: $\mathbf{v}(t) = \mathbf{r}'(t) = \langle 1, 2t\rangle$ and $\mathbf{a}(t) = \mathbf{r}''(t) = \langle 0, 2\rangle$. The goal is to express $\mathbf{a} = \langle 0, 2\rangle$ in terms of $\mathbf{T}$ and $\mathbf{N}$. A short calculation reveals that

$$\mathbf{T} = \frac{\mathbf{v}}{|\mathbf{v}|} = \frac{\langle 1, 2t\rangle}{\sqrt{1 + 4t^2}} \quad \text{and} \quad \mathbf{N} = \frac{d\mathbf{T}/dt}{|d\mathbf{T}/dt|} = \frac{\langle -2t, 1\rangle}{\sqrt{1 + 4t^2}}.$$

We now have two ways to proceed. One is to compute the normal and tangential components of the acceleration directly using the definitions. More efficient is to note that $\mathbf{T}$ and $\mathbf{N}$ are orthogonal unit vectors, and then to compute the scalar projections of $\mathbf{a} = \langle 0, 2\rangle$ in the directions of $\mathbf{T}$ and $\mathbf{N}$. We find that

$$a_N = \mathbf{a} \cdot \mathbf{N} = \langle 0, 2\rangle \cdot \frac{\langle -2t, 1\rangle}{\sqrt{1 + 4t^2}} = \frac{2}{\sqrt{1 + 4t^2}}$$

and

$$a_T = \mathbf{a} \cdot \mathbf{T} = \langle 0, 2\rangle \cdot \frac{\langle 1, 2t\rangle}{\sqrt{1 + 4t^2}} = \frac{4t}{\sqrt{1 + 4t^2}}.$$

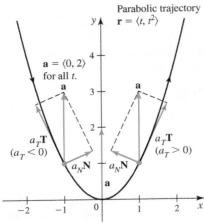

Figure 11.109

You should verify that at all times (Exercise 76),

$$\mathbf{a} = a_N \mathbf{N} + a_T \mathbf{T} = \frac{2}{\sqrt{1 + 4t^2}} (\mathbf{N} + 2t\,\mathbf{T}) = \langle 0, 2 \rangle.$$

Let's interpret these results. First notice that the driver negotiates the curve in a sensible way: The speed $|\mathbf{v}| = \sqrt{1 + 4t^2}$ decreases as the car approaches the origin (the tightest part of the curve) and increases as it moves away from the origin (Figure 11.109). As the car approaches the origin ($t < 0$), $\mathbf{T}$ points in the direction of the trajectory and $\mathbf{N}$ points to the inside of the curve. However, $a_T = \frac{d^2s}{dt^2} < 0$ when $t < 0$, so $a_T\mathbf{T}$ points in the direction opposite that of $\mathbf{T}$ (corresponding to a deceleration). As the car leaves the origin ($t > 0$), $a_T > 0$ (corresponding to an acceleration) and $a_T\mathbf{T}$ and $\mathbf{T}$ point in the direction of the trajectory. At all times, $\mathbf{N}$ points to the inside of the curve (Figure 11.109; Exercise 78).

Related Exercises 35–40 ◄

QUICK CHECK 5 Verify that $\mathbf{T}$ and $\mathbf{N}$ given in Example 7 satisfy $|\mathbf{T}| = |\mathbf{N}| = 1$ and that $\mathbf{T} \cdot \mathbf{N} = 0$. ◄

The Binormal Vector and Torsion

We have seen that the curvature function and the principal unit normal vector tell us how quickly and in what direction a curve turns. For curves in two dimensions, these quantities give a fairly complete description of motion along the curve. However, in three dimensions, a curve has more "room" in which to change its course, and another descriptive function is often useful. Figure 11.110 shows a smooth parameterized curve C with its unit tangent vector $\mathbf{T}$ and its principal unit normal vector $\mathbf{N}$ at two different points. These two vectors determine a plane called the *osculating plane* (Figure 11.110b). The question we now ask is, How quickly does the curve C move out of the plane determined by $\mathbf{T}$ and $\mathbf{N}$?

➤ The TNB frame is also called the Frenet-Serret frame, after two 19th-century French mathematicians, Jean Frenet and Joseph Serret.

To answer this question, we begin by defining the *unit binormal vector* $\mathbf{B} = \mathbf{T} \times \mathbf{N}$. By the definition of the cross product, $\mathbf{B}$ is orthogonal to $\mathbf{T}$ and $\mathbf{N}$. Because $\mathbf{T}$ and $\mathbf{N}$ are unit vectors, $\mathbf{B}$ is also a unit vector. Notice that $\mathbf{T}$, $\mathbf{N}$, and $\mathbf{B}$ form a right-handed coordinate system (like the *xyz*-coordinate system) that changes its orientation as we move along the curve. This coordinate system is often called the **TNB frame** (Figure 11.110).

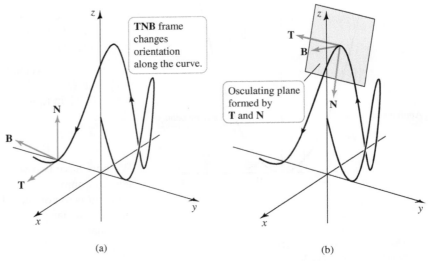

(a)   (b)

Figure 11.110

QUICK CHECK 6 Explain why $\mathbf{B} = \mathbf{T} \times \mathbf{N}$ is a unit vector. ◄

The rate at which the curve C twists out of the plane determined by $\mathbf{T}$ and $\mathbf{N}$ is the rate at which $\mathbf{B}$ changes as we move along C, which is $\frac{d\mathbf{B}}{ds}$. A short calculation leads to a practical formula for the twisting of the curve. Differentiating the cross product $\mathbf{T} \times \mathbf{N}$, we find that

$$\frac{d\mathbf{B}}{ds} = \frac{d}{ds}(\mathbf{T} \times \mathbf{N})$$

$$= \underbrace{\frac{d\mathbf{T}}{ds} \times \mathbf{N}}_{\text{parallel vectors}} + \mathbf{T} \times \frac{d\mathbf{N}}{ds} \qquad \text{Product Rule for cross products}$$

$$= \mathbf{T} \times \frac{d\mathbf{N}}{ds}. \qquad \frac{d\mathbf{T}}{ds} \text{ and } \mathbf{N} \text{ are parallel; } \frac{d\mathbf{T}}{ds} \times \mathbf{N} = \mathbf{0}.$$

Notice that by definition, $\mathbf{N} = \frac{1}{\kappa}\frac{d\mathbf{T}}{ds}$, which implies that $\mathbf{N}$ and $\frac{d\mathbf{T}}{ds}$ are scalar multiples of each other. Therefore, their cross product is the zero vector.

The properties of $\frac{d\mathbf{B}}{ds}$ become clear with the following observations.

- $\frac{d\mathbf{B}}{ds}$ is orthogonal to both $\mathbf{T}$ and $\frac{d\mathbf{N}}{ds}$, because it is the cross product of $\mathbf{T}$ and $\frac{d\mathbf{N}}{ds}$.

- Applying Theorem 11.8 to the unit vector $\mathbf{B}$, it follows that $\frac{d\mathbf{B}}{ds}$ is also orthogonal to $\mathbf{B}$.

- By the previous two observations, $\frac{d\mathbf{B}}{ds}$ is orthogonal to both $\mathbf{B}$ and $\mathbf{T}$, so it must be parallel to $\mathbf{N}$.

> Note that $\mathbf{B}$ is a unit vector (of constant length). Therefore, by Theorem 11.8, $\mathbf{B}$ and $\mathbf{B}'(t)$ are orthogonal. Because $\mathbf{B}'(t)$ and $\mathbf{B}'(s)$ are parallel, it follows that $\mathbf{B}$ and $\mathbf{B}'(s)$ are orthogonal.

Because $\frac{d\mathbf{B}}{ds}$ is parallel to (a scalar multiple of) $\mathbf{N}$, we write

$$\frac{d\mathbf{B}}{ds} = -\tau\mathbf{N},$$

> The negative sign in the definition of the torsion is conventional. However, τ may be positive or negative (or zero), and in general, it varies along the curve.

where the scalar τ is the *torsion*. Notice that $\left|\frac{d\mathbf{B}}{ds}\right| = |-\tau\mathbf{N}| = |-\tau|$, so the magnitude of the torsion equals the magnitude of $\frac{d\mathbf{B}}{ds}$, which is the rate at which the curve twists out of the **TN**-plane.

A short calculation gives a method for computing the torsion. We take the dot product of both sides of the equation defining the torsion with $\mathbf{N}$:

$$\frac{d\mathbf{B}}{ds} \cdot \mathbf{N} = -\tau\underbrace{\mathbf{N} \cdot \mathbf{N}}_{1}$$

> Notice that $\mathbf{B}$ and τ depend on the orientation of the curve.

$$\frac{d\mathbf{B}}{ds} \cdot \mathbf{N} = -\tau. \qquad \mathbf{N} \text{ is a unit vector.}$$

QUICK CHECK 7 Explain why $\mathbf{N} \cdot \mathbf{N} = 1$. ◄

DEFINITION Unit Binormal Vector and Torsion

Let C be a smooth parameterized curve with unit tangent and principal unit normal vectors $\mathbf{T}$ and $\mathbf{N}$, respectively. Then at each point of the curve at which the curvature is nonzero, the **unit binormal vector** is

$$\mathbf{B} = \mathbf{T} \times \mathbf{N},$$

and the **torsion** is

$$\tau = -\frac{d\mathbf{B}}{ds} \cdot \mathbf{N}.$$

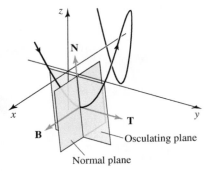

Figure 11.111

▶ The third plane formed by the vectors **T** and **B** is called the *rectifying plane*.

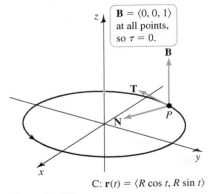

$B = \langle 0, 0, 1 \rangle$ at all points, so $\tau = 0$.

C: $\mathbf{r}(t) = \langle R \cos t, R \sin t \rangle$

Figure 11.112

Figure 11.111 provides some interpretation of the curvature and the torsion. First, we see a smooth curve C passing through a point where the mutually orthogonal vectors **T**, **N**, and **B** are defined. The **osculating plane** is defined by the vectors **T** and **N**. The plane orthogonal to the osculating plane containing **N** is called the **normal plane**. Because **N** and $\dfrac{d\mathbf{B}}{ds}$ are parallel, $\dfrac{d\mathbf{B}}{ds}$ also lies in the normal plane. The torsion, which is equal in magnitude to $\left| \dfrac{d\mathbf{B}}{ds} \right|$, gives the rate at which the curve moves *out of* the osculating plane. In a complementary way, the curvature, which is equal to $\left| \dfrac{d\mathbf{T}}{ds} \right|$, gives the rate at which the curve turns *within* the osculating plane. Two examples will clarify these concepts.

EXAMPLE 8   **Unit binormal vector**   Consider the circle C defined by

$$\mathbf{r}(t) = \langle R \cos t, R \sin t \rangle, \text{ for } 0 \le t \le 2\pi, \text{ with } R > 0.$$

a. Without doing any calculations, find the unit binormal vector **B** and determine the torsion.

b. Use the definition of **B** to calculate **B** and confirm your answer in part (a).

SOLUTION

a. The circle C lies in the xy-plane, so at all points on the circle, **T** and **N** are in the xy-plane. Therefore, at all points of the circle, $\mathbf{B} = \mathbf{T} \times \mathbf{N}$ is the unit vector in the positive z-direction (by the right-hand rule); that is, $\mathbf{B} = \mathbf{k}$. Because **B** changes neither in length nor direction, $\dfrac{d\mathbf{B}}{ds} = \mathbf{0}$ and $\tau = 0$ (Figure 11.112).

b. Building on the calculations of Example 2, we find that

$$\mathbf{T} = \langle -\sin t, \cos t \rangle \quad \text{and} \quad \mathbf{N} = \langle -\cos t, -\sin t \rangle.$$

Therefore, the unit binormal vector is

$$\mathbf{B} = \mathbf{T} \times \mathbf{N} = \begin{vmatrix} \mathbf{i} & \mathbf{j} & \mathbf{k} \\ -\sin t & \cos t & 0 \\ -\cos t & -\sin t & 0 \end{vmatrix} = 0 \cdot \mathbf{i} - 0 \cdot \mathbf{j} + 1 \cdot \mathbf{k} = \mathbf{k}.$$

As in part (a), it follows that the torsion is zero.

Related Exercises 41–48 ◀

Generalizing Example 8, it can be shown that the binormal vector of any curve that lies in the xy-plane is always parallel to the z-axis; therefore, the torsion of the curve is everywhere zero.

EXAMPLE 9   **Torsion of a helix**   Compute the torsion of the helix $\mathbf{r}(t) = \langle a \cos t, a \sin t, bt \rangle$, for $t \ge 0$, $a > 0$, and $b > 0$.

SOLUTION   In Example 5, we found that

$$\mathbf{T} = \frac{\langle -a \sin t, a \cos t, b \rangle}{\sqrt{a^2 + b^2}} \quad \text{and} \quad \mathbf{N} = \langle -\cos t, -\sin t, 0 \rangle.$$

Therefore,

$$\mathbf{B} = \mathbf{T} \times \mathbf{N} = \frac{1}{\sqrt{a^2 + b^2}} \begin{vmatrix} \mathbf{i} & \mathbf{j} & \mathbf{k} \\ -a \sin t & a \cos t & b \\ -\cos t & -\sin t & 0 \end{vmatrix} = \frac{\langle b \sin t, -b \cos t, a \rangle}{\sqrt{a^2 + b^2}}.$$

The next step is to determine $\dfrac{d\mathbf{B}}{ds}$, which we do in the same way we computed $\dfrac{d\mathbf{T}}{ds}$, by writing

$$\frac{d\mathbf{B}}{dt} = \frac{d\mathbf{B}}{ds} \cdot \frac{ds}{dt} \quad \text{or} \quad \frac{d\mathbf{B}}{ds} = \frac{d\mathbf{B}/dt}{ds/dt}.$$

In this case,

$$\frac{ds}{dt} = |\mathbf{r}'(t)| = \sqrt{a^2 \sin^2 t + a^2 \cos^2 t + b^2} = \sqrt{a^2 + b^2}.$$

Computing $\frac{d\mathbf{B}}{dt}$, we have

$$\frac{d\mathbf{B}}{ds} = \frac{d\mathbf{B}/dt}{ds/dt} = \frac{\langle b \cos t, b \sin t, 0 \rangle}{a^2 + b^2}.$$

The final step is to compute the torsion:

$$\tau = -\frac{d\mathbf{B}}{ds} \cdot \mathbf{N} = -\frac{\langle b \cos t, b \sin t, 0 \rangle}{a^2 + b^2} \cdot \langle -\cos t, -\sin t, 0 \rangle = \frac{b}{a^2 + b^2}.$$

We see that the torsion is constant over the helix. In Example 4, we found that the curvature of a helix is also constant. This special property of circular helices means that the curve turns about its axis at a constant rate and rises vertically at a constant rate (Figure 11.113).

Related Exercises 41–48 ◄

Example 9 suggests that the computation of the binormal vector and the torsion can be involved. We close by stating some alternative formulas for $\mathbf{B}$ and τ that *may* simplify calculations in some cases. Letting $\mathbf{v} = \mathbf{r}'(t)$ and $\mathbf{a} = \mathbf{v}'(t) = \mathbf{r}''(t)$, the binormal vector can be written compactly as (Exercise 83)

$$\mathbf{B} = \mathbf{T} \times \mathbf{N} = \frac{\mathbf{v} \times \mathbf{a}}{|\mathbf{v} \times \mathbf{a}|}.$$

We also state without proof that the torsion may be expressed in either of the forms

$$\tau = \frac{(\mathbf{v} \times \mathbf{a}) \cdot \mathbf{a}'}{|\mathbf{v} \times \mathbf{a}|^2} \quad \text{or} \quad \tau = \frac{(\mathbf{r}' \times \mathbf{r}'') \cdot \mathbf{r}'''}{|\mathbf{r}' \times \mathbf{r}''|^2}.$$

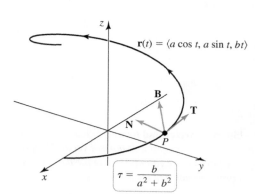

$\mathbf{r}(t) = \langle a \cos t, a \sin t, bt \rangle$

$\tau = \dfrac{b}{a^2 + b^2}$

Figure 11.113

SUMMARY   **Formulas for Curves in Space**

Position function: $\mathbf{r}(t) = \langle x(t), y(t), z(t) \rangle$

Velocity: $\mathbf{v} = \mathbf{r}'$

Acceleration: $\mathbf{a} = \mathbf{v}'$

Unit tangent vector: $\mathbf{T} = \dfrac{\mathbf{v}}{|\mathbf{v}|}$

Principal unit normal vector: $\mathbf{N} = \dfrac{d\mathbf{T}/dt}{|d\mathbf{T}/dt|}$ (provided $d\mathbf{T}/dt \neq \mathbf{0}$)

Curvature: $\kappa = \left| \dfrac{d\mathbf{T}}{ds} \right| = \dfrac{1}{|\mathbf{v}|} \left| \dfrac{d\mathbf{T}}{dt} \right| = \dfrac{|\mathbf{v} \times \mathbf{a}|}{|\mathbf{v}|^3}$

Components of acceleration: $\mathbf{a} = a_N \mathbf{N} + a_T \mathbf{T}$, where $a_N = \kappa |\mathbf{v}|^2 = \dfrac{|\mathbf{v} \times \mathbf{a}|}{|\mathbf{v}|}$
and $a_T = \dfrac{d^2 s}{dt^2} = \dfrac{\mathbf{v} \cdot \mathbf{a}}{|\mathbf{v}|}$

Unit binormal vector: $\mathbf{B} = \mathbf{T} \times \mathbf{N} = \dfrac{\mathbf{v} \times \mathbf{a}}{|\mathbf{v} \times \mathbf{a}|}$

Torsion: $\tau = -\dfrac{d\mathbf{B}}{ds} \cdot \mathbf{N} = \dfrac{(\mathbf{v} \times \mathbf{a}) \cdot \mathbf{a}'}{|\mathbf{v} \times \mathbf{a}|^2} = \dfrac{(\mathbf{r}' \times \mathbf{r}'') \cdot \mathbf{r}'''}{|\mathbf{r}' \times \mathbf{r}''|^2}$

SECTION 11.9 EXERCISES

Review Questions

1. What is the curvature of a straight line?

2. Explain the meaning of *the curvature of a curve*. Is it a scalar function or a vector function?

3. Give a practical formula for computing the curvature.

4. Interpret *the principal unit normal vector of a curve*. Is it a scalar function or a vector function?

5. Give a practical formula for computing the principal unit normal vector.

6. Explain how to decompose the acceleration vector of a moving object into its tangential and normal components.

7. Explain how the vectors **T**, **N**, and **B** are related geometrically.

8. How do you compute **B**?

9. Give a geometrical interpretation of the torsion.

10. How do you compute the torsion?

Basic Skills

11–20. Curvature *Find the unit tangent vector* **T** *and the curvature* κ *for the following parameterized curves.*

11. $\mathbf{r}(t) = \langle 2t + 1, 4t - 5, 6t + 12 \rangle$

12. $\mathbf{r}(t) = \langle 2\cos t, -2\sin t \rangle$

13. $\mathbf{r}(t) = \langle 2t, 4\sin t, 4\cos t \rangle$

14. $\mathbf{r}(t) = \langle \cos t^2, \sin t^2 \rangle$

15. $\mathbf{r}(t) = \langle \sqrt{3}\sin t, \sin t, 2\cos t \rangle$

16. $\mathbf{r}(t) = \langle t, \ln \cos t \rangle$

17. $\mathbf{r}(t) = \langle t, 2t^2 \rangle$

18. $\mathbf{r}(t) = \langle \cos^3 t, \sin^3 t \rangle$

19. $\mathbf{r}(t) = \left\langle \int_0^t \cos(\pi u^2/2)\, du, \int_0^t \sin(\pi u^2/2)\, du \right\rangle, t > 0$

20. $\mathbf{r}(t) = \left\langle \int_0^t \cos u^2\, du, \int_0^t \sin u^2\, du \right\rangle, t > 0$

21–26. Alternative curvature formula *Use the alternative curvature formula* $\kappa = |\mathbf{v} \times \mathbf{a}|/|\mathbf{v}|^3$ *to find the curvature of the following parameterized curves.*

21. $\mathbf{r}(t) = \langle -3\cos t, 3\sin t, 0 \rangle$

22. $\mathbf{r}(t) = \langle 4t, 3\sin t, 3\cos t \rangle$

23. $\mathbf{r}(t) = \langle 4 + t^2, t, 0 \rangle$

24. $\mathbf{r}(t) = \langle \sqrt{3}\sin t, \sin t, 2\cos t \rangle$

25. $\mathbf{r}(t) = \langle 4\cos t, \sin t, 2\cos t \rangle$

26. $\mathbf{r}(t) = \langle e^t \cos t, e^t \sin t, e^t \rangle$

27–34. Principal unit normal vector *Find the unit tangent vector* **T** *and the principal unit normal vector* **N** *for the following parameterized curves. In each case, verify that* $|\mathbf{T}| = |\mathbf{N}| = 1$ *and* $\mathbf{T} \cdot \mathbf{N} = 0$.

27. $\mathbf{r}(t) = \langle 2\sin t, 2\cos t \rangle$

28. $\mathbf{r}(t) = \langle 4\sin t, 4\cos t, 10t \rangle$

29. $\mathbf{r}(t) = \langle t^2/2, 4 - 3t, 1 \rangle$

30. $\mathbf{r}(t) = \langle t^2/2, t^3/3 \rangle, t > 0$

31. $\mathbf{r}(t) = \langle \cos t^2, \sin t^2 \rangle$

32. $\mathbf{r}(t) = \langle \cos^3 t, \sin^3 t \rangle$

33. $\mathbf{r}(t) = \langle t^2, t \rangle$

34. $\mathbf{r}(t) = \langle t, \ln \cos t \rangle$

35–40. Components of the acceleration *Consider the following trajectories of moving objects. Find the tangential and normal components of the acceleration.*

35. $\mathbf{r}(t) = \langle t, 1 + 4t, 2 - 6t \rangle$

36. $\mathbf{r}(t) = \langle 10\cos t, -10\sin t \rangle$

37. $\mathbf{r}(t) = \langle e^t \cos t, e^t \sin t, e^t \rangle$

38. $\mathbf{r}(t) = \langle t, t^2 + 1 \rangle$

39. $\mathbf{r}(t) = \langle t^3, t^2 \rangle$

40. $\mathbf{r}(t) = \langle 20\cos t, 20\sin t, 30t \rangle$

41–44. Computing the binormal vector and torsion *In Exercises 27–30, the unit tangent vector* **T** *and the principal unit normal vector* **N** *were computed for the following parameterized curves. Use the definitions to compute their unit binormal vector and torsion.*

41. $\mathbf{r}(t) = \langle 2\sin t, 2\cos t \rangle$

42. $\mathbf{r}(t) = \langle 4\sin t, 4\cos t, 10t \rangle$

43. $\mathbf{r}(t) = \langle t^2/2, 4 - 3t, 1 \rangle$

44. $\mathbf{r}(t) = \langle t^2/2, t^3/3 \rangle, t > 0$

45–48. Computing the binormal vector and torsion *Use the definitions to compute the unit binormal vector and torsion of the following curves.*

45. $\mathbf{r}(t) = \langle 2\cos t, 2\sin t, -t \rangle$

46. $\mathbf{r}(t) = \langle t, \cosh t, -\sinh t \rangle$

47. $\mathbf{r}(t) = \langle 12t, 5\cos t, 5\sin t \rangle$

48. $\mathbf{r}(t) = \langle \sin t - t\cos t, \cos t + t\sin t, t \rangle$

Further Explorations

49. **Explain why or why not** Determine whether the following statements are true and give an explanation or counterexample.

    a. The position, unit tangent, and principal unit normal vectors (**r**, **T**, and **N**) at a point lie in the same plane.
    b. The vectors **T** and **N** at a point depend on the orientation of a curve.
    c. The curvature at a point depends on the orientation of a curve.
    d. An object with unit speed ($|\mathbf{v}| = 1$) on a circle of radius R has an acceleration of $\mathbf{a} = \mathbf{N}/R$.
    e. If the speedometer of a car reads a constant 60 mi/hr, the car is not accelerating.
    f. A curve in the *xy*-plane that is concave up at all points has positive torsion.
    g. A curve with large curvature also has large torsion.

50. **Special formula: Curvature for** $y = f(x)$ Assume that f is twice differentiable. Prove that the curve $y = f(x)$ has curvature

$$\kappa(x) = \frac{|f''(x)|}{(1 + f'(x)^2)^{3/2}}.$$

(*Hint:* Use the parametric description $x = t$, $y = f(t)$.)

51–54. Curvature for $y = f(x)$ *Use the result of Exercise 50 to find the curvature function of the following curves.*

51. $f(x) = x^2$

52. $f(x) = \sqrt{a^2 - x^2}$

53. $f(x) = \ln x$

54. $f(x) = \ln \cos x$

55. Special formula: Curvature for plane curves Show that the parametric curve $\mathbf{r}(t) = \langle f(t), g(t) \rangle$, where f and g are twice differentiable, has curvature

$$\kappa(t) = \frac{|f'g'' - f''g'|}{((f')^2 + (g')^2)^{3/2}},$$

where all derivatives are taken with respect to t.

56–59. Curvature for plane curves *Use the result of Exercise 55 to find the curvature function of the following curves.*

56. $\mathbf{r}(t) = \langle a \sin t, a \cos t \rangle$ (circle)

57. $\mathbf{r}(t) = \langle a \sin t, b \cos t \rangle$ (ellipse)

58. $\mathbf{r}(t) = \langle a \cos^3 t, a \sin^3 t \rangle$ (astroid)

59. $\mathbf{r}(t) = \langle t, at^2 \rangle$ (parabola)

When appropriate, consider using the special formulas derived in Exercises 50 and 55 in the remaining exercises.

60–63. Same paths, different velocity *The position functions of objects A and B describe different motion along the same path, for $t \geq 0$.*

a. *Sketch the path followed by both A and B.*

b. *Find the velocity and acceleration of A and B and discuss the differences.*

c. *Express the acceleration of A and B in terms of the tangential and normal components and discuss the differences.*

60. A: $\mathbf{r}(t) = \langle 1 + 2t, 2 - 3t, 4t \rangle$, B: $\mathbf{r}(t) = \langle 1 + 6t, 2 - 9t, 12t \rangle$

61. A: $\mathbf{r}(t) = \langle t, 2t, 3t \rangle$, B: $\mathbf{r}(t) = \langle t^2, 2t^2, 3t^2 \rangle$

62. A: $\mathbf{r}(t) = \langle \cos t, \sin t \rangle$, B: $\mathbf{r}(t) = \langle \cos 3t, \sin 3t \rangle$

63. A: $\mathbf{r}(t) = \langle \cos t, \sin t \rangle$, B: $\mathbf{r}(t) = \langle \cos t^2, \sin t^2 \rangle$

▣ 64–67. Graphs of the curvature *Consider the following curves.*

a. *Graph the curve.*

b. *Compute the curvature.*

c. *Graph the curvature as a function of the parameter.*

d. *Identify the points (if any) at which the curve has a maximum or minimum curvature.*

e. *Verify that the graph of the curvature is consistent with the graph of the curve.*

64. $\mathbf{r}(t) = \langle t, t^2 \rangle$, for $-2 \leq t \leq 2$ (parabola)

65. $\mathbf{r}(t) = \langle t - \sin t, 1 - \cos t \rangle$, for $0 \leq t \leq 2\pi$ (cycloid)

66. $\mathbf{r}(t) = \langle t, \sin t \rangle$, for $0 \leq t \leq \pi$ (sine curve)

67. $\mathbf{r}(t) = \langle t^2/2, t^3/3 \rangle$, for $t > 0$

68. Curvature of $\ln x$ Find the curvature of $f(x) = \ln x$, for $x > 0$, and find the point at which it is a maximum. What is the value of the maximum curvature?

69. Curvature of e^x Find the curvature of $f(x) = e^x$ and find the point at which it is a maximum. What is the value of the maximum curvature?

70. Circle and radius of curvature Choose a point P on a smooth curve C in the plane. The **circle of curvature** (or **osculating circle**) at P is the circle that (a) is tangent to C at P, (b) has the same curvature as C at P, and (c) lies on the same side of C as the principal unit normal $\mathbf{N}$ (see figure). The **radius of curvature** is the radius of the circle of curvature. Show that the radius of curvature is $1/\kappa$, where κ is the curvature of C at P.

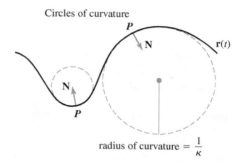

Circles of curvature

radius of curvature $= \dfrac{1}{\kappa}$

71–74. Finding radii of curvature *Find the radius of curvature (see Exercise 70) of the following curves at the given point. Then write an equation of the circle of curvature at the point.*

71. $\mathbf{r}(t) = \langle t, t^2 \rangle$ (parabola) at $t = 0$

72. $y = \ln x$ at $x = 1$

73. $\mathbf{r}(t) = \langle t - \sin t, 1 - \cos t \rangle$ (cycloid) at $t = \pi$

74. $y = \sin x$ at $x = \pi/2$

75. Curvature of the sine curve The function $f(x) = \sin nx$, where n is a positive real number, has a local maximum at $x = \pi/(2n)$. Compute the curvature κ of f at this point. How does κ vary (if at all) as n varies?

Applications

76. Parabolic trajectory In Example 7 it was shown that for the parabolic trajectory $\mathbf{r}(t) = \langle t, t^2 \rangle$, $\mathbf{a} = \langle 0, 2 \rangle$ and

$$\mathbf{a} = \frac{2}{\sqrt{1 + 4t^2}} (\mathbf{N} + 2t\,\mathbf{T}).$$ Show that the second expression for $\mathbf{a}$ reduces to the first expression.

▣ 77. Parabolic trajectory Consider the parabolic trajectory

$$x = (V_0 \cos \alpha)\, t, \quad y = (V_0 \sin \alpha)\, t - \tfrac{1}{2} gt^2,$$

where V_0 is the initial speed, α is the angle of launch, and g is the acceleration due to gravity. Consider all times $[0, T]$ for which $y \geq 0$.

a. Find and graph the speed, for $0 \leq t \leq T$.

b. Find and graph the curvature, for $0 \leq t \leq T$.

c. At what times (if any) do the speed and curvature have maximum and minimum values?

78. Relationship between T, N, and a Show that if an object accelerates in the sense that $d^2s/dt^2 > 0$ and $\kappa \neq 0$, then the acceleration vector lies between $\mathbf{T}$ and $\mathbf{N}$ in the plane of $\mathbf{T}$ and $\mathbf{N}$. If an object decelerates in the sense that $d^2s/dt^2 < 0$, then the acceleration vector lies in the plane of $\mathbf{T}$ and $\mathbf{N}$, but not between $\mathbf{T}$ and $\mathbf{N}$.

Additional Exercises

79. Zero curvature Prove that the curve

$$\mathbf{r}(t) = \langle a + bt^p, c + dt^p, e + ft^p \rangle,$$

where a, b, c, d, e, and f are real numbers and p is a positive integer, has zero curvature. Give an explanation.

80. Practical formula for N Show that the definition of the principal unit normal vector $\mathbf{N} = \dfrac{d\mathbf{T}/ds}{|d\mathbf{T}/ds|}$ implies the practical formula

$\mathbf{N} = \dfrac{d\mathbf{T}/dt}{|d\mathbf{T}/dt|}$. Use the Chain Rule and recall that

$|\mathbf{v}| = ds/dt > 0$.

T 81. Maximum curvature Consider the "superparabolas" $f_n(x) = x^{2n}$, where n is a positive integer.

    a. Find the curvature function of f_n, for $n = 1, 2$, and 3.
    b. Plot f_n and their curvature functions, for $n = 1, 2$, and 3, and check for consistency.
    c. At what points does the maximum curvature occur, for $n = 1, 2, 3$?
    d. Let the maximum curvature for f_n occur at $x = \pm z_n$. Using either analytical methods or a calculator, determine $\lim_{n \to \infty} z_n$. Interpret your result.

82. Alternative derivation of the curvature Derive the computational formula for curvature using the following steps.

    a. Use the tangential and normal components of the acceleration to show that $\mathbf{v} \times \mathbf{a} = \kappa |\mathbf{v}|^3 \mathbf{B}$. (Note that $\mathbf{T} \times \mathbf{T} = \mathbf{0}$.)
    b. Solve the equation in part (a) for κ and conclude that $\kappa = \dfrac{|\mathbf{v} \times \mathbf{a}|}{|\mathbf{v}^3|}$, as shown in the text.

83. Computational formula for B Use the result of part (a) of Exercise 82 and the formula for κ to show that

$$\mathbf{B} = \frac{\mathbf{v} \times \mathbf{a}}{|\mathbf{v} \times \mathbf{a}|}.$$

84. Torsion formula Show that the formula defining the torsion, $\tau = -\dfrac{d\mathbf{B}}{ds} \cdot \mathbf{N}$, is equivalent to $\tau = -\dfrac{1}{|\mathbf{v}|}\dfrac{d\mathbf{B}}{dt} \cdot \mathbf{N}$. The second formula is generally easier to use.

85. Descartes' four-circle solution Consider the four mutually tangent circles shown in the figure that have radii a, b, c, and d, and curvatures $A = 1/a, B = 1/b, C = 1/c$, and $D = 1/d$. Prove Descartes' result (1643) that

$$(A + B + C + D)^2 = 2(A^2 + B^2 + C^2 + D^2).$$

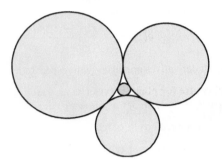

QUICK CHECK ANSWERS

1. $\kappa = \frac{1}{3}$ 2. $\kappa = 0$ 3. Negative y-direction
4. $\kappa = 0$, so $\mathbf{N}$ is undefined.   6. $|\mathbf{T}| = |\mathbf{N}| = 1$, so $|\mathbf{B}| = 1$ 7. For any vector, $\mathbf{u} \cdot \mathbf{u} = |\mathbf{u}|^2$. Because $|\mathbf{N}| = 1, \mathbf{N} \cdot \mathbf{N} = 1$. ◄

CHAPTER 11   REVIEW EXERCISES

1. Explain why or why not Determine whether the following statements are true and give an explanation or counterexample.

    a. Given two vectors $\mathbf{u}$ and $\mathbf{v}$, it is always true that $2\mathbf{u} + \mathbf{v} = \mathbf{v} + 2\mathbf{u}$.
    b. The vector in the direction of $\mathbf{u}$ with the length of $\mathbf{v}$ equals the vector in the direction of $\mathbf{v}$ with the length of $\mathbf{u}$.
    c. If $\mathbf{u} \neq \mathbf{0}$ and $\mathbf{u} + \mathbf{v} = \mathbf{0}$, then $\mathbf{u}$ and $\mathbf{v}$ are parallel.
    d. If $\mathbf{r}'(t) = \mathbf{0}$, then $\mathbf{r}(t) = \langle a, b, c \rangle$, where a, b, and c are real numbers.
    e. The parameterized curve $\mathbf{r}(t) = \langle 5 \cos t, 12 \cos t, 13 \sin t \rangle$ has arc length as a parameter.
    f. The position vector and the principal unit normal are always parallel on a smooth curve.

2–5. Drawing vectors *Let* $\mathbf{u} = \langle 3, -4 \rangle$ *and* $\mathbf{v} = \langle -1, 2 \rangle$. *Use geometry to sketch* $\mathbf{u}$, $\mathbf{v}$, *and the following vectors.*

2. $\mathbf{u} - \mathbf{v}$ **3.** $-3\mathbf{v}$

4. $\mathbf{u} + 2\mathbf{v}$ **5.** $2\mathbf{v} - \mathbf{u}$

6–11. Working with vectors *Let* $\mathbf{u} = \langle 2, 4, -5 \rangle$ *and* $\mathbf{v} = \langle -6, 10, 2 \rangle$.

6. Compute $\mathbf{u} - 3\mathbf{v}$.

7. Compute $|\mathbf{u} + \mathbf{v}|$.

8. Find the unit vector with the same direction as $\mathbf{u}$.

9. Find a vector parallel to $\mathbf{v}$ with length 20.

10. Compute $\mathbf{u} \cdot \mathbf{v}$ and the angle between $\mathbf{u}$ and $\mathbf{v}$.

11. Compute $\mathbf{u} \times \mathbf{v}, \mathbf{v} \times \mathbf{u}$, and the area of the triangle with vertices $(0, 0, 0), (2, 4, -5)$, and $(-6, 10, 2)$.

12. Scalar multiples Find scalars a, b, and c such that

$$\langle 2, 2, 2 \rangle = a\langle 1, 1, 0 \rangle + b\langle 0, 1, 1 \rangle + c\langle 1, 0, 1 \rangle.$$

13. Velocity vectors Assume the positive x-axis points east and the positive y-axis points north.

    a. An airliner flies northwest at a constant altitude at 550 mi/hr in calm air. Find a and b such that its velocity may be expressed in the form $\mathbf{v} = a\mathbf{i} + b\mathbf{j}$.

b. An airliner flies northwest at a constant altitude at 550 mi/hr relative to the air in a southerly crosswind $\mathbf{w} = \langle 0, 40 \rangle$. Find the velocity of the airliner relative to the ground.

14. Position vectors Let $\vec{PQ}$ extend from $P(2, 0, 6)$ to $Q(2, -8, 5)$.

   a. Find the position vector equal to $\vec{PQ}$.

   b. Find the midpoint M of the line segment PQ. Then find the magnitude of $\vec{PM}$.

   c. Find a vector of length 8 with direction opposite that of $\vec{PQ}$.

15–17. Spheres and balls *Use set notation to describe the following sets.*

15. The sphere of radius 4 centered at $(1, 0, -1)$

16. The points inside the sphere of radius 10 centered at $(2, 4, -3)$

17. The points outside the sphere of radius 2 centered at $(0, 1, 0)$

18–21. Identifying sets. *Give a geometric description of the following sets of points.*

18. $x^2 - 6x + y^2 + 8y + z^2 - 2z - 23 = 0$

19. $x^2 - x + y^2 + 4y + z^2 - 6z + 11 \leq 0$

20. $x^2 + y^2 - 10y + z^2 - 6z = -34$

21. $x^2 - 6x + y^2 + z^2 - 20z + 9 > 0$

22. Combined force An object at the origin is acted on by the forces $\mathbf{F}_1 = -10\,\mathbf{i} + 20\,\mathbf{k}$, $\mathbf{F}_2 = 40\,\mathbf{j} + 10\,\mathbf{k}$, and $\mathbf{F}_3 = -50\mathbf{i} + 20\mathbf{j}$. Find the magnitude of the combined force and use a sketch to illustrate the direction of the combined force.

23. Falling probe A remote sensing probe falls vertically with a terminal velocity of 60 m/s when it encounters a horizontal crosswind blowing north at 4 m/s and an updraft blowing vertically at 10 m/s. Find the magnitude and direction of the resulting velocity relative to the ground.

24. Crosswinds A small plane is flying north in calm air at 250 mi/hr when it is hit by a horizontal crosswind blowing northeast at 40 mi/hr and a 25 mi/hr downdraft. Find the resulting velocity and speed of the plane.

25. Sets of points Describe the set of points satisfying both the equation $x^2 + z^2 = 1$ and $y = 2$.

26–27. Angles and projections

a. Find the angle between $\mathbf{u}$ *and* $\mathbf{v}$.

b. Compute $\text{proj}_{\mathbf{v}}\mathbf{u}$ *and* $\text{scal}_{\mathbf{v}}\mathbf{u}$.

c. Compute $\text{proj}_{\mathbf{u}}\mathbf{v}$ *and* $\text{scal}_{\mathbf{u}}\mathbf{v}$.

26. $\mathbf{u} = -3\mathbf{j} + 4\mathbf{k}, \mathbf{v} = -4\mathbf{i} + \mathbf{j} + 5\mathbf{k}$

27. $\mathbf{u} = -\mathbf{i} + 2\mathbf{j} + 2\mathbf{k}, \mathbf{v} = 3\mathbf{i} + 6\mathbf{j} + 6\mathbf{k}$

28. Work A 180-lb man stands on a hillside that makes an angle of $30°$ with the horizontal, producing a force of $\mathbf{W} = \langle 0, -180 \rangle$.

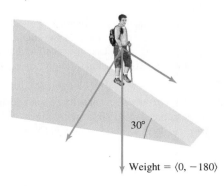

30°

Weight $= \langle 0, -180 \rangle$

a. Find the component of his weight in the downward direction perpendicular to the hillside and in the downward direction parallel to the hillside.

b. How much work is done when the man moves 10 ft up the hillside?

29. Vectors normal to a plane Find a unit vector normal to the vectors $\langle 2, -6, 9 \rangle$ and $\langle -1, 0, 6 \rangle$.

30. Angle in two ways Find the angle between $\langle 2, 0, -2 \rangle$ and $\langle 2, 2, 0 \rangle$ using (a) the dot product and (b) the cross product.

31. Knee torque Jan does leg lifts with a 10-kg weight attached to her foot, so the resulting force is $mg \approx 98$ N directed vertically downward. If the distance from her knee to the weight is 0.4 m and her lower leg makes an angle of θ to the vertical, find the magnitude of the torque about her knee as her leg is lifted (as a function of θ). What are the minimum and maximum magnitudes of the torque? Does the direction of the torque change as her leg is lifted?

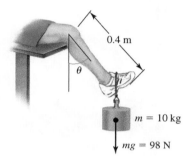

0.4 m

θ

$m = 10$ kg

$mg = 98$ N

32–36. Lines in space *Find an equation of the following lines or line segments.*

32. The line that passes through the points $(2, 6, -1)$ and $(-6, 4, 0)$

33. The line segment that joins the points $(0, -3, 9)$ and $(2, -8, 1)$

34. The line through the point $(0, 1, 1)$ and parallel to the line $\mathbf{R}(t) = \langle 1 + 2t, 3 - 5t, 7 + 6t \rangle$

35. The line through the point $(0, 1, 1)$ that is orthogonal to both $\langle 0, -1, 3 \rangle$ and $\langle 2, -1, 2 \rangle$

36. The line through the point $(0, 1, 4)$ and orthogonal to the vector $\langle -2, 1, 7 \rangle$ and the y-axis

37. Area of a parallelogram Find the area of the parallelogram with vertices $(1, 2, 3)$, $(1, 0, 6)$, and $(4, 2, 4)$.

38. Area of a triangle Find the area of the triangle with vertices $(1, 0, 3)$, $(5, 0, -1)$, and $(0, 2, -2)$.

T 39–41. Curves in space *Sketch the curves described by the following functions, indicating the orientation of the curve. Use analysis and describe the shape of the curve before using a graphing utility.*

39. $\mathbf{r}(t) = 4\cos t\,\mathbf{i} + \mathbf{j} + 4\sin t\,\mathbf{k}$, for $0 \leq t \leq 2\pi$

40. $\mathbf{r}(t) = e^t\,\mathbf{i} + 2e^t\,\mathbf{j} + \mathbf{k}$, for $t \geq 0$

41. $\mathbf{r}(t) = \sin t\,\mathbf{i} + \sqrt{2}\cos t\,\mathbf{j} + \sin t\,\mathbf{k}$, for $0 \leq t \leq 2\pi$

42–45. Working with vector-valued functions *For each vector-valued function* $\mathbf{r}$, *carry out the following steps.*

a. Evaluate $\lim\limits_{t \to 0} \mathbf{r}(t)$ *and* $\lim\limits_{t \to \infty} \mathbf{r}(t)$, *if each exists.*

b. Find $\mathbf{r}'(t)$ *and evaluate* $\mathbf{r}'(0)$.

c. Find $\mathbf{r}''(t)$.

d. Evaluate $\int \mathbf{r}(t)\, dt$.

42. $\mathbf{r}(t) = \langle t + 1, t^2 - 3 \rangle$

43. $\mathbf{r}(t) = \left\langle \dfrac{1}{2t + 1}, \dfrac{t}{t + 1} \right\rangle$

44. $\mathbf{r}(t) = \langle e^{-2t}, te^{-t}, \tan^{-1} t \rangle$

45. $\mathbf{r}(t) = \langle \sin 2t, 3 \cos 4t, t \rangle$

T 46. Orthogonal r and r' Find all points on the ellipse $\mathbf{r}(t) = \langle 1, 8 \sin t, \cos t \rangle$, for $0 \leq t \leq 2\pi$, at which $\mathbf{r}(t)$ and $\mathbf{r}'(t)$ are orthogonal. Sketch the curve and the tangent vectors to verify your conclusion.

T 47. Projectile motion A projectile is launched from the origin, which is a point 50 ft from a 30-ft vertical cliff (see figure). It is launched at a speed of $50\sqrt{2}$ ft/s at an angle of $45°$ to the horizontal. Assume that the ground is horizontal on top of the cliff and that only the gravitational force affects the motion of the object.

a. Give the coordinates of the landing spot of the projectile on the top of the cliff.
b. What is the maximum height reached by the projectile?
c. What is the time of flight?
d. Write an integral that gives the length of the trajectory.
e. Approximate the length of the trajectory.
f. What is the range of launch angles needed to clear the edge of the cliff?

48. Baseball motion A toddler on level ground throws a baseball into the air at an angle of $30°$ with the ground from a height of 2 ft. If the ball lands 10 ft from the child, determine the initial speed of the ball.

49. Shooting a basket A basketball player tosses a basketball into the air at an angle of $45°$ with the ground from a height of 6 ft above the ground. If the ball goes through the basket 15 ft away and 10 ft above the ground, determine the initial velocity of the ball.

50–52. Arc length *Find the arc length of the following curves.*

50. $\mathbf{r}(t) = \langle 2t^{9/2}, t^3 \rangle$, for $0 \leq t \leq 2$

51. $\mathbf{r}(t) = \left\langle t^2, \dfrac{4\sqrt{2}}{3} t^{3/2}, 2t \right\rangle$, for $1 \leq t \leq 3$

52. $\mathbf{r}(t) = \langle t, \ln \sec t, \ln (\sec t + \tan t) \rangle$, for $0 \leq t \leq \pi/4$

53. Velocity and trajectory length The acceleration of a wayward firework is given by $\mathbf{a}(t) = \sqrt{2}\,\mathbf{j} + 2t\,\mathbf{k}$, for $0 \leq t \leq 3$. Suppose the initial velocity of the firework is $\mathbf{v}(0) = \mathbf{i}$.

a. Find the velocity of the firework, for $0 \leq t \leq 3$.
b. Find the length of the trajectory of the firework over the interval $0 \leq t \leq 3$.

T 54–55. Arc length of polar curves *Find the approximate length of the following curves.*

54. The limaçon $r = 3 + 2 \cos \theta$

55. The limaçon $r = 3 - 6 \cos \theta$

56–57. Arc length parameterization *Find the description of the following curves that uses arc length as a parameter.*

56. $\mathbf{r}(t) = (1 + 4t)\mathbf{i} - 3t\,\mathbf{j}$, for $t \geq 1$

57. $\mathbf{r}(t) = \left\langle t^2, \dfrac{4\sqrt{2}}{3} t^{3/2}, 2t \right\rangle$, for $t \geq 0$

58. Tangents and normals for an ellipse Consider the ellipse $\mathbf{r}(t) = \langle 3 \cos t, 4 \sin t \rangle$, for $0 \leq t \leq 2\pi$.

a. Find the tangent vector $\mathbf{r}'$, the unit tangent vector $\mathbf{T}$, and the principal unit normal vector $\mathbf{N}$ at all points on the curve.
b. At what points does $|\mathbf{r}'|$ have maximum and minimum values?
c. At what points does the curvature have maximum and minimum values? Interpret this result in light of part (b).
d. Find the points (if any) at which $\mathbf{r}$ and $\mathbf{N}$ are parallel.

T 59–62. Properties of space curves *Do the following calculations.*

a. Find the tangent vector and the unit tangent vector.
b. Find the curvature.
c. Find the principal unit normal vector.
d. Verify that $|\mathbf{N}| = 1$ and $\mathbf{T} \cdot \mathbf{N} = 0$.
e. Graph the curve and sketch $\mathbf{T}$ and $\mathbf{N}$ at two points.

59. $\mathbf{r}(t) = \langle 6 \cos t, 3 \sin t \rangle$, for $0 \leq t \leq 2\pi$

60. $\mathbf{r}(t) = \cos t\,\mathbf{i} + 2 \sin t\,\mathbf{j} + \mathbf{k}$, for $0 \leq t \leq 2\pi$

61. $\mathbf{r}(t) = \cos t\,\mathbf{i} + 2 \cos t\,\mathbf{j} + \sqrt{5} \sin t\,\mathbf{k}$, for $0 \leq t \leq 2\pi$

62. $\mathbf{r}(t) = t\,\mathbf{i} + 2 \cos t\,\mathbf{j} + 2 \sin t\,\mathbf{k}$, for $0 \leq t \leq 2\pi$

63–66. Analyzing motion *Consider the position vector of the following moving objects.*

a. Find the normal and tangential components of the acceleration.
b. Graph the trajectory and sketch the normal and tangential components of the acceleration at two points on the trajectory. Show that their sum gives the total acceleration.

63. $\mathbf{r}(t) = 2 \cos t\,\mathbf{i} + 2 \sin t\,\mathbf{j}$, for $0 \leq t \leq 2\pi$

64. $\mathbf{r}(t) = 3t\,\mathbf{i} + (4 - t)\,\mathbf{j} + t\,\mathbf{k}$, for $t \geq 0$

65. $\mathbf{r}(t) = (t^2 + 1)\,\mathbf{i} + 2t\,\mathbf{j}$, for $t \geq 0$

66. $\mathbf{r}(t) = 2 \cos t\,\mathbf{i} + 2 \sin t\,\mathbf{j} + 10t\,\mathbf{k}$, for $0 \leq t \leq 2\pi$

67. Lines in the plane

a. Use a dot product to find an equation of the line in the xy-plane passing through the point (x_0, y_0) perpendicular to the vector $\langle a, b \rangle$.
b. Given a point $(x_0, y_0, 0)$ and a vector $\mathbf{v} = \langle a, b, 0 \rangle$ in $\mathbb{R}^3$, describe the set of points that satisfy the equation $\langle a, b, 0 \rangle \times \langle x - x_0, y - y_0, 0 \rangle = \mathbf{0}$. Use this result to determine an equation of a line in $\mathbb{R}^2$ passing through (x_0, y_0) parallel to the vector $\langle a, b \rangle$.

68. Length of a DVD groove The capacity of a single-sided, single-layer digital versatile disc (DVD) is approximately 4.7 billion bytes—enough to store a two-hour movie. (Newer double-sided, double-layer DVDs have about four times that capacity, and Blu-ray discs are in the range of 50 gigabytes.) A DVD consists of a single "groove" that spirals outward from the inner edge to the outer edge of the storage region.

a. First consider the spiral given in polar coordinates by $r = t\theta/(2\pi)$, where $0 \le \theta \le 2\pi N$ and successive loops of the spiral are t units apart. Explain why this spiral has N loops and why the entire spiral has a radius of $R = Nt$ units. Sketch three loops of the spiral.

b. Write an integral for the length L of the spiral with N loops.

c. The integral in part (b) can be evaluated exactly, but a good approximation can also be made. Assuming N is large, explain why $\theta^2 + 1 \approx \theta^2$. Use this approximation to simplify the integral in part (b) and show that $L \approx t\pi N^2 = \dfrac{\pi R^2}{t}$.

d. Now consider a DVD with an inner radius of $r = 2.5$ cm and an outer radius of $R = 5.9$ cm. Model the groove by a spiral with a thickness of $t = 1.5$ microns $= 1.5 \times 10^{-6}$ m. Because of the hole in the DVD, the lower limit in the arc length integral is not $\theta = 0$. What are the limits of integration?

e. Use the approximation in part (c) to find the length of the DVD groove. Express your answer in centimeters and miles.

69. Computing the binormal vector and torsion Compute the unit binormal vector $\mathbf{B}$ and the torsion of the curve $\mathbf{r}(t) = \langle t, t^2, t^3 \rangle$ at $t = 1$.

70–71. Curve analysis *Carry out the following steps for the given curves C.*

a. *Find $\mathbf{T}(t)$ at all points of C.*
b. *Find $\mathbf{N}(t)$ and the curvature at all points of C.*
c. *Sketch the curve and show $\mathbf{T}(t)$ and $\mathbf{N}(t)$ at the points of C corresponding to $t = 0$ and $t = \pi/2$.*
d. *Are the results of parts (a) and (b) consistent with the graph?*
e. *Find $\mathbf{B}(t)$ at all points of C.*

f. *On the graph of part (c), plot $\mathbf{B}(t)$ at the points of C corresponding to $t = 0$ and $t = \pi/2$.*
g. *Describe three calculations that serve to check the accuracy of your results in part (a)–(f).*
h. *Compute the torsion at all points of C. Interpret this result.*

70. C: $\mathbf{r}(t) = \langle 3 \sin t, 4 \sin t, 5 \cos t \rangle$, for $0 \le t \le 2\pi$

71. C: $\mathbf{r}(t) = \langle 3 \sin t, 3 \cos t, 4t \rangle$, for $0 \le t \le 2\pi$

72. Torsion of a plane curve Suppose $\mathbf{r}(t) = \langle f(t), g(t), h(t) \rangle$, where f, g, and h are the quadratic functions $f(t) = a_1 t^2 + b_1 t + c_1$, $g(t) = a_2 t^2 + b_2 t + c_2$, and $h(t) = a_3 t^2 + b_3 t + c_3$, and where at least one of the leading coefficients a_1, a_2, or a_3 is nonzero. Apart from a set of degenerate cases (for example, $\mathbf{r}(t) = \langle t^2, t^2, t^2 \rangle$, whose graph is a line), it can be shown that the graph of $\mathbf{r}(t)$ is a parabola that lies in a plane (Exercise 73).

a. Show by direct computation that $\mathbf{v} \times \mathbf{a}$ is constant. Then explain why the unit binormal vector is constant at all points on the curve. What does this result say about the torsion of the curve?

b. Compute $\mathbf{a}'(t)$ and explain why the torsion is zero at all points on the curve for which the torsion is defined.

73. Families of plane curves Let f and g be continuous on an interval I. Consider the curve

$$C: \mathbf{r}(t) = \langle a_1 f(t) + a_2 g(t) + a_3, b_1 f(t) + b_2 g(t) + b_3, c_1 f(t) + c_2 g(t) + c_3 \rangle,$$

for t in I, and where a_i, b_i, and c_i, for $i = 1, 2$, and 3, are real numbers.

a. Show that, in general, apart from a set of special cases, C lies in a plane.
b. Explain why the torsion is zero at all points of C for which the torsion is defined.
c. Find the plane in which C: $\mathbf{r}(t) = \langle t^2 - 2, -t^2 + t + 2, t - 4 \rangle$ lies.

Chapter 11 Guided Projects

Applications of the material in this chapter and related topics can be found in the following Guided Projects. For additional information, see the Preface.

- Designing a trajectory
- Intercepting a UFO
- CORDIC algorithms: How your calculator works

- Bezier curves for graphic design
- Kepler's laws

12

Functions of Several Variables

Chapter Preview Chapter 11 was devoted to vector-valued functions, which generally have one independent variable and two or more dependent variables. In this chapter, we step into three-dimensional space along a different path by considering functions with several independent variables and one dependent variable. All the familiar properties of single-variable functions—domains, graphs, limits, continuity, and derivatives—have generalizations for multivariable functions, although there are often subtle differences when compared to single-variable functions. With functions of several independent variables, we work with *partial derivatives*, which, in turn, give rise to directional derivatives and the *gradient*, a fundamental concept in calculus. Partial derivatives allow us to find maximum and minimum values of multivariable functions. We define tangent planes, rather than tangent lines, that allow us to make linear approximations. The chapter ends with a survey of optimization problems in several variables.

12.1 Planes and Surfaces

Functions with one independent variable, such as $f(x) = xe^{-x}$, or *equations* in two variables, such as $x^2 + y^2 = 4$, describe curves in $\mathbb{R}^2$. We now add a third variable to the picture and consider functions of two independent variables (for example, $f(x, y) = x^2 + 2y^2$) and equations in three variables (for example, $x^2 + y^2 + 2z^2 = 4$). We see in this chapter that such functions and equations describe *surfaces* that may be displayed in $\mathbb{R}^3$. Just as a line is the simplest curve in $\mathbb{R}^2$, a plane is the simplest surface in $\mathbb{R}^3$.

Equations of Planes

Intuitively, a plane is a flat surface with infinite extent in all directions. Three noncollinear points (not all on the same line) determine a unique plane in $\mathbb{R}^3$. A plane in $\mathbb{R}^3$ is also uniquely determined by one point in the plane and any nonzero vector orthogonal (perpendicular) to the plane. Such a vector, called a *normal vector*, specifies the orientation of the plane.

> Just as the slope determines the orientation of a line in $\mathbb{R}^2$, a normal vector determines the orientation of a plane.

DEFINITION **Plane in $\mathbb{R}^3$**

Given a fixed point P_0 and a nonzero **normal vector n**, the set of points P in $\mathbb{R}^3$ for which $\overrightarrow{P_0P}$ is orthogonal to **n** is called a **plane** (Figure 12.1).

QUICK CHECK 1 Describe the plane that is orthogonal to the unit vector $\mathbf{i} = \langle 1, 0, 0 \rangle$ and passes through the point $(1, 2, 3)$. ◄

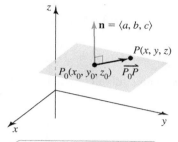

The orientation of a plane is specified by a normal vector **n**. All vectors $\overrightarrow{P_0P}$ in the plane are orthogonal to **n**.

Figure 12.1

▶ A vector $\mathbf{n} = \langle a, b, c \rangle$ is used to describe a *plane* by specifying a direction *orthogonal* to the plane. By contrast, a vector $\mathbf{v} = \langle a, b, c \rangle$ is used to describe a *line* by specifying a direction *parallel* to the line (Section 11.5).

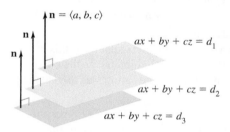

The normal vectors of parallel planes have the same direction.

Figure 12.2

We now derive an equation of the plane passing through the point $P_0(x_0, y_0, z_0)$ with nonzero normal vector $\mathbf{n} = \langle a, b, c \rangle$. Notice that for any point $P(x, y, z)$ in the plane, the vector $\overrightarrow{P_0P} = \langle x - x_0, y - y_0, z - z_0 \rangle$ lies in the plane and is orthogonal to **n**. This orthogonality relationship is written and simplified as follows:

$$\mathbf{n} \cdot \overrightarrow{P_0P} = 0 \qquad \text{Dot product of orthogonal vectors}$$
$$\langle a, b, c \rangle \cdot \langle x - x_0, y - y_0, z - z_0 \rangle = 0 \qquad \text{Substitute vector components.}$$
$$a(x - x_0) + b(y - y_0) + c(z - z_0) = 0 \qquad \text{Expand the dot product.}$$
$$ax + by + cz = d. \qquad d = ax_0 + by_0 + cz_0$$

This important result states that the most general linear equation in three variables, $ax + by + cz = d$, describes a plane in $\mathbb{R}^3$.

General Equation of a Plane in $\mathbb{R}^3$

The plane passing through the point $P_0(x_0, y_0, z_0)$ with a nonzero normal vector $\mathbf{n} = \langle a, b, c \rangle$ is described by the equation

$$a(x - x_0) + b(y - y_0) + c(z - z_0) = 0 \quad \text{or} \quad ax + by + cz = d,$$

where $d = ax_0 + by_0 + cz_0$.

The coefficients a, b, and c in the equation of a plane determine the *orientation* of the plane, while the constant term d determines the *location* of the plane. If a, b, and c are held constant and d is varied, a family of parallel planes is generated, all with the same orientation (Figure 12.2).

QUICK CHECK 2 Consider the equation of a plane in the form $\mathbf{n} \cdot \overrightarrow{P_0P} = 0$. Explain why the equation of the plane depends only on the direction, but not the length, of the normal vector **n**. ◀

EXAMPLE 1 **Equation of a plane** Find an equation of the plane passing through $P_0(2, -3, 4)$ with a normal vector $\mathbf{n} = \langle -1, 2, 3 \rangle$.

SOLUTION Substituting the components of **n** ($a = -1$, $b = 2$, and $c = 3$) and the coordinates of P_0 ($x_0 = 2$, $y_0 = -3$, and $z_0 = 4$) into the equation of a plane, we have

$$a(x - x_0) + b(y - y_0) + c(z - z_0) = 0 \qquad \text{General equation of a plane}$$
$$(-1)(x - 2) + 2(y - (-3)) + 3(z - 4) = 0 \qquad \text{Substitute.}$$
$$-x + 2y + 3z = 4. \qquad \text{Simplify.}$$

The plane is shown in Figure 12.3.

Related Exercises 11–16 ◀

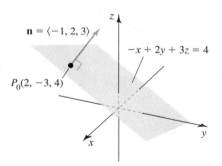

Figure 12.3

▶ Three points P, Q, and R determine a plane provided they are not collinear. If P, Q, and R *are* collinear, then the vectors $\overrightarrow{PQ}$ and $\overrightarrow{PR}$ are parallel, which implies that $\overrightarrow{PQ} \times \overrightarrow{PR} = \mathbf{0}$.

EXAMPLE 2 **A plane through three points** Find an equation of the plane that passes through the (noncollinear) points $P(2, -1, 3)$, $Q(1, 4, 0)$, and $R(0, -1, 5)$.

SOLUTION To write an equation of the plane, we must find a normal vector. Because P, Q, and R lie in the plane, the vectors $\overrightarrow{PQ} = \langle -1, 5, -3 \rangle$ and $\overrightarrow{PR} = \langle -2, 0, 2 \rangle$ also lie in the plane. The cross product $\overrightarrow{PQ} \times \overrightarrow{PR}$ is perpendicular to both $\overrightarrow{PQ}$ and $\overrightarrow{PR}$; therefore, a vector normal to the plane is

$$\mathbf{n} = \overrightarrow{PQ} \times \overrightarrow{PR} = \begin{vmatrix} \mathbf{i} & \mathbf{j} & \mathbf{k} \\ -1 & 5 & -3 \\ -2 & 0 & 2 \end{vmatrix} = 10\mathbf{i} + 8\mathbf{j} + 10\mathbf{k}.$$

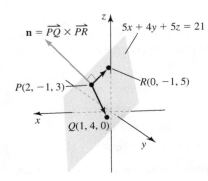

$\overrightarrow{PQ}$ and $\overrightarrow{PR}$ lie in the same plane.
$\overrightarrow{PQ} \times \overrightarrow{PR}$ is orthogonal to the plane.

Figure 12.4

Any nonzero scalar multiple of **n** may be used as the normal vector. Choosing **n** = $\langle 5, 4, 5 \rangle$ and $P_0(2, -1, 3)$ as the fixed point in the plane (Figure 12.4), an equation of the plane is

$$5(x - 2) + 4(y - (-1)) + 5(z - 3) = 0 \quad \text{or} \quad 5x + 4y + 5z = 21.$$

Using either Q or R as the fixed point in the plane leads to an equivalent equation of the plane.

Related Exercises 17–20 ◀

QUICK CHECK 3 Verify in Example 2 that the same equation for the plane results if either Q or R is used as the fixed point in the plane. ◀

EXAMPLE 3   Properties of a plane Let Q be the plane described by the equation $2x - 3y - z = 6$.

a. Find a vector normal to Q.

b. Find the points at which Q intersects the coordinate axes and plot Q.

c. Describe the sets of points at which Q intersects the yz-plane, the xz-plane, and the xy-plane.

SOLUTION

a. The coefficients of x, y, and z in the equation of Q are the components of a vector normal to Q. Therefore, a normal vector is **n** = $\langle 2, -3, -1 \rangle$ (or any nonzero multiple of **n**).

b. The point (x, y, z) at which Q intersects the x-axis must have $y = z = 0$. Substituting $y = z = 0$ into the equation of Q gives $x = 3$, so Q intersects the x-axis at $(3, 0, 0)$. Similarly, Q intersects the y-axis at $(0, -2, 0)$, and Q intersects the z-axis at $(0, 0, -6)$. Connecting the three intercepts with straight lines allows us to visualize the plane (Figure 12.5).

▶ There is a possibility for confusion here. Working in $\mathbb{R}^3$ with no other restrictions, the equation $-3y - z = 6$ describes a plane that is parallel to the x-axis (because x is unspecified). To make it clear that $-3y - z = 6$ is a line in the yz-plane, the condition $x = 0$ is included.

c. All points in the yz-plane have $x = 0$. Setting $x = 0$ in the equation of Q gives the equation $-3y - z = 6$, which, with the condition $x = 0$, describes a line in the yz-plane. If we set $y = 0$, Q intersects the xz-plane in the line $2x - z = 6$, where $y = 0$. If $z = 0$, Q intersects the xy-plane in the line $2x - 3y = 6$, where $z = 0$ (Figure 12.5).

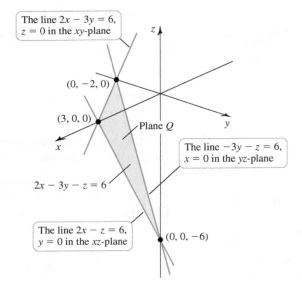

Figure 12.5

Related Exercises 21–24 ◀

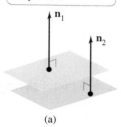

Two distinct planes are parallel if $\mathbf{n}_1$ and $\mathbf{n}_2$ are parallel.

(a)

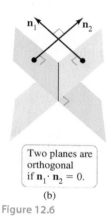

Two planes are orthogonal if $\mathbf{n}_1 \cdot \mathbf{n}_2 = 0$.

(b)

Figure 12.6

QUICK CHECK 4 Verify in Example 4 that $\mathbf{n}_R \cdot \mathbf{n}_S = 0$ and $\mathbf{n}_R \cdot \mathbf{n}_T = 0$. ◄

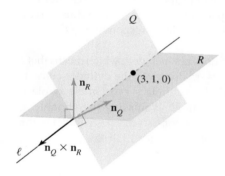

Figure 12.7

➤ By setting $z = 0$ and solving these two equations, we find the point that lies on both planes *and* lies in the *xy*-plane ($z = 0$).

Parallel and Orthogonal Planes

The normal vectors of distinct planes tell us about the relative orientation of the planes. Two cases are of particular interest: Two distinct planes may be *parallel* (Figure 12.6a) and two intersecting planes may be *orthogonal* (Figure 12.6b).

DEFINITION Parallel and Orthogonal Planes

Two distinct planes are **parallel** if their respective normal vectors are parallel (that is, the normal vectors are scalar multiples of each other). Two planes are **orthogonal** if their respective normal vectors are orthogonal (that is, the dot product of the normal vectors is zero).

EXAMPLE 4 Parallel and orthogonal planes Which of the following distinct planes are parallel and which are orthogonal?

$$Q: \quad 2x - 3y + 6z = 12 \qquad R: \quad -x + \tfrac{3}{2}y - 3z = 14$$
$$S: \quad 6x + 8y + 2z = 1 \qquad T: \quad -9x - 12y - 3z = 7$$

SOLUTION Let $\mathbf{n}_Q$, $\mathbf{n}_R$, $\mathbf{n}_S$, and $\mathbf{n}_T$ be vectors normal to Q, R, S, and T, respectively. Normal vectors may be read from the coefficients of x, y, and z in the equations of the planes.

$$\mathbf{n}_Q = \langle 2, -3, 6 \rangle \qquad \mathbf{n}_R = \left\langle -1, \tfrac{3}{2}, -3 \right\rangle$$
$$\mathbf{n}_S = \langle 6, 8, 2 \rangle \qquad \mathbf{n}_T = \langle -9, -12, -3 \rangle$$

Notice that $\mathbf{n}_Q = -2\mathbf{n}_R$, which implies that Q and R are parallel. Similarly, $\mathbf{n}_T = -\tfrac{3}{2}\mathbf{n}_S$, so S and T are parallel. Furthermore, $\mathbf{n}_Q \cdot \mathbf{n}_S = 0$ and $\mathbf{n}_Q \cdot \mathbf{n}_T = 0$, which implies that Q is orthogonal to both S and T. Because Q and R are parallel, it follows that R is also orthogonal to both S and T.

Related Exercises 25–30 ◄

EXAMPLE 5 Parallel planes Find an equation of the plane Q that passes through the point $(-2, 4, 1)$ and is parallel to the plane $R: 3x - 2y + z = 4$.

SOLUTION The vector $\mathbf{n} = \langle 3, -2, 1 \rangle$ is normal to R. Because Q and R are parallel, $\mathbf{n}$ is also normal to Q. Therefore, an equation of Q, passing through $(-2, 4, 1)$ with normal vector $\langle 3, -2, 1 \rangle$, is

$$3(x + 2) - 2(y - 4) + (z - 1) = 0 \quad \text{or} \quad 3x - 2y + z = -13.$$

Related Exercises 31–34 ◄

EXAMPLE 6 Intersecting planes Find an equation of the line of intersection of the planes $Q: x + 2y + z = 5$ and $R: 2x + y - z = 7$.

SOLUTION First note that the vectors normal to the planes, $\mathbf{n}_Q = \langle 1, 2, 1 \rangle$ and $\mathbf{n}_R = \langle 2, 1, -1 \rangle$, are *not* multiples of each other. Therefore, the planes are not parallel and they must intersect in a line; call it ℓ. To find an equation of ℓ, we need two pieces of information: a point on ℓ and a vector pointing in the direction of ℓ. Here is one of several ways to find a point on ℓ. Setting $z = 0$ in the equations of the planes gives equations of the lines in which the planes intersect the *xy*-plane:

$$x + 2y = 5$$
$$2x + y = 7.$$

Solving these equations simultaneously, we find that $x = 3$ and $y = 1$. Combining this result with $z = 0$, we see that $(3, 1, 0)$ is a point on ℓ (Figure 12.7).

We next find a vector parallel to ℓ. Because ℓ lies in Q and R, it is orthogonal to the normal vectors $\mathbf{n}_Q$ and $\mathbf{n}_R$. Therefore, the cross product of $\mathbf{n}_Q$ and $\mathbf{n}_R$ is a vector parallel to ℓ (Figure 12.7). In this case, the cross product is

$$\mathbf{n}_Q \times \mathbf{n}_R = \begin{vmatrix} \mathbf{i} & \mathbf{j} & \mathbf{k} \\ 1 & 2 & 1 \\ 2 & 1 & -1 \end{vmatrix} = -3\,\mathbf{i} + 3\,\mathbf{j} - 3\,\mathbf{k} = \langle -3, 3, -3 \rangle.$$

▶ Another question related to Example 6 concerns the angle between two planes. See Exercise 95 for an example.

An equation of the line ℓ in the direction of the vector $\langle -3, 3, -3 \rangle$ passing through the point $(3, 1, 0)$ is

$$\begin{aligned} \mathbf{r}(t) &= \langle x_0, y_0, z_0 \rangle + t\langle a, b, c \rangle && \text{Equation of a line (Section 11.5)} \\ &= \langle 3, 1, 0 \rangle + t\langle -3, 3, -3 \rangle && \text{Substitute.} \\ &= \langle 3 - 3t, 1 + 3t, -3t \rangle, && \text{Simplify.} \end{aligned}$$

▶ Any nonzero scalar multiple of $\langle -3, 3, -3 \rangle$ can be used for the direction of ℓ. For example, another equation of ℓ is $\mathbf{r}(t) = \langle 3 + t, 1 - t, t \rangle$.

where $-\infty < t < \infty$. You can check that any point (x, y, z) with $x = 3 - 3t$, $y = 1 + 3t$, and $z = -3t$ satisfies the equations of both planes.

Related Exercises 35–38 ◀

Cylinders and Traces

In everyday language, we use the word *cylinder* to describe the surface that forms, say, the wall of a paint can. In the context of three-dimensional surfaces, the term *cylinder* has a more general meaning.

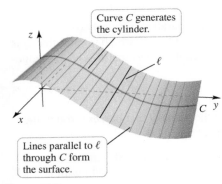

Curve C generates the cylinder.

Lines parallel to ℓ through C form the surface.

Figure 12.8

> **DEFINITION Cylinder**
>
> Given a curve C in a plane P and a line ℓ not in P, a **cylinder** is the surface consisting of all lines parallel to ℓ that pass through C (Figure 12.8).

A common situation arises when ℓ is one of the coordinate axes or is parallel to a coordinate axis. In these cases, the cylinder is also parallel to one of the coordinate axes. Equations for such cylinders are easy to identify: The variable corresponding to the coordinate axis parallel to ℓ is missing.

For example, working in $\mathbb{R}^3$, the equation $y = x^2$ does not include z, which means that z is arbitrary and can take on all values. Therefore, $y = x^2$ describes the cylinder consisting of all lines parallel to the z-axis that pass through the parabola $y = x^2$ in the xy-plane (Figure 12.9a). In a similar way, the equation $z^2 = y$ in $\mathbb{R}^3$ is missing the variable x, so it describes a cylinder parallel to the x-axis. The cylinder consists of lines parallel to the x-axis that pass through the parabola $z^2 = y$ in the yz-plane (Figure 12.9b).

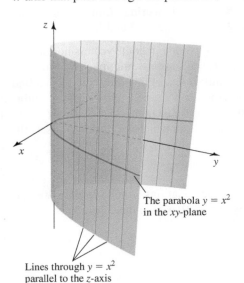

The parabola $y = x^2$ in the xy-plane

Lines through $y = x^2$ parallel to the z-axis

(a)

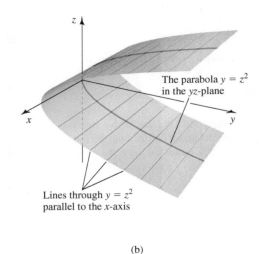

The parabola $y = z^2$ in the yz-plane

Lines through $y = z^2$ parallel to the x-axis

(b)

Figure 12.9

QUICK CHECK 5 To which coordinate axis in $\mathbb{R}^3$ is the cylinder $z - 2 \ln x = 0$ parallel? To which coordinate axis in $\mathbb{R}^3$ is the cylinder $y = 4z^2 - 1$ parallel? ◄

Graphing surfaces—and cylinders in particular—is facilitated by identifying the *traces* of the surface.

> **DEFINITION Trace**
>
> A **trace** of a surface is the set of points at which the surface intersects a plane that is parallel to one of the coordinate planes. The traces in the coordinate planes are called the **xy-trace**, the **yz-trace**, and the **xz-trace** (Figure 12.10).

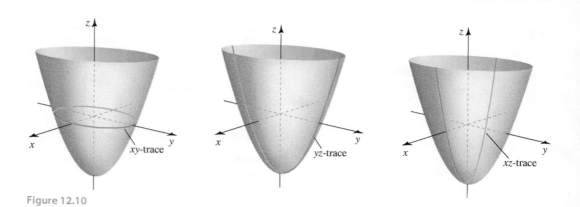

Figure 12.10

EXAMPLE 7 Graphing cylinders Sketch the graphs of the following cylinders in $\mathbb{R}^3$. Identify the axis to which each cylinder is parallel.

a. $x^2 + 4y^2 = 16$ **b.** $x - \sin z = 0$

SOLUTION

a. As an equation in $\mathbb{R}^3$, the variable z is absent. Therefore, z assumes all real values and the graph is a cylinder consisting of lines parallel to the z-axis passing through the curve $x^2 + 4y^2 = 16$ in the xy-plane. You can sketch the cylinder in the following steps.

   1. Rewriting the given equation as $\dfrac{x^2}{4^2} + \dfrac{y^2}{2^2} = 1$, we see that the trace of the cylinder in the xy-plane (the xy-trace) is an ellipse. We begin by drawing this ellipse.

   2. Next draw a second trace (a copy of the ellipse in Step 1) in a plane parallel to the xy-plane.

   3. Now draw lines parallel to the z-axis through the two traces to fill out the cylinder (Figure 12.11a).

   The resulting surface, called an *elliptic cylinder*, runs parallel to the z-axis (Figure 12.11b).

b. As an equation in $\mathbb{R}^3$, $x - \sin z = 0$ is missing the variable y. Therefore, y assumes all real values and the graph is a cylinder consisting of lines parallel to the y-axis passing through the curve $x = \sin z$ in the xz-plane. You can sketch the cylinder in the following steps.

   1. Graph the curve $x = \sin z$ in the xz-plane, which is the xz-trace of the surface.

   2. Draw a second trace (a copy of the curve in Step 1) in a plane parallel to the xz-plane.

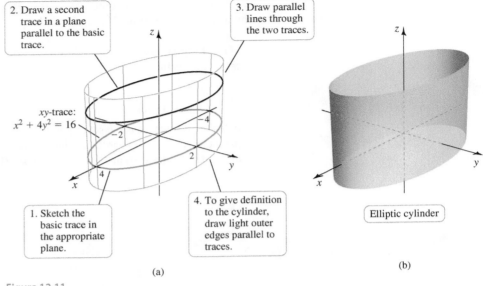

2. Draw a second trace in a plane parallel to the basic trace.

3. Draw parallel lines through the two traces.

xy-trace:
$x^2 + 4y^2 = 16$

1. Sketch the basic trace in the appropriate plane.

4. To give definition to the cylinder, draw light outer edges parallel to traces.

(a)

Elliptic cylinder

(b)

Figure 12.11

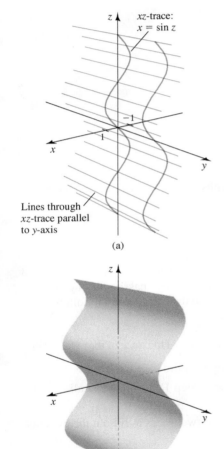

xz-trace:
$x = \sin z$

Lines through
xz-trace parallel
to y-axis

(a)

(b)

Figure 12.12

➤ Working with quadric surfaces requires familiarity with conic sections (Section 10.4).

3. Draw lines parallel to the y-axis passing through the two traces. (Figure 12.12a).

The result is a cylinder, running parallel to the y-axis, consisting of copies of the curve $x = \sin z$ (Figure 12.12b).

Related Exercises 39–46 ◄

Quadric Surfaces

Quadric surfaces are described by the general quadratic (second-degree) equation in three variables,

$$Ax^2 + By^2 + Cz^2 + Dxy + Exz + Fyz + Gx + Hy + Iz + J = 0,$$

where the coefficients $A, \ldots, J$ are constants and not all of A, B, C, D, E, and F are zero. We do not attempt a detailed study of this large family of surfaces. However, a few standard surfaces are worth investigating.

Apart from their mathematical interest, quadric surfaces have a variety of practical uses. Paraboloids (defined in Example 9) share the reflective properties of their two-dimensional counterparts (Section 10.4) and are used to design satellite dishes, headlamps, and mirrors in telescopes. Cooling towers for nuclear power plants have the shape of hyperboloids of one sheet. Ellipsoids appear in the design of water tanks and gears.

Making hand sketches of quadric surfaces can be challenging. Here are a few general ideas to keep in mind as you sketch their graphs.

1. Intercepts Determine the points, if any, where the surface intersects the coordinate axes. To find these intercepts, set x, y, and z equal to zero in pairs in the equation of the surface and solve for the third coordinate.

2. Traces As illustrated in the following examples, finding traces of the surface helps visualize the surface. For example, setting $z = 0$ or $z = z_0$ (a constant) gives the traces in planes parallel to the xy-plane.

3. Sketch at least two traces in parallel planes (for example, traces with $z = 0$ and $z = \pm 1$). Then draw smooth curves that pass through the traces to fill out the surface.

QUICK CHECK 6 Explain why the elliptic cylinder discussed in Example 7a is a quadric surface. ◄

EXAMPLE 8 **An ellipsoid** The surface defined by the equation $\dfrac{x^2}{a^2} + \dfrac{y^2}{b^2} + \dfrac{z^2}{c^2} = 1$ is an *ellipsoid*. Graph the ellipsoid with $a = 3$, $b = 4$, and $c = 5$.

SOLUTION Setting x, y, and z equal to zero in pairs gives the intercepts $(\pm 3, 0, 0)$, $(0, \pm 4, 0)$, and $(0, 0, \pm 5)$. Note that points in $\mathbb{R}^3$ with $|x| > 3$ or $|y| > 4$ or $|z| > 5$ do not satisfy the equation of the surface (because the left side of the equation is a sum of nonnegative terms that cannot exceed 1). Therefore, the entire surface is contained in the rectangular box defined by $|x| \leq 3$, $|y| \leq 4$, and $|z| \leq 5$.

The trace in the horizontal plane $z = z_0$ is found by substituting $z = z_0$ into the equation of the ellipsoid, which gives

$$\frac{x^2}{9} + \frac{y^2}{16} + \frac{z_0^2}{25} = 1 \quad \text{or} \quad \frac{x^2}{9} + \frac{y^2}{16} = 1 - \frac{z_0^2}{25}.$$

> The name *ellipsoid* is used in Example 8 because all traces of this surface, when they exist, are ellipses.

If $|z_0| < 5$, then $1 - \dfrac{z_0^2}{25} > 0$, and the equation describes an ellipse in the horizontal plane $z = z_0$. The largest ellipse parallel to the xy-plane occurs with $z_0 = 0$; it is the xy-trace, which is the ellipse $\dfrac{x^2}{9} + \dfrac{y^2}{16} = 1$ with axes of length 6 and 8 (Figure 12.13a). You can check that the yz-trace, found by setting $x = 0$, is the ellipse $\dfrac{y^2}{16} + \dfrac{z^2}{25} = 1$. The xz-trace (set $y = 0$) is the ellipse $\dfrac{x^2}{9} + \dfrac{z^2}{25} = 1$ (Figure 12.13b). By sketching the xy-, xz-, and yz-traces, an outline of the ellipsoid emerges (Figure 12.13c).

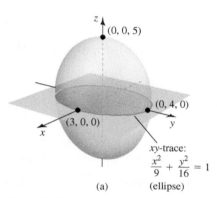

(a)

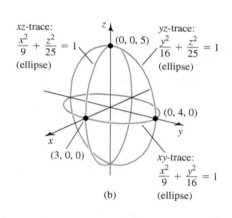

(b)

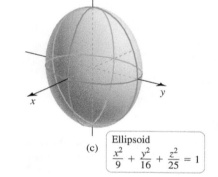

(c)

Figure 12.13

Related Exercises 47–50 ◄

QUICK CHECK 7 Assume that $0 < c < b < a$ in the general equation of an ellipsoid. Along which coordinate axis does the ellipsoid have its longest axis? Its shortest axis? ◄

EXAMPLE 9 **An elliptic paraboloid** The surface defined by the equation $z = \dfrac{x^2}{a^2} + \dfrac{y^2}{b^2}$ is an *elliptic paraboloid*. Graph the elliptic paraboloid with $a = 4$ and $b = 2$.

SOLUTION Note that the only intercept of the coordinate axes is $(0, 0, 0)$, which is the *vertex* of the paraboloid. The trace in the horizontal plane $z = z_0$, where $z_0 > 0$, satisfies the equation $\dfrac{x^2}{16} + \dfrac{y^2}{4} = z_0$, which describes an ellipse; there is no horizontal trace when $z_0 < 0$ (Figure 12.14a). The trace in the vertical plane $x = x_0$ is the parabola $z = \dfrac{x_0^2}{16} + \dfrac{y^2}{4}$ (Figure 12.14b); the trace in the vertical plane $y = y_0$ is the parabola $z = \dfrac{x^2}{16} + \dfrac{y_0^2}{4}$ (Figure 12.14c).

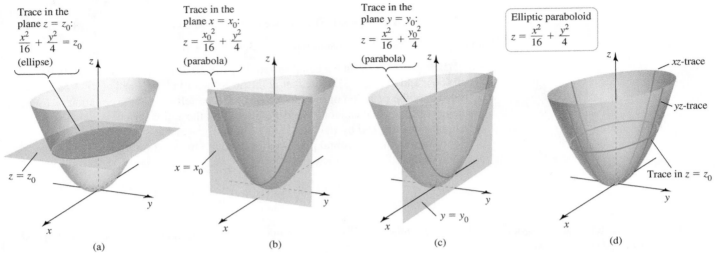

Figure 12.14

▶ The name *elliptic paraboloid* says that the traces of this surface are parabolas and ellipses. Two of the three traces in the coordinate planes are parabolas, so it is called a paraboloid rather than an ellipsoid.

To graph the surface, we sketch the xz-trace $z = \dfrac{x^2}{16}$ (setting $y = 0$) and the yz-trace $z = \dfrac{y^2}{4}$ (setting $x = 0$). When these traces are combined with an elliptical trace $\dfrac{x^2}{16} + \dfrac{y^2}{4} = z_0$ in a plane $z = z_0$, an outline of the surface appears (Figure 12.14d).

Related Exercises 51–54 ◀

QUICK CHECK 8 The elliptic paraboloid $x = \dfrac{y^2}{3} + \dfrac{z^2}{7}$ is a bowl-shaped surface. Along which axis does the bowl open? ◀

EXAMPLE 10   A hyperboloid of one sheet Graph the surface defined by the equation $\dfrac{x^2}{4} + \dfrac{y^2}{9} - z^2 = 1$.

▶ To be completely accurate, this surface should be called an *elliptic hyperboloid of one sheet* because the traces are ellipses and hyperbolas.

SOLUTION The intercepts of the coordinate axes are $(0, \pm 3, 0)$ and $(\pm 2, 0, 0)$. Setting $z = z_0$, the traces in horizontal planes are ellipses of the form $\dfrac{x^2}{4} + \dfrac{y^2}{9} = 1 + z_0^2$. This equation has solutions for all choices of z_0, so the surface has traces in all horizontal planes. These elliptical traces increase in size as $|z_0|$ increases (Figure 12.15a), with the smallest trace being the ellipse $\dfrac{x^2}{4} + \dfrac{y^2}{9} = 1$ in the xy-plane. Setting $y = 0$, the xz-trace is the hyperbola $\dfrac{x^2}{4} - z^2 = 1$; with $x = 0$, the yz-trace is the hyperbola $\dfrac{y^2}{9} - z^2 = 1$ (Figure 12.15b, c). In fact, the intersection of the surface with any vertical plane is a hyperbola. The resulting surface is a *hyperboloid of one sheet* (Figure 12.15d).

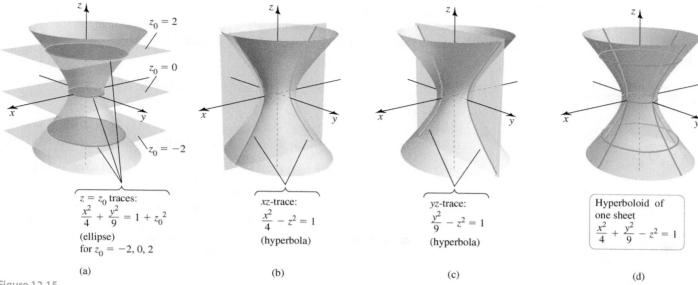

$z = z_0$ traces:
$$\frac{x^2}{4} + \frac{y^2}{9} = 1 + z_0^2$$
(ellipse)
for $z_0 = -2, 0, 2$

(a)

xz-trace:
$$\frac{x^2}{4} - z^2 = 1$$
(hyperbola)

(b)

yz-trace:
$$\frac{y^2}{9} - z^2 = 1$$
(hyperbola)

(c)

Hyperboloid of one sheet
$$\frac{x^2}{4} + \frac{y^2}{9} - z^2 = 1$$

(d)

Figure 12.15

Related Exercises 55–58 ◄

QUICK CHECK 9 Which coordinate axis is the axis of the hyperboloid $\dfrac{y^2}{a^2} + \dfrac{z^2}{b^2} - \dfrac{x^2}{c^2} = 1$? ◄

EXAMPLE 11   A hyperbolic paraboloid Graph the surface defined by the equation $z = x^2 - \dfrac{y^2}{4}$.

▶ The name *hyperbolic paraboloid* tells us that the traces are hyperbolas and parabolas. Two of the three traces in the coordinate planes are parabolas, so it is a paraboloid rather than a hyperboloid.

SOLUTION Setting $z = 0$ in the equation of the surface, we see that the xy-trace consists of the two lines $y = \pm 2x$. However, slicing the surface with any other horizontal plane $z = z_0$ produces a hyperbola $x^2 - \dfrac{y^2}{4} = z_0$. If $z_0 > 0$, then the axis of the hyperbola is parallel to the x-axis. On the other hand, if $z_0 < 0$, then the axis of the hyperbola is parallel to the y-axis (Figure 12.16a). Setting $x = x_0$ produces the trace $z = x_0^2 - \dfrac{y^2}{4}$, which

▶ The hyperbolic paraboloid has a feature called a *saddle point*. For the surface in Example 11, if you walk from the saddle point at the origin in the direction of the x-axis, you move uphill. If you walk from the saddle point in the direction of the y-axis, you move downhill. Saddle points are examined in detail in Section 12.8.

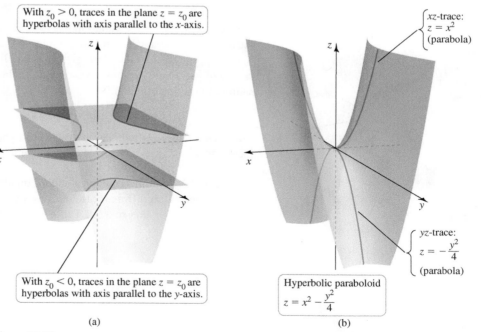

With $z_0 > 0$, traces in the plane $z = z_0$ are hyperbolas with axis parallel to the x-axis.

With $z_0 < 0$, traces in the plane $z = z_0$ are hyperbolas with axis parallel to the y-axis.

(a)

xz-trace:
$z = x^2$
(parabola)

yz-trace:
$z = -\dfrac{y^2}{4}$
(parabola)

Hyperbolic paraboloid
$z = x^2 - \dfrac{y^2}{4}$

(b)

Figure 12.16

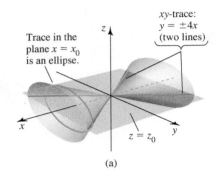

Trace in the plane $x = x_0$ is an ellipse.

xy-trace: $y = \pm 4x$ (two lines)

$z = z_0$

(a)

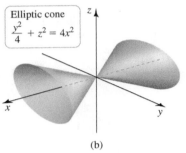

Elliptic cone $\dfrac{y^2}{4} + z^2 = 4x^2$

(b)

Figure 12.17

▶ The equation $-x^2 - \dfrac{y^2}{4} + \dfrac{z^2}{16} = 1$ describes a hyperboloid of two sheets with its axis on the z-axis. Therefore, the equation in Example 13 describes the same surface shifted 2 units in the positive x-direction.

Hyperboloid of two sheets
$-(x - 2)^2 - \dfrac{y^2}{4} + \dfrac{z^2}{16} = 1$

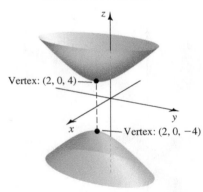

Vertex: $(2, 0, 4)$

Vertex: $(2, 0, -4)$

Figure 12.18

is the equation of a parabola that opens downward in a plane parallel to the yz-plane. You can check that traces in planes parallel to the xz-plane are parabolas that open upward. The resulting surface is a *hyperbolic paraboloid* (Figure 12.16b).

Related Exercises 59–62 ◀

EXAMPLE 12 Elliptic cones Graph the surface defined by the equation
$$\frac{y^2}{4} + z^2 = 4x^2.$$

SOLUTION The only point at which the surface intersects the coordinate axes is $(0, 0, 0)$. Traces in the planes $x = x_0$ are ellipses of the form $\dfrac{y^2}{4} + z^2 = 4x_0{}^2$ that shrink in size as x_0 approaches 0. Setting $y = 0$, the xz-trace satisfies the equation $z^2 = 4x^2$ or $z = \pm 2x$, which are equations of two lines in the xz-plane that intersect at the origin. Setting $z = 0$, the xy-trace satisfies $y^2 = 16x^2$ or $y = \pm 4x$, which describes two lines in the xy-plane that intersect at the origin (Figure 12.17a). The complete surface consists of two *cones* opening in opposite directions along the x-axis with a common vertex at the origin (Figure 12.17b).

Related Exercises 63–66 ◀

EXAMPLE 13 A hyperboloid of two sheets Graph the surface defined by the equation
$$-16x^2 - 4y^2 + z^2 + 64x - 80 = 0.$$

SOLUTION We first regroup terms, giving
$$-16\underbrace{(x^2 - 4x)}_{\text{complete the square}} - 4y^2 + z^2 - 80 = 0,$$

and then complete the square in x:
$$-16(\underbrace{x^2 - 4x + 4}_{(x - 2)^2} - 4) - 4y^2 + z^2 - 80 = 0.$$

Collecting terms and dividing by 16 gives the equation
$$-(x - 2)^2 - \frac{y^2}{4} + \frac{z^2}{16} = 1.$$

Notice that if $z = 0$, the equation has no solution, so the surface does not intersect the xy-plane. The traces in planes parallel to the xz- and yz-planes are hyperbolas. If $|z_0| \geq 4$, the trace in the plane $z = z_0$ is an ellipse. This equation describes a *hyperboloid of two sheets*, with its axis parallel to the z-axis and shifted 2 units in the positive x-direction (Figure 12.18).

Related Exercises 67–70 ◀

QUICK CHECK 10 In which variable(s) should you complete the square to identify the surface $x = y^2 + 2y + z^2 - 4z + 16$? Name and describe the surface. ◀

Table 12.1 summarizes the standard quadric surfaces. It is important to note that the same surfaces with different orientations are obtained when the roles of the variables are interchanged. For this reason, Table 12.1 summarizes many more surfaces than those listed.

Table 12.1

Name	Standard Equation	Features	Graph
Ellipsoid	$\dfrac{x^2}{a^2} + \dfrac{y^2}{b^2} + \dfrac{z^2}{c^2} = 1$	All traces are ellipses.	
Elliptic paraboloid	$z = \dfrac{x^2}{a^2} + \dfrac{y^2}{b^2}$	Traces with $z = z_0 > 0$ are ellipses. Traces with $x = x_0$ or $y = y_0$ are parabolas.	
Hyperboloid of one sheet	$\dfrac{x^2}{a^2} + \dfrac{y^2}{b^2} - \dfrac{z^2}{c^2} = 1$	Traces with $z = z_0$ are ellipses for all z_0. Traces with $x = x_0$ or $y = y_0$ are hyperbolas.	
Hyperboloid of two sheets	$-\dfrac{x^2}{a^2} - \dfrac{y^2}{b^2} + \dfrac{z^2}{c^2} = 1$	Traces with $z = z_0$ with $|z_0| > |c|$ are ellipses. Traces with $x = x_0$ and $y = y_0$ are hyperbolas.	
Elliptic cone	$\dfrac{x^2}{a^2} + \dfrac{y^2}{b^2} = \dfrac{z^2}{c^2}$	Traces with $z = z_0 \neq 0$ are ellipses. Traces with $x = x_0$ or $y = y_0$ are hyperbolas or intersecting lines.	
Hyperbolic paraboloid	$z = \dfrac{x^2}{a^2} - \dfrac{y^2}{b^2}$	Traces with $z = z_0 \neq 0$ are hyperbolas. Traces with $x = x_0$ or $y = y_0$ are parabolas.	

SECTION 12.1 EXERCISES

Review Questions

1. Give two pieces of information which, taken together, uniquely determine a plane.

2. Find a vector normal to the plane $-2x - 3y + 4z = 12$.

3. Where does the plane $-2x - 3y + 4z = 12$ intersect the coordinate axes?

4. Give an equation of the plane with a normal vector $\mathbf{n} = \langle 1, 1, 1 \rangle$ that passes through the point $(1, 0, 0)$.

5. To which coordinate axes are the following cylinders in $\mathbb{R}^3$ parallel: $x^2 + 2y^2 = 8$, $z^2 + 2y^2 = 8$, and $x^2 + 2z^2 = 8$?

6. Describe the graph of $x = z^2$ in $\mathbb{R}^3$.

7. What is a trace of a surface?

8. What is the name of the surface defined by the equation $y = \dfrac{x^2}{4} + \dfrac{z^2}{8}$?

9. What is the name of the surface defined by the equation $x^2 + \dfrac{y^2}{3} + 2z^2 = 1$?

10. What is the name of the surface defined by the equation $-y^2 - \dfrac{z^2}{2} + x^2 = 1$?

Basic Skills

11–16. Equations of planes *Find an equation of the plane that passes through the point P_0 with a normal vector $\mathbf{n}$.*

11. $P_0(0, 2, -2)$; $\mathbf{n} = \langle 1, 1, -1 \rangle$

12. $P_0(1, 0, -3)$; $\mathbf{n} = \langle 1, -1, 2 \rangle$

13. $P_0(2, 3, 0)$; $\mathbf{n} = \langle -1, 2, -3 \rangle$

14. $P_0(1, 2, -3)$; $\mathbf{n} = \langle -1, 4, -3 \rangle$

15. **Equation of a plane** Find an equation of the plane that is parallel to the vectors $\langle 1, 0, 1 \rangle$ and $\langle 0, 2, 1 \rangle$, passing through the point $(1, 2, 3)$.

16. **Equation of a plane** Find an equation of the plane that is parallel to the vectors $\langle 1, -3, 1 \rangle$ and $\langle 4, 2, 0 \rangle$, passing through the point $(3, 0, -2)$.

17–20. Equations of planes *Find an equation of the following planes.*

17. The plane passing through the points $(1, 0, 3)$, $(0, 4, 2)$, and $(1, 1, 1)$

18. The plane passing through the points $(-1, 1, 1)$, $(0, 0, 2)$, and $(3, -1, -2)$

19. The plane passing through the points $(2, -1, 4)$, $(1, 1, -1)$, and $(-4, 1, 1)$

20. The plane passing through the points $(5, 3, 1)$, $(1, 3, -5)$, and $(-1, 3, 1)$

21–24. Properties of planes *Find the points at which the following planes intersect the coordinate axes and find equations of the lines where the planes intersect the coordinate planes. Sketch a graph of the plane.*

21. $3x - 2y + z = 6$

22. $-4x + 8z = 16$

23. $x + 3y - 5z - 30 = 0$

24. $12x - 9y + 4z + 72 = 0$

25–28. Pairs of planes *Determine whether the following pairs of planes are parallel, orthogonal, or neither.*

25. $x + y + 4z = 10$ and $-x - 3y + z = 10$

26. $2x + 2y - 3z = 10$ and $-10x - 10y + 15z = 10$

27. $3x + 2y - 3z = 10$ and $-6x - 10y + z = 10$

28. $3x + 2y + 2z = 10$ and $-6x - 10y + 19z = 10$

29–30. Equations of planes *For the following sets of planes, determine which pairs of planes in the set are parallel, orthogonal, or identical.*

29. $Q\colon 3x - 2y + z = 12$; $R\colon -x + 2y/3 - z/3 = 0$; $S\colon -x + 2y + 7z = 1$; $T\colon 3x/2 - y + z/2 = 6$

30. $Q\colon x + y - z = 0$; $R\colon y + z = 0$; $S\colon x - y = 0$; $T\colon x + y + z = 0$

31–34. Parallel planes *Find an equation of the plane parallel to the plane Q passing through the point P_0.*

31. $Q\colon -x + 2y - 4z = 1$; $P_0(1, 0, 4)$

32. $Q\colon 2x + y - z = 1$; $P_0(0, 2, -2)$

33. $Q\colon 4x + 3y - 2z = 12$; $P_0(1, -1, 3)$

34. $Q\colon x - 5y - 2z = 1$; $P_0(1, 2, 0)$

35–38. Intersecting planes *Find an equation of the line of intersection of the planes Q and R.*

35. $Q\colon -x + 2y + z = 1$; $R\colon x + y + z = 0$

36. $Q\colon x + 2y - z = 1$; $R\colon x + y + z = 1$

37. $Q\colon 2x - y + 3z - 1 = 0$; $R\colon -x + 3y + z - 4 = 0$

38. $Q\colon x - y - 2z = 1$; $R\colon x + y + z = -1$

39–46. Cylinders in $\mathbb{R}^3$ *Consider the following cylinders in $\mathbb{R}^3$.*

a. Identify the coordinate axis to which the cylinder is parallel.
b. Sketch the cylinder.

39. $z = y^2$

40. $x^2 + 4y^2 = 4$

41. $x^2 + z^2 = 4$

42. $x = z^2 - 4$

43. $y - x^3 = 0$

44. $x - 2z^2 = 0$

45. $z - \ln y = 0$

46. $x - 1/y = 0$

47–70. Quadric surfaces *Consider the following equations of quadric surfaces.*

a. Find the intercepts with the three coordinate axes, when they exist.
b. Find the equations of the xy-, xz-, and yz-traces, when they exist.
c. Sketch a graph of the surface.

Ellipsoids

47. $x^2 + \dfrac{y^2}{4} + \dfrac{z^2}{9} = 1$

48. $4x^2 + y^2 + \dfrac{z^2}{2} = 1$

49. $\dfrac{x^2}{3} + 3y^2 + \dfrac{z^2}{12} = 3$

50. $\dfrac{x^2}{6} + 24y^2 + \dfrac{z^2}{24} - 6 = 0$

Elliptic paraboloids

51. $x = y^2 + z^2$

52. $z = \dfrac{x^2}{4} + \dfrac{y^2}{9}$

53. $9x - 81y^2 - \dfrac{z^2}{4} = 0$

54. $2y - \dfrac{x^2}{8} - \dfrac{z^2}{18} = 0$

Hyperboloids of one sheet

55. $\dfrac{x^2}{25} + \dfrac{y^2}{9} - z^2 = 1$

56. $\dfrac{y^2}{4} + \dfrac{z^2}{9} - \dfrac{x^2}{16} = 1$

57. $\dfrac{y^2}{16} + 36z^2 - \dfrac{x^2}{4} - 9 = 0$

58. $9z^2 + x^2 - \dfrac{y^2}{3} - 1 = 0$

Hyperbolic paraboloids

59. $z = \dfrac{x^2}{9} - y^2$

60. $y = \dfrac{x^2}{16} - 4z^2$

61. $5x - \dfrac{y^2}{5} + \dfrac{z^2}{20} = 0$

62. $6y + \dfrac{x^2}{6} - \dfrac{z^2}{24} = 0$

Elliptic cones

63. $x^2 + \dfrac{y^2}{4} = z^2$

64. $4y^2 + z^2 = x^2$

65. $\dfrac{z^2}{32} + \dfrac{y^2}{18} = 2x^2$

66. $\dfrac{x^2}{3} + \dfrac{z^2}{12} = 3y^2$

Hyperboloids of two sheets

67. $-x^2 + \dfrac{y^2}{4} - \dfrac{z^2}{9} = 1$

68. $1 - 4x^2 + y^2 + \dfrac{z^2}{2} = 0$

69. $-\dfrac{x^2}{3} + 3y^2 - \dfrac{z^2}{12} = 1$

70. $-\dfrac{x^2}{6} - 24y^2 + \dfrac{z^2}{24} - 6 = 0$

Further Explorations

71. **Explain why or why not** Determine whether the following statements are true and give an explanation or counterexample.

a. The plane passing through the point $(1, 1, 1)$ with a normal vector $\mathbf{n} = \langle 1, 2, -3 \rangle$ is the same as the plane passing through the point $(3, 0, 1)$ with a normal vector $\mathbf{n} = \langle -2, -4, 6 \rangle$.

b. The equations $x + y - z = 1$ and $-x - y + z = 1$ describe the same plane.

c. Given a plane Q, there is exactly one plane orthogonal to Q.

d. Given a line ℓ and a point P_0 not on ℓ, there is exactly one plane that contains ℓ and passes through P_0.

e. Given a plane R and a point P_0, there is exactly one plane that is orthogonal to R and passes through P_0.

f. Any two distinct lines in $\mathbb{R}^3$ determine a unique plane.

g. If plane Q is orthogonal to plane R and plane R is orthogonal to plane S, then plane Q is orthogonal to plane S.

72. **Plane containing a line and a point** Find an equation of the plane that passes through the point P_0 and contains the line ℓ.

a. $P_0(1, -2, 3)$; ℓ: $\mathbf{r} = \langle t, -t, 2t \rangle$

b. $P_0(-4, 1, 2)$; ℓ: $\mathbf{r} = \langle 2t, -2t, -4t \rangle$

73–74. Lines normal to planes *Find an equation of the line passing through P_0 and normal to the plane P.*

73. $P_0(2, 1, 3)$; P: $2x - 4y + z = 10$

74. $P_0(0, -10, -3)$; P: $x + 4z = 2$

75. **A family of orthogonal planes** Find an equation for a family of planes that are orthogonal to the planes $2x + 3y = 4$ and $-x - y + 2z = 8$.

76. **Orthogonal plane** Find an equation of the plane passing through $(0, -2, 4)$ that is orthogonal to the planes $2x + 5y - 3z = 0$ and $-x + 5y + 2z = 8$.

77. **Three intersecting planes** Describe the set of all points (if any) at which all three planes $x + 3z = 3$, $y + 4z = 6$, and $x + y + 6z = 9$ intersect.

78. **Three intersecting planes** Describe the set of all points (if any) at which all three planes $x + 2y + 2z = 3$, $y + 4z = 6$, and $x + 2y + 8z = 9$ intersect.

79. **Matching graphs with equations** Match equations a–f with surfaces A–F.

a. $y - z^2 = 0$

b. $2x + 3y - z = 5$

c. $4x^2 + \dfrac{y^2}{9} + z^2 = 1$

d. $x^2 + \dfrac{y^2}{9} - z^2 = 1$

e. $x^2 + \dfrac{y^2}{9} = z^2$

f. $y = |x|$

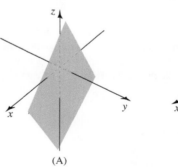

(A)

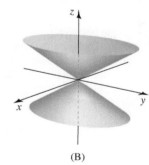

(B)

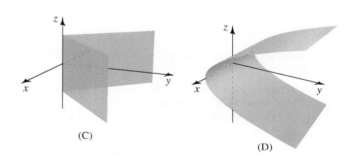

(C)

(D)

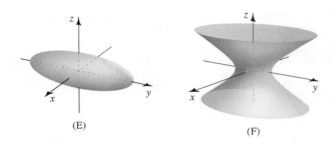

(E)   (F)

80–89. Identifying surfaces *Identify and briefly describe the surfaces defined by the following equations.*

80. $z^2 + 4y^2 - x^2 = 1$ **81.** $y = 4z^2 - x^2$

82. $-y^2 - 9z^2 + x^2/4 = 1$ **83.** $y = x^2/6 + z^2/16$

84. $x^2 + y^2 + 4z^2 + 2x = 0$ **85.** $9x^2 + y^2 - 4z^2 + 2y = 0$

86. $x^2 + 4y^2 = 1$ **87.** $y^2 - z^2 = 2$

88. $-x^2 - y^2 + z^2/9 + 6x - 8y = 26$

89. $x^2/4 + y^2 - 2x - 10y - z^2 + 41 = 0$

90–93. Curve–plane intersections *Find the points (if they exist) at which the following planes and curves intersect.*

90. $y = 2x + 1$; $\mathbf{r}(t) = \langle 10 \cos t, 2 \sin t, 1 \rangle$, for $0 \le t \le 2\pi$

91. $8x + y + z = 60$; $\mathbf{r}(t) = \langle t, t^2, 3t^2 \rangle$, for $-\infty < t < \infty$

92. $8x + 15y + 3z = 20$; $\mathbf{r}(t) = \langle 1, \sqrt{t}, -t \rangle$, for $t > 0$

93. $2x + 3y - 12z = 0$; $\mathbf{r}(t) = \langle 4 \cos t, 4 \sin t, \cos t \rangle$, for $0 \le t \le 2\pi$

94.   Intercepts Let a, b, c, and d be constants. Find the points at which the plane $ax + by + cz = d$ intersects the x-, y-, and z-axes.

T 95.   Angle between planes The angle between two planes is the angle θ between the normal vectors of the planes, where the directions of the normal vectors are chosen so that $0 \le \theta < \pi$. Find the angle between the planes $5x + 2y - z = 0$ and $-3x + y + 2z = 0$.

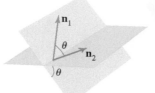

96.   Solids of revolution Consider the ellipse $x^2 + 4y^2 = 1$ in the xy-plane.

   a. If this ellipse is revolved about the x-axis, what is the equation of the resulting ellipsoid?
   b. If this ellipse is revolved about the y-axis, what is the equation of the resulting ellipsoid?

97.   Solids of revolution Which of the quadric surfaces in Table 12.1 can be generated by revolving a curve in one of the coordinate planes about a coordinate axis, assuming $a = b = c \ne 0$?

Applications

98.   Light cones The idea of a *light cone* appears in the Special Theory of Relativity. The xy-plane (see figure) represents all of three-dimensional space, and the z-axis is the time axis (t-axis). If an event E occurs at the origin, the interior of the future light cone ($t > 0$) represents all events in the future that could be affected by E, assuming that no signal travels faster than the speed of light. The interior of the past light cone ($t < 0$) represents all events in the past that could have affected E, again assuming that no signal travels faster than the speed of light.

   a. If time is measured in seconds and distance (x and y) is measured in light-seconds (the distance light travels in 1 s), the light cone makes a 45° angle with the xy-plane. Write the equation of the light cone in this case.
   b. Suppose distance is measured in meters and time is measured in seconds. Write the equation of the light cone in this case given that the speed of light is 3×10^8 m/s.

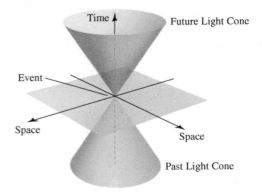

99.   T-shirt profits A clothing company makes a profit of \$10 on its long-sleeved T-shirts and \$5 on its short-sleeved T-shirts. Assuming there is a \$200 setup cost, the profit on T-shirt sales is $z = 10x + 5y - 200$, where x is the number of long-sleeved T-shirts sold and y is the number of short-sleeved T-shirts sold. Assume x and y are nonnegative.

   a. Graph the plane that gives the profit using the window $[0, 40] \times [0, 40] \times [-400, 400]$.
   b. If $x = 20$ and $y = 10$, is the profit positive or negative?
   c. Describe the values of x and y for which the company breaks even (for which the profit is zero). Mark this set on your graph.

Additional Exercises

100.   Parallel line and plane Show that the plane $ax + by + cz = d$ and the line $\mathbf{r}(t) = \mathbf{r}_0 + \mathbf{v}t$, not in the plane, have no points of intersection if and only if $\mathbf{v} \cdot \langle a, b, c \rangle = 0$. Give a geometric explanation of this result.

101.   Tilted ellipse Consider the curve $\mathbf{r}(t) = \langle \cos t, \sin t, c \sin t \rangle$, for $0 \le t \le 2\pi$, where c is a real number.

   a. What is the equation of the plane P in which the curve lies?
   b. What is the angle between P and the xy-plane?
   c. Prove that the curve is an ellipse in P.

102.   Distance from a point to a plane

   a. Show that the point in the plane $ax + by + cz = d$ nearest the origin is $P(ad/D^2, bd/D^2, cd/D^2)$, where $D^2 = a^2 + b^2 + c^2$. Conclude that the least distance from the plane to the origin is $|d|/D$. (*Hint:* The least distance is along a normal to the plane.)

b. Show that the least distance from the point $P_0(x_0, y_0, z_0)$ to the plane $ax + by + cz = d$ is $|ax_0 + by_0 + cz_0 - d|/D$. (*Hint:* Find the point P on the plane closest to P_0.)

103. Another distance formula. Suppose P is a point in the plane $ax + by + cz = d$. Then the least distance from any point Q to the plane equals the length of the orthogonal projection of $\overrightarrow{PQ}$ onto the normal vector $\mathbf{n} = \langle a, b. c \rangle$.

a. Use this information to show that the least distance from Q to the plane is $\dfrac{|\overrightarrow{PQ} \cdot \mathbf{n}|}{|\mathbf{n}|}$.

b. Find the least distance from the point $(1, 2, -4)$ to the plane $2x - y + 3z = 1$.

104. Ellipsoid–plane intersection Let E be the ellipsoid $x^2/9 + y^2/4 + z^2 = 1$, P be the plane $z = Ax + By$, and C be the intersection of E and P.

a. Is C an ellipse for all values of A and B? Explain.

b. Sketch and interpret the situation in which $A = 0$ and $B \neq 0$.

c. Find an equation of the projection of C on the xy-plane.

d. Assume $A = \frac{1}{6}$ and $B = \frac{1}{2}$. Find a parametric description of C as a curve in $\mathbb{R}^3$. (*Hint:* Assume C is described by $\langle a \cos t + b \sin t, c \cos t + d \sin t, e \cos t + f \sin t \rangle$ and find a, b, c, d, e, and f.)

QUICK CHECK ANSWERS

1. The plane passes through $(1, 2, 3)$ and is parallel to the yz-plane; its equation is $x = 1$. **2.** Because the right side of the equation is 0, the equation can be multiplied by any nonzero constant (changing the length of $\mathbf{n}$) without changing the graph. **5.** y-axis; x-axis **6.** The equation $x^2 + 4y^2 = 16$ is a special case of the general equation for quadric surfaces; all the coefficients except A, B, and J are zero. **7.** x-axis; z-axis **8.** Positive x-axis **9.** x-axis **10.** Complete the square in y and z; elliptic paraboloid with its axis parallel to the x-axis ◄

12.2 Graphs and Level Curves

In Chapter 11, we discussed vector-valued functions with one independent variable and several dependent variables. We now reverse the situation and consider functions with several independent variables and one dependent variable. Such functions are aptly called *functions of several variables* or *multivariable functions*.

To set the stage, consider the following practical questions that illustrate a few of the many applications of functions of several variables.

• What is the probability that one man selected randomly from a large group of men weighs more than 200 pounds and is over 6 feet tall?

• Where on the wing of an airliner flying at a speed of 550 mi/hr is the pressure greatest?

• A physician knows the optimal blood concentration of an antibiotic needed by a patient. What dosage of antibiotic is needed and how often should it be given to reach this optimal level?

Although we don't answer these questions immediately, they provide an idea of the scope and importance of the topic. First, we must introduce the idea of a function of several variables.

Functions of Two Variables

The key concepts related to functions of several variables are most easily presented in the case of two independent variables; the extension to three or more variables is then straightforward. In general, functions of two variables are written *explicitly* in the form

$$z = f(x, y)$$

or *implicitly* in the form

$$F(x, y, z) = 0.$$

Both forms are important, but for now, we consider explicitly defined functions.

The concepts of domain and range carry over directly from functions of a single variable.

> **DEFINITION Function, Domain, and Range with Two Independent Variables**
>
> A **function** $z = f(x, y)$ assigns to each point (x, y) in a set D in $\mathbb{R}^2$ a unique real number z in a subset of $\mathbb{R}$. The set D is the **domain** of f. The **range** of f is the set of real numbers z that are assumed as the points (x, y) vary over the domain (Figure 12.19).

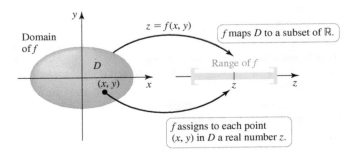

Figure 12.19

As with functions of one variable, a function of several variables may have a domain that is restricted by the context of the problem. For example, if the independent variables correspond to price or length or population, they take only nonnegative values, even though the associated function may be defined for negative values of the variables. If not stated otherwise, D is the set of all points for which the function is defined.

A polynomial in x and y consists of sums and products of polynomials in x and polynomials in y; for example, $f(x, y) = x^2 y - 2xy - xy^2$. Such polynomials are defined for all values of x and y, so their domain is $\mathbb{R}^2$. A quotient of two polynomials in x and y, such as $h(x, y) = \dfrac{xy}{x - y}$, is a rational function in x and y. The domain of a rational function excludes points at which the denominator is zero, so the domain of h is $\{(x, y): x \neq y\}$.

EXAMPLE 1 Finding domains Find the domain of the function
$g(x, y) = \sqrt{4 - x^2 - y^2}$.

SOLUTION Because g involves a square root, its domain consists of ordered pairs (x, y) for which $4 - x^2 - y^2 \geq 0$ or $x^2 + y^2 \leq 4$. Therefore, the domain of g is $\{(x, y): x^2 + y^2 \leq 4\}$, which is the set of points on or within the circle of radius 2 centered at the origin in the xy-plane (a *disk* of radius 2) (Figure 12.20).

Related Exercises 11–20 ◄

QUICK CHECK 1 Find the domains of $f(x, y) = \sin xy$ and $g(x, y) = \sqrt{(x^2 + 1)y}$. ◄

Graphs of Functions of Two Variables

The **graph** of a function f of two variables is the set of points (x, y, z) that satisfy the equation $z = f(x, y)$. More specifically, for each point (x, y) in the domain of f, the point $(x, y, f(x, y))$ lies on the graph of f (Figure 12.21). A similar definition applies to relations of the form $F(x, y, z) = 0$.

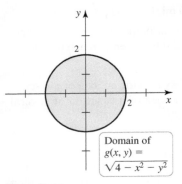

Domain of
$g(x, y) = \sqrt{4 - x^2 - y^2}$

Figure 12.20

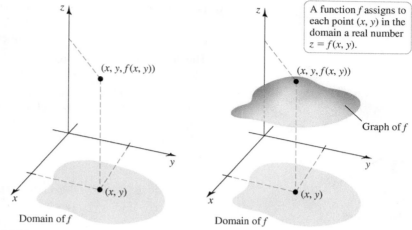

Figure 12.21

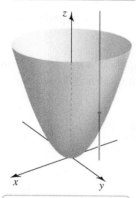

An ellipsoid does not pass the vertical line test: not the graph of a function.

Like functions of one variable, functions of two variables must pass a **vertical line test**. A relation of the form $F(x, y, z) = 0$ is a function provided every line parallel to the z-axis intersects the graph of the relation at most once. For example, an ellipsoid (discussed in Section 12.1) is not the graph of a function because some vertical lines intersect the surface twice. On the other hand, an elliptic paraboloid of the form $z = ax^2 + by^2$ does represent a function (Figure 12.22).

QUICK CHECK 2 Does the graph of a hyperboloid of one sheet represent a function? Does the graph of a cone with its axis parallel to the x-axis represent a function? ◄

EXAMPLE 2   Graphing two-variable functions Find the domain and range of the following functions. Then sketch a graph.

a. $f(x, y) = 2x + 3y - 12$ **b.** $g(x, y) = x^2 + y^2$
c. $h(x, y) = \sqrt{1 + x^2 + y^2}$

SOLUTION

a. Letting $z = f(x, y)$, we have the equation $z = 2x + 3y - 12$, or $2x + 3y - z = 12$, which describes a plane with a normal vector $\langle 2, 3, -1 \rangle$ (Section 12.1). The domain consists of all points in $\mathbb{R}^2$, and the range is $\mathbb{R}$. We sketch the surface by noting that the x-intercept is $(6, 0, 0)$ (setting $y = z = 0$); the y-intercept is $(0, 4, 0)$ and the z-intercept is $(0, 0, -12)$ (Figure 12.23).

This elliptic paraboloid passes the vertical line test: graph of a function.

Figure 12.22

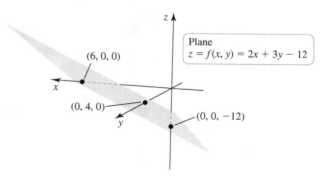

Figure 12.23

Paraboloid
$z = f(x, y) = x^2 + y^2$

Figure 12.24

b. Letting $z = g(x, y)$, we have the equation $z = x^2 + y^2$, which describes an elliptic paraboloid that opens upward with vertex $(0, 0, 0)$. The domain is $\mathbb{R}^2$ and the range consists of all nonnegative real numbers (Figure 12.24).

c. The domain of the function is $\mathbb{R}^2$ because the quantity under the square root is always positive. Note that $1 + x^2 + y^2 \geq 1$, so the range is $\{z : z \geq 1\}$. Squaring both sides of $z = \sqrt{1 + x^2 + y^2}$, we obtain $z^2 = 1 + x^2 + y^2$, or $-x^2 - y^2 + z^2 = 1$. This is the equation of a hyperboloid of two sheets that opens along the z-axis. Because the range is $\{z : z \geq 1\}$, the given function represents only the upper sheet of the hyperboloid (Figure 12.25; the lower sheet was introduced when we squared the original equation).

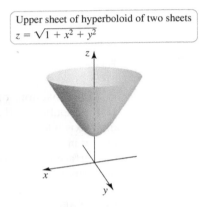

Upper sheet of hyperboloid of two sheets
$z = \sqrt{1 + x^2 + y^2}$

Figure 12.25

Related Exercises 21–29 ◄

QUICK CHECK 3 Find a function whose graph is the lower half of the hyperboloid $-x^2 - y^2 + z^2 = 1$. ◄

➤ To anticipate results that appear later in the chapter, notice how the streams in the topographic map—which flow downhill—cross the level curves roughly at right angles.

Level Curves   Functions of two variables are represented by surfaces in $\mathbb{R}^3$. However, such functions can be represented in another illuminating way, which is used to make topographic maps (Figure 12.26).

Closely spaced contours: rapid changes in elevation

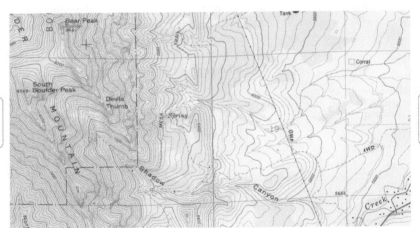

Widely spaced contours: slow changes in elevation

Figure 12.26

▶ A contour curve is a trace in the plane $z = z_0$.

▶ A level curve may not always be a single curve. It might consist of a point ($x^2 + y^2 = 0$) or it might consist of several lines or curves ($xy = 0$).

Consider a surface defined by the function $z = f(x, y)$ (Figure 12.27). Now imagine stepping onto the surface and walking along a path on which your elevation has the constant value $z = z_0$. The path you walk on the surface is part of a **contour curve**; the complete contour curve is the intersection of the surface and the horizontal plane $z = z_0$. When the contour curve is projected onto the xy-plane, the result is the curve $f(x, y) = z_0$. This curve in the xy-plane is called a **level curve**.

Imagine repeating this process with a different constant value of z, say, $z = z_1$. The path you walk this time when projected onto the xy-plane is part of another level curve $f(x, y) = z_1$. A collection of such level curves, corresponding to different values of z, provides a useful two-dimensional representation of the surface (Figure 12.28).

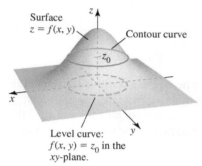

Surface $z = f(x, y)$

Contour curve

z_0

Level curve: $f(x, y) = z_0$ in the xy-plane.

Figure 12.27

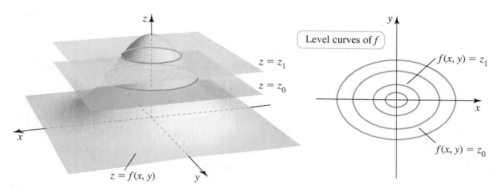

Level curves of f

$z = z_1$

$z = z_0$

$f(x, y) = z_1$

$f(x, y) = z_0$

$z = f(x, y)$

Figure 12.28

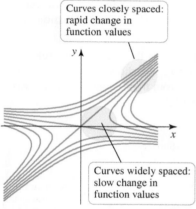

Curves closely spaced: rapid change in function values

Curves widely spaced: slow change in function values

Figure 12.29

QUICK CHECK 4 Can two level curves of a function intersect? Explain. ◀

Assuming that two adjacent level curves always correspond to the same change in z, widely spaced level curves indicate gradual changes in z-values, while closely spaced level curves indicate rapid changes in some directions (Figure 12.29). Concentric closed level curves indicate either a peak or a depression on the surface.

QUICK CHECK 5 Describe in words the level curves of the top half of the sphere $x^2 + y^2 + z^2 = 1$. ◀

EXAMPLE 3   Level curves Find and sketch the level curves of the following surfaces.

a. $f(x, y) = y - x^2 - 1$ **b.** $f(x, y) = e^{-x^2 - y^2}$

SOLUTION

a. The level curves are described by the equation $y - x^2 - 1 = z_0$, where z_0 is a constant in the range of f. For all values of z_0, these curves are parabolas in the xy-plane, as seen by writing the equation in the form $y = x^2 + z_0 + 1$. For example:

- With $z_0 = 0$, the level curve is the parabola $y = x^2 + 1$; along this curve, the surface has an elevation (z-coordinate) of 0.

- With $z_0 = -1$, the level curve is $y = x^2$; along this curve, the surface has an elevation of -1.

- With $z_0 = 1$, the level curve is $y = x^2 + 2$, along which the surface has an elevation of 1.

As shown in Figure 12.30a, the level curves form a family of shifted parabolas. When these level curves are labeled with their z-coordinates, the graph of the surface $z = f(x, y)$ can be visualized (Figure 12.30b).

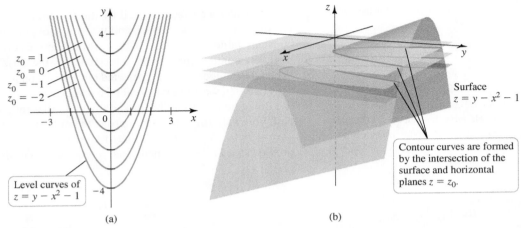

Level curves of
$z = y - x^2 - 1$

(a)

Surface
$z = y - x^2 - 1$

Contour curves are formed
by the intersection of the
surface and horizontal
planes $z = z_0$.

(b)

Figure 12.30

b. The level curves satisfy the equation $e^{-x^2-y^2} = z_0$, where z_0 is a positive constant. Taking the natural logarithm of both sides gives the equation $x^2 + y^2 = -\ln z_0$, which describes circular level curves. These curves can be sketched for all values of z_0 with $0 < z_0 \le 1$ (because the right side of $x^2 + y^2 = -\ln z_0$ must be nonnegative). For example:

- With $z_0 = 1$, the level curve satisfies the equation $x^2 + y^2 = 0$, whose solution is the single point $(0, 0)$; at this point, the surface has an elevation of 1.

- With $z_0 = e^{-1}$, the level curve is $x^2 + y^2 = -\ln e^{-1} = 1$, which is a circle centered at $(0, 0)$ with a radius of 1; along this curve the surface has an elevation of $e^{-1} \approx 0.37$.

In general, the level curves are circles centered at $(0, 0)$; as the radii of the circles increase, the corresponding z-values decrease. Figure 12.31a shows the level curves, with larger z-values corresponding to darker shades. From these labeled level curves, we can reconstruct the graph of the surface (Figure 12.31b).

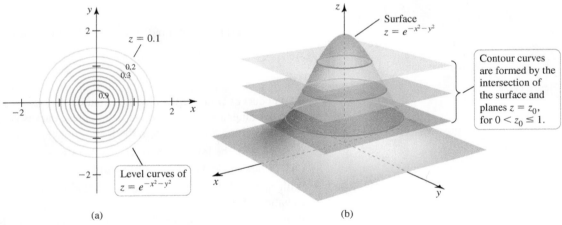

$z = 0.1$

0.2
0.3

0.9

Level curves of
$z = e^{-x^2-y^2}$

(a)

Surface
$z = e^{-x^2-y^2}$

Contour curves
are formed by the
intersection of
the surface and
planes $z = z_0$,
for $0 < z_0 \le 1$.

(b)

Figure 12.31

Related Exercises 30–38 ◄

QUICK CHECK 6 Does the surface in Example 3b have a level curve for $z_0 = 0$? Explain. ◄

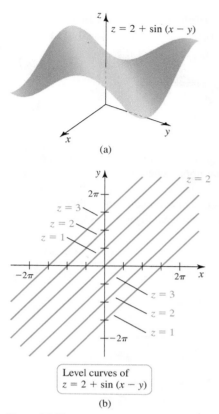

Figure 12.32

EXAMPLE 4 Level curves The graph of the function

$$f(x, y) = 2 + \sin(x - y)$$

is shown in Figure 12.32a. Sketch several level curves of the function.

SOLUTION The level curves are $f(x, y) = 2 + \sin(x - y) = z_0$, or $\sin(x - y) = z_0 - 2$. Because $-1 \le \sin(x - y) \le 1$, the admissible values of z_0 satisfy $-1 \le z_0 - 2 \le 1$, or, equivalently, $1 \le z_0 \le 3$. For example, when $z_0 = 2$, the level curves satisfy $\sin(x - y) = 0$. The solutions of this equation are $x - y = k\pi$, or $y = x - k\pi$, where k is an integer. Therefore, the surface has an elevation of 2 on this set of lines. With $z_0 = 1$ (the minimum value of z), the level curves satisfy $\sin(x - y) = -1$. The solutions are $x - y = -\pi/2 + 2k\pi$, where k is an integer; along these lines, the surface has an elevation of 1. Here we have an example in which each level curve is an infinite collection of lines of slope 1 (Figure 12.32b).

Related Exercises 30–38 ◄

Applications of Functions of Two Variables

The following examples offer two of many applications of functions of two variables.

EXAMPLE 5 A probability function of two variables Suppose that on a particular day, the fraction of students on campus infected with flu is r, where $0 \le r \le 1$. If you have n random (possibly repeated) encounters with students during the day, the probability of meeting *at least* one infected person is $p(n, r) = 1 - (1 - r)^n$ (Figure 12.33a). Discuss this probability function.

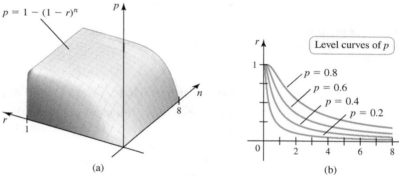

Figure 12.33

Table 12.2

			n		
	2	**5**	**10**	**15**	**20**
0.05	0.10	0.23	0.40	0.54	0.64
0.1	0.19	0.41	0.65	0.79	0.88
r **0.3**	0.51	0.83	0.97	1	1
0.5	0.75	0.97	1	1	1
0.7	0.91	1	1	1	1

SOLUTION The independent variable r is restricted to the interval $[0, 1]$ because it is a fraction of the population. The other independent variable n is any nonnegative integer; for the purposes of graphing, we treat n as a real number in the interval $[0, 8]$. With $0 \le r \le 1$, note that $0 \le 1 - r \le 1$. If n is nonnegative, then $0 \le (1 - r)^n \le 1$, and it follows that $0 \le p(n, r) \le 1$. Therefore, the range of the function is $[0, 1]$, which is consistent with the fact that p is a probability.

The level curves (Figure 12.33b) show that for a fixed value of n, the probability of at least one encounter increases with r; and for a fixed value of r, the probability increases with n. Therefore, as r increases or as n increases, the probability approaches 1 (at a surprising rate). If 10% of the population is infected ($r = 0.1$) and you have $n = 10$ encounters, then the probability of at least one encounter with an infected person is $p(0.1, 10) \approx 0.651$, which is about 2 in 3.

A numerical view of this function is given in Table 12.2, where we see probabilities tabulated for various values of n and r (rounded to two digits). The numerical values confirm the preceding observations.

Related Exercises 39–45 ◄

QUICK CHECK 7 In Example 5, if 50% of the population is infected, what is the probability of meeting at least one infected person in five encounters? ◄

EXAMPLE 6 **Electric potential function in two variables** The electric field at points in the xy-plane due to two point charges located at $(0, 0)$ and $(1, 0)$ is related to the electric potential function

$$\varphi(x, y) = \frac{2}{\sqrt{x^2 + y^2}} + \frac{2}{\sqrt{(x - 1)^2 + y^2}}.$$

Discuss the electric potential function.

▶ The electric potential function, often denoted φ (pronounced *fee* or *fie*), is a scalar-valued function from which the electric field can be computed. Potential functions are discussed in detail in Chapter 14.

▶ A function that grows without bound near a point, as in the case of the electric potential function, is said to have a *singularity* at that point. A singularity is analogous to a vertical asymptote in a function of one variable.

SOLUTION The domain of the function contains all points of $\mathbb{R}^2$ except $(0, 0)$ and $(1, 0)$ where the charges are located. As these points are approached, the potential function becomes arbitrarily large (Figure 12.34a). The potential approaches zero as x or y increases in magnitude. These observations imply that the range of the potential function is all positive real numbers. The level curves of φ are closed curves, encircling either a single charge (at small distances) or both charges (at larger distances; Figure 12.34b).

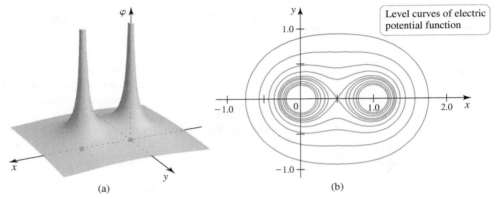

(a)

(b)

QUICK CHECK 8 In Example 6, what is the electric potential at the point $\left(\frac{1}{2}, 0\right)$? ◄

Figure 12.34

Related Exercises 39–45 ◄

Functions of More Than Two Variables

Many properties of functions of two independent variables extend naturally to functions of three or more variables. A function of three variables is defined explicitly in the form $w = f(x, y, z)$ and implicitly in the form $F(x, y, z, w) = 0$. With more than three independent variables, the variables are usually written $x_1, \ldots, x_n$. Table 12.3 shows the progression of functions of several variables.

Table 12.3

Number of Independent Variables	Explicit Form	Implicit Form	Graph Resides In ...
1	$y = f(x)$	$F(x, y) = 0$	$\mathbb{R}^2$ (xy-plane)
2	$z = f(x, y)$	$F(x, y, z) = 0$	$\mathbb{R}^3$ (xyz-space)
3	$w = f(x, y, z)$	$F(x, y, z, w) = 0$	$\mathbb{R}^4$
n	$x_{n+1} = f(x_1, x_2, \ldots, x_n)$	$F(x_1, x_2, \ldots, x_n, x_{n+1}) = 0$	$\mathbb{R}^{n+1}$

The concepts of domain and range extend from the one- and two-variable cases in an obvious way.

DEFINITION Function, Domain, and Range with n Independent Variables

The **function** $x_{n+1} = f(x_1, x_2, \ldots, x_n)$ assigns a unique real number x_{n+1} to each point $(x_1, x_2, \ldots, x_n)$ in a set D in $\mathbb{R}^n$. The set D is the **domain** of f. The **range** is the set of real numbers x_{n+1} that are assumed as the points $(x_1, x_2, \ldots, x_n)$ vary over the domain.

EXAMPLE 7   **Finding domains**   Find the domain of the following functions.

a. $g(x, y, z) = \sqrt{16 - x^2 - y^2 - z^2}$ **b.** $h(x, y, z) = \dfrac{12y^2}{z - y}$

SOLUTION

a. Values of the variables that make the argument of a square root negative must be excluded from the domain. In this case, the quantity under the square root is nonnegative provided

$$16 - x^2 - y^2 - z^2 \geq 0, \quad \text{or} \quad x^2 + y^2 + z^2 \leq 16.$$

> Recall that a closed ball of radius r is the set of all points on or within a sphere of radius r.

Therefore, the domain of g is a closed ball in $\mathbb{R}^3$ of radius 4 centered at the origin.

b. Values of the variables that make a denominator zero must be excluded from the domain. In this case, the denominator vanishes for all points in $\mathbb{R}^3$ that satisfy $z - y = 0$, or $y = z$. Therefore, the domain of h is the set $\{(x, y, z): y \neq z\}$. This set is $\mathbb{R}^3$ excluding the points on the plane $y = z$.

Related Exercises 46–52 ◄

QUICK CHECK 9   What is the domain of the function $w = f(x, y, z) = 1/xyz$? ◄

Graphs of Functions of More Than Two Variables

Graphing functions of *two* independent variables requires a three-dimensional coordinate system, which is the limit of ordinary graphing methods. Clearly, difficulties arise in graphing functions with three or more independent variables. For example, the graph of the function $w = f(x, y, z)$ resides in four dimensions. Here are two approaches to representing functions of three independent variables.

The idea of level curves can be extended. With the function $w = f(x, y, z)$, level curves become **level surfaces**, which are surfaces in $\mathbb{R}^3$ on which w is constant. For example, the level surfaces of the function

$$w = f(x, y, z) = \sqrt{z - x^2 - 2y^2}$$

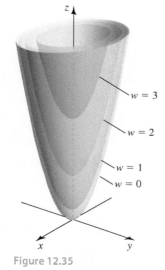

Figure 12.35

satisfy $w = \sqrt{z - x^2 - 2y^2} = C$, where C is a nonnegative constant. This equation is satisfied when $z = x^2 + 2y^2 + C^2$. Therefore, the level surfaces are elliptic paraboloids, stacked one inside another (Figure 12.35).

Another approach to displaying functions of three variables is to use colors to represent the fourth dimension. Figure 12.36a shows the electrical activity of the heart at one snapshot in time. The three independent variables correspond to locations in the heart. At each point, the value of the electrical activity, which is the dependent variable, is coded by colors.

In Figure 12.36b, the dependent variable is the switching speed in an integrated circuit, again represented by colors, as it varies over points of the domain. Software to produce such images, once expensive and inefficient, has become much more accessible.

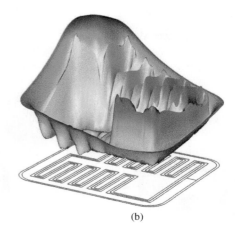

(a)   (b)

Figure 12.36

SECTION 12.2 EXERCISES

Review Questions

1. A function is defined by $z = x^2y - xy^2$. Identify the independent and dependent variables.

2. What is the domain of $f(x, y) = x^2y - xy^2$?

3. What is the domain of $g(x, y) = 1/(xy)$?

4. What is the domain of $h(x, y) = \sqrt{x - y}$?

5. How many axes (or how many dimensions) are needed to graph the function $z = f(x, y)$? Explain.

6. Explain how to graph the level curves of a surface $z = f(x, y)$.

7. Describe in words the level curves of the paraboloid $z = x^2 + y^2$.

8. How many axes (or how many dimensions) are needed to graph the level surfaces of $w = f(x, y, z)$? Explain.

9. The domain of $Q = f(u, v, w, x, y, z)$ lies in $\mathbb{R}^n$ for what value of n? Explain.

10. Give two methods for graphically representing a function with three independent variables.

Basic Skills

11–20. Domains *Find the domain of the following functions.*

11. $f(x, y) = 2xy - 3x + 4y$

12. $f(x, y) = \cos(x^2 - y^2)$

13. $f(x, y) = \sqrt{25 - x^2 - y^2}$

14. $f(x, y) = \dfrac{1}{\sqrt{x^2 + y^2 - 25}}$

15. $f(x, y) = \sin\dfrac{x}{y}$

16. $f(x, y) = \dfrac{12}{y^2 - x^2}$

17. $g(x, y) = \ln(x^2 - y)$

18. $f(x, y) = \sin^{-1}(y - x^2)$

19. $g(x, y) = \sqrt{\dfrac{xy}{x^2 + y^2}}$

20. $h(x, y) = \sqrt{x - 2y + 4}$

21–28. Graphs of familiar functions *Use what you learned about surfaces in Section 12.1 to sketch a graph of the following functions. In each case identify the surface and state the domain and range of the function.*

21. $f(x, y) = 3x - 6y + 18$

22. $h(x, y) = 2x^2 + 3y^2$

23. $p(x, y) = x^2 - y^2$

24. $F(x, y) = \sqrt{1 - x^2 - y^2}$

25. $G(x, y) = -\sqrt{1 + x^2 + y^2}$

26. $H(x, y) = \sqrt{x^2 + y^2}$

27. $P(x, y) = \sqrt{x^2 + y^2 - 1}$

28. $g(x, y) = y^3 + 1$

29. **Matching surfaces** Match functions a–d with surfaces A–D in the figure.

   a. $f(x, y) = \cos xy$

   b. $g(x, y) = \ln(x^2 + y^2)$

   c. $h(x, y) = 1/(x - y)$

   d. $p(x, y) = 1/(1 + x^2 + y^2)$

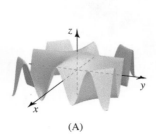

(A)

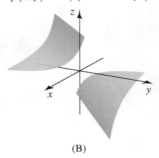

(B)

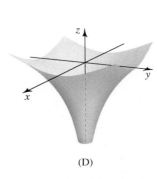

(C)

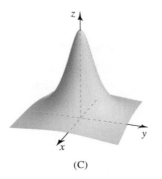

(D)

▣ 30–37. Level curves *Graph several level curves of the following functions using the given window. Label at least two level curves with their z-values.*

30. $z = x^2 + y^2$; $[-4, 4] \times [-4, 4]$

31. $z = x - y^2$; $[0, 4] \times [-2, 2]$

32. $z = 2x - y$; $[-2, 2] \times [-2, 2]$

33. $z = \sqrt{x^2 + 4y^2}$; $[-8, 8] \times [-8, 8]$

34. $z = e^{-x^2 - 2y^2}$; $[-2, 2] \times [-2, 2]$

35. $z = \sqrt{25 - x^2 - y^2}$; $[-6, 6] \times [-6, 6]$

36. $z = \sqrt{y - x^2 - 1}$; $[-5, 5] \times [-5, 5]$

37. $z = 3\cos(2x + y)$; $[-2, 2] \times [-2, 2]$

38. **Matching level curves with surfaces** Match surfaces a–f in the figure with level curves A–F.

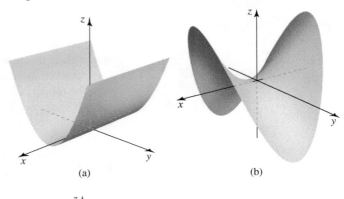

(a)   (b)

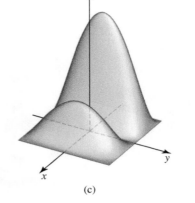

(c)

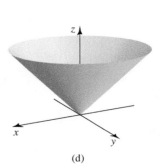

(d)

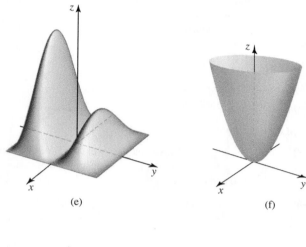

(e)

(f)

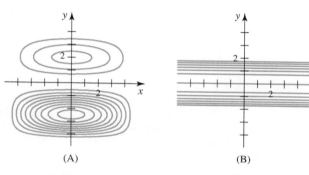

(A)

(B)

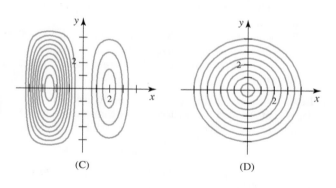

(C)

(D)

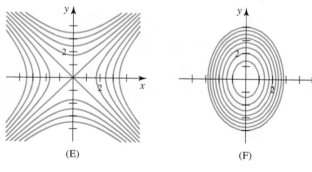

(E)

(F)

T 39. A volume function The volume of a right circular cone of radius r and height h is $V(r, h) = \pi r^2 h/3$.

a. Graph the function in the window $[0, 5] \times [0, 5] \times [0, 150]$.
b. What is the domain of the volume function?
c. What is the relationship between the values of r and h when $V = 100$?

40. Earned run average A baseball pitcher's earned run average (ERA) is $A(e, i) = 9e/i$, where e is the number of earned runs given up by the pitcher and i is the number of innings pitched. Good pitchers have low ERAs. Assume that $e \geq 0$ and $i > 0$ are real numbers.

a. The single-season major league record for the lowest ERA was set by Dutch Leonard of the Detroit Tigers in 1914. During that season, Dutch pitched a total of 224 innings and gave up just 24 earned runs. What was his ERA?
b. Determine the ERA of a relief pitcher who gives up 4 earned runs in one-third of an inning.
c. Graph the level curve $A(e, i) = 3$ and describe the relationship between e and i in this case.

T 41. Electric potential function The electric potential function for two positive charges, one at $(0, 1)$ with twice the strength as the charge at $(0, -1)$, is given by

$$\varphi(x, y) = \frac{2}{\sqrt{x^2 + (y-1)^2}} + \frac{1}{\sqrt{x^2 + (y+1)^2}}.$$

a. Graph the electric potential using the window $[-5, 5] \times [-5, 5] \times [0, 10]$.
b. For what values of x and y is the potential φ defined?
c. Is the electric potential greater at $(3, 2)$ or $(2, 3)$?
d. Describe how the electric potential varies along the line $y = x$.

T 42. Cobb-Douglas production function The output Q of an economic system subject to two inputs, such as labor L and capital K, is often modeled by the Cobb-Douglas production function $Q(L, K) = cL^aK^b$, where a, b, and c are positive real numbers. When $a + b = 1$, the case is called *constant returns to scale*. Suppose $a = \frac{1}{3}$, $b = \frac{2}{3}$, and $c = 40$.

a. Graph the output function using the window $[0, 20] \times [0, 20] \times [0, 500]$.
b. If L is held constant at $L = 10$, write the function that gives the dependence of Q on K.
c. If K is held constant at $K = 15$, write the function that gives the dependence of Q on L.

T 43. Resistors in parallel Two resistors wired in parallel in an electrical circuit give an effective resistance of $R(x, y) = \dfrac{xy}{x + y}$, where x and y are the positive resistances of the individual resistors (typically measured in ohms).

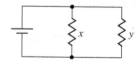

a. Graph the resistance function using the window $[0, 10] \times [0, 10] \times [0, 5]$.
b. Estimate the maximum value of R, for $0 < x \leq 10$ and $0 < y \leq 10$.
c. Explain what it means to say that the resistance function is symmetric in x and y.

T 44. Water waves A snapshot of a water wave moving toward shore is described by the function $z = 10 \sin (2x - 3y)$, where z is the height of the water surface above (or below) the xy-plane, which is the level of undisturbed water.

a. Graph the height function using the window $[-5, 5] \times [-5, 5] \times [-15, 15]$.
b. For what values of x and y is z defined?

c. What are the maximum and minimum values of the water height?

d. Give a vector in the xy-plane that is orthogonal to the level curves of the crests and troughs of the wave (which is parallel to the direction of wave propagation).

45. Approximate mountains Suppose the elevation of Earth's surface over a 16-mi by 16-mi region is approximated by the function

$$z = 10e^{-(x^2+y^2)} + 5e^{-((x+5)^2+(y-3)^2)/10} + 4e^{-2((x-4)^2+(y+1)^2)}.$$

a. Graph the height function using the window $[-8, 8] \times [-8, 8] \times [0, 15]$.

b. Approximate the points (x, y) where the peaks in the landscape appear.

c. What are the approximate elevations of the peaks?

46–52. Domains of functions of three or more variables *Find the domain of the following functions. If possible, give a description of the domains (for example, all points outside a sphere of radius 1 centered at the origin).*

46. $f(x, y, z) = 2xyz - 3xz + 4yz$

47. $g(x, y, z) = \dfrac{1}{x - z}$

48. $p(x, y, z) = \sqrt{x^2 + y^2 + z^2 - 9}$

49. $f(x, y, z) = \sqrt{y - z}$

50. $Q(x, y, z) = \dfrac{10}{1 + x^2 + y^2 + 4z^2}$

51. $F(x, y, z) = \sqrt{y - x^2}$

52. $f(w, x, y, z) = \sqrt{1 - w^2 - x^2 - y^2 - z^2}$

Further Explorations

53. Explain why or why not Determine whether the following statements are true and give an explanation or counterexample.

a. The domain of the function $f(x, y) = 1 - |x - y|$ is $\{(x, y): x \geq y\}$.

b. The domain of the function $Q = g(w, x, y, z)$ is a region in $\mathbb{R}^3$.

c. All level curves of the plane $z = 2x - 3y$ are lines.

54–60. Graphing functions

a. *Determine the domain and range of the following functions.*

b. *Graph each function using a graphing utility. Be sure to experiment with the graphing window and orientation to give the best perspective of the surface.*

54. $g(x, y) = e^{-xy}$

55. $f(x, y) = |xy|$

56. $p(x, y) = 1 - |x - 1| + |y + 1|$

57. $h(x, y) = (x + y)/(x - y)$

58. $G(x, y) = \ln(2 + \sin(x + y))$

59. $F(x, y) = \tan^2(x - y)$

60. $P(x, y) = \cos x \sin 2y$

61–64. Peaks and valleys *The following functions have exactly one isolated peak or one isolated depression (one local maximum or minimum). Use a graphing utility to approximate the coordinates of the peak or depression.*

61. $f(x, y) = x^2y^2 - 8x^2 - y^2 + 6$

62. $g(x, y) = (x^2 - x - 2)(y^2 + 2y)$

63. $h(x, y) = 1 - e^{-(x^2+y^2-2x)}$

64. $p(x, y) = 2 + |x - 1| + |y - 1|$

65. Level curves of planes Prove that the level curves of the plane $ax + by + cz = d$ are parallel lines in the xy-plane, provided $a^2 + b^2 \neq 0$ and $c \neq 0$.

66–69. Level surfaces *Find an equation for the family of level surfaces corresponding to f. Describe the level surfaces.*

66. $f(x, y, z) = \dfrac{1}{x^2 + y^2 + z^2}$

67. $f(x, y, z) = x^2 + y^2 - z$

68. $f(x, y, z) = x^2 - y^2 - z$

69. $f(x, y, z) = \sqrt{x^2 + 2z^2}$

Applications

70. Level curves of a savings account Suppose you make a one-time deposit of P dollars into a savings account that earns interest at an annual rate of $p\%$ compounded continuously. The balance in the account after t years is $B(P, r, t) = Pe^{rt}$, where $r = p/100$ (for example, if the annual interest rate is 4%, then $r = 0.04$). Let the interest rate be fixed at $r = 0.04$.

a. With a target balance of \$2000, find the set of all points (P, t) that satisfy $B = 2000$. This curve gives all deposits P and times t that result in a balance of \$2000.

b. Repeat part (a) with $B = \$500, \$1000, \$1500,$ and \$2500, and draw the resulting level curves of the balance function.

c. In general, on one level curve, if t increases, does P increase or decrease?

71. Level curves of a savings plan Suppose you make monthly deposits of P dollars into an account that earns interest at a *monthly* rate of $p\%$. The balance in the account after t years is

$$B(P, r, t) = P\left(\frac{(1 + r)^{12t} - 1}{r}\right), \text{ where } r = p/100 \text{ (for}$$

example, if the annual interest rate is 9%, then $p = \frac{9}{12} = 0.75$ and $r = 0.0075$). Let the time of investment be fixed at $t = 20$ years.

a. With a target balance of \$20,000, find the set of all points (P, r) that satisfy $B = 20,000$. This curve gives all deposits P and monthly interest rates r that result in a balance of \$20,000 after 20 years.

b. Repeat part (a) with $B = \$5000, \$10,000, \$15,000,$ and \$25,000, and draw the resulting level curves of the balance function.

72. Quarterback passer ratings One measurement of the quality of a quarterback in the National Football League is known as the *quarterback passer rating*. The rating formula is

$$R(c, t, i, y) = \frac{50 + 20c + 80t - 100i + 100y}{24},$$ where c is the

percentage of passes completed, t is the percentage of passes thrown for touchdowns, i is the percentage of intercepted passes, and y is the yards gained per attempted pass.

a. In 2012, Green Bay quarterback Aaron Rodgers had the highest passer rating. He completed 67.21% of his passes, 7.07% of his passes were thrown for touchdowns, 1.45% of his passes were intercepted, and he gained an average of 7.78 yards per passing attempt. What was his passer rating in the 2012 season?

b. If c, t, and y remained fixed, what happens to the quarterback passer rating as i increases? Explain your answer with and without mathematics.

(*Source: The College Mathematics Journal,* 24, 5, Nov 1993)

T 73. Ideal Gas Law Many gases can be modeled by the Ideal Gas Law, $PV = nRT$, which relates the temperature (T, measured in Kelvin (K)), pressure (P, measured in Pascals (Pa)), and volume (V, measured in m^3) of a gas. Assume that the quantity of gas in question is $n = 1$ mole (mol). The gas constant has a value of $R = 8.3$ m^3-Pa/mol-K.

a. Consider T to be the dependent variable and plot several level curves (called *isotherms*) of the temperature surface in the region $0 \leq P \leq 100,000$ and $0 \leq V \leq 0.5$.

b. Consider P to be the dependent variable and plot several level curves (called *isobars*) of the pressure surface in the region $0 \leq T \leq 900$ and $0 < V \leq 0.5$.

c. Consider V to be the dependent variable and plot several level curves of the volume surface in the region $0 \leq T \leq 900$ and $0 < P \leq 100,000$.

Additional Exercises

74–77. Challenge domains *Find the domains of the following functions. Specify the domain mathematically and then describe it in words or with a sketch.*

74. $g(x, y, z) = \dfrac{10}{x^2 - (y + z)x + yz}$

75. $f(x, y) = \sin^{-1}(x - y)^2$

76. $f(x, y, z) = \ln(z - x^2 - y^2 + 2x + 3)$

77. $h(x, y, z) = \sqrt[4]{z^2 - xz + yz - xy}$

78. Other balls The closed unit ball in $\mathbb{R}^3$ centered at the origin is the set $\{(x, y, z): x^2 + y^2 + z^2 \leq 1\}$. Describe the following alternative unit balls.

a. $\{(x, y, z): |x| + |y| + |z| \leq 1\}$

b. $\{(x, y, z): \max\{|x|, |y|, |z|\} \leq 1\}$, where $\max\{a, b, c\}$ is the maximum value of a, b, and c.

QUICK CHECK ANSWERS

1. $\mathbb{R}^2$; $\{(x, y): y \geq 0\}$ **2.** No; no
3. $z = -\sqrt{1 + x^2 + y^2}$ **4.** No; otherwise the function would have two values at a single point.   **5.** Concentric circles   **6.** No; $z = 0$ is not in the range of the function.
7. 0.97   **8.** 8   **9.** $\{(x, y, z): x \neq 0 \text{ and } y \neq 0 \text{ and } z \neq 0\}$ (which is $\mathbb{R}^3$, excluding the coordinate planes) ◄

12.3 Limits and Continuity

You have now seen examples of functions of several variables, but calculus has not yet entered the picture. In this section, we revisit topics encountered in single-variable calculus and see how they apply to functions of several variables. We begin with the fundamental concepts of limits and continuity.

Limit of a Function of Two Variables

A function f of two variables has a limit L as $P(x, y)$ approaches a fixed point $P_0(a, b)$ if $|f(x, y) - L|$ can be made arbitrarily small for all P in the domain that are sufficiently close to P_0. If such a limit exists, we write

$$\lim_{(x,y) \to (a,b)} f(x, y) = \lim_{P \to P_0} f(x, y) = L.$$

To make this definition more precise, *close to* must be defined carefully.

A point x on the number line is close to another point a provided the distance $|x - a|$ is small (Figure 12.37a). In $\mathbb{R}^2$, a point $P(x, y)$ is close to another point $P_0(a, b)$ if the distance between them $|PP_0| = \sqrt{(x - a)^2 + (y - b)^2}$ is small (Figure 12.37b). When we say *for all P close to P_0*, it means that $|PP_0|$ is small for points P on all sides of P_0.

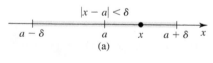

(a)

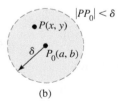

(b)

Figure 12.37

> The formal definition extends naturally to any number of variables. With n variables, the limit point is $P_0(a_1, \ldots, a_n)$, the variable point is $P(x_1, \ldots, x_n)$, and $|PP_0| = \sqrt{(x_1 - a_1)^2 + \cdots + (x_n - a_n)^2}$.

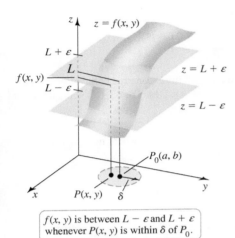

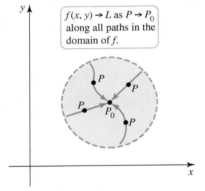

$f(x, y)$ is between $L - \varepsilon$ and $L + \varepsilon$ whenever $P(x, y)$ is within δ of P_0.

Figure 12.38

Figure 12.39

With this understanding of closeness, we can give a formal definition of a limit with two independent variables. This definition parallels the formal definition of a limit given in Section 2.7 (Figure 12.38).

DEFINITION   Limit of a Function of Two Variables

The function f has the **limit** L as $P(x, y)$ approaches $P_0(a, b)$, written

$$\lim_{(x,y) \to (a,b)} f(x, y) = \lim_{P \to P_0} f(x, y) = L,$$

if, given any $\varepsilon > 0$, there exists a $\delta > 0$ such that

$$|f(x, y) - L| < \varepsilon$$

whenever (x, y) is in the domain of f and

$$0 < |PP_0| = \sqrt{(x - a)^2 + (y - b)^2} < \delta.$$

The condition $|PP_0| < \delta$ means that the distance between $P(x, y)$ and $P_0(a, b)$ is less than δ as P approaches P_0 from all possible directions (Figure 12.39). Therefore, the limit exists only if $f(x, y)$ approaches L as P approaches P_0 *along all possible paths* in the domain of f. As shown in upcoming examples, this interpretation is critical in determining whether a limit exists.

As with functions of one variable, we first establish limits of the simplest functions.

THEOREM 12.1   Limits of Constant and Linear Functions

Let a, b, and c be real numbers.

1. Constant function $f(x, y) = c$: $\displaystyle \lim_{(x,y) \to (a,b)} c = c$

2. Linear function $f(x, y) = x$: $\displaystyle \lim_{(x,y) \to (a,b)} x = a$

3. Linear function $f(x, y) = y$: $\displaystyle \lim_{(x,y) \to (a,b)} y = b$

Proof:

1. Consider the constant function $f(x, y) = c$ and assume $\varepsilon > 0$ is given. To prove that the value of the limit is $L = c$, we must produce a $\delta > 0$ such that $|f(x, y) - L| < \varepsilon$ whenever $0 < \sqrt{(x - a)^2 + (y - b)^2} < \delta$. For constant functions, we may use *any* $\delta > 0$. Then for every (x, y) in the domain of f,

$$|f(x, y) - L| = |f(x, y) - c| = |c - c| = 0 < \varepsilon$$

whenever $0 < \sqrt{(x - a)^2 + (y - b)^2} < \delta$.

2. Assume $\varepsilon > 0$ is given and take $\delta = \varepsilon$. The condition $0 < \sqrt{(x - a)^2 + (y - b)^2} < \delta$ implies that

$$0 < \sqrt{(x - a)^2 + (y - b)^2} < \varepsilon \qquad \delta = \varepsilon$$
$$\sqrt{(x - a)^2} < \varepsilon \qquad (x - a)^2 \le (x - a)^2 + (y - b)^2$$
$$|x - a| < \varepsilon. \qquad \sqrt{x^2} = |x| \text{ for real numbers } x$$

Because $f(x, y) = x$ and $L = a$, we have shown that $|f(x, y) - L| < \varepsilon$ whenever $0 < \sqrt{(x - a)^2 + (y - b)^2} < \delta$. Therefore, $\displaystyle \lim_{(x,y) \to (a,b)} f(x, y) = L$, or $\displaystyle \lim_{(x,y) \to (a,b)} x = a$. The proof that $\displaystyle \lim_{(x,y) \to (a,b)} y = b$ is similar (Exercise 82).   ◄

Using the three basic limits in Theorem 12.1, we can compute limits of more complicated functions. The only tools needed are limit laws analogous to those given in Theorem 2.3. The proofs of these laws are examined in Exercises 84–85.

THEOREM 12.2   Limit Laws for Functions of Two Variables

Let L and M be real numbers and suppose that $\lim\limits_{(x,y)\to(a,b)} f(x, y) = L$ and $\lim\limits_{(x,y)\to(a,b)} g(x, y) = M$. Assume c is a constant, and m and n are integers.

1. **Sum** $\lim\limits_{(x,y)\to(a,b)} (f(x, y) + g(x, y)) = L + M$

2. **Difference** $\lim\limits_{(x,y)\to(a,b)} (f(x, y) - g(x, y)) = L - M$

3. **Constant multiple** $\lim\limits_{(x,y)\to(a,b)} cf(x, y) = cL$

4. **Product** $\lim\limits_{(x,y)\to(a,b)} f(x, y)g(x, y) = LM$

5. **Quotient** $\lim\limits_{(x,y)\to(a,b)} \dfrac{f(x, y)}{g(x, y)} = \dfrac{L}{M}$, provided $M \neq 0$

6. **Power** $\lim\limits_{(x,y)\to(a,b)} (f(x, y))^n = L^n$

7. **Fractional power** If m and n have no common factors and $n \neq 0$, then $\lim\limits_{(x,y)\to(a,b)} (f(x, y))^{m/n} = L^{m/n}$, where we assume $L > 0$ if n is even.

▶ Recall that a polynomial in two variables consists of sums and products of polynomials in x and polynomials in y. A rational function is the quotient of two polynomials.

Combining Theorems 12.1 and 12.2 allows us to find limits of polynomial, rational, and algebraic functions in two variables.

EXAMPLE 1   Limits of two-variable functions Evaluate $\lim\limits_{(x,y)\to(2,8)} (3x^2y + \sqrt{xy})$.

SOLUTION All the operations in this function appear in Theorem 12.2. Therefore, we can apply the limit laws directly.

$$
\begin{aligned}
\lim_{(x,y)\to(2,8)} (3x^2y + \sqrt{xy}) &= \lim_{(x,y)\to(2,8)} 3x^2y + \lim_{(x,y)\to(2,8)} \sqrt{xy} \quad &\text{Law 1}\\
&= 3 \lim_{(x,y)\to(2,8)} x^2 \cdot \lim_{(x,y)\to(2,8)} y \\
&\quad + \sqrt{\lim_{(x,y)\to(2,8)} x \cdot \lim_{(x,y)\to(2,8)} y} \quad &\text{Laws 3, 4, 6, 7}\\
&= 3 \cdot 2^2 \cdot 8 + \sqrt{2 \cdot 8} = 100 \quad &\text{Theorem 12.1}
\end{aligned}
$$

Related Exercises 11–18 ◀

In Example 1, the value of the limit equals the value of the function at (a, b); in other words, $\lim\limits_{(x,y)\to(a,b)} f(x, y) = f(a, b)$ and the limit can be evaluated by substitution. This is a property of *continuous* functions, discussed later in this section.

QUICK CHECK 1 Which of the following limits exist?

a. $\lim\limits_{(x,y)\to(1,1)} 3x^{12}y^2$ **b.** $\lim\limits_{(x,y)\to(0,0)} 3x^{-2}y^2$ **c.** $\lim\limits_{(x,y)\to(1,2)} \sqrt{x - y^2}$ ◀

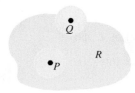

Figure 12.40

▶ The definitions of interior point and boundary point apply to regions in $\mathbb{R}^3$ if we replace *disk* by *ball*.

▶ Many sets, such as the annulus $\{(x, y): 2 \leq x^2 + y^2 < 5\}$, are neither open nor closed.

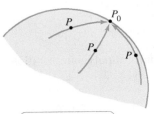

Figure 12.41

▶ Recall that this same method was used with functions of one variable. For example, after the common factor $x - 2$ is canceled, the function

$$g(x) = \frac{x^2 - 4}{x - 2}$$

becomes $g(x) = x + 2$, provided $x \neq 2$. In this case, 2 plays the role of a boundary point.

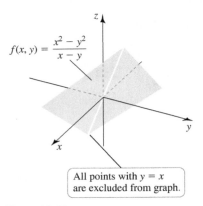

$$f(x, y) = \frac{x^2 - y^2}{x - y}$$

Figure 12.42

Limits at Boundary Points

This is an appropriate place to make some definitions that are used in the remainder of the book.

DEFINITION Interior and Boundary Points

Let R be a region in $\mathbb{R}^2$. An **interior point** P of R lies entirely within R, which means it is possible to find a disk centered at P that contains only points of R (Figure 12.40).

A **boundary point** Q of R lies on the edge of R in the sense that *every* disk centered at Q contains at least one point in R and at least one point not in R.

For example, let R be the points in $\mathbb{R}^2$ satisfying $x^2 + y^2 < 9$. The boundary points of R lie on the circle $x^2 + y^2 = 9$. The interior points lie inside that circle and satisfy $x^2 + y^2 < 9$. Notice that the boundary points of a set need not lie in the set.

DEFINITION Open and Closed Sets

A region is **open** if it consists entirely of interior points. A region is **closed** if it contains all its boundary points.

An example of an open region in $\mathbb{R}^2$ is the open disk $\{(x, y): x^2 + y^2 < 9\}$. An example of a closed region in $\mathbb{R}^2$ is the square $\{(x, y): |x| \leq 1, |y| \leq 1\}$. Later in the book, we encounter interior and boundary points of three-dimensional sets such as balls, boxes, and pyramids.

QUICK CHECK 2 Give an example of a set that contains none of its boundary points. ◀

Suppose $P_0(a, b)$ is a boundary point of the domain of f. The limit $\lim\limits_{(x,y) \to (a,b)} f(x, y)$ exists, even if P_0 is not in the domain of f, provided $f(x, y)$ approaches the same value as (x, y) approaches (a, b) *along all paths that lie in the domain* (Figure 12.41).

Consider the function $f(x, y) = \dfrac{x^2 - y^2}{x - y}$ whose domain is $\{(x, y): x \neq y\}$. Provided $x \neq y$, we may cancel the factor $(x - y)$ from the numerator and denominator and write

$$f(x, y) = \frac{x^2 - y^2}{x - y} = \frac{(x - y)(x + y)}{x - y} = x + y.$$

The graph of f (Figure 12.42) is the plane $z = x + y$, with points corresponding to the line $x = y$ removed.

Now we examine $\lim\limits_{(x,y) \to (4,4)} \dfrac{x^2 - y^2}{x - y}$, where $(4, 4)$ is a boundary point of the domain of f but does not lie in the domain. For this limit to exist, $f(x, y)$ must approach the same value along all paths to $(4, 4)$ that lie in the domain of f—that is, all paths approaching $(4, 4)$ that do not intersect $x = y$. To evaluate the limit, we proceed as follows:

$$\lim_{(x,y) \to (4,4)} \frac{x^2 - y^2}{x - y} = \lim_{(x,y) \to (4,4)} (x + y) \qquad \text{Assume } x \neq y, \text{ cancel } x - y.$$

$$= 4 + 4 = 8. \qquad \text{Same limit along all paths in the domain}$$

To emphasize, we let $(x, y) \to (4, 4)$ along all paths that do not intersect $x = y$, which lies outside the domain of f. Along all admissible paths, the function approaches 8.

QUICK CHECK 3 Can the limit $\lim\limits_{(x,y) \to (0,0)} \dfrac{x^2 - xy}{x}$ be evaluated by direct substitution? ◀

EXAMPLE 2 **Limits at boundary points** Evaluate $\lim\limits_{(x,y)\to(4,1)} \dfrac{xy - 4y^2}{\sqrt{x} - 2\sqrt{y}}$.

SOLUTION Points in the domain of this function satisfy $x \geq 0$ and $y \geq 0$ (because of the square roots) and $x \neq 4y$ (to ensure the denominator is nonzero). We see that the point $(4, 1)$ lies on the boundary of the domain. Multiplying the numerator and denominator by the algebraic conjugate of the denominator, the limit is computed as follows:

$$\lim_{(x,y)\to(4,1)} \frac{xy - 4y^2}{\sqrt{x} - 2\sqrt{y}} = \lim_{(x,y)\to(4,1)} \frac{(xy - 4y^2)(\sqrt{x} + 2\sqrt{y})}{(\sqrt{x} - 2\sqrt{y})(\sqrt{x} + 2\sqrt{y})} \quad \text{Multiply by conjugate.}$$

$$= \lim_{(x,y)\to(4,1)} \frac{y(x - 4y)(\sqrt{x} + 2\sqrt{y})}{x - 4y} \quad \text{Simplify.}$$

$$= \lim_{(x,y)\to(4,1)} y(\sqrt{x} + 2\sqrt{y}) \quad \begin{array}{l}\text{Cancel } x - 4y, \\ \text{assumed to be nonzero.}\end{array}$$

$$= 4. \quad \text{Evaluate limit.}$$

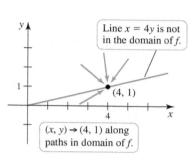

Line $x = 4y$ is not in the domain of f.

$(4, 1)$

$(x, y) \to (4, 1)$ along paths in domain of f.

Figure 12.43

Because points on the line $x = 4y$ are outside the domain of the function, we assume that $x - 4y \neq 0$. Along all other paths to $(4, 1)$, the function values approach 4 (Figure 12.43).

Related Exercises 19–26 ◄

EXAMPLE 3 **Nonexistence of a limit** Investigate the limit $\lim\limits_{(x,y)\to(0,0)} \dfrac{(x + y)^2}{x^2 + y^2}$.

SOLUTION The domain of the function is $\{(x, y): (x, y) \neq (0, 0)\}$; therefore, the limit is at a boundary point outside the domain. Suppose we let (x, y) approach $(0, 0)$ along the line $y = mx$ for a fixed constant m. Substituting $y = mx$ and noting that $y \to 0$ as $x \to 0$, we have

➤ Notice that if we choose any path of the form $y = mx$, then $y \to 0$ as $x \to 0$. Therefore, $\lim\limits_{(x,y)\to(0,0)}$ can be replaced by $\lim\limits_{x\to0}$ along this path. A similar argument applies to paths of the form $y = mx^p$, for $p > 0$.

$$\lim_{\substack{(x,y)\to(0,0) \\ (\text{along } y = mx)}} \frac{(x + y)^2}{x^2 + y^2} = \lim_{x\to0} \frac{(x + mx)^2}{x^2 + m^2x^2} = \lim_{x\to0} \frac{x^2(1 + m)^2}{x^2(1 + m^2)} = \frac{(1 + m)^2}{1 + m^2}.$$

The constant m determines the direction of approach to $(0, 0)$. Therefore, depending on m, the function approaches different values as (x, y) approaches $(0, 0)$ (Figure 12.44). For example, if $m = 0$, the corresponding limit is 1 and if $m = -1$, the limit is 0. The reason for this behavior is revealed if we plot the surface and look at two level curves. The lines $y = x$ and $y = -x$ (excluding the origin) are level curves of the function for $z = 2$ and $z = 0$, respectively. (Figure 12.45). Therefore, as $(x, y) \to (0, 0)$ along $y = x, f(x, y) \to 2$, and as $(x, y) \to (0, 0)$ along $y = -x, f(x, y) \to 0$. Because the function approaches different values along different paths, we conclude that the *limit does not exist*.

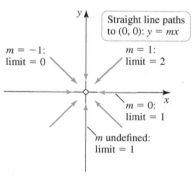

Straight line paths to $(0, 0)$: $y = mx$

$m = -1$: limit = 0

$m = 1$: limit = 2

$m = 0$: limit = 1

m undefined: limit = 1

Figure 12.44

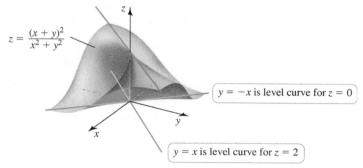

$z = \dfrac{(x + y)^2}{x^2 + y^2}$

$y = -x$ is level curve for $z = 0$

$y = x$ is level curve for $z = 2$

Figure 12.45

Related Exercises 27–32 ◄

The strategy used in Example 3 is an effective way to prove the nonexistence of a limit.

QUICK CHECK 4 What is the analog of the Two-Path Test for functions of a single variable? ◄

> **PROCEDURE   Two-Path Test for Nonexistence of Limits**
>
> If $f(x, y)$ approaches two different values as (x, y) approaches (a, b) along two different paths in the domain of f, then $\lim\limits_{(x,y)\to(a,b)} f(x, y)$ does not exist.

Continuity of Functions of Two Variables

The following definition of continuity for functions of two variables is analogous to the continuity definition for functions of one variable.

> **DEFINITION Continuity**
>
> The function f is continuous at the point (a, b) provided
>
> **1.** f is defined at (a, b).
>
> **2.** $\lim\limits_{(x,y)\to(a,b)} f(x, y)$ exists.
>
> **3.** $\lim\limits_{(x,y)\to(a,b)} f(x, y) = f(a, b)$.

A function of two (or more) variables is continuous at a point, provided its limit equals its value at that point (which implies the limit and the value both exist). The definition of continuity applies at boundary points of the domain of f provided the limits in the definition are taken along all paths that lie in the domain. Because limits of polynomials and rational functions can be evaluated by substitution at points of their domains (that is, $\lim\limits_{(x,y)\to(a,b)} f(x, y) = f(a, b)$), it follows that polynomials and rational functions are continuous at all points of their domains.

EXAMPLE 4   Checking continuity Determine the points at which the following function is continuous.

$$f(x, y) = \begin{cases} \dfrac{3xy^2}{x^2 + y^4} & \text{if } (x, y) \neq (0, 0) \\ 0 & \text{if } (x, y) = (0, 0) \end{cases}$$

SOLUTION The function $\dfrac{3xy^2}{x^2 + y^4}$ is a rational function, so it is continuous at all points of its domain, which consists of all points of $\mathbb{R}^2$ except $(0, 0)$. To determine whether f is continuous at $(0, 0)$, we must show that

$$\lim_{(x,y)\to(0,0)} \frac{3xy^2}{x^2 + y^4}$$

exists and equals $f(0, 0) = 0$ along all paths that approach $(0, 0)$.

You can verify that as (x, y) approaches $(0, 0)$ along paths of the form $y = mx$, where m is any constant, the function values approach $f(0, 0) = 0$. However, along parabolic paths of the form $x = my^2$ (where m is a nonzero constant), the limit behaves

▶ The choice of $x = my^2$ for paths to $(0, 0)$ is not obvious. Notice that if x is replaced with my^2 in f, the result involves the same power of y (in this case, y^4) in the numerator and denominator, which may be canceled.

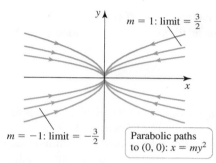

$m = 1$: limit $= \frac{3}{2}$

$m = -1$: limit $= -\frac{3}{2}$

Parabolic paths to $(0, 0)$: $x = my^2$

Figure 12.46

differently (Figure 12.46). This time we substitute $x = my^2$ and note that $x \to 0$ as $y \to 0$:

$$\lim_{\substack{(x,y)\to(0,0)\\ (\text{along } x = my^2)}} \frac{3xy^2}{x^2 + y^4} = \lim_{y\to0} \frac{3(my^2)y^2}{(my^2)^2 + y^4} \quad \text{Substitute } x = my^2.$$

$$= \lim_{y\to0} \frac{3my^4}{m^2y^4 + y^4} \quad \text{Simplify.}$$

$$= \lim_{y\to0} \frac{3m}{m^2 + 1} \quad \text{Cancel } y^4.$$

$$= \frac{3m}{m^2 + 1}.$$

We see that along parabolic paths, the limit depends on the approach path. For example, with $m = 1$, along the path $x = y^2$, the function values approach $\frac{3}{2}$; with $m = -1$, along the path $x = -y^2$, the function values approach $-\frac{3}{2}$ (Figure 12.47). Because $f(x, y)$ approaches two different numbers along two different paths, the limit at $(0, 0)$ does not exist, and f is not continuous at $(0, 0)$.

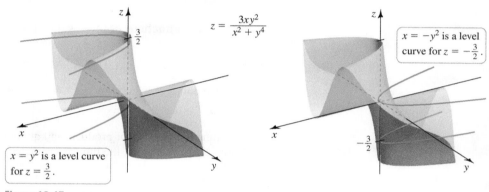

$z = \frac{3xy^2}{x^2 + y^4}$

$x = y^2$ is a level curve for $z = \frac{3}{2}$.

$x = -y^2$ is a level curve for $z = -\frac{3}{2}$.

Figure 12.47

Related Exercises 33–40 ◀

QUICK CHECK 5 Which of the following functions are continuous at $(0, 0)$?

a. $f(x, y) = 2x^2y^5$

b. $f(x, y) = \frac{2x^2y^5}{x - 1}$

c. $f(x, y) = 2x^{-2}y^5$ ◀

Composite Functions Recall that for functions of a single variable, compositions of continuous functions are also continuous. The following theorem gives the analogous result for functions of two variables; it is proved in Appendix B.

THEOREM 12.3 Continuity of Composite Functions
If $u = g(x, y)$ is continuous at (a, b) and $z = f(u)$ is continuous at $g(a, b)$, then the composite function $z = f(g(x, y))$ is continuous at (a, b).

With Theorem 12.3, we can easily analyze the continuity of many functions. For example, $\sin x$, $\cos x$, and e^x are continuous functions of a single variable, for all real values of x. Therefore, compositions of these functions with polynomials in x and y (for example, $\sin(x^2y)$ and $e^{x^4-y^2}$) are continuous for all real numbers x and y. Similarly, $\sqrt{x}$ is a continuous function of a single variable, for $x \geq 0$. Therefore, $\sqrt{u(x, y)}$ is continuous at (x, y) provided u is continuous at (x, y) and $u(x, y) \geq 0$. As long as we observe restrictions on domains, then compositions of continuous functions are also continuous.

EXAMPLE 5 Continuity of composite functions. Determine the points at which the following functions are continuous.

a. $h(x, y) = \ln(x^2 + y^2 + 4)$ **b.** $h(x, y) = e^{x/y}$

SOLUTION

a. This function is the composition $f(g(x, y))$, where

$$f(u) = \ln u \quad \text{and} \quad u = g(x, y) = x^2 + y^2 + 4.$$

As a polynomial, g is continuous for all (x, y) in $\mathbb{R}^2$. The function f is continuous for $u > 0$. Because $u = x^2 + y^2 + 4 > 0$ for all (x, y), it follows that h is continuous at all points of $\mathbb{R}^2$.

b. Letting $f(u) = e^u$ and $u = g(x, y) = x/y$, we have $h(x, y) = f(g(x, y))$. Note that f is continuous at all points of $\mathbb{R}$ and g is continuous at all points of $\mathbb{R}^2$ provided $y \neq 0$. Therefore, h is continuous on the set $\{(x, y): y \neq 0\}$.

Related Exercises 41–52 ◀

Functions of Three Variables

The work we have done with limits and continuity of functions of two variables extends to functions of three or more variables. Specifically, the limit laws of Theorem 12.2 apply to functions of the form $w = f(x, y, z)$. Polynomials and rational functions are continuous at all points of their domains, and limits of these functions may be evaluated by direct substitution at all points of their domains. Compositions of continuous functions of the form $f(g(x, y, z))$ are also continuous at points at which $g(x, y, z)$ is in the domain of f.

EXAMPLE 6   Functions of three variables

a. Evaluate $\displaystyle\lim_{(x,y,z)\to(2,\pi/2,0)} \frac{x^2 \sin y}{z^2 + 4}$.

b. Find the points at which $h(x, y, z) = \sqrt{x^2 + y^2 + z^2 - 1}$ is continuous.

SOLUTION

a. This function consists of products and quotients of functions that are continuous at $(2, \pi/2, 0)$. Therefore, the limit is evaluated by direct substitution:

$$\lim_{(x,y,z)\to(2,\pi/2,0)} \frac{x^2 \sin y}{z^2 + 4} = \frac{2^2 \sin(\pi/2)}{0^2 + 4} = 1.$$

b. This function is a composition in which the outer function $f(u) = \sqrt{u}$ is continuous for $u \geq 0$. The inner function

$$g(x, y, z) = x^2 + y^2 + z^2 - 1$$

is nonnegative provided $x^2 + y^2 + z^2 \geq 1$. Therefore, h is continuous at all points on or outside the unit sphere in $\mathbb{R}^3$.

Related Exercises 53–58 ◀

SECTION 12.3 EXERCISES

Review Questions

1. Explain what $\displaystyle\lim_{(x,y)\to(a,b)} f(x, y) = L$ means.

2. Explain why $f(x, y)$ must approach a unique number L as (x, y) approaches (a, b) along *all* paths in the domain in order for $\displaystyle\lim_{(x,y)\to(a,b)} f(x, y)$ to exist.

3. What does it mean to say that limits of polynomials may be evaluated by direct substitution?

4. Suppose (a, b) is on the boundary of the domain of f. Explain how you would determine whether $\displaystyle\lim_{(x,y)\to(a,b)} f(x, y)$ exists.

5. Explain how examining limits along multiple paths may prove the nonexistence of a limit.

6. Explain why evaluating a limit along a finite number of paths does not prove the existence of a limit of a function of several variables.

7. What three conditions must be met for a function f to be continuous at the point (a, b)?

8. Let R be the unit disk $\{(x, y): x^2 + y^2 \leq 1\}$ with $(0, 0)$ removed. Is $(0, 0)$ a boundary point of R? Is R open or closed?

9. At what points of $\mathbb{R}^2$ is a rational function of two variables continuous?

10. Evaluate $\displaystyle\lim_{(x,y,z)\to(1,1,-1)} xy^2z^3$.

Basic Skills

11–18. Limits of functions *Evaluate the following limits.*

11. $\displaystyle\lim_{(x,y)\to(2,9)} 101$

12. $\displaystyle\lim_{(x,y)\to(1,-3)} (3x + 4y - 2)$

13. $\displaystyle\lim_{(x,y)\to(-3,3)} (4x^2 - y^2)$

14. $\displaystyle\lim_{(x,y)\to(2,-1)} (xy^8 - 3x^2y^3)$

15. $\displaystyle\lim_{(x,y)\to(0,\pi)} \frac{\cos xy + \sin xy}{2y}$

16. $\displaystyle\lim_{(x,y)\to(e^2,4)} \ln\sqrt{xy}$

17. $\displaystyle\lim_{(x,y)\to(2,0)} \frac{x^2 - 3xy^2}{x + y}$

18. $\displaystyle\lim_{(u,v)\to(1,-1)} \frac{10uv - 2v^2}{u^2 + v^2}$

19–26. Limits at boundary points *Evaluate the following limits.*

19. $\displaystyle\lim_{(x,y)\to(6,2)} \frac{x^2 - 3xy}{x - 3y}$

20. $\displaystyle\lim_{(x,y)\to(1,-2)} \frac{y^2 + 2xy}{y + 2x}$

21. $\displaystyle\lim_{(x,y)\to(3,1)} \frac{x^2 - 7xy + 12y^2}{x - 3y}$

22. $\displaystyle\lim_{(x,y)\to(-1,1)} \frac{2x^2 - xy - 3y^2}{x + y}$

23. $\displaystyle\lim_{(x,y)\to(2,2)} \frac{y^2 - 4}{xy - 2x}$

24. $\displaystyle\lim_{(x,y)\to(4,5)} \frac{\sqrt{x + y} - 3}{x + y - 9}$

25. $\displaystyle\lim_{(x,y)\to(1,2)} \frac{\sqrt{y} - \sqrt{x + 1}}{y - x - 1}$

26. $\displaystyle\lim_{(u,v)\to(8,8)} \frac{u^{1/3} - v^{1/3}}{u^{2/3} - v^{2/3}}$

27–32. Nonexistence of limits *Use the Two-Path Test to prove that the following limits do not exist.*

27. $\displaystyle\lim_{(x,y)\to(0,0)} \frac{x + 2y}{x - 2y}$

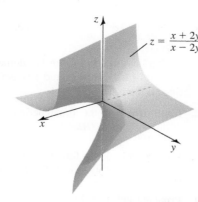

$z = \dfrac{x + 2y}{x - 2y}$

28. $\displaystyle\lim_{(x,y)\to(0,0)} \frac{4xy}{3x^2 + y^2}$

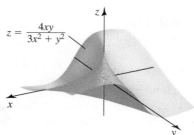

$z = \dfrac{4xy}{3x^2 + y^2}$

29. $\displaystyle\lim_{(x,y)\to(0,0)} \frac{y^4 - 2x^2}{y^4 + x^2}$

30. $\displaystyle\lim_{(x,y)\to(0,0)} \frac{x^3 - y^2}{x^3 + y^2}$

31. $\displaystyle\lim_{(x,y)\to(0,0)} \frac{y^3 + x^3}{xy^2}$

32. $\displaystyle\lim_{(x,y)\to(0,0)} \frac{y}{\sqrt{x^2 - y^2}}$

33–40. Continuity *At what points of $\mathbb{R}^2$ are the following functions continuous?*

33. $f(x, y) = x^2 + 2xy - y^3$

34. $f(x, y) = \dfrac{xy}{x^2 y^2 + 1}$

35. $p(x, y) = \dfrac{4x^2 y^2}{x^4 + y^2}$

36. $S(x, y) = \dfrac{2xy}{x^2 - y^2}$

37. $f(x, y) = \dfrac{2}{x(y^2 + 1)}$

38. $f(x, y) = \dfrac{x^2 + y^2}{x(y^2 - 1)}$

39. $f(x, y) = \begin{cases} \dfrac{xy}{x^2 + y^2} & \text{if } (x, y) \neq (0, 0) \\ 0 & \text{if } (x, y) = (0, 0) \end{cases}$

40. $f(x, y) = \begin{cases} \dfrac{y^4 - 2x^2}{y^4 + x^2} & \text{if } (x, y) \neq (0, 0) \\ 0 & \text{if } (x, y) = (0, 0) \end{cases}$

41–52. Continuity of composite functions *At what points of $\mathbb{R}^2$ are the following functions continuous?*

41. $f(x, y) = \sqrt{x^2 + y^2}$

42. $f(x, y) = e^{x^2 + y^2}$

43. $f(x, y) = \sin xy$

44. $g(x, y) = \ln(x - y)$

45. $h(x, y) = \cos(x + y)$

46. $p(x, y) = e^{x - y}$

47. $f(x, y) = \ln(x^2 + y^2)$

48. $f(x, y) = \sqrt{4 - x^2 - y^2}$

49. $g(x, y) = \sqrt[3]{x^2 + y^2 - 9}$

50. $h(x, y) = \dfrac{\sqrt{x - y}}{4}$

51. $f(x, y) = \begin{cases} \dfrac{\sin(x^2 + y^2)}{x^2 + y^2} & \text{if } (x, y) \neq (0, 0) \\ 1 & \text{if } (x, y) = (0, 0) \end{cases}$

52. $f(x, y) = \begin{cases} \dfrac{1 - \cos(x^2 + y^2)}{x^2 + y^2} & \text{if } (x, y) \neq (0, 0) \\ 0 & \text{if } (x, y) = (0, 0) \end{cases}$

53–58. Limits of functions of three variables *Evaluate the following limits.*

53. $\displaystyle\lim_{(x,y,z)\to(1,\ln 2,3)} z e^{xy}$

54. $\displaystyle\lim_{(x,y,z)\to(0,1,0)} (1 + y) \ln e^{xz}$

55. $\displaystyle\lim_{(x,y,z)\to(1,1,1)} \frac{yz - xy - xz - x^2}{yz + xy + xz - y^2}$

56. $\displaystyle\lim_{(x,y,z)\to(1,1,1)} \frac{x - \sqrt{xz} - \sqrt{xy} + \sqrt{yz}}{x - \sqrt{xz} + \sqrt{xy} - \sqrt{yz}}$

57. $\displaystyle\lim_{(x,y,z)\to(1,1,1)} \frac{x^2 + xy - xz - yz}{x - z}$

58. $\displaystyle\lim_{(x,y,z)\to(1,-1,1)} \frac{xz + 5x + yz + 5y}{x + y}$

Further Explorations

59. Explain why or why not Determine whether the following statements are true and give an explanation or counterexample.

a. If the limits $\displaystyle\lim_{(x,0)\to(0,0)} f(x, 0)$ and $\displaystyle\lim_{(0,y)\to(0,0)} f(0, y)$ exist and equal L, then $\displaystyle\lim_{(x,y)\to(0,0)} f(x, y) = L$.

b. If $\displaystyle\lim_{(x,y)\to(a,b)} f(x, y)$ equals a finite number L, then f is continuous at (a, b).

c. If f is continuous at (a, b), then $\displaystyle\lim_{(x,y)\to(a,b)} f(x, y)$ exists.

d. If P is a boundary point of the domain of f, then P is in the domain of f.

60–67. Miscellaneous limits *Use the method of your choice to evaluate the following limits.*

60. $\lim\limits_{(x,y)\to(0,0)} \dfrac{y^2}{x^8 + y^2}$

61. $\lim\limits_{(x,y)\to(0,1)} \dfrac{y \sin x}{x(y + 1)}$

62. $\lim\limits_{(x,y)\to(1,1)} \dfrac{x^2 + xy - 2y^2}{2x^2 - xy - y^2}$

63. $\lim\limits_{(x,y)\to(1,0)} \dfrac{y \ln y}{x}$

64. $\lim\limits_{(x,y)\to(0,0)} \dfrac{|xy|}{xy}$

65. $\lim\limits_{(x,y)\to(0,0)} \dfrac{|x - y|}{|x + y|}$

66. $\lim\limits_{(u,v)\to(-1,0)} \dfrac{uve^{-v}}{u^2 + v^2}$

67. $\lim\limits_{(x,y)\to(2,0)} \dfrac{1 - \cos y}{xy^2}$

68–71. Limits using polar coordinates *Limits at $(0, 0)$ may be easier to evaluate by converting to polar coordinates. Remember that the same limit must be obtained as $r \to 0$ along all paths in the domain to $(0, 0)$. Evaluate the following limits or state that they do not exist.*

68. $\lim\limits_{(x,y)\to(0,0)} \dfrac{x - y}{\sqrt{x^2 + y^2}}$

69. $\lim\limits_{(x,y)\to(0,0)} \dfrac{x^2 y}{x^2 + y^2}$

70. $\lim\limits_{(x,y)\to(0,0)} \tan^{-1}\left(\dfrac{(2 + (x + y)^2 + (x - y)^2)}{2e^{x^2+y^2}} \right)$

71. $\lim\limits_{(x,y)\to(0,0)} \dfrac{x^2 + y^2 + x^2 y^2}{x^2 + y^2}$

Additional Exercises

72. Sine limits Evaluate the following limits.

a. $\lim\limits_{(x,y)\to(0,0)} \dfrac{\sin (x + y)}{x + y}$

b. $\lim\limits_{(x,y)\to(0,0)} \dfrac{\sin x + \sin y}{x + y}$

73. Piecewise function Let

$$f(x, y) = \begin{cases} \dfrac{\sin (x^2 + y^2 - 1)}{x^2 + y^2 - 1} & \text{if } x^2 + y^2 \neq 1 \\ b & \text{if } x^2 + y^2 = 1. \end{cases}$$

Find the value of b for which f is continuous at all points in $\mathbb{R}^2$.

74. Piecewise function Let

$$f(x, y) = \begin{cases} \dfrac{1 + 2xy - \cos xy}{xy} & \text{if } xy \neq 0 \\ a & \text{if } xy = 0. \end{cases}$$

Find the value of a for which f is continuous at all points in $\mathbb{R}^2$.

75. Nonexistence of limits Show that $\lim\limits_{(x,y)\to(0,0)} \dfrac{ax^m y^n}{bx^{m+n} + cy^{m+n}}$ does not exist when a, b, and c are nonzero real numbers and m and n are positive integers.

76. Nonexistence of limits Show that $\lim\limits_{(x,y)\to(0,0)} \dfrac{ax^{2(p-n)} y^n}{bx^{2p} + cy^p}$ does not exist when a, b, and c are nonzero real numbers and n and p are positive integers with $p \geq n$.

77–80. Limits of composite functions *Evaluate the following limits.*

77. $\lim\limits_{(x,y)\to(1,0)} \dfrac{\sin xy}{xy}$

78. $\lim\limits_{(x,y)\to(4,0)} x^2 y \ln xy$

79. $\lim\limits_{(x,y)\to(0,2)} (2xy)^{xy}$

80. $\lim\limits_{(x,y)\to(0,\pi/2)} \dfrac{1 - \cos xy}{4x^2 y^3}$

81. Filling in a function value The domain of $f(x, y) = e^{-1/(x^2+y^2)}$ excludes $(0, 0)$. How should f be defined at $(0, 0)$ to make it continuous there?

82. Limit proof Use the formal definition of a limit to prove that $\lim\limits_{(x,y)\to(a,b)} y = b$. (*Hint:* Take $\delta = \varepsilon$.)

83. Limit proof Use the formal definition of a limit to prove that $\lim\limits_{(x,y)\to(a,b)} (x + y) = a + b$. (*Hint:* Take $\delta = \varepsilon/2$.)

84. Proof of Limit Law 1 Use the formal definition of a limit to prove that $\lim\limits_{(x,y)\to(a,b)} (f(x, y) + g(x, y)) = \lim\limits_{(x,y)\to(a,b)} f(x, y) + \lim\limits_{(x,y)\to(a,b)} g(x, y)$.

85. Proof of Limit Law 3 Use the formal definition of a limit to prove that $\lim\limits_{(x,y)\to(a,b)} cf(x, y) = c \lim\limits_{(x,y)\to(a,b)} f(x, y)$.

QUICK CHECK ANSWERS

1. The limit exists only for (a). **2.** $\{(x, y): x^2 + y^2 < 2\}$
3. If a factor of x is first canceled, then the limit may be evaluated by substitution. **4.** If the left and right limits at a point are not equal, then the two-sided limit does not exist. **5.** (a) and (b) are continuous at $(0, 0)$. ◄

12.4 Partial Derivatives

The derivative of a function of one variable, $y = f(x)$, measures the rate of change of y with respect to x, and it gives slopes of tangent lines. The analogous idea for functions of several variables presents a new twist: Derivatives may be defined with respect to any of the independent variables. For example, we can compute the derivative of $f(x, y)$ with respect to x or y. The resulting derivatives are called *partial derivatives*; they still represent rates of change and they are associated with slopes of tangents. Therefore, much of what you have learned about derivatives applies to functions of several variables. However, much is also different.

Derivatives with Two Variables

Consider a function f defined on a domain D in the xy-plane. Suppose that f represents the elevation of the land (above sea level) over D. Imagine that you are on the surface $z = f(x, y)$ at the point $(a, b, f(a, b))$ and you are asked to determine the slope of the surface where you are standing. Your answer should be, *it depends*!

Figure 12.48a shows a function that resembles the landscape in Figure 12.48b. Suppose you are standing at the point $P(0, 0, f(0, 0))$, which lies on the pass or the saddle. The surface behaves differently depending on the direction in which you walk. If you walk east (positive x-direction), the elevation increases and your path takes you upward on the surface. If you walk north (positive y-direction), the elevation decreases and your path takes you downward on the surface. In fact, in every direction you walk from the point P, the function values change at different rates. So how should the slope or the rate of change at a given point be defined?

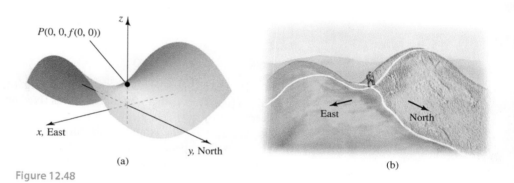

(a)   (b)

Figure 12.48

The answer to this question involves *partial derivatives*, which arise when we hold all but one independent variable fixed and then compute an ordinary derivative with respect to the remaining variable. Suppose we move along the surface $z = f(x, y)$, starting at the point $(a, b, f(a, b))$ in such a way that $y = b$ is fixed and only x varies. The resulting path is a curve (a trace) on the surface that varies in the x-direction (Figure 12.49). This curve is the intersection of the surface with the vertical plane $y = b$; it is described by $z = f(x, b)$, which is a function of the single variable x. We know how to compute the slope of this curve: It is the ordinary derivative of $f(x, b)$ with respect to x. This derivative is called the *partial derivative of f with respect to x*, denoted $\partial f/\partial x$ or f_x. When evaluated at (a, b), its value is defined by the limit

$$f_x(a, b) = \lim_{h \to 0} \frac{f(a + h, b) - f(a, b)}{h},$$

provided this limit exists. Notice that the y-coordinate is fixed at $y = b$ in this limit. If we replace (a, b) with the variable point (x, y), then f_x becomes a function of x and y.

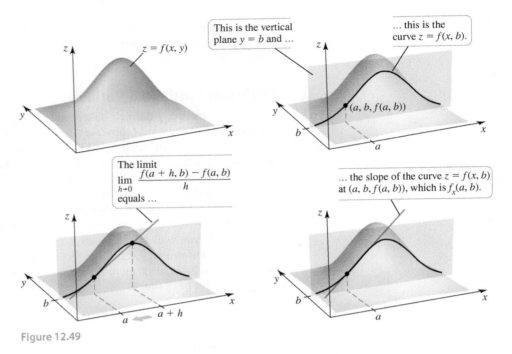

Figure 12.49

In a similar way, we can move along the surface $z = f(x, y)$ from the point $(a, b, f(a, b))$ in such a way that $x = a$ is fixed and only y varies. Now the result is a trace described by $z = f(a, y)$, which is the intersection of the surface and the plane $x = a$ (Figure 12.50). The slope of this curve at (a, b) is given by the ordinary derivative of $f(a, y)$ with respect to y. This derivative is called the *partial derivative of f with respect to y*, denoted $\partial f / \partial y$ or f_y. When evaluated at (a, b), it is defined by the limit

$$f_y(a, b) = \lim_{h \to 0} \frac{f(a, b + h) - f(a, b)}{h},$$

provided this limit exists. If we replace (a, b) with the variable point (x, y), then f_y becomes a function of x and y.

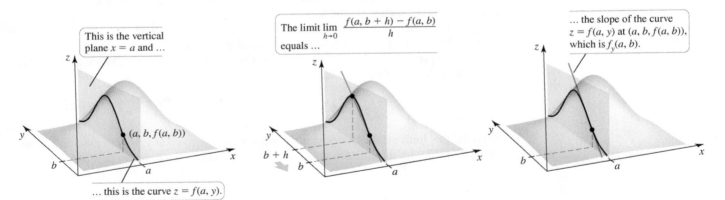

Figure 12.50

DEFINITION Partial Derivatives

The **partial derivative of f with respect to x at the point (a, b)** is

$$f_x(a, b) = \lim_{h \to 0} \frac{f(a + h, b) - f(a, b)}{h}.$$

The **partial derivative of f with respect to y at the point (a, b)** is

$$f_y(a, b) = \lim_{h \to 0} \frac{f(a, b + h) - f(a, b)}{h},$$

provided these limits exist.

▶ Recall that f' is a function, while $f'(a)$ is the value of the derivative at $x = a$. In the same way, f_x and f_y are functions of x and y, while $f_x(a, b)$ and $f_y(a, b)$ are their values at (a, b).

Notation The partial derivatives evaluated at a point (a, b) are denoted in any of the following ways:

$$\frac{\partial f}{\partial x}(a, b) = \left.\frac{\partial f}{\partial x}\right|_{(a,b)} = f_x(a, b) \quad \text{and} \quad \frac{\partial f}{\partial y}(a, b) = \left.\frac{\partial f}{\partial y}\right|_{(a,b)} = f_y(a, b).$$

Notice that the d in the ordinary derivative df/dx has been replaced with ∂ in the partial derivatives $\partial f/\partial x$ and $\partial f/\partial y$. The notation $\partial/\partial x$ is an instruction or operator: It says, "take the partial derivative with respect to x of the function that follows."

Calculating Partial Derivatives We begin by calculating partial derivatives using the limit definition. The procedure in Example 1 should look familiar. It echoes the method used in Chapter 3 when we first introduced ordinary derivatives.

EXAMPLE 1   Partial derivatives from the definition Suppose $f(x, y) = x^2 y$. Use the limit definition of partial derivatives to compute $f_x(x, y)$ and $f_y(x, y)$.

SOLUTION We compute the partial derivatives at an arbitrary point (x, y) in the domain. The partial derivative with respect to x is

$$
\begin{aligned}
f_x(x, y) &= \lim_{h \to 0} \frac{f(x + h, y) - f(x, y)}{h} &&\text{Definition of } f_x \text{ at } (x, y)\\
&= \lim_{h \to 0} \frac{(x + h)^2 y - x^2 y}{h} &&\text{Substitute for } f(x + h, y) \text{ and } f(x, y).\\
&= \lim_{h \to 0} \frac{(x^2 + 2xh + h^2 - x^2)y}{h} &&\text{Factor and expand.}\\
&= \lim_{h \to 0} (2x + h)y &&\text{Simplify and cancel } h.\\
&= 2xy. &&\text{Evaluate limit.}
\end{aligned}
$$

In a similar way, the partial derivative with respect to y is

$$
\begin{aligned}
f_y(x, y) &= \lim_{h \to 0} \frac{f(x, y + h) - f(x, y)}{h} &&\text{Definition of } f_y \text{ at } (x, y)\\
&= \lim_{h \to 0} \frac{x^2(y + h) - x^2 y}{h} &&\text{Substitute for } f(x, y + h) \text{ and } f(x, y).\\
&= \lim_{h \to 0} \frac{x^2(y + h - y)}{h} &&\text{Factor.}\\
&= x^2. &&\text{Simplify and evaluate limit.}
\end{aligned}
$$

Related Exercises 7–10 ◀

A careful examination of Example 1 reveals a shortcut for evaluating partial derivatives. To compute the partial derivative of f with respect to x, we treat y as a constant and take an ordinary derivative with respect to x:

$$\frac{\partial}{\partial x}(x^2 y) = y\underbrace{\frac{\partial}{\partial x}(x^2)}_{2x} = 2xy. \quad \text{Treat } y \text{ as a constant.}$$

Similarly, we treat x (and therefore x^2) as a constant to evaluate the partial derivative of f with respect to y:

$$\frac{\partial}{\partial y}(x^2 y) = x^2\underbrace{\frac{\partial}{\partial y}(y)}_{1} = x^2. \quad \text{Treat } x \text{ as a constant.}$$

The next two examples illustrate the process.

EXAMPLE 2   Partial derivatives Let $f(x, y) = x^3 - y^2 + 4$.

a. Compute $\dfrac{\partial f}{\partial x}$ and $\dfrac{\partial f}{\partial y}$.

b. Evaluate each derivative at $(2, -4)$.

SOLUTION

a. We compute the partial derivative with respect to x assuming that y is a constant; the Power Rule gives

$$\frac{\partial f}{\partial x} = \frac{\partial}{\partial x}(\underbrace{x^3}_{\text{variable}} - \underbrace{y^2 + 4}_{\substack{\text{constant with} \\ \text{respect to } x}}) = 3x^2 + 0 = 3x^2.$$

The partial derivative with respect to y is computed by treating x as a constant; using the Power Rule gives

$$\frac{\partial f}{\partial y} = \frac{\partial}{\partial y}(\underbrace{x^3}_{\substack{\text{constant} \\ \text{with respect} \\ \text{to } y}} - \underbrace{y^2}_{\text{variable}} + \underbrace{4}_{\text{constant}}) = -2y.$$

QUICK CHECK 1 Compute f_x and f_y for $f(x, y) = 2xy$. ◄

b. It follows that $f_x(2, -4) = (3x^2)|_{(2,-4)} = 12$ and $f_y(2, -4) = (-2y)|_{(2,-4)} = 8$.

Related Exercises 11–28 ◄

EXAMPLE 3   Partial derivatives Compute the partial derivatives of the following functions.

a. $f(x, y) = \sin xy$ **b.** $g(x, y) = x^2 e^{xy}$

SOLUTION

a. Treating y as a constant and differentiating with respect to x, we have

$$\frac{\partial f}{\partial x} = \frac{\partial}{\partial x}(\sin xy) = y \cos xy.$$

► Recall that

$$\frac{d}{dx}(\sin 2x) = 2 \cos 2x.$$

Replacing 2 with the constant y, we have

$$\frac{\partial}{\partial x}(\sin xy) = y \cos xy.$$

Holding x fixed and differentiating with respect to y, we have

$$\frac{\partial f}{\partial y} = \frac{\partial}{\partial y}(\sin xy) = x \cos xy.$$

b. To compute the partial derivative with respect to x, we call on the Product Rule. Holding y fixed, we have

$$\frac{\partial g}{\partial x} = \frac{\partial}{\partial x}\left(x^2 e^{xy}\right)$$

$$= \frac{\partial}{\partial x}\left(x^2\right)e^{xy} + x^2\frac{\partial}{\partial x}\left(e^{xy}\right) \quad \text{Product Rule}$$

$$= 2xe^{xy} + x^2ye^{xy} \quad\quad\quad\quad \text{Evaluate partial derivatives.}$$

$$= xe^{xy}(2 + xy). \quad\quad\quad\quad\quad \text{Simplify.}$$

> Because x and y are *independent* variables,
>
> $$\frac{\partial}{\partial x}(y) = 0 \quad \text{and} \quad \frac{\partial}{\partial y}(x) = 0.$$

Treating x as a constant, the partial derivative with respect to y is

$$\frac{\partial g}{\partial y} = \frac{\partial}{\partial y}\left(x^2 e^{xy}\right) = x^2 \underbrace{\frac{\partial}{\partial y}\left(e^{xy}\right)}_{xe^{xy}} = x^3 e^{xy}.$$

Related Exercises 11–28 ◄

Higher-Order Partial Derivatives

Just as we have higher-order derivatives of functions of one variable, we also have higher-order partial derivatives. For example, given a function f and its partial derivative f_x, we can take the derivative of f_x with respect to x or with respect to y, which accounts for two of the four possible *second-order partial derivatives*. Table 12.4 summarizes the notation for second partial derivatives.

Table 12.4

Notation 1	Notation 2	What we say ...
$\dfrac{\partial}{\partial x}\left(\dfrac{\partial f}{\partial x}\right) = \dfrac{\partial^2 f}{\partial x^2}$	$(f_x)_x = f_{xx}$	*d squared f dx squared* or *f-x-x*
$\dfrac{\partial}{\partial y}\left(\dfrac{\partial f}{\partial y}\right) = \dfrac{\partial^2 f}{\partial y^2}$	$(f_y)_y = f_{yy}$	*d squared f dy squared* or *f-y-y*
$\dfrac{\partial}{\partial x}\left(\dfrac{\partial f}{\partial y}\right) = \dfrac{\partial^2 f}{\partial x \partial y}$	$(f_y)_x = f_{yx}$	*f-y-x*
$\dfrac{\partial}{\partial y}\left(\dfrac{\partial f}{\partial x}\right) = \dfrac{\partial^2 f}{\partial y \partial x}$	$(f_x)_y = f_{xy}$	*f-x-y*

The order of differentiation can make a difference in the **mixed partial derivatives** f_{xy} and f_{yx}. So it is important to use the correct notation to reflect the order in which derivatives are taken. For example, the notations $\dfrac{\partial^2 f}{\partial x \partial y}$ and f_{yx} both mean $\dfrac{\partial}{\partial x}\left(\dfrac{\partial f}{\partial y}\right)$; that is, differentiate first with respect to y, then with respect to x.

QUICK CHECK 2 Which of the following expressions are equivalent to each other: (a) f_{xy}, (b) f_{yx}, or (c) $\dfrac{\partial^2 f}{\partial y \partial x}$? Write $\dfrac{\partial^2 f}{\partial p \partial q}$ in subscript notation. ◄

EXAMPLE 4   Second partial derivatives Find the four second partial derivatives of $f(x, y) = 3x^4 y - 2xy + 5xy^3$.

SOLUTION First, we compute

$$\frac{\partial f}{\partial x} = \frac{\partial}{\partial x}\left(3x^4 y - 2xy + 5xy^3\right) = 12x^3 y - 2y + 5y^3$$

and

$$\frac{\partial f}{\partial y} = \frac{\partial}{\partial y}(3x^4y - 2xy + 5xy^3) = 3x^4 - 2x + 15xy^2.$$

For the second partial derivatives, we have

$$\frac{\partial^2 f}{\partial x^2} = \frac{\partial}{\partial x}\left(\frac{\partial f}{\partial x}\right) = \frac{\partial}{\partial x}(12x^3y - 2y + 5y^3) = 36x^2y,$$

$$\frac{\partial^2 f}{\partial y^2} = \frac{\partial}{\partial y}\left(\frac{\partial f}{\partial y}\right) = \frac{\partial}{\partial y}(3x^4 - 2x + 15xy^2) = 30xy,$$

$$\frac{\partial^2 f}{\partial x \partial y} = \frac{\partial}{\partial x}\left(\frac{\partial f}{\partial y}\right) = \frac{\partial}{\partial x}(3x^4 - 2x + 15xy^2) = 12x^3 - 2 + 15y^2, \text{ and}$$

$$\frac{\partial^2 f}{\partial y \partial x} = \frac{\partial}{\partial y}\left(\frac{\partial f}{\partial x}\right) = \frac{\partial}{\partial y}(12x^3y - 2y + 5y^3) = 12x^3 - 2 + 15y^2.$$

QUICK CHECK 3 Compute f_{xxx} and f_{xxy} for $f(x, y) = x^3 y$. ◄

Related Exercises 29–44 ◄

Equality of Mixed Partial Derivatives   Notice that the two mixed partial derivatives in Example 4 are equal; that is, $f_{xy} = f_{yx}$. It turns out that most of the functions we encounter in this book have this property. Sufficient conditions for equality of mixed partial derivatives are given in a theorem attributed to the French mathematician Alexis Clairaut (1713–1765). The proof is found in advanced texts.

THEOREM 12.4   (Clairaut) Equality of Mixed Partial Derivatives
Assume that f is defined on an open set D of $\mathbb{R}^2$, and that f_{xy} and f_{yx} are continuous throughout D. Then $f_{xy} = f_{yx}$ at all points of D.

Assuming sufficient continuity, Theorem 12.4 can be extended to higher derivatives of f. For example, $f_{xyx} = f_{xxy} = f_{yxx}$.

Functions of Three Variables

Everything we learned about partial derivatives of functions with two variables carries over to functions of three or more variables, as illustrated in Example 5.

EXAMPLE 5   **Partial derivatives with more than two variables**   Find f_x, f_y, and f_z when $f(x, y, z) = e^{-xy}\cos z$.

SOLUTION   To find f_x, we treat y and z as constants and differentiate with respect to x:

$$\frac{\partial f}{\partial x} = \frac{\partial}{\partial x}\left(\underbrace{e^{-xy}}_{\substack{y\text{ is}\\ \text{constant}}} \quad \underbrace{\cos z}_{\text{constant}}\right) = -ye^{-xy}\cos z.$$

Holding x and z constant and differentiating with respect to y, we have

$$\frac{\partial f}{\partial y} = \frac{\partial}{\partial y}\left(\underbrace{e^{-xy}}_{\substack{x\text{ is}\\ \text{constant}}} \quad \underbrace{\cos z}_{\text{constant}}\right) = -xe^{-xy}\cos z.$$

To find f_z, we hold x and y constant and differentiate with respect to z:

$$\frac{\partial f}{\partial z} = \frac{\partial}{\partial z}\left(\underbrace{e^{-xy}}_{\text{constant}}\cos z\right) = -e^{-xy}\sin z.$$

QUICK CHECK 4 Compute f_{xz} and f_{zz} for $f(x, y, z) = xyz - x^2z + yz^2$. ◄

Related Exercises 45–54 ◄

Applications of Partial Derivatives When functions are used in realistic applications (for example, to describe velocity, pressure, investment fund balance, or population), they often involve more than one independent variable. For this reason, partial derivatives appear frequently in mathematical modeling.

EXAMPLE 6 **Ideal Gas Law** The pressure P, volume V, and temperature T of an ideal gas are related by the equation $PV = kT$, where $k > 0$ is a constant depending on the amount of gas.

a. Determine the rate of change of the pressure with respect to the volume at constant temperature. Interpret the result.

b. Determine the rate of change of the pressure with respect to the temperature at constant volume. Interpret the result.

c. Explain these results using level curves.

> Implicit differentiation can also be used with partial derivatives. Instead of solving for P, we could differentiate both sides of $PV = kT$ with respect to V holding T fixed. Using the Product Rule, $P + VP_V = 0$, which implies that $P_V = -P/V$. Substituting $P = kT/V$, we have $P_V = -kT/V^2$.

SOLUTION Expressing the pressure as a function of volume and temperature, we have
$$P = k\frac{T}{V}.$$

a. We find the partial derivative $\partial P/\partial V$ by holding T constant and differentiating P with respect to V:
$$\frac{\partial P}{\partial V} = \frac{\partial}{\partial V}\left(k\frac{T}{V}\right) = kT\frac{\partial}{\partial V}\left(V^{-1}\right) = -\frac{kT}{V^2}.$$

> In the Ideal Gas Law, temperature is a positive variable because it is measured in degrees Kelvin.

Recognizing that P, V, and T are always positive, we see that $\dfrac{\partial P}{\partial V} < 0$, which means that the pressure is a decreasing function of volume at a constant temperature.

b. The partial derivative $\partial P/\partial T$ is found by holding V constant and differentiating P with respect to T:
$$\frac{\partial P}{\partial T} = \frac{\partial}{\partial T}\left(k\frac{T}{V}\right) = \frac{k}{V}.$$

In this case, $\partial P/\partial T > 0$, which says that the pressure is an increasing function of temperature at constant volume.

c. The level curves (Section 12.2) of the pressure function are curves in the VT-plane that satisfy $k\dfrac{T}{V} = P_0$, where P_0 is a constant. Solving for T, the level curves are given by $T = \dfrac{1}{k}P_0V$. Because $\dfrac{P_0}{k}$ is a positive constant, the level curves are lines in the first quadrant (Figure 12.51) with slope P_0/k. The fact that $\dfrac{\partial P}{\partial V} < 0$ (from part (a)) means that if we hold $T > 0$ fixed and move in the direction of increasing V on a *horizontal* line, we cross level curves corresponding to decreasing pressures. Similarly, $\dfrac{\partial P}{\partial T} > 0$ (from part (b)) means that if we hold $V > 0$ fixed and move in the direction of increasing T on a *vertical* line, we cross level curves corresponding to increasing pressures.

Related Exercises 51–52 ◄

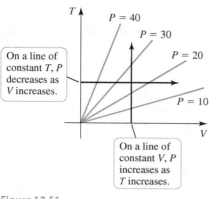

On a line of constant T, P decreases as V increases.

On a line of constant V, P increases as T increases.

Figure 12.51

QUICK CHECK 5 Explain why, in Figure 12.51, the slopes of the level curves increase as the pressure increases. ◄

Differentiability

We close this section with a technical matter that bears on the remainder of the chapter. Although we know how to compute partial derivatives of a function of several variables, we have not said what it means for such a function to be *differentiable* at a point. It is tempting to conclude that if the partial derivatives f_x and f_y exist at a point, then f is differentiable there. However, it is not so simple.

Recall that a function f of one variable is differentiable at $x = a$ provided the limit

$$f'(a) = \lim_{\Delta x \to 0} \frac{f(a + \Delta x) - f(a)}{\Delta x}$$

exists. If f is differentiable at a, it means that the curve is smooth at the point $(a, f(a))$ (no jumps, corners, or cusps); furthermore, the curve has a unique tangent line at that point with slope $f'(a)$. Differentiability for a function of several variables should carry the same properties: The surface should be smooth at the point in question and something analogous to a unique tangent line should exist at the point.

Staying with the one-variable case, we define the quantity

$$\varepsilon = \underbrace{\frac{f(a + \Delta x) - f(a)}{\Delta x}}_{\text{slope of secant line}} - \underbrace{f'(a)}_{\substack{\text{slope of} \\ \text{tangent line}}},$$

where ε is viewed as a function of Δx. Notice that ε is the difference between the slopes of secant lines and the slope of the tangent line at the point $(a, f(a))$. If f is differentiable at a, then this difference approaches zero as $\Delta x \to 0$; therefore, $\lim_{\Delta x \to 0} \varepsilon = 0$. Multiplying both sides of the definition of ε by Δx gives

$$\varepsilon \Delta x = f(a + \Delta x) - f(a) - f'(a) \Delta x.$$

Rearranging, we have the change in the function $y = f(x)$:

$$\Delta y = f(a + \Delta x) - f(a) = f'(a) \Delta x + \underbrace{\varepsilon \, \Delta x}_{\varepsilon \,\to\, 0 \text{ as } \Delta x \,\to\, 0}.$$

➤ Notice that $f'(a) \Delta x$ is the approximate change in the function given by a linear approximation.

This expression says that in the one-variable case, if f is differentiable at a, then the change in f between a and a nearby point $a + \Delta x$ is represented by $f'(a) \Delta x$ plus a quantity $\varepsilon \, \Delta x$, where $\lim_{\Delta x \to 0} \varepsilon = 0$.

The analogous requirement with several variables is the definition of differentiability for functions or two (or more) variables.

DEFINITION Differentiability

The function $z = f(x, y)$ is **differentiable at** (a, b) provided $f_x(a, b)$ and $f_y(a, b)$ exist and the change $\Delta z = f(a + \Delta x, b + \Delta y) - f(a, b)$ equals

$$\Delta z = f_x(a, b) \Delta x + f_y(a, b) \Delta y + \varepsilon_1 \Delta x + \varepsilon_2 \Delta y,$$

where for fixed a and b, ε_1 and ε_2 are functions that depend only on Δx and Δy, with $(\varepsilon_1, \varepsilon_2) \to (0, 0)$ as $(\Delta x, \Delta y) \to (0, 0)$. A function is **differentiable** on an open set R if it is differentiable at every point of R.

Several observations are needed here. First, the definition extends to functions of more than two variables. Second, we show how differentiability is related to linear approximation and the existence of a *tangent plane* in Section 12.7. Finally, the conditions of the definition are generally difficult to verify. The following theorem may be useful in checking differentiability.

THEOREM 12.5 Conditions for Differentiability
Suppose the function f has partial derivatives f_x and f_y defined on an open set containing (a, b), with f_x and f_y continuous at (a, b). Then f is differentiable at (a, b).

As shown in Example 7, the existence of f_x and f_y at (a, b) is not enough to ensure differentiability of f at (a, b). However, by Theorem 12.5, if f_x and f_y are continuous at (a, b) (and defined in an open set containing (a, b)), then we can conclude f is differentiable there. Polynomials and rational functions are differentiable at all points of their domains, as are compositions of exponential, logarithmic, and trigonometric functions with other differentiable functions. The proof of this theorem is given in Appendix B.

We close with the analog of Theorem 3.1, which states that differentiability implies continuity.

THEOREM 12.6 Differentiable Implies Continuous
If a function f is differentiable at (a, b), then it is continuous at (a, b).

Proof: By the definition of differentiability,

$$\Delta z = f_x(a, b)\,\Delta x + f_y(a, b)\,\Delta y + \varepsilon_1\Delta x + \varepsilon_2\Delta y,$$

where $(\varepsilon_1, \varepsilon_2) \to (0, 0)$ as $(\Delta x, \Delta y) \to (0, 0)$. Because f is assumed to be differentiable, as Δx and Δy approach 0, we see that

$$\lim_{(\Delta x, \Delta y)\to(0,0)} \Delta z = 0.$$

Also, because $\Delta z = f(a + \Delta x, b + \Delta y) - f(a, b)$, it follows that

$$\lim_{(\Delta x, \Delta y)\to(0,0)} f(a + \Delta x, b + \Delta y) = f(a, b),$$

which implies continuity of f at (a, b).   ◄

> Recall that continuity requires that
> $$\lim_{(x,y)\to(a,b)} f(x, y) = f(a, b),$$
> which is equivalent to
> $$\lim_{(\Delta x, \Delta y)\to(0,0)} f(a + \Delta x, b + \Delta y) = f(a, b).$$

EXAMPLE 7 A nondifferentiable function Discuss the differentiability and continuity of the function

$$f(x, y) = \begin{cases} \dfrac{3xy}{x^2 + y^2} & \text{if } (x, y) \neq (0, 0) \\ 0 & \text{if } (x, y) = (0, 0). \end{cases}$$

SOLUTION As a rational function, f is continuous and differentiable at all points $(x, y) \neq (0, 0)$. The interesting behavior occurs at the origin. Using calculations similar to those in Example 4 in Section 12.3, it can be shown that if the origin is approached along the line $y = mx$, then

$$\lim_{\substack{(x,y)\to(0,0) \\ \text{(along } y = mx)}} \frac{3xy}{x^2 + y^2} = \frac{3m}{m^2 + 1}.$$

Therefore, the value of the limit depends on the direction of approach, which implies that the limit does not exist, and f is not continuous at $(0, 0)$. By Theorem 12.6, it follows that f is not differentiable at $(0, 0)$. Figure 12.52 shows the discontinuity of f at the origin.

Let's look at the first partial derivatives of f at $(0, 0)$. A short calculation shows that

$$f_x(0, 0) = \lim_{h\to 0} \frac{f(0 + h, 0) - f(0, 0)}{h} = \lim_{h\to 0} \frac{0 - 0}{h} = 0,$$

$$f_y(0, 0) = \lim_{h\to 0} \frac{f(0, 0 + h) - f(0, 0)}{h} = \lim_{h\to 0} \frac{0 - 0}{h} = 0.$$

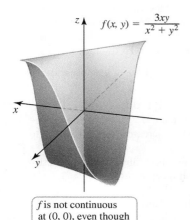

$$f(x, y) = \frac{3xy}{x^2 + y^2}$$

f is not continuous at $(0, 0)$, even though $f_x(0, 0) = f_y(0, 0) = 0$.

Figure 12.52

▶ The relationships between the existence and continuity of partial derivatives and whether a function is differentiable are further explored in Exercises 90–91.

Despite the fact that its first partial derivatives exist at $(0, 0)$, f is not differentiable at $(0, 0)$. As noted earlier, the existence of first partial derivatives at a point is not enough to ensure differentiability at that point.

Related Exercises 57–58 ◀

SECTION 12.4 EXERCISES

Review Questions

1. Suppose you are standing on the surface $z = f(x, y)$ at the point $(a, b, f(a, b))$. Interpret the meaning of $f_x(a, b)$ and $f_y(a, b)$ in terms of slopes or rates of change.

2. Find f_x and f_y when $f(x, y) = 3x^2y + xy^3$.

3. Find f_x and f_y when $f(x, y) = x \cos xy$.

4. Find the four second partial derivatives of $f(x, y) = 3x^2y + xy^3$.

5. Explain how you would evaluate f_z for the differentiable function $w = f(x, y, z)$.

6. The volume of a right circular cylinder with radius r and height h is $V = \pi r^2 h$. Is the volume an increasing or decreasing function of the radius at a fixed height (assume $r > 0$ and $h > 0$)?

Basic Skills

7–10. Evaluating partial derivatives using limits *Use the limit definition of partial derivatives to evaluate $f_x(x, y)$ and $f_y(x, y)$ for each of the following functions.*

7. $f(x, y) = 5xy$

8. $f(x, y) = x + y^2 + 4$

9. $f(x, y) = \dfrac{x}{y}$

10. $f(x, y) = \sqrt{xy}$

11–28. Partial derivatives *Find the first partial derivatives of the following functions.*

11. $f(x, y) = 3x^2 + 4y^3$

12. $f(x, y) = x^2y$

13. $f(x, y) = 3x^2y + 2$

14. $f(x, y) = y^8 + 2x^6 + 2xy$

15. $f(x, y) = xe^y$

16. $f(x, y) = \ln(x/y)$

17. $g(x, y) = \cos 2xy$

18. $h(x, y) = (y^2 + 1)e^x$

19. $f(x, y) = e^{x^2y}$

20. $f(s, t) = \dfrac{s - t}{s + t}$

21. $f(w, z) = \dfrac{w}{w^2 + z^2}$

22. $g(x, z) = x \ln(z^2 + x^2)$

23. $s(y, z) = z^2 \tan yz$

24. $F(p, q) = \sqrt{p^2 + pq + q^2}$

25. $G(s, t) = \dfrac{\sqrt{st}}{s + t}$

26. $h(u, v) = \sqrt{\dfrac{uv}{u - v}}$

27. $f(x, y) = x^{2y}$

28. $f(x, y) = \sqrt{x^2y^3}$

29–38. Second partial derivatives *Find the four second partial derivatives of the following functions.*

29. $h(x, y) = x^3 + xy^2 + 1$

30. $f(x, y) = 2x^5y^2 + x^2y$

31. $f(x, y) = x^2y^3$

32. $f(x, y) = (x + 3y)^2$

33. $f(x, y) = y^3 \sin 4x$

34. $f(x, y) = \cos xy$

35. $p(u, v) = \ln(u^2 + v^2 + 4)$

36. $Q(r, s) = r/s$

37. $F(r, s) = re^s$

38. $H(x, y) = \sqrt{4 + x^2 + y^2}$

39–44. Equality of mixed partial derivatives *Verify that $f_{xy} = f_{yx}$ for the following functions.*

39. $f(x, y) = 2x^3 + 3y^2 + 1$

40. $f(x, y) = xe^y$

41. $f(x, y) = \cos xy$

42. $f(x, y) = 3x^2y^{-1} - 2x^{-1}y^2$

43. $f(x, y) = e^{x+y}$

44. $f(x, y) = \sqrt{xy}$

45–54. Partial derivatives with more than two variables *Find the first partial derivatives of the following functions.*

45. $f(x, y, z) = xy + xz + yz$

46. $g(x, y, z) = 2x^2y - 3xz^4 + 10y^2z^2$

47. $h(x, y, z) = \cos(x + y + z)$

48. $Q(x, y, z) = \tan xyz$

49. $F(u, v, w) = \dfrac{u}{v + w}$

50. $G(r, s, t) = \sqrt{rs + rt + st}$

51. $f(w, x, y, z) = w^2xy^2 + xy^3z^2$

52. $g(w, x, y, z) = \cos(w + x)\sin(y - z)$

53. $h(w, x, y, z) = \dfrac{wz}{xy}$

54. $F(w, x, y, z) = w\sqrt{x + 2y + 3z}$

55. **Gas law calculations** Consider the Ideal Gas Law $PV = kT$, where $k > 0$ is a constant. Solve this equation for V in terms of P and T.

   a. Determine the rate of change of the volume with respect to the pressure at constant temperature. Interpret the result.
   b. Determine the rate of change of the volume with respect to the temperature at constant pressure. Interpret the result.
   c. Assuming $k = 1$, draw several level curves of the volume function and interpret the results as in Example 5.

56. **Volume of a box** A box with a square base of length x and height h has a volume $V = x^2h$.

   a. Compute the partial derivatives V_x and V_h.
   b. For a box with $h = 1.5$ m, use linear approximation to estimate the change in volume if x increases from $x = 0.5$ m to $x = 0.51$ m.
   c. For a box with $x = 0.5$ m, use linear approximation to estimate the change in volume if h decreases from $h = 1.5$ m to $h = 1.49$ m.
   d. For a fixed height, does a 10% change in x always produce (approximately) a 10% change in V? Explain.
   e. For a fixed base length, does a 10% change in h always produce (approximately) a 10% change in V? Explain.

57–58. Nondifferentiability? *Consider the following functions f.*

a. *Is f continuous at* $(0, 0)$?
b. *Is f differentiable at* $(0, 0)$?
c. *If possible, evaluate* $f_x(0, 0)$ *and* $f_y(0, 0)$.
d. *Determine whether* f_x *and* f_y *are continuous at* $(0, 0)$.
e. *Explain why Theorems 12.5 and 12.6 are consistent with the results in parts (a)–(d).*

57. $f(x, y) = \begin{cases} -\dfrac{xy}{x^2 + y^2} & \text{if } (x, y) \neq (0, 0) \\ 0 & \text{if } (x, y) = (0, 0) \end{cases}$

58. $f(x, y) = \begin{cases} \dfrac{2xy^2}{x^2 + y^4} & \text{if } (x, y) \neq (0, 0) \\ 0 & \text{if } (x, y) = (0, 0) \end{cases}$

Further Explorations

59. Explain why or why not Determine whether the following statements are true and give an explanation or counterexample.

a. $\dfrac{\partial}{\partial x}(y^{10}) = 10y^9$.

b. $\dfrac{\partial^2}{\partial x \partial y}(\sqrt{xy}) = \dfrac{1}{\sqrt{xy}}$.

c. If f has continuous partial derivatives of all orders, then $f_{xxy} = f_{yxx}$.

60–63. Estimating partial derivatives *The following table shows values of a function $f(x, y)$ for values of x from 2 to 2.5 and values of y from 3 to 3.5. Use this table to estimate the values of the following partial derivates.*

y \ x	2	2.1	2.2	2.3	2.4	2.5
3	4.243	4.347	4.450	4.550	4.648	4.743
3.1	4.384	4.492	4.598	4.701	4.802	4.902
3.2	4.525	4.637	4.746	4.853	4.957	5.060
3.3	4.667	4.782	4.895	5.005	5.112	5.218
3.4	4.808	4.930	5.043	5.156	5.267	5.376
3.5	4.950	5.072	5.191	5.308	5.422	5.534

60. $f_x(2, 3)$

61. $f_y(2, 3)$

62. $f_x(2.2, 3.4)$

63. $f_y(2.4, 3.3)$

64–68. Miscellaneous partial derivatives *Compute the first partial derivatives of the following functions.*

64. $f(x, y) = \ln(1 + e^{-xy})$

65. $f(x, y) = 1 - \tan^{-1}(x^2 + y^2)$

66. $f(x, y) = 1 - \cos(2(x + y)) + \cos^2(x + y)$

67. $h(x, y, z) = (1 + x + 2y)^z$

68. $g(x, y, z) = \dfrac{4x - 2y - 2z}{3y - 6x - 3z}$

69. Partial derivatives and level curves Consider the function $z = x/y^2$.

a. Compute z_x and z_y.
b. Sketch the level curves for $z = 1, 2, 3,$ and 4.
c. Move along the horizontal line $y = 1$ in the xy-plane and describe how the corresponding z-values change. Explain how this observation is consistent with z_x as computed in part (a).

d. Move along the vertical line $x = 1$ in the xy-plane and describe how the corresponding z-values change. Explain how this observation is consistent with z_y as computed in part (a).

70. Spherical caps The volume of the cap of a sphere of radius r and thickness h is $V = \dfrac{\pi}{3}h^2(3r - h)$, for $0 \leq h \leq 2r$.

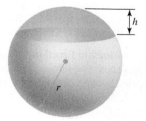

$V = \frac{\pi}{3}h^2(3r - h)$

a. Compute the partial derivatives V_h and V_r.
b. For a sphere of any radius, is the rate of change of volume with respect to r greater when $h = 0.2r$ or when $h = 0.8r$?
c. For a sphere of any radius, for what value of h is the rate of change of volume with respect to r equal to 1?
d. For a fixed radius r, for what value of h $(0 \leq h \leq 2r)$ is the rate of change of volume with respect to h the greatest?

71. Law of Cosines All triangles satisfy the Law of Cosines $c^2 = a^2 + b^2 - 2ab \cos \theta$ (see figure). Notice that when $\theta = \pi/2$, the Law of Cosines becomes the Pythagorean Theorem. Consider all triangles with a fixed angle $\theta = \pi/3$, in which case c is a function of a and b, where $a > 0$ and $b > 0$.

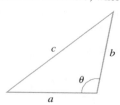

a. Compute $\dfrac{\partial c}{\partial a}$ and $\dfrac{\partial c}{\partial b}$ by solving for c and differentiating.

b. Compute $\dfrac{\partial c}{\partial a}$ and $\dfrac{\partial c}{\partial b}$ by implicit differentiation. Check for agreement with part (a).

c. What relationship between a and b makes c an increasing function of a (for constant b)?

Applications

72. Body mass index The body mass index (BMI) for an adult human is given by the function $B = w/h^2$, where w is the weight measured in kilograms and h is the height measured in meters. (The BMI for units of pounds and inches is $B = 703 \, w/h^2$.)

a. Find the rate of change of the BMI with respect to weight at a constant height.
b. For fixed h, is the BMI an increasing or decreasing function of w? Explain.
c. Find the rate of change of the BMI with respect to height at a constant weight.
d. For fixed w, is the BMI an increasing or decreasing function of h? Explain.

73. Electric potential function The electric potential in the xy-plane associated with two positive charges, one at $(0, 1)$ with twice the magnitude as the charge at $(0, -1)$, is

$$\varphi(x, y) = \frac{2}{\sqrt{x^2 + (y - 1)^2}} + \frac{1}{\sqrt{x^2 + (y + 1)^2}}.$$

a. Compute φ_x and φ_y.
b. Describe how φ_x and φ_y behave as $x, y \to \pm \infty$.
c. Evaluate $\varphi_x(0, y)$, for all $y \ne \pm 1$. Interpret this result.
d. Evaluate $\varphi_y(x, 0)$, for all x. Interpret this result.

T 74. Cobb-Douglas production function The output Q of an economic system subject to two inputs, such as labor L and capital K, is often modeled by the Cobb-Douglas production function $Q(L, K) = cL^aK^b$. Suppose $a = \frac{1}{3}$, $b = \frac{2}{3}$, and $c = 1$.

a. Evaluate the partial derivatives Q_L and Q_K.
b. Suppose $L = 10$ is fixed and K increases from $K = 20$ to $K = 20.5$. Use linear approximation to estimate the change in Q.
c. Suppose $K = 20$ is fixed and L decreases from $L = 10$ to $L = 9.5$. Use linear approximation to estimate the change in Q.
d. Graph the level curves of the production function in the first quadrant of the LK-plane for $Q = 1, 2$, and 3.
e. Use the graph of part (d). If you move along the vertical line $L = 2$ in the positive K-direction, how does Q change? Is this consistent with Q_K computed in part (a)?
f. Use the graph of part (d). If you move along the horizontal line $K = 2$ in the positive L-direction, how does Q change? Is this consistent with Q_L computed in part (a)?

75. Resistors in parallel Two resistors in an electrical circuit with resistance R_1 and R_2 wired in parallel with a constant voltage give an effective resistance of R, where $\dfrac{1}{R} = \dfrac{1}{R_1} + \dfrac{1}{R_2}$.

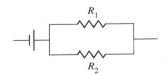

a. Find $\dfrac{\partial R}{\partial R_1}$ and $\dfrac{\partial R}{\partial R_2}$ by solving for R and differentiating.
b. Find $\dfrac{\partial R}{\partial R_1}$ and $\dfrac{\partial R}{\partial R_2}$ by differentiating implicitly.
c. Describe how an increase in R_1 with R_2 constant affects R.
d. Describe how a decrease in R_2 with R_1 constant affects R.

76. Wave on a string Imagine a string that is fixed at both ends (for example, a guitar string). When plucked, the string forms a standing wave. The displacement u of the string varies with position x and with time t. Suppose it is given by $u = f(x, t) = 2 \sin(\pi x) \sin(\pi t/2)$, for $0 \le x \le 1$ and $t \ge 0$ (see figure). At a fixed point in time, the string forms a wave on $[0, 1]$. Alternatively, if you focus on a point on the string (fix a value of x), that point oscillates up and down in time.

a. What is the period of the motion in time?
b. Find the rate of change of the displacement with respect to time at a constant position (which is the vertical velocity of a point on the string).

c. At a fixed time, what point on the string is moving fastest?
d. At a fixed position on the string, when is the string moving fastest?
e. Find the rate of change of the displacement with respect to position at a constant time (which is the slope of the string).
f. At a fixed time, where is the slope of the string greatest?

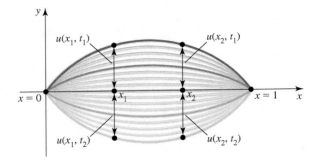

77–79. Wave equation *Traveling waves (for example, water waves or electromagnetic waves) exhibit periodic motion in both time and position. In one dimension, some types of wave motion are governed by the one-dimensional wave equation*

$$\frac{\partial^2 u}{\partial t^2} = c^2 \frac{\partial^2 u}{\partial x^2},$$

where $u(x, t)$ is the height or displacement of the wave surface at position x and time t, and c is the constant speed of the wave. Show that the following functions are solutions of the wave equation.

77. $u(x, t) = \cos(2(x + ct))$

78. $u(x, t) = 5 \cos(2(x + ct)) + 3 \sin(x - ct)$

79. $u(x, t) = A f(x + ct) + B g(x - ct)$, where A and B are constants and f and g are twice differentiable functions of one variable

80–83. Laplace's equation *A classical equation of mathematics is Laplace's equation, which arises in both theory and applications. It governs ideal fluid flow, electrostatic potentials, and the steady-state distribution of heat in a conducting medium. In two dimensions, Laplace's equation is*

$$\frac{\partial^2 u}{\partial x^2} + \frac{\partial^2 u}{\partial y^2} = 0.$$

*Show that the following functions are **harmonic**; that is, they satisfy Laplace's equation.*

80. $u(x, y) = e^{-x} \sin y$

81. $u(x, y) = x(x^2 - 3y^2)$

82. $u(x, y) = e^{ax} \cos ay$, for any real number a

83. $u(x, y) = \tan^{-1}\left(\dfrac{y}{x - 1}\right) - \tan^{-1}\left(\dfrac{y}{x + 1}\right)$

84–87. Heat equation *The flow of heat along a thin conducting bar is governed by the one-dimensional heat equation (with analogs for thin plates in two dimensions and for solids in three dimensions)*

$$\frac{\partial u}{\partial t} = k\frac{\partial^2 u}{\partial x^2},$$

where u is a measure of the temperature at a location x on the bar at time t and the positive constant k is related to the conductivity of the material. Show that the following functions satisfy the heat equation with k = 1.

84. $u(x, t) = 10e^{-t}\sin x$

85. $u(x, t) = 4e^{-4t}\cos 2x$

86. $u(x, t) = e^{-t}(2\sin x + 3\cos x)$

87. $u(x, t) = Ae^{-a^2 t}\cos ax$, for any real numbers a and A

Additional Exercises

88–89. Differentiability *Use the definition of differentiability to prove that the following functions are differentiable at $(0, 0)$. You must produce functions ε_1 and ε_2 with the required properties.*

88. $f(x, y) = x + y$ **89.** $f(x, y) = xy$

90–91. Nondifferentiability? *Consider the following functions f.*

a. Is f continuous at $(0, 0)$?
b. Is f differentiable at $(0, 0)$?
c. If possible, evaluate $f_x(0, 0)$ and $f_y(0, 0)$.
d. Determine whether f_x and f_y are continuous at $(0, 0)$.
e. Explain why Theorems 12.5 and 12.6 are consistent with the results in parts (a)–(d).

90. $f(x, y) = 1 - |xy|$ **91.** $f(x, y) = \sqrt{|xy|}$

92. Mixed partial derivatives

    a. Consider the function $w = f(x, y, z)$. List all possible second partial derivatives that could be computed.
    b. Let $f(x, y, z) = x^2 y + 2xz^2 - 3y^2 z$ and determine which second partial derivatives are equal.

    c. How many second partial derivatives does $p = g(w, x, y, z)$ have?

93. Derivatives of an integral Let h be continuous for all real numbers.

    a. Find f_x and f_y when $f(x, y) = \displaystyle\int_x^y h(s)\, ds.$

    b. Find f_x and f_y when $f(x, y) = \displaystyle\int_1^{xy} h(s)\, ds.$

94. An identity Show that if $f(x, y) = \dfrac{ax + by}{cx + dy}$, where a, b, c, and d are real numbers with $ad - bc = 0$, then $f_x = f_y = 0$, for all x and y in the domain of f. Give an explanation.

95. Cauchy-Riemann equations In the advanced subject of complex variables, a function typically has the form $f(x, y) = u(x, y) + iv(x, y)$, where u and v are real-valued functions and $i = \sqrt{-1}$ is the imaginary unit. A function $f = u + iv$ is said to be *analytic* (analogous to differentiable) if it satisfies the Cauchy-Riemann equations: $u_x = v_y$ and $u_y = -v_x$.

    a. Show that $f(x, y) = (x^2 - y^2) + i(2xy)$ is analytic.
    b. Show that $f(x, y) = x(x^2 - 3y^2) + iy(3x^2 - y^2)$ is analytic.
    c. Show that if $f = u + iv$ is analytic, then $u_{xx} + u_{yy} = 0$ and $v_{xx} + v_{yy} = 0$. Assume u and v satisfy the conditions in Theorem 12.4.

QUICK CHECK ANSWERS

1. $f_x = 2y; f_y = 2x$ **2.** (a) and (c) are the same; f_{qp}
3. $f_{xxx} = 6y; f_{xxy} = 6x$ **4.** $f_{xz} = y - 2x; f_{zz} = 2y$

5. The equations of the level curves are $T = \dfrac{1}{k}P_0 V$. As the pressure P_0 increases, the slopes of these lines increase. ◀

12.5 The Chain Rule

In this section, we combine ideas based on the Chain Rule (Section 3.6) with what we know about partial derivatives (Section 12.4) to develop new methods for finding derivatives of functions of several variables. To illustrate the importance of these methods, consider the following situation.

Economists modeling manufacturing systems often work with *production functions* that relate the productivity (output) of the system to all the variables on which it depends (input). A simplified production function might take the form $P = F(L, K, R)$, where L, K, and R represent the availability of labor, capital, and natural resources, respectively. However, the variables L, K, and R may be intermediate variables that depend on other variables. For example, it might be that L is a function of the unemployment rate u, K is a function of the prime interest rate i, and R is a function of time t (seasonal availability of resources). Even in this simplified model, we see that productivity, which is the dependent variable, is ultimately related to many other variables

(Figure 12.53). Of critical interest to an economist is how changes in one variable determine changes in other variables. For instance, if the unemployment rate increases by 0.1% and the interest rate decreases by 0.2%, what is the effect on productivity? In this section, we develop the tools needed to answer such questions.

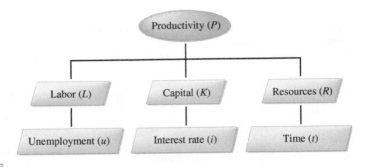

Figure 12.53

The Chain Rule with One Independent Variable

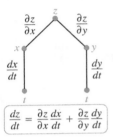

Figure 12.54

Recall the basic Chain Rule: If y is a function of u and u is a function of t, then $\dfrac{dy}{dt} = \dfrac{dy}{du}\dfrac{du}{dt}$. We first extend the Chain Rule to composite functions of the form $z = f(x, y)$, where x and y are functions of t. What is $\dfrac{dz}{dt}$?

We illustrate the relationships among the variables $t, x, y,$ and z using a *tree diagram* (Figure 12.54). To find dz/dt, first notice that z depends on x, which in turn depends on t. The change in z with respect to x is the partial derivative $\partial z/\partial x$, while the change in x with respect to t is the ordinary derivative dx/dt. These derivatives appear on the corresponding branches of the tree diagram. Using the Chain Rule idea, the product of these derivatives gives the change in z with respect to t through x.

Similarly, z also depends on y. The change in z with respect to y is $\partial z/\partial y$, while the change in y with respect to t is dy/dt. The product of these derivatives, which appear on the corresponding branches of the tree, gives the change in z with respect to t through y. Summing the contributions to dz/dt along each branch of the tree leads to the following theorem, whose proof is found in Appendix B.

> A subtle observation about notation should be made. If $z = f(x, y)$, where x and y are functions of another variable t, it is common to write $z = f(t)$ to show that z ultimately depends on t. However, the two functions denoted f are actually different. We *should* write (or at least remember) that in fact $z = F(t)$, where F is a function other than f. This distinction is often overlooked for the sake of convenience.

THEOREM 12.7   Chain Rule (One Independent Variable)
Let z be a differentiable function of x and y on its domain, where x and y are differentiable functions of t on an interval I. Then

$$\frac{dz}{dt} = \frac{\partial z}{\partial x}\frac{dx}{dt} + \frac{\partial z}{\partial y}\frac{dy}{dt}.$$

QUICK CHECK 1 Explain why Theorem 12.7 reduces to the Chain Rule for a function of one variable in the case that $z = f(x)$ and $x = g(t)$. ◄

Before presenting examples, several comments are in order.

• With $z = f(x(t), y(t))$, the dependent variable is z and the sole independent variable is t. The variables x and y are **intermediate variables**.

• The choice of notation for partial and ordinary derivatives in the Chain Rule is important. We write the ordinary derivatives dx/dt and dy/dt because x and y depend only on t. We write the partial derivatives $\partial z/\partial x$ and $\partial z/\partial y$ because z is a function of both x and y. Finally, we write dz/dt as an ordinary derivative because z ultimately depends only on t.

• Theorem 12.7 generalizes directly to functions of more than two intermediate variables (Figure 12.55). For example, if $w = f(x, y, z)$, where $x, y,$ and z are functions of the single independent variable t, then

$$\frac{dw}{dt} = \frac{\partial w}{\partial x}\frac{dx}{dt} + \frac{\partial w}{\partial y}\frac{dy}{dt} + \frac{\partial w}{\partial z}\frac{dz}{dt}.$$

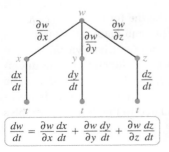

Figure 12.55

▶ If f, x, and y are simple, as in Example 1, it is possible to substitute $x(t)$ and $y(t)$ into f, producing a function of t only, and then differentiate with respect to t. But this approach quickly becomes impractical with more complicated functions, and the Chain Rule offers a great advantage.

EXAMPLE 1 Chain Rule with one independent variable Let $z = x^2 - 3y^2 + 20$, where $x = 2 \cos t$ and $y = 2 \sin t$.

a. Find $\dfrac{dz}{dt}$ and evaluate it at $t = \pi/4$.

b. Interpret the result geometrically.

SOLUTION

a. Computing the intermediate derivatives and applying the Chain Rule (Theorem 12.7), we find that

$$\frac{dz}{dt} = \frac{\partial z}{\partial x}\frac{dx}{dt} + \frac{\partial z}{\partial y}\frac{dy}{dt}$$

$$= \underbrace{(2x)}_{\frac{\partial z}{\partial x}}\underbrace{(-2\sin t)}_{\frac{dx}{dt}} + \underbrace{(-6y)}_{\frac{\partial z}{\partial y}}\underbrace{(2\cos t)}_{\frac{dy}{dt}} \quad \text{Evaluate derivatives.}$$

$$= -4x\sin t - 12y\cos t \qquad \text{Simplify.}$$

$$= -8\cos t \sin t - 24 \sin t \cos t \qquad \text{Substitute } x = 2\cos t, y = 2\sin t.$$

$$= -16 \sin 2t. \qquad \text{Simplify; } \sin 2t = 2\sin t \cos t.$$

Substituting $t = \pi/4$ gives $\dfrac{dz}{dt}\bigg|_{t=\pi/4} = -16.$

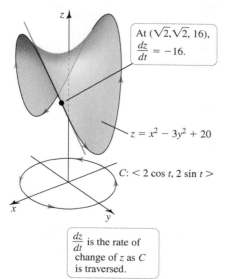

At $(\sqrt{2}, \sqrt{2}, 16)$, $\dfrac{dz}{dt} = -16.$

$z = x^2 - 3y^2 + 20$

C: $\langle 2\cos t, 2\sin t \rangle$

$\dfrac{dz}{dt}$ is the rate of change of z as C is traversed.

Figure 12.56

b. The parametric equations $x = 2 \sin t$, $y = 2 \sin t$, for $0 \le t \le 2\pi$, describe a circle C of radius 2 in the xy-plane. Imagine walking on the surface $z = x^2 - 3y^2 + 20$ directly above the circle C consistent with positive (counterclockwise) orientation of C. Your path rises and falls as you walk (Figure 12.56); the rate of change of your elevation z with respect to t is given by dz/dt. For example, when $t = \pi/4$, the corresponding point on the surface is $(\sqrt{2}, \sqrt{2}, 16)$. At that point, z decreases at a rate of -16 (by part (a)) as you walk on the surface above C.

Related Exercises 7–18 ◀

The Chain Rule with Several Independent Variables

The ideas behind the Chain Rule of Theorem 12.7 can be modified to cover a variety of situations in which functions of several variables are composed with one another. For example, suppose z depends on two intermediate variables x and y, each of which depends on the independent variables s and t. Once again, a tree diagram (Figure 12.57) helps organize the relationships among variables. The dependent variable z now ultimately depends on the two independent variables s and t, so it makes sense to ask about the rates of change of z with respect to either s or t, which are $\partial z/\partial s$ and $\partial z/\partial t$, respectively.

To compute $\partial z/\partial s$, we note that there are two paths in the tree (in red in Figure 12.57) that connect z to s and contribute to $\partial z/\partial s$. Along one path, z changes with respect to x (with rate of change $\partial z/\partial x$) and x changes with respect to s (with rate of change $\partial x/\partial s$). Along the other path, z changes with respect to y (with rate of change $\partial z/\partial y$) and y changes with respect to s (with rate of change $\partial y/\partial s$). We use a Chain Rule calculation along each path and combine the results. A similar argument leads to $\partial z/\partial t$ (Figure 12.58).

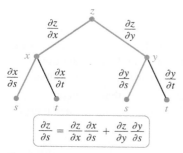

$$\frac{\partial z}{\partial s} = \frac{\partial z}{\partial x}\frac{\partial x}{\partial s} + \frac{\partial z}{\partial y}\frac{\partial y}{\partial s}$$

Figure 12.57

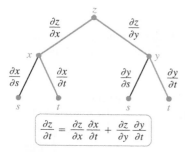

$$\frac{\partial z}{\partial t} = \frac{\partial z}{\partial x}\frac{\partial x}{\partial t} + \frac{\partial z}{\partial y}\frac{\partial y}{\partial t}$$

Figure 12.58

THEOREM 12.8 Chain Rule (Two Independent Variables)

Let z be a differentiable function of x and y, where x and y are differentiable functions of s and t. Then

$$\frac{\partial z}{\partial s} = \frac{\partial z}{\partial x}\frac{\partial x}{\partial s} + \frac{\partial z}{\partial y}\frac{\partial y}{\partial s} \quad \text{and} \quad \frac{\partial z}{\partial t} = \frac{\partial z}{\partial x}\frac{\partial x}{\partial t} + \frac{\partial z}{\partial y}\frac{\partial y}{\partial t}.$$

QUICK CHECK 2 Suppose that $w = f(x, y, z)$, where $x = g(s, t)$, $y = h(s, t)$, and $z = p(s, t)$. Extend Theorem 12.8 to write a formula for $\partial w/\partial t$. ◀

EXAMPLE 2   Chain Rule with two independent variables Let $z = \sin 2x \cos 3y$, where $x = s + t$ and $y = s - t$. Evaluate $\partial z / \partial s$ and $\partial z / \partial t$.

SOLUTION The tree diagram in Figure 12.57 gives the Chain Rule formula for $\partial z / \partial s$: We form products of the derivatives along the red branches connecting z to s and add the results. The partial derivative is

$$\frac{\partial z}{\partial s} = \frac{\partial z}{\partial x}\frac{\partial x}{\partial s} + \frac{\partial z}{\partial y}\frac{\partial y}{\partial s}$$

$$= \underbrace{2\cos 2x \cos 3y}_{\frac{\partial z}{\partial x}} \cdot \underbrace{1}_{\frac{\partial x}{\partial s}} + \underbrace{(-3\sin 2x \sin 3y)}_{\frac{\partial z}{\partial y}} \cdot \underbrace{1}_{\frac{\partial y}{\partial s}}$$

$$= 2\cos\,(2\underbrace{(s + t)}_{x})\cos\,(3\underbrace{(s - t)}_{y}) - 3\sin\,(2\underbrace{(s + t)}_{x})\sin\,(3\underbrace{(s - t)}_{y}).$$

Following the branches of Figure 12.58 connecting z to t, we have

$$\frac{\partial z}{\partial t} = \frac{\partial z}{\partial x}\frac{\partial x}{\partial t} + \frac{\partial z}{\partial y}\frac{\partial y}{\partial t}$$

$$= \underbrace{2\cos 2x \cos 3y}_{\frac{\partial z}{\partial x}} \cdot \underbrace{1}_{\frac{\partial x}{\partial t}} + \underbrace{(-3\sin 2x \sin 3y)}_{\frac{\partial z}{\partial y}} \cdot \underbrace{-1}_{\frac{\partial y}{\partial t}}$$

$$= 2\cos\,(2\underbrace{(s + t)}_{x})\cos\,(3\underbrace{(s - t)}_{y}) + 3\sin\,(2\underbrace{(s + t)}_{x})\sin\,(3\underbrace{(s - t)}_{y}).$$

Related Exercises 19–26 ◄

EXAMPLE 3   More variables Let w be a function of x, y, and z, each of which is a function of s and t.

a. Draw a labeled tree diagram showing the relationships among the variables.

b. Write the Chain Rule formula for $\dfrac{\partial w}{\partial s}$.

SOLUTION

a. Because w is a function of x, y, and z, the upper branches of the tree (Figure 12.59) are labeled with the partial derivatives w_x, w_y, and w_z. Each of x, y, and z is a function of two variables, so the lower branches of the tree also require partial derivative labels.

b. Extending Theorem 12.8, we take the three paths through the tree that connect w to s (red branches in Figure 12.59). Multiplying the derivatives that appear on each path and adding gives the result

$$\frac{\partial w}{\partial s} = \frac{\partial w}{\partial x}\frac{\partial x}{\partial s} + \frac{\partial w}{\partial y}\frac{\partial y}{\partial s} + \frac{\partial w}{\partial z}\frac{\partial z}{\partial s}.$$

Related Exercises 19–26 ◄

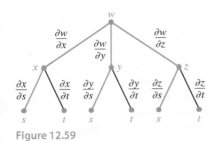

Figure 12.59

QUICK CHECK 3 If Q is a function of w, x, y, and z, each of which is a function of r, s, and t, how many dependent variables, intermediate variables, and independent variables are there? ◄

It is probably clear by now that we can create a Chain Rule for any set of relationships among variables. The key is to draw an accurate tree diagram and label the branches of the tree with the appropriate derivatives.

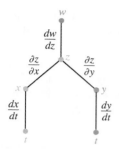

Figure 12.60

EXAMPLE 4 **A different kind of tree** Let w be a function of z, where z is a function of x and y, and each of x and y is a function of t. Draw a labeled tree diagram and write the Chain Rule formula for dw/dt.

SOLUTION The dependent variable w is related to the independent variable t through two paths in the tree: $w \rightarrow z \rightarrow x \rightarrow t$ and $w \rightarrow z \rightarrow y \rightarrow t$ (Figure 12.60). At the top of the tree, w is a function of the single variable z, so the rate of change is the ordinary derivative dw/dz. The tree below z looks like Figure 12.54. Multiplying the derivatives on each of the two branches connecting w to t and adding the results, we have

$$\frac{dw}{dt} = \frac{dw}{dz}\frac{\partial z}{\partial x}\frac{dx}{dt} + \frac{dw}{dz}\frac{\partial z}{\partial y}\frac{dy}{dt} = \frac{dw}{dz}\left(\frac{\partial z}{\partial x}\frac{dx}{dt} + \frac{\partial z}{\partial y}\frac{dy}{dt}\right).$$

Related Exercises 27–30 ◄

Implicit Differentiation

Using the Chain Rule for partial derivatives, the technique of implicit differentiation can be put in a larger perspective. Recall that if x and y are related through an implicit relationship, such as $\sin xy + \pi y^2 = x$, then dy/dx is computed using implicit differentiation (Section 3.8). Another way to compute dy/dx is to define the function $F(x, y) = \sin xy + \pi y^2 - x$. Notice that the original relationship $\sin xy + \pi y^2 = x$ is $F(x, y) = 0$.

To find dy/dx, we treat x as the independent variable and differentiate both sides of $F(x, y(x)) = 0$ with respect to x. The derivative of the right side is 0. On the left side, we use the Chain Rule of Theorem 12.7:

$$\frac{\partial F}{\partial x}\underbrace{\frac{dx}{dx}}_{1} + \frac{\partial F}{\partial y}\frac{dy}{dx} = 0.$$

Noting that $dx/dx = 1$ and solving for dy/dx, we obtain the following theorem.

> ► The question of whether a relationship of the form $F(x, y) = 0$ or $F(x, y, z) = 0$ determines one or more functions is addressed by a theorem of advanced calculus called the Implicit Function Theorem.

THEOREM 12.9 **Implicit Differentiation**
Let F be differentiable on its domain and suppose that $F(x, y) = 0$ defines y as a differentiable function of x. Provided $F_y \neq 0$,

$$\frac{dy}{dx} = -\frac{F_x}{F_y}.$$

> ► The method of Theorem 12.9 generalizes to computing $\frac{\partial z}{\partial x}$ and $\frac{\partial z}{\partial y}$ with functions of the form $F(x, y, z) = 0$ (Exercise 48).

EXAMPLE 5 **Implicit differentiation** Find dy/dx when $F(x, y) = \sin xy + \pi y^2 - x = 0$.

SOLUTION Computing the partial derivatives of F with respect to x and y, we find that

$$F_x = y\cos xy - 1 \quad \text{and} \quad F_y = x\cos xy + 2\pi y.$$

Therefore,

$$\frac{dy}{dx} = -\frac{F_x}{F_y} = -\frac{y\cos xy - 1}{x\cos xy + 2\pi y}.$$

As with many implicit differentiation calculations, the result is left in terms of both x and y. The same result is obtained using the methods of Section 3.8.

Related Exercises 31–36 ◄

QUICK CHECK 4 Use the method of Example 5 to find dy/dx when $F(x, y) = x^2 + xy - y^3 - 7 = 0$. Compare your solution to Example 3 in Section 3.8. Which method is easier? ◄

EXAMPLE 6   Fluid flow A basin of circulating water is represented by the square region $\{(x, y): 0 \leq x \leq 1, 0 \leq y \leq 1\}$, where x is positive in the eastward direction and y is positive in the northward direction. The velocity components of the water are

the east-west velocity $u(x, y) = 2 \sin \pi x \cos \pi y$ and

the north-south velocity $v(x, y) = -2 \cos \pi x \sin \pi y$;

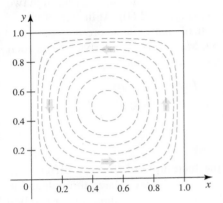

Figure 12.61

these velocity components produce the flow pattern shown in Figure 12.61. The *streamlines* shown in the figure are the paths followed by small parcels of water. The speed of the water at a point (x, y) is given by the function $s(x, y) = \sqrt{u(x, y)^2 + v(x, y)^2}$. Find $\partial s/\partial x$ and $\partial s/\partial y$, the rates of change of the water speed in the x- and y-directions, respectively.

SOLUTION The dependent variable s depends on the independent variables x and y through the intermediate variables u and v (Figure 12.62). Theorem 12.8 applies here in the form

$$\frac{\partial s}{\partial x} = \frac{\partial s}{\partial u}\frac{\partial u}{\partial x} + \frac{\partial s}{\partial v}\frac{\partial v}{\partial x} \quad \text{and} \quad \frac{\partial s}{\partial y} = \frac{\partial s}{\partial u}\frac{\partial u}{\partial y} + \frac{\partial s}{\partial v}\frac{\partial v}{\partial y}.$$

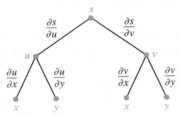

Figure 12.62

The derivatives $\partial s/\partial u$ and $\partial s/\partial v$ are easier to find if we square the speed function to obtain $s^2 = u^2 + v^2$ and then use implicit differentiation. To compute $\partial s/\partial u$, we differentiate both sides of $s^2 = u^2 + v^2$ with respect to u:

$$2s\frac{\partial s}{\partial u} = 2u, \quad \text{which implies that} \quad \frac{\partial s}{\partial u} = \frac{u}{s}.$$

Similarly, differentiating $s^2 = u^2 + v^2$ with respect to v gives

$$2s\frac{\partial s}{\partial v} = 2v, \quad \text{which implies that} \quad \frac{\partial s}{\partial v} = \frac{v}{s}.$$

Now the Chain Rule leads to $\dfrac{\partial s}{\partial x}$:

$$\frac{\partial s}{\partial x} = \frac{\partial s}{\partial u}\frac{\partial u}{\partial x} + \frac{\partial s}{\partial v}\frac{\partial v}{\partial x}$$

$$= \underbrace{\frac{u}{s}}_{\frac{\partial s}{\partial u}} \underbrace{(2\pi \cos \pi x \cos \pi y)}_{\frac{\partial u}{\partial x}} + \underbrace{\frac{v}{s}}_{\frac{\partial s}{\partial v}} \underbrace{(2\pi \sin \pi x \sin \pi y)}_{\frac{\partial v}{\partial x}}$$

$$= \frac{2\pi}{s}(u \cos \pi x \cos \pi y + v \sin \pi x \sin \pi y).$$

A similar calculation shows that

$$\frac{\partial s}{\partial y} = -\frac{2\pi}{s}(u \sin \pi x \sin \pi y + v \cos \pi x \cos \pi y).$$

As a final step, you could replace s, u, and v with their definitions in terms of x and y.

Related Exercises 37–38 ◄

SECTION 12.5 EXERCISES

Review Questions

1. Suppose $z = f(x, y)$, where x and y are functions of t. How many dependent, intermediate, and independent variables are there?

2. Let z be a function of x and y, while x and y are functions of t. Explain how to find $\dfrac{dz}{dt}$.

3. Suppose w is a function of x, y, and z, which are each functions of t. Explain how to find $\dfrac{dw}{dt}$.

4. Let $z = f(x, y)$, $x = g(s, t)$, and $y = h(s, t)$. Explain how to find $\partial z/\partial t$.

5. Given that $w = F(x, y, z)$, and x, y, and z are functions of r and s, sketch a Chain Rule tree diagram with branches labeled with the appropriate derivatives.

6. Suppose $F(x, y) = 0$ and y is a differentiable function of x. Explain how to find dy/dx.

Basic Skills

7–16. Chain Rule with one independent variable *Use Theorem 12.7 to find the following derivatives. When feasible, express your answer in terms of the independent variable.*

7. dz/dt, where $z = x^2 + y^3$, $x = t^2$, and $y = t$

8. dz/dt, where $z = xy^2$, $x = t^2$, and $y = t$

9. dz/dt, where $z = x \sin y$, $x = t^2$, and $y = 4t^3$

10. dz/dt, where $z = x^2y - xy^3$, $x = t^2$, and $y = t^{-2}$

11. dw/dt, where $w = \cos 2x \sin 3y$, $x = t/2$, and $y = t^4$

12. dz/dt, where $z = \sqrt{r^2 + s^2}$, $r = \cos 2t$, and $s = \sin 2t$

13. dw/dt, where $w = xy \sin z$, $x = t^2$, $y = 4t^3$, and $z = t + 1$

14. dQ/dt, where $Q = \sqrt{x^2 + y^2 + z^2}$, $x = \sin t$, $y = \cos t$, and $z = \cos t$

15. dU/dt, where $U = \ln(x + y + z)$, $x = t$, $y = t^2$, and $z = t^3$

16. dV/dt, where $V = \dfrac{x - y}{y + z}$, $x = t$, $y = 2t$, and $z = 3t$

17. **Changing cylinder** The volume of a right circular cylinder with radius r and height h is $V = \pi r^2 h$.
   a. Assume that r and h are functions of t. Find $V'(t)$.
   b. Suppose that $r = e^t$ and $h = e^{-2t}$, for $t \geq 0$. Use part (a) to find $V'(t)$.
   c. Does the volume of the cylinder in part (b) increase or decrease as t increases?

18. **Changing pyramid** The volume of a pyramid with a square base x units on a side and a height of h is $V = \frac{1}{3}x^2h$.
   a. Assume that x and h are functions of t. Find $V'(t)$.
   b. Suppose that $x = t/(t + 1)$ and $h = 1/(t + 1)$, for $t \geq 0$. Use part (a) to find $V'(t)$.
   c. Does the volume of the pyramid in part (b) increase or decrease as t increases?

19–26. Chain Rule with several independent variables *Find the following derivatives.*

19. z_s and z_t, where $z = x^2 \sin y$, $x = s - t$, and $y = t^2$

20. z_s and z_t, where $z = \sin(2x + y)$, $x = s^2 - t^2$, and $y = s^2 + t^2$

21. z_s and z_t, where $z = xy - x^2y$, $x = s + t$, and $y = s - t$

22. z_s and z_t, where $z = \sin x \cos 2y$, $x = s + t$, and $y = s - t$

23. z_s and z_t, where $z = e^{x+y}$, $x = st$, and $y = s + t$

24. z_s and z_t, where $z = xy - 2x + 3y$, $x = \cos s$, and $y = \sin t$

25. w_s and w_t, where $w = \dfrac{x - z}{y + z}$, $x = s + t$, $y = st$, and $z = s - t$

26. w_r, w_s, and w_t, where $w = \sqrt{x^2 + y^2 + z^2}$, $x = st$, $y = rs$, and $z = rt$

27–30. Making trees *Use a tree diagram to write the required Chain Rule formula.*

27. w is a function of z, where z is a function of x and y, each of which is a function of t. Find dw/dt.

28. $w = f(x, y, z)$, where $x = g(t)$, $y = h(s, t)$, and $z = p(r, s, t)$. Find $\partial w/\partial t$.

29. $u = f(v)$, where $v = g(w, x, y)$, $w = h(z)$, $x = p(t, z)$, and $y = q(t, z)$. Find $\partial u/\partial z$.

30. $u = f(v, w, x)$, where $v = g(r, s, t)$, $w = h(r, s, t)$, $x = p(r, s, t)$, and $r = F(z)$. Find $\partial u/\partial z$.

31–36. Implicit differentiation *Given the following equations, evaluate dy/dx. Assume that each equation implicitly defines y as a differentiable function of x.*

31. $x^2 - 2y^2 - 1 = 0$
32. $x^3 + 3xy^2 - y^5 = 0$
33. $2 \sin xy = 1$
34. $ye^{xy} - 2 = 0$
35. $\sqrt{x^2 + 2xy + y^4} = 3$
36. $y \ln(x^2 + y^2 + 4) = 3$

37–38. Fluid flow *The x- and y-components of a fluid moving in two dimensions are given by the following functions u and v. The speed of the fluid at (x, y) is $s(x, y) = \sqrt{u(x, y)^2 + v(x, y)^2}$. Use the Chain Rule to find $\partial s/\partial x$ and $\partial s/\partial y$.*

37. $u(x, y) = 2y$ and $v(x, y) = -2x$; $x \geq 0$ and $y \geq 0$

38. $u(x, y) = x(1 - x)(1 - 2y)$ and $v(x, y) = y(y - 1)(1 - 2x)$; $0 \leq x \leq 1$, $0 \leq y \leq 1$

Further Explorations

39. **Explain why or why not** Determine whether the following statements are true and give an explanation or counterexample. Assume all partial derivatives exist.
   a. If $z = (x + y)\sin xy$, where x and y are functions of s, then $\dfrac{\partial z}{\partial s} = \dfrac{dz}{dx}\dfrac{dx}{ds}$.
   b. Given that $w = f(x(s, t), y(s, t), z(s, t))$, the rate of change of w with respect to t is dw/dt.

40–41. Derivative practice two ways *Find the indicated derivative in two ways:*

a. *Replace x and y to write z as a function of t and differentiate.*

b. *Use the Chain Rule.*

40. $z'(t)$, where $z = \ln(x + y)$, $x = te^t$, and $y = e^t$

41. $z'(t)$, where $z = \dfrac{1}{x} + \dfrac{1}{y}$, $x = t^2 + 2t$, and $y = t^3 - 2$

42–46. Derivative practice *Find the indicated derivative for the following functions.*

42. $\partial z/\partial p$, where $z = x/y$, $x = p + q$, and $y = p - q$

43. dw/dt, where $w = xyz$, $x = 2t^4$, $y = 3t^{-1}$, and $z = 4t^{-3}$

44. $\partial w/\partial x$, where $w = \cos z - \cos x \cos y + \sin x \sin y$ and $z = x + y$

45. $\dfrac{\partial z}{\partial x}$, where $\dfrac{1}{x} + \dfrac{1}{y} + \dfrac{1}{z} = 1$

46. $\partial z/\partial x$, where $xy - z = 1$

47. Change on a line Suppose $w = f(x, y, z)$ and ℓ is the line $r(t) = \langle at, bt, ct \rangle$, for $-\infty < t < \infty$.

a. Find $w'(t)$ on ℓ (in terms of a, b, c, w_x, w_y, and w_z).
b. Apply part (a) to find $w'(t)$ when $f(x, y, z) = xyz$.
c. Apply part (a) to find $w'(t)$ when $f(x, y, z) = \sqrt{x^2 + y^2 + z^2}$.
d. For a general function $w = f(x, y, z)$, find $w''(t)$.

48. Implicit differentiation rule with three variables Assume that $F(x, y, z(x, y)) = 0$ implicitly defines z as a differentiable function of x and y. Extend Theorem 12.9 to show that

$$\frac{\partial z}{\partial x} = -\frac{F_x}{F_z} \quad \text{and} \quad \frac{\partial z}{\partial y} = -\frac{F_y}{F_z}.$$

49–51. Implicit differentiation with three variables *Use the result of Exercise 48 to evaluate $\dfrac{\partial z}{\partial x}$ and $\dfrac{\partial z}{\partial y}$ for the following relations.*

49. $xy + xz + yz = 3$

50. $x^2 + 2y^2 - 3z^2 = 1$

51. $xyz + x + y - z = 0$

52. More than one way Let $e^{xyz} = 2$. Find z_x and z_y in three ways (and check for agreement).

a. Use the result of Exercise 48.
b. Take logarithms of both sides and differentiate $xyz = \ln 2$.
c. Solve for z and differentiate $z = \ln 2/(xy)$.

53–56. Walking on a surface *Consider the following surfaces specified in the form $z = f(x, y)$ and the oriented curve C in the xy-plane.*

a. *In each case, find $z'(t)$.*

b. *Imagine that you are walking on the surface directly above the curve C in the direction of positive orientation. Find the values of t for which you are walking uphill (that is, z is increasing).*

53. $z = x^2 + 4y^2 + 1$, $C: x = \cos t, y = \sin t; \ 0 \le t \le 2\pi$

54. $z = 4x^2 - y^2 + 1$, $C: x = \cos t, y = \sin t; \ 0 \le t \le 2\pi$

55. $z = \sqrt{1 - x^2 - y^2}$, $C: x = e^{-t}, y = e^{-t}; \ t \ge \frac{1}{2}\ln 2$

56. $z = 2x^2 + y^2 + 1$, $C: x = 1 + \cos t, y = \sin t; \ 0 \le t \le 2\pi$

Applications

57. Conservation of energy A projectile with mass m is launched into the air on a parabolic trajectory. For $t \ge 0$, its horizontal and vertical coordinates are $x(t) = u_0 t$ and $y(t) = -\frac{1}{2}gt^2 + v_0 t$, respectively, where u_0 is the initial horizontal velocity, v_0 is the initial vertical velocity, and g is the acceleration due to gravity. Recalling that $u(t) = x'(t)$ and $v(t) = y'(t)$ are the components of the velocity, the energy of the projectile (kinetic plus potential) is

$$E(t) = \frac{1}{2}m(u^2 + v^2) + mgy.$$

Use the Chain Rule to compute $E'(t)$ and show that $E'(t) = 0$, for all $t \ge 0$. Interpret the result.

58. Utility functions in economics Economists use *utility functions* to describe consumers' relative preference for two or more commodities (for example, vanilla vs. chocolate ice cream or leisure time vs. material goods). The Cobb-Douglas family of utility functions has the form $U(x, y) = x^a y^{1-a}$, where x and y are the amounts of two commodities and $0 < a < 1$ is a parameter. Level curves on which the utility function is constant are called *indifference curves*; the utility is the same for all combinations of x and y along an indifference curve (see figure).

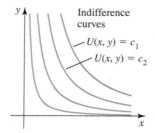

a. The marginal utilities of the commodities x and y are defined to be $\partial U/\partial x$ and $\partial U/\partial y$, respectively. Compute the marginal utilities for the utility function $U(x, y) = x^a y^{1-a}$.

b. The marginal rate of substitution (MRS) is the slope of the indifference curve at the point (x, y). Use the Chain Rule to show that for $U(x, y) = x^a y^{1-a}$, the MRS is $-\dfrac{a}{1 - a}\dfrac{y}{x}$.

c. Find the MRS for the utility function $U(x, y) = x^{0.4}y^{0.6}$ at $(x, y) = (8, 12)$.

59. Constant volume tori The volume of a solid torus is given by $V = (\pi^2/4)(R + r)(R - r)^2$, where r and R are the inner and outer radii and $R > r$ (see figure).

a. If R and r increase at the same rate, does the volume of the torus increase, decrease, or remain constant?

b. If R and r decrease at the same rate, does the volume of the torus increase, decrease, or remain constant?

60. Body surface area One of several empirical formulas that relates the surface area S of a human body to the height h and weight w of the body is the Mosteller formula $S(h, w) = \frac{1}{60} \sqrt{hw}$, where h is measured in centimeters, w is measured in kilograms, and S is measured in square meters. Suppose that h and w are functions of t.

   a. Find $S'(t)$.

   b. Show that the condition that the surface area remains constant as h and w change is $wh'(t) + hw'(t) = 0$.

   c. Show that part (b) implies that for constant surface area, h and w must be inversely related; that is, $h = C/w$, where C is a constant.

61. The Ideal Gas Law The pressure, temperature, and volume of an ideal gas are related by $PV = kT$, where $k > 0$ is a constant. Any two of the variables may be considered independent, which determines the third variable.

   a. Use implicit differentiation to compute the partial derivatives $\frac{\partial P}{\partial V}, \frac{\partial T}{\partial P}$, and $\frac{\partial V}{\partial T}$.

   b. Show that $\frac{\partial P}{\partial V} \frac{\partial T}{\partial P} \frac{\partial V}{\partial T} = -1$. (See Exercise 67 for a generalization.)

62. Variable density The density of a thin circular plate of radius 2 is given by $\rho(x, y) = 4 + xy$. The edge of the plate is described by the parametric equations $x = 2 \cos t, y = 2 \sin t$, for $0 \le t \le 2\pi$.

   a. Find the rate of change of the density with respect to t on the edge of the plate.

   b. At what point(s) on the edge of the plate is the density a maximum?

T 63. Spiral through a domain Suppose you follow the spiral path $C: x = \cos t, y = \sin t, z = t$, for $t \ge 0$, through the domain of the function $w = f(x, y, z) = xyz/(z^2 + 1)$.

   a. Find $w'(t)$ along C.

   b. Estimate the point (x, y, z) on C at which w has its maximum value.

Additional Exercises

64. Change of coordinates Recall that Cartesian and polar coordinates are related through the transformation equations

$$\begin{cases} x = r \cos \theta \\ y = r \sin \theta \end{cases} \quad \text{or} \quad \begin{cases} r^2 = x^2 + y^2 \\ \tan \theta = y/x. \end{cases}$$

   a. Evaluate the partial derivatives x_r, y_r, x_θ, and y_θ.

   b. Evaluate the partial derivatives r_x, r_y, θ_x, and θ_y.

   c. For a function $z = f(x, y)$, find z_r and z_θ, where x and y are expressed in terms of r and θ.

   d. For a function $z = g(r, \theta)$, find z_x and z_y, where r and θ are expressed in terms of x and y.

   e. Show that $\left(\frac{\partial z}{\partial x} \right)^2 + \left(\frac{\partial z}{\partial y} \right)^2 = \left(\frac{\partial z}{\partial r} \right)^2 + \frac{1}{r^2} \left(\frac{\partial z}{\partial \theta} \right)^2$.

65. Change of coordinates continued An important derivative operation in many applications is called the Laplacian; in Cartesian coordinates, for $z = f(x, y)$, the Laplacian is $z_{xx} + z_{yy}$. Determine the Laplacian in polar coordinates using the following steps.

   a. Begin with $z = g(r, \theta)$ and write z_x and z_y in terms of polar coordinates (see Exercise 64).

   b. Use the Chain Rule to find $z_{xx} = \frac{\partial}{\partial x} (z_x)$. There should be two major terms, which, when expanded and simplified, result in five terms.

   c. Use the Chain Rule to find $z_{yy} = \frac{\partial}{\partial y} (z_y)$. There should be two major terms, which, when expanded and simplified, result in five terms.

   d. Combine parts (b) and (c) to show that

$$z_{xx} + z_{yy} = z_{rr} + \frac{1}{r} z_r + \frac{1}{r^2} z_{\theta\theta}.$$

66. Geometry of implicit differentiation Suppose x and y are related by the equation $F(x, y) = 0$. Interpret the solution of this equation as the set of points (x, y) that lie on the intersection of the surface $z = F(x, y)$ with the xy-plane $(z = 0)$.

   a. Make a sketch of a surface and its intersection with the xy-plane. Give a geometric interpretation of the result that $\frac{dy}{dx} = -\frac{F_x}{F_y}$.

   b. Explain geometrically what happens at points where $F_y = 0$.

67. General three-variable relationship In the implicit relationship $F(x, y, z) = 0$, any two of the variables may be considered independent, which then determines the third variable. To avoid confusion, we use a subscript to indicate which variable is held fixed in a derivative calculation; for example, $\left(\frac{\partial z}{\partial x} \right)_y$ means that y is held fixed in taking the partial derivative of z with respect to x. (In this context, the subscript does *not* mean a derivative.)

   a. Differentiate $F(x, y, z) = 0$ with respect to x holding y fixed to show that $\left(\frac{\partial z}{\partial x} \right)_y = -\frac{F_x}{F_z}$.

   b. As in part (a), find $\left(\frac{\partial y}{\partial z} \right)_x$ and $\left(\frac{\partial x}{\partial y} \right)_z$.

   c. Show that $\left(\frac{\partial z}{\partial x} \right)_y \left(\frac{\partial y}{\partial z} \right)_x \left(\frac{\partial x}{\partial y} \right)_z = -1$.

   d. Find the relationship analogous to part (c) for the case $F(w, x, y, z) = 0$.

68. Second derivative Let $f(x, y) = 0$ define y as a twice differentiable function of x.

   a. Show that $y''(x) = -\frac{f_{xx} f_y^2 - 2 f_x f_y f_{xy} + f_{yy} f_x^2}{f_y^3}$.

   b. Verify part (a) using the function $f(x, y) = xy - 1$.

69. Subtleties of the Chain Rule Let $w = f(x, y, z) = 2x + 3y + 4z$, which is defined for all (x, y, z) in $\mathbb{R}^3$. Suppose that we are interested in the partial derivative w_x on a subset of $\mathbb{R}^3$, such as the plane P given by $z = 4x - 2y$. The point to be made is that the result is not unique unless we specify which variables are considered independent.

   a. We could proceed as follows. On the plane P, consider x and y as the independent variables, which means z depends on x and y, so we write $w = f(x, y, z(x, y))$. Differentiate with respect to x holding y fixed to show that $\left(\frac{\partial w}{\partial x} \right)_y = 18$, where the subscript y indicates that y is held fixed.

b. Alternatively, on the plane P, we could consider x and z as the independent variables, which means y depends on x and z, so we write $w = f(x, y(x, z), z)$ and differentiate with respect to x holding z fixed. Show that $\left(\dfrac{\partial w}{\partial x}\right)_z = 8$, where the subscript z indicates that z is held fixed.

c. Make a sketch of the plane $z = 4x - 2y$ and interpret the results of parts (a) and (b) geometrically.

d. Repeat the arguments of parts (a) and (b) to find $\left(\dfrac{\partial w}{\partial y}\right)_x$, $\left(\dfrac{\partial w}{\partial y}\right)_z$, $\left(\dfrac{\partial w}{\partial z}\right)_x$, and $\left(\dfrac{\partial w}{\partial z}\right)_y$.

QUICK CHECK ANSWERS

1. If $z = f(x(t))$, then $\dfrac{\partial z}{\partial y} = 0$, and the original Chain Rule results. **2.** $\dfrac{\partial w}{\partial t} = \dfrac{\partial w}{\partial x}\dfrac{\partial x}{\partial t} + \dfrac{\partial w}{\partial y}\dfrac{\partial y}{\partial t} + \dfrac{\partial w}{\partial z}\dfrac{\partial z}{\partial t}$

3. One dependent variable, four intermediate variables, and three independent variables

4. $\dfrac{dy}{dx} = \dfrac{2x + y}{3y^2 - x}$; in this case, using $\dfrac{dy}{dx} = -\dfrac{F_x}{F_y}$ is more efficient. ◄

12.6 Directional Derivatives and the Gradient

Partial derivatives tell us a lot about the rate of change of a function on its domain. However, they do not *directly* answer some important questions. For example, suppose you are standing at a point $(a, b, f(a, b))$ on the surface $z = f(x, y)$. The partial derivatives f_x and f_y tell you the rate of change (or slope) of the surface at that point in the directions parallel to the x-axis and y-axis, respectively. But you could walk in an infinite number of directions from that point and find a different rate of change in every direction. With this observation in mind, we pose several questions.

- Suppose you are standing on a surface and you walk in a direction *other* than a coordinate direction—say, northwest or south-southeast. What is the rate of change of the function in such a direction?

- Suppose you are standing on a surface and you release a ball at your feet and let it roll. In which direction will it roll?

- If you are hiking up a mountain, in what direction should you walk after each step if you want to follow the steepest path?

These questions are answered in this section by introducing the *directional derivative*, followed by one of the central concepts of calculus—the *gradient*.

Directional Derivatives

Let $(a, b, f(a, b))$ be a point on the surface $z = f(x, y)$ and let **u** be a unit vector in the xy-plane (Figure 12.63). Our aim is to find the rate of change of f in the direction **u** at $P_0(a, b)$. In general, this rate of change is neither $f_x(a, b)$ nor $f_y(a, b)$ (unless $\mathbf{u} = \langle 1, 0 \rangle$ or $\mathbf{u} = \langle 0, 1 \rangle$), but it turns out to be a combination of $f_x(a, b)$ and $f_y(a, b)$.

Figure 12.64a shows the unit vector $\mathbf{u} = \langle u_1, u_2 \rangle$; its horizontal and vertical components are u_1 and u_2, respectively. The derivative we seek must be computed along the line ℓ in the xy-plane through P_0 in the direction of **u**. A neighboring point P, which is h units from P_0 along ℓ, has coordinates $P(a + hu_1, b + hu_2)$ (Figure 12.64b).

Now imagine the plane Q perpendicular to the xy-plane, containing ℓ. This plane cuts the surface $z = f(x, y)$ in a curve C. Consider two points on C corresponding to P_0 and P; they have z-coordinates $f(a, b)$ and $f(a + hu_1, b + hu_2)$ (Figure 12.65). The slope of the secant line between these points is

$$\frac{f(a + hu_1, b + hu_2) - f(a, b)}{h}.$$

The derivative of f in the direction of **u** is obtained by letting $h \to 0$; when the limit exists, it is called the *directional derivative of f at (a, b) in the direction of* **u**. It gives the slope of the line tangent to the curve C in the plane Q.

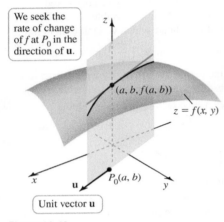

We seek the rate of change of f at P_0 in the direction of **u**.

$(a, b, f(a, b))$

$z = f(x, y)$

$P_0(a, b)$

Unit vector **u**

Figure 12.63

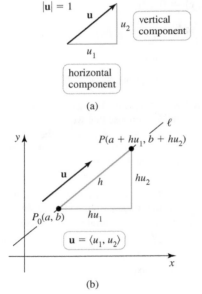

$|\mathbf{u}| = 1$

u

u_2 vertical component

u_1 horizontal component

(a)

ℓ

$P(a + hu_1, b + hu_2)$

u h hu_2

$P_0(a, b)$ hu_1

$\mathbf{u} = \langle u_1, u_2 \rangle$

(b)

Figure 12.64

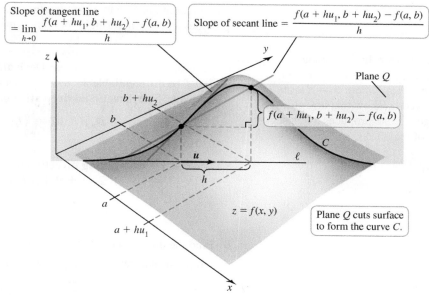

Slope of tangent line
$$= \lim_{h \to 0} \frac{f(a + hu_1, b + hu_2) - f(a, b)}{h}$$

Slope of secant line $= \dfrac{f(a + hu_1, b + hu_2) - f(a, b)}{h}$

Plane Q

$f(a + hu_1, b + hu_2) - f(a, b)$

$b + hu_2$

b

C

u

ℓ

h

a

$z = f(x, y)$

$a + hu_1$

Plane Q cuts surface to form the curve C.

Figure 12.65

> The definition of the directional derivative looks like the definition of the ordinary derivative if we write it as
>
> $$\lim_{P \to P_0} \frac{f(P) - f(P_0)}{|P - P_0|},$$
>
> where P approaches P_0 along the line ℓ.

DEFINITION **Directional Derivative**

Let f be differentiable at (a, b) and let $\mathbf{u} = \langle u_1, u_2 \rangle$ be a unit vector in the xy-plane. The **directional derivative of f at (a, b) in the direction of u** is

$$D_{\mathbf{u}}f(a, b) = \lim_{h \to 0} \frac{f(a + hu_1, b + hu_2) - f(a, b)}{h},$$

provided the limit exists.

QUICK CHECK 1 Explain why, when $\mathbf{u} = \langle 1, 0 \rangle$ in the definition of the directional derivative, the result is $f_x(a, b)$ and when $\mathbf{u} = \langle 0, 1 \rangle$, the result is $f_y(a, b)$. ◄

> To see that s is an arc length parameter, note that the line ℓ may be written in the form
>
> $$\mathbf{r}(s) = \langle a + su_1, b + su_2 \rangle.$$
>
> Therefore, $\mathbf{r}'(s) = \langle u_1, u_2 \rangle$ and $|\mathbf{r}'(s)| = 1$. It follows by the discussion in Section 11.8 that s is an arc length parameter. Because the directional derivative is a derivative with respect to length along ℓ, it is essential that s be an arc length parameter, which occurs only if $\mathbf{u}$ is a unit vector.

As with ordinary derivatives, we would prefer to evaluate directional derivatives without taking limits. Fortunately, there is an easy way to express a directional derivative in terms of partial derivatives.

The key is to define a function that is equal to f along the line ℓ through (a, b) in the direction of the unit vector $\mathbf{u} = \langle u_1, u_2 \rangle$. The points on ℓ satisfy the parametric equations

$$x = a + su_1 \quad \text{and} \quad y = b + su_2,$$

where $-\infty < s < \infty$. Because $\mathbf{u}$ is a unit vector, the parameter s corresponds to arc length. As s increases, the points (x, y) move along ℓ in the direction of $\mathbf{u}$ with $s = 0$ corresponding to (a, b). Now we define the function

$$g(s) = f(\underbrace{a + su_1}_{x}, \underbrace{b + su_2}_{y}),$$

which gives the values of f along ℓ. The derivative of f along ℓ is $g'(s)$, and when evaluated at $s = 0$, it is the directional derivative of f at (a, b); that is, $g'(0) = D_{\mathbf{u}}f(a, b)$.

Noting that $\dfrac{dx}{ds} = u_1$ and $\dfrac{dy}{ds} = u_2$, we apply the Chain Rule to find that

$$D_{\mathbf{u}}f(a, b) = g'(0) = \left(\frac{\partial f}{\partial x} \underbrace{\frac{dx}{ds}}_{u_1} + \frac{\partial f}{\partial y} \underbrace{\frac{dy}{ds}}_{u_2} \right)\Bigg|_{s=0} \quad \text{Chain Rule}$$

$$= f_x(a, b)u_1 + f_y(a, b)u_2. \quad s = 0 \text{ corresponds to } (a, b).$$

We see that the directional derivative is a weighted average of the partial derivatives $f_x(a, b)$ and $f_y(a, b)$, with the components of $\mathbf{u}$ serving as the weights. In other words, knowing the slope of the surface in the x- and y-directions allows us to find the slope in any direction. Notice that the directional derivative can be written as a dot product, which provides a practical formula for computing directional derivatives.

QUICK CHECK 2 In the parametric description $x = a + su_1$ and $y = b + su_2$, where $\mathbf{u} = \langle u_1, u_2 \rangle$ is a unit vector, show that any positive change Δs in s produces a line segment of length Δs. ◄

THEOREM 12.10   Directional Derivative

Let f be differentiable at (a, b) and let $\mathbf{u} = \langle u_1, u_2 \rangle$ be a unit vector in the xy-plane. The **directional derivative of f at (a, b) in the direction of u** is

$$D_{\mathbf{u}}f(a, b) = \langle f_x(a, b), f_y(a, b) \rangle \cdot \langle u_1, u_2 \rangle.$$

EXAMPLE 1   Computing directional derivatives Consider the paraboloid $z = f(x, y) = \frac{1}{4}(x^2 + 2y^2) + 2$. Let P_0 be the point $(3, 2)$ and consider the unit vectors

$$\mathbf{u} = \left\langle \frac{1}{\sqrt{2}}, \frac{1}{\sqrt{2}} \right\rangle \quad \text{and} \quad \mathbf{v} = \left\langle \frac{1}{2}, -\frac{\sqrt{3}}{2} \right\rangle.$$

a. Find the directional derivative of f at P_0 in the directions of **u** and **v**.

b. Graph the surface and interpret the directional derivatives.

SOLUTION

a. We see that $f_x = x/2$ and $f_y = y$; evaluated at $(3, 2)$, we have $f_x(3, 2) = 3/2$ and $f_y(3, 2) = 2$. The directional derivatives in the directions **u** and **v** are

$$\begin{aligned} D_{\mathbf{u}}f(3, 2) &= \langle f_x(3, 2), f_y(3, 2) \rangle \cdot \langle u_1, u_2 \rangle \\ &= \frac{3}{2} \cdot \frac{1}{\sqrt{2}} + 2 \cdot \frac{1}{\sqrt{2}} = \frac{7}{2\sqrt{2}} \approx 2.47 \text{ and} \end{aligned}$$

$$\begin{aligned} D_{\mathbf{v}}f(3, 2) &= \langle f_x(3, 2), f_y(3, 2) \rangle \cdot \langle v_1, v_2 \rangle \\ &= \frac{3}{2} \cdot \frac{1}{2} + 2\left(-\frac{\sqrt{3}}{2} \right) = \frac{3}{4} - \sqrt{3} \approx -0.98. \end{aligned}$$

> ► It is understood that the line tangent to C in the direction of **u** lies in the vertical plane Q containing **u**.

b. In the direction of **u**, the directional derivative is approximately 2.47. Because it is positive, the function is increasing at $(3, 2)$ in this direction. Equivalently, if Q is the vertical plane containing **u** and C is the curve along which the surface intersects Q, then the slope of the line tangent to C is approximately 2.47 (Figure 12.66a). In the direction of **v**, the directional derivative is approximately -0.98. Because it is negative, the function is decreasing in this direction. In this case, the vertical plane Q contains **v** and again C is the curve along which the surface intersects Q; the slope of the line tangent to C is approximately -0.98 (Figure 12.66b).

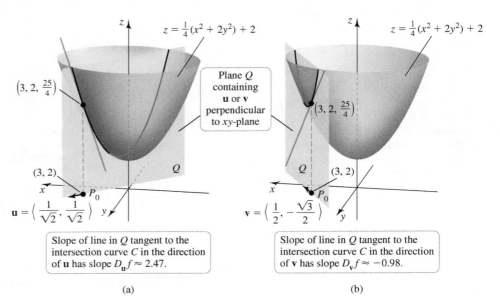

Slope of line in Q tangent to the intersection curve C in the direction of **u** has slope $D_{\mathbf{u}}f \approx 2.47$.

Slope of line in Q tangent to the intersection curve C in the direction of **v** has slope $D_{\mathbf{v}}f \approx -0.98$.

(a)   (b)

Figure 12.66

QUICK CHECK 3 In Example 1, evaluate $D_{-\mathbf{u}}f(3, 2)$ and $D_{-\mathbf{v}}f(3, 2)$. ◄

Related Exercises 7–8 ◄

The Gradient Vector

We have seen that the directional derivative can be written as a dot product: $D_{\mathbf{u}}f(a, b) = \langle f_x(a, b), f_y(a, b) \rangle \cdot \langle u_1, u_2 \rangle$. The vector $\langle f_x(a, b), f_y(a, b) \rangle$ that appears in the dot product is important in its own right and is called the *gradient* of f.

> ▶ Recall that the unit coordinate vectors in $\mathbb{R}^2$ are $\mathbf{i} = \langle 1, 0 \rangle$ and $\mathbf{j} = \langle 0, 1 \rangle$. The gradient of f is also written grad f, read *grad f*.

DEFINITION Gradient (Two Dimensions)

Let f be differentiable at the point (x, y). The **gradient** of f at (x, y) is the vector-valued function

$$\nabla f(x, y) = \langle f_x(x, y), f_y(x, y) \rangle = f_x(x, y)\,\mathbf{i} + f_y(x, y)\,\mathbf{j}.$$

With the definition of the gradient, the directional derivative of f at (a, b) in the direction of the unit vector $\mathbf{u}$ can be written

$$D_{\mathbf{u}}f(a, b) = \nabla f(a, b) \cdot \mathbf{u}.$$

The gradient satisfies sum, product, and quotient rules analogous to those for ordinary derivatives (Exercise 81).

EXAMPLE 2   Computing gradients Find $\nabla f(3, 2)$ for $f(x, y) = x^2 + 2xy - y^3$.

SOLUTION Computing $f_x = 2x + 2y$ and $f_y = 2x - 3y^2$, we have

$$\nabla f(x, y) = \langle 2(x + y), 2x - 3y^2 \rangle = 2(x + y)\,\mathbf{i} + (2x - 3y^2)\,\mathbf{j}.$$

Substituting $x = 3$ and $y = 2$ gives

$$\nabla f(3, 2) = \langle 10, -6 \rangle = 10\,\mathbf{i} - 6\,\mathbf{j}.$$

Related Exercises 9–16 ◀

EXAMPLE 3   Computing directional derivatives with gradients Let
$$f(x, y) = 3 - \frac{x^2}{10} + \frac{xy^2}{10}.$$

a. Compute $\nabla f(3, -1)$.

b. Compute $D_{\mathbf{u}}f(3, -1)$, where $\mathbf{u} = \left\langle \dfrac{1}{\sqrt{2}}, -\dfrac{1}{\sqrt{2}} \right\rangle$.

c. Compute the directional derivative of f at $(3, -1)$ in the direction of the vector $\langle 3, 4 \rangle$.

SOLUTION

a. Note that $f_x = -x/5 + y^2/10$ and $f_y = xy/5$. Therefore,

$$\nabla f(3, -1) = \left\langle -\frac{x}{5} + \frac{y^2}{10}, \frac{xy}{5} \right\rangle \bigg|_{(3, -1)} = \left\langle -\frac{1}{2}, -\frac{3}{5} \right\rangle.$$

b. Before computing the directional derivative, it is important to verify that $\mathbf{u}$ is a unit vector (in this case, it is). The required directional derivative is

$$D_{\mathbf{u}}f(3, -1) = \nabla f(3, -1) \cdot \mathbf{u} = \left\langle -\frac{1}{2}, -\frac{3}{5} \right\rangle \cdot \left\langle \frac{1}{\sqrt{2}}, -\frac{1}{\sqrt{2}} \right\rangle = \frac{1}{10\sqrt{2}}.$$

Figure 12.67 shows the line tangent to the intersection curve in the plane corresponding to $\mathbf{u}$; its slope is $D_{\mathbf{u}}f(3, -1)$.

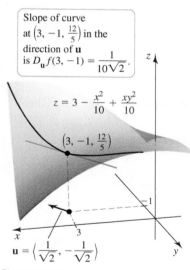

Slope of curve at $\left(3, -1, \frac{12}{5}\right)$ in the direction of $\mathbf{u}$ is $D_{\mathbf{u}}f(3, -1) = \dfrac{1}{10\sqrt{2}}$.

$z = 3 - \dfrac{x^2}{10} + \dfrac{xy^2}{10}$

$\left(3, -1, \dfrac{12}{5}\right)$

$\mathbf{u} = \left\langle \dfrac{1}{\sqrt{2}}, -\dfrac{1}{\sqrt{2}} \right\rangle$

Figure 12.67

c. In this case, the direction is given in terms of a nonunit vector. The vector $\langle 3, 4 \rangle$ has length 5, so the unit vector in the direction of $\langle 3, 4 \rangle$ is $\mathbf{u} = \left\langle \frac{3}{5}, \frac{4}{5} \right\rangle$. The directional derivative at $(3, -1)$ in the direction of $\mathbf{u}$ is

$$D_{\mathbf{u}} f(3, -1) = \nabla f(3, -1) \cdot \mathbf{u} = \left\langle -\frac{1}{2}, -\frac{3}{5} \right\rangle \cdot \left\langle \frac{3}{5}, \frac{4}{5} \right\rangle = -\frac{39}{50},$$

which gives the slope of the surface in the direction of $\mathbf{u}$ at $(3, -1)$.

Related Exercises 17–26 ◀

Interpretations of the Gradient

The gradient is important not only in calculating directional derivatives; it plays many other roles in multivariable calculus. Our present goal is to develop some intuition about the meaning of the gradient.

> Recall that $\mathbf{u} \cdot \mathbf{v} = |\mathbf{u}||\mathbf{v}| \cos \theta$, where θ is the angle between $\mathbf{u}$ and $\mathbf{v}$.

We have seen that the directional derivative of f at (a, b) in the direction of the unit vector $\mathbf{u}$ is $D_{\mathbf{u}} f(a, b) = \nabla f(a, b) \cdot \mathbf{u}$. Using properties of the dot product, we have

$$\begin{aligned} D_{\mathbf{u}} f(a, b) &= \nabla f(a, b) \cdot \mathbf{u} \\ &= |\nabla f(a, b)||\mathbf{u}| \cos \theta \\ &= |\nabla f(a, b)| \cos \theta, \qquad |\mathbf{u}| = 1 \end{aligned}$$

> It is important to remember and easy to forget that $\nabla f(a, b)$ lies in the same plane as the domain of f.

where θ is the angle between $\nabla f(a, b)$ and $\mathbf{u}$. It follows that $D_{\mathbf{u}} f(a, b)$ has its maximum value when $\cos \theta = 1$, which corresponds to $\theta = 0$. Therefore, $D_{\mathbf{u}} f(a, b)$ has its maximum value and f has its greatest rate of *increase* when $\nabla f(a, b)$ and $\mathbf{u}$ point in the same direction. Notice that when $\cos \theta = 1$, the actual rate of increase is $D_{\mathbf{u}} f(a, b) = |\nabla f(a, b)|$ (Figure 12.68).

Similarly, when $\theta = \pi$, we have $\cos \theta = -1$, and f has its greatest rate of *decrease* when $\nabla f(a, b)$ and $\mathbf{u}$ point in opposite directions. The actual rate of decrease is $D_{\mathbf{u}} f(a, b) = -|\nabla f(a, b)|$. These observations are summarized as follows: The gradient $\nabla f(a, b)$ points in the *direction of steepest ascent* at (a, b), while $-\nabla f(a, b)$ points in the *direction of steepest descent*.

Notice that $D_{\mathbf{u}} f(a, b) = 0$ when the angle between $\nabla f(a, b)$ and $\mathbf{u}$ is $\pi/2$, which means $\nabla f(a, b)$ and $\mathbf{u}$ are orthogonal (Figure 12.68). These observations justify the following theorem.

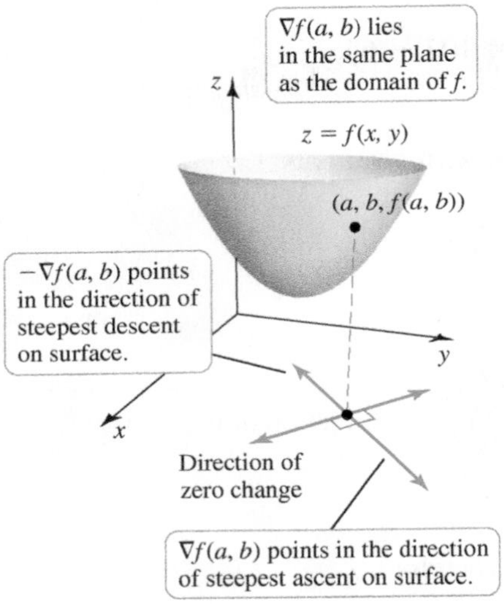

$\nabla f(a, b)$ lies in the same plane as the domain of f.

$z = f(x, y)$

$(a, b, f(a, b))$

$-\nabla f(a, b)$ points in the direction of steepest descent on surface.

Direction of zero change

$\nabla f(a, b)$ points in the direction of steepest ascent on surface.

Figure 12.68

THEOREM 12.11   Directions of Change

Let f be differentiable at (a, b) with $\nabla f(a, b) \neq \mathbf{0}$.

1. f has its maximum rate of increase at (a, b) in the direction of the gradient $\nabla f(a, b)$. The rate of change in this direction is $|\nabla f(a, b)|$.

2. f has its maximum rate of decrease at (a, b) in the direction of $-\nabla f(a, b)$. The rate of change in this direction is $-|\nabla f(a, b)|$.

3. The directional derivative is zero in any direction orthogonal to $\nabla f(a, b)$.

EXAMPLE 4   Steepest ascent and descent Consider the bowl-shaped paraboloid $z = f(x, y) = 4 + x^2 + 3y^2$.

a. If you are located on the paraboloid at the point $\left(2, -\frac{1}{2}, \frac{35}{4} \right)$, in which direction should you move in order to *ascend* on the surface at the maximum rate? What is the rate of change?

b. If you are located at the point $\left(2, -\frac{1}{2}, \frac{35}{4} \right)$, in which direction should you move in order to *descend* on the surface at the maximum rate? What is the rate of change?

c. At the point $(3, 1, 16)$, in what direction(s) is there no change in the function values?

SOLUTION

a. At the point $\left(2, -\frac{1}{2}\right)$, the value of the gradient is

$$\nabla f\left(2, -\tfrac{1}{2}\right) = \langle 2x, 6y \rangle \big|_{(2, -1/2)} = \langle 4, -3 \rangle.$$

Therefore, the direction of steepest ascent in the xy-plane is in the direction of the gradient vector $\langle 4, -3 \rangle$ (or $\mathbf{u} = \frac{1}{5}\langle 4, -3 \rangle$, as a unit vector). The rate of change is $\left|\nabla f\left(2, -\frac{1}{2}\right)\right| = |\langle 4, -3 \rangle| = 5$ (Figure 12.69a).

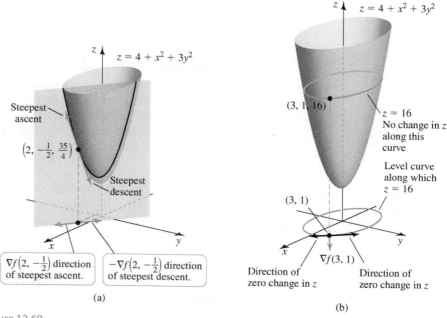

Figure 12.69

b. The direction of steepest *descent* is the direction of $-\nabla f\left(2, -\frac{1}{2}\right) = \langle -4, 3 \rangle$ (or $\mathbf{u} = \frac{1}{5}\langle -4, 3 \rangle$, as a unit vector). The rate of change is $-\left|\nabla f\left(2, -\frac{1}{2}\right)\right| = -5$.

c. At the point $(3, 1)$, the value of the gradient is $\nabla f(3, 1) = \langle 6, 6 \rangle$. The function has zero change if we move in either of the two directions orthogonal to $\langle 6, 6 \rangle$; these two directions are parallel to $\langle 6, -6 \rangle$. In terms of unit vectors, the directions of no change are $\mathbf{u} = \dfrac{1}{\sqrt{2}}\langle -1, 1 \rangle$ and $\mathbf{u} = \dfrac{1}{\sqrt{2}}\langle 1, -1 \rangle$ (Figure 12.69b).

> Note that $\langle 6, 6 \rangle$ and $\langle 6, -6 \rangle$ are orthogonal because $\langle 6, 6 \rangle \cdot \langle 6, -6 \rangle = 0$.

Related Exercises 27–32 ◀

EXAMPLE 5 Interpreting directional derivatives Consider the function $f(x, y) = 3x^2 - 2y^2$.

a. Compute $\nabla f(x, y)$ and $\nabla f(2, 3)$.

b. Let $\mathbf{u} = \langle \cos\theta, \sin\theta \rangle$ be a unit vector. At $(2, 3)$, for what values of θ (measured relative to the positive x-axis), with $0 \le \theta < 2\pi$, does the directional derivative have its maximum and minimum values and what are those values?

SOLUTION

a. The gradient is $\nabla f(x, y) = \langle f_x, f_y \rangle = \langle 6x, -4y \rangle$, and at $(2, 3)$, we have $\nabla f(2, 3) = \langle 12, -12 \rangle$.

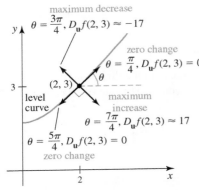

Figure 12.70

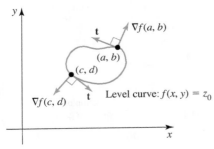

Figure 12.71

► We have used the fact that the vector $\langle a, b \rangle$ has slope b/a.

b. The gradient $\nabla f(2, 3) = \langle 12, -12 \rangle$ makes an angle of $7\pi/4$ with the positive x-axis. So the maximum rate of change of f occurs in this direction, and that rate of change is $|\nabla f(2, 3)| = |\langle 12, -12 \rangle| = 12\sqrt{2} \approx 17$. The direction of maximum decrease is opposite the direction of the gradient, which corresponds to $\theta = 3\pi/4$. The maximum rate of decrease is the negative of the maximum rate of increase, or $-12\sqrt{2} \approx -17$. The function has zero change in the directions orthogonal to the gradient, which correspond to $\theta = \pi/4$ and $\theta = 5\pi/4$.

Figure 12.70 summarizes these conclusions. Notice that the gradient at $(2, 3)$ appears to be orthogonal to the level curve of f passing through $(2, 3)$. We next see that this is always the case.

Related Exercises 33–42 ◄

The Gradient and Level Curves

Theorem 12.11 states that in any direction orthogonal to the gradient $\nabla f(a, b)$, the function f does not change at (a, b). Recall from Section 12.2 that the curve $f(x, y) = z_0$, where z_0 is a constant, is a *level curve*, on which function values are constant. Combining these two observations, we conclude that the gradient $\nabla f(a, b)$ is orthogonal to the line tangent to the level curve through (a, b).

THEOREM 12.12 The Gradient and Level Curves
Given a function f differentiable at (a, b), the line tangent to the level curve of f at (a, b) is orthogonal to the gradient $\nabla f(a, b)$, provided $\nabla f(a, b) \neq \mathbf{0}$.

Proof: A level curve of the function $z = f(x, y)$ is a curve in the xy-plane of the form $f(x, y) = z_0$, where z_0 is a constant. By Theorem 12.9, the slope of the line tangent to the level curve is $y'(x) = -f_x/f_y$.

It follows that any vector pointing in the direction of the tangent line at the point (a, b) is a scalar multiple of the vector $\mathbf{t} = \langle -f_y(a, b), f_x(a, b) \rangle$ (Figure 12.71). At that same point, the gradient points in the direction $\nabla f(a, b) = \langle f_x(a, b), f_y(a, b) \rangle$. The dot product of $\mathbf{t}$ and $\nabla f(a, b)$ is

$$\mathbf{t} \cdot \nabla f(a, b) = \langle -f_y(a, b), f_x(a, b) \rangle \cdot \langle f_x(a, b), f_y(a, b) \rangle$$
$$= -f_x(a, b)\, f_y(a, b) + f_x(a, b)f_y(a, b)$$
$$= 0$$

which implies that $\mathbf{t}$ and $\nabla f(a, b)$ are orthogonal.   ◄

An immediate consequence of Theorem 12.12 is an alternative equation of the tangent line. The curve described by $f(x, y) = z_0$ can be viewed as a level curve in the xy-plane for a surface. By Theorem 12.12, the line tangent to the curve at (a, b) is orthogonal to $\nabla f(a, b)$. Therefore, if (x, y) is a point on the tangent line, then $\nabla f(a, b) \cdot \langle x - a, y - b \rangle = 0$, which, when simplified, gives an equation of the line tangent to the curve $f(x, y) = z_0$:

$$f_x(a, b)(x - a) + f_y(a, b)(y - b) = 0.$$

QUICK CHECK 4 Draw a circle in the xy-plane centered at the origin and regard it is as a level curve of the surface $z = x^2 + y^2$. At the point (a, a) of the level curve in the xy-plane, the slope of the tangent line is -1. Show that the gradient at (a, a) is orthogonal to the tangent line. ◄

EXAMPLE 6 Gradients and level curves Consider the upper sheet $z = f(x, y) = \sqrt{1 + 2x^2 + y^2}$ of a hyperboloid of two sheets.

a. Verify that the gradient at $(1, 1)$ is orthogonal to the corresponding level curve at that point.

b. Find an equation of the line tangent to the level curve at $(1, 1)$.

▶ The fact that $y' = -2x/y$ may also be obtained using Theorem 12.9: If $F(x, y) = 0$, then $y'(x) = -F_x/F_y$.

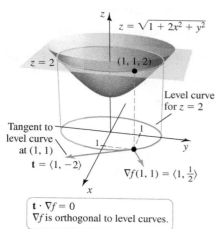

$z = \sqrt{1 + 2x^2 + y^2}$

$z = 2$

$(1, 1, 2)$

Level curve for $z = 2$

Tangent to level curve at $(1, 1)$
$\mathbf{t} = \langle 1, -2 \rangle$

$\nabla f(1, 1) = \langle 1, \frac{1}{2} \rangle$

$\mathbf{t} \cdot \nabla f = 0$
∇f is orthogonal to level curves.

Figure 12.72

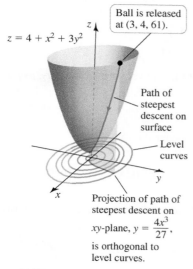

$z = 4 + x^2 + 3y^2$

Ball is released at $(3, 4, 61)$.

Path of steepest descent on surface

Level curves

Projection of path of steepest descent on xy-plane, $y = \dfrac{4x^3}{27}$, is orthogonal to level curves.

Figure 12.73

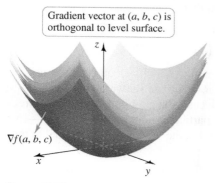

Gradient vector at (a, b, c) is orthogonal to level surface.

$\nabla f(a, b, c)$

Figure 12.74

SOLUTION

a. You can verify that $(1, 1, 2)$ is on the surface; therefore, $(1, 1)$ is on the level curve corresponding to $z = 2$. Setting $z = 2$ in the equation of the surface and squaring both sides, the equation of the level curve is $4 = 1 + 2x^2 + y^2$, or $2x^2 + y^2 = 3$, which is the equation of an ellipse (Figure 12.72). Differentiating $2x^2 + y^2 = 3$ with respect to x gives $4x + 2yy'(x) = 0$, which implies that the slope of the level curve is $y'(x) = -\dfrac{2x}{y}$. Therefore, at the point $(1, 1)$, the slope of the tangent line is -2. Any vector proportional to $\mathbf{t} = \langle 1, -2 \rangle$ has slope -2 and points in the direction of the tangent line.

We now compute the gradient:

$$\nabla f(x, y) = \langle f_x, f_y \rangle = \left\langle \frac{2x}{\sqrt{1 + 2x^2 + y^2}}, \frac{y}{\sqrt{1 + 2x^2 + y^2}} \right\rangle.$$

It follows that $\nabla f(1, 1) = \langle 1, \frac{1}{2} \rangle$ (Figure 12.72). The tangent vector $\mathbf{t}$ and the gradient are orthogonal because

$$\mathbf{t} \cdot \nabla f(1, 1) = \langle 1, -2 \rangle \cdot \langle 1, \tfrac{1}{2} \rangle = 0.$$

b. An equation of the line tangent to the level curve at $(1, 1)$ is

$$\underbrace{f_x(1, 1)}_{1}(x - 1) + \underbrace{f_y(1, 1)}_{\frac{1}{2}}(y - 1) = 0,$$

or $y = -2x + 3$.

Related Exercises 43–50 ◀

EXAMPLE 7   Path of steepest descent Consider the paraboloid $z = f(x, y) = 4 + x^2 + 3y^2$ (Figure 12.73). Beginning at the point $(3, 4, 61)$ on the surface, find the projection in the xy-plane of the path of steepest descent on the surface.

SOLUTION Imagine releasing a ball at $(3, 4, 61)$ and assume that it rolls in the direction of steepest descent at all points. The projection of this path in the xy-plane points in the direction of $-\nabla f(x, y) = \langle -2x, -6y \rangle$, which means that at the point (x, y), the line tangent to the path has slope $y'(x) = (-6y)/(-2x) = 3y/x$. Therefore, the path in the xy-plane satisfies $y'(x) = 3y/x$ and passes through the initial point $(3, 4)$. You can verify that the solution to this differential equation is $y = 4x^3/27$. Therefore, the projection of the path of steepest descent in the xy-plane is the curve $y = 4x^3/27$. The descent ends at $(0, 0)$, which corresponds to the vertex of the paraboloid (Figure 12.73). At all points of the descent, the curve in the xy-plane is orthogonal to the level curves of the surface.

Related Exercises 51–54 ◀

QUICK CHECK 5 Verify that $y = 4x^3/27$ satisfies the equation $y'(x) = 3y/x$, with $y(3) = 4$. ◀

The Gradient in Three Dimensions

The directional derivative, the gradient, and the idea of a level curve extend immediately to functions of three variables of the form $w = f(x, y, z)$. The main differences are that the gradient is a vector in $\mathbb{R}^3$ and level curves become *level surfaces* (Section 12.2). Here is how the gradient looks when we step up one dimension.

The easiest way to visualize the surface $w = f(x, y, z)$ is to picture its level surfaces—the surfaces in $\mathbb{R}^3$ on which f has a constant value. The level surfaces are given by the equation $f(x, y, z) = C$, where C is a constant (Figure 12.74). The level surfaces *can* be graphed, and they may be viewed as layers of the full four-dimensional surface (like layers of an onion). With this image in mind, we now extend the concept of a gradient.

Given the function $w = f(x, y, z)$, we argue just as we did in the two-variable case and define the directional derivative. Given a unit vector $\mathbf{u} = \langle u_1, u_2, u_3 \rangle$, the directional derivative of f in the direction of $\mathbf{u}$ at the point (a, b, c) is

$$D_{\mathbf{u}} f(a, b, c) = f_x(a, b, c) u_1 + f_y(a, b, c) u_2 + f_z(a, b, c) u_3.$$

As before, we recognize this expression as a dot product of the vector $\mathbf{u}$ and the vector $\nabla f(x, y, z) = \left\langle \dfrac{\partial f}{\partial x}, \dfrac{\partial f}{\partial y}, \dfrac{\partial f}{\partial z} \right\rangle$, which is the *gradient* in three dimensions. Therefore, the directional derivative in the direction of $\mathbf{u}$ at the point (a, b, c) is

$$D_{\mathbf{u}} f(a, b, c) = \nabla f(a, b, c) \cdot \mathbf{u}.$$

▶ When we introduce the tangent plane in Section 12.7, we can also claim that $\nabla f(a, b, c)$ is orthogonal to the level surface that passes through (a, b, c).

Following the line of reasoning in the two-variable case, f has its maximum rate of *increase* in the direction of $\nabla f(a, b, c)$. The actual rate of increase is $|\nabla f(a, b, c)|$. Similarly, f has its maximum rate of *decrease* in the direction of $-\nabla f(a, b, c)$. Also, in all directions orthogonal to $\nabla f(a, b, c)$, the directional derivative at (a, b, c) is zero.

QUICK CHECK 6 Compute $\nabla f(-1, 2, 1)$, where $f(x, y, z) = xy/z$. ◀

> **DEFINITION Gradient and Directional Derivative in Three Dimensions**
>
> Let f be differentiable at the point (x, y, z). The **gradient** of f at (x, y, z) is the vector-valued function
>
> $$\nabla f(x, y, z) = \langle f_x(x, y, z), f_y(x, y, z), f_z(x, y, z) \rangle$$
> $$= f_x(x, y, z)\,\mathbf{i} + f_y(x, y, z)\,\mathbf{j} + f_z(x, y, z)\,\mathbf{k}.$$
>
> The **directional derivative** of f in the direction of the unit vector $\mathbf{u} = \langle u_1, u_2, u_3 \rangle$ at the point (a, b, c) is $D_{\mathbf{u}} f(a, b, c) = \nabla f(a, b, c) \cdot \mathbf{u}$.

EXAMPLE 8　Gradients in three dimensions Consider the function $f(x, y, z) = x^2 + 2y^2 + 4z^2 - 1$ and its level surface $f(x, y, z) = 3$.

a. Find and interpret the gradient at the points $P(2, 0, 0)$, $Q(0, \sqrt{2}, 0)$, $R(0, 0, 1)$, and $S\left(1, 1, \frac{1}{2}\right)$ on the level surface.

b. What are the actual rates of change of f in the directions of the gradients in part (a)?

SOLUTION

a. The gradient is

$$\nabla f = \langle f_x, f_y, f_z \rangle = \langle 2x, 4y, 8z \rangle.$$

Evaluating the gradient at the four points we find that

$$\nabla f(2, 0, 0) = \langle 4, 0, 0 \rangle, \qquad \nabla f(0, \sqrt{2}, 0) = \langle 0, 4\sqrt{2}, 0 \rangle,$$
$$\nabla f(0, 0, 1) = \langle 0, 0, 8 \rangle, \qquad \nabla f\left(1, 1, \tfrac{1}{2}\right) = \langle 2, 4, 4 \rangle.$$

The level surface $f(x, y, z) = 3$ is an ellipsoid (Figure 12.75), which is one layer of a four-dimensional surface. The four points P, Q, R, and S are shown on the level surface with the respective gradient vectors. In each case, the gradient points in the direction that f has its maximum rate of increase. Of particular importance is the fact—to be made clear in the next section—that at each point, the gradient is orthogonal to the level surface.

b. The actual rate of increase of f at (a, b, c) in the direction of the gradient is $|\nabla f(a, b, c)|$. At P, the rate of increase of f in the direction of the gradient is $|\langle 4, 0, 0 \rangle| = 4$; at Q, the rate of increase is $|\langle 0, 4\sqrt{2}, 0 \rangle| = 4\sqrt{2}$; at R, the rate of increase is $|\langle 0, 0, 8 \rangle| = 8$; and at S, the rate of increase is $|\langle 2, 4, 4 \rangle| = 6$.

Related Exercises 55–62 ◀

Level surface of $f(x, y, z) = x^2 + 2y^2 + 4z^2 - 1$
$f(x, y, z) = 3$

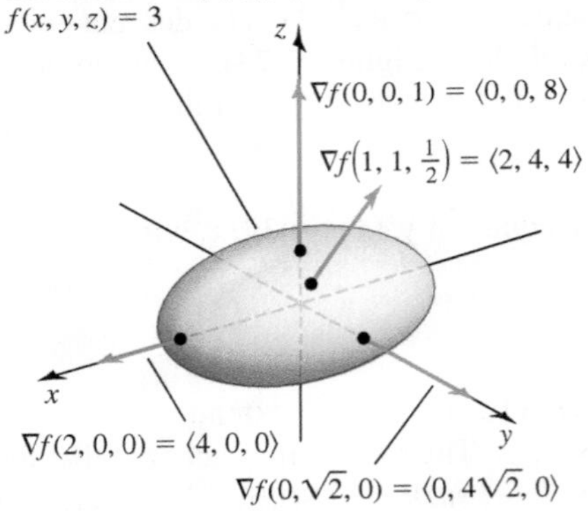

Figure 12.75

SECTION 12.6 EXERCISES

Review Questions

1. Explain how a directional derivative is formed from the two partial derivatives f_x and f_y.

2. How do you compute the gradient of the functions $f(x, y)$ and $f(x, y, z)$?

3. Interpret the direction of the gradient vector at a point.

4. Interpret the magnitude of the gradient vector at a point.

5. Given a function f, explain the relationship between the gradient and the level curves of f.

6. The level curves of the surface $z = x^2 + y^2$ are circles in the xy-plane centered at the origin. Without computing the gradient, what is the direction of the gradient at $(1, 1)$ and $(-1, -1)$ (determined up to a scalar multiple)?

Basic Skills

7. **Directional derivatives** Consider the function $f(x, y) = 8 - x^2/2 - y^2$, whose graph is a paraboloid (see figure).

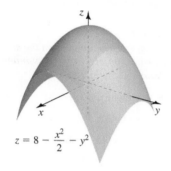

$$z = 8 - \frac{x^2}{2} - y^2$$

a. Fill in the table with the values of the directional derivative at the points (a, b) in the directions given by the unit vectors **u**, **v**, and **w**.

	$(a, b) = (2, 0)$	$(a, b) = (0, 2)$	$(a, b) = (1, 1)$
$\mathbf{u} = \left\langle \frac{\sqrt{2}}{2}, \frac{\sqrt{2}}{2} \right\rangle$			
$\mathbf{v} = \left\langle -\frac{\sqrt{2}}{2}, \frac{\sqrt{2}}{2} \right\rangle$			
$\mathbf{w} = \left\langle -\frac{\sqrt{2}}{2}, -\frac{\sqrt{2}}{2} \right\rangle$			

b. Interpret each of the directional derivatives computed in part (a) at the point $(2, 0)$.

8. **Directional derivatives** Consider the function $f(x, y) = 2x^2 + y^2$, whose graph is a paraboloid (see figure).

a. Fill in the table with the values of the directional derivative at the points (a, b) in the directions given by the unit vectors **u**, **v**, and **w**.

	$(a, b) = (1, 0)$	$(a, b) = (1, 1)$	$(a, b) = (1, 2)$
$\mathbf{u} = \langle 1, 0 \rangle$			
$\mathbf{v} = \left\langle \frac{\sqrt{2}}{2}, \frac{\sqrt{2}}{2} \right\rangle$			
$\mathbf{w} = \langle 0, 1 \rangle$			

b. Interpret each of the directional derivatives computed in part (a) at the point $(1, 0)$.

9–16. Computing gradients *Compute the gradient of the following functions and evaluate it at the given point P.*

9. $f(x, y) = 2 + 3x^2 - 5y^2$; $P(2, -1)$

10. $f(x, y) = 4x^2 - 2xy + y^2$; $P(-1, -5)$

11. $g(x, y) = x^2 - 4x^2y - 8xy^2$; $P(-1, 2)$

12. $p(x, y) = \sqrt{12 - 4x^2 - y^2}$; $P(-1, -1)$

13. $f(x, y) = xe^{2xy}$; $P(1, 0)$

14. $f(x, y) = \sin(3x + 2y)$; $P(\pi, 3\pi/2)$

15. $F(x, y) = e^{-x^2 - 2y^2}$; $P(-1, 2)$

16. $h(x, y) = \ln(1 + x^2 + 2y^2)$; $P(2, -3)$

17–26. Computing directional derivatives with the gradient *Compute the directional derivative of the following functions at the given point P in the direction of the given vector. Be sure to use a unit vector for the direction vector.*

17. $f(x, y) = x^2 - y^2$; $P(-1, -3)$; $\left\langle \frac{3}{5}, -\frac{4}{5} \right\rangle$

18. $f(x, y) = 3x^2 + y^3$; $P(3, 2)$; $\left\langle \frac{5}{13}, \frac{12}{13} \right\rangle$

19. $f(x, y) = 10 - 3x^2 + \dfrac{y^4}{4}$; $P(2, -3)$; $\left\langle \dfrac{\sqrt{3}}{2}, -\dfrac{1}{2} \right\rangle$

20. $g(x, y) = \sin \pi(2x - y)$; $P(-1, -1)$; $\left\langle \dfrac{5}{13}, -\dfrac{12}{13} \right\rangle$

21. $f(x, y) = \sqrt{4 - x^2 - 2y}$; $P(2, -2)$; $\left\langle \dfrac{1}{\sqrt{5}}, \dfrac{2}{\sqrt{5}} \right\rangle$

22. $f(x, y) = 13e^{xy}$; $P(1, 0)$; $\langle 5, 12 \rangle$

23. $f(x, y) = 3x^2 + 2y + 5$; $P(1, 2)$; $\langle -3, 4 \rangle$

24. $h(x, y) = e^{-x-y}$; $P(\ln 2, \ln 3)$; $\langle 1, 1 \rangle$

25. $g(x, y) = \ln(4 + x^2 + y^2)$; $P(-1, 2)$; $\langle 2, 1 \rangle$

26. $f(x, y) = x/(x - y)$; $P(4, 1)$; $\langle -1, 2 \rangle$

27–32. Direction of steepest ascent and descent *Consider the following functions and points P.*

a. *Find the unit vectors that give the direction of steepest ascent and steepest descent at P.*
b. *Find a vector that points in a direction of no change in the function at P.*

27. $f(x, y) = x^2 - 4y^2 - 9$; $P(1, -2)$

28. $f(x, y) = x^2 + 4xy - y^2$; $P(2, 1)$

29. $f(x, y) = x^4 - x^2y + y^2 + 6$; $P(-1, 1)$

30. $p(x, y) = \sqrt{20 + x^2 + 2xy - y^2}$; $P(1, 2)$

31. $F(x, y) = e^{-x^2/2 - y^2/2}$; $P(-1, 1)$

32. $f(x, y) = 2 \sin(2x - 3y)$; $P(0, \pi)$

33–38. Interpreting directional derivatives *A function f and a point P are given. Let θ correspond to the direction of the directional derivative.*

a. *Find the gradient and evaluate it at P.*
b. *Find the angles θ (with respect to the positive x-axis) associated with the directions of maximum increase, maximum decrease, and zero change.*
c. *Write the directional derivative at P as a function of θ; call this function g.*
d. *Find the value of θ that maximizes g(θ) and find the maximum value.*
e. *Verify that the value of θ that maximizes g corresponds to the direction of the gradient. Verify that the maximum value of g equals the magnitude of the gradient.*

33. $f(x, y) = 10 - 2x^2 - 3y^2$; $P(3, 2)$

34. $f(x, y) = 8 + x^2 + 3y^2$; $P(-3, -1)$

35. $f(x, y) = \sqrt{2 + x^2 + y^2}$; $P(\sqrt{3}, 1)$

36. $f(x, y) = \sqrt{12 - x^2 - y^2}$; $P(-1, -1/\sqrt{3})$

37. $f(x, y) = e^{-x^2 - 2y^2}$; $P(-1, 0)$

T 38. $f(x, y) = \ln(1 + 2x^2 + 3y^2)$; $P\left(\frac{3}{4}, -\sqrt{3}\right)$

39–42. Directions of change *Consider the following functions f and points P. Sketch the xy-plane showing P and the level curve through P. Indicate (as in Figure 12.70) the directions of maximum increase, maximum decrease, and no change for f.*

39. $f(x, y) = 8 + 4x^2 + 2y^2$; $P(2, -4)$

40. $f(x, y) = -4 + 6x^2 + 3y^2$; $P(-1, -2)$

T 41. $f(x, y) = x^2 + xy + y^2 + 7$; $P(-3, 3)$

T 42. $f(x, y) = \tan(2x + 2y)$; $P(\pi/16, \pi/16)$

43–46. Level curves *Consider the paraboloid $f(x, y) = 16 - x^2/4 - y^2/16$ and the point P on the given level curve of f. Compute the slope of the line tangent to the level curve at P and verify that the tangent line is orthogonal to the gradient at that point.*

43. $f(x, y) = 0$; $P(0, 16)$ 44. $f(x, y) = 0$; $P(8, 0)$

45. $f(x, y) = 12$; $P(4, 0)$ 46. $f(x, y) = 12$; $P(2\sqrt{3}, 4)$

47–50. Level curves *Consider the upper half of the ellipsoid*
$$f(x, y) = \sqrt{1 - \dfrac{x^2}{4} - \dfrac{y^2}{16}}$$
and the point P on the given level curve of f. Compute the slope of the line tangent to the level curve at P and verify that the tangent line is orthogonal to the gradient at that point.

47. $f(x, y) = \sqrt{3}/2$; $P(1/2, \sqrt{3})$

48. $f(x, y) = 1/\sqrt{2}$; $P(0, \sqrt{8})$

49. $f(x, y) = 1/\sqrt{2}$; $P(\sqrt{2}, 0)$

50. $f(x, y) = 1/\sqrt{2}$; $P(1, 2)$

51–54. Path of steepest descent *Consider each of the following surfaces and the point P on the surface.*

a. *Find the gradient of f.*
b. *Let C′ be the path of steepest descent on the surface beginning at P and let C be the projection of C′ on the xy-plane. Find an equation of C in the xy-plane.*

51. $f(x, y) = 4 + x$ (a plane); $P(4, 4, 8)$

52. $f(x, y) = y + x$ (a plane); $P(2, 2, 4)$

53. $f(x, y) = 4 - x^2 - 2y^2$ (a paraboloid); $P(1, 1, 1)$

54. $f(x, y) = y + x^{-1}$; $P(1, 2, 3)$

55–62. Gradients in three dimensions *Consider the following functions f, points P, and unit vectors u.*

a. *Compute the gradient of f and evaluate it at P.*
b. *Find the unit vector in the direction of maximum increase of f at P.*
c. *Find the rate of change of the function in the direction of maximum increase at P.*
d. *Find the directional derivative at P in the direction of the given vector.*

55. $f(x, y, z) = x^2 + 2y^2 + 4z^2 + 10$; $P(1, 0, 4)$; $\left\langle \dfrac{1}{\sqrt{2}}, 0, \dfrac{1}{\sqrt{2}} \right\rangle$

56. $f(x, y, z) = 4 - x^2 + 3y^2 + \dfrac{z^2}{2}$; $P(0, 2, -1)$; $\left\langle 0, \dfrac{1}{\sqrt{2}}, -\dfrac{1}{\sqrt{2}} \right\rangle$

57. $f(x, y, z) = 1 + 4xyz$; $P(1, -1, -1)$; $\left\langle \dfrac{1}{\sqrt{3}}, \dfrac{1}{\sqrt{3}}, -\dfrac{1}{\sqrt{3}} \right\rangle$

58. $f(x, y, z) = xy + yz + xz + 4$; $P(2, -2, 1)$; $\left\langle 0, -\dfrac{1}{\sqrt{2}}, -\dfrac{1}{\sqrt{2}} \right\rangle$

59. $f(x, y, z) = 1 + \sin(x + 2y - z)$; $P\left(\dfrac{\pi}{6}, \dfrac{\pi}{6}, -\dfrac{\pi}{6}\right)$; $\left\langle \dfrac{1}{3}, \dfrac{2}{3}, \dfrac{2}{3} \right\rangle$

60. $f(x, y, z) = e^{xyz-1}$; $P(0, 1, -1)$; $\left\langle -\dfrac{2}{3}, \dfrac{2}{3}, -\dfrac{1}{3} \right\rangle$

61. $f(x, y, z) = \ln(1 + x^2 + y^2 + z^2)$; $P(1, 1, -1)$; $\left\langle \frac{2}{3}, \frac{2}{3}, -\frac{1}{3} \right\rangle$

62. $f(x, y, z) = \dfrac{x - z}{y - z}$; $P(3, 2, -1)$; $\left\langle \frac{1}{3}, \frac{2}{3}, -\frac{1}{3} \right\rangle$

Further Explorations

63. Explain why or why not Determine whether the following statements are true and give an explanation or counterexample.

a. If $f(x, y) = x^2 + y^2 - 10$, then $\nabla f(x, y) = 2x + 2y$.
b. Because the gradient gives the direction of maximum increase of a function, the gradient is always positive.
c. The gradient of $f(x, y, z) = 1 + xyz$ has four components.
d. If $f(x, y, z) = 4$, then $\nabla f = \mathbf{0}$.

64. Gradient of a composite function Consider the function $F(x, y, z) = e^{xyz}$.

a. Write F as a composite function $f \circ g$, where f is a function of one variable and g is a function of three variables.
b. Relate ∇F to ∇g.

65–68. Directions of zero change *Find the directions in the xy-plane in which the following functions have zero change at the given point. Express the directions in terms of unit vectors.*

65. $f(x, y) = 12 - 4x^2 - y^2$; $P(1, 2, 4)$

66. $f(x, y) = x^2 - 4y^2 - 8$; $P(4, 1, 4)$

67. $f(x, y) = \sqrt{3 + 2x^2 + y^2}$; $P(1, -2, 3)$

68. $f(x, y) = e^{1-xy}$; $P(1, 0, e)$

69. Steepest ascent on a plane Suppose a long sloping hillside is described by the plane $z = ax + by + c$, where a, b, and c are constants. Find the path in the xy-plane, beginning at (x_0, y_0), that corresponds to the path of steepest ascent on the hillside.

70. Gradient of a distance function Let (a, b) be a given point in $\mathbb{R}^2$ and let $d = f(x, y)$ be the distance between (a, b) and the variable point (x, y).

a. Show that the graph of f is a cone.
b. Show that the gradient of f at any point other than (a, b) is a unit vector.
c. Interpret the direction and magnitude of ∇f.

71–74. Looking ahead—tangent planes *Consider the following surfaces $f(x, y, z) = 0$, which may be regarded as a level surface of the function $w = f(x, y, z)$. A point $P(a, b, c)$ on the surface is also given.*

a. Find the (three-dimensional) gradient of f and evaluate it at P.
b. The set of all vectors orthogonal to the gradient with their tails at P form a plane. Find an equation of that plane (soon to be called the tangent plane).

71. $f(x, y, z) = x^2 + y^2 + z^2 - 3 = 0$; $P(1, 1, 1)$

72. $f(x, y, z) = 8 - xyz = 0$; $P(2, 2, 2)$

73. $f(x, y, z) = e^{x+y-z} - 1 = 0$; $P(1, 1, 2)$

74. $f(x, y, z) = xy + xz - yz - 1$; $P(1, 1, 1)$

Applications

T 75. A traveling wave A snapshot (frozen in time) of a water wave is described by the function $z = 1 + \sin(x - y)$, where z gives the height of the wave and (x, y) are coordinates in the horizontal plane $z = 0$.

a. Use a graphing utility to graph $z = 1 + \sin(x - y)$.
b. The crests and the troughs of the waves are aligned in the direction in which the height function has zero change. Find the direction in which the crests and troughs are aligned.
c. If you were surfing on this wave and wanted the steepest descent from a crest to a trough, in which direction would you point your surfboard (given in terms of a unit vector in the xy-plane)?
d. Check that your answers to parts (b) and (c) are consistent with the graph of part (a).

76. Traveling waves in general Generalize Exercise 75 by considering a wave described by the function $z = A + \sin(ax - by)$, where a, b, and A are real numbers.

a. Find the direction in which the crests and troughs of the wave are aligned. Express your answer as a unit vector in terms of a and b.
b. Find the surfer's direction—that is, the direction of steepest descent from a crest to a trough. Express your answer as a unit vector in terms of a and b.

77–79. Potential functions *Potential functions arise frequently in physics and engineering. A potential function has the property that a field of interest (for example, an electric field, a gravitational field, or a velocity field) is the gradient of the potential (or sometimes the negative of the gradient of the potential). (Potential functions are considered in depth in Chapter 14.)*

77. Electric potential due to a point charge The electric field due to a point charge of strength Q at the origin has a potential function $\varphi = kQ/r$, where $r^2 = x^2 + y^2 + z^2$ is the square of the distance between a variable point $P(x, y, z)$ and the charge, and $k > 0$ is a physical constant. The electric field is given by $\mathbf{E} = -\nabla\varphi$, where $\nabla\varphi$ is the gradient in three dimensions.

a. Show that the three-dimensional electric field due to a point charge is given by

$$\mathbf{E}(x, y, z) = kQ \left\langle \frac{x}{r^3}, \frac{y}{r^3}, \frac{z}{r^3} \right\rangle.$$

b. Show that the electric field at a point has a magnitude $|\mathbf{E}| = kQ/r^2$. Explain why this relationship is called an inverse square law.

78. Gravitational potential The gravitational potential associated with two objects of mass M and m is $\varphi = -GMm/r$, where G is the gravitational constant. If one of the objects is at the origin and the other object is at $P(x, y, z)$, then $r^2 = x^2 + y^2 + z^2$ is the square of the distance between the objects. The gravitational field at P is given by $\mathbf{F} = -\nabla\varphi$, where $\nabla\varphi$ is the gradient in three dimensions. Show that the force has a magnitude $|\mathbf{F}| = GMm/r^2$. Explain why this relationship is called an inverse square law.

79. Velocity potential In two dimensions, the motion of an ideal fluid (an incompressible and irrotational fluid) is governed by a velocity potential φ. The velocity components of the fluid, u in the x-direction and v in the y-direction, are given by

$\langle u, v \rangle = \nabla \varphi$. Find the velocity components associated with the velocity potential $\varphi(x, y) = \sin \pi x \sin 2\pi y$.

Additional Exercises

80. Gradients for planes Prove that for the plane described by $f(x, y) = Ax + By$, where A and B are nonzero constants, the gradient is constant (independent of (x, y)). Interpret this result.

81. Rules for gradients Use the definition of the gradient (in two or three dimensions), assume that f and g are differentiable functions on $\mathbb{R}^2$ or $\mathbb{R}^3$, and let c be a constant. Prove the following gradient rules.

  a. Constants Rule: $\nabla(cf) = c\nabla f$
  b. Sum Rule: $\nabla(f + g) = \nabla f + \nabla g$
  c. Product Rule: $\nabla(fg) = (\nabla f)\, g + f\nabla g$
  d. Quotient Rule: $\nabla\left(\dfrac{f}{g}\right) = \dfrac{g\nabla f - f\nabla g}{g^2}$
  e. Chain Rule: $\nabla(f \circ g) = f'(g)\nabla g$, where f is a function of one variable

82–87. Using gradient rules *Use the gradient rules of Exercise 81 to find the gradient of the following functions.*

82. $f(x, y) = xy \cos xy$

83. $f(x, y) = \dfrac{x + y}{x^2 + y^2}$

84. $f(x, y) = \ln(1 + x^2 + y^2)$

85. $f(x, y, z) = \sqrt{25 - x^2 - y^2 - z^2}$

86. $f(x, y, z) = (x + y + z)\, e^{xyz}$

87. $f(x, y, z) = \dfrac{x + yz}{y + xz}$

QUICK CHECK ANSWERS

1. If $\mathbf{u} = \langle u_1, u_2 \rangle = \langle 1, 0 \rangle$ then

$$D_\mathbf{u} f(a, b) = \lim_{h \to 0} \frac{f(a + hu_1, b + hu_2) - f(a, b)}{h}$$

$$= \lim_{h \to 0} \frac{f(a + h, b) - f(a, b)}{h} = f_x(a, b).$$

Similarly, when $\mathbf{u} = \langle 0, 1 \rangle$, the partial derivative $f_y(a, b)$ results. **2.** The vector from (a, b) to $(a + \Delta s u_1, b + \Delta s u_2)$ is $\langle \Delta s u_1, \Delta s u_2 \rangle = \Delta s \langle u_1, u_2 \rangle = \Delta s \mathbf{u}$. Its length is $|\Delta s \mathbf{u}| = \Delta s |\mathbf{u}| = \Delta s$. Therefore, s measures arc length. **3.** Reversing (negating) the direction vector negates the directional derivative. So the respective values are approximately -2.47 and 0.98. **4.** The gradient is $\langle 2x, 2y \rangle$, which, evaluated at (a, a), is $\langle 2a, 2a \rangle$. Taking the dot product of the gradient and the vector $\langle -1, 1 \rangle$ (a vector parallel to a line of slope -1), we see that $\langle 2a, 2a \rangle \cdot \langle -1, 1 \rangle = 0$. **6.** $\langle 2, -1, 2 \rangle$ ◄

12.7 Tangent Planes and Linear Approximation

In Section 4.5, we saw that if we zoom in on a point on a smooth curve (one described by a differentiable function), the curve looks more and more like the tangent line at that point. Once we have the tangent line at a point, it can be used to approximate function values and to estimate changes in the dependent variable. In this section, the analogous story is developed in three dimensions. Now we see that differentiability at a point (as discussed in Section 12.4) implies the existence of a tangent *plane* at that point (Figure 12.76).

Consider a smooth surface described by a differentiable function f and focus on a single point on the surface. As we zoom in on that point (Figure 12.77), the surface appears more and more like a plane. The first step is to define this plane carefully; it is called the *tangent plane*. Once we have the tangent plane, we can use it to approximate function values and to estimate changes in the dependent variable.

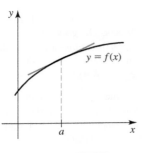

f differentiable at $a \Rightarrow$ tangent line at $(a, f(a))$

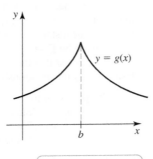

g not differentiable at $b \Rightarrow$ no tangent line at $(b, f(b))$

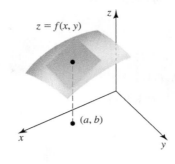

f differentiable at $(a, b) \Rightarrow$ tangent plane at $(a, b, f(a, b))$

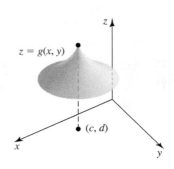

g not differentiable at $(c, d) \Rightarrow$ no tangent plane at $(c, d, g(c, d))$

Figure 12.76

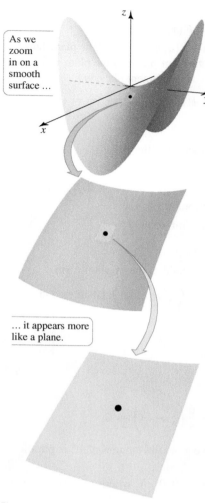

As we zoom in on a smooth surface ...

... it appears more like a plane.

Figure 12.77

▶ Recall that an equation of the plane passing though (a, b, c) with a normal vector $\mathbf{n} = \langle n_1, n_2, n_3 \rangle$ is $n_1(x - a) + n_2(y - b) + n_3(z - c) = 0$.

▶ If $\mathbf{r}$ is a position vector corresponding to an arbitrary point on the tangent plane and $\mathbf{r}_0$ is a position vector corresponding to a fixed point (a, b, c) on the plane, then an equation of the tangent plane may be written concisely as

$$\nabla F(a, b, c) \cdot (\mathbf{r} - \mathbf{r}_0) = 0.$$

Notice the analogy with tangent lines and level curves (Section 12.6). An equation of the line tangent to $f(x, y) = 0$ at (a, b) is

$$\nabla f(a, b) \cdot \langle x - a, y - b \rangle = 0.$$

Tangent Planes

Recall that a surface in $\mathbb{R}^3$ may be defined in at least two different ways:

- **Explicitly** in the form $z = f(x, y)$ or
- **Implicitly** in the form $F(x, y, z) = 0$.

It is easiest to begin by considering a surface defined implicitly by $F(x, y, z) = 0$, where F is differentiable at a particular point. Such a surface may be viewed as a level surface of a function $w = F(x, y, z)$; it is the level surface for $w = 0$.

QUICK CHECK 1 Write the function $z = xy + x - y$ in the form $F(x, y, z) = 0$. ◀

Tangent Planes for $F(x, y, z) = 0$ To find an equation of the tangent plane, consider a smooth curve $C: \mathbf{r} = \langle x(t), y(t), z(t) \rangle$ that lies on the surface $F(x, y, z) = 0$ (Figure 12.78a). Because the points of C lie on the surface, we have $F(x(t), y(t), z(t)) = 0$. Differentiating both sides of this equation with respect to t, a useful relationship emerges. The derivative of the right side is 0. The Chain Rule applied to the left side yields

$$\frac{d}{dt}\left(F(x(t), y(t), z(t))\right) = \frac{\partial F}{\partial x}\frac{dx}{dt} + \frac{\partial F}{\partial y}\frac{dy}{dt} + \frac{\partial F}{\partial z}\frac{dz}{dt}$$

$$= \underbrace{\left\langle \frac{\partial F}{\partial x}, \frac{\partial F}{\partial y}, \frac{\partial F}{\partial z} \right\rangle}_{\nabla F(x, y, z)} \cdot \underbrace{\left\langle \frac{dx}{dt}, \frac{dy}{dt}, \frac{dz}{dt} \right\rangle}_{\mathbf{r}'(t)}$$

$$= \nabla F(x, y, z) \cdot \mathbf{r}'(t).$$

Therefore, $\nabla F(x, y, z) \cdot \mathbf{r}'(t) = 0$ and at any point on the curve, the tangent vector $\mathbf{r}'(t)$ is orthogonal to the gradient.

Now fix a point $P_0(a, b, c)$ on the surface, assume that $\nabla F(a, b, c) \neq \mathbf{0}$, and let C be any smooth curve on the surface passing through P_0. We have shown that any vector tangent to C is orthogonal to $\nabla F(a, b, c)$ at P_0. Because this argument applies to *all* smooth curves on the surface passing through P_0, the tangent vectors for all these curves (with their tails at P_0) are orthogonal to $\nabla F(a, b, c)$; therefore, they all lie in the same plane (Figure 12.78b). This plane is called the *tangent plane* at P_0. We can easily find an equation of the tangent plane because we know both a point on the plane $P_0(a, b, c)$ and a normal vector $\nabla F(a, b, c)$; an equation is

$$\nabla F(a, b, c) \cdot \langle x - a, y - b, z - c \rangle = 0.$$

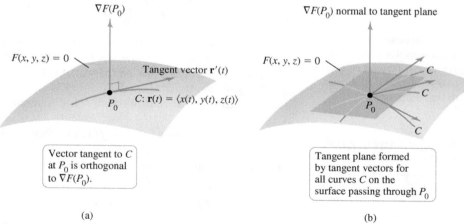

Vector tangent to C at P_0 is orthogonal to $\nabla F(P_0)$.

(a)

Tangent plane formed by tangent vectors for all curves C on the surface passing through P_0

(b)

Figure 12.78

> **DEFINITION Equation of the Tangent Plane for $F(x, y, z) = 0$**
>
> Let F be differentiable at the point $P_0(a, b, c)$ with $\nabla F(a, b, c) \neq \mathbf{0}$. The plane tangent to the surface $F(x, y, z) = 0$ at P_0, called the **tangent plane**, is the plane passing through P_0 orthogonal to $\nabla F(a, b, c)$. An equation of the tangent plane is
>
> $$F_x(a, b, c)(x - a) + F_y(a, b, c)(y - b) + F_z(a, b, c)(z - c) = 0.$$

EXAMPLE 1   Equation of a tangent plane Consider the ellipsoid

$$F(x, y, z) = \frac{x^2}{9} + \frac{y^2}{25} + z^2 - 1 = 0.$$

a. Find the equation of the plane tangent to the ellipsoid at $\left(0, 4, \frac{3}{5}\right)$.

b. At what points on the ellipsoid is the tangent plane horizontal?

SOLUTION

a. Notice that we have written the equation of the ellipsoid in the implicit form $F(x, y, z) = 0$. The gradient of F is $\nabla F(x, y, z) = \left\langle \frac{2x}{9}, \frac{2y}{25}, 2z \right\rangle$. Evaluated at $\left(0, 4, \frac{3}{5}\right)$, we have

$$\nabla F\left(0, 4, \frac{3}{5}\right) = \left\langle 0, \frac{8}{25}, \frac{6}{5} \right\rangle.$$

An equation of the tangent plane at this point is

$$0 \cdot (x - 0) + \frac{8}{25}(y - 4) + \frac{6}{5}\left(z - \frac{3}{5}\right) = 0,$$

or $4y + 15z = 25$. The equation does not involve x, so the tangent plane is parallel to (does not intersect) the x-axis (Figure 12.79).

b. A horizontal plane has a normal vector of the form $\langle 0, 0, c \rangle$, where $c \neq 0$. A plane tangent to the ellipsoid has a normal vector $\nabla F(x, y, z) = \left\langle \frac{2x}{9}, \frac{2y}{25}, 2z \right\rangle$. Therefore, the ellipsoid has a horizontal tangent plane when $F_x = \frac{2x}{9} = 0$ and $F_y = \frac{2y}{25} = 0$, or when $x = 0$ and $y = 0$. Substituting these values into the original equation for the ellipsoid, we find that horizontal planes occur at $(0, 0, 1)$ and $(0, 0, -1)$.

Related Exercises 9–16 ◀

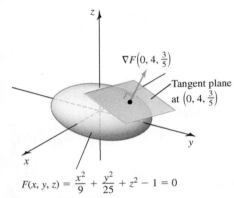

$\nabla F\left(0, 4, \frac{3}{5}\right)$

Tangent plane at $\left(0, 4, \frac{3}{5}\right)$

$F(x, y, z) = \dfrac{x^2}{9} + \dfrac{y^2}{25} + z^2 - 1 = 0$

Figure 12.79

The preceding discussion allows us to confirm a claim made in Section 12.6. The surface $F(x, y, z) = 0$ is a level surface of the function $w = F(x, y, z)$ (corresponding to $w = 0$). At any point on that surface, the tangent plane has a normal vector $\nabla F(x, y, z)$. Therefore, the gradient $\nabla F(x, y, z)$ is orthogonal to the level surface $F(x, y, z) = 0$ at all points of the domain at which F is differentiable.

> ▶ This result extends Theorem 12.12, which states that for functions $f(x, y) = 0$, the gradient at a point is orthogonal to the level curve that passes through that point.

Tangent Planes for $z = f(x, y)$ Surfaces in $\mathbb{R}^3$ are often defined explicitly in the form $z = f(x, y)$. In this situation, the equation of the tangent plane is a special case of the general equation just derived. The equation $z = f(x, y)$ is written as $F(x, y, z) = z - f(x, y) = 0$, and the gradient of F at the point $(a, b, f(a, b))$ is

> ▶ To be clear, when $F(x, y, z) = z - f(x, y)$, we have $F_x = -f_x$, $F_y = -f_y$, and $F_z = 1$.

$$\nabla F(a, b, f(a, b)) = \langle F_x(a, b, f(a, b)), F_y(a, b, f(a, b)), F_z(a, b, f(a, b)) \rangle$$
$$= \langle -f_x(a, b), -f_y(a, b), 1 \rangle.$$

Using the tangent plane definition, an equation of the plane tangent to the surface $z = f(x, y)$ at the point $(a, b, f(a, b))$ is

$$-f_x(a, b)(x - a) - f_y(a, b)(y - b) + 1(z - f(a, b)) = 0.$$

After some rearranging, we obtain an equation of the tangent plane.

Tangent Plane for $z = f(x, y)$

Let f be differentiable at the point (a, b). An equation of the plane tangent to the surface $z = f(x, y)$ at the point $(a, b, f(a, b))$ is

$$z = f_x(a, b)(x - a) + f_y(a, b)(y - b) + f(a, b).$$

EXAMPLE 2   **Tangent plane for $z = f(x, y)$**   Find an equation of the plane tangent to the paraboloid $z = f(x, y) = 32 - 3x^2 - 4y^2$ at $(2, 1, 16)$.

SOLUTION   The partial derivatives are $f_x = -6x$ and $f_y = -8y$. Evaluating the partial derivatives at $(2, 1)$, we have $f_x(2, 1) = -12$ and $f_y(2, 1) = -8$. Therefore, an equation of the tangent plane (Figure 12.80) is

$$\begin{aligned} z &= f_x(a, b)(x - a) + f_y(a, b)(y - b) + f(a, b) \\ &= -12(x - 2) - 8(y - 1) + 16 \\ &= -12x - 8y + 48. \end{aligned}$$

Related Exercises 17–24 ◄

Linear Approximation

With a function of the form $y = f(x)$, the tangent line at a point often gives good approximations to the function near that point. A straightforward extension of this idea applies to approximating functions of two variables with tangent planes. As before, the method is called *linear approximation*.

Figure 12.81 shows the details of linear approximation in the one- and two-variable cases. In the one-variable case (Section 4.5), if f is differentiable at a, the equation of the line tangent to the curve $y = f(x)$ at the point $(a, f(a))$ is

$$L(x) = f(a) + f'(a)(x - a).$$

The tangent line gives an approximation to the function. At points near a, we have $f(x) \approx L(x)$.

The two-variable case is analogous. If f is differentiable at (a, b), an equation of the plane tangent to the surface $z = f(x, y)$ at the point $(a, b, f(a, b))$ is

$$L(x, y) = f_x(a, b)(x - a) + f_y(a, b)(y - b) + f(a, b).$$

This tangent plane is the linear approximation to f at (a, b). At points near (a, b), we have $f(x, y) \approx L(x, y)$.

DEFINITION **Linear Approximation**

Let f be differentiable at (a, b). The linear approximation to the surface $z = f(x, y)$ at the point $(a, b, f(a, b))$ is the tangent plane at that point, given by the equation

$$L(x, y) = f_x(a, b)(x - a) + f_y(a, b)(y - b) + f(a, b).$$

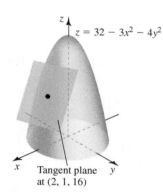

Figure 12.80

➤ The term *linear approximation* applies in both $\mathbb{R}^2$ and $\mathbb{R}^3$ because lines in $\mathbb{R}^2$ and planes in $\mathbb{R}^3$ are described by linear functions of the independent variables. In both cases, we call the linear approximation L.

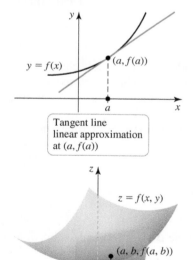

Figure 12.81

EXAMPLE 3 Linear approximation Let $f(x, y) = \dfrac{5}{x^2 + y^2}$.

a. Find the linear approximation to the function at the point $(-1, 2, 1)$.

b. Use the linear approximation to estimate the value of $f(-1.05, 2.1)$.

SOLUTION

a. The partial derivatives of f are

$$f_x = -\frac{10x}{(x^2 + y^2)^2} \quad \text{and} \quad f_y = -\frac{10y}{(x^2 + y^2)^2}.$$

Evaluated at $(-1, 2)$, we have $f_x(-1, 2) = \frac{2}{5} = 0.4$ and $f_y(-1, 2) = -\frac{4}{5} = -0.8$.
Therefore, the linear approximation to the function at $(-1, 2, 1)$ is

$$
\begin{aligned}
L(x, y) &= f_x(-1, 2)(x - (-1)) + f_y(-1, 2)(y - 2) + f(-1, 2) \\
&= 0.4(x + 1) - 0.8(y - 2) + 1 \\
&= 0.4x - 0.8y + 3.
\end{aligned}
$$

The surface and the tangent plane are shown in Figure 12.82.

b. The value of the function at the point $(-1.05, 2.1)$ is approximated by the value of the linear approximation at that point, which is

$$L(-1.05, 2.1) = 0.4(-1.05) - 0.8(2.1) + 3 = 0.90.$$

In this case, we can easily evaluate $f(-1.05, 2.1) \approx 0.907$ and compare the linear approximation with the exact value; the approximation has a relative error of about 0.8%.

Related Exercises 25–30 ◄

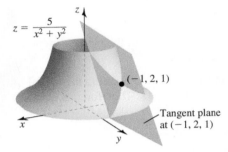

$z = \dfrac{5}{x^2 + y^2}$

$(-1, 2, 1)$

Tangent plane at $(-1, 2, 1)$

Figure 12.82

➤ Relative error $=$
$\dfrac{|\text{approximation} - \text{exact value}|}{|\text{exact value}|}$

QUICK CHECK 2 Look at the graph of the surface in Example 3 (Figure 12.82) and explain why $f_x(-1, 2) > 0$ and $f_y(-1, 2) < 0$. ◄

Differentials and Change

Recall that for a function of the form $y = f(x)$, if the independent variable changes from x to $x + dx$, the corresponding change Δy in the dependent variable is approximated by the differential $dy = f'(x)\, dx$, which is the change in the linear approximation. Therefore, $\Delta y \approx dy$, with the approximation improving as dx approaches 0.

For functions of the form $z = f(x, y)$, we start with the linear approximation to the surface

$$f(x, y) \approx L(x, y) = f_x(a, b)(x - a) + f_y(a, b)(y - b) + f(a, b).$$

The exact change in the function between the points (a, b) and (x, y) is

$$\Delta z = f(x, y) - f(a, b).$$

Replacing $f(x, y)$ with its linear approximation, the change Δz is approximated by

$$\Delta z \approx \underbrace{L(x, y) - f(a, b) = f_x(a, b)\underbrace{(x - a)}_{dx} + f_y(a, b)\underbrace{(y - b)}_{dy}}_{dz}.$$

➤ Alternative notation for the differential at (a, b) is $dz|_{(a,b)}$ or $df|_{(a,b)}$.

The change in the x-coordinate is $dx = x - a$ and the change in the y-coordinate is $dy = y - b$ (Figure 12.83). As before, we let the differential dz denote the change in the linear approximation. Therefore, the approximate change in the z-coordinate is

$$\Delta z \approx dz = \underbrace{f_x(a, b)\, dx}_{\substack{\text{change in } z \text{ due} \\ \text{to change in } x}} + \underbrace{f_y(a, b)\, dy}_{\substack{\text{change in } z \text{ due} \\ \text{to change in } y}}.$$

This expression says that if we move the independent variables from (a, b) to $(x, y) = (a + dx, b + dy)$, the corresponding change in the dependent variable Δz has two contributions—one due to the change in x and one due to the change in y. If dx and dy are small in magnitude, then so is Δz. The approximation $\Delta z \approx dz$ improves as dx and dy approach 0. The relationships among the differentials are illustrated in Figure 12.83.

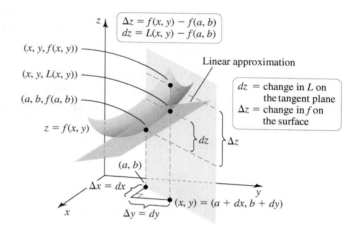

Figure 12.83

QUICK CHECK 3 Explain why, if $dx = 0$ or $dy = 0$ in the change formula for Δz, the result is the change formula for one variable. ◄

DEFINITION The differential dz

Let f be differentiable at the point (a, b). The change in $z = f(x, y)$ as the independent variables change from (a, b) to $(a + dx, b + dy)$ is denoted Δz and is approximated by the differential dz:

$$\Delta z \approx dz = f_x(a, b)\, dx + f_y(a, b)\, dy.$$

EXAMPLE 4   Approximating function change Let $z = f(x, y) = \dfrac{5}{x^2 + y^2}$.

Approximate the change in z when the independent variables change from $(-1, 2)$ to $(-0.93, 1.94)$.

SOLUTION If the independent variables change from $(-1, 2)$ to $(-0.93, 1.94)$, then $dx = 0.07$ (an increase) and $dy = -0.06$ (a decrease). Using the values of the partial derivatives evaluated in Example 3, the corresponding change in z is approximately

$$\begin{aligned}
dz &= f_x(-1, 2)\, dx + f_y(-1, 2)\, dy \\
&= 0.4(0.07) + (-0.8)(-0.06) \\
&= 0.076.
\end{aligned}$$

Again, we can check the accuracy of the approximation. The actual change is $f(-0.93, 1.94) - f(-1, 2) \approx 0.080$, so the approximation has a 5% error.

Related Exercises 31–34 ◄

EXAMPLE 5 **Body mass index** The body mass index (BMI) for an adult human is given by the function $B(w, h) = w/h^2$, where w is weight measured in kilograms and h is height measured in meters.

a. Use differentials to approximate the change in the BMI when weight increases from 55 to 56.5 kg and height increases from 1.65 to 1.66 m.

b. Which produces a greater *percentage* change in the BMI, a 1% change in the weight (at a constant height) or a 1% change in the height (at a constant weight)?

SOLUTION

a. The approximate change in the BMI is $dB = B_w\, dw + B_h\, dh$, where the derivatives are evaluated at $w = 55$ and $h = 1.65$, and the changes in the independent variables are $dw = 1.5$ and $dh = 0.01$. Evaluating the partial derivatives, we find that

$$B_w(w, h) = \frac{1}{h^2}, \qquad B_w(55, 1.65) \approx 0.37,$$

$$B_h(w, h) = -\frac{2w}{h^3}, \qquad B_h(55, 1.65) \approx -24.49.$$

Therefore, the approximate change in the BMI is

$$\begin{aligned}
dB &= B_w(55, 1.65)\, dw + B_h(55, 1.65)\, dh \\
&\approx (0.37)(1.5) + (-24.49)(0.01) \\
&\approx 0.56 - 0.25 \\
&= 0.31.
\end{aligned}$$

As expected, an increase in weight *increases* the BMI, while an increase in height *decreases* the BMI. In this case, the two contributions combine for a net increase in the BMI.

b. The changes dw, dh, and dB that appear in the differential change formula in part (a) are *absolute changes*. The corresponding *relative*, or *percentage*, changes are $\dfrac{dw}{w}$, $\dfrac{dh}{h}$, and $\dfrac{dB}{B}$. To introduce relative changes into the change formula, we divide both sides of $dB = B_w\, dw + B_h\, dh$ by $B = w/h^2 = wh^{-2}$. The result is

$$\begin{aligned}
\frac{dB}{B} &= B_w \frac{dw}{wh^{-2}} + B_h \frac{dh}{wh^{-2}} \\[1mm]
&= \frac{1}{h^2}\frac{dw}{wh^{-2}} - \frac{2w}{h^3}\frac{dh}{wh^{-2}} \qquad \text{Substitute for } B_w \text{ and } B_h. \\[1mm]
&= \underbrace{\frac{dw}{w}}_{\substack{\text{relative}\\\text{change}\\\text{in } w}} - 2\underbrace{\frac{dh}{h}}_{\substack{\text{relative}\\\text{change}\\\text{in } h}}. \qquad \text{Simplify.}
\end{aligned}$$

➤ See Exercises 64–65 for general results about relative or percentage changes in functions.

This expression relates the relative changes in w, h, and B. With h constant ($dh = 0$), a 1% change in w ($dw/w = 0.01$) produces approximately a 1% change of the same sign in B. With w constant ($dw = 0$), a 1% change in h ($dh/h = 0.01$) produces approximately a 2% change in B of the opposite sign. We see that the BMI formula is more sensitive to small changes in h than in w.

Related Exercises 35–38 ◄

QUICK CHECK 4 In Example 5, interpret the facts that $B_w > 0$ and $B_h < 0$, for $w, h > 0$. ◄

The differential for functions of two variables extends naturally to more variables. For example, if f is differentiable at (a, b, c) with $w = f(x, y, z)$, then

$$dw = f_x(a, b, c)\, dx + f_y(a, b, c)\, dy + f_z(a, b, c)\, dz.$$

The differential dw (or df) gives the approximate change in f at the point (a, b, c) due to changes of dx, dy, and dz in the independent variables.

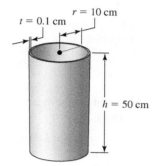

$r = 10$ cm
$t = 0.1$ cm
$h = 50$ cm

Figure 12.84

EXAMPLE 6   Manufacturing errors A company manufactures cylindrical aluminum tubes to rigid specifications. The tubes are designed to have an outside radius of $r = 10$ cm, a height of $h = 50$ cm, and a thickness of $t = 0.1$ cm (Figure 12.84). The manufacturing process produces tubes with a maximum error of ± 0.05 cm in the radius and height and a maximum error of ± 0.0005 cm in the thickness. The volume of the material used to construct a cylindrical tube is $V(r, h, t) = \pi h t(2r - t)$. Use differentials to estimate the maximum error in the volume of a tube.

SOLUTION The approximate change in the volume of a tube due to changes dr, dh, and dt in the radius, height, and thickness, respectively, is

$$dV = V_r\, dr + V_h\, dh + V_t\, dt.$$

The partial derivatives evaluated at $r = 10$, $h = 50$, and $t = 0.1$ are

$$V_r(r, h, t) = 2\pi ht, \qquad V_r(10, 50, 0.1) = 10\pi,$$
$$V_h(r, h, t) = \pi t(2r - t), \qquad V_h(10, 50, 0.1) = 1.99\pi,$$
$$V_t(r, h, t) = 2\pi h(r - t), \qquad V_t(10, 50, 0.1) = 990\pi.$$

We let $dr = dh = 0.05$ and $dt = 0.0005$ be the maximum errors in the radius, height, and thickness, respectively. The maximum error in the volume is approximately

$$\begin{aligned}
dV &= V_r(10, 50, 0.1)\, dr + V_h(10, 50, 0.1)\, dh + V_t(10, 50, 0.1)\, dt \\
&= 10\pi(0.05) + 1.99\pi(0.05) + 990\pi(0.0005) \\
&\approx 1.57 + 0.31 + 1.56 \\
&= 3.44.
\end{aligned}$$

The maximum error in the volume is approximately 3.44 cm^3. Notice that the "magnification factor" for the thickness (990π) is roughly 100 and 500 times greater than the magnification factors for the radius and height, respectively. This means that for the same errors in r, h, and t, the volume is far more sensitive to errors in the thickness. The partial derivatives allow us to do a sensitivity analysis to determine which independent (input) variables are most critical in producing change in the dependent (output) variable.

Related Exercises 39–44 ◀

SECTION 12.7 EXERCISES

Review Questions

1. Suppose **n** is a vector normal to the tangent plane of the surface $F(x, y, z) = 0$ at a point. How is **n** related to the gradient of F at that point?

2. Write the explicit function $z = xy^2 + x^2y - 10$ in the implicit form $F(x, y, z) = 0$.

3. Write an equation for the plane tangent to the surface $F(x, y, z) = 0$ at the point (a, b, c).

4. Write an equation for the plane tangent to the surface $z = f(x, y)$ at the point $(a, b, f(a, b))$.

5. Explain how to approximate a function f at a point near (a, b) where the values of $f, f_x,$ and f_y are known at (a, b).

6. Explain how to approximate the change in a function f when the independent variables change from (a, b) to $(a + \Delta x, b + \Delta y)$.

7. Write the approximate change formula for a function $z = f(x, y)$ at the point (a, b) in terms of differentials.

8. Write the differential dw for the function $w = f(x, y, z)$.

Basic Skills

9–16. Tangent planes for $F(x, y, z) = 0$ *Find an equation of the plane tangent to the following surfaces at the given points (two planes and two equations).*

9. $x^2 + y + z = 3$; $(1, 1, 1)$ and $(2, 0, -1)$

10. $x^2 + y^3 + z^4 = 2$; $(1, 0, 1)$ and $(-1, 0, 1)$

11. $xy + xz + yz - 12 = 0$; $(2, 2, 2)$ and $(2, 0, 6)$

12. $x^2 + y^2 - z^2 = 0$; $(3, 4, 5)$ and $(-4, -3, 5)$

13. $xy \sin z = 1$; $(1, 2, \pi/6)$ and $(-2, -1, 5\pi/6)$

14. $yze^{xz} - 8 = 0$; $(0, 2, 4)$ and $(0, -8, -1)$

15. $z^2 - x^2/16 - y^2/9 - 1 = 0$; $(4, 3, -\sqrt{3})$ and $(-8, 9, \sqrt{14})$

16. $2x + y^2 - z^2 = 0$; $(0, 1, 1)$ and $(4, 1, -3)$

17–24. Tangent planes for $z = f(x, y)$ *Find an equation of the plane tangent to the following surfaces at the given points (two planes and two equations).*

17. $z = 4 - 2x^2 - y^2$; $(2, 2, -8)$ and $(-1, -1, 1)$

18. $z = 2 + 2x^2 + \dfrac{y^2}{2}$; $\left(-\dfrac{1}{2}, 1, 3\right)$ and $(3, -2, 22)$

19. $z = e^{xy}$; $(1, 0, 1)$ and $(0, 1, 1)$

20. $z = \sin xy + 2$; $(1, 0, 2)$ and $(0, 5, 2)$

21. $z = x^2 e^{x-y}$; $(2, 2, 4)$ and $(-1, -1, 1)$

22. $z = \ln(1 + xy)$; $(1, 2, \ln 3)$ and $(-2, -1, \ln 3)$

23. $z = (x - y)/(x^2 + y^2)$; $\left(1, 2, -\frac{1}{5}\right)$ and $\left(2, -1, \frac{3}{5}\right)$

24. $z = 2\cos(x - y) + 2$; $(\pi/6, -\pi/6, 3)$ and $(\pi/3, \pi/3, 4)$

25–30. Linear approximation

a. *Find the linear approximation to the function f at the given point.*
b. *Use part (a) to estimate the given function value.*

25. $f(x, y) = xy + x - y$; $(2, 3)$; estimate $f(2.1, 2.99)$.

26. $f(x, y) = 12 - 4x^2 - 8y^2$; $(-1, 4)$; estimate $f(-1.05, 3.95)$.

27. $f(x, y) = -x^2 + 2y^2$; $(3, -1)$; estimate $f(3.1, -1.04)$.

28. $f(x, y) = \sqrt{x^2 + y^2}$; $(3, -4)$; estimate $f(3.06, -3.92)$.

29. $f(x, y) = \ln(1 + x + y)$; $(0, 0)$; estimate $f(0.1, -0.2)$.

30. $f(x, y) = (x + y)/(x - y)$; $(3, 2)$; estimate $f(2.95, 2.05)$.

31–34. Approximate function change *Use differentials to approximate the change in z for the given changes in the independent variables.*

31. $z = 2x - 3y - 2xy$ when (x, y) changes from $(1, 4)$ to $(1.1, 3.9)$

32. $z = -x^2 + 3y^2 + 2$ when (x, y) changes from $(-1, 2)$ to $(-1.05, 1.9)$

33. $z = e^{x+y}$ when (x, y) changes from $(0, 0)$ to $(0.1, -0.05)$

34. $z = \ln(1 + x + y)$ when (x, y) changes from $(0, 0)$ to $(-0.1, 0.03)$

35. Changes in torus surface area The surface area of a torus with an inner radius r and an outer radius $R > r$ is $S = 4\pi^2(R^2 - r^2)$.

   a. If r increases and R decreases, does S increase or decrease, or is it impossible to say?
   b. If r increases and R increases, does S increase or decrease, or is it impossible to say?
   c. Estimate the change in the surface area of the torus when r changes from $r = 3.00$ to $r = 3.05$ and R changes from $R = 5.50$ to $R = 5.65$.
   d. Estimate the change in the surface area of the torus when r changes from $r = 3.00$ to $r = 2.95$ and R changes from $R = 7.00$ to $R = 7.04$.
   e. Find the relationship between the changes in r and R that leaves the surface area (approximately) unchanged.

36. Changes in cone volume The volume of a right circular cone with radius r and height h is $V = \pi r^2 h/3$.

   a. Approximate the change in the volume of the cone when the radius changes from $r = 6.5$ to $r = 6.6$ and the height changes from $h = 4.20$ to $h = 4.15$.
   b. Approximate the change in the volume of the cone when the radius changes from $r = 5.40$ to $r = 5.37$ and the height changes from $h = 12.0$ to $h = 11.96$.

37. Area of an ellipse The area of an ellipse with axes of length $2a$ and $2b$ is $A = \pi ab$. Approximate the percent change in the area when a increases by 2% and b increases by 1.5%.

38. Volume of a paraboloid The volume of a segment of a circular paraboloid (see figure) with radius r and height h is $V = \pi r^2 h/2$. Approximate the percent change in the volume when the radius decreases by 1.5% and the height increases by 2.2%.

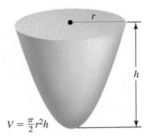

$$V = \frac{\pi}{2} r^2 h$$

39–42. Differentials with more than two variables *Write the differential dw in terms of the differentials of the independent variables.*

39. $w = f(x, y, z) = xy^2 + x^2 z + yz^2$

40. $w = f(x, y, z) = \sin(x + y - z)$

41. $w = f(u, x, y, z) = (u + x)/(y + z)$

42. $w = f(p, q, r, s) = pq/(rs)$

⊤ 43. Law of Cosines The side lengths of any triangle are related by the Law of Cosines,

$$c^2 = a^2 + b^2 - 2ab\cos\theta.$$

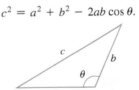

   a. Estimate the change in the side length c when a changes from $a = 2$ to $a = 2.03$, b changes from $b = 4.00$ to $b = 3.96$, and θ changes from $\theta = \pi/3$ to $\theta = \pi/3 + \pi/90$.
   b. If a changes from $a = 2$ to $a = 2.03$ and b changes from $b = 4.00$ to $b = 3.96$, is the resulting change in c greater in magnitude when $\theta = \pi/20$ (small angle) or when $\theta = 9\pi/20$ (close to a right angle)?

44. Travel cost The cost of a trip that is L miles long, driving a car that gets m miles per gallon, with gas costs of $\$p$/gal is $C = Lp/m$ dollars. Suppose you plan a trip of $L = 1500$ mi in a car that gets $m = 32$ mi/gal, with gas costs of $p = \$3.80$/gal.

   a. Explain how the cost function is derived.
   b. Compute the partial derivatives C_L, C_m, and C_p. Explain the meaning of the signs of the derivatives in the context of this problem.

c. Estimate the change in the total cost of the trip if L changes from $L = 1500$ to $L = 1520$, m changes from $m = 32$ to 31, and p changes from \$3.80 to \$3.85.

d. Is the total cost of the trip (with $L = 1500$ mi, $m = 32$ mi/gal, and $p = \$3.80$) more sensitive to a 1% change in L, m, or p (assuming the other two variables are fixed)? Explain.

Further Explorations

45. Explain why or why not Determine whether the following statements are true and give an explanation or counterexample.

a. The planes tangent to the cylinder $x^2 + z^2 = 1$ in $\mathbb{R}^3$ all have the form $ax + bz + c = 0$.

b. Suppose $w = xy/z$, for $x > 0$, $y > 0$, and $z > 0$. A decrease in z with x and y fixed results in an increase in w.

c. The gradient $\nabla F(a, b, c)$ lies in the plane tangent to the surface $F(x, y, z) = 0$ at (a, b, c).

46–49. Tangent planes *Find an equation of the plane tangent to the following surfaces at the given point.*

46. $z = \tan^{-1}(x + y);\ (0, 0, 0)$

47. $z = \tan^{-1} xy;\ (1, 1, \pi/4)$

48. $(x + z)/(y - z) = 2;\ (4, 2, 0)$

49. $\sin xyz = \frac{1}{2};\ \left(\pi, 1, \frac{1}{6}\right)$

50–53. Horizontal tangent planes *Find the points at which the following surfaces have horizontal tangent planes.*

50. $z = \sin(x - y)$ in the region $-2\pi \le x \le 2\pi,\ -2\pi \le y \le 2\pi$

51. $x^2 + y^2 - z^2 - 2x + 2y + 3 = 0$

52. $x^2 + 2y^2 + z^2 - 2x - 2z - 2 = 0$

53. $z = \cos 2x \sin y$ in the region $-\pi \le x \le \pi,\ -\pi \le y \le \pi$

54. Heron's formula The area of a triangle with sides of length a, b, and c is given by a formula from antiquity called Heron's formula:

$$A = \sqrt{s(s - a)(s - b)(s - c)},$$

where $s = (a + b + c)/2$ is the *semiperimeter* of the triangle.

a. Find the partial derivatives A_a, A_b, and A_c.

b. A triangle has sides of length $a = 2$, $b = 4$, and $c = 5$. Estimate the change in the area when a increases by 0.03, b decreases by 0.08, and c increases by 0.6.

c. For an equilateral triangle with $a = b = c$, estimate the percent change in the area when all sides increase in length by $p\%$.

55. Surface area of a cone A cone with height h and radius r has a lateral surface area (the curved surface only, excluding the base) of $S = \pi r \sqrt{r^2 + h^2}$.

a. Estimate the change in the surface area when r increases from $r = 2.50$ to $r = 2.55$ and h decreases from $h = 0.60$ to $h = 0.58$.

b. When $r = 100$ and $h = 200$, is the surface area more sensitive to a small change in r or a small change in h? Explain.

56. Line tangent to an intersection curve Consider the paraboloid $z = x^2 + 3y^2$ and the plane $z = x + y + 4$, which intersects the paraboloid in a curve C at $(2, 1, 7)$ (see figure). Find the equation of the line tangent to C at the point $(2, 1, 7)$. Proceed as follows.

a. Find a vector normal to the plane at $(2, 1, 7)$.

b. Find a vector normal to the plane tangent to the paraboloid at $(2, 1, 7)$.

c. Argue that the line tangent to C at $(2, 1, 7)$ is orthogonal to both normal vectors found in parts (a) and (b). Use this fact to find a direction vector for the tangent line.

d. Knowing a point on the tangent line and the direction of the tangent line, write an equation of the tangent line in parametric form.

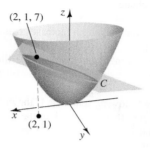

Applications

57. Batting averages Batting averages in baseball are defined by $A = x/y$, where $x \ge 0$ is the total number of hits and $y > 0$ is the total number of at bats. Treat x and y as positive real numbers and note that $0 \le A \le 1$.

a. Use differentials to estimate the change in the batting average if the number of hits increases from 60 to 62 and the number of at bats increases from 175 to 180.

b. If a batter currently has a batting average of $A = 0.350$, does the average decrease if the batter fails to get a hit more than it increases if the batter gets a hit?

c. Does the answer to part (b) depend on the current batting average? Explain.

58. Water-level changes A conical tank with radius 0.50 m and height 2.00 m is filled with water (see figure). Water is released from the tank, and the water level drops by 0.05 m (from 2.00 m to 1.95 m). Approximate the change in the volume of water in the tank. (*Hint:* When the water level drops, both the radius and height of the cone of water change.)

59. Flow in a cylinder Poiseuille's Law is a fundamental law of fluid dynamics that describes the flow velocity of a viscous incompressible fluid in a cylinder (it is used to model blood flow through veins and arteries). It says that in a cylinder of radius R and length L, the velocity of the fluid $r \le R$ units from the center-line of the cylinder is $V = \dfrac{P}{4L\nu}(R^2 - r^2)$, where P is the difference in the pressure between the ends of the cylinder and ν is the viscosity of the fluid (see figure). Assuming that P and ν are constant, the velocity V along the centerline of the cylinder ($r = 0$) is $V = kR^2/L$, where k is a constant that we will take to be $k = 1$.

a. Estimate the change in the centerline velocity ($r = 0$) if the radius of the flow cylinder increases from $R = 3$ cm to $R = 3.05$ cm and the length increases from $L = 50$ cm to $L = 50.5$ cm.

b. Estimate the percent change in the centerline velocity if the radius of the flow cylinder R decreases by 1% and the length L increases by 2%.

c. Complete the following sentence: If the radius of the cylinder increases by $p\%$, then the length of the cylinder must increase by approximately _____ % in order for the velocity to remain constant.

60. Floating-point operations In general, real numbers (with infinite decimal expansions) cannot be represented exactly in a computer by floating-point numbers (with finite decimal expansions). Suppose that floating-point numbers on a particular computer carry an error of at most 10^{-16}. Estimate the maximum error that is committed in doing the following arithmetic operations. Express the error in absolute and relative (percent) terms.

a. $f(x, y) = xy$
b. $f(x, y) = x/y$
c. $F(x, y, z) = xyz$
d. $F(x, y, z) = (x/y)/z$

61. Probability of at least one encounter Suppose that in a large group of people, a fraction $0 \le r \le 1$ of the people have flu. The probability that in n random encounters you will meet at least one person with flu is $P = f(n, r) = 1 - (1 - r)^n$. Although n is a positive integer, regard it as a positive real number.

a. Compute f_r and f_n.
b. How sensitive is the probability P to the flu rate r? Suppose you meet $n = 20$ people. Approximately how much does the probability P increase if the flu rate increases from $r = 0.1$ to $r = 0.11$ (with n fixed)?
c. Approximately how much does the probability P increase if the flu rate increases from $r = 0.9$ to $r = 0.91$ with $n = 20$?
d. Interpret the results of parts (b) and (c).

62. Two electrical resistors When two electrical resistors with resistance $R_1 > 0$ and $R_2 > 0$ are wired in parallel in a circuit (see figure), the combined resistance R, measured in ohms (Ω), is given by $\dfrac{1}{R} = \dfrac{1}{R_1} + \dfrac{1}{R_2}$.

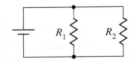

a. Estimate the change in R if R_1 increases from 2 Ω to 2.05 Ω and R_2 decreases from 3 Ω to 2.95 Ω.
b. Is it true that if $R_1 = R_2$ and R_1 increases by the same small amount as R_2 decreases, then R is approximately unchanged? Explain.
c. Is it true that if R_1 and R_2 increase, then R increases? Explain.
d. Suppose $R_1 > R_2$ and R_1 increases by the same small amount as R_2 decreases. Does R increase or decrease?

63. Three electrical resistors Extending Exercise 62, when three electrical resistors with resistance $R_1 > 0$, $R_2 > 0$, and $R_3 > 0$

are wired in parallel in a circuit (see figure), the combined resistance R, measured in ohms (Ω), is given by $\dfrac{1}{R} = \dfrac{1}{R_1} + \dfrac{1}{R_2} + \dfrac{1}{R_3}$.

Estimate the change in R if R_1 increases from 2 Ω to 2.05 Ω, R_2 decreases from 3 Ω to 2.95 Ω, and R_3 increases from 1.5 Ω to 1.55 Ω.

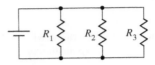

Additional Exercises

64. Power functions and percent change Suppose that $z = f(x, y) = x^a y^b$, where a and b are real numbers. Let dx/x, dy/y, and dz/z be the approximate relative (percent) changes in x, y, and z, respectively. Show that $dz/z = a(dx)/x + b(dy)/y$; that is, the relative changes are additive when weighted by the exponents a and b.

65. Logarithmic differentials Let f be a differentiable function of one or more variables that is positive on its domain.

a. Show that $d(\ln f) = \dfrac{df}{f}$.
b. Use part (a) to explain the statement that the absolute change in $\ln f$ is approximately equal to the relative change in f.
c. Let $f(x, y) = xy$, note that $\ln f = \ln x + \ln y$, and show that relative changes add; that is, $df/f = dx/x + dy/y$.
d. Let $f(x, y) = x/y$, note that $\ln f = \ln x - \ln y$, and show that relative changes subtract; that is $df/f = dx/x - dy/y$.
e. Show that in a product of n numbers, $f = x_1 x_2 \cdots x_n$, the relative change in f is approximately equal to the sum of the relative changes in the variables.

66. Distance from a plane to an ellipsoid (Adapted from 1938 Putnam Exam) Consider the ellipsoid $x^2/a^2 + y^2/b^2 + z^2/c^2 = 1$ and the plane P given by $Ax + By + Cz + 1 = 0$. Let $h = (A^2 + B^2 + C^2)^{-1/2}$ and $m = (a^2 A^2 + b^2 B^2 + c^2 C^2)^{1/2}$.

a. Find the equation of the plane tangent to the ellipsoid at the point (p, q, r).
b. Find the two points on the ellipsoid at which the tangent plane is parallel to P and find equations of the tangent planes.
c. Show that the distance between the origin and the plane P is h.
d. Show that the distance between the origin and the tangent planes is hm.
e. Find a condition that guarantees that the plane P does not intersect the ellipsoid.

QUICK CHECK ANSWERS

1. $F(x, y, z) = z - xy - x + y = 0$ **2.** If you walk in the positive x-direction from $(-1, 2, 1)$, then you walk uphill. If you walk in the positive y-direction from $(-1, 2, 1)$, then you walk downhill.   **3.** If $\Delta x = 0$, then the change formula becomes $\Delta z \approx f_y(a, b)\, \Delta y$, which is the change formula for the single variable y. If $\Delta y = 0$, then the change formula becomes $\Delta z \approx f_x(a, b)\, \Delta x$, which is the change formula for the single variable x.   **4.** The BMI increases with weight w and decreases with height h.◀

12.8 Maximum/Minimum Problems

In Chapter 4, we showed how to use derivatives to find maximum and minimum values of functions of a single variable. When those techniques are extended to functions of two variables, we discover both similarities and differences. The landscape of a surface is far more complicated than the profile of a curve in the plane, so we see more interesting features when working with several variables. In addition to peaks (maximum values) and hollows (minimum values), we encounter winding ridges, long valleys, and mountain passes. Yet despite these complications, many of the ideas used for single-variable functions reappear in higher dimensions. For example, the Second Derivative Test, suitably adapted for two variables, plays a central role. As with single-variable functions, the techniques developed here are useful for solving practical optimization problems.

Local Maximum / Minimum Values

The concepts of local maximum and minimum values encountered in Chapter 4 extend readily to functions of two variables of the form $z = f(x, y)$. Figure 12.85 shows a general surface defined on a domain D, which is a subset of $\mathbb{R}^2$. The surface has peaks (local high points) and hollows (local low points) at points in the interior of D. The goal is to locate and classify these extreme points.

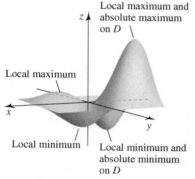

Local maximum and absolute maximum on D

Local maximum

Local minimum

Local minimum and absolute minimum on D

Figure 12.85

> We maintain the convention adopted in Chapter 4 that local maxima or minima occur at interior points of the domain. Recall that an open disk centered at (a, b) is the set of points within a circle centered at (a, b).

DEFINITION Local Maximum / Minimum Values

A function f has a **local maximum value** at (a, b) if $f(x, y) \leq f(a, b)$ for all (x, y) in the domain of f in some open disk centered at (a, b). A function f has a **local minimum value** at (a, b) if $f(x, y) \geq f(a, b)$ for all (x, y) in the domain of f in some open disk centered at (a, b). Local maximum and local minimum values are also called **local extreme values** or **local extrema**.

In familiar terms, a local maximum is a point on a surface from which you cannot walk uphill. A local minimum is a point from which you cannot walk downhill. The following theorem is the analog of Theorem 4.2.

THEOREM 12.13   Derivatives and Local Maximum / Minimum Values

If f has a local maximum or minimum value at (a, b) and the partial derivatives f_x and f_y exist at (a, b), then $f_x(a, b) = f_y(a, b) = 0$.

Proof: Suppose f has a local maximum value at (a, b). The function of one variable $g(x) = f(x, b)$, obtained by holding $y = b$ fixed, also has a local maximum at (a, b). By Theorem 4.2, $g'(a) = 0$. However, $g'(a) = f_x(a, b)$; therefore, $f_x(a, b) = 0$. Similarly, the function $h(y) = f(a, y)$, obtained by holding $x = a$ fixed, has a local maximum at (a, b), which implies that $f_y(a, b) = h'(b) = 0$. An analogous argument is used for the local minimum case. ◄

Suppose f is differentiable at (a, b) (ensuring the existence of a tangent plane) and f has a local extremum at (a, b). Then $f_x(a, b) = f_y(a, b) = 0$, which, when substituted into the equation of the tangent plane, gives the equation $z = f(a, b)$ (a constant). Therefore, if the tangent plane exists at a local extremum, then it is horizontal there.

QUICK CHECK 1 The paraboloid $z = x^2 + y^2 - 4x + 2y + 5$ has a local minimum at $(2, -1)$. Verify the conclusion of Theorem 12.13 for this function. ◄

Recall that for a function of one variable, the condition $f'(a) = 0$ does not guarantee a local extremum at a. A similar precaution must be taken with Theorem 12.13. The conditions $f_x(a, b) = f_y(a, b) = 0$ do not imply that f has a local extremum at (a, b), as we show momentarily. Theorem 12.13 provides *candidates* for local extrema. We call these candidates *critical points*, as we did for functions of one variable. Therefore, the procedure for locating local maximum and minimum values is to find the critical points and then determine whether these candidates correspond to genuine local maximum and minimum values.

DEFINITION Critical Point

An interior point (a, b) in the domain of f is a **critical point** of f if either

1. $f_x(a, b) = f_y(a, b) = 0$, or

2. at least one of the partial derivatives f_x and f_y does not exist at (a, b).

EXAMPLE 1   Finding critical points Find the critical points of
$f(x, y) = xy(x - 2)(y + 3)$.

SOLUTION This function is differentiable at all points of $\mathbb{R}^2$, so the critical points occur only at points where $f_x(x, y) = f_y(x, y) = 0$. Computing and simplifying the partial derivatives, these conditions become

$$f_x(x, y) = 2y(x - 1)(y + 3) = 0$$
$$f_y(x, y) = x(x - 2)(2y + 3) = 0.$$

We must now identify all (x, y) pairs that satisfy both equations. The first equation is satisfied if and only if $y = 0, x = 1$, or $y = -3$. We consider each of these cases.

- Substituting $y = 0$, the second equation is $3x(x - 2) = 0$, which has solutions $x = 0$ and $x = 2$. So $(0, 0)$ and $(2, 0)$ are critical points.
- Substituting $x = 1$, the second equation is $-(2y + 3) = 0$, which has the solution $y = -\frac{3}{2}$. So $\left(1, -\frac{3}{2}\right)$ is a critical point.
- Substituting $y = -3$, the second equation is $-3x(x - 2) = 0$, which has roots $x = 0$ and $x = 2$. So $(0, -3)$ and $(2, -3)$ are critical points.

We find that there are five critical points: $(0, 0), (2, 0), \left(1, -\frac{3}{2}\right), (0, -3)$, and $(2, -3)$. Some of these critical points may correspond to local maximum or minimum values. We return to this example and a complete analysis shortly.

Related Exercises 9–18 ◄

Second Derivative Test

Critical points are candidates for local extreme values. With functions of one variable, the Second Derivative Test is used to determine whether critical points correspond to local maxima or minima (the test can also be inconclusive). The analogous test for functions of two variables not only detects local maxima and minima, but also identifies another type of point known as a *saddle point*.

> The usual image of a saddle point is that of a mountain pass (or a horse saddle), where you can walk upward in some directions and downward in other directions. The definition of a saddle point given here includes other less common situations. For example, with this definition, the cylinder $z = x^3$ has a line of saddle points along the y-axis.

DEFINITION Saddle Point

A function f has a **saddle point** at a critical point (a, b) if, in every open disk centered at (a, b), there are points (x, y) for which $f(x, y) > f(a, b)$ and points for which $f(x, y) < f(a, b)$.

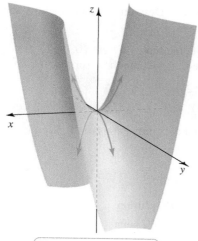

The hyperbolic paraboloid $z = x^2 - y^2$ has a saddle point at $(0, 0)$.

Figure 12.86

If (a, b) is a critical point of f and f has a saddle point at (a, b), then from the point $(a, b, f(a, b))$, it is possible to walk uphill in some directions and downhill in other directions. The function $f(x, y) = x^2 - y^2$ (a hyperbolic paraboloid) is a good example to remember. The surface *rises* from the critical point $(0, 0)$ along the x-axis and *falls* from $(0, 0)$ along the y-axis (Figure 12.86). We can easily check that $f_x(0, 0) = f_y(0, 0) = 0$, demonstrating that critical points do not necessarily correspond to local maxima or minima.

QUICK CHECK 2 Consider the plane tangent to a surface at a saddle point. In what direction does the normal to the plane point? ◄

THEOREM 12.14   Second Derivative Test

Suppose that the second partial derivatives of f are continuous throughout an open disk centered at the point (a, b), where $f_x(a, b) = f_y(a, b) = 0$. Let $D(x, y) = f_{xx}(x, y) f_{yy}(x, y) - (f_{xy}(x, y))^2$.

1. If $D(a, b) > 0$ and $f_{xx}(a, b) < 0$, then f has a local maximum value at (a, b).
2. If $D(a, b) > 0$ and $f_{xx}(a, b) > 0$, then f has a local minimum value at (a, b).
3. If $D(a, b) < 0$, then f has a saddle point at (a, b).
4. If $D(a, b) = 0$, then the test is inconclusive.

▶ The Second Derivative Test for functions of a single variable states that if a is a critical point with $f'(a) = 0$, then $f''(a) > 0$ implies that f has a local minimum at a, $f''(a) < 0$ implies that f has a local maximum at a, and if $f''(a) = 0$, the test is inconclusive. Theorem 12.14 is easier to remember if you notice the parallels between the two second derivative tests.

The proof of this theorem is given in Appendix B, but a few comments are in order. The test relies on the quantity $D(x, y) = f_{xx}f_{yy} - (f_{xy})^2$, which is called the **discriminant** of f. It can be remembered as the 2×2 determinant of the **Hessian** matrix $\begin{pmatrix} f_{xx} & f_{xy} \\ f_{yx} & f_{yy} \end{pmatrix}$, where $f_{xy} = f_{yx}$, provided these derivatives are continuous (Theorem 12.4). The condition $D(x, y) > 0$ means that the surface has the same general behavior in all directions near (a, b); either the surface rises in all directions or it falls in all directions. In the case that $D(a, b) = 0$, the test is inconclusive: (a, b) could correspond to a local maximum, a local minimum, or a saddle point.

Finally, another useful characterization of a saddle point can be derived from Theorem 12.14: The tangent plane at a saddle point lies both above and below the surface.

QUICK CHECK 3 Compute the discriminant $D(x, y)$ of $f(x, y) = x^2y^2$. ◄

EXAMPLE 2   Analyzing critical points Use the Second Derivative Test to classify the critical points of $f(x, y) = x^2 + 2y^2 - 4x + 4y + 6$.

SOLUTION We begin with the following derivative calculations:

$$f_x = 2x - 4 \qquad f_y = 4y + 4$$
$$f_{xx} = 2 \qquad f_{xy} = f_{yx} = 0 \qquad f_{yy} = 4.$$

Setting both f_x and f_y equal to zero yields the single critical point $(2, -1)$. The value of the discriminant at the critical point is $D(2, -1) = f_{xx}f_{yy} - (f_{xy})^2 = 8 > 0$. Furthermore, $f_{xx}(2, -1) = 2 > 0$. By the Second Derivative Test, f has a local minimum at $(2, -1)$; the value of the function at that point is $f(2, -1) = 0$ (Figure 12.87).

Related Exercises 19–34 ◄

$z = x^2 + 2y^2 - 4x + 4y + 6$

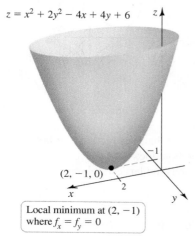

Local minimum at $(2, -1)$ where $f_x = f_y = 0$

Figure 12.87

EXAMPLE 3   Analyzing critical points Use the Second Derivative Test to classify the critical points of $f(x, y) = xy(x - 2)(y + 3)$.

SOLUTION In Example 1, we determined that the critical points of f are $(0, 0)$, $(2, 0)$, $\left(1, -\frac{3}{2}\right)$, $(0, -3)$, and $(2, -3)$. The derivatives needed to evaluate the discriminant are

$$f_x = 2y(x - 1)(y + 3), \qquad f_y = x(x - 2)(2y + 3),$$
$$f_{xx} = 2y(y + 3), \qquad\qquad f_{xy} = 2(2y + 3)(x - 1), \qquad f_{yy} = 2x(x - 2).$$

The values of the discriminant at the critical points and the conclusions of the Second Derivative Test are shown in Table 12.5.

Table 12.5

(x, y)	$D(x, y)$	f_{xx}	Conclusion
$(0, 0)$	-36	0	Saddle point
$(2, 0)$	-36	0	Saddle point
$\left(1, -\frac{3}{2}\right)$	9	$-\frac{9}{2}$	Local maximum
$(0, -3)$	-36	0	Saddle point
$(2, -3)$	-36	0	Saddle point

The surface described by f has one local maximum at $\left(1, -\frac{3}{2}\right)$, surrounded by four saddle points (Figure 12.88a). The structure of the surface may also be visualized by plotting the level curves of f (Figure 12.88b).

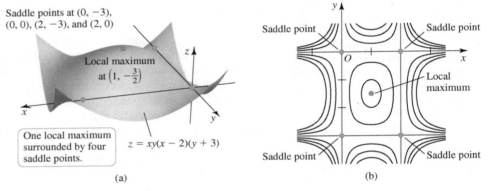

Saddle points at $(0, -3)$, $(0, 0)$, $(2, -3)$, and $(2, 0)$

Local maximum at $\left(1, -\frac{3}{2}\right)$

One local maximum surrounded by four saddle points.

$z = xy(x - 2)(y + 3)$

(a)

Saddle point   Saddle point   Local maximum   Saddle point   Saddle point

(b)

Figure 12.88

Related Exercises 19–34 ◄

▶ Example 4 is a *constrained optimization problem*, in which the goal is to maximize the volume subject to an additional condition called a *constraint*. We return to such problems in the next section and present another method of solution.

EXAMPLE 4   Shipping regulations A shipping company handles rectangular boxes provided the sum of the length, width, and height of the box does not exceed 96 in. Find the dimensions of the box that meets this condition and has the largest volume.

SOLUTION Let x, y, and z be the dimensions of the box; its volume is $V = xyz$. The box with the maximum volume satisfies the condition $x + y + z = 96$, which is used to eliminate any one of the variables from the volume function. Noting that $z = 96 - x - y$, the volume function becomes

$$V(x, y) = xy(96 - x - y).$$

Notice that because x, y, and $96 - x - y$ are dimensions of the box, they must be non-negative. The condition $96 - x - y \geq 0$ implies that $x + y \leq 96$. Therefore, among points in the xy-plane, the constraint is met only if (x, y) lies in the triangle bounded by the lines $x = 0$, $y = 0$, and $x + y = 96$ (Figure 12.89). This triangle is the domain of the problem, and on its boundary, $V = 0$.

The goal is to find the maximum value of V. The critical points of V satisfy

$$V_x = 96y - 2xy - y^2 = y(96 - 2x - y) = 0$$
$$V_y = 96x - 2xy - x^2 = x(96 - 2y - x) = 0.$$

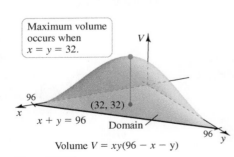

Maximum volume occurs when $x = y = 32$.

$x + y = 96$ Domain

Volume $V = xy(96 - x - y)$

Figure 12.89

You can check that these two equations have four solutions: $(0, 0)$, $(96, 0)$, $(0, 96)$, and $(32, 32)$. The first three solutions lie on the boundary of the domain, where $V = 0$. Therefore, the remaining critical point is $(32, 32)$. The required second derivatives are

$$V_{xx} = -2y, \qquad V_{xy} = 96 - 2x - 2y, \qquad V_{yy} = -2x.$$

The discriminant is

$$D(x, y) = V_{xx}V_{yy} - (V_{xy})^2 = 4xy - (96 - 2x - 2y)^2,$$

which, when evaluated at $(32, 32)$, has the value $D(32, 32) = 3072 > 0$. Therefore, the critical point corresponds to a local maximum or minimum. Noting that $V_{xx}(32, 32) = -64 < 0$, we conclude that the critical point corresponds to a local maximum. The dimensions of the box with maximum volume are $x = 32$, $y = 32$, and $z = 96 - x - y = 32$ (it is a cube). Its volume is 32,768 in³, which is the maximum volume on the domain.

Related Exercises 35–38 ◄

EXAMPLE 5   **Inconclusive tests** Apply the Second Derivative Test to the following functions and interpret the results.

a. $f(x, y) = 2x^4 + y^4$ **b.** $f(x, y) = 2 - xy^2$

SOLUTION

a. The critical points of f satisfy the conditions

$$f_x = 8x^3 = 0 \quad \text{and} \quad f_y = 4y^3 = 0,$$

so the sole critical point is $(0, 0)$. The second partial derivatives evaluated at $(0, 0)$ are

$$f_{xx}(0, 0) = f_{xy}(0, 0) = f_{yy}(0, 0) = 0.$$

We see that $D(0, 0) = 0$, and the Second Derivative Test is inconclusive. While the bowl-shaped surface (Figure 12.90) described by f has a local minimum at $(0, 0)$, the surface also has a broad flat bottom, which makes the local minimum "invisible" to the Second Derivative Test.

b. The critical points of this function satisfy

$$f_x(x, y) = -y^2 = 0 \quad \text{and} \quad f_y(x, y) = -2xy = 0.$$

The solutions of these equations have the form $(a, 0)$, where a is a real number. It is easy to check that the second partial derivatives evaluated at $(a, 0)$ are

$$f_{xx}(a, 0) = f_{xy}(a, 0) = 0 \quad \text{and} \quad f_{yy}(a, 0) = -2a.$$

Therefore, the discriminant is $D(a, 0) = 0$, and the Second Derivative Test is inconclusive. Figure 12.91 shows that f has a flat ridge above the x-axis that the Second Derivative Test is unable to classify.

Related Exercises 39–42 ◄

Absolute Maximum and Minimum Values

As in the one-variable case, we are often interested in knowing where a function of two or more variables attains its extreme values over its domain (or a subset of its domain).

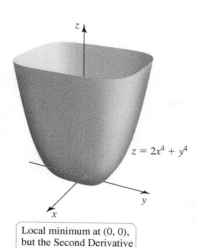

$z = 2x^4 + y^4$

Local minimum at $(0, 0)$, but the Second Derivative Test is inconclusive.

Figure 12.90

➤ The same "flat" behavior occurs with functions of one variable, such as $f(x) = x^4$. Although f has a local minimum at $x = 0$, the Second Derivative Test is inconclusive.

➤ It is not surprising that the Second Derivative Test is inconclusive in Example 5b. The function has a line of local maxima at $(a, 0)$ for $a > 0$, a line of local minima at $(a, 0)$ for $a < 0$, and a saddle point at $(0, 0)$.

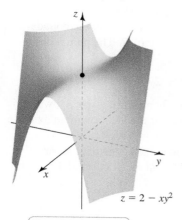

$z = 2 - xy^2$

Second derivative test fails to detect saddle point at $(0, 0)$.

Figure 12.91

DEFINITION **Absolute Maximum/Minimum Values**

Let f be defined on a set R in $\mathbb{R}^2$ containing the point (a, b). If $f(a, b) \geq f(x, y)$ for every (x, y) in R, then $f(a, b)$ is an **absolute maximum value** of f on R. If $f(a, b) \leq f(x, y)$ for every (x, y) in R, then $f(a, b)$ is an **absolute minimum value** of f on R.

It should be noted that the Extreme Value Theorem of Chapter 4 has an analog in $\mathbb{R}^2$ (or in higher dimensions): A function that is continuous on a closed bounded set in $\mathbb{R}^2$ attains its absolute maximum and absolute minimum values on that set. Absolute maximum and minimum values on a closed bounded set R occur in two ways.

▶ Recall that a *closed set* in $\mathbb{R}^2$ is a set that includes its boundary. A *bounded set* in $\mathbb{R}^2$ is a set that may be enclosed by a circle of finite radius.

• They may be local maximum or minimum values at interior points of R, where they are associated with critical points.

• They may occur on the boundary of R.

Therefore, the search for absolute maximum and minimum values on a closed bounded set is accomplished in the following three steps.

PROCEDURE   Finding Absolute Maximum / Minimum Values on Closed Bounded Sets

Let f be continuous on a closed bounded set R in $\mathbb{R}^2$. To find the absolute maximum and minimum values of f on R:

1. Determine the values of f at all critical points in R.

2. Find the maximum and minimum values of f on the boundary of R.

3. The greatest function value found in Steps 1 and 2 is the absolute maximum value of f on R, and the least function value found in Steps 1 and 2 is the absolute minimum value of f on R.

The techniques for carrying out Step 1 of this process have been presented. The challenge often lies in locating extreme values on the boundary. Examples 6 and 7 illustrate two approaches to handling the boundary of R. The first expresses the boundary using functions of a single variable, and the second describes the boundary parametrically. In both cases, finding extreme values on the boundary becomes a one-variable problem. In the next section, we discuss an alternative method for finding extreme values on boundaries.

EXAMPLE 6   Extreme values over a region Find the absolute maximum and minimum values of $f(x, y) = xy - 8x - y^2 + 12y + 160$ over the triangular region $R = \{(x, y): 0 \le x \le 15, 0 \le y \le 15 - x\}$.

SOLUTION Figure 12.92 shows the graph of f over the region R. The goal is to determine the absolute maximum and minimum values of f over R—including the boundary of R. We begin by finding the critical points of f on the interior of R. The partial derivatives of f are

$$f_x(x, y) = y - 8 \quad \text{and} \quad f_y(x, y) = x - 2y + 12.$$

The conditions $f_x(x, y) = f_y(x, y) = 0$ are satisfied only when $(x, y) = (4, 8)$, which is a point in the interior of R. This critical point is a candidate for the location of an extreme value of f, and the value of the function at this point is $f(4, 8) = 192$.

To search for extrema on the boundary of R, we consider each edge of R separately. Let C_1 be the line segment $\{(x, y): y = 0, \text{ for } 0 \le x \le 15\}$ on the x-axis and define the

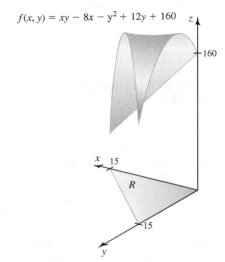

$f(x, y) = xy - 8x - y^2 + 12y + 160$

Figure 12.92

single-variable function g_1 to equal f at all points along C_1 (Figure 12.93). We substitute $y = 0$ and find that g_1 has the form

$$g_1(x) = f(x, 0) = 160 - 8x.$$

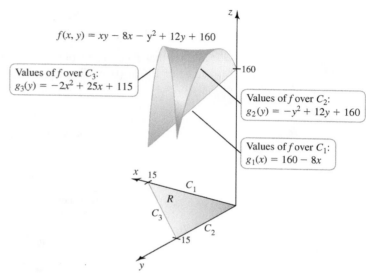

$f(x, y) = xy - 8x - y^2 + 12y + 160$

Values of f over C_3:
$g_3(y) = -2x^2 + 25x + 115$

Values of f over C_2:
$g_2(y) = -y^2 + 12y + 160$

Values of f over C_1:
$g_1(x) = 160 - 8x$

Figure 12.93

Using what we learned in Chapter 4, the candidates for absolute extreme values of g_1 on $0 \leq x \leq 15$ occur at critical points and endpoints. Specifically, the critical points of g_1 correspond to values where its derivative is zero, but in this case $g_1'(x) = -8$. So there is no critical point, which implies that the extreme values of g_1 occur at the endpoints of the interval $[0, 15]$. At the endpoints, we find that

$$g_1(0) = f(0, 0) = 160 \quad \text{and} \quad g_1(15) = f(15, 0) = 40.$$

Let's set aside this information while we do a similar analysis on the other two edges of the boundary of R.

Let C_2 be the line segment $\{(x, y): x = 0, \text{for } 0 \leq y \leq 15\}$ and define g_2 to equal f on C_2 (Figure 12.93). Substituting $x = 0$, we see that

$$g_2(y) = f(0, y) = -y^2 + 12y + 160.$$

The critical points of g_2 satisfy

$$g_2'(y) = -2y + 12 = 0,$$

which has the single root $y = 6$. Evaluating g_2 at this point and the endpoints, we have

$$g_2(6) = f(0, 6) = 196, \quad g_2(0) = f(0, 0) = 160, \quad \text{and} \quad g_2(15) = f(0, 15) = 115.$$

Observe that $g_1(0) = g_2(0)$ because C_1 and C_2 intersect at the origin.

Finally, we let C_3 be the line segment $\{(x, y): y = 15 - x, 0 \leq x \leq 15\}$ and define g_3 to equal f on C_3 (Figure 12.93). Substituting $y = 15 - x$ and simplifying, we find that

$$g_3(x) = f(x, 15 - x) = -2x^2 + 25x + 115.$$

The critical points of g_3 satisfy

$$g_3'(x) = -4x + 25,$$

whose only root on the interval $0 \leq x \leq 15$ is $x = 6.25$. Evaluating g_3 at this critical point and the endpoints, we have

$$g_3(6.25) = f(6.25, 8.75) = 193.125, \quad g_3(15) = f(15, 0) = 40, \quad \text{and}$$
$$g_3(0) = f(0, 15) = 115.$$

Observe that $g_3(15) = g_1(15)$ and $g_3(0) = g_2(15)$, so only one new candidate for the location of an extreme value is the point $(6.25, 8.75)$.

Collecting and summarizing our work, we have 6 candidates for absolute extreme values:

$$f(4, 8) = 192, \quad f(0, 0) = 160, \quad f(15, 0) = 40, \quad f(0, 6) = 196,$$
$$f(0, 15) = 115, \quad \text{and} \quad f(6.25, 8.75) = 193.125.$$

We see that f has an absolute minimum value of 40 at $(15, 0)$ and an absolute maximum value of 196 at $(0, 6)$. These findings are illustrated in Figure 12.94.

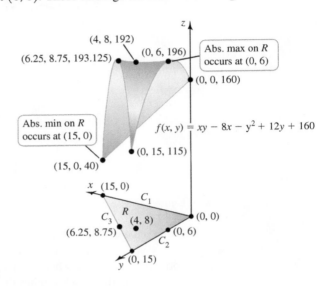

Figure 12.94

Related Exercises 43–52 ◀

EXAMPLE 7 Absolute maximum and minimum values Find the absolute maximum and minimum values of $f(x, y) = x^2 + y^2 - 2x + 2y + 5$ on the region $R = \{(x, y): x^2 + y^2 \le 4\}$ (the closed disk centered at $(0, 0)$ with radius 2).

SOLUTION We begin by locating the critical points and the local maxima and minima. The critical points satisfy the equations

$$f_x(x, y) = 2x - 2 = 0 \quad \text{and} \quad f_y(x, y) = 2y + 2 = 0,$$

which have the solution $x = 1$ and $y = -1$. The value of the function at this point is $f(1, -1) = 3$.

We now determine the maximum and minimum values of f on the boundary of R, which is a circle of radius 2 described by the parametric equations

$$x = 2 \cos \theta, \quad y = 2 \sin \theta, \quad \text{for} \quad 0 \le \theta \le 2\pi.$$

> Recall that a parametric description of a circle of radius a centered at the origin is $x = a \cos \theta$, $y = a \sin \theta$, for $0 \le \theta \le 2\pi$.

Substituting x and y in terms of θ into the function f, we obtain a new function $g(\theta)$ that gives the values of f on the boundary of R:

$$g(\theta) = (2 \cos \theta)^2 + (2 \sin \theta)^2 - 2(2 \cos \theta) + 2(2 \sin \theta) + 5$$
$$= 4(\cos^2 \theta + \sin^2 \theta) - 4 \cos \theta + 4 \sin \theta + 5$$
$$= -4 \cos \theta + 4 \sin \theta + 9.$$

Finding the maximum and minimum boundary values is now a one-variable problem. The critical points of g satisfy

$$g'(\theta) = 4 \sin \theta + 4 \cos \theta = 0,$$

or $\tan\theta = -1$. Therefore, on the interval $[0, 2\pi]$, g has critical points $\theta = 3\pi/4$ and $\theta = 7\pi/4$, which correspond to the points $(-\sqrt{2}, \sqrt{2})$ and $(\sqrt{2}, -\sqrt{2})$, respectively. Notice that the endpoints of the interval ($\theta = 0$ and $\theta = 2\pi$) correspond to the same point on the boundary of R, namely $(2, 0)$.

Having completed the first two steps of this procedure, we have four function values to consider:

- $f(1, -1) = 3$ (critical point),
- $f(\sqrt{2}, -\sqrt{2}) = 9 - 4\sqrt{2} \approx 3.3$ (boundary point),
- $f(-\sqrt{2}, \sqrt{2}) = 9 + 4\sqrt{2} \approx 14.7$ (boundary point), and
- $f(2, 0) = 5$ (boundary point).

The greatest value of f on R, $f(-\sqrt{2}, \sqrt{2}) = 9 + 4\sqrt{2}$, is the absolute maximum value, and it occurs at a boundary point. The least value, $f(1, -1) = 3$, is the absolute minimum value, and it occurs at an interior point (Figure 12.95a). Also revealing is the plot of the level curves of the surface with the boundary of R superimposed (Figure 12.95b). As the boundary of R is traversed, the values of f vary, reaching a maximum value at $\theta = 3\pi/4$, or $(-\sqrt{2}, \sqrt{2})$, and a minimum value at $\theta = 7\pi/4$, or $(\sqrt{2}, -\sqrt{2})$.

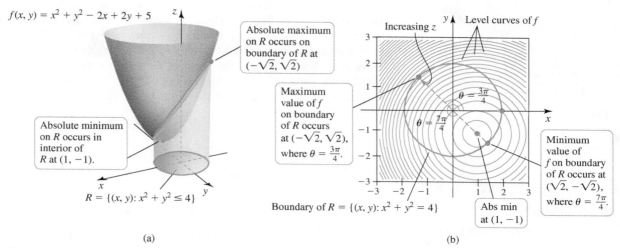

(a)

(b)

Figure 12.95

Related Exercises 43–52 ◄

Open and/or Unbounded Regions   Finding absolute maximum and minimum values of a function on an open region (for example, $R = \{(x, y) = x^2 + y^2 < 9\}$) or an unbounded domain (for example, $R = \{(x, y): x > 0, y > 0\}$) presents additional challenges. Because there is no systematic procedure for dealing with such problems, some ingenuity is generally needed. Notice that absolute extrema may not exist on such regions.

EXAMPLE 8   Absolute extreme values on an open region   Find the absolute maximum and minimum values of $f(x, y) = 4 - x^2 - y^2$ on the open disk $R = \{(x, y): x^2 + y^2 < 1\}$ (if they exist).

SOLUTION   You should verify that f has a critical point at $(0, 0)$ and it corresponds to a local maximum (on an inverted paraboloid). Moving away from $(0, 0)$ in all directions, the function values decrease, so f also has an absolute maximum value of 4 at $(0, 0)$. The boundary of R is the unit circle $\{(x, y): x^2 + y^2 = 1\}$, which is not contained in R. As (x, y) approaches any point on the unit circle along any path in R, the function values $f(x, y) = 4 - (x^2 + y^2)$ decrease and approach 3 but never reach 3. Therefore, f does not have an absolute minimum on R.

Related Exercises 53–60 ◄

QUICK CHECK 4   Does the linear function $f(x, y) = 2x + 3y$ have an absolute maximum or minimum value on the open unit square $\{(x, y): 0 < x < 1, 0 < y < 1\}$? ◄

EXAMPLE 9 **Absolute extreme values on an open region** Find the point(s) on the plane $x + 2y + z = 2$ closest to the point $P(2, 0, 4)$.

SOLUTION Suppose that (x, y, z) is a point on the plane, which means that $z = 2 - x - 2y$. The distance between $P(2, 0, 4)$ and (x, y, z) that we seek to minimize is

$$d(x, y, z) = \sqrt{(x - 2)^2 + y^2 + (z - 4)^2}.$$

It is easier to minimize d^2, which has the same critical points as d. Squaring d and eliminating z using $z = 2 - x - 2y$, we have

$$f(x, y) = (d(x, y, z))^2 = (x - 2)^2 + y^2 + \underbrace{(-x - 2y - 2)^2}_{z - 4}$$

$$= 2x^2 + 5y^2 + 4xy + 8y + 8.$$

The critical points of f satisfy the equations

$$f_x = 4x + 4y = 0 \quad \text{and} \quad f_y = 4x + 10y + 8 = 0,$$

whose only solution is $x = \frac{4}{3}, y = -\frac{4}{3}$. The Second Derivative Test confirms that this point corresponds to a local minimum of f. We now ask: Does $\left(\frac{4}{3}, -\frac{4}{3}\right)$ correspond to the *absolute* minimum value of f over the entire domain of the problem, which is $\mathbb{R}^2$? Because the domain has no boundary, we cannot check values of f on the boundary. Instead, we argue geometrically that there is exactly one point on the plane that is closest to P. We have found a point that is closest to P among nearby points on the plane. As we move away from this point, the values of f increase without bound. Therefore, $\left(\frac{4}{3}, -\frac{4}{3}\right)$ corresponds to the absolute minimum value of f. A graph of f (Figure 12.96) confirms this reasoning, and we conclude that the point $\left(\frac{4}{3}, -\frac{4}{3}, \frac{10}{3}\right)$ is the point on the plane nearest P.

Related Exercises 53–60 ◄

▶ Notice that $\frac{\partial}{\partial x}(d^2) = 2d\frac{\partial d}{\partial x}$ and $\frac{\partial}{\partial y}(d^2) = 2d\frac{\partial d}{\partial y}$. Because $d \geq 0$, d^2 and d have the same critical points.

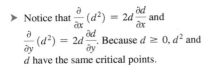

Distance squared:
$f(x, y) = 2x^2 + 5y^2 + 4xy + 8y + 8$

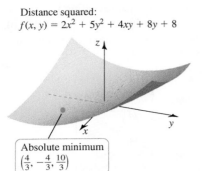

Absolute minimum
$\left(\frac{4}{3}, -\frac{4}{3}, \frac{10}{3}\right)$

Figure 12.96

SECTION 12.8 EXERCISES

Review Questions

1. Describe the appearance of a smooth surface with a local maximum at a point.

2. Describe the usual appearance of a smooth surface at a saddle point.

3. What are the conditions for a critical point of a function f?

4. If $f_x(a, b) = f_y(a, b) = 0$, does it follow that f has a local maximum or local minimum at (a, b)? Explain.

5. Consider the function $z = f(x, y)$. What is the discriminant of f, and how do you compute it?

6. Explain how the Second Derivative Test is used.

7. What is an absolute minimum value of a function f on a set R in $\mathbb{R}^2$?

8. What is the procedure for locating absolute maximum and minimum values on a closed bounded domain?

Basic Skills

9–18. Critical points *Find all critical points of the following functions.*

9. $f(x, y) = 1 + x^2 + y^2$

10. $f(x, y) = x^2 - 6x + y^2 + 8y$

11. $f(x, y) = (3x - 2)^2 + (y - 4)^2$

12. $f(x, y) = 3x^2 - 4y^2$

13. $f(x, y) = x^4 + y^4 - 16xy$

14. $f(x, y) = x^3/3 - y^3/3 + 3xy$

15. $f(x, y) = x^4 - 2x^2 + y^2 - 4y + 5$

16. $f(x, y) = x^2 + xy - 2x - y + 1$

17. $f(x, y) = x^2 + 6x + y^2 + 8$

18. $f(x, y) = e^{x^2y^2 - 2xy^2 + y^2}$

19–34. Analyzing critical points *Find the critical points of the following functions. Use the Second Derivative Test to determine (if possible) whether each critical point corresponds to a local maximum, local minimum, or saddle point. Confirm your results using a graphing utility.*

19. $f(x, y) = 4 + 2x^2 + 3y^2$

20. $f(x, y) = (4x - 1)^2 + (2y + 4)^2 + 1$

21. $f(x, y) = -4x^2 + 8y^2 - 3$

22. $f(x, y) = x^4 + y^4 - 4x - 32y + 10$

23. $f(x, y) = x^4 + 2y^2 - 4xy$

24. $f(x, y) = xye^{-x-y}$

25. $f(x, y) = \sqrt{x^2 + y^2 - 4x + 5}$

26. $f(x, y) = \tan^{-1} xy$

27. $f(x, y) = 2xye^{-x^2 - y^2}$

28. $f(x, y) = x^2 + xy^2 - 2x + 1$

29. $f(x, y) = \dfrac{x}{1 + x^2 + y^2}$

30. $f(x, y) = \dfrac{x - 1}{x^2 + y^2}$

31. $f(x, y) = x^4 + 4x^2(y - 2) + 8(y - 1)^2$

32. $f(x, y) = xe^{-x-y} \sin y$, for $|x| \le 2, 0 \le y \le \pi$

33. $f(x, y) = ye^x - e^y$

34. $f(x, y) = \sin(2\pi x) \cos(\pi y)$, for $|x| \le \tfrac{1}{2}$ and $|y| \le \tfrac{1}{2}$.

35. Shipping regulations A shipping company handles rectangular boxes provided the sum of the height and the girth of the box does not exceed 96 in. (The girth is the perimeter of the smallest side of the box.) Find the dimensions of the box that meets this condition and has the largest volume.

36. Cardboard boxes A lidless box is to be made using 2 m² of cardboard. Find the dimensions of the box with the largest possible volume.

37. Cardboard boxes A lidless cardboard box is to be made with a volume of 4 m³. Find the dimensions of the box that requires the least amount of cardboard.

38. Optimal box Find the dimensions of the largest rectangular box in the first octant of the xyz-coordinate system that has one vertex at the origin and the opposite vertex on the plane $x + 2y + 3z = 6$.

39–42. Inconclusive tests *Show that the Second Derivative Test is inconclusive when applied to the following functions at $(0, 0)$. Describe the behavior of the function at the critical point.*

39. $f(x, y) = 4 + x^4 + 3y^4$ **40.** $f(x, y) = x^2 y - 3$

41. $f(x, y) = x^4 y^2$ **42.** $f(x, y) = \sin(x^2 y^2)$

43–52. Absolute maxima and minima *Find the absolute maximum and minimum values of the following functions on the given region R.*

43. $f(x, y) = x^2 + y^2 - 2y + 1$; $R = \{(x, y): x^2 + y^2 \le 4\}$

44. $f(x, y) = 2x^2 + y^2$; $R = \{(x, y): x^2 + y^2 \le 16\}$

45. $f(x, y) = 4 + 2x^2 + y^2$;
$R = \{(x, y): -1 \le x \le 1, -1 \le y \le 1\}$

46. $f(x, y) = 6 - x^2 - 4y^2$;
$R = \{(x, y): -2 \le x \le 2, -1 \le y \le 1\}$

47. $f(x, y) = 2x^2 - 4x + 3y^2 + 2$;
$R = \{(x, y): (x - 1)^2 + y^2 \le 1\}$

48. $f(x, y) = x^2 + y^2 - 2x - 2y$; R is the closed region bounded by the triangle with vertices $(0, 0)$, $(2, 0)$, and $(0, 2)$.

49. $f(x, y) = -2x^2 + 4x - 3y^2 - 6y - 1$;
$R = \{(x, y): (x - 1)^2 + (y + 1)^2 \le 1\}$

50. $f(x, y) = \sqrt{x^2 + y^2 - 2x + 2}$; $R = \{(x, y): x^2 + y^2 \le 4,$
$y \ge 0\}$

51. $f(x, y) = \dfrac{2y^2 - x^2}{2 + 2x^2 y^2}$; R is the closed region bounded by the lines $y = x, y = 2x$, and $y = 2$.

52. $f(x, y) = \sqrt{x^2 + y^2}$; R is the closed region bounded by the ellipse $\dfrac{x^2}{4} + y^2 = 1$.

53–56. Absolute extrema on open and/or unbounded regions *If possible, find the absolute maximum and minimum values of the following functions on the region R.*

53. $f(x, y) = x^2 + y^2 - 4$; $R = \{(x, y): x^2 + y^2 < 4\}$

54. $f(x, y) = x + 3y$; $R = \{(x, y): |x| < 1, |y| < 2\}$

55. $f(x, y) = 2e^{-x-y}$; $R = \{(x, y): x \ge 0, y \ge 0\}$

56. $f(x, y) = x^2 - y^2$; $R = \{(x, y); |x| < 1, |y| < 1\}$

57–60. Absolute extrema on open and/or unbounded regions

57. Find the point on the plane $x + y + z = 4$ nearest the point $P(0, 3, 6)$.

58. Find the point(s) on the cone $z^2 = x^2 + y^2$ nearest the point $P(1, 4, 0)$.

59. Find the point on the curve $y = x^2$ nearest the line $y = x - 1$. Identify the point on the line.

60. Rectangular boxes with a volume of 10 m³ are made of two materials. The material for the top and bottom of the box costs $\$10/\text{m}^2$ and the material for the sides of the box costs $\$1/\text{m}^2$. What are the dimensions of the box that minimize the cost of the box?

Further Explorations

61. Explain why or why not Determine whether the following statements are true and give an explanation or counterexample. Assume that f is differentiable at the points in question.

a. The fact that $f_x(2, 2) = f_y(2, 2) = 0$ implies that f has a local maximum, local minimum, or saddle point at $(2, 2)$.

b. The function f could have a local maximum at (a, b) where $f_y(a, b) \ne 0$.

c. The function f could have both an absolute maximum and an absolute minimum at two different points that are not critical points.

d. The tangent plane is horizontal at a point on a smooth surface corresponding to a critical point.

62–63. Extreme points from contour plots *Based on the level curves that are visible in the following graphs, identify the approximate locations of the local maxima, local minima, and saddle points.*

62.

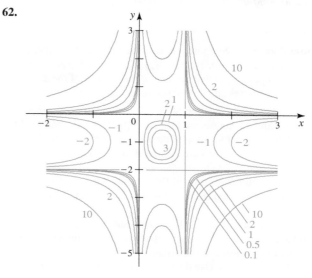

63.

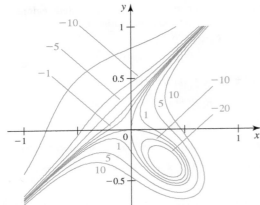

64. Optimal box Find the dimensions of the rectangular box with maximum volume in the first octant with one vertex at the origin and the opposite vertex on the ellipsoid $36x^2 + 4y^2 + 9z^2 = 36$.

65. Least distance What point on the plane $x - y + z = 2$ is closest to the point $(1, 1, 1)$?

66. Maximum/minimum of linear functions Let R be a closed bounded region in $\mathbb{R}^2$ and let $f(x, y) = ax + by + c$, where a, b, and c are real numbers, with a and b not both zero. Give a geometrical argument explaining why the absolute maximum and minimum values of f over R occur on the boundaries of R.

67. Magic triples Let x, y, and z be nonnegative numbers with $x + y + z = 200$.

  a. Find the values of $x, y,$ and z that minimize $x^2 + y^2 + z^2$.
  b. Find the values of $x, y,$ and z that minimize $\sqrt{x^2 + y^2 + z^2}$.
  c. Find the values of $x, y,$ and z that maximize xyz.
  d. Find the values of $x, y,$ and z that maximize $x^2y^2z^2$.

68. Powers and roots Assume that $x + y + z = 1$ with $x \geq 0$, $y \geq 0$, and $z \geq 0$.

  a. Find the maximum and minimum values of $(1 + x^2)(1 + y^2)(1 + z^2)$.
  b. Find the maximum and minimum values of $(1 + \sqrt{x})(1 + \sqrt{y})(1 + \sqrt{z})$.
  (Source: Math Horizons, Apr 2004)

Applications

T 69. Optimal locations Suppose n houses are located at the distinct points $(x_1, y_1), (x_2, y_2), \ldots, (x_n, y_n)$. A power substation must be located at a point such that the *sum of the squares* of the distances between the houses and the substation is minimized.

  a. Find the optimal location of the substation in the case that $n = 3$ and the houses are located at $(0, 0), (2, 0),$ and $(1, 1)$.
  b. Find the optimal location of the substation in the case that $n = 3$ and the houses are located at distinct points (x_1, y_1), (x_2, y_2), and (x_3, y_3).
  c. Find the optimal location of the substation in the general case of n houses located at distinct points $(x_1, y_1), (x_2, y_2), \ldots,$ (x_n, y_n).
  d. You might argue that the locations found in parts (a), (b), and (c) are not optimal because they result from minimizing the sum of the *squares* of the distances, not the sum of the distances themselves. Use the locations in part (a) and write the function that gives the sum of the distances. Note that minimizing this function is much more difficult than in part (a).

Then use a graphing utility to determine whether the optimal location is the same in the two cases. (Also see Exercise 77 about Steiner's problem.)

70–71. Least squares approximation *In its many guises, the least squares approximation arises in numerous areas of mathematics and statistics. Suppose you collect data for two variables (for example, height and shoe size) in the form of pairs $(x_1, y_1), (x_2, y_2), \ldots, (x_n, y_n)$. The data may be plotted as a scatterplot in the xy-plane, as shown in the figure. The technique known as* linear regression *asks the question: What is the equation of the line that "best fits" the data? The least squares criterion for best fit requires that the sum of the squares of the vertical distances between the line and the data points is a minimum.*

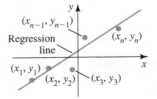

70. Let the equation of the best-fit line be $y = mx + b$, where the slope m and the y-intercept b must be determined using the least squares condition. First assume that there are three data points $(1, 2), (3, 5),$ and $(4, 6)$. Show that the function of m and b that gives the sum of the squares of the vertical distances between the line and the three data points is

$$E(m, b) = ((m + b) - 2)^2 + ((3m + b) - 5)^2$$
$$+ ((4m + b) - 6)^2.$$

Find the critical points of E and find the values of m and b that minimize E. Graph the three data points and the best-fit line.

T 71. Generalize the procedure in Exercise 70 by assuming that n data points $(x_1, y_1), (x_2, y_2), \ldots, (x_n, y_n)$ are given. Write the function $E(m, b)$ (summation notation allows for a more compact calculation). Show that the coefficients of the best-fit line are

$$m = \frac{\left(\sum x_k\right)\left(\sum y_k\right) - n\sum x_k y_k}{\left(\sum x_k\right)^2 - n\sum x_k^2} \text{ and}$$

$$b = \frac{1}{n}\left(\sum y_k - m\sum x_k\right),$$

where all sums run from $k = 1$ to $k = n$.

T 72–73. Least squares practice *Use the results of Exercise 71 to find the best-fit line for the following data sets. Plot the points and the best-fit line.*

72. $(0, 0), (2, 3), (4, 5)$ **73.** $(-1, 0), (0, 6), (3, 8)$

Additional Exercises

74. Second Derivative Test Use the Second Derivative Test to prove that if (a, b) is a critical point of f at which $f_x(a, b) = f_y(a, b) = 0$ and $f_{xx}(a, b) < 0 < f_{yy}(a, b)$ or $f_{yy}(a, b) < 0 < f_{xx}(a, b)$, then f has a saddle point at (a, b).

75. Maximum area triangle Among all triangles with a perimeter of 9 units, find the dimensions of the triangle with the maximum area. It may be easiest to use Heron's formula, which states that the area of a triangle with side length a, b, and c is $A = \sqrt{s(s - a)(s - b)(s - c)}$, where $2s$ is the perimeter of the triangle.

76. Ellipsoid inside a tetrahedron (1946 Putnam Exam) Let P be a plane tangent to the ellipsoid $x^2/a^2 + y^2/b^2 + z^2/c^2 = 1$ at a point in the first octant. Let T be the tetrahedron in the first octant bounded by P and the coordinate planes $x = 0$, $y = 0$, and $z = 0$. Find the minimum volume of T. (The volume of a tetrahedron is one-third the area of the base times the height.)

T 77. Steiner's problem for three points Given three distinct noncollinear points A, B, and C in the plane, find the point P in the plane such that the sum of the distances $|AP| + |BP| + |CP|$ is a minimum. Here is how to proceed with three points, assuming that the triangle formed by the three points has no angle greater than $2\pi/3$ $(120°)$.

   a. Assume the coordinates of the three given points are $A(x_1, y_1)$, $B(x_2, y_2)$, and $C(x_3, y_3)$. Let $d_1(x, y)$ be the distance between $A(x_1, y_1)$ and a variable point $P(x, y)$. Compute the gradient of d_1 and show that it is a unit vector pointing along the line between the two points.
   b. Define d_2 and d_3 in a similar way and show that ∇d_2 and ∇d_3 are also unit vectors in the direction of the line between the two points.
   c. The goal is to minimize $f(x, y) = d_1 + d_2 + d_3$. Show that the condition $f_x = f_y = 0$ implies that $\nabla d_1 + \nabla d_2 + \nabla d_3 = 0$.
   d. Explain why part (c) implies that the optimal point P has the property that the three line segments AP, BP, and CP all intersect symmetrically in angles of $2\pi/3$.
   e. What is the optimal solution if one of the angles in the triangle is greater than $2\pi/3$ (just draw a picture)?
   f. Estimate the Steiner point for the three points $(0, 0)$, $(0, 1)$, and $(2, 0)$.

78. Slicing plane Find an equation of the plane passing through the point $(3, 2, 1)$ that slices off the solid in the first octant with the least volume.

T 79. Two mountains without a saddle Show that the following two functions have two local maxima but no other extreme points (therefore, there is no saddle or basin between the mountains).

   a. $f(x, y) = -(x^2 - 1)^2 - (x^2 - e^y)^2$
   b. $f(x, y) = 4x^2 e^y - 2x^4 - e^{4y}$

(*Source: Ira Rosenholtz, Mathematics Magazine, Feb 1987*)

T 80. Solitary critical points A function of *one* variable has the property that a local maximum (or minimum) occurring at the only critical point is also the absolute maximum (or minimum) (for example, $f(x) = x^2$). Does the same result hold for a function of *two* variables? Show that the following functions have the property that they have a single local maximum (or minimum), occurring at the only critical point, but that the local maximum (or minimum) is not an absolute maximum (or minimum) on $\mathbb{R}^2$.

   a. $f(x, y) = 3xe^y - x^3 - e^{3y}$
   b. $f(x, y) = (2y^2 - y^4)\left(e^x + \dfrac{1}{1 + x^2}\right) - \dfrac{1}{1 + x^2}$

This property has the following interpretation. Suppose that a surface has a single local minimum that is not the absolute minimum. Then water can be poured into the basin around the local minimum and the surface never overflows, even though there are points on the surface below the local minimum.

(*Source: Mathematics Magazine, May 1985, and Calculus and Analytical Geometry, 2nd ed., Philip Gillett, 1984*)

QUICK CHECK ANSWERS

1. $f_x(2, -1) = f_y(2, -1) = 0$ 2. Vertically, in the directions $\langle 0, 0, \pm 1 \rangle$ 3. $D(x, y) = -12x^2 y^2$
4. It has neither an absolute maximum nor absolute minimum value on this set. ◄

12.9 Lagrange Multipliers

One of many challenges in economics and marketing is predicting the behavior of consumers. Basic models of consumer behavior often involve a *utility function* that expresses consumers' combined preference for several different amenities. For example, a simple utility function might have the form $U = f(\ell, g)$, where ℓ represents the amount of leisure time and g represents the number of consumable goods. The model assumes that consumers try to maximize their utility function, but they do so under certain constraints on the variables of the problem. For example, increasing leisure time may increase utility, but leisure time produces no income for consumable goods. Similarly, consumable goods may also increase utility, but they require income, which reduces leisure time. We first develop a general method for solving such constrained optimization problems and then return to economics problems later in the section.

The Basic Idea

We start with a typical constrained optimization problem with two independent variables and give its method of solution; a generalization to more variables then follows. We seek maximum and/or minimum values of a differentiable **objective function** f with the restriction that x and y must lie on a **constraint** curve C in the xy-plane given by $g(x, y) = 0$ (Figure 12.97).

The problem and a method of solution are easy to visualize if we return to Example 7 of Section 12.8. Part of that problem was to find the maximum value of $f(x, y) = x^2 + y^2 - 2x + 2y + 5$ on the circle $C: \{(x, y): x^2 + y^2 = 4\}$ (Figure 12.98a). In

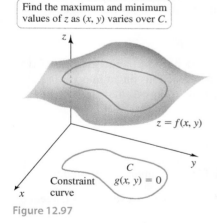

Find the maximum and minimum values of z as (x, y) varies over C.

$z = f(x, y)$

C

Constraint curve $g(x, y) = 0$

Figure 12.97

Figure 12.98b, we see the level curves of f and the point $P(-\sqrt{2}, \sqrt{2})$ on C at which f has a maximum value. Imagine moving along C toward P; as we approach P, the values of f increase and reach a maximum value at P. Moving past P, the values of f decrease.

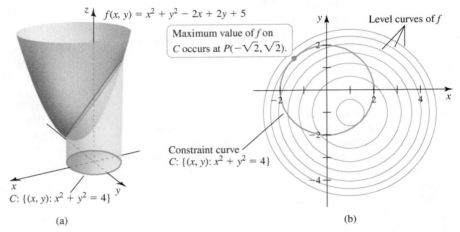

Maximum value of f on C occurs at $P(-\sqrt{2}, \sqrt{2})$.

Level curves of f

Constraint curve
C: $\{(x, y): x^2 + y^2 = 4\}$

$f(x, y) = x^2 + y^2 - 2x + 2y + 5$

C: $\{(x, y): x^2 + y^2 = 4\}$

(a)

(b)

Figure 12.98

Figure 12.99 shows what is special about the point P. We already know that the line tangent to the level curve of f at P is orthogonal to the gradient $\nabla f(P)$ (Theorem 12.12). We also see that the line tangent to the level curve at P is tangent to the constraint curve C at P. We prove this fact shortly.

Furthermore, if we think of the constraint curve C as just one level curve of the function $z = g(x, y)$, then it follows that the gradient $\nabla g(P)$ is also orthogonal to C at P, where we assume that $\nabla g(P) \neq \mathbf{0}$ (Theorem 12.12). Therefore, the gradients $\nabla f(P)$ and $\nabla g(P)$ are parallel. These properties characterize the point P at which f has an extreme value on the constraint curve. They are the basis for the method of *Lagrange multipliers* that we now formalize.

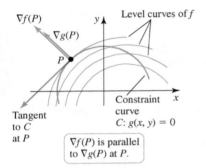

$\nabla f(P)$

$\nabla g(P)$

Level curves of f

P

Tangent to C at P

Constraint curve
C: $g(x, y) = 0$

$\nabla f(P)$ is parallel to $\nabla g(P)$ at P.

Figure 12.99

➤ The Greek lowercase ℓ is λ; it is read *lambda*.

Lagrange Multipliers with Two Independent Variables

The major step in establishing the method of Lagrange multipliers is to prove that Figure 12.99 is drawn correctly; that is, at the point on the constraint curve C where f has an extreme value, the line tangent to C is orthogonal to $\nabla f(a, b)$ and $\nabla g(a, b)$.

THEOREM 12.15   Parallel Gradients (Ball Park Theorem)
Let f be a differentiable function in a region of $\mathbb{R}^2$ that contains the smooth curve C given by $g(x, y) = 0$. Assume that f has a local extreme value on C at a point $P(a, b)$. Then $\nabla f(a, b)$ is orthogonal to the line tangent to C at P. Assuming $\nabla g(a, b) \neq \mathbf{0}$, it follows that there is a real number λ (called a **Lagrange multiplier**) such that $\nabla f(a, b) = \lambda \nabla g(a, b)$.

Proof: Because C is smooth, it can be expressed parametrically in the form $C: \mathbf{r}(t) = \langle x(t), y(t) \rangle$, where x and y are differentiable functions on an interval in t that contains t_0 with $P(a, b) = (x(t_0), y(t_0))$. As we vary t and follow C, the rate of change of f is given by the Chain Rule:

$$\frac{df}{dt} = \frac{\partial f}{\partial x}\frac{dx}{dt} + \frac{\partial f}{\partial y}\frac{dy}{dt} = \nabla f \cdot \mathbf{r}'(t).$$

At the point $(x(t_0), y(t_0)) = (a, b)$ at which f has a local maximum or minimum value, we have $\left.\dfrac{df}{dt}\right|_{t=t_0} = 0$, which implies that $\nabla f(a, b) \cdot \mathbf{r}'(t_0) = 0$. Because $\mathbf{r}'(t)$ is tangent to C, the gradient $\nabla f(a, b)$ is orthogonal to the line tangent to C at P.

To prove the second assertion, note that the constraint curve C given by $g(x, y) = 0$ is also a level curve of the surface $z = g(x, y)$. Recall that gradients are orthogonal to

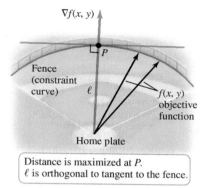

$\nabla f(x, y)$

P

Fence
(constraint
curve)

ℓ

$f(x, y)$
objective
function

Home plate

Distance is maximized at P.
ℓ is orthogonal to tangent to the fence.

Figure 12.100

QUICK CHECK 1 Explain in terms of functions and gradients why the ballpark analogy for Theorem 12.15 is true. ◄

➤ *In principle*, it is possible to solve a constrained optimization problem by solving the constraint equation for one of the variables and eliminating that variable in the objective function. In practice, this method is often prohibitive, particularly with three or more variables or two or more constraints.

level curves. Therefore, at the point $P(a, b)$, $\nabla g(a, b)$ is orthogonal to C at (a, b). Because both $\nabla f(a, b)$ and $\nabla g(a, b)$ are orthogonal to C, the two gradients are parallel, so there is a real number λ such that $\nabla f(a, b) = \lambda \nabla g(a, b)$. ◄

Theorem 12.15 has a nice geometric interpretation that makes it easy to remember. Suppose you walk along the outfield fence at a ballpark, which represents the constraint curve C, and record the distance $f(x, y)$ between you and home plate (which is the objective function). At some instant, you reach a point P that maximizes the distance; it is the point on the fence farthest from home plate. The point P has the property that the line ℓ from home plate to P, which points in the direction of maximum increase of f, is orthogonal to the (line tangent to the) fence at P (Figure 12.100).

PROCEDURE   **Method of Lagrange Multipliers in Two Variables**

Let the objective function f and the constraint function g be differentiable on a region of $\mathbb{R}^2$ with $\nabla g(x, y) \neq \mathbf{0}$ on the curve $g(x, y) = 0$. To locate the maximum and minimum values of f subject to the constraint $g(x, y) = 0$, carry out the following steps.

1. Find the values of x, y, and λ (if they exist) that satisfy the equations
$$\nabla f(x, y) = \lambda \nabla g(x, y) \quad \text{and} \quad g(x, y) = 0.$$

2. Among the values (x, y) found in Step 1, select the largest and smallest corresponding function values. These values are the maximum and minimum values of f subject to the constraint.

Notice that $\nabla f = \lambda \nabla g$ is a vector equation: $\langle f_x, f_y \rangle = \lambda \langle g_x, g_y \rangle$. It is satisfied provided $f_x = \lambda g_x$ and $f_y = \lambda g_y$. Therefore, the crux of the method is solving the three equations

$$f_x = \lambda g_x, \qquad f_y = \lambda g_y, \qquad \text{and} \qquad g(x, y) = 0$$

for the three variables x, y, and λ.

EXAMPLE 1   Lagrange multipliers with two variables Find the maximum and minimum values of the objective function $f(x, y) = 2x^2 + y^2 + 2$, where x and y lie on the ellipse C given by $g(x, y) = x^2 + 4y^2 - 4 = 0$.

SOLUTION Figure 12.101a shows the elliptic paraboloid $z = f(x, y)$ above the ellipse C in the xy-plane. As the ellipse is traversed, the corresponding function values on the surface vary. The goal is to find the minimum and maximum of these function values. An alternative view is given in Figure 12.101b, where we see the level curves of f and the constraint curve C. As the ellipse is traversed, the values of f vary, reaching maximum and minimum values along the way.

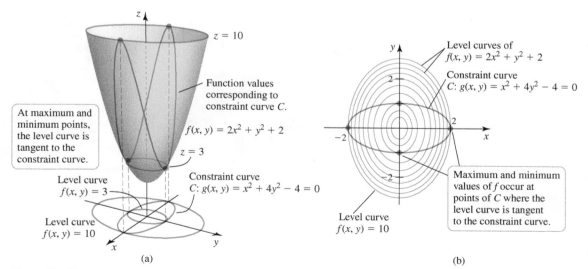

At maximum and minimum points, the level curve is tangent to the constraint curve.

$z = 10$

Function values corresponding to constraint curve C.

$f(x, y) = 2x^2 + y^2 + 2$

$z = 3$

Level curve
$f(x, y) = 3$

Constraint curve
$C: g(x, y) = x^2 + 4y^2 - 4 = 0$

Level curve
$f(x, y) = 10$

Level curves of
$f(x, y) = 2x^2 + y^2 + 2$

Constraint curve
$C: g(x, y) = x^2 + 4y^2 - 4 = 0$

Maximum and minimum values of f occur at points of C where the level curve is tangent to the constraint curve.

Level curve
$f(x, y) = 10$

(a)   (b)

Figure 12.101

Noting that $\nabla f(x, y) = \langle 4x, 2y \rangle$ and $\nabla g(x, y) = \langle 2x, 8y \rangle$, the equations that result from $\nabla f = \lambda \nabla g$ and the constraint are

$$\underbrace{4x = \lambda(2x),}_{f_x = \lambda g_x} \qquad \underbrace{2y = \lambda(8y),}_{f_y = \lambda g_y} \qquad \text{and} \qquad \underbrace{x^2 + 4y^2 - 4 = 0,}_{g(x, y) = 0}$$

which reduce to the system of equations

$$x(2 - \lambda) = 0, \ (1) \qquad y(1 - 4\lambda) = 0, \quad \text{and} \quad (2) \qquad x^2 + 4y^2 - 4 = 0. \ (3)$$

The solutions of equation (1) are $x = 0$ or $\lambda = 2$. If $x = 0$, then equation (3) implies that $y = \pm 1$ and (2) implies that $\lambda = \frac{1}{4}$. On the other hand, if $\lambda = 2$ in equation (1), then equation (2) implies that $y = 0$; from (3), we get $x = \pm 2$. Therefore, the candidates for locations of extreme values are $(0, \pm 1)$, with $f(0, \pm 1) = 3$, and $(\pm 2, 0)$, with $f(\pm 2, 0) = 10$. We see that the maximum value of f on C is 10, which occurs at $(2, 0)$ and $(-2, 0)$; the minimum value of f on C is 3, which occurs at $(0, 1)$ and $(0, -1)$. Notice that the value of λ is not used in the final result.

Related Exercises 5–14 ◄

QUICK CHECK 2 Choose any point on the constraint curve in Figure 12.101b other than a solution point. Draw ∇f and ∇g at that point and show that they are not parallel. ◄

Lagrange Multipliers with Three Independent Variables

The technique just outlined extends to three or more independent variables. With three variables, suppose an objective function $w = f(x, y, z)$ is given; its level surfaces are surfaces in $\mathbb{R}^3$ (Figure 12.102a). The constraint equation takes the form $g(x, y, z) = 0$, which is another surface S in $\mathbb{R}^3$ (Figure 12.102b). To find the maximum and minimum values of f on S (assuming they exist), we must find the points (a, b, c) on S at which $\nabla f(a, b, c)$ is parallel to $\nabla g(a, b, c)$, assuming $\nabla g(a, b, c) \neq \mathbf{0}$ (Figure 12.102c, d). The procedure for finding the maximum and minimum values of $f(x, y, z)$, where the point (x, y, z) is constrained to lie on S, is similar to the procedure for two variables.

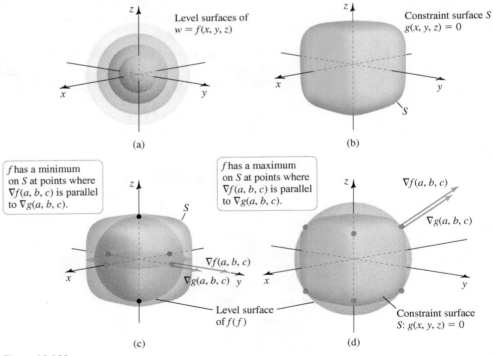

Figure 12.102

> **PROCEDURE**   **Method of Lagrange Multipliers in Three Variables**
>
> Let f and g be differentiable on a region of $\mathbb{R}^3$ with $\nabla g(x, y, z) \neq \mathbf{0}$ on the surface $g(x, y, z) = 0$. To locate the maximum and minimum values of f subject to the constraint $g(x, y, z) = 0$, carry out the following steps.
>
> **1.** Find the values of x, y, z, and λ that satisfy the equations
> $$\nabla f(x, y, z) = \lambda \nabla g(x, y, z) \quad \text{and} \quad g(x, y, z) = 0.$$
>
> **2.** Among the points (x, y, z) found in Step 1, select the largest and smallest corresponding function values. These values are the maximum and minimum values of f subject to the constraint.

▶ Some books formulate the Lagrange multiplier method by defining $L = f - \lambda g$. The conditions of the method then become $\nabla L = \mathbf{0}$, where $\nabla L = \langle L_x, L_y, L_z, L_\lambda \rangle$.

Now there are four equations to be solved for x, y, z, and λ:

$$f_x(x, y, z) = \lambda g_x(x, y, z), \qquad f_y(x, y, z) = \lambda g_y(x, y, z),$$
$$f_z(x, y, z) = \lambda g_z(x, y, z), \quad \text{and} \quad g(x, y, z) = 0.$$

▶ Problems similar to Example 2 were solved in Section 12.8 using ordinary optimization techniques. These methods may or may not be easier to apply than Lagrange multipliers.

EXAMPLE 2   A geometry problem Find the least distance between the point $P(3, 4, 0)$ and the surface of the cone $z^2 = x^2 + y^2$.

SOLUTION Figure 12.103 shows both sheets of the cone and the point $P(3, 4, 0)$. Because P is in the xy-plane, we anticipate two solutions, one for each sheet of the cone. The distance between P and any point $Q(x, y, z)$ on the cone is

$$d(x, y, z) = \sqrt{(x - 3)^2 + (y - 4)^2 + z^2}.$$

In many distance problems, it is easier to work with the *square* of the distance to avoid dealing with square roots. This maneuver is allowable because if a point minimizes $(d(x, y, z))^2$, it also minimizes $d(x, y, z)$. Therefore, we define

$$f(x, y, z) = (d(x, y, z))^2 = (x - 3)^2 + (y - 4)^2 + z^2.$$

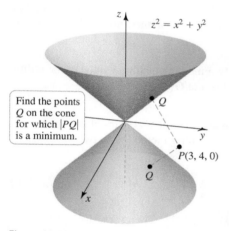

Figure 12.103

Find the points Q on the cone for which $|PQ|$ is a minimum.

$z^2 = x^2 + y^2$

The constraint is the condition that the point (x, y, z) must lie on the cone, which implies $z^2 = x^2 + y^2$, or $g(x, y, z) = z^2 - x^2 - y^2 = 0$.
    Now we proceed with Lagrange multipliers; the conditions are

$$f_x(x, y, z) = \lambda g_x(x, y, z), \text{ or } 2(x - 3) = \lambda(-2x), \text{ or } x(1 + \lambda) = 3, \tag{4}$$
$$f_y(x, y, z) = \lambda g_y(x, y, z), \text{ or } 2(y - 4) = \lambda(-2y), \text{ or } y(1 + \lambda) = 4, \tag{5}$$
$$f_z(x, y, z) = \lambda g_z(x, y, z), \text{ or } 2z = \lambda(2z), \text{ or } z = \lambda z, \text{ and} \tag{6}$$
$$g(x, y, z) = z^2 - x^2 - y^2 = 0. \tag{7}$$

The solutions of equation (6) (the simplest of the four equations) are either $z = 0$, or $\lambda = 1$ and $z \neq 0$. In the first case, if $z = 0$, then by equation (7), $x = y = 0$; however, $x = 0$ and $y = 0$ do not satisfy (4) and (5). So no solution results from this case.
    On the other hand, if $\lambda = 1$ in equation (6), then by (4) and (5), we find that $x = \frac{3}{2}$ and $y = 2$. Using (7), the corresponding values of z are $\pm\frac{5}{2}$. Therefore, the two solutions and the values of f are

$$x = \tfrac{3}{2}, \quad y = 2, \quad z = \tfrac{5}{2} \quad \text{with } f\left(\tfrac{3}{2}, 2, \tfrac{5}{2}\right) = \tfrac{25}{2}, \text{ and}$$
$$x = \tfrac{3}{2}, \quad y = 2, \quad z = -\tfrac{5}{2} \quad \text{with } f\left(\tfrac{3}{2}, 2, -\tfrac{5}{2}\right) = \tfrac{25}{2}.$$

▶ With three independent variables, it is possible to impose two constraints. These problems are explored in Exercises 61–65.

You can check that moving away from $\left(\frac{3}{2}, 2, \pm\frac{5}{2}\right)$ in any direction on the cone has the effect of increasing the values of f. Therefore, the points correspond to *local* minima of f. Do these points also correspond to *absolute* minima? The domain of this problem is unbounded; however, one can argue geometrically that f increases without bound moving away from $\left(\frac{3}{2}, 2, \pm\frac{5}{2}\right)$ on the cone with $|x| \to \infty$ and $|y| \to \infty$. Therefore, these points correspond to absolute minimum values and the points on the cone nearest to $(3, 4, 0)$ are

QUICK CHECK 3 In Example 2, is there a point that *maximizes* the distance between $(3, 4, 0)$ and the cone? If the point $(3, 4, 0)$ were replaced by $(3, 4, 1)$, how many minimizing solutions would there be? ◀

$\left(\frac{3}{2}, 2, \pm\frac{5}{2}\right)$, at a distance of $\sqrt{\dfrac{25}{2}} = \dfrac{5}{\sqrt{2}}$. (Recall that $f = d^2$.)

Related Exercises 15–34 ◀

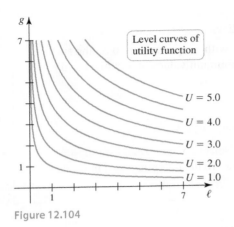

Figure 12.104

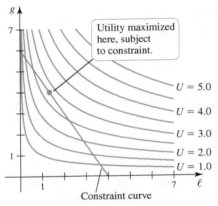

Figure 12.105

Economic Models   In the opening of this section, we briefly described how utility functions are used to model consumer behavior. We now look in more detail at some specific—admittedly simple—utility functions and the constraints that are imposed upon them.

As described earlier, a prototype model for consumer behavior uses two independent variables: leisure time ℓ and consumable goods g. A utility function $U = f(\ell, g)$ measures consumer preferences for various combinations of leisure time and consumable goods. The following assumptions about utility functions are commonly made.

1. Utility increases if any variable increases (essentially, *more is better*).

2. Various combinations of leisure time and consumable goods have the same utility; that is, giving up some leisure time for additional consumable goods results in the same utility.

The level curves of a typical utility function are shown in Figure 12.104. Assumption 1 is reflected by the fact that the utility values on the level curves increase as either ℓ or g increases. Consistent with Assumption 2, a single level curve shows the combinations of ℓ and g that have the same utility; for this reason, economists call the level curves *indifference curves*. Notice that if ℓ increases, then g must decrease on a level curve to maintain the same utility, and vice versa.

Economic models assert that consumers maximize utility subject to constraints on leisure time and consumable goods. One assumption that leads to a reasonable constraint is that an increase in leisure time implies a linear decrease in consumable goods. Therefore, the constraint curve is a line with negative slope (Figure 12.105). When such a constraint is superimposed on the level curves of the utility function, the optimization problem becomes evident. Among all points on the constraint line, which one maximizes utility? A solution is marked in the figure; at this point, the utility has a maximum value (between 2.5 and 3.0).

EXAMPLE 3   Constrained optimization of utility   Find the maximum value of the utility function $U = f(\ell, g) = \ell^{1/3} g^{2/3}$, subject to the constraint $G(\ell, g) = 3\ell + 2g - 12 = 0$, where $\ell \geq 0$ and $g \geq 0$.

SOLUTION   The level curves of the utility function and the linear constraint are shown in Figure 12.105. The solution follows the Lagrange multiplier method with two variables. The gradient of the utility function is

$$\nabla f(\ell, g) = \left\langle \frac{\ell^{-2/3} g^{2/3}}{3}, \frac{2\ell^{1/3} g^{-1/3}}{3} \right\rangle = \frac{1}{3}\left\langle \left(\frac{g}{\ell}\right)^{2/3}, 2\left(\frac{\ell}{g}\right)^{1/3} \right\rangle.$$

The gradient of the constraint function is $\nabla G(\ell, g) = \langle 3, 2 \rangle$. Therefore, the equations that must be solved are

$$\frac{1}{3}\left(\frac{g}{\ell}\right)^{2/3} = 3\lambda, \qquad \frac{2}{3}\left(\frac{\ell}{g}\right)^{1/3} = 2\lambda, \qquad \text{and} \qquad G(\ell, g) = 3\ell + 2g - 12 = 0.$$

Eliminating λ from the first two equations leads to the condition $g = 3\ell$, which, when substituted into the constraint equation, gives the solution $\ell = \frac{4}{3}$ and $g = 4$. The actual value of the utility function at this point is $U = f\left(\frac{4}{3}, 4\right) = 4/\sqrt[3]{3} \approx 2.8$. This solution is consistent with Figure 12.105.

Related Exercises 35–38 ◄

QUICK CHECK 4   In Figure 12.105, explain why, if you move away from the optimal point along the constraint line, the utility decreases. ◄

SECTION 12.9 EXERCISES

Review Questions

1. Explain why, at a point that maximizes or minimizes f subject to a constraint $g(x, y) = 0$, the gradient of f is parallel to the gradient of g. Use a diagram.

2. If $f(x, y) = x^2 + y^2$ and $g(x, y) = 2x + 3y - 4 = 0$, write the Lagrange multiplier conditions that must be satisfied by a point that maximizes or minimizes f subject to $g(x, y) = 0$.

3. If $f(x, y, z) = x^2 + y^2 + z^2$ and $g(x, y, z) = 2x + 3y - 5z + 4 = 0$, write the Lagrange multiplier conditions that must be satisfied by a point that maximizes or minimizes f subject to $g(x, y, z) = 0$.

4. Sketch several level curves of $f(x, y) = x^2 + y^2$ and sketch the constraint line $g(x, y) = 2x + 3y - 4 = 0$. Describe the extrema (if any) that f attains on the constraint line.

Basic Skills

5–14. Lagrange multipliers in two variables *Use Lagrange multipliers to find the maximum and minimum values of f (when they exist) subject to the given constraint.*

5. $f(x, y) = x + 2y$ subject to $x^2 + y^2 = 4$

6. $f(x, y) = xy^2$ subject to $x^2 + y^2 = 1$

7. $f(x, y) = x + y$ subject to $x^2 - xy + y^2 = 1$

8. $f(x, y) = x^2 + y^2$ subject to $2x^2 + 3xy + 2y^2 = 7$

9. $f(x, y) = xy$ subject to $x^2 + y^2 - xy = 9$

10. $f(x, y) = x - y$ subject to $x^2 + y^2 - 3xy = 20$

11. $f(x, y) = e^{2xy}$ subject to $x^2 + y^2 = 16$

12. $f(x, y) = x^2 + y^2$ subject to $x^6 + y^6 = 1$

13. $f(x, y) = y^2 - 4x^2$ subject to $x^2 + 2y^2 = 4$

14. $f(x, y) = xy + x + y$ subject to $x^2 y^2 = 4$

15–24. Lagrange multipliers in three variables *Use Lagrange multipliers to find the maximum and minimum values of f (when they exist) subject to the given constraint.*

15. $f(x, y, z) = x + 3y - z$ subject to $x^2 + y^2 + z^2 = 4$

16. $f(x, y, z) = xyz$ subject to $x^2 + 2y^2 + 4z^2 = 9$

17. $f(x, y, z) = x$ subject to $x^2 + y^2 + z^2 - z = 1$

18. $f(x, y, z) = x - z$ subject to $x^2 + y^2 + z^2 - y = 2$

19. $f(x, y, z) = x^2 + y^2 + z^2$ subject to $x^2 + y^2 + z^2 - 4xy = 1$

20. $f(x, y, z) = x + y + z$ subject to $x^2 + y^2 + z^2 - 2x - 2y = 1$

21. $f(x, y, z) = 2x + z^2$ subject to $x^2 + y^2 + 2z^2 = 25$

22. $f(x, y, z) = x^2 + y^2 - z$ subject to $z = 2x^2 y^2 + 1$

23. $f(x, y, z) = x^2 + y^2 + z^2$ subject to $xyz = 4$

24. $f(x, y, z) = (xyz)^{1/2}$ subject to $x + y + z = 1$ with $x \geq 0$, $y \geq 0, z \geq 0$

25–34. Applications of Lagrange multipliers *Use Lagrange multipliers in the following problems. When the domain of the objective function is unbounded or open, explain why you have found an absolute maximum or minimum value.*

25. **Shipping regulations** A shipping company requires that the sum of length plus girth of rectangular boxes must not exceed 108 in. Find the dimensions of the box with maximum volume that meets this condition. (The girth is the perimeter of the smallest side of the box.)

26. **Box with minimum surface area** Find the rectangular box with a volume of 16 ft^3 that has minimum surface area.

T 27. **Extreme distances to an ellipse** Find the minimum and maximum distances between the ellipse $x^2 + xy + 2y^2 = 1$ and the origin.

28. **Maximum area rectangle in an ellipse** Find the dimensions of the rectangle of maximum area with sides parallel to the coordinate axes that can be inscribed in the ellipse $4x^2 + 16y^2 = 16$.

29. **Maximum perimeter rectangle in an ellipse** Find the dimensions of the rectangle of maximum perimeter with sides parallel to the coordinate axes that can be inscribed in the ellipse $2x^2 + 4y^2 = 3$.

30. **Minimum distance to a plane** Find the point on the plane $2x + 3y + 6z - 10 = 0$ closest to the point $(-2, 5, 1)$.

31. **Minimum distance to a surface** Find the point on the surface $4x + y - 1 = 0$ closest to the point $(1, 2, -3)$.

32. **Minimum distance to a cone** Find the points on the cone $z^2 = x^2 + y^2$ closest to the point $(1, 2, 0)$.

33. **Extreme distances to a sphere** Find the minimum and maximum distances between the sphere $x^2 + y^2 + z^2 = 9$ and the point $(2, 3, 4)$.

34. **Maximum volume cylinder in a sphere** Find the dimensions of a right circular cylinder of maximum volume that can be inscribed in a sphere of radius 16.

35–38. Maximizing utility functions *Find the values of ℓ and g with $\ell \geq 0$ and $g \geq 0$ that maximize the following utility functions subject to the given constraints. Give the value of the utility function at the optimal point.*

35. $U = f(\ell, g) = 10\ell^{1/2} g^{1/2}$ subject to $3\ell + 6g = 18$

36. $U = f(\ell, g) = 32\ell^{2/3} g^{1/3}$ subject to $4\ell + 2g = 12$

37. $U = f(\ell, g) = 8\ell^{4/5} g^{1/5}$ subject to $10\ell + 8g = 40$

38. $U = f(\ell, g) = \ell^{1/6} g^{5/6}$ subject to $4\ell + 5g = 20$

Further Explorations

39. **Explain why or why not** Determine whether the following statements are true and give an explanation or counterexample.

   a. Suppose you are standing at the center of a sphere looking at a point P on the surface of the sphere. Your line of sight to P is orthogonal to the plane tangent to the sphere at P.

   b. At a point that maximizes f on the curve $g(x, y) = 0$, the dot product $\nabla f \cdot \nabla g$ is zero.

40–45. Alternative method *Solve the following problems from Section 12.8 using Lagrange multipliers.*

40. Exercise 35   **41.** Exercise 36   **42.** Exercise 37

43. Exercise 38   **44.** Exercise 64   **45.** Exercise 65

 46–49. Absolute maximum and minimum values *Find the absolute maximum and minimum values of the following functions over the given regions R. Use Lagrange multipliers to check for extreme points on the boundary.*

46. $f(x, y) = x^2 + 4y^2 + 1$; $R = \{(x, y): x^2 + 4y^2 \leq 1\}$

47. $f(x, y) = x^2 - 4y^2 + xy$; $R = \{(x, y): 4x^2 + 9y^2 \leq 36\}$

48. $f(x, y) = 2x^2 + y^2 + 2x - 3y$; $R = \{(x, y): x^2 + y^2 \leq 1\}$

49. $f(x, y) = (x - 1)^2 + (y + 1)^2$; $R = \{(x, y): x^2 + y^2 \leq 4\}$

50–51. Graphical Lagrange multipliers *The following figures show the level curves of f and the constraint curve $g(x, y) = 0$. Estimate the maximum and minimum values of f subject to the constraint. At each point where an extreme value occurs, indicate the direction of ∇f and the direction of ∇g.*

50.

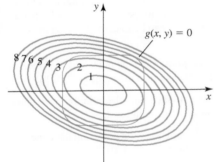

51.

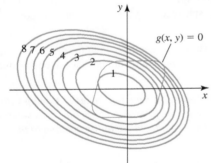

52. Extreme points on flattened spheres The equation $x^{2n} + y^{2n} + z^{2n} = 1$, where n is a positive integer, describes a flattened sphere. Define the extreme points to be the points on the flattened sphere with a maximum distance from the origin.

a. Find all the extreme points on the flattened sphere with $n = 2$. What is the distance between the extreme points and the origin?

b. Find all the extreme points on the flattened sphere for integers $n > 2$. What is the distance between the extreme points and the origin?

c. Give the location of the extreme points in the limit as $n \to \infty$. What is the limiting distance between the extreme points and the origin as $n \to \infty$?

Applications

53–55. Production functions *Economists model the output of manufacturing systems using production functions that have many of the same properties as utility functions. The family of Cobb-Douglas production functions has the form $P = f(K, L) = CK^a L^{1-a}$, where K represents capital, L represents labor, and C and a are positive real numbers with $0 < a < 1$. If the cost of capital is p dollars per unit, the cost of labor is q dollars per unit, and the total available budget is B, then the constraint takes the form $pK + qL = B$. Find the values of K and L that maximize the following production functions subject to the given constraint, assuming $K \geq 0$ and $L \geq 0$.*

53. $P = f(K, L) = K^{1/2} L^{1/2}$ for $20K + 30L = 300$

54. $P = f(K, L) = 10K^{1/3} L^{2/3}$ for $30K + 60L = 360$

55. Given the production function $P = f(K, L) = K^a L^{1-a}$ and the budget constraint $pK + qL = B$, where a, p, q, and B are given, show that P is maximized when $K = aB/p$ and $L = (1 - a)B/q$.

56. Temperature of an elliptical plate The temperature of points on an elliptical plate $x^2 + y^2 + xy \leq 1$ is given by $T(x, y) = 25(x^2 + y^2)$. Find the hottest and coldest temperatures on the edge of the elliptical plate.

Additional Exercises

57–59. Maximizing a sum

57. Find the maximum value of $x_1 + x_2 + x_3 + x_4$ subject to the condition that $x_1^2 + x_2^2 + x_3^2 + x_4^2 = 16$.

58. Generalize Exercise 57 and find the maximum value of $x_1 + x_2 + \cdots + x_n$ subject to the condition that $x_1^2 + x_2^2 + \cdots + x_n^2 = c^2$, for a real number c and a positive integer n.

59. Generalize Exercise 57 and find the maximum value of $a_1x_1 + a_2x_2 + \cdots + a_nx_n$ subject to the condition that $x_1^2 + x_2^2 + \cdots + x_n^2 = 1$, for given positive real numbers $a_1, \ldots, a_n$ and a positive integer n.

60. Geometric and arithmetic means Given positive numbers $x_1, \ldots, x_n$, prove that the geometric mean $(x_1x_2\cdots x_n)^{1/n}$ is no greater than the arithmetic mean $(x_1 + \cdots + x_n)/n$ in the following cases.

a. Find the maximum value of xyz, subject to $x + y + z = k$, where k is a real number and $x > 0, y > 0$, and $z > 0$. Use the result to prove that

$$(xyz)^{1/3} \leq \frac{x + y + z}{3}.$$

b. Generalize part (a) and show that

$$(x_1x_2 \cdots x_n)^{1/n} \leq \frac{x_1 + \cdots + x_n}{n}.$$

61. Problems with two constraints Given a differentiable function $w = f(x, y, z)$, the goal is to find its maximum and minimum values subject to the constraints $g(x, y, z) = 0$ and $h(x, y, z) = 0$, where g and h are also differentiable.

   a. Imagine a level surface of the function f and the constraint surfaces $g(x, y, z) = 0$ and $h(x, y, z) = 0$. Note that g and h intersect (in general) in a curve C on which maximum and minimum values of f must be found. Explain why ∇g and ∇h are orthogonal to their respective surfaces.

   b. Explain why ∇f lies in the plane formed by ∇g and ∇h at a point of C where f has a maximum or minimum value.

   c. Explain why part (b) implies that $\nabla f = \lambda \nabla g + \mu \nabla h$ at a point of C where f has a maximum or minimum value, where λ and μ (the Lagrange multipliers) are real numbers.

   d. Conclude from part (c) that the equations that must be solved for maximum or minimum values of f subject to two constraints are $\nabla f = \lambda \nabla g + \mu \nabla h$, $g(x, y, z) = 0$ and $h(x, y, z) = 0$.

62–65. Two-constraint problems *Use the result of Exercise 61 to solve the following problems.*

62. The planes $x + 2z = 12$ and $x + y = 6$ intersect in a line L. Find the point on L nearest the origin.

63. Find the maximum and minimum values of $f(x, y, z) = xyz$ subject to the conditions that $x^2 + y^2 = 4$ and $x + y + z = 1$.

64. The paraboloid $z = x^2 + 2y^2 + 1$ and the plane $x - y + 2z = 4$ intersect in a curve C. Find the points on C that have maximum and minimum distance from the origin.

65. Find the maximum and minimum values of $f(x, y, z) = x^2 + y^2 + z^2$ on the curve on which the cone $z^2 = 4x^2 + 4y^2$ and the plane $2x + 4z = 5$ intersect.

QUICK CHECK ANSWERS

1. Let $f(x, y)$ be the distance between any point $P(x, y)$ on the fence and home plate O. The key fact is that ∇f always points along the line OP. As P moves along the fence (the constraint curve), $f(x, y)$ increases until a point is reached at which ∇f is orthogonal to the fence. At such a point, f has a maximum value.   **3.** The distance between $(3, 4, 0)$ and the cone can be arbitrarily large, so there is no maximizing solution. If the point of interest is not in the xy-plane, there is one minimizing solution.   **4.** If you move along the constraint line away from the optimal solution in either direction, you cross level curves of the utility function with decreasing values.◄

CHAPTER 12   REVIEW EXERCISES

1. **Explain why or why not** Determine whether the following statements are true and give an explanation or counterexample.

   a. The equation $4x - 3y = 12$ describes a line in $\mathbb{R}^3$.

   b. The equation $z^2 = 2x^2 - 6y^2$ determines z as a single function of x and y.

   c. If f has continuous partial derivatives of all orders, then $f_{xxy} = f_{yyx}$.

   d. Given the surface $z = f(x, y)$, the gradient $\nabla f(a, b)$ lies in the plane tangent to the surface at $(a, b, f(a, b))$.

   e. There is always a plane orthogonal to both of two distinct intersecting planes.

2. **Equations of planes** Consider the plane that passes through the point $(6, 0, 1)$ with a normal vector $\mathbf{n} = \langle 3, 4, -6 \rangle$.

   a. Find an equation of the plane.

   b. Find the intercepts of the plane with the three coordinate axes.

   c. Make a sketch of the plane.

3. **Equations of planes** Consider the plane passing through the points $(0, 0, 3)$, $(1, 0, -6)$, and $(1, 2, 3)$.

   a. Find an equation of the plane.

   b. Find the intercepts of the plane with the three coordinate axes.

   c. Make a sketch of the plane.

4–5. Intersecting planes *Find an equation of the line of intersection of the planes Q and R.*

4. $Q: 2x + y - z = 0$, $R: -x + y + z = 1$

5. $Q: -3x + y + 2z = 0$, $R: 3x + 3y + 4z - 12 = 0$

6–7. Equations of planes *Find an equation of the following planes.*

6. The plane passing through $(2, -3, 1)$ normal to the line $\langle x, y, z \rangle = \langle 2 + t, 3t, 2 - 3t \rangle$

7. The plane passing through $(-2, 3, 1)$, $(1, 1, 0)$, and $(-1, 0, 1)$

8–22. Identifying surfaces *Consider the surfaces defined by the following equations.*

   a. *Identify and briefly describe the surface.*

   b. *Find the xy-, xz-, and yz-traces, when they exist.*

   c. *Find the intercepts with the three coordinate axes, when they exist.*

   d. *Make a sketch of the surface.*

8. $z - \sqrt{x} = 0$

9. $3z = \dfrac{x^2}{12} - \dfrac{y^2}{48}$

10. $\dfrac{x^2}{100} + 4y^2 + \dfrac{z^2}{16} = 1$

11. $y^2 = 4x^2 + z^2/25$

12. $\dfrac{4x^2}{9} + \dfrac{9z^2}{4} = y^2$

13. $4z = \dfrac{x^2}{4} + \dfrac{y^2}{9}$

14. $\dfrac{x^2}{16} + \dfrac{z^2}{36} - \dfrac{y^2}{100} = 1$

15. $y^2 + 4z^2 - 2x^2 = 1$

16. $-\dfrac{x^2}{16} + \dfrac{z^2}{36} - \dfrac{y^2}{25} = 4$

17. $\dfrac{x^2}{4} + \dfrac{y^2}{16} - z^2 = 4$

18. $x = \dfrac{y^2}{64} - \dfrac{z^2}{9}$

19. $\dfrac{x^2}{4} + \dfrac{y^2}{16} + z^2 = 4$

20. $y - e^{-x} = 0$

21. $\dfrac{y^2}{49} + \dfrac{x^2}{9} = \dfrac{z^2}{64}$

22. $y = 4x^2 + \dfrac{z^2}{9}$

23–26. Domains *Find the domain of the following functions. Make a sketch of the domain in the xy-plane.*

23. $f(x, y) = \dfrac{1}{x^2 + y^2}$

24. $f(x, y) = \ln xy$

25. $f(x, y) = \sqrt{x - y^2}$

26. $f(x, y) = \tan(x + y)$

27. Matching surfaces Match functions a–d with surfaces A–D.

   a. $z = \sqrt{2x^2 + 3y^2 + 1} - 1$
   b. $z = -3y^2$
   c. $z = 2x^2 - 3y^2 + 1$
   d. $z = \sqrt{2x^2 + 3y^2} - 1$

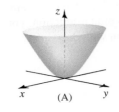

(A)

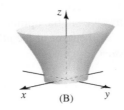

(B)

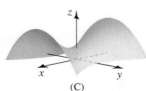

(C)

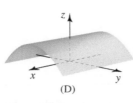

(D)

28–29. Level curves *Make a sketch of several level curves of the following functions. Label at least two level curves with their z-values.*

28. $f(x, y) = x^2 - y$

29. $f(x, y) = 2x^2 + 4y^2$

30. Matching level curves with surfaces Match level curve plots a–d with surfaces A–D.

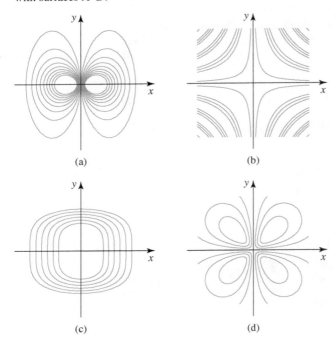

(a)

(b)

(c)

(d)

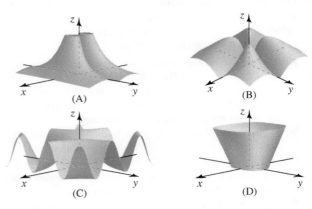

(A)

(B)

(C)

(D)

31–38. Limits *Evaluate the following limits or determine that they do not exist.*

31. $\displaystyle\lim_{(x,y)\to(4,-2)} (10x - 5y + 6xy)$

32. $\displaystyle\lim_{(x,y)\to(1,1)} \dfrac{xy}{x + y}$

33. $\displaystyle\lim_{(x,y)\to(0,0)} \dfrac{x + y}{xy}$

34. $\displaystyle\lim_{(x,y)\to(0,0)} \dfrac{\sin xy}{x^2 + y^2}$

35. $\displaystyle\lim_{(x,y)\to(-1,1)} \dfrac{x^2 - y^2}{x^2 - xy - 2y^2}$

36. $\displaystyle\lim_{(x,y)\to(1,2)} \dfrac{x^2 y}{x^4 + 2y^2}$

37. $\displaystyle\lim_{(x,y,z)\to(\frac{\pi}{2},0,\frac{\pi}{2})} 4\cos y \sin\sqrt{xz}$

38. $\displaystyle\lim_{(x,y,z)\to(5,2,-3)} \tan^{-1}\left(\dfrac{x + y^2}{z^2}\right)$

39–46. Partial derivatives *Find the first partial derivatives of the following functions.*

39. $f(x, y) = 3x^2 y^5$

40. $g(x, y, z) = 4xyz^2 - \dfrac{3x}{y}$

41. $f(x, y) = \dfrac{x^2}{x^2 + y^2}$

42. $g(x, y, z) = \dfrac{xyz}{x + y}$

43. $f(x, y) = xye^{xy}$

44. $g(u, v) = u\cos v - v\sin u$

45. $f(x, y, z) = e^{x + 2y + 3z}$

46. $H(p, q, r) = p^2\sqrt{q + r}$

47–48. Laplace's equation *Verify that the following functions satisfy Laplace's equation* $\dfrac{\partial^2 u}{\partial x^2} + \dfrac{\partial^2 u}{\partial y^2} = 0.$

47. $u(x, y) = y(3x^2 - y^2)$

48. $u(x, y) = \ln(x^2 + y^2)$

49. Region between spheres Two spheres have the same center and radii r and R, where $0 < r < R$. The volume of the region between the spheres is $V(r, R) = \dfrac{4\pi}{3}(R^3 - r^3)$.

   a. First use your intuition. If r is held fixed, how does V change as R increases? What is the sign of V_R? If R is held fixed, how does V change as r increases (up to the value of R)? What is the sign of V_r?

   b. Compute V_r and V_R. Are the results consistent with part (a)?

   c. Consider spheres with $R = 3$ and $r = 1$. Does the volume change more if R is increased by $\Delta R = 0.1$ (with r fixed) or if r is decreased by $\Delta r = 0.1$ (with R fixed)?

50–53. Chain Rule *Use the Chain Rule to evaluate the following derivatives.*

50. $w'(t)$, where $w = xy \sin z, x = t^2, y = 4t^3$, and $z = t + 1$

51. $w'(t)$, where $w = \sqrt{x^2 + y^2 + z^2}, x = \sin t, y = \cos t$, and $z = \cos t$

52. w_s and w_t, where $w = xyz, x = 2st, y = st^2$, and $z = s^2t$

53. w_r, w_s, and w_t, where $w = \ln(xy^2), x = rst$, and $y = r + s$

54–55. Implicit differentiation *Find dy/dx for the following implicit relations.*

54. $2x^2 + 3xy - 3y^4 = 2$ **55.** $y \ln(x^2 + y^2) = 4$

56–57. Walking on a surface *Consider the following surfaces and parameterized curves C in the xy-plane.*

a. *In each case, find $z'(t)$ on C.*

b. *Imagine that you are walking on the surface directly above C consistent with the positive orientation of C. Find the values of t for which you are walking uphill.*

56. $z = 4x^2 + y^2 - 2$; $C: x = \cos t, y = \sin t$, for $0 \le t \le 2\pi$

57. $z = x^2 - 2y^2 + 4$; $C: x = 2 \cos t, y = 2 \sin t$, for $0 \le t \le 2\pi$

58. Constant volume cones Suppose the radius of a right circular cone increases as $r(t) = t^a$ and the height decreases as $h(t) = t^{-b}$, for $t \ge 1$, where a and b are positive constants. What is the relationship between a and b such that the volume of the cone remains constant (that is, $V'(t) = 0$, where $V = (\pi/3)r^2h$)?

59. Directional derivatives Consider the function $f(x, y) = 2x^2 - 4y^2 + 10$, whose graph is shown in the figure.

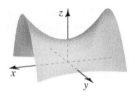

a. Fill in the table showing the value of the directional derivative at points (a, b) in the direction given by the unit vectors $\mathbf{u, v}$, and $\mathbf{w}$.

	$(a, b) = (0, 0)$	$(a, b) = (2, 0)$	$(a, b) = (1, 1)$
$\mathbf{u} = \left\langle \frac{\sqrt{2}}{2}, \frac{\sqrt{2}}{2} \right\rangle$			
$\mathbf{v} = \left\langle -\frac{\sqrt{2}}{2}, \frac{\sqrt{2}}{2} \right\rangle$			
$\mathbf{w} = \left\langle -\frac{\sqrt{2}}{2}, -\frac{\sqrt{2}}{2} \right\rangle$			

b. Interpret each of the directional derivatives computed in part (a) at the point $(2, 0)$.

60–65. Computing gradients *Compute the gradient of the following functions, evaluate it at the given point P, and evaluate the directional derivative at that point in the given direction.*

60. $f(x, y) = x^2$; $P(1, 2)$; $\mathbf{u} = \left\langle \frac{1}{\sqrt{2}}, -\frac{1}{\sqrt{2}} \right\rangle$

61. $g(x, y) = x^2y^3$; $P(-1, 1)$; $\mathbf{u} = \left\langle \frac{5}{13}, \frac{12}{13} \right\rangle$

62. $f(x, y) = \frac{x}{y^2}$; $P(0, 3)$; $\mathbf{u} = \left\langle \frac{\sqrt{3}}{2}, \frac{1}{2} \right\rangle$

63. $h(x, y) = \sqrt{2 + x^2 + 2y^2}$; $P(2, 1)$; $\mathbf{u} = \left\langle \frac{3}{5}, \frac{4}{5} \right\rangle$

64. $f(x, y, z) = xy + yz + xz + 4$; $P(2, -2, 1)$;
$\mathbf{u} = \left\langle 0, -\frac{1}{\sqrt{2}}, -\frac{1}{\sqrt{2}} \right\rangle$

65. $f(x, y, z) = 1 + \sin(x + 2y - z)$; $P\left(\frac{\pi}{6}, \frac{\pi}{6}, -\frac{\pi}{6} \right)$;
$\mathbf{u} = \left\langle \frac{1}{3}, \frac{2}{3}, \frac{2}{3} \right\rangle$

66–67. Direction of steepest ascent and descent

a. *Find the unit vectors that give the direction of steepest ascent and steepest descent at P.*

b. *Find a unit vector that points in a direction of no change.*

66. $f(x, y) = \ln(1 + xy)$; $P(2, 3)$

67. $f(x, y) = \sqrt{4 - x^2 - y^2}$; $P(-1, 1)$

68–69. Level curves *Let $f(x, y) = 8 - 2x^2 - y^2$. For the following level curves $f(x, y) = C$ and points (a, b), compute the slope of the line tangent to the level curve at (a, b) and verify that the tangent line is orthogonal to the gradient at that point.*

68. $f(x, y) = 5$; $(a, b) = (1, 1)$

69. $f(x, y) = 0$; $(a, b) = (2, 0)$

70. Directions of zero change Find the directions in which the function $f(x, y) = 4x^2 - y^2$ has zero change at the point $(1, 1, 3)$. Express the directions in terms of unit vectors.

71. Electric potential due to a charged cylinder. An infinitely long charged cylinder of radius R with its axis along the z-axis has an electric potential $V = k \ln(R/r)$, where r is the distance between a variable point $P(x, y)$ and the axis of the cylinder $(r^2 = x^2 + y^2)$ and k is a physical constant. The electric field at a point (x, y) in the xy-plane is given by $\mathbf{E} = -\nabla V$, where ∇V is the two-dimensional gradient. Compute the electric field at a point (x, y) with $r > R$.

72–77. Tangent planes *Find an equation of the plane tangent to the following surfaces at the given points.*

72. $z = 2x^2 + y^2$; $(1, 1, 3)$ and $(0, 2, 4)$

73. $x^2 + \frac{y^2}{4} - \frac{z^2}{9} = 1$; $(0, 2, 0)$ and $\left(1, 1, \frac{3}{2} \right)$

74. $xy \sin z - 1 = 0$; $\left(1, 2, \frac{\pi}{6} \right)$ and $\left(-2, -1, \frac{5\pi}{6} \right)$

75. $yze^{xz} - 8 = 0$; $(0, 2, 4)$ and $(0, -8, -1)$

76. $z = x^2e^{x-y}$; $(2, 2, 4)$ and $(-1, -1, 1)$

77. $z = \ln(1 + xy)$; $(1, 2, \ln 3)$ and $(-2, -1, \ln 3)$

78–79. Linear approximation

a. *Find the linear approximation to the function f at the point (a, b).*

b. *Use part (a) to estimate the given function value.*

78. $f(x, y) = 4 \cos(2x - y)$; $(a, b) = \left(\frac{\pi}{4}, \frac{\pi}{4} \right)$; estimate $f(0.8, 0.8)$.

79. $f(x, y) = (x + y)e^{xy}$; $(a, b) = (2, 0)$; estimate $f(1.95, 0.05)$.

80. Changes in a function Estimate the change in the function $f(x, y) = -2y^2 + 3x^2 + xy$ when (x, y) changes from $(1, -2)$ to $(1.05, -1.9)$.

81. Volume of a cylinder The volume of a cylinder with radius r and height h is $V = \pi r^2 h$. Find the approximate percentage change in the volume when the radius decreases by 3% and the height increases by 2%.

82. Volume of an ellipsoid The volume of an ellipsoid with axes of length $2a$, $2b$, and $2c$ is $V = \pi abc$. Find the percentage change in the volume when a increases by 2%, b increases by 1.5%, and c decreases by 2.5%.

83. Water-level changes A hemispherical tank with a radius of 1.50 m is filled with water to a depth of 1.00 m. Water is released from the tank and the water level drops by 0.05 m (from 1.00 m to 0.95 m).

    a. Approximate the change in the volume of water in the tank. The volume of a spherical cap is $V = \pi h^2(3r - h)/3$, where r is the radius of the sphere and h is the thickness of the cap (in this case, the depth of the water).

    b. Approximate the change in the surface area of the water in the tank.

1.5 m

1 m

84–87. Analyzing critical points *Identify the critical points of the following functions. Then determine whether each critical point corresponds to a local maximum, local minimum, or saddle point. State when your analysis is inconclusive. Confirm your results using a graphing utility.*

84. $f(x, y) = x^4 + y^4 - 16xy$

85. $f(x, y) = x^3/3 - y^3/3 + 2xy$

86. $f(x, y) = xy(2 + x)(y - 3)$

87. $f(x, y) = 10 - x^3 - y^3 - 3x^2 + 3y^2$

88–91. Absolute maxima and minima *Find the absolute maximum and minimum values of the following functions on the specified region R.*

88. $f(x, y) = x^3/3 - y^3/3 + 2xy$ on the rectangle $R = \{(x, y): 0 \le x \le 3, -1 \le y \le 1\}$

89. $f(x, y) = x^4 + y^4 - 4xy + 1$ on the square $R = \{(x, y): -2 \le x \le 2, -2 \le y \le 2\}$

90. $f(x, y) = x^2y - y^3$ on the triangle $R = \{(x, y): 0 \le x \le 2, 0 \le y \le 2 - x\}$

91. $f(x, y) = xy$ on the semicircular disk $R = \{(x, y): -1 \le x \le 1, 0 \le y \le \sqrt{1 - x^2}\}$

92. Least distance What point on the plane $x + y + 4z = 8$ is closest to the origin? Give an argument showing you have found an absolute minimum of the distance function.

93–96. Lagrange multipliers *Use Lagrange multipliers to find the maximum and minimum values of f (when they exist) subject to the given constraint.*

93. $f(x, y) = 2x + y + 10$ subject to $2(x - 1)^2 + 4(y - 1)^2 = 1$

94. $f(x, y) = x^2y^2$ subject to $2x^2 + y^2 = 1$

95. $f(x, y, z) = x + 2y - z$ subject to $x^2 + y^2 + z^2 = 1$

96. $f(x, y, z) = x^2y^2z$ subject to $2x^2 + y^2 + z^2 = 25$

97. Maximum perimeter rectangle Use Lagrange multipliers to find the dimensions of the rectangle with the maximum perimeter that can be inscribed with sides parallel to the coordinate axes in the ellipse $x^2/a^2 + y^2/b^2 = 1$.

98. Minimum surface area cylinder Use Lagrange multipliers to find the dimensions of the right circular cylinder of minimum surface area (including the circular ends) with a volume of 32π in^3.

99. Minimum distance to a cone Find the point(s) on the cone $z^2 - x^2 - y^2 = 0$ that are closest to the point $(1, 3, 1)$. Give an argument showing you have found an absolute minimum of the distance function.

100. Gradient of a distance function Let $P_0(a, b, c)$ be a fixed point in $\mathbb{R}^3$ and let $d(x, y, z)$ be the distance between P_0 and a variable point $P(x, y, z)$.

    a. Compute $\nabla d(x, y, z)$.

    b. Show that $\nabla d(x, y, z)$ points in the direction from P_0 to P and has magnitude 1 for all (x, y, z).

    c. Describe the level surfaces of d and give the direction of $\nabla d(x, y, z)$ relative to the level surfaces of d.

    d. Discuss $\lim_{P \to P_0} \nabla d(x, y, z)$.

Chapter 12 Guided Projects

Applications of the material in this chapter and related topics can be found in the following Guided Projects. For additional information, see the Preface.

- Traveling waves
- Ecological diversity
- Economic production functions

13

Multiple Integration

Chapter Preview We have now generalized limits and derivatives to functions of several variables. The next step is to carry out a similar process with respect to integration. As you know, single (one-variable) integrals are developed from Riemann sums and are used to compute areas of regions in $\mathbb{R}^2$. In an analogous way, we use Riemann sums to develop double (two-variable) and triple (three-variable) integrals, which are used to compute volumes of solid regions in $\mathbb{R}^3$. These multiple integrals have many applications in statistics, science, and engineering, including calculating the mass, the center of mass, and moments of inertia of solids with a variable density. Another significant development in this chapter is the appearance of cylindrical and spherical coordinates. These alternative coordinate systems often simplify the evaluation of integrals in three-dimensional space. The chapter closes with the two- and three-dimensional versions of the substitution (change of variables) rule. The overall lesson of the chapter is that we can integrate functions over most geometrical objects, from intervals on the x-axis to regions in the plane bounded by curves to complicated three-dimensional solids.

13.1 Double Integrals over Rectangular Regions

In Chapter 12 the concept of differentiation was extended to functions of several variables. In this chapter, we extend integration to multivariable functions. By the close of the chapter, we will have completed Table 13.1, which is a basic road map for calculus.

Table 13.1

	Derivatives	Integrals
Single variable: $f(x)$	$f'(x)$	$\displaystyle\int_a^b f(x)\, dx$
Several variables: $f(x, y)$ and $f(x, y, z)$	$\dfrac{\partial f}{\partial x}, \dfrac{\partial f}{\partial y}, \dfrac{\partial f}{\partial z}$	$\displaystyle\iint_R f(x, y)\, dA, \iiint_D f(x, y, z)\, dV$

Volumes of Solids

The problem of finding the net area of a region bounded by a curve led to the definite integral in Chapter 5. Recall that we began that discussion by approximating the region with a collection of rectangles and then formed a Riemann sum of the areas of the rectangles. Under appropriate conditions, as the number of rectangles increases, the sum approaches the value of the definite integral, which is the net area of the region.

We now carry out an analogous procedure with surfaces defined by functions of the form $z = f(x, y)$, where, for the moment, we assume that $f(x, y) \geq 0$ on a region R in the xy-plane (Figure 13.1a). The goal is to determine the volume of the solid bounded by the surface and R. In general terms, the solid is first approximated by *boxes* (Figure 13.1b). The sum of the volumes of these boxes, which is a Riemann sum, approximates the volume of the solid. Under appropriate conditions, as the number of boxes increases, the approximations converge to the value of a *double integral*, which is the volume of the solid.

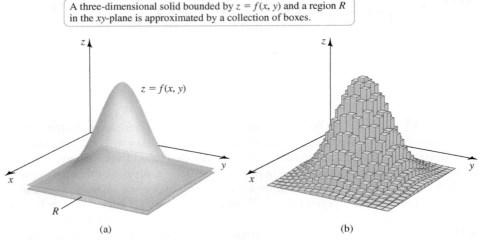

A three-dimensional solid bounded by $z = f(x, y)$ and a region R in the xy-plane is approximated by a collection of boxes.

$z = f(x, y)$

(a)   (b)

Figure 13.1

> We adopt the convention that Δx_k and Δy_k are the side lengths of the kth rectangle, for $k = 1, \ldots, n$, even though there are generally fewer than n different values of Δx_k and Δy_k. This convention is used throughout the chapter.

We assume that $z = f(x, y)$ is a nonnegative function defined on a *rectangular* region $R = \{(x, y): a \leq x \leq b, c \leq y \leq d\}$. A **partition** of R is formed by dividing R into n rectangular subregions using lines parallel to the x- and y-axes (not necessarily uniformly spaced). The rectangles may be numbered in any systematic way; for example, left to right and then bottom to top. The side lengths of the kth rectangle are denoted Δx_k and Δy_k, so the area of the kth rectangle is $\Delta A_k = \Delta x_k \, \Delta y_k$. We also let (x_k^*, y_k^*) be any point in the kth rectangle, for $1 \leq k \leq n$ (Figure 13.2).

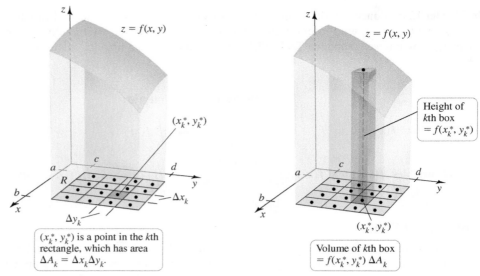

$z = f(x, y)$ $z = f(x, y)$

(x_k^*, y_k^*)

Height of
kth box
$= f(x_k^*, y_k^*)$

Δx_k

Δy_k (x_k^*, y_k^*)

(x_k^*, y_k^*) is a point in the kth rectangle, which has area $\Delta A_k = \Delta x_k \Delta y_k$.

Volume of kth box
$= f(x_k^*, y_k^*) \, \Delta A_k$

Figure 13.2   Figure 13.3

To approximate the volume of the solid bounded by the surface $z = f(x, y)$ and the region R, we construct boxes on each of the n rectangles; each box has a height of $f(x_k^*, y_k^*)$ and a base with area ΔA_k, for $1 \leq k \leq n$ (Figure 13.3). Therefore, the volume of the kth box is

$$f(x_k^*, y_k^*)\Delta A_k = f(x_k^*, y_k^*)\Delta x_k \, \Delta y_k.$$

The sum of the volumes of the n boxes gives an approximation to the volume of the solid:

$$V \approx \sum_{k=1}^{n} f(x_k^*, y_k^*)\, \Delta A_k.$$

QUICK CHECK 1 Explain why the preceding sum for the volume is an approximation. How can the approximation be improved? ◄

We now let Δ be the maximum length of the diagonals of the rectangles in the partition. As $\Delta \to 0$, the areas of *all* the rectangles approach zero $(\Delta A_k \to 0)$ and the number of rectangles increases $(n \to \infty)$. If the approximations given by these Riemann sums have a limit as $\Delta \to 0$, then we define the volume of the solid to be that limit (Figure 13.4).

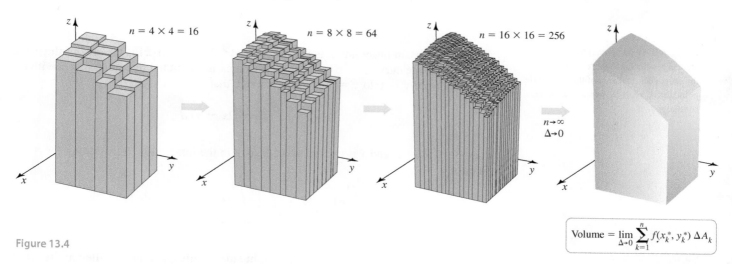

$n = 4 \times 4 = 16$ $n = 8 \times 8 = 64$ $n = 16 \times 16 = 256$

$n \to \infty$
$\Delta \to 0$

$$\text{Volume} = \lim_{\Delta \to 0} \sum_{k=1}^{n} f(x_k^*, y_k^*)\, \Delta A_k$$

Figure 13.4

> The functions that we encounter in this book are integrable. Advanced methods are needed to prove that continuous functions and many functions with finite discontinuities are also integrable.

DEFINITION Double Integrals

A function f defined on a rectangular region R in the xy-plane is **integrable** on R if $\lim\limits_{\Delta \to 0} \sum\limits_{k=1}^{n} f(x_k^*, y_k^*) \Delta A_k$ exists for all partitions of R and for all choices of (x_k^*, y_k^*) within those partitions. The limit is the **double integral of f over R**, which we write

$$\iint\limits_{R} f(x, y)\, dA = \lim_{\Delta \to 0} \sum_{k=1}^{n} f(x_k^*, y_k^*) \Delta A_k.$$

If f is nonnegative on R, then the double integral equals the volume of the solid bounded by $z = f(x, y)$ and the xy-plane over R. If f is negative on parts of R, the value of the double integral may be zero or negative, and the result is interpreted as a *net volume* (in analogy with *net area* for single variable integrals).

Iterated Integrals

Evaluating double integrals using limits of Riemann sums is tedious and rarely done. Fortunately, there is a practical method for evaluating double integrals that is based on the general slicing method (Section 6.3). An example illustrates the technique.

▶ The general slicing method was introduced in Section 6.3.

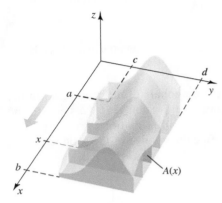

If a solid is sliced parallel to the *y*-axis and perpendicular to the *xy*-plane, and the cross-sectional area of the slice at the point *x* is $A(x)$, then the volume of the solid region is

$$V = \int_a^b A(x)\, dx.$$

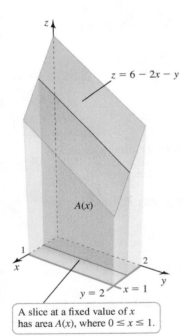

$z = 6 - 2x - y$

$A(x)$

$y = 2$ $x = 1$

A slice at a fixed value of *x* has area $A(x)$, where $0 \le x \le 1$.

Figure 13.5

Suppose we wish to compute the volume of the solid region bounded by the plane $z = f(x, y) = 6 - 2x - y$ over the rectangular region $R = \{(x, y) : 0 \le x \le 1, 0 \le y \le 2\}$ (Figure 13.5). By definition, the volume is given by the double integral

$$V = \iint_R f(x, y)\, dA = \iint_R (6 - 2x - y)\, dA.$$

According to the general slicing method (see margin note and figure), we can compute this volume by taking vertical slices through the solid parallel to the *yz*-plane (Figure 13.5). The slice at the point *x* has a cross-sectional area denoted $A(x)$. In general, as *x* varies, the area $A(x)$ also changes, so we integrate these cross-sectional areas from $x = 0$ to $x = 1$ to obtain the volume

$$V = \int_0^1 A(x)\, dx.$$

The important observation is that for a fixed value of *x*, $A(x)$ is the area of the plane region under the curve $z = 6 - 2x - y$. This area is computed by integrating *f* with respect to *y* from $y = 0$ to $y = 2$, holding *x* fixed; that is,

$$A(x) = \int_0^2 (6 - 2x - y)\, dy,$$

where $0 \le x \le 1$, and *x* is treated as a constant in the integration. Substituting for $A(x)$, we have

$$V = \int_0^1 A(x)\, dx = \int_0^1 \left(\underbrace{\int_0^2 (6 - 2x - y)\, dy}_{A(x)} \right) dx.$$

The expression that appears on the right side of this equation is called an **iterated integral** (meaning repeated integral). We first evaluate the inner integral with respect to *y* holding *x* fixed; the result is a function of *x*. Then the outer integral is evaluated with respect to *x*; the result is a real number, which is the volume of the solid in Figure 13.5. Both of these integrals are ordinary one-variable integrals.

EXAMPLE 1   Evaluating an iterated integral Evaluate $V = \int_0^1 A(x)\, dx$, where $A(x) = \int_0^2 (6 - 2x - y)\, dy$.

SOLUTION Using the Fundamental Theorem of Calculus, holding *x* constant, we have

$$A(x) = \int_0^2 (6 - 2x - y)\, dy$$

$$= \left(6y - 2xy - \frac{y^2}{2} \right) \Big|_0^2 \quad \text{Evaluate integral with respect to } y; \, x \text{ is constant.}$$

$$= (12 - 4x - 2) - 0 \quad \text{Simplify; limits are in } y.$$

$$= 10 - 4x. \quad \text{Simplify.}$$

Substituting $A(x) = 10 - 4x$ into the volume integral, we have

$$V = \int_0^1 A(x)\, dx$$

$$= \int_0^1 (10 - 4x)\, dx \quad \text{Substitute for } A(x).$$

$$= (10x - 2x^2) \Big|_0^1 \quad \text{Evaluate integral with respect to } x.$$

$$= 8. \quad \text{Simplify.}$$

Related Exercises 5–25 ◀

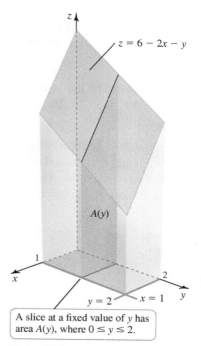

A slice at a fixed value of y has area $A(y)$, where $0 \le y \le 2$.

Figure 13.6

EXAMPLE 2 **Same double integral, different order** Example 1 used slices through the solid parallel to the yz-plane. Compute the volume of the same solid using vertical slices through the solid parallel to the xz-plane, for $0 \le y \le 2$ (Figure 13.6).

SOLUTION In this case, $A(y)$ is the area of a slice through the solid for a fixed value of y in the interval $0 \le y \le 2$. This area is computed by integrating $z = 6 - 2x - y$ from $x = 0$ to $x = 1$, holding y fixed; that is,

$$A(y) = \int_0^1 (6 - 2x - y)\, dx,$$

where $0 \le y \le 2$.

Using the general slicing method again, the volume is

$$V = \int_0^2 A(y)\, dy \qquad \text{General slicing method}$$

$$= \int_0^2 \left(\underbrace{\int_0^1 (6 - 2x - y)\, dx}_{A(y)} \right) dy \qquad \text{Substitute for } A(y).$$

$$= \int_0^2 \left((6x - x^2 - yx) \Big|_0^1 \right) dy \qquad \begin{array}{l}\text{Evaluate inner integral with respect}\\ \text{to } x;\ y \text{ is constant.}\end{array}$$

$$= \int_0^2 (5 - y)\, dy \qquad \text{Simplify; limits are in } x.$$

$$= \left(5y - \frac{y^2}{2} \right) \Big|_0^2 \qquad \text{Evaluate outer integral with respect to } y.$$

$$= 8. \qquad \text{Simplify.}$$

Related Exercises 5–25 ◀

Several important comments are in order. First, the two iterated integrals give the same value for the double integral. Second, the notation of the iterated integral must be used carefully. When we write $\int_c^d \int_a^b f(x, y)\, dx\, dy$, it means $\int_c^d \left(\int_a^b f(x, y)\, dx \right) dy$. The *inner* integral with respect to x is evaluated first, holding y fixed, and the variable runs from $x = a$ to $x = b$. The result of that integration is a constant or a function of y, which is then integrated in the *outer* integral, with the variable running from $y = c$ to $y = d$. The order of integration is signified by the order of dx and dy.

Similarly, $\int_a^b \int_c^d f(x, y)\, dy\, dx$ means $\int_a^b \left(\int_c^d f(x, y)\, dy \right) dx$. The inner integral with respect to y is evaluated first, holding x fixed. The result is then integrated with respect to x. In both cases, the limits of integration in the iterated integrals determine the boundaries of the rectangular *region of integration*.

Examples 1 and 2 illustrate one version of *Fubini's Theorem*, a deep result that relates double integrals to iterated integrals. The first version of the theorem applies to double integrals over rectangular regions.

QUICK CHECK 2 Consider the integral $\int_3^4 \int_1^2 f(x, y)\, dx\, dy$. Give the limits of integration and the variable of integration for the first (inner) integral and the second (outer) integral. Sketch the region of integration. ◀

➤ The area of the kth rectangle in the partition is $\Delta A_k = \Delta x_k \Delta y_k$, where Δx_k and Δy_k are the lengths of the sides of that rectangle. Accordingly, the *element of area dA* in the double integral becomes $dx\, dy$ or $dy\, dx$ in the iterated integral.

THEOREM 13.1 (Fubini) **Double Integrals on Rectangular Regions**

Let f be continuous on the rectangular region $R = \{(x, y) : a \le x \le b, c \le y \le d\}$. The double integral of f over R may be evaluated by either of two iterated integrals:

$$\iint_R f(x, y)\, dA = \int_c^d \int_a^b f(x, y)\, dx\, dy = \int_a^b \int_c^d f(x, y)\, dy\, dx.$$

The importance of Fubini's Theorem is twofold: It says that double integrals may be evaluated by iterated integrals. It also says that the order of integration in the iterated integrals does not matter (although in practice, one order of integration is often easier to use than the other).

EXAMPLE 3   A double integral Find the volume of the solid bounded by the surface $f(x, y) = 4 + 9x^2y^2$ over the region $R = \{(x, y): -1 \le x \le 1, 0 \le y \le 2\}$. Use both possible orders of integration.

SOLUTION Because $f(x, y) > 0$ on R, the volume of the region is given by the double integral $\iint_R (4 + 9x^2y^2)\, dA$. By Fubini's Theorem, the double integral is evaluated as an iterated integral. If we first integrate with respect to x, the area of a cross section of the solid for a fixed value of y is given by $A(y)$ (Figure 13.7a). The volume of the region is

$$\iint\limits_R (4 + 9x^2y^2)\, dA = \int_0^2 \underbrace{\int_{-1}^1 (4 + 9x^2y^2)\, dx}_{A(y)}\, dy \qquad \text{Convert to an iterated integral.}$$

$$= \int_0^2 (4x + 3x^3y^2)\Big|_{-1}^1\, dy \qquad \begin{array}{l}\text{Evaluate inner integral}\\ \text{with respect to } x.\end{array}$$

$$= \int_0^2 (8 + 6y^2)\, dy \qquad \text{Simplify.}$$

$$= (8y + 2y^3)\Big|_0^2 \qquad \begin{array}{l}\text{Evaluate outer integral}\\ \text{with respect to } y.\end{array}$$

$$= 32. \qquad \text{Simplify.}$$

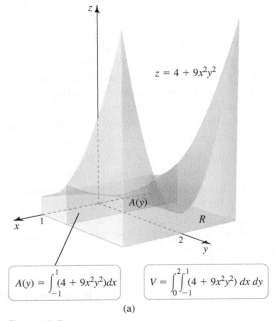

$z = 4 + 9x^2y^2$

$A(y) = \int_{-1}^1 (4 + 9x^2y^2)dx$ $V = \int_0^2 \int_{-1}^1 (4 + 9x^2y^2)\, dx\, dy$

(a)

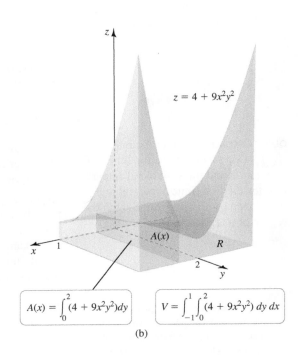

$z = 4 + 9x^2y^2$

$A(x) = \int_0^2 (4 + 9x^2y^2)dy$ $V = \int_{-1}^1 \int_0^2 (4 + 9x^2y^2)\, dy\, dx$

(b)

Figure 13.7

Alternatively, if we integrate first with respect to y, the area of a cross section of the solid for a fixed value of x is given by $A(x)$ (Figure 13.7b). The volume of the region is

$$\iint_R (4 + 9x^2y^2)\, dA = \int_{-1}^{1} \underbrace{\int_0^2 (4 + 9x^2y^2)\, dy}_{A(x)}\, dx \qquad \text{Convert to an iterated integral.}$$

$$= \int_{-1}^{1} (4y + 3x^2y^3)\Big|_0^2\, dx \qquad \text{Evaluate inner integral with respect to } y.$$

$$= \int_{-1}^{1} (8 + 24x^2)\, dx \qquad \text{Simplify.}$$

$$= (8x + 8x^3)\Big|_{-1}^{1} = 32. \qquad \text{Evaluate outer integral with respect to } x.$$

As guaranteed by Fubini's Theorem, the two iterated integrals are equal, both giving the value of the double integral and the volume of the solid.

Related Exercises 5–25 ◄

QUICK CHECK 3 Write the iterated integral $\int_{-10}^{10}\int_0^{20}(x^2y + 2xy^3)\, dy\, dx$ with the order of integration reversed. ◄

The following example shows that sometimes the order of integration must be chosen carefully either to save work or to make the integration possible.

EXAMPLE 4 Choosing a convenient order of integration Evaluate $\iint_R ye^{xy}\, dA$, where $R = \{(x, y): 0 \le x \le 1, 0 \le y \le \ln 2\}$.

SOLUTION The iterated integral $\int_0^1 \int_0^{\ln 2} ye^{xy}\, dy\, dx$ requires first integrating ye^{xy} with respect to y, which entails integration by parts. An easier approach is to integrate first with respect to x:

$$\int_0^{\ln 2} \int_0^1 ye^{xy}\, dx\, dy = \int_0^{\ln 2} e^{xy}\Big|_0^1\, dy \qquad \text{Evaluate inner integral with respect to } x.$$

$$= \int_0^{\ln 2} (e^y - 1)\, dy \qquad \text{Simplify.}$$

$$= (e^y - y)\Big|_0^{\ln 2} \qquad \text{Evaluate outer integral with respect to } y.$$

$$= 1 - \ln 2. \qquad \text{Simplify.}$$

Related Exercises 26–31 ◄

Average Value

The concept of the average value of a function (Section 5.4) extends naturally to functions of two variables. Recall that the average value of the integrable function f over the interval $[a, b]$ is

$$\bar{f} = \frac{1}{b - a} \int_a^b f(x)\, dx.$$

To find the average value of an integrable function f over a region R, we integrate f over R and divide the result by the "size" of R, which is the area of R in the two-variable case.

➤ The same definition of average value applies to more general regions in the plane.

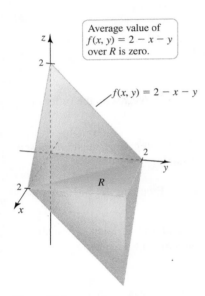

Figure 13.8

➤ An average value of 0 means that over the region R, the volume of the solid above the xy-plane and below the surface equals the volume of the solid below the xy-plane and above the surface.

DEFINITION Average Value of a Function over a Plane Region

The **average value** of an integrable function f over a region R is

$$\bar{f} = \frac{1}{\text{area of } R} \iint_R f(x, y)\, dA.$$

EXAMPLE 5 Average value Find the average value of the quantity $2 - x - y$ over the square $R = \{(x, y): 0 \le x \le 2, 0 \le y \le 2\}$ (Figure 13.8).

SOLUTION The area of the region R is 4. Letting $f(x, y) = 2 - x - y$, the average value of f is

$$\frac{1}{\text{area of } R} \iint_R f(x, y)\, dA = \frac{1}{4} \iint_R (2 - x - y)\, dA$$

$$= \frac{1}{4} \int_0^2 \int_0^2 (2 - x - y)\, dx\, dy \quad \text{Convert to an iterated integral.}$$

$$= \frac{1}{4} \int_0^2 \left(2x - \frac{x^2}{2} - xy \right) \Big|_0^2 dy \quad \begin{array}{l}\text{Evaluate inner integral} \\ \text{with respect to } x.\end{array}$$

$$= \frac{1}{4} \int_0^2 (2 - 2y)\, dy \quad \text{Simplify.}$$

$$= 0. \quad \begin{array}{l}\text{Evaluate outer integral} \\ \text{with respect to } y.\end{array}$$

Related Exercises 32–36 ◄

SECTION 13.1 EXERCISES

Review Questions

1. Write an iterated integral that gives the volume of the solid bounded by the surface $f(x, y) = xy$ over the square $R = \{(x, y): 0 \le x \le 2, 1 \le y \le 3\}$.

2. Write an iterated integral that gives the volume of a box with height 10 and base $R = \{(x, y): 0 \le x \le 5, -2 \le y \le 4\}$.

3. Write two iterated integrals that equal $\iint_R f(x, y)\, dA$, where $R = \{(x, y): -2 \le x \le 4, 1 \le y \le 5\}$.

4. Consider the integral $\int_1^3 \int_{-1}^1 (2y^2 + xy)\, dy\, dx$. State the variable of integration in the first (inner) integral and the limits of integration. State the variable of integration in the second (outer) integral and the limits of integration.

Basic Skills

5–16. Iterated integrals *Evaluate the following iterated integrals.*

5. $\displaystyle \int_0^2 \int_0^1 4xy\, dx\, dy$

6. $\displaystyle \int_1^2 \int_0^1 (3x^2 + 4y^3)\, dy\, dx$

7. $\displaystyle \int_1^3 \int_0^2 x^2 y\, dx\, dy$

8. $\displaystyle \int_0^3 \int_{-2}^1 (2x + 3y)\, dx\, dy$

9. $\displaystyle \int_1^3 \int_0^{\pi/2} x \sin y\, dy\, dx$

10. $\displaystyle \int_1^3 \int_1^2 (y^2 + y)\, dx\, dy$

11. $\displaystyle \int_1^4 \int_0^4 \sqrt{uv}\, du\, dv$

12. $\displaystyle \int_0^{\pi/2} \int_0^1 x \cos xy\, dy\, dx$

13. $\displaystyle\int_0^{\ln 2}\int_0^1 6xe^{3y}\,dx\,dy$

14. $\displaystyle\int_0^1\int_0^1 \frac{y}{1+x^2}\,dx\,dy$

15. $\displaystyle\int_1^{\ln 5}\int_0^{\ln 3} e^{x+y}\,dx\,dy$

16. $\displaystyle\int_0^{\pi/4}\int_0^3 r\sec\theta\,dr\,d\theta$

17–25. Double integrals *Evaluate each double integral over the region R by converting it to an iterated integral.*

17. $\displaystyle\iint_R (x+2y)\,dA;\ R=\{(x,y): 0\le x\le 3, 1\le y\le 4\}$

18. $\displaystyle\iint_R (x^2+xy)\,dA;\ R=\{(x,y): 1\le x\le 2, -1\le y\le 1\}$

19. $\displaystyle\iint_R 4x^3\cos y\,dA;\ R=\{(x,y): 1\le x\le 2, 0\le y\le \pi/2\}$

20. $\displaystyle\iint_R \frac{y}{\sqrt{1-x^2}}\,dA;\ R=\{(x,y): \tfrac12\le x\le \tfrac{\sqrt3}{2}, 1\le y\le 2\}$

21. $\displaystyle\iint_R \sqrt{\frac{x}{y}}\,dA;\ R=\{(x,y): 0\le x\le 1, 1\le y\le 4\}$

22. $\displaystyle\iint_R xy\sin x^2\,dA;\ R=\{(x,y): 0\le x\le \sqrt{\pi/2}, 0\le y\le 1\}$

23. $\displaystyle\iint_R e^{x+2y}\,dA;\ R=\{(x,y): 0\le x\le \ln 2, 1\le y\le \ln 3\}$

24. $\displaystyle\iint_R (x^2-y^2)^2\,dA;\ R=\{(x,y): -1\le x\le 2, 0\le y\le 1\}$

25. $\displaystyle\iint_R (x^5-y^5)^2\,dA;\ R=\{(x,y): 0\le x\le 1, -1\le y\le 1\}$

26–31. Choose a convenient order *When converted to an iterated integral, the following double integrals are easier to evaluate in one order than the other. Find the best order and evaluate the integral.*

26. $\displaystyle\iint_R y\cos xy\,dA;\ R=\{(x,y): 0\le x\le 1, 0\le y\le \pi/3\}$

27. $\displaystyle\iint_R (y+1)e^{x(y+1)}\,dA;\ R=\{(x,y): 0\le x\le 1, -1\le y\le 1\}$

28. $\displaystyle\iint_R x\sec^2 xy\,dA;\ R=\{(x,y): 0\le x\le \pi/3, 0\le y\le 1\}$

29. $\displaystyle\iint_R 6x^5 e^{x^3 y}\,dA;\ R=\{(x,y): 0\le x\le 2, 0\le y\le 2\}$

30. $\displaystyle\iint_R y^3\sin xy^2\,dA;\ R=\{(x,y): 0\le x\le 2, 0\le y\le \sqrt{\pi/2}\}$

31. $\displaystyle\iint_R \frac{x}{(1+xy)^2}\,dA;\ R=\{(x,y): 0\le x\le 4, 1\le y\le 2\}$

32–34. Average value *Compute the average value of the following functions over the region R.*

32. $f(x,y)=4-x-y;\ R=\{(x,y): 0\le x\le 2, 0\le y\le 2\}$

33. $f(x,y)=e^{-y};\ R=\{(x,y): 0\le x\le 6, 0\le y\le \ln 2\}$

34. $f(x,y)=\sin x\sin y;\ R=\{(x,y): 0\le x\le \pi, 0\le y\le \pi\}$

35–36. Average value

35. Find the average squared distance between the points of $R=\{(x,y): -2\le x\le 2, 0\le y\le 2\}$ and the origin.

36. Find the average squared distance between the points of $R=\{(x,y): 0\le x\le 3, 0\le y\le 3\}$ and the point $(3,3)$.

Further Explorations

37. Explain why or why not Determine whether the following statements are true and give an explanation or counterexample.

    a. The region of integration for $\int_4^6\int_1^3 4\,dx\,dy$ is a square.

    b. If f is continuous on $\mathbb{R}^2$, then
$$\int_4^6\int_1^3 f(x,y)\,dx\,dy = \int_4^6\int_1^3 f(x,y)\,dy\,dx.$$

    c. If f is continuous on $\mathbb{R}^2$, then
$$\int_4^6\int_1^3 f(x,y)\,dx\,dy = \int_1^3\int_4^6 f(x,y)\,dy\,dx.$$

38. Symmetry Evaluate the following integrals using symmetry arguments. Let $R=\{(x,y): -a\le x\le a, -b\le y\le b\}$, where a and b are positive real numbers.

    a. $\displaystyle\iint_R xye^{-(x^2+y^2)}\,dA$

    b. $\displaystyle\iint_R \frac{\sin(x-y)}{x^2+y^2+1}\,dA$

39. Computing populations The population densities in nine districts of a rectangular county are shown in the figure.

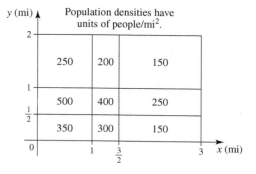

    a. Use the fact that population = (population density) × (area) to estimate the population of the county.

    b. Explain how the calculation of part (a) is related to Riemann sums and double integrals.

T 40. Approximating water volume The varying depth of an 18 m × 25 m swimming pool is measured in 15 different rectangles of equal area (see figure). Approximate the volume of water in the pool.

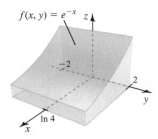

0.75	1.25	1.75	2.25	2.75
1	1.5	2.0	2.5	3.0
1	1.5	2.0	2.5	3.0

Depth readings have units of m.

41–42. Pictures of solids *Draw the solid whose volume is given by the following iterated integrals. Then find the volume of the solid.*

41. $\int_0^6 \int_1^2 10 \, dy \, dx$

42. $\int_0^1 \int_{-1}^1 (4 - x^2 - y^2) \, dx \, dy$

43–46. More integration practice *Evaluate the following iterated integrals.*

43. $\int_1^2 \int_1^2 \frac{x}{x+y} \, dy \, dx$

44. $\int_0^2 \int_0^1 x^5 y^2 e^{x^3 y^3} \, dy \, dx$

45. $\int_0^1 \int_1^4 \frac{3y}{\sqrt{x+y^2}} \, dx \, dy$

46. $\int_1^4 \int_0^2 e^{y\sqrt{x}} \, dy \, dx$

47–50. Volumes of solids *Find the volume of the following solids.*

47. The solid beneath the cylinder $f(x, y) = e^{-x}$ and above the region $R = \{(x, y): 0 \le x \le \ln 4, -2 \le y \le 2\}$

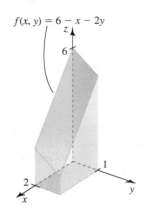

48. The solid beneath the plane $f(x, y) = 6 - x - 2y$ and above the region $R = \{(x, y): 0 \le x \le 2, 0 \le y \le 1\}$

$f(x, y) = 6 - x - 2y$

49. The solid beneath the plane $f(x, y) = 24 - 3x - 4y$ and above the region $R = \{(x, y): -1 \le x \le 3, 0 \le y \le 2\}$

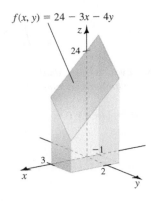

$f(x, y) = 24 - 3x - 4y$

50. The solid beneath the paraboloid $f(x, y) = 12 - x^2 - 2y^2$ and above the region $R = \{(x, y): 1 \le x \le 2, 0 \le y \le 1\}$

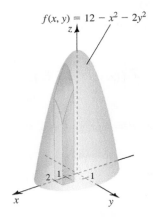

$f(x, y) = 12 - x^2 - 2y^2$

51. Solving for a parameter Let $R = \{(x, y): 0 \le x \le \pi, 0 \le y \le a\}$. For what values of a, with $0 \le a \le \pi$, is $\iint_R \sin(x + y) \, dA$ equal to 1?

52–53. Zero average value *Find the value of $a > 0$ such that the average value of the following functions over $R = \{(x, y): 0 \le x \le a, 0 \le y \le a\}$ is zero.*

52. $f(x, y) = x + y - 8$ **53.** $f(x, y) = 4 - x^2 - y^2$

54. Maximum integral Consider the plane $x + 3y + z = 6$ over the rectangle R with vertices at $(0, 0)$, $(a, 0)$, $(0, b)$, and (a, b), where the vertex (a, b) lies on the line where the plane intersects the xy-plane (so $a + 3b = 6$). Find the point (a, b) for which the volume of the solid between the plane and R is a maximum.

Applications

55. Density and mass Suppose a thin rectangular plate, represented by a region R in the xy-plane, has a density given by the function $\rho(x, y)$; this function gives the *area density* in units such as grams per square centimeter (g/cm^2). The mass of the plate is $\iint_R \rho(x, y) \, dA$. Assume that $R = \{(x, y): 0 \le x \le \pi/2, 0 \le y \le \pi\}$ and find the mass of the plates with the following density functions.

a. $\rho(x, y) = 1 + \sin x$
b. $\rho(x, y) = 1 + \sin y$
c. $\rho(x, y) = 1 + \sin x \sin y$

56. Approximating volume Propose a method based on Riemann sums to approximate the volume of the shed shown in the figure (the peak of the roof is directly above the rear corner of the shed). Carry out the method and provide an estimate of the volume.

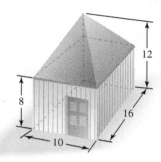

Additional Exercises

57. Cylinders Let S be the solid in $\mathbb{R}^3$ between the cylinder $z = f(x)$ and the region $R = \{(x, y): a \le x \le b, c \le y \le d\}$, where $f(x) \ge 0$ on R. Explain why $\int_c^d \int_a^b f(x)\, dx\, dy$ equals the area of the constant cross section of S multiplied by $(d - c)$, which is the volume of S.

58. Product of integrals Suppose $f(x, y) = g(x)h(y)$, where g and h are continuous functions for all real values of x and y.

  a. Show that $\int_c^d \int_a^b f(x, y)\, dx\, dy = \left(\int_a^b g(x)\, dx\right)\left(\int_c^d h(y)\, dy\right)$. Interpret this result geometrically.

  b. Write $\left(\int_a^b g(x)\, dx\right)^2$ as an iterated integral.

  c. Use the result of part (a) to evaluate $\int_0^{2\pi} \int_{10}^{30} e^{-4y^2} \cos x\, dy\, dx$.

59. An identity Suppose the second partial derivatives of f are continuous on $R = \{(x, y): 0 \le x \le a, 0 \le y \le b\}$. Simplify

$$\iint\limits_R \frac{\partial^2 f}{\partial x\, \partial y}\, dA.$$

60. Two integrals Let $R = \{(x, y): 0 \le x \le 1, 0 \le y \le 1\}$.

  a. Evaluate $\iint\limits_R \cos(x\sqrt{y})\, dA$.

  b. Evaluate $\iint\limits_R x^3 y \cos(x^2 y^2)\, dA$.

61. A generalization Let R be as in Exercise 60, let F be an antiderivative of f with $F(0) = 0$, and let G be an antiderivative of F. Show that if f and F are integrable and $r \ge 1$ and $s \ge 1$ are real numbers, then

$$\iint\limits_R x^{2r-1} y^{s-1} f(x^r y^s)\, dA = \frac{G(1) - G(0)}{rs}.$$

QUICK CHECK ANSWERS

1. The sum gives the volume of a collection of rectangular boxes, and these boxes do not exactly fill the solid region under the surface. The approximation is improved by using more boxes.   **2.** Inner integral: x runs from $x = 1$ to $x = 2$; outer integral: y runs from $y = 3$ to $y = 4$. The region is the rectangle $\{(x, y): 1 \le x \le 2, 3 \le y \le 4\}$.
3. $\int_0^{20} \int_{-10}^{10} (x^2 y + 2xy^3)\, dx\, dy$ ◄

13.2 Double Integrals over General Regions

Evaluating double integrals over rectangular regions is a useful place to begin our study of multiple integrals. Problems of practical interest, however, usually involve nonrectangular regions of integration. The goal of this section is to extend the methods presented in Section 13.1 so that they apply to more general regions of integration.

General Regions of Integration

Consider a function f defined over a closed bounded *nonrectangular* region R in the xy-plane. As with rectangular regions, we use a partition consisting of rectangles, but now, such a partition does not cover R exactly. In this case, only the n rectangles that lie entirely within R are considered to be in the partition (Figure 13.9). When f is nonnegative on R, the volume of the solid bounded by the surface $z = f(x, y)$ and the xy-plane over R is approximated by the Riemann sum

$$V \approx \sum_{k=1}^{n} f(x_k^*, y_k^*) \Delta A_k,$$

where $\Delta A_k = \Delta x_k \Delta y_k$ is the area of the kth rectangle and (x_k^*, y_k^*) is any point in the kth rectangle, for $1 \le k \le n$. As before, we define Δ to be the maximum length of the diagonals of the rectangles in the partition.

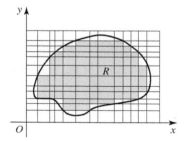

Figure 13.9

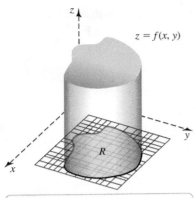

$$\text{Volume of solid} = \iint_R f(x, y) \, dA$$
$$= \lim_{\Delta \to 0} \sum_{k=1}^{n} f(x_k^*, y_k^*) \, \Delta A_k$$

Figure 13.10

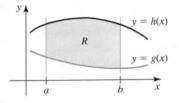

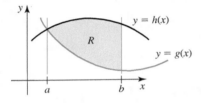

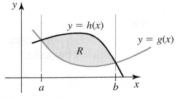

Figure 13.11

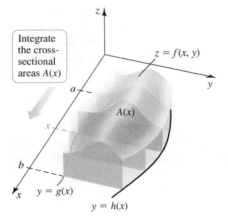

Integrate the cross-sectional areas $A(x)$

Figure 13.12

Under the assumptions that f is continuous on R and that the boundary of R consists of a finite number of smooth curves, two things occur as $\Delta \to 0$ and the number of rectangles increases $(n \to \infty)$.

- The rectangles in the partition fill R more and more completely; that is, the union of the rectangles approaches R.

- Over all partitions and all choices of (x_k^*, y_k^*) within a partition, the Riemann sums approach a (unique) limit.

The limit approached by the Riemann sums is the **double integral of f over R**; that is,

$$\iint_R f(x, y) \, dA = \lim_{\Delta \to 0} \sum_{k=1}^{n} f(x_k^*, y_k^*) \Delta A_k.$$

When this limit exists, f is **integrable** over R. If f is nonnegative on R, then the double integral equals the volume of the solid bounded by the surface $z = f(x, y)$ and the xy-plane over R (Figure 13.10).

The double integral $\iint_R f(x, y) \, dA$ has another common interpretation. Suppose R represents a thin plate whose density at the point (x, y) is $f(x, y)$. The units of density are mass per unit area, so the product $f(x_k^*, y_k^*) \Delta A_k$ approximates the mass of the kth rectangle in R. Summing the masses of the rectangles gives an approximation to the total mass of R. In the limit as $n \to \infty$ and $\Delta \to 0$, the double integral equals the mass of the plate.

Iterated Integrals

Double integrals over nonrectangular regions are also evaluated using iterated integrals. However, in this more general setting, the order of integration is critical. Most of the double integrals we encounter fall into one of two categories determined by the shape of the region R.

The first type of region has the property that its lower and upper boundaries are the graphs of continuous functions $y = g(x)$ and $y = h(x)$, respectively, for $a \le x \le b$. Such regions have any of the forms shown in Figure 13.11.

Once again, we appeal to the general slicing method. Assume for the moment that f is nonnegative on R and consider the solid bounded by the surface $z = f(x, y)$ and R (Figure 13.12). Imagine taking vertical slices through the solid parallel to the yz-plane. The cross section through the solid at a fixed value of x extends from the lower curve $y = g(x)$ to the upper curve $y = h(x)$. The area of that cross section is

$$A(x) = \int_{g(x)}^{h(x)} f(x, y) \, dy, \qquad \text{for } a \le x \le b.$$

The volume of the solid is given by a double integral; it is evaluated by integrating the cross-sectional areas $A(x)$ from $x = a$ to $x = b$:

$$\iint_R f(x, y) \, dA = \int_a^b \underbrace{\int_{g(x)}^{h(x)} f(x, y) \, dy \, dx.}_{A(x)}$$

The limits of integration in the iterated integral describe the boundaries of the region of integration R.

EXAMPLE 1 **Evaluating a double integral** Express the integral $\iint_R 2x^2 y \, dA$ as an iterated integral, where R is the region bounded by the parabolas $y = 3x^2$ and $y = 16 - x^2$. Then evaluate the integral.

The bounding curves
determine the limits
of integration in y.

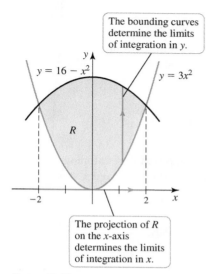

The projection of R
on the x-axis
determines the limits
of integration in x.

Figure 13.13

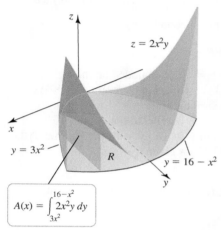

$$A(x) = \int_{3x^2}^{16-x^2} 2x^2y \, dy$$

Figure 13.14

SOLUTION The region R is bounded below and above by the graphs of $g(x) = 3x^2$ and $h(x) = 16 - x^2$, respectively. Solving $3x^2 = 16 - x^2$, we find that these curves intersect at $x = -2$ and $x = 2$, which are the limits of integration in the x-direction (Figure 13.13).

Figure 13.14 shows the solid bounded by the surface $z = 2x^2y$ and the region R. A typical vertical cross section through the solid parallel to the yz-plane at a fixed value of x has area

$$A(x) = \int_{3x^2}^{16-x^2} 2x^2y \, dy.$$

Integrating these cross-sectional areas between $x = -2$ and $x = 2$, the iterated integral becomes

$$\iint_R 2x^2y \, dA = \int_{-2}^{2} \underbrace{\int_{3x^2}^{16-x^2} 2x^2y \, dy}_{A(x)} \, dx \qquad \text{Convert to an iterated integral.}$$

$$= \int_{-2}^{2} x^2y^2 \Big|_{3x^2}^{16-x^2} \, dx \qquad \text{Evaluate inner integral with respect to } y.$$

$$= \int_{-2}^{2} x^2((16 - x^2)^2 - (3x^2)^2) \, dx \qquad \text{Simplify.}$$

$$= \int_{-2}^{2} (-8x^6 - 32x^4 + 256x^2) \, dx \qquad \text{Simplify.}$$

$$\approx 663.2. \qquad \text{Evaluate outer integral with respect to } x.$$

Because $z = 2x^2y \geq 0$ on R, the value of the integral is the volume of the solid shown in Figure 13.14.

Related Exercises 7–30 ◄

QUICK CHECK 1 A region R is bounded by the x- and y-axes and the line $x + y = 2$. Suppose you integrate first with respect to y. Give the limits of the iterated integral over R. ◄

Change of Perspective Suppose that the region of integration R is bounded on the left and right by the graphs of continuous functions $x = g(y)$ and $x = h(y)$, respectively, on the interval $c \leq y \leq d$. Such regions may take any of the forms shown in Figure 13.15.

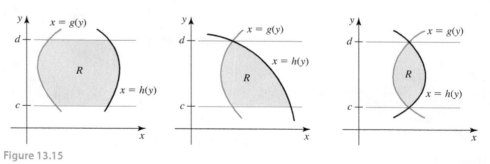

Figure 13.15

To find the volume of the solid bounded by the surface $z = f(x, y)$ and R, we now take vertical slices parallel to the xz-plane. In so doing, the double integral $\iint_R f(x, y) \, dA$ is converted to an iterated integral in which the inner integration is with respect to x over the interval $g(y) \leq x \leq h(y)$ and the outer integration is with respect to y over the interval $c \leq y \leq d$. The evaluation of double integrals in these two cases is summarized in the following theorem.

▶ Theorem 13.2 is another version of Fubini's Theorem. With integrals over nonrectangular regions, the order of integration cannot be simply switched; that is,

$$\int_a^b \int_{g(x)}^{h(x)} f(x, y) \, dy \, dx$$

$$\neq \int_{g(x)}^{h(x)} \int_a^b f(x, y) \, dx \, dy.$$

The *element of area dA* corresponds to the area of a small rectangle in the partition. Comparing the double integral to the iterated integral, we see that the element of area is $dA = dy \, dx$ or $dA = dx \, dy$, which is consistent with the area formula for rectangles.

THEOREM 13.2   Double Integrals over Nonrectangular Regions

Let R be a region bounded below and above by the graphs of the continuous functions $y = g(x)$ and $y = h(x)$, respectively, and by the lines $x = a$ and $x = b$ (Figure 13.11). If f is continuous on R, then

$$\iint_R f(x, y) \, dA = \int_a^b \int_{g(x)}^{h(x)} f(x, y) \, dy \, dx.$$

Let R be a region bounded on the left and right by the graphs of the continuous functions $x = g(y)$ and $x = h(y)$, respectively, and the lines $y = c$ and $y = d$ (Figure 13.15). If f is continuous on R, then

$$\iint_R f(x, y) \, dA = \int_c^d \int_{g(y)}^{h(y)} f(x, y) \, dx \, dy.$$

EXAMPLE 2   Computing a volume Find the volume of the solid below the surface $f(x, y) = 2 + \dfrac{1}{y}$ and above the region R in the xy-plane bounded by the lines $y = x$, $y = 8 - x$, and $y = 1$. Notice that $f(x, y) > 0$ on R.

SOLUTION The region R is bounded on the left by $x = y$ and bounded on the right by $y = 8 - x$, or $x = 8 - y$ (Figure 13.16). These lines intersect at the point $(4, 4)$. We take vertical slices through the solid parallel to the xz-plane from $y = 1$ to $y = 4$. To visualize these slices, it helps to draw lines through R parallel to the x-axis.

Integrating the cross-sectional areas of slices from $y = 1$ to $y = 4$, the volume of the solid beneath the graph of f and above R (Figure 13.17) is given by

$$\iint_R \left(2 + \frac{1}{y}\right) dA = \int_1^4 \int_y^{8-y} \left(2 + \frac{1}{y}\right) dx \, dy \qquad \text{Convert to an iterated integral.}$$

$$= \int_1^4 \left(2 + \frac{1}{y}\right) x \Big|_y^{8-y} \, dy \qquad \begin{array}{l}\text{Evaluate inner integral}\\ \text{with respect to } x.\end{array}$$

$$= \int_1^4 \left(2 + \frac{1}{y}\right)(8 - 2y) \, dy \qquad \text{Simplify.}$$

$$= \int_1^4 \left(14 - 4y + \frac{8}{y}\right) dy \qquad \text{Simplify.}$$

$$= \left(14y - 2y^2 + 8 \ln |y|\right)\Big|_1^4 \qquad \begin{array}{l}\text{Evaluate outer integral}\\ \text{with respect to } y.\end{array}$$

$$= 12 + 8 \ln 4 \approx 23.09. \qquad \text{Simplify.}$$

Related Exercises 31–52 ◀

The bounding curves determine the limits of integration in x.

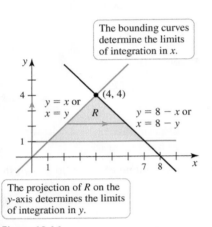

The projection of R on the y-axis determines the limits of integration in y.

Figure 13.16

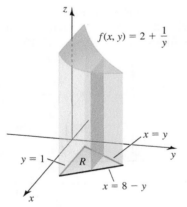

Figure 13.17

QUICK CHECK 2 Could the integral in Example 2 be evaluated by integrating first (inner integral) with respect to y? ◀

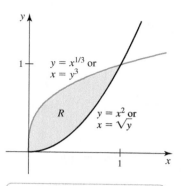

$y = x^{1/3}$ or
$x = y^3$

R

$y = x^2$ or
$x = \sqrt{y}$

*R is bounded above and below,
and on the right and left by curves.*

Figure 13.18

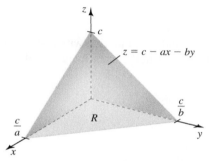

$z = c - ax - by$

$\dfrac{c}{b}$

R

$\dfrac{c}{a}$

Figure 13.19

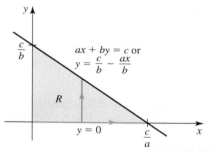

$\dfrac{c}{b}$

$ax + by = c$ or
$y = \dfrac{c}{b} - \dfrac{ax}{b}$

R

$y = 0$

$\dfrac{c}{a}$

Figure 13.20

▶ In Example 3, it is just as easy to view R as being bounded on the left and the right by the lines $x = 0$ and $x = c/a - by/a$, respectively, and integrating first with respect to x.

▶ The volume of *any* tetrahedron is $\dfrac{1}{3}$ (area of base)(height), where any of the faces may be chosen as the base (Exercise 98).

Choosing and Changing the Order of Integration

Occasionally, a region of integration is bounded above and below by a pair of curves *and* the region is bounded on the right and left by a pair of curves. For example, the region R in Figure 13.18 is bounded above by $y = x^{1/3}$ and below by $y = x^2$, and it is bounded on the right by $x = \sqrt{y}$ and on the left by $x = y^3$. In these cases, we can choose either of two orders of integration; however, one order of integration may be preferable. The following examples illustrate the valuable techniques of choosing and changing the order of integration.

EXAMPLE 3   **Volume of a tetrahedron**   Find the volume of the tetrahedron (pyramid with four triangular faces) in the first octant bounded by the plane $z = c - ax - by$ and the coordinate planes ($x = 0, y = 0$, and $z = 0$). Assume a, b, and c are positive real numbers (Figure 13.19).

SOLUTION   Let R be the triangular base of the tetrahedron in the xy-plane; it is bounded by the x- and y-axes and the line $ax + by = c$ (found by setting $z = 0$ in the equation of the plane; Figure 13.20). We can view R as being bounded below and above by the lines $y = 0$ and $y = c/b - ax/b$, respectively. The boundaries on the left and right are then $x = 0$ and $x = c/a$, respectively. Therefore, the volume of the solid region between the plane and R is

$$\iint\limits_R (c - ax - by) \, dA = \int_0^{c/a} \int_0^{c/b - ax/b} (c - ax - by) \, dy \, dx \qquad \text{Convert to an iterated integral.}$$

$$= \int_0^{c/a} \left(cy - axy - \frac{by^2}{2} \right) \Big|_0^{c/b - ax/b} dx \qquad \text{Evaluate inner integral with respect to } y.$$

$$= \int_0^{c/a} \frac{(ax - c)^2}{2b} \, dx \qquad \text{Simplify and factor.}$$

$$= \frac{c^3}{6ab}. \qquad \text{Evaluate outer integral with respect to } x.$$

This result illustrates the volume formula for a tetrahedron. The lengths of the legs of the triangular base are c/a and c/b, which means the area of the base is $c^2/(2ab)$. The height of the tetrahedron is c. The general volume formula is

$$V = \frac{c^3}{6ab} = \frac{1}{3} \underbrace{\frac{c^2}{2ab}}_{\substack{\text{area of} \\ \text{base}}} \cdot \underbrace{c}_{\text{height}} = \frac{1}{3} (\text{area of base})(\text{height}).$$

Related Exercises 53–56 ◀

EXAMPLE 4   **Changing the order of integration**   Consider the iterated integral $\int_0^{\sqrt{\pi}} \int_y^{\sqrt{\pi}} \sin x^2 \, dx \, dy$. Sketch the region of integration determined by the limits of integration and then evaluate the iterated integral.

SOLUTION   The region of integration is $R = \{(x, y): y \le x \le \sqrt{\pi}, 0 \le y \le \sqrt{\pi}\}$, which is a triangle (Figure 13.21a). Evaluating the iterated integral as given (integrating first with respect to x) requires integrating $\sin x^2$, a function whose antiderivative is not expressible in terms of elementary functions. Therefore, this order of integration is not feasible.

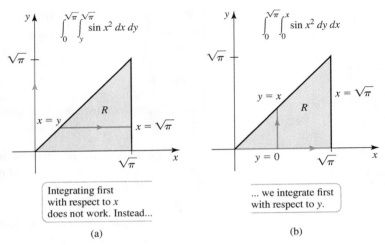

Figure 13.21

Instead, we change our perspective (Figure 13.21b) and integrate first with respect to y. With this order of integration, y runs from $y = 0$ to $y = x$ in the inner integral and x runs from $x = 0$ to $x = \sqrt{\pi}$ in the outer integral:

$$\iint\limits_{R} \sin x^2 \, dA = \int_0^{\sqrt{\pi}} \int_0^x \sin x^2 \, dy \, dx$$

$$= \int_0^{\sqrt{\pi}} y \sin x^2 \Big|_0^x \, dx \qquad \text{Evaluate inner integral with respect to } y; \sin x^2 \text{ is constant.}$$

$$= \int_0^{\sqrt{\pi}} x \sin x^2 \, dx \qquad \text{Simplify.}$$

$$= -\frac{1}{2} \cos x^2 \Big|_0^{\sqrt{\pi}} \qquad \text{Evaluate outer integral with respect to } x.$$

$$= 1. \qquad \text{Simplify.}$$

This example shows that the order of integration can make a practical difference.

Related Exercises 57–68 ◄

QUICK CHECK 3 Change the order of integration of the integral $\int_0^1 \int_0^y f(x, y) \, dx \, dy$. ◄

Regions Between Two Surfaces

An extension of the preceding ideas allows us to solve more general volume problems. Let $z = f(x, y)$ and $z = g(x, y)$ be continuous functions with $f(x, y) \geq g(x, y)$ on a region R in the xy-plane. Suppose we wish to compute the volume of the solid between the two surfaces over the region R (Figure 13.22). Forming a Riemann sum for the volume, the height of a typical box within the solid is the vertical distance $f(x, y) - g(x, y)$ between the upper and lower surfaces. Therefore, the volume of the solid between the surfaces is

$$V = \iint\limits_{R} (f(x, y) - g(x, y)) \, dA.$$

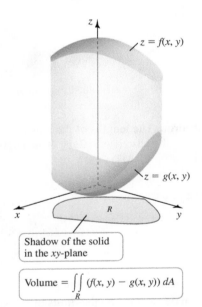

Shadow of the solid in the xy-plane

Volume $= \iint\limits_{R} (f(x, y) - g(x, y)) \, dA$

Figure 13.22

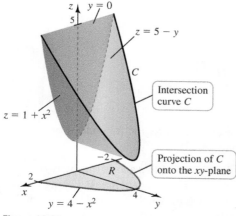

Figure 13.23

EXAMPLE 5   Region bounded by two surfaces Find the volume of the solid bounded by the parabolic cylinder $z = 1 + x^2$ and the planes $z = 5 - y$ and $y = 0$ (Figure 13.23).

SOLUTION The upper surface bounding the solid is $z = 5 - y$ and the lower surface is $z = 1 + x^2$; these two surfaces intersect along a curve C. Solving $5 - y = 1 + x^2$, we find that $y = 4 - x^2$, which is the projection of C onto the xy-plane. The back wall of the solid is the plane $y = 0$, and its projection onto the xy-plane is the x-axis. This line ($y = 0$) intersects the parabola $y = 4 - x^2$ at $x = \pm 2$. Therefore, the region of integration (Figure 13.23) is

$$R = \{(x, y): 0 \le y \le 4 - x^2, -2 \le x \le 2\}.$$

Notice that both R and the solid are symmetric about the yz-plane. Therefore, the volume of the entire solid is twice the volume of that part of the solid that lies in the first octant. The volume of the solid is

$$2 \int_0^2 \int_0^{4-x^2} (\underbrace{(5 - y)}_{f(x,\,y)} - \underbrace{(1 + x^2)}_{g(x,\,y)}) \, dy \, dx$$

$$= 2 \int_0^2 \int_0^{4-x^2} (4 - x^2 - y) \, dy \, dx \qquad \text{Simplify the integrand.}$$

$$= 2 \int_0^2 \left((4 - x^2)y - \frac{y^2}{2} \right) \Big|_0^{4-x^2} dx \qquad \begin{array}{l}\text{Evaluate inner integral with}\\ \text{respect to } y.\end{array}$$

$$= \int_0^2 (x^4 - 8x^2 + 16) \, dx \qquad \text{Simplify.}$$

$$= \left(\frac{x^5}{5} - \frac{8x^3}{3} + 16x \right) \Big|_0^2 \qquad \begin{array}{l}\text{Evaluate outer integral with}\\ \text{respect to } x.\end{array}$$

$$= \frac{256}{15}. \qquad \text{Simplify.}$$

Related Exercises 69–74 ◄

▶ To use symmetry to simplify a double integral, you must check that both the region of integration and the integrand have the same symmetry.

Decomposition of Regions

We occasionally encounter regions that are more complicated than those considered so far. A technique called *decomposition* allows us to subdivide a region of integration into two (or more) subregions. If the integrals over the subregions can be evaluated separately, the results are added to obtain the value of the original integral. For example, the region R in Figure 13.24 is divided into two nonoverlapping subregions R_1 and R_2. By partitioning these regions and using Riemann sums, it can be shown that

$$\iint\limits_R f(x, y) \, dA = \iint\limits_{R_1} f(x, y) \, dA + \iint\limits_{R_2} f(x, y) \, dA.$$

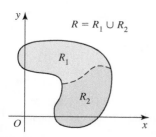

Figure 13.24

This method is illustrated in Example 6. The analogue of decomposition with single variable integrals is the property $\int_a^b f(x) \, dx = \int_a^p f(x) \, dx + \int_p^b f(x) \, dx$.

Finding Area by Double Integrals

An interesting application of double integrals arises when the integrand is $f(x, y) = 1$. The integral $\iint_R 1 \, dA$ gives the volume of the solid between the horizontal plane $z = 1$ and the region R. Because the height of this solid is 1, its volume equals (numerically) the area of R (Figure 13.25). Therefore, we have a way to compute areas of regions in the xy-plane using double integrals.

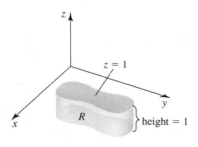

Volume of solid = (Area of R) × (height)

= Area of R = $\iint\limits_R 1 \, dA$

Figure 13.25

> We are solving a familiar area problem first encountered in Section 6.2. Suppose R is bounded above by $y = h(x)$ and below by $y = g(x)$, for $a \le x \le b$. Using a double integral, the area of R is

$$\iint\limits_R dA = \int_a^b \int_{g(x)}^{h(x)} dy\, dx$$

$$= \int_a^b (h(x) - g(x))\, dx,$$

which is a result obtained in Section 6.2.

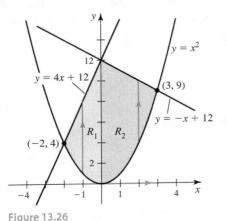

Figure 13.26

Areas of Regions by Double Integrals

Let R be a region in the xy-plane. Then

$$\text{area of } R = \iint\limits_R dA.$$

EXAMPLE 6   **Area of a plane region**   Find the area of the region R bounded by $y = x^2$, $y = -x + 12$, and $y = 4x + 12$ (Figure 13.26).

SOLUTION   The region R in its entirety is bounded neither above and below by two curves, nor on the left and right by two curves. However, when decomposed along the y-axis, R may be viewed as two regions R_1 and R_2, each of which is bounded above and below by a pair of curves. Notice that the parabola $y = x^2$ and the line $y = -x + 12$ intersect in the first quadrant at the point $(3, 9)$, while the parabola and the line $y = 4x + 12$ intersect in the second quadrant at the point $(-2, 4)$.

To find the area of R, we integrate the function $f(x, y) = 1$ over R_1 and R_2; the area is

$$\iint\limits_{R_1} 1\, dA + \iint\limits_{R_2} 1\, dA \qquad \text{Decompose region.}$$

$$= \int_{-2}^0 \int_{x^2}^{4x+12} 1\, dy\, dx + \int_0^3 \int_{x^2}^{-x+12} 1\, dy\, dx \qquad \text{Convert to iterated integrals.}$$

$$= \int_{-2}^0 (4x + 12 - x^2)\, dx + \int_0^3 (-x + 12 - x^2)\, dx \qquad \begin{array}{l}\text{Evaluate inner integral} \\ \text{with respect to } y.\end{array}$$

$$= \left(2x^2 + 12x - \frac{x^3}{3}\right)\Big|_{-2}^0 + \left(-\frac{x^2}{2} + 12x - \frac{x^3}{3}\right)\Big|_0^3 \qquad \begin{array}{l}\text{Evaluate outer integral} \\ \text{with respect to } x.\end{array}$$

$$= \frac{40}{3} + \frac{45}{2} = \frac{215}{6}. \qquad \text{Simplify.}$$

Related Exercises 75–80 ◄

QUICK CHECK 4   Consider the triangle R with vertices $(-1, 0)$, $(1, 0)$, and $(0, 1)$ as a region of integration. If we integrate first with respect to x, does R need to be decomposed? If we integrate first with respect to y, does R need to be decomposed? ◄

SECTION 13.2 EXERCISES

Review Questions

1. Describe and sketch a region that is bounded above and below by two curves.

2. Describe and a sketch a region that is bounded on the left and on the right by two curves.

3. Which order of integration is preferable to integrate $f(x, y) = xy$ over $R = \{(x, y): y - 1 \le x \le 1 - y, 0 \le y \le 1\}$?

4. Which order of integration would you use to find the area of the region bounded by the x-axis and the lines $y = 2x + 3$ and $y = 3x - 4$ using a double integral?

5. Change the order of integration in the integral $\int_0^1 \int_{y^2}^{\sqrt{y}} f(x, y)\, dx\, dy$.

6. Sketch the region of integration for $\int_{-2}^2 \int_{x^2}^4 e^{xy}\, dy\, dx$.

Basic Skills

7–8. Regions of integration *Consider the regions R shown in the figures and write an iterated integral of a continuous function f over R.*

7.   8.

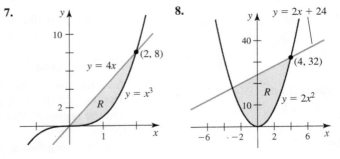

9–16. Regions of integration *Sketch each region and write an iterated integral of a continuous function f over the region. Use the order dy dx.*

9. $R = \{(x, y): 0 \le x \le \pi/4, \sin x \le y \le \cos x\}$

10. $R = \{(x, y): 0 \le x \le 2, 3x^2 \le y \le -6x + 24\}$

11. $R = \{(x, y): 1 \le x \le 2, x + 1 \le y \le 2x + 4\}$

12. $R = \{(x, y): 0 \le x \le 4, x^2 \le y \le 8\sqrt{x}\}$

13. R is the triangular region with vertices $(0, 0)$, $(0, 2)$, and $(1, 0)$.

14. R is the triangular region with vertices $(0, 0)$, $(0, 2)$, and $(1, 1)$.

15. R is the region in the first quadrant bounded by a circle of radius 1 centered at the origin.

16. R is the region in the first quadrant bounded by the y-axis and the parabolas $y = x^2$ and $y = 1 - x^2$.

17–26. Evaluating integrals *Evaluate the following integrals as they are written.*

17. $\displaystyle\int_0^1 \int_x^1 6y \, dy \, dx$

18. $\displaystyle\int_0^1 \int_0^{2x} 15\, xy^2 \, dy \, dx$

19. $\displaystyle\int_0^2 \int_{x^2}^{2x} xy \, dy \, dx$

20. $\displaystyle\int_0^3 \int_{x^2}^{x+6} (x - 1) \, dy \, dx$

21. $\displaystyle\int_{-\pi/4}^{\pi/4} \int_{\sin x}^{\cos x} dy \, dx$

22. $\displaystyle\int_0^1 \int_{-\sqrt{1-x^2}}^{\sqrt{1-x^2}} 2x^2 y \, dy \, dx$

23. $\displaystyle\int_{-2}^2 \int_{x^2}^{8-x^2} x \, dy \, dx$

24. $\displaystyle\int_0^{\ln 2} \int_{e^x}^2 dy \, dx$

25. $\displaystyle\int_0^1 \int_0^x 2e^{x^2} dy \, dx$

26. $\displaystyle\int_0^{\sqrt[3]{\pi/2}} \int_0^x y \cos x^3 \, dy \, dx$

27–30. Evaluating integrals *Evaluate the following integrals. A sketch is helpful.*

27. $\iint_R xy \, dA$; R is bounded by $x = 0$, $y = 2x + 1$, and $y = -2x + 5$.

28. $\iint_R (x + y) \, dA$; R is the region in the first quadrant bounded by $x = 0$, $y = x^2$, and $y = 8 - x^2$.

29. $\iint_R y^2 \, dA$; R is bounded by $x = 1$, $y = 2x + 2$, and $y = -x - 1$.

30. $\iint_R x^2 y \, dA$; R is the region in quadrants 1 and 4 bounded by the semicircle of radius 4 centered at $(0, 0)$.

31–32. Regions of integration *Write an iterated integral of a continuous function f over the region R shown in the figure.*

31.

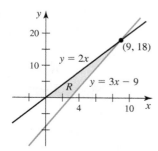

32.

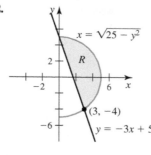

33–38. Regions of integration *Sketch each region and write an iterated integral of a continuous function f over the region. Use the order dx dy.*

33. The region bounded by $y = 2x + 3$, $y = 3x - 7$, and $y = 0$

34. $R = \{(x, y): 0 \le x \le y(1 - y)\}$

35. The region bounded by $y = 4 - x$, $y = 1$, and $x = 0$

36. The region in quadrants 2 and 3 bounded by the semicircle with radius 3 centered at $(0, 0)$

37. The region bounded by the triangle with vertices $(0, 0)$, $(2, 0)$, and $(1, 1)$

38. The region in the first quadrant bounded by the x-axis, the line $x = 6 - y$, and the curve $y = \sqrt{x}$

39–46. Evaluating integrals *Evaluate the following integrals as they are written.*

39. $\displaystyle\int_{-1}^2 \int_y^{4-y} dx \, dy$

40. $\displaystyle\int_0^2 \int_0^{4-y^2} y \, dx \, dy$

41. $\displaystyle\int_0^4 \int_{-\sqrt{16-y^2}}^{\sqrt{16-y^2}} 2xy \, dx \, dy$

42. $\displaystyle\int_0^1 \int_{-2\sqrt{1-y^2}}^{2\sqrt{1-y^2}} 2x \, dx \, dy$

43. $\displaystyle\int_0^{\ln 2} \int_{e^y}^2 \frac{y}{x} \, dx \, dy$

44. $\displaystyle\int_0^4 \int_y^{2y} xy \, dx \, dy$

45. $\displaystyle\int_0^{\pi/2} \int_y^{\pi/2} 6 \sin (2x - 3y) \, dx \, dy$

46. $\displaystyle\int_0^{\pi/2} \int_0^{\cos y} e^{\sin y} \, dx \, dy$

47–52. Evaluating integrals *Evaluate the following integrals. A sketch is helpful.*

47. $\iint_R 12y \, dA$; R is bounded by $y = 2 - x$, $y = \sqrt{x}$, and $y = 0$.

48. $\iint_R y^2 \, dA$; R is bounded by $y = 1$, $y = 1 - x$, and $y = x - 1$.

49. $\iint_R 3xy \, dA$; R is bounded by $y = 2 - x$, $y = 0$, and $x = 4 - y^2$ in the first quadrant.

50. $\iint_R (x + y) \, dA$; R is bounded by $y = |x|$ and $y = 4$.

51. $\iint_R 3x^2 \, dA$; R is bounded by $y = 0$, $y = 2x + 4$, and $y = x^3$.

52. $\iint_R x^2 y \, dA$; R is bounded by $y = 0$, $y = \sqrt{x}$, and $y = x - 2$.

53–56. Volumes *Use double integrals to calculate the volume of the following regions.*

53. The tetrahedron bounded by the coordinate planes $(x = 0, y = 0, z = 0)$ and the plane $z = 8 - 2x - 4y$

54. The solid in the first octant bounded by the coordinate planes and the surface $z = 1 - y - x^2$

55. The segment of the cylinder $x^2 + y^2 = 1$ bounded above by the plane $z = 12 + x + y$ and below by $z = 0$

56. The solid beneath the cylinder $z = y^2$ and above the region $R = \{(x, y): 0 \le y \le 1, y \le x \le 1\}$

57–62. Changing order of integration *Reverse the order of integration in the following integrals.*

57. $\displaystyle\int_0^2 \int_{x^2}^{2x} f(x, y) \, dy \, dx$

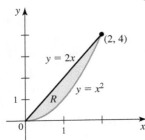

58. $\displaystyle\int_0^3 \int_0^{6-2x} f(x, y) \, dy \, dx$

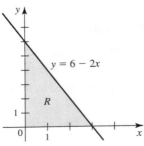

59. $\displaystyle\int_{1/2}^1 \int_0^{-\ln y} f(x, y) \, dx \, dy$

60. $\displaystyle\int_0^1 \int_1^{e^y} f(x, y) \, dx \, dy$

61. $\displaystyle\int_0^1 \int_0^{\cos^{-1} y} f(x, y) \, dx \, dy$

62. $\displaystyle\int_1^e \int_0^{\ln x} f(x, y) \, dy \, dx$

63–68. Changing order of integration *The following integrals can be evaluated only by reversing the order of integration. Sketch the region of integration, reverse the order of integration, and evaluate the integral.*

63. $\displaystyle\int_0^1 \int_y^1 e^{x^2} \, dx \, dy$

64. $\displaystyle\int_0^\pi \int_x^\pi \sin y^2 \, dy \, dx$

65. $\displaystyle\int_0^{1/2} \int_{y^2}^{1/4} y \cos (16\pi x^2) \, dx \, dy$

66. $\displaystyle\int_0^4 \int_{\sqrt{x}}^2 \frac{x}{y^5 + 1} \, dy \, dx$

67. $\displaystyle\int_0^{\sqrt[3]{\pi}} \int_y^{\sqrt[3]{\pi}} x^4 \cos (x^2 y) \, dx \, dy$

68. $\displaystyle\int_0^2 \int_0^{4-x^2} \frac{x e^{2y}}{4 - y} \, dy \, dx$

69–74. Regions between surfaces *Find the volume of the following solid regions.*

69. The solid above the region
$R = \{(x, y): 0 \le x \le 1,$
$0 \le y \le 1 - x\}$
bounded by the parabo-
loids $z = x^2 + y^2$ and
$z = 2 - x^2 - y^2$, and the
coordinate planes in the first
octant

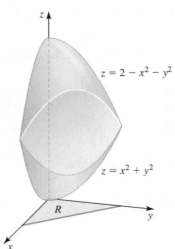

70. The solid above the
parabolic region
$R = \{(x, y): 0 \le x \le 1,$
$0 \le y \le 1 - x^2\}$ and
between the planes $z = 1$
and $z = 2 - y$

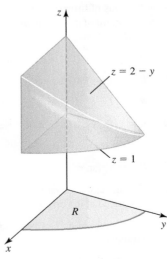

71. The solid bounded by the
paraboloid $z = x^2 + y^2$ and
the plane $z = 9$

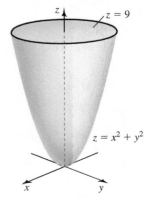

72. The solid bounded by
the parabolic cylinder
$z = x^2 + 1$, and the planes
$z = y + 1$ and $y = 1$

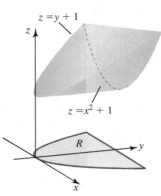

73. The solid above the region
$R = \{(x, y): 0 \le x \le 1,$
$0 \le y \le 2 - x\}$ and
between the planes
$-4x - 4y + z = 0$ and
$-2x - y + z = 8$

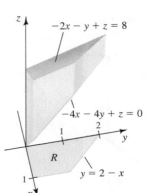

74. The solid S between the surfaces $z = e^{x-y}$ and $z = -e^{x-y}$, where S intersects the xy-plane in the region $R = \{(x, y): 0 \le x \le y, 0 \le y \le 1\}$

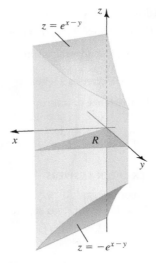

75–80. Area of plane regions *Use double integrals to compute the area of the following regions. Make a sketch of the region.*

75. The region bounded by the parabola $y = x^2$ and the line $y = 4$

76. The region bounded by the parabola $y = x^2$ and the line $y = x + 2$

77. The region in the first quadrant bounded by $y = e^x$ and $x = \ln 2$

78. The region bounded by $y = 1 + \sin x$ and $y = 1 - \sin x$ on the interval $[0, \pi]$

79. The region in the first quadrant bounded by $y = x^2$, $y = 5x + 6$, and $y = 6 - x$

80. The region bounded by the lines $x = 0$, $x = 4$, $y = x$, and $y = 2x + 1$

Further Explorations

81. Explain why or why not Determine whether the following statements are true and give an explanation or counterexample.

   a. In the iterated integral $\int_c^d \int_a^b f(x, y)\, dx\, dy$, the limits a and b must be constants or functions of x.

   b. In the iterated integral $\int_c^d \int_a^b f(x, y)\, dx\, dy$, the limits c and d must be functions of y.

   c. Changing the order of integration gives $\int_0^2 \int_1^y f(x, y)\, dx\, dy = \int_1^y \int_0^2 f(x, y)\, dy\, dx$.

82–85. Miscellaneous integrals *Evaluate the following integrals.*

82. $\displaystyle\iint\limits_{R} y\, dA; \quad R = \{(x, y): 0 \le y \le \sec x, 0 \le x \le \pi/3\}$

83. $\displaystyle\iint\limits_{R} (x + y)\, dA; \ R$ is the region bounded by $y = 1/x$ and $y = 5/2 - x$.

84. $\displaystyle\iint\limits_{R} \frac{xy}{1 + x^2 + y^2}\, dA; \ R = \{(x, y): 0 \le y \le x, 0 \le x \le 2\}$

85. $\displaystyle\iint\limits_{R} x \sec^2 y\, dA; \ R = \{(x, y): 0 \le y \le x^2, 0 \le x \le \sqrt{\pi}/2\}$

86. Paraboloid sliced by plane Find the volume of the solid between the paraboloid $z = x^2 + y^2$ and the plane $z = 1 - 2y$.

87. Two integrals to one Draw the regions of integration and write the following integrals as a single iterated integral:
$$\int_0^1 \int_{e^y}^e f(x, y)\, dx\, dy + \int_{-1}^0 \int_{e^{-y}}^e f(x, y)\, dx\, dy.$$

88. Square region Consider the region $R = \{(x, y): |x| + |y| \le 1\}$ shown in the figure.

   a. Use a double integral to verify that the area of R is 2.

   b. Find the volume of the square column whose base is R and whose upper surface is $z = 12 - 3x - 4y$.

   c. Find the volume of the solid above R and beneath the cylinder $x^2 + z^2 = 1$.

   d. Find the volume of the pyramid whose base is R and whose vertex is on the z-axis at $(0, 0, 6)$.

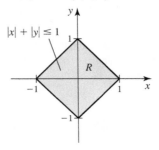

89–90. Average value *Use the definition for the average value of a function over a region R (Section 13.1),* $\bar{f} = \dfrac{1}{\text{area of } R} \displaystyle\iint\limits_{R} f(x, y)\, dA.$

89. Find the average value of $a - x - y$ over the region $R = \{(x, y): x + y \le a, x \ge 0, y \ge 0\}$, where $a > 0$.

90. Find the average value of $z = a^2 - x^2 - y^2$ over the region $R = \{(x, y): x^2 + y^2 \le a^2\}$, where $a > 0$.

91–92. Area integrals *Consider the following regions R.*

   a. Sketch the region R.

   b. Evaluate $\iint_R dA$ to determine the area of the region.

   c. Evaluate $\iint_R xy\, dA$.

91. R is the region between both branches of $y = 1/x$ and the lines $y = x + 3/2$ and $y = x - 3/2$.

92. R is the region bounded by the ellipse $x^2/18 + y^2/36 = 1$ with $y \le 4x/3$.

93–96. Improper integrals *Many improper double integrals may be handled using the techniques for improper integrals in one variable (Section 7.8). For example, under suitable conditions on f,*
$$\int_a^\infty \int_{g(x)}^{h(x)} f(x, y)\, dy\, dx = \lim_{b \to \infty} \int_a^b \int_{g(x)}^{h(x)} f(x, y)\, dy\, dx.$$

Use or extend the one-variable methods for improper integrals to evaluate the following integrals.

93. $\displaystyle\int_1^\infty \int_0^{e^{-x}} xy\, dy\, dx$

94. $\displaystyle\int_1^\infty \int_0^{1/x^2} \frac{2y}{x}\, dy\, dx$

95. $\displaystyle\int_0^\infty \int_0^\infty e^{-x-y}\, dy\, dx$

96. $\displaystyle\int_{-\infty}^\infty \int_{-\infty}^\infty \frac{1}{(x^2+1)(y^2+1)}\, dy\, dx$

97–101. Volumes *Compute the volume of the following solids.*

97. **Sliced block** The solid bounded by the planes $x = 0, x = 5$, $z = y - 1, z = -2y - 1, z = 0$, and $z = 2$

98. **Tetrahedron** A tetrahedron with vertices $(0, 0, 0), (a, 0, 0)$, $(b, c, 0)$, and $(0, 0, d)$, where a, b, c, and d are positive real numbers

99. **Square column** The column with a square base $R = \{(x, y): |x| \leq 1, |y| \leq 1\}$ cut by the plane $z = 4 - x - y$

100. **Wedge** The wedge sliced from the cylinder $x^2 + y^2 = 1$ by the planes $z = 1 - x$ and $z = x - 1$

101. **Wedge** The wedge sliced from the cylinder $x^2 + y^2 = 1$ by the planes $z = a(2 - x)$ and $z = a(x - 2)$, where $a > 0$

Additional Exercises

102. Existence of improper double integral For what values of m and n does the integral $\displaystyle\int_1^\infty \int_0^{1/x} \frac{y^m}{x^n}\, dy\, dx$ have a finite value? See Exercises 93–96.

103. Existence of improper double integral Let $R_1 = \{(x, y): x \geq 1, 1 \leq y \leq 2\}$ and $R_2 = \{(x, y): 1 \leq x \leq 2, y \geq 1\}$. For $n > 1$, which integral(s) have finite values: $\iint_{R_1} x^{-n}\, dA$ or $\iint_{R_2} x^{-n}\, dA$?

QUICK CHECK ANSWERS

1. Inner integral: $0 \leq y \leq 2 - x$; outer integral: $0 \leq x \leq 2$
2. Yes; however, two separate iterated integrals would be required.   **3.** $\int_0^1 \int_x^1 f(x, y)\, dy\, dx$ **4.** No; yes ◄

13.3 Double Integrals in Polar Coordinates

> Recall the conversions between Cartesian and polar coordinates (Section 10.2):
>
> $x = r\cos\theta, y = r\sin\theta,$ or
> $r^2 = x^2 + y^2, \tan\theta = y/x.$

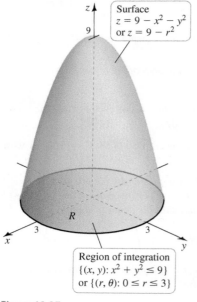

Figure 13.27

In Chapter 10, we explored polar coordinates and saw that in certain situations, they simplify problems considerably. The same is true when it comes to integration over plane regions. In this section, we learn how to formulate double integrals in polar coordinates and how to change double integrals from Cartesian coordinates to polar coordinates.

Polar Rectangular Regions

Suppose we want to find the volume of the solid bounded by the paraboloid $z = 9 - x^2 - y^2$ and the xy-plane (Figure 13.27). The intersection of the paraboloid and the xy-plane ($z = 0$) is the curve $9 - x^2 - y^2 = 0$, or $x^2 + y^2 = 9$. Therefore, the region of integration R is the disk of radius 3 centered at the origin in the xy-plane, which, when expressed in Cartesian coordinates, is $R = \{(x, y): -\sqrt{9 - x^2} \leq y \leq \sqrt{9 - x^2}, -3 \leq x \leq 3\}$. However, we use the relationship $r^2 = x^2 + y^2$ for converting Cartesian to polar coordinates, the region of integration is simply $R = \{(r, \theta): 0 \leq r \leq 3, 0 \leq \theta \leq 2\pi\}$. Furthermore, the paraboloid is expressed in polar coordinates as $z = 9 - r^2$. This problem (which is solved in Example 1) illustrates how both the integrand and the region of integration in a double integral can be simplified by working in polar coordinates.

The region of integration in this problem is an example of a **polar rectangle**. It has the form $R = \{(r, \theta): 0 \leq a \leq r \leq b, \alpha \leq \theta \leq \beta\}$, where $\beta - \alpha \leq 2\pi$ and a, b, α, and β are constants (Figure 13.28). Polar rectangles are the analogs of rectangles in Cartesian coordinates. For this reason, the methods used in Section 13.1 for evaluating double integrals over rectangles can be extended to polar rectangles. The goal is to evaluate integrals of the form $\iint_R f(r, \theta)\, dA$, where f is a continuous function of r and θ, and R is a polar rectangle. If f is nonnegative on R, this integral equals the volume of the solid bounded by the surface $z = f(r, \theta)$ and the region R in the xy-plane.

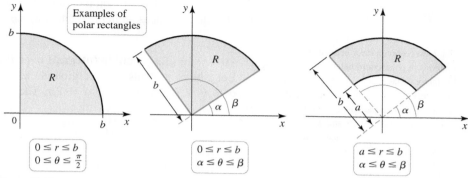

Figure 13.28

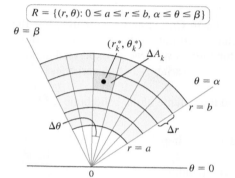

$$R = \{(r, \theta): 0 \le a \le r \le b, \alpha \le \theta \le \beta\}$$

Figure 13.29

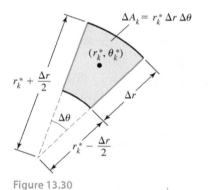

Figure 13.30

▶ Recall that the area of a sector of a circle of radius r subtended by an angle θ is $\frac{1}{2} r^2 \theta$.

$$\text{Area} = \frac{1}{2} r^2 \theta$$

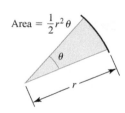

Our approach is to divide $[a, b]$ into M subintervals of equal length $\Delta r = (b - a)/M$. We similarly divide $[\alpha, \beta]$ into m subintervals of equal length $\Delta \theta = (\beta - \alpha)/m$. Now look at the arcs of the circles centered at the origin with radii

$$r = a, r = a + \Delta r, r = a + 2\Delta r, \ldots, r = b$$

and the rays

$$\theta = \alpha, \theta = \alpha + \Delta\theta, \theta = \alpha + 2\Delta\theta, \ldots, \theta = \beta$$

emanating from the origin (Figure 13.29). These arcs and rays divide the region R into $n = Mm$ polar rectangles that we number in a convenient way from $k = 1$ to $k = n$. The area of the kth rectangle is denoted ΔA_k, and we let (r_k^*, θ_k^*) be an arbitrary point in that rectangle.

Consider the "box" whose base is the kth polar rectangle and whose height is $f(r_k^*, \theta_k^*)$; its volume is $f(r_k^*, \theta_k^*) \Delta A_k$, for $k = 1, \ldots, n$. Therefore, the volume of the solid region beneath the surface $z = f(r, \theta)$ with a base R is approximately

$$V \approx \sum_{k=1}^{n} f(r_k^*, \theta_k^*) \Delta A_k.$$

This approximation to the volume is another Riemann sum. We let Δ be the maximum value of Δr and $\Delta \theta$. If f is continuous on R, then as $n \to \infty$ and $\Delta \to 0$, the sum approaches a double integral; that is,

$$\iint\limits_{R} f(r, \theta) \, dA = \lim_{\Delta \to 0} \sum_{k=1}^{n} f(r_k^*, \theta_k^*) \Delta A_k. \tag{1}$$

The next step is to write the double integral as an iterated integral. In order to do so, we must express ΔA_k in terms of Δr and $\Delta \theta$. Figure 13.30 shows the kth polar rectangle, with an area ΔA_k. The point (r_k^*, θ_k^*) is chosen so that the outer arc of the polar rectangle has radius $r_k^* + \Delta r/2$ and the inner arc has radius $r_k^* - \Delta r/2$. The area of the polar rectangle is

$$\Delta A_k = (\text{area of outer sector}) - (\text{area of inner sector})$$
$$= \frac{1}{2}\left(r_k^* + \frac{\Delta r}{2}\right)^2 \Delta\theta - \frac{1}{2}\left(r_k^* - \frac{\Delta r}{2}\right)^2 \Delta\theta \qquad \text{Area of sector} = \frac{1}{2} r^2 \Delta\theta$$
$$= r_k^* \Delta r \Delta\theta. \qquad \text{Expand and simplify.}$$

Substituting this expression for ΔA_k into equation (1), we have

$$\iint\limits_{R} f(r, \theta) \, dA = \lim_{\Delta \to 0} \sum_{k=1}^{n} f(r_k^*, \theta_k^*) \Delta A_k = \lim_{\Delta \to 0} \sum_{k=1}^{n} f(r_k^*, \theta_k^*) r_k^* \Delta r \Delta\theta.$$

This observation leads to another version of Fubini's Theorem, which is needed to write the double integral as an iterated integral; the proof is found in advanced texts.

▶ The most common error in evaluating integrals in polar coordinates is to omit the factor r that appears in the integrand. In Cartesian coordinates, the element of area is $dx\,dy$; in polar coordinates, the element of area is $r\,dr\,d\theta$, and without the factor of r, area is not measured correctly.

> **THEOREM 13.3   Double Integrals over Polar Rectangular Regions**
> Let f be continuous on the region in the xy-plane $R = \{(r, \theta): 0 \le a \le r \le b, \alpha \le \theta \le \beta\}$, where $\beta - \alpha \le 2\pi$. Then
> $$\iint_R f(r, \theta)\, dA = \int_\alpha^\beta \int_a^b f(r, \theta)\, r\,dr\,d\theta.$$

QUICK CHECK 1 Describe in polar coordinates the region in the first quadrant between the circles of radius 1 and 2. ◀

Frequently, an integral $\iint_R f(x, y)\, dA$ is given in Cartesian coordinates, but the region of integration is easier to handle in polar coordinates. By using the relations $x = r\cos\theta$, $y = r\sin\theta$, and $x^2 + y^2 = r^2$, the function $f(x, y)$ can be expressed in polar form as $f(r\cos\theta, r\sin\theta)$. This procedure is a change of variables in two variables.

EXAMPLE 1   Volume of a paraboloid cap Find the volume of the solid bounded by the paraboloid $z = 9 - x^2 - y^2$ and the xy-plane.

SOLUTION Using $x^2 + y^2 = r^2$, the surface is described in polar coordinates by $z = 9 - r^2$. The paraboloid intersects the xy-plane ($z = 0$) when $z = 9 - r^2 = 0$, or $r = 3$. Therefore, the intersection curve is the circle of radius 3 centered at the origin. The resulting region of integration is the disk $R = \{(r, \theta): 0 \le r \le 3, 0 \le \theta \le 2\pi\}$ (Figure 13.31). Integrating over R in polar coordinates, the volume is

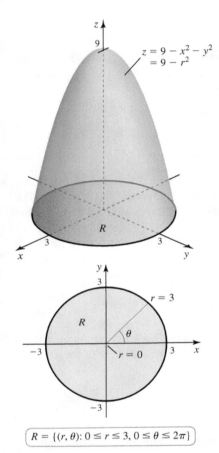

$R = \{(r, \theta): 0 \le r \le 3, 0 \le \theta \le 2\pi\}$

Figure 13.31

$$V = \int_0^{2\pi} \int_0^3 \underbrace{(9 - r^2)}_{z}\, r\,dr\,d\theta \qquad \text{Iterated integral for volume}$$

$$= \int_0^{2\pi} \left(\frac{9r^2}{2} - \frac{r^4}{4}\right)\Big|_0^3\, d\theta \qquad \text{Evaluate inner integral with respect to } r.$$

$$= \int_0^{2\pi} \frac{81}{4}\, d\theta = \frac{81\pi}{2}. \qquad \text{Evaluate outer integral with respect to } \theta.$$

Related Exercises 7–18 ◀

QUICK CHECK 2 Express the functions $f(x, y) = (x^2 + y^2)^{5/2}$ and $h(x, y) = x^2 - y^2$ in polar coordinates. ◀

EXAMPLE 2   Region bounded by two surfaces Find the volume of the region bounded by the paraboloids $z = x^2 + y^2$ and $z = 8 - x^2 - y^2$.

SOLUTION As shown in Figure 13.32, the two surfaces intersect in a curve C whose projection onto the xy-plane is the circle $x^2 + y^2 = 4$. This circle is the boundary of the region of integration R, which is written in polar coordinates as

$$R = \{(r, \theta): 0 \le r \le 2, 0 \le \theta \le 2\pi\}.$$

▶ In rectangular coordinates, the volume integral in Example 2 is

$$V = \int_{-2}^2 \int_{-\sqrt{4-x^2}}^{\sqrt{4-x^2}} (8 - 2x^2 - 2y^2)\, dy\,dx.$$

Evaluating this integral is decidedly more difficult than evaluating it in polar coordinates.

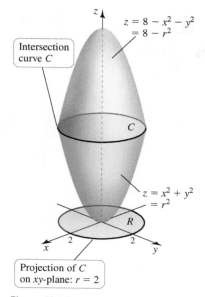

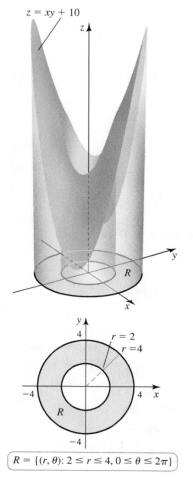

Figure 13.32

Figure 13.33

$R = \{(r, \theta): 2 \le r \le 4, 0 \le \theta \le 2\pi\}$

In polar coordinates, the upper bounding surface of the solid is $z = 8 - r^2$, and the lower bounding surface is $z = r^2$. The volume of the solid is

$$V = \int_0^{2\pi} \int_0^2 (\underbrace{(8 - r^2)}_{\text{upper}} - \underbrace{r^2}_{\text{lower}}) \, r \, dr \, d\theta$$

$$= \int_0^{2\pi} \int_0^2 (8r - 2r^3) \, dr \, d\theta \qquad \text{Simplify integrand.}$$

$$= \int_0^{2\pi} \left(4r^2 - \frac{r^4}{2}\right)\Big|_0^2 \, d\theta \qquad \text{Evaluate inner integral with respect to } r.$$

$$= \int_0^{2\pi} 8 \, d\theta \qquad \text{Simplify.}$$

$$= 16\pi. \qquad \text{Evaluate outer integral with respect to } \theta.$$

Related Exercises 19–22 ◄

EXAMPLE 3 Annular region Find the volume of the region beneath the surface $z = xy + 10$ and above the annular region $R = \{(r, \theta): 2 \le r \le 4, 0 \le \theta \le 2\pi\}$. (An *annulus* is the region between two concentric circles.)

SOLUTION The region of integration suggests working in polar coordinates (Figure 13.33). Substituting $x = r \cos \theta$ and $y = r \sin \theta$, the integrand becomes

$$xy + 10 = (r \cos \theta)(r \sin \theta) + 10 \qquad \text{Substitute for } x \text{ and } y.$$

$$= r^2 \sin \theta \cos \theta + 10 \qquad \text{Simplify.}$$

$$= \tfrac{1}{2} r^2 \sin 2\theta + 10. \qquad \sin 2\theta = 2 \sin \theta \cos \theta$$

Substituting the integrand into the volume integral, we have

$$V = \int_0^{2\pi} \int_2^4 \left(\tfrac{1}{2} r^2 \sin 2\theta + 10\right) r \, dr \, d\theta \qquad \text{Iterated integral for volume}$$

$$= \int_0^{2\pi} \int_2^4 \left(\tfrac{1}{2} r^3 \sin 2\theta + 10r\right) dr \, d\theta \qquad \text{Simplify.}$$

$$= \int_0^{2\pi} \left(\frac{r^4}{8} \sin 2\theta + 5r^2\right)\Big|_2^4 \, d\theta \qquad \text{Evaluate inner integral with respect to } r.$$

$$= \int_0^{2\pi} (30 \sin 2\theta + 60) \, d\theta \qquad \text{Simplify.}$$

$$= (15(-\cos 2\theta) + 60\theta)\Big|_0^{2\pi} = 120\pi. \qquad \text{Evaluate outer integral with respect to } \theta.$$

Related Exercises 23–32 ◄

More General Polar Regions

In Section 13.2 we generalized double integrals over rectangular regions to double integrals over nonrectangular regions. In an analogous way, the method for integrating over a polar rectangle may be extended to more general regions. Consider a region bounded by two rays $\theta = \alpha$ and $\theta = \beta$, where $\beta - \alpha \le 2\pi$, and two curves $r = g(\theta)$ and $r = h(\theta)$ (Figure 13.34):

$$R = \{(r, \theta): 0 \le g(\theta) \le r \le h(\theta), \alpha \le \theta \le \beta\}.$$

The double integral $\iint_R f(r, \theta)\, dA$ is expressed as an iterated integral in which the inner integral has limits $r = g(\theta)$ and $r = h(\theta)$, and the outer integral runs from $\theta = \alpha$ to $\theta = \beta$. If f is nonnegative on R, the double integral gives the volume of the solid bounded by the surface $z = f(r, \theta)$ and R.

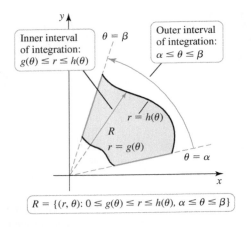

Inner interval of integration: $g(\theta) \le r \le h(\theta)$

$\theta = \beta$

Outer interval of integration: $\alpha \le \theta \le \beta$

$r = h(\theta)$

R

$r = g(\theta)$

$\theta = \alpha$

$R = \{(r, \theta): 0 \le g(\theta) \le r \le h(\theta),\ \alpha \le \theta \le \beta\}$

Figure 13.34

> For the type of region described in Theorem 13.4, with the boundaries in the radial direction expressed as functions of θ, the inner integral is always with respect to r.

THEOREM 13.4   Double Integrals over More General Polar Regions

Let f be continuous on the region in the xy-plane

$$R = \{(r, \theta): 0 \le g(\theta) \le r \le h(\theta),\ \alpha \le \theta \le \beta\},$$

where $0 < \beta - \alpha \le 2\pi$. Then

$$\iint_R f(r, \theta)\, dA = \int_\alpha^\beta \int_{g(\theta)}^{h(\theta)} f(r, \theta)\, r\, dr\, d\theta.$$

> Recall from Section 10.2 that the polar equation $r = 2a \sin\theta$ describes a circle of radius $|a|$ with center $(0, a)$. The polar equation $r = 2a \cos\theta$ describes a circle of radius $|a|$ with center $(a, 0)$.

EXAMPLE 4   Specifying regions Write an iterated integral for $\iint_R f(r, \theta)\, dA$ for the following regions R in the xy-plane.

a. The region outside the circle $r = 2$ (with radius 2 centered at $(0, 0)$) and inside the circle $r = 4 \cos\theta$ (with radius 2 centered at $(2, 0)$)

b. The region inside both circles of part (a)

SOLUTION

a. Equating the two expressions for r, we have $4 \cos\theta = 2$ or $\cos\theta = \frac{1}{2}$, so the circles intersect when $\theta = \pm \pi/3$ (Figure 13.35). The inner boundary of R is the circle $r = 2$, and the outer boundary is the circle $r = 4 \cos\theta$. Therefore, the region of integration is $R = \{(r, \theta): 2 \le r \le 4 \cos\theta,\ -\pi/3 \le \theta \le \pi/3\}$ and the iterated integral is

$$\iint_R f(r, \theta)\, dA = \int_{-\pi/3}^{\pi/3} \int_2^{4\cos\theta} f(r, \theta)\, r\, dr\, d\theta.$$

b. From part (a), we know that the circles intersect when $\theta = \pm \pi/3$. The region R consists of three subregions R_1, R_2, and R_3 (Figure 13.36a).

• For $-\pi/2 \le \theta \le -\pi/3$, R_1 is bounded by $r = 0$ (inner curve) and $r = 4 \cos\theta$ (outer curve) (Figure 13.36b).

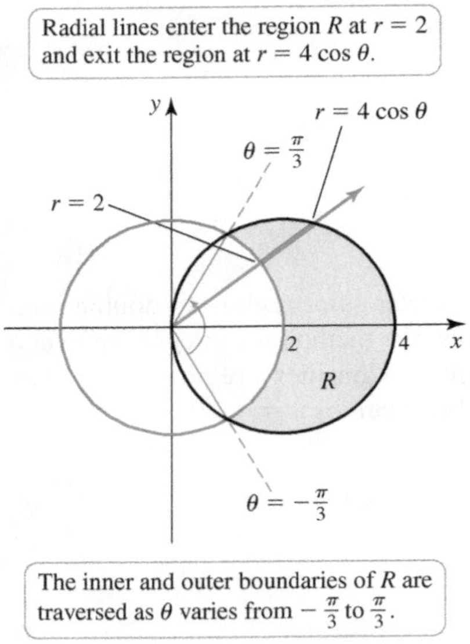

Radial lines enter the region R at $r = 2$ and exit the region at $r = 4 \cos\theta$.

y

$r = 4 \cos\theta$

$\theta = \dfrac{\pi}{3}$

$r = 2$

2 4 x

R

$\theta = -\dfrac{\pi}{3}$

The inner and outer boundaries of R are traversed as θ varies from $-\dfrac{\pi}{3}$ to $\dfrac{\pi}{3}$.

Figure 13.35

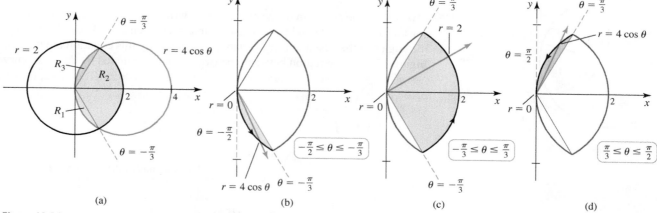

Figure 13.36

- For $-\pi/3 \leq \theta \leq \pi/3$, R_2 is bounded by $r = 0$ (inner curve) and $r = 2$ (outer curve) (Figure 13.36c).

- For $\pi/3 \leq \theta \leq \pi/2$, R_3 is bounded by $r = 0$ (inner curve) and $r = 4 \cos \theta$ (outer curve) (Figure 13.36d).

Therefore, the double integral is expressed in three parts:

$$\iint\limits_{R} f(r, \theta) \, dA = \int_{-\pi/2}^{-\pi/3} \int_{0}^{4 \cos \theta} f(r, \theta) \, r \, dr \, d\theta + \int_{-\pi/3}^{\pi/3} \int_{0}^{2} f(r, \theta) \, r \, dr \, d\theta$$

$$+ \int_{\pi/3}^{\pi/2} \int_{0}^{4 \cos \theta} f(r, \theta) \, r \, dr \, d\theta.$$

Related Exercises 33–38 ◄

Areas of Regions

In Cartesian coordinates, the area of a region R in the xy-plane is computed by integrating the function $f(x, y) = 1$ over R; that is, $A = \iint_R dA$. This fact extends to polar coordinates.

> ➤ Do not forget the factor of r in the area integral!

Area of Polar Regions

The area of the region $R = \{(r, \theta): 0 \leq g(\theta) \leq r \leq h(\theta), \alpha \leq \theta \leq \beta\}$, where $0 < \beta - \alpha \leq 2\pi$, is

$$A = \iint\limits_{R} dA = \int_{\alpha}^{\beta} \int_{g(\theta)}^{h(\theta)} r \, dr \, d\theta.$$

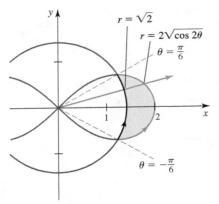

Figure 13.37

EXAMPLE 5   Area within a lemniscate Compute the area of the region in the first and fourth quadrants outside the circle $r = \sqrt{2}$ and inside the lemniscate $r^2 = 4\cos 2\theta$ (Figure 13.37).

SOLUTION The equation of the circle can be written as $r^2 = 2$. Equating the two expressions for r^2, the circle and the lemniscate intersect when $2 = 4\cos 2\theta$, or $\cos 2\theta = \frac{1}{2}$. The angles in the first and fourth quadrants that satisfy this equation are $\theta = \pm \pi/6$ (Figure 13.37). The region between the two curves is bounded by the inner curve $r = g(\theta) = \sqrt{2}$ and the outer curve $r = h(\theta) = 2\sqrt{\cos 2\theta}$. Therefore, the area of the region is

$$A = \int_{-\pi/6}^{\pi/6} \int_{\sqrt{2}}^{2\sqrt{\cos 2\theta}} r\,dr\,d\theta$$

$$= \int_{-\pi/6}^{\pi/6} \left(\frac{r^2}{2}\right)\Bigg|_{\sqrt{2}}^{2\sqrt{\cos 2\theta}} d\theta \qquad \text{Evaluate inner integral with respect to } r.$$

$$= \int_{-\pi/6}^{\pi/6} (2\cos 2\theta - 1)\,d\theta \qquad \text{Simplify.}$$

$$= (\sin 2\theta - \theta)\Bigg|_{-\pi/6}^{\pi/6} \qquad \text{Evaluate outer integral with respect to } \theta.$$

$$= \sqrt{3} - \frac{\pi}{3}. \qquad \text{Simplify.}$$

Related Exercises 39–44 ◄

QUICK CHECK 3 Express the area of the disk $R = \{(r, \theta): 0 \le r \le a, 0 \le \theta \le 2\pi\}$ in terms of a double integral in polar coordinates. ◄

Average Value over a Planar Polar Region

We have encountered the average value of a function in several different settings. To find the average value of a function over a region in polar coordinates, we again integrate the function over the region and divide by the area of the region.

EXAMPLE 6   Average y-coordinate Find the average value of the y-coordinates of the points in the semicircular disk of radius a given by $R = \{(r, \theta): 0 \le r \le a, 0 \le \theta \le \pi\}$.

SOLUTION Because the y-coordinates of points in the disk are given by $y = r\sin\theta$, the function whose average value we seek is $f(r, \theta) = r\sin\theta$. We use the fact that the area of R is $\pi a^2/2$. Evaluating the average value integral we find that

$$\bar{y} = \frac{1}{\pi a^2/2} \int_0^\pi \int_0^a r\sin\theta\,r\,dr\,d\theta$$

$$= \frac{2}{\pi a^2} \int_0^\pi \sin\theta \left(\frac{r^3}{3}\right)\Bigg|_0^a d\theta \qquad \text{Evaluate inner integral with respect to } r.$$

$$= \frac{2}{\pi a^2}\frac{a^3}{3} \int_0^\pi \sin\theta\,d\theta \qquad \text{Simplify.}$$

$$= \frac{2a}{3\pi}(-\cos\theta)\Bigg|_0^\pi \qquad \text{Evaluate outer integral with respect to } \theta.$$

$$= \frac{4a}{3\pi}. \qquad \text{Simplify.}$$

Note that $4/(3\pi) \approx 0.42$, so the average value of the y-coordinates is less than half the radius of the disk.

Related Exercises 45–48 ◄

SECTION 13.3 EXERCISES

Review Questions

1. Draw the region $\{(r, \theta): 1 \le r \le 2, 0 \le \theta \le \pi/2\}$. Why is it called a polar rectangle?

2. Write the double integral $\iint_R f(x, y)\, dA$ as an iterated integral in polar coordinates when $R = \{(r, \theta): a \le r \le b, \alpha \le \theta \le \beta\}$.

3. Sketch the region of integration for the integral
$$\int_{-\pi/6}^{\pi/6} \int_{1/2}^{\cos 2\theta} f(r, \theta)\, r\, dr\, d\theta.$$

4. Explain why the element of area in Cartesian coordinates $dx\, dy$ becomes $r\, dr\, d\theta$ in polar coordinates.

5. How do you find the area of a region $R = \{(r, \theta): 0 \le g(\theta) \le r \le h(\theta), \alpha \le \theta \le \beta\}$?

6. How do you find the average value of a function over a region that is expressed in polar coordinates?

Basic Skills

7–10. Polar rectangles *Sketch the following polar rectangles.*

7. $R = \{(r, \theta): 0 \le r \le 5, 0 \le \theta \le \pi/2\}$

8. $R = \{(r, \theta): 2 \le r \le 3, \pi/4 \le \theta \le 5\pi/4\}$

9. $R = \{(r, \theta): 1 \le r \le 4, -\pi/4 \le \theta \le 2\pi/3\}$

10. $R = \{(r, \theta): 4 \le r \le 5, -\pi/3 \le \theta \le \pi/2\}$

11–14. Solids bounded by paraboloids *Find the volume of the solid below the paraboloid $z = 4 - x^2 - y^2$ and above the following regions.*

11. $R = \{(r, \theta): 0 \le r \le 1, 0 \le \theta \le 2\pi\}$

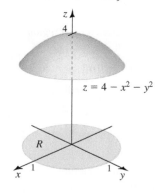

12. $R = \{(r, \theta): 0 \le r \le 2, 0 \le \theta \le 2\pi\}$

13. $R = \{(r, \theta): 1 \le r \le 2, 0 \le \theta \le 2\pi\}$

14. $R = \{(r, \theta): 1 \le r \le 2, -\pi/2 \le \theta \le \pi/2\}$

15–18. Solids bounded by hyperboloids *Find the volume of the solid below the hyperboloid $z = 5 - \sqrt{1 + x^2 + y^2}$ and above the following regions.*

15. $R = \{(r, \theta): 0 \le r \le 2, 0 \le \theta \le 2\pi\}$

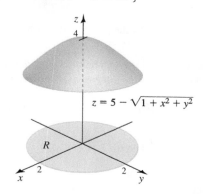

16. $R = \{(r, \theta): 0 \le r \le 1, 0 \le \theta \le \pi\}$

17. $R = \{(r, \theta): \sqrt{3} \le r \le 2\sqrt{2}, 0 \le \theta \le 2\pi\}$

18. $R = \{(r, \theta): \sqrt{3} \le r \le \sqrt{15}, -\pi/2 \le \theta \le \pi\}$

19–22. Volume between surfaces *Find the volume of the following solids.*

19. The solid bounded by the paraboloids $z = x^2 + y^2$ and $z = 2 - x^2 - y^2$

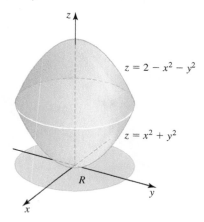

20. The solid bounded by the paraboloids $z = 2x^2 + y^2$ and $z = 27 - x^2 - 2y^2$

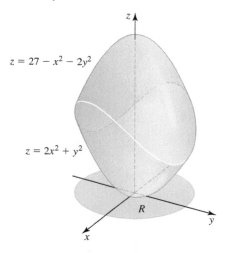

21. The solid bounded by the paraboloid $z = 2 - x^2 - y^2$ and the plane $z = 1$

22. The solid bounded by the paraboloid $z = 8 - x^2 - 3y^2$ and the hyperbolic paraboloid $z = x^2 - y^2$

23–28. Cartesian to polar coordinates *Sketch the given region of integration R and evaluate the integral over R using polar coordinates.*

23. $\iint\limits_R (x^2 + y^2)\, dA; \quad R = \{(r, \theta): 0 \le r \le 4, 0 \le \theta \le 2\pi\}$

24. $\iint\limits_R 2xy\, dA; \quad R = \{(r, \theta): 1 \le r \le 3, 0 \le \theta \le \pi/2\}$

25. $\iint\limits_R 2xy\, dA; \quad R = \{(x, y): x^2 + y^2 \le 9, y \ge 0\}$

26. $\iint\limits_R \dfrac{dA}{1 + x^2 + y^2}; \quad R = \{(r, \theta): 1 \le r \le 2, 0 \le \theta \le \pi\}$

27. $\iint\limits_R \dfrac{dA}{\sqrt{16 - x^2 - y^2}};$
$R = \{(x, y): x^2 + y^2 \le 4, x \ge 0, y \ge 0\}$

28. $\iint\limits_R e^{-x^2 - y^2}\, dA; \quad R = \{(x, y): x^2 + y^2 \le 9\}$

29–32. Island problems *The surface of an island is defined by the following functions over the region on which the function is nonnegative. Find the volume of the island.*

29. $z = e^{-(x^2 + y^2)/8} - e^{-2}$

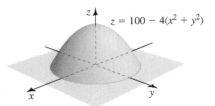
$z = e^{-(x^2+y^2)/8} - e^{-2}$

30. $z = 100 - 4(x^2 + y^2)$

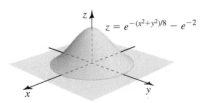
$z = 100 - 4(x^2 + y^2)$

31. $z = 25 - \sqrt{x^2 + y^2}$

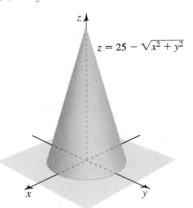
$z = 25 - \sqrt{x^2 + y^2}$

32. $z = \dfrac{20}{1 + x^2 + y^2} - 2$

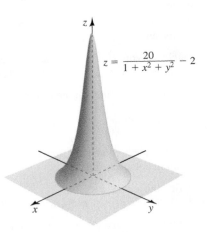
$z = \dfrac{20}{1 + x^2 + y^2} - 2$

33–38. Describing general regions *Sketch the following regions R. Then express $\iint_R f(r, \theta)\, dA$ as an iterated integral over R.*

33. The region inside the limaçon $r = 1 + \frac{1}{2}\cos\theta$

34. The region inside the leaf of the rose $r = 2\sin 2\theta$ in the first quadrant

35. The region inside the lobe of the lemniscate $r^2 = 2\sin 2\theta$ in the first quadrant

36. The region outside the circle $r = 2$ and inside the circle $r = 4\sin\theta$

37. The region outside the circle $r = 1$ and inside the rose $r = 2\sin 3\theta$ in the first quadrant

38. The region outside the circle $r = \frac{1}{2}$ and inside the cardioid $r = 1 + \cos\theta$

39–44. Computing areas *Sketch each region and use a double integral to find its area.*

39. The annular region $\{(r, \theta): 1 \le r \le 2, 0 \le \theta \le \pi\}$

40. The region bounded by the cardioid $r = 2(1 - \sin\theta)$

41. The region bounded by all leaves of the rose $r = 2\cos 3\theta$

42. The region inside both the cardioid $r = 1 - \cos\theta$ and the circle $r = 1$

43. The region inside both the cardioid $r = 1 + \sin\theta$ and the cardioid $r = 1 + \cos\theta$

44. The region bounded by the spiral $r = 2\theta$, for $0 \le \theta \le \pi$, and the x-axis

45–48. Average values *Find the following average values.*

45. The average distance between points of the disk $\{(r, \theta): 0 \le r \le a\}$ and the origin

46. The average distance between points within the cardioid $r = 1 + \cos\theta$ and the origin

47. The average distance squared between points on the unit disk $\{(r, \theta): 0 \le r \le 1\}$ and the point $(1, 1)$

48. The average value of $1/r^2$ over the annulus $\{(r, \theta): 2 \le r \le 4\}$

Further Explorations

49. Explain why or why not Determine whether the following statements are true and give an explanation or counterexample.

  a. Let R be the unit disk centered at $(0, 0)$. Then $\iint_R (x^2 + y^2)\, dA = \int_0^{2\pi} \int_0^1 r^2\, dr\, d\theta$.

  b. The average distance between the points of the hemisphere $z = \sqrt{4 - x^2 - y^2}$ and the origin is 2 (calculus not required).

  c. The integral $\int_0^1 \int_0^{\sqrt{1-y^2}} e^{x^2+y^2}\, dx\, dy$ is easier to evaluate in polar coordinates than in Cartesian coordinates.

50–57. Miscellaneous integrals *Evaluate the following integrals using the method of your choice. A sketch is helpful.*

50. $\int_0^3 \int_0^{\sqrt{9-x^2}} \sqrt{x^2 + y^2}\, dy\, dx$

51. $\int_{-1}^1 \int_{-\sqrt{1-x^2}}^{\sqrt{1-x^2}} (x^2 + y^2)^{3/2}\, dy\, dx$

52. $\int_{-4}^4 \int_0^{\sqrt{16-y^2}} (16 - x^2 - y^2)\, dx\, dy$

53. $\int_0^{\pi/4} \int_0^{\sec\theta} r^3\, dr\, d\theta$

54. $\iint_R \sqrt{x^2 + y^2}\, dA;\ R = \{(x, y) : 0 \le y \le x \le 1\}$

55. $\iint_R \sqrt{x^2 + y^2}\, dA;\ R = \{(x, y) : 1 \le x^2 + y^2 \le 4\}$

56. $\iint_R \dfrac{x - y}{x^2 + y^2 + 1}\, dA;\ R$ is the region bounded by the unit circle centered at the origin.

57. $\iint_R \dfrac{dA}{4 + \sqrt{x^2 + y^2}};\ R = \{(r, \theta) : 0 \le r \le 2,\ \pi/2 \le \theta \le 3\pi/2\}$

58. Areas of circles Use integration to show that the circles $r = 2a \cos\theta$ and $r = 2a \sin\theta$ have the same area, which is πa^2.

59. Filling bowls with water Which bowl holds more water if it is filled to a depth of 4 units?

  • The paraboloid $z = x^2 + y^2$, for $0 \le z \le 4$
  • The cone $z = \sqrt{x^2 + y^2}$, for $0 \le z \le 4$
  • The hyperboloid $z = \sqrt{1 + x^2 + y^2}$, for $1 \le z \le 5$

60. Equal volumes To what height (above the bottom of the bowl) must the cone and paraboloid bowls of Exercise 59 be filled to hold the same volume of water as the hyperboloid bowl filled to a depth of 4 units $(1 \le z \le 5)$?

61. Volume of a hyperbolic paraboloid Consider the surface $z = x^2 - y^2$.

  a. Find the region in the xy-plane in polar coordinates for which $z \ge 0$.

  b. Let $R = \{(r, \theta) : 0 \le r \le a,\ -\pi/4 \le \theta \le \pi/4\}$, which is a sector of a circle of radius a. Find the volume of the region below the hyperbolic paraboloid and above the region R.

62. Slicing a hemispherical cake A cake is shaped like a hemisphere of radius 4 with its base on the xy-plane. A wedge of the cake is removed by making two slices from the center of the cake outward, perpendicular to the xy-plane and separated by an angle of φ.

  a. Use a double integral to find the volume of the slice for $\varphi = \pi/4$. Use geometry to check your answer.

  b. Now suppose the cake is sliced by a plane perpendicular to the xy-plane at $x = a > 0$. Let D be the smaller of the two pieces produced. For what value of a is the volume of D equal to the volume in part (a)?

63–66. Improper integrals *Improper integrals arise in polar coordinates when the radial coordinate r becomes arbitrarily large. Under certain conditions, these integrals are treated in the usual way:*

$$\int_\alpha^\beta \int_a^\infty f(r, \theta)\, r\, dr\, d\theta = \lim_{b \to \infty} \int_\alpha^\beta \int_a^b f(r, \theta)\, r\, dr\, d\theta.$$

Use this technique to evaluate the following integrals.

63. $\int_0^{\pi/2} \int_1^\infty \dfrac{\cos\theta}{r^3}\, r\, dr\, d\theta$

64. $\iint_R \dfrac{dA}{(x^2 + y^2)^{5/2}};\ R = \{(r, \theta) : 1 \le r < \infty,\ 0 \le \theta \le 2\pi\}$

65. $\iint_R e^{-x^2-y^2}\, dA;\ R = \{(r, \theta) : 0 \le r < \infty,\ 0 \le \theta \le \pi/2\}$

66. $\iint_R \dfrac{dA}{(1 + x^2 + y^2)^2};\ R$ is the first quadrant.

67. Limaçon loops The limaçon $r = b + a \cos\theta$ has an inner loop if $b < a$ and no inner loop if $b > a$.

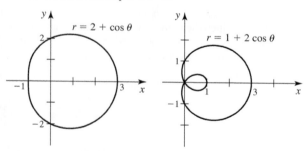

  a. Find the area of the region bounded by the limaçon $r = 2 + \cos\theta$.

  b. Find the area of the region outside the inner loop and inside the outer loop of the limaçon $r = 1 + 2 \cos\theta$.

  c. Find the area of the region inside the inner loop of the limaçon $r = 1 + 2 \cos\theta$.

Applications

T 68. Mass from density data The following table gives the density (in units of g/cm^2) at selected points of a thin semicircular plate of radius 3. Estimate the mass of the plate and explain your method.

	$\theta = 0$	$\theta = \pi/4$	$\theta = \pi/2$	$\theta = 3\pi/4$	$\theta = \pi$
$r = 1$	2.0	2.1	2.2	2.3	2.4
$r = 2$	2.5	2.7	2.9	3.1	3.3
$r = 3$	3.2	3.4	3.5	3.6	3.7

69. A mass calculation Suppose the density of a thin plate represented by the region R is $\rho(r, \theta)$ (in units of mass per area). The mass of the plate is $\iint_R \rho(r, \theta)\, dA$. Find the mass of the thin half annulus $R = \{(r, \theta): 1 \le r \le 4, 0 \le \theta \le \pi\}$ with a density $\rho(r, \theta) = 4 + r \sin \theta$.

Additional Exercises

70. Area formula In Section 10.3 it was shown that the area of a region enclosed by the polar curve $r = g(\theta)$ and the rays $\theta = \alpha$ and $\theta = \beta$, where $\beta - \alpha \le 2\pi$, is $A = \frac{1}{2}\int_\alpha^\beta r^2\, d\theta$. Prove this result using the area formula with double integrals.

71. Normal distribution An important integral in statistics associated with the normal distribution is $I = \int_{-\infty}^{\infty} e^{-x^2}\, dx$. It is evaluated in the following steps.

a. Assume that

$$I^2 = \left(\int_{-\infty}^{\infty} e^{-x^2}\, dx\right)\left(\int_{-\infty}^{\infty} e^{-y^2}\, dy\right)$$

$$= \int_{-\infty}^{\infty}\int_{-\infty}^{\infty} e^{-x^2 - y^2}\, dx\, dy,$$

where we have chosen the variables of integration to be x and y and then written the product as an iterated integral. Evaluate this integral in polar coordinates and show that $I = \sqrt{\pi}$. Why is the solution $I = -\sqrt{\pi}$ rejected?

b. Evaluate $\int_0^{\infty} e^{-x^2}\, dx$, $\int_0^{\infty} xe^{-x^2}\, dx$, and $\int_0^{\infty} x^2 e^{-x^2}\, dx$ (using part (a) if needed).

72. Existence of integrals For what values of p does the integral

$$\iint_R \frac{dA}{(x^2 + y^2)^p}$$ exist in the following cases?

a. $R = \{(r, \theta): 1 \le r < \infty, 0 \le \theta \le 2\pi\}$
b. $R = \{(r, \theta): 0 \le r \le 1, 0 \le \theta \le 2\pi\}$

73. Integrals in strips Consider the integral

$$I = \iint_R \frac{dA}{(1 + x^2 + y^2)^2},$$

where $R = \{(x, y): 0 \le x \le 1, 0 \le y \le a\}$.

a. Evaluate I for $a = 1$. (*Hint:* Use polar coordinates.)
b. Evaluate I for arbitrary $a > 0$.
c. Let $a \to \infty$ in part (b) to find I over the infinite strip $R = \{(x, y): 0 \le x \le 1, 0 \le y < \infty\}$.

T 74. Area of an ellipse In polar coordinates an equation of an ellipse with eccentricity $0 < e < 1$ and semimajor axis a is

$$r = \frac{a(1 - e^2)}{1 + e \cos \theta}.$$

a. Write the integral that gives the area of the ellipse.
b. Show that the area of an ellipse is πab, where $b^2 = a^2(1 - e^2)$.

QUICK CHECK ANSWERS

1. $R = \{(r, \theta): 1 \le r \le 2, 0 \le \theta \le \pi/2\}$
2. $r^5, r^2(\cos^2\theta - \sin^2\theta) = r^2\cos 2\theta$
3. $\int_0^{2\pi}\int_0^a r\, dr\, d\theta = \pi a^2$ ◄

13.4 Triple Integrals

At this point, you may see a pattern that is developing with respect to integration. In Chapter 5, we introduced integrals of single-variable functions. In the first three sections of this chapter, we moved up one dimension to double integrals of two-variable functions. In this section, we take another step and investigate triple integrals of three-variable functions. There is no end to the progression of multiple integrals. It is possible to define integrals with respect to any number of variables. For example, problems in statistics and statistical mechanics involve integration over regions of many dimensions.

Triple Integrals in Rectangular Coordinates

Consider a function $w = f(x, y, z)$ that is defined on a closed and bounded region D of $\mathbb{R}^3$. The graph of f lies in four-dimensional space and is the set of points $(x, y, z, f(x, y, z))$, where (x, y, z) is in D. Despite the difficulty in representing f in $\mathbb{R}^3$, we may still define the integral of f over D. We first create a partition of D by slicing the region with three sets of planes that run parallel to the xz-, yz-, and xy-planes (Figure 13.38). This partition subdivides D into small boxes that are ordered in a convenient way from $k = 1$ to $k = n$. The partition includes all boxes that are wholly contained in D. The kth box has side lengths Δx_k, Δy_k, and Δz_k, and volume $\Delta V_k = \Delta x_k\, \Delta y_k\, \Delta z_k$. We let (x_k^*, y_k^*, z_k^*) be an arbitrary point in the kth box, for $k = 1, \ldots, n$.

A Riemann sum is now formed, in which the kth term is the function value $f(x_k^*, y_k^*, z_k^*)$ multiplied by the volume of the kth box:

$$\sum_{k=1}^{n} f(x_k^*, y_k^*, z_k^*) \Delta V_k.$$

We let Δ denote the maximum length of the diagonals of the boxes. As the number of boxes n increases, while Δ approaches zero, two things happen.

- For commonly encountered regions, the region formed by the collection of boxes approaches the region D.
- If f is continuous, the Riemann sum approaches a limit.

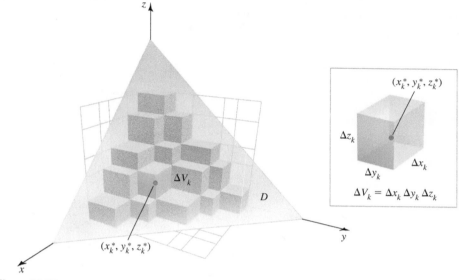

Figure 13.38

The limit of the Riemann sum is the **triple integral of f over D**, and we write

$$\iiint_D f(x, y, z)\, dV = \lim_{\Delta \to 0} \sum_{k=1}^{n} f(x_k^*, y_k^*, z_k^*) \Delta V_k.$$

The kth box in the partition has volume $\Delta V_k = \Delta x_k \Delta y_k \Delta z_k$, where Δx_k, Δy_k, and Δz_k are the side lengths of the box. Accordingly, the *element of volume* in the triple integral, which we denote dV, becomes $dx\, dy\, dz$ (or some rearrangement of dx, dy, and dz) in an iterated integral.

We give two immediate interpretations of a triple integral. First, if $f(x, y, z) = 1$, then the Riemann sum simply adds up the volumes of the boxes in the partition. In the limit as $\Delta \to 0$, the triple integral $\iiint_D dV$ gives the volume of the region D. Second, suppose that D is a solid three-dimensional object and its density varies from point to point according to the function $f(x, y, z)$. The units of density are mass per unit volume, so the product $f(x_k^*, y_k^*, z_k^*) \Delta V_k$ approximates the mass of the kth box in D. Summing the masses of the boxes gives an approximation to the total mass of D. In the limit as $\Delta \to 0$, the triple integral gives the mass of the object.

As with double integrals, a version of Fubini's Theorem expresses a triple integral in terms of an iterated integral in x, y, and z. The situation becomes interesting because with three variables, there are *six* possible orders of integration.

QUICK CHECK 1 List the six orders in which the three differentials dx, dy, and dz may be written. ◄

> ➤ Notice the analogy between double and triple integrals:
>
> $$\text{area}\,(R) = \iint_R dA \quad \text{and}$$
>
> $$\text{volume}\,(D) = \iiint_D dV.$$
>
> The use of triple integrals to compute the mass of an object is discussed in detail in Section 13.6.

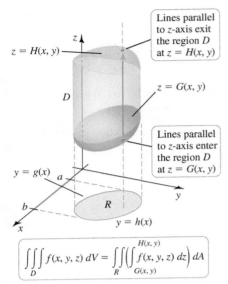

$$\iiint\limits_{D} f(x, y, z)\, dV = \iint\limits_{R}\left(\int\limits_{G(x, y)}^{H(x, y)} f(x, y, z)\, dz\right) dA$$

Figure 13.39

Finding Limits of Integration We discuss one of the six orders of integration in detail; the others are examined in the examples. Suppose a region D in $\mathbb{R}^3$ is bounded above by a surface $z = H(x, y)$ and below by a surface $z = G(x, y)$ (Figure 13.39). These two surfaces determine the limits of integration in the z-direction. The next step is to project the region D onto the xy-plane to form a region that we call R (Figure 13.40). You can think of R as the shadow of D in the xy-plane. At this point, we can begin to write the triple integral as an iterated integral. So far, we have

$$\iiint\limits_{D} f(x, y, z)\, dV = \iint\limits_{R}\left(\int\limits_{G(x, y)}^{H(x, y)} f(x, y, z)\, dz\right) dA.$$

Now assume that R is bounded above and below by the curves $y = h(x)$ and $y = g(x)$, respectively, and bounded on the right and left by the lines $x = a$ and $x = b$, respectively (Figure 13.40). The remaining integration over R is carried out as a double integral (Section 13.2).

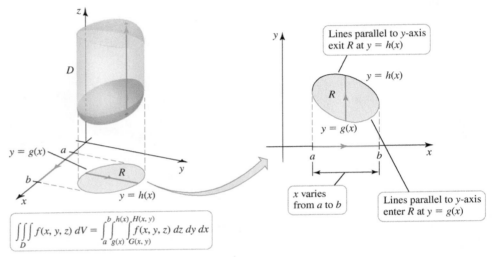

$$\iiint\limits_{D} f(x, y, z)\, dV = \int_{a}^{b}\int_{g(x)}^{h(x)}\int_{G(x, y)}^{H(x, y)} f(x, y, z)\, dz\, dy\, dx$$

Figure 13.40

Table 13.2

Integral	Variable	Interval
Inner	z	$G(x, y) \le z \le H(x, y)$
Middle	y	$g(x) \le y \le h(x)$
Outer	x	$a \le x \le b$

The intervals that describe D are summarized in Table 13.2, which can then be used to formulate the limits of integration. To integrate over all points of D, we carry out the following steps.

1. Integrate with respect to z from $z = G(x, y)$ to $z = H(x, y)$; the result (in general) is a function of x and y.

2. Integrate with respect to y from $y = g(x)$ to $y = h(x)$; the result (in general) is a function of x.

3. Integrate with respect to x from $x = a$ to $x = b$; the result is (always) a real number.

▶ Theorem 13.5 is a version of Fubini's Theorem. Five other versions could be written for the other orders of integration.

THEOREM 13.5   Triple Integrals

Let f be continuous over the region

$$D = \{(x, y, z): a \le x \le b, g(x) \le y \le h(x), G(x, y) \le z \le H(x, y)\},$$

where g, h, G, and H are continuous functions. Then f is integrable over D and the triple integral is evaluated as the iterated integral

$$\iiint\limits_{D} f(x, y, z)\, dV = \int_{a}^{b}\int_{g(x)}^{h(x)}\int_{G(x, y)}^{H(x, y)} f(x, y, z)\, dz\, dy\, dx.$$

We now illustrate this procedure with several examples.

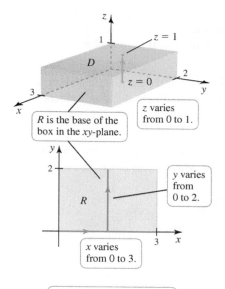

R is the base of the box in the xy-plane.

z varies from 0 to 1.

y varies from 0 to 2.

x varies from 0 to 3.

$$M = \int_0^3\int_0^2\int_0^1 (2-z)\,dz\,dy\,dx$$

Figure 13.41

Table 13.3

Integral	Variable	Interval
Inner	z	$0 \le z \le 1$
Middle	y	$0 \le y \le 2$
Outer	x	$0 \le x \le 3$

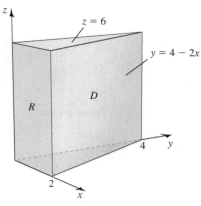

Figure 13.42

EXAMPLE 1 Mass of a box A solid box D is bounded by the planes $x = 0$, $x = 3$, $y = 0$, $y = 2$, $z = 0$, and $z = 1$. The density of the box decreases linearly in the positive z-direction and is given by $f(x, y, z) = 2 - z$. Find the mass of the box.

SOLUTION The mass of the box is found by integrating the density $f(x, y, z) = 2 - z$ over the box. Because the limits of integration for all three variables are constant, the iterated integral may be written in any order. Using the order of integration $dz\,dy\,dx$ (Figure 13.41), the limits of integration are shown in Table 13.3.

The mass of the box is

$$M = \iiint_D (2-z)\,dV$$

$$= \int_0^3\int_0^2\int_0^1 (2-z)\,dz\,dy\,dx \quad \text{Convert to an iterated integral.}$$

$$= \int_0^3\int_0^2 \left(2z - \frac{z^2}{2}\right)\Big|_0^1 dy\,dx \quad \text{Evaluate inner integral with respect to } z.$$

$$= \int_0^3\int_0^2 \frac{3}{2}\,dy\,dx \quad \text{Simplify.}$$

$$= \int_0^3 \left(\frac{3y}{2}\right)\Big|_0^2 dx \quad \text{Evaluate middle integral with respect to } y.$$

$$= \int_0^3 3\,dx = 9. \quad \text{Evaluate outer integral with respect to } x \text{ and simplify.}$$

The result makes sense: The density of the box varies linearly from 1 (at the top of the box) to 2 (at the bottom); if the box had a constant density of 1, its mass would be (volume) · (density) $= 6$; if the box had a constant density of 2, its mass would be 12. The actual mass is the average of 6 and 12, as you might expect.

Any other order of integration produces the same result. For example with the order $dy\,dx\,dz$, the iterated integral is

$$M = \iiint_D (2-z)\,dV = \int_0^1\int_0^3\int_0^2 (2-z)\,dy\,dx\,dz = 9.$$

Related Exercises 7–14 ◄

QUICK CHECK 2 Write the integral in Example 1 in the orders $dx\,dy\,dz$ and $dx\,dz\,dy$. ◄

EXAMPLE 2 Volume of a prism Find the volume of the prism D in the first octant bounded by the planes $y = 4 - 2x$ and $z = 6$ (Figure 13.42).

SOLUTION The prism may be viewed in several different ways. Letting the base of the prism be in the xz-plane, the upper surface of the prism is the plane $y = 4 - 2x$, and the lower surface is $y = 0$. The projection of the prism onto the xz-plane is the rectangle $R = \{(x, z): 0 \le x \le 2, 0 \le z \le 6\}$. One possible order of integration in this case is $dy\,dx\,dz$.

Inner integral with respect to y: A line through the prism parallel to the y-axis enters the prism through the rectangle R at $y = 0$ and exits the prism at the plane $y = 4 - 2x$. Therefore, we first integrate with respect to y over the interval $0 \le y \le 4 - 2x$ (Figure 13.43a).

Middle integral with respect to x: The limits of integration for the middle and outer integrals must cover the region R in the xz-plane. A line parallel to the x-axis enters R at $x = 0$ and exits R at $x = 2$. So we integrate with respect to x over the interval $0 \le x \le 2$ (Figure 13.43b).

Outer integral with respect to z: To cover all of R, the line segments from $x = 0$ to $x = 2$ must run from $z = 0$ to $z = 6$. So we integrate with respect to z over the interval $0 \le z \le 6$ (Figure 13.43b).

Integrating $f(x, y, z) = 1$, the volume of the prism is

$$V = \iiint\limits_{D} dV = \int_0^6 \int_0^2 \int_0^{4-2x} dy\, dx\, dz$$

> The volume of the prism could also be found using geometry: The area of the triangular base in the xy-plane is 4 and the height of the prism is 6. Therefore, the volume is $6 \cdot 4 = 24$.

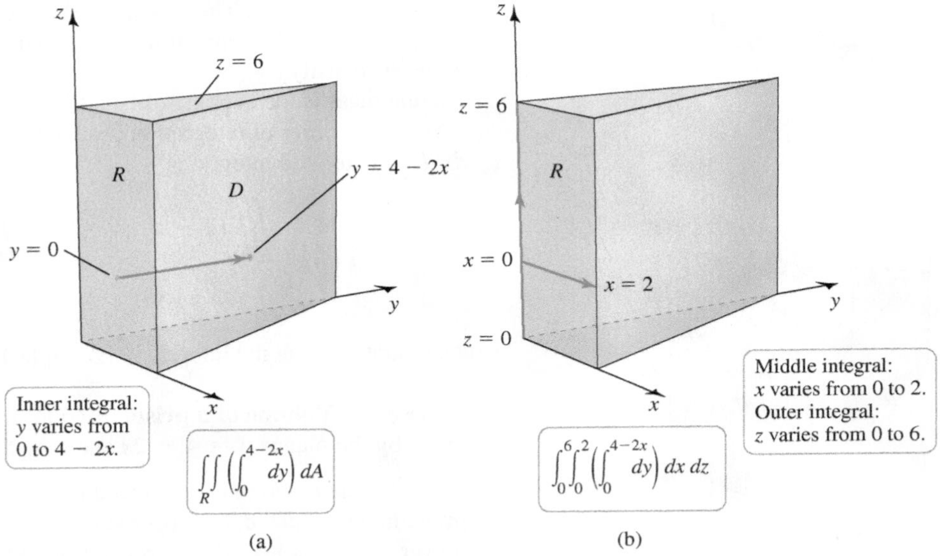

$$= \int_0^6 \int_0^2 (4 - 2x)\, dx\, dz \qquad \text{Evaluate inner integral with respect to } y.$$

$$= \int_0^6 \left(4x - x^2\right)\Big|_0^2 dz \qquad \text{Evaluate middle integral with respect to } x.$$

$$= \int_0^6 4\, dz \qquad \text{Simplify.}$$

$$= 24. \qquad \text{Evaluate outer integral with respect to } z.$$

Inner integral:
y varies from
0 to 4 − 2x.

$$\iint\limits_R \left(\int_0^{4-2x} dy \right) dA$$

(a)

Middle integral:
x varies from 0 to 2.
Outer integral:
z varies from 0 to 6.

$$\int_0^6 \int_0^2 \left(\int_0^{4-2x} dy \right) dx\, dz$$

(b)

Figure 13.43

Related Exercises 15–24 ◄

QUICK CHECK 3 Write the integral in Example 2 in the orders $dz\, dy\, dx$ and $dx\, dy\, dz$. ◄

EXAMPLE 3   A volume integral Find the volume of the region D bounded by the paraboloids $y = x^2 + z^2$ and $y = 16 - 3x^2 - z^2$ (Figure 13.44).

SOLUTION We identify the right boundary of D as the surface $y = 16 - 3x^2 - z^2$; the left boundary is $y = x^2 + z^2$. These surfaces are functions of x and z, so they determine the limits of integration for the inner integral in the y-direction.

A key step in the calculation is finding the curve of intersection between the two surfaces and projecting it onto the xz-plane to form the boundary of the region R. Equating the y-coordinates of the two surfaces, we have $x^2 + z^2 = 16 - 3x^2 - z^2$, which becomes the equation of an ellipse:

$$4x^2 + 2z^2 = 16, \quad \text{or} \quad z = \pm \sqrt{8 - 2x^2}.$$

The projection of the solid region D onto the xz-plane is the region R bounded by this ellipse (centered at the origin with axes of length 4 and $4\sqrt{2}$). Here are the observations that lead to the limits of integration with the ordering $dy\, dz\, dx$.

Inner integral with respect to y: A line through the solid parallel to the y-axis enters the solid at $y = x^2 + z^2$ and exits at $y = 16 - 3x^2 - z^2$. Therefore, for fixed values of x and z, we integrate over the interval $x^2 + z^2 \le y \le 16 - 3x^2 - z^2$ (Figure 13.44a).

Middle integral with respect to z: Now we must cover the region R. A line parallel to the z-axis enters R at $z = -\sqrt{8 - 2x^2}$ and exits R at $z = \sqrt{8 - 2x^2}$. Therefore, for a fixed value of x, we integrate over the interval $-\sqrt{8 - 2x^2} \le z \le \sqrt{8 - 2x^2}$ (Figure 13.44b).

Outer integral with respect to x: To cover all of R, x must run from $x = -2$ to $x = 2$ (Figure 13.44b).

➤ Note that the problem is symmetric about the x- and z-axes. Therefore, the integral over R could be evaluated over one-quarter of R,

$$\{(x, z): 0 \le z \le \sqrt{8 - 2x^2},$$
$$0 \le x \le 2\},$$

in which case the final result must be multiplied by 4.

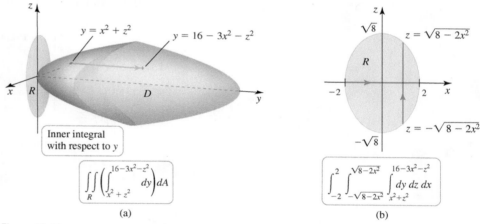

Figure 13.44

Integrating $f(x, y, z) = 1$, the iterated integral for the volume is

$$V = \int_{-2}^{2} \int_{-\sqrt{8 - 2x^2}}^{\sqrt{8 - 2x^2}} \int_{x^2 + z^2}^{16 - 3x^2 - z^2} dy\, dz\, dx$$

$$= \int_{-2}^{2} \int_{-\sqrt{8 - 2x^2}}^{\sqrt{8 - 2x^2}} (16 - 4x^2 - 2z^2)\, dz\, dx \qquad \text{Evaluate inner integral with respect to } y \text{ and simplify.}$$

$$= \int_{-2}^{2} \left(16z - 4x^2 z - \frac{2z^3}{3} \right) \Big|_{-\sqrt{8 - 2x^2}}^{\sqrt{8 - 2x^2}} dx \qquad \text{Evaluate middle integral with respect to } z.$$

$$= \frac{16\sqrt{2}}{3} \int_{-2}^{2} (4 - x^2)^{3/2}\, dx = 32\pi\sqrt{2}. \qquad \text{Evaluate outer integral with respect to } x.$$

The last (outer) integral in this calculation requires the trigonometric substitution $x = 2\sin\theta$.

Related Exercises 25–38 ◄

Changing the Order of Integration

As with double integrals, choosing an appropriate order of integration may simplify the evaluation of a triple integral. Therefore, it is important to become proficient at changing the order of integration.

EXAMPLE 4   Changing the order of integration Consider the integral

$$\int_0^{\sqrt[4]{\pi}} \int_0^z \int_y^z 12y^2 z^3 \sin x^4 \, dx \, dy \, dz.$$

a. Sketch the region of integration D.

b. Evaluate the integral by changing the order of integration.

SOLUTION

a. We begin by finding the projection of the region of integration D on the appropriate coordinate plane; call the projection R. Because the inner integration is with respect to x, R lies in the yz-plane, and it is determined by the limits on the middle and outer integrals. We see that

$$R = \{(y, z) : 0 \le y \le z, 0 \le z \le \sqrt[4]{\pi}\},$$

which is a triangular region in the yz-plane bounded by the z-axis and the lines $y = z$ and $z = \sqrt[4]{\pi}$. Using the limits on the inner integral, for each point in R, we let x vary from the plane $x = y$ to the plane $x = z$. In so doing, the points fill an inverted tetrahedron in the first octant with its vertex at the origin, which is D (Figure 13.45).

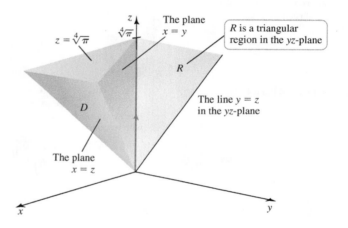

Figure 13.45

▶ How do we know to switch the order of integration so the inner integral is with respect to y? Often we do not know in advance whether a new order of integration will work, and some trial and error is needed. In this case, either y^2 or z^3 is easier to integrate than $\sin x^4$, so either y or z is a likely variable for the inner integral.

b. It is difficult to evaluate the integral in the given order ($dx \, dy \, dz$) because the antiderivative of $\sin x^4$ is not expressible in terms of elementary functions. If we integrate first with respect to y, we introduce a factor in the integrand that enables us to use a substitution to integrate $\sin x^4$. With the order of integration $dy \, dx \, dz$, the bounds of integration for the inner integral extend from the plane $y = 0$ to the plane $y = x$ (Figure 13.46a). Furthermore, the projection of D onto the xz-plane is the region R, which must be covered by the middle and outer integrals (Figure 13.46b). In this case, we draw a line segment parallel to the x-axis to see that the limits of the middle integral run from $x = 0$ to $x = z$. Then we include all these segments from $z = 0$

to $z = \sqrt[4]{\pi}$ to obtain the outer limits of integration in z. The integration proceeds as follows:

$$\int_0^{\sqrt[4]{\pi}} \int_0^z \int_0^x 12y^2z^3 \sin x^4 \, dy \, dx \, dz = \int_0^{\sqrt[4]{\pi}} \int_0^z (4y^3z^3 \sin x^4)\Big|_0^x \, dx \, dz \qquad \begin{array}{l}\text{Evaluate inner}\\ \text{integral with}\\ \text{respect to } y.\end{array}$$

$$= \int_0^{\sqrt[4]{\pi}} \int_0^z 4x^3z^3 \sin x^4 \, dx \, dz \qquad \text{Simplify.}$$

$$= \int_0^{\sqrt[4]{\pi}} z^3(-\cos x^4)\Big|_0^z \, dz \qquad \begin{array}{l}\text{Evaluate middle}\\ \text{integral with res-}\\ \text{pect to } x; u = x^4.\end{array}$$

$$= \int_0^{\sqrt[4]{\pi}} z^3(1 - \cos z^4) \, dz \qquad \text{Simplify.}$$

$$= \left(\frac{z^4}{4} - \frac{\sin z^4}{4}\right)\Big|_0^{\sqrt[4]{\pi}} \qquad \begin{array}{l}\text{Evaluate outer}\\ \text{integral with res-}\\ \text{pect to } z; u = z^4.\end{array}$$

$$= \frac{\pi}{4}. \qquad \text{Simplify.}$$

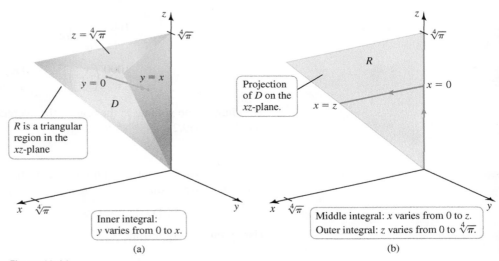

Figure 13.46

Related Exercises 39–42 ◀

Average Value of a Function of Three Variables

The idea of the average value of a function extends naturally from the one- and two-variable cases. The average value of a function of three variables is found by integrating the function over the region of interest and dividing by the volume of the region.

> **DEFINITION Average Value of a Function of Three Variables**
>
> If f is continuous on a region D of $\mathbb{R}^3$, then the average value of f over D is
>
> $$\bar{f} = \frac{1}{\text{volume }(D)} \iiint_D f(x, y, z) \, dV.$$

EXAMPLE 5   Average temperature Consider a block of a conducting material occupying the region

$$D = \{(x, y, z): 0 \le x \le 2, 0 \le y \le 2, 0 \le z \le 1\}.$$

Due to heat sources on its boundaries, the temperature in the block is given by $T(x, y, z) = 250xy \sin \pi z$. Find the average temperature of the block.

SOLUTION We must integrate the temperature function over the block and divide by the volume of the block, which is 4. One way to evaluate the temperature integral is as follows:

$$\iiint_D 250xy \sin \pi z \, dV = 250 \int_0^2 \int_0^2 \int_0^1 xy \sin \pi z \, dz \, dy \, dx \qquad \text{Convert to an iterated integral.}$$

$$= 250 \int_0^2 \int_0^2 xy \frac{1}{\pi} (-\cos \pi z) \Big|_0^1 dy \, dx \qquad \begin{array}{l}\text{Evaluate inner integral with} \\ \text{respect to } z.\end{array}$$

$$= \frac{500}{\pi} \int_0^2 \int_0^2 xy \, dy \, dx \qquad \text{Simplify.}$$

$$= \frac{500}{\pi} \int_0^2 x \left(\frac{y^2}{2}\right)\Big|_0^2 dx \qquad \begin{array}{l}\text{Evaluate middle integral with} \\ \text{respect to } y.\end{array}$$

$$= \frac{1000}{\pi} \int_0^2 x \, dx \qquad \text{Simplify.}$$

$$= \frac{1000}{\pi} \left(\frac{x^2}{2}\right)\Big|_0^2 = \frac{2000}{\pi}. \qquad \begin{array}{l}\text{Evaluate outer integral with} \\ \text{respect to } x.\end{array}$$

Dividing by the volume of the region, the average temperature is $(2000/\pi)/4 = 500/\pi \approx 159.2$.

Related Exercises 43–48 ◄

QUICK CHECK 4 Without integrating, what is the average value of $f(x, y, z) = \sin x \sin y \sin z$ on the cube

$$\{(x, y, z): -1 \le x \le 1, -1 \le y \le 1, -1 \le z \le 1\}?$$

Use symmetry arguments. ◄

SECTION 13.4 EXERCISES

Review Questions

1. Sketch the region $D = \{(x, y, z): x^2 + y^2 \le 4, 0 \le z \le 4\}$.

2. Write an iterated integral for $\iiint_D f(x, y, z) \, dV$, where D is the box $\{(x, y, z): 0 \le x \le 3, 0 \le y \le 6, 0 \le z \le 4\}$.

3. Write an iterated integral for $\iiint_D f(x, y, z) \, dV$, where D is a sphere of radius 9 centered at $(0, 0, 0)$. Use the order $dz \, dy \, dx$.

4. Sketch the region of integration for the integral

$$\int_0^1 \int_0^{\sqrt{1-z^2}} \int_0^{\sqrt{1-y^2-z^2}} f(x, y, z) \, dx \, dy \, dz.$$

5. Write the integral in Exercise 4 in the order $dy \, dx \, dz$.

6. Write an integral for the average value of $f(x, y, z) = xyz$ over the region bounded by the paraboloid $z = 9 - x^2 - y^2$ and the xy-plane (assuming the volume of the region is known).

Basic Skills

7–14. Integrals over boxes *Evaluate the following integrals. A sketch of the region of integration may be useful.*

7. $\int_{-2}^2 \int_3^6 \int_0^2 dx \, dy \, dz$

8. $\int_{-1}^1 \int_{-1}^2 \int_0^1 6xyz \, dy \, dx \, dz$

9. $\int_{-2}^2 \int_1^2 \int_1^e \frac{xy^2}{z} \, dz \, dx \, dy$

10. $\int_0^{\ln 4} \int_0^{\ln 3} \int_0^{\ln 2} e^{-x+y+z} \, dx \, dy \, dz$

11. $\displaystyle\int_0^{\pi/2}\int_0^1\int_0^{\pi/2} \sin \pi x \cos y \sin 2z\, dy\, dx\, dz$

12. $\displaystyle\int_0^2\int_1^2\int_0^1 yze^x\, dx\, dz\, dy$

13. $\displaystyle\iiint_D (xy + xz + yz)\, dV;\ D = \{(x, y, z): -1 \le x \le 1,$
$-2 \le y \le 2, -3 \le z \le 3\}$

14. $\displaystyle\iiint_D xyze^{-x^2-y^2}\, dV;\ D = \{(x, y, z): 0 \le x \le \sqrt{\ln 2},$
$0 \le y \le \sqrt{\ln 4}, 0 \le z \le 1\}$

15–24. Volumes of solids *Find the volume of the following solids using triple integrals.*

15. The solid in the first octant bounded by the plane $2x + 3y + 6z = 12$ and the coordinate planes

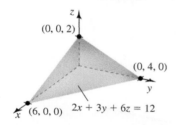

16. The solid in the first octant formed when the cylinder $z = \sin y$, for $0 \le y \le \pi$, is sliced by the planes $y = x$ and $x = 0$

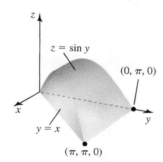

17. The solid bounded below by the cone $z = \sqrt{x^2 + y^2}$ and bounded above by the sphere $x^2 + y^2 + z^2 = 8$

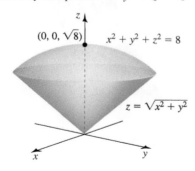

18. The prism in the first octant bounded by $z = 2 - 4x$ and $y = 8$

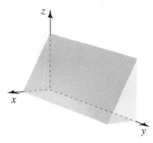

19. The wedge above the xy-plane formed when the cylinder $x^2 + y^2 = 4$ is cut by the planes $z = 0$ and $y = -z$

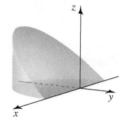

20. The wedge bounded by the parabolic cylinder $y = x^2$ and the planes $z = 3 - y$ and $z = 0$

21. The solid between the sphere $x^2 + y^2 + z^2 = 19$ and the hyperboloid $z^2 - x^2 - y^2 = 1$, for $z > 0$

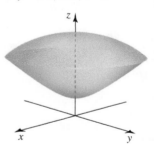

22. The solid bounded by the surfaces $z = e^y$ and $z = 1$ over the rectangle $\{(x, y): 0 \le x \le 1, 0 \le y \le \ln 2\}$

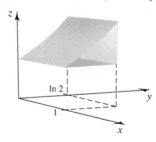

23. The wedge of the cylinder $x^2 + 4y^2 = 4$ created by the planes $z = 3 - x$ and $z = x - 3$

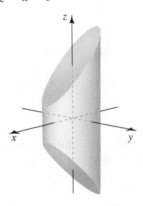

24. The solid in the first octant bounded by the cone $z = 1 - \sqrt{x^2 + y^2}$ and the plane $x + y + z = 1$

25–34. Triple integrals *Evaluate the following integrals.*

25. $\displaystyle\int_0^1 \int_0^{\sqrt{1-x^2}} \int_0^{\sqrt{1-x^2}} dz\, dy\, dx$

26. $\displaystyle\int_0^1 \int_0^{\sqrt{1-x^2}} \int_0^{\sqrt{1-x^2-y^2}} 2xz\, dz\, dy\, dx$

27. $\displaystyle\int_0^4 \int_{-2\sqrt{16-y^2}}^{2\sqrt{16-y^2}} \int_0^{16-x^2/4-y^2} dz\, dx\, dy$

28. $\displaystyle\int_1^6 \int_0^{4-2y/3} \int_0^{12-2y-3z} \frac{1}{y}\, dx\, dz\, dy$

29. $\displaystyle\int_0^3 \int_0^{\sqrt{9-z^2}} \int_0^{\sqrt{1+x^2+z^2}} dy\, dx\, dz$

30. $\displaystyle\int_0^\pi \int_0^\pi \int_0^{\sin x} \sin y\, dz\, dx\, dy$

31. $\displaystyle\int_1^{\ln 8} \int_1^{\sqrt{z}} \int_{\ln y}^{\ln 2y} e^{x+y^2-z}\, dx\, dy\, dz$

32. $\displaystyle\int_0^1 \int_0^{\sqrt{1-x^2}} \int_0^{2-x} 4yz\, dz\, dy\, dx$

33. $\displaystyle\int_0^2 \int_0^4 \int_{y^2}^4 \sqrt{x}\, dz\, dx\, dy$

34. $\displaystyle\int_0^1 \int_y^{2-y} \int_0^{2-x-y} xy\, dz\, dx\, dy$

35–38. Finding an appropriate order of integration *Find the volume of the following solids.*

35. The solid bounded by $x = 0, x = 1 - z^2, y = 0, z = 0$, and $z = 1 - y$

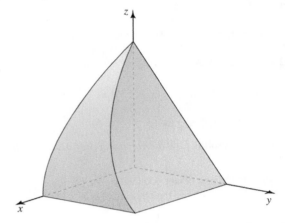

36. The solid bounded by $x = 0, x = 2, y = 0, y = e^{-z}, z = 0$, and $z = 1$

37. The solid bounded by $x = 0, x = 2, y = z, y = z + 1, z = 0$, and $z = 4$

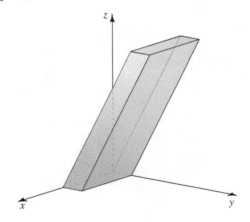

38. The solid bounded by $x = 0$, $y = z^2$, $z = 0$, and $z = 2 - x - y$

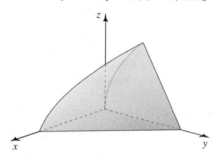

39–42. Changing the order of integration *Rewrite the following integrals using the indicated order of integration and then evaluate the resulting integral.*

39. $\displaystyle\int_0^5 \int_{-1}^0 \int_0^{4x+4} dy\, dx\, dz$ in the order $dz\, dx\, dy$

40. $\displaystyle\int_0^1 \int_{-2}^2 \int_0^{\sqrt{4-y^2}} dz\, dy\, dx$ in the order $dy\, dz\, dx$

41. $\displaystyle\int_0^1 \int_0^{\sqrt{1-x^2}} \int_0^{\sqrt{1-x^2}} dy\, dz\, dx$ in the order $dz\, dy\, dx$

42. $\displaystyle\int_0^4 \int_0^{\sqrt{16-x^2}} \int_0^{\sqrt{16-x^2-z^2}} dy\, dz\, dx$ in the order $dx\, dy\, dz$

43–48. Average value *Find the following average values.*

43. The average temperature in the box $D = \{(x, y, z): 0 \le x \le \ln 2, 0 \le y \le \ln 4, 0 \le z \le \ln 8\}$ with a temperature distribution of $T(x, y, z) = 128\, e^{-x-y-z}$

44. The average value of $f(x, y, z) = 6xyz$ over the points inside the hemisphere of radius 4 centered at the origin with its base in the xy-plane

45. The average of the *squared* distance between the origin and points in the solid cylinder $D = \{(x, y, z): x^2 + y^2 \le 4, 0 \le z \le 2\}$

46. The average of the *squared* distance between the origin and points in the solid paraboloid $D = \{(x, y, z): 0 \le z \le 4 - x^2 - y^2\}$

47. The average z-coordinate of points on and within a hemisphere of radius 4 centered at the origin with its base in the xy-plane

48. The average of the *squared* distance between the z-axis and points in the conical solid $D = \{(x, y, z): 2\sqrt{x^2 + y^2} \le z \le 8\}$

Further Explorations

49. Explain why or why not Determine whether the following statements are true and give an explanation or counterexample.

  a. An iterated integral of a function over the box $D = \{(x, y, z): 0 \le x \le a, 0 \le y \le b, 0 \le z \le c\}$ can be expressed in eight different ways.

  b. One possible iterated integral of f over the prism $D = \{(x, y, z): 0 \le x \le 1, 0 \le y \le 3x - 3, 0 \le z \le 5\}$ is $\int_0^{3x-3} \int_0^1 \int_0^5 f(x, y, z)\, dz\, dx\, dy$.

c. The region $D = \{(x, y, z): 0 \le x \le 1, 0 \le y \le \sqrt{1 - x^2}, 0 \le z \le \sqrt{1 - x^2}\}$ is a sphere.

50. Changing the order of integration Use another order of integration to evaluate $\displaystyle\int_1^4 \int_z^{4z} \int_0^{\pi^2} \frac{\sin\sqrt{yz}}{x^{3/2}}\, dy\, dx\, dz$.

51–55. Miscellaneous volumes *Use a triple integral to compute the volume of the following regions.*

51. The parallelepiped (slanted box) with vertices $(0, 0, 0)$, $(1, 0, 0)$, $(0, 1, 0)$, $(1, 1, 0)$, $(0, 1, 1)$, $(1, 1, 1)$, $(0, 2, 1)$, and $(1, 2, 1)$. (Use integration and find the best order of integration.)

52. The larger of two solids formed when the parallelepiped (slanted box) with vertices $(0, 0, 0)$, $(2, 0, 0)$, $(0, 2, 0)$, $(2, 2, 0)$, $(0, 1, 1)$, $(2, 1, 1)$, $(0, 3, 1)$, and $(2, 3, 1)$ is sliced by the plane $y = 2$.

53. The pyramid with vertices $(0, 0, 0)$, $(2, 0, 0)$, $(2, 2, 0)$, $(0, 2, 0)$, and $(0, 0, 4)$

54. The solid common to the cylinders $z = \sin x$ and $z = \sin y$ over the square $R = \{(x, y): 0 \le x \le \pi, 0 \le y \le \pi\}$ (The figure shows the cylinders, but not the common region.)

55. The wedge of the square column $|x| + |y| = 1$ created by the planes $z = 0$ and $x + y + z = 1$

56. Partitioning a cube Consider the region $D_1 = \{(x, y, z): 0 \le x \le y \le z \le 1\}$.

  a. Find the volume of D_1.

  b. Let $D_2, \ldots, D_6$ be the "cousins" of D_1 formed by rearranging x, y, and z in the inequality $0 \le x \le y \le z \le 1$. Show that the volumes of $D_1, \ldots, D_6$ are equal.

  c. Show that the union of $D_1, \ldots, D_6$ is a unit cube.

57. Changing order of integration Write the integral $\displaystyle\int_0^2 \int_0^1 \int_0^{1-y} dz\, dy\, dx$ in the five other possible orders of integration.

58. All six orders Let D be the solid bounded by $y = x$, $z = 1 - y^2$, $x = 0$, and $z = 0$. Write triple integrals over D in all six possible orders of integration.

Applications

59. Comparing two masses Two different tetrahedrons fill the region in the first octant bounded by the coordinate planes and the plane $x + y + z = 4$. Both solids have densities that vary in the z-direction between $\rho = 4$ and $\rho = 8$, according to the functions $\rho_1 = 8 - z$ and $\rho_2 = 4 + z$. Find the mass of each solid.

60. Dividing the cheese Suppose a wedge of cheese fills the region in the first octant bounded by the planes $y = z$, $y = 4$, and $x = 4$. You could divide the wedge into two pieces of equal volume by slicing the wedge with the plane $x = 2$. Instead find a with $0 < a < 4$ such that slicing the wedge with the plane $y = a$ divides the wedge into two pieces of equal volume.

61–65. General volume formulas *Find equations for the bounding surfaces, set up a volume integral, and evaluate the integral to obtain a volume formula for each region. Assume that a, b, c, r, R, and h are positive constants.*

61. Cone Find the volume of a right circular cone with height h and base radius r.

62. Tetrahedron Find the volume of a tetrahedron whose vertices are located at $(0, 0, 0)$, $(a, 0, 0)$, $(0, b, 0)$, and $(0, 0, c)$.

63. Spherical cap Find the volume of the cap of a sphere of radius R with height h.

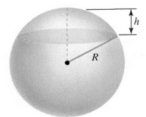

64. Frustum of a cone Find the volume of a truncated cone of height h whose ends have radii r and R.

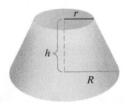

65. Ellipsoid Find the volume of an ellipsoid with axes of length $2a$, $2b$, and $2c$.

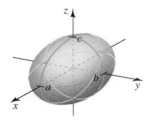

66. Exponential distribution The occurrence of random events (such as phone calls or e-mail messages) is often idealized using an exponential distribution. If λ is the average rate of occurrence of such an event, assumed to be constant over time, then the average time between occurrences is λ^{-1} (for example, if phone calls arrive at a rate of $\lambda = 2/\text{min}$, then the mean time between phone calls is $\lambda^{-1} = \frac{1}{2}$ min). The exponential distribution is given by $f(t) = \lambda e^{-\lambda t}$, for $0 \le t < \infty$.

a. Suppose you work at a customer service desk and phone calls arrive at an average rate of $\lambda_1 = 0.8/\text{min}$ (meaning the average time between phone calls is $1/0.8 = 1.25$ min). The probability that a phone call arrives during the interval $[0, T]$ is $p(T) = \int_0^T \lambda_1 e^{-\lambda_1 t}\, dt$. Find the probability that a phone call arrives during the first 45 s (0.75 min) that you work at the desk.

b. Now suppose that walk-in customers also arrive at your desk at an average rate of $\lambda_2 = 0.1/\text{min}$. The probability that a phone call *and* a customer arrive during the interval $[0, T]$ is

$$p(T) = \int_0^T \int_0^T \lambda_1 e^{-\lambda_1 t} \lambda_2 e^{-\lambda_2 s}\, dt\, ds.$$

Find the probability that a phone call and a customer arrive during the first 45 s that you work at the desk.

c. E-mail messages also arrive at your desk at an average rate of $\lambda_3 = 0.05/\text{min}$. The probability that a phone call *and* a customer *and* an e-mail message arrive during the interval $[0, T]$ is

$$p(T) = \int_0^T \int_0^T \int_0^T \lambda_1 e^{-\lambda_1 t} \lambda_2 e^{-\lambda_2 s} \lambda_3 e^{-\lambda_3 u}\, dt\, ds\, du.$$

Find the probability that a phone call and a customer and an e-mail message arrive during the first 45 s that you work at the desk.

Additional Exercises

67. Hypervolume Find the "volume" of the four-dimensional pyramid bounded by $w + x + y + z + 1 = 0$ and the coordinate planes $w = 0$, $x = 0$, $y = 0$, and $z = 0$.

68. An identity (Putnam Exam 1941) Let f be a continuous function on $[0, 1]$. Prove that

$$\int_0^1 \int_x^1 \int_x^y f(x)f(y)f(z)\, dz\, dy\, dx = \frac{1}{6}\left(\int_0^1 f(x)\, dx\right)^3.$$

QUICK CHECK ANSWERS

1. $dx\, dy\, dz$, $dx\, dz\, dy$, $dy\, dx\, dz$, $dy\, dz\, dx$, $dz\, dx\, dy$, $dz\, dy\, dx$

2. $\displaystyle\int_0^1 \int_0^2 \int_0^3 (2 - z)\, dx\, dy\, dz$, $\displaystyle\int_0^2 \int_0^1 \int_0^3 (2 - z)\, dx\, dz\, dy$

3. $\displaystyle\int_0^2 \int_0^{4-2x} \int_0^6 dz\, dy\, dx$, $\displaystyle\int_0^6 \int_0^4 \int_0^{2-y/2} dx\, dy\, dz$

4. 0 ($\sin x$, $\sin y$, and $\sin z$ are odd functions.)◄

13.5 Triple Integrals in Cylindrical and Spherical Coordinates

When evaluating triple integrals, you may have noticed that some regions (such as spheres, cones, and cylinders) have awkward descriptions in Cartesian coordinates. In this section, we examine two other coordinate systems in $\mathbb{R}^3$ that are easier to use when working with certain types of regions. These coordinate systems are helpful not only for integration, but also for general problem solving.

Cylindrical Coordinates

When we extend polar coordinates from $\mathbb{R}^2$ to $\mathbb{R}^3$, the result is *cylindrical coordinates*. In this coordinate system, a point P in $\mathbb{R}^3$ has coordinates (r, θ, z), where r and θ are polar coordinates for the point P^*, which is the projection of P onto the xy-plane (Figure 13.47). As in Cartesian coordinates, the z-coordinate is the signed vertical distance between P and the xy-plane. Any point in $\mathbb{R}^3$ can be represented by cylindrical coordinates using the intervals $0 \leq r < \infty$, $0 \leq \theta \leq 2\pi$, and $-\infty < z < \infty$.

Many sets of points have simple representations in cylindrical coordinates. For example, the set $\{(r, \theta, z): r = a\}$ is the set of points whose distance from the z-axis is a, which is a right circular cylinder of radius a. The set $\{(r, \theta, z): \theta = \theta_0\}$ is the set of points with a constant θ coordinate; it is a vertical half plane emanating from the z-axis in the direction $\theta = \theta_0$. Table 13.4 summarizes these and other sets that are ideal for integration in cylindrical coordinates.

> ➤ In cylindrical coordinates, r and θ are the usual polar coordinates, with the additional restriction that $r \geq 0$. Adding the z-coordinate lifts points in the polar plane into $\mathbb{R}^3$.

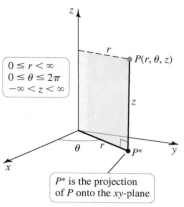

$0 \leq r < \infty$
$0 \leq \theta \leq 2\pi$
$-\infty < z < \infty$

P^* is the projection of P onto the xy-plane

Figure 13.47

Table 13.4

Name	Description	Example
Cylinder	$\{(r, \theta, z): r = a\}, a > 0$	
Cylindrical shell	$\{(r, \theta, z): 0 < a \leq r \leq b\}$	
Vertical half plane	$\{(r, \theta, z): \theta = \theta_0\}$	

(Continued)

Table 13.4   (Continued)

Name	Description	Example
Horizontal plane	$\{(r, \theta, z): z = a\}$	
Cone	$\{(r, \theta, z): z = ar\}, a \neq 0$	

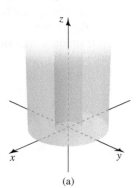

(a)

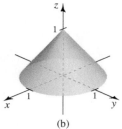

(b)

Figure 13.48

EXAMPLE 1   Sets in cylindrical coordinates Identify and sketch the following sets in cylindrical coordinates.

a. $Q = \{(r, \theta, z): 1 \leq r \leq 3, z \geq 0\}$
b. $S = \{(r, \theta, z): z = 1 - r, 0 \leq r \leq 1\}$

SOLUTION

a. The set Q is a cylindrical shell with inner radius 1 and outer radius 3 that extends indefinitely along the positive z-axis (Figure 13.48a). Because θ is unspecified, it takes on all values.

b. To identify this surface, it helps to work in steps. The set $S_1 = \{(r, \theta, z): z = r\}$ is a cone that opens *upward* with its vertex at the origin. Similarly, the set $S_2 = \{(r, \theta, z): z = -r\}$ is a cone that opens *downward* with its vertex at the origin. Therefore, S is S_2 shifted vertically upward by 1 unit; it is a cone that opens downward with its vertex at $(0, 0, 1)$. Because $0 \leq r \leq 1$, the base of the cone is on the xy-plane (Figure 13.48b).

Related Exercises 11–14 ◄

Equations for transforming Cartesian coordinates to cylindrical coordinates, and vice versa, are often needed for integration. We simply use the rules for polar coordinates (Section 10.2) with no change in the z-coordinate (Figure 13.49).

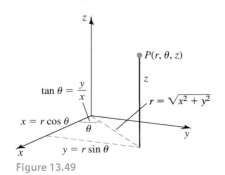

Figure 13.49

Transformations Between Cylindrical and Rectangular Coordinates

Rectangular → Cylindrical	**Cylindrical → Rectangular**
$r^2 = x^2 + y^2$	$x = r\cos\theta$
$\tan\theta = y/x$	$y = r\sin\theta$
$z = z$	$z = z$

QUICK CHECK 1 Find the cylindrical coordinates of the point with rectangular coordinates $(1, -1, 5)$. Find the rectangular coordinates of the point with cylindrical coordinates $(2, \pi/3, 5)$. ◄

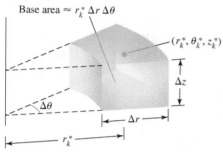

Base area $\approx r_k^* \, \Delta r \, \Delta \theta$

Approximate volume $\Delta V_k \approx r_k^* \, \Delta r \, \Delta \theta \, \Delta z$

Figure 13.50

Integration in Cylindrical Coordinates

Among the uses of cylindrical coordinates is the evaluation of triple integrals. We begin with a region D in $\mathbb{R}^3$ and partition it into cylindrical wedges formed by changes of Δr, $\Delta \theta$, and Δz in the coordinate directions (Figure 13.50). Those wedges that lie entirely within D are labeled from $k = 1$ to $k = n$ in some convenient order. We let $(r_k^*, \theta_k^*, z_k^*)$ be an arbitrary point in the kth wedge.

As shown in Figure 13.50, the base of the kth wedge is a polar rectangle with an approximate area of $r_k^* \, \Delta r \, \Delta \theta$ (Section 13.3). The height of the wedge is Δz. Multiplying these dimensions together, the approximate volume of the wedge is $\Delta V_k = r_k^* \Delta r \, \Delta \theta \, \Delta z$, for $k = 1, \ldots, n$.

We now assume that f is continuous on D and form a Riemann sum over the region by adding function values multiplied by the corresponding approximate volumes:

$$\sum_{k=1}^{n} f(r_k^*, \theta_k^*, z_k^*) \Delta V_k = \sum_{k=1}^{n} f(r_k^*, \theta_k^*, z_k^*) \, r_k^* \Delta r \, \Delta \theta \, \Delta z.$$

Let Δ be the maximum value of Δr, $\Delta \theta$, and Δz, for $k = 1, 2, \ldots, n$. As $n \to \infty$ and $\Delta \to 0$, the Riemann sums approach a limit called the **triple integral of f over D in cylindrical coordinates**:

$$\iiint_D f(r, \theta, z) \, dV = \lim_{\Delta \to 0} \sum_{k=1}^{n} f(r_k^*, \theta_k^*, z_k^*) \, r_k^* \Delta r \, \Delta \theta \, \Delta z.$$

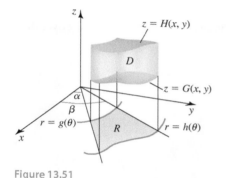

Figure 13.51

Finding Limits of Integration We show how to find the limits of integration in one common situation involving cylindrical coordinates. Suppose D is a region in $\mathbb{R}^3$ consisting of points between the surfaces $z = G(x, y)$ and $z = H(x, y)$, where x and y belong to a region R in the xy-plane and $G(x, y) \leq H(x, y)$ on R (Figure 13.51). Assuming f is continuous on D, the triple integral of f over D may be expressed as the iterated integral

$$\iiint_D f(x, y, z) \, dV = \iint_R \left(\int_{G(x,y)}^{H(x,y)} f(x, y, z) \, dz \right) dA.$$

The inner integral with respect to z runs from the lower surface $z = G(x, y)$ to the upper surface $z = H(x, y)$, leaving an outer double integral over R.

If the region R is described in polar coordinates by

$$\{(r, \theta): g(\theta) \leq r \leq h(\theta), \alpha \leq \theta \leq \beta\},$$

then it makes sense to evaluate the double integral over R in polar coordinates (Section 13.3). The effect is a change of variables from rectangular to cylindrical coordinates. Letting $x = r \cos \theta$ and $y = r \sin \theta$, we have the following result, which is another version of Fubini's Theorem.

▶ The order of the differentials specifies the order in which the integrals are evaluated, so we write the volume element dV as $dz \, r \, dr \, d\theta$. Do not lose sight of the factor of r in the integrand! It plays the same role as it does in the area element $dA = r \, dr \, d\theta$ in polar coordinates.

THEOREM 13.6 Triple Integrals in Cylindrical Coordinates

Let f be continuous over the region

$$D = \{(r, \theta, z): 0 \leq g(\theta) \leq r \leq h(\theta), \alpha \leq \theta \leq \beta, G(x, y) \leq z \leq H(x, y)\}.$$

Then f is integrable over D, and the triple integral of f over D in cylindrical coordinates is

$$\iiint_D f(x, y, z) \, dV = \int_\alpha^\beta \int_{g(\theta)}^{h(\theta)} \int_{G(r \cos \theta, \, r \sin \theta)}^{H(r \cos \theta, \, r \sin \theta)} f(r \cos \theta, r \sin \theta, z) \, dz \, r \, dr \, d\theta.$$

Notice that the integrand and the limits of integration are converted from Cartesian to cylindrical coordinates. As with triple integrals in Cartesian coordinates, there are two immediate interpretations of this integral. If $f = 1$, then the triple integral $\iiint_D dV$ equals the volume of the region D. Also, if f describes the density of an object occupying the region D, the triple integral equals the mass of the object.

EXAMPLE 2   **Switching coordinate systems**   Evaluate the integral

$$I = \int_0^{2\sqrt{2}} \int_{-\sqrt{8-x^2}}^{\sqrt{8-x^2}} \int_{-1}^{2} \sqrt{1 + x^2 + y^2} \, dz \, dy \, dx.$$

SOLUTION   Evaluating this integral as it is given in Cartesian coordinates requires a tricky trigonometric substitution in the middle integral, followed by an even more difficult integral. Notice that z varies between the planes $z = -1$ and $z = 2$, while x and y vary over half of a disk in the xy-plane. Therefore, D is half of a solid cylinder (Figure 13.52a), which suggests a change to cylindrical coordinates.

The limits of integration in cylindrical coordinates are determined as follows:

Inner integral with respect to z A line through the half cylinder parallel to the z-axis enters at $z = -1$ and leaves at $z = 2$, so we integrate over the interval $-1 \le z \le 2$ (Figure 13.52b).

Middle integral with respect to r The projection of the half cylinder onto the xy-plane is the half disk R of radius $2\sqrt{2}$ centered at the origin, so r varies over the interval $0 \le r \le 2\sqrt{2}$.

Outer integral with respect to θ The half disk R is swept out by letting θ vary over the interval $-\pi/2 \le \theta \le \pi/2$ (Figure 13.52c).

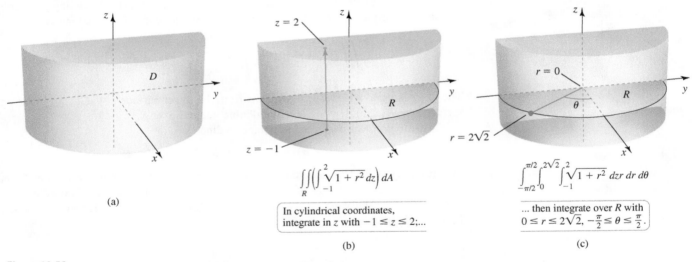

$$\iint_R \left(\int_{-1}^{2} \sqrt{1 + r^2} \, dz \right) dA$$

In cylindrical coordinates, integrate in z with $-1 \le z \le 2$;...

$$\int_{-\pi/2}^{\pi/2} \int_0^{2\sqrt{2}} \int_{-1}^{2} \sqrt{1 + r^2} \, dz \, r \, dr \, d\theta$$

... then integrate over R with $0 \le r \le 2\sqrt{2}$, $-\frac{\pi}{2} \le \theta \le \frac{\pi}{2}$.

(a)   (b)   (c)

Figure 13.52

We also convert the integrand to cylindrical coordinates:

$$f(x, y, z) = \sqrt{1 + \underbrace{x^2 + y^2}_{r^2}} = \sqrt{1 + r^2}.$$

The evaluation of the integral in cylindrical coordinates now follows:

$$I = \int_{-\pi/2}^{\pi/2} \int_0^{2\sqrt{2}} \int_{-1}^2 \sqrt{1 + r^2} \, dz \, r \, dr \, d\theta \qquad \text{Convert to cylindrical coordinates.}$$

$$= 3 \int_{-\pi/2}^{\pi/2} \int_0^{2\sqrt{2}} \sqrt{1 + r^2} \, r \, dr \, d\theta \qquad \text{Evaluate inner integral with respect to } z.$$

$$= \int_{-\pi/2}^{\pi/2} (1 + r^2)^{3/2} \Big|_0^{2\sqrt{2}} \, d\theta \qquad \text{Evaluate middle integral with respect to } r.$$

$$= \int_{-\pi/2}^{\pi/2} 26 \, d\theta = 26\pi. \qquad \text{Evaluate outer integral with respect to } \theta.$$

QUICK CHECK 2 Find the limits of integration for a triple integral in cylindrical coordinates that gives the volume of a cylinder with height 20 and a circular base centered at the origin in the xy-plane of radius 10. ◄

Related Exercises 15–22 ◄

As illustrated in Example 2, triple integrals given in rectangular coordinates may be more easily evaluated after converting to cylindrical coordinates. The following questions may help you choose the best coordinate system for a particular integral.

• In which coordinate system is the region of integration most easily described?
• In which coordinate system is the integrand most easily expressed?
• In which coordinate system is the triple integral most easily evaluated?

In general, if an integral in one coordinate system is difficult to evaluate, consider using a different coordinate system.

EXAMPLE 3 **Mass of a solid paraboloid** Find the mass of the solid D bounded by the paraboloid $z = 4 - r^2$ and the plane $z = 0$ (Figure 13.53a), where the density of the solid is $f(r, \theta, z) = 5 - z$ (heavy near the base and light near the vertex).

SOLUTION The z-coordinate runs from the base ($z = 0$) to the surface $z = 4 - r^2$ (Figure 13.53b). The projection R of the region D onto the xy-plane is found by setting $z = 0$ in the equation of the surface, $z = 4 - r^2$. The positive value of r satisfying the equation $4 - r^2 = 0$ is $r = 2$, so $R = \{(r, \theta): 0 \le r \le 2, 0 \le \theta \le 2\pi\}$, which is a disk of radius 2 (Figure 13.53c).

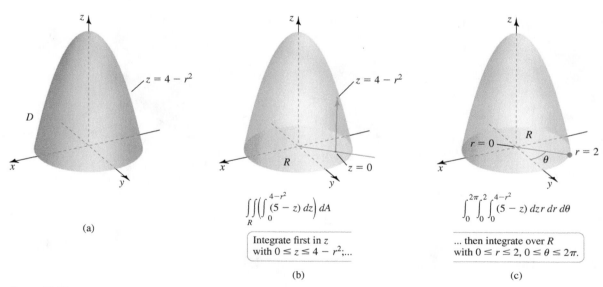

(a)

$$\iint_R \left(\int_0^{4-r^2} (5 - z) \, dz \right) dA$$

Integrate first in z
with $0 \le z \le 4 - r^2;...$

(b)

$$\int_0^{2\pi} \int_0^2 \int_0^{4-r^2} (5 - z) \, dz \, r \, dr \, d\theta$$

... then integrate over R
with $0 \le r \le 2, 0 \le \theta \le 2\pi.$

(c)

Figure 13.53

> In Example 3, the integrand is independent of θ, so the integral with respect to θ could have been done first, producing a factor of 2π.

The mass is computed by integrating the density function over D:

$$\iiint_D f(r, \theta, z)\, dV = \int_0^{2\pi} \int_0^2 \int_0^{4-r^2} (5 - z)\, dz\, r\, dr\, d\theta \qquad \text{Integrate density.}$$

$$= \int_0^{2\pi} \int_0^2 \left(5z - \frac{z^2}{2}\right)\Bigg|_0^{4-r^2} r\, dr\, d\theta \qquad \begin{array}{l}\text{Evaluate inner integral}\\ \text{with respect to } z.\end{array}$$

$$= \frac{1}{2}\int_0^{2\pi} \int_0^2 (24r - 2r^3 - r^5)\, dr\, d\theta \qquad \text{Simplify.}$$

$$= \int_0^{2\pi} \frac{44}{3}\, d\theta \qquad \begin{array}{l}\text{Evaluate middle integral}\\ \text{with respect to } r.\end{array}$$

$$= \frac{88\pi}{3}. \qquad \begin{array}{l}\text{Evaluate outer integral}\\ \text{with respect to } \theta.\end{array}$$

Related Exercises 23–28 ◄

> Recall that to find the volume of a region D using a triple integral, we set $f = 1$ and evaluate
>
> $$V = \iiint_D dV.$$

EXAMPLE 4   Volume between two surfaces Find the volume of the solid D between the cone $z = \sqrt{x^2 + y^2}$ and the inverted paraboloid $z = 12 - x^2 - y^2$ (Figure 13.54a).

SOLUTION Because $x^2 + y^2 = r^2$, the equation of the cone in cylindrical coordinates becomes $z = r$, and the equation of the paraboloid becomes $z = 12 - r^2$. The inner integral in z runs from the cone $z = r$ (the lower surface) to the paraboloid $z = 12 - r^2$ (the upper surface) (Figure 13.54b). We project D onto the xy-plane to produce the region R, whose boundary is determined by the intersection of the two surfaces. Equating the z-coordinates in the equations of the two surfaces, we have $12 - r^2 = r$, or $(r - 3)(r + 4) = 0$. Because $r \geq 0$, the relevant root is $r = 3$. Therefore, the projection of D onto the xy-plane is $R = \{(r, \theta) : 0 \leq r \leq 3, 0 \leq \theta \leq 2\pi\}$, which is a disk of radius 3 centered at $(0, 0)$ (Figure 13.54c).

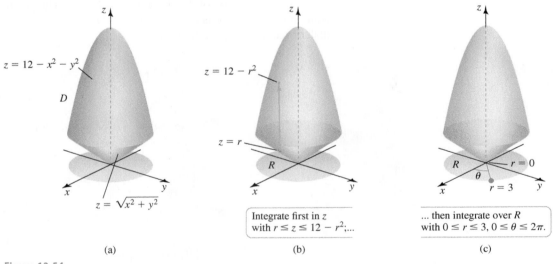

(a)	(b)	(c)

Figure 13.54

The volume of the region is

$$\iiint\limits_{D} dV = \int_{0}^{2\pi} \int_{0}^{3} \int_{r}^{12-r^2} dz\, r\, dr\, d\theta$$

$$= \int_{0}^{2\pi} \int_{0}^{3} (12 - r^2 - r)\, r\, dr\, d\theta \qquad \text{Evaluate inner integral with respect to } z.$$

$$= \int_{0}^{2\pi} \frac{99}{4}\, d\theta \qquad \text{Evaluate middle integral with respect to } r.$$

$$= \frac{99\pi}{2}. \qquad \text{Evaluate outer integral with respect to } \theta.$$

Related Exercises 29–34 ◄

Spherical Coordinates

In spherical coordinates, a point P in $\mathbb{R}^3$ is represented by three coordinates (ρ, φ, θ) (Figure 13.55).

- ρ is the distance from the origin to P.
- φ is the angle between the positive z-axis and the line OP.
- θ is the same angle as in cylindrical coordinates; it measures rotation about the z-axis relative to the positive x-axis.

All points in $\mathbb{R}^3$ can be represented by spherical coordinates using the intervals $0 \le \rho < \infty$, $0 \le \varphi \le \pi$, and $0 \le \theta \le 2\pi$.

Figure 13.56 allows us to find the relationships among rectangular and spherical coordinates. Given the spherical coordinates (ρ, φ, θ) of a point P, the distance from P to the z-axis is $r = \rho \sin \varphi$. We also see from Figure 13.56 that $x = r \cos \theta = \rho \sin \varphi \cos \theta$, $y = r \sin \theta = \rho \sin \varphi \sin \theta$, and $z = \rho \cos \varphi$.

> ▶ The coordinate ρ (pronounced "rho") in spherical coordinates should not be confused with r in cylindrical coordinates, which is the distance from P to the z-axis.

> ▶ The coordinate φ is called the *colatitude* because it is $\pi/2$ minus the latitude of points in the northern hemisphere. Physicists may reverse the roles of θ and φ; that is, θ is the colatitude and φ is the polar angle.

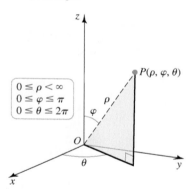

$0 \le \rho < \infty$
$0 \le \varphi \le \pi$
$0 \le \theta \le 2\pi$

Figure 13.55

Transformations Between Spherical and Rectangular Coordinates	
Rectangular → Spherical	**Spherical → Rectangular**
$\rho^2 = x^2 + y^2 + z^2$	$x = \rho \sin \varphi \cos \theta$
Use trigonometry to find	$y = \rho \sin \varphi \sin \theta$
φ and θ	$z = \rho \cos \varphi$

QUICK CHECK 3 Find the spherical coordinates of the point with rectangular coordinates $(1, \sqrt{3}, 2)$. Find the rectangular coordinates of the point with spherical coordinates $(2, \pi/4, \pi/4)$. ◄

In spherical coordinates, some sets of points have simple representations. For instance, the set $\{(\rho, \varphi, \theta) : \rho = a\}$ is the set of points whose ρ-coordinate is constant, which is a sphere of radius a centered at the origin. The set $\{(\rho, \varphi, \theta) : \varphi = \varphi_0\}$ is the set of points with a constant φ-coordinate; it is a cone with its vertex at the origin and whose sides make an angle φ_0 with the positive z-axis.

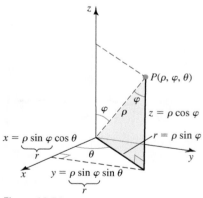

Figure 13.56

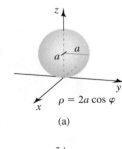

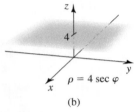

$\rho = 2a \cos \varphi$

(a)

$\rho = 4 \sec \varphi$

(b)

Figure 13.57

EXAMPLE 5   Sets in spherical coordinates Express the following sets in rectangular coordinates and identify the set. Assume that a is a positive real number.

a. $\{(\rho, \varphi, \theta): \rho = 2a \cos \varphi, 0 \leq \varphi \leq \pi/2, 0 \leq \theta \leq 2\pi\}$

b. $\{(\rho, \varphi, \theta): \rho = 4 \sec \varphi, 0 \leq \varphi < \pi/2, 0 \leq \theta \leq 2\pi\}$

SOLUTION

a. To avoid working with square roots, we multiply both sides of $\rho = 2a \cos \varphi$ by ρ to obtain $\rho^2 = 2a \rho \cos \varphi$. Substituting rectangular coordinates, we have $x^2 + y^2 + z^2 = 2az$. Completing the square results in the equation

$$x^2 + y^2 + (z - a)^2 = a^2.$$

This is the equation of a sphere centered at $(0, 0, a)$ with radius a (Figure 13.57a). With the limits $0 \leq \varphi \leq \pi/2$ and $0 \leq \theta \leq 2\pi$, the set describes a full sphere.

b. The equation $\rho = 4 \sec \varphi$ is first written $\rho \cos \varphi = 4$. Noting that $z = \rho \cos \varphi$, the set consists of all points with $z = 4$, which is a horizontal plane (Figure 13.57b).

Related Exercises 35–38 ◄

Table 13.5 summarizes some sets that have simple descriptions in spherical coordinates.

Table 13.5

Name	Description	Example
Sphere, radius a, center $(0, 0, 0)$	$\{(\rho, \varphi, \theta): \rho = a\}, a > 0$	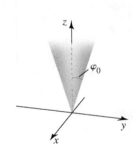
Cone	$\{(\rho, \varphi, \theta): \varphi = \varphi_0\}, \varphi_0 \neq 0, \pi/2, \pi$	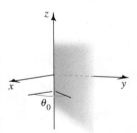
Vertical half plane	$\{(\rho, \varphi, \theta): \theta = \theta_0\}$	

➤ Notice that the set (ρ, φ, θ) with $\varphi = \pi/2$ is the xy-plane, and if $\pi/2 < \varphi_0 < \pi$, the set $\varphi = \varphi_0$ is a cone that opens downward.

(Continued)

Table 13.5   **(Continued)**

Name	Description	Example
Horizontal plane, $z = a$	$a > 0: \{(\rho, \varphi, \theta): \rho = a \sec \varphi, 0 \leq \varphi < \pi/2\}$ $a < 0: \{(\rho, \varphi, \theta): \rho = a \sec \varphi, \pi/2 < \varphi \leq \pi\}$	
Cylinder, radius $a > 0$	$\{(\rho, \varphi, \theta): \rho = a \csc \varphi, 0 < \varphi < \pi\}$	
Sphere, radius $a > 0$, center $(0, 0, a)$	$\{(\rho, \varphi, \theta): \rho = 2a \cos \varphi, 0 \leq \varphi \leq \pi/2\}$	

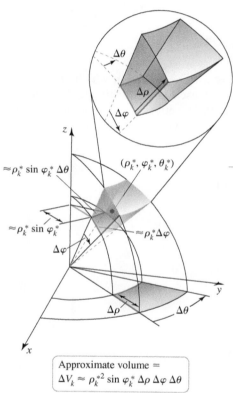

Approximate volume =
$$\Delta V_k \approx \rho_k^{*2} \sin \varphi_k^* \, \Delta \rho \, \Delta \varphi \, \Delta \theta$$

Figure 13.58

▶ Recall that the length s of a circular arc of radius r subtended by an angle θ is $s = r\theta$.

Integration in Spherical Coordinates

We now investigate triple integrals in spherical coordinates over a region D in $\mathbb{R}^3$. The region D is partitioned into "spherical boxes" that are formed by changes of $\Delta \rho$, $\Delta \varphi$, and $\Delta \theta$ in the coordinate directions (Figure 13.58). Those boxes that lie entirely within D are labeled from $k = 1$ to $k = n$. We let $(\rho_k^*, \varphi_k^*, \theta_k^*)$ be an arbitrary point in the kth box.

To approximate the volume of a typical box, note that the length of the box in the ρ-direction is $\Delta \rho$ (Figure 13.58). The approximate length of the kth box in the θ-direction is the length of an arc of a circle of radius $\rho_k^* \sin \varphi_k^*$ subtended by an angle $\Delta \theta$; this length is $\rho_k^* \sin \varphi_k^* \Delta \theta$. The approximate length of the box in the φ-direction is the length of an arc of radius ρ_k^* subtended by an angle $\Delta \varphi$; this length is $\rho_k^* \Delta \varphi$. Multiplying these dimensions together, the approximate volume of the kth spherical box is $\Delta V_k = \rho_k^{*2} \sin \varphi_k^* \Delta \rho \, \Delta \varphi \, \Delta \theta$, for $k = 1, \ldots, n$.

We now assume that f is continuous on D and form a Riemann sum over the region by adding function values multiplied by the corresponding approximate volumes:

$$\sum_{k=1}^{n} f(\rho_k^*, \varphi_k^*, \theta_k^*) \Delta V_k = \sum_{k=1}^{n} f(\rho_k^*, \varphi_k^*, \theta_k^*) \, \rho_k^{*2} \sin \varphi_k^* \Delta \rho \, \Delta \varphi \, \Delta \theta.$$

We let Δ denote the maximum value of $\Delta \rho$, $\Delta \varphi$, and $\Delta \theta$. As $n \to \infty$ and $\Delta \to 0$, the Riemann sums approach a limit called the **triple integral of f over D in spherical coordinates**:

$$\iiint\limits_{D} f(\rho, \varphi, \theta) \, dV = \lim_{\Delta \to 0} \sum_{k=1}^{n} f(\rho_k^*, \varphi_k^*, \theta_k^*) \, \rho_k^{*2} \sin \varphi_k^* \Delta \rho \, \Delta \varphi \, \Delta \theta.$$

Finding Limits of Integration   We consider a common situation in which the region of integration has the form

$$D = \{(\rho, \varphi, \theta): 0 \leq g(\varphi, \theta) \leq \rho \leq h(\varphi, \theta), a \leq \varphi \leq b, \alpha \leq \theta \leq \beta\}.$$

In other words, D is bounded in the ρ-direction by two surfaces given by g and h. In the angular directions, the region lies between two cones ($a \leq \varphi \leq b$) and two half planes ($\alpha \leq \theta \leq \beta$) (Figure 13.59).

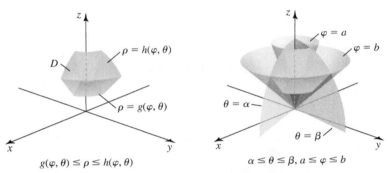

Figure 13.59

For this type of region, the inner integral is with respect to ρ, which varies from $\rho = g(\varphi, \theta)$ to $\rho = h(\varphi, \theta)$. As ρ varies between these limits, imagine letting θ and φ vary over the intervals $a \leq \varphi \leq b$ and $\alpha \leq \theta \leq \beta$. The effect is to sweep out all points of D. Notice that the middle and outer integrals, with respect to θ and φ, may be done in either order (Figure 13.60).

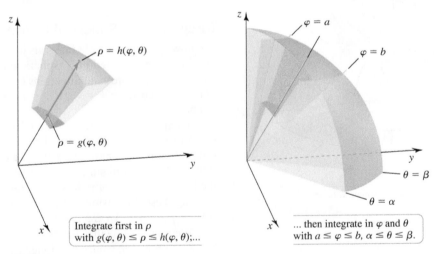

Figure 13.60

In summary, to integrate over all points of D, we carry out the following steps.

1. Integrate with respect to ρ from $\rho = g(\varphi, \theta)$ to $\rho = h(\varphi, \theta)$; the result (in general) is a function of φ and θ.

2. Integrate with respect to φ from $\varphi = a$ to $\varphi = b$; the result (in general) is a function of θ.

3. Integrate with respect to θ from $\theta = \alpha$ to $\theta = \beta$; the result is (always) a real number.

Another version of Fubini's Theorem expresses the triple integral as an iterated integral.

> The element of volume in spherical coordinates is $dV = \rho^2 \sin\varphi \, d\rho \, d\varphi \, d\theta$.

THEOREM 13.7   Triple Integrals in Spherical Coordinates

Let f be continuous over the region

$$D = \{(\rho, \varphi, \theta) : 0 \le g(\varphi, \theta) \le \rho \le h(\varphi, \theta), a \le \varphi \le b, \alpha \le \theta \le \beta\}.$$

Then f is integrable over D, and the triple integral of f over D in spherical coordinates is

$$\iiint_D f(\rho, \varphi, \theta) \, dV = \int_\alpha^\beta \int_a^b \int_{g(\varphi,\theta)}^{h(\varphi,\theta)} f(\rho, \varphi, \theta) \, \rho^2 \sin\varphi \, d\rho \, d\varphi \, d\theta.$$

If the integrand is given in terms of Cartesian coordinates x, y, and z, it must be expressed in spherical coordinates before integrating. As with other triple integrals, if $f = 1$, then the triple integral equals the volume of D. If f is a density function for an object occupying the region D, then the triple integral equals the mass of the object.

EXAMPLE 6   A triple integral Evaluate $\iiint_D (x^2 + y^2 + z^2)^{-3/2} \, dV$, where D is the region in the first octant between two spheres of radius 1 and 2 centered at the origin.

SOLUTION Both the integrand f and region D are greatly simplified when expressed in spherical coordinates. The integrand becomes

$$(x^2 + y^2 + z^2)^{-3/2} = (\rho^2)^{-3/2} = \rho^{-3},$$

while the region of integration (Figure 13.61) is

$$D = \{(\rho, \varphi, \theta) : 1 \le \rho \le 2, 0 \le \varphi \le \pi/2, 0 \le \theta \le \pi/2\}.$$

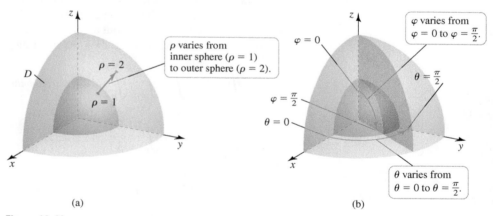

(a)   (b)

Figure 13.61

The integral is evaluated as follows:

$$\iiint_D f(x, y, z) \, dV = \int_0^{\pi/2} \int_0^{\pi/2} \int_1^2 \rho^{-3} \rho^2 \sin\varphi \, d\rho \, d\varphi \, d\theta \qquad \text{Convert to spherical coordinates.}$$

$$= \int_0^{\pi/2} \int_0^{\pi/2} \int_1^2 \rho^{-1} \sin\varphi \, d\rho \, d\varphi \, d\theta \qquad \text{Simplify.}$$

$$= \int_0^{\pi/2} \int_0^{\pi/2} \ln|\rho| \Big|_1^2 \sin\varphi \, d\varphi \, d\theta \qquad \text{Evaluate inner integral with respect to } \rho.$$

$$= \ln 2 \int_0^{\pi/2} \int_0^{\pi/2} \sin\varphi \, d\varphi \, d\theta \qquad \text{Simplify.}$$

$$= \ln 2 \int_0^{\pi/2} (-\cos \varphi) \Big|_0^{\pi/2} d\theta \qquad \text{Evaluate middle integral with respect to } \varphi.$$

$$= \ln 2 \int_0^{\pi/2} d\theta = \frac{\pi \ln 2}{2}. \qquad \text{Evaluate outer integral with respect to } \theta.$$

Related Exercises 39–45 ◄

EXAMPLE 7 **Ice cream cone** Find the volume of the solid region D that lies inside the cone $\varphi = \pi/6$ and inside the sphere $\rho = 4$ (Figure 13.62a).

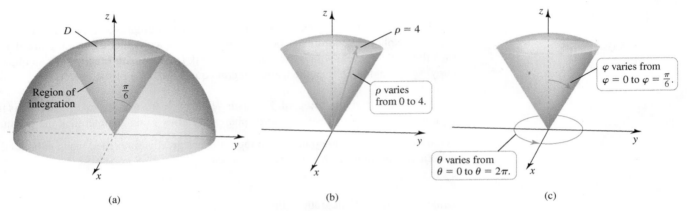

Figure 13.62

SOLUTION To find the volume, we evaluate a triple integral with $f(\rho, \varphi, \theta) = 1$. In the radial direction, the region extends from the origin $\rho = 0$ to the sphere $\rho = 4$ (Figure 13.62b). To sweep out all points of D, φ varies from 0 to $\pi/6$ and θ varies from 0 to 2π (Figure 13.62c). Integrating the function $f = 1$, the volume of the region is

$$\iiint\limits_D dV = \int_0^{2\pi} \int_0^{\pi/6} \int_0^4 \rho^2 \sin \varphi \, d\rho \, d\varphi \, d\theta \qquad \text{Convert to an iterated integral.}$$

$$= \int_0^{2\pi} \int_0^{\pi/6} \frac{\rho^3}{3} \Big|_0^4 \sin \varphi \, d\varphi \, d\theta \qquad \text{Evaluate inner integral with respect to } \rho.$$

$$= \frac{64}{3} \int_0^{2\pi} \int_0^{\pi/6} \sin \varphi \, d\varphi \, d\theta \qquad \text{Simplify.}$$

$$= \frac{64}{3} \int_0^{2\pi} \underbrace{(-\cos \varphi) \Big|_0^{\pi/6}}_{1 - \sqrt{3}/2} d\theta \qquad \text{Evaluate middle integral with respect to } \varphi.$$

$$= \frac{32}{3} (2 - \sqrt{3}) \int_0^{2\pi} d\theta \qquad \text{Simplify.}$$

$$= \frac{64\pi}{3} (2 - \sqrt{3}). \qquad \text{Evaluate outer integral with respect to } \theta.$$

Related Exercises 46–52 ◄

SECTION 13.5 EXERCISES

Review Questions

1. Explain how cylindrical coordinates are used to describe a point in $\mathbb{R}^3$.

2. Explain how spherical coordinates are used to describe a point in $\mathbb{R}^3$.

3. Describe the set $\{(r, \theta, z): r = 4z\}$ in cylindrical coordinates.

4. Describe the set $\{(\rho, \varphi, \theta): \varphi = \pi/4\}$ in spherical coordinates.

5. Explain why $dz\, r\, dr\, d\theta$ is the volume of a small "box" in cylindrical coordinates.

6. Explain why $\rho^2 \sin \varphi\, d\rho\, d\varphi\, d\theta$ is the volume of a small "box" in spherical coordinates.

7. Write the integral $\iiint_D f(r, \theta, z)\, dV$ as an iterated integral where
$D = \{(r, \theta, z): G(r, \theta) \le z \le H(r, \theta), g(\theta) \le r \le h(\theta), \alpha \le \theta \le \beta\}$.

8. Write the integral $\iiint_D f(\rho, \varphi, \theta)\, dV$ as an iterated integral,
where $D = \{(\rho, \varphi, \theta): g(\varphi, \theta) \le \rho \le h(\varphi, \theta), a \le \varphi \le b, \alpha \le \theta \le \beta\}$.

9. What coordinate system is *suggested* if the integrand of a triple integral involves $x^2 + y^2$?

10. What coordinate system is *suggested* if the integrand of a triple integral involves $x^2 + y^2 + z^2$?

Basic Skills

11–14. Sets in cylindrical coordinates *Identify and sketch the following sets in cylindrical coordinates.*

11. $\{(r, \theta, z): 0 \le r \le 3, 0 \le \theta \le \pi/3, 1 \le z \le 4\}$

12. $\{(r, \theta, z): 0 \le \theta \le \pi/2, z = 1\}$

13. $\{(r, \theta, z): 2r \le z \le 4\}$

14. $\{(r, \theta, z): 0 \le z \le 8 - 2r\}$

15–18. Integrals in cylindrical coordinates *Evaluate the following integrals in cylindrical coordinates. The figures illustrate the region of integration.*

15. $\displaystyle\int_0^{2\pi} \int_0^1 \int_{-1}^1 dz\, r\, dr\, d\theta$

16. $\displaystyle\int_0^3 \int_{-\sqrt{9-y^2}}^{\sqrt{9-y^2}} \int_0^{9-3\sqrt{x^2+y^2}} dz\, dx\, dy$

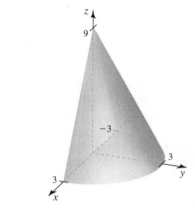

17. $\displaystyle\int_{-1}^1 \int_{-\sqrt{1-y^2}}^{\sqrt{1-y^2}} \int_{-1}^1 (x^2 + y^2)^{3/2}\, dz\, dx\, dy$

18. $\displaystyle\int_{-3}^3 \int_0^{\sqrt{9-x^2}} \int_0^2 \frac{1}{1 + x^2 + y^2}\, dz\, dy\, dx$

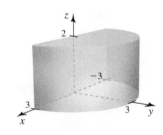

19–22. Integrals in cylindrical coordinates *Evaluate the following integrals in cylindrical coordinates.*

19. $\displaystyle\int_0^4 \int_0^{\sqrt{2}/2} \int_x^{\sqrt{1-x^2}} e^{-x^2-y^2}\, dy\, dx\, dz$

20. $\displaystyle\int_{-4}^4 \int_{-\sqrt{16-x^2}}^{\sqrt{16-x^2}} \int_{\sqrt{x^2+y^2}}^4 dz\, dy\, dx$

21. $\displaystyle\int_0^3 \int_0^{\sqrt{9-x^2}} \int_0^{\sqrt{x^2+y^2}} (x^2 + y^2)^{-1/2} dz\, dy\, dx$

22. $\displaystyle\int_{-1}^1 \int_0^{1/2} \int_{\sqrt{3}y}^{\sqrt{1-y^2}} (x^2 + y^2)^{1/2}\, dx\, dy\, dz$

23–26. Mass from density *Find the mass of the following objects with the given density functions.*

23. The solid cylinder $D = \{(r, \theta, z): 0 \le r \le 4, 0 \le z \le 10\}$ with density $\rho(r, \theta, z) = 1 + z/2$

24. The solid cylinder $D = \{(r, \theta, z): 0 \le r \le 3, 0 \le z \le 2\}$ with density $\rho(r, \theta, z) = 5e^{-r^2}$

25. The solid cone $D = \{(r, \theta, z): 0 \le z \le 6 - r, 0 \le r \le 6\}$ with density $\rho(r, \theta, z) = 7 - z$

26. The solid paraboloid $D = \{(r, \theta, z): 0 \le z \le 9 - r^2, 0 \le r \le 3\}$ with density $\rho(r, \theta, z) = 1 + z/9$

27. **Which weighs more?** For $0 \le r \le 1$, the solid bounded by the cone $z = 4 - 4r$ and the solid bounded by the paraboloid $z = 4 - 4r^2$ have the same base in the xy-plane and the same height. Which object has the greater mass if the density of both objects is $\rho(r, \theta, z) = 10 - 2z$?

28. **Which weighs more?** Which of the objects in Exercise 27 weighs more if the density of both objects is $\rho(r, \theta, z) = \dfrac{8}{\pi}e^{-z}$?

29–34. Volumes in cylindrical coordinates *Use cylindrical coordinates to find the volume of the following solids.*

29. The solid bounded by the plane $z = 0$ and the hyperboloid $z = \sqrt{17} - \sqrt{1 + x^2 + y^2}$

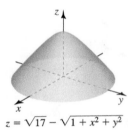

$$z = \sqrt{17} - \sqrt{1 + x^2 + y^2}$$

30. The solid bounded by the plane $z = 25$ and the paraboloid $z = x^2 + y^2$

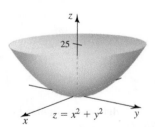

$$z = x^2 + y^2$$

31. The solid bounded by the plane $z = \sqrt{29}$ and the hyperboloid $z = \sqrt{4 + x^2 + y^2}$

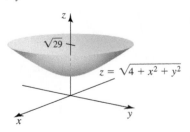

$$z = \sqrt{4 + x^2 + y^2}$$

32. The solid cylinder whose height is 4 and whose base is the disk $\{(r, \theta): 0 \le r \le 2\cos\theta\}$

33. The solid in the first octant bounded by the cylinder $r = 1$, and the planes $z = x$ and $z = 0$

34. The solid bounded by the cylinders $r = 1$ and $r = 2$, and the planes $z = 4 - x - y$ and $z = 0$

35–38. Sets in spherical coordinates *Identify and sketch the following sets in spherical coordinates.*

35. $\{(\rho, \varphi, \theta): 1 \le \rho \le 3\}$

36. $\{(\rho, \varphi, \theta): \rho = 2\csc\varphi, 0 < \varphi < \pi\}$

37. $\{(\rho, \varphi, \theta): \rho = 4\cos\varphi, 0 \le \varphi \le \pi/2\}$

38. $\{(\rho, \varphi, \theta): \rho = 2\sec\varphi, 0 \le \varphi < \pi/2\}$

39–45. Integrals in spherical coordinates *Evaluate the following integrals in spherical coordinates.*

39. $\displaystyle\iiint_D (x^2 + y^2 + z^2)^{5/2}\, dV$; D is the unit ball.

40. $\displaystyle\iiint_D e^{-(x^2+y^2+z^2)^{3/2}}\, dV$; D is the unit ball.

41. $\displaystyle\iiint_D \frac{dV}{(x^2 + y^2 + z^2)^{3/2}}$; D is the solid between the spheres of radius 1 and 2 centered at the origin.

42. $\displaystyle\int_0^{2\pi}\int_0^{\pi/3}\int_0^{4\sec\varphi} \rho^2 \sin\varphi\, d\rho\, d\varphi\, d\theta$

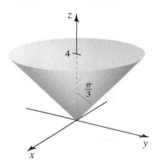

43. $\displaystyle\int_0^{\pi}\int_0^{\pi/6}\int_{2\sec\varphi}^{4} \rho^2 \sin\varphi\, d\rho\, d\varphi\, d\theta$

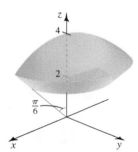

44. $\displaystyle\int_0^{2\pi}\int_0^{\pi/4}\int_1^{2\sec\varphi}(\rho^{-3})\,\rho^2\sin\varphi\,d\rho\,d\varphi\,d\theta$

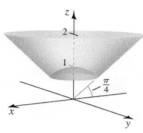

45. $\displaystyle\int_0^{2\pi}\int_{\pi/6}^{\pi/3}\int_0^{2\csc\varphi}\rho^2\sin\varphi\,d\rho\,d\varphi\,d\theta$

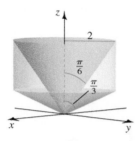

46–52. Volumes in spherical coordinates *Use spherical coordinates to find the volume of the following solids.*

46. A ball of radius $a > 0$

47. The solid bounded by the sphere $\rho = 2\cos\varphi$ and the hemisphere $\rho = 1, z \geq 0$

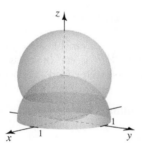

48. The solid cardioid of revolution
$$D = \{(\rho,\varphi,\theta): 0 \leq \rho \leq 1 + \cos\varphi, 0 \leq \varphi \leq \pi, 0 \leq \theta \leq 2\pi\}$$

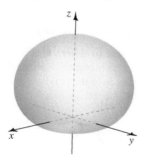

49. The solid outside the cone $\varphi = \pi/4$ and inside the sphere $\rho = 4\cos\varphi$

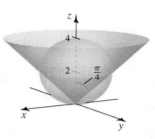

50. The solid bounded by the cylinders $r = 1$ and $r = 2$, and the cones $\varphi = \pi/6$ and $\varphi = \pi/3$

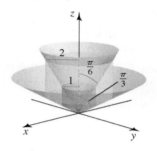

51. That part of the ball $\rho \leq 4$ that lies between the planes $z = 2$ and $z = 2\sqrt{3}$

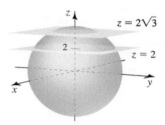

52. The solid inside the cone $z = (x^2 + y^2)^{1/2}$ that lies between the planes $z = 1$ and $z = 2$

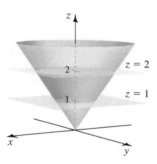

Further Explorations

53. Explain why or why not Determine whether the following statements are true and give an explanation or counterexample.

a. Any point on the z-axis has more than one representation in both cylindrical and spherical coordinates.

b. The sets $\{(r, \theta, z): r = z\}$ and $\{(\rho, \varphi, \theta): \varphi = \pi/4\}$ are the same.

54. Spherical to rectangular Convert the equation $\rho^2 = \sec 2\varphi$, where $0 \le \varphi < \pi/4$, to rectangular coordinates and identify the surface.

55. Spherical to rectangular Convert the equation $\rho^2 = -\sec 2\varphi$, where $\pi/4 < \varphi \le \pi/2$, to rectangular coordinates and identify the surface.

56–59. Mass from density *Find the mass of the following solids with the given density functions. Note that density is described by the function f to avoid confusion with the radial spherical coordinate ρ.*

56. The ball of radius 4 centered at the origin with a density $f(\rho, \varphi, \theta) = 1 + \rho$

57. The ball of radius 8 centered at the origin with a density $f(\rho, \varphi, \theta) = 2e^{-\rho^3}$

58. The solid cone $\{(r, \theta, z): 0 \le z \le 4, 0 \le r \le \sqrt{3}z, 0 \le \theta \le 2\pi\}$ with a density $f(r, \theta, z) = 5 - z$

59. The solid cylinder $\{(r, \theta, z): 0 \le r \le 2, 0 \le \theta \le 2\pi, -1 \le z \le 1\}$ with a density of $f(r, \theta, z) = (2 - |z|)(4 - r)$

60–61. Changing order of integration *If possible, write iterated integrals in cylindrical coordinates for the following regions in the specified orders. Sketch the region of integration.*

60. The solid outside the cylinder $r = 1$ and inside the sphere $\rho = 5$, for $z \ge 0$, in the orders $dz\, dr\, d\theta$, $dr\, dz\, d\theta$, and $d\theta\, dz\, dr$

61. The solid above the cone $z = r$ and below the sphere $\rho = 2$, for $z \ge 0$, in the orders $dz\, dr\, d\theta$, $dr\, dz\, d\theta$, and $d\theta\, dz\, dr$

62–63. Changing order of integration *If possible, write iterated integrals in spherical coordinates for the following regions in the specified orders. Sketch the region of integration. Assume that f is continuous on the region.*

62. $\displaystyle\int_0^{2\pi} \int_0^{\pi/4} \int_0^{4\sec\varphi} f(\rho, \varphi, \theta)\, \rho^2 \sin\varphi\, d\rho\, d\varphi\, d\theta$ in the orders $d\rho\, d\theta\, d\varphi$ and $d\theta\, d\rho\, d\varphi$

63. $\displaystyle\int_0^{2\pi} \int_{\pi/6}^{\pi/2} \int_{\csc\varphi}^{2} f(\rho, \varphi, \theta)\, \rho^2 \sin\varphi\, d\rho\, d\varphi\, d\theta$ in the orders $d\rho\, d\theta\, d\varphi$ and $d\theta\, d\rho\, d\varphi$

64–72. Miscellaneous volumes *Choose the best coordinate system for finding the volume of the following solids. Surfaces are specified using the coordinates that give the simplest description, but the simplest integration may be with respect to different variables.*

64. The solid inside the sphere $\rho = 1$ and below the cone $\varphi = \pi/4$, for $z \ge 0$

65. That part of the solid cylinder $r \le 2$ that lies between the cones $\varphi = \pi/3$ and $\varphi = 2\pi/3$

66. That part of the ball $\rho \le 2$ that lies between the cones $\varphi = \pi/3$ and $\varphi = 2\pi/3$

67. The solid bounded by the cylinder $r = 1$, for $0 \le z \le x + y$

68. The solid inside the cylinder $r = 2\cos\theta$, for $0 \le z \le 4 - x$

69. The wedge cut from the cardioid cylinder $r = 1 + \cos\theta$ by the planes $z = 2 - x$ and $z = x - 2$

70. Volume of a drilled hemisphere Find the volume of material remaining in a hemisphere of radius 2 after a cylindrical hole of radius 1 is drilled through the center of the hemisphere perpendicular to its base.

71. Two cylinders The x- and y-axes form the axes of two right circular cylinders with radius 1 (see figure). Find the volume of the solid that is common to the two cylinders.

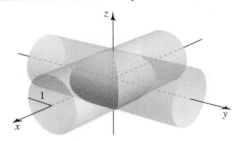

72. Three cylinders The coordinate axes form the axes of three right circular cylinders with radius 1 (see figure). Find the volume of the solid that is common to the three cylinders.

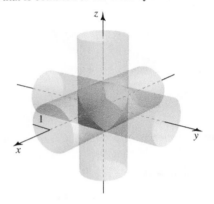

Applications

73. Density distribution A right circular cylinder with height 8 cm and radius 2 cm is filled with water. A heated filament running along its axis produces a variable density in the water given by $\rho(r) = 1 - 0.05e^{-0.01r^2}$ g/cm^3 (ρ stands for density here, not the radial spherical coordinate). Find the mass of the water in the cylinder. Neglect the volume of the filament.

74. Charge distribution A spherical cloud of electric charge has a known charge density $Q(\rho)$, where ρ is the spherical coordinate. Find the total charge in the interior of the cloud in the following cases.

a. $Q(\rho) = \dfrac{2 \times 10^{-4}}{\rho^4}, 1 \le \rho < \infty$

b. $Q(\rho) = (2 \times 10^{-4})e^{-0.01\rho^3}, 0 \le \rho < \infty$

75. Gravitational field due to spherical shell A point mass m is a distance d from the center of a thin spherical shell of mass M and radius R. The magnitude of the gravitational force on the point mass is given by the integral

$$F(d) = \frac{GMm}{4\pi} \int_0^{2\pi} \int_0^{\pi} \frac{(d - R\cos\varphi)\sin\varphi}{(R^2 + d^2 - 2Rd\cos\varphi)^{3/2}}\, d\varphi\, d\theta,$$

where G is the gravitational constant.

a. Use the change of variable $x = \cos\varphi$ to evaluate the integral and show that if $d > R$, then $F(d) = \dfrac{GMm}{d^2}$, which means the force is the same as if the mass of the shell were concentrated at its center.

b. Show that if $d < R$ (the point mass is inside the shell), then $F = 0$.

76. Water in a gas tank Before a gasoline-powered engine is started, water must be drained from the bottom of the fuel tank. Suppose the tank is a right circular cylinder on its side with a length of 2 ft and a radius of 1 ft. If the water level is 6 in above the lowest part of the tank, determine how much water must be drained from the tank.

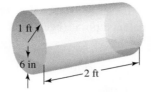

Additional Exercises

77–80. General volume formulas *Use integration to find the volume of the following solids. In each case, choose a convenient coordinate system, find equations for the bounding surfaces, set up a triple integral, and evaluate the integral. Assume that a, b, c, r, R, and h are positive constants.*

77. Cone Find the volume of a solid right circular cone with height h and base radius r.

78. Spherical cap Find the volume of the cap of a sphere of radius R with thickness h.

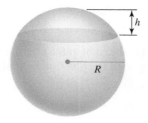

79. Frustum of a cone Find the volume of a truncated solid cone of height h whose ends have radii r and R.

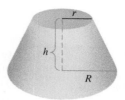

80. Ellipsoid Find the volume of a solid ellipsoid with axes of length $2a$, $2b$, and $2c$.

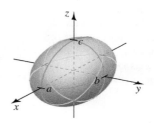

81. Intersecting spheres One sphere is centered at the origin and has a radius of R. Another sphere is centered at $(0, 0, r)$ and has a radius of r, where $r > R/2$. What is the volume of the region common to the two spheres?

QUICK CHECK ANSWERS

1. $\left(\sqrt{2}, 7\pi/4, 5\right), \left(1, \sqrt{3}, 5\right)$
2. $0 \le r \le 10, 0 \le \theta \le 2\pi, 0 \le z \le 20$
3. $\left(2\sqrt{2}, \pi/4, \pi/3\right), \left(1, 1, \sqrt{2}\right)$ ◄

13.6 Integrals for Mass Calculations

Intuition says that a thin circular disk (like a DVD without a hole) should balance on a pencil placed at the center of the disk (Figure 13.63). If, however, you were given a thin plate with an irregular shape, then at what point does it balance? This question asks about the *center of mass* of a thin object (thin enough that it can be treated as a two-dimensional region). Similarly, given a solid object with an irregular shape and variable density, where is the point at which all of the mass of the object would be located if it were treated as a point mass? In this section, we use integration to compute the center of mass of one-, two-, and three-dimensional objects.

Sets of Individual Objects

Methods for finding the center of mass of an object are ultimately based on a well-known playground principle: If two people with masses m_1 and m_2 sit at distances d_1 and d_2 from the pivot point of a seesaw (with no mass), then the seesaw balances provided $m_1 d_1 = m_2 d_2$ (Figure 13.64).

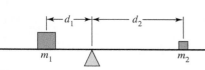

Figure 13.63

Figure 13.64

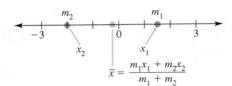

Figure 13.65

➤ The center of mass may be viewed as the weighted average of the x-coordinates with the masses serving as the weights. Notice how the units work out: If x_1 and x_2 have units of meters and m_1 and m_2 have units of kilograms, then $\bar{x}$ has units of meters.

QUICK CHECK 1 A 90-kg person sits 2 m from the balance point of a seesaw. How far from that point must a 60-kg person sit to balance the seesaw? Assume the seesaw has no mass. ◄

To generalize the problem, we introduce a coordinate system with the origin at $x = 0$ (Figure 13.65). Suppose the location of the balance point $\bar{x}$ is unknown. The coordinates of the two masses m_1 and m_2 are denoted x_1 and x_2, respectively, with $x_1 > x_2$. The mass m_1 is a distance $x_1 - \bar{x}$ from the balance point (because distance is positive and $x_1 > \bar{x}$). The mass m_2 is a distance $\bar{x} - x_2$ from the balance point (because $\bar{x} > x_2$). The playground principle becomes

$$m_1\underbrace{(x_1 - \bar{x})}_{\substack{\text{distance from} \\ \text{balance point} \\ \text{to } m_1}} = m_2\underbrace{(\bar{x} - x_2)}_{\substack{\text{distance from} \\ \text{balance point} \\ \text{to } m_2}},$$

or $m_1(x_1 - \bar{x}) + m_2(x_2 - \bar{x}) = 0$.

Solving this equation for $\bar{x}$, the balance point or *center of mass* of the two-mass system is located at

$$\bar{x} = \frac{m_1x_1 + m_2x_2}{m_1 + m_2}.$$

The quantities m_1x_1 and m_2x_2 are called *moments about the origin* (or just *moments*). The location of the center of mass is the sum of the moments divided by the sum of the masses.

QUICK CHECK 2 Solve the equation $m_1(x_1 - \bar{x}) + m_2(x_2 - \bar{x}) = 0$ for $\bar{x}$ to verify the preceding expression for the center of mass. ◄

For example, an 80-kg man standing 2 m to the right of the origin will balance a 160-kg gorilla sitting 4 m to the left of the origin provided the pivot on their seesaw is placed at

$$\bar{x} = \frac{80 \cdot 2 + 160(-4)}{80 + 160} = -2,$$

or 2 m to the left of the origin (Figure 13.66).

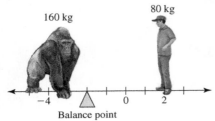

Figure 13.66

Several Objects on a Line   Generalizing the preceding argument to n objects having masses $m_1, m_2, \ldots,$ and m_n with coordinates $x_1, x_2, \ldots,$ and x_n, respectively, the balance condition becomes

$$m_1(x_1 - \bar{x}) + m_2(x_2 - \bar{x}) + \cdots + m_n(x_n - \bar{x}) = \sum_{k=1}^{n} m_k(x_k - \bar{x}) = 0.$$

Solving this equation for the location of the center of mass, we find that

$$\bar{x} = \frac{m_1x_1 + m_2x_2 + \cdots + m_nx_n}{m_1 + m_2 + \cdots + m_n} = \frac{\sum_{k=1}^{n} m_kx_k}{\sum_{k=1}^{n} m_k}.$$

Again, the location of the center of mass is the sum of the moments $m_1x_1, m_2x_2, \ldots,$ and m_nx_n divided by the sum of the masses.

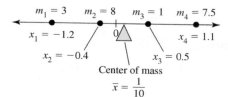

Figure 13.67

EXAMPLE 1   Center of mass for four objects Find the point at which the system shown in Figure 13.67 balances.

SOLUTION The center of mass is

$$
\bar{x} = \frac{m_1 x_1 + m_2 x_2 + m_3 x_3 + m_4 x_4}{m_1 + m_2 + m_3 + m_4}
$$

$$
= \frac{3(-1.2) + 8(-0.4) + 1(0.5) + 7.5(1.1)}{3 + 8 + 1 + 7.5}
$$

$$
= \frac{1}{10}.
$$

The balancing point is slightly to the right of the origin.

Related Exercises 7–8 ◄

Continuous Objects in One Dimension

Now consider a thin rod or wire with density ρ that varies along the length of the rod (Figure 13.68). The density in this case has units of mass per length (for example, g/cm). As before, we want to determine the location $\bar{x}$ at which the rod balances on a pivot.

> Density is usually measured in units of *mass per volume*. However, for thin, narrow objects such as rods and wires, linear density with units of *mass per length* is used. For thin, flat objects such as plates and sheets, area density with units of *mass per area* is used.

QUICK CHECK 3 In Figure 13.68, suppose $a = 0$, $b = 3$, and the density of the rod in g/cm is $\rho(x) = 4 - x$. Where is the rod lightest? Heaviest? ◄

Using the slice-and-sum strategy, we divide the rod, which corresponds to the interval $a \le x \le b$, into n subintervals, each with a width of $\Delta x = \dfrac{b - a}{n}$ (Figure 13.69). The corresponding grid points are

$$
x_0 = a, x_1 = a + \Delta x, \ldots, x_k = a + k\,\Delta x, \ldots, \text{ and } x_n = b.
$$

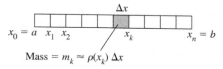

$x = a$ $x = b$

Density (mass per unit length) varies with x.

Figure 13.68

The mass of the kth segment of the rod is approximately the density at x_k multiplied by the length of the interval, or $m_k \approx \rho(x_k)\,\Delta x$.

We now use the center-of-mass formula for several distinct objects to write the approximate center of mass of the rod as

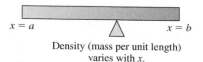

Δx

$x_0 = a$ x_1 x_2 x_k $x_n = b$

Mass $= m_k \approx \rho(x_k)\,\Delta x$

Figure 13.69

$$
\bar{x} = \frac{\displaystyle\sum_{k=1}^{n} m_k x_k}{\displaystyle\sum_{k=1}^{n} m_k} \approx \frac{\displaystyle\sum_{k=1}^{n} (\rho(x_k)\Delta x)\, x_k}{\displaystyle\sum_{k=1}^{n} \rho(x_k)\Delta x}.
$$

> An object consisting of two different materials that meet at an interface has a discontinuous density function. Physical density functions either are continuous or have a finite number of discontinuities.

> We assume that the rod has positive mass and the limits in the numerator and denominator exist, so the limit of the quotient is the quotient of the limits.

To model a rod with a continuous density, we let $\Delta x \to 0$ and $n \to \infty$; the center of mass of the rod is

$$
\bar{x} = \lim_{\Delta x \to 0} \frac{\displaystyle\sum_{k=1}^{n} (\rho(x_k)\Delta x)\, x_k}{\displaystyle\sum_{k=1}^{n} \rho(x_k)\Delta x} = \frac{\displaystyle\lim_{\Delta x \to 0} \sum_{k=1}^{n} x_k\, \rho(x_k)\Delta x}{\displaystyle\lim_{\Delta x \to 0} \sum_{k=1}^{n} \rho(x_k)\Delta x} = \frac{\displaystyle\int_a^b x\rho(x)\, dx}{\displaystyle\int_a^b \rho(x)\, dx}.
$$

As discussed in Section 6.7, the denominator of the last fraction, $\int_a^b \rho(x)\, dx$, is the mass of the rod. The numerator is the "sum" of the moments of each piece of the rod, which is called the *total moment*.

▶ The units of a moment are mass × length. The center of mass is a moment divided by a mass, which has units of length. Notice that if the density is constant, then ρ effectively does not enter the calculation of $\bar{x}$.

> **DEFINITION**   **Center of Mass in One Dimension**
>
> Let ρ be an integrable density function on the interval $[a, b]$ (which represents a thin rod or wire). The **center of mass** is located at the point $\bar{x} = \dfrac{M}{m}$, where the **total moment** M and mass m are
>
> $$M = \int_a^b x\rho(x)\,dx \quad \text{and} \quad m = \int_a^b \rho(x)\,dx.$$

Observe the parallels between the discrete and continuous cases:

$$n \text{ individual objects:} \quad \bar{x} = \frac{\displaystyle\sum_{k=1}^{n} x_k m_k}{\displaystyle\sum_{k=1}^{n} m_k}; \quad \text{continuous object:} \quad \bar{x} = \frac{\displaystyle\int_a^b x\rho(x)\,dx}{\displaystyle\int_a^b \rho(x)\,dx}.$$

EXAMPLE 2   Center of mass of a one-dimensional object   Suppose a thin 2-m bar is made of an alloy whose density in kg/m is $\rho(x) = 1 + x^2$, where $0 \le x \le 2$. Find the center of mass of the bar.

SOLUTION   The total mass of the bar in kilograms is

$$m = \int_a^b \rho(x)\,dx = \int_0^2 (1 + x^2)\,dx = \left(x + \frac{x^3}{3} \right)\Big|_0^2 = \frac{14}{3}.$$

▶ Notice that the density of the bar increases with x. As a consistency check, our calculation must result in a center of mass to the right of the midpoint of the bar.

The total moment of the bar, with units kg-m, is

$$M = \int_a^b x\rho(x)\,dx = \int_0^2 x(1 + x^2)\,dx = \left(\frac{x^2}{2} + \frac{x^4}{4} \right)\Big|_0^2 = 6.$$

Therefore, the center of mass is located at $\bar{x} = \dfrac{M}{m} = \dfrac{9}{7} \approx 1.29$ m.

Related Exercises 9–14 ◀

Two-Dimensional Objects

In two dimensions, we start with an integrable density function $\rho(x, y)$ defined over a closed bounded region R in the xy-plane. The density is now an *area density* with units of mass per area (for example, kg/m^2). The region represents a thin plate (or *lamina*). The center of mass is the point at which a pivot must be located to balance the plate. If the density is constant, the location of the center of mass depends only on the shape of the plate, in which case the center of mass is called the *centroid*.

For a two- or three-dimensional object, the coordinates for the center of mass are computed independently by applying the one-dimensional argument in each coordinate direction (Figure 13.70). The mass of the plate is the integral of the density function over R:

$$m = \iint_R \rho(x, y)\,dA.$$

In analogy with the moment calculation in the one-dimensional case, we now define two moments.

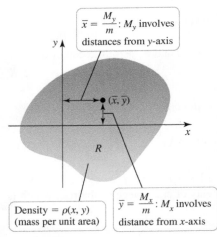

$\bar{x} = \dfrac{M_y}{m}$: M_y involves distances from y-axis

$(\bar{x}, \bar{y})$

R

Density $= \rho(x, y)$ (mass per unit area)

$\bar{y} = \dfrac{M_x}{m}$: M_x involves distance from x-axis

Figure 13.70

> The moment with respect to the y-axis M_y is a weighted average of distances from the y-axis, so it has x in the integrand (the distance between a point and the y-axis). Similarly, the moment with respect to the x-axis M_x is a weighted average of distances from the x-axis, so it has y in the integrand.

DEFINITION Center of Mass in Two Dimensions

Let ρ be an integrable area density function defined over a closed bounded region R in $\mathbb{R}^2$. The coordinates of the center of mass of the object represented by R are

$$\bar{x} = \frac{M_y}{m} = \frac{1}{m}\iint_R x\rho(x, y)\, dA \quad \text{and} \quad \bar{y} = \frac{M_x}{m} = \frac{1}{m}\iint_R y\rho(x, y)\, dA,$$

where $m = \iint_R \rho(x, y)\, dA$ is the mass, and M_y and M_x are the moments with respect to the y-axis and x-axis, respectively. If ρ is constant, the center of mass is called the **centroid** and is independent of the density.

As before, the center of mass coordinates are weighted averages of the distances from the coordinate axes. For two- and three-dimensional objects, the center of mass need not lie within the object (Exercises 51, 61, and 62).

QUICK CHECK 4 Explain why the integral for M_y has x in the integrand. Explain why the density drops out of the center of mass calculation if it is constant. ◄

EXAMPLE 3 Centroid calculation Find the centroid (center of mass) of the unit density, dart-shaped region bounded by the y-axis and the curves $y = e^{-x} - \frac{1}{2}$ and $y = \frac{1}{2} - e^{-x}$ (Figure 13.71).

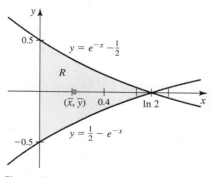

Figure 13.71

> The density does not enter the center of mass calculation when the density is constant. So it is easiest to set $\rho = 1$.

> If possible, try to arrange the coordinate system so that at least one of the integrations in the center of mass calculation can be avoided by using symmetry. Often the mass (or area) can be found using geometry if the density is constant.

SOLUTION Because the region is symmetric about the x-axis and the density is constant, the y-coordinate of the center of mass is $\bar{y} = 0$. This leaves the integrals for m and M_y to evaluate.

The first task is to find the point at which the curves intersect. Solving $e^{-x} - \frac{1}{2} = \frac{1}{2} - e^{-x}$, we find that $x = \ln 2$, from which it follows that $y = 0$. Therefore, the intersection point is $(\ln 2, 0)$. The moment M_y (with $\rho = 1$) is given by

$$M_y = \int_0^{\ln 2} \int_{1/2 - e^{-x}}^{e^{-x} - 1/2} x\, dy\, dx \qquad \text{Definition of } M_y$$

$$= \int_0^{\ln 2} x\left(\left(e^{-x} - \frac{1}{2}\right) - \left(\frac{1}{2} - e^{-x}\right)\right)dx \qquad \text{Evaluate inner integral.}$$

$$= \int_0^{\ln 2} x(2e^{-x} - 1)\, dx. \qquad \text{Simplify.}$$

Using integration by parts for this integral, we find that

$$M_y = \int_0^{\ln 2} \underbrace{x}_{u}\; \underbrace{(2e^{-x} - 1)\, dx}_{dv}$$

$$= -x(2e^{-x} + x)\Big|_0^{\ln 2} + \int_0^{\ln 2}(2e^{-x} + x)\, dx \qquad \text{Integration by parts}$$

$$= 1 - \ln 2 - \frac{1}{2}\ln^2 2 \approx 0.067. \qquad \text{Evaluate and simplify.}$$

With $\rho = 1$, the mass of the region is given by

$$
\begin{aligned}
m &= \int_0^{\ln 2} \int_{1/2 - e^{-x}}^{e^{-x} - 1/2} dy\, dx && \text{Definition of } m \\[2mm]
&= \int_0^{\ln 2} (2e^{-x} - 1)\, dx && \text{Evaluate inner integral.} \\[2mm]
&= (-2e^{-x} - x)\Big|_0^{\ln 2} && \text{Evaluate outer integral.} \\[2mm]
&= 1 - \ln 2 \approx 0.307. && \text{Simplify.}
\end{aligned}
$$

Therefore, the x-coordinate of the center of mass is $\bar{x} = \dfrac{M_y}{m} \approx 0.217$. The center of mass is located approximately at $(0.217, 0)$.

Related Exercises 15–20 ◀

EXAMPLE 4 Variable-density plate Find the center of mass of the rectangular plate $R = \{(x, y): -1 \le x \le 1, 0 \le y \le 1\}$ with a density of $\rho(x, y) = 2 - y$ (heavy at the lower edge and light at the top edge; Figure 13.72).

SOLUTION Because the plate is symmetric with respect to the y-axis and because the density is independent of x, we have $\bar{x} = 0$. We must still compute m and M_x.

$$
m = \iint\limits_R \rho(x, y)\, dA = \int_{-1}^{1} \int_0^1 (2 - y)\, dy\, dx = \frac{3}{2} \int_{-1}^{1} dx = 3
$$

$$
M_x = \iint\limits_R y\rho(x, y)\, dA = \int_{-1}^{1} \int_0^1 y(2 - y)\, dy\, dx = \frac{2}{3} \int_{-1}^{1} dx = \frac{4}{3}
$$

Therefore, the center of mass coordinates are

$$
\bar{x} = \frac{M_y}{m} = 0 \quad \text{and} \quad \bar{y} = \frac{M_x}{m} = \frac{4/3}{3} = \frac{4}{9}.
$$

Related Exercises 21–26 ◀

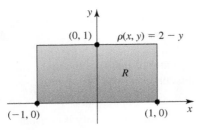

Figure 13.72

➤ To verify that $\bar{x} = 0$, notice that to find M_y, we integrate an odd function in x over $-1 \le x \le 1$; the result is zero.

Three-Dimensional Objects

We now extend the preceding arguments to compute the center of mass of three-dimensional solids. Assume that D is a closed bounded region in $\mathbb{R}^3$, on which an integrable density function ρ is defined. The units of the density are mass per volume (for example, g/cm^3). The coordinates of the center of mass depend on the mass of the region, which by Section 13.4 is the integral of the density function over D. Three moments enter the picture: M_{yz} involves distances from the yz-plane; therefore, it has an x in the integrand. Similarly, M_{xz} involves distances from the xz-plane, so it has a y in the integrand, and M_{xy} involves distances from the xy-plane, so it has a z in the integrand. As before, the coordinates of the center of mass are the total moments divided by the total mass (Figure 13.73).

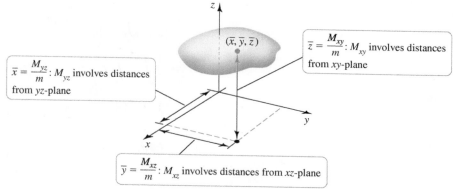

Figure 13.73

QUICK CHECK 5 Explain why the integral for the moment M_{xy} has z in the integrand. ◄

DEFINITION Center of Mass in Three Dimensions

Let ρ be an integrable density function on a closed bounded region D in $\mathbb{R}^3$. The coordinates of the center of mass of the region are

$$\bar{x} = \frac{M_{yz}}{m} = \frac{1}{m}\iiint\limits_{D} x\rho(x, y, z)\, dV, \quad \bar{y} = \frac{M_{xz}}{m} = \frac{1}{m}\iiint\limits_{D} y\rho(x, y, z)\, dV, \text{ and}$$

$$\bar{z} = \frac{M_{xy}}{m} = \frac{1}{m}\iiint\limits_{D} z\rho(x, y, z)\, dV,$$

where $m = \iiint_D \rho(x, y, z)\, dV$ is the mass, and M_{yz}, M_{xz}, and M_{xy} are the moments with respect to the coordinate planes.

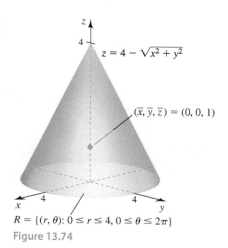

$z = 4 - \sqrt{x^2 + y^2}$

$(\bar{x}, \bar{y}, \bar{z}) = (0, 0, 1)$

$R = \{(r, \theta): 0 \le r \le 4, 0 \le \theta \le 2\pi\}$

Figure 13.74

EXAMPLE 5 Center of mass with constant density Find the center of mass of the constant-density solid cone D bounded by the surface $z = 4 - \sqrt{x^2 + y^2}$ and $z = 0$ (Figure 13.74).

SOLUTION Because the cone is symmetric about the z-axis and has uniform density, the center of mass lies on the z-axis; that is, $\bar{x} = 0$ and $\bar{y} = 0$. Setting $z = 0$, the base of the cone in the xy-plane is the disk of radius 4 centered at the origin. Therefore, the cone has height 4 and radius 4; by the volume formula, its volume is $\pi r^2 h / 3 = 64\pi / 3$. The cone has a constant density, so we assume that $\rho = 1$ and its mass is $m = 64\pi / 3$.

To obtain the value of $\bar{z}$, only M_{xy} needs to be calculated, which is most easily done in cylindrical coordinates. The cone is described by the equation $z = 4 - \sqrt{x^2 + y^2} = 4 - r$. The projection of the cone onto the xy-plane, which is the region of integration in the xy-plane, is $R = \{(r, \theta): 0 \le r \le 4, 0 \le \theta \le 2\pi\}$. The integration for M_{xy} now follows:

$$M_{xy} = \iiint\limits_{D} z\, dV \qquad \text{Definition of } M_{xy} \text{ with } \rho = 1$$

$$= \int_0^{2\pi} \int_0^4 \int_0^{4-r} z\, dz\, r\, dr\, d\theta \qquad \text{Convert to an iterated integral.}$$

$$= \int_0^{2\pi} \int_0^4 \frac{z^2}{2} \Big|_0^{4-r} r \, dr \, d\theta \qquad \text{Evaluate inner integral with respect to } z.$$

$$= \frac{1}{2} \int_0^{2\pi} \int_0^4 r(4-r)^2 \, dr \, d\theta \qquad \text{Simplify.}$$

$$= \frac{1}{2} \int_0^{2\pi} \frac{64}{3} \, d\theta \qquad \text{Evaluate middle integral with respect to } r.$$

$$= \frac{64\pi}{3}. \qquad \text{Evaluate outer integral with respect to } \theta.$$

The z-coordinate of the center of mass is $\bar{z} = \dfrac{M_{xy}}{m} = \dfrac{64\pi/3}{64\pi/3} = 1$, and the center of

mass is located at $(0, 0, 1)$. It can be shown (Exercise 55) that the center of mass of a constant-density cone of height h is located $h/4$ units from the base on the axis of the cone, independent of the radius.

Related Exercises 27–32 ◄

EXAMPLE 6   Center of mass with variable density Find the center of mass of the interior of the hemisphere D of radius a with its base on the xy-plane. The density of the object is $f(\rho, \varphi, \theta) = 2 - \rho/a$ (heavy near the center and light near the outer surface; Figure 13.75).

SOLUTION The center of mass lies on the z-axis because of the symmetry of both the solid and the density function; therefore, $\bar{x} = \bar{y} = 0$. Only the integrals for m and M_{xy} need to be evaluated, and they should be done in spherical coordinates.

The integral for the mass is

$$m = \iiint\limits_D f(\rho, \varphi, \theta) \, dV \qquad \text{Definition of } m.$$

$$= \int_0^{2\pi} \int_0^{\pi/2} \int_0^a \left(2 - \frac{\rho}{a}\right) \rho^2 \sin\varphi \, d\rho \, d\varphi \, d\theta \qquad \text{Convert to an iterated integral.}$$

$$= \int_0^{2\pi} \int_0^{\pi/2} \left(\frac{2\rho^3}{3} - \frac{\rho^4}{4a}\right)\Big|_0^a \sin\varphi \, d\varphi \, d\theta \qquad \text{Evaluate inner integral with respect to } \rho.$$

$$= \int_0^{2\pi} \int_0^{\pi/2} \frac{5a^3}{12} \sin\varphi \, d\varphi \, d\theta \qquad \text{Simplify.}$$

$$= \frac{5a^3}{12} \int_0^{2\pi} \underbrace{(-\cos\varphi)\Big|_0^{\pi/2}}_{1} d\theta \qquad \text{Evaluate middle integral with respect to } \varphi.$$

$$= \frac{5a^3}{12} \int_0^{2\pi} d\theta \qquad \text{Simplify.}$$

$$= \frac{5\pi a^3}{6}. \qquad \text{Evaluate outer integral with respect to } \theta.$$

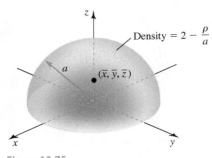

Density $= 2 - \dfrac{\rho}{a}$

a

$(\bar{x}, \bar{y}, \bar{z})$

Figure 13.75

In spherical coordinates, $z = \rho \cos \varphi$, so the integral for the moment M_{xy} is

$$M_{xy} = \iiint_D z\, f(\rho, \varphi, \theta)\, dV \qquad \text{Definition of } M_{xy}$$

$$= \int_0^{2\pi} \int_0^{\pi/2} \int_0^a \underbrace{\rho \cos \varphi}_{z} \left(2 - \frac{\rho}{a}\right) \rho^2 \sin \varphi\, d\rho\, d\varphi\, d\theta \qquad \text{Convert to an iterated integral.}$$

$$= \int_0^{2\pi} \int_0^{\pi/2} \left(\frac{\rho^4}{2} - \frac{\rho^5}{5a}\right)\Big|_0^a \sin \varphi \cos \varphi\, d\varphi\, d\theta \qquad \text{Evaluate inner integral with respect to } \rho.$$

$$= \int_0^{2\pi} \int_0^{\pi/2} \frac{3a^4}{10} \underbrace{\sin \varphi \cos \varphi}_{(\sin 2\varphi)/2}\, d\varphi\, d\theta \qquad \text{Simplify.}$$

$$= \frac{3a^4}{10} \int_0^{2\pi} \underbrace{\left(-\frac{\cos 2\varphi}{4}\right)\Big|_0^{\pi/2}}_{1/2}\, d\theta \qquad \text{Evaluate middle integral with respect to } \varphi.$$

$$= \frac{3a^4}{20} \int_0^{2\pi} d\theta \qquad \text{Simplify.}$$

$$= \frac{3\pi a^4}{10}. \qquad \text{Evaluate outer integral with respect to } \theta.$$

The z-coordinate of the center of mass is $\bar{z} = \dfrac{M_{xy}}{m} = \dfrac{3\pi a^4/10}{5\pi a^3/6} = \dfrac{9a}{25} = 0.36a$. It can be shown (Exercise 56) that the center of mass of a uniform-density hemispherical solid of radius a is $3a/8 = 0.375a$ units above the base. In this case, the variable density lowers the center of mass toward the base.

Related Exercises 33–38 ◀

SECTION 13.6 EXERCISES

Review Questions

1. Explain how to find the balance point for two people on opposite ends of a (massless) plank that rests on a pivot.

2. If a thin 1-m cylindrical rod has a density of $\rho = 1$ g/cm for its left half and a density of $\rho = 2$ g/cm for its right half, what is its mass and where is its center of mass?

3. Explain how to find the center of mass of a thin plate with a variable density.

4. In the integral for the moment M_x of a thin plate, why does y appear in the integrand?

5. Explain how to find the center of mass of a three-dimensional object with a variable density.

6. In the integral for the moment M_{xz} with respect to the xz-plane of a solid, why does y appear in the integrand?

Basic Skills

7–8. Individual masses on a line *Sketch the following systems on a number line and find the location of the center of mass.*

7. $m_1 = 10$ kg located at $x = 3$ m; $m_2 = 3$ kg located at $x = -1$ m

8. $m_1 = 8$ kg located at $x = 2$ m; $m_2 = 4$ kg located at $x = -4$ m; $m_3 = 1$ kg located at $x = 0$ m

9–14. One-dimensional objects *Find the mass and center of mass of the thin rods with the following density functions.*

9. $\rho(x) = 1 + \sin x$, for $0 \le x \le \pi$

10. $\rho(x) = 1 + x^3$, for $0 \le x \le 1$

11. $\rho(x) = 2 - x^2/16$, for $0 \le x \le 4$

12. $\rho(x) = 2 + \cos x$, for $0 \le x \le \pi$

13. $\rho(x) = \begin{cases} 1 & \text{if } 0 \le x \le 2 \\ 1 + x & \text{if } 2 < x \le 4 \end{cases}$

14. $\rho(x) = \begin{cases} x^2 & \text{if } 0 \le x \le 1 \\ x(2 - x) & \text{if } 1 < x \le 2 \end{cases}$

15–20. Centroid calculations *Find the mass and centroid (center of mass) of the following thin plates, assuming constant density. Sketch the region corresponding to the plate and indicate the location of the center of mass. Use symmetry when possible to simplify your work.*

15. The region bounded by $y = \sin x$ and $y = 1 - \sin x$ between $x = \pi/4$ and $x = 3\pi/4$

16. The region in the first quadrant bounded by $x^2 + y^2 = 16$

17. The region bounded by $y = 1 - |x|$ and the x-axis

18. The region bounded by $y = e^x, y = e^{-x}, x = 0$, and $x = \ln 2$

19. The region bounded by $y = \ln x$, the x-axis, and $x = e$

20. The region bounded by $x^2 + y^2 = 1$ and $x^2 + y^2 = 9$, for $y \geq 0$

21–26. Variable-density plates *Find the center of mass of the following plane regions with variable density. Describe the distribution of mass in the region.*

21. $R = \{(x, y): 0 \leq x \leq 4, 0 \leq y \leq 2\}; \ \rho(x, y) = 1 + x/2$

22. $R = \{(x, y): 0 \leq x \leq 1, 0 \leq y \leq 5\}; \ \rho(x, y) = 2e^{-y/2}$

23. The triangular plate in the first quadrant bounded by $x + y = 4$ with $\rho(x, y) = 1 + x + y$

24. The upper half $(y \geq 0)$ of the disk bounded by the circle $x^2 + y^2 = 4$ with $\rho(x, y) = 1 + y/2$

25. The upper half $(y \geq 0)$ of the plate bounded by the ellipse $x^2 + 9y^2 = 9$ with $\rho(x, y) = 1 + y$

26. The quarter disk in the first quadrant bounded by $x^2 + y^2 = 4$ with $\rho(x, y) = 1 + x^2 + y^2$

27–32. Center of mass of constant-density solids *Find the center of mass of the following solids, assuming a constant density of 1. Sketch the region and indicate the location of the centroid. Use symmetry when possible and choose a convenient coordinate system.*

27. The upper half of the ball $x^2 + y^2 + z^2 \leq 16$ (for $z \geq 0$)

28. The solid bounded by the paraboloid $z = x^2 + y^2$ and the plane $z = 25$

29. The tetrahedron in the first octant bounded by $z = 1 - x - y$ and the coordinate planes

30. The solid bounded by the cone $z = 16 - r$ and the plane $z = 0$

31. The sliced solid cylinder bounded by $x^2 + y^2 = 1, z = 0$, and $y + z = 1$

32. The solid bounded by the upper half $(z \geq 0)$ of the ellipsoid $4x^2 + 4y^2 + z^2 = 16$

33–38. Variable-density solids *Find the coordinates of the center of mass of the following solids with variable density.*

33. $R = \{(x, y, z): 0 \leq x \leq 4, 0 \leq y \leq 1, 0 \leq z \leq 1\}; \ \rho(x, y, z) = 1 + x/2$

34. The solid bounded by the paraboloid $z = 4 - x^2 - y^2$ and $z = 0$ with $\rho(x, y, z) = 5 - z$

35. The solid bounded by the upper half of the sphere $\rho = 6$ and $z = 0$ with density $f(\rho, \varphi, \theta) = 1 + \rho/4$

36. The interior of the cube in the first octant formed by the planes $x = 1, y = 1$, and $z = 1$ with $\rho(x, y, z) = 2 + x + y + z$

37. The interior of the prism formed by $z = x, x = 1, y = 4$, and the coordinate planes with $\rho(x, y, z) = 2 + y$

38. The solid bounded by the cone by $z = 9 - r$ and $z = 0$ with $\rho(r, \theta, z) = 1 + z$

Further Explorations

39. Explain why or why not Determine whether the following statements are true and give an explanation or counterexample.

   a. A thin plate of constant density that is symmetric about the x-axis has a center of mass with an x-coordinate of zero.

   b. A thin plate of constant density that is symmetric about both the x-axis and the y-axis has its center of mass at the origin.

   c. The center of mass of a thin plate must lie on the plate.

   d. The center of mass of a connected solid region (all in one piece) must lie within the region.

40. Limiting center of mass A thin rod of length L has a linear density given by $\rho(x) = 2e^{-x/3}$ on the interval $0 \leq x \leq L$. Find the mass and center of mass of the rod. How does the center of mass change as $L \to \infty$?

41. Limiting center of mass A thin rod of length L has a linear density given by $\rho(x) = \dfrac{10}{1 + x^2}$ on the interval $0 \leq x \leq L$. Find the mass and center of mass of the rod. How does the center of mass change as $L \to \infty$?

42. Limiting center of mass A thin plate is bounded by the graphs of $y = e^{-x}, y = -e^{-x}, x = 0$, and $x = L$. Find its center of mass. How does the center of mass change as $L \to \infty$?

43–44. Two-dimensional plates *Find the mass and center of mass of the thin constant-density plates shown in the figure.*

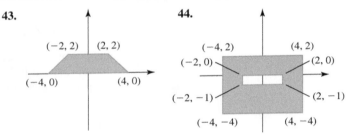

43.

$(-2, 2)$ | $(2, 2)$

$(-4, 0)$ $(4, 0)$

44.

$(-4, 2)$ $(4, 2)$

$(-2, 0)$ $(2, 0)$

$(-2, -1)$ $(2, -1)$

$(-4, -4)$ $(4, -4)$

45–50. Centroids *Use polar coordinates to find the centroid of the following constant-density plane regions.*

45. The semicircular disk $R = \{(r, \theta): 0 \leq r \leq 2, 0 \leq \theta \leq \pi\}$

46. The quarter-circular disk $R = \{(r, \theta): 0 \leq r \leq 2, 0 \leq \theta \leq \pi/2\}$

47. The region bounded by the cardioid $r = 1 + \cos \theta$

48. The region bounded by the cardioid $r = 3 - 3 \cos \theta$

49. The region bounded by one leaf of the rose $r = \sin 2\theta$, for $0 \leq \theta \leq \pi/2$

50. The region bounded by the limaçon $r = 2 + \cos \theta$

51. Semicircular wire A thin (one-dimensional) wire of constant density is bent into the shape of a semicircle of radius a. Find the location of its center of mass. (*Hint:* Treat the wire as a thin half-annulus with width Δa, and then let $\Delta a \to 0$.)

52. Parabolic region A thin plate of unit density occupies the region between the parabola $y = ax^2$ and the horizontal line $y = b$, where $a > 0$ and $b > 0$. Show that the center of mass is $\left(0, \dfrac{3b}{5}\right)$, independent of a.

53. Circular crescent Find the center of mass of the region in the first quadrant bounded by the circle $x^2 + y^2 = a^2$ and the lines $x = a$ and $y = a$, where $a > 0$.

54–59. Centers of mass for general objects *Consider the following two- and three-dimensional regions. Specify the surfaces and curves that bound the region, choose a convenient coordinate system, and compute the center of mass assuming constant density. All parameters are positive real numbers.*

54. A solid rectangular box has sides of length a, b, and c. Where is the center of mass relative to the faces of the box?

55. A solid cone has a base with a radius of a and a height of h. How far from the base is the center of mass?

56. A solid is enclosed by a hemisphere of radius a. How far from the base is the center of mass?

57. A region is enclosed by an isosceles triangle with two sides of length s and a base of length b. How far from the base is the center of mass?

58. A tetrahedron is bounded by the coordinate planes and the plane $x/a + y/a + z/a = 1$. What are the coordinates of the center of mass?

59. A solid is enclosed by the upper half of an ellipsoid with a circular base of radius r and a height of a. How far from the base is the center of mass?

Applications

60. Geographic vs. population center Geographers measure the *geographical center* of a country (which is the centroid) and the *population center* of a country (which is the center of mass computed with the population density). A hypothetical country is shown in the figure with the location and population of five towns. Assuming no one lives outside the towns, find the geographical center of the country and the population center of the country.

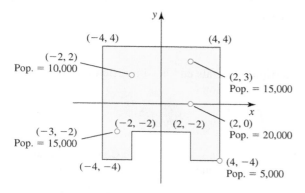

61. Center of mass on the edge Consider the thin constant-density plate $\{(r, \theta): 0 < a \le r \le 1, 0 \le \theta \le \pi\}$ bounded by two semicircles and the x-axis.

    a. Find and graph the y-coordinate of the center of mass of the plate as a function of a.

    b. For what value of a is the center of mass on the edge of the plate?

62. Center of mass on the edge Consider the constant-density solid $\{(\rho, \varphi, \theta): 0 < a \le \rho \le 1, 0 \le \varphi \le \pi/2, 0 \le \theta \le 2\pi\}$ bounded by two hemispheres and the xy-plane.

    a. Find and graph the z-coordinate of the center of mass of the plate as a function of a.

    b. For what value of a is the center of mass on the edge of the solid?

63. Draining a soda can A cylindrical soda can has a radius of 4 cm and a height of 12 cm. When the can is full of soda, the center of mass of the contents of the can is 6 cm above the base on the axis of the can (halfway along the axis of the can). As the can is drained, the center of mass descends for a while. However, when the can is empty (filled only with air), the center of mass is once again 6 cm above the base on the axis of the can. Find the depth of soda in the can for which the center of mass is at its lowest point. Neglect the mass of the can and assume the density of the soda is 1 g/cm³ and the density of air is 0.001 g/cm³.

Additional Exercises

64. Triangle medians A triangular region has a base that connects the vertices $(0, 0)$ and $(b, 0)$, and a third vertex at (a, h), where $a > 0, b > 0$, and $h > 0$.

    a. Show that the centroid of the triangle is $\left(\dfrac{a + b}{3}, \dfrac{h}{3}\right)$.

    b. Recall that the three medians of a triangle extend from each vertex to the midpoint of the opposite side. Knowing that the medians of a triangle intersect in a point M and that each median bisects the triangle, conclude that the centroid of the triangle is M.

65. The golden earring A disk of radius r is removed from a larger disk of radius R to form an earring (see figure). Assume the earring is a thin plate of uniform density.

    a. Find the center of mass of the earring in terms of r and R. (*Hint:* Place the origin of a coordinate system either at the center of the large disk or at Q; either way, the earring is symmetric about the x-axis.)

    b. Show that the ratio R/r such that the center of mass lies at the point P (on the edge of the inner disk) is the golden mean $(1 + \sqrt{5})/2 \approx 1.618$.

(*Source:* P. Glaister, *Golden Earrings, Mathematical Gazette*, 80, 1996)

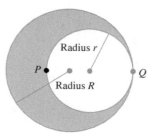

13.7 Change of Variables in Multiple Integrals

Converting double integrals from rectangular coordinates to polar coordinates (Section 13.3) and converting triple integrals from rectangular coordinates to cylindrical or spherical coordinates (Section 13.5) are examples of a general procedure known as a *change of variables*. The idea is not new: The Substitution Rule introduced in Chapter 5 with single-variable integrals is also a change of variables. The aim of this section is to show how to change variables in double and triple integrals.

Recap of Change of Variables

Recall how a change of variables is used to simplify a single-variable integral. For example, to simplify the integral $\int_0^1 2\sqrt{2x+1}\,dx$, we choose a new variable $u = 2x + 1$, which means that $du = 2\,dx$. Therefore,

$$\int_0^1 2\sqrt{2x+1}\,dx = \int_1^3 \sqrt{u}\,du.$$

This equality means that the area under the curve $y = 2\sqrt{2x+1}$ from $x = 0$ to $x = 1$ equals the area under the curve $y = \sqrt{u}$ from $u = 1$ to $u = 3$ (Figure 13.76). The relation $du = 2\,dx$ relates the length of a small interval on the u-axis to the length of the corresponding interval on the x-axis.

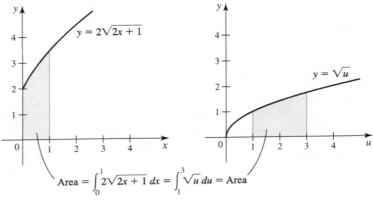

$$\text{Area} = \int_0^1 2\sqrt{2x+1}\,dx = \int_1^3 \sqrt{u}\,du = \text{Area}$$

Figure 13.76

Similarly, some double and triple integrals can be simplified through a change of variables. For example, the region of integration for

$$\int_0^1 \int_0^{\sqrt{1-x^2}} e^{1-x^2-y^2}\,dy\,dx$$

is the quarter disk $R = \{(x, y) : x \geq 0, y \geq 0, x^2 + y^2 \leq 1\}$. Changing variables to polar coordinates with $x = r\cos\theta$, $y = r\sin\theta$, and $dy\,dx = r\,dr\,d\theta$, we have

$$\int_0^1 \int_0^{\sqrt{1-x^2}} e^{1-x^2-y^2}\,dy\,dx \quad \overset{\substack{x = r\cos\theta \\ y = r\sin\theta}}{=} \quad \int_0^{\pi/2} \int_0^1 e^{1-r^2} r\,dr\,d\theta.$$

In this case, the original region of integration R is transformed into a new region $S = \{(r, \theta) : 0 \leq r \leq 1, 0 \leq \theta \leq \pi/2\}$, which is a rectangle in the $r\theta$-plane.

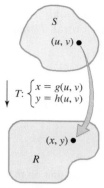

Figure 13.77

➤ In Example 1, we have replaced the coordinates u and v with the familiar polar coordinates r and θ.

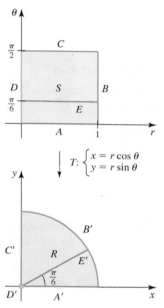

Figure 13.78

Transformations in the Plane

A change of variables in a double integral is a *transformation* that relates two sets of variables, (u, v) and (x, y). It is written compactly as $(x, y) = T(u, v)$. Because it relates pairs of variables, T has two components,

$$T: x = g(u, v) \quad \text{and} \quad y = h(u, v).$$

Geometrically, T takes a region S in the uv-plane and "maps" it point by point to a region R in the xy-plane (Figure 13.77). We write the outcome of this process as $R = T(S)$ and call R the **image** of S under T.

EXAMPLE 1 Image of a transformation Consider the transformation from polar to rectangular coordinates given by

$$T: \quad x = g(r, \theta) = r \cos \theta \quad \text{and} \quad y = h(r, \theta) = r \sin \theta.$$

Find the image under this transformation of the rectangle

$$S = \{(r, \theta): 0 \le r \le 1, 0 \le \theta \le \pi/2\}.$$

SOLUTION If we apply T to every point of S (Figure 13.78), what is the resulting set R in the xy-plane? One way to answer this question is to walk around the boundary of S, let's say counterclockwise, and determine the corresponding path in the xy-plane. In the $r\theta$-plane, we let the horizontal axis be the r-axis and the vertical axis be the θ-axis. Starting at the origin, we denote the edges of the rectangle S as follows.

$$A = \{(r, \theta): 0 \le r \le 1, \theta = 0\} \qquad \text{Lower boundary}$$

$$B = \left\{(r, \theta): r = 1, 0 \le \theta \le \frac{\pi}{2}\right\} \qquad \text{Right boundary}$$

$$C = \left\{(r, \theta): 0 \le r \le 1, \theta = \frac{\pi}{2}\right\} \qquad \text{Upper boundary}$$

$$D = \left\{(r, \theta): r = 0, 0 \le \theta \le \frac{\pi}{2}\right\} \qquad \text{Left boundary}$$

Table 13.6 shows the effect of the transformation on the four boundaries of S; the corresponding boundaries of R in the xy-plane are denoted A', B', C', and D' (Figure 13.78).

Table 13.6

Boundary of S in $r\theta$-plane	Transformation equations	Boundary of R in xy-plane
A: $0 \le r \le 1, \theta = 0$	$x = r \cos \theta = r,$ $y = r \sin \theta = 0$	A': $0 \le x \le 1, y = 0$
B: $r = 1, 0 \le \theta \le \pi/2$	$x = r \cos \theta = \cos \theta,$ $y = r \sin \theta = \sin \theta$	B': quarter unit circle
C: $0 \le r \le 1, \theta = \pi/2$	$x = r \cos \theta = 0,$ $y = r \sin \theta = r$	C': $x = 0, 0 \le y \le 1$
D: $r = 0, 0 \le \theta \le \pi/2$	$x = r \cos \theta = 0,$ $y = r \sin \theta = 0$	D': single point $(0, 0)$

The image of the rectangular boundary of S is the boundary of R. Furthermore, it can be shown that every point in the interior of R is the image of one point in the interior of S. (For example, the horizontal line segment E in the $r\theta$-plane in Figure 13.78 is mapped to the line segment E' in the xy-plane.) Therefore, the image of S is the quarter disk R in the xy-plane.

Related Exercises 5–16 ◄

QUICK CHECK 1 How would the image of S change in Example 1 if $S = \{(r, \theta): 0 \le r \le 1, 0 \le \theta \le \pi\}$? ◄

Recall that a function f is *one-to-one* on an interval I if $f(x_1) = f(x_2)$ only when $x_1 = x_2$, where x_1 and x_2 are points of I. We need an analogous property for transformations when changing variables.

DEFINITION One-to-One Transformation

A transformation T from a region S to a region R is one-to-one on S if $T(P) = T(Q)$ only when $P = Q$, where P and Q are points in S.

Notice that the polar coordinate transformation in Example 1 is not one-to-one on the rectangle $S = \{(r, \theta): 0 \le r \le 1, 0 \le \theta \le \pi/2\}$ (because all points with $r = 0$ map to the point $(0, 0)$). However, this transformation *is* one-to-one on the interior of S.

We can now anticipate how a transformation (change of variables) is used to simplify a double integral. Suppose we have the integral $\iint_R f(x, y)\, dA$. The goal is to find a transformation to a new set of coordinates (u, v) such that the new equivalent integral $\iint_S f(x(u, v), y(u, v))\, dA$ involves a simple region S (such as a rectangle), a simple integrand, or both. The next theorem allows us to do exactly that, but it first requires a new concept.

> ▶ The Jacobian is named after the German mathematician Carl Gustav Jacob Jacobi (1804–1851). In some books, the Jacobian is the matrix of partial derivatives. In others, as here, the Jacobian is the determinant of the matrix of partial derivatives. Both $J(u, v)$ and $\dfrac{\partial(x, y)}{\partial(u, v)}$ are used to refer to the Jacobian.

DEFINITION Jacobian Determinant of a Transformation of Two Variables

Given a transformation $T: x = g(u, v), y = h(u, v)$, where g and h are differentiable on a region of the uv-plane, the **Jacobian determinant** (or **Jacobian**) of T is

$$J(u, v) = \frac{\partial(x, y)}{\partial(u, v)} = \begin{vmatrix} \dfrac{\partial x}{\partial u} & \dfrac{\partial x}{\partial v} \\[2mm] \dfrac{\partial y}{\partial u} & \dfrac{\partial y}{\partial v} \end{vmatrix} = \frac{\partial x}{\partial u}\frac{\partial y}{\partial v} - \frac{\partial x}{\partial v}\frac{\partial y}{\partial u}.$$

> **QUICK CHECK 2** Find $J(u, v)$ if $x = u + v, y = 2v$. ◀

The Jacobian is easiest to remember as the determinant of a 2×2 matrix of partial derivatives. With the Jacobian in hand, we can state the change-of-variables rule for double integrals.

> ▶ The condition that g and h have continuous first partial derivatives ensures that the new integrand is integrable.

THEOREM 13.8   Change of Variables for Double Integrals

Let $T: x = g(u, v), y = h(u, v)$ be a transformation that maps a closed bounded region S in the uv-plane onto a region R in the xy-plane. Assume that T is one-to-one on the interior of S and that g and h have continuous first partial derivatives there. If f is continuous on R, then

$$\iint\limits_R f(x, y)\, dA = \iint\limits_S f(g(u, v), h(u, v))\, |J(u, v)|\, dA.$$

> ▶ In the integral over R, dA corresponds to $dx\, dy$. In the integral over S, dA corresponds to $du\, dv$. The relation $dx\, dy = |J|\, du\, dv$ is the analog of $du = g'(x)\, dx$ in a change of variables with one variable.

The proof of this result is technical and is found in advanced texts. The factor $|J(u, v)|$ that appears in the second integral is the absolute value of the Jacobian. Matching the area elements in the two integrals of Theorem 13.8, we see that $dx\, dy = |J(u, v)|\, du\, dv$. This expression shows that the Jacobian is a magnification (or reduction) factor: It relates the area of a small region $dx\, dy$ in the xy-plane to the area of the corresponding region $du\, dv$ in the uv-plane. If the transformation equations are linear, then this relationship is exact in the sense that $\text{area}(T(S)) = |J(u, v)|\, \text{area}(S)$ (see Exercise 60). The way in which the Jacobian arises is explored in Exercise 61.

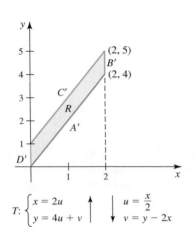

$$T: \begin{cases} x = 2u \\ y = 4u + v \end{cases} \qquad \begin{cases} u = \dfrac{x}{2} \\ v = y - 2x \end{cases}$$

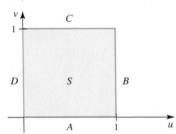

Figure 13.79

▶ The relations that "go the other direction" comprise the inverse transformation, usually denoted T^{-1}.

Table 13.7

(x, y)	(u, v)
$(0, 0)$	$(0, 0)$
$(0, 1)$	$(0, 1)$
$(2, 5)$	$(1, 1)$
$(2, 4)$	$(1, 0)$

EXAMPLE 2   Jacobian of the polar-to-rectangular transformation Compute the Jacobian of the transformation

$$T: \quad x = g(r, \theta) = r \cos \theta, \qquad y = h(r, \theta) = r \sin \theta.$$

SOLUTION The necessary partial derivatives are

$$\frac{\partial x}{\partial r} = \cos \theta, \qquad \frac{\partial x}{\partial \theta} = -r \sin \theta, \qquad \frac{\partial y}{\partial r} = \sin \theta, \quad \text{and} \quad \frac{\partial y}{\partial \theta} = r \cos \theta.$$

Therefore,

$$J(r, \theta) = \frac{\partial(x, y)}{\partial(r, \theta)} = \begin{vmatrix} \dfrac{\partial x}{\partial r} & \dfrac{\partial x}{\partial \theta} \\ \dfrac{\partial y}{\partial r} & \dfrac{\partial y}{\partial \theta} \end{vmatrix} = \begin{vmatrix} \cos \theta & -r \sin \theta \\ \sin \theta & r \cos \theta \end{vmatrix} = r(\cos^2 \theta + \sin^2 \theta) = r.$$

This determinant calculation confirms the change-of-variables formula for polar coordinates: $dx \, dy$ becomes $r \, dr \, d\theta$.

Related Exercises 17–26 ◀

We are now ready for a change of variables. To transform the integral $\iint_R f(x, y) \, dA$ into $\iint_S f(x(u, v), y(u, v)) |J(u, v)| \, dA$, we must find the transformation $x = g(u, v)$ and $y = h(u, v)$, and then use it to find the new region of integration S. The next example illustrates how the region S is found, assuming the transformation is given.

EXAMPLE 3   Double integral with a change of variables given Evaluate the integral $\iint_R \sqrt{2x(y - 2x)} \, dA$, where R is the parallelogram in the xy-plane with vertices $(0, 0)$, $(0, 1)$, $(2, 4)$, and $(2, 5)$ (Figure 13.79). Use the transformation

$$T: x = 2u, \, y = 4u + v.$$

SOLUTION To what region S in the uv-plane is R mapped? Because T takes points in the uv-plane and assigns them to points in the xy-plane, we must reverse the process by solving $x = 2u, y = 4u + v$ for u and v.

$$\text{First equation: } x = 2u \implies u = \frac{x}{2}$$

$$\text{Second equation: } y = 4u + v \implies v = y - 4u = y - 2x$$

Rather than walk around the boundary of R in the xy-plane to determine the resulting region S in the uv-plane, it suffices to find the images of the vertices of R. You should confirm that the vertices map as shown in Table 13.7.

Connecting the points in the uv-plane in order, we see that S is the unit square $\{(u, v): 0 \le u \le 1, 0 \le v \le 1\}$ (Figure 13.79). These inequalities determine the limits of integration in the uv-plane.

Replacing $2x$ with $4u$ and $y - 2x$ with v, the original integrand becomes $\sqrt{2x(y - 2x)} = \sqrt{4uv}$. The Jacobian is

$$J(u, v) = \begin{vmatrix} \dfrac{\partial x}{\partial u} & \dfrac{\partial x}{\partial v} \\ \dfrac{\partial y}{\partial u} & \dfrac{\partial y}{\partial v} \end{vmatrix} = \begin{vmatrix} 2 & 0 \\ 4 & 1 \end{vmatrix} = 2.$$

> ➤ T is an example of a *shearing transformation*. The greater the u-coordinate of a point, the more that point is displaced in the v-direction. It also involves a uniform stretch in the u-direction.

The integration now follows:

$$\iint_R \sqrt{2x(y-2x)}\, dA = \iint_S \sqrt{4uv}\, \underbrace{|J(u,v)|}_{2}\, dA \qquad \text{Change variables.}$$

$$= \int_0^1 \int_0^1 \sqrt{4uv}\, 2\, du\, dv \qquad \text{Convert to an iterated integral.}$$

$$= 4 \int_0^1 \frac{2}{3} \sqrt{v}\, (u^{3/2}) \Big|_0^1\, dv \qquad \text{Evaluate inner integral.}$$

$$= \frac{8}{3} \cdot \frac{2}{3} (v^{3/2}) \Big|_0^1 = \frac{16}{9}. \qquad \text{Evaluate outer integral.}$$

The effect of the change of variables is illustrated in Figure 13.80, where we see the surface $z = \sqrt{2x(y-2x)}$ over the region R and the surface $w = 2\sqrt{4uv}$ over the region S. The volumes of the solids beneath the two surfaces are equal, but the integral over S is easier to evaluate.

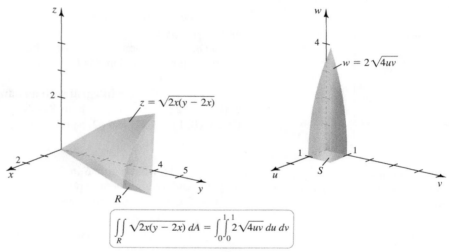

$$\iint_R \sqrt{2x(y-2x)}\, dA = \int_0^1 \int_0^1 2\sqrt{4uv}\, du\, dv$$

Figure 13.80

Related Exercises 27–30 ◄

QUICK CHECK 3 Solve the equations $u = x + y$, $v = -x + 2y$ for x and y. ◄

In Example 3, the required transformation was given. More practically, we must deduce an appropriate transformation from the form of either the integrand or the region of integration.

EXAMPLE 4 Change of variables determined by the integrand Evaluate $\iint_R \sqrt{\dfrac{x-y}{x+y+1}}\, dA$, where R is the square with vertices $(0,0)$, $(1,-1)$, $(2,0)$, and $(1,1)$ (Figure 13.81).

SOLUTION Evaluating the integral as it stands requires splitting the region R into two subregions; furthermore, the integrand presents difficulties. The terms $x + y$ and $x - y$ in the integrand suggest the new variables

$$u = x - y \quad \text{and} \quad v = x + y.$$

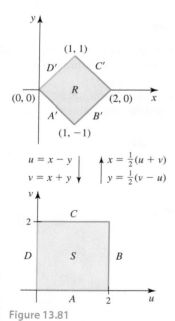

Figure 13.81

▶ The transformation in Example 4 is a *rotation*. It rotates the points of R about the origin 45° in the counterclockwise direction (it also increases lengths by a factor of $\sqrt{2}$). In this example, the change of variables $u = x + y$ and $v = x - y$ would work just as well.

To determine the region S in the uv-plane that corresponds to R under this transformation, we find the images of the vertices of R in the uv-plane and connect them in order. The result is the square $S = \{(u, v): 0 \leq u \leq 2, 0 \leq v \leq 2\}$ (Figure 13.81). Before computing the Jacobian, we express x and y in terms of u and v. Adding the two equations and solving for x, we have $x = (u + v)/2$. Subtracting the two equations and solving for y gives $y = (v - u)/2$. The Jacobian now follows:

$$J(u, v) = \begin{vmatrix} \dfrac{\partial x}{\partial u} & \dfrac{\partial x}{\partial v} \\ \dfrac{\partial y}{\partial u} & \dfrac{\partial y}{\partial v} \end{vmatrix} = \begin{vmatrix} \dfrac{1}{2} & \dfrac{1}{2} \\ -\dfrac{1}{2} & \dfrac{1}{2} \end{vmatrix} = \dfrac{1}{2}.$$

▶ An appropriate change of variables for a double integral is not always obvious. Some trial and error is often needed to come up with a transformation that simplifies the integrand and/or the region of integration. Strategies are discussed at the end of this section.

With the choice of new variables, the original integrand $\sqrt{\dfrac{x - y}{x + y + 1}}$ becomes $\sqrt{\dfrac{u}{v + 1}}$. The integration in the uv-plane may now be done:

$$\iint_R \sqrt{\dfrac{x - y}{x + y + 1}}\, dA = \iint_S \sqrt{\dfrac{u}{v + 1}}\, |J(u, v)|\, dA \qquad \text{Change of variables}$$

$$= \int_0^2 \int_0^2 \sqrt{\dfrac{u}{v + 1}}\, \dfrac{1}{2}\, du\, dv \qquad \text{Convert to an iterated integral.}$$

$$= \dfrac{1}{2} \int_0^2 (v + 1)^{-1/2} \dfrac{2}{3}\, (u^{3/2}) \Big|_0^2 dv \qquad \text{Evaluate inner integral.}$$

$$= \dfrac{2^{3/2}}{3}\, 2(v + 1)^{1/2} \Big|_0^2 \qquad \text{Evaluate outer integral.}$$

$$= \dfrac{4\sqrt{2}}{3} (\sqrt{3} - 1). \qquad \text{Simplify.}$$

Related Exercises 31–36 ◄

QUICK CHECK 4 In Example 4, what is the ratio of the area of S to the area of R? How is this ratio related to J? ◄

EXAMPLE 5 **Change of variables determined by the region** Let R be the region in the first quadrant bounded by the parabolas $x = y^2$, $x = y^2 - 4$, $x = 9 - y^2$, and $x = 16 - y^2$ (Figure 13.82). Evaluate $\iint_R y^2\, dA$.

SOLUTION Notice that the bounding curves may be written as $x - y^2 = 0$, $x - y^2 = -4$, $x + y^2 = 9$, and $x + y^2 = 16$. The first two parabolas have the form $x - y^2 = C$, where C is a constant, which suggests the new variable $u = x - y^2$. The last two parabolas have the form $x + y^2 = C$, which suggests the new variable $v = x + y^2$. Therefore, the new variables are

$$u = x - y^2, \quad v = x + y^2.$$

The boundary curves of S are $u = -4$, $u = 0$, $v = 9$, and $v = 16$. Therefore, the new region is $S = \{(u, v): -4 \leq u \leq 0, 9 \leq v \leq 16\}$ (Figure 13.82). To compute the Jacobian, we must find the transformation T by writing x and y in terms of u and v. Solving for x and y, and observing that $y \geq 0$ for all points in R, we find that

$$T: \quad x = \dfrac{u + v}{2}, \quad y = \sqrt{\dfrac{v - u}{2}}.$$

The points of S satisfy $v > u$, so $\sqrt{v - u}$ is defined. Now the Jacobian may be computed:

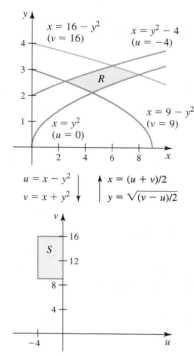

Figure 13.82

$$J(u, v) = \begin{vmatrix} \dfrac{\partial x}{\partial u} & \dfrac{\partial x}{\partial v} \\ \dfrac{\partial y}{\partial u} & \dfrac{\partial y}{\partial v} \end{vmatrix} = \begin{vmatrix} \dfrac{1}{2} & \dfrac{1}{2} \\ -\dfrac{1}{2\sqrt{2(v - u)}} & \dfrac{1}{2\sqrt{2(v - u)}} \end{vmatrix} = \dfrac{1}{2\sqrt{2(v - u)}}.$$

The change of variables proceeds as follows:

$$\iint\limits_{R} y^2 \, dA = \int_{9}^{16} \int_{-4}^{0} \underbrace{\frac{v - u}{2}}_{y^2} \underbrace{\frac{1}{2\sqrt{2(v - u)}}}_{|J(u, v)|} \, du \, dv \qquad \text{Convert to an iterated integral.}$$

$$= \frac{1}{4\sqrt{2}} \int_{9}^{16} \int_{-4}^{0} \sqrt{v - u} \, du \, dv \qquad \text{Simplify.}$$

$$= \frac{1}{4\sqrt{2}} \frac{2}{3} \int_{9}^{16} \left. \left(-(v - u)^{3/2} \right) \right|_{-4}^{0} dv \qquad \text{Evaluate inner integral.}$$

$$= \frac{1}{6\sqrt{2}} \int_{9}^{16} \left((v + 4)^{3/2} - v^{3/2} \right) dv \qquad \text{Simplify.}$$

$$= \frac{1}{6\sqrt{2}} \frac{2}{5} \left. \left((v + 4)^{5/2} - v^{5/2} \right) \right|_{9}^{16} \qquad \text{Evaluate outer integral.}$$

$$= \frac{\sqrt{2}}{30} \left(32 \cdot 5^{5/2} - 13^{5/2} - 781 \right) \qquad \text{Simplify.}$$

$$\approx 18.79.$$

Related Exercises 31–36 ◄

Change of Variables in Triple Integrals

With triple integrals, we work with a transformation T of the form

$$T: \qquad x = g(u, v, w), \quad y = h(u, v, w), \quad z = p(u, v, w).$$

In this case, T maps a region S in uvw-space to a region D in xyz-space. As before, the goal is to transform the integral $\iiint_{D} f(x, y, z) \, dV$ into a new integral over the region S that is easier to evaluate. First, we need a Jacobian.

> Recall that by expanding about the first row,
>
> $$\begin{vmatrix} a_{11} & a_{12} & a_{13} \\ a_{21} & a_{22} & a_{23} \\ a_{31} & a_{32} & a_{33} \end{vmatrix}$$
>
> $$= a_{11}(a_{22}a_{33} - a_{23}a_{32})$$
> $$- a_{12}(a_{21}a_{33} - a_{23}a_{31})$$
> $$+ a_{13}(a_{21}a_{32} - a_{22}a_{31}).$$

DEFINITION Jacobian Determinant of a Transformation of Three Variables

Given a transformation $T: x = g(u, v, w)$, $y = h(u, v, w)$, and $z = p(u, v, w)$, where g, h, and p are differentiable on a region of uvw-space, the **Jacobian determinant** (or **Jacobian**) of T is

$$J(u, v, w) = \frac{\partial(x, y, z)}{\partial(u, v, w)} = \begin{vmatrix} \dfrac{\partial x}{\partial u} & \dfrac{\partial x}{\partial v} & \dfrac{\partial x}{\partial w} \\[2mm] \dfrac{\partial y}{\partial u} & \dfrac{\partial y}{\partial v} & \dfrac{\partial y}{\partial w} \\[2mm] \dfrac{\partial z}{\partial u} & \dfrac{\partial z}{\partial v} & \dfrac{\partial z}{\partial w} \end{vmatrix}.$$

The Jacobian is evaluated as a 3×3 determinant and is a function of u, v, and w. A change of variables with respect to three variables proceeds in analogy to the two-variable case.

> If we match the elements of volume in both integrals, then $dx \, dy \, dz = |J(u, v, w)| \, du \, dv \, dw$. As before, the Jacobian is a magnification (or reduction) factor, now relating the volume of a small region in xyz-space to the volume of the corresponding region in uvw-space.

THEOREM 13.9   Change of Variables for Triple Integrals

Let $T: x = g(u, v, w)$, $y = h(u, v, w)$, and $z = p(u, v, w)$ be a transformation that maps a closed bounded region S in uvw-space to a region $D = T(S)$ in xyz-space. Assume that T is one-to-one on the interior of S and that g, h, and p have continuous first partial derivatives there. If f is continuous on D, then

$$\iiint\limits_{D} f(x, y, z) \, dV = \iiint\limits_{S} f(g(u, v, w), h(u, v, w), p(u, v, w)) \, |J(u, v, w)| \, dV.$$

▶ To see that triple integrals in cylindrical and spherical coordinates as derived in Section 13.5 are consistent with this change-of-variables formulation, see Exercises 46 and 47.

EXAMPLE 6 **A triple integral** Use a change of variables to evaluate $\iiint_D xz \, dV$, where D is a parallelepiped bounded by the planes

$$y = x, \quad y = x + 2, \quad z = x, \quad z = x + 3, \quad z = 0, \quad \text{and} \quad z = 4$$

(Figure 13.83a).

SOLUTION The key is to note that D is bounded by three pairs of parallel planes.

- $y - x = 0$ and $y - x = 2$
- $z - x = 0$ and $z - x = 3$
- $z = 0$ and $z = 4$

These combinations of variables suggest the new variables

$$u = y - x, \quad v = z - x, \quad \text{and} \quad w = z.$$

With this choice, the new region of integration (Figure 13.83b) is the rectangular box

$$S = \{(u, v, w): 0 \le u \le 2, 0 \le v \le 3, 0 \le w \le 4\}.$$

To compute the Jacobian, we must express x, y, and z in terms of u, v, and w. A few steps of algebra lead to the transformation

$$T: \quad x = w - v, \quad y = u - v + w, \quad \text{and} \quad z = w.$$

The resulting Jacobian is

$$J(u, v, w) = \begin{vmatrix} \dfrac{\partial x}{\partial u} & \dfrac{\partial x}{\partial v} & \dfrac{\partial x}{\partial w} \\ \dfrac{\partial y}{\partial u} & \dfrac{\partial y}{\partial v} & \dfrac{\partial y}{\partial w} \\ \dfrac{\partial z}{\partial u} & \dfrac{\partial z}{\partial v} & \dfrac{\partial z}{\partial w} \end{vmatrix} = \begin{vmatrix} 0 & -1 & 1 \\ 1 & -1 & 1 \\ 0 & 0 & 1 \end{vmatrix} = 1.$$

Noting that the integrand is $xz = (w - v)w = w^2 - vw$, the integral may now be evaluated:

▶ It is easiest to expand the Jacobian determinant in Example 6 about the third row.

$$\iiint_D xz \, dV = \iiint_S (w^2 - vw) \, |J(u, v, w)| \, dV \qquad \text{Change variables.}$$

$$= \int_0^4 \int_0^3 \int_0^2 (w^2 - vw) \underbrace{1}_{|J(u, v, w)|} du \, dv \, dw \qquad \text{Convert to an iterated integral.}$$

$$= \int_0^4 \int_0^3 2(w^2 - vw) \, dv \, dw \qquad \text{Evaluate inner integral.}$$

$$= 2 \int_0^4 \left(vw^2 - \frac{v^2 w}{2} \right) \Big|_0^3 dw \qquad \text{Evaluate middle integral.}$$

$$= 2 \int_0^4 \left(3w^2 - \frac{9w}{2} \right) dw \qquad \text{Simplify.}$$

$$= 2 \left(w^3 - \frac{9w^2}{4} \right) \Big|_0^4 = 56. \qquad \text{Evaluate outer integral.}$$

Related Exercises 37–44 ◄

QUICK CHECK 5 Interpret a Jacobian with a value of 1 (as in Example 6). ◄

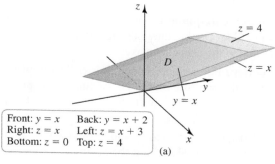

Front: $y = x$ Back: $y = x + 2$
Right: $z = x$ Left: $z = x + 3$
Bottom: $z = 0$ Top: $z = 4$

(a)

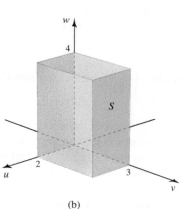

(b)

Figure 13.83

Strategies for Choosing New Variables

Sometimes a change of variables simplifies the integrand but leads to an awkward region of integration. Conversely, the new region of integration may be simplified at the expense of additional complications in the integrand. Here are a few suggestions for finding new variables of integration. The observations are made with respect to double integrals, but they also apply to triple integrals. As before, R is the original region of integration in the xy-plane and S is the new region in the uv-plane.

1. **Aim for simple regions of integration in the uv-plane** The new region of integration in the uv-plane should be as simple as possible. Double integrals are easiest to evaluate over rectangular regions with sides parallel to the coordinate axes.

➤ Inverting the transformation means solving for x and y in terms of u and v, or vice versa.

2. **Is $(x, y) \rightarrow (u, v)$ or $(u, v) \rightarrow (x, y)$ better?** For some problems it is easiest to write (x, y) as functions of (u, v); in other cases, the opposite is true. Depending on the problem, inverting the transformation (finding relations that go in the opposite direction) may be easy, difficult, or impossible.

   • If you know (x, y) in terms of (u, v) (that is, $x = g(u, v)$ and $y = h(u, v)$), then computing the Jacobian is straightforward, as is sketching the region R given the region S. However, the transformation must be inverted to determine the shape of S.

   • If you know (u, v) in terms of (x, y) (that is, $u = G(x, y)$ and $v = H(x, y)$), then sketching the region S is straightforward. However, the transformation must be inverted to compute the Jacobian.

3. **Let the integrand suggest new variables** New variables are often chosen to simplify the integrand. For example, the integrand $\sqrt{\dfrac{x - y}{x + y}}$ calls for new variables $u = x - y$ and $v = x + y$ (or $u = x + y, v = x - y$). There is, however, no guarantee that this change of variables will simplify the region of integration. In cases in which only one combination of variables appears, let one new variable be that combination and let the other new variable be unchanged. For example, if the integrand is $(x + 4y)^{3/2}$, try letting $u = x + 4y$ and $v = y$.

4. **Let the region suggest new variables** Example 5 illustrates an ideal situation. It occurs when the region R is bounded by two pairs of "parallel" curves in the families $g(x, y) = C_1$ and $h(x, y) = C_2$ (Figure 13.84). In this case, the new region of integration is a rectangle $S = \{(u, v): a_1 \le u \le a_2, b_1 \le v \le b_2\}$, where $u = g(x, y)$ and $v = h(x, y)$.

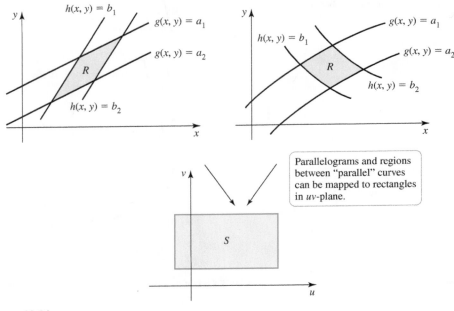

Parallelograms and regions between "parallel" curves can be mapped to rectangles in uv-plane.

Figure 13.84

As another example, suppose the region is bounded by the lines $y = x$ (or $y/x = 1$) and $y = 2x$ (or $y/x = 2$) and by the hyperbolas $xy = 1$ and $xy = 3$. Then the new variables should be $u = xy$ and $v = y/x$ (or vice versa). The new region of integration is the rectangle $S = \{(u, v): 1 \le u \le 3, 1 \le v \le 2\}$.

SECTION 13.7 EXERCISES

Review Questions

1. Suppose S is the unit square in the first quadrant of the uv-plane. Describe the image of the transformation $T: x = 2u, y = 2v$.

2. Explain how to compute the Jacobian of the transformation $T: x = g(u, v), y = h(u, v)$.

3. Using the transformation $T: x = u + v, y = u - v$, the image of the unit square $S = \{(u, v): 0 \le u \le 1, 0 \le v \le 1\}$ is a region R in the xy-plane. Explain how to change variables in the integral $\iint_R f(x, y)\, dA$ to find a new integral over S.

4. Suppose S is the unit cube in the first octant of uvw-space with one vertex at the origin. What is the image of the transformation $T: x = u/2, y = v/2, z = w/2$?

Basic Skills

5–12. Transforming a square *Let $S = \{(u, v): 0 \le u \le 1, 0 \le v \le 1\}$ be a unit square in the uv-plane. Find the image of S in the xy-plane under the following transformations.*

5. $T: x = 2u, y = v/2$

6. $T: x = -u, y = -v$

7. $T: x = (u + v)/2, y = (u - v)/2$

8. $T: x = 2u + v, y = 2u$

9. $T: x = u^2 - v^2, y = 2uv$

10. $T: x = 2uv, y = u^2 - v^2$

11. $T: x = u \cos \pi v, y = u \sin \pi v$

12. $T: x = v \sin \pi u, y = v \cos \pi u$

13–16. Images of regions *Find the image R in the xy-plane of the region S using the given transformation T. Sketch both R and S.*

13. $S = \{(u, v): v \le 1 - u, u \ge 0, v \ge 0\}$; $T: x = u, y = v^2$

14. $S = \{(u, v): u^2 + v^2 \le 1\}$; $T: x = 2u, y = 4v$

15. $S = \{(u, v): 1 \le u \le 3, 2 \le v \le 4\}$; $T: x = u/v, y = v$

16. $S = \{(u, v): 2 \le u \le 3, 3 \le v \le 6\}$; $T: x = u, y = v/u$

17–22. Computing Jacobians *Compute the Jacobian $J(u, v)$ for the following transformations.*

17. $T: x = 3u, y = -3v$

18. $T: x = 4v, y = -2u$

19. $T: x = 2uv, y = u^2 - v^2$

20. $T: x = u \cos \pi v, y = u \sin \pi v$

21. $T: x = (u + v)/\sqrt{2}, y = (u - v)/\sqrt{2}$

22. $T: x = u/v, y = v$

23–26. Solve and compute Jacobians *Solve the following relations for x and y, and compute the Jacobian $J(u, v)$.*

23. $u = x + y, v = 2x - y$

24. $u = xy, v = x$

25. $u = 2x - 3y, v = y - x$

26. $u = x + 4y, v = 3x + 2y$

27–30. Double integrals—transformation given *To evaluate the following integrals, carry out these steps.*

a. *Sketch the original region of integration R in the xy-plane and the new region S in the uv-plane using the given change of variables.*

b. *Find the limits of integration for the new integral with respect to u and v.*

c. *Compute the Jacobian.*

d. *Change variables and evaluate the new integral.*

27. $\iint_R xy\, dA$, where R is the square with vertices $(0, 0)$, $(1, 1)$, $(2, 0)$, and $(1, -1)$; use $x = u + v, y = u - v$.

28. $\iint_R x^2 y\, dA$, where $R = \{(x, y): 0 \le x \le 2, x \le y \le x + 4\}$; use $x = 2u, y = 4v + 2u$.

29. $\iint_R x^2 \sqrt{x + 2y}\, dA$, where $R = \{(x, y): 0 \le x \le 2, -x/2 \le y \le 1 - x\}$; use $x = 2u, y = v - u$.

30. $\iint_R xy\, dA$, where R is bounded by the ellipse $9x^2 + 4y^2 = 36$; use $x = 2u, y = 3v$.

31–36. Double integrals—your choice of transformation *Evaluate the following integrals using a change of variables. Sketch the original and new regions of integration, R and S.*

31. $\int_0^1 \int_y^{y+2} \sqrt{x - y}\, dx\, dy$

32. $\iint_R \sqrt{y^2 - x^2}\, dA$, where R is the diamond bounded by $y - x = 0, y - x = 2, y + x = 0$, and $y + x = 2$

33. $\iint_R \left(\dfrac{y - x}{y + 2x + 1}\right)^4 dA$, where R is the parallelogram bounded by $y - x = 1, y - x = 2, y + 2x = 0$, and $y + 2x = 4$

34. $\iint_R e^{xy}\, dA$, where R is the region bounded by the hyperbolas $xy = 1$ and $xy = 4$, and the lines $y/x = 1$ and $y/x = 3$

35. $\iint\limits_{R} xy\, dA$, where R is the region bounded by the hyperbolas

$xy = 1$ and $xy = 4$, and the lines $y = 1$ and $y = 3$

36. $\iint\limits_{R} (x - y)\sqrt{x - 2y}\, dA$, where R is the triangular region

bounded by $y = 0, x - 2y = 0$, and $x - y = 1$

37–40. Jacobians in three variables *Evaluate the Jacobians $J(u, v, w)$ for the following transformations.*

37. $x = v + w, y = u + w, z = u + v$

38. $x = u + v - w, y = u - v + w, z = -u + v + w$

39. $x = vw, y = uw, z = u^2 - v^2$

40. $u = x - y, v = x - z, w = y + z$ (Solve for $x, y,$ and z first.)

41–44. Triple integrals *Use a change of variables to evaluate the following integrals.*

41. $\iiint\limits_{D} xy\, dV;$ D is bounded by the planes $y - x = 0,$

$y - x = 2, z - y = 0, z - y = 1, z = 0,$ and $z = 3.$

42. $\iiint\limits_{D} dV;$ D is bounded by the planes $y - 2x = 0, y - 2x = 1,$

$z - 3y = 0, z - 3y = 1, z - 4x = 0,$ and $z - 4x = 3.$

43. $\iiint\limits_{D} z\, dV;$ D is bounded by the paraboloid $z = 16 - x^2 - 4y^2$

and the xy-plane. Use $x = 4u \cos v, y = 2u \sin v, z = w.$

44. $\iiint\limits_{D} dV;$ D is bounded by the upper half of the ellipsoid

$x^2/9 + y^2/4 + z^2 = 1$ and the xy-plane. Use $x = 3u,$ $y = 2v, z = w.$

Further Explorations

45. Explain why or why not Determine whether the following statements are true and give an explanation or counterexample.

   a. If the transformation $T: x = g(u, v), y = h(u, v)$ is linear in u and v, then the Jacobian is a constant.

   b. The transformation $x = au + bv, y = cu + dv$ generally maps triangular regions to triangular regions.

   c. The transformation $x = 2v, y = -2u$ maps circles to circles.

46. Cylindrical coordinates Evaluate the Jacobian for the transformation from cylindrical coordinates (r, θ, Z) to rectangular coordinates $(x, y, z): x = r \cos \theta, y = r \sin \theta, z = Z.$ Show that $J(r, \theta, Z) = r.$

47. Spherical coordinates Evaluate the Jacobian for the transformation from spherical to rectangular coordinates: $x = \rho \sin \varphi \cos \theta, y = \rho \sin \varphi \sin \theta, z = \rho \cos \varphi.$ Show that $J(\rho, \varphi, \theta) = \rho^2 \sin \varphi.$

48–52. Ellipse problems *Let R be the region bounded by the ellipse $x^2/a^2 + y^2/b^2 = 1$, where $a > 0$ and $b > 0$ are real numbers. Let T be the transformation $x = au, y = bv.$*

48. Find the area of $R.$

49. Evaluate $\iint\limits_{R} |xy|\, dA.$

50. Find the center of mass of the upper half of R $(y \geq 0)$ assuming it has a constant density.

51. Find the average square of the distance between points of R and the origin.

52. Find the average distance between points in the upper half of R and the x-axis.

53–56. Ellipsoid problems *Let D be the solid bounded by the ellipsoid $x^2/a^2 + y^2/b^2 + z^2/c^2 = 1$, where $a > 0, b > 0,$ and $c > 0$ are real numbers. Let T be the transformation $x = au, y = bv, z = cw.$*

53. Find the volume of $D.$

54. Evaluate $\iiint\limits_{D} |xyz|\, dA.$

55. Find the center of mass of the upper half of D $(z \geq 0)$ assuming it has a constant density.

56. Find the average square of the distance between points of D and the origin.

57. Parabolic coordinates Let T be the transformation $x = u^2 - v^2,$ $y = 2uv.$

   a. Show that the lines $u = a$ in the uv-plane map to parabolas in the xy-plane that open in the negative x-direction with vertices on the positive x-axis.

   b. Show that the lines $v = b$ in the uv-plane map to parabolas in the xy-plane that open in the positive x-direction with vertices on the negative x-axis.

   c. Evaluate $J(u, v).$

   d. Use a change of variables to find the area of the region bounded by $x = 4 - y^2/16$ and $x = y^2/4 - 1.$

   e. Use a change of variables to find the area of the curved rectangle above the x-axis bounded by $x = 4 - y^2/16,$ $x = 9 - y^2/36, x = y^2/4 - 1,$ and $x = y^2/64 - 16.$

   f. Describe the effect of the transformation $x = 2uv,$ $y = u^2 - v^2$ on horizontal and vertical lines in the uv-plane.

Applications

58. Shear transformations in $\mathbb{R}^2$ The transformation T in $\mathbb{R}^2$ given by $x = au + bv, y = cv,$ where $a, b,$ and c are positive real numbers, is a *shear transformation*. Let S be the unit square $\{(u, v): 0 \leq u \leq 1, 0 \leq v \leq 1\}.$ Let $R = T(S)$ be the image of $S.$

   a. Explain with pictures the effect of T on $S.$

   b. Compute the Jacobian of $T.$

   c. Find the area of R and compare it to the area of S (which is 1).

   d. Assuming a constant density, find the center of mass of R (in terms of $a, b,$ and c) and compare it to the center of mass of S (which is $\left(\frac{1}{2}, \frac{1}{2}\right)$).

   e. Find an analogous transformation that gives a shear in the y-direction.

59. Shear transformations in $\mathbb{R}^3$ The transformation T in $\mathbb{R}^3$ given by

$$x = au + bv + cw, \qquad y = dv + ew, \qquad z = w,$$

where $a, b, c, d,$ and e are positive real numbers, is one of many possible shear transformations in $\mathbb{R}^3$. Let S be the unit cube

$\{(u, v, w): 0 \leq u \leq 1, 0 \leq v \leq 1, 0 \leq w \leq 1\}$. Let $D = T(S)$ be the image of S.

a. Explain with pictures and words the effect of T on S.

b. Compute the Jacobian of T.

c. Find the volume of D and compare it to the volume of S (which is 1).

d. Assuming a constant density, find the center of mass of D and compare it to the center of mass of S (which is $\left(\frac{1}{2}, \frac{1}{2}, \frac{1}{2}\right)$).

Additional Exercises

60. Linear transformations Consider the linear transformation T in $\mathbb{R}^2$ given by $x = au + bv, y = cu + dv$, where a, b, c, and d are real numbers, with $ad \neq bc$.

a. Find the Jacobian of T.

b. Let S be the square in the uv-plane with vertices $(0, 0)$, $(1, 0)$, $(0, 1)$, and $(1, 1)$, and let $R = T(S)$. Show that area$(R) = |J(u, v)|$.

c. Let ℓ be the line segment joining the points P and Q in the uv-plane. Show that $T(\ell)$ (the image of ℓ under T) is the line segment joining $T(P)$ and $T(Q)$ in the xy-plane. (*Hint:* Use vectors.)

d. Show that if S is a parallelogram in the uv-plane and $R = T(S)$, then area$(R) = |J(u, v)|$ area(S). (*Hint:* Without loss of generality, assume the vertices of S are $(0, 0)$, $(A, 0)$, (B, C), and $(A + B, C)$, where A, B, and C are positive, and use vectors.)

61. Meaning of the Jacobian The Jacobian is a magnification (or reduction) factor that relates the area of a small region near the point (u, v) to the area of the image of that region near the point (x, y).

a. Suppose S is a rectangle in the uv-plane with vertices $O(0, 0)$, $P(\Delta u, 0)$, $(\Delta u, \Delta v)$, and $Q(0, \Delta v)$ (see figure). The image of S under the transformation $x = g(u, v), y = h(u, v)$ is a region R in the xy-plane. Let O', P', and Q' be the images of O, P, and Q, respectively, in the xy-plane, where O', P', and Q' do not all lie on the same line. Explain why the coordinates of O', P', and Q' are $(g(0, 0), h(0, 0))$, $(g(\Delta u, 0), h(\Delta u, 0))$, and $(g(0, \Delta v), h(0, \Delta v))$, respectively.

b. Use a Taylor series in both variables to show that

$$g(\Delta u, 0) \approx g(0, 0) + g_u(0, 0)\Delta u$$
$$g(0, \Delta v) \approx g(0, 0) + g_v(0, 0)\Delta v$$
$$h(\Delta u, 0) \approx h(0, 0) + h_u(0, 0)\Delta u$$
$$h(0, \Delta v) \approx h(0, 0) + h_v(0, 0)\Delta v$$

where $g_u(0, 0)$ is $\dfrac{\partial x}{\partial u}$ evaluated at $(0, 0)$, with similar meanings for g_v, h_u, and h_v.

c. Consider the vectors $\overrightarrow{O'P'}$ and $\overrightarrow{O'Q'}$ and the parallelogram, two of whose sides are $\overrightarrow{O'P'}$ and $\overrightarrow{O'Q'}$. Use the cross product to show that the area of the parallelogram is approximately $|J(u, v)| \, \Delta u \, \Delta v$.

d. Explain why the ratio of the area of R to the area of S is approximately $|J(u, v)|$.

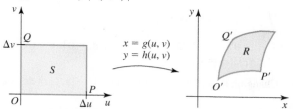

62. Open and closed boxes Consider the region R bounded by three pairs of parallel planes: $ax + by = 0, ax + by = 1$, $cx + dz = 0, cx + dz = 1, ey + fz = 0$, and $ey + fz = 1$, where a, b, c, d, e, and f are real numbers. For the purposes of evaluating triple integrals, when do these six planes bound a finite region? Carry out the following steps.

a. Find three vectors $\mathbf{n}_1, \mathbf{n}_2$, and $\mathbf{n}_3$ each of which is normal to one of the three pairs of planes.

b. Show that the three normal vectors lie in a plane if their triple scalar product $\mathbf{n}_1 \cdot (\mathbf{n}_2 \times \mathbf{n}_3)$ is zero.

c. Show that the three normal vectors lie in a plane if $ade + bcf = 0$.

d. Assuming $\mathbf{n}_1, \mathbf{n}_2$, and $\mathbf{n}_3$ lie in a plane P, find a vector $\mathbf{N}$ that is normal to P. Explain why a line in the direction of $\mathbf{N}$ does not intersect any of the six planes and therefore the six planes do not form a bounded region.

e. Consider the change of variables $u = ax + by, v = cx + dz$, $w = ey + fz$. Show that

$$J(x, y, z) = \frac{\partial(u, v, w)}{\partial(x, y, z)} = -ade - bcf.$$

What is the value of the Jacobian if R is unbounded?

QUICK CHECK ANSWERS

1. The image is a semicircular disk of radius 1.
2. $J(u, v) = 2$ **3.** $x = 2u/3 - v/3, y = u/3 + v/3$
4. The ratio is 2, which is $1/J(u, v)$.   **5.** It means that the volume of a small region in xyz-space is unchanged when it is transformed by T to a small region in uvw-space. ◄

CHAPTER 13 REVIEW EXERCISES

1. Explain why or why not Determine whether the following statements are true and give an explanation or counterexample.

   a. Assuming g is integrable and $a, b, c,$ and d are constants,
$$\int_c^d \int_a^b g(x, y)\, dx\, dy = \left(\int_a^b g(x, y)\, dx \right)\left(\int_c^d g(x, y)\, dy \right).$$

   b. $\{(\rho, \varphi, \theta): \varphi = \pi/2\} = \{(r, \theta, z): z = 0\} = \{(x, y, z): z = 0\}$

   c. Changing the order of integration in $\iiint_D f(x, y, z)\, dx\, dy\, dz$ from $dx\, dy\, dz$ to $dy\, dz\, dx$ also requires changing the integrand from $f(x, y, z)$ to $f(y, z, x)$.

   d. The transformation $T: x = v, y = -u$ maps a square in the uv-plane into a triangle in the xy-plane.

2–4. Evaluating integrals Evaluate the following integrals as they are written.

2. $\displaystyle\int_1^2 \int_1^4 \frac{xy}{(x^2 + y^2)^2}\, dx\, dy$ **3.** $\displaystyle\int_1^3 \int_1^{e^x} \frac{x}{y}\, dy\, dx$

4. $\displaystyle\int_1^2 \int_0^{\ln x} x^3 e^y\, dy\, dx$

5–7. Changing the order of integration Assuming f is integrable, change the order of integration in the following integrals.

5. $\displaystyle\int_{-1}^1 \int_{x^2}^1 f(x, y)\, dy\, dx$ **6.** $\displaystyle\int_0^2 \int_{y-1}^1 f(x, y)\, dx\, dy$

7. $\displaystyle\int_0^1 \int_0^{\sqrt{1-y^2}} f(x, y)\, dx\, dy$

8–10. Area of plane regions Use double integrals to compute the area of the following regions. Make a sketch of the region.

8. The region bounded by the lines $y = -x - 4, y = x,$ and $y = 2x - 4$

9. The region bounded by $y = |x|$ and $y = 20 - x^2$

10. The region between the curves $y = x^2$ and $y = 1 + x - x^2$

11–16. Miscellaneous double integrals Choose a convenient method for evaluating the following integrals.

11. $\displaystyle\iint_R \frac{2y}{\sqrt{x^4 + 1}}\, dA;$ R is the region bounded by $x = 1, x = 2,$ $y = x^{3/2},$ and $y = 0.$

12. $\displaystyle\iint_R x^{-1/2} e^y\, dA;$ R is the region bounded by $x = 1, x = 4,$ $y = \sqrt{x},$ and $y = 0.$

13. $\displaystyle\iint_R (x + y)\, dA;$ R is the disk bounded by the circle $r = 4 \sin \theta.$

14. $\displaystyle\iint_R (x^2 + y^2)\, dA;$ R is the region $\{(x, y): 0 \le x \le 2,$ $0 \le y \le x\}.$

15. $\displaystyle\int_0^1 \int_{y^{1/3}}^1 x^{10} \cos(\pi x^4 y)\, dx\, dy$

16. $\displaystyle\int_0^2 \int_{y^2}^4 x^8 y \sqrt{1 + x^4 y^2}\, dx\, dy$

17–18. Cartesian to polar coordinates Evaluate the following integrals over the specified region.

17. $\displaystyle\iint_R 3x^2 y\, dA;$ $R = \{(r, \theta): 0 \le r \le 1, 0 \le \theta \le \pi/2\}$

18. $\displaystyle\iint_R \frac{dA}{(1 + x^2 + y^2)^2};$ $R = \{(r, \theta): 1 \le r \le 4, 0 \le \theta \le \pi\}$

19–21. Computing areas Sketch the following regions and use integration to find their areas.

19. The region bounded by all leaves of the rose $r = 3 \cos 2\theta$

20. The region inside both the circles $r = 2$ and $r = 4 \cos \theta$

21. The region that lies inside both the cardioids $r = 2 - 2 \cos \theta$ and $r = 2 + 2 \cos \theta$

22–23. Average values

22. Find the average value of $z = \sqrt{16 - x^2 - y^2}$ over the disk in the xy-plane centered at the origin with radius 4.

23. Find the average distance from the points in the solid cone bounded by $z = 2\sqrt{x^2 + y^2}$ to the z-axis, for $0 \le z \le 8.$

24–26. Changing order of integration Rewrite the following integrals using the indicated order of integration.

24. $\displaystyle\int_0^1 \int_0^{\sqrt{1-x^2}} \int_0^{\sqrt{1-x^2}} f(x, y, z)\, dy\, dz\, dx$ in the order $dz\, dy\, dx$

25. $\displaystyle\int_0^4 \int_0^{\sqrt{16-x^2}} \int_0^{\sqrt{16-x^2-z^2}} f(x, y, z)\, dy\, dz\, dx$ in the order $dx\, dy\, dz$

26. $\displaystyle\int_0^2 \int_0^{9-x^2} \int_0^x f(x, y, z)\, dy\, dz\, dx$ in the order $dz\, dx\, dy$

27–31. Triple integrals Evaluate the following integrals, changing the order of integration if needed.

27. $\displaystyle\int_0^1 \int_{-z}^z \int_{-\sqrt{1-x^2}}^{\sqrt{1-x^2}} dy\, dx\, dz$ **28.** $\displaystyle\int_0^\pi \int_0^y \int_0^{\sin x} dz\, dx\, dy$

29. $\displaystyle\int_1^9 \int_0^1 \int_{2y}^2 \frac{4 \sin x^2}{\sqrt{z}}\, dx\, dy\, dz$

30. $\displaystyle\int_0^2 \int_{-\sqrt{2-x^2/2}}^{\sqrt{2-x^2/2}} \int_{x^2+3y^2}^{8-x^2-y^2} dz\, dy\, dx$

31. $\int_0^2 \int_0^{y^{1/3}} \int_0^{y^2} yz^5(1 + x + y^2 + z^6)^2 \, dx \, dz \, dy$

32–36. Volumes of solids *Find the volume of the following solids.*

32. The prism in the first octant bounded by the planes $y = 3 - 3x$ and $z = 2$

33. One of the wedges formed when the cylinder $x^2 + y^2 = 4$ is cut by the planes $z = 0$ and $y = z$

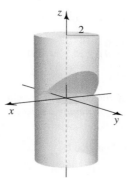

34. The solid bounded by the parabolic cylinders $z = y^2 + 1$ and $z = 2 - x^2$

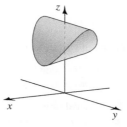

35. The solid common to the two cylinders $x^2 + y^2 = 4$ and $x^2 + z^2 = 4$

36. The tetrahedron with vertices $(0, 0, 0)$, $(1, 0, 0)$, $(1, 1, 0)$, and $(1, 1, 1)$

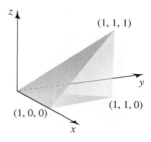

37. Single to double integral Evaluate $\int_0^{1/2}(\sin^{-1} 2x - \sin^{-1} x) \, dx$ by converting it to a double integral.

38. Tetrahedron limits Let D be the tetrahedron with vertices at $(0, 0, 0)$, $(1, 0, 0)$, $(0, 2, 0)$, and $(0, 0, 3)$. Suppose the volume of D is to be found using a triple integral. Give the limits of integration for the six possible orderings of the variables.

39. A "polynomial cube" Let $D = \{(x, y, z): 0 \le x \le y^2,\ 0 \le y \le z^3, 0 \le z \le 2\}$.

    a. Use a triple integral to find the volume of D.

    b. In theory, how many other possible orderings of the variables (besides the one used in part (a)) can be used to find the volume of D? Verify the result of part (a) using one of these other orderings.

    c. What is the volume of the region $D = \{(x, y, z): 0 \le x \le y^p,\ 0 \le y \le z^q, 0 \le z \le 2\}$, where p and q are positive real numbers?

40–41. Average value

40. Find the average of the *square* of the distance between the origin and the points in the solid paraboloid $D = \{(x, y, z): 0 \le z \le 4 - x^2 - y^2\}$.

41. Find the average x-coordinate of the points in the prism $D = \{(x, y, z): 0 \le x \le 1, 0 \le y \le 3 - 3x, 0 \le z \le 2\}$.

42–43. Integrals in cylindrical coordinates *Evaluate the following integrals in cylindrical coordinates.*

42. $\int_0^3 \int_0^{\sqrt{9-x^2}} \int_0^3 (x^2 + y^2)^{3/2} \, dz \, dy \, dx$

43. $\int_{-1}^1 \int_{-2}^2 \int_0^{\sqrt{1-y^2}} \frac{1}{(1 + x^2 + y^2)^2} \, dx \, dz \, dy$

44–45. Volumes in cylindrical coordinates *Use integration in cylindrical coordinates to find the volume of the following solids.*

44. The solid bounded by the plane $z = \sqrt{29}$ and the hyperboloid $z = \sqrt{4 + x^2 + y^2}$

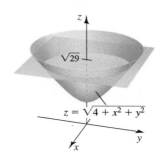

45. The solid cylinder whose height is 4 and whose base is the disk $\{(r, \theta): 0 \leq r \leq 2\cos\theta\}$

46–47. Integrals in spherical coordinates *Evaluate the following integrals in spherical coordinates.*

46. $\int_0^{2\pi} \int_0^{\pi/2} \int_0^{2\cos\varphi} \rho^2 \sin\varphi \, d\rho \, d\varphi \, d\theta$

47. $\int_0^{\pi} \int_0^{\pi/4} \int_{2\sec\varphi}^{4\sec\varphi} \rho^2 \sin\varphi \, d\rho \, d\varphi \, d\theta$

48–50. Volumes in spherical coordinates *Use integration in spherical coordinates to find the volume of the following solids.*

48. The solid cardioid of revolution $D = \{(\rho, \varphi, \theta): 0 \leq \rho \leq (1 - \cos\varphi)/2, 0 \leq \varphi \leq \pi, 0 \leq \theta \leq 2\pi\}$

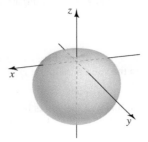

49. The solid rose petal of revolution $D = \{(\rho, \varphi, \theta): 0 \leq \rho \leq 4\sin 2\varphi, 0 \leq \varphi \leq \pi/2, 0 \leq \theta \leq 2\pi\}$

50. The solid above the cone $\varphi = \pi/4$ and inside the sphere $\rho = 4\cos\varphi$

51–54. Center of mass of constant-density plates *Find the center of mass (centroid) of the following thin constant-density plates. Sketch the region corresponding to the plate and indicate the location of the center of mass. Use symmetry whenever possible to simplify your work.*

51. The region bounded by $y = \sin x$ and $y = 0$ between $x = 0$ and $x = \pi$

52. The region bounded by $y = x^3$ and $y = x^2$ between $x = 0$ and $x = 1$

53. The half-annulus $\{(r, \theta): 2 \leq r \leq 4, 0 \leq \theta \leq \pi\}$

54. The region bounded by $y = x^2$ and $y = a^2 - x^2$, where $a > 0$

55–56. Center of mass of constant-density solids *Find the center of mass of the following solids, assuming a constant density. Use symmetry whenever possible and choose a convenient coordinate system.*

55. The paraboloid bowl bounded by $z = x^2 + y^2$ and $z = 36$

56. The tetrahedron bounded by $z = 4 - x - 2y$ and the coordinate planes

57–58. Variable-density solids *Find the coordinates of the center of mass of the following solids with the given density.*

57. The upper half of a ball $\left\{(\rho, \varphi, \theta): 0 \leq \rho \leq 16, 0 \leq \varphi \leq \dfrac{\pi}{2},\right.$ $\left. 0 \leq \theta \leq 2\pi\right\}$ with density $f(\rho, \varphi, \theta) = 1 + \rho/4$

58. The cube in the first octant bounded by the planes $x = 2, y = 2$, and $z = 2$, with $\rho(x, y, z) = 1 + x + y + z$

59–62. Center of mass for general objects *Consider the following two- and three-dimensional regions. Compute the center of mass assuming constant density. All parameters are positive real numbers.*

59. A solid is bounded by a paraboloid with a circular base of radius R and height h. How far from the base is the center of mass?

60. Let R be the region enclosed by an equilateral triangle with sides of length s. What is the perpendicular distance between the center of mass of R and the edges of R?

61. An isosceles triangle has two sides of length s and a base of length b. How far from the base is the center of mass of the region enclosed by the triangle?

62. A tetrahedron is bounded by the coordinate planes and the plane $x + y/2 + z/3 = 1$. What are the coordinates of the center of mass?

63. Slicing a conical cake A cake is shaped like a solid cone with radius 4 and height 2, with its base on the xy-plane. A wedge of the cake is removed by making two slices from the axis of the cone outward, perpendicular to the xy-plane separated by an angle of Q radians, where $0 < Q < 2\pi$.

   a. Use a double integral to find the volume of the slice for $Q = \pi/4$. Use geometry to check your answer.

   b. Use a double integral to find the volume of the slice for any $0 < Q < 2\pi$. Use geometry to check your answer.

64. Volume and weight of a fish tank A spherical fish tank with a radius of 1 ft is filled with water to a level 6 in below the top of the tank.

   a. Determine the volume and weight of the water in the fish tank. (The weight density of water is about 62.5 lb/ft^3.)

   b. How much additional water must be added to completely fill the tank?

65–68. Transforming a square Let $S = \{(u, v): 0 \le u \le 1, 0 \le v \le 1\}$ be a unit square in the uv-plane. Find the image of S in the xy-plane under the following transformations.

65. $T: x = v, y = u$

66. $T: x = -v, y = u$

67. $T: x = (u + v)/2, y = (u - v)/2$

68. $T: x = u, y = 2v + 2$

69–72. Computing Jacobians Compute the Jacobian $J(u, v)$ of the following transformations.

69. $T: x = 4u - v, y = -2u + 3v$

70. $T: x = u + v, y = u - v$

71. $T: x = 3u, y = 2v + 2$

72. $T: x = u^2 - v^2, y = 2uv$

73–76. Double integrals—transformation given To evaluate the following integrals, carry out the following steps.

a. Sketch the original region of integration R and the new region S using the given change of variables.

b. Find the limits of integration for the new integral with respect to u and v.

c. Compute the Jacobian.

d. Change variables and evaluate the new integral.

73. $\iint\limits_R xy^2 \, dA; \ R = \{(x, y): y/3 \le x \le (y + 6)/3, 0 \le y \le 3\}$; use $x = u + v/3, y = v$.

74. $\iint\limits_R 3xy^2 \, dA; \ R = \{(x, y): 0 \le x \le 2, x \le y \le x + 4\}$; use $x = 2u, y = 4v + 2u$.

75. $\iint\limits_R x^2\sqrt{x + 2y} \, dA; \ R = \{(x, y): 0 \le x \le 2, -x/2 \le y \le 1 - x\}$; use $x = 2u, y = v - u$.

76. $\iint\limits_R xy^2 \, dA; \ R$ is the region between the hyperbolas $xy = 1$ and $xy = 4$ and the lines $y = 1$ and $y = 4$; use $x = u/v, y = v$.

77–78. Double integrals Evaluate the following integrals using a change of variables. Sketch the original and new regions of integration, R and S.

77. $\iint\limits_R y^4 \, dA; \ R$ is the region bounded by the hyperbolas $xy = 1$ and $xy = 4$ and the lines $y/x = 1$ and $y/x = 3$.

78. $\iint\limits_R (y^2 + xy - 2x^2) \, dA; \ R$ is the region bounded by the lines $y = x, y = x - 3, y = -2x + 3$, and $y = -2x - 3$.

79–80. Triple integrals Use a change of variables to evaluate the following integrals.

79. $\iiint\limits_D yz \, dV; \ D$ is bounded by the planes $x + 2y = 1, x + 2y = 2, x - z = 0, x - z = 2, 2y - z = 0$, and $2y - z = 3$.

80. $\iiint\limits_D x \, dV; \ D$ is bounded by the planes $y - 2x = 0, y - 2x = 1, z - 3y = 0, z - 3y = 1, z - 4x = 0$, and $z - 4x = 3$.

Chapter 13 Guided Projects

Applications of the material in this chapter and related topics can be found in the following Guided Projects. For additional information, see the Preface.

- How big are n-balls?
- Electrical field integrals
- The tilted cylinder problem
- The exponential Eiffel Tower
- Moments of inertia
- Gravitational fields

14

Vector Calculus

Chapter Preview This culminating chapter of the book provides a beautiful, unifying conclusion to our study of calculus. Many ideas and themes that have appeared throughout the book come together in these final pages. First, we combine vector-valued functions (Chapter 11) and functions of several variables (Chapter 12) to form *vector fields*. Once vector fields have been introduced and illustrated through their many applications, we begin exploring the calculus of vector fields. Concepts such as limits and continuity carry over directly. The extension of derivatives to vector fields leads to two new operations that underlie this chapter: the *curl* and the *divergence*. When integration is extended to vector fields, we discover new versions of the Fundamental Theorem of Calculus. The chapter ends with a final look at the Fundamental Theorem of Calculus and the several related forms in which it has appeared throughout the book.

14.1 Vector Fields

We live in a world filled with phenomena that can be represented by vector fields. Imagine sitting in a window seat looking out at the wing of an airliner. Although you can't see it, air is rushing over and under the wing. Focus on a point near the wing and visualize the motion of the air at that point at a single instant of time. The motion is described by a velocity vector with three components—for example, east-west, north-south, and up-down. At another point near the wing at the same time, the air is moving at a different speed and direction, and a different velocity vector is associated with that point. In general, at one instant in time, every point around the wing has a velocity vector associated with it (Figure 14.1). This collection of velocity vectors—a unique vector for each point in space—is a function called a *vector field*.

Other examples of vector fields include the wind patterns in a hurricane (Figure 14.2a) and the circulation of water in a heat exchanger (Figure 14.2b). Gravitational, magnetic, and electric force fields are also represented by vector fields (Figure 14.2c), as are the stresses and strains in buildings and bridges. Beyond

Figure 14.1

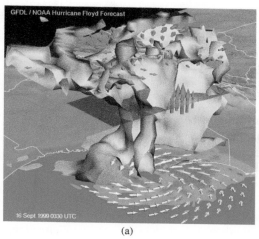

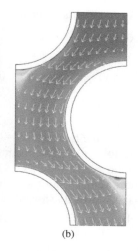

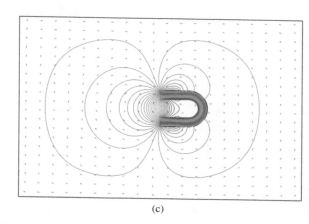

(a)   (b)   (c)

Figure 14.2

physics and engineering, the transport of a chemical pollutant in a lake or human migration patterns can be modeled by vector fields.

Vector Fields in Two Dimensions

To solidify the idea of a vector field, we begin by exploring vector fields in $\mathbb{R}^2$. From there, it is a short step to vector fields in $\mathbb{R}^3$.

> ➤ Notice that a vector field is both a vector-valued function (Chapter 11) and a function of several variables (Chapter 12).

DEFINITION   **Vector Fields in Two Dimensions**

Let f and g be defined on a region R of $\mathbb{R}^2$. A **vector field** in $\mathbb{R}^2$ is a function $\mathbf{F}$ that assigns to each point in R a vector $\langle f(x, y), g(x, y) \rangle$. The vector field is written as

$$\mathbf{F}(x, y) = \langle f(x, y), g(x, y) \rangle \quad \text{or}$$
$$\mathbf{F}(x, y) = f(x, y)\,\mathbf{i} + g(x, y)\,\mathbf{j}.$$

A vector field $\mathbf{F} = \langle f, g \rangle$ is continuous or differentiable on a region R of $\mathbb{R}^2$ if f and g are continuous or differentiable on R, respectively.

A vector field cannot be represented graphically in its entirety. Instead, we plot a representative sample of vectors that illustrates the general appearance of the vector field. Consider the vector field defined by

$$\mathbf{F}(x, y) = \langle 2x, 2y \rangle = 2x\,\mathbf{i} + 2y\,\mathbf{j}.$$

At selected points $P(x, y)$, we plot a vector with its tail at P equal to the value of $\mathbf{F}(x, y)$. For example, $\mathbf{F}(1, 1) = \langle 2, 2 \rangle$, so we draw a vector equal to $\langle 2, 2 \rangle$ with its tail at the point $(1, 1)$. Similarly, $\mathbf{F}(-2, -3) = \langle -4, -6 \rangle$, so at the point $(-2, -3)$, we draw a vector equal to $\langle -4, -6 \rangle$. We can make the following general observations about the vector field $\mathbf{F}(x, y) = \langle 2x, 2y \rangle$.

- For every (x, y) except $(0, 0)$, the vector $\mathbf{F}(x, y)$ points in the direction of $\langle 2x, 2y \rangle$, which is directly outward from the origin.

- The length of $\mathbf{F}(x, y)$ is $|\mathbf{F}| = |\langle 2x, 2y \rangle| = 2\sqrt{x^2 + y^2}$, which increases with distance from the origin.

The vector field $\mathbf{F} = \langle 2x, 2y \rangle$ is an example of a *radial vector field* because its vectors point radially away from the origin (Figure 14.3). If $\mathbf{F}$ represents the velocity of a fluid moving in two dimensions, the graph of the vector field gives a vivid image of how a small object, such as a cork, moves through the fluid. In this case, at every point of the vector field, a particle moves in the direction of the arrow at that point with a speed equal to the length of the arrow. For this reason, vector fields are sometimes called *flows*. When sketching vector fields, it is often useful to draw continuous curves that are aligned with the vector field. Such curves are called *flow curves* or *streamlines*; we examine their properties in greater detail later in this section.

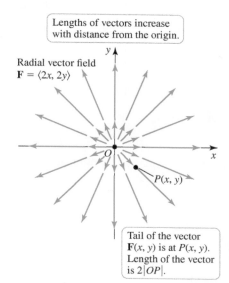

Lengths of vectors increase with distance from the origin.

Radial vector field
$\mathbf{F} = \langle 2x, 2y \rangle$

$P(x, y)$

Tail of the vector $\mathbf{F}(x, y)$ is at $P(x, y)$. Length of the vector is $2|OP|$.

Figure 14.3

Shear vector field
$\mathbf{F} = \langle 0, x \rangle$

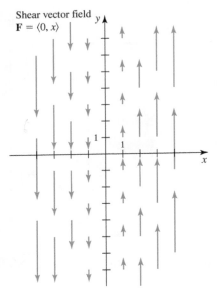

Figure 14.4

▶ Drawing vectors with their actual length often leads to cluttered pictures of vector fields. For this reason, most of the vector fields in this chapter are illustrated with proportional scaling: All vectors are multiplied by a scalar chosen to make the vector field as understandable as possible.

▶ A useful observation for two-dimensional vector fields $\mathbf{F} = \langle f, g \rangle$ is that the slope of the vector at (x, y) is $g(x, y)/f(x, y)$. In Example 1a, the slopes are everywhere undefined; in part (b), the slopes are everywhere 0, and in part (c), the slopes are $-x/y$.

EXAMPLE 1   Vector fields Sketch representative vectors of the following vector fields.

a. $\mathbf{F}(x, y) = \langle 0, x \rangle = x\,\mathbf{j}$ (a shear field)

b. $\mathbf{F}(x, y) = \langle 1 - y^2, 0 \rangle = (1 - y^2)\,\mathbf{i}$, for $|y| \leq 1$ (channel flow)

c. $\mathbf{F}(x, y) = \langle -y, x \rangle = -y\,\mathbf{i} + x\,\mathbf{j}$ (a rotation field)

SOLUTION

a. This vector field is independent of y. Furthermore, because the x-component of $\mathbf{F}$ is zero, all vectors in the field (for $x \neq 0$) point in the y-direction: upward for $x > 0$ and downward for $x < 0$. The magnitudes of the vectors in the field increase with distance from the y-axis (Figure 14.4). The flow curves for this field are vertical lines. If $\mathbf{F}$ represents a velocity field, a particle right of the y-axis moves upward, a particle left of the y-axis moves downward, and a particle on the y-axis is stationary.

b. In this case, the vector field is independent of x and the y-component of $\mathbf{F}$ is zero. Because $1 - y^2 > 0$ for $|y| < 1$, vectors in this region point in the positive x-direction. The x-component of the vector field is zero at the boundaries $y = \pm 1$ and increases to 1 along the center of the strip, $y = 0$. This vector field might model the flow of water in a straight shallow channel (Figure 14.5); its flow curves are horizontal lines, indicating motion in the direction of the positive x-axis.

c. It often helps to determine the vector field along the coordinate axes.

- When $y = 0$ (along the x-axis), we have $\mathbf{F}(x, 0) = \langle 0, x \rangle$. With $x > 0$, this vector field consists of vectors pointing upward, increasing in length as x increases. With $x < 0$, the vectors point downward, increasing in length as $|x|$ increases.

- When $x = 0$ (along the y-axis), we have $\mathbf{F}(0, y) = \langle -y, 0 \rangle$. If $y > 0$, the vectors point in the negative x-direction, increasing in length as y increases. If $y < 0$, the vectors point in the positive x-direction, increasing in length as $|y|$ increases.

A few more representative vectors show that this vector field has a counterclockwise rotation about the origin; the magnitudes of the vectors increase with distance from the origin (Figure 14.6).

Channel flow
$\mathbf{F} = \langle 1 - y^2, 0 \rangle$

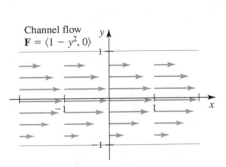

Figure 14.5

Rotation vector field
$\mathbf{F} = \langle -y, x \rangle$

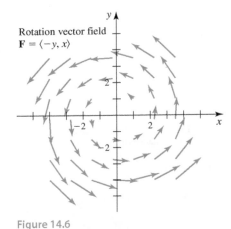

Figure 14.6

Related Exercises 6–16 ◀

QUICK CHECK 1 If the vector field in Example 1c describes the velocity of a fluid and you place a small cork in the plane at $(2, 0)$, what path will it follow? ◀

Radial Vector Fields in $\mathbb{R}^2$ Radial vector fields in $\mathbb{R}^2$ have the property that their vectors point directly toward or away from the origin at all points (except the origin), parallel to the position vectors $\mathbf{r} = \langle x, y \rangle$. We will work with radial vector fields of the form

$$\mathbf{F}(x, y) = \frac{\mathbf{r}}{|\mathbf{r}|^p} = \frac{\langle x, y \rangle}{|\mathbf{r}|^p} = \underbrace{\frac{\mathbf{r}}{|\mathbf{r}|}}_{\substack{\text{unit} \\ \text{vector}}} \underbrace{\frac{1}{|\mathbf{r}|^{p-1}}}_{\text{magnitude}},$$

where p is a real number. Figure 14.7 illustrates radial fields with $p = 1$ and $p = 3$. These vector fields (and their three-dimensional counterparts) play an important role in many applications. For example, central forces, such as gravitational or electrostatic forces between point masses or charges, are described by radial vector fields with $p = 3$. These forces obey an inverse square law in which the magnitude of the force is proportional to $1/|\mathbf{r}|^2$.

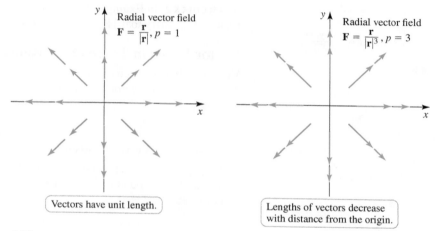

Figure 14.7

DEFINITION Radial Vector Fields in $\mathbb{R}^2$

Let $\mathbf{r} = \langle x, y \rangle$. A vector field of the form $\mathbf{F} = f(x, y)\,\mathbf{r}$, where f is a scalar-valued function, is a **radial vector field**. Of specific interest are the radial vector fields

$$\mathbf{F}(x, y) = \frac{\mathbf{r}}{|\mathbf{r}|^p} = \frac{\langle x, y \rangle}{|\mathbf{r}|^p},$$

where p is a real number. At every point (except the origin), the vectors of this field are directed outward from the origin with a magnitude of $|\mathbf{F}| = \dfrac{1}{|\mathbf{r}|^{p-1}}$.

EXAMPLE 2 Normal and tangent vectors Let C be the circle $x^2 + y^2 = a^2$, where $a > 0$.

a. Show that at each point of C, the radial vector field $\mathbf{F}(x, y) = \dfrac{\mathbf{r}}{|\mathbf{r}|} = \dfrac{\langle x, y \rangle}{\sqrt{x^2 + y^2}}$ is orthogonal to the line tangent to C at that point.

b. Show that at each point of C, the rotation vector field $\mathbf{G}(x, y) = \dfrac{\langle -y, x \rangle}{\sqrt{x^2 + y^2}}$ is parallel to the line tangent to C at that point.

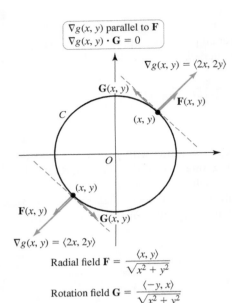

$\nabla g(x, y)$ parallel to $\mathbf{F}$
$\nabla g(x, y) \cdot \mathbf{G} = 0$

$\nabla g(x, y) = \langle 2x, 2y \rangle$

$\mathbf{G}(x, y)$

$\mathbf{F}(x, y)$

(x, y)

C

O

(x, y)

$\mathbf{F}(x, y)$

$\mathbf{G}(x, y)$

$\nabla g(x, y) = \langle 2x, 2y \rangle$

Radial field $\mathbf{F} = \dfrac{\langle x, y \rangle}{\sqrt{x^2 + y^2}}$

Rotation field $\mathbf{G} = \dfrac{\langle -y, x \rangle}{\sqrt{x^2 + y^2}}$

Figure 14.8

SOLUTION Let $g(x, y) = x^2 + y^2$. The circle C described by the equation $g(x, y) = a^2$ may be viewed as a level curve of the surface $z = x^2 + y^2$. As shown in Theorem 12.12 (Section 12.6), the gradient $\nabla g(x, y) = \langle 2x, 2y \rangle$ is orthogonal to the line tangent to C at (x, y) (Figure 14.8).

a. Notice that $\nabla g(x, y)$ is parallel to $\mathbf{F} = \langle x, y \rangle / |\mathbf{r}|$ at the point (x, y). It follows that $\mathbf{F}$ is also orthogonal the line tangent to C at (x, y).

b. Notice that

$$\nabla g(x, y) \cdot \mathbf{G}\langle x, y \rangle = \langle 2x, 2y \rangle \cdot \frac{\langle -y, x \rangle}{|\mathbf{r}|} = 0.$$

Therefore, $\nabla g(x, y)$ is orthogonal to the vector field $\mathbf{G}$ at (x, y), which implies that $\mathbf{G}$ is parallel to the tangent line at (x, y).

Related Exercises 17–20 ◄

QUICK CHECK 2 In Example 2, verify that $\nabla g(x, y) \cdot \mathbf{G}(x, y) = 0$. In parts (a) and (b) of Example 2, verify that $|\mathbf{F}| = 1$ and $|\mathbf{G}| = 1$ at all points excluding the origin. ◄

Vector Fields in Three Dimensions

Vector fields in three dimensions are conceptually the same as vector fields in two dimensions. The vector $\mathbf{F}$ now has three components, each of which depends on three variables.

DEFINITION Vector Fields and Radial Vector Fields in $\mathbb{R}^3$

Let f, g, and h be defined on a region D of $\mathbb{R}^3$. A **vector field** in $\mathbb{R}^3$ is a function $\mathbf{F}$ that assigns to each point in D a vector $\langle f(x, y, z), g(x, y, z), h(x, y, z) \rangle$. The vector field is written as

$$\mathbf{F}(x, y, z) = \langle f(x, y, z), g(x, y, z), h(x, y, z) \rangle \quad \text{or}$$
$$\mathbf{F}(x, y, z) = f(x, y, z)\,\mathbf{i} + g(x, y, z)\,\mathbf{j} + h(x, y, z)\,\mathbf{k}.$$

A vector field $\mathbf{F} = \langle f, g, h \rangle$ is continuous or differentiable on a region D of $\mathbb{R}^3$ if f, g, and h are continuous or differentiable on D, respectively. Of particular importance are the **radial vector fields**

$$\mathbf{F}(x, y, z) = \frac{\mathbf{r}}{|\mathbf{r}|^p} = \frac{\langle x, y, z \rangle}{|\mathbf{r}|^p},$$

where p is a real number.

EXAMPLE 3 Vector fields in $\mathbb{R}^3$ Sketch and discuss the following vector fields.

a. $\mathbf{F}(x, y, z) = \langle x, y, e^{-z} \rangle$, for $z \geq 0$
b. $\mathbf{F}(x, y, z) = \langle 0, 0, 1 - x^2 - y^2 \rangle$, for $x^2 + y^2 \leq 1$

SOLUTION

a. First consider the x- and y-components of $\mathbf{F}$ in the xy-plane ($z = 0$), where $\mathbf{F} = \langle x, y, 1 \rangle$. This vector field looks like a radial field in the first two components, increasing in magnitude with distance from the z-axis. However, each vector also has a constant vertical component of 1. In horizontal planes $z = z_0 > 0$, the radial pattern remains the same, but the vertical component decreases as z increases. As $z \to \infty$, $e^{-z} \to 0$ and the vector field approaches a horizontal radial field (Figure 14.9).

$$\mathbf{F} = \langle x, y, e^{-z} \rangle, \text{ for } z \geq 0$$

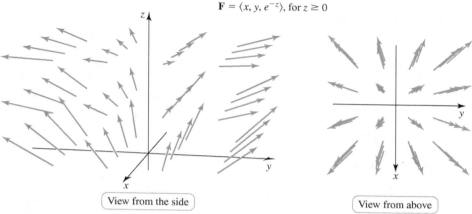

View from the side   View from above

Figure 14.9

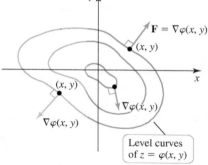

$\mathbf{F} = \langle 0, 0, 1 - x^2 - y^2 \rangle$, for $x^2 + y^2 \leq 1$

Cylinder $x^2 + y^2 = 1$

Figure 14.10

b. Regarding $\mathbf{F}$ as a velocity field, for points in and on the cylinder $x^2 + y^2 = 1$, there is no motion in the x- or y-directions. The z-component of the vector field may be written $1 - r^2$, where $r^2 = x^2 + y^2$ is the square of the distance from the z-axis. We see that the z-component increases from 0 on the boundary of the cylinder ($r = 1$) to a maximum value of 1 along the centerline of the cylinder ($r = 0$) (Figure 14.10). This vector field models the flow of a fluid inside a tube (such as a blood vessel).

Related Exercises 21–24 ◄

> Physicists often use the convention that a gradient field and its potential function are related by $\mathbf{F} = -\nabla\varphi$ (with a negative sign).

The vector field $\mathbf{F} = \nabla\varphi$ is orthogonal to the level curves of φ at (x, y).

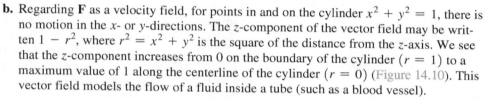

$\mathbf{F} = \nabla\varphi(x, y)$

(x, y)

$\nabla\varphi(x, y)$

(x, y)

$\nabla\varphi(x, y)$

Level curves of $z = \varphi(x, y)$

Figure 14.11

Gradient Fields and Potential Functions One way to generate a vector field is to start with a differentiable scalar-valued function φ, take its gradient, and let $\mathbf{F} = \nabla\varphi$. A vector field defined as the gradient of a scalar-valued function φ is called a *gradient field*, and φ is called a *potential function*.

Suppose φ is a differentiable function on a region R of $\mathbb{R}^2$ and consider the surface $z = \varphi(x, y)$. Recall from Chapter 12 that this function may also be represented by level curves in the xy-plane. At each point (a, b) on a level curve, the gradient $\nabla\varphi(a, b) = \langle \varphi_x(a, b), \varphi_y(a, b) \rangle$ is orthogonal to the level curve at (a, b) (Figure 14.11). Therefore, the vectors of $\mathbf{F} = \nabla\varphi$ point in a direction orthogonal to the level curves of φ.

The idea extends to gradients of functions of three variables. If φ is differentiable on a region D of $\mathbb{R}^3$, then $\mathbf{F} = \nabla\varphi = \langle \varphi_x, \varphi_y, \varphi_z \rangle$ is a vector field that points in a direction orthogonal to the level *surfaces* of φ.

Gradient fields are useful because of the physical meaning of the gradient. For example, if φ represents the temperature in a conducting material, then the gradient field $\mathbf{F} = \nabla\varphi$ evaluated at a point indicates the direction in which the temperature increases most rapidly at that point. According to a basic physical law, heat diffuses in the direction of the vector field $-\mathbf{F} = -\nabla\varphi$, the direction in which the temperature *decreases* most rapidly; that is, heat flows "down the gradient" from relatively hot regions to cooler regions. Similarly, water on a smooth surface tends to flow down the elevation gradient.

QUICK CHECK 3 Find the gradient field associated with the function $\varphi(x, y, z) = xyz$. ◄

▶ A potential function plays the role of an antiderivative of a vector field: Derivatives of the potential function produce the vector field. If φ is a potential function for a gradient field, then $\varphi + C$ is also a potential function for that gradient field, for any constant C.

DEFINITION Gradient Fields and Potential Functions

Let φ be differentiable on a region of $\mathbb{R}^2$ or $\mathbb{R}^3$. The vector field $\mathbf{F} = \nabla\varphi$ is a **gradient field** and the function φ is a **potential function** for $\mathbf{F}$.

EXAMPLE 4   Gradient fields

a. Sketch and interpret the gradient field associated with the temperature function $T = 200 - x^2 - y^2$ on the circular plate $R = \{(x, y) : x^2 + y^2 \leq 25\}$.

b. Sketch and interpret the gradient field associated with the velocity potential $\varphi = \tan^{-1}(y/x)$.

SOLUTION

a. The gradient field associated with T is

$$\mathbf{F} = \nabla T = \langle -2x, -2y \rangle = -2\langle x, y \rangle.$$

This vector field points inward toward the origin at all points of R except $(0, 0)$. The magnitudes of the vectors,

$$|\mathbf{F}| = \sqrt{(-2x)^2 + (-2y)^2} = 2\sqrt{x^2 + y^2},$$

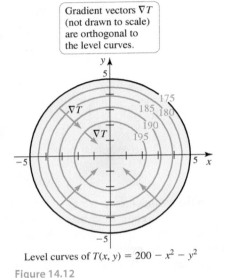

Gradient vectors ∇T (not drawn to scale) are orthogonal to the level curves.

Level curves of $T(x, y) = 200 - x^2 - y^2$

Figure 14.12

are greatest on the edge of the disk R, where $x^2 + y^2 = 25$ and $|\mathbf{F}| = 10$. The magnitudes of the vectors in the field decrease toward the center of the plate with $|\mathbf{F}(0, 0)| = 0$. Figure 14.12 shows the level curves of the temperature function with several gradient vectors, all orthogonal to the level curves. Note that the plate is hottest at the center and coolest on the edge, so heat diffuses *outward*, in the direction opposite that of the gradient.

b. The gradient of a velocity potential gives the velocity components of a two-dimensional flow; that is, $\mathbf{F} = \langle u, v \rangle = \nabla\varphi$, where u and v are the velocities in the x- and y-directions, respectively. Computing the gradient, we find that

$$\mathbf{F} = \langle \varphi_x, \varphi_y \rangle = \left\langle \frac{1}{1 + (y/x)^2} \cdot -\frac{y}{x^2}, \frac{1}{1 + (y/x)^2} \cdot \frac{1}{x} \right\rangle = \left\langle -\frac{y}{x^2 + y^2}, \frac{x}{x^2 + y^2} \right\rangle.$$

Notice that the level curves of φ are the lines $\frac{y}{x} = C$ or $y = Cx$. At all points off the y-axis, the vector field is orthogonal to the level curves, which gives a rotation field (Figure 14.13).

Related Exercises 25–36 ◀

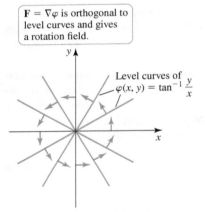

$\mathbf{F} = \nabla\varphi$ is orthogonal to level curves and gives a rotation field.

Level curves of $\varphi(x, y) = \tan^{-1}\dfrac{y}{x}$

Figure 14.13

Equipotential Curves and Surfaces   The preceding example illustrates a beautiful geometric connection between a gradient field and its associated potential function. Let φ be a potential function for the vector field $\mathbf{F}$ in $\mathbb{R}^2$; that is, $\mathbf{F} = \nabla\varphi$. The level curves of a potential function are called **equipotential curves** (curves on which the potential function is constant).

Because the equipotential curves are level curves of φ, the vector field $\mathbf{F} = \nabla\varphi$ is everywhere orthogonal to the equipotential curves (Figure 14.14). The vector field may be visualized by drawing continuous **flow curves** or **streamlines** that are everywhere orthogonal to the equipotential curves. These ideas also apply to vector fields in $\mathbb{R}^3$ in which case the vector field is orthogonal to the **equipotential surfaces**.

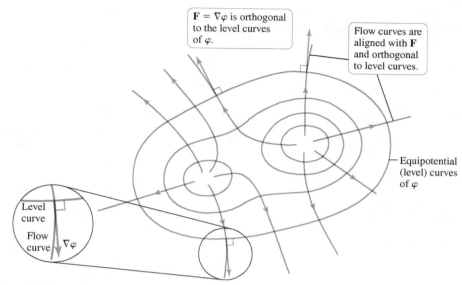

Figure 14.14

Level curves of
$\varphi(x, y) = \frac{1}{2}(x^2 - y^2)$

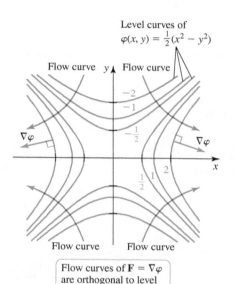

Flow curves of $\mathbf{F} = \nabla\varphi$
are orthogonal to level
curves of φ everywhere.

Figure 14.15

➤ We use the fact that a line with slope
a/b points in the direction of the vectors
$\langle 1, a/b \rangle$ or $\langle b, a \rangle$.

EXAMPLE 5   **Equipotential curves**   The equipotential curves for the potential function $\varphi(x, y) = (x^2 - y^2)/2$ are shown in green in Figure 14.15.

a. Find the gradient field associated with φ and verify that the gradient field is orthogonal to the equipotential curve at $(2, 1)$.

b. Verify that the vector field $\mathbf{F} = \nabla\varphi$ is orthogonal to the equipotential curves at all points (x, y).

SOLUTION

a. The level (or equipotential) curves are the hyperbolas $(x^2 - y^2)/2 = C$, where C is a constant. The slope at any point on a level curve $\varphi(x, y) = C$ (Section 12.5) is

$$\frac{dy}{dx} = -\frac{\varphi_x}{\varphi_y} = \frac{x}{y}.$$

At the point $(2, 1)$, the slope of the level curve is $dy/dx = 2$, so the vector tangent to the curve points in the direction $\langle 1, 2 \rangle$. The gradient field is given by $\mathbf{F} = \nabla\varphi = \langle x, -y \rangle$, so $\mathbf{F}(2, 1) = \nabla\varphi(2, 1) = \langle 2, -1 \rangle$. The dot product of the tangent vector $\langle 1, 2 \rangle$ and the gradient is $\langle 1, 2 \rangle \cdot \langle 2, -1 \rangle = 0$; therefore, the two vectors are orthogonal.

b. In general, the line tangent to the equipotential curve at (x, y) is parallel to the vector $\langle y, x \rangle$, while the vector field at that point is $\mathbf{F} = \langle x, -y \rangle$. The vector field and the tangent vectors are orthogonal because $\langle y, x \rangle \cdot \langle x, -y \rangle = 0$.

Related Exercises 37–40 ◄

SECTION 14.1 EXERCISES

Review Questions

1. How is a vector field $\mathbf{F} = \langle f, g, h \rangle$ used to describe the motion of air at one instant in time?

2. Sketch the vector field $\mathbf{F} = \langle x, y \rangle$.

3. How do you graph the vector field $\mathbf{F} = \langle f(x, y), g(x, y) \rangle$?

4. Given a function φ, why is the gradient of φ a vector field?

5. Interpret the gradient field of the temperature function $T = f(x, y)$.

Basic Skills

6–15. Two-dimensional vector fields *Sketch the following vector fields.*

6. $\mathbf{F} = \langle 1, y \rangle$ **7.** $\mathbf{F} = \langle x, 0 \rangle$ **8.** $\mathbf{F} = \langle -x, -y \rangle$

9. $\mathbf{F} = \langle x, -y \rangle$ **10.** $\mathbf{F} = \langle 2x, 3y \rangle$ **11.** $\mathbf{F} = \langle y, -x \rangle$

12. $\mathbf{F} = \langle x + y, y \rangle$ **13.** $\mathbf{F} = \langle x, y - x \rangle$

14. $\mathbf{F} = \left\langle \dfrac{x}{\sqrt{x^2 + y^2}}, \dfrac{y}{\sqrt{x^2 + y^2}} \right\rangle$ **15.** $\mathbf{F} = \langle e^{-x}, 0 \rangle$

16. Matching vector fields with graphs Match vector fields a–d with graphs A–D.

    a. $\mathbf{F} = \langle 0, x^2 \rangle$ **b.** $\mathbf{F} = \langle x - y, x \rangle$
    c. $\mathbf{F} = \langle 2x, -y \rangle$ **d.** $\mathbf{F} = \langle y, x \rangle$

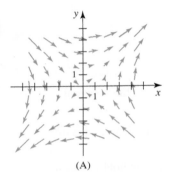

(A)

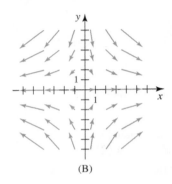

(B)

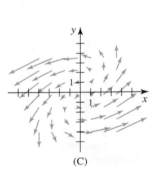

(C)

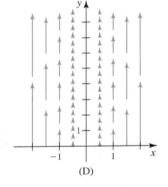

(D)

17–20. Normal and tangential components *Determine the points (if any) on the curve C at which the vector field* $\mathbf{F}$ *is tangent to C and normal to C. Sketch C and a few representative vectors of* $\mathbf{F}$.

17. $\mathbf{F} = \langle x, y \rangle$, where $C = \{(x, y): x^2 + y^2 = 4\}$

18. $\mathbf{F} = \langle y, -x \rangle$, where $C = \{(x, y): x^2 + y^2 = 1\}$

19. $\mathbf{F} = \langle x, y \rangle$, where $C = \{(x, y): x = 1\}$

20. $\mathbf{F} = \langle y, x \rangle$, where $C = \{(x, y): x^2 + y^2 = 1\}$

T **21–24. Three-dimensional vector fields** *Sketch a few representative vectors of the following vector fields.*

21. $\mathbf{F} = \langle 1, 0, z \rangle$ **22.** $\mathbf{F} = \langle x, y, z \rangle$

23. $\mathbf{F} = \langle y, -x, 0 \rangle$

24. $\mathbf{F} = \dfrac{\langle x, y, z \rangle}{\sqrt{x^2 + y^2 + z^2}}$

T **25–28. Gradient fields** *Find the gradient field* $\mathbf{F} = \nabla \varphi$ *for the potential function* φ. *Sketch a few level curves of* φ *and a few vectors of* $\mathbf{F}$.

25. $\varphi(x, y) = x^2 + y^2$, for $x^2 + y^2 \le 16$

26. $\varphi(x, y) = \sqrt{x^2 + y^2}$, for $x^2 + y^2 \le 9$, $(x, y) \ne (0, 0)$

27. $\varphi(x, y) = x + y$, for $|x| \le 2$, $|y| \le 2$

28. $\varphi(x, y) = 2xy$, for $|x| \le 2$, $|y| \le 2$

29–36. Gradient fields *Find the gradient field* $\mathbf{F} = \nabla \varphi$ *for the following potential functions* φ.

29. $\varphi(x, y) = x^2 y - y^2 x$

30. $\varphi(x, y) = \sqrt{xy}$

31. $\varphi(x, y) = x/y$

32. $\varphi(x, y) = \tan^{-1}(y/x)$

33. $\varphi(x, y, z) = (x^2 + y^2 + z^2)/2$

34. $\varphi(x, y, z) = \ln(1 + x^2 + y^2 + z^2)$

35. $\varphi(x, y, z) = (x^2 + y^2 + z^2)^{-1/2}$

36. $\varphi(x, y, z) = e^{-z} \sin(x + y)$

37–40. Equipotential curves *Consider the following potential functions and graphs of their equipotential curves.*

a. *Find the associated gradient field* $\mathbf{F} = \nabla \varphi$.
b. *Show that the vector field is orthogonal to the equipotential curve at the point* $(1, 1)$. *Illustrate this result on the figure.*
c. *Show that the vector field is orthogonal to the equipotential curve at all points* (x, y).
d. *Sketch two flow curves representing* $\mathbf{F}$ *that are everywhere orthogonal to the equipotential curves.*

37. $\varphi(x, y) = 2x + 3y$ 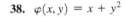   **38.** $\varphi(x, y) = x + y^2$

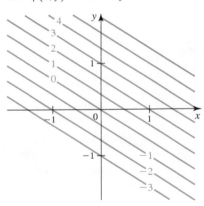

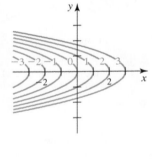

39. $\varphi(x, y) = e^{x - y}$ **40.** $\varphi(x, y) = x^2 + 2y^2$

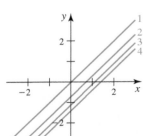

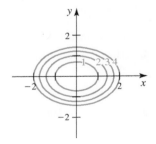

Further Explorations

41. Explain why or why not Determine whether the following statements are true and give an explanation or counterexample.

   a. The vector field $\mathbf{F} = \langle 3x^2, 1 \rangle$ is a gradient field for both $\varphi_1(x, y) = x^3 + y$ and $\varphi_2(x, y) = y + x^3 + 100$.

   b. The vector field $\mathbf{F} = \dfrac{\langle y, x \rangle}{\sqrt{x^2 + y^2}}$ is constant in direction and magnitude on the unit circle.

   c. The vector field $\mathbf{F} = \dfrac{\langle y, x \rangle}{\sqrt{x^2 + y^2}}$ is neither a radial field nor a rotation field.

42–43. Vector fields on regions *Let* $S = \{(x, y): |x| \leq 1, |y| \leq 1\}$ *(a square centered at the origin),* $D = \{(x, y): |x| + |y| \leq 1\}$ *(a diamond centered at the origin), and* $C = \{(x, y): x^2 + y^2 \leq 1\}$ *(a disk centered at the origin). For each vector field* $\mathbf{F}$, *draw pictures and analyze the vector field to answer the following questions.*

a. *At what points of S, D, and C does the vector field have its maximum magnitude?*

b. *At what points on the boundary of each region is the vector field directed out of the region?*

42. $\mathbf{F} = \langle x, y \rangle$ **43.** $\mathbf{F} = \langle -y, x \rangle$

44–47. Design your own vector field *Specify the component functions of a vector field* $\mathbf{F}$ *in* $\mathbb{R}^2$ *with the following properties. Solutions are not unique.*

44. $\mathbf{F}$ is everywhere normal to the line $x = 2$.

45. $\mathbf{F}$ is everywhere normal to the line $x = y$.

46. The flow of $\mathbf{F}$ is counterclockwise around the origin, increasing in magnitude with distance from the origin.

47. At all points except $(0, 0)$, $\mathbf{F}$ has unit magnitude and points away from the origin along radial lines.

Applications

48. Electric field due to a point charge The electric field in the xy-plane due to a point charge at $(0, 0)$ is a gradient field with a potential function $V(x, y) = \dfrac{k}{\sqrt{x^2 + y^2}}$, where $k > 0$ is a physical constant.

   a. Find the components of the electric field in the x- and y-directions, where $\mathbf{E}(x, y) = -\nabla V(x, y)$.

   b. Show that the vectors of the electric field point in the radial direction (outward from the origin) and the radial component of $\mathbf{E}$ can be expressed as $E_r = k/r^2$, where $r = \sqrt{x^2 + y^2}$.

   c. Show that the vector field is orthogonal to the equipotential curves at all points in the domain of V.

49. Electric field due to a line of charge The electric field in the xy-plane due to an infinite line of charge along the z-axis is a gradient field with a potential function $V(x, y) = c \ln \left(\dfrac{r_0}{\sqrt{x^2 + y^2}} \right)$,

where $c > 0$ is a constant and r_0 is a reference distance at which the potential is assumed to be 0 (see figure).

   a. Find the components of the electric field in the x- and y-directions, where $\mathbf{E}(x, y) = -\nabla V(x, y)$.

   b. Show that the electric field at a point in the xy-plane is directed outward from the origin and has magnitude $|\mathbf{E}| = c/r$, where $r = \sqrt{x^2 + y^2}$.

   c. Show that the vector field is orthogonal to the equipotential curves at all points in the domain of V.

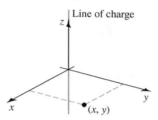

50. Gravitational force due to a mass The gravitational force on a point mass m due to a point mass M at the origin is a gradient field with potential $U(r) = \dfrac{GMm}{r}$, where G is the gravitational constant and $r = \sqrt{x^2 + y^2 + z^2}$ is the distance between the masses.

   a. Find the components of the gravitational force in the x-, y-, and z-directions, where $\mathbf{F}(x, y, z) = -\nabla U(x, y, z)$.

   b. Show that the gravitational force points in the radial direction (outward from point mass M) and the radial component is $F(r) = \dfrac{GMm}{r^2}$.

   c. Show that the vector field is orthogonal to the equipotential surfaces at all points in the domain of U.

Additional Exercises

51–55. Flow curves in the plane *Let* $\mathbf{F}(x, y) = \langle f(x, y), g(x, y) \rangle$ *be defined on* $\mathbb{R}^2$.

51. Explain why the flow curves or streamlines of $\mathbf{F}$ satisfy $y' = g(x, y)/f(x, y)$ and are everywhere tangent to the vector field.

T 52. Find and graph the flow curves for the vector field $\mathbf{F} = \langle 1, x \rangle$.

T 53. Find and graph the flow curves for the vector field $\mathbf{F} = \langle x, x \rangle$.

T 54. Find and graph the flow curves for the vector field $\mathbf{F} = \langle y, x \rangle$. Note that $d/dx(y^2) = 2yy'(x)$.

T 55. Find and graph the flow curves for the vector field $\mathbf{F} = \langle -y, x \rangle$.

56–57. Unit vectors in polar coordinates

56. Vectors in $\mathbb{R}^2$ may also be expressed in terms of polar coordinates. The standard coordinate unit vectors in polar coordinates are denoted $\mathbf{u}_r$ and $\mathbf{u}_\theta$ (see figure). Unlike the coordinate unit vectors in Cartesian coordinates, $\mathbf{u}_r$ and $\mathbf{u}_\theta$ change their direction depending on the point (r, θ). Use the figure to show that for $r > 0$, the following relationships among the unit vectors in Cartesian and polar coordinates hold:

$$\mathbf{u}_r = \cos\theta\,\mathbf{i} + \sin\theta\,\mathbf{j} \qquad \mathbf{i} = \mathbf{u}_r\cos\theta - \mathbf{u}_\theta\sin\theta$$

$$\mathbf{u}_\theta = -\sin\theta\,\mathbf{i} + \cos\theta\,\mathbf{j} \qquad \mathbf{j} = \mathbf{u}_r\sin\theta + \mathbf{u}_\theta\cos\theta.$$

57. Verify that the relationships in Exercise 56 are consistent when $\theta = 0, \pi/2, \pi,$ and $3\pi/2$.

58–60. Vector fields in polar coordinates *A vector field in polar coordinates has the form* $\mathbf{F}(r, \theta) = f(r, \theta)\,\mathbf{u}_r + g(r, \theta)\,\mathbf{u}_\theta$, *where the unit vectors are defined in Exercise 56. Sketch the following vector fields and express them in Cartesian coordinates.*

58. $\mathbf{F} = \mathbf{u}_r$ **59.** $\mathbf{F} = \mathbf{u}_\theta$ **60.** $\mathbf{F} = r\,\mathbf{u}_\theta$

61. Cartesian-to-polar vector field Write the vector field $\mathbf{F} = \langle -y, x \rangle$ in polar coordinates and sketch the field.

QUICK CHECK ANSWERS

1. The particle follows a circular path around the origin. **3.** $\nabla\varphi = \langle yz, xz, xy \rangle$ ◀

14.2 Line Integrals

With integrals of a single variable, we integrate over intervals in $\mathbb{R}$ (the real line). With double and triple integrals, we integrate over regions in $\mathbb{R}^2$ or $\mathbb{R}^3$. *Line integrals* (which really should be called *curve integrals*) are another class of integrals that play an important role in vector calculus. They are used to integrate either scalar-valued functions or vector fields along curves.

Suppose a thin, circular plate has a known temperature distribution and you must compute the average temperature along the edge of the plate. The required calculation involves integrating the temperature function over the *curved* boundary of the plate. Similarly, to calculate the amount of work needed to put a satellite into orbit, we integrate the gravitational force (a vector field) along the curved path of the satellite. Both these calculations require line integrals. As you will see, line integrals take several different forms. It is the goal of this section to distinguish these various forms and show how and when each form should be used.

Scalar Line Integrals in the Plane

We first consider line integrals of scalar-valued functions over curves in the plane. Figure 14.16 shows a surface $z = f(x, y)$ and a parameterized curve C in the xy-plane; for the moment, we assume that $f(x, y) \geq 0$, for (x, y) on C. Now visualize the curtain-like surface formed by the vertical line segments joining the surface $z = f(x, y)$ and C. The goal is to find the area of one side of this curtain in terms of a line integral. As with other integrals we have studied, we begin with Riemann sums.

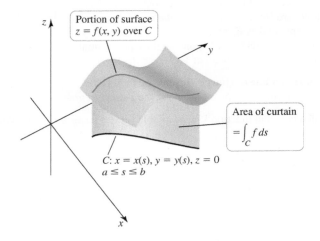

Figure 14.16

Assume that C is a smooth curve of finite length, parameterized in terms of arc length as $\mathbf{r}(s) = \langle x(s), y(s) \rangle$, for $a \le s \le b$, and let f be defined on C. We subdivide C into n small arcs by forming a partition of $[a, b]$:

$$a = s_0 < s_1 < \cdots < s_{n-1} < s_n = b.$$

Let s_k^* be a point in the kth subinterval $[s_{k-1}, s_k]$, which corresponds to a point $(x(s_k^*), y(s_k^*))$ on the kth arc of C, for $k = 1, 2, \ldots, n$. The length of the kth arc is denoted Δs_k. This partition also divides the curtain into n panels. The kth panel has an approximate height of $f(x(s_k^*), y(s_k^*))$ and a base of length Δs_k; therefore, the approximate area of the kth panel is $f(x(s_k^*), y(s_k^*)) \Delta s_k$ (Figure 14.17). Summing the areas of the panels, the approximate area of the curtain is given by the Riemann sum

$$\text{area} \approx \sum_{k=1}^{n} f(x(s_k^*), y(s_k^*)) \Delta s_k.$$

▶ The parameter s resides on the s-axis. As s varies from a to b on the s-axis, the curve C in the xy-plane is generated from the point $(x(a), y(a))$ to the point $(x(b), y(b))$.

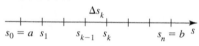

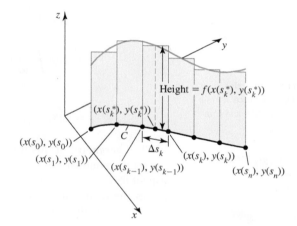

Figure 14.17

We now let Δ be the maximum value of $\Delta s_1, \ldots, \Delta s_n$. If the limit of the Riemann sums as $n \to \infty$ and $\Delta \to 0$ exists over all partitions, the limit is called a *line integral*, and it gives the area of the curtain.

DEFINITION **Scalar Line Integral in the Plane, Arc Length Parameter**

Suppose the scalar-valued function f is defined on the smooth curve
$C: \mathbf{r}(s) = \langle x(s), y(s) \rangle$, parameterized by the arc length s. The **line integral of f over C** is

$$\int_C f(x(s), y(s)) \, ds = \lim_{\Delta \to 0} \sum_{k=1}^{n} f(x(s_k^*), y(s_k^*)) \Delta s_k,$$

provided this limit exists over all partitions of C. When the limit exists, f is said to be **integrable** on C.

The more compact notations $\int_C f(\mathbf{r}(s)) \, ds$, $\int_C f(x, y) \, ds$, or $\int_C f \, ds$ are also used for the line integral of f over C. It can be shown that if f is continuous on a region containing C, then the line integral of f over C exists. If $f(x, y) = 1$, the line integral $\int_C ds$ gives the length of the curve, just as the ordinary integral $\int_a^b dx$ gives the length of the interval $[a, b]$, which is $b - a$.

▶ When we compute the average value by an ordinary integral, we divide by the length of the interval of integration. Analogously, when we compute the average value by a line integral, we divide by the length of the curve L:

$$\bar{f} = \frac{1}{L} \int_C f \, ds.$$

EXAMPLE 1   Average temperature on a circle The temperature of the circular plate $R = \{(x, y): x^2 + y^2 \leq 1\}$ is $T(x, y) = 100(x^2 + 2y^2)$. Find the average temperature along the edge of the plate.

SOLUTION Calculating the average value requires integrating the temperature function over the boundary circle $C = \{(x, y): x^2 + y^2 = 1\}$ and dividing by the length (circumference) of C. The first step is to find a parametric description for C. Recall from Section 11.8 that a parametric description of a unit circle using arc length as the parameter is $\mathbf{r} = \langle x, y \rangle = \langle \cos s, \sin s \rangle$, for $0 \leq s \leq 2\pi$. We substitute $x = \cos s$ and $y = \sin s$ into the temperature function and express the line integral as an ordinary integral with respect to s:

$$\int_C T(x, y) \, ds = \int_0^{2\pi} \underbrace{100(x(s)^2 + 2y(s)^2)}_{T(s)} ds \qquad \text{Write the line integral as an ordinary integral with respect to } s.$$

$$= 100 \int_0^{2\pi} (\cos^2 s + 2\sin^2 s) \, ds \qquad \text{Substitute for } x \text{ and } y.$$

$$= 100 \underbrace{\int_0^{2\pi} (1 + \sin^2 s) \, ds}_{3\pi} \qquad \cos^2 s + \sin^2 s = 1$$

$$= 300\pi. \qquad \text{Use } \sin^2 s = \frac{1 - \cos 2s}{2} \text{ and integrate.}$$

▶ The line integral in Example 1 also gives the area of the vertical cylindrical curtain that hangs between the surface and C in Figure 14.18.

The geometry of this line integral is shown in Figure 14.18. The temperature function on the boundary of C is a function of s. The line integral is an ordinary integral with respect to s over the interval $[0, 2\pi]$. To find the average value, we divide the line integral of the temperature by the length of the curve, which is 2π. Therefore, the average temperature on the boundary of the plate is $300\pi/(2\pi) = 150$.

Related Exercises 11–14 ◀

Parameters Other Than Arc Length The line integral in Example 1 is straightforward because a circle is easily parameterized in terms of the arc length. Suppose we wish to compute the value of a line integral over a curve C that is described with a parameter t that is *not* the arc length. The key is a change of variables. Assume the curve C is described by $\mathbf{r}(t) = \langle x(t), y(t) \rangle$, for $a \leq t \leq b$. Recall from Section 11.8 that the length of C over the interval $[a, t]$ is

$$s(t) = \int_a^t |\mathbf{r}'(u)| \, du.$$

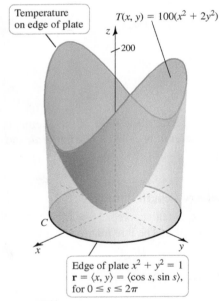

Temperature on edge of plate

$T(x, y) = 100(x^2 + 2y^2)$

z

200

C

x y

Edge of plate $x^2 + y^2 = 1$
$\mathbf{r} = \langle x, y \rangle = \langle \cos s, \sin s \rangle$,
for $0 \leq s \leq 2\pi$

Figure 14.18

Differentiating both sides of this equation and using the Fundamental Theorem of Calculus yields $s'(t) = |\mathbf{r}'(t)|$. We now make a standard change of variables using the relationship

$$ds = s'(t) \, dt = |\mathbf{r}'(t)| \, dt.$$

▶ If t represents time, then the relationship $ds = |\mathbf{r}'(t)| \, dt$ is a generalization of the familiar formula

$$distance = speed \cdot time.$$

The original line integral with respect to s is now converted into an ordinary integral with respect to t:

$$\int_C f \, ds = \int_a^b f(x(t), y(t)) \underbrace{|\mathbf{r}'(t)| \, dt}_{ds}.$$

QUICK CHECK 1 Explain mathematically why differentiating the arc length integral leads to $s'(t) = |\mathbf{r}'(t)|$. ◀

➤ The value of a line integral of a scalar-valued function is independent of the parameterization of C and independent of the direction in which C is traversed (Exercises 54–55).

THEOREM 14.1   Evaluating Scalar Line Integrals in $\mathbb{R}^2$

Let f be continuous on a region containing a smooth curve C: $\mathbf{r}(t) = \langle x(t), y(t) \rangle$, for $a \leq t \leq b$. Then

$$\int_C f \, ds = \int_a^b f(x(t), y(t)) |\mathbf{r}'(t)| \, dt$$

$$= \int_a^b f(x(t), y(t)) \sqrt{x'(t)^2 + y'(t)^2} \, dt.$$

If t represents time and C is the path of a moving object, then $|\mathbf{r}'(t)|$ is the speed of the object. The *speed factor* $|\mathbf{r}'(t)|$ that appears in the integral relates distance traveled along the curve as measured by s to the elapsed time as measured by the parameter t.

Notice that if t is the arc length s, then $|\mathbf{r}'(t)| = 1$ and we recover the line integral with respect to the arc length s:

$$\int_C f \, ds = \int_a^b f(x(s), y(s)) \, ds.$$

If $f(x, y) = 1$, then the line integral is $\int_a^b \sqrt{x'(t)^2 + y'(t)^2} \, dt$, which is the arc length formula for C. Theorem 14.1 leads to the following procedure for evaluating line integrals.

PROCEDURE   Evaluating the Line Integral $\displaystyle\int_C f \, ds$

1. Find a parametric description of C in the form $\mathbf{r}(t) = \langle x(t), y(t) \rangle$, for $a \leq t \leq b$.

2. Compute $|\mathbf{r}'(t)| = \sqrt{x'(t)^2 + y'(t)^2}$.

3. Make substitutions for x and y in the integrand and evaluate an ordinary integral:

$$\int_C f \, ds = \int_a^b f(x(t), y(t)) |\mathbf{r}'(t)| \, dt.$$

EXAMPLE 2   Average temperature on a circle The temperature of the circular plate $R = \{(x, y): x^2 + y^2 \leq 1\}$ is $T(x, y) = 100(x^2 + 2y^2)$ as in Example 1. Confirm the average temperature computed in Example 1 when the circle has the parametric description

$$C = \{(x, y): x = \cos t^2, y = \sin t^2, 0 \leq t \leq \sqrt{2\pi}\}.$$

SOLUTION The speed factor on C (using $\sin^2 t^2 + \cos^2 t^2 = 1$) is

$$|\mathbf{r}'(t)| = \sqrt{x'(t)^2 + y'(t)^2} = \sqrt{(-2t \sin t^2)^2 + (2t \cos t^2)^2} = 2t.$$

Making the appropriate substitutions, the value of the line integral is

$$\int_C T \, ds = \int_0^{\sqrt{2\pi}} 100(x(t)^2 + 2y(t)^2)|\mathbf{r}'(t)| \, dt \qquad \text{Write the line integral with respect to } t.$$

$$= \int_0^{\sqrt{2\pi}} 100(\cos^2 t^2 + 2\sin^2 t^2) \underbrace{2t \, dt}_{|\mathbf{r}'(t)|} \qquad \text{Substitute for } x \text{ and } y.$$

$$= 100 \int_0^{2\pi} \underbrace{(\cos^2 u + 2\sin^2 u) \, du}_{\pi + 2\pi} \qquad \text{Simplify and let } u = t^2, \, du = 2t \, dt.$$

$$= 300\pi. \qquad \text{Evaluate integral.}$$

Dividing by the length of C, the average temperature on the boundary of the plate is $300\pi/(2\pi) = 150$, as found in Example 1.

Related Exercises 15–24 ◄

Line Integrals in $\mathbb{R}^3$

The argument that leads to line integrals on plane curves extends immediately to three or more dimensions. Here is the corresponding evaluation theorem for line integrals in $\mathbb{R}^3$.

THEOREM 14.2   Evaluating Scalar Line Integrals in $\mathbb{R}^3$

Let f be continuous on a region containing a smooth curve $C : \mathbf{r}(t) = \langle x(t), y(t), z(t) \rangle$, for $a \le t \le b$. Then

$$\int_C f \, ds = \int_a^b f(x(t), y(t), z(t))|\mathbf{r}'(t)| \, dt$$

$$= \int_a^b f(x(t), y(t), z(t))\sqrt{x'(t)^2 + y'(t)^2 + z'(t)^2} \, dt.$$

As before, if t is the arc length s, then $|\mathbf{r}'(t)| = 1$ and

$$\int_C f \, ds = \int_a^b f(x(s), y(s), z(s)) \, ds.$$

If $f(x, y, z) = 1$, then the line integral gives the length of C.

▶ Recall that a parametric equation of a line is

$$\mathbf{r}(t) = \langle x_0, y_0, z_0 \rangle + t \langle a, b, c \rangle,$$

where $\langle x_0, y_0, z_0 \rangle$ is a position vector associated with a fixed point on the line and $\langle a, b, c \rangle$ is a vector parallel to the line.

EXAMPLE 3   Line integrals in $\mathbb{R}^3$ Evaluate $\int_C (xy + 2z) \, ds$ on the following line segments.

a. The line segment from $P(1, 0, 0)$ to $Q(0, 1, 1)$
b. The line segment from $Q(0, 1, 1)$ to $P(1, 0, 0)$

SOLUTION

a. A parametric description of the line segment from $P(1, 0, 0)$ to $Q(0, 1, 1)$ is

$$\mathbf{r}(t) = \langle 1, 0, 0 \rangle + t \langle -1, 1, 1 \rangle = \langle 1 - t, t, t \rangle, \qquad \text{for } 0 \le t \le 1.$$

The speed factor is

$$|r'(t)| = \sqrt{x'(t)^2 + y'(t)^2 + z'(t)^2} = \sqrt{(-1)^2 + 1^2 + 1^2} = \sqrt{3}.$$

Substituting $x = 1 - t$, $y = t$, and $z = t$, the value of the line integral is

$$\int_C (xy + 2z)\, ds = \int_0^1 (\underbrace{(1-t)}_{x}\underbrace{t}_{y} + \underbrace{2t}_{2z})\sqrt{3}\, dt \quad \text{Substitute for } x, y, z.$$

$$= \sqrt{3}\int_0^1 (3t - t^2)\, dt \quad\quad \text{Simplify.}$$

$$= \sqrt{3}\left(\frac{3t^2}{2} - \frac{t^3}{3}\right)\Big|_0^1 \quad\quad \text{Integrate.}$$

$$= \frac{7\sqrt{3}}{6}. \quad\quad\quad\quad \text{Evaluate.}$$

b. The line segment from $Q(0, 1, 1)$ to $P(1, 0, 0)$ may be described parametrically by

$$\mathbf{r}(t) = \langle 0, 1, 1 \rangle + t\langle 1, -1, -1 \rangle = \langle t, 1 - t, 1 - t \rangle, \quad \text{for } 0 \le t \le 1.$$

The speed factor is

$$|\mathbf{r}'(t)| = \sqrt{x'(t)^2 + y'(t)^2 + z'(t)^2} = \sqrt{1^2 + (-1)^2 + (-1)^2} = \sqrt{3}.$$

We substitute $x = t$, $y = 1 - t$, and $z = 1 - t$ and do a calculation similar to that in part (a). The value of the line integral is again $\dfrac{7\sqrt{3}}{6}$, emphasizing the fact that a scalar line integral is independent of the orientation and parameterization of the curve.

Related Exercises 25–30 ◄

EXAMPLE 4   **Flight of an eagle** An eagle soars on the ascending spiral path

$$C: \mathbf{r}(t) = \langle x(t), y(t), z(t) \rangle = \left\langle 2400 \cos\frac{t}{2}, 2400 \sin\frac{t}{2}, 500t \right\rangle,$$

where x, y, and z are measured in feet and t is measured in minutes. How far does the eagle fly over the time interval $0 \le t \le 10$?

> ▶ Because we are finding the length of a curve, the integrand in this line integral is $f(x, y, z) = 1$.

SOLUTION The distance traveled is found by integrating the element of arc length ds along C, that is, $L = \int_C ds$. We now make a change of variables to the parameter t using

$$|\mathbf{r}'(t)| = \sqrt{x'(t)^2 + y'(t)^2 + z'(t)^2}$$

$$= \sqrt{\left(-1200 \sin\frac{t}{2}\right)^2 + \left(1200 \cos\frac{t}{2}\right)^2 + 500^2} \quad \text{Substitute derivatives.}$$

$$= \sqrt{1200^2 + 500^2} = 1300. \quad\quad\quad\quad \sin^2\frac{t}{2} + \cos^2\frac{t}{2} = 1$$

It follows that the distance traveled is

$$L = \int_C ds = \int_0^{10} |\mathbf{r}'(t)|\, dt = \int_0^{10} 1300\, dt = 13{,}000 \text{ ft.}$$

Related Exercises 31–32 ◄

QUICK CHECK 2 What is the speed of the eagle in Example 4? ◄

Line Integrals of Vector Fields

Line integrals along curves in $\mathbb{R}^2$ or $\mathbb{R}^3$ may also have integrands that involve vector fields. Such line integrals are different from scalar line integrals in two respects.

• Recall that an *oriented curve* is a parameterized curve for which a direction is specified. The *positive* orientation is the direction in which the curve is generated as the parameter increases. For example, the positive orientation of the circle $\mathbf{r}(t) = \langle \cos t, \sin t \rangle$, for

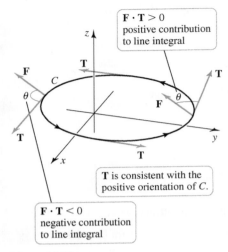

F · T > 0
positive contribution
to line integral

**T is consistent with the
positive orientation of C.**

F · T < 0
negative contribution
to line integral

Figure 14.19

➤ The component of **F** in the direction of **T** is the scalar component of **F** in the direction of **T**, scal$_\text{T}$ **F**, as defined in Section 11.3. Note that $|\textbf{T}| = 1$.

➤ Some books let $d\textbf{s}$ stand for **T** ds. Then the line integral $\int_C \textbf{F} \cdot \textbf{T} \, ds$ is written $\int_C \textbf{F} \cdot d\textbf{s}$.

➤ Keep in mind that $f(t)$ stands for $f(x(t), y(t), z(t))$ with analogous expressions for $g(t)$ and $h(t)$.

$0 \le t \le 2\pi$, is counterclockwise. As we will see, vector line integrals must be evaluated on oriented curves, and the value of a line integral depends on the orientation.

• The line integral of a vector field **F** along an oriented curve involves a specific component of **F** relative to the curve. We begin by defining vector line integrals for the *tangential* component of **F**, a situation that has many physical applications.

Let $C: \textbf{r}(s) = \langle x(s), y(s), z(s) \rangle$ be a smooth oriented curve in $\mathbb{R}^3$ parameterized by arc length and let **F** be a vector field that is continuous on a region containing C. At each point of C, the unit tangent vector **T** points in the positive direction on C (Figure 14.19). The component of **F** in the direction of **T** at a point of C is $|\textbf{F}| \cos \theta$, where θ is the angle between **F** and **T**. Because **T** is a unit vector,

$$|\textbf{F}| \cos \theta = |\textbf{F}||\textbf{T}| \cos \theta = \textbf{F} \cdot \textbf{T}.$$

The first line integral of a vector field **F** that we introduce is the line integral of the scalar **F** · **T** along the curve C. When we integrate **F** · **T** along C, the effect is to add up the components of **F** in the direction of C at each point of C.

DEFINITION Line Integral of a Vector Field

Let **F** be a vector field that is continuous on a region containing a smooth oriented curve C parameterized by arc length. Let **T** be the unit tangent vector at each point of C consistent with the orientation. The line integral of **F** over C is $\int_C \textbf{F} \cdot \textbf{T} \, ds$.

We need a method for evaluating vector line integrals, particularly when the parameter is *not* the arc length. Suppose that C has a parameterization $\textbf{r}(t) = \langle x(t), y(t), z(t) \rangle$, for $a \le t \le b$. Recall from Section 11.6 that the unit tangent vector at a point on the curve is $\textbf{T} = \dfrac{\textbf{r}'(t)}{|\textbf{r}'(t)|}$. Using the fact that $ds = |\textbf{r}'(t)| \, dt$, the line integral becomes

$$\int_C \textbf{F} \cdot \textbf{T} \, ds = \int_a^b \textbf{F} \cdot \underbrace{\frac{\textbf{r}'(t)}{|\textbf{r}'(t)|}}_{\textbf{T}} \underbrace{|\textbf{r}'(t)| \, dt}_{ds} = \int_a^b \textbf{F} \cdot \textbf{r}'(t) \, dt.$$

This integral may be written in several equivalent forms. If $\textbf{F} = \langle f, g, h \rangle$, then the line integral is expressed in component form as

$$\int_C \textbf{F} \cdot \textbf{T} \, ds = \int_a^b \textbf{F} \cdot \textbf{r}'(t) \, dt = \int_a^b (f(t)x'(t) + g(t)y'(t) + h(t)z'(t)) \, dt.$$

Another useful form is obtained by noting that

$$dx = x'(t) \, dt, \qquad dy = y'(t) \, dt, \qquad dz = z'(t) \, dt.$$

Making these replacements in the previous integral results in the form

$$\int_C \textbf{F} \cdot \textbf{T} \, ds = \int_C f \, dx + g \, dy + h \, dz.$$

Finally, if we let $d\textbf{r} = \langle dx, dy, dz \rangle$, then $f \, dx + g \, dy + h \, dz = \textbf{F} \cdot d\textbf{r}$, and we have

$$\int_C \textbf{F} \cdot \textbf{T} \, ds = \int_C \textbf{F} \cdot d\textbf{r}.$$

It is helpful to become familiar with these various forms of the line integral.

Different Forms of Line Integrals of Vector Fields

The line integral $\int_C \mathbf{F} \cdot \mathbf{T}\, ds$ may be expressed in the following forms, where $\mathbf{F} = \langle f, g, h \rangle$ and C has a parameterization $\mathbf{r}(t) = \langle x(t), y(t), z(t) \rangle$, for $a \le t \le b$:

$$\int_a^b \mathbf{F} \cdot \mathbf{r}'(t)\, dt = \int_a^b \left(f(t)x'(t) + g(t)y'(t) + h(t)z'(t) \right) dt$$

$$= \int_C f\, dx + g\, dy + h\, dz$$

$$= \int_C \mathbf{F} \cdot d\mathbf{r}.$$

For line integrals in the plane, we let $\mathbf{F} = \langle f, g \rangle$ and assume C is parameterized in the form $\mathbf{r}(t) = \langle x(t), y(t) \rangle$, for $a \le t \le b$. Then

$$\int_a^b \mathbf{F} \cdot \mathbf{r}'(t)\, dt = \int_a^b \left(f(t)x'(t) + g(t)y'(t) \right) dt = \int_C f\, dx + g\, dy = \int_C \mathbf{F} \cdot d\mathbf{r}.$$

➤ We use the convention that $-C$ is the curve C with the opposite orientation.

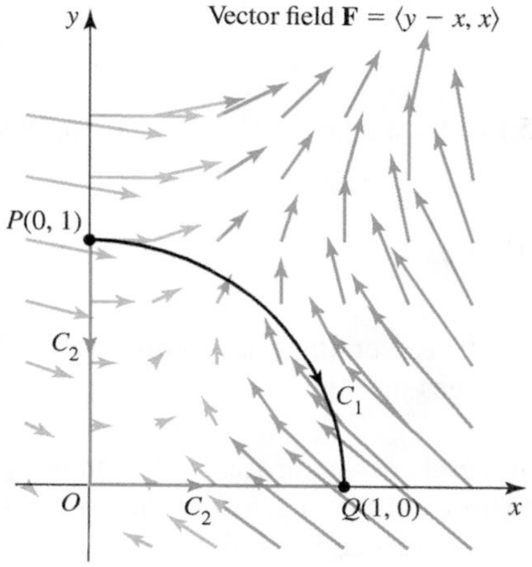

EXAMPLE 5 Different paths Evaluate $\int_C \mathbf{F} \cdot \mathbf{T}\, ds$ with $\mathbf{F} = \langle y - x, x \rangle$ on the following oriented paths in $\mathbb{R}^2$ (Figure 14.20).

a. The quarter circle C_1 from $P(0, 1)$ to $Q(1, 0)$

b. The quarter circle $-C_1$ from $Q(1, 0)$ to $P(0, 1)$

c. The path C_2 from $P(0, 1)$ to $Q(1, 0)$ via two line segments through $O(0, 0)$

SOLUTION

a. Working in $\mathbb{R}^2$, a parametric description of the curve C_1 with the required (clockwise) orientation is $\mathbf{r}(t) = \langle \sin t, \cos t \rangle$, for $0 \le t \le \pi/2$. Along C_1, the vector field is

$$\mathbf{F} = \langle y - x, x \rangle = \langle \cos t - \sin t, \sin t \rangle.$$

The velocity vector is $\mathbf{r}'(t) = \langle \cos t, -\sin t \rangle$, so the integrand of the line integral is

$$\mathbf{F} \cdot \mathbf{r}'(t) = \langle \cos t - \sin t, \sin t \rangle \cdot \langle \cos t, -\sin t \rangle = \underbrace{\cos^2 t - \sin^2 t}_{\cos 2t} - \underbrace{\sin t \cos t}_{\frac{1}{2}\sin 2t}.$$

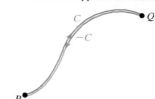

Vector field $\mathbf{F} = \langle y - x, x \rangle$

Figure 14.20

The value of the line integral of $\mathbf{F}$ over C_1 is

$$\int_0^{\pi/2} \mathbf{F} \cdot \mathbf{r}'(t)\, dt = \int_0^{\pi/2} \left(\cos 2t - \frac{1}{2}\sin 2t \right) dt \quad \text{Substitute for } \mathbf{F} \cdot \mathbf{r}'(t).$$

$$= \left(\frac{1}{2}\sin 2t + \frac{1}{4}\cos 2t \right) \Big|_0^{\pi/2} \quad \text{Evaluate integral.}$$

$$= -\frac{1}{2}. \quad \text{Simplify.}$$

b. A parameterization of the curve $-C_1$ from Q to P is $\mathbf{r}(t) = \langle \cos t, \sin t \rangle$, for $0 \le t \le \pi/2$. The vector field along the curve is

$$\mathbf{F} = \langle y - x, x \rangle = \langle \sin t - \cos t, \cos t \rangle,$$

and the velocity vector is $\mathbf{r}'(t) = \langle -\sin t, \cos t \rangle$. A calculation similar to that in part (a) results in

$$\int_{-C} \mathbf{F} \cdot \mathbf{T} \, ds = \int_0^{\pi/2} \mathbf{F} \cdot \mathbf{r}'(t) \, dt = \frac{1}{2}.$$

Comparing the results of parts (a) and (b), we see that reversing the orientation of C_1 reverses the sign of the line integral of the vector field.

c. The path C_2 consists of two line segments.

- The segment from P to O is parameterized by $\mathbf{r}(t) = \langle 0, 1 - t \rangle$, for $0 \leq t \leq 1$. Therefore, $\mathbf{r}'(t) = \langle 0, -1 \rangle$ and $\mathbf{F} = \langle y - x, x \rangle = \langle 1 - t, 0 \rangle$. On this segment, $\mathbf{T} = \langle 0, -1 \rangle$.
- The line segment from O to Q is parameterized by $\mathbf{r}(t) = \langle t, 0 \rangle$, for $0 \leq t \leq 1$. Therefore, $\mathbf{r}'(t) = \langle 1, 0 \rangle$ and $\mathbf{F} = \langle y - x, x \rangle = \langle -t, t \rangle$. On this segment, $\mathbf{T} = \langle 1, 0 \rangle$.

The line integral is split into two parts and evaluated as follows:

$$\int_{C_2} \mathbf{F} \cdot \mathbf{T} \, ds = \int_{PO} \mathbf{F} \cdot \mathbf{T} \, ds + \int_{OQ} \mathbf{F} \cdot \mathbf{T} \, ds$$

$$= \int_0^1 \langle 1 - t, 0 \rangle \cdot \langle 0, -1 \rangle \, dt + \int_0^1 \langle -t, t \rangle \cdot \langle 1, 0 \rangle \, dt \qquad \text{Substitute for } x, y, \mathbf{r}'.$$

$$= \int_0^1 0 \, dt + \int_0^1 (-t) \, dt \qquad \text{Simplify.}$$

$$= -\frac{1}{2}. \qquad \text{Evaluate integrals.}$$

The line integrals in parts (a) and (c) have the same value and run from P to Q, but along different paths. We might ask: For what vector fields are the values of a line integral independent of path? We return to this question in Section 14.3.

Related Exercises 33–38 ◄

> Line integrals of vector fields satisfy properties similar to those of ordinary integrals. If C is a smooth curve from A to B and P is a point on C between A and B, then
>
> $$\int_{AB} \mathbf{F} \cdot d\mathbf{r} = \int_{AP} \mathbf{F} \cdot d\mathbf{r} + \int_{PB} \mathbf{F} \cdot d\mathbf{r}.$$

The solutions to parts (a) and (b) of Example 5 illustrate a general result that applies to line integrals of vector fields:

$$\int_{-C} \mathbf{F} \cdot \mathbf{T} \, ds = -\int_C \mathbf{F} \cdot \mathbf{T} \, ds.$$

Figure 14.21 provides the justification of the this fact: Reversing the orientation of C changes the sign of $\mathbf{F} \cdot \mathbf{T}$ at each point of C, which changes the sign of the line integral.

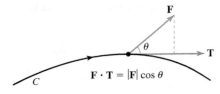

$$\mathbf{F} \cdot \mathbf{T} = |\mathbf{F}| \cos \theta$$

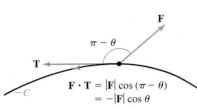

$$\mathbf{F} \cdot \mathbf{T} = |\mathbf{F}| \cos (\pi - \theta) = -|\mathbf{F}| \cos \theta$$

Reversing the orientation of C changes the sign of $\mathbf{F} \cdot \mathbf{T}$ at each point on C.

Figure 14.21

> Remember that the value of $\int_C f \, ds$ (the line integral of a *scalar* function) does not depend on the orientation of C.

Work Integrals A common application of line integrals of vector fields is computing the work done in moving an object in a force field (for example, a gravitational or electric field). First recall (Section 6.7) that if $\mathbf{F}$ is a *constant* force field, the work done in moving an object a distance d along the x-axis is $W = F_x d$, where $F_x = |\mathbf{F}| \cos \theta$ is the component of the force along the x-axis (Figure 14.22a). Only the component of $\mathbf{F}$ in the direction of motion contributes to the work. More generally, if $\mathbf{F}$ is a *variable* force field, the work done in moving an object from $x = a$ to $x = b$ is $W = \int_a^b F_x(x) \, dx$, where again F_x is the component of the force $\mathbf{F}$ in the direction of motion (parallel to the x-axis, Figure 14.22b).

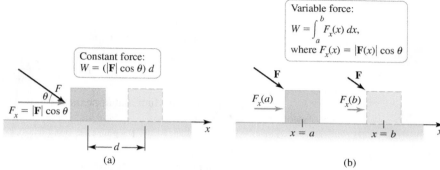

Figure 14.22

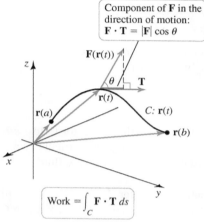

Figure 14.23

> Just to be clear, a work integral is nothing more than a line integral of the tangential component of a force field.

QUICK CHECK 3 Suppose a two-dimensional force field is everywhere directed outward from the origin and C is a circle centered at the origin. What is the angle between the field and the unit vectors tangent to C? ◄

We now take this progression one step further. Let $\mathbf{F}$ be a variable force field defined in a region D of $\mathbb{R}^3$ and suppose C is a smooth, oriented curve in D, along which an object moves. The direction of motion at each point of C is given by the unit tangent vector $\mathbf{T}$. Therefore, the component of $\mathbf{F}$ in the direction of motion is $\mathbf{F} \cdot \mathbf{T}$, which is the tangential component of $\mathbf{F}$ along C. Summing the contributions to the work at each point of C, the work done in moving an object along C in the presence of the force is the line integral of $\mathbf{F} \cdot \mathbf{T}$ (Figure 14.23).

DEFINITION Work Done in a Force Field

Let $\mathbf{F}$ be a continuous force field in a region D of $\mathbb{R}^3$. Let $C: \mathbf{r}(t) = \langle x(t), y(t), z(t) \rangle$, for $a \le t \le b$, be a smooth curve in D with a unit tangent vector $\mathbf{T}$ consistent with the orientation. The work done in moving an object along C in the positive direction is

$$ W = \int_C \mathbf{F} \cdot \mathbf{T} \, ds = \int_a^b \mathbf{F} \cdot \mathbf{r}'(t) \, dt. $$

EXAMPLE 6 An inverse square force Gravitational and electrical forces between point masses and point charges obey inverse square laws: They act along the line joining the centers and they vary as $1/r^2$, where r is the distance between the centers. The force of attraction (or repulsion) of an inverse square force field is given by the vector field $\mathbf{F} = \dfrac{k\langle x, y, z \rangle}{(x^2 + y^2 + z^2)^{3/2}}$, where k is a physical constant. Because $\mathbf{r} = \langle x, y, z \rangle$, this force may also be written $\mathbf{F} = \dfrac{k\mathbf{r}}{|\mathbf{r}|^3}$. Find the work done in moving an object along the following paths.

a. C_1 is the line segment from $(1, 1, 1)$ to (a, a, a), where $a > 1$.

b. C_2 is the extension of C_1 produced by letting $a \to \infty$.

SOLUTION

a. A parametric description of C_1 consistent with the orientation is $\mathbf{r}(t) = \langle t, t, t \rangle$, for $1 \le t \le a$, with $\mathbf{r}'(t) = \langle 1, 1, 1 \rangle$. In terms of the parameter t, the force field is

$$\mathbf{F} = \frac{k \langle x, y, z \rangle}{(x^2 + y^2 + z^2)^{3/2}} = \frac{k \langle t, t, t \rangle}{(3t^2)^{3/2}}.$$

The dot product that appears in the work integral is

$$\mathbf{F} \cdot \mathbf{r}'(t) = \frac{k \langle t, t, t \rangle}{(3t^2)^{3/2}} \cdot \langle 1, 1, 1 \rangle = \frac{3kt}{3\sqrt{3}\, t^3} = \frac{k}{\sqrt{3}\, t^2}.$$

Therefore, the work done is

$$W = \int_1^a \mathbf{F} \cdot \mathbf{r}'(t)\, dt = \frac{k}{\sqrt{3}} \int_1^a t^{-2}\, dt = \frac{k}{\sqrt{3}} \left(1 - \frac{1}{a} \right).$$

b. The path C_2 is obtained by letting $a \to \infty$ in part (a). The required work is

$$W = \lim_{a \to \infty} \frac{k}{\sqrt{3}} \left(1 - \frac{1}{a} \right) = \frac{k}{\sqrt{3}}.$$

If $\mathbf{F}$ is a gravitational field, this result implies that the work required to escape Earth's gravitational field is finite (which makes space flight possible).

Related Exercises 39–46 ◄

Circulation and Flux of a Vector Field

Line integrals are useful for investigating two important properties of vector fields: *circulation* and *flux*. These properties apply to any vector field, but they are particularly relevant and easy to visualize if you think of $\mathbf{F}$ as the velocity field for a moving fluid.

> ► In the definition of circulation, a *closed curve* is a curve whose initial and terminal points are the same, as defined formally in Section 14.3.

Circulation   We assume that $\mathbf{F} = \langle f, g, h \rangle$ is a continuous vector field on a region D of $\mathbb{R}^3$, and we take C to be a *closed* smooth oriented curve in D. The *circulation* of $\mathbf{F}$ along C is a measure of how much of the vector field points in the direction of C. More simply, as you travel along C in the positive direction, how much of the vector field is at your back and how much of it is in your face? To determine the circulation, we simply "add up" the components of $\mathbf{F}$ in the direction of the unit tangent vector $\mathbf{T}$ at each point. Therefore, circulation integrals are another example of line integrals of vector fields.

> ► Though we define circulation integrals for smooth curves, these integrals may be computed on piecewise-smooth curves. We adopt the convention that *piecewise* refers to a curve with finitely many pieces.

DEFINITION   Circulation

Let $\mathbf{F}$ be a continuous vector field on a region D of $\mathbb{R}^3$ and let C be a closed smooth oriented curve in D. The **circulation** of $\mathbf{F}$ on C is $\int_C \mathbf{F} \cdot \mathbf{T}\, ds$, where $\mathbf{T}$ is the unit vector tangent to C consistent with the orientation.

EXAMPLE 7   Circulation of two-dimensional flows   Let C be the unit circle with counterclockwise orientation. Find the circulation on C of the following vector fields.

a. The radial vector field $\mathbf{F} = \langle x, y \rangle$

b. The rotation vector field $\mathbf{F} = \langle -y, x \rangle$

SOLUTION

a. The unit circle with the specified orientation is described parametrically by
$\mathbf{r}(t) = \langle \cos t, \sin t \rangle$, for $0 \leq t \leq 2\pi$. Therefore, $\mathbf{r}'(t) = \langle -\sin t, \cos t \rangle$ and the circulation of the radial field $\mathbf{F} = \langle x, y \rangle$ is

$$\int_C \mathbf{F} \cdot \mathbf{T} \, ds = \int_0^{2\pi} \mathbf{F} \cdot \mathbf{r}'(t) \, dt \qquad \text{Evaluation of a line integral}$$

$$= \int_0^{2\pi} \underbrace{\langle \cos t, \sin t \rangle}_{\mathbf{F} = \langle x, y \rangle} \cdot \underbrace{\langle -\sin t, \cos t \rangle}_{\mathbf{r}'(t)} \, dt \quad \text{Substitute for } \mathbf{F} \text{ and } \mathbf{r}'.$$

$$= \int_0^{2\pi} 0 \, dt = 0. \qquad \text{Simplify.}$$

The tangential component of the radial field is zero everywhere on C, so the circulation is zero (Figure 14.24a).

b. The circulation for the rotation field $\mathbf{F} = \langle -y, x \rangle$ is

$$\int_C \mathbf{F} \cdot \mathbf{T} \, ds = \int_0^{2\pi} \mathbf{F} \cdot \mathbf{r}'(t) \, dt \qquad \text{Evaluation of a line integral}$$

$$= \int_0^{2\pi} \underbrace{\langle -\sin t, \cos t \rangle}_{\mathbf{F} = \langle -y, x \rangle} \cdot \underbrace{\langle -\sin t, \cos t \rangle}_{\mathbf{r}'(t)} \, dt \quad \text{Substitute for } \mathbf{F} \text{ and } \mathbf{r}'.$$

$$= \int_0^{2\pi} \underbrace{(\sin^2 t + \cos^2 t)}_{1} \, dt \qquad \text{Simplify.}$$

$$= 2\pi.$$

In this case, at every point of C, the rotation field is in the direction of the tangent vector; the result is a positive circulation (Figure 14.24b).

Related Exercises 47–48 ◄

EXAMPLE 8 Circulation of a three-dimensional flow Find the circulation of the vector field $\mathbf{F} = \langle z, x, -y \rangle$ on the tilted ellipse C: $\mathbf{r}(t) = \langle \cos t, \sin t, \cos t \rangle$, for $0 \leq t \leq 2\pi$ (Figure 14.25a).

SOLUTION We first determine that

$$\mathbf{r}'(t) = \langle x'(t), y'(t), z'(t) \rangle = \langle -\sin t, \cos t, -\sin t \rangle.$$

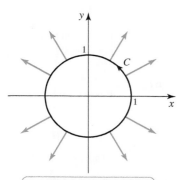

On the unit circle, $\mathbf{F} = \langle x, y \rangle$ is orthogonal to C and has zero circulation on C.

(a)

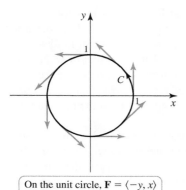

On the unit circle, $\mathbf{F} = \langle -y, x \rangle$ is tangent to C and has positive circulation on C.

(b)

Figure 14.24

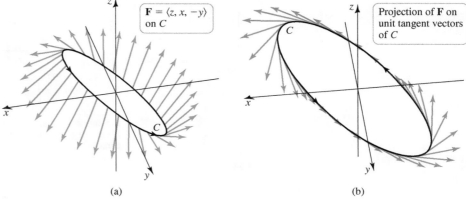

(a)   (b)

Figure 14.25

Substituting $x = \cos t$, $y = \sin t$, and $z = \cos t$ into $\mathbf{F} = \langle z, x, -y \rangle$, the circulation is

$$
\begin{aligned}
\int_C \mathbf{F} \cdot \mathbf{T}\, ds &= \int_0^{2\pi} \mathbf{F} \cdot \mathbf{r}'(t)\, dt & & \text{Evaluation of a} \\
& & & \text{line integral} \\[1em]
&= \int_0^{2\pi} \langle \cos t, \cos t, -\sin t \rangle \cdot \langle -\sin t, \cos t, -\sin t \rangle\, dt & & \text{Substitute for} \\
& & & \mathbf{F} \text{ and } \mathbf{r}'. \\[1em]
&= \int_0^{2\pi} (-\sin t \cos t + 1)\, dt & & \text{Simplify;} \\
& & & \sin^2 t + \cos^2 t = 1. \\[1em]
&= 2\pi. & & \text{Evaluate integral.}
\end{aligned}
$$

Figure 14.25b shows the projection of the vector field on the unit tangent vectors at various points on C. The circulation is the "sum" of the scalar components associated with these projections, which, in this case, is positive.

Related Exercises 47–48 ◄

> In the definition of flux, the non-self-intersecting property of C means that C is a *simple* curve, as defined formally in Section 14.3.

Flux of Two-Dimensional Vector Fields

Assume that $\mathbf{F} = \langle f, g \rangle$ is a continuous vector field on a region R of $\mathbb{R}^2$. We let C be a smooth oriented curve in R that does not intersect itself; C may or may not be closed. To compute the *flux* of the vector field across C, we "add up" the components of $\mathbf{F}$ *orthogonal* or *normal* to C at each point of C. Notice that every point on C has two unit vectors normal to C. Therefore, we let $\mathbf{n}$ denote the unit vector in the xy-plane normal to C in a direction to be defined momentarily. Once the direction of $\mathbf{n}$ is defined, the component of $\mathbf{F}$ normal to C is $\mathbf{F} \cdot \mathbf{n}$, and the flux is the line integral of $\mathbf{F} \cdot \mathbf{n}$ along C, which we denote $\int_C \mathbf{F} \cdot \mathbf{n}\, ds$.

> Recall that $\mathbf{a} \times \mathbf{b}$ is orthogonal to both $\mathbf{a}$ and $\mathbf{b}$.

The first step is to define the unit normal vector at a point P of C. Because C lies in the xy-plane, the unit vector $\mathbf{T}$ tangent at P also lies in the xy-plane. Therefore, its z-component is 0, and we let $\mathbf{T} = \langle T_x, T_y, 0 \rangle$. As always, $\mathbf{k} = \langle 0, 0, 1 \rangle$ is the unit vector in the z-direction. Because a unit vector $\mathbf{n}$ in the xy-plane normal to C is orthogonal to both $\mathbf{T}$ and $\mathbf{k}$, we determine the direction of $\mathbf{n}$ by letting $\mathbf{n} = \mathbf{T} \times \mathbf{k}$. This choice has two implications.

• If C is a closed curve oriented counterclockwise (when viewed from above), the unit normal vector points *outward* along the curve (Figure 14.26a). When $\mathbf{F}$ also points outward at a point on C, the angle θ between $\mathbf{F}$ and $\mathbf{n}$ satisfies $0 \le \theta < \frac{\pi}{2}$ (Figure 14.26b). At all such points, $\mathbf{F} \cdot \mathbf{n} > 0$ and there is a positive contribution to the flux across C. When $\mathbf{F}$ points inward at a point on C, $\frac{\pi}{2} < \theta \le \pi$ and $\mathbf{F} \cdot \mathbf{n} < 0$, which means there is a negative contribution to the flux at that point.

• If C is not a closed curve, the unit normal vector points to the right (when viewed from above) as the curve is traversed in the positive direction.

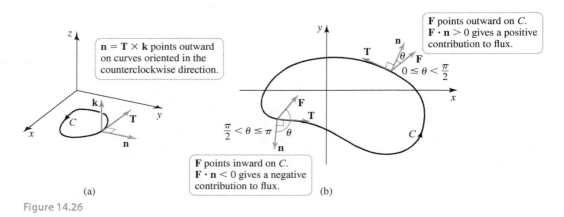

(a)

(b)

Figure 14.26

QUICK CHECK 4 Sketch a closed curve on a sheet of paper and draw a unit tangent vector **T** on the curve pointing in the counterclockwise direction. Explain why $\mathbf{n} = \mathbf{T} \times \mathbf{k}$ is an *outward* unit normal vector. ◄

Calculating the cross product that defines the unit normal vector **n**, we find that

$$\mathbf{n} = \mathbf{T} \times \mathbf{k} = \begin{vmatrix} \mathbf{i} & \mathbf{j} & \mathbf{k} \\ T_x & T_y & 0 \\ 0 & 0 & 1 \end{vmatrix} = T_y\,\mathbf{i} - T_x\,\mathbf{j}.$$

Because $\mathbf{T} = \dfrac{\mathbf{r}'(t)}{|\mathbf{r}'(t)|}$, the components of **T** are

$$\mathbf{T} = \langle T_x, T_y, 0 \rangle = \frac{\langle x'(t), y'(t), 0 \rangle}{|\mathbf{r}'(t)|}.$$

We now have an expression for the unit normal vector:

$$\mathbf{n} = T_y\,\mathbf{i} - T_x\,\mathbf{j} = \frac{y'(t)}{|\mathbf{r}'(t)|}\,\mathbf{i} - \frac{x'(t)}{|\mathbf{r}'(t)|}\,\mathbf{j} = \frac{\langle y'(t), -x'(t) \rangle}{|\mathbf{r}'(t)|}.$$

To evaluate the flux integral $\int_C \mathbf{F} \cdot \mathbf{n}\, ds$, we make a familiar change of variables by letting $ds = |\mathbf{r}'(t)|\, dt$. The flux of $\mathbf{F} = \langle f, g \rangle$ across C is then

$$\int_C \mathbf{F} \cdot \mathbf{n}\, ds = \int_a^b \mathbf{F} \cdot \underbrace{\frac{\langle y'(t), -x'(t) \rangle}{|\mathbf{r}'(t)|}}_{\mathbf{n}} \underbrace{|\mathbf{r}'(t)|\, dt}_{ds} = \int_a^b (f(t)y'(t) - g(t)x'(t))\, dt.$$

This is one useful form of the flux integral. Alternatively, we can note that $dx = x'(t)\, dt$ and $dy = y'(t)\, dt$ and write

$$\int_C \mathbf{F} \cdot \mathbf{n}\, ds = \int_C f\, dy - g\, dx.$$

➤ As with circulation integrals, flux integrals may be computed on piecewise-smooth curves by finding the flux on each piece and adding the results.

DEFINITION Flux

Let $\mathbf{F} = \langle f, g \rangle$ be a continuous vector field on a region R of $\mathbb{R}^2$. Let $C\colon \mathbf{r}(t) = \langle x(t), y(t) \rangle$, for $a \le t \le b$, be a smooth oriented curve in R that does not intersect itself. The **flux** of the vector field $\mathbf{F}$ across C is

$$\int_C \mathbf{F} \cdot \mathbf{n}\, ds = \int_a^b (f(t)y'(t) - g(t)x'(t))\, dt,$$

where $\mathbf{n} = \mathbf{T} \times \mathbf{k}$ is the unit normal vector and **T** is the unit tangent vector consistent with the orientation. If C is a closed curve with counterclockwise orientation, **n** is the outward normal vector and the flux integral gives the **outward flux** across C.

EXAMPLE 9 Flux of two-dimensional flows Find the outward flux across the unit circle with counterclockwise orientation for the following vector fields.

a. The radial vector field $\mathbf{F} = \langle x, y \rangle$

b. The rotation vector field $\mathbf{F} = \langle -y, x \rangle$

SOLUTION

a. The unit circle with counterclockwise orientation has a description $\mathbf{r}(t) = \langle x(t),$ $y(t) \rangle = \langle \cos t, \sin t \rangle$, for $0 \le t \le 2\pi$. Therefore, $x'(t) = -\sin t$ and $y'(t) = \cos t$. The components of $\mathbf{F}$ are $f = x(t) = \cos t$ and $g = y(t) = \sin t$. It follows that the outward flux is

$$\int_a^b (f(t)y'(t) - g(t)x'(t))\, dt = \int_0^{2\pi} (\underbrace{\cos t}_{f(t)}\underbrace{\cos t}_{y'(t)} - \underbrace{\sin t}_{g(t)}\underbrace{(-\sin t)}_{x'(t)})\, dt$$

$$= \int_0^{2\pi} 1\, dt = 2\pi. \qquad \cos^2 t + \sin^2 t = 1$$

Because the radial field points outward and is aligned with the unit normal vectors on C, the outward flux is positive (Figure 14.27a).

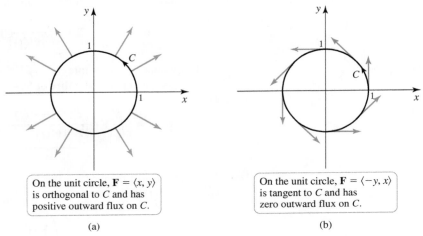

On the unit circle, $\mathbf{F} = \langle x, y \rangle$ is orthogonal to C and has positive outward flux on C.

(a)

On the unit circle, $\mathbf{F} = \langle -y, x \rangle$ is tangent to C and has zero outward flux on C.

(b)

Figure 14.27

b. For the rotation field, $f = -y(t) = -\sin t$ and $g = x(t) = \cos t$. The outward flux is

$$\int_a^b (f(t)y'(t) - g(t)x'(t))\, dt = \int_0^{2\pi} (\underbrace{-\sin t}_{f(t)}\underbrace{\cos t}_{y'(t)} - \underbrace{\cos t}_{g(t)}\underbrace{(-\sin t)}_{x'(t)})\, dt$$

$$= \int_0^{2\pi} 0\, dt = 0.$$

Because the rotation field is orthogonal to $\mathbf{n}$ at all points of C, the outward flux across C is zero (Figure 14.27b). The results of Examples 7 and 9 are worth remembering: On a unit circle centered at the origin, the *radial* vector field $\langle x, y \rangle$ has outward flux 2π and zero circulation. The *rotation* vector field $\langle -y, x \rangle$ has zero outward flux and circulation 2π.

Related Exercises 49–50 ◄

SECTION 14.2 EXERCISES

Review Questions

1. How does a line integral differ from the single-variable integral $\int_a^b f(x)\,dx$?

2. How do you evaluate the line integral $\int_C f\,ds$, where C is parameterized by a parameter other than arc length?

3. If a curve C is given by $\mathbf{r}(t) = \langle t, t^2 \rangle$, what is $|\mathbf{r}'(t)|$?

4. Given a vector field $\mathbf{F}$ and a parameterized curve C, explain how to evaluate the line integral $\int_C \mathbf{F} \cdot \mathbf{T}\,ds$.

5. How can $\int_C \mathbf{F} \cdot \mathbf{T}\,ds$ be written in the alternative form $\int_a^b (f(t)x'(t) + g(t)y'(t) + h(t)z'(t))\,dt$?

6. Given a vector field $\mathbf{F}$ and a closed smooth oriented curve C, what is the meaning of the circulation of $\mathbf{F}$ on C?

7. How is the circulation of a vector field on a closed smooth oriented curve calculated?

8. Given a two-dimensional vector field $\mathbf{F}$ and a smooth oriented curve C, what is the meaning of the flux of $\mathbf{F}$ across C?

9. How do you calculate the flux of a two-dimensional vector field across a smooth oriented curve C?

10. Sketch the oriented quarter circle from $(1, 0)$ to $(0, 1)$ and supply a parameterization for the curve. Draw the unit normal vector at several points on the curve.

Basic Skills

11–14. Scalar line integrals with arc length as parameter *Evaluate the following line integrals.*

11. $\displaystyle\int_C xy\,ds$; C is the unit circle $\mathbf{r}(s) = \langle \cos s, \sin s \rangle$, for $0 \le s \le 2\pi$.

12. $\displaystyle\int_C (x + y)\,ds$; C is the circle of radius 1 centered at $(0, 0)$.

13. $\displaystyle\int_C (x^2 - 2y^2)\,ds$; C is the line $\mathbf{r}(s) = \langle s/\sqrt{2}, s/\sqrt{2} \rangle$, for $0 \le s \le 4$.

14. $\displaystyle\int_C x^2 y\,ds$; C is the line $\mathbf{r}(s) = \langle s/\sqrt{2}, 1 - s/\sqrt{2} \rangle$, for $0 \le s \le 4$.

15–20. Scalar line integrals in the plane

a. *Find a parametric description for C in the form* $\mathbf{r}(t) = \langle x(t), y(t) \rangle$, *if it is not given.*
b. *Evaluate* $|\mathbf{r}'(t)|$.
c. *Convert the line integral to an ordinary integral with respect to the parameter and evaluate it.*

15. $\displaystyle\int_C (x^2 + y^2)\,ds$; C is the circle of radius 4 centered at $(0, 0)$.

16. $\displaystyle\int_C (x^2 + y^2)\,ds$; C is the line segment from $(0, 0)$ to $(5, 5)$.

17. $\displaystyle\int_C \frac{x}{x^2 + y^2}\,ds$; C is the line segment from $(1, 1)$ to $(10, 10)$.

18. $\displaystyle\int_C (xy)^{1/3}\,ds$; C is the curve $y = x^2$, for $0 \le x \le 1$.

19. $\displaystyle\int_C xy\,ds$; C is the portion of the ellipse $\dfrac{x^2}{4} + \dfrac{y^2}{16} = 1$ in the first quadrant, oriented counterclockwise.

20. $\displaystyle\int_C (2x - 3y)\,ds$; C is the line segment from $(-1, 0)$ to $(0, 1)$ followed by the line segment from $(0, 1)$ to $(1, 0)$.

21–24. Average values *Find the average value of the following functions on the given curves.*

21. $f(x, y) = x + 2y$ on the line segment from $(1, 1)$ to $(2, 5)$

22. $f(x, y) = x^2 + 4y^2$ on the circle of radius 9 centered at the origin

23. $f(x, y) = \sqrt{4 + 9y^{2/3}}$ on the curve $y = x^{3/2}$, for $0 \le x \le 5$

24. $f(x, y) = xe^y$ on the unit circle centered at the origin

25–30. Scalar line integrals in $\mathbb{R}^3$ *Convert the line integral to an ordinary integral with respect to the parameter and evaluate it.*

25. $\displaystyle\int_C (x + y + z)\,ds$; C is the circle $\mathbf{r}(t) = \langle 2\cos t, 0, 2\sin t \rangle$, for $0 \le t \le 2\pi$.

26. $\displaystyle\int_C (x - y + 2z)\,ds$; C is the circle $\mathbf{r}(t) = \langle 1, 3\cos t, 3\sin t \rangle$, for $0 \le t \le 2\pi$.

27. $\displaystyle\int_C xyz\,ds$; C is the line segment from $(0, 0, 0)$ to $(1, 2, 3)$.

28. $\displaystyle\int_C \frac{xy}{z}\,ds$; C is the line segment from $(1, 4, 1)$ to $(3, 6, 3)$.

29. $\displaystyle\int_C (y - z)\,ds$; C is the helix $\mathbf{r}(t) = \langle 3\cos t, 3\sin t, t \rangle$, for $0 \le t \le 2\pi$.

30. $\displaystyle\int_C xe^{yz}\,ds$; C is $\mathbf{r}(t) = \langle t, 2t, -4t \rangle$, for $1 \le t \le 2$.

31–32. Length of curves *Use a scalar line integral to find the length of the following curves.*

31. $\mathbf{r}(t) = \left\langle 20\sin\dfrac{t}{4}, 20\cos\dfrac{t}{4}, \dfrac{t}{2} \right\rangle$, for $0 \le t \le 2$

32. $\mathbf{r}(t) = \langle 30\sin t, 40\sin t, 50\cos t \rangle$, for $0 \le t \le 2\pi$

33–38. Line integrals of vector fields in the plane *Given the following vector fields and oriented curves C, evaluate $\int_C \mathbf{F} \cdot \mathbf{T}\,ds$.*

33. $\mathbf{F} = \langle x, y \rangle$ on the parabola $\mathbf{r}(t) = \langle 4t, t^2 \rangle$, for $0 \le t \le 1$

34. $\mathbf{F} = \langle -y, x \rangle$ on the semicircle $\mathbf{r}(t) = \langle 4\cos t, 4\sin t \rangle$, for $0 \le t \le \pi$

35. $\mathbf{F} = \langle y, x \rangle$ on the line segment from $(1, 1)$ to $(5, 10)$

36. $\mathbf{F} = \langle -y, x \rangle$ on the parabola $y = x^2$ from $(0, 0)$ to $(1, 1)$

37. $\mathbf{F} = \dfrac{\langle x, y \rangle}{(x^2 + y^2)^{3/2}}$ on the curve $\mathbf{r}(t) = \langle t^2, 3t^2 \rangle$, for $1 \le t \le 2$

38. $\mathbf{F} = \dfrac{\langle x, y \rangle}{x^2 + y^2}$ on the line $\mathbf{r}(t) = \langle t, 4t \rangle$, for $1 \le t \le 10$

39–42. Work integrals *Given the force field* $\mathbf{F}$, *find the work required to move an object on the given oriented curve.*

39. $\mathbf{F} = \langle y, -x \rangle$ on the path consisting of the line segment from $(1, 2)$ to $(0, 0)$ followed by the line segment from $(0, 0)$ to $(0, 4)$

40. $\mathbf{F} = \langle x, y \rangle$ on the path consisting of the line segment from $(-1, 0)$ to $(0, 8)$ followed by the line segment from $(0, 8)$ to $(2, 8)$

41. $\mathbf{F} = \langle y, x \rangle$ on the parabola $y = 2x^2$ from $(0, 0)$ to $(2, 8)$

42. $\mathbf{F} = \langle y, -x \rangle$ on the line $y = 10 - 2x$ from $(1, 8)$ to $(3, 4)$

43–46. Work integrals in $\mathbb{R}^3$ *Given the force field* $\mathbf{F}$, *find the work required to move an object on the given oriented curve.*

43. $\mathbf{F} = \langle x, y, z \rangle$ on the tilted ellipse $\mathbf{r}(t) = \langle 4 \cos t, 4 \sin t, 4 \cos t \rangle$, for $0 \le t \le 2\pi$

44. $\mathbf{F} = \langle -y, x, z \rangle$ on the helix $\mathbf{r}(t) = \langle 2 \cos t, 2 \sin t, t/2\pi \rangle$, for $0 \le t \le 2\pi$

45. $\mathbf{F} = \dfrac{\langle x, y, z \rangle}{(x^2 + y^2 + z^2)^{3/2}}$ on the line segment from $(1, 1, 1)$ to $(10, 10, 10)$

46. $\mathbf{F} = \dfrac{\langle x, y, z \rangle}{x^2 + y^2 + z^2}$ on the line segment from $(1, 1, 1)$ to $(8, 4, 2)$

47–48. Circulation *Consider the following vector fields* $\mathbf{F}$ *and closed oriented curves* C *in the plane (see figures).*

a. Based on the picture, make a conjecture about whether the circulation of $\mathbf{F}$ *on* C *is positive, negative, or zero.*

b. Compute the circulation and interpret the result.

47. $\mathbf{F} = \langle y - x, x \rangle$; $C: \mathbf{r}(t) = \langle 2 \cos t, 2 \sin t \rangle$, for $0 \le t \le 2\pi$

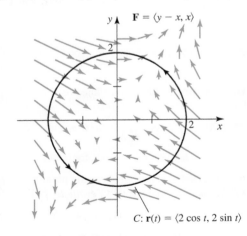

$C: \mathbf{r}(t) = \langle 2 \cos t, 2 \sin t \rangle$

48. $\mathbf{F} = \dfrac{\langle x, y \rangle}{(x^2 + y^2)^{1/2}}$; C is the boundary of the square with vertices $(\pm 2, \pm 2)$, traversed counterclockwise.

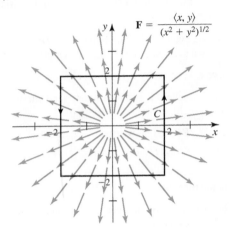

49–50. Flux *Consider the vector fields and curves in Exercises 47–48.*

a. Based on the picture, make a conjecture about whether the outward flux of $\mathbf{F}$ *across* C *is positive, negative, or zero.*

b. Compute the flux for the vector fields and curves.

49. $\mathbf{F}$ and C given in Exercise 47

50. $\mathbf{F}$ and C given in Exercise 48

Further Explorations

51. Explain why or why not Determine whether the following statements are true and give an explanation or counterexample.

   a. If a curve has a parametric description $\mathbf{r}(t) = \langle x(t), y(t), z(t) \rangle$, where t is the arc length, then $|\mathbf{r}'(t)| = 1$.

   b. The vector field $\mathbf{F} = \langle y, x \rangle$ has both zero circulation along and zero flux across the unit circle centered at the origin.

   c. If at all points of a path a force acts in a direction orthogonal to the path, then no work is done in moving an object along the path.

   d. The flux of a vector field across a curve in $\mathbb{R}^2$ can be computed using a line integral.

52. Flying into a headwind An airplane flies in the xz-plane, where x increases in the eastward direction and $z \ge 0$ represents vertical distance above the ground. A wind blows horizontally out of the west, producing a force $\mathbf{F} = \langle 150, 0 \rangle$. On which path between the points $(100, 50)$ and $(-100, 50)$ is the most work done overcoming the wind?

   a. The straight line $\mathbf{r}(t) = \langle x(t), z(t) \rangle = \langle -t, 50 \rangle$, for $-100 \le t \le 100$

   b. The arc of a circle $\mathbf{r}(t) = \langle 100 \cos t, 50 + 100 \sin t \rangle$, for $0 \le t \le \pi$

53. Flying into a headwind

   a. How does the result of Exercise 52 change if the force due to the wind is $\mathbf{F} = \langle 141, 50 \rangle$ (approximately the same magnitude, but different direction)?

   b. How does the result of Exercise 52 change if the force due to the wind is $\mathbf{F} = \langle 141, -50 \rangle$ (approximately the same magnitude, but different direction)?

54. Changing orientation Let $f(x, y) = x + 2y$ and let C be the unit circle.

    a. Find a parameterization of C with counterclockwise orientation and evaluate $\int_C f\, ds$.

    b. Find a parameterization of C with clockwise orientation and evaluate $\int_C f\, ds$.

    c. Compare the results of (a) and (b).

55. Changing orientation Let $f(x, y) = x$ and let C be the segment of the parabola $y = x^2$ joining $O(0, 0)$ and $P(1, 1)$.

    a. Find a parameterization of C in the direction from O to P. Evaluate $\int_C f\, ds$.

    b. Find a parameterization of C in the direction from P to O. Evaluate $\int_C f\, ds$.

    c. Compare the results of (a) and (b).

56–57. Zero circulation fields

56. For what values of b and c does the vector field $\mathbf{F} = \langle by, cx \rangle$ have zero circulation on the unit circle centered at the origin and oriented counterclockwise?

57. Consider the vector field $\mathbf{F} = \langle ax + by, cx + dy \rangle$. Show that $\mathbf{F}$ has zero circulation on any oriented circle centered at the origin, for any $a, b, c,$ and d, provided $b = c$.

58–59. Zero flux fields

58. For what values of a and d does the vector field $\mathbf{F} = \langle ax, dy \rangle$ have zero flux across the unit circle centered at the origin and oriented counterclockwise?

59. Consider the vector field $\mathbf{F} = \langle ax + by, cx + dy \rangle$. Show that $\mathbf{F}$ has zero flux across any oriented circle centered at the origin, for any $a, b, c,$ and d, provided $a = -d$.

60. Work in a rotation field Consider the rotation field $\mathbf{F} = \langle -y, x \rangle$ and the three paths shown in the figure. Compute the work done in the presence of the force field $\mathbf{F}$ on each of the three paths. Does it appear that the line integral $\int_C \mathbf{F} \cdot \mathbf{T}\, ds$ is independent of the path, where C is any path from $(1, 0)$ to $(0, 1)$?

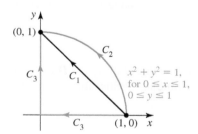

61. Work in a hyperbolic field Consider the hyperbolic force field $\mathbf{F} = \langle y, x \rangle$ (the streamlines are hyperbolas) and the three paths shown in the figure for Exercise 60. Compute the work done in the presence of $\mathbf{F}$ on each of the three paths. Does it appear that the line integral $\int_C \mathbf{F} \cdot \mathbf{T}\, ds$ is independent of the path, where C is any path from $(1, 0)$ to $(0, 1)$?

Applications

62–63. Mass and density *A thin wire represented by the smooth curve C with a density ρ (units of mass per length) has a mass $M = \int_C \rho\, ds$. Find the mass of the following wires with the given density.*

62. $C: \mathbf{r}(\theta) = \langle \cos\theta, \sin\theta \rangle$, for $0 \le \theta \le \pi$; $\rho(\theta) = 2\theta/\pi + 1$

63. $C: \{(x, y): y = 2x^2, 0 \le x \le 3\}$; $\rho(x, y) = 1 + xy$

64. Heat flux in a plate A square plate $R = \{(x, y): 0 \le x \le 1, 0 \le y \le 1\}$ has a temperature distribution $T(x, y) = 100 - 50x - 25y$.

    a. Sketch two level curves of the temperature in the plate.

    b. Find the gradient of the temperature $\nabla T(x, y)$.

    c. Assume that the flow of heat is given by the vector field $\mathbf{F} = -\nabla T(x, y)$. Compute $\mathbf{F}$.

    d. Find the outward heat flux across the boundary $\{(x, y): x = 1, 0 \le y \le 1\}$.

    e. Find the outward heat flux across the boundary $\{(x, y): 0 \le x \le 1, y = 1\}$.

65. Inverse force fields Consider the radial field

$$\mathbf{F} = \frac{\mathbf{r}}{|\mathbf{r}|^p} = \frac{\langle x, y, z \rangle}{|\mathbf{r}|^p},$$ where $p > 1$ (the inverse square law corresponds to $p = 3$). Let C be the line from $(1, 1, 1)$ to (a, a, a), where $a > 1$, given by $\mathbf{r}(t) = \langle t, t, t \rangle$, for $1 \le t \le a$.

    a. Find the work done in moving an object along C with $p = 2$.

    b. If $a \to \infty$ in part (a), is the work finite?

    c. Find the work done in moving an object moving along C with $p = 4$.

    d. If $a \to \infty$ in part (c), is the work finite?

    e. Find the work done in moving an object moving along C for any $p > 1$.

    f. If $a \to \infty$ in part (e), for what values of p is the work finite?

66. Flux across curves in a vector field Consider the vector field $\mathbf{F} = \langle y, x \rangle$ shown in the figure.

    a. Compute the outward flux across the quarter circle $C: \mathbf{r}(t) = \langle 2\cos t, 2\sin t \rangle$, for $0 \le t \le \pi/2$.

    b. Compute the outward flux across the quarter circle $C: \mathbf{r}(t) = \langle 2\cos t, 2\sin t \rangle$, for $\pi/2 \le t \le \pi$.

    c. Explain why the flux across the quarter circle in the third quadrant equals the flux computed in part (a).

    d. Explain why the flux across the quarter circle in the fourth quadrant equals the flux computed in part (b).

    e. What is the outward flux across the full circle?

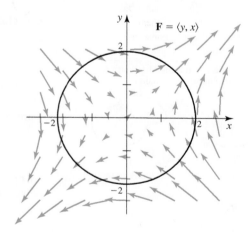

Additional Exercises

67–68. Looking ahead: Area from line integrals *The area of a region R in the plane, whose boundary is the closed curve C, may be computed using line integrals with the formula*

$$\text{area of } R = \int_C x\, dy = -\int_C y\, dx.$$

These ideas reappear later in the chapter.

67. Let R be the rectangle with vertices $(0, 0)$, $(a, 0)$, $(0, b)$, and (a, b), and let C be the boundary of R oriented counterclockwise. Use the formula $A = \int_C x \, dy$ to verify that the area of the rectangle is ab.

68. Let $R = \{(r, \theta): 0 \le r \le a, 0 \le \theta \le 2\pi\}$ be the disk of radius a centered at the origin and let C be the boundary of R oriented counterclockwise. Use the formula $A = -\int_C y \, dx$ to verify that the area of the disk is πr^2.

QUICK CHECK ANSWERS

1. The Fundamental Theorem of Calculus says that $\dfrac{d}{dt} \displaystyle\int_a^t f(u) \, du = f(t)$, which applies to differentiating the arc length integral.   **2.** 1300 ft/min   **3.** $\pi/2$ **4.** $\mathbf{T}$ and $\mathbf{k}$ are unit vectors, so $\mathbf{n}$ is a unit vector. By the right-hand rule for cross products, $\mathbf{n}$ points outward from the curve. ◄

14.3 Conservative Vector Fields

This is an action-packed section in which several fundamental ideas come together. At the heart of the matter are two questions.

- When can a vector field be expressed as the gradient of a potential function? A vector field with this property will be defined as a *conservative* vector field.

- What special properties do conservative vector fields have?

After some preliminary definitions, we present a test to determine whether a vector field in $\mathbb{R}^2$ or $\mathbb{R}^3$ is conservative. This test is followed by a procedure to find a potential function for a conservative field. We then develop several equivalent properties shared by all conservative vector fields.

Types of Curves and Regions

Many of the results in the remainder of the book rely on special properties of regions and curves. It's best to collect these definitions in one place for easy reference.

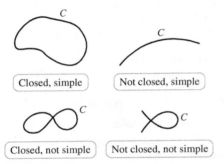

Figure 14.28

> Recall that all points of an open set are interior points. An open set does not contain its boundary points.

> Roughly speaking, connected means that R is all in one piece and simply connected in $\mathbb{R}^2$ means that R has no holes. $\mathbb{R}^2$ and $\mathbb{R}^3$ are themselves connected and simply connected.

DEFINITION **Simple and Closed Curves**

Suppose a curve C (in $\mathbb{R}^2$ or $\mathbb{R}^3$) is described parametrically by $\mathbf{r}(t)$, where $a \le t \le b$. Then C is a **simple curve** if $\mathbf{r}(t_1) \ne \mathbf{r}(t_2)$ for all t_1 and t_2, with $a < t_1 < t_2 < b$; that is, C never intersects itself between its endpoints. The curve C is **closed** if $\mathbf{r}(a) = \mathbf{r}(b)$; that is, the initial and terminal points of C are the same (Figure 14.28).

In all that follows, we generally assume that R in $\mathbb{R}^2$ (or D in $\mathbb{R}^3$) is an open region. Open regions are further classified according to whether they are *connected* and whether they are *simply connected*.

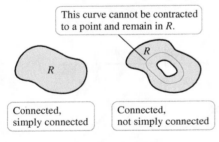

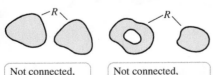

Figure 14.29

DEFINITION **Connected and Simply Connected Regions**

An open region R in $\mathbb{R}^2$ (or D in $\mathbb{R}^3$) is **connected** if it is possible to connect any two points of R by a continuous curve lying in R. An open region R is **simply connected** if every closed simple curve in R can be deformed and contracted to a point in R (Figure 14.29).

QUICK CHECK 1 Is a figure-8 curve simple? Closed? Is a torus connected? Simply connected? ◄

Test for Conservative Vector Fields

We begin with the central definition of this section.

> ► The term *conservative* refers to conservation of energy. See Exercise 52 for an example of conservation of energy in a conservative force field.

> ► Depending on the context and the interpretation of the vector field, the potential function φ may be defined such that $\mathbf{F} = -\nabla\varphi$ (with a negative sign).

DEFINITION **Conservative Vector Field**

A vector field $\mathbf{F}$ is said to be **conservative** on a region (in $\mathbb{R}^2$ or $\mathbb{R}^3$) if there exists a scalar function φ such that $\mathbf{F} = \nabla\varphi$ on that region.

Suppose that the components of $\mathbf{F} = \langle f, g, h \rangle$ have continuous first partial derivatives on a region D in $\mathbb{R}^3$. Also assume that $\mathbf{F}$ is conservative, which means by definition that there is a potential function φ such that $\mathbf{F} = \nabla\varphi$. Matching the components of $\mathbf{F}$ and $\nabla\varphi$, we see that $f = \varphi_x$, $g = \varphi_y$, and $h = \varphi_z$. Recall from Theorem 12.4 that if a function has continuous second partial derivatives, the order of differentiation in the second partial derivatives does not matter. Under these conditions on φ, we conclude the following:

- $\varphi_{xy} = \varphi_{yx}$, which implies that $f_y = g_x$,
- $\varphi_{xz} = \varphi_{zx}$, which implies that $f_z = h_x$, and
- $\varphi_{yz} = \varphi_{zy}$, which implies that $g_z = h_y$.

These observations comprise half of the proof of the following theorem. The remainder of the proof is given in Section 14.4.

THEOREM 14.3 **Test for Conservative Vector Fields**

Let $\mathbf{F} = \langle f, g, h \rangle$ be a vector field defined on a connected and simply connected region D of $\mathbb{R}^3$, where f, g, and h have continuous first partial derivatives on D. Then $\mathbf{F}$ is a conservative vector field on D (there is a potential function φ such that $\mathbf{F} = \nabla\varphi$) if and only if

$$\frac{\partial f}{\partial y} = \frac{\partial g}{\partial x}, \qquad \frac{\partial f}{\partial z} = \frac{\partial h}{\partial x}, \quad \text{and} \quad \frac{\partial g}{\partial z} = \frac{\partial h}{\partial y}.$$

For vector fields in $\mathbb{R}^2$, we have the single condition $\dfrac{\partial f}{\partial y} = \dfrac{\partial g}{\partial x}$.

EXAMPLE 1 **Testing for conservative fields** Determine whether the following vector fields are conservative on $\mathbb{R}^2$ and $\mathbb{R}^3$, respectively.

a. $\mathbf{F} = \langle e^x \cos y, -e^x \sin y \rangle$

b. $\mathbf{F} = \langle 2xy - z^2, x^2 + 2z, 2y - 2xz \rangle$

SOLUTION

a. Letting $f(x, y) = e^x \cos y$ and $g(x, y) = -e^x \sin y$, we see that

$$\frac{\partial f}{\partial y} = -e^x \sin y = \frac{\partial g}{\partial x}.$$

The conditions of Theorem 14.3 are met and $\mathbf{F}$ is conservative.

b. Letting $f(x, y, z) = 2xy - z^2$, $g(x, y, z) = x^2 + 2z$, and $h(x, y, z) = 2y - 2xz$, we have

$$\frac{\partial f}{\partial y} = 2x = \frac{\partial g}{\partial x}, \qquad \frac{\partial f}{\partial z} = -2z = \frac{\partial h}{\partial x}, \qquad \frac{\partial g}{\partial z} = 2 = \frac{\partial h}{\partial y}.$$

By Theorem 14.3, $\mathbf{F}$ is conservative.

Related Exercises 9–14 ◄

Finding Potential Functions

Like antiderivatives, potential functions are determined up to an arbitrary additive constant. Unless an additive constant in a potential function has some physical meaning, it is usually omitted. Given a conservative vector field, there are several methods for finding a potential function. One method is shown in the following example. Another approach is illustrated in Exercise 57.

QUICK CHECK 2 Explain why a potential function for a conservative vector field is determined up to an additive constant. ◄

EXAMPLE 2   Finding potential functions Find a potential function for the conservative vector fields in Example 1.

a. $\mathbf{F} = \langle e^x \cos y, -e^x \sin y \rangle$

b. $\mathbf{F} = \langle 2xy - z^2, x^2 + 2z, 2y - 2xz \rangle$

SOLUTION

a. A potential function φ for $\mathbf{F} = \langle f, g \rangle$ has the property that $\mathbf{F} = \nabla\varphi$ and satisfies the conditions

$$\varphi_x = f(x, y) = e^x \cos y \quad \text{and} \quad \varphi_y = g(x, y) = -e^x \sin y.$$

The first equation is integrated with respect to x (holding y fixed) to obtain

$$\int \varphi_x \, dx = \int e^x \cos y \, dx,$$

which implies that

$$\varphi(x, y) = e^x \cos y + c(y).$$

> This procedure may begin with either of the two conditions, $\varphi_x = f$ or $\varphi_y = g$.

In this case, the "constant of integration" $c(y)$ is an arbitrary function of y. You can check the preceding calculation by noting that

$$\frac{\partial \varphi}{\partial x} = \frac{\partial}{\partial x}(e^x \cos y + c(y)) = e^x \cos y = f(x, y).$$

To find the arbitrary function $c(y)$, we differentiate $\varphi(x, y) = e^x \cos y + c(y)$ with respect to y and equate the result to g (recall that $\varphi_y = g$):

$$\varphi_y = -e^x \sin y + c'(y) \quad \text{and} \quad g = -e^x \sin y.$$

We conclude that $c'(y) = 0$, which implies that $c(y)$ is any real number, which we typically take to be zero. So a potential function is $\varphi(x, y) = e^x \cos y$, a result that may be checked by differentiation.

b. The method of part (a) is more elaborate with three variables. A potential function φ must now satisfy these conditions:

> This procedure may begin with any of the three conditions.

$$\varphi_x = f = 2xy - z^2 \qquad \varphi_y = g = x^2 + 2z \qquad \varphi_z = h = 2y - 2xz.$$

Integrating the first condition with respect to x (holding y and z fixed), we have

$$\varphi = \int (2xy - z^2) \, dx = x^2 y - xz^2 + c(y, z).$$

Because the integration is with respect to x, the arbitrary "constant" is a function of y and z. To find $c(y, z)$, we differentiate φ with respect to y, which results in

$$\varphi_y = x^2 + c_y(y, z).$$

Equating φ_y and $g = x^2 + 2z$, we see that $c_y(y, z) = 2z$. To obtain $c(y, z)$, we integrate $c_y(y, z) = 2z$ with respect to y (holding z fixed), which results in $c(y, z) = 2yz + d(z)$. The "constant" of integration is now a function of z, which we call $d(z)$. At this point, a potential function looks like

$$\varphi(x, y, z) = x^2 y - xz^2 + 2yz + d(z).$$

To determine $d(z)$, we differentiate φ with respect to z:

$$\varphi_z = -2xz + 2y + d'(z).$$

Equating φ_z and $h = 2y - 2xz$, we see that $d'(z) = 0$, or $d(z)$ is a real number, which we generally take to be zero. Putting it all together, a potential function is

$$\varphi = x^2y - xz^2 + 2yz.$$

Related Exercises 15–26 ◀

QUICK CHECK 3 Verify by differentiation that the potential functions found in Example 2 produce the corresponding vector fields. ◀

PROCEDURE   **Finding Potential Functions in $\mathbb{R}^3$**

Suppose $\mathbf{F} = \langle f, g, h \rangle$ is a conservative vector field. To find φ such that $\mathbf{F} = \nabla\varphi$, use the following steps:

1. Integrate $\varphi_x = f$ with respect to x to obtain φ, which includes an arbitrary function $c(y, z)$.

2. Compute φ_y and equate it to g to obtain an expression for $c_y(y, z)$.

3. Integrate $c_y(y, z)$ with respect to y to obtain $c(y, z)$, including an arbitrary function $d(z)$.

4. Compute φ_z and equate it to h to get $d(z)$.

A similar procedure beginning with $\varphi_y = g$ or $\varphi_z = h$ may be easier in some cases.

Fundamental Theorem for Line Integrals and Path Independence

Knowing how to find potential functions, we now investigate their properties. The first property is one of several beautiful parallels to the Fundamental Theorem of Calculus.

➤ Compare the two versions of the Fundamental Theorem.

$$\int_a^b F'(x)\, dx = F(b) - F(a)$$

$$\int_C \nabla\varphi \cdot d\mathbf{r} = \varphi(B) - \varphi(A)$$

THEOREM 14.4   **Fundamental Theorem for Line Integrals**

Let $\mathbf{F}$ be a continuous vector field on an open connected region R in $\mathbb{R}^2$ (or D in $\mathbb{R}^3$). There exists a potential function φ with $\mathbf{F} = \nabla\varphi$ (which means that $\mathbf{F}$ is conservative) if and only if

$$\int_C \mathbf{F} \cdot \mathbf{T}\, ds = \int_C \mathbf{F} \cdot d\mathbf{r} = \varphi(B) - \varphi(A),$$

for all points A and B in R (or D) and all piecewise-smooth oriented curves C in R (or D) from A to B.

Here is the meaning of this theorem: If $\mathbf{F}$ is a conservative vector field, then the value of a line integral of $\mathbf{F}$ depends only on the endpoints of the path. More simply, *the line integral is independent of path*, which means a parameterization of the path is not needed to evaluate line integrals of conservative fields.

If we think of φ as an antiderivative of the vector field $\mathbf{F}$, then the parallel to the Fundamental Theorem of Calculus is clear. The line integral of $\mathbf{F}$ is the difference of the values of φ evaluated at the endpoints.

Proof: We prove the theorem in one direction: If $\mathbf{F}$ is conservative, then the line integral is path independent. The technical proof in the other direction is omitted.

Let the curve C in $\mathbb{R}^3$ be given by $\mathbf{r}(t) = \langle x(t), y(t), z(t) \rangle$, for $a \leq t \leq b$, where $\mathbf{r}(a)$ and $\mathbf{r}(b)$ are the position vectors for the points A and B, respectively. By the Chain Rule, the rate of change of φ with respect to t along C is

$$
\begin{aligned}
\frac{d\varphi}{dt} &= \frac{\partial \varphi}{\partial x}\frac{dx}{dt} + \frac{\partial \varphi}{\partial y}\frac{dy}{dt} + \frac{\partial \varphi}{\partial z}\frac{dz}{dt} && \text{Chain Rule} \\
&= \left\langle \frac{\partial \varphi}{\partial x}, \frac{\partial \varphi}{\partial y}, \frac{\partial \varphi}{\partial z} \right\rangle \cdot \left\langle \frac{dx}{dt}, \frac{dy}{dt}, \frac{dz}{dt} \right\rangle && \text{Identify the dot product.} \\
&= \nabla\varphi \cdot \mathbf{r}'(t) && \mathbf{r} = \langle x, y, z \rangle \\
&= \mathbf{F} \cdot \mathbf{r}'(t). && \mathbf{F} = \nabla\varphi
\end{aligned}
$$

Evaluating the line integral and using the Fundamental Theorem of Calculus, it follows that

$$
\begin{aligned}
\int_C \mathbf{F} \cdot d\mathbf{r} &= \int_a^b \mathbf{F} \cdot \mathbf{r}'(t)\, dt \\
&= \int_a^b \frac{d\varphi}{dt}\, dt && \mathbf{F} \cdot \mathbf{r}'(t) = \frac{d\varphi}{dt} \\
&= \varphi(B) - \varphi(A). && \text{Fundamental Theorem of Calculus; } t = b \text{ corresponds} \\
& && \text{to } B \text{ and } t = a \text{ corresponds to } A.
\end{aligned}
$$

◄

EXAMPLE 3 **Verifying path independence** Consider the potential function $\varphi(x, y) = (x^2 - y^2)/2$ and its gradient field $\mathbf{F} = \langle x, -y \rangle$.

- Let C_1 be the quarter circle $\mathbf{r}(t) = \langle \cos t, \sin t \rangle$, for $0 \leq t \leq \pi/2$, from $A(1, 0)$ to $B(0, 1)$.
- Let C_2 be the line $\mathbf{r}(t) = \langle 1 - t, t \rangle$, for $0 \leq t \leq 1$, also from A to B.

Evaluate the line integrals of $\mathbf{F}$ on C_1 and C_2, and show that both are equal to $\varphi(B) - \varphi(A)$.

SOLUTION On C_1, we have $\mathbf{r}'(t) = \langle -\sin t, \cos t \rangle$ and $\mathbf{F} = \langle x, -y \rangle = \langle \cos t, -\sin t \rangle$. The line integral on C_1 is

$$
\begin{aligned}
\int_{C_1} \mathbf{F} \cdot d\mathbf{r} &= \int_{C_1} \mathbf{F} \cdot \mathbf{r}'(t)\, dt \\
&= \int_0^{\pi/2} \underbrace{\langle \cos t, -\sin t \rangle}_{\mathbf{F}} \cdot \underbrace{\langle -\sin t, \cos t \rangle\, dt}_{\mathbf{r}'(t)\, dt} && \text{Substitute for } \mathbf{F} \text{ and } \mathbf{r}'. \\
&= \int_0^{\pi/2} (-\sin 2t)\, dt && 2 \sin t \cos t = \sin 2t \\
&= \left(\frac{1}{2} \cos 2t \right)\Big|_0^{\pi/2} = -1. && \text{Evaluate the integral.}
\end{aligned}
$$

On C_2, we have $\mathbf{r}'(t) = \langle -1, 1 \rangle$ and $\mathbf{F} = \langle x, -y \rangle = \langle 1 - t, -t \rangle$; therefore,

$$
\begin{aligned}
\int_{C_2} \mathbf{F} \cdot d\mathbf{r} &= \int_0^1 \underbrace{\langle 1 - t, -t \rangle}_{\mathbf{F}} \cdot \underbrace{\langle -1, 1 \rangle\, dt}_{d\mathbf{r}} && \text{Substitute for } \mathbf{F} \text{ and } d\mathbf{r}. \\
&= \int_0^1 (-1)\, dt = -1. && \text{Simplify.}
\end{aligned}
$$

The two line integrals have the same value, which is

$$
\varphi(B) - \varphi(A) = \varphi(0, 1) - \varphi(1, 0) = -\frac{1}{2} - \frac{1}{2} = -1.
$$

Related Exercises 27–32 ◄

EXAMPLE 4 **Line integral of a conservative vector field** Evaluate

$$\int_C ((2xy - z^2)\,\mathbf{i} + (x^2 + 2z)\,\mathbf{j} + (2y - 2xz)\,\mathbf{k}) \cdot d\mathbf{r},$$

where C is a simple curve from $A(-3, -2, -1)$ to $B(1, 2, 3)$.

SOLUTION This vector field is conservative and has a potential function $\varphi = x^2y - xz^2 + 2yz$ (Example 2). By the Fundamental Theorem for line integrals,

$$\int_C ((2xy - z^2)\,\mathbf{i} + (x^2 + 2z)\,\mathbf{j} + (2y - 2xz)\,\mathbf{k}) \cdot d\mathbf{r}$$

$$= \int_C \nabla \underbrace{(x^2y - xz^2 + 2yz)}_{\varphi} \cdot d\mathbf{r}$$

$$= \varphi(1, 2, 3) - \varphi(-3, -2, -1) = 16.$$

Related Exercises 27–32 ◄

QUICK CHECK 4 Explain why the vector field $\nabla(xy + xz - yz)$ is conservative. ◄

Line Integrals on Closed Curves

It is a short step to another characterization of conservative vector fields. Suppose C is a simple *closed* piecewise-smooth oriented curve in $\mathbb{R}^2$ or $\mathbb{R}^3$. To distinguish line integrals on closed curves, we adopt the notation $\oint_C \mathbf{F} \cdot d\mathbf{r}$, where the small circle on the integral sign indicates that C is a closed curve. Let A be any point on C and think of A as both the initial point and the final point of C. Assuming that $\mathbf{F}$ is a conservative vector field on an open connected region R containing C, it follows by Theorem 14.4 that

> ► Notice the analogy with $\int_a^a f(x)\,dx = 0$, which is true of all integrable functions.

$$\oint_C \mathbf{F} \cdot d\mathbf{r} = \varphi(A) - \varphi(A) = 0.$$

Because A is an arbitrary point on C, we see that the line integral of a conservative vector field on a closed curve is zero.

An argument can be made in the opposite direction as well: Suppose $\oint_C \mathbf{F} \cdot d\mathbf{r} = 0$ on all simple closed piecewise-smooth oriented curves in a region R, and let A and B be distinct points in R. Let C_1 denote any curve from A to B, let C_2 be any curve from B to A (distinct from and not intersecting C_1), and let C be the closed curve consisting of C_1 followed by C_2 (Figure 14.30). Then

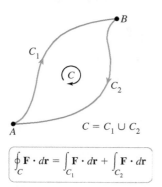

$$0 = \oint_C \mathbf{F} \cdot d\mathbf{r} = \int_{C_1} \mathbf{F} \cdot d\mathbf{r} + \int_{C_2} \mathbf{F} \cdot d\mathbf{r}.$$

$C = C_1 \cup C_2$

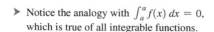

$$\oint_C \mathbf{F} \cdot d\mathbf{r} = \int_{C_1} \mathbf{F} \cdot d\mathbf{r} + \int_{C_2} \mathbf{F} \cdot d\mathbf{r}$$

Figure 14.30

Therefore, $\int_{C_1} \mathbf{F} \cdot d\mathbf{r} = -\int_{C_2} \mathbf{F} \cdot d\mathbf{r} = \int_{-C_2} \mathbf{F} \cdot d\mathbf{r}$, where $-C_2$ is the curve C_2 traversed in the opposite direction (from A to B). We see that the line integral has the same value on two arbitrary paths between A and B. It follows that the value of the line integral is independent of path, and by Theorem 14.4, $\mathbf{F}$ is conservative. This argument is a proof of the following theorem.

> **THEOREM 14.5** **Line Integrals on Closed Curves**
> Let R in $\mathbb{R}^2$ (or D in $\mathbb{R}^3$) be an open connected region. Then $\mathbf{F}$ is a conservative vector field on R if and only if $\oint_C \mathbf{F} \cdot d\mathbf{r} = 0$ on all simple closed piecewise-smooth oriented curves C in R.

EXAMPLE 5 **A closed curve line integral in $\mathbb{R}^3$** Evaluate $\int_C \nabla(-xy + xz + yz) \cdot d\mathbf{r}$ on the curve $C: \mathbf{r}(t) = \langle \sin t, \cos t, \sin t \rangle$, for $0 \le t \le 2\pi$, without using Theorems 14.4 or 14.5.

SOLUTION The components of the vector field are

$$\mathbf{F} = \nabla(-xy + xz + yz) = \langle -y + z, -x + z, x + y \rangle.$$

Note that $\mathbf{r}'(t) = \langle \cos t, -\sin t, \cos t \rangle$ and $d\mathbf{r} = \mathbf{r}'(t)\, dt$. Substituting values of x, y, and z, the value of the line integral is

$$\oint_C \mathbf{F} \cdot d\mathbf{r} = \oint_C \langle -y + z, -x + z, x + y \rangle \cdot d\mathbf{r} \qquad \text{Substitute for } \mathbf{F}.$$

$$= \int_0^{2\pi} \sin 2t \, dt \qquad\qquad \text{Substitute for } x, y, z, d\mathbf{r}.$$

$$= -\frac{1}{2} \cos 2t \Big|_0^{2\pi} = 0. \qquad\qquad \text{Evaluate integral.}$$

The line integral of this conservative vector field on the closed curve C is zero. In fact, by Theorem 14.5, the line integral vanishes on any simple closed piecewise-smooth oriented curve.

Related Exercises 33–38 ◀

Summary of the Properties of Conservative Vector Fields

We have established three equivalent properties of conservative vector fields $\mathbf{F}$ defined on an open connected region R in $\mathbb{R}^2$ (or D in $\mathbb{R}^3$).

- There exists a potential function φ such that $\mathbf{F} = \nabla\varphi$ (definition).
- $\int_C \mathbf{F} \cdot d\mathbf{r} = \varphi(B) - \varphi(A)$ for all points A and B in R and all piecewise-smooth oriented curves C in R from A to B (path independence).
- $\oint_C \mathbf{F} \cdot d\mathbf{r} = 0$ on all simple piecewise-smooth closed oriented curves C in R.

The connections between these properties were established by Theorems 14.4 and 14.5 in the following way:

$$\overset{\text{Theorem 14.4}}{\text{Path independence} \quad \Longleftrightarrow} \quad \mathbf{F} \text{ is conservative } (\nabla\varphi = \mathbf{F}) \quad \overset{\text{Theorem 14.5}}{\Longleftrightarrow} \quad \oint_C \mathbf{F} \cdot d\mathbf{r} = 0.$$

SECTION 14.3 EXERCISES

Review Questions

1. Explain with pictures what is meant by a simple curve and a closed curve.

2. Explain with pictures what is meant by a connected region and a simply connected region.

3. How do you determine whether a vector field in $\mathbb{R}^2$ is conservative (has a potential function φ such that $\mathbf{F} = \nabla\varphi$)?

4. How do you determine whether a vector field in $\mathbb{R}^3$ is conservative?

5. Briefly describe how to find a potential function φ for a conservative vector field $\mathbf{F} = \langle f, g \rangle$.

6. If $\mathbf{F}$ is a conservative vector field on a region R, how do you evaluate $\int_C \mathbf{F} \cdot d\mathbf{r}$, where C is a path between two points A and B in R?

7. If $\mathbf{F}$ is a conservative vector field on a region R, what is the value of $\oint_C \mathbf{F} \cdot d\mathbf{r}$, where C is a simple closed piecewise-smooth oriented curve in R?

8. Give three equivalent properties of conservative vector fields.

Basic Skills

9–14. Testing for conservative vector fields *Determine whether the following vector fields are conservative on $\mathbb{R}^2$.*

9. $\mathbf{F} = \langle 1, 1 \rangle$

10. $\mathbf{F} = \langle x, y \rangle$

11. $\mathbf{F} = \langle -y, -x \rangle$

12. $\mathbf{F} = \langle -y, x + y \rangle$

13. $\mathbf{F} = \langle e^{-x} \cos y, e^{-x} \sin y \rangle$

14. $\mathbf{F} = \langle 2x^3 + xy^2, 2y^3 + x^2y \rangle$

15–26. Finding potential functions *Determine whether the following vector fields are conservative on the specified region. If so, determine a potential function. Let R^* and D^* be open regions of $\mathbb{R}^2$ and $\mathbb{R}^3$, respectively, that do not include the origin.*

15. $\mathbf{F} = \langle x, y \rangle$ on $\mathbb{R}^2$

16. $\mathbf{F} = \langle -y, -x \rangle$ on $\mathbb{R}^2$

17. $\mathbf{F} = \left\langle x^3 - xy, \dfrac{x^2}{2} + y \right\rangle$ on $\mathbb{R}^2$

18. $\mathbf{F} = \dfrac{\langle x, y \rangle}{x^2 + y^2}$ on R^*

19. $\mathbf{F} = \dfrac{\langle x, y \rangle}{\sqrt{x^2 + y^2}}$ on R^*

20. $\mathbf{F} = \langle y, x, 1 \rangle$ on $\mathbb{R}^3$

21. $\mathbf{F} = \langle z, 1, x \rangle$ on $\mathbb{R}^3$

22. $\mathbf{F} = \langle yz, xz, xy \rangle$ on $\mathbb{R}^3$

23. $\mathbf{F} = \langle y + z, x + z, x + y \rangle$ on $\mathbb{R}^3$

24. $\mathbf{F} = \dfrac{\langle x, y, z \rangle}{x^2 + y^2 + z^2}$ on D^*

25. $\mathbf{F} = \dfrac{\langle x, y, z \rangle}{\sqrt{x^2 + y^2 + z^2}}$ on D^*

26. $\mathbf{F} = \langle x^3, 2y, -z^3 \rangle$ on $\mathbb{R}^3$

27–32. Evaluating line integrals *Evaluate the line integral* $\int_C \nabla\varphi \cdot d\mathbf{r}$ *for the following functions* φ *and oriented curves* C *in two ways.*

a. Use a parametric description of C *to evaluate the integral directly.*
b. Use the Fundamental Theorem for line integrals.

27. $\varphi(x, y) = xy$; $C: \mathbf{r}(t) = \langle \cos t, \sin t \rangle$, for $0 \le t \le \pi$

28. $\varphi(x, y) = (x^2 + y^2)/2$; $C: \mathbf{r}(t) = \langle \sin t, \cos t \rangle$, for $0 \le t \le \pi$

29. $\varphi(x, y) = x + 3y$; $C: \mathbf{r}(t) = \langle 2 - t, t \rangle$, for $0 \le t \le 2$

30. $\varphi(x, y, z) = x + y + z$; $C: \mathbf{r}(t) = \langle \sin t, \cos t, t/\pi \rangle$, for $0 \le t \le \pi$

31. $\varphi(x, y, z) = (x^2 + y^2 + z^2)/2$; $C: \mathbf{r}(t) = \langle \cos t, \sin t, t/\pi \rangle$, for $0 \le t \le 2\pi$

32. $\varphi(x, y, z) = xy + xz + yz$; $C: \mathbf{r}(t) = \langle t, 2t, 3t \rangle$, for $0 \le t \le 4$

33–38. Line integrals of vector fields on closed curves *Evaluate* $\oint_C \mathbf{F} \cdot d\mathbf{r}$ *for the following vector fields and closed oriented curves* C *by parameterizing* C. *If the integral is not zero, give an explanation.*

33. $\mathbf{F} = \langle x, y \rangle$; C is the circle of radius 4 centered at the origin oriented counterclockwise.

34. $\mathbf{F} = \langle y, x \rangle$; C is the circle of radius 8 centered at the origin oriented counterclockwise.

35. $\mathbf{F} = \langle x, y \rangle$; C is the triangle with vertices $(0, \pm 1)$ and $(1, 0)$ oriented counterclockwise.

36. $\mathbf{F} = \langle y, -x \rangle$; C is the circle of radius 3 centered at the origin oriented counterclockwise.

37. $\mathbf{F} = \langle x, y, z \rangle$; $C: \mathbf{r}(t) = \langle \cos t, \sin t, 2 \rangle$, for $0 \le t \le 2\pi$

38. $\mathbf{F} = \langle y - z, z - x, x - y \rangle$; $C: \mathbf{r}(t) = \langle \cos t, \sin t, \cos t \rangle$, for $0 \le t \le 2\pi$

Further Explorations

39. Explain why or why not Determine whether the following statements are true and give an explanation or counterexample.

    a. If $\mathbf{F} = \langle -y, x \rangle$ and C is the circle of radius 4 centered at $(1, 0)$ oriented counterclockwise, then $\oint_C \mathbf{F} \cdot d\mathbf{r} = 0$.

    b. If $\mathbf{F} = \langle x, -y \rangle$ and C is the circle of radius 4 centered at $(1, 0)$ oriented counterclockwise, then $\oint_C \mathbf{F} \cdot d\mathbf{r} = 0$.

    c. A constant vector field is conservative on $\mathbb{R}^2$.

    d. The vector field $\mathbf{F} = \langle f(x), g(y) \rangle$ is conservative on $\mathbb{R}^2$ (assume f and g are defined for all real numbers).

    e. Gradient fields are conservative.

40–43. Line integrals *Evaluate each line integral using a method of your choice.*

40. $\displaystyle\int_C \nabla(1 + x^2 yz) \cdot d\mathbf{r}$, where C is the helix

    $\mathbf{r}(t) = \langle \cos 2t, \sin 2t, t \rangle$, for $0 \le t \le 4\pi$

41. $\displaystyle\int_C \nabla(e^{-x} \cos y) \cdot d\mathbf{r}$, where C is the line segment from $(0, 0)$ to

    $(\ln 2, 2\pi)$

42. $\displaystyle\oint_C e^{-x}(\cos y \, dx + \sin y \, dy)$, where C is the square with vertices

    $(\pm 1, \pm 1)$ oriented counterclockwise

43. $\displaystyle\oint_C \mathbf{F} \cdot d\mathbf{r}$, where $\mathbf{F} = \langle 2xy + z^2, x^2, 2xz \rangle$ and C is the circle

    $\mathbf{r}(t) = \langle 3 \cos t, 4 \cos t, 5 \sin t \rangle$, for $0 \le t \le 2\pi$.

44. Closed curve integrals Evaluate $\oint_C ds$, $\oint_C dx$, and $\oint_C dy$, where C is the unit circle oriented counterclockwise.

45–48. Work in force fields *Find the work required to move an object in the following force fields along a line segment between the given points. Check to see whether the force is conservative.*

45. $\mathbf{F} = \langle x, 2 \rangle$ from $A(0, 0)$ to $B(2, 4)$

46. $\mathbf{F} = \langle x, y \rangle$ from $A(1, 1)$ to $B(3, -6)$

47. $\mathbf{F} = \langle x, y, z \rangle$ from $A(1, 2, 1)$ to $B(2, 4, 6)$

48. $\mathbf{F} = e^{x+y} \langle 1, 1, z \rangle$ from $A(0, 0, 0)$ to $B(-1, 2, -4)$

49–50. Work from graphs *Determine whether* $\int_C \mathbf{F} \cdot d\mathbf{r}$ *along the paths* C_1 *and* C_2 *shown in the following vector fields is positive or negative. Explain your reasoning.*

49.

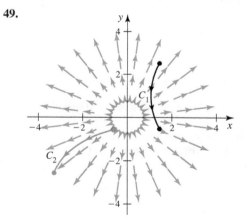

50.

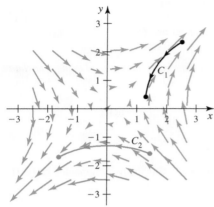

Applications

51. Work by a constant force Evaluate a line integral to show that the work done in moving an object from point A to point B in the presence of a constant force $\mathbf{F} = \langle a, b, c \rangle$ is $\mathbf{F} \cdot \overrightarrow{AB}$.

52. Conservation of energy Suppose an object with mass m moves in a region R in a conservative force field given by $\mathbf{F} = -\nabla\varphi$, where φ is a potential function in a region R. The motion of the object is governed by Newton's Second Law of Motion, $\mathbf{F} = m\mathbf{a}$, where $\mathbf{a}$ is the acceleration. Suppose the object moves from point A to point B in R.

a. Show that the equation of motion is $m\dfrac{d\mathbf{v}}{dt} = -\nabla\varphi$.

b. Show that $\dfrac{d\mathbf{v}}{dt} \cdot \mathbf{v} = \dfrac{1}{2}\dfrac{d}{dt}(\mathbf{v} \cdot \mathbf{v})$.

c. Take the dot product of both sides of the equation in part (a) with $\mathbf{v}(t) = \mathbf{r}'(t)$ and integrate along a curve between A and B. Use part (b) and the fact that $\mathbf{F}$ is conservative to show that the total energy (kinetic plus potential) $\frac{1}{2}m|\mathbf{v}|^2 + \varphi$ is the same at A and B. Conclude that because A and B are arbitrary, energy is conserved in R.

53. Gravitational potential The gravitational force between two point masses M and m is

$$\mathbf{F} = GMm\frac{\mathbf{r}}{|\mathbf{r}|^3} = GMm\frac{\langle x, y, z \rangle}{(x^2 + y^2 + z^2)^{3/2}},$$

where G is the gravitational constant.

a. Verify that this force field is conservative on any region excluding the origin.
b. Find a potential function φ for this force field such that $\mathbf{F} = -\nabla\varphi$.
c. Suppose the object with mass m is moved from a point A to a point B, where A is a distance r_1 from M and B is a distance r_2 from M. Show that the work done in moving the object is
$$GMm\left(\frac{1}{r_2} - \frac{1}{r_1}\right).$$
d. Does the work depend on the path between A and B? Explain.

Additional Exercises

54. Radial fields in $\mathbb{R}^3$ are conservative Prove that the radial field $\mathbf{F} = \dfrac{\mathbf{r}}{|\mathbf{r}|^p}$, where $\mathbf{r} = \langle x, y, z \rangle$ and p is a real number, is conservative on any region not containing the origin. For what values of p is $\mathbf{F}$ conservative on a region that contains the origin?

55. Rotation fields are usually not conservative

a. Prove that the rotation field $\mathbf{F} = \dfrac{\langle -y, x \rangle}{|\mathbf{r}|^p}$, where $\mathbf{r} = \langle x, y \rangle$, is not conservative for $p \neq 2$.
b. For $p = 2$, show that $\mathbf{F}$ is conservative on any region not containing the origin.
c. Find a potential function for $\mathbf{F}$ when $p = 2$.

56. Linear and quadratic vector fields

a. For what values of a, b, c, and d is the field $\mathbf{F} = \langle ax + by, cx + dy \rangle$ conservative?
b. For what values of a, b, and c is the field $\mathbf{F} = \langle ax^2 - by^2, cxy \rangle$ conservative?

57. Alternative construction of potential functions in $\mathbb{R}^2$ Assume that the vector field $\mathbf{F}$ is conservative in $\mathbb{R}^2$, so that the line integral $\int_C \mathbf{F} \cdot d\mathbf{r}$ is independent of path. Use the following procedure to construct a potential function φ for the vector field $\mathbf{F} = \langle f, g \rangle = \langle 2x - y, -x + 2y \rangle$.

a. Let A be $(0, 0)$ and let B be an arbitrary point (x, y). Define $\varphi(x, y)$ to be the work required to move an object from A to B, where $\varphi(A) = 0$. Let C_1 be the path from A to $(x, 0)$ to B and let C_2 be the path from A to $(0, y)$ to B. Draw a picture.
b. Evaluate $\int_{C_1} \mathbf{F} \cdot d\mathbf{r} = \int_{C_1} f\,dx + g\,dy$ and conclude that $\varphi(x, y) = x^2 - xy + y^2$.
c. Verify that the same potential function is obtained by evaluating the line integral over C_2.

58–61. Alternative construction of potential functions *Use the procedure in Exercise 57 to construct potential functions for the following fields.*

58. $\mathbf{F} = \langle -y, -x \rangle$ **59.** $\mathbf{F} = \langle x, y \rangle$

60. $\mathbf{F} = \mathbf{r}/|\mathbf{r}|$, where $\mathbf{r} = \langle x, y \rangle$

61. $\mathbf{F} = \langle 2x^3 + xy^2, 2y^3 + x^2y \rangle$

QUICK CHECK ANSWERS

1. A figure-8 is closed but not simple; a torus is connected but not simply connected. **2.** The vector field is obtained by differentiating the potential function. So additive constants in the potential give the same vector field: $\nabla(\varphi + C) = \nabla\varphi$, when C is a constant. **3.** Show that $\nabla(e^x \cos y) = \langle e^x \cos y, -e^x \sin y \rangle$, which is the original vector field. A similar calculation may be done for part (b). **4.** The vector field $\nabla(xy + xz - yz)$ is the gradient of $xy + xz - yz$, so the vector field is conservative.◀

14.4 Green's Theorem

The preceding section gave a version of the Fundamental Theorem of Calculus that applies to line integrals. In this and the remaining sections of the book, you will see additional extensions of the Fundamental Theorem that apply to regions in $\mathbb{R}^2$ and $\mathbb{R}^3$. All these fundamental theorems share a common feature. Part 2 of the Fundamental Theorem of Calculus (Chapter 5) says

$$\int_a^b \frac{df}{dx}\, dx = f(b) - f(a),$$

which relates the integral of $\dfrac{df}{dx}$ on an interval $[a, b]$ to the values of f on the boundary of $[a, b]$. The Fundamental Theorem for line integrals says

$$\int_C \nabla\varphi \cdot d\mathbf{r} = \varphi(B) - \varphi(A),$$

which relates the integral of $\nabla\varphi$ on a piecewise-smooth oriented curve C to the boundary values of φ. (The boundary consists of the two endpoints A and B.)

The subject of this section is Green's Theorem, which is another step in this progression. It relates the double integral of derivatives of a function over a region in $\mathbb{R}^2$ to function values on the boundary of that region.

Circulation Form of Green's Theorem

Throughout this section, unless otherwise stated, we assume that curves in the plane are simple closed piecewise-smooth oriented curves. By a result called the *Jordan Curve Theorem*, such curves have a well-defined interior such that when the curve is traversed in the counterclockwise direction (viewed from above), the interior is on the left. With this orientation, there is a unique outward unit normal vector that points to the right (at points where the curve is smooth). We also assume that curves in the plane lie in regions that are both connected and simply connected.

Suppose the vector field $\mathbf{F}$ is defined on a region R whose boundary is the closed curve C. As we have seen, the circulation $\oint_C \mathbf{F} \cdot d\mathbf{r}$ (Section 14.2) measures the net component of $\mathbf{F}$ in the direction tangent to C. It is easiest to visualize the circulation when $\mathbf{F}$ represents the velocity of a fluid moving in two dimensions. For example, let C be the unit circle with a counterclockwise orientation. The vector field $\mathbf{F} = \langle -y, x \rangle$ has a positive circulation of 2π on C (Section 14.2) because the vector field is everywhere tangent to C (Figure 14.31). A nonzero circulation on a closed curve says that the vector field must have some property *inside* the curve that produces the circulation. You can think of this property as a *net rotation*.

To visualize the rotation of a vector field, imagine a small paddle wheel, fixed at a point in the vector field, with its axis perpendicular to the xy-plane (Figure 14.31). The strength of the rotation at that point is seen in the speed at which the paddle wheel spins, while the direction of the rotation is the direction in which the paddle wheel spins. At a different point in the vector field, the paddle wheel will, in general, have a different speed and direction of rotation.

The first form of Green's Theorem relates the circulation on C to the double integral, over the region R, of a quantity that measures rotation at each point of R.

Paddle wheel at one point of vector field.

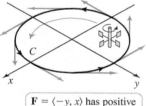

$\mathbf{F} = \langle -y, x \rangle$ has positive (counterclockwise) circulation on C.

Figure 14.31

> The circulation form of Green's Theorem is also called the *tangential*, or *curl*, form.

THEOREM 14.6 Green's Theorem—Circulation Form

Let C be a simple closed piecewise-smooth curve, oriented counterclockwise, that encloses a connected and simply connected region R in the plane. Assume $\mathbf{F} = \langle f, g \rangle$, where f and g have continuous first partial derivatives in R. Then

$$\underbrace{\oint_C \mathbf{F} \cdot d\mathbf{r}}_{\text{circulation}} = \underbrace{\oint_C f\,dx + g\,dy}_{\text{circulation}} = \iint_R \left(\frac{\partial g}{\partial x} - \frac{\partial f}{\partial y} \right) dA.$$

The proof of a special case of the theorem is given at the end of this section. Notice that the two line integrals on the left side of Green's Theorem give the circulation of the vector field on C. The double integral on the right side involves the quantity $\dfrac{\partial g}{\partial x} - \dfrac{\partial f}{\partial y}$, which describes the rotation of the vector field *within* C that produces the circulation *on* C. This quantity is called the *two-dimensional curl* of the vector field.

Figure 14.32 illustrates how the curl measures the rotation of a particular vector field at a point P. If the horizontal component of the field decreases in the y-direction at P ($f_y < 0$) and the vertical component increases in the x-direction at P ($g_x > 0$), then $\dfrac{\partial g}{\partial x} - \dfrac{\partial f}{\partial y} > 0$, and the field has a counterclockwise rotation at P. The double integral in Green's Theorem computes the net rotation of the field throughout R. The theorem says that the net rotation throughout R equals the circulation on the boundary of R.

QUICK CHECK 1 Compute $\dfrac{\partial g}{\partial x} - \dfrac{\partial f}{\partial y}$ for the radial vector field $\mathbf{F} = \langle x, y \rangle$. What does this tell you about the circulation on a simple closed curve? ◄

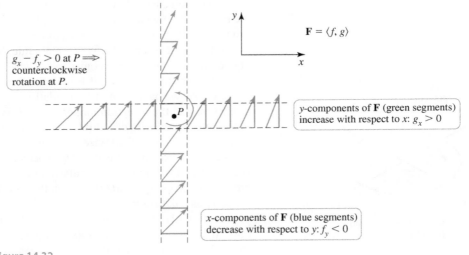

Figure 14.32

Green's Theorem has an important consequence when applied to a conservative vector field. Recall from Theorem 14.3 that if $\mathbf{F} = \langle f, g \rangle$ is conservative, then its components satisfy the condition $f_y = g_x$. If R is a region of $\mathbb{R}^2$ on which the conditions of Green's Theorem are satisfied, then for a conservative field, we have

$$\oint_C \mathbf{F} \cdot d\mathbf{r} = \iint_R \underbrace{\left(\frac{\partial g}{\partial x} - \frac{\partial f}{\partial y} \right)}_{0} dA = 0.$$

▶ In some cases, the rotation of a vector field is not obvious. For example, the parallel flow in a channel $\mathbf{F} = \langle 0, 1 - x^2 \rangle$, for $|x| \leq 1$, has a nonzero curl for $x \neq 0$. See Exercise 66.

Green's Theorem confirms the fact (Theorem 14.5) that if $\mathbf{F}$ is a conservative vector field in a region, then the circulation $\oint_C \mathbf{F} \cdot d\mathbf{r}$ is zero on any simple closed curve in the region. A two-dimensional vector field $\mathbf{F} = \langle f, g \rangle$ for which $\frac{\partial g}{\partial x} - \frac{\partial f}{\partial y} = 0$ at all points of a region is said to be *irrotational*, because it produces zero circulation on closed curves in the region. Irrotational vector fields on simply connected regions in $\mathbb{R}^2$ are conservative.

DEFINITION Two-Dimensional Curl

The **two-dimensional curl** of the vector field $\mathbf{F} = \langle f, g \rangle$ is $\frac{\partial g}{\partial x} - \frac{\partial f}{\partial y}$. If the curl is zero throughout a region, the vector field is **irrotational** on that region.

Evaluating circulation integrals of conservative vector fields on closed curves is easy. The integral is always zero. Green's Theorem provides a way to evaluate circulation integrals for nonconservative vector fields.

EXAMPLE 1   Circulation of a rotation field Consider the rotation vector field $\mathbf{F} = \langle -y, x \rangle$ on the unit disk $R = \{(x, y): x^2 + y^2 \leq 1\}$ (Figure 14.31). In Example 7 of Section 14.2, we showed that $\oint_C \mathbf{F} \cdot d\mathbf{r} = 2\pi$, where C is the boundary of R oriented counterclockwise. Confirm this result using Green's Theorem.

SOLUTION Note that $f(x, y) = -y$ and $g(x, y) = x$; therefore, the curl of $\mathbf{F}$ is $\frac{\partial g}{\partial x} - \frac{\partial f}{\partial y} = 2$. By Green's Theorem,

$$\oint_C \mathbf{F} \cdot d\mathbf{r} = \iint_R \underbrace{\left(\frac{\partial g}{\partial x} - \frac{\partial f}{\partial y} \right)}_{2} dA = \iint_R 2\, dA = 2 \times (\text{area of } R) = 2\pi.$$

The curl $\frac{\partial g}{\partial x} - \frac{\partial f}{\partial y}$ is nonzero on R, which results in a nonzero circulation on the boundary of R.

Related Exercises 11–16 ◀

Calculating Area by Green's Theorem A useful consequence of Green's Theorem arises with the vector fields $\mathbf{F} = \langle f, g \rangle = \langle 0, x \rangle$ and $\mathbf{F} = \langle f, g \rangle = \langle y, 0 \rangle$. In the first case, we have $g_x = 1$ and $f_y = 0$; therefore, by Green's Theorem,

$$\oint_C \mathbf{F} \cdot d\mathbf{r} = \oint_C \underbrace{x\, dy}_{\mathbf{F} \cdot d\mathbf{r}} = \iint_R \underbrace{dA}_{\frac{\partial g}{\partial x} - \frac{\partial f}{\partial y} = 1} = \text{area of } R.$$

In the second case, $g_x = 0$ and $f_y = 1$, and Green's Theorem says

$$\oint_C \mathbf{F} \cdot d\mathbf{r} = \oint_C y\, dx = -\iint_R dA = -\text{area of } R.$$

These two results may also be combined in one statement to give the following theorem.

Area of a Plane Region by Line Integrals

Under the conditions of Green's Theorem, the area of a region R enclosed by a curve C is

$$\oint_C x \, dy = -\oint_C y \, dx = \frac{1}{2}\oint_C (x \, dy - y \, dx).$$

A remarkably simple calculation of the area of an ellipse follows from this result.

EXAMPLE 2   Area of an ellipse Find the area of the ellipse $\dfrac{x^2}{a^2} + \dfrac{y^2}{b^2} = 1$.

SOLUTION An ellipse with counterclockwise orientation is described parametrically by $\mathbf{r}(t) = \langle x, y \rangle = \langle a \cos t, b \sin t \rangle$, for $0 \le t \le 2\pi$. Noting that $dx = -a \sin t \, dt$ and $dy = b \cos t \, dt$, we have

$$
\begin{aligned}
x \, dy - y \, dx &= (a \cos t)(b \cos t) \, dt - (b \sin t)(-a \sin t) \, dt \\
&= ab \, (\cos^2 t + \sin^2 t) \, dt \\
&= ab \, dt.
\end{aligned}
$$

Expressing the line integral as an ordinary integral with respect to t, the area of the ellipse is

$$\frac{1}{2}\oint_C \underbrace{(x \, dy - y \, dx)}_{ab \, dt} = \frac{ab}{2}\int_0^{2\pi} dt = \pi ab.$$

Related Exercises 17–22 ◄

Flux Form of Green's Theorem

Let C be a closed curve enclosing a region R in $\mathbb{R}^2$ and let $\mathbf{F}$ be a vector field defined on R. We assume that C and R have the previously stated properties; specifically, C is oriented counterclockwise with an outward normal vector $\mathbf{n}$. Recall that the outward flux of $\mathbf{F}$ across C is $\oint_C \mathbf{F} \cdot \mathbf{n} \, ds$ (Section 14.2). The second form of Green's Theorem relates the flux across C to a property of the vector field within R that produces the flux.

> ▶ The flux form of Green's Theorem is also called the *normal*, or *divergence*, form.

> ▶ The two forms of Green's Theorem are related in the following way: Applying the circulation form of the theorem to $\mathbf{F} = \langle -g, f \rangle$ results in the flux form, and applying the flux form of the theorem to $\mathbf{F} = \langle g, -f \rangle$ results in the circulation form.

THEOREM 14.7   Green's Theorem, Flux Form

Let C be a simple closed piecewise-smooth curve, oriented counterclockwise, that encloses a connected and simply connected region R in the plane. Assume $\mathbf{F} = \langle f, g \rangle$, where f and g have continuous first partial derivatives in R. Then

$$\underbrace{\oint_C \mathbf{F} \cdot \mathbf{n} \, ds}_{\text{outward flux}} = \underbrace{\oint_C f \, dy - g \, dx}_{\text{outward flux}} = \iint_R \left(\frac{\partial f}{\partial x} + \frac{\partial g}{\partial y}\right) dA,$$

where $\mathbf{n}$ is the outward unit normal vector on the curve.

The two line integrals on the left side of Theorem 14.7 give the outward flux of the vector field across C. The double integral on the right side involves the quantity $\dfrac{\partial f}{\partial x} + \dfrac{\partial g}{\partial y}$, which is the property of the vector field that produces the flux across C. This quantity is called the *two-dimensional divergence*.

Figure 14.33 illustrates how the divergence measures the flux of a particular vector field at a point P. If $f_x > 0$ at P, it indicates an expansion of the vector field in the x-direction (if f_x is negative, it indicates a contraction). Similarly, if $g_y > 0$ at P, it indicates an expansion of the vector field in the y-direction. The combined effect of $f_x + g_y > 0$ at a point is a net outward flux across a small circle enclosing P.

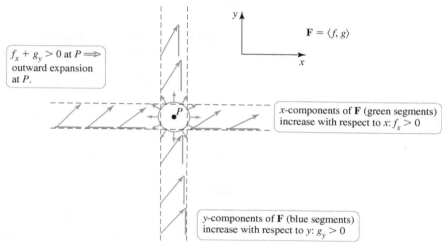

$f_x + g_y > 0$ at $P \Longrightarrow$ outward expansion at P.

$\mathbf{F} = \langle f, g \rangle$

x-components of $\mathbf{F}$ (green segments) increase with respect to x: $f_x > 0$

y-components of $\mathbf{F}$ (blue segments) increase with respect to y: $g_y > 0$

Figure 14.33

If the divergence of $\mathbf{F}$ is zero throughout a region on which $\mathbf{F}$ satisfies the conditions of Theorem 14.7, then the outward flux across the boundary is zero. Vector fields with a zero divergence are said to be *source free*. If the divergence is positive throughout R, the outward flux across C is positive, meaning that the vector field acts as a *source* in R. If the divergence is negative throughout R, the outward flux across C is negative, meaning that the vector field acts as a *sink* in R.

DEFINITION   **Two-Dimensional Divergence**

The **two-dimensional divergence** of the vector field $\mathbf{F} = \langle f, g \rangle$ is $\dfrac{\partial f}{\partial x} + \dfrac{\partial g}{\partial y}$. If the divergence is zero throughout a region, the vector field is **source free** on that region.

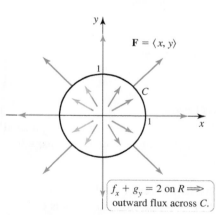

$\mathbf{F} = \langle x, y \rangle$

C

$f_x + g_y = 2$ on $R \Longrightarrow$ outward flux across C.

Figure 14.34

QUICK CHECK 2   Compute $\dfrac{\partial f}{\partial x} + \dfrac{\partial g}{\partial y}$ for the rotation field $\mathbf{F} = \langle -y, x \rangle$. What does this tell you about the outward flux of $\mathbf{F}$ across a simple closed curve? ◄

EXAMPLE 3   **Outward flux of a radial field**   Use Green's Theorem to compute the outward flux of the radial field $\mathbf{F} = \langle x, y \rangle$ across the unit circle $C = \{(x, y) : x^2 + y^2 = 1\}$ (Figure 14.34). Interpret the result.

SOLUTION We have already calculated the outward flux of the radial field across C as a line integral and found it to be 2π (Section 14.2). Computing the outward flux using Green's Theorem, note that $f(x, y) = x$ and $g(x, y) = y$; therefore, the divergence of $\mathbf{F}$ is $\dfrac{\partial f}{\partial x} + \dfrac{\partial g}{\partial y} = 2$. By Green's Theorem, we have

$$\oint_C \mathbf{F} \cdot \mathbf{n}\, ds = \iint_R \underbrace{\left(\frac{\partial f}{\partial x} + \frac{\partial g}{\partial y} \right)}_{2} dA = \iint_R 2\, dA = 2 \times (\text{area of } R) = 2\pi.$$

The positive divergence on R results in an outward flux of the vector field across the boundary of R.

Related Exercises 23–28 ◄

As with the circulation form, the flux form of Green's Theorem can be used in either direction: to simplify line integrals or to simplify double integrals.

EXAMPLE 4   Line integral as a double integral Evaluate

$$\oint_C (4x^3 + \sin y^2)\, dy - (4y^3 + \cos x^2)\, dx,$$

where C is the boundary of the disk $R = \{(x, y): x^2 + y^2 \le 4\}$ oriented counterclockwise.

SOLUTION Letting $f(x, y) = 4x^3 + \sin y^2$ and $g(x, y) = 4y^3 + \cos x^2$, Green's Theorem takes the form

$$\oint_C \underbrace{(4x^3 + \sin y^2)}_{f}\, dy - \underbrace{(4y^3 + \cos x^2)}_{g}\, dx$$

$$= \iint_R (\underbrace{12x^2}_{f_x} + \underbrace{12y^2}_{g_y})\, dA \qquad \text{Green's Theorem, flux form}$$

$$= 12 \int_0^{2\pi} \int_0^2 r^2 \underbrace{r\, dr\, d\theta}_{dA} \qquad \text{Polar coordinates; } x^2 + y^2 = r^2$$

$$= 12 \int_0^{2\pi} \frac{r^4}{4}\Big|_0^2\, d\theta \qquad \text{Evaluate inner integral.}$$

$$= 48 \int_0^{2\pi} d\theta = 96\pi. \qquad \text{Evaluate outer integral.}$$

Related Exercises 29–34 ◄

Circulation and Flux on More General Regions

Some ingenuity is required to extend both forms of Green's Theorem to more complicated regions. The next two examples illustrate Green's Theorem on two such regions: a half annulus and a full annulus.

EXAMPLE 5   Circulation on a half annulus Consider the vector field $\mathbf{F} = \langle y^2, x^2 \rangle$ on the half annulus $R = \{(x, y): 1 \le x^2 + y^2 \le 9, y \ge 0\}$, whose boundary is C. Find the circulation on C, assuming it has the orientation shown in Figure 14.35.

SOLUTION The circulation on C is

$$\oint_C f\, dx + g\, dy = \oint_C y^2\, dx + x^2\, dy.$$

With the given orientation, the curve runs counterclockwise on the outer semicircle and clockwise on the inner semicircle. Identifying $f(x, y) = y^2$ and $g(x, y) = x^2$, the

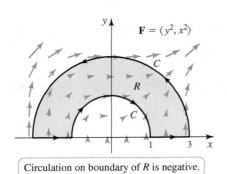

$\mathbf{F} = \langle y^2, x^2 \rangle$

Circulation on boundary of R is negative.

Figure 14.35

circulation form of Green's Theorem converts the line integral into a double integral. The double integral is most easily evaluated in polar coordinates using $x = r \cos \theta$ and $y = r \sin \theta$:

$$\oint_C \underbrace{y^2}_{f} \, dx + \underbrace{x^2}_{g} \, dy = \iint_R (\underbrace{2x}_{g_x} - \underbrace{2y}_{f_y}) \, dA \qquad \text{Green's Theorem, circulation form}$$

$$= 2 \int_0^\pi \int_1^3 (r \cos \theta - r \sin \theta) \underbrace{r \, dr \, d\theta}_{dA} \qquad \text{Convert to polar coordinates.}$$

$$= 2 \int_0^\pi (\cos \theta - \sin \theta) \frac{r^3}{3}\Big|_1^3 \, d\theta \qquad \text{Evaluate inner integral.}$$

$$= \frac{52}{3} \int_0^\pi (\cos \theta - \sin \theta) \, d\theta \qquad \text{Simplify.}$$

$$= -\frac{104}{3}. \qquad \text{Evaluate outer integral.}$$

The vector field (Figure 14.35) suggests why the circulation is negative. The field is roughly *opposed* to the direction of C on the outer semicircle but roughly aligned with the direction of C on the inner semicircle. Because the outer semicircle is longer and the field has greater magnitudes on the outer curve than the inner curve, the greater contribution to the circulation is negative.

Related Exercises 35–38 ◄

EXAMPLE 6 **Flux across the boundary of an annulus** Find the outward flux of the vector field $\mathbf{F} = \langle xy^2, x^2y \rangle$ across the boundary of the annulus $R = \{(x, y): 1 \le x^2 + y^2 \le 4\} = \{(r, \theta): 1 \le r \le 2, 0 \le \theta \le 2\pi\}$ (Figure 14.36).

SOLUTION Because the annulus R is not simply connected, Green's Theorem does not apply as stated in Theorem 14.7. This difficulty is overcome by defining the curve C shown in Figure 14.36, which is simple, closed, and piecewise smooth. The connecting links L_1 and L_2 below and above the x-axis are traversed in opposite directions. Letting L_1 and L_2 approach the x-axis, the contributions to the line integral cancel on L_1 and L_2. Because of this cancellation, we take C to be the curve that runs counterclockwise on the outer boundary and clockwise on the inner boundary.

Using the flux form of Green's Theorem and converting to polar coordinates, we have

$$\oint_C \mathbf{F} \cdot \mathbf{n} \, ds = \oint_C f \, dy - g \, dx = \oint_C xy^2 \, dy - x^2y \, dx \qquad \text{Substitute for } f \text{ and } g.$$

$$= \iint_R (\underbrace{y^2}_{f_x} + \underbrace{x^2}_{g_y}) \, dA \qquad \text{Green's Theorem, flux form}$$

$$= \int_0^{2\pi} \int_1^2 (r^2) \, r \, dr \, d\theta \qquad \text{Polar coordinates; } x^2 + y^2 = r^2$$

$$= \int_0^{2\pi} \frac{r^4}{4}\Big|_1^2 \, d\theta \qquad \text{Evaluate inner integral.}$$

$$= \frac{15}{4} \int_0^{2\pi} d\theta \qquad \text{Simplify.}$$

$$= \frac{15\pi}{2}. \qquad \text{Evaluate outer integral.}$$

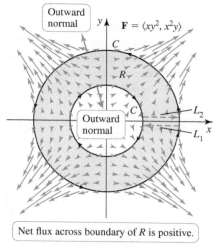

Outward normal
$\mathbf{F} = \langle xy^2, x^2y \rangle$
C
R
Outward normal
C
L_2
L_1

Net flux across boundary of R is positive.

Figure 14.36

➤ Another way to deal with the flux across the annulus is to apply Green's Theorem to the entire disk $|r| \le 2$ and compute the flux across the outer circle. Then apply Green's Theorem to the disk $|r| \le 1$ and compute the flux across the inner circle. Note that the flux *out* of the inner disk is a flux *into* the annulus. Therefore, the difference of the two fluxes gives the net flux for the annulus.

> Notice that the divergence of the vector field in Example 6 is $x^2 + y^2$, which is positive on R, also explaining the outward flux across C.

Figure 14.36 shows the vector field and explains why the flux across C is positive. Because the field increases in magnitude moving away from the origin, the outward flux across the outer boundary is greater than the inward flux across the inner boundary. Hence, the net outward flux across C is positive.

Related Exercises 35–38 ◄

Stream Functions

We can now see a wonderful parallel between circulation properties (and conservative vector fields) and flux properties (and source-free fields). We need one more piece to complete the picture; it is the *stream function*, which plays the same role for source-free fields that the potential function plays for conservative fields.

> Potential function for $\mathbf{F} = \langle f, g \rangle$:
>
> $$\varphi_x = f \quad \text{and} \quad \varphi_y = g$$
>
> Stream function for $\mathbf{F} = \langle f, g \rangle$:
>
> $$\psi_x = -g \quad \text{and} \quad \psi_y = f$$

Consider a two-dimensional vector field $\mathbf{F} = \langle f, g \rangle$ that is differentiable on a region R. A **stream function** for the vector field—if it exists—is a function ψ (pronounced *psigh* or *psee*) that satisfies

$$\frac{\partial \psi}{\partial y} = f, \qquad \frac{\partial \psi}{\partial x} = -g.$$

If we compute the divergence of a vector field $\mathbf{F} = \langle f, g \rangle$ that has a stream function and use the fact that $\psi_{xy} = \psi_{yx}$, then

$$\frac{\partial f}{\partial x} + \frac{\partial g}{\partial y} = \frac{\partial}{\partial x}\left(\frac{\partial \psi}{\partial y} \right) + \frac{\partial}{\partial y}\left(-\frac{\partial \psi}{\partial x} \right) = 0.$$

$$\underbrace{\qquad\qquad\qquad\qquad}_{\psi_{yx} = \psi_{xy}}$$

We see that the existence of a stream function guarantees that the vector field has zero divergence or, equivalently, is source free. The converse is also true on simply connected regions of $\mathbb{R}^2$.

As discussed in Section 14.1, the level curves of a stream function are called flow curves or streamlines—and for good reason. It can be shown (Exercise 64) that the vector field $\mathbf{F}$ is everywhere tangent to the streamlines, which means that a graph of the streamlines shows the flow of the vector field. Finally, just as circulation integrals of a conservative vector field are path-independent, flux integrals of a source-free field are also path-independent (Exercise 63).

QUICK CHECK 3 Show that $\psi = \dfrac{1}{2}(y^2 - x^2)$ is a stream function for the vector field $\mathbf{F} = \langle y, x \rangle$. Show that $\mathbf{F}$ has zero divergence. ◄

> In fluid dynamics, velocity fields that are both conservative and source free are called *ideal flows*. They model fluids that are irrotational and incompressible.

Vector fields that are both conservative and source free are quite interesting mathematically. They have both a potential function and a stream function whose level curves form orthogonal families. Such vector fields have zero curl $(g_x - f_y = 0)$ and zero divergence $(f_x + g_y = 0)$. If we write the zero divergence condition in terms of the potential function φ, we find that

$$0 = f_x + g_y = \varphi_{xx} + \varphi_{yy}.$$

Writing the zero curl condition in terms of the stream function ψ, we find that

$$0 = g_x - f_y = -\psi_{xx} - \psi_{yy}.$$

> Methods for finding solutions of Laplace's equation are discussed in advanced mathematics courses.

We see that the potential function and the stream function both satisfy an important equation known as **Laplace's equation**:

$$\varphi_{xx} + \varphi_{yy} = 0 \quad \text{and} \quad \psi_{xx} + \psi_{yy} = 0.$$

Any function satisfying Laplace's equation can be used as a potential function or stream function for a conservative, source-free vector field. These vector fields are used in fluid dynamics, electrostatics, and other modeling applications.

Table 14.1 shows the parallel properties of conservative and source-free vector fields in two dimensions. We assume that C is a simple piecewise-smooth oriented curve and is either closed or has endpoints A and B.

Table 14.1

Conservative Fields $\mathbf{F} = \langle f, g \rangle$	Source-Free Fields $\mathbf{F} = \langle f, g \rangle$
• curl $= \dfrac{\partial g}{\partial x} - \dfrac{\partial f}{\partial y} = 0$	• divergence $= \dfrac{\partial f}{\partial x} + \dfrac{\partial g}{\partial y} = 0$
• Potential function φ with $$\mathbf{F} = \nabla\varphi \quad \text{or} \quad f = \frac{\partial \varphi}{\partial x}, \quad g = \frac{\partial \varphi}{\partial y}$$	• Stream function ψ with $$f = \frac{\partial \psi}{\partial y}, \quad g = -\frac{\partial \psi}{\partial x}$$
• Circulation $= \oint_C \mathbf{F} \cdot d\mathbf{r} = 0$ on all closed curves C.	• Flux $= \oint_C \mathbf{F} \cdot \mathbf{n}\, ds = 0$ on all closed curves C.
• Path independence $$\int_C \mathbf{F} \cdot d\mathbf{r} = \varphi(B) - \varphi(A)$$	• Path independence $$\int_C \mathbf{F} \cdot \mathbf{n}\, ds = \psi(B) - \psi(A)$$

With Green's Theorem in the picture, we may also give a concise summary of the various cases that arise with line integrals of both the circulation and flux types (Table 14.2).

Table 14.2

Circulation/work integrals: $\displaystyle\int_C \mathbf{F} \cdot \mathbf{T}\, ds = \int_C \mathbf{F} \cdot d\mathbf{r} = \int_C f\, dx + g\, dy$

	C **closed**	C **not closed**
F conservative ($\mathbf{F} = \nabla\varphi$)	$\displaystyle\oint_C \mathbf{F} \cdot d\mathbf{r} = 0$	$\displaystyle\int_C \mathbf{F} \cdot d\mathbf{r} = \varphi(B) - \varphi(A)$
F not conservative	Green's Theorem $$\oint_C \mathbf{F} \cdot d\mathbf{r} = \iint_R (g_x - f_y)\, dA$$	Direct evaluation $$\int_C \mathbf{F} \cdot d\mathbf{r} = \int_a^b (fx' + gy')\, dt$$

Flux integrals: $\displaystyle\int_C \mathbf{F} \cdot \mathbf{n}\, ds = \int_C f\, dy - g\, dx$

	C **closed**	C **not closed**
F source free ($f = \psi_y,\, g = -\psi_x$)	$\displaystyle\oint_C \mathbf{F} \cdot \mathbf{n}\, ds = 0$	$\displaystyle\int_C \mathbf{F} \cdot \mathbf{n}\, ds = \psi(B) - \psi(A)$
F not source free	Green's Theorem $$\oint_C \mathbf{F} \cdot \mathbf{n}\, ds = \iint_R (f_x + g_y)\, dA$$	Direct evaluation $$\int_C \mathbf{F} \cdot \mathbf{n}\, ds = \int_a^b (fy' - gx')\, dt$$

Proof of Green's Theorem on Special Regions

The proof of Green's Theorem is straightforward when restricted to special regions. We consider regions R enclosed by a simple closed smooth curve C oriented in the counterclockwise direction. Furthermore, we require that there are functions $G_1, G_2, H_1,$ and H_2 such that the region can be expressed in two ways (Figure 14.37):

- $R = \{(x, y): a \le x \le b, G_1(x) \le y \le G_2(x)\}$ or
- $R = \{(x, y): H_1(y) \le x \le H_2(y), c \le y \le d\}$.

> ➤ This restriction on R means that lines parallel to the coordinate axes intersect the boundary of R at most twice.

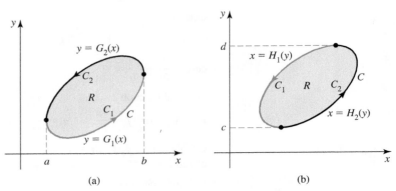

Figure 14.37

Under these conditions, we prove the circulation form of Green's Theorem:

$$\oint_C f\, dx + g\, dy = \iint_R \left(\frac{\partial g}{\partial x} - \frac{\partial f}{\partial y} \right) dA.$$

Beginning with the term $\iint_R \dfrac{\partial f}{\partial y}\, dA$, we write this double integral as an iterated integral, where $G_1(x) \le y \le G_2(x)$ in the inner integral and $a \le x \le b$ in the outer integral (Figure 14.37a). The upper curve is labeled C_2 and the lower curve is labeled C_1. Notice that the inner integral of $\dfrac{\partial f}{\partial y}$ with respect to y gives $f(x, y)$. Therefore, the first step of the double integration is

$$\iint_R \frac{\partial f}{\partial y}\, dA = \int_a^b \int_{G_1(x)}^{G_2(x)} \frac{\partial f}{\partial y}\, dy\, dx \qquad \text{Convert to an iterated integral.}$$

$$= \int_a^b \Big(\underbrace{f(x, G_2(x))}_{\text{on } C_2} - \underbrace{f(x, G_1(x))}_{\text{on } C_1} \Big) dx.$$

Over the interval $a \le x \le b$, the points $(x, G_2(x))$ trace out the upper part of C (labeled C_2) in the *negative* (clockwise) direction. Similarly, over the interval $a \le x \le b$, the points $(x, G_1(x))$ trace out the lower part of C (labeled C_1) in the *positive* (counterclockwise) direction.

Therefore,

$$\iint_R \frac{\partial f}{\partial y}\, dA = \int_a^b \big(f(x, G_2(x)) - f(x, G_1(x)) \big) dx$$

$$= \int_{-C_2} f\, dx - \int_{C_1} f\, dx$$

$$= -\int_{C_2} f\, dx - \int_{C_1} f\, dx \qquad\qquad \int_{-C_2} f\, dx = -\int_{C_2} f\, dx$$

$$= -\oint_C f\, dx. \qquad\qquad \int_C f\, dx = \int_{C_1} f\, dx + \int_{C_2} f\, dx$$

A similar argument applies to the double integral of $\dfrac{\partial g}{\partial x}$, except we use the bounding curves $x = H_1(y)$ and $x = H_2(y)$, where C_1 is now the left curve and C_2 is the right curve (Figure 14.37b). We have

$$\iint\limits_{R} \frac{\partial g}{\partial x}\, dA = \int_{c}^{d} \int_{H_1(y)}^{H_2(y)} \frac{\partial g}{\partial x}\, dx\, dy \qquad \text{Convert to an iterated integral.}$$

$$= \int_{c}^{d} \big(\underbrace{g(H_2(y), y)}_{C_2} - \underbrace{g(H_1(y), y)}_{-C_1} \big)\, dy \qquad \int \frac{\partial g}{\partial x}\, dx = g$$

$$= \int_{C_2} g\, dy - \int_{-C_1} g\, dy$$

$$= \int_{C_2} g\, dy + \int_{C_1} g\, dy \qquad \int_{-C_1} g\, dy = -\int_{C_1} g\, dy$$

$$= \oint_{C} g\, dy. \qquad \int_{C} g\, dy = \int_{C_1} g\, dy + \int_{C_2} g\, dy$$

Combining these two calculations results in

$$\iint\limits_{R} \left(\frac{\partial g}{\partial x} - \frac{\partial f}{\partial y} \right) dA = \oint_{C} f\, dx + g\, dy.$$

As mentioned earlier, with a change of notation (replace g with f and f with $-g$), the flux form of Green's Theorem is obtained. This proof also completes the list of equivalent properties of conservative fields given in Section 14.3: From Green's Theorem, it follows that if $\dfrac{\partial g}{\partial x} = \dfrac{\partial f}{\partial y}$ on a simply connected region R, then the vector field $\mathbf{F} = \langle f, g \rangle$ is conservative on R.

QUICK CHECK 4 Explain why Green's Theorem proves that if $g_x = f_y$, then the vector field $\mathbf{F} = \langle f, g \rangle$ is conservative. ◄

SECTION 14.4 EXERCISES

Review Questions

1. Explain why the two forms of Green's Theorem are analogs of the Fundamental Theorem of Calculus.

2. Referring to both forms of Green's Theorem, match each idea in Column 1 to an idea in Column 2:

Line integral for flux	Double integral of the curl
Line integral for circulation	Double integral of the divergence

3. Compute the two-dimensional curl of $\mathbf{F} = \langle 4x^3 y, xy^2 + x^4 \rangle$.

4. Compute the two-dimensional divergence of $\mathbf{F} = \langle 4x^3 y, xy^2 + x^4 \rangle$.

5. How do you use a line integral to compute the area of a plane region?

6. Why does a two-dimensional vector field with zero curl on a region have zero circulation on a closed curve that bounds the region?

7. Why does a two-dimensional vector field with zero divergence on a region have zero outward flux across a closed curve that bounds the region?

8. Sketch a two-dimensional vector field that has zero curl everywhere in the plane.

9. Sketch a two-dimensional vector field that has zero divergence everywhere in the plane.

10. Discuss one of the parallels between a conservative vector field and a source-free vector field.

Basic Skills

11–16. Green's Theorem, circulation form *Consider the following regions R and vector fields* **F**.

a. *Compute the two-dimensional curl of the vector field.*
b. *Evaluate both integrals in Green's Theorem and check for consistency.*
c. *Is the vector field conservative?*

11. $\mathbf{F} = \langle x, y \rangle$; $R = \{(x, y): x^2 + y^2 \leq 2\}$

12. $\mathbf{F} = \langle y, x \rangle$; R is the square with vertices $(0, 0)$, $(1, 0)$, $(1, 1)$, and $(0, 1)$.

13. $\mathbf{F} = \langle 2y, -2x \rangle$; R is the region bounded by $y = \sin x$ and $y = 0$, for $0 \leq x \leq \pi$.

14. $\mathbf{F} = \langle -3y, 3x \rangle$; R is the triangle with vertices $(0, 0)$, $(1, 0)$, and $(0, 2)$.

15. $\mathbf{F} = \langle 2xy, x^2 - y^2 \rangle$; R is the region bounded by $y = x(2 - x)$ and $y = 0$.

16. $\mathbf{F} = \langle 0, x^2 + y^2 \rangle$; $R = \{(x, y): x^2 + y^2 \leq 1\}$

17–22. Area of regions *Use a line integral on the boundary to find the area of the following regions.*

17. A disk of radius 5

18. A region bounded by an ellipse with major and minor axes of length 12 and 8, respectively.

19. $\{(x, y): x^2 + y^2 \leq 16\}$

20. The region shown in the figure

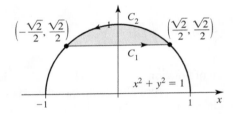

21. The region bounded by the parabolas $\mathbf{r}(t) = \langle t, 2t^2 \rangle$ and $\mathbf{r}(t) = \langle t, 12 - t^2 \rangle$, for $-2 \leq t \leq 2$

22. The region bounded by the curve $\mathbf{r}(t) = \langle t(1 - t^2), 1 - t^2 \rangle$, for $-1 \leq t \leq 1$ (*Hint:* Plot the curve.)

23–28. Green's Theorem, flux form *Consider the following regions R and vector fields $\mathbf{F}$.*

a. Compute the two-dimensional divergence of the vector field.
b. Evaluate both integrals in Green's Theorem and check for consistency.
c. State whether the vector field is source free.

23. $\mathbf{F} = \langle x, y \rangle$; $R = \{(x, y): x^2 + y^2 \leq 4\}$

24. $\mathbf{F} = \langle y, -x \rangle$; R is the square with vertices $(0, 0)$, $(1, 0)$, $(1, 1)$, and $(0, 1)$.

25. $\mathbf{F} = \langle y, -3x \rangle$; R is the region bounded by $y = 4 - x^2$ and $y = 0$.

26. $\mathbf{F} = \langle -3y, 3x \rangle$; R is the triangle with vertices $(0, 0)$, $(3, 0)$, and $(0, 1)$.

27. $\mathbf{F} = \langle 2xy, x^2 - y^2 \rangle$; R is the region bounded by $y = x(2 - x)$ and $y = 0$.

28. $\mathbf{F} = \langle x^2 + y^2, 0 \rangle$; $R = \{(x, y): x^2 + y^2 \leq 1\}$

29–34. Line integrals *Use Green's Theorem to evaluate the following line integrals. Unless stated otherwise, assume all curves are oriented counterclockwise.*

29. $\oint_C (2x + e^{y^2}) \, dy - (4y^2 + e^{x^2}) \, dx$, where C is the boundary of the square with vertices $(0, 0)$, $(1, 0)$, $(1, 1)$, and $(0, 1)$

30. $\oint_C (2x - 3y) \, dy - (3x + 4y) \, dx$, where C is the unit circle

31. $\oint_C f \, dy - g \, dx$, where $\langle f, g \rangle = \langle 0, xy \rangle$ and C is the triangle with vertices $(0, 0)$, $(2, 0)$, and $(0, 4)$

32. $\oint_C f \, dy - g \, dx$, where $\langle f, g \rangle = \langle x^2, 2y^2 \rangle$ and C is the upper half of the unit circle and the line segment $-1 \leq x \leq 1$ oriented *clockwise*

33. The circulation line integral of $\mathbf{F} = \langle x^2 + y^2, 4x + y^3 \rangle$, where C is the boundary of $\{(x, y): 0 \leq y \leq \sin x, 0 \leq x \leq \pi\}$

34. The flux line integral of $\mathbf{F} = \langle e^{x-y}, e^{y-x} \rangle$, where C is the boundary of $\{(x, y): 0 \leq y \leq x, 0 \leq x \leq 1\}$

35–38. General regions *For the following vector fields, compute (a) the circulation on and (b) the outward flux across the boundary of the given region. Assume boundary curves are oriented counterclockwise.*

35. $\mathbf{F} = \langle x, y \rangle$; R is the half-annulus $\{(r, \theta): 1 \leq r \leq 2, 0 \leq \theta \leq \pi\}$.

36. $\mathbf{F} = \langle -y, x \rangle$; R is the annulus $\{(r, \theta): 1 \leq r \leq 3, 0 \leq \theta \leq 2\pi\}$.

37. $\mathbf{F} = \langle 2x + y, x - 4y \rangle$; R is the quarter-annulus $\{(r, \theta): 1 \leq r \leq 4, 0 \leq \theta \leq \pi/2\}$.

38. $\mathbf{F} = \langle x - y, -x + 2y \rangle$; R is the parallelogram $\{(x, y): 1 - x \leq y \leq 3 - x, 0 \leq x \leq 1\}$.

Further Explorations

39. Explain why or why not Determine whether the following statements are true and give an explanation or counterexample.

    a. The work required to move an object around a closed curve C in the presence of a vector force field is the circulation of the force field on the curve.

    b. If a vector field has zero divergence throughout a region (on which the conditions of Green's Theorem are met), then the circulation on the boundary of that region is zero.

    c. If the two-dimensional curl of a vector field is positive throughout a region (on which the conditions of Green's Theorem are met), then the circulation on the boundary of that region is positive (assuming counterclockwise orientation).

40–43. Circulation and flux *For the following vector fields, compute (a) the circulation on and (b) the outward flux across the boundary of the given region. Assume boundary curves have counterclockwise orientation.*

40. $\mathbf{F} = \left\langle \ln(x^2 + y^2), \tan^{-1}\dfrac{y}{x} \right\rangle$, where R is the annulus $\{(r, \theta): 1 \leq r \leq 2, 0 \leq \theta \leq 2\pi\}$

41. $\mathbf{F} = \nabla\left(\sqrt{x^2 + y^2}\right)$, where R is the half annulus $\{(r, \theta): 1 \leq r \leq 3, 0 \leq \theta \leq \pi\}$

42. $\mathbf{F} = \langle y \cos x, -\sin x \rangle$, where R is the square $\{(x, y): 0 \leq x \leq \pi/2, 0 \leq y \leq \pi/2\}$

43. $\mathbf{F} = \langle x + y^2, x^2 - y \rangle$, where $R = \{(x, y): 3y^2 \leq x \leq 36 - y^2\}$

44–45. Special line integrals *Prove the following identities, where C is a simple closed smooth oriented curve.*

44. $\oint_C dx = \oint_C dy = 0$

45. $\oint_C f(x)\,dx + g(y)\,dy = 0$, where f and g have continuous

derivatives on the region enclosed by C.

46. Double integral to line integral Use the flux form of Green's Theorem to evaluate $\iint_R (2xy + 4y^3)\,dA$, where R is the triangle with vertices $(0, 0)$, $(1, 0)$, and $(0, 1)$.

47. Area line integral Show that the value of

$$\oint_C xy^2\,dx + (x^2 y + 2x)\,dy$$

depends only on the area of the region enclosed by C.

48. Area line integral In terms of the parameters a and b, how is the value of $\oint_C ay\,dx + bx\,dy$ related to the area of the region enclosed by C, assuming counterclockwise orientation of C?

49–52. Stream function *Recall that if the vector field $\mathbf{F} = \langle f, g \rangle$ is source free (zero divergence), then a stream function ψ exists such that $f = \psi_y$ and $g = -\psi_x$.*

a. *Verify that the given vector field has zero divergence.*
b. *Integrate the relations $f = \psi_y$ and $g = -\psi_x$ to find a stream function for the field.*

49. $\mathbf{F} = \langle 4, 2 \rangle$ **50.** $\mathbf{F} = \langle y^2, x^2 \rangle$

51. $\mathbf{F} = \langle -e^{-x} \sin y, e^{-x} \cos y \rangle$ **52.** $\mathbf{F} = \langle x^2, -2xy \rangle$

Applications

53–56. Ideal flow *A two-dimensional vector field describes **ideal flow** if it has both zero curl and zero divergence on a simply connected region (excluding the origin if necessary).*

a. *Verify that the curl and divergence of the given field is zero.*
b. *Find a potential function φ and a stream function ψ for the field.*
c. *Verify that φ and ψ satisfy Laplace's equation $\varphi_{xx} + \varphi_{yy} = \psi_{xx} + \psi_{yy} = 0$.*

53. $\mathbf{F} = \langle e^x \cos y, -e^x \sin y \rangle$

54. $\mathbf{F} = \langle x^3 - 3xy^2, y^3 - 3x^2 y \rangle$

55. $\mathbf{F} = \left\langle \tan^{-1} \dfrac{y}{x}, \dfrac{1}{2} \ln (x^2 + y^2) \right\rangle$

56. $\mathbf{F} = \dfrac{\langle x, y \rangle}{x^2 + y^2}$

57. Flow in an ocean basin An idealized two-dimensional ocean is modeled by the square region $R = [-\pi/2, \pi/2] \times [-\pi/2, \pi/2]$ with boundary C. Consider the stream function $\psi(x, y) = 4 \cos x \cos y$ defined on R (see figure).

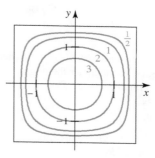

a. The horizontal (east-west) component of the velocity is $u = \psi_y$ and the vertical (north-south) component of the velocity is $v = -\psi_x$. Sketch a few representative velocity vectors and show that the flow is counterclockwise around the region.
b. Is the velocity field source free? Explain.
c. Is the velocity field irrotational? Explain.
d. Let C be the boundary of R. Find the total outward flux across C.
e. Find the circulation on C assuming counterclockwise orientation.

Additional Exercises

58. Green's Theorem as a Fundamental Theorem of Calculus Show that if the circulation form of Green's Theorem is applied to the vector field $\left\langle 0, \dfrac{f(x)}{c} \right\rangle$ and $R = \{ (x, y) : a \le x \le b, 0 \le y \le c \}$, then the result is the Fundamental Theorem of Calculus,

$$\int_a^b \frac{df}{dx}\,dx = f(b) - f(a).$$

59. Green's Theorem as a Fundamental Theorem of Calculus Show that if the flux form of Green's Theorem is applied to the vector field $\left\langle \dfrac{f(x)}{c}, 0 \right\rangle$ and $R = \{ (x, y) : a \le x \le b, 0 \le y \le c \}$, then the result is the Fundamental Theorem of Calculus,

$$\int_a^b \frac{df}{dx}\,dx = f(b) - f(a).$$

60. What's wrong? Consider the rotation field $\mathbf{F} = \dfrac{\langle -y, x \rangle}{x^2 + y^2}$.

a. Verify that the two-dimensional curl of $\mathbf{F}$ is zero, which suggests that the double integral in the circulation form of Green's Theorem is zero.
b. Use a line integral to verify that the circulation on the unit circle of the vector field is 2π.
c. Explain why the results of parts (a) and (b) do not agree.

61. What's wrong? Consider the radial field $\mathbf{F} = \dfrac{\langle x, y \rangle}{x^2 + y^2}$.

a. Verify that the divergence of $\mathbf{F}$ is zero, which suggests that the double integral in the flux form of Green's Theorem is zero.
b. Use a line integral to verify that the outward flux across the unit circle of the vector field is 2π.
c. Explain why the results of parts (a) and (b) do not agree.

62. Conditions for Green's Theorem Consider the radial field

$$\mathbf{F} = \langle f, g \rangle = \frac{\langle x, y \rangle}{\sqrt{x^2 + y^2}} = \frac{\mathbf{r}}{|\mathbf{r}|}.$$

a. Explain why the conditions of Green's Theorem do not apply to $\mathbf{F}$ on a region that includes the origin.

b. Let R be the unit disk centered at the origin and compute

$$\iint\limits_{R} \left(\frac{\partial f}{\partial x} + \frac{\partial g}{\partial y} \right) dA.$$

c. Evaluate the line integral in the flux form of Green's Theorem on the boundary of R.

d. Do the results of parts (b) and (c) agree? Explain.

63. Flux integrals Assume the vector field $\mathbf{F} = \langle f, g \rangle$ is source free (zero divergence) with stream function ψ. Let C be any smooth simple curve from A to the distinct point B. Show that the flux integral $\int_C \mathbf{F} \cdot \mathbf{n} \, ds$ is independent of path; that is, $\int_C \mathbf{F} \cdot \mathbf{n} \, ds = \psi(B) - \psi(A)$.

64. Streamlines are tangent to the vector field Assume that the vector field $\mathbf{F} = \langle f, g \rangle$ is related to the stream function ψ by $\psi_y = f$ and $\psi_x = -g$ on a region R. Prove that at all points of R, the vector field is tangent to the streamlines (the level curves of the stream function).

65. Streamlines and equipotential lines Assume that on $\mathbb{R}^2$, the vector field $\mathbf{F} = \langle f, g \rangle$ has a potential function φ such that $f = \varphi_x$ and $g = \varphi_y$, and it has a stream function ψ such that $f = \psi_y$ and $g = -\psi_x$. Show that the equipotential curves (level curves of φ) and the streamlines (level curves of ψ) are everywhere orthogonal.

66. Channel flow The flow in a long shallow channel is modeled by the velocity field $\mathbf{F} = \langle 0, 1 - x^2 \rangle$, where $R = \{(x, y): |x| \leq 1 \text{ and } |y| \leq 5\}$.

a. Sketch R and several streamlines of $\mathbf{F}$.

b. Evaluate the curl of $\mathbf{F}$ on the lines $x = 0$, $x = \frac{1}{4}$, $x = \frac{1}{2}$, and $x = 1$.

c. Compute the circulation on the boundary of R.

d. How do you explain the fact that the curl of $\mathbf{F}$ is nonzero at points of R, but the circulation is zero?

QUICK CHECK ANSWERS

1. $g_x - f_y = 0$, which implies zero circulation on a closed curve.   **2.** $f_x + g_y = 0$, which implies zero flux across a closed curve.   **3.** $\psi_y = y$ is the x-component of $\mathbf{F} = \langle y, x \rangle$, and $-\psi_x = x$ is the y-component of $\mathbf{F}$. Also, the divergence of $\mathbf{F}$ is $y_x + x_y = 0$.   **4.** If the curl is zero on a region, then all closed-path integrals are zero, which is a condition (Section 14.3) for a conservative field. ◄

14.5 Divergence and Curl

Green's Theorem sets the stage for the final act in our exploration of calculus. The last four sections of the book have the following goal: to lift both forms of Green's Theorem out of the plane ($\mathbb{R}^2$) and into space ($\mathbb{R}^3$). It is done as follows.

- The circulation form of Green's Theorem relates a line integral over a simple closed oriented curve in the plane to a double integral over the enclosed region. In an analogous manner, we will see that *Stokes' Theorem* (Section 14.7) relates a line integral over a simple closed oriented curve in $\mathbb{R}^3$ to a double integral over a surface whose boundary is that curve.

- The flux form of Green's Theorem relates a line integral over a simple closed oriented curve in the plane to a double integral over the enclosed region. Similarly, the *Divergence Theorem* (Section 14.8) relates an integral over a closed oriented surface in $\mathbb{R}^3$ to a triple integral over the region enclosed by that surface.

In order to make these extensions, we need a few more tools.

- The two-dimensional divergence and two-dimensional curl must be extended to three dimensions (this section).

- The idea of a *surface integral* must be introduced (Section 14.6).

The Divergence

> Review: The divergence measures the expansion or contraction of a vector field at each point. The flux form of Green's Theorem implies that if the two-dimensional divergence of a vector field is zero throughout a simply connected plane region, then the outward flux across the boundary of the region is zero. If the divergence is nonzero, Green's Theorem gives the outward flux across the boundary.

Recall that in two dimensions, the divergence of the vector field $\mathbf{F} = \langle f, g \rangle$ is $\dfrac{\partial f}{\partial x} + \dfrac{\partial g}{\partial y}$. The extension to three dimensions is straightforward. If $\mathbf{F} = \langle f, g, h \rangle$ is a differentiable vector field defined on a region of $\mathbb{R}^3$, the divergence of $\mathbf{F}$ is $\dfrac{\partial f}{\partial x} + \dfrac{\partial g}{\partial y} + \dfrac{\partial h}{\partial z}$. The interpretation of the three-dimensional divergence is much the same as it is in two dimensions. It measures the expansion or contraction of the vector field at each point. If the divergence is zero at all points of a region, the vector field is *source free* on that region.

Recall the *del operator* ∇ that was introduced in Section 12.6 to define the gradient:

$$\nabla = \mathbf{i} \frac{\partial}{\partial x} + \mathbf{j} \frac{\partial}{\partial y} + \mathbf{k} \frac{\partial}{\partial z} = \left\langle \frac{\partial}{\partial x}, \frac{\partial}{\partial y}, \frac{\partial}{\partial z} \right\rangle.$$

This object is not really a vector; it is an operation that is applied to a function or a vector field. Applying it directly to a scalar function f results in the gradient of f:

$$\nabla f = \frac{\partial f}{\partial x}\mathbf{i} + \frac{\partial f}{\partial y}\mathbf{j} + \frac{\partial f}{\partial z}\mathbf{k} = \langle f_x, f_y, f_z \rangle.$$

However, if we form the *dot product* of ∇ and a vector field $\mathbf{F} = \langle f, g, h \rangle$, the result is

$$\nabla \cdot \mathbf{F} = \left\langle \frac{\partial}{\partial x}, \frac{\partial}{\partial y}, \frac{\partial}{\partial z} \right\rangle \cdot \langle f, g, h \rangle = \frac{\partial f}{\partial x} + \frac{\partial g}{\partial y} + \frac{\partial h}{\partial z},$$

which is the divergence of $\mathbf{F}$, also denoted div $\mathbf{F}$. Like all dot products, the divergence is a scalar; in this case, it is a scalar-valued function.

> In evaluating $\nabla \cdot \mathbf{F}$ as a dot product, each component of ∇ is applied to the corresponding component of $\mathbf{F}$, producing $f_x + g_y + h_z$.

DEFINITION Divergence of a Vector Field

The **divergence** of a vector field $\mathbf{F} = \langle f, g, h \rangle$ that is differentiable on a region of $\mathbb{R}^3$ is

$$\text{div } \mathbf{F} = \nabla \cdot \mathbf{F} = \frac{\partial f}{\partial x} + \frac{\partial g}{\partial y} + \frac{\partial h}{\partial z}.$$

If $\nabla \cdot \mathbf{F} = 0$, the vector field is **source free**.

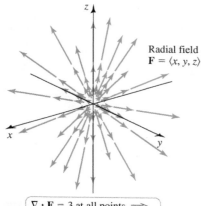

Radial field
$\mathbf{F} = \langle x, y, z \rangle$

$\nabla \cdot \mathbf{F} = 3$ at all points $\Longrightarrow$ vector field expands outward at all points.

(a)

EXAMPLE 1 Computing the divergence Compute the divergence of the following vector fields.

a. $\mathbf{F} = \langle x, y, z \rangle$ (a radial field)

b. $\mathbf{F} = \langle -y, x - z, y \rangle$ (a rotation field)

c. $\mathbf{F} = \langle -y, x, z \rangle$ (a spiral flow)

SOLUTION

a. The divergence is $\nabla \cdot \mathbf{F} = \nabla \cdot \langle x, y, z \rangle = \dfrac{\partial x}{\partial x} + \dfrac{\partial y}{\partial y} + \dfrac{\partial z}{\partial z} = 1 + 1 + 1 = 3.$

Because the divergence is positive, the flow expands outward at all points (Figure 14.38a).

b. The divergence is

$$\nabla \cdot \mathbf{F} = \nabla \cdot \langle -y, x - z, y \rangle = \frac{\partial(-y)}{\partial x} + \frac{\partial(x - z)}{\partial y} + \frac{\partial y}{\partial z} = 0 + 0 + 0 = 0,$$

so the field is source free.

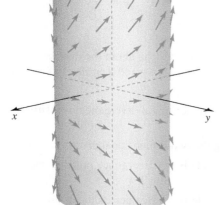

Spiral flow
$\mathbf{F} = \langle -y, x, z \rangle$

(b)

Figure 14.38

c. This field is a combination of the two-dimensional rotation field $\mathbf{F} = \langle -y, x \rangle$ and a vertical flow in the z-direction; the net effect is a field that spirals upward for $z > 0$ and spirals downward for $z < 0$ (Figure 14.38b). The divergence is

$$\nabla \cdot \mathbf{F} = \nabla \cdot \langle -y, x, z \rangle = \frac{\partial(-y)}{\partial x} + \frac{\partial x}{\partial y} + \frac{\partial z}{\partial z} = 0 + 0 + 1 = 1.$$

The rotational part of the field in x and y does not contribute to the divergence. However, the z-component of the field produces a nonzero divergence.

Related Exercises 9–16 ◀

QUICK CHECK 1 Show that if a vector field has the form $\mathbf{F} = \langle f(y, z), g(x, z), h(x, y) \rangle$, then div $\mathbf{F} = 0$. ◀

Divergence of a Radial Vector Field The vector field considered in Example 1a is just one of many radial fields that have important applications (for example, the inverse square laws of gravitation and electrostatics). The following example leads to a general result for the divergence of radial vector fields.

EXAMPLE 2 Divergence of a radial field Compute the divergence of the radial vector field

$$\mathbf{F} = \frac{\mathbf{r}}{|\mathbf{r}|} = \frac{\langle x, y, z \rangle}{\sqrt{x^2 + y^2 + z^2}}.$$

SOLUTION This radial field has the property that is it directed outward from the origin and all vectors have unit length ($|\mathbf{F}| = 1$). Let's compute one piece of the divergence; the others follow the same pattern. Using the Quotient Rule, the derivative with respect to x of the first component of $\mathbf{F}$ is

$$\frac{\partial}{\partial x}\left(\frac{x}{(x^2 + y^2 + z^2)^{1/2}}\right) = \frac{(x^2 + y^2 + z^2)^{1/2} - x^2(x^2 + y^2 + z^2)^{-1/2}}{x^2 + y^2 + z^2} \quad \text{Quotient Rule}$$

$$= \frac{|\mathbf{r}| - x^2|\mathbf{r}|^{-1}}{|\mathbf{r}|^2} \quad \sqrt{x^2 + y^2 + z^2} = |\mathbf{r}|$$

$$= \frac{|\mathbf{r}|^2 - x^2}{|\mathbf{r}|^3}. \quad \text{Simplify.}$$

A similar calculation of the y- and z-derivatives yields $\dfrac{|\mathbf{r}|^2 - y^2}{|\mathbf{r}|^3}$ and $\dfrac{|\mathbf{r}|^2 - z^2}{|\mathbf{r}|^3}$, respectively.

Adding the three terms, we find that

$$\nabla \cdot \mathbf{F} = \frac{|\mathbf{r}|^2 - x^2}{|\mathbf{r}|^3} + \frac{|\mathbf{r}|^2 - y^2}{|\mathbf{r}|^3} + \frac{|\mathbf{r}|^2 - z^2}{|\mathbf{r}|^3}$$

$$= 3\frac{|\mathbf{r}|^2}{|\mathbf{r}|^3} - \frac{x^2 + y^2 + z^2}{|\mathbf{r}|^3} \quad \text{Collect terms.}$$

$$= \frac{2}{|\mathbf{r}|}. \quad x^2 + y^2 + z^2 = |\mathbf{r}|^2$$

Related Exercises 17–20 ◄

Examples 1a and 2 give two special cases of the following theorem about the divergence of radial vector fields (Exercise 73).

THEOREM 14.8   Divergence of Radial Vector Fields
For a real number p, the divergence of the radial vector field

$$\mathbf{F} = \frac{\mathbf{r}}{|\mathbf{r}|^p} = \frac{\langle x, y, z\rangle}{(x^2 + y^2 + z^2)^{p/2}} \quad \text{is} \quad \nabla \cdot \mathbf{F} = \frac{3 - p}{|\mathbf{r}|^p}.$$

EXAMPLE 3   Divergence from a graph To gain some intuition about the divergence, consider the two-dimensional vector field $\mathbf{F} = \langle f, g\rangle = \langle x^2, y\rangle$ and a circle C of radius 2 centered at the origin (Figure 14.39).

a. Without computing it, determine whether the two-dimensional divergence is positive or negative at the point $Q(1, 1)$. Why?

b. Confirm your conjecture in part (a) by computing the two-dimensional divergence at Q.

c. Based on part (b), over what regions within the circle is the divergence positive and over what regions within the circle is the divergence negative?

d. By inspection of the figure, on what part of the circle is the flux across the boundary outward? Is the net flux out of the circle positive or negative?

SOLUTION

a. At $Q(1, 1)$ the x-component and the y-component of the field are increasing ($f_x > 0$ and $g_y > 0$), so the field is expanding at that point and the two-dimensional divergence is positive.

b. Calculating the two-dimensional divergence, we find that

$$\nabla \cdot \mathbf{F} = \frac{\partial}{\partial x}(x^2) + \frac{\partial}{\partial y}(y) = 2x + 1.$$

At $Q(1, 1)$ the divergence is 3, confirming part (a).

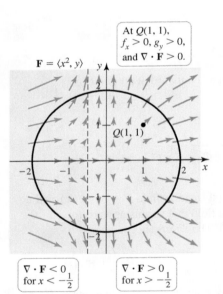

At $Q(1, 1)$,
$f_x > 0, g_y > 0$,
and $\nabla \cdot \mathbf{F} > 0$.

$\mathbf{F} = \langle x^2, y\rangle$

$\nabla \cdot \mathbf{F} < 0$ for $x < -\frac{1}{2}$

$\nabla \cdot \mathbf{F} > 0$ for $x > -\frac{1}{2}$

Figure 14.39

➤ To understand the conclusion of Example 3a, note that as you move through the point Q from left to right, the horizontal components of the vectors increase in length ($f_x > 0$). As you move through the point Q in the upward direction, the vertical components of the vectors also increase in length ($g_y > 0$).

QUICK CHECK 2 Verify the claim made in Example 3d by showing that the net outward flux of **F** across C is positive. (*Hint:* If you use Green's Theorem to evaluate the integral $\int_C f\,dy - g\,dx$, convert to polar coordinates.) ◄

c. From part (b), we see that $\nabla \cdot \mathbf{F} = 2x + 1 > 0$, for $x > -\frac{1}{2}$, and $\nabla \cdot \mathbf{F} < 0$, for $x < -\frac{1}{2}$. To the left of the line $x = -\frac{1}{2}$ the field is contracting and to the right of the line the field is expanding.

d. Using Figure 14.39, it appears that the field is tangent to the circle at two points with $x \approx -1$. For points on the circle with $x < -1$, the flow is into the circle; for points on the circle with $x > -1$, the flow is out of the circle. It appears that the net outward flux across C is positive. The points where the field changes from inward to outward may be determined exactly (Exercise 46).

Related Exercises 21–22 ◄

The Curl

> ► Review: The *two-dimensional curl* $g_x - f_y$ measures the rotation of a vector field at a point. The circulation form of Green's theorem implies that if the two-dimensional curl of a vector field is zero throughout a simply connected region, then the circulation on the boundary of the region is also zero. If the curl is nonzero, Green's Theorem gives the circulation along the curve.

Just as the divergence $\nabla \cdot \mathbf{F}$ is the dot product of the *del operator* and **F**, the three-dimensional curl is the cross product $\nabla \times \mathbf{F}$. If we formally use the notation for the cross product in terms of a 3×3 determinant, we obtain the definition of the curl:

$$\nabla \times \mathbf{F} = \begin{vmatrix} \mathbf{i} & \mathbf{j} & \mathbf{k} \\ \dfrac{\partial}{\partial x} & \dfrac{\partial}{\partial y} & \dfrac{\partial}{\partial z} \\ f & g & h \end{vmatrix} \begin{matrix} \leftarrow \text{Unit vectors} \\ \leftarrow \text{Components of } \nabla \\ \leftarrow \text{Components of } \mathbf{F} \end{matrix}$$

$$= \left(\frac{\partial h}{\partial y} - \frac{\partial g}{\partial z} \right) \mathbf{i} + \left(\frac{\partial f}{\partial z} - \frac{\partial h}{\partial x} \right) \mathbf{j} + \left(\frac{\partial g}{\partial x} - \frac{\partial f}{\partial y} \right) \mathbf{k}.$$

The curl of a vector field, also denoted curl **F**, is a vector with three components. Notice that the **k**-component of the curl $(g_x - f_y)$ is the two-dimensional curl, which gives the rotation in the xy-plane at a point. The **i**- and **j**-components of the curl correspond to the rotation of the vector field in planes parallel to the yz-plane (orthogonal to **i**) and in planes parallel to the xz-plane (orthogonal to **j**) (Figure 14.40).

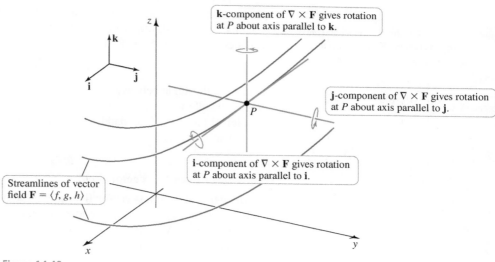

Figure 14.40

DEFINITION Curl of a Vector Field

The **curl** of a vector field $\mathbf{F} = \langle f, g, h \rangle$ that is differentiable on a region of $\mathbb{R}^3$ is

$$\nabla \times \mathbf{F} = \text{curl } \mathbf{F}$$

$$= \left(\frac{\partial h}{\partial y} - \frac{\partial g}{\partial z} \right) \mathbf{i} + \left(\frac{\partial f}{\partial z} - \frac{\partial h}{\partial x} \right) \mathbf{j} + \left(\frac{\partial g}{\partial x} - \frac{\partial f}{\partial y} \right) \mathbf{k}.$$

If $\nabla \times \mathbf{F} = \mathbf{0}$, the vector field is **irrotational**.

Curl of a General Rotation Vector Field We can clarify the physical meaning of the curl by considering the vector field $\mathbf{F} = \mathbf{a} \times \mathbf{r}$, where $\mathbf{a} = \langle a_1, a_2, a_3 \rangle$ is a nonzero constant vector and $\mathbf{r} = \langle x, y, z \rangle$. Writing out its components, we see that

$$\mathbf{F} = \mathbf{a} \times \mathbf{r} = \begin{vmatrix} \mathbf{i} & \mathbf{j} & \mathbf{k} \\ a_1 & a_2 & a_3 \\ x & y & z \end{vmatrix} = (a_2 z - a_3 y)\,\mathbf{i} + (a_3 x - a_1 z)\,\mathbf{j} + (a_1 y - a_2 x)\,\mathbf{k}.$$

This vector field is a *general rotation field* in three dimensions. With $a_1 = a_2 = 0$ and $a_3 = 1$, we have the familiar two-dimensional rotation field $\langle -y, x \rangle$ with its axis in the **k**-direction. More generally, **F** is the superposition of three rotation fields with axes in the **i**-, **j**-, and **k**-directions. The result is a single rotation field with an axis in the direction of **a** (Figure 14.41).

Three calculations tell us a lot about the general rotation field. The first calculation confirms that $\nabla \cdot \mathbf{F} = 0$ (Exercise 42). Just as with rotation fields in two dimensions, the divergence of a general rotation field is zero.

The second calculation (Exercises 43–44) uses the right-hand rule for cross products to show that the vector field $\mathbf{F} = \mathbf{a} \times \mathbf{r}$ is indeed a rotation field that circles the vector **a** in a counterclockwise direction looking along the length of **a** from head to tail (Figure 14.41).

The third calculation (Exercise 45) says that $\nabla \times \mathbf{F} = 2\mathbf{a}$. Therefore, the curl of the general rotation field is in the direction of the axis of rotation **a** (Figure 14.41). The magnitude of the curl is $|\nabla \times \mathbf{F}| = 2|\mathbf{a}|$. It can be shown (Exercise 52) that if **F** is a velocity field, then $|\mathbf{a}|$ is the constant angular speed of rotation of the field, denoted ω. The angular speed is the rate (radians per unit time) at which a small particle in the vector field rotates about the axis of the field. Therefore, the angular speed is half the magnitude of the curl, or

$$\omega = |\mathbf{a}| = \frac{1}{2} |\nabla \times \mathbf{F}|.$$

The rotation field $\mathbf{F} = \mathbf{a} \times \mathbf{r}$ suggests a related question. Suppose a paddle wheel is placed in the vector field **F** at a point P with the axis of the wheel in the direction of a unit vector **n** (Figure 14.42). How should **n** be chosen so the paddle wheel spins fastest? The scalar component of $\nabla \times \mathbf{F}$ in the direction of **n** is

$$(\nabla \times \mathbf{F}) \cdot \mathbf{n} = |\nabla \times \mathbf{F}| \cos \theta, \quad (|n| = 1)$$

where θ is the angle between $\nabla \times \mathbf{F}$ and **n**. The scalar component is greatest in magnitude and the paddle wheel spins fastest when $\theta = 0$ or $\theta = \pi$; that is, when **n** and $\nabla \times \mathbf{F}$ are parallel. If the axis of the paddle wheel is orthogonal to $\nabla \times \mathbf{F}$ ($\theta = \pm \pi/2$), the wheel doesn't spin.

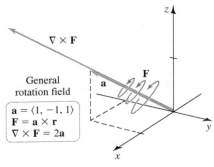

$\nabla \times \mathbf{F}$

General
rotation field

$\mathbf{a} = \langle 1, -1, 1 \rangle$
$\mathbf{F} = \mathbf{a} \times \mathbf{r}$
$\nabla \times \mathbf{F} = 2\mathbf{a}$

Figure 14.41

➤ Just as $\nabla f \cdot \mathbf{n}$ is the directional derivative in the direction **n**, $(\nabla \times \mathbf{F}) \cdot \mathbf{n}$ is the directional spin in the direction **n**.

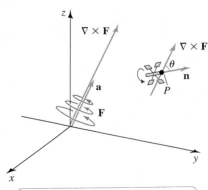

Paddle wheel at P with axis **n** measures rotation about **n**. Rotation is a maximum when $\nabla \times \mathbf{F}$ is parallel to **n**.

Figure 14.42

General Rotation Vector Field

The **general rotation vector field** is $\mathbf{F} = \mathbf{a} \times \mathbf{r}$, where the nonzero constant vector $\mathbf{a} = \langle a_1, a_2, a_3 \rangle$ is the axis of rotation and $\mathbf{r} = \langle x, y, z \rangle$. For all nonzero choices of **a**, $|\nabla \times \mathbf{F}| = 2|\mathbf{a}|$ and $\nabla \cdot \mathbf{F} = 0$. If **F** is a velocity field, then the constant angular speed of the field is

$$\omega = |\mathbf{a}| = \frac{1}{2} |\nabla \times \mathbf{F}|.$$

QUICK CHECK 3 Show that if a vector field has the form $\mathbf{F} = \langle f(x), g(y), h(z) \rangle$, then $\nabla \times \mathbf{F} = \mathbf{0}$.◄

EXAMPLE 4 Curl of a rotation field Compute the curl of the rotational field $\mathbf{F} = \mathbf{a} \times \mathbf{r}$, where $\mathbf{a} = \langle 1, -1, 1 \rangle$ and $\mathbf{r} = \langle x, y, z \rangle$ (Figure 14.41). What is the direction and the magnitude of the curl?

SOLUTION A quick calculation shows that

$$\mathbf{F} = \mathbf{a} \times \mathbf{r} = (-y - z)\,\mathbf{i} + (x - z)\,\mathbf{j} + (x + y)\,\mathbf{k}.$$

The curl of the vector field is

$$\nabla \times \mathbf{F} = \begin{vmatrix} \mathbf{i} & \mathbf{j} & \mathbf{k} \\ \dfrac{\partial}{\partial x} & \dfrac{\partial}{\partial y} & \dfrac{\partial}{\partial z} \\ -y - z & x - z & x + y \end{vmatrix} = 2\mathbf{i} - 2\mathbf{j} + 2\mathbf{k} = 2\mathbf{a}.$$

We have confirmed that $\nabla \times \mathbf{F} = 2\mathbf{a}$ and that the direction of the curl is the direction of $\mathbf{a}$, which is the axis of rotation. The magnitude of $\nabla \times \mathbf{F}$ is $|2\mathbf{a}| = 2\sqrt{3}$, which is twice the angular speed of rotation.

Related Exercises 23–34 ◀

Working with Divergence and Curl

The divergence and curl satisfy some of the same properties that ordinary derivatives satisfy. For example, given a real number c and differentiable vector fields $\mathbf{F}$ and $\mathbf{G}$, we have the following properties.

<table>
<tr><td align="center">**Divergence Properties**</td><td align="center">**Curl Properties**</td></tr>
<tr><td align="center">$\nabla \cdot (\mathbf{F} + \mathbf{G}) = \nabla \cdot \mathbf{F} + \nabla \cdot \mathbf{G}$</td><td align="center">$\nabla \times (\mathbf{F} + \mathbf{G}) = (\nabla \times \mathbf{F}) + (\nabla \times \mathbf{G})$</td></tr>
<tr><td align="center">$\nabla \cdot (c\mathbf{F}) = c(\nabla \cdot \mathbf{F})$</td><td align="center">$\nabla \times (c\mathbf{F}) = c(\nabla \times \mathbf{F})$</td></tr>
</table>

These and other properties are explored in Exercises 65–72.

Additional properties that have importance in theory and applications are presented in the following theorems and examples.

THEOREM 14.9   Curl of a Conservative Vector Field

Suppose that $\mathbf{F}$ is a conservative vector field on an open region D of $\mathbb{R}^3$. Let $\mathbf{F} = \nabla \varphi$, where φ is a potential function with continuous second partial derivatives on D. Then $\nabla \times \mathbf{F} = \nabla \times \nabla \varphi = \mathbf{0}$: The curl of the gradient is the zero vector and $\mathbf{F}$ is irrotational.

Proof: We must calculate $\nabla \times \nabla \varphi$:

$$\nabla \times \nabla \varphi = \begin{vmatrix} \mathbf{i} & \mathbf{j} & \mathbf{k} \\ \dfrac{\partial}{\partial x} & \dfrac{\partial}{\partial y} & \dfrac{\partial}{\partial z} \\ \varphi_x & \varphi_y & \varphi_z \end{vmatrix} = \underbrace{(\varphi_{zy} - \varphi_{yz})}_{0}\mathbf{i} + \underbrace{(\varphi_{xz} - \varphi_{zx})}_{0}\mathbf{j} + \underbrace{(\varphi_{yx} - \varphi_{xy})}_{0}\mathbf{k} = \mathbf{0}.$$

The mixed partial derivatives are equal by Clairaut's Theorem (Theorem 12.4).

The converse of this theorem (if $\nabla \times \mathbf{F} = \mathbf{0}$, then $\mathbf{F}$ is a conservative field) is handled in Section 14.7 by means of Stokes' Theorem. ◀

▶ First note that $\nabla \times \mathbf{F}$ is a vector, so it makes sense to take the divergence of the curl.

THEOREM 14.10   Divergence of the Curl

Suppose that $\mathbf{F} = \langle f, g, h \rangle$, where f, g, and h have continuous second partial derivatives. Then $\nabla \cdot (\nabla \times \mathbf{F}) = 0$: The divergence of the curl is zero.

Proof: Again, a calculation is needed:

$$\nabla \cdot (\nabla \times \mathbf{F})$$

$$= \frac{\partial}{\partial x}\left(\frac{\partial h}{\partial y} - \frac{\partial g}{\partial z}\right) + \frac{\partial}{\partial y}\left(\frac{\partial f}{\partial z} - \frac{\partial h}{\partial x}\right) + \frac{\partial}{\partial z}\left(\frac{\partial g}{\partial x} - \frac{\partial f}{\partial y}\right)$$

$$= \underbrace{(h_{yx} - h_{xy})}_{0} + \underbrace{(g_{xz} - g_{zx})}_{0} + \underbrace{(f_{zy} - f_{yz})}_{0} = 0.$$

Clairaut's Theorem (Theorem 12.4) ensures that the mixed partial derivatives are equal. ◀

The gradient, the divergence, and the curl may be combined in many ways—some of which are undefined. For example, the gradient of the curl $(\nabla(\nabla \times \mathbf{F}))$ and the curl of the divergence $(\nabla \times (\nabla \cdot \mathbf{F}))$ are undefined. However, a combination that *is* defined and is important is the divergence of the gradient $\nabla \cdot \nabla u$, where u is a scalar-valued function. This combination is denoted $\nabla^2 u$ and is called the **Laplacian** of u; it arises in many physical situations (Exercises 56–58, 62). Carrying out the calculation, we find that

$$\nabla \cdot \nabla u = \frac{\partial}{\partial x}\frac{\partial u}{\partial x} + \frac{\partial}{\partial y}\frac{\partial u}{\partial y} + \frac{\partial}{\partial z}\frac{\partial u}{\partial z} = \frac{\partial^2 u}{\partial x^2} + \frac{\partial^2 u}{\partial y^2} + \frac{\partial^2 u}{\partial z^2}.$$

We close with a result that is useful in its own right but also intriguing because it parallels the Product Rule from single-variable calculus.

THEOREM 14.11 Product Rule for the Divergence

Let u be a scalar-valued function that is differentiable on a region D and let $\mathbf{F}$ be a vector field that is differentiable on D. Then

$$\nabla \cdot (u\mathbf{F}) = \nabla u \cdot \mathbf{F} + u(\nabla \cdot \mathbf{F}).$$

The rule says that the "derivative" of the product is the "derivative" of the first function multiplied by the second function plus the first function multiplied by the "derivative" of the second function. However, in each instance, "derivative" must be interpreted correctly for the operations to make sense. The proof of the theorem requires a direct calculation (Exercise 67). Other similar vector calculus identities are presented in Exercises 68–72.

QUICK CHECK 4 Is $\nabla \cdot (u\mathbf{F})$ a vector function or a scalar function? ◄

EXAMPLE 5 More properties of radial fields Let $\mathbf{r} = \langle x, y, z \rangle$ and let $\varphi = \dfrac{1}{|\mathbf{r}|} = (x^2 + y^2 + z^2)^{-1/2}$ be a potential function.

a. Find the associated gradient field $\mathbf{F} = \nabla\!\left(\dfrac{1}{|\mathbf{r}|}\right)$.

b. Compute $\nabla \cdot \mathbf{F}$.

SOLUTION

a. The gradient has three components. Computing the first component reveals a pattern:

$$\frac{\partial \varphi}{\partial x} = \frac{\partial}{\partial x}(x^2 + y^2 + z^2)^{-1/2} = -\frac{1}{2}(x^2 + y^2 + z^2)^{-3/2}\,2x = -\frac{x}{|\mathbf{r}|^3}.$$

Making a similar calculation for the y- and z-derivatives, the gradient is

$$\mathbf{F} = \nabla\!\left(\frac{1}{|\mathbf{r}|}\right) = -\frac{\langle x, y, z \rangle}{|\mathbf{r}|^3} = -\frac{\mathbf{r}}{|\mathbf{r}|^3}.$$

This result reveals that $\mathbf{F}$ is an inverse square vector field (for example, a gravitational or electric field), and its potential function is $\varphi = \dfrac{1}{|\mathbf{r}|}$.

b. The divergence $\nabla \cdot \mathbf{F} = \nabla \cdot \left(-\dfrac{\mathbf{r}}{|\mathbf{r}|^3}\right)$ involves a product of the vector function $\mathbf{r} = \langle x, y, z \rangle$ and the scalar function $|\mathbf{r}|^{-3}$. Applying Theorem 14.11, we find that

$$\nabla \cdot \mathbf{F} = \nabla \cdot \left(-\frac{\mathbf{r}}{|\mathbf{r}|^3}\right) = -\nabla\frac{1}{|\mathbf{r}|^3} \cdot \mathbf{r} - \frac{1}{|\mathbf{r}|^3}\,\nabla \cdot \mathbf{r}.$$

A calculation similar to part (a) shows that $\nabla\dfrac{1}{|\mathbf{r}|^3} = -\dfrac{3\,\mathbf{r}}{|\mathbf{r}|^5}$ (Exercise 35). Therefore,

$$\nabla \cdot \mathbf{F} = \nabla \cdot \left(-\frac{\mathbf{r}}{|\mathbf{r}|^3}\right) = \underbrace{-\nabla\frac{1}{|\mathbf{r}|^3}}_{-3\mathbf{r}/|\mathbf{r}|^5} \cdot \mathbf{r} - \frac{1}{|\mathbf{r}|^3}\underbrace{\nabla \cdot \mathbf{r}}_{3}$$

$$= \frac{3\mathbf{r}}{|\mathbf{r}|^5}\cdot\mathbf{r} - \frac{3}{|\mathbf{r}|^3} \qquad \text{Substitute for } \nabla\frac{1}{|\mathbf{r}|^3}.$$

$$= \frac{3|\mathbf{r}|^2}{|\mathbf{r}|^5} - \frac{3}{|\mathbf{r}|^3} \qquad \mathbf{r}\cdot\mathbf{r} = |\mathbf{r}|^2$$

$$= 0.$$

The result is consistent with Theorem 14.8 (with $p = 3$): The divergence of an inverse square vector field in $\mathbb{R}^3$ is zero. It does not happen for any other radial fields of this form.

Related Exercises 35–38 ◄

Summary of Properties of Conservative Vector Fields

We can now extend the list of equivalent properties of conservative vector fields **F** defined on an open connected region. Theorem 14.9 is added to the list given at the end of Section 14.3.

> **Properties of a Conservative Vector Field**
>
> Let **F** be a conservative vector field whose components have continuous second partial derivatives on an open connected region D in $\mathbb{R}^3$. Then **F** has the following equivalent properties.
>
> 1. There exists a potential function φ such that $\mathbf{F} = \nabla\varphi$ (definition).
> 2. $\int_C \mathbf{F}\cdot d\mathbf{r} = \varphi(B) - \varphi(A)$ for all points A and B in D and all piecewise-smooth oriented curves C in D from A to B.
> 3. $\oint_C \mathbf{F}\cdot d\mathbf{r} = 0$ on all simple piecewise-smooth closed oriented curves C in D.
> 4. $\nabla \times \mathbf{F} = \mathbf{0}$ at all points of D.

SECTION 14.5 EXERCISES

Review Questions

1. Explain how to compute the divergence of the vector field $\mathbf{F} = \langle f, g, h \rangle$.

2. Interpret the divergence of a vector field.

3. What does it mean if the divergence of a vector field is zero throughout a region?

4. Explain how to compute the curl of the vector field $\mathbf{F} = \langle f, g, h \rangle$.

5. Interpret the curl of a general rotation vector field.

6. What does it mean if the curl of a vector field is zero throughout a region?

7. What is the value of $\nabla \cdot (\nabla \times \mathbf{F})$?

8. What is the value of $\nabla \times \nabla u$?

Basic Skills

9–16. Divergence of vector fields *Find the divergence of the following vector fields.*

9. $\mathbf{F} = \langle 2x, 4y, -3z \rangle$

10. $\mathbf{F} = \langle -2y, 3x, z \rangle$

11. $\mathbf{F} = \langle 12x, -6y, -6z \rangle$

12. $\mathbf{F} = \langle x^2yz, -xy^2z, -xyz^2 \rangle$

13. $\mathbf{F} = \langle x^2 - y^2, y^2 - z^2, z^2 - x^2 \rangle$

14. $\mathbf{F} = \langle e^{-x+y}, e^{-y+z}, e^{-z+x} \rangle$

15. $\mathbf{F} = \dfrac{\langle x, y, z \rangle}{1 + x^2 + y^2}$

16. $\mathbf{F} = \langle yz \sin x, xz \cos y, xy \cos z \rangle$

17–20. Divergence of radial fields *Calculate the divergence of the following radial fields. Express the result in terms of the position vector **r** and its length $|\mathbf{r}|$. Check for agreement with Theorem 14.8.*

17. $\mathbf{F} = \dfrac{\langle x, y, z \rangle}{x^2 + y^2 + z^2} = \dfrac{\mathbf{r}}{|\mathbf{r}|^2}$

18. $\mathbf{F} = \dfrac{\langle x, y, z \rangle}{(x^2 + y^2 + z^2)^{3/2}} = \dfrac{\mathbf{r}}{|\mathbf{r}|^3}$

19. $\mathbf{F} = \dfrac{\langle x, y, z \rangle}{(x^2 + y^2 + z^2)^2} = \dfrac{\mathbf{r}}{|\mathbf{r}|^4}$

20. $\mathbf{F} = \langle x, y, z \rangle (x^2 + y^2 + z^2) = \mathbf{r}|\mathbf{r}|^2$

21–22. Divergence and flux from graphs *Consider the following vector fields, the circle C, and two points P and Q.*

a. *Without computing the divergence, does the graph suggest that the divergence is positive or negative at P and Q? Justify your answer.*
b. *Compute the divergence and confirm your conjecture in part (a).*
c. *On what part of C is the flux outward? Inward?*
d. *Is the net outward flux across C positive or negative?*

21. $\mathbf{F} = \langle x, x + y \rangle$

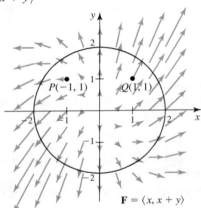

$$\mathbf{F} = \langle x, x + y \rangle$$

22. $\mathbf{F} = \langle x, y^2 \rangle$

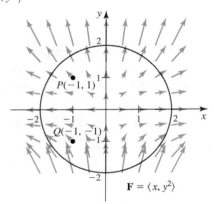

$$\mathbf{F} = \langle x, y^2 \rangle$$

23–26. Curl of a rotational field *Consider the following vector fields, where $\mathbf{r} = \langle x, y, z \rangle$.*

a. *Compute the curl of the field and verify that it has the same direction as the axis of rotation.*
b. *Compute the magnitude of the curl of the field.*

23. $\mathbf{F} = \langle 1, 0, 0 \rangle \times \mathbf{r}$

24. $\mathbf{F} = \langle 1, -1, 0 \rangle \times \mathbf{r}$

25. $\mathbf{F} = \langle 1, -1, 1 \rangle \times \mathbf{r}$

26. $\mathbf{F} = \langle 1, -2, -3 \rangle \times \mathbf{r}$

27–34. Curl of a vector field *Compute the curl of the following vector fields.*

27. $\mathbf{F} = \langle x^2 - y^2, xy, z \rangle$

28. $\mathbf{F} = \langle 0, z^2 - y^2, -yz \rangle$

29. $\mathbf{F} = \langle x^2 - z^2, 1, 2xz \rangle$

30. $\mathbf{F} = \mathbf{r} = \langle x, y, z \rangle$

31. $\mathbf{F} = \dfrac{\langle x, y, z \rangle}{(x^2 + y^2 + z^2)^{3/2}} = \dfrac{\mathbf{r}}{|\mathbf{r}|^3}$

32. $\mathbf{F} = \dfrac{\langle x, y, z \rangle}{(x^2 + y^2 + z^2)^{1/2}} = \dfrac{\mathbf{r}}{|\mathbf{r}|}$

33. $\mathbf{F} = \langle z^2 \sin y, xz^2 \cos y, 2xz \sin y \rangle$

34. $\mathbf{F} = \langle 3xz^3 e^{y^2}, 2xz^3 e^{y^2}, 3xz^2 e^{y^2} \rangle$

35–38. Derivative rules *Prove the following identities. Use Theorem 14.11 (Product Rule) whenever possible.*

35. $\nabla \left(\dfrac{1}{|\mathbf{r}|^3} \right) = \dfrac{-3\mathbf{r}}{|\mathbf{r}|^5}$ (used in Example 5)

36. $\nabla \left(\dfrac{1}{|\mathbf{r}|^2} \right) = \dfrac{-2\mathbf{r}}{|\mathbf{r}|^4}$

37. $\nabla \cdot \nabla \left(\dfrac{1}{|\mathbf{r}|^2} \right) = \dfrac{2}{|\mathbf{r}|^4}$ (use Exercise 36)

38. $\nabla (\ln |\mathbf{r}|) = \dfrac{\mathbf{r}}{|\mathbf{r}|^2}$

Further Explorations

39. Explain why or why not Determine whether the following statements are true and give an explanation or counterexample.

a. For a function f of a single variable, if $f'(x) = 0$ for all x in the domain, then f is a constant function. If $\nabla \cdot \mathbf{F} = 0$ for all points in the domain, then $\mathbf{F}$ is constant.
b. If $\nabla \times \mathbf{F} = \mathbf{0}$, then $\mathbf{F}$ is constant.
c. A vector field consisting of parallel vectors has zero curl.
d. A vector field consisting of parallel vectors has zero divergence.
e. curl $\mathbf{F}$ is orthogonal to $\mathbf{F}$.

40. Another derivative combination Let $\mathbf{F} = \langle f, g, h \rangle$ and let u be a differentiable scalar-valued function.

a. Take the dot product of $\mathbf{F}$ and the del operator; then apply the result to u to show that

$$(\mathbf{F} \cdot \nabla) u = \left(f \frac{\partial}{\partial x} + g \frac{\partial}{\partial y} + h \frac{\partial}{\partial z} \right) u$$

$$= f \frac{\partial u}{\partial x} + g \frac{\partial u}{\partial y} + h \frac{\partial u}{\partial z}.$$

b. Evaluate $(\mathbf{F} \cdot \nabla)(xy^2 z^3)$ at $(1, 1, 1)$, where $\mathbf{F} = \langle 1, 1, 1 \rangle$.

41. Does it make sense? Are the following expressions defined? If so, state whether the result is a scalar or a vector. Assume $\mathbf{F}$ is a sufficiently differentiable vector field and φ is a sufficiently differentiable scalar-valued function.

a. $\nabla \cdot \varphi$ **b.** $\nabla \mathbf{F}$ **c.** $\nabla \cdot \nabla \varphi$
d. $\nabla (\nabla \cdot \varphi)$ **e.** $\nabla (\nabla \times \varphi)$ **f.** $\nabla \cdot (\nabla \cdot \mathbf{F})$
g. $\nabla \times \nabla \varphi$ **h.** $\nabla \times (\nabla \cdot \mathbf{F})$ **i.** $\nabla \times (\nabla \times \mathbf{F})$

42. Zero divergence of the rotation field Show that the general rotation field $\mathbf{F} = \mathbf{a} \times \mathbf{r}$, where $\mathbf{a}$ is a nonzero constant vector and $\mathbf{r} = \langle x, y, z \rangle$, has zero divergence.

43. General rotation fields

a. Let $\mathbf{a} = \langle 0, 1, 0 \rangle$, $\mathbf{r} = \langle x, y, z \rangle$, and consider the rotation field $\mathbf{F} = \mathbf{a} \times \mathbf{r}$. Use the right-hand rule for cross products to find the direction of $\mathbf{F}$ at the points $(0, 1, 1)$, $(1, 1, 0)$, $(0, 1, -1)$, and $(-1, 1, 0)$.

b. With $\mathbf{a} = \langle 0, 1, 0 \rangle$, explain why the rotation field $\mathbf{F} = \mathbf{a} \times \mathbf{r}$ circles the y-axis in the counterclockwise direction looking along $\mathbf{a}$ from head to tail (that is, in the negative y-direction).

44. General rotation fields Generalize Exercise 43 to show that the rotation field $\mathbf{F} = \mathbf{a} \times \mathbf{r}$ circles the vector $\mathbf{a}$ in the counterclockwise direction looking along $\mathbf{a}$ from head to tail.

45. Curl of the rotation field For the general rotation field $\mathbf{F} = \mathbf{a} \times \mathbf{r}$, where $\mathbf{a}$ is a nonzero constant vector and $\mathbf{r} = \langle x, y, z \rangle$, show that curl $\mathbf{F} = 2\mathbf{a}$.

46. Inward to outward Find the exact points on the circle $x^2 + y^2 = 2$ at which the field $\mathbf{F} = \langle f, g \rangle = \langle x^2, y \rangle$ switches from pointing inward to outward on the circle, or vice versa.

47. Maximum divergence Within the cube $\{(x, y, z): |x| \le 1, |y| \le 1, |z| \le 1\}$, where does div $\mathbf{F}$ have the greatest magnitude when $\mathbf{F} = \langle x^2 - y^2, xy^2z, 2xz \rangle$?

48. Maximum curl Let $\mathbf{F} = \langle z, 0, -y \rangle$.

a. What is the component of curl $\mathbf{F}$ in the direction $\mathbf{n} = \langle 1, 0, 0 \rangle$?

b. What is the component of curl $\mathbf{F}$ in the direction $\mathbf{n} = \langle 1, -1, 1 \rangle$?

c. In what direction $\mathbf{n}$ is the dot product (curl $\mathbf{F}$) $\cdot \mathbf{n}$ a maximum?

49. Zero component of the curl For what vectors $\mathbf{n}$ is (curl $\mathbf{F}$) $\cdot \mathbf{n} = 0$ when $\mathbf{F} = \langle y, -2z, -x \rangle$?

50–51. Find a vector field Find a vector field $\mathbf{F}$ *with the given curl. In each case, is the vector field you found unique?*

50. curl $\mathbf{F} = \langle 0, 1, 0 \rangle$ **51.** curl $\mathbf{F} = \langle 0, z, -y \rangle$

52. Curl and angular speed Consider the rotational velocity field $\mathbf{v} = \mathbf{a} \times \mathbf{r}$, where $\mathbf{a}$ is a nonzero constant vector and $\mathbf{r} = \langle x, y, z \rangle$. Use the fact that an object moving in a circular path of radius R with speed $|\mathbf{v}|$ has an angular speed of $\omega = |\mathbf{v}|/R$.

a. Sketch a position vector $\mathbf{a}$, which is the axis of rotation for the vector field, and a position vector $\mathbf{r}$ of a point P in $\mathbb{R}^3$. Let θ be the angle between the two vectors. Show that the perpendicular distance from P to the axis of rotation is $R = |\mathbf{r}| \sin \theta$.

b. Show that the speed of a particle in the velocity field is $|\mathbf{a} \times \mathbf{r}|$ and that the angular speed of the object is $|\mathbf{a}|$.

c. Conclude that $\omega = \frac{1}{2}|\nabla \times \mathbf{v}|$.

53. Paddle wheel in a vector field Let $\mathbf{F} = \langle z, 0, 0 \rangle$ and let $\mathbf{n}$ be a unit vector aligned with the axis of a paddle wheel located on the x-axis (see figure).

a. If the paddle wheel is oriented with $\mathbf{n} = \langle 1, 0, 0 \rangle$, in what direction (if any) does the wheel spin?

b. If the paddle wheel is oriented with $\mathbf{n} = \langle 0, 1, 0 \rangle$, in what direction (if any) does the wheel spin?

c. If the paddle wheel is oriented with $\mathbf{n} = \langle 0, 0, 1 \rangle$, in what direction (if any) does the wheel spin?

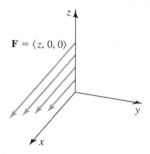

54. Angular speed Consider the rotational velocity field $\mathbf{v} = \langle -2y, 2z, 0 \rangle$.

a. If a paddle wheel is placed in the xy-plane with its axis normal to this plane, what is its angular speed?

b. If a paddle wheel is placed in the xz-plane with its axis normal to this plane, what is its angular speed?

c. If a paddle wheel is placed in the yz-plane with its axis normal to this plane, what is its angular speed?

55. Angular speed Consider the rotational velocity field $\mathbf{v} = \langle 0, 10z, -10y \rangle$. If a paddle wheel is placed in the plane $x + y + z = 1$ with its axis normal to this plane, how fast does the paddle wheel spin (revolutions per unit time)?

Applications

56–58. Heat flux *Suppose a solid object in $\mathbb{R}^3$ has a temperature distribution given by $T(x, y, z)$. The heat flow vector field in the object is $\mathbf{F} = -k\nabla T$, where the conductivity $k > 0$ is a property of the material. Note that the heat flow vector points in the direction opposite that of the gradient, which is the direction of greatest temperature decrease. The divergence of the heat flow vector is $\nabla \cdot \mathbf{F} = -k\nabla \cdot \nabla T = -k\nabla^2 T$ (the Laplacian of T). Compute the heat flow vector field and its divergence for the following temperature distributions.*

56. $T(x, y, z) = 100e^{-\sqrt{x^2+y^2+z^2}}$

57. $T(x, y, z) = 100e^{-x^2+y^2+z^2}$

58. $T(x, y, z) = 100(1 + \sqrt{x^2 + y^2 + z^2})$

59. Gravitational potential The potential function for the gravitational force field due to a mass M at the origin acting on a mass m is $\varphi = GMm/|\mathbf{r}|$, where $\mathbf{r} = \langle x, y, z \rangle$ is the position vector of the mass m and G is the gravitational constant.

a. Compute the gravitational force field $\mathbf{F} = -\nabla\varphi$.

b. Show that the field is irrotational; that is, $\nabla \times \mathbf{F} = \mathbf{0}$.

60. Electric potential The potential function for the force field due to a charge q at the origin is $\varphi = \dfrac{1}{4\pi\varepsilon_0} \dfrac{q}{|\mathbf{r}|}$, where $\mathbf{r} = \langle x, y, z \rangle$ is the position vector of a point in the field and ε_0 is the permittivity of free space.

a. Compute the force field $\mathbf{F} = -\nabla\varphi$.

b. Show that the field is irrotational; that is $\nabla \times \mathbf{F} = \mathbf{0}$.

61. Navier-Stokes equation The Navier-Stokes equation is the fundamental equation of fluid dynamics that models the flow in everything from bathtubs to oceans. In one of its many forms (incompressible, viscous flow), the equation is

$$\rho \left(\frac{\partial \mathbf{V}}{\partial t} + (\mathbf{V} \cdot \nabla)\,\mathbf{V} \right) = -\nabla p + \mu(\nabla \cdot \nabla)\,\mathbf{V}.$$

In this notation, $\mathbf{V} = \langle u, v, w \rangle$ is the three-dimensional velocity field, p is the (scalar) pressure, ρ is the constant density of the fluid, and μ is the constant viscosity. Write out the three component equations of this vector equation. (See Exercise 40 for an interpretation of the operations.)

T 62. Stream function and vorticity The rotation of a three-dimensional velocity field $\mathbf{V} = \langle u, v, w \rangle$ is measured by the **vorticity** $\boldsymbol{\omega} = \nabla \times \mathbf{V}$. If $\boldsymbol{\omega} = \mathbf{0}$ at all points in the domain, the flow is irrotational.

a. Which of the following velocity fields is irrotational:
   $\mathbf{V} = \langle 2, -3y, 5z \rangle$ or $\mathbf{V} = \langle y, x - z, -y \rangle$?

b. Recall that for a two-dimensional source-free flow
   $\mathbf{V} = (u, v, 0)$, a stream function $\psi(x, y)$ may be defined such that $u = \psi_y$ and $v = -\psi_x$. For such a two-dimensional flow, let $\zeta = \mathbf{k} \cdot \nabla \times \mathbf{V}$ be the $\mathbf{k}$-component of the vorticity. Show that $\nabla^2 \psi = \nabla \cdot \nabla \psi = -\zeta$.

c. Consider the stream function $\psi(x, y) = \sin x \sin y$ on the square region $R = \{(x, y): 0 \le x \le \pi, 0 \le y \le \pi\}$. Find the velocity components u and v; then sketch the velocity field.

d. For the stream function in part (c), find the vorticity function ζ as defined in part (b). Plot several level curves of the vorticity function. Where on R is it a maximum? A minimum?

63. Ampere's Law One of Maxwell's equations for electromagnetic waves is $\nabla \times \mathbf{B} = C \dfrac{\partial \mathbf{E}}{\partial t}$, where $\mathbf{E}$ is the electric field, $\mathbf{B}$ is the magnetic field, and C is a constant.

a. Show that the fields
   $$\mathbf{E}(z, t) = A \sin (kz - \omega t)\, \mathbf{i} \qquad \mathbf{B}(z, t) = A \sin (kz - \omega t)\, \mathbf{j}$$
   satisfy the equation for constants A, k, and ω, provided $\omega = k/C$.

b. Make a rough sketch showing the directions of $\mathbf{E}$ and $\mathbf{B}$.

Additional Exercises

64. Splitting a vector field Express the vector field $\mathbf{F} = \langle xy, 0, 0 \rangle$ in the form $\mathbf{V} + \mathbf{W}$, where $\nabla \cdot \mathbf{V} = 0$ and $\nabla \times \mathbf{W} = \mathbf{0}$.

65. Properties of div and curl Prove the following properties of the divergence and curl. Assume $\mathbf{F}$ and $\mathbf{G}$ are differentiable vector fields and c is a real number.

a. $\nabla \cdot (\mathbf{F} + \mathbf{G}) = \nabla \cdot \mathbf{F} + \nabla \cdot \mathbf{G}$
b. $\nabla \times (\mathbf{F} + \mathbf{G}) = (\nabla \times \mathbf{F}) + (\nabla \times \mathbf{G})$
c. $\nabla \cdot (c\mathbf{F}) = c(\nabla \cdot \mathbf{F})$
d. $\nabla \times (c\mathbf{F}) = c(\nabla \times \mathbf{F})$

66. Equal curls If two functions of one variable, f and g, have the property that $f' = g'$, then f and g differ by a constant. Prove or disprove: If $\mathbf{F}$ and $\mathbf{G}$ are nonconstant vector fields in $\mathbb{R}^2$ with curl $\mathbf{F} = $ curl $\mathbf{G}$ and div $\mathbf{F} = $ div $\mathbf{G}$ at all points of $\mathbb{R}^2$, then $\mathbf{F}$ and $\mathbf{G}$ differ by a constant vector.

67–72. Identities *Prove the following identities. Assume that φ is a differentiable scalar-valued function and $\mathbf{F}$ and $\mathbf{G}$ are differentiable vector fields, all defined on a region of $\mathbb{R}^3$.*

67. $\nabla \cdot (\varphi \mathbf{F}) = \nabla\varphi \cdot \mathbf{F} + \varphi\nabla \cdot \mathbf{F}$ (Product Rule)

68. $\nabla \times (\varphi \mathbf{F}) = (\nabla\varphi \times \mathbf{F}) + (\varphi\nabla \times \mathbf{F})$ (Product Rule)

69. $\nabla \cdot (\mathbf{F} \times \mathbf{G}) = \mathbf{G} \cdot (\nabla \times \mathbf{F}) - \mathbf{F} \cdot (\nabla \times \mathbf{G})$

70. $\nabla \times (\mathbf{F} \times \mathbf{G}) = (\mathbf{G} \cdot \nabla)\mathbf{F} - \mathbf{G}(\nabla \cdot \mathbf{F}) - (\mathbf{F} \cdot \nabla)\mathbf{G} + \mathbf{F}(\nabla \cdot \mathbf{G})$

71. $\nabla(\mathbf{F} \cdot \mathbf{G}) = (\mathbf{G} \cdot \nabla)\mathbf{F} + (\mathbf{F} \cdot \nabla)\mathbf{G} + \mathbf{G} \times (\nabla \times \mathbf{F}) + \mathbf{F} \times (\nabla \times \mathbf{G})$

72. $\nabla \times (\nabla \times \mathbf{F}) = \nabla(\nabla \cdot \mathbf{F}) - (\nabla \cdot \nabla)\mathbf{F}$

73. Divergence of radial fields Prove that for a real number p, with $\mathbf{r} = \langle x, y, z \rangle$, $\nabla \cdot \dfrac{\langle x, y, z \rangle}{|\mathbf{r}|^p} = \dfrac{3 - p}{|\mathbf{r}|^p}$.

74. Gradients and radial fields Prove that for a real number p, with $\mathbf{r} = \langle x, y, z \rangle$, $\nabla\left(\dfrac{1}{|\mathbf{r}|^p}\right) = \dfrac{-p\mathbf{r}}{|\mathbf{r}|^{p+2}}$.

75. Divergence of gradient fields Prove that for a real number p, with $\mathbf{r} = \langle x, y, z \rangle$, $\nabla \cdot \nabla\left(\dfrac{1}{|\mathbf{r}|^p}\right) = \dfrac{p(p - 1)}{|\mathbf{r}|^{p+2}}$.

QUICK CHECK ANSWERS

1. The x-derivative of the divergence is applied to $f(y, z)$, which gives zero. Similarly, the y- and z-derivatives are zero. 2. Net outward flux is 4π 3. In the curl, the first component of $\mathbf{F}$ is differentiated only with respect to y and z, so the contribution from the first component is zero. Similarly, the second and third components of $\mathbf{F}$ make no contribution to the curl. 4. The divergence is a scalar-valued function. ◀

14.6 Surface Integrals

We have studied integrals on the real line, on regions in the plane, on solid regions in space, and along curves in space. One situation is still unexplored. Suppose a sphere has a known temperature distribution; perhaps it is cold near the poles and warm near the equator. How do you find the average temperature over the entire sphere? In analogy with other average value calculations, we should expect to "add up" the temperature values over the sphere and divide by the surface area of the sphere. Because the temperature varies continuously over the sphere, adding up means integrating. How do you integrate a function over a surface? This question leads to *surface integrals*.

It helps to keep curves, arc length, and line integrals in mind as we discuss surfaces, surface area, and surface integrals. What we discover about surfaces parallels what we already know about curves—all "lifted" up one dimension.

Parallel Concepts	
Curves	**Surfaces**
Arc length	Surface area
Line integrals	Surface integrals
One-parameter description	Two-parameter description

Parameterized Surfaces

A curve in $\mathbb{R}^2$ is defined parametrically by $\mathbf{r}(t) = \langle x(t), y(t) \rangle$, for $a \le t \le b$; it requires one parameter and two dependent variables. Stepping up one dimension to define a surface in $\mathbb{R}^3$, we need *two* parameters and *three* dependent variables. Letting u and v be parameters, the general parametric description of a surface has the form

$$\mathbf{r}(u, v) = \langle x(u, v), y(u, v), z(u, v) \rangle.$$

We make the assumption that the parameters vary over a rectangle $R = \{(u, v):$ $a \le u \le b, c \le v \le d\}$ (Figure 14.43). As the parameters (u, v) vary over R, the vector $\mathbf{r}(u, v) = \langle x(u, v), y(u, v), z(u, v) \rangle$ sweeps out a surface S in $\mathbb{R}^3$.

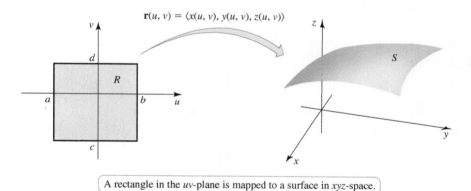

A rectangle in the *uv*-plane is mapped to a surface in *xyz*-space.

Figure 14.43

We work extensively with three surfaces that are easily described in parametric form. As with parameterized curves, a parametric description of a surface is not unique.

Cylinders   In Cartesian coordinates, the set

$$\{(x, y, z): x = a \cos \theta, y = a \sin \theta, 0 \le \theta \le 2\pi, 0 \le z \le h\},$$

where $a > 0$, is a cylindrical surface of radius a and height h with its axis along the z-axis. Using the parameters $u = \theta$ and $v = z$, a parametric description of the cylinder is

$$\mathbf{r}(u, v) = \langle x(u, v), y(u, v), z(u, v) \rangle = \langle a \cos u, a \sin u, v \rangle,$$

where $0 \le u \le 2\pi$ and $0 \le v \le h$ (Figure 14.44).

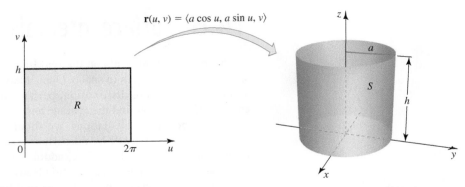

Figure 14.44

QUICK CHECK 1 Describe the surface $\mathbf{r}(u, v) = \langle 2 \cos u, 2 \sin u, v \rangle$, for $0 \leq u \leq \pi$ and $0 \leq v \leq 1$. ◄

> Note that when $r = 0$, $z = 0$ and when $r = a$, $z = h$.

> Recall the relationships among polar and rectangular coordinates:
>
> $x = r \cos \theta$, $y = r \sin \theta$, and $x^2 + y^2 = r^2$.

Cones   The surface of a cone of height h and radius a with its vertex at the origin is described in cylindrical coordinates by

$$\{(r, \theta, z): 0 \leq r \leq a, 0 \leq \theta \leq 2\pi, z = rh/a\}.$$

For a fixed value of z, we have $r = az/h$; therefore, on the surface of the cone

$$x = r \cos \theta = \frac{az}{h} \cos \theta \quad \text{and} \quad y = r \sin \theta = \frac{az}{h} \sin \theta.$$

Using the parameters $u = \theta$ and $v = z$, the parametric description of the conical surface is

$$\mathbf{r}(u, v) = \langle x(u, v), y(u, v), z(u, v) \rangle = \left\langle \frac{av}{h} \cos u, \frac{av}{h} \sin u, v \right\rangle,$$

where $0 \leq u \leq 2\pi$ and $0 \leq v \leq h$ (Figure 14.45).

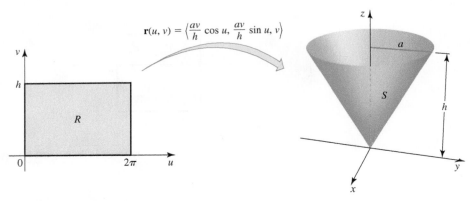

Figure 14.45

QUICK CHECK 2 Describe the surface $\mathbf{r}(u, v) = \langle v \cos u, v \sin u, v \rangle$, for $0 \leq u \leq \pi$ and $0 \leq v \leq 10$. ◄

> The complete cylinder, cone, and sphere are generated as the angle variable θ varies over the half-open interval $[0, 2\pi)$. As in previous chapters, we will use the closed interval $[0, 2\pi]$.

Spheres   The parametric description of a sphere of radius a centered at the origin comes directly from spherical coordinates:

$$\{(\rho, \varphi, \theta): \rho = a, 0 \leq \varphi \leq \pi, 0 \leq \theta \leq 2\pi\}.$$

Recall the following relationships among spherical and rectangular coordinates (Section 13.5):

$$x = a \sin \varphi \cos \theta, \qquad y = a \sin \varphi \sin \theta, \qquad z = a \cos \varphi.$$

When we define the parameters $u = \varphi$ and $v = \theta$, a parametric description of the sphere is

$$\mathbf{r}(u, v) = \langle a \sin u \cos v, a \sin u \sin v, a \cos u \rangle,$$

where $0 \leq u \leq \pi$ and $0 \leq v \leq 2\pi$ (Figure 14.46).

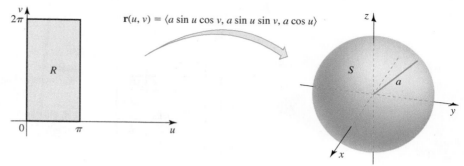

Figure 14.46

QUICK CHECK 3 Describe the surface $\mathbf{r}(u, v) = \langle 4 \sin u \cos v, 4 \sin u \sin v, 4 \cos u \rangle$, for $0 \le u \le \pi/2$ and $0 \le v \le \pi$. ◄

EXAMPLE 1 Parametric surfaces Find parametric descriptions for the following surfaces.

a. The plane $3x - 2y + z = 2$

b. The paraboloid $z = x^2 + y^2$, for $0 \le z \le 9$

SOLUTION

a. Defining the parameters $u = x$ and $v = y$, we find that

$$z = 2 - 3x + 2y = 2 - 3u + 2v.$$

Therefore, a parametric description of the plane is

$$\mathbf{r}(u, v) = \langle u, v, 2 - 3u + 2v \rangle,$$

for $-\infty < u < \infty$ and $-\infty < v < \infty$.

b. Thinking in terms of polar coordinates, we let $u = \theta$ and $v = \sqrt{z}$, which means that $z = v^2$. The equation of the paraboloid is $x^2 + y^2 = z = v^2$, so v plays the role of the polar coordinate r. Therefore, $x = v \cos \theta = v \cos u$ and $y = v \sin \theta = v \sin u$. A parametric description for the paraboloid is

$$\mathbf{r}(u, v) = \langle v \cos u, v \sin u, v^2 \rangle,$$

where $0 \le u \le 2\pi$ and $0 \le v \le 3$.

Alternatively, we could choose $u = \theta$ and $v = z$. The resulting description is

$$\mathbf{r}(u, v) = \langle \sqrt{v} \cos u, \sqrt{v} \sin u, v \rangle,$$

where $0 \le u \le 2\pi$ and $0 \le v \le 9$.

Related Exercises 11–20 ◄

Surface Integrals of Scalar-Valued Functions

We now develop the surface integral of a scalar-valued function f defined on a smooth parameterized surface S described by the equation

$$\mathbf{r}(u, v) = \langle x(u, v), y(u, v), z(u, v) \rangle,$$

where the parameters vary over a rectangle $R = \{(u, v): a \le u \le b, c \le v \le d\}$. The functions x, y, and z are assumed to have continuous partial derivatives with respect to u and v. The rectangular region R in the uv-plane is partitioned into rectangles, with sides of length Δu and Δv, that are ordered in some convenient way, for $k = 1, \ldots, n$. The kth rectangle R_k, which has area $\Delta A = \Delta u \Delta v$, corresponds to a curved patch S_k on the surface S (Figure 14.47), which has area ΔS_k. We let (u_k, v_k) be the lower-left corner point of R_k. The parameterization then assigns (u_k, v_k) to a point $P(x(u_k, v_k), y(u_k, v_k), z(u_k, v_k))$, or more simply, $P(x_k, y_k, z_k)$, on S_k. To construct

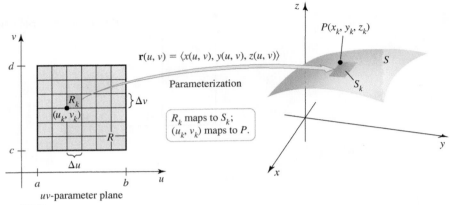

Figure 14.47

> A more general approach allows (u_k, v_k) to be an arbitrary point in the kth rectangle. The outcome of the two approaches is the same.

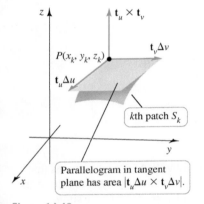

Figure 14.48

> In general, the vectors $\mathbf{t}_u$ and $\mathbf{t}_v$ are different for each patch, so they should carry a subscript k. To keep the notation as simple as possible, we have suppressed the subscripts on these vectors with the understanding that they change with k. These tangent vectors are given by partial derivatives because in each case, either u or v is held constant, while the other variable changes.

the surface integral, we define a Riemann sum, which adds up function values multiplied by areas of the respective patches:

$$\sum_{k=1}^{n} f(x(u_k, v_k), y(u_k, v_k), z(u_k, v_k)) \Delta S_k.$$

The crucial step is computing ΔS_k, the area of the kth patch S_k.

Figure 14.48 shows the patch S_k and the point $P(x_k, y_k, z_k)$. Two special vectors are tangent to the surface at P.

• $\mathbf{t}_u$ is a vector tangent to the surface corresponding to a change in u with v constant in the uv-plane.

• $\mathbf{t}_v$ is a vector tangent to the surface corresponding to a change in v with u constant in the uv-plane.

Because the surface S may be written $\mathbf{r}(u, v) = \langle x(u, v), y(u, v), z(u, v) \rangle$, a tangent vector corresponding to a change in u with v fixed is

$$\mathbf{t}_u = \frac{\partial \mathbf{r}}{\partial u} = \left\langle \frac{\partial x}{\partial u}, \frac{\partial y}{\partial u}, \frac{\partial z}{\partial u} \right\rangle.$$

Similarly, a tangent vector corresponding to a change in v with u fixed is

$$\mathbf{t}_v = \frac{\partial \mathbf{r}}{\partial v} = \left\langle \frac{\partial x}{\partial v}, \frac{\partial y}{\partial v}, \frac{\partial z}{\partial v} \right\rangle.$$

Now consider an increment Δu in u with v fixed. The tangent vector $\mathbf{t}_u \Delta u$ forms one side of a parallelogram (Figure 14.48). Similarly, with an increment Δv in v with u fixed, the tangent vector $\mathbf{t}_v \Delta v$ forms the other side of that parallelogram. The area of this parallelogram is an approximation to the area of the patch S_k, which is ΔS_k.

Appealing to the cross product (Section 11.4), the area of the parallelogram is

$$|\mathbf{t}_u \Delta u \times \mathbf{t}_v \Delta v| = |\mathbf{t}_u \times \mathbf{t}_v| \, \Delta u \, \Delta v \approx \Delta S_k.$$

Note that $\mathbf{t}_u \times \mathbf{t}_v$ is evaluated at (u_k, v_k) and is a vector normal to the surface at P, which we assume to be nonzero at all points of S.

We write the Riemann sum with the observation that the areas of the parallelograms approximate the areas of the patches S_k:

$$\sum_{k=1}^{n} f(x(u_k, v_k), y(u_k, v_k), z(u_k, v_k)) \Delta S_k$$

$$\approx \sum_{k=1}^{n} f(x(u_k, v_k), y(u_k, v_k), z(u_k, v_k)) \underbrace{|\mathbf{t}_u \times \mathbf{t}_v| \, \Delta u \, \Delta v}_{\approx \Delta S_k}.$$

We now assume that f is continuous on S. As Δu and Δv approach zero, the areas of the parallelograms approach the areas of the corresponding patches on S. We define the limit

> The factor $|\mathbf{t}_u \times \mathbf{t}_v|\, dA$ plays an analogous role in surface integrals as the factor $|\mathbf{r}'(t)|\, dt$ in line integrals.

of this Riemann sum to be the surface integral of f over S, which we write $\iint_S f(x, y, z)\, dS$. The surface integral is evaluated as an ordinary double integral over the region R in the uv-plane:

$$\iint\limits_S f(x, y, z)\, dS = \lim_{\Delta u, \Delta v \to 0} \sum_{k=1}^{n} f(x(u_k, v_k), y(u_k, v_k), z(u_k, v_k))\, |\mathbf{t}_u \times \mathbf{t}_v|\, \Delta u\, \Delta v$$

$$= \iint\limits_R f(x(u, v), y(u, v), z(u, v))\, |\mathbf{t}_u \times \mathbf{t}_v|\, dA.$$

If R is a rectangular region, as we have assumed, the double integral becomes an iterated integral with respect to u and v with constant limits. In the special case that $f(x, y, z) = 1$, the integral gives the surface area of S.

> The condition that $\mathbf{t}_u \times \mathbf{t}_v$ be nonzero means $\mathbf{t}_u$ and $\mathbf{t}_v$ are nonzero and not parallel. If $\mathbf{t}_u \times \mathbf{t}_v \neq \mathbf{0}$ at all points, then the surface is *smooth*. The value of the integral is independent of the parameterization of S.

DEFINITION Surface Integral of Scalar-Valued Functions on Parameterized Surfaces

Let f be a continuous scalar-valued function on a smooth surface S given parametrically by $\mathbf{r}(u, v) = \langle x(u, v), y(u, v), z(u, v) \rangle$, where u and v vary over $R = \{(u, v): a \leq u \leq b, c \leq v \leq d\}$. Assume also that the tangent vectors

$$\mathbf{t}_u = \frac{\partial \mathbf{r}}{\partial u} = \left\langle \frac{\partial x}{\partial u}, \frac{\partial y}{\partial u}, \frac{\partial z}{\partial u} \right\rangle \quad \text{and} \quad \mathbf{t}_v = \frac{\partial \mathbf{r}}{\partial v} = \left\langle \frac{\partial x}{\partial v}, \frac{\partial y}{\partial v}, \frac{\partial z}{\partial v} \right\rangle \text{ are continuous on } R \text{ and}$$

the normal vector $\mathbf{t}_u \times \mathbf{t}_v$ is nonzero on R. Then the **surface integral** of f over S is

$$\iint\limits_S f(x, y, z)\, dS = \iint\limits_R f(x(u, v), y(u, v), z(u, v))\, |\mathbf{t}_u \times \mathbf{t}_v|\, dA.$$

If $f(x, y, z) = 1$, this integral equals the surface area of S.

EXAMPLE 2 Surface area of a cylinder and sphere Find the surface area of the following surfaces.

a. A cylinder with radius $a > 0$ and height h (excluding the circular ends)

b. A sphere of radius a

SOLUTION The critical step is evaluating the normal vector $\mathbf{t}_u \times \mathbf{t}_v$. It needs to be done only once for any given surface.

a. As shown before, a parametric description of the cylinder is

$$\mathbf{r}(u, v) = \langle x(u, v), y(u, v), z(u, v) \rangle = \langle a \cos u, a \sin u, v \rangle,$$

where $0 \leq u \leq 2\pi$ and $0 \leq v \leq h$. The required normal vector is

$$\mathbf{t}_u \times \mathbf{t}_v = \begin{vmatrix} \mathbf{i} & \mathbf{j} & \mathbf{k} \\ \frac{\partial x}{\partial u} & \frac{\partial y}{\partial u} & \frac{\partial z}{\partial u} \\ \frac{\partial x}{\partial v} & \frac{\partial y}{\partial v} & \frac{\partial z}{\partial v} \end{vmatrix} \qquad \text{Definition of cross product}$$

$$= \begin{vmatrix} \mathbf{i} & \mathbf{j} & \mathbf{k} \\ -a \sin u & a \cos u & 0 \\ 0 & 0 & 1 \end{vmatrix} \qquad \text{Evaluate derivatives.}$$

$$= \langle a \cos u, a \sin u, 0 \rangle. \qquad \text{Compute cross product.}$$

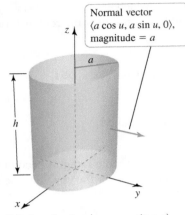

Cylinder: $\mathbf{r}(u, v) = \langle a \cos u, a \sin u, v \rangle$,
$0 \le u \le 2\pi$ and $0 \le v \le h$

Figure 14.49

➤ Recall that for the sphere, $u = \varphi$ and $v = \theta$, where φ and θ are spherical coordinates. The element of surface area in spherical coordinates is $dS = a^2 \sin \varphi \, d\varphi \, d\theta$.

Sphere:
$\mathbf{r}(u, v) = \langle a \sin u \cos v, a \sin u \sin v, a \cos u \rangle$,
$0 \le u \le \pi$ and $0 \le v \le 2\pi$

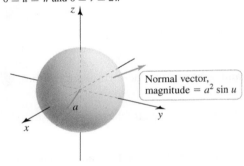

Figure 14.50

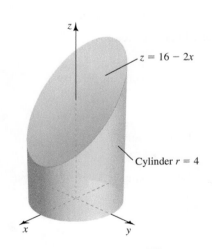

Sliced cylinder is generated by
$\mathbf{r}(u, v) = \langle 4 \cos u, 4 \sin u, v \rangle$, where
$0 \le u \le 2\pi, 0 \le v \le 16 - 8 \cos u.$

Figure 14.51

Notice that this normal vector points outward from the cylinder, away from the z-axis (Figure 14.49). It follows that

$$|\mathbf{t}_u \times \mathbf{t}_v| = \sqrt{a^2 \cos^2 u + a^2 \sin^2 u} = a.$$

Setting $f(x, y, z) = 1$, the surface area of the cylinder is

$$\iint_S 1 \, dS = \iint_R \underbrace{|\mathbf{t}_u \times \mathbf{t}_v|}_{a} \, dA = \int_0^{2\pi} \int_0^h a \, dv \, du = 2\pi a h,$$

confirming the formula for the surface area of a cylinder (excluding the ends).

b. A parametric description of the sphere is

$$\mathbf{r}(u, v) = \langle a \sin u \cos v, a \sin u \sin v, a \cos u \rangle,$$

where $0 \le u \le \pi$ and $0 \le v \le 2\pi$. The required normal vector is

$$\mathbf{t}_u \times \mathbf{t}_v = \begin{vmatrix} \mathbf{i} & \mathbf{j} & \mathbf{k} \\ a \cos u \cos v & a \cos u \sin v & -a \sin u \\ -a \sin u \sin v & a \sin u \cos v & 0 \end{vmatrix}$$

$$= \langle a^2 \sin^2 u \cos v, a^2 \sin^2 u \sin v, a^2 \sin u \cos u \rangle.$$

Computing $|\mathbf{t}_u \times \mathbf{t}_v|$ requires several steps (Exercise 70). However, the needed result is quite simple: $|\mathbf{t}_u \times \mathbf{t}_v| = a^2 \sin u$ and the normal vector $\mathbf{t}_u \times \mathbf{t}_v$ points outward from the surface of the sphere (Figure 14.50). With $f(x, y, z) = 1$, the surface area of the sphere is

$$\iint_S 1 \, dS = \iint_R \underbrace{|\mathbf{t}_u \times \mathbf{t}_v|}_{a^2 \sin u} \, dA = \int_0^{2\pi} \int_0^\pi a^2 \sin u \, du \, dv = 4\pi a^2,$$

confirming the formula for the surface area of a sphere.

Related Exercises 21–26 ◄

EXAMPLE 3 Surface area of a partial cylinder Find the surface area of the cylinder $\{(r, \theta): r = 4, 0 \le \theta \le 2\pi\}$ between the planes $z = 0$ and $z = 16 - 2x$ (excluding the top and bottom surfaces).

SOLUTION Figure 14.51 shows the cylinder bounded by the two planes. With $u = \theta$ and $v = z$, a parametric description of the cylinder is

$$\mathbf{r}(u, v) = \langle x(u, v), y(u, v), z(u, v) \rangle = \langle 4 \cos u, 4 \sin u, v \rangle.$$

The challenge is finding the limits on v, which is the z-coordinate. The plane $z = 16 - 2x$ intersects the cylinder in an ellipse; along this ellipse, as u varies between 0 and 2π, the parameter v also changes. To find the relationship between u and v along this intersection curve, notice that at any point on the cylinder, we have $x = 4 \cos u$ (remember that $u = \theta$). Making this substitution in the equation of the plane, we have

$$z = 16 - 2x = 16 - 2(4 \cos u) = 16 - 8 \cos u.$$

Substituting $v = z$, the relationship between u and v is $v = 16 - 8 \cos u$ (Figure 14.52). Therefore, the region of integration in the uv-plane is

$$R = \{(u, v): 0 \le u \le 2\pi, 0 \le v \le 16 - 8 \cos u\}.$$

Recall from Example 2a that for the cylinder, $|\mathbf{t}_u \times \mathbf{t}_v| = a = 4$. Setting $f(x, y, z) = 1$, the surface integral for the area is

$$\iint_S 1 \, dS = \iint_R \underbrace{|\mathbf{t}_u \times \mathbf{t}_v|}_{4} \, dA$$

$$= \int_0^{2\pi} \int_0^{16 - 8 \cos u} 4 \, dv \, du$$

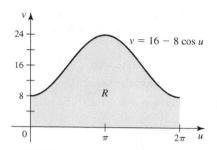

Region of integration in the uv-plane is
$R = \{(u, v): 0 \le u \le 2\pi,$
$0 \le v \le 16 - 8 \cos u\}$.

Figure 14.52

$$= 4 \int_0^{2\pi} (16 - 8 \cos u)\, du \quad \text{Evaluate inner integral.}$$

$$= 4(16u - 8 \sin u)\Big|_0^{2\pi} \quad \text{Evaluate outer integral.}$$

$$= 128\pi. \quad \text{Simplify.}$$

Related Exercises 21–26 ◄

EXAMPLE 4   **Average temperature on a sphere**   The temperature on the surface of a sphere of radius a varies with latitude according to the function $T(\varphi, \theta) = 10 + 50 \sin \varphi$, for $0 \le \varphi \le \pi$ and $0 \le \theta \le 2\pi$ (φ and θ are spherical coordinates, so the temperature is $10°$ at the poles, increasing to $60°$ at the equator). Find the average temperature over the sphere.

SOLUTION   We use the parametric description of a sphere. With $u = \varphi$ and $v = \theta$, the temperature function becomes $f(u, v) = 10 + 50 \sin u$. Integrating the temperature over the sphere using the fact that $|\mathbf{t}_u \times \mathbf{t}_v| = a^2 \sin u$ (Example 2b), we have

$$\iint_S (10 + 50 \sin u)\, dS = \iint_R (10 + 50 \sin u)\underbrace{|\mathbf{t}_u \times \mathbf{t}_v|}_{a^2 \sin u}\, dA$$

$$= \int_0^\pi \int_0^{2\pi} (10 + 50 \sin u)a^2 \sin u\, dv\, du$$

$$= 2\pi a^2 \int_0^\pi (10 + 50 \sin u) \sin u\, du \quad \text{Evaluate inner integral.}$$

$$= 10\pi a^2(4 + 5\pi). \quad \text{Evaluate outer integral.}$$

The average temperature is the integrated temperature $10\pi a^2(4 + 5\pi)$ divided by the surface area of the sphere $4\pi a^2$; so the average temperature is $(20 + 25\pi)/2 \approx 49.3°$.

Related Exercises 27–30 ◄

Surface Integrals on Explicitly Defined Surfaces

Suppose a smooth surface S is defined not parametrically, but explicitly, in the form $z = g(x, y)$ over a region R in the xy-plane. Such a surface may be treated as a parameterized surface. We simply define the parameters to be $u = x$ and $v = y$. Making these substitutions into the expression for $\mathbf{t}_u$ and $\mathbf{t}_v$, a short calculation (Exercise 71) reveals that $\mathbf{t}_u = \langle 1, 0, z_x \rangle$, $\mathbf{t}_v = \langle 0, 1, z_y \rangle$, and the required normal vector is

$$\mathbf{t}_u \times \mathbf{t}_v = \langle -z_x, -z_y, 1 \rangle.$$

It follows that

$$|\mathbf{t}_x \times \mathbf{t}_y| = |\langle -z_x, -z_y, 1 \rangle| = \sqrt{z_x^2 + z_y^2 + 1}.$$

With these observations, the surface integral over S can be expressed as a double integral over a region R in the xy-plane.

> ➤ This is a familiar result: A normal to the surface $z = g(x, y)$ at a point is a constant multiple of the gradient of $z - g(x, y)$, which is $\langle -g_x, -g_y, 1 \rangle = \langle -z_x, -z_y, 1 \rangle$. The factor $\sqrt{z_x^2 + z_y^2 + 1}$ is analogous to the factor $\sqrt{f'(x)^2 + 1}$ that appears in arc length integrals.

> ➤ If the surface S in Theorem 14.12 is generated by revolving a curve in the xy-plane about the x-axis, the theorem gives the surface area formula derived in Section 6.6 (Exercise 75).

THEOREM 14.12   **Evaluation of Surface Integrals of Scalar-Valued Functions on Explicitly Defined Surfaces**

Let f be a continuous function on a smooth surface S given by $z = g(x, y)$, for (x, y) in a region R. The surface integral of f over S is

$$\iint_S f(x, y, z)\, dS = \iint_R f(x, y, g(x, y))\sqrt{z_x^2 + z_y^2 + 1}\, dA.$$

If $f(x, y, z) = 1$, the surface integral equals the area of the surface.

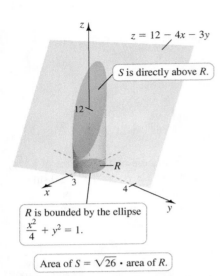

$z = 12 - 4x - 3y$

S is directly above R.

12

R

3

4

x

y

R is bounded by the ellipse
$\frac{x^2}{4} + y^2 = 1$.

Area of $S = \sqrt{26}$ · area of R.

Figure 14.53

EXAMPLE 5   Area of a roof over an ellipse Find the area of the surface S that lies in the plane $z = 12 - 4x - 3y$ directly above the region R bounded by the ellipse $x^2/4 + y^2 = 1$ (Figure 14.53).

SOLUTION Because we are computing the area of the surface, we take $f(x, y, z) = 1$. Note that $z_x = -4$ and $z_y = -3$, so the factor $\sqrt{z_x^2 + z_y^2 + 1}$ has the value $\sqrt{(-4)^2 + (-3)^2 + 1} = \sqrt{26}$ (a constant because the surface is a plane). The relevant surface integral is

$$\iint\limits_S 1 \, dS = \iint\limits_R \underbrace{\sqrt{z_x^2 + z_y^2 + 1}}_{\sqrt{26}} \, dA = \sqrt{26} \iint\limits_R dA.$$

The double integral that remains is simply the area of the region R bounded by the ellipse. Because the ellipse has semiaxes of length $a = 2$ and $b = 1$, its area is $\pi ab = 2\pi$. Therefore, the area of S is $2\pi\sqrt{26}$.

This result has a useful interpretation. The plane surface S is not horizontal, so it has a greater area than the horizontal region R beneath it. The factor that converts the area of R to the area of S is $\sqrt{26}$. Notice that if the roof *were* horizontal, then the surface would be $z = c$, the area conversion factor would be 1, and the area of the roof would equal the area of the floor beneath it.

Related Exercises 31–34 ◄

QUICK CHECK 4 The plane $z = y$ forms a 45° angle with the xy-plane. Suppose the plane is the roof of a room and the xy-plane is the floor of the room. Then 1 ft^2 on the floor becomes how many square feet when projected on the roof?◄

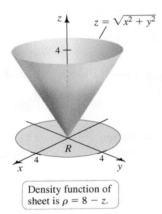

$z = \sqrt{x^2 + y^2}$

4

R

4

4

x

y

Density function of
sheet is $\rho = 8 - z$.

Figure 14.54

EXAMPLE 6   Mass of a conical sheet A thin conical sheet is described by the surface $z = (x^2 + y^2)^{1/2}$, for $0 \le z \le 4$. The density of the sheet in g/cm^2 is $\rho = f(x, y, z) = (8 - z)$ (decreasing from 8 g/cm^2 at the vertex to 4 g/cm^2 at the top of the cone; Figure 14.54). What is the mass of the cone?

SOLUTION We find the mass by integrating the density function over the surface of the cone. The projection of the cone on the xy-plane is found by setting $z = 4$ (the top of the cone) in the equation of the cone. We find that $(x^2 + y^2)^{1/2} = 4$; therefore, the region of integration is the disk $R = \{(x, y): x^2 + y^2 \le 16\}$. The next step is to compute z_x and z_y in order to evaluate $\sqrt{z_x^2 + z_y^2 + 1}$. Differentiating $z^2 = x^2 + y^2$ implicitly gives $2zz_x = 2x$, or $z_x = x/z$. Similarly, $z_y = y/z$. Using the fact that $z^2 = x^2 + y^2$, we have

$$\sqrt{z_x^2 + z_y^2 + 1} = \sqrt{(x/z)^2 + (y/z)^2 + 1} = \sqrt{\underbrace{\frac{x^2 + y^2}{z^2}}_{1} + 1} = \sqrt{2}.$$

To integrate the density over the conical surface, we set $f(x, y, z) = 8 - z$. Replacing z in the integrand by $r = (x^2 + y^2)^{1/2}$ and using polar coordinates, the mass in grams is given by

$$\iint\limits_S f(x, y, z) \, dS = \iint\limits_R f(x, y, z) \underbrace{\sqrt{z_x^2 + z_y^2 + 1}}_{\sqrt{2}} \, dA$$

$$= \sqrt{2} \iint\limits_R (8 - z) \, dA \qquad \text{Substitute.}$$

$$= \sqrt{2} \iint\limits_R (8 - \sqrt{x^2 + y^2}) \, dA \qquad z = \sqrt{x^2 + y^2}$$

$$= \sqrt{2} \int_0^{2\pi} \int_0^4 (8 - r) \, r \, dr \, d\theta \qquad \text{Polar coordinates}$$

$$= \sqrt{2} \int_0^{2\pi} \left(4r^2 - \frac{r^3}{3} \right) \Big|_0^4 \, d\theta \qquad \text{Evaluate inner integral.}$$

$$= \frac{128\sqrt{2}}{3} \int_0^{2\pi} d\theta \qquad \text{Simplify.}$$

$$= \frac{256\pi\sqrt{2}}{3} \approx 379. \qquad \text{Evaluate outer integral.}$$

As a check, note that the surface area of the cone is $\pi r \sqrt{r^2 + h^2} \approx 71 \text{ cm}^2$. If the entire cone had the maximum density $\rho = 8 \text{ g/cm}^2$, its mass would be approximately 568 g. If the entire cone had the minimum density $\rho = 4 \text{ g/cm}^2$, its mass would be approximately 284 g. The actual mass is between these extremes and closer to the low value because the cone is lighter at the top, where the surface area is greater.

Related Exercises 35–42 ◄

Table 14.3 summarizes the essential relationships for the explicit and parametric descriptions of cylinders, cones, spheres, and paraboloids. The listed normal vectors are chosen to point away from the z-axis.

Table 14.3

Surface	Explicit Description $z = g(x,y)$		Parametric Description	
	Equation	Normal vector; magnitude $\pm \langle -z_x, -z_y, 1 \rangle; |\langle -z_x, -z_y, 1 \rangle|$	Equation	Normal vector; magnitude $t_u \times t_v ; |t_u \times t_v|$
Cylinder	$x^2 + y^2 = a^2,$ $0 \le z \le h$	$\langle x, y, 0 \rangle; a$	$\mathbf{r} = \langle a \cos u, a \sin u, v \rangle,$ $0 \le u \le 2\pi, 0 \le v \le h$	$\langle a \cos u, a \sin u, 0 \rangle; a$
Cone	$z^2 = x^2 + y^2,$ $0 \le z \le h$	$\langle x/z, y/z, -1 \rangle; \sqrt{2}$	$\mathbf{r} = \langle v \cos u, v \sin u, v \rangle,$ $0 \le u \le 2\pi, 0 \le v \le h$	$\langle v \cos u, v \sin u, -v \rangle; \sqrt{2}v$
Sphere	$x^2 + y^2 + z^2 = a^2$	$\langle x/z, y/z, 1 \rangle; a/z$	$\mathbf{r} = \langle a \sin u \cos v,$ $a \sin u \sin v, a \cos u \rangle,$ $0 \le u \le \pi, 0 \le v \le 2\pi$	$\langle a^2 \sin^2 u \cos v, a^2 \sin^2 u \sin v,$ $a^2 \sin u \cos u \rangle; a^2 \sin u$
Paraboloid	$z = x^2 + y^2,$ $0 \le z \le h$	$\langle 2x, 2y, -1 \rangle; \sqrt{1 + 4(x^2 + y^2)}$	$\mathbf{r} = \langle v \cos u, v \sin u, v^2 \rangle,$ $0 \le u \le 2\pi, 0 \le v \le \sqrt{h}$	$\langle 2v^2 \cos u, 2v^2 \sin u, -v \rangle; v\sqrt{1 + 4v^2}$

QUICK CHECK 5 Explain why the explicit description for a cylinder $x^2 + y^2 = a^2$ cannot be used for a surface integral over a cylinder and a parametric description must be used. ◄

Surface Integrals of Vector Fields

Before beginning a discussion of surface integrals of vector fields, two technical issues about surfaces and normal vectors must be addressed.

The surfaces we consider in this book are called **two-sided**, or **orientable**, surfaces. To be orientable, a surface must have the property that the normal vectors vary continuously over the surface. In other words, when you walk on any closed path on an orientable surface and return to your starting point, your head must point in the same direction it did when you started. A well-known example of a *nonorientable* surface is the Möbius strip (Figure 14.55). Suppose you start walking the length of the Möbius strip at a point P with your head pointing upward. When you return to P, your head points in the opposite direction, or downward. Therefore, the Möbius strip is not orientable.

At any point of a parameterized orientable surface, there are two unit normal vectors. Therefore, the second point concerns the orientation of the surface or, equivalently,

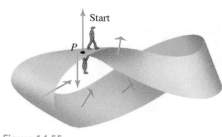

Start

P

Figure 14.55

Surfaces that enclose a region are oriented so normal vectors point in the outward direction.

For other surfaces, the orientation of the surface must be specified.

Figure 14.56

the direction of the normal vector. Once the direction of the normal vector is determined, the surface becomes **oriented**.

We make the common assumption that—unless specified otherwise—a closed orientable surface that fully encloses a region (such as a sphere) is oriented so that the normal vectors point in the *outward direction*. For a surface that does not enclose a region in $\mathbb{R}^3$, the orientation must be specified in some way. For example, we might specify that the normal vectors for a particular surface point in the general direction of the positive z-axis; that is, in an upward direction (Figure 14.56).

Now recall that the parameterization of a surface defines a normal vector $\mathbf{t}_u \times \mathbf{t}_v$ at each point. In many cases, the normal vectors are consistent with the specified orientation, in which case no adjustments need to be made. If the direction of $\mathbf{t}_u \times \mathbf{t}_v$ is not consistent with the specified orientation, then the sign of $\mathbf{t}_u \times \mathbf{t}_v$ must be reversed before doing calculations. This process is demonstrated in the following examples.

Flux Integrals   It turns out that the most common surface integral of a vector field is a *flux integral*. Consider a vector field $\mathbf{F} = \langle f, g, h \rangle$, continuous on a region in $\mathbb{R}^3$, that represents the flow of a fluid or the transport of a substance. Given a smooth oriented surface S, we aim to compute the net flux of the vector field across the surface. In a small region containing a point P, the flux across the surface is proportional to the component of $\mathbf{F}$ in the direction of the unit normal vector $\mathbf{n}$ at P. If θ is the angle between $\mathbf{F}$ and $\mathbf{n}$, then this component is $\mathbf{F} \cdot \mathbf{n} = |\mathbf{F}| \, |\mathbf{n}| \cos \theta = |\mathbf{F}| \cos \theta$ (because $|\mathbf{n}| = 1$; Figure 14.57a). We have the following special cases.

• If $\mathbf{F}$ and the unit normal vector are aligned at P ($\theta = 0$), then the component of $\mathbf{F}$ in the direction $\mathbf{n}$ is $\mathbf{F} \cdot \mathbf{n} = |\mathbf{F}|$; that is, all of $\mathbf{F}$ flows across the surface in the direction of $\mathbf{n}$ (Figure 14.57b).

• If $\mathbf{F}$ and the unit normal vector point in opposite directions at P ($\theta = \pi$), then the component of $\mathbf{F}$ in the direction $\mathbf{n}$ is $\mathbf{F} \cdot \mathbf{n} = -|\mathbf{F}|$; that is, all of $\mathbf{F}$ flows across the surface in the direction opposite that of $\mathbf{n}$ (Figure 14.57c).

• If $\mathbf{F}$ and the unit normal vector are orthogonal at P ($\theta = \pi/2$), then the component of $\mathbf{F}$ in the direction $\mathbf{n}$ is $\mathbf{F} \cdot \mathbf{n} = 0$; that is, none of $\mathbf{F}$ flows across the surface at that point (Figure 14.57d).

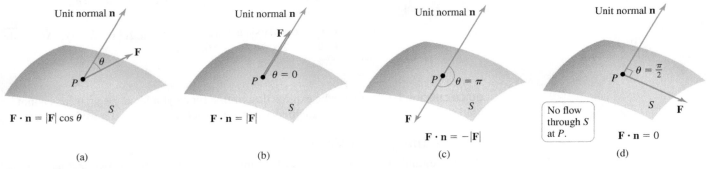

Figure 14.57

The flux integral, denoted $\iint_S \mathbf{F} \cdot \mathbf{n} \, dS$ or $\iint_S \mathbf{F} \cdot d\mathbf{S}$, simply adds up the components of $\mathbf{F}$ normal to the surface at all points of the surface. Notice that $\mathbf{F} \cdot \mathbf{n}$ is a scalar-valued function. Here is how the flux integral is computed.

Suppose the smooth oriented surface S is parameterized in the form

$$\mathbf{r}(u, v) = \langle x(u, v), y(u, v), z(u, v) \rangle,$$

▶ If $\mathbf{t}_u \times \mathbf{t}_v$ is not consistent with the specified orientation, its sign must be reversed.

where u and v vary over a region R in the uv-plane. The required vector normal to the surface at a point is $\mathbf{t}_u \times \mathbf{t}_v$, which we assume to be consistent with the orientation of S.

Therefore, the *unit* normal vector consistent with the orientation is $\mathbf{n} = \dfrac{\mathbf{t}_u \times \mathbf{t}_v}{|\mathbf{t}_u \times \mathbf{t}_v|}$.

Appealing to the definition of the surface integral for parameterized surfaces, the flux integral is

$$\iint_S \mathbf{F} \cdot \mathbf{n}\, dS = \iint_R \mathbf{F} \cdot \mathbf{n} |\mathbf{t}_u \times \mathbf{t}_v|\, dA \qquad \text{Definition of surface integral}$$

$$= \iint_R \mathbf{F} \cdot \underbrace{\frac{\mathbf{t}_u \times \mathbf{t}_v}{|\mathbf{t}_u \times \mathbf{t}_v|}}_{\mathbf{n}} |\mathbf{t}_u \times \mathbf{t}_v|\, dA \qquad \text{Substitute for } \mathbf{n}.$$

$$= \iint_R \mathbf{F} \cdot (\mathbf{t}_u \times \mathbf{t}_v)\, dA. \qquad \text{Convenient cancellation}$$

The remarkable occurrence in the flux integral is the cancellation of the factor $|\mathbf{t}_u \times \mathbf{t}_v|$.

The special case in which the surface S is specified in the form $z = g(x, y)$ follows directly by recalling that the required normal vector is $\mathbf{t}_u \times \mathbf{t}_v = \langle -z_x, -z_y, 1 \rangle$. In this case, with $\mathbf{F} = \langle f, g, h \rangle$, the integrand of the surface integral is $\mathbf{F} \cdot (\mathbf{t}_u \times \mathbf{t}_v) = -fz_x - gz_y + h$.

▶ The value of the surface integral is independent of the parameterization. However, in contrast to a surface integral of a scalar-valued function, the value of a surface integral of a vector field depends on the orientation of the surface. Changing the orientation changes the sign of the result.

DEFINITION Surface Integral of a Vector Field

Suppose $\mathbf{F} = \langle f, g, h \rangle$ is a continuous vector field on a region of $\mathbb{R}^3$ containing a smooth oriented surface S. If S is defined parametrically as $\mathbf{r}(u, v) = \langle x(u, v), y(u, v), z(u, v) \rangle$, for (u, v) in a region R, then

$$\iint_S \mathbf{F} \cdot \mathbf{n}\, dS = \iint_R \mathbf{F} \cdot (\mathbf{t}_u \times \mathbf{t}_v)\, dA,$$

where $\mathbf{t}_u = \dfrac{\partial \mathbf{r}}{\partial u} = \left\langle \dfrac{\partial x}{\partial u}, \dfrac{\partial y}{\partial u}, \dfrac{\partial z}{\partial u} \right\rangle$ and $\mathbf{t}_v = \dfrac{\partial \mathbf{r}}{\partial v} = \left\langle \dfrac{\partial x}{\partial v}, \dfrac{\partial y}{\partial v}, \dfrac{\partial z}{\partial v} \right\rangle$ are continuous on R, the normal vector $\mathbf{t}_u \times \mathbf{t}_v$ is nonzero on R, and the direction of the normal vector is consistent with the orientation of S. If S is defined in the form $z = g(x, y)$, for (x, y) in a region R, then

$$\iint_S \mathbf{F} \cdot \mathbf{n}\, dS = \iint_R (-fz_x - gz_y + h)\, dA.$$

EXAMPLE 7 Rain on a roof Consider the vertical vector field $\mathbf{F} = \langle 0, 0, -1 \rangle$, corresponding to a constant downward flow. Find the flux in the downward direction across the surface S, which is the plane $z = 4 - 2x - y$ in the first octant.

SOLUTION In this case, the surface is given explicitly. With $z = 4 - 2x - y$, we have $z_x = -2$ and $z_y = -1$. Therefore, the required normal vector is $\langle -z_x, -z_y, 1 \rangle = \langle 2, 1, 1 \rangle$, which points *upward* (the z-component of the vector is positive). Because we are interested in the *downward* flux of $\mathbf{F}$ across S, the surface must be oriented so the normal vectors point downward. So we take the normal vector to be $\langle -2, -1, -1 \rangle$ (Figure 14.58). Letting R be the region in the xy-plane beneath S and noting that $\mathbf{F} = \langle f, g, h \rangle = \langle 0, 0, -1 \rangle$, the flux integral is

$$\iint_S \mathbf{F} \cdot \mathbf{n}\, dS = \iint_R \langle 0, 0, -1 \rangle \cdot \langle -2, -1, -1 \rangle\, dA = \iint_R dA = \text{area}(R).$$

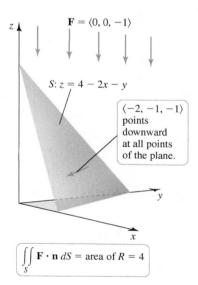

$\mathbf{F} = \langle 0, 0, -1 \rangle$

$S: z = 4 - 2x - y$

$\langle -2, -1, -1 \rangle$ points downward at all points of the plane.

$\iint_S \mathbf{F} \cdot \mathbf{n}\, dS = \text{area of } R = 4$

Figure 14.58

The base R is a triangle in the xy-plane with vertices $(0, 0)$, $(2, 0)$, and $(0, 4)$, so its area is 4. Therefore, the *downward* flux across S is 4. This flux integral has an interesting interpretation. If the vector field $\mathbf{F}$ represents the rate of rainfall with units of, say, g/m^2 per unit time, then the flux integral gives the mass of rain (in grams) that falls on the surface in a unit of time. This result says that (because the vector field is vertical) the mass of rain that falls on the roof equals the mass that would fall on the floor beneath the roof if the roof were not there. This property is explored further in Exercise 73.

Related Exercises 43–48 ◄

EXAMPLE 8   Flux of the radial field Consider the radial vector field $\mathbf{F} = \langle f, g, h \rangle = \langle x, y, z \rangle$. Is the upward flux of the field greater across the hemisphere $x^2 + y^2 + z^2 = 1$, for $z \geq 0$, or across the paraboloid $z = 1 - x^2 - y^2$, for $z \geq 0$? Note that the two surfaces have the same base in the xy-plane and the same high point $(0, 0, 1)$. Use the explicit description for the hemisphere and a parametric description for the paraboloid.

SOLUTION The base of both surfaces in the xy-plane is the unit disk $R = \{(x, y): x^2 + y^2 \leq 1\} = \{(r, \theta): 0 \leq r \leq 1, 0 \leq \theta \leq 2\pi\}$. To use the explicit description for the hemisphere, we must compute z_x and z_y. Differentiating $x^2 + y^2 + z^2 = 1$ implicitly, we find that $z_x = -x/z$ and $z_y = -y/z$. Therefore, the required normal vector is $\langle x/z, y/z, 1 \rangle$, which points upward on the surface. The flux integral is evaluated by substituting for f, g, h, z_x, and z_y; eliminating z from the integrand; and converting the integral in x and y to an integral in polar coordinates:

> ▶ Recall that the required normal vector for an explicitly defined surface $z = g(x, y)$ is $\langle -z_x, -z_y, 1 \rangle$.

$$\iint_S \mathbf{F} \cdot \mathbf{n} \, dS = \iint_R (-fz_x - gz_y + h) \, dA$$

$$= \iint_R \left(x\frac{x}{z} + y\frac{y}{z} + z \right) dA \qquad \text{Substitute.}$$

$$= \iint_R \left(\frac{x^2 + y^2 + z^2}{z} \right) dA \qquad \text{Simplify.}$$

$$= \iint_R \left(\frac{1}{z} \right) dA \qquad x^2 + y^2 + z^2 = 1$$

$$= \iint_R \left(\frac{1}{\sqrt{1 - x^2 - y^2}} \right) dA \qquad z = \sqrt{1 - x^2 - y^2}$$

$$= \int_0^{2\pi} \int_0^1 \left(\frac{1}{\sqrt{1 - r^2}} \right) r \, dr \, d\theta \qquad \text{Polar coordinates}$$

$$= \int_0^{2\pi} \left. \left(-\sqrt{1 - r^2} \right) \right|_0^1 d\theta \qquad \begin{array}{l}\text{Evaluate inner integral} \\ \text{as an improper integral.}\end{array}$$

$$= \int_0^{2\pi} d\theta = 2\pi. \qquad \text{Evaluate outer integral.}$$

For the paraboloid $z = 1 - x^2 - y^2$, we use the parametric description (Example 1b or Table 14.3)

$$\mathbf{r}(u, v) = \langle x, y, z \rangle = \langle v \cos u, v \sin u, 1 - v^2 \rangle,$$

for $0 \leq u \leq 2\pi$ and $0 \leq v \leq 1$. The required vector normal to the surface is

$$\mathbf{t}_u \times \mathbf{t}_v = \begin{vmatrix} \mathbf{i} & \mathbf{j} & \mathbf{k} \\ -v\sin u & v\cos u & 0 \\ \cos u & \sin u & -2v \end{vmatrix}$$

$$= \langle -2v^2\cos u, -2v^2\sin u, -v \rangle.$$

Notice that the normal vectors point downward on the surface (because the z-component is negative for $0 \leq v \leq 1$). In order to find the upward flux, we negate the normal vector and use the upward normal vector

$$-(\mathbf{t}_u \times \mathbf{t}_v) = \langle 2v^2\cos u, 2v^2\sin u, v \rangle.$$

The flux integral is evaluated by substituting for $\mathbf{F} = \langle x, y, z \rangle$ and $-(\mathbf{t}_u \times \mathbf{t}_v)$, and then evaluating an iterated integral in u and v:

$$\iint_S \mathbf{F} \cdot \mathbf{n} \, dS = \int_0^1 \int_0^{2\pi} \langle v\cos u, v\sin u, 1 - v^2 \rangle \cdot \langle 2v^2\cos u, 2v^2\sin u, v \rangle \, du\, dv$$

Substitute for F and $-(\mathbf{t}_u \times \mathbf{t}_v)$.

$$= \int_0^1 \int_0^{2\pi} (v^3 + v) \, du\, dv \quad \text{Simplify.}$$

QUICK CHECK 6 Explain why the upward flux for the radial field in Example 8 is greater for the hemisphere than for the paraboloid. ◄

$$= 2\pi\left(\frac{v^4}{4} + \frac{v^2}{2}\right)\Big|_0^1 = \frac{3\pi}{2}. \quad \text{Evaluate integrals.}$$

We see that the upward flux is greater for the hemisphere than for the paraboloid.

Related Exercises 43–48 ◄

SECTION 14.6 EXERCISES

Review Questions

1. Give a parametric description for a cylinder with radius a and height h, including the intervals for the parameters.

2. Give a parametric description for a cone with radius a and height h, including the intervals for the parameters.

3. Give a parametric description for a sphere with radius a, including the intervals for the parameters.

4. Explain how to compute the surface integral of a scalar-valued function f over a cone using an explicit description of the cone.

5. Explain how to compute the surface integral of a scalar-valued function f over a sphere using a parametric description of the sphere.

6. Explain how to compute a surface integral $\iint_S \mathbf{F} \cdot \mathbf{n} \, dS$ over a cone using an explicit description and a given orientation of the cone.

7. Explain how to compute a surface integral $\iint_S \mathbf{F} \cdot \mathbf{n} \, dS$ over a sphere using a parametric description of the sphere and a given orientation.

8. Explain what it means for a surface to be orientable.

9. Describe the usual orientation of a closed surface such as a sphere.

10. Why is the upward flux of a vertical vector field $\mathbf{F} = \langle 0, 0, 1 \rangle$ across a surface equal to the area of the projection of the surface in the xy-plane?

Basic Skills

11–16. Parametric descriptions *Give a parametric description of the form* $\mathbf{r}(u, v) = \langle x(u, v), y(u, v), z(u, v) \rangle$ *for the following surfaces. The descriptions are not unique. Specify the required rectangle in the uv-plane.*

11. The plane $2x - 4y + 3z = 16$

12. The cap of the sphere $x^2 + y^2 + z^2 = 16$, for $2\sqrt{2} \leq z \leq 4$

13. The frustum of the cone $z^2 = x^2 + y^2$, for $2 \leq z \leq 8$

14. The cone $z^2 = 4(x^2 + y^2)$, for $0 \leq z \leq 4$

15. The portion of the cylinder $x^2 + y^2 = 9$ in the first octant, for $0 \leq z \leq 3$

16. The cylinder $y^2 + z^2 = 36$, for $0 \leq x \leq 9$

17–20. Identify the surface *Describe the surface with the given parametric representation.*

17. $\mathbf{r}(u, v) = \langle u, v, 2u + 3v - 1 \rangle$, for $1 \leq u \leq 3, 2 \leq v \leq 4$

18. $\mathbf{r}(u, v) = \langle u, u + v, 2 - u - v \rangle$, for $0 \leq u \leq 2, 0 \leq v \leq 2$

19. $\mathbf{r}(u, v) = \langle v\cos u, v\sin u, 4v \rangle$, for $0 \leq u \leq \pi, 0 \leq v \leq 3$

20. $\mathbf{r}(u, v) = \langle v, 6\cos u, 6\sin u \rangle$, for $0 \leq u \leq 2\pi, 0 \leq v \leq 2$

21–26. Surface area using a parametric description *Find the area of the following surfaces using a parametric description of the surface.*

21. The half-cylinder $\{(r, \theta, z): r = 4, 0 \leq \theta \leq \pi, 0 \leq z \leq 7\}$

22. The plane $z = 3 - x - 3y$ in the first octant

23. The plane $z = 10 - x - y$ above the square $|x| \le 2, |y| \le 2$

24. The hemisphere $x^2 + y^2 + z^2 = 100$, for $z \ge 0$

25. A cone with base radius r and height h, where r and h are positive constants

26. The cap of the sphere $x^2 + y^2 + z^2 = 4$, for $1 \le z \le 2$

27–30. Surface integrals using a parametric description *Evaluate the surface integral $\iint_S f(x, y, z) \, dS$ using a parametric description of the surface.*

27. $f(x, y, z) = x^2 + y^2$, where S is the hemisphere $x^2 + y^2 + z^2 = 36$, for $z \ge 0$

28. $f(x, y, z) = y$, where S is the cylinder $x^2 + y^2 = 9, 0 \le z \le 3$

29. $f(x, y, z) = x$, where S is the cylinder $x^2 + z^2 = 1, 0 \le y \le 3$

30. $f(\rho, \varphi, \theta) = \cos \varphi$, where S is the part of the unit sphere in the first octant

31–34. Surface area using an explicit description *Find the area of the following surfaces using an explicit description of the surface.*

31. The cone $z^2 = 4(x^2 + y^2)$, for $0 \le z \le 4$

32. The paraboloid $z = 2(x^2 + y^2)$, for $0 \le z \le 8$

33. The trough $z = x^2$, for $-2 \le x \le 2, 0 \le y \le 4$

34. The part of the hyperbolic paraboloid $z = x^2 - y^2$ above the sector $R = \{(r, \theta): 0 \le r \le 4, -\pi/4 \le \theta \le \pi/4\}$

35–38. Surface integrals using an explicit description *Evaluate the surface integral $\iint_S f(x, y, z) \, dS$ using an explicit representation of the surface.*

35. $f(x, y, z) = xy$; S is the plane $z = 2 - x - y$ in the first octant.

36. $f(x, y, z) = x^2 + y^2$; S is the paraboloid $z = x^2 + y^2$, for $0 \le z \le 4$.

37. $f(x, y, z) = 25 - x^2 - y^2$; S is the hemisphere centered at the origin with radius 5, for $z \ge 0$.

38. $f(x, y, z) = e^z$; S is the plane $z = 8 - x - 2y$ in the first octant.

39–42. Average values

39. Find the average temperature on that part of the plane $3x + 4y + z = 6$ over the square $|x| \le 1, |y| \le 1$, where the temperature is given by $T(x, y, z) = e^{-z}$.

40. Find the average squared distance between the origin and the points on the paraboloid $z = 4 - x^2 - y^2$, for $z \ge 0$.

41. Find the average value of the function $f(x, y, z) = xyz$ on the unit sphere in the first octant.

42. Find the average value of the temperature function $T(x, y, z) = 100 - 25z$ on the cone $z^2 = x^2 + y^2$, for $0 \le z \le 2$.

43–48. Surface integrals of vector fields *Find the flux of the following vector fields across the given surface with the specified orientation. You may use either an explicit or parametric description of the surface.*

43. $\mathbf{F} = \langle 0, 0, -1 \rangle$ across the slanted face of the tetrahedron $z = 4 - x - y$ in the first octant; normal vectors point upward.

44. $\mathbf{F} = \langle x, y, z \rangle$ across the slanted face of the tetrahedron $z = 10 - 2x - 5y$ in the first octant; normal vectors point upward.

45. $\mathbf{F} = \langle x, y, z \rangle$ across the slanted surface of the cone $z^2 = x^2 + y^2$, for $0 \le z \le 1$; normal vectors point upward.

46. $\mathbf{F} = \langle e^{-y}, 2z, xy \rangle$ across the curved sides of the surface $S = \{(x, y, z): z = \cos y, |y| \le \pi, 0 \le x \le 4\}$; normal vectors point upward.

47. $\mathbf{F} = \mathbf{r}/|\mathbf{r}|^3$ across the sphere of radius a centered at the origin, where $\mathbf{r} = \langle x, y, z \rangle$; normal vectors point outward.

48. $\mathbf{F} = \langle -y, x, 1 \rangle$ across the cylinder $y = x^2$, for $0 \le x \le 1$, $0 \le z \le 4$; normal vectors point in the general direction of the positive y-axis.

Further Explorations

49. **Explain why or why not** Determine whether the following statements are true and give an explanation or counterexample.

   a. If the surface S is given by $\{(x, y, z): 0 \le x \le 1, 0 \le y \le 1, z = 10\}$, then $\iint_S f(x, y, z) \, dS = \int_0^1 \int_0^1 f(x, y, 10) \, dx \, dy$.

   b. If the surface S is given by $\{(x, y, z): 0 \le x \le 1, 0 \le y \le 1, z = x\}$, then $\iint_S f(x, y, z) \, dS = \int_0^1 \int_0^1 f(x, y, x) \, dx \, dy$.

   c. The surface $\mathbf{r} = \langle v \cos u, v \sin u, v^2 \rangle$, for $0 \le u \le \pi$, $0 \le v \le 2$, is the same as the surface $\mathbf{r} = \langle \sqrt{v} \cos 2u, \sqrt{v} \sin 2u, v \rangle$, for $0 \le u \le \pi/2, 0 \le v \le 4$.

   d. Given the standard parameterization of a sphere, the normal vectors $\mathbf{t}_u \times \mathbf{t}_v$ are outward normal vectors.

50–53. Miscellaneous surface integrals *Evaluate the following integrals using the method of your choice. Assume normal vectors point either outward or upward.*

50. $\iint_S \nabla \ln |\mathbf{r}| \cdot \mathbf{n} \, dS$, where S is the hemisphere $x^2 + y^2 + z^2 = a^2$, for $z \ge 0$, and where $\mathbf{r} = \langle x, y, z \rangle$

51. $\iint_S |\mathbf{r}| \, dS$, where S is the cylinder $x^2 + y^2 = 4$, for $0 \le z \le 8$, and where $\mathbf{r} = \langle x, y, z \rangle$

52. $\iint_S xyz \, dS$, where S is that part of the plane $z = 6 - y$ that lies in the cylinder $x^2 + y^2 = 4$

53. $\iint_S \dfrac{\langle x, 0, z \rangle}{\sqrt{x^2 + z^2}} \cdot \mathbf{n} \, dS$, where S is the cylinder $x^2 + z^2 = a^2$, $|y| \le 2$

54. **Cone and sphere** The cone $z^2 = x^2 + y^2$, for $z \ge 0$, cuts the sphere $x^2 + y^2 + z^2 = 16$ along a curve C.

   a. Find the surface area of the sphere below C, for $z \ge 0$.
   b. Find the surface area of the sphere above C.
   c. Find the surface area of the cone below C, for $z \ge 0$.

55. **Cylinder and sphere** Consider the sphere $x^2 + y^2 + z^2 = 4$ and the cylinder $(x - 1)^2 + y^2 = 1$, for $z \ge 0$.

   a. Find the surface area of the cylinder inside the sphere.
   b. Find the surface area of the sphere inside the cylinder.

56. **Flux on a tetrahedron** Find the upward flux of the field $\mathbf{F} = \langle x, y, z \rangle$ across the plane $x/a + y/b + z/c = 1$ in the first octant. Show that the flux equals c times the area of the base of the region. Interpret the result physically.

57. Flux across a cone Consider the field $\mathbf{F} = \langle x, y, z \rangle$ and the cone $z^2 = (x^2 + y^2)/a^2$, for $0 \leq z \leq 1$.

    a. Show that when $a = 1$, the outward flux across the cone is zero. Interpret the result.

    b. Find the outward flux (away from the z-axis), for any $a > 0$. Interpret the result.

58. Surface area formula for cones Find the general formula for the surface area of a cone with height h and base radius a (excluding the base).

59. Surface area formula for spherical cap A sphere of radius a is sliced parallel to the equatorial plane at a distance $a - h$ from the equatorial plane (see figure). Find the general formula for the surface area of the resulting spherical cap (excluding the base) with thickness h.

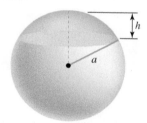

60. Radial fields and spheres Consider the radial field $\mathbf{F} = \mathbf{r}/|\mathbf{r}|^p$, where $\mathbf{r} = \langle x, y, z \rangle$ and p is a real number. Let S be the sphere of radius a centered at the origin. Show that the outward flux of $\mathbf{F}$ across the sphere is $4\pi/a^{p-3}$. It is instructive to do the calculation using both an explicit and parametric description of the sphere.

Applications

61–63. Heat flux *The heat flow vector field for conducting objects is* $\mathbf{F} = -k\nabla T$, *where* $T(x, y, z)$ *is the temperature in the object and* $k > 0$ *is a constant that depends on the material. Compute the outward flux of* $\mathbf{F}$ *across the following surfaces S for the given temperature distributions. Assume $k = 1$.*

61. $T(x, y, z) = 100e^{-x-y}$; S consists of the faces of the cube $|x| \leq 1, |y| \leq 1, |z| \leq 1$.

62. $T(x, y, z) = 100e^{-x^2-y^2-z^2}$; S is the sphere $x^2 + y^2 + z^2 = a^2$.

63. $T(x, y, z) = -\ln(x^2 + y^2 + z^2)$; S is the sphere $x^2 + y^2 + z^2 = a^2$.

64. Flux across a cylinder Let S be the cylinder $x^2 + y^2 = a^2$, for $-L \leq z \leq L$.

    a. Find the outward flux of the field $\mathbf{F} = \langle x, y, 0 \rangle$ across S.

    b. Find the outward flux of the field $\mathbf{F} = \dfrac{\langle x, y, 0 \rangle}{(x^2 + y^2)^{p/2}} = \dfrac{\mathbf{r}}{|\mathbf{r}|^p}$ across S, where $|\mathbf{r}|$ is the distance from the z-axis and p is a real number.

    c. In part (b), for what values of p is the outward flux finite as $a \to \infty$ (with L fixed)?

    d. In part (b), for what values of p is the outward flux finite as $L \to \infty$ (with a fixed)?

65. Flux across concentric spheres Consider the radial fields
$$\mathbf{F} = \frac{\langle x, y, z \rangle}{(x^2 + y^2 + z^2)^{p/2}} = \frac{\mathbf{r}}{|\mathbf{r}|^p},$$
where p is a real number. Let S consist of the spheres A and B centered at the origin with radii $0 < a < b$, respectively. The total outward flux across S consists of the flux out of S across the outer sphere B minus the flux into S across the inner sphere A.

    a. Find the total flux across S with $p = 0$. Interpret the result.

    b. Show that for $p = 3$ (an inverse square law), the flux across S is independent of a and b.

66–69. Mass and center of mass *Let S be a surface that represents a thin shell with density ρ. The moments about the coordinate planes (see Section 13.6) are* $M_{yz} = \iint_S x\rho(x, y, z)\,dS$, $M_{xz} = \iint_S y\rho(x, y, z)\,dS$, *and* $M_{xy} = \iint_S z\rho(x, y, z)\,dS$. *The coordinates of the center of mass of the shell are* $\bar{x} = \dfrac{M_{yz}}{m}$, $\bar{y} = \dfrac{M_{xz}}{m}$, $\bar{z} = \dfrac{M_{xy}}{m}$, *where m is the mass of the shell. Find the mass and center of mass of the following shells. Use symmetry whenever possible.*

66. The constant-density hemispherical shell $x^2 + y^2 + z^2 = a^2, z \geq 0$

67. The constant-density cone with radius a, height h, and base in the xy-plane

68. The constant-density half cylinder $x^2 + z^2 = a^2, -h/2 \leq y \leq h/2, z \geq 0$

69. The cylinder $x^2 + y^2 = a^2, 0 \leq z \leq 2$, with density $\rho(x, y, z) = 1 + z$

Additional Exercises

70. Outward normal to a sphere Show that $|\mathbf{t}_u \times \mathbf{t}_v| = a^2 \sin u$ for a sphere of radius a defined parametrically by $\mathbf{r}(u, v) = \langle a \sin u \cos v, a \sin u \sin v, a \cos u \rangle$, where $0 \leq u \leq \pi$ and $0 \leq v \leq 2\pi$.

71. Special case of surface integrals of scalar-valued functions Suppose that a surface S is defined as $z = g(x, y)$ on a region R. Show that $\mathbf{t}_x \times \mathbf{t}_y = \langle -z_x, -z_y, 1 \rangle$ and that
$$\iint_S f(x, y, z)\,dS = \iint_R f(x, y, z)\sqrt{z_x^2 + z_y^2 + 1}\,dA.$$

72. Surfaces of revolution Suppose $y = f(x)$ is a continuous and positive function on $[a, b]$. Let S be the surface generated when the graph of f on $[a, b]$ is revolved about the x-axis.

    a. Show that S is described parametrically by $\mathbf{r}(u, v) = \langle u, f(u) \cos v, f(u) \sin v \rangle$, for $a \leq u \leq b, 0 \leq v \leq 2\pi$.

    b. Find an integral that gives the surface area of S.

    c. Apply the result of part (b) to find the area of the surface generated with $f(x) = x^3$, for $1 \leq x \leq 2$.

    d. Apply the result of part (b) to find the area of the surface generated with $f(x) = (25 - x^2)^{1/2}$, for $3 \leq x \leq 4$.

73. Rain on roofs Let $z = s(x, y)$ define a surface over a region R in the xy-plane, where $z \geq 0$ on R. Show that the downward flux of the vertical vector field $\mathbf{F} = \langle 0, 0, -1 \rangle$ across S equals the area of R. Interpret the result physically.

74. Surface area of a torus

a. Show that a torus with radii $R > r$ (see figure) may be described parametrically by
$r(u, v) = \langle (R + r \cos u) \cos v, (R + r \cos u) \sin v, r \sin u \rangle$,
for $0 \le u \le 2\pi, 0 \le v \le 2\pi$.

b. Show that the surface area of the torus is $4\pi^2 Rr$.

75. Surfaces of revolution—single variable Let f be differentiable and positive on the interval $[a, b]$. Let S be the surface generated when the graph of f on $[a, b]$ is revolved about the x-axis. Use Theorem 14.12 to show that the area of S (as given in Section 6.6) is

$$\int_a^b 2\pi f(x) \sqrt{1 + f'(x)^2} \, dx.$$

QUICK CHECK ANSWERS

1. A half-cylinder with height 1 and radius 2 with its axis along the z-axis **2.** A half-cone with height 10 and radius 10 **3.** A quarter-sphere with radius 4 **4.** $\sqrt{2}$ **5.** The cylinder $x^2 + y^2 = a^2$ does not represent a function, so z_x and z_y cannot be computed. **6.** The vector field is everywhere orthogonal to the hemisphere, so the hemisphere has maximum flux at every point. ◀

14.7 Stokes' Theorem

> ➤ Born in Ireland, George Gabriel Stokes (1819–1903) led a long and distinguished life as one of the prominent mathematicians and physicists of his day. He entered Cambridge University as a student and remained there as a professor for most of his life, taking the Lucasian chair of mathematics once held by Sir Isaac Newton. The first statement of Stokes' Theorem was given by William Thomson (Lord Kelvin).

With the divergence, the curl, and surface integrals in hand, we are ready to present two of the crowning results of calculus. Fortunately, all of the heavy lifting has been done. In this section, you will see Stokes' Theorem, and in the next section, we present the Divergence Theorem.

Stokes' Theorem

Stokes' Theorem is the three-dimensional version of the circulation form of Green's Theorem. Recall that if C is a closed simple piecewise-smooth oriented curve in the xy-plane enclosing a simply connected region R and $\mathbf{F} = \langle f, g \rangle$ is a differentiable vector field on R, Green's Theorem says that

$$\underbrace{\oint_C \mathbf{F} \cdot d\mathbf{r}}_{\text{circulation}} = \iint_R \underbrace{(g_x - f_y)}_{\text{curl or rotation}} dA.$$

The line integral on the left gives the circulation along the boundary of R. The double integral on the right sums the curl of the vector field over all points of R. If $\mathbf{F}$ represents a fluid flow, the theorem says that the cumulative rotation of the flow within R equals the circulation along the boundary.

In Stokes' Theorem, the plane region R in Green's Theorem becomes an oriented surface S in $\mathbb{R}^3$. The circulation integral in Green's Theorem remains a circulation integral, but now over the closed simple piecewise-smooth oriented curve C that forms the boundary of S. The double integral of the curl in Green's Theorem becomes a surface integral of the three-dimensional curl (Figure 14.59).

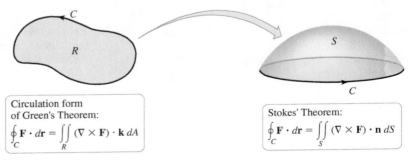

Circulation form of Green's Theorem:
$$\oint_C \mathbf{F} \cdot d\mathbf{r} = \iint_R (\nabla \times \mathbf{F}) \cdot \mathbf{k} \, dA$$

Stokes' Theorem:
$$\oint_C \mathbf{F} \cdot d\mathbf{r} = \iint_S (\nabla \times \mathbf{F}) \cdot \mathbf{n} \, dS$$

Figure 14.59

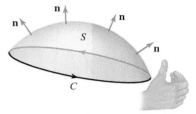

Figure 14.60

▶ The right-hand rule tells you which of two normal vectors at a point of S to use. Remember that the direction of normal vectors changes continuously on an oriented surface.

Stokes' Theorem involves an oriented curve C and an oriented surface S on which there are two unit normal vectors at every point. These orientations must be consistent and the normal vectors must be chosen correctly. Here is the right-hand rule that relates the orientations of S and C, and determines the choice of the normal vectors:

> If the fingers of your right hand curl in the positive direction around C, then your right thumb points in the (general) direction of the vectors normal to S (Figure 14.60).

A common situation occurs when C has a counterclockwise orientation when viewed from above; then the vectors normal to S point upward.

THEOREM 14.13   Stokes' Theorem
Let S be an oriented surface in $\mathbb{R}^3$ with a piecewise-smooth closed boundary C whose orientation is consistent with that of S. Assume that $\mathbf{F} = \langle f, g, h \rangle$ is a vector field whose components have continuous first partial derivatives on S. Then

$$\oint_C \mathbf{F} \cdot d\mathbf{r} = \iint_S (\nabla \times \mathbf{F}) \cdot \mathbf{n} \, dS,$$

where $\mathbf{n}$ is the unit vector normal to S determined by the orientation of S.

QUICK CHECK 1 Suppose that S is a region in the xy-plane with a boundary oriented counterclockwise. What is the normal to S? Explain why Stokes' Theorem becomes the circulation form of Green's Theorem. ◀

The meaning of Stokes' Theorem is much the same as for the circulation form of Green's Theorem: Under the proper conditions, the accumulated rotation of the vector field over the surface S (as given by the normal component of the curl) equals the net circulation on the boundary of S. An outline of the proof of Stokes' Theorem is given at the end of this section. First, we look at some special cases that give further insight into the theorem.

If $\mathbf{F}$ is a conservative vector field on a domain D, then it has a potential function φ such that $\mathbf{F} = \nabla\varphi$. Because $\nabla \times \nabla\varphi = \mathbf{0}$, it follows that $\nabla \times \mathbf{F} = \mathbf{0}$ (Theorem 14.9); therefore, the circulation integral is zero on all closed curves in D. Recall that the circulation integral is also a work integral for the force field $\mathbf{F}$, which emphasizes the fact that no work is done in moving an object on a closed path in a conservative force field. Among the important conservative vector fields are the radial fields $\mathbf{F} = \mathbf{r}/|\mathbf{r}|^p$, which generally have zero curl and zero circulation on closed curves.

▶ Recall that for a constant nonzero vector $\mathbf{a}$ and the position vector $\mathbf{r} = \langle x, y, z \rangle$, the field $\mathbf{F} = \mathbf{a} \times \mathbf{r}$ is a rotational field. In Example 1,

$$\mathbf{F} = \langle 0, 1, 1 \rangle \times \langle x, y, z \rangle.$$

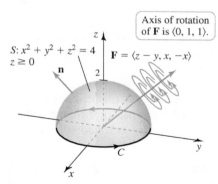

Figure 14.61

EXAMPLE 1   Verifying Stokes' Theorem Confirm that Stokes' Theorem holds for the vector field $\mathbf{F} = \langle z - y, x, -x \rangle$, where S is the hemisphere $x^2 + y^2 + z^2 = 4$, for $z \geq 0$, and C is the circle $x^2 + y^2 = 4$ oriented counterclockwise.

SOLUTION The orientation of C implies that vectors normal to S should point in the outward direction. The vector field is a rotation field $\mathbf{a} \times \mathbf{r}$, where $\mathbf{a} = \langle 0, 1, 1 \rangle$ and $\mathbf{r} = \langle x, y, z \rangle$; so the axis of rotation points in the direction of the vector $\langle 0, 1, 1 \rangle$ (Figure 14.61). We first compute the circulation integral in Stokes' Theorem. The curve C with the given orientation is parameterized as $\mathbf{r}(t) = \langle 2\cos t, 2\sin t, 0 \rangle$, for $0 \leq t \leq 2\pi$; therefore, $\mathbf{r}'(t) = \langle -2\sin t, 2\cos t, 0 \rangle$. The circulation integral is

$$\oint_C \mathbf{F} \cdot d\mathbf{r} = \int_0^{2\pi} \mathbf{F} \cdot \mathbf{r}'(t) \, dt \qquad \text{Definition of line integral}$$

$$= \int_0^{2\pi} \langle \underbrace{z - y}_{-2\sin t}, x, -x \rangle \cdot \langle -2\sin t, 2\cos t, 0 \rangle \, dt \qquad \text{Substitute.}$$

$$= \int_0^{2\pi} 4(\sin^2 t + \cos^2 t) \, dt \qquad \text{Simplify.}$$

$$= 4\int_0^{2\pi} dt \qquad \sin^2 t + \cos^2 t = 1$$

$$= 8\pi. \qquad \text{Evaluate integral.}$$

The surface integral requires computing the curl of the vector field:

$$\nabla \times \mathbf{F} = \nabla \times \langle z - y, x, -x \rangle = \begin{vmatrix} \mathbf{i} & \mathbf{j} & \mathbf{k} \\ \dfrac{\partial}{\partial x} & \dfrac{\partial}{\partial y} & \dfrac{\partial}{\partial z} \\ z - y & x & -x \end{vmatrix} = \langle 0, 2, 2 \rangle.$$

Recall from Section 14.6 (Table 14.3) that the required outward normal to the hemisphere is $\langle x/z, y/z, 1 \rangle$. The region of integration is the base of the hemisphere in the xy-plane, which is

$$R = \{(x, y): x^2 + y^2 \le 4\} = \{(r, \theta): 0 \le r \le 2, 0 \le \theta \le 2\pi\}.$$

Combining these results, the surface integral in Stokes' Theorem is

$$\iint\limits_{S} (\nabla \times \mathbf{F}) \cdot \mathbf{n} \, dS = \iint\limits_{R} \underbrace{\langle 0, 2, 2 \rangle}_{\langle 0, 2, 2 \rangle} \cdot \left\langle \frac{x}{z}, \frac{y}{z}, 1 \right\rangle dA \qquad \text{Substitute and convert to a double integral over } R.$$

$$= \iint\limits_{R} \left(\frac{2y}{\sqrt{4 - x^2 - y^2}} + 2 \right) dA \qquad \text{Simplify and use } z = \sqrt{4 - x^2 - y^2}.$$

$$= \int_0^{2\pi} \int_0^2 \left(\frac{2r \sin \theta}{\sqrt{4 - r^2}} + 2 \right) r \, dr \, d\theta. \qquad \text{Convert to polar coordinates.}$$

We integrate first with respect to θ because the integral of $\sin \theta$ from 0 to 2π is zero and the first term in the integral is eliminated. Therefore, the surface integral reduces to

> ➤ In eliminating the first term of this double integral, we note that the improper integral $\displaystyle\int_0^2 \frac{r^2}{\sqrt{4 - r^2}} \, dr$ has a finite value.

$$\iint\limits_{S} (\nabla \times \mathbf{F}) \cdot \mathbf{n} \, dS = \int_0^2 \int_0^{2\pi} \left(\frac{2r^2 \sin \theta}{\sqrt{4 - r^2}} + 2r \right) d\theta \, dr$$

$$= \int_0^2 \int_0^{2\pi} 2r \, d\theta \, dr \qquad \int_0^{2\pi} \sin \theta \, d\theta = 0$$

$$= 4\pi \int_0^2 r \, dr \qquad \text{Evaluate inner integral.}$$

$$= 8\pi. \qquad \text{Evaluate outer integral.}$$

Computed either as a line integral or a surface integral, the vector field has a positive circulation along the boundary of S, which is produced by the net rotation of the field over the surface S.

Related Exercises 5–10 ◀

In Example 1, it was possible to evaluate both the line integral and the surface integral that appear in Stokes' Theorem. Often the theorem provides an easier way to evaluate difficult line integrals.

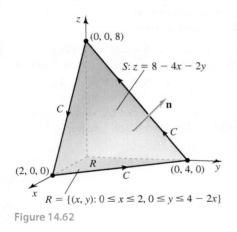

$R = \{(x, y): 0 \le x \le 2, 0 \le y \le 4 - 2x\}$

Figure 14.62

EXAMPLE 2   Using Stokes' Theorem to evaluate a line integral Evaluate the line integral $\oint_C \mathbf{F} \cdot d\mathbf{r}$, where $\mathbf{F} = z\mathbf{i} - z\mathbf{j} + (x^2 - y^2)\mathbf{k}$ and C consists of the three line segments that bound the plane $z = 8 - 4x - 2y$ in the first octant, oriented as shown in Figure 14.62.

SOLUTION Evaluating the line integral directly involves parameterizing the three line segments. Instead, we use Stokes' Theorem to convert the line integral to a surface integral, where S is that portion of the plane $z = 8 - 4x - 2y$ that lies in the first octant. The curl of the vector field is

$$\nabla \times \mathbf{F} = \nabla \times \langle z, -z, x^2 - y^2 \rangle = \begin{vmatrix} \mathbf{i} & \mathbf{j} & \mathbf{k} \\ \dfrac{\partial}{\partial x} & \dfrac{\partial}{\partial y} & \dfrac{\partial}{\partial z} \\ z & -z & x^2 - y^2 \end{vmatrix} = \langle 1 - 2y, 1 - 2x, 0 \rangle.$$

> Recall that for an explicitly defined surface S given by $z = g(x, y)$ over a region R with $\mathbf{F} = \langle f, g, h \rangle$,
>
> $$\iint_S \mathbf{F} \cdot \mathbf{n} \, dS = \iint_R (-f z_x - g z_y + h) \, dA.$$
>
> In Example 2, $\mathbf{F}$ is replaced with $\nabla \times \mathbf{F}$.

The appropriate vector normal to the plane $z = 8 - 4x - 2y$ is $\langle -z_x, -z_y, 1 \rangle = \langle 4, 2, 1 \rangle$, which points upward, consistent with the orientation of C. The triangular region R in the xy-plane beneath S is found by setting $z = 0$ in the equation of the plane; we find that $R = \{(x, y): 0 \le x \le 2, 0 \le y \le 4 - 2x\}$. The surface integral in Stokes' Theorem may now be evaluated:

$$\iint_S \underbrace{(\nabla \times \mathbf{F})}_{\langle 1 - 2y, 1 - 2x, 0 \rangle} \cdot \mathbf{n} \, dS = \iint_R \langle 1 - 2y, 1 - 2x, 0 \rangle \cdot \langle 4, 2, 1 \rangle \, dA \quad \text{Substitute and convert to a double integral over } R.$$

$$= \int_0^2 \int_0^{4-2x} (6 - 4x - 8y) \, dy \, dx \quad \text{Simplify.}$$

$$= -\frac{88}{3}. \quad \text{Evaluate integrals.}$$

The circulation around the boundary of R is negative, indicating a net circulation in the clockwise direction on C (looking from above).

Related Exercises 11–16 ◄

In other situations, Stokes' Theorem may be used to convert a difficult surface integral into a relatively easy line integral, as illustrated in the next example.

EXAMPLE 3 Using Stokes' Theorem to evaluate a surface integral Evaluate the integral $\iint_S (\nabla \times \mathbf{F}) \cdot \mathbf{n} \, dS$, where $\mathbf{F} = -xz \, \mathbf{i} + yz \, \mathbf{j} + xye^z \, \mathbf{k}$ and S is the cap of the paraboloid $z = 5 - x^2 - y^2$ above the plane $z = 3$ (Figure 14.63). Assume $\mathbf{n}$ points in the upward direction on S.

SOLUTION We use Stokes' Theorem to convert the surface integral to a line integral along the curve C that bounds S. That curve is the intersection between the paraboloid $z = 5 - x^2 - y^2$ and the plane $z = 3$. Eliminating z from these equations, we find that C is the circle $x^2 + y^2 = 2$, with $z = 3$. By the orientation of S, we see that C must be oriented counterclockwise, so a parametric description of C is $\mathbf{r}(t) = \langle \sqrt{2} \cos t, \sqrt{2} \sin t, 3 \rangle$, which implies that $\mathbf{r}'(t) = \langle -\sqrt{2} \sin t, \sqrt{2} \cos t, 0 \rangle$. The value of the surface integral is

$$\iint_S (\nabla \times \mathbf{F}) \cdot \mathbf{n} \, dS = \oint_C \mathbf{F} \cdot d\mathbf{r} \quad \text{Stokes' Theorem}$$

$$= \int_0^{2\pi} \mathbf{F} \cdot \mathbf{r}'(t) \, dt \quad \text{Definition of line integral}$$

$$= \int_0^{2\pi} \langle -xz, yz, xye^z \rangle \cdot \langle -\sqrt{2} \sin t, \sqrt{2} \cos t, 0 \rangle \, dt \quad \text{Substitute.}$$

$$= \int_0^{2\pi} 12 \sin t \cos t \, dt \quad \text{Substitute for } x, y, \text{ and } z, \text{ and simplify.}$$

$$= 6 \int_0^{2\pi} \sin 2t \, dt = 0. \quad \sin 2t = 2 \sin t \cos t$$

Related Exercises 17–20 ◄

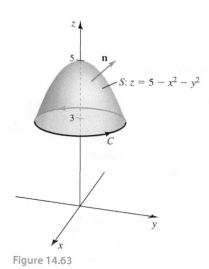

Figure 14.63

QUICK CHECK 2 In Example 3, the z-component of the vector field did not enter the calculation; it could have been anything. Explain why. ◄

Interpreting the Curl

Stokes' Theorem leads to another interpretation of the curl at a point in a vector field. We need the idea of the **average circulation**. If C is the boundary of an oriented surface S, we define the average circulation of $\mathbf{F}$ over S as

$$\frac{1}{\text{area}(S)} \oint_C \mathbf{F} \cdot d\mathbf{r} = \frac{1}{\text{area}(S)} \iint_S (\nabla \times \mathbf{F}) \cdot \mathbf{n}\, dS,$$

where Stokes' Theorem is used to convert the circulation integral to a surface integral.

First consider a general rotation field $\mathbf{F} = \mathbf{a} \times \mathbf{r}$, where $\mathbf{a} = \langle a_1, a_2, a_3 \rangle$ is a constant nonzero vector and $\mathbf{r} = \langle x, y, z \rangle$. Recall that $\mathbf{F}$ describes the rotation about an axis in the direction of $\mathbf{a}$ with angular speed $\omega = |\mathbf{a}|$. We also showed that $\mathbf{F}$ has a constant curl, $\nabla \times \mathbf{F} = \nabla \times (\mathbf{a} \times \mathbf{r}) = 2\mathbf{a}$. We now take S to be a small circular disk centered at a point P, whose normal vector $\mathbf{n}$ makes an angle θ with the axis $\mathbf{a}$ (Figure 14.64). Let C be the boundary of S with a counterclockwise orientation.

The average circulation of this vector field on S is

$$\frac{1}{\text{area }(S)} \iint_S \underbrace{(\nabla \times \mathbf{F}) \cdot \mathbf{n}}_{\text{constant}}\, dS \qquad \text{Definition}$$

$$= \frac{1}{\text{area }(S)} (\nabla \times \mathbf{F}) \cdot \mathbf{n} \cdot \text{area }(S) \qquad \iint_S dS = \text{area }(S)$$

$$= \underbrace{(\nabla \times \mathbf{F})}_{2\mathbf{a}} \cdot \mathbf{n} \qquad \text{Simplify.}$$

$$= 2|\mathbf{a}| \cos \theta. \qquad |\mathbf{n}| = 1,\ |\nabla \times \mathbf{F}| = 2|\mathbf{a}|$$

If the normal vector $\mathbf{n}$ is aligned with $\nabla \times \mathbf{F}$ (which is parallel to $\mathbf{a}$), then $\theta = 0$ and the average circulation on S has its maximum value of $2|\mathbf{a}|$. However, if the vector normal to the surface S is orthogonal to the axis of rotation ($\theta = \pi/2$), the average circulation is zero.

We see that for a general rotation field $\mathbf{F} = \mathbf{a} \times \mathbf{r}$, the curl of $\mathbf{F}$ has the following interpretations, where S is a small disk centered at a point P with a normal vector $\mathbf{n}$.

- The scalar component of $\nabla \times \mathbf{F}$ at P in the direction of $\mathbf{n}$, which is $(\nabla \times \mathbf{F}) \cdot \mathbf{n} = 2|\mathbf{a}| \cos \theta$, is the average circulation of $\mathbf{F}$ on S.
- The direction of $\nabla \times \mathbf{F}$ at P is the direction that maximizes the average circulation of $\mathbf{F}$ on S. Equivalently, it is the direction in which you should orient the axis of a paddle wheel to obtain the maximum angular speed.

A similar argument may be applied to a general vector field (with a variable curl) to give an analogous interpretation of the curl at a point (Exercise 44).

EXAMPLE 4   Horizontal channel flow Consider the velocity field $\mathbf{v} = \langle 0, 1 - x^2, 0 \rangle$, for $|x| \le 1$ and $|z| \le 1$, which represents a horizontal flow in the y-direction (Figure 14.65a).

a. Suppose you place a paddle wheel at the point $P\left(\frac{1}{2}, 0, 0\right)$. Using physical arguments, in which of the coordinate directions should the axis of the wheel point in order for the wheel to spin? In which direction does it spin? What happens if you place the wheel at $Q\left(-\frac{1}{2}, 0, 0\right)$?

b. Compute and graph the curl of $\mathbf{v}$ and provide an interpretation.

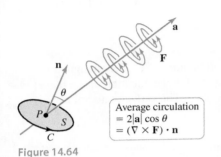

Figure 14.64

Average circulation
$= 2|\mathbf{a}| \cos \theta$
$= (\nabla \times \mathbf{F}) \cdot \mathbf{n}$

➤ Recall that $\mathbf{n}$ is a unit normal vector with $|\mathbf{n}| = 1$. By definition, the dot product gives $\mathbf{a} \cdot \mathbf{n} = |\mathbf{a}| \cos \theta$.

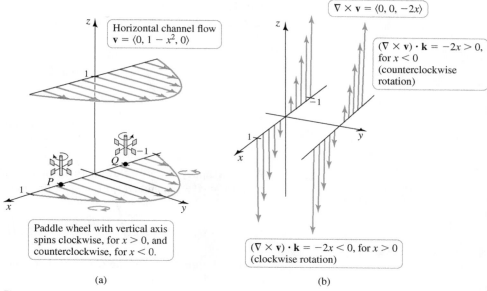

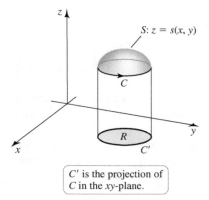

Figure 14.65

SOLUTION

a. If the axis of the wheel is aligned with the x-axis at P, the flow strikes the upper and lower halves of the wheel symmetrically and the wheel does not spin. If the axis of the wheel is aligned with the y-axis, the flow is parallel to the axis of the wheel and the wheel does not spin. If the axis of the wheel is aligned with the z-axis at P, the flow in the y-direction is greater for $x < \frac{1}{2}$ than it is for $x > \frac{1}{2}$. Therefore, a wheel located at $P\left(\frac{1}{2}, 0, 0\right)$ spins in the clockwise direction, looking from above (Figure 14.65a). Using a similar argument, we conclude that a vertically oriented paddle wheel placed at $Q\left(-\frac{1}{2}, 0, 0\right)$ spins in the counterclockwise direction (when viewed from above).

b. A short calculation shows that

$$\nabla \times \mathbf{v} = \begin{vmatrix} \mathbf{i} & \mathbf{j} & \mathbf{k} \\ \dfrac{\partial}{\partial x} & \dfrac{\partial}{\partial y} & \dfrac{\partial}{\partial z} \\ 0 & 1 - x^2 & 0 \end{vmatrix} = -2x\,\mathbf{k}.$$

QUICK CHECK 3 In Example 4, explain why a paddle wheel with its axis aligned with the z-axis does not spin when placed on the y-axis. ◄

As shown in Figure 14.65b, the curl points in the z-direction, which is the direction of the paddle wheel axis that gives the maximum angular speed of the wheel. Consider the z-component of the curl, which is $(\nabla \times \mathbf{v}) \cdot \mathbf{k} = -2x$. At $x = 0$, this component is zero, meaning the wheel does not spin at any point along the y-axis when its axis is aligned with the z-axis. For $x > 0$, we see that $(\nabla \times \mathbf{v}) \cdot \mathbf{k} < 0$, which corresponds to clockwise rotation of the vector field. For $x < 0$, we have $(\nabla \times \mathbf{v}) \cdot \mathbf{k} > 0$, corresponding to counterclockwise rotation.

Related Exercises 21–24 ◄

Proof of Stokes' Theorem

The proof of the most general case of Stokes' Theorem is intricate. However, a proof of a special case is instructive and it relies on several previous results.

Consider the case in which the surface S is the graph of the function $z = s(x, y)$, defined on a region in the xy-plane. Let C be the curve that bounds S with a counterclockwise orientation, let R be the projection of S in the xy-plane, and let C' be the projection of C in the xy-plane (Figure 14.66).

Letting $\mathbf{F} = \langle f, g, h \rangle$, the line integral in Stokes' Theorem is

$$\oint_C \mathbf{F} \cdot d\mathbf{r} = \oint_C f\,dx + g\,dy + h\,dz.$$

Figure 14.66

The key observation for this integral is that along C (which is the boundary of S), $dz = z_x\, dx + z_y\, dy$. Making this substitution, we convert the line integral on C to a line integral on C' in the xy-plane:

$$\oint_C \mathbf{F} \cdot d\mathbf{r} = \oint_{C'} f\, dx + g\, dy + h\underbrace{(z_x\, dx + z_y\, dy)}_{dz}$$

$$= \oint_{C'} \underbrace{(f + hz_x)}_{M(x,\,y)}\, dx + \underbrace{(g + hz_y)}_{N(x,\,y)}\, dy.$$

We now apply the circulation form of Green's Theorem to this line integral with $M(x, y) = f + hz_x$ and $N(x, y) = g + hz_y$; the result is

$$\oint_{C'} M\, dx + N\, dy = \iint_R (N_x - M_y)\, dA.$$

A careful application of the Chain Rule (remembering that z is a function of x and y, Exercise 45) reveals that

$$M_y = f_y + f_z z_y + hz_{xy} + z_x(h_y + h_z z_y) \quad \text{and}$$
$$N_x = g_x + g_z z_x + hz_{yx} + z_y(h_x + h_z z_x).$$

Making these substitutions in the line integral and simplifying (note that $z_{xy} = z_{yx}$ is needed), we have

$$\oint_C \mathbf{F} \cdot d\mathbf{r} = \iint_R (z_x(g_z - h_y) + z_y(h_x - f_z) + (g_x - f_y))\, dA. \qquad (1)$$

Now let's look at the surface integral in Stokes' Theorem. The upward vector normal to the surface is $\langle -z_x, -z_y, 1 \rangle$. Substituting the components of $\nabla \times \mathbf{F}$, the surface integral takes the form

$$\iint_S (\nabla \times \mathbf{F}) \cdot \mathbf{n}\, dS = \iint_R ((h_y - g_z)(-z_x) + (f_z - h_x)(-z_y) + (g_x - f_y))\, dA,$$

which upon rearrangement becomes the integral in (1).　　　◄

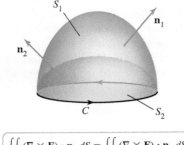

$$\boxed{\iint_{S_1} (\nabla \times \mathbf{F}) \cdot \mathbf{n}_1\, dS = \iint_{S_2} (\nabla \times \mathbf{F}) \cdot \mathbf{n}_2\, dS}$$

(a)

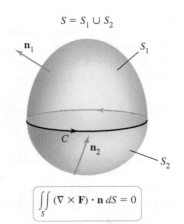

$$S = S_1 \cup S_2$$

$$\boxed{\iint_S (\nabla \times \mathbf{F}) \cdot \mathbf{n}\, dS = 0}$$

(b)

Figure 14.67

Two Final Notes on Stokes' Theorem

1. Stokes' Theorem allows a surface integral $\iint_S (\nabla \times \mathbf{F}) \cdot \mathbf{n}\, dS$ to be evaluated using only the values of the vector field on the boundary C. This means that if a closed curve C is the boundary of two different smooth oriented surfaces S_1 and S_2, which both have an orientation consistent with that of C, then the integrals of $(\nabla \times \mathbf{F}) \cdot \mathbf{n}$ on the two surfaces are equal; that is,

$$\iint_{S_1} (\nabla \times \mathbf{F}) \cdot \mathbf{n}_1\, dS = \iint_{S_2} (\nabla \times \mathbf{F}) \cdot \mathbf{n}_2\, dS,$$

where $\mathbf{n}_1$ and $\mathbf{n}_2$ are the respective unit normal vectors consistent with the orientation of the surfaces (Figure 14.67a).

　　　Now let's take a different perspective. Suppose S is a *closed* surface consisting of S_1 and S_2 with a common boundary curve C (Figure 14.67b). Let $\mathbf{n}$ represent the outward unit normal vectors for the entire surface S. Either the vectors normal to S_1 point out of the enclosed region (in the direction of $\mathbf{n}$) and the vectors normal to S_2 point into that region (opposite $\mathbf{n}$), or vice versa. In either case, $\iint_{S_1} (\nabla \times \mathbf{F}) \cdot \mathbf{n}_1\, dS$ and $\iint_{S_2} (\nabla \times \mathbf{F}) \cdot \mathbf{n}_2\, dS$ are equal in magnitude and of opposite sign; therefore,

$$\iint_S (\nabla \times \mathbf{F}) \cdot \mathbf{n}\, dS = \iint_{S_1} (\nabla \times \mathbf{F}) \cdot \mathbf{n}_1\, dS + \iint_{S_2} (\nabla \times \mathbf{F}) \cdot \mathbf{n}_2\, dS = 0.$$

This argument can be adapted to show that $\iint_S (\nabla \times \mathbf{F}) \cdot \mathbf{n} \, dS = 0$ over any closed oriented surface S (Exercise 46).

2. We can now resolve an assertion made in Section 14.5. There we proved (Theorem 14.9) that if $\mathbf{F}$ is a conservative vector field, then $\nabla \times \mathbf{F} = \mathbf{0}$; we claimed, but did not prove, that the converse is true. The converse follows directly from Stokes' Theorem.

> **THEOREM 14.14   Curl F = 0 Implies F Is Conservative**
> Suppose that $\nabla \times \mathbf{F} = \mathbf{0}$ throughout an open simply connected region D of $\mathbb{R}^3$. Then $\oint_C \mathbf{F} \cdot d\mathbf{r} = 0$ on all closed simple smooth curves C in D and $\mathbf{F}$ is a conservative vector field on D.

Proof: Given a closed simple smooth curve C, an advanced result states that C is the boundary of at least one smooth oriented surface S in D. By Stokes' Theorem

$$\oint_C \mathbf{F} \cdot d\mathbf{r} = \iint_S \underbrace{(\nabla \times \mathbf{F})}_{0} \cdot \mathbf{n} \, dS = 0.$$

Because the line integral equals zero over all such curves in D, the vector field is conservative on D by Theorem 14.5.   ◄

SECTION 14.7 EXERCISES

Review Questions

1. Explain the meaning of the integral $\oint_C \mathbf{F} \cdot d\mathbf{r}$ in Stokes' Theorem.

2. Explain the meaning of the integral $\iint_S (\nabla \times \mathbf{F}) \cdot \mathbf{n} \, dS$ in Stokes' Theorem.

3. Explain the meaning of Stokes' Theorem.

4. Why does a conservative vector field produce zero circulation around a closed curve?

Basic Skills

5–10. Verifying Stokes' Theorem *Verify that the line integral and the surface integral of Stokes' Theorem are equal for the following vector fields, surfaces S, and closed curves C. Assume that C has counterclockwise orientation and S has a consistent orientation.*

5. $\mathbf{F} = \langle y, -x, 10 \rangle$; S is the upper half of the sphere $x^2 + y^2 + z^2 = 1$ and C is the circle $x^2 + y^2 = 1$ in the xy-plane.

6. $\mathbf{F} = \langle 0, -x, y \rangle$; S is the upper half of the sphere $x^2 + y^2 + z^2 = 4$ and C is the circle $x^2 + y^2 = 4$ in the xy-plane.

7. $\mathbf{F} = \langle x, y, z \rangle$; S is the paraboloid $z = 8 - x^2 - y^2$, for $0 \leq z \leq 8$, and C is the circle $x^2 + y^2 = 8$ in the xy-plane.

8. $\mathbf{F} = \langle 2z, -4x, 3y \rangle$; S is the cap of the sphere $x^2 + y^2 + z^2 = 169$ above the plane $z = 12$ and C is the boundary of S.

9. $\mathbf{F} = \langle y - z, z - x, x - y \rangle$; S is the cap of the sphere $x^2 + y^2 + z^2 = 16$ above the plane $z = \sqrt{7}$ and C is the boundary of S.

10. $\mathbf{F} = \langle -y, -x - z, y - x \rangle$; S is the part of the plane $z = 6 - y$ that lies in the cylinder $x^2 + y^2 = 16$ and C is the boundary of S.

11–16. Stokes' Theorem for evaluating line integrals *Evaluate the line integral $\oint_C \mathbf{F} \cdot d\mathbf{r}$ by evaluating the surface integral in Stokes' Theorem with an appropriate choice of S. Assume that C has a counterclockwise orientation.*

11. $\mathbf{F} = \langle 2y, -z, x \rangle$; C is the circle $x^2 + y^2 = 12$ in the plane $z = 0$.

12. $\mathbf{F} = \langle y, xz, -y \rangle$; C is the ellipse $x^2 + y^2/4 = 1$ in the plane $z = 1$.

13. $\mathbf{F} = \langle x^2 - z^2, y, 2xz \rangle$; C is the boundary of the plane $z = 4 - x - y$ in the first octant.

14. $\mathbf{F} = \langle x^2 - y^2, z^2 - x^2, y^2 - z^2 \rangle$; C is the boundary of the square $|x| \leq 1$, $|y| \leq 1$ in the plane $z = 0$.

15. $\mathbf{F} = \langle y^2, -z^2, x \rangle$; C is the circle $\mathbf{r}(t) = \langle 3 \cos t, 4 \cos t, 5 \sin t \rangle$, for $0 \leq t \leq 2\pi$.

16. $\mathbf{F} = \langle 2xy \sin z, x^2 \sin z, x^2 y \cos z \rangle$; C is the boundary of the plane $z = 8 - 2x - 4y$ in the first octant.

17–20. Stokes' Theorem for evaluating surface integrals *Evaluate the line integral in Stokes' Theorem to determine the value of the surface integral $\iint_S (\nabla \times \mathbf{F}) \cdot \mathbf{n} \, dS$. Assume that $\mathbf{n}$ points in an upward direction.*

17. $\mathbf{F} = \langle x, y, z \rangle$; S is the upper half of the ellipsoid $x^2/4 + y^2/9 + z^2 = 1$.

18. $\mathbf{F} = \mathbf{r}/|\mathbf{r}|$; S is the paraboloid $x = 9 - y^2 - z^2$, for $0 \leq x \leq 9$ (excluding its base), where $\mathbf{r} = \langle x, y, z \rangle$.

19. $\mathbf{F} = \langle 2y, -z, x - y - z \rangle$; S is the cap of the sphere (excluding its base) $x^2 + y^2 + z^2 = 25$, for $3 \leq x \leq 5$.

20. $\mathbf{F} = \langle x + y, y + z, z + x \rangle$; S is the tilted disk enclosed by $\mathbf{r}(t) = \langle \cos t, 2 \sin t, \sqrt{3} \cos t \rangle$.

21–24. Interpreting and graphing the curl *For the following velocity fields, compute the curl, make a sketch of the curl, and interpret the curl.*

21. $\mathbf{v} = \langle 0, 0, y \rangle$

22. $\mathbf{v} = \langle 1 - z^2, 0, 0 \rangle$

23. $\mathbf{v} = \langle -2z, 0, 1 \rangle$

24. $\mathbf{v} = \langle 0, -z, y \rangle$

Further Explorations

25. Explain why or why not Determine whether the following statements are true and give an explanation or counterexample.

    a. A paddle wheel with its axis in the direction $\langle 0, 1, -1 \rangle$ would not spin when put in the vector field $\mathbf{F} = \langle 1, 1, 2 \rangle \times \langle x, y, z \rangle$.

    b. Stokes' Theorem relates the flux of a vector field $\mathbf{F}$ across a surface to the values of $\mathbf{F}$ on the boundary of the surface.

    c. A vector field of the form $\mathbf{F} = \langle a + f(x), b + g(y), c + h(z) \rangle$, where a, b, and c are constants, has zero circulation on a closed curve.

    d. If a vector field has zero circulation on all simple closed smooth curves C in a region D, then $\mathbf{F}$ is conservative on D.

26–29. Conservative fields *Use Stokes' Theorem to find the circulation of the following vector fields around any simple closed smooth curve C.*

26. $\mathbf{F} = \langle 2x, -2y, 2z \rangle$

27. $\mathbf{F} = \nabla (x \sin y \, e^z)$

28. $\mathbf{F} = \langle 3x^2 y, x^3 + 2yz^2, 2y^2 z \rangle$

29. $\mathbf{F} = \langle y^2 z^3, 2xyz^3, 3xy^2 z^2 \rangle$

30–34. Tilted disks *Let S be the disk enclosed by the curve $C: \mathbf{r}(t) = \langle \cos \varphi \cos t, \sin t, \sin \varphi \cos t \rangle$, for $0 \le t \le 2\pi$, where $0 \le \varphi \le \pi/2$ is a fixed angle.*

30. What is the area of S? Find a vector normal to S.

31. What is the length of C?

32. Use Stokes' Theorem and a surface integral to find the circulation on C of the vector field $\mathbf{F} = \langle -y, x, 0 \rangle$ as a function of φ. For what value of φ is the circulation a maximum?

33. What is the circulation on C of the vector field $\mathbf{F} = \langle -y, -z, x \rangle$ as a function of φ? For what value of φ is the circulation a maximum?

34. Consider the vector field $\mathbf{F} = \mathbf{a} \times \mathbf{r}$, where $\mathbf{a} = \langle a_1, a_2, a_3 \rangle$ is a constant nonzero vector and $\mathbf{r} = \langle x, y, z \rangle$. Show that the circulation is a maximum when $\mathbf{a}$ points in the direction of the normal to S.

35. Circulation in a plane A circle C in the plane $x + y + z = 8$ has a radius of 4 and center $(2, 3, 3)$. Evaluate $\oint_C \mathbf{F} \cdot d\mathbf{r}$ for $\mathbf{F} = \langle 0, -z, 2y \rangle$ where C has a counterclockwise orientation when viewed from above. Does the circulation depend on the radius of the circle? Does it depend on the location of the center of the circle?

36. No integrals Let $\mathbf{F} = \langle 2z, z, 2y + x \rangle$ and let S be the hemisphere of radius a with its base in the xy-plane and center at the origin.

    a. Evaluate $\iint_S (\nabla \times \mathbf{F}) \cdot \mathbf{n} \, dS$ by computing $\nabla \times \mathbf{F}$ and appealing to symmetry.

    b. Evaluate the line integral using Stokes' Theorem to check part (a).

37. Compound surface and boundary Begin with the paraboloid $z = x^2 + y^2$, for $0 \le z \le 4$, and slice it with the plane $y = 0$. Let S be the surface that remains for $y \ge 0$ (including the planar surface in the xz-plane) (see figure). Let C be the semicircle and line segment that bound the cap of S in the plane $z = 4$ with counterclockwise orientation. Let $\mathbf{F} = \langle 2z + y, 2x + z, 2y + x \rangle$.

    a. Describe the direction of the vectors normal to the surface that are consistent with the orientation of C.

    b. Evaluate $\iint_S (\nabla \times \mathbf{F}) \cdot \mathbf{n} \, dS$.

    c. Evaluate $\oint_C \mathbf{F} \cdot d\mathbf{r}$ and check for agreement with part (b).

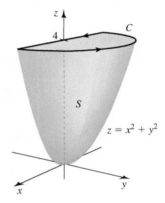

Applications

38. Ampère's Law The French physicist André-Marie Ampère (1775–1836) discovered that an electrical current I in a wire produces a magnetic field $\mathbf{B}$. A special case of Ampère's Law relates the current to the magnetic field through the equation $\oint_C \mathbf{B} \cdot d\mathbf{r} = \mu I$, where C is any closed curve through which the wire passes and μ is a physical constant. Assume that the current I is given in terms of the current density $\mathbf{J}$ as $I = \iint_S \mathbf{J} \cdot \mathbf{n} \, dS$, where S is an oriented surface with C as a boundary. Use Stokes' Theorem to show that an equivalent form of Ampère's Law is $\nabla \times \mathbf{B} = \mu \mathbf{J}$.

39. Maximum surface integral Let S be the paraboloid $z = a(1 - x^2 - y^2)$, for $z \ge 0$, where $a > 0$ is a real number. Let $\mathbf{F} = \langle x - y, y + z, z - x \rangle$. For what value(s) of a (if any) does $\iint_S (\nabla \times \mathbf{F}) \cdot \mathbf{n} \, dS$ have its maximum value?

40. Area of a region in a plane Let R be a region in a plane that has a unit normal vector $\mathbf{n} = \langle a, b, c \rangle$ and boundary C. Let $\mathbf{F} = \langle bz, cx, ay \rangle$.

    a. Show that $\nabla \times \mathbf{F} = \mathbf{n}$.

    b. Use Stokes' Theorem to show that

$$\text{area of } R = \oint_C \mathbf{F} \cdot d\mathbf{r}.$$

    c. Consider the curve C given by $\mathbf{r} = \langle 5 \sin t, 13 \cos t, 12 \sin t \rangle$, for $0 \le t \le 2\pi$. Prove that C lies in a plane by showing that $\mathbf{r} \times \mathbf{r}'$ is constant for all t.

    d. Use part (b) to find the area of the region enclosed by C in part (c). (*Hint:* Find the unit normal vector that is consistent with the orientation of C.)

41. Choosing a more convenient surface The goal is to evaluate $A = \iint_S (\nabla \times \mathbf{F}) \cdot \mathbf{n} \, dS$, where $\mathbf{F} = \langle yz, -xz, xy \rangle$ and S is the surface of the upper half of the ellipsoid $x^2 + y^2 + 8z^2 = 1 \, (z \geq 0)$.

a. Evaluate a surface integral over a more convenient surface to find the value of A.

b. Evaluate A using a line integral.

Additional Exercises

42. Radial fields and zero circulation Consider the radial vector fields $\mathbf{F} = \mathbf{r}/|\mathbf{r}|^p$, where p is a real number and $\mathbf{r} = \langle x, y, z \rangle$. Let C be any circle in the xy-plane centered at the origin.

a. Evaluate a line integral to show that the field has zero circulation on C.

b. For what values of p does Stokes' Theorem apply? For those values of p, use the surface integral in Stokes' Theorem to show that the field has zero circulation on C.

43. Zero curl Consider the vector field

$$\mathbf{F} = \frac{-y}{x^2 + y^2} \mathbf{i} + \frac{x}{x^2 + y^2} \mathbf{j} + z \mathbf{k}.$$

a. Show that $\nabla \times \mathbf{F} = \mathbf{0}$.

b. Show that $\oint_C \mathbf{F} \cdot d\mathbf{r}$ is not zero on a circle C in the xy-plane enclosing the origin.

c. Explain why Stokes' Theorem does not apply in this case.

44. Average circulation Let S be a small circular disk of radius R centered at the point P with a unit normal vector $\mathbf{n}$. Let C be the boundary of S.

a. Express the average circulation of the vector field $\mathbf{F}$ on S as a surface integral of $\nabla \times \mathbf{F}$.

b. Argue that for small R, the average circulation approaches $(\nabla \times \mathbf{F})|_P \cdot \mathbf{n}$ (the component of $\nabla \times \mathbf{F}$ in the direction of $\mathbf{n}$ evaluated at P) with the approximation improving as $R \to 0$.

45. Proof of Stokes' Theorem Confirm the following step in the proof of Stokes' Theorem. If $z = s(x, y)$ and f, g, and h are functions of x, y, and z, with $M = f + hz_x$ and $N = g + hz_y$, then

$$M_y = f_y + f_z z_y + h z_{xy} + z_x (h_y + h_z z_y) \quad \text{and}$$
$$N_x = g_x + g_z z_x + h z_{yx} + z_y (h_x + h_z z_x).$$

46. Stokes' Theorem on closed surfaces Prove that if $\mathbf{F}$ satisfies the conditions of Stokes' Theorem, then $\iint_S (\nabla \times \mathbf{F}) \cdot \mathbf{n} \, dS = 0$, where S is a smooth surface that encloses a region.

47. Rotated Green's Theorem Use Stokes' Theorem to write the circulation form of Green's Theorem in the yz-plane.

QUICK CHECK ANSWERS

1. If S is a region in the xy-plane, $\mathbf{n} = \mathbf{k}$ and $(\nabla \times \mathbf{F}) \cdot \mathbf{n}$ becomes $g_x - f_y$. **2.** The tangent vector $\mathbf{r}'$ lies in the xy-plane and is orthogonal to the z-component of $\mathbf{F}$. This component does not contribute to the circulation along C. **3.** The vector field is symmetric about the y-axis. ◄

14.8 Divergence Theorem

Vector fields can represent electric or magnetic fields, air velocities in hurricanes, or blood flow in an artery. These and other vector phenomena suggest movement of a "substance." A frequent question concerns the amount of a substance that flows across a surface—for example, the amount of water that passes across the membrane of a cell per unit time. Such flux calculations may be done using flux integrals as in Section 14.6. The Divergence Theorem offers an alternative method. In effect, it says that instead of integrating the flow in and out of a region across its boundary, you may also add up all the sources (or sinks) of the flow throughout the region.

Divergence Theorem

> Circulation form of Green's Theorem → Stokes' Theorem
>
> Flux form of Green's Theorem → Divergence Theorem

The Divergence Theorem is the three-dimensional version of the flux form of Green's Theorem. Recall that if R is a region in the xy-plane, C is the simple closed piecewise-smooth oriented boundary of R, and $\mathbf{F} = \langle f, g \rangle$ is a vector field, Green's Theorem says that

$$\underbrace{\oint_C \mathbf{F} \cdot \mathbf{n} \, ds}_{\text{flux across } C} = \iint_R \underbrace{(f_x + g_y)}_{\text{divergence}} \, dA.$$

The line integral on the left gives the flux across the boundary of R. The double integral on the right measures the net expansion or contraction of the vector field within R. If $\mathbf{F}$ represents a fluid flow or the transport of a material, the theorem says that the cumulative effect of the sources (or sinks) of the flow within R equals the net flow across its boundary.

The Divergence Theorem is a direct extension of Green's Theorem. The plane region in Green's Theorem becomes a solid region D in $\mathbb{R}^3$, and the closed curve in Green's Theorem becomes the oriented surface S that encloses D. The flux integral in Green's Theorem becomes a surface integral over S, and the double integral in Green's Theorem becomes a triple integral over D of the three-dimensional divergence (Figure 14.68).

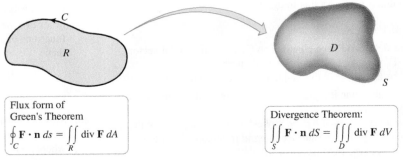

Flux form of
Green's Theorem

$$\oint_C \mathbf{F} \cdot \mathbf{n}\, ds = \iint_R \text{div } \mathbf{F}\, dA$$

Divergence Theorem:

$$\iint_S \mathbf{F} \cdot \mathbf{n}\, dS = \iiint_D \text{div } \mathbf{F}\, dV$$

Figure 14.68

> **THEOREM 14.15   Divergence Theorem**
> Let $\mathbf{F}$ be a vector field whose components have continuous first partial derivatives in a connected and simply connected region D in $\mathbb{R}^3$ enclosed by an oriented surface S. Then
>
> $$\iint_S \mathbf{F} \cdot \mathbf{n}\, dS = \iiint_D \nabla \cdot \mathbf{F}\, dV,$$
>
> where $\mathbf{n}$ is the outward unit normal vector on S.

The surface integral on the left gives the flux of the vector field across the boundary; a positive flux integral means there is a net flow of the field out of the region. The triple integral on the right is the cumulative expansion or contraction of the field over the region D. The proof of a special case of the theorem is given later in this section.

QUICK CHECK 1 Interpret the Divergence Theorem in the case that $\mathbf{F} = \langle a, b, c \rangle$ is a constant vector field and D is a ball. ◄

EXAMPLE 1   Verifying the Divergence Theorem   Consider the radial field $\mathbf{F} = \langle x, y, z \rangle$ and let S be the sphere $x^2 + y^2 + z^2 = a^2$ that encloses the region D. Assume $\mathbf{n}$ is the outward unit normal vector on the sphere. Evaluate both integrals of the Divergence Theorem.

SOLUTION   The divergence of $\mathbf{F}$ is

$$\nabla \cdot \mathbf{F} = \frac{\partial}{\partial x}(x) + \frac{\partial}{\partial y}(y) + \frac{\partial}{\partial z}(z) = 3.$$

Integrating over D, we have

$$\iiint_D \nabla \cdot \mathbf{F}\, dV = \iiint_D 3\, dV = 3 \cdot \text{volume}(D) = 3 \cdot \frac{4}{3}\pi a^3 = 4\pi a^3.$$

To evaluate the surface integral, we parameterize the sphere (Section 14.6, Table 14.3) in the form

$$\mathbf{r} = \langle x, y, z \rangle = \langle a \sin u \cos v, a \sin u \sin v, a \cos u \rangle,$$

where $R = \{(u, v): 0 \le u \le \pi, 0 \le v \le 2\pi\}$ (u and v are the spherical coordinates φ and θ, respectively). The surface integral is

$$\iint\limits_{S} \mathbf{F} \cdot \mathbf{n}\, dS = \iint\limits_{R} \mathbf{F} \cdot (\mathbf{t}_u \times \mathbf{t}_v)\, dA,$$

where the required vector normal to the surface is

$$\mathbf{t}_u \times \mathbf{t}_v = \langle a^2 \sin^2 u \cos v, a^2 \sin^2 u \sin v, a^2 \sin u \cos u \rangle.$$

Substituting for $\mathbf{F} = \langle x, y, z \rangle$ and $\mathbf{t}_u \times \mathbf{t}_v$, we find after simplifying that $\mathbf{F} \cdot (\mathbf{t}_u \times \mathbf{t}_v) = a^3 \sin u$. Therefore, the surface integral becomes

> ▶ See Exercise 32 for an alternative evaluation of the surface integral.

$$\iint\limits_{S} \mathbf{F} \cdot \mathbf{n}\, dS = \iint\limits_{R} \underbrace{\mathbf{F} \cdot (\mathbf{t}_u \times \mathbf{t}_v)}_{a^3 \sin u}\, dA$$

$$= \int_0^{2\pi} \int_0^{\pi} a^3 \sin u\, du\, dv \quad \text{Substitute for } \mathbf{F} \text{ and } \mathbf{t}_u \times \mathbf{t}_v.$$

$$= 4\pi a^3. \qquad\qquad \text{Evaluate integrals.}$$

The two integrals of the Divergence Theorem are equal.

Related Exercises 9–12 ◀

EXAMPLE 2   Divergence Theorem with a rotation field Consider the rotation field

$$\mathbf{F} = \mathbf{a} \times \mathbf{r} = \langle 1, 0, 1 \rangle \times \langle x, y, z \rangle = \langle -y, x - z, y \rangle.$$

Let S be the hemisphere $x^2 + y^2 + z^2 = a^2$, for $z \ge 0$, together with its base in the xy-plane. Find the net outward flux across S.

SOLUTION To find the flux using surface integrals, two surfaces must be considered (the hemisphere and its base). The Divergence Theorem gives a simpler solution. Note that

$$\nabla \cdot \mathbf{F} = \frac{\partial}{\partial x}(-y) + \frac{\partial}{\partial y}(x - z) + \frac{\partial}{\partial z}(y) = 0.$$

We see that the flux across the hemisphere is zero.

Related Exercises 13–16 ◀

With Stokes' Theorem, rotation fields are noteworthy because they have a nonzero curl. With the Divergence Theorem, the situation is reversed. As suggested by Example 2, pure rotation fields of the form $\mathbf{F} = \mathbf{a} \times \mathbf{r}$ have zero divergence (Exercise 16). However, with the Divergence Theorem, radial fields are interesting and have many physical applications.

EXAMPLE 3   Computing flux with the Divergence Theorem Find the net outward flux of the field $\mathbf{F} = xyz\langle 1, 1, 1 \rangle$ across the boundaries of the cube $D = \{(x, y, z): 0 \le x \le 1, 0 \le y \le 1, 0 \le z \le 1\}$.

SOLUTION Computing a surface integral involves the six faces of the cube. The Divergence Theorem gives the outward flux with a single integral over D. The divergence of the field is

$$\nabla \cdot \mathbf{F} = \frac{\partial}{\partial x}(xyz) + \frac{\partial}{\partial y}(xyz) + \frac{\partial}{\partial z}(xyz) = yz + xz + xy.$$

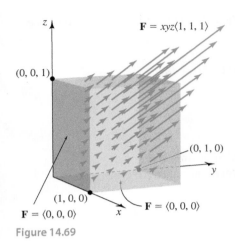

F = xyz⟨1, 1, 1⟩

(0, 0, 1)

(0, 1, 0)

(1, 0, 0)

F = ⟨0, 0, 0⟩   F = ⟨0, 0, 0⟩

Figure 14.69

The integral over D is a standard triple integral:

$$\iiint_D \nabla \cdot \mathbf{F} \, dV = \iiint_D (yz + xz + xy) \, dV$$

$$= \int_0^1 \int_0^1 \int_0^1 (yz + xz + xy) \, dx \, dy \, dz \quad \text{Convert to a triple integral.}$$

$$= \frac{3}{4}. \qquad\qquad\qquad\qquad \text{Evaluate integrals.}$$

On three faces of the cube (those that lie in the coordinate planes), we see that $\mathbf{F}(0, y, z) = \mathbf{F}(x, 0, z) = \mathbf{F}(x, y, 0) = \mathbf{0}$, so there is no contribution to the flux on these faces (Figure 14.69). On the other three faces, the vector field has components out of the cube. Therefore, the net outward flux is positive, as calculated.

Related Exercises 17–24 ◄

QUICK CHECK 2 In Example 3, does the vector field have negative components anywhere in the cube D? Is the divergence negative anywhere in D? ◄

> ▶ The mass transport is also called the *flux density*; when multiplied by an area, it gives the flux. We use the convention that flux has units of mass per unit time.

> ▶ Check the units: If **F** has units of mass/(area · time), then the flux has units of mass/time (**n** has no units).

Interpretation of the Divergence Theorem Using Mass Transport

Suppose that **v** is the velocity field of a material, such as water or molasses, and ρ is its constant density. The vector field $\mathbf{F} = \rho\mathbf{v} = \langle f, g, h \rangle$ describes the **mass transport** of the material, with units of (mass/vol) × (length/time) = mass/(area · time); typical units of mass transport are $g/m^2/s$. This means that **F** gives the mass of material flowing past a point (in each of the three coordinate directions) per unit of surface area per unit of time. When **F** is multiplied by an area, the result is the **flux**, with units of mass/unit time.

Now consider a small cube located in the vector field with its faces parallel to the coordinate planes. One vertex is located at $(0, 0, 0)$, the opposite vertex is at $(\Delta x, \Delta y, \Delta z)$, and (x, y, z) is an arbitrary point in the cube (Figure 14.70). The goal is to compute the approximate flux of material across the faces of the cube. We begin with the flux across the two parallel faces $x = 0$ and $x = \Delta x$.

The outward unit vectors normal to the faces $x = 0$ and $x = \Delta x$ are $\langle -1, 0, 0 \rangle$ and $\langle 1, 0, 0 \rangle$, respectively. Each face has area $\Delta y \, \Delta z$, so the approximate net flux across these faces is

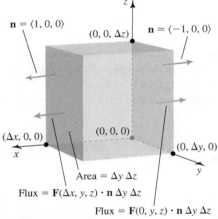

n = ⟨1, 0, 0⟩

(0, 0, Δz)   n = ⟨-1, 0, 0⟩

(Δx, 0, 0)   (0, 0, 0)

(0, Δy, 0)

Area = Δy Δz

Flux = **F**(Δx, y, z) · **n** Δy Δz

Flux = **F**(0, y, z) · **n** Δy Δz

Figure 14.70

$$\underbrace{\mathbf{F}(\Delta x, y, z)}_{x = \Delta x \text{ face}} \cdot \underbrace{\mathbf{n}}_{\langle 1, 0, 0 \rangle} \Delta y \, \Delta z + \underbrace{\mathbf{F}(0, y, z)}_{x = 0 \text{ face}} \cdot \underbrace{\mathbf{n}}_{\langle -1, 0, 0 \rangle} \Delta y \, \Delta z$$

$$= (f(\Delta x, y, z) - f(0, y, z)) \, \Delta y \, \Delta z.$$

Note that if $f(\Delta x, y, z) > f(0, y, z)$, the net flux across these two faces of the cube is positive, which means the net flow is *out* of the cube. Letting $\Delta V = \Delta x \, \Delta y \, \Delta z$ be the volume of the cube, we rewrite the net flux as

$$(f(\Delta x, y, z) - f(0, y, z)) \, \Delta y \, \Delta z$$

$$= \frac{f(\Delta x, y, z) - f(0, y, z)}{\Delta x} \, \Delta x \, \Delta y \, \Delta z \quad \text{Multiply by } \frac{\Delta x}{\Delta x}$$

$$= \frac{f(\Delta x, y, z) - f(0, y, z)}{\Delta x} \, \Delta V. \qquad \Delta V = \Delta x \, \Delta y \, \Delta z$$

A similar argument can be applied to the other two pairs of faces. The approximate net flux across the faces $y = 0$ and $y = \Delta y$ is

$$\frac{g(x, \Delta y, z) - g(x, 0, z)}{\Delta y} \, \Delta V,$$

and the approximate net flux across the faces $z = 0$ and $z = \Delta z$ is

$$\frac{h(x, y, \Delta z) - h(x, y, 0)}{\Delta z} \, \Delta V.$$

Adding these three individual fluxes gives the approximate net flux out of the cube:

$$\text{net flux out of cube} \approx \left(\underbrace{\frac{f(\Delta x, y, z) - f(0, y, z)}{\Delta x}}_{\approx \frac{\partial f}{\partial x}(0,0,0)} + \underbrace{\frac{g(x, \Delta y, z) - g(x, 0, z)}{\Delta y}}_{\approx \frac{\partial g}{\partial y}(0,0,0)} \right.$$

$$\left. + \underbrace{\frac{h(x, y, \Delta z) - h(x, y, 0)}{\Delta z}}_{\approx \frac{\partial h}{\partial z}(0,0,0)} \right) \Delta V$$

$$\approx \left(\frac{\partial f}{\partial x} + \frac{\partial g}{\partial y} + \frac{\partial h}{\partial z} \right)\Bigg|_{(0,0,0)} \Delta V$$

$$= (\nabla \cdot \mathbf{F})(0, 0, 0)\, \Delta V.$$

Notice how the three quotients approximate partial derivatives when Δx, Δy, and Δz are small. A similar argument may be made at any point in the region.

Taking one more step, we show informally how the Divergence Theorem arises. Suppose the small cube we just analyzed is one of many small cubes of volume ΔV that fill a region D. We label the cubes $k = 1, \ldots, n$ and apply the preceding argument to each cube, letting $(\nabla \cdot \mathbf{F})_k$ be the divergence evaluated at a point in the kth cube. Adding the individual contributions to the net flux from each cube, we obtain the approximate net flux across the boundary of D:

$$\text{net flux out of } D \approx \sum_{k=1}^{n} (\nabla \cdot \mathbf{F})_k\, \Delta V.$$

> In making this argument, notice that for two adjacent cubes, the flux into one cube equals the flux out of the other cube across the common face. Therefore, there is a cancellation of fluxes throughout the interior of D.

Letting the volume of the cubes ΔV approach 0 and letting the number of cubes n increase, we obtain an integral over D:

$$\text{net flux out of } D = \lim_{n \to \infty} \sum_{k=1}^{n} (\nabla \cdot \mathbf{F})_k\, \Delta V = \iiint_D \nabla \cdot \mathbf{F}\, dV.$$

The net flux across the boundary of D is also given by $\iint_S \mathbf{F} \cdot \mathbf{n}\, dS$. Equating the surface integral and the volume integral gives the Divergence Theorem. Now we look at a formal proof.

QUICK CHECK 3 Draw the unit cube $D = \{(x, y, z): 0 \le x \le 1, 0 \le y \le 1, 0 \le z \le 1\}$ and sketch the vector field $\mathbf{F} = \langle x, -y, 2z \rangle$ on the six faces of the cube. Compute and interpret div $\mathbf{F}$. ◄

Proof of the Divergence Theorem

We prove the Divergence Theorem under special conditions on the region D. Let R be the projection of D in the xy-plane (Figure 14.71); that is,

$$R = \{(x, y): (x, y, z) \text{ is in } D\}.$$

Assume that the boundary of D is S and let $\mathbf{n}$ be the unit vector normal to S that points outward.

Letting $\mathbf{F} = \langle f, g, h \rangle = f\mathbf{i} + g\mathbf{j} + h\mathbf{k}$, the surface integral in the Divergence Theorem is

$$\iint_S \mathbf{F} \cdot \mathbf{n}\, dS = \iint_S (f\mathbf{i} + g\mathbf{j} + h\mathbf{k}) \cdot \mathbf{n}\, dS$$

$$= \iint_S f\mathbf{i} \cdot \mathbf{n}\, dS + \iint_S g\mathbf{j} \cdot \mathbf{n}\, dS + \iint_S h\mathbf{k} \cdot \mathbf{n}\, dS.$$

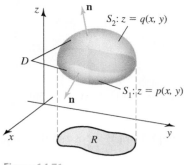

Figure 14.71

The volume integral in the Divergence Theorem is

$$\iiint_D \nabla \cdot \mathbf{F} \, dV = \iiint_D \left(\frac{\partial f}{\partial x} + \frac{\partial g}{\partial y} + \frac{\partial h}{\partial z} \right) dV.$$

Matching terms of the surface and volume integrals, the theorem is proved by showing that

$$\iint_S f\mathbf{i} \cdot \mathbf{n} \, dS = \iiint_D \frac{\partial f}{\partial x} \, dV, \tag{1}$$

$$\iint_S g\mathbf{j} \cdot \mathbf{n} \, dS = \iiint_D \frac{\partial g}{\partial y} \, dV, \text{ and} \tag{2}$$

$$\iint_S h\mathbf{k} \cdot \mathbf{n} \, dS = \iiint_D \frac{\partial h}{\partial z} \, dV. \tag{3}$$

We work on equation (3) assuming special properties for D. Suppose D is bounded by two surfaces S_1: $z = p(x, y)$ and S_2: $z = q(x, y)$, where $p(x, y) \le q(x, y)$ on R (Figure 14.71). The Fundamental Theorem of Calculus is used in the triple integral to show that

$$\iiint_D \frac{\partial h}{\partial z} \, dV = \iint_R \int_{p(x, y)}^{q(x, y)} \frac{\partial h}{\partial z} \, dz \, dx \, dy$$

$$= \iint_R \left(h(x, y, q(x, y)) - h(x, y, p(x, y)) \right) dx \, dy. \quad \text{Evaluate inner integral.}$$

Now let's turn to the surface integral in equation (3), $\iint_S h\mathbf{k} \cdot \mathbf{n} \, dS$, and note that S consists of three pieces: the lower surface S_1, the upper surface S_2, and the vertical sides S_3 of the surface (if they exist). The normal to S_3 is everywhere orthogonal to $\mathbf{k}$, so $\mathbf{k} \cdot \mathbf{n} = 0$ and the S_3 integral makes no contribution. What remains is to compute the surface integrals over S_1 and S_2.

The required outward normal to S_2 (which is the graph of $z = q(x, y)$) is $\langle -q_x, -q_y, 1 \rangle$. The outward normal to S_1 (which is the graph of $z = p(x, y)$) points *downward*, so it is given by $\langle p_x, p_y, -1 \rangle$. The surface integral of (3) becomes

$$\iint_S h\mathbf{k} \cdot \mathbf{n} \, dS = \iint_{S_2} h(x, y, z)\, \mathbf{k} \cdot \mathbf{n} \, dS + \iint_{S_1} h(x, y, z)\, \mathbf{k} \cdot \mathbf{n} \, dS$$

$$= \iint_R h(x, y, q(x, y))\, \underbrace{\mathbf{k} \cdot \langle -q_x, -q_y, 1 \rangle}_{1} \, dx \, dy$$

$$+ \iint_R h(x, y, p(x, y))\, \underbrace{\mathbf{k} \cdot \langle p_x, p_y, -1 \rangle}_{-1} \, dx \, dy$$

$$= \iint_R h(x, y, q(x, y)) \, dx \, dy - \iint_R h(x, y, p(x, y)) \, dx \, dy. \quad \text{Simplify.}$$

Observe that both the volume integral and the surface integral of (3) reduce to the same integral over R. Therefore, $\iint_S h\mathbf{k} \cdot \mathbf{n} \, dS = \iiint_D \frac{\partial h}{\partial z} \, dV$.

Equations (1) and (2) are handled in a similar way.

- To prove (1), we make the special assumption that D is also bounded by two surfaces, $S_1: x = s(y, z)$ and $S_2: x = t(y, z)$, where $s(y, z) \leq t(y, z)$.
- To prove (2), we assume that D is bounded by two surfaces, $S_1: y = u(x, z)$ and $S_2: y = v(x, z)$, where $u(x, z) \leq v(x, z)$.

When combined, equations (1), (2), and (3) yield the Divergence Theorem.   ◀

Divergence Theorem for Hollow Regions

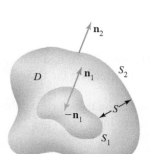

$\mathbf{n}_1$ is the outward unit normal to S_1 and points into D. The outward unit normal to S on S_1 is $-\mathbf{n}_1$.

Figure 14.72

The Divergence Theorem may be extended to more general solid regions. Here we consider the important case of hollow regions. Suppose that D is a region consisting of all points inside a closed oriented surface S_2 and outside a closed oriented surface S_1, where S_1 lies within S_2 (Figure 14.72). Therefore, the boundary of D consists of S_1 and S_2, which we denote S. (Note that D *is* simply connected.)

We let $\mathbf{n}_1$ and $\mathbf{n}_2$ be the outward unit normal vectors for S_1 and S_2, respectively. Note that $\mathbf{n}_1$ points into D, so the outward normal to S on S_1 is $-\mathbf{n}_1$. With this observation, the Divergence Theorem takes the following form.

> ➤ It's important to point out again that $\mathbf{n}_1$ is the unit normal that we would use for S_1 alone, independent of S. It is the outward unit normal to S_1, but it points into D.

THEOREM 14.16   Divergence Theorem for Hollow Regions
Suppose the vector field $\mathbf{F}$ satisfies the conditions of the Divergence Theorem on a region D bounded by two oriented surfaces S_1 and S_2, where S_1 lies within S_2. Let S be the entire boundary of D ($S = S_1 \cup S_2$) and let $\mathbf{n}_1$ and $\mathbf{n}_2$ be the outward unit normal vectors for S_1 and S_2, respectively. Then

$$\iiint_D \nabla \cdot \mathbf{F} \, dV = \iint_S \mathbf{F} \cdot \mathbf{n} \, dS = \iint_{S_2} \mathbf{F} \cdot \mathbf{n}_2 \, dS - \iint_{S_1} \mathbf{F} \cdot \mathbf{n}_1 \, dS.$$

This form of the Divergence Theorem is applicable to vector fields that are not differentiable at the origin, as is the case with some important radial vector fields.

EXAMPLE 4   Flux for an inverse square field Consider the inverse square vector field

$$\mathbf{F} = \frac{\mathbf{r}}{|\mathbf{r}|^3} = \frac{\langle x, y, z \rangle}{(x^2 + y^2 + z^2)^{3/2}}.$$

> ➤ Recall that an inverse square force is proportional to $1/|\mathbf{r}|^2$ multiplied by a unit vector in the radial direction, which is $\mathbf{r}/|\mathbf{r}|$. Combining these two factors gives $\mathbf{F} = \mathbf{r}/|\mathbf{r}|^3$.

a. Find the net outward flux of $\mathbf{F}$ across the surface of the region $D = \{(x, y, z): a^2 \leq x^2 + y^2 + z^2 \leq b^2\}$ that lies between concentric spheres with radii a and b.

b. Find the outward flux of $\mathbf{F}$ across any sphere that encloses the origin.

SOLUTION

a. Although the vector field is undefined at the origin, it is defined and differentiable in D, which excludes the origin. In Section 14.5 (Exercise 71) it was shown that the divergence of the radial field $\mathbf{F} = \dfrac{\mathbf{r}}{|\mathbf{r}|^p}$ with $p = 3$ is 0. We let S be the union of S_2, the larger sphere of radius b, and S_1, the smaller sphere of radius a. Because $\iiint_D \nabla \cdot \mathbf{F} \, dV = 0$, the Divergence Theorem implies that

$$\iint_S \mathbf{F} \cdot \mathbf{n} \, dS = \iint_{S_2} \mathbf{F} \cdot \mathbf{n}_2 \, dS - \iint_{S_1} \mathbf{F} \cdot \mathbf{n}_1 \, dS = 0.$$

Therefore, the next flux across S is zero.

b. Part (a) implies that

$$\underbrace{\iint_{S_2} \mathbf{F} \cdot \mathbf{n}_2 \, dS}_{\text{out of } D} = \underbrace{\iint_{S_1} \mathbf{F} \cdot \mathbf{n}_1 \, dS.}_{\text{into } D}$$

We see that the flux out of D across S_2 equals the flux into D across S_1. To find that flux, we evaluate the surface integral over S_1 on which $|\mathbf{r}| = a$. (Because the fluxes are equal, S_2 could also be used.)

The easiest way to evaluate the surface integral is to note that on the sphere S_1, the unit outward normal vector is $\mathbf{n}_1 = \mathbf{r}/|\mathbf{r}|$. Therefore, the surface integral is

$$\iint_{S_1} \mathbf{F} \cdot \mathbf{n}_1 \, dS = \iint_{S_1} \frac{\mathbf{r}}{|\mathbf{r}|^3} \cdot \frac{\mathbf{r}}{|\mathbf{r}|} \, dS \quad \text{Substitute for } \mathbf{F} \text{ and } \mathbf{n}_1.$$

$$= \iint_{S_1} \frac{|\mathbf{r}|^2}{|\mathbf{r}|^4} \, dS \quad \mathbf{r} \cdot \mathbf{r} = |\mathbf{r}|^2$$

$$= \iint_{S_1} \frac{1}{a^2} \, dS \quad |\mathbf{r}| = a$$

$$= \frac{4\pi a^2}{a^2} \quad \text{Surface area} = 4\pi a^2$$

$$= 4\pi.$$

The same result is obtained using S_2 or any smooth surface enclosing the origin. The flux of the inverse square field across *any* surface enclosing the origin is 4π. As shown in Exercise 46, among radial fields, this property holds only for the inverse square field ($p = 3$).

Related Exercises 25–30 ◄

Gauss' Law

Applying the Divergence Theorem to electric fields leads to one of the fundamental laws of physics. The electric field due to a point charge Q located at the origin is given by the inverse square law,

$$\mathbf{E}(x, y, z) = \frac{Q}{4\pi\varepsilon_0} \frac{\mathbf{r}}{|\mathbf{r}|^3},$$

where $\mathbf{r} = \langle x, y, z \rangle$ and ε_0 is a physical constant called the *permittivity of free space*.

According to the calculation of Example 4, the flux of the field $\dfrac{\mathbf{r}}{|\mathbf{r}|^3}$ across any surface that encloses the origin is 4π. Therefore, the flux of the electric field across any surface enclosing the origin is $\dfrac{Q}{4\pi\varepsilon_0} \cdot 4\pi = \dfrac{Q}{\varepsilon_0}$ (Figure 14.73a). This is one statement of Gauss' Law: If S is a surface that encloses a point charge Q, then the flux of the electric field across S is

$$\iint_S \mathbf{E} \cdot \mathbf{n} \, dS = \frac{Q}{\varepsilon_0}.$$

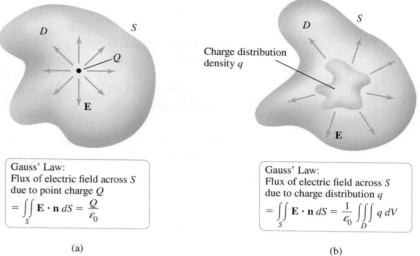

Figure 14.73

In fact, Gauss' Law applies to more general charge distributions (Exercise 39). If $q(x, y, z)$ is a charge density (charge per unit volume) defined on a region D enclosed by S, then the total charge within D is $Q = \iiint_D q(x, y, z)\, dV$ (Figure 14.73b). Replacing Q with this triple integral, Gauss' Law takes the form

$$\iint_S \mathbf{E} \cdot \mathbf{n}\, dS = \frac{1}{\varepsilon_0} \underbrace{\iiint_D q(x, y, z)\, dV}_{Q}.$$

Gauss' Law applies to other inverse square fields. In a slightly different form, it also governs heat transfer. If T is the temperature distribution in a solid body D, then the heat flow vector field is $\mathbf{F} = -k\nabla T$. (Heat flows down the temperature gradient.) If $q(x, y, z)$ represents the sources of heat within D, Gauss' Law says

$$\iint_S \mathbf{F} \cdot \mathbf{n}\, dS = -k \iint_S \nabla T \cdot \mathbf{n}\, dS = \iiint_D q(x, y, z)\, dV.$$

We see that, in general, the flux of material (fluid, heat, electric field lines) across the boundary of a region is the cumulative effect of the sources within the region.

A Final Perspective

Table 14.4 offers a look at the progression of fundamental theorems of calculus that have appeared throughout this book. Each theorem builds on its predecessors, extending the same basic idea to a different situation or to higher dimensions.

In all cases, the statement is effectively the same: The cumulative (integrated) effect of the *derivatives* of a function throughout a region is determined by the values of the function on the boundary of that region. This principle underlies much of our understanding of the world around us.

Table 14.4

Fundamental Theorem of Calculus	$\displaystyle\int_a^b f'(x)\,dx = f(b) - f(a)$	
Fundamental Theorem of Line Integrals	$\displaystyle\int_C \nabla f \cdot d\mathbf{r} = f(B) - f(A)$	
Green's Theorem (Circulation form)	$\displaystyle\iint_R (g_x - f_y)\,dA = \oint_C f\,dx + g\,dy$	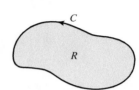
Stokes' Theorem	$\displaystyle\iint_S (\nabla \times \mathbf{F}) \cdot \mathbf{n}\,dS = \oint_C \mathbf{F} \cdot d\mathbf{r}$	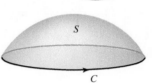
Divergence Theorem	$\displaystyle\iiint_D \nabla \cdot \mathbf{F}\,dV = \iint_S \mathbf{F} \cdot \mathbf{n}\,dS$	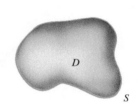

SECTION 14.8 EXERCISES

Review Questions

1. Explain the meaning of the surface integral in the Divergence Theorem.

2. Interpret the volume integral in the Divergence Theorem.

3. Explain the meaning of the Divergence Theorem.

4. What is the net outward flux of the rotation field $\mathbf{F} = \langle 2z + y, -x, -2x \rangle$ across the surface that encloses any region?

5. What is the net outward flux of the radial field $\mathbf{F} = \langle x, y, z \rangle$ across the sphere of radius 2 centered at the origin?

6. What is the divergence of an inverse square vector field?

7. Suppose div $\mathbf{F} = 0$ in a region enclosed by two concentric spheres. What is the relationship between the outward fluxes across the two spheres?

8. If div $\mathbf{F} > 0$ in a region enclosed by a small cube, is the net flux of the field into or out of the cube?

Basic Skills

9–12. Verifying the Divergence Theorem *Evaluate both integrals of the Divergence Theorem for the following vector fields and regions. Check for agreement.*

9. $\mathbf{F} = \langle 2x, 3y, 4z \rangle$; $D = \{(x, y, z): x^2 + y^2 + z^2 \le 4\}$

10. $\mathbf{F} = \langle -x, -y, -z \rangle$;
$D = \{(x, y, z): |x| \le 1, |y| \le 1, |z| \le 1\}$

11. $\mathbf{F} = \langle z - y, x, -x \rangle$;
$D = \{(x, y, z): x^2/4 + y^2/8 + z^2/12 \le 1\}$

12. $\mathbf{F} = \langle x^2, y^2, z^2 \rangle$; $D = \{(x, y, z): |x| \le 1, |y| \le 2, |z| \le 3\}$

13–16. Rotation fields

13. Find the net outward flux of the field $\mathbf{F} = \langle 2z - y, x, -2x \rangle$ across the sphere of radius 1 centered at the origin.

14. Find the net outward flux of the field $\mathbf{F} = \langle z - y, x - z, y - x \rangle$ across the boundary of the cube $\{(x, y, z): |x| \le 1, |y| \le 1, |z| \le 1\}$.

15. Find the net outward flux of the field $\mathbf{F} = \langle bz - cy, cx - az, ay - bx \rangle$ across any smooth closed surface in $\mathbb{R}^3$, where a, b, and c are constants.

16. Find the net outward flux of $\mathbf{F} = \mathbf{a} \times \mathbf{r}$ across any smooth closed surface in $\mathbb{R}^3$, where $\mathbf{a}$ is a constant nonzero vector and $\mathbf{r} = \langle x, y, z \rangle$.

17–24. Computing flux *Use the Divergence Theorem to compute the net outward flux of the following fields across the given surfaces S.*

17. $\mathbf{F} = \langle x, -2y, 3z \rangle$; S is the sphere $\{(x, y, z): x^2 + y^2 + z^2 = 6\}$.

18. $\mathbf{F} = \langle x^2, 2xz, y^2 \rangle$; S is the surface of the cube cut from the first octant by the planes $x = 1$, $y = 1$, and $z = 1$.

19. $\mathbf{F} = \langle x, 2y, z \rangle$; S is the boundary of the tetrahedron in the first octant formed by the plane $x + y + z = 1$.

20. $\mathbf{F} = \langle x^2, y^2, z^2 \rangle$; S is the sphere $\{(x, y, z): x^2 + y^2 + z^2 = 25\}$.

21. $\mathbf{F} = \langle y - 2x, x^3 - y, y^2 - z \rangle$; S is the sphere $\{(x, y, z): x^2 + y^2 + z^2 = 4\}$.

22. $\mathbf{F} = \langle y + z, x + z, x + y \rangle$; S consists of the faces of the cube $\{(x, y, z): |x| \leq 1, |y| \leq 1, |z| \leq 1\}$.

23. $\mathbf{F} = \langle x, y, z \rangle$; S is the surface of the paraboloid $z = 4 - x^2 - y^2$, for $z \geq 0$, plus its base in the xy-plane.

24. $\mathbf{F} = \langle x, y, z \rangle$; S is the surface of the cone $z^2 = x^2 + y^2$, for $0 \leq z \leq 4$, plus its top surface in the plane $z = 4$.

25–30. Divergence Theorem for more general regions *Use the Divergence Theorem to compute the net outward flux of the following vector fields across the boundary of the given regions D.*

25. $\mathbf{F} = \langle z - x, x - y, 2y - z \rangle$; D is the region between the spheres of radius 2 and 4 centered at the origin.

26. $\mathbf{F} = \mathbf{r}|\mathbf{r}| = \langle x, y, z \rangle \sqrt{x^2 + y^2 + z^2}$; D is the region between the spheres of radius 1 and 2 centered at the origin.

27. $\mathbf{F} = \dfrac{\mathbf{r}}{|\mathbf{r}|} = \dfrac{\langle x, y, z \rangle}{\sqrt{x^2 + y^2 + z^2}}$; D is the region between the spheres of radius 1 and 2 centered at the origin.

28. $\mathbf{F} = \langle z - y, x - z, 2y - x \rangle$; D is the region between two cubes: $\{(x, y, z): 1 \leq |x| \leq 3, 1 \leq |y| \leq 3, 1 \leq |z| \leq 3\}$.

29. $\mathbf{F} = \langle x^2, -y^2, z^2 \rangle$; D is the region in the first octant between the planes $z = 4 - x - y$ and $z = 2 - x - y$.

30. $\mathbf{F} = \langle x, 2y, 3z \rangle$; D is the region between the cylinders $x^2 + y^2 = 1$ and $x^2 + y^2 = 4$, for $0 \leq z \leq 8$.

Further Explorations

31. Explain why or why not Determine whether the following statements are true and give an explanation or counterexample.

   a. If $\nabla \cdot \mathbf{F} = 0$ at all points of a region D, then $\mathbf{F} \cdot \mathbf{n} = 0$ at all points of the boundary of D.

   b. If $\iint_S \mathbf{F} \cdot \mathbf{n}\, dS = 0$ on all closed surfaces in $\mathbb{R}^3$, then $\mathbf{F}$ is constant.

   c. If $|\mathbf{F}| < 1$, then $\left| \iiint_D \nabla \cdot \mathbf{F}\, dV \right|$ is less than the area of the surface of D.

32. Flux across a sphere Consider the radial field $\mathbf{F} = \langle x, y, z \rangle$ and let S be the sphere of radius a centered at the origin. Compute the outward flux of $\mathbf{F}$ across S using the representation $z = \pm \sqrt{a^2 - x^2 - y^2}$ for the sphere (either symmetry or two surfaces must be used).

33–35. Flux integrals *Compute the outward flux of the following vector fields across the given surfaces S. You should decide which integral of the Divergence Theorem to use.*

33. $\mathbf{F} = \langle x^2 e^y \cos z, -4xe^y \cos z, 2xe^y \sin z \rangle$; S is the boundary of the ellipsoid $x^2/4 + y^2 + z^2 = 1$.

34. $\mathbf{F} = \langle -yz, xz, 1 \rangle$; S is the boundary of the ellipsoid $x^2/4 + y^2/4 + z^2 = 1$.

35. $\mathbf{F} = \langle x \sin y, -\cos y, z \sin y \rangle$; S is the boundary of the region bounded by the planes $x = 1$, $y = 0$, $y = \pi/2$, $z = 0$, and $z = x$.

36. Radial fields Consider the radial vector field $\mathbf{F} = \dfrac{\mathbf{r}}{|\mathbf{r}|^p} = \dfrac{\langle x, y, z \rangle}{(x^2 + y^2 + z^2)^{p/2}}$. Let S be the sphere of radius a centered at the origin.

   a. Use a surface integral to show that the outward flux of $\mathbf{F}$ across S is $4\pi a^{3-p}$. Recall that the unit normal to the sphere is $\mathbf{r}/|\mathbf{r}|$.

   b. For what values of p does $\mathbf{F}$ satisfy the conditions of the Divergence Theorem? For these values of p, use the fact (Theorem 14.8) that $\nabla \cdot \mathbf{F} = \dfrac{3 - p}{|\mathbf{r}|^p}$ to compute the flux across S using the Divergence Theorem.

37. Singular radial field Consider the radial field

$$\mathbf{F} = \frac{\mathbf{r}}{|\mathbf{r}|} = \frac{\langle x, y, z \rangle}{(x^2 + y^2 + z^2)^{1/2}}.$$

   a. Evaluate a surface integral to show that $\iint_S \mathbf{F} \cdot \mathbf{n}\, dS = 4\pi a^2$, where S is the surface of a sphere of radius a centered at the origin.

   b. Note that the first partial derivatives of the components of $\mathbf{F}$ are undefined at the origin, so the Divergence Theorem does not apply directly. Nevertheless, the flux across the sphere as computed in part (a) is finite. Evaluate the triple integral of the Divergence Theorem as an improper integral as follows. Integrate div $\mathbf{F}$ over the region between two spheres of radius a and $0 < \varepsilon < a$. Then let $\varepsilon \to 0^+$ to obtain the flux computed in part (a).

38. Logarithmic potential Consider the potential function $\varphi(x, y, z) = \frac{1}{2} \ln(x^2 + y^2 + z^2) = \ln |\mathbf{r}|$, where $\mathbf{r} = \langle x, y, z \rangle$.

   a. Show that the gradient field associated with φ is

$$\mathbf{F} = \frac{\mathbf{r}}{|\mathbf{r}|^2} = \frac{\langle x, y, z \rangle}{x^2 + y^2 + z^2}.$$

   b. Show that $\iint_S \mathbf{F} \cdot \mathbf{n}\, dS = 4\pi a$, where S is the surface of a sphere of radius a centered at the origin.

   c. Compute div $\mathbf{F}$.

   d. Note that $\mathbf{F}$ is undefined at the origin, so the Divergence Theorem does not apply directly. Evaluate the volume integral as described in Exercise 37.

Applications

39. Gauss' Law for electric fields The electric field due to a point charge Q is $\mathbf{E} = \dfrac{Q}{4\pi\varepsilon_0}\dfrac{\mathbf{r}}{|\mathbf{r}|^3}$, where $\mathbf{r} = \langle x, y, z \rangle$, and ε_0 is a constant.

   a. Show that the flux of the field across a sphere of radius a centered at the origin is $\iint_S \mathbf{E} \cdot \mathbf{n}\, dS = \dfrac{Q}{\varepsilon_0}$.

   b. Let S be the boundary of the region between two spheres centered at the origin of radius a and b with $a < b$. Use the Divergence Theorem to show that the net outward flux across S is zero.

   c. Suppose there is a distribution of charge within a region D. Let $q(x, y, z)$ be the charge density (charge per unit volume). Interpret the statement that

$$\iint_S \mathbf{E} \cdot \mathbf{n}\, dS = \frac{1}{\varepsilon_0} \iiint_D q(x, y, z)\, dV.$$

   d. Assuming $\mathbf{E}$ satisfies the conditions of the Divergence Theorem on D, conclude from part (c) that $\nabla \cdot \mathbf{E} = \dfrac{q}{\varepsilon_0}$.

e. Because the electric force is conservative, it has a potential function φ. From part (d), conclude that

$$\nabla^2 \varphi = \nabla \cdot \nabla \varphi = \frac{q}{\varepsilon_0}.$$

40. **Gauss' Law for gravitation** The gravitational force due to a point mass M at the origin is proportional to $\mathbf{F} = GM\mathbf{r}/|\mathbf{r}|^3$, where $\mathbf{r} = \langle x, y, z \rangle$ and G is the gravitational constant.

a. Show that the flux of the force field across a sphere of radius a centered at the origin is $\iint_S \mathbf{F} \cdot \mathbf{n}\, dS = 4\pi GM$.
b. Let S be the boundary of the region between two spheres centered at the origin of radius a and b with $a < b$. Use the Divergence Theorem to show that the net outward flux across S is zero.
c. Suppose there is a distribution of mass within a region D. Let $\rho(x, y, z)$ be the mass density (mass per unit volume). Interpret the statement that

$$\iint_S \mathbf{F} \cdot \mathbf{n}\, dS = 4\pi G \iiint_D \rho(x, y, z)\, dV.$$

d. Assuming $\mathbf{F}$ satisfies the conditions of the Divergence Theorem on D, conclude from part (c) that $\nabla \cdot \mathbf{F} = 4\pi G\rho$.
e. Because the gravitational force is conservative, it has a potential function φ. From part (d), conclude that $\nabla^2 \varphi = 4\pi G\rho$.

41–45. Heat transfer *Fourier's Law of heat transfer (or heat conduction) states that the heat flow vector $\mathbf{F}$ at a point is proportional to the negative gradient of the temperature; that is, $\mathbf{F} = -k\nabla T$, which means that heat energy flows from hot regions to cold regions. The constant $k > 0$ is called the conductivity, which has metric units of J/m-s-K. A temperature function for a region D is given. Find the net outward heat flux $\iint_S \mathbf{F} \cdot \mathbf{n}\, dS = -k \iint_S \nabla T \cdot \mathbf{n}\, dS$ across the boundary S of D. In some cases, it may be easier to use the Divergence Theorem and evaluate a triple integral. Assume that $k = 1$.*

41. $T(x, y, z) = 100 + x + 2y + z;$
    $D = \{(x, y, z): 0 \le x \le 1, 0 \le y \le 1, 0 \le z \le 1\}$

42. $T(x, y, z) = 100 + x^2 + y^2 + z^2;$
    $D = \{(x, y, z): 0 \le x \le 1, 0 \le y \le 1, 0 \le z \le 1\}$

43. $T(x, y, z) = 100 + e^{-z};$
    $D = \{(x, y, z): 0 \le x \le 1, 0 \le y \le 1, 0 \le z \le 1\}$

44. $T(x, y, z) = 100 + x^2 + y^2 + z^2;$ D is the unit sphere centered at the origin.

T 45. $T(x, y, z) = 100e^{-x^2-y^2-z^2};$ D is the sphere of radius a centered at the origin.

Additional Exercises

46. **Inverse square fields are special** Let $\mathbf{F}$ be a radial field $\mathbf{F} = \mathbf{r}/|\mathbf{r}|^p$, where p is a real number and $\mathbf{r} = \langle x, y, z \rangle$. With $p = 3$, $\mathbf{F}$ is an inverse square field.

a. Show that the net flux across a sphere centered at the origin is independent of the radius of the sphere only for $p = 3$.
b. Explain the observation in part (a) by finding the flux of $\mathbf{F} = \mathbf{r}/|\mathbf{r}|^p$ across the boundaries of a spherical box $\{(\rho, \varphi, \theta): a \le \rho \le b, \varphi_1 \le \varphi \le \varphi_2, \theta_1 \le \theta \le \theta_2\}$ for various values of p.

47. **A beautiful flux integral** Consider the potential function $\varphi(x, y, z) = G(\rho)$, where G is any twice differentiable function and $\rho = \sqrt{x^2 + y^2 + z^2}$; therefore, G depends only on the distance from the origin.

a. Show that the gradient vector field associated with φ is

$$\mathbf{F} = \nabla\varphi = G'(\rho)\frac{\mathbf{r}}{\rho}, \text{ where } \mathbf{r} = \langle x, y, z \rangle \text{ and } \rho = |\mathbf{r}|.$$

b. Let S be the sphere of radius a centered at the origin and let D be the region enclosed by S. Show that the flux of $\mathbf{F}$ across S is $\iint_S \mathbf{F} \cdot \mathbf{n}\, dS = 4\pi a^2 G'(a)$.
c. Show that $\nabla \cdot \mathbf{F} = \nabla \cdot \nabla\varphi = \dfrac{2G'(\rho)}{\rho} + G''(\rho)$.

d. Use part (c) to show that the flux across S (as given in part (b)) is also obtained by the volume integral $\iiint_D \nabla \cdot \mathbf{F}\, dV$. (*Hint:* use spherical coordinates and integrate by parts.)

48. **Integration by parts (Gauss' Formula)** Recall the Product Rule of Theorem 14.11: $\nabla \cdot (u\mathbf{F}) = \nabla u \cdot \mathbf{F} + u(\nabla \cdot \mathbf{F})$.

a. Integrate both sides of this identity over a solid region D with a closed boundary S and use the Divergence Theorem to prove an integration by parts rule:

$$\iiint_D u(\nabla \cdot \mathbf{F})\, dV = \iint_S u\mathbf{F} \cdot \mathbf{n}\, dS - \iiint_D \nabla u \cdot \mathbf{F}\, dV.$$

b. Explain the correspondence between this rule and the integration by parts rule for single-variable functions.
c. Use integration by parts to evaluate $\iiint_D (x^2y + y^2z + z^2x)\, dV$, where D is the cube in the first octant cut by the planes $x = 1$, $y = 1$, and $z = 1$.

49. **Green's Formula** Write Gauss' Formula of Exercise 48 in two dimensions—that is, where $\mathbf{F} = \langle f, g \rangle$, D is a plane region R and C is the boundary of R. Show that the result is Green's Formula:

$$\iint_R u(f_x + g_y)\, dA = \oint_C u(\mathbf{F} \cdot \mathbf{n})\, ds - \iint_R (fu_x + gu_y)\, dA.$$

Show that with $u = 1$, one form of Green's Theorem appears. Which form of Green's Theorem is it?

50. **Green's First Identity** Prove Green's First Identity for twice differentiable scalar-valued functions u and v defined on a region D:

$$\iiint_D (u\nabla^2 v + \nabla u \cdot \nabla v)\, dV = \iint_S u\nabla v \cdot \mathbf{n}\, dS,$$

where $\nabla^2 v = \nabla \cdot \nabla v$. You may apply Gauss' Formula in Exercise 48 to $\mathbf{F} = \nabla v$ or apply the Divergence Theorem to $\mathbf{F} = u\nabla v$.

51. **Green's Second Identity** Prove Green's Second Identity for scalar-valued functions u and v defined on a region D:

$$\iiint_D (u\nabla^2 v - v\nabla^2 u)\, dV = \iint_S (u\nabla v - v\nabla u) \cdot \mathbf{n}\, dS.$$

(*Hint:* Reverse the roles of u and v in Green's First Identity.)

52–54. Harmonic functions *A scalar-valued function φ is harmonic on a region D if $\nabla^2\varphi = \nabla \cdot \nabla\varphi = 0$ at all points of D.*

52. Show that the potential function $\varphi(x, y, z) = |\mathbf{r}|^{-p}$ is harmonic provided $p = 0$ or $p = 1$, where $\mathbf{r} = \langle x, y, z \rangle$. To what vector fields do these potentials correspond?

53. Show that if φ is harmonic on a region D enclosed by a surface S, then
$$\iint_S \nabla\varphi \cdot \mathbf{n} \, dS = 0.$$

54. Show that if u is harmonic on a region D enclosed by a surface S, then
$$\iint_S u\,\nabla u \cdot \mathbf{n} \, dS = \iiint_D |\nabla u|^2 \, dV.$$

55. Miscellaneous integral identities Prove the following identities.

a. $\iiint_D \nabla \times \mathbf{F} \, dV = \iint_S (\mathbf{n} \times \mathbf{F}) \, dS$ (*Hint:* Apply the Divergence Theorem to each component of the identity.)

b. $\iint_S (\mathbf{n} \times \nabla\varphi) \, dS = \oint_C \varphi \, d\mathbf{r}$ (*Hint:* Apply Stokes' Theorem to each component of the identity.)

QUICK CHECK ANSWERS

1. If $\mathbf{F}$ is constant, then div $\mathbf{F} = 0$, so $\iiint_D \nabla \cdot \mathbf{F} \, dV = \iint_S \mathbf{F} \cdot \mathbf{n} \, dS = 0$. This means that all the "material" that flows into one side of D flows out of the other side of D. **2.** The vector field and the divergence are positive throughout D. **3.** The vector field has no flow into or out of the cube on the faces $x = 0$, $y = 0$, and $z = 0$ because the vectors of $\mathbf{F}$ on these faces are parallel to the faces. The vector field points out of the cube on the $x = 1$ and $z = 1$ faces and into the cube on the $y = 1$ face. div$(\mathbf{F}) = 2$, so there is a net flow out of the cube.◄

CHAPTER 14 REVIEW EXERCISES

1. Explain why or why not Determine whether the following statements are true and give an explanation or counterexample.

a. The rotational field $\mathbf{F} = \langle -y, x \rangle$ has zero curl and zero divergence.

b. $\nabla \times \nabla\varphi = \mathbf{0}$

c. Two vector fields with the same curl differ by a constant vector field.

d. Two vector fields with the same divergence differ by a constant vector field.

e. If $\mathbf{F} = \langle x, y, z \rangle$ and S encloses a region D, then $\iint_S \mathbf{F} \cdot \mathbf{n} \, dS$ is three times the volume of D.

2. Matching vector fields Match vector fields a–f with the graphs A–F. Let $\mathbf{r} = \langle x, y \rangle$.

a. $\mathbf{F} = \langle x, y \rangle$
b. $\mathbf{F} = \langle -2y, 2x \rangle$
c. $\mathbf{F} = \mathbf{r}/|\mathbf{r}|$
d. $\mathbf{F} = \langle y - x, x \rangle$
e. $\mathbf{F} = \langle e^{-y}, e^{-x} \rangle$
f. $\mathbf{F} = \langle \sin \pi x, \sin \pi y \rangle$

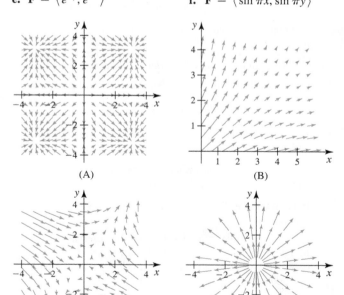

(A) (B) (C) (D)

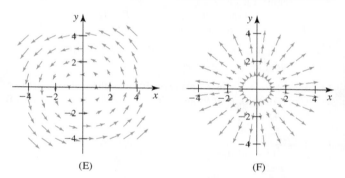

(E) (F)

3–4. Gradient fields in $\mathbb{R}^2$ *Find the vector field $\mathbf{F} = \nabla\varphi$ for the following potential functions. Sketch a few level curves of φ and sketch the general appearance of $\mathbf{F}$ in relation to the level curves.*

3. $\varphi(x, y) = x^2 + 4y^2$, for $|x| \le 5$, $|y| \le 5$

4. $\varphi(x, y) = (x^2 - y^2)/2$, for $|x| \le 2$, $|y| \le 2$

5–6. Gradient fields in $\mathbb{R}^3$ *Find the vector field $\mathbf{F} = \nabla\varphi$ for the following potential functions.*

5. $\varphi(x, y, z) = 1/|\mathbf{r}|$, where $\mathbf{r} = \langle x, y, z \rangle$

6. $\varphi(x, y, z) = \dfrac{1}{2}e^{-x^2-y^2-z^2}$

7. Normal component Let C be the circle of radius 2 centered at the origin with counterclockwise orientation.

a. Give the unit outward normal vector at any point (x, y) on C.

b. Find the normal component of the vector field $\mathbf{F} = 2\langle y, -x \rangle$ at any point on C.

c. Find the normal component of the vector field $\mathbf{F} = \dfrac{\langle x, y \rangle}{x^2 + y^2}$ at any point on C.

8–10. Line integrals *Evaluate the following line integrals.*

8. $\displaystyle\int_C (x^2 - 2xy + y^2)\, ds$; C is the upper half of the circle

   $\mathbf{r}(t) = \langle 5\cos t, 5\sin t\rangle$, for $0 \le t \le \pi$.

9. $\displaystyle\int_C ye^{-xz}\, ds$; C is the path $\mathbf{r}(t) = \langle t, 3t, -6t\rangle$, for $0 \le t \le \ln 8$.

10. $\displaystyle\int_C (xz - y^2)\, ds$; C is the line segment from $(0, 1, 2)$ to

    $(-3, 7, -1)$.

11. **Two parameterizations** Verify that $\oint_C (x - 2y + 3z)\, ds$ has the same value when C is given by $\mathbf{r}(t) = \langle 2\cos t, 2\sin t, 0\rangle$, for $0 \le t \le 2\pi$, and by $\mathbf{r}(t) = \langle 2\cos t^2, 2\sin t^2, 0\rangle$, for $0 \le t \le \sqrt{2\pi}$.

12. **Work integral** Find the work done in moving an object from $P(1, 0, 0)$ to $Q(0, 1, 0)$ in the presence of the force $\mathbf{F} = \langle 1, 2y, -4z\rangle$ along the following paths.

    a. The line segment from P to Q
    b. The line segment from P to $O(0, 0, 0)$ followed by the line segment from O to Q
    c. The arc of the quarter circle from P to Q
    d. Is the work independent of the path?

13–14. Work integrals in $\mathbb{R}^3$ *Given the following force fields, find the work required to move an object on the given curve.*

13. $\mathbf{F} = \langle -y, z, x\rangle$ on the path consisting of the line segment from $(0, 0, 0)$ to $(0, 1, 0)$ followed by the line segment from $(0, 1, 0)$ to $(0, 1, 4)$

14. $\mathbf{F} = \dfrac{\langle x, y, z\rangle}{(x^2 + y^2 + z^2)^{3/2}}$ on the path $\mathbf{r}(t) = \langle t^2, 3t^2, -t^2\rangle$, for $1 \le t \le 2$

15–18. Circulation and flux *Find the circulation and the outward flux of the following vector fields for the curve $\mathbf{r}(t) = \langle 2\cos t, 2\sin t\rangle$, for $0 \le t \le 2\pi$.*

15. $\mathbf{F} = \langle y - x, y\rangle$

16. $\mathbf{F} = \langle x, y\rangle$

17. $\mathbf{F} = \mathbf{r}/|\mathbf{r}|^2$, where $\mathbf{r} = \langle x, y\rangle$

18. $\mathbf{F} = \langle x - y, x\rangle$

19. **Flux in channel flow** Consider the flow of water in a channel whose boundaries are the planes $y = \pm L$ and $z = \pm\frac{1}{2}$. The velocity field in the channel is $\mathbf{v} = \langle v_0(L^2 - y^2), 0, 0\rangle$. Find the flux across the cross section of the channel at $x = 0$ in terms of v_0 and L.

20–23. Conservative vector fields and potentials *Determine whether the following vector fields are conservative on their domains. If so, find a potential function.*

20. $\mathbf{F} = \langle y^2, 2xy\rangle$

21. $\mathbf{F} = \langle y, x + z^2, 2yz\rangle$

22. $\mathbf{F} = \langle e^x \cos y, -e^x \sin y\rangle$

23. $\mathbf{F} = e^z\langle y, x, xy\rangle$

24–27. Evaluating line integrals *Evaluate the line integral $\int_C \mathbf{F}\cdot d\mathbf{r}$ for the following vector fields $\mathbf{F}$ and curves C in two ways.*

a. By parameterizing C
b. By using the Fundamental Theorem for line integrals, if possible

24. $\mathbf{F} = \nabla(x^2y)$; $C: \mathbf{r}(t) = \langle 9 - t^2, t\rangle$, for $0 \le t \le 3$

25. $\mathbf{F} = \nabla(xyz)$; $C: \mathbf{r}(t) = \langle \cos t, \sin t, t/\pi\rangle$, for $0 \le t \le \pi$

26. $\mathbf{F} = \langle x, -y\rangle$; C is the square with vertices $(\pm 1, \pm 1)$ with counterclockwise orientation.

27. $\mathbf{F} = \langle y, z, -x\rangle$; $C: \mathbf{r}(t) = \langle \cos t, \sin t, 4\rangle$, for $0 \le t \le 2\pi$

28. **Radial fields in $\mathbb{R}^2$ are conservative** Prove that the radial field $\mathbf{F} = \dfrac{\mathbf{r}}{|\mathbf{r}|^p}$, where $\mathbf{r} = \langle x, y\rangle$ and p is a real number, is conservative on $\mathbb{R}^2$ with the origin removed. For what value of p is $\mathbf{F}$ conservative on $\mathbb{R}^2$ (including the origin)?

29–32. Green's Theorem for line integrals *Use either form of Green's Theorem to evaluate the following line integrals.*

29. $\oint_C xy^2\, dx + x^2y\, dy$; C is the triangle with vertices $(0, 0)$, $(2, 0)$, and $(0, 2)$ with counterclockwise orientation.

30. $\oint_C (-3y + x^{3/2})\, dx + (x - y^{2/3})\, dy$; C is the boundary of the half disk $\{(x, y): x^2 + y^2 \le 2, y \ge 0\}$ with counterclockwise orientation.

31. $\oint_C (x^3 + xy)\, dy + (2y^2 - 2x^2y)\, dx$; C is the square with vertices $(\pm 1, \pm 1)$ with counterclockwise orientation.

32. $\oint_C 3x^3\, dy - 3y^3\, dx$; C is the circle of radius 4 centered at the origin with *clockwise* orientation.

33–34. Areas of plane regions *Find the area of the following regions using a line integral.*

33. The region enclosed by the ellipse $x^2 + 4y^2 = 16$

34. The region bounded by the hypocycloid $\mathbf{r}(t) = \langle \cos^3 t, \sin^3 t\rangle$, for $0 \le t \le 2\pi$

35–36. Circulation and flux *Consider the following vector fields.*

a. Compute the circulation on the boundary of the region R (with counterclockwise orientation).
b. Compute the outward flux across the boundary of R.

35. $\mathbf{F} = \mathbf{r}/|\mathbf{r}|$, where $\mathbf{r} = \langle x, y\rangle$ and R is the half-annulus $\{(r, \theta): 1 \le r \le 3, 0 \le \theta \le \pi\}$

36. $\mathbf{F} = \langle -\sin y, x\cos y\rangle$, where R is the square $\{(x, y): 0 \le x \le \pi/2, 0 \le y \le \pi/2\}$

37. **Parameters** Let $\mathbf{F} = \langle ax + by, cx + dy\rangle$, where $a, b, c,$ and d are constants.

    a. For what values of $a, b, c,$ and d is $\mathbf{F}$ conservative?
    b. For what values of $a, b, c,$ and d is $\mathbf{F}$ source free?
    c. For what values of $a, b, c,$ and d is $\mathbf{F}$ conservative and source free?

38–41. Divergence and curl *Compute the divergence and curl of the following vector fields. State whether the field is source free or irrotational.*

38. $\mathbf{F} = \langle yz, xz, xy \rangle$

39. $\mathbf{F} = \mathbf{r}|\mathbf{r}| = \langle x, y, z \rangle \sqrt{x^2 + y^2 + z^2}$

40. $\mathbf{F} = \langle \sin xy, \cos yz, \sin xz \rangle$

41. $\mathbf{F} = \langle 2xy + z^4, x^2, 4xz^3 \rangle$

42. Identities Prove that $\nabla\left(\dfrac{1}{|\mathbf{r}|^4}\right) = -\dfrac{4\mathbf{r}}{|\mathbf{r}|^6}$ and use the result to prove that $\nabla \cdot \nabla\left(\dfrac{1}{|\mathbf{r}|^4}\right) = \dfrac{12}{|\mathbf{r}|^6}$.

43. Maximum curl Let $\mathbf{F} = \langle z, x, -y \rangle$.

   a. What is the component of curl $\mathbf{F}$ in the directions $\mathbf{n} = \langle 1, 0, 0 \rangle$ and $\mathbf{n} = \langle 0, -1/\sqrt{2}, 1/\sqrt{2} \rangle$?

   b. In what direction is the scalar component of curl $\mathbf{F}$ a maximum?

44. Paddle wheel in a vector field Let $\mathbf{F} = \langle 0, 2x, 0 \rangle$ and let $\mathbf{n}$ be a unit vector aligned with the axis of a paddle wheel located on the y-axis.

   a. If the axis of the paddle wheel is aligned with $\mathbf{n} = \langle 1, 0, 0 \rangle$, how fast does it spin?

   b. If the axis of the paddle wheel is aligned with $\mathbf{n} = \langle 0, 0, 1 \rangle$, how fast does it spin?

   c. For what direction $\mathbf{n}$ does the paddle wheel spin fastest?

45–48. Surface areas *Use a surface integral to find the area of the following surfaces.*

45. The hemisphere $x^2 + y^2 + z^2 = 9$, for $z \geq 0$ (excluding the base)

46. The frustum of the cone $z^2 = x^2 + y^2$, for $2 \leq z \leq 4$ (excluding the bases)

47. The plane $z = 6 - x - y$ above the square $|x| \leq 1, |y| \leq 1$

48. The surface $f(x, y) = \sqrt{2}\, xy$ above the region $\{(r, \theta): 0 \leq r \leq 2, 0 \leq \theta \leq 2\pi\}$

49–51. Surface integrals *Evaluate the following surface integrals.*

49. $\displaystyle\iint_S (1 + yz)\, dS$; S is the plane $x + y + z = 2$ in the first octant.

50. $\displaystyle\iint_S \langle 0, y, z \rangle \cdot \mathbf{n}\, dS$; S is the curved surface of the cylinder $y^2 + z^2 = a^2, |x| \leq 8$ with outward normal vectors.

51. $\displaystyle\iint_S (x - y + z)\, dS$; S is the entire surface including the base of the hemisphere $x^2 + y^2 + z^2 = 4$, for $z \geq 0$.

52–53. Flux integrals *Find the flux of the following vector fields across the given surface. Assume the vectors normal to the surface point outward.*

52. $\mathbf{F} = \langle x, y, z \rangle$ across the curved surface of the cylinder $x^2 + y^2 = 1$, for $|z| \leq 8$

53. $\mathbf{F} = \mathbf{r}/|\mathbf{r}|$ across the sphere of radius a centered at the origin, where $\mathbf{r} = \langle x, y, z \rangle$

54. Three methods Find the surface area of the paraboloid $z = x^2 + y^2$, for $0 \leq z \leq 4$, in three ways.

   a. Use an explicit description of the surface.

   b. Use the parametric description $\mathbf{r} = \langle v \cos u, v \sin u, v^2 \rangle$.

   c. Use the parametric description $\mathbf{r} = \langle \sqrt{v} \cos u, \sqrt{v} \sin u, v \rangle$.

55. Flux across hemispheres and paraboloids Let S be the hemisphere $x^2 + y^2 + z^2 = a^2$, for $z \geq 0$, and let T be the paraboloid $z = a - (x^2 + y^2)/a$, for $z \geq 0$, where $a > 0$. Assume the surfaces have outward normal vectors.

   a. Verify that S and T have the same base ($x^2 + y^2 \leq a^2$) and the same high point $(0, 0, a)$.

   b. Which surface has the greater area?

   c. Show that the flux of the radial field $\mathbf{F} = \langle x, y, z \rangle$ across S is $2\pi a^3$.

   d. Show that the flux of the radial field $\mathbf{F} = \langle x, y, z \rangle$ across T is $3\pi a^3/2$.

56. Surface area of an ellipsoid Consider the ellipsoid $x^2/a^2 + y^2/b^2 + z^2/c^2 = 1$, where a, b, and c are positive real numbers.

   a. Show that the surface is described by the parametric equations

$$\mathbf{r}(u, v) = \langle a \cos u \sin v, b \sin u \sin v, c \cos v \rangle$$

   for $0 \leq u \leq 2\pi, 0 \leq v \leq \pi$.

   b. Write an integral for the surface area of the ellipsoid.

57–58. Stokes' Theorem for line integrals *Evaluate the line integral $\oint_C \mathbf{F} \cdot d\mathbf{r}$ using Stokes' Theorem. Assume C has counterclockwise orientation.*

57. $\mathbf{F} = \langle xz, yz, xy \rangle$; C is the circle $x^2 + y^2 = 4$ in the xy-plane.

58. $\mathbf{F} = \langle x^2 - y^2, x, 2yz \rangle$; C is the boundary of the plane $z = 6 - 2x - y$ in the first octant.

59–60. Stokes' Theorem for surface integrals *Use Stokes' Theorem to evaluate the surface integral $\iint_S (\nabla \times \mathbf{F}) \cdot \mathbf{n}\, dS$. Assume that $\mathbf{n}$ is the outward normal.*

59. $\mathbf{F} = \langle -z, x, y \rangle$, where S is the hyperboloid $z = 10 - \sqrt{1 + x^2 + y^2}$, for $z \geq 0$

60. $\mathbf{F} = \langle x^2 - z^2, y^2, xz \rangle$, where S is the hemisphere $x^2 + y^2 + z^2 = 4$, for $y \geq 0$

61. Conservative fields Use Stokes' Theorem to find the circulation of the vector field $\mathbf{F} = \nabla(10 - x^2 + y^2 + z^2)$ around any smooth closed curve C with counterclockwise orientation.

62–64. Computing fluxes *Use the Divergence Theorem to compute the outward flux of the following vector fields across the given surfaces S.*

62. $\mathbf{F} = \langle -x, x - y, x - z \rangle$; S is the surface of the cube cut from the first octant by the planes $x = 1, y = 1$, and $z = 1$.

63. $\mathbf{F} = \langle x^3, y^3, z^3 \rangle/3$; S is the sphere $\{(x, y, z): x^2 + y^2 + z^2 = 9\}$.

64. $\mathbf{F} = \langle x^2, y^2, z^2 \rangle$; S is the cylinder $\{(x, y, z): x^2 + y^2 = 4, 0 \leq z \leq 8\}$.

65–66. General regions *Use the Divergence Theorem to compute the outward flux of the following vector fields across the boundary of the given regions D.*

65. $\mathbf{F} = \langle x^3, y^3, 10 \rangle$; D is the region between the hemispheres of radius 1 and 2 centered at the origin with bases in the xy-plane.

66. $\mathbf{F} = \dfrac{\mathbf{r}}{|\mathbf{r}|^3} = \dfrac{\langle x, y, z \rangle}{(x^2 + y^2 + z^2)^{3/2}}$; D is the region between two spheres with radii 1 and 2 centered at $(5, 5, 5)$.

67. Flux integrals Compute the outward flux of the field $\mathbf{F} = \langle x^2 + x \sin y, y^2 + 2 \cos y, z^2 + z \sin y \rangle$ across the surface S that is the boundary of the prism bounded by the planes $y = 1 - x$, $x = 0$, $y = 0$, $z = 0$, and $z = 4$.

68. Stokes' Theorem on a compound surface Consider the surface S consisting of the quarter-sphere $x^2 + y^2 + z^2 = a^2$, for $z \geq 0$ and $x \geq 0$, and the half-disk in the yz-plane $y^2 + z^2 \leq a^2$, for $z \geq 0$. The boundary of S in the xy-plane is C, which consists of the semicircle $x^2 + y^2 = a^2$, for $x \geq 0$, and the line segment $[-a, a]$ on the y-axis, with a counterclockwise orientation. Let $\mathbf{F} = \langle 2z - y, x - z, y - 2x \rangle$.

a. Describe the direction in which the normal vectors point on S.
b. Evaluate $\oint_C \mathbf{F} \cdot d\mathbf{r}$.
c. Evaluate $\iint_S (\nabla \times \mathbf{F}) \cdot \mathbf{n} \, dS$ and check for agreement with part (b).

Chapter 14 Guided Projects

Applications of the material in this chapter and related topics can be found in the following Guided Projects. For additional information, see the Preface.

- Ideal fluid flow
- Maxwell's equations

- Planimeters and vector fields
- Vector calculus in other coordinate systems

A

Appendix

The goal of this appendix is to establish the essential notation, terminology, and algebraic skills that are used throughout the book.

Algebra

EXAMPLE 1 Algebra review

a. Evaluate $(-32)^{2/5}$.

b. Simplify $\dfrac{1}{x-2} - \dfrac{1}{x+2}$.

c. Solve the equation $\dfrac{x^4 - 5x^2 + 4}{x-1} = 0$.

SOLUTION

a. Recall that $(-32)^{2/5} = ((-32)^{1/5})^2$. Because $(-32)^{1/5} = \sqrt[5]{-32} = -2$, we have $(-32)^{2/5} = (-2)^2 = 4$.

   Another option is to write $(-32)^{2/5} = ((-32)^2)^{1/5} = 1024^{1/5} = 4$.

b. Finding a common denominator and simplifying leads to

$$\frac{1}{x-2} - \frac{1}{x+2} = \frac{(x+2)-(x-2)}{(x-2)(x+2)} = \frac{4}{x^2-4}.$$

c. Notice that $x = 1$ cannot be a solution of the equation because the left side of the equation is undefined at $x = 1$. Because $x - 1 \neq 0$, both sides of the equation can be multiplied by $x - 1$ to produce $x^4 - 5x^2 + 4 = 0$. After factoring, this equation becomes $(x^2 - 4)(x^2 - 1) = 0$, which implies $x^2 - 4 = (x - 2)(x + 2) = 0$ or $x^2 - 1 = (x - 1)(x + 1) = 0$. The roots of $x^2 - 4 = 0$ are $x = \pm 2$, and the roots of $x^2 - 1 = 0$ are $x = \pm 1$. Excluding $x = 1$, the roots of the original equation are $x = -1$ and $x = \pm 2$.

Related Exercises 15–26 ◄

Sets of Real Numbers

Figure A.1 shows the notation for **open intervals**, **closed intervals**, and various **bounded** and **unbounded intervals**. Notice that either interval notation or set notation may be used.

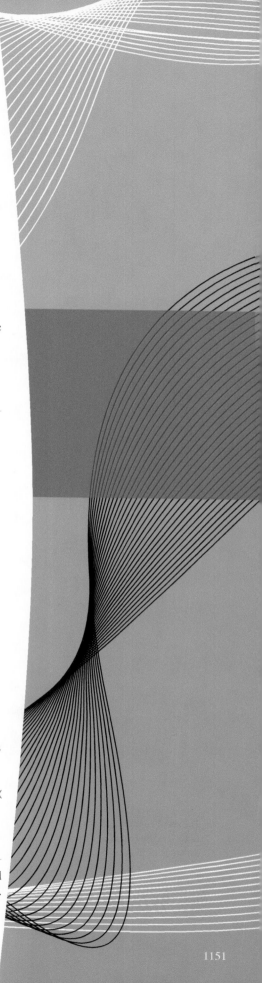

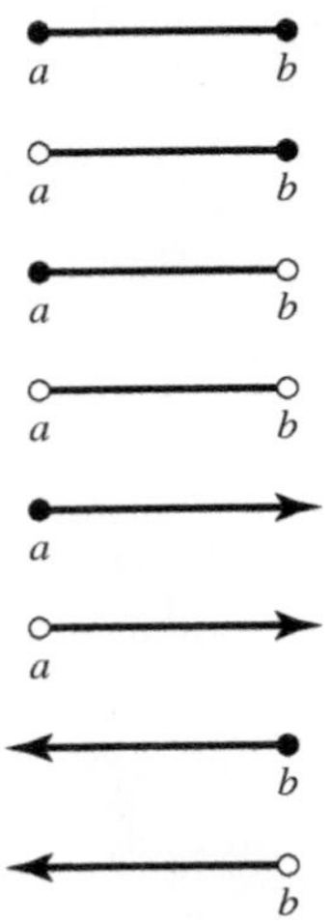

$[a, b] = \{x: a \leq x \leq b\}$	Closed, bounded interval
$(a, b] = \{x: a < x \leq b\}$	Bounded interval
$[a, b) = \{x: a \leq x < b\}$	Bounded interval
$(a, b) = \{x: a < x < b\}$	Open, bounded interval
$[a, \infty) = \{x: x \geq a\}$	Unbounded interval
$(a, \infty) = \{x: x > a\}$	Unbounded interval
$(-\infty, b] = \{x: x \leq b\}$	Unbounded interval
$(-\infty, b) = \{x: x < b\}$	Unbounded interval
$(-\infty, \infty) = \{x: -\infty < x < \infty\}$	Unbounded interval

Figure A.1

EXAMPLE 2   Solving inequalities Solve the following inequalities.

a. $-x^2 + 5x - 6 < 0$ **b.** $\dfrac{x^2 - x - 2}{x - 3} \leq 0$

SOLUTION

a. We multiply by -1, reverse the inequality, and then factor:

$$x^2 - 5x + 6 > 0 \quad \text{Multiply by } -1.$$
$$(x - 2)(x - 3) > 0. \quad \text{Factor.}$$

The roots of the corresponding equation $(x - 2)(x - 3) = 0$ are $x = 2$ and $x = 3$. These roots partition the number line (Figure A.2) into three intervals: $(-\infty, 2)$, $(2, 3)$, and $(3, \infty)$. On each interval, the product $(x - 2)(x - 3)$ does not change sign. To determine the sign of the product on a given interval, a **test value** x is selected and the sign of $(x - 2)(x - 3)$ is determined at x.

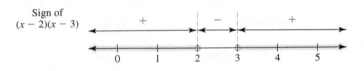

Figure A.2

A convenient choice for x in $(-\infty, 2)$ is $x = 0$. At this test value,

$$(x - 2)(x - 3) = (-2)(-3) > 0.$$

Using a test value of $x = 2.5$ in the interval $(2, 3)$, we have

$$(x - 2)(x - 3) = (0.5)(-0.5) < 0.$$

A test value of $x = 4$ in $(3, \infty)$ gives

$$(x - 2)(x - 3) = (2)(1) > 0.$$

▶ The set of numbers $\{x: x$ is in $(-\infty, 2)$ or $(3, \infty)\}$ may also be expressed using the union symbol:

$$(-\infty, 2) \cup (3, \infty).$$

Therefore, $(x - 2)(x - 3) > 0$ on $(-\infty, 2)$ and $(3, \infty)$. We conclude that the inequality $-x^2 + 5x - 6 < 0$ is satisfied for all x in either $(-\infty, 2)$ or $(3, \infty)$ (Figure A.2).

b. The expression $\dfrac{x^2 - x - 2}{x - 3}$ can change sign only at points where the numerator or denominator of $\dfrac{x^2 - x - 2}{x - 3}$ equals 0. Because

$$\frac{x^2 - x - 2}{x - 3} = \frac{(x + 1)(x - 2)}{x - 3},$$

the numerator is 0 when $x = -1$ or $x = 2$, and the denominator is 0 at $x = 3$. Therefore, we examine the sign of $\dfrac{(x + 1)(x - 2)}{x - 3}$ on the intervals $(-\infty, -1)$, $(-1, 2)$, $(2, 3)$, and $(3, \infty)$.

Using test values on these intervals, we see that $\dfrac{(x + 1)(x - 2)}{x - 3} < 0$ on $(-\infty, -1)$ and $(2, 3)$. Furthermore, the expression is 0 when $x = -1$ and $x = 2$. Therefore, $\dfrac{x^2 - x - 2}{x - 3} \leq 0$ for all values of x in either $(-\infty, -1]$ or $[2, 3)$ (Figure A.3).

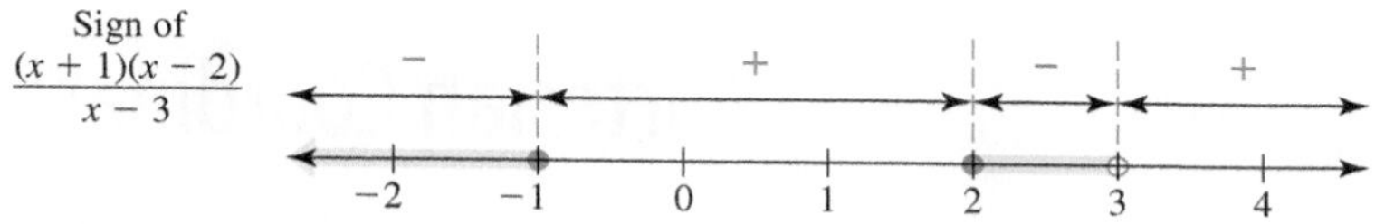

Test Value	$x + 1$	$x - 2$	$x - 3$	Result
-2	$-$	$-$	$-$	$-$
0	$+$	$-$	$-$	$+$
2.5	$+$	$+$	$-$	$-$
4	$+$	$+$	$+$	$+$

Sign of
$\dfrac{(x + 1)(x - 2)}{x - 3}$

Figure A.3

Related Exercises 27–30 ◄

Absolute Value

The **absolute value** of a real number x, denoted $|x|$, is the distance between x and the origin on the number line (Figure A.4). More generally, $|x - y|$ is the distance between the points x and y on the number line. The absolute value has the following definition and properties.

▶ The absolute value is useful in simplifying square roots. Because $\sqrt{a}$ is nonnegative, we have $\sqrt{a^2} = |a|$. For example, $\sqrt{3^2} = 3$ and $\sqrt{(-3)^2} = \sqrt{9} = 3$. Note that the solutions of $x^2 = 9$ are $|x| = 3$ or $x = \pm 3$.

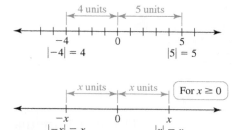

Figure A.4

Definition and Properties of the Absolute Value

The absolute value of a real number x is defined as

$$|x| = \begin{cases} x & \text{if } x \geq 0 \\ -x & \text{if } x < 0. \end{cases}$$

Let a be a positive real number.

1. $|x| = a \Leftrightarrow x = \pm a$ **2.** $|x| < a \Leftrightarrow -a < x < a$

3. $|x| > a \Leftrightarrow x > a$ or $x < -a$ **4.** $|x| \leq a \Leftrightarrow -a \leq x \leq a$

5. $|x| \geq a \Leftrightarrow x \geq a$ or $x \leq -a$ **6.** $|x + y| \leq |x| + |y|$

▶ Property 6 is called the **triangle inequality**.

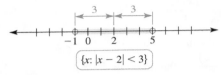

$\{x: |x - 2| < 3\}$

Figure A.5

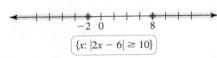

$\{x: |2x - 6| \geq 10\}$

Figure A.6

EXAMPLE 3   Inequalities with absolute values Solve the following inequalities. Then sketch the solution on the number line and express it in interval notation.

a. $|x - 2| < 3$ **b.** $|2x - 6| \geq 10$

SOLUTION

a. Using property 2 of the absolute value, $|x - 2| < 3$ is written as

$$-3 < x - 2 < 3.$$

Adding 2 to each term of these inequalities results in $-1 < x < 5$ (Figure A.5). This set of numbers is written as $(-1, 5)$ in interval notation.

b. Using property 5, the inequality $|2x - 6| \geq 10$ implies that

$$2x - 6 \geq 10 \quad \text{or} \quad 2x - 6 \leq -10.$$

We add 6 to both sides of the first inequality to obtain $2x \geq 16$, which implies $x \geq 8$. Similarly, the second inequality yields $x \leq -2$ (Figure A.6). In interval notation, the solution is $(-\infty, -2]$ or $[8, \infty)$.

Related Exercises 31–34 ◄

Cartesian Coordinate System

The conventions of the **Cartesian coordinate system** or **xy-coordinate system** are illustrated in Figure A.7. The set of real numbers is often denoted $\mathbb{R}$. The set of all ordered pairs of real numbers, which comprise the *xy*-plane, is often denoted $\mathbb{R}^2$.

► The familiar (x, y) coordinate system is named after René Descartes (1596–1650). However, it was introduced independently and simultaneously by Pierre de Fermat (1601–1665).

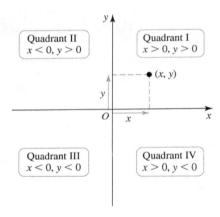

Figure A.7

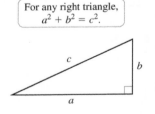

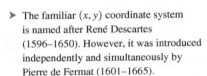

Figure A.8

Distance Formula and Circles

By the Pythagorean theorem (Figure A.8), we have the following formula for the distance between two points $P_1(x_1, y_1)$ and $P_2(x_2, y_2)$.

Distance Formula

The distance between the points $P_1(x_1, y_1)$ and $P_2(x_2, y_2)$ is

$$|P_1P_2| = \sqrt{(x_2 - x_1)^2 + (y_2 - y_1)^2}.$$

A **circle** is the set of points in the plane whose distance from a fixed point (the **center**) is constant (the **radius**). This definition leads to the following equations that describe a circle.

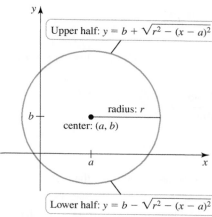

Upper half: $y = b + \sqrt{r^2 - (x - a)^2}$

radius: r

center: (a, b)

b

a

Lower half: $y = b - \sqrt{r^2 - (x - a)^2}$

Figure A.9

Equation of a Circle

The equation of a circle centered at (a, b) with radius r is

$$(x - a)^2 + (y - b)^2 = r^2.$$

Solving for y, the equations of the upper and lower halves of the circle (Figure A.9) are

$$y = b + \sqrt{r^2 - (x - a)^2} \qquad \text{Upper half of the circle}$$

$$y = b - \sqrt{r^2 - (x - a)^2}. \qquad \text{Lower half of the circle}$$

EXAMPLE 4   Sets involving circles

a. Find the equation of the circle with center $(2, 4)$ passing through $(-2, 1)$.

b. Describe the set of points satisfying $x^2 + y^2 - 4x - 6y < 12$.

SOLUTION

a. The radius of the circle equals the length of the line segment between the center $(2, 4)$ and the point on the circle $(-2, 1)$, which is

$$\sqrt{(2 - (-2))^2 + (4 - 1)^2} = 5.$$

Therefore, the equation of the circle is

$$(x - 2)^2 + (y - 4)^2 = 25.$$

> Recall that the procedure shown here for completing the square works when the coefficient on the quadratic term is 1. When the coefficient is not 1, it must be factored out before completing the square.

b. To put this inequality in a recognizable form, we complete the square on the left side of the inequality:

$$x^2 + y^2 - 4x - 6y = x^2 - 4x \underbrace{+ 4 - 4}_{\substack{\text{Add and subtract the square} \\ \text{of half the coefficient of } x}} + y^2 - 6y \underbrace{+ 9 - 9}_{\substack{\text{Add and subtract the square} \\ \text{of half the coefficient of } y.}}$$

$$= \underbrace{x^2 - 4x + 4}_{(x - 2)^2} + \underbrace{y^2 - 6y + 9}_{(y - 3)^2} - 4 - 9$$

$$= (x - 2)^2 + (y - 3)^2 - 13.$$

Therefore, the original inequality becomes

$$(x - 2)^2 + (y - 3)^2 - 13 < 12, \quad \text{or} \quad (x - 2)^2 + (y - 3)^2 < 25.$$

> A **circle** is the set of all points whose distance from a fixed point is a constant. A **disk** is the set of all points within and possibly on a circle.

This inequality describes those points that lie within the circle centered at $(2, 3)$ with radius 5 (Figure A.10). Note that a dashed curve is used to indicate that the circle itself is not part of the solution.

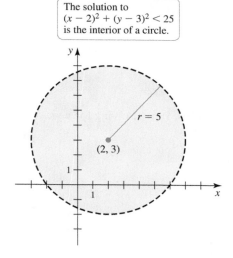

The solution to $(x - 2)^2 + (y - 3)^2 < 25$ is the interior of a circle.

$r = 5$

$(2, 3)$

Figure A.10

Related Exercises 35–36 ◄

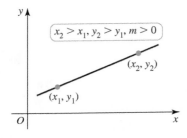

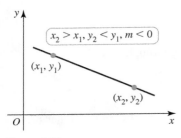

Figure A.11

Equations of Lines

The **slope** m of the line passing through the points $P_1(x_1, y_1)$ and $P_2(x_2, y_2)$ is the *rise over run* (Figure A.11), computed as

$$m = \frac{\text{change in vertical coordinate}}{\text{change in horizontal coordinate}} = \frac{y_2 - y_1}{x_2 - x_1}.$$

> **Equations of a Line**
>
> **Point-slope form** The equation of the line with slope m passing through the point (x_1, y_1) is $y - y_1 = m(x - x_1)$.
>
> **Slope-intercept form** The equation of the line with slope m and y-intercept $(0, b)$ is $y = mx + b$ (Figure A.12a).
>
> **General linear equation** The equation $Ax + By + C = 0$ describes a line in the plane, provided A and B are not both zero.
>
> **Vertical and horizontal lines** The vertical line that passes through $(a, 0)$ has an equation $x = a$; its slope is undefined. The horizontal line through $(0, b)$ has an equation $y = b$, with slope equal to 0 (Figure A.12b).

▶ Given a particular line, we often talk about *the* equation of a line. But the equation of a specific line is not unique. Having found one equation, we can multiply it by any nonzero constant to produce another equation of the same line.

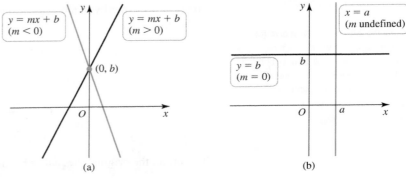

Figure A.12

EXAMPLE 5   Working with linear equations Find an equation of the line passing through the points $(1, -2)$ and $(-4, 5)$.

SOLUTION The slope of the line through the points $(1, -2)$ and $(-4, 5)$ is

$$m = \frac{5 - (-2)}{-4 - 1} = \frac{7}{-5} = -\frac{7}{5}.$$

Using the point $(1, -2)$, the point-slope form of the equation is

$$y - (-2) = -\frac{7}{5}(x - 1).$$

▶ Because both points $(1, -2)$ and $(-4, 5)$ lie on the line and must satisfy the equation of the line, either point can be used to determine an equation of the line.

Solving for y yields the slope-intercept form of the equation:

$$y = -\frac{7}{5}x - \frac{3}{5}.$$

Related Exercises 37–40 ◀

Parallel and Perpendicular Lines

Two lines in the plane may have either of two special relationships to each other: They may be parallel or perpendicular.

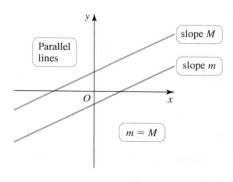

Parallel lines
slope M
slope m
O
$m = M$

Parallel Lines

Two distinct nonvertical lines are **parallel** if they have the same slope; that is, the lines with equations $y = mx + b$ and $y = Mx + B$ are parallel if and only if $m = M$. Two distinct vertical lines are parallel.

EXAMPLE 6   Parallel lines Find an equation of the line parallel to $3x - 6y + 12 = 0$ that intersects the x-axis at $(4, 0)$.

SOLUTION Solving the equation $3x - 6y + 12 = 0$ for y, we have

$$y = \frac{1}{2}x + 2.$$

This line has a slope of $\frac{1}{2}$ and any line parallel to it has a slope of $\frac{1}{2}$. Therefore, the line that passes through $(4, 0)$ with slope $\frac{1}{2}$ has the point-slope equation $y - 0 = \frac{1}{2}(x - 4)$. After simplifying, an equation of the line is

$$y = \frac{1}{2}x - 2.$$

Notice that the slopes of the two lines are the same; only the y-intercepts differ.

Related Exercises 41–42 ◄

▶ The slopes of perpendicular lines are *negative reciprocals* of each other.

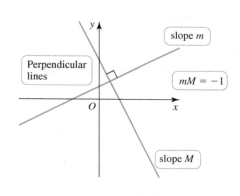

Perpendicular lines
slope m
$mM = -1$
O
slope M

Perpendicular Lines

Two lines with slopes $m \neq 0$ and $M \neq 0$ are **perpendicular** if and only if $mM = -1$, or equivalently, $m = -1/M$.

EXAMPLE 7   Perpendicular lines Find an equation of the line passing through the point $(-2, 5)$ perpendicular to the line $\ell: 4x - 2y + 7 = 0$.

SOLUTION The equation of ℓ can be written $y = 2x + \frac{7}{2}$, which reveals that its slope is 2. Therefore, the slope of any line perpendicular to ℓ is $-\frac{1}{2}$. The line with slope $-\frac{1}{2}$ passing through the point $(-2, 5)$ is

$$y - 5 = -\frac{1}{2}(x + 2), \quad \text{or} \quad y = -\frac{x}{2} + 4.$$

Related Exercises 43–44 ◄

APPENDIX A EXERCISES

Review Questions

1. State the meaning of $\{x: -4 < x \leq 10\}$. Express the set $\{x: -4 < x \leq 10\}$ using interval notation and draw it on a number line.

2. Write the interval $(-\infty, 2)$ in set notation and draw it on a number line.

3. Give the definition of $|x|$.

4. Write the inequality $|x - 2| \leq 3$ without absolute value symbols.

5. Write the inequality $|2x - 4| \geq 3$ without absolute value symbols.

6. Write an equation of the set of all points that are a distance 5 units from the point $(2, 3)$.

7. Explain how to find the distance between two points whose coordinates are known.

8. Sketch the set of points $\{(x, y): x^2 + (y - 2)^2 > 16\}$.

9. Give an equation of the upper half of the circle centered at the origin with radius 6.

10. What are the possible solution sets of the equation $x^2 + y^2 + Cx + Dy + E = 0$?

11. Give an equation of the line with slope m that passes through the point $(4, -2)$.

12. Give an equation of the line with slope m and y-intercept $(0, 6)$.

13. What is the relationship between the slopes of two parallel lines?

14. What is the relationship between the slopes of two perpendicular lines?

Basic Skills

15–20. Algebra review *Simplify or evaluate the following expressions without a calculator.*

15. $(1/8)^{-2/3}$

16. $\sqrt[3]{-125} + \sqrt{1/25}$

17. $(u + v)^2 - (u - v)^2$

18. $\dfrac{(a + h)^2 - a^2}{h}$

19. $\dfrac{1}{x + h} - \dfrac{1}{x}$

20. $\dfrac{2}{x + 3} - \dfrac{2}{x - 3}$

21–26. Algebra review

21. Factor $y^2 - y^{-2}$.

22. Solve $x^3 - 9x = 0$.

23. Solve $u^4 - 11u^2 + 18 = 0$.

24. Solve $4^x - 6(2^x) = -8$.

25. Simplify $\dfrac{(x + h)^3 - x^3}{h}$, for $h \neq 0$.

26. Rewrite $\dfrac{\sqrt{x + h} - \sqrt{x}}{h}$, where $h \neq 0$, without square roots in the numerator.

27–30. Solving inequalities *Solve the following inequalities and draw the solution on a number line.*

27. $x^2 - 6x + 5 < 0$

28. $\dfrac{x + 1}{x + 2} < 6$

29. $\dfrac{x^2 - 9x + 20}{x - 6} \leq 0$

30. $x\sqrt{x - 1} > 0$

31–34. Inequalities with absolute values *Solve the following inequalities. Then draw the solution on a number line and express it using interval notation.*

31. $|3x - 4| > 8$

32. $1 \leq |x| \leq 10$

33. $3 < |2x - 1| < 5$

34. $2 < \left|\frac{x}{2} - 5\right| < 6$

35–36. Circle calculations *Solve the following problems.*

35. Find the equation of the lower half of the circle with center $(-1, 2)$ and radius 3.

36. Describe the set of points that satisfy $x^2 + y^2 + 6x + 8y \geq 25$.

37–40. Working with linear equations *Find an equation of the line ℓ that satisfies the given condition. Then draw the graph of ℓ.*

37. ℓ has slope $5/3$ and y-intercept $(0, 4)$.

38. ℓ has undefined slope and passes through $(0, 5)$.

39. ℓ has y-intercept $(0, -4)$ and x-intercept $(5, 0)$.

40. ℓ is parallel to the x-axis and passes through the point $(2, 3)$.

41–42. Parallel lines *Find an equation of the following lines and draw their graphs.*

41. The line with y-intercept $(0, 12)$ parallel to the line $x + 2y = 8$

42. The line with x-intercept $(-6, 0)$ parallel to the line $2x - 5 = 0$

43–44. Perpendicular lines *Find an equation of the following lines.*

43. The line passing through $(3, -6)$ perpendicular to the line $y = -3x + 2$

44. The perpendicular bisector of the line joining the points $(-9, 2)$ and $(3, -5)$

Further Explorations

45. **Explain why or why not** State whether the following statements are true and give an explanation or counterexample.

  a. $\sqrt{16} = \pm 4$.

  b. $\sqrt{4^2} = \sqrt{(-4)^2}$.

  c. There are two real numbers that satisfy the condition $|x| = -2$.

  d. $|\pi^2 - 9| < 0$.

  e. The point $(1, 1)$ is inside the circle of radius 1 centered at the origin.

  f. $\sqrt{x^4} = x^2$ for all real numbers x.

  g. $\sqrt{a^2} < \sqrt{b^2}$ implies $a < b$ for all real numbers a and b.

46–48. Intervals to sets *Express the following intervals in set notation. Use absolute value notation when possible.*

46. $(-\infty, 12)$

47. $(-\infty, -2]$ or $[4, \infty)$

48. $(2, 3]$ or $[4, 5)$

49–50. Sets in the plane *Graph each set in the xy-plane.*

49. $\{(x, y): |x - y| = 0\}$

50. $\{(x, y): |x| = |y|\}$

B

Appendix

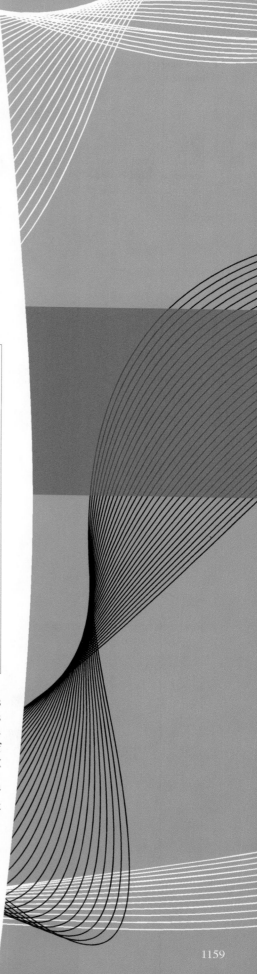

Proofs of Selected Theorems

THEOREM 2.3 Limit Laws

Assume $\lim\limits_{x \to a} f(x)$ and $\lim\limits_{x \to a} g(x)$ exist. The following properties hold, where c is a real number, and $m > 0$ and $n > 0$ are integers.

1. **Sum** $\lim\limits_{x \to a} (f(x) + g(x)) = \lim\limits_{x \to a} f(x) + \lim\limits_{x \to a} g(x)$

2. **Difference** $\lim\limits_{x \to a} (f(x) - g(x)) = \lim\limits_{x \to a} f(x) - \lim\limits_{x \to a} g(x)$

3. **Constant multiple** $\lim\limits_{x \to a} (cf(x)) = c \lim\limits_{x \to a} f(x)$

4. **Product** $\lim\limits_{x \to a} (f(x)g(x)) = \left(\lim\limits_{x \to a} f(x)\right)\left(\lim\limits_{x \to a} g(x)\right)$

5. **Quotient** $\lim\limits_{x \to a} \dfrac{f(x)}{g(x)} = \dfrac{\lim\limits_{x \to a} f(x)}{\lim\limits_{x \to a} g(x)}$, provided $\lim\limits_{x \to a} g(x) \neq 0$

6. **Power** $\lim\limits_{x \to a} (f(x))^n = \left(\lim\limits_{x \to a} f(x)\right)^n$

7. **Fractional power** $\lim\limits_{x \to a} (f(x))^{n/m} = \left(\lim\limits_{x \to a} f(x)\right)^{n/m}$, provided $f(x) \geq 0$, for x near a, if m is even and n/m is reduced to lowest terms

---

Proof: The proof of Law 1 is given in Example 5 of Section 2.7. The proof of Law 2 is analogous to that of Law 1; the triangle inequality in the form $|x - y| \leq |x| + |y|$ is used. The proof of Law 3 is outlined in Exercise 26 of Section 2.7. The proofs of Laws 4 and 5 are given below. The proof of Law 6 involves the repeated use of Law 4. The proof of Law 7 is given in advanced texts. ◀

Proof of Product Law: Let $L = \lim\limits_{x \to a} f(x)$ and $M = \lim\limits_{x \to a} g(x)$. Using the definition of a limit, the goal is to show that given any $\varepsilon > 0$, it is possible to specify a $\delta > 0$ such that $|f(x)g(x) - LM| < \varepsilon$ whenever $0 < |x - a| < \delta$. Notice that

$$
\begin{aligned}
|f(x)g(x) - LM| &= |f(x)g(x) - Lg(x) + Lg(x) - LM| &&\text{Add and subtract } Lg(x).\\
&= |(f(x) - L)g(x) + (g(x) - M)L| &&\text{Group terms.}\\
&\leq |(f(x) - L)g(x)| + |(g(x) - M)L| &&\text{Triangle inequality}\\
&= |f(x) - L||g(x)| + |g(x) - M||L|. &&|xy| = |x||y|
\end{aligned}
$$

> Real numbers x and y obey the triangle inequality $|x + y| \leq |x| + |y|$.

We now use the definition of the limits of f and g, and note that L and M are fixed real numbers. Given $\varepsilon > 0$, there exist $\delta_1 > 0$ and $\delta_2 > 0$ such that

$$|f(x) - L| < \frac{\varepsilon}{2(|M| + 1)} \quad \text{and} \quad |g(x) - M| < \frac{\varepsilon}{2(|L| + 1)}$$

> $|g(x) - M| < 1$ implies that $g(x)$ is less than 1 unit from M. Therefore, whether $g(x)$ and M are positive or negative, $|g(x)| < |M| + 1$.

whenever $0 < |x - a| < \delta_1$ and $0 < |x - a| < \delta_2$, respectively. Furthermore, by the definition of the limit of g, there exits a $\delta_3 > 0$ such that $|g(x) - M| < 1$ whenever $0 < |x - a| < \delta_3$. It follows that $|g(x)| < |M| + 1$ whenever $0 < |x - a| < \delta_3$. Now take δ to be the minimum of δ_1, δ_2, and δ_3. Then for $0 < |x - a| < \delta$, we have

$$|f(x)g(x) - LM| \leq \underbrace{|f(x) - L|}_{< \frac{\varepsilon}{2(|M| + 1)}}\underbrace{|g(x)|}_{<(|M| + 1)} + \underbrace{|g(x) - M|}_{< \frac{\varepsilon}{2(|L| + 1)}}|L|$$

$$< \frac{\varepsilon}{2} + \frac{\varepsilon}{2}\underbrace{\frac{|L|}{|L| + 1}}_{<1} < \frac{\varepsilon}{2} + \frac{\varepsilon}{2} = \varepsilon.$$

It follows that $\lim_{x \to a} [f(x)g(x)] = LM$.   ◄

Proof of Quotient Law: We first prove that if $\lim_{x \to a} g(x) = M$ exists, where $M \neq 0$, then $\lim_{x \to a} \frac{1}{g(x)} = \frac{1}{M}$. The Quotient Law then follows when we replace g with $1/g$ in the Product Law. Therefore, the goal is to show that given any $\varepsilon > 0$, it is possible to specify a $\delta > 0$ such that $\left|\frac{1}{g(x)} - \frac{1}{M}\right| < \varepsilon$ whenever $0 < |x - a| < \delta$. First note that $M \neq 0$ and $g(x)$ can be made arbitrarily close to M. For this reason, there exists a $\delta_1 > 0$ such that $|g(x)| > |M|/2$, or equivalently, $1/|g(x)| < 2/|M|$, whenever $0 < |x - a| < \delta_1$. Furthermore, using the definition of the limit of g, given any $\varepsilon > 0$, there exists a $\delta_2 > 0$ such that $|g(x) - M| < \frac{\varepsilon|M|^2}{2}$ whenever $0 < |x - a| < \delta_2$. Now take δ to be the minimum of δ_1 and δ_2. Then for $0 < |x - a| < \delta$, we have

$$\left|\frac{1}{g(x)} - \frac{1}{M}\right| = \left|\frac{M - g(x)}{Mg(x)}\right| \qquad \text{Common denominator}$$

> Note that if $|g(x)| > |M|/2$, then $1/|g(x)| < 2/|M|$.

$$= \frac{1}{|M|}\underbrace{\frac{1}{|g(x)|}}_{< \frac{2}{|M|}}\underbrace{|g(x) - M|}_{< \frac{\varepsilon|M|^2}{2}} \qquad \text{Rewrite.}$$

$$< \frac{1}{|M|}\frac{2}{|M|}\frac{\varepsilon|M|^2}{2} = \varepsilon. \qquad \text{Simplify.}$$

By the definition of a limit, we have $\lim_{x \to a} \frac{1}{g(x)} = \frac{1}{M}$. The proof can be completed by applying the Product Law with g replaced with $1/g$.   ◄

THEOREM 8.14   Ratio Test

Let $\sum a_k$ be an infinite series with positive terms and let $r = \lim_{k \to \infty} \frac{a_{k+1}}{a_k}$.

1. If $0 \leq r < 1$, the series converges.

2. If $r > 1$ (including $r = \infty$), the series diverges.

3. If $r = 1$, the test is inconclusive.

Proof: We consider three cases: $0 \le r < 1, r > 1$, and $r = 1$.

1. Assume $0 \le r < 1$ and choose a number R such that $r < R < 1$. Because the sequence $\left\{\dfrac{a_{k+1}}{a_k}\right\}$ converges to a number r less than R, eventually all the terms in the tail of the sequence $\left\{\dfrac{a_{k+1}}{a_k}\right\}$ are less than R. That is, there is a positive integer N such that $\dfrac{a_{k+1}}{a_k} < R$, for all $k > N$. Multiplying both sides of this inequality by $\dfrac{a_k}{R^{k+1}}$, we have $\dfrac{a_{k+1}}{R^{k+1}} < \dfrac{a_k}{R^k}$, for all $k > N$. So the sequence $\left\{\dfrac{a_k}{R^k}\right\}_{k=N+1}^{\infty}$ is decreasing and it follows that $\dfrac{a_k}{R^k} < \dfrac{a_{N+1}}{R^{N+1}}$, for all $k \ge N + 1$. By letting $c = \dfrac{a_{N+1}}{R^{N+1}}$, we have

$0 < a_k \le cR^k$, for all $k \ge N + 1$. Let S_n represent the nth partial sum of $\displaystyle\sum_{k=N+1}^{\infty} a_k$; note that the partial sums of this series are bounded by a convergent geometric series:

$$
\begin{aligned}
S_n &= a_{N+1} + a_{N+2} + \cdots + a_{N+n} \\
&\le cR^{N+1} + cR^{N+2} + \cdots + cR^{N+n} \\
&< cR^{N+1} + cR^{N+2} + \cdots + cR^{N+n} + \cdots \\
&= \frac{cR^{N+1}}{1 - R}.
\end{aligned}
$$

Because the sequence $\{S_n\}$ is increasing (each partial sum in the sequence consists of positive terms) and is bounded above by $\dfrac{cR^{N+1}}{1 - R}$, it converges by the Bounded Monotonic Sequences Theorem (Theorem 8.5). Therefore, $\displaystyle\sum_{k=N+1}^{\infty} a_k$ converges and we conclude that $\displaystyle\sum_{k=1}^{\infty} a_k$ converges (Theorem 8.13).

2. If $r > 1$, there is a positive integer N for which $\dfrac{a_{k+1}}{a_k} > 1$, or equivalently $a_{k+1} > a_k$, for all $k > N$. So every term in the sequence $\{a_k\}_{k=N+1}^{\infty}$ is greater than or equal to the positive number a_{N+1}, which implies that $\displaystyle\lim_{n\to\infty} a_n \ne 0$. Therefore, the series $\displaystyle\sum_{k=N+1}^{\infty} a_k$ diverges by the Divergence Test, and we conclude that $\displaystyle\sum_{k=1}^{\infty} a_k$ diverges (Theorem 8.13).

3. In the case that $r = 1$, the series $\displaystyle\sum_{k=1}^{\infty} a_k$ may or may not converge. For example, both the divergent harmonic series $\displaystyle\sum_{k=1}^{\infty} \dfrac{1}{k}$ and the convergent p-series $\displaystyle\sum_{k=1}^{\infty} \dfrac{1}{k^2}$ produce a value of $r = 1$. ◄

THEOREM 8.15   Root Test

Let $\sum a_k$ be an infinite series with nonnegative terms and let $\rho = \displaystyle\lim_{k\to\infty} \sqrt[k]{a_k}$.

1. If $0 \le \rho < 1$, the series converges.
2. If $\rho > 1$ (including $\rho = \infty$), the series diverges.
3. If $\rho = 1$, the test is inconclusive.

Proof: We consider three cases: $0 \le \rho < 1, \rho > 1$, and $\rho = 1$.

1. Assume $0 \le \rho < 1$ and choose a number R such that $\rho < R < 1$. Because the sequence $\{\sqrt[k]{a_k}\}$ converges to a number less than R, there is a positive integer N such that

$\sqrt[k]{a_k} < R$, or equivalently $a_k < R^k$, for all $k > N$. Let S_n represent the nth partial sum of $\sum\limits_{k=N+1}^{\infty} a_k$; note that the partial sums of this series are bounded by a convergent geometric series:

$$
\begin{aligned}
S_n &= a_{N+1} + a_{N+2} + \cdots + a_{N+n} \\
&\leq R^{N+1} + R^{N+2} + \cdots + R^{N+n} \\
&< R^{N+1} + R^{N+2} + \cdots + R^{N+n} + \cdots \\
&= \frac{R^{N+1}}{1-R}.
\end{aligned}
$$

Because the sequence $\{S_n\}$ is increasing (each partial sum in the sequence consists of positive terms) and is bounded above by $\dfrac{R^{N+1}}{1-R}$, it converges by the Bounded Monotonic Sequences Theorem (Theorem 8.5). Therefore, $\sum\limits_{k=N+1}^{\infty} a_k$ converges and we conclude that $\sum\limits_{k=1}^{\infty} a_k$ converges (Theorem 8.13).

2. If $\rho > 1$, there is an integer N for which $\sqrt[k]{a_k} > 1$, or equivalently $a_k > 1$, for all $k > N$. So every term in the sequence $\{a_k\}_{k=N+1}^{\infty}$ is greater than or equal to 1, which implies that $\lim\limits_{n\to\infty} a_n \neq 0$. Therefore, the series $\sum\limits_{k=N+1}^{\infty} a_k$ diverges by the Divergence Test, and we conclude that $\sum\limits_{k=1}^{\infty} a_k$ diverges (Theorem 8.13).

3. If $\rho = 1$, the series $\sum\limits_{k=1}^{\infty} a_k$ may or may not converge. For example, both the divergent harmonic series $\sum\limits_{k=1}^{\infty} \dfrac{1}{k}$ and the convergent p-series $\sum\limits_{k=1}^{\infty} \dfrac{1}{k^2}$ produce a value of $\rho = 1$. ◄

THEOREM 9.3   Convergence of Power Series

A power series $\sum\limits_{k=0}^{\infty} c_k(x-a)^k$ centered at a converges in one of three ways.

1. The series converges for all x, in which case the interval of convergence is $(-\infty, \infty)$ and the radius of convergence is $R = \infty$.

2. There is a real number $R > 0$ such that the series converges for $|x - a| < R$ and diverges for $|x - a| > R$, in which case the radius of convergence is R.

3. The series converges only at a, in which case the radius of convergence is $R = 0$.

Proof: Without loss of generality, we take $a = 0$. (If $a \neq 0$, the following argument may be shifted so it is centered at $x = a$.) The proof hinges on a preliminary result:

If $\sum\limits_{k=0}^{\infty} c_k x^k$ converges for $x = b \neq 0$, then it converges absolutely, for $|x| < |b|$. If $\sum\limits_{k=0}^{\infty} c_k x^k$ diverges for $x = d$, then it diverges, for $|x| > |d|$.

To prove these facts, assume that $\sum\limits_{k=0}^{\infty} c_k b^k$ converges, which implies that $\lim\limits_{k\to\infty} c_k b^k = 0$. Then there exists a real number $M > 0$ such that $|c_k b^k| < M$, for $k = 0, 1, 2, 3, \ldots$. It follows that

$$
\sum_{k=0}^{\infty} |c_k x^k| = \sum_{k=0}^{\infty} \underbrace{|c_k b^k|}_{< M} \left|\frac{x}{b}\right|^k < M \sum_{k=0}^{\infty} \left|\frac{x}{b}\right|^k.
$$

If $|x| < |b|$, then $|x/b| < 1$ and $\sum_{k=0}^{\infty} \left|\dfrac{x}{b}\right|^k$ is a convergent geometric series. Therefore, $\sum_{k=0}^{\infty} |c_k x^k|$ converges by the comparison test, which implies that $\sum_{k=0}^{\infty} c_k x^k$ converges absolutely for $|x| < |b|$. The second half of the preliminary result is proved by supposing the series diverges at $x = d$. The series cannot converge at a point x_0 with $|x_0| > |d|$ because by the preceding argument, it would converge for $|x| < |x_0|$, which includes $x = d$. Therefore, the series diverges for $|x| > |d|$.

Now we may deal with the three cases in the theorem. Let S be the set of real numbers for which the series converges, which always includes 0. If $S = \{0\}$, then we have Case 3. If S consists of all real numbers, then we have Case 1. For Case 2, assume that $d \neq 0$ is a point at which the series diverges. By the preliminary result, the series diverges for $|x| > |d|$. Therefore, if x is in S, then $|x| < |d|$, which implies that S is bounded. By the Least Upper Bound Property for real numbers, S has a least upper bound R, such that $x \leq R$, for all x in S. If $|x| > R$, then x is not in S and the series diverges. If $|x| < R$, then x is not the least upper bound of S and there exists a number b in S with $|x| < b \leq R$.

Because the series converges at $x = b$, by the preliminary result, $\sum_{k=0}^{\infty} |c_k x^k|$ converges for $|x| < |b|$. Therefore, the series $\sum_{k=0}^{\infty} c_k x^k$ converges absolutely for $|x| < R$ and diverges for $|x| > R$. ◄

> The Least Upper Bound Property for real numbers states that if a nonempty set S is bounded (that is, there exists a number M, called an *upper bound*, such that $x \leq M$ for all x in S), then S has a *least upper bound* L, which is the smallest of the upper bounds.

THEOREM 10.3   Eccentricity-Directrix Theorem

Let ℓ be a line, F a point not on ℓ, and $e > 0$ a real number. Let C be the set of points P in a plane with the property that $\dfrac{|PF|}{|PL|} = e$, where $|PL|$ is the perpendicular distance from P to ℓ.

1. If $e = 1$, C is a **parabola**.

2. If $0 < e < 1$, C is an **ellipse**.

3. If $e > 1$, C is a **hyperbola**.

Proof: If $e = 1$, then the defining property becomes $|PF| = |PL|$, which is the standard definition of a parabola (Section 11.4). We prove the result for ellipses ($0 < e < 1$); a small modification handles the case of hyperbolas ($e > 1$).

Let E be the curve whose points satisfy $|PF| = e|PL|$; the goal is to show that E is an ellipse. There are two points on the x-axis (the *vertices*), call them V and V', that satisfy $|VF| = e|VL|$ and $|V'F| = e|V'L|$. We choose the origin such that V and V' have coordinates $(a, 0)$ and $(-a, 0)$, respectively (Figure B.1). We locate the point F (a *focus*) at $(c, 0)$ and let ℓ (a *directrix*) be the line $x = d$, where $c > 0$ and $d > 0$. These choices place the center of E at the origin. Notice that we have four parameters (a, c, d, and e) that must be related.

Because the vertex $V(a, 0)$ is on E, it satisfies the defining property $|PF| = e|PL|$, with $P = V$. This condition implies that $a - c = e(d - a)$. Because the vertex $V'(-a, 0)$ is on the curve E, it also satisfies the defining property $|PF| = e|PL|$, with $P = V'$. This condition implies that $a + c = e(d + a)$. Solving these two equations for c and d, we find that $c = ae$ and $d = a/e$. To summarize, the parameters a, c, d, and e are related by the equations

$$c = ae \quad \text{and} \quad a = de.$$

Because $e < 1$, it follows that $c < a < d$.

We now use the property $|PF| = e|PL|$ with an arbitrary point $P(x, y)$ on the curve E. Figure B.1 shows the geometry with the focus $(c, 0) = (ae, 0)$ and the directrix $x = d = a/e$. The condition $|PF| = e|PL|$ becomes

$$\sqrt{(x - ae)^2 + y^2} = e\left(\frac{a}{e} - x\right).$$

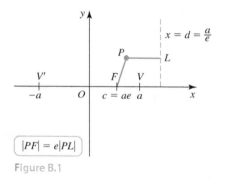

Figure B.1

The goal is to find the simplest possible relationship between x and y. Squaring both sides and collecting terms, we have

$$(1 - e^2)x^2 + y^2 = a^2(1 - e^2).$$

Dividing through by $a^2(1 - e^2)$ gives the equation of the standard ellipse:

$$\frac{x^2}{a^2} + \frac{y^2}{a^2(1 - e^2)} = \frac{x^2}{a^2} + \frac{y^2}{b^2} = 1, \quad \text{where} \quad b^2 = a^2(1 - e^2).$$

This is the equation of an ellipse centered at the origin with vertices and foci on the x-axis.

The preceding proof is now applied with $e > 1$. The argument for ellipses with $0 < e < 1$ led to the equation

$$\frac{x^2}{a^2} + \frac{y^2}{a^2(1 - e^2)} = 1.$$

With $e > 1$, we have $1 - e^2 < 0$, so we write $(1 - e^2) = -(e^2 - 1)$. The resulting equation describes a hyperbola centered at the origin with the foci on the x-axis:

$$\frac{x^2}{a^2} - \frac{y^2}{b^2} = 1, \quad \text{where} \quad b^2 = a^2(e^2 - 1). \qquad \blacktriangleleft$$

THEOREM 12.3   Continuity of Composite Functions

If $u = g(x, y)$ is continuous at (a, b) and $z = f(u)$ is continuous at $g(a, b)$, then the composite function $z = f(g(x, y))$ is continuous at (a, b).

Proof: Let P and P_0 represent the points (x, y) and (a, b), respectively. Let $u = g(P)$ and $u_0 = g(P_0)$. The continuity of f at u_0 means that $\lim_{u \to u_0} f(u) = f(u_0)$. This limit implies that given any $\varepsilon > 0$, there exists a $\delta^* > 0$ such that

$$|f(u) - f(u_0)| < \varepsilon \quad \text{whenever} \quad 0 < |u - u_0| < \delta^*.$$

The continuity of g at P_0 means that $\lim_{P \to P_0} g(P) = g(P_0)$. Letting $|P - P_0|$ denote the distance between P and P_0, this limit implies that given any $\delta^* > 0$, there exists a $\delta > 0$ such that

$$|g(P) - g(P_0)| = |u - u_0| < \delta^* \quad \text{whenever} \quad 0 < |P - P_0| < \delta.$$

We now combine these two statements. Given any $\varepsilon > 0$, there exists a $\delta > 0$ such that

$$|f(g(P)) - f(g(P_0))| = |f(u) - f(u_0)| < \varepsilon \quad \text{whenever} \quad 0 < |P - P_0| < \delta.$$

Therefore, $\lim_{(x,y) \to (a,b)} f(g(x, y)) = f(g(a, b))$ and $z = f(g(x, y))$ is continuous at (a, b). $\blacktriangleleft$

THEOREM 12.5   Conditions for Differentiability

Suppose the function f has partial derivatives f_x and f_y defined in a region containing (a, b), with f_x and f_y continuous at (a, b). Then f is differentiable at (a, b).

Proof: Figure B.2 shows a region on which the conditions of the theorem are satisfied containing the points $P_0(a, b)$, $Q(a + \Delta x, b)$, and $P(a + \Delta x, b + \Delta y)$. By the definition of differentiability of f at P_0, we must show that

$$\Delta z = f(P) - f(P_0) = f_x(a, b)\Delta x + f_y(a, b)\Delta y + \varepsilon_1 \Delta x + \varepsilon_2 \Delta y,$$

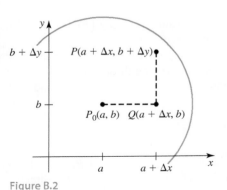

Figure B.2

where ε_1 and ε_2 depend only on $a, b, \Delta x$, and Δy, with $(\varepsilon_1, \varepsilon_2) \to (0, 0)$ as $(\Delta x, \Delta y) \to (0, 0)$. We can view the change Δz taking place in two stages:

- $\Delta z_1 = f(a + \Delta x, b) - f(a, b)$ is the change in z as (x, y) moves from P_0 to Q.
- $\Delta z_2 = f(a + \Delta x, b + \Delta y) - f(a + \Delta x, b)$ is the change in z as (x, y) moves from Q to P.

Applying the Mean Value Theorem to the first variable and noting that f is differentiable with respect to x, we have

$$\Delta z_1 = f(a + \Delta x, b) - f(a, b) = f_x(c, b)\Delta x,$$

where c lies in the interval $(a, a + \Delta x)$. Similarly, applying the Mean Value Theorem to the second variable and noting that f is differentiable with respect to y, we have

$$\Delta z_2 = f(a + \Delta x, b + \Delta y) - f(a + \Delta x, b) = f_y(a + \Delta x, d)\Delta y,$$

where d lies in the interval $(b, b + \Delta y)$. We now express Δz as the sum of Δz_1 and Δz_2:

$$\begin{aligned}
\Delta z &= \Delta z_1 + \Delta z_2 \\
&= f_x(c, b)\Delta x + f_y(a + \Delta x, d)\Delta y \\
&= \underbrace{(f_x(c, b) - f_x(a, b) + f_x(a, b))}_{\varepsilon_1}\Delta x \qquad \text{Add and subtract } f_x(a, b). \\
&\quad + \underbrace{(f_y(a + \Delta x, d) - f_y(a, b) + f_y(a, b))}_{\varepsilon_2}\Delta y \qquad \text{Add and subtract } f_y(a, b). \\
&= (f_x(a, b) + \varepsilon_1)\Delta x + (f_y(a, b) + \varepsilon_2)\Delta y.
\end{aligned}$$

Note that as $\Delta x \to 0$ and $\Delta y \to 0$, we have $c \to a$ and $d \to b$. Because f_x and f_y are continuous at (a, b), it follows that as $\Delta x \to 0$ and $\Delta y \to 0$,

$$\varepsilon_1 = f_x(c, b) - f_x(a, b) \to 0 \quad \text{and} \quad \varepsilon_2 = f_y(a + \Delta x, d) - f_y(a, b) \to 0.$$

Therefore, the condition for differentiability of f at (a, b) has been proved. ◄

THEOREM 12.7   Chain Rule (One Independent Variable)
Let $z = f(x, y)$ be a differentiable function of x and y on its domain, where x and y are differentiable functions of t on an interval I. Then

$$\frac{dz}{dt} = \frac{\partial f}{\partial x}\frac{dx}{dt} + \frac{\partial f}{\partial y}\frac{dy}{dt}.$$

Proof: Assume $(a, b) = (x(t), y(t))$ is in the domain of f, where t is in I. Let $\Delta x = x(t + \Delta t) - x(t)$ and $\Delta y = y(t + \Delta t) - y(t)$. Because f is differentiable at (a, b), we know (Section 13.4) that

$$\Delta z = \frac{\partial f}{\partial x}(a, b)\Delta x + \frac{\partial f}{\partial y}(a, b)\Delta y + \varepsilon_1\Delta x + \varepsilon_2\Delta y,$$

where $(\varepsilon_1, \varepsilon_2) \to (0, 0)$ as $(\Delta x, \Delta y) \to (0, 0)$. Dividing this equation by Δt gives

$$\frac{\Delta z}{\Delta t} = \frac{\partial f}{\partial x}\frac{\Delta x}{\Delta t} + \frac{\partial f}{\partial y}\frac{\Delta y}{\Delta t} + \varepsilon_1\frac{\Delta x}{\Delta t} + \varepsilon_2\frac{\Delta y}{\Delta t}.$$

As $\Delta t \to 0$, several things occur. First, because $x = g(t)$ and $y = h(t)$ are differentiable on I, $\dfrac{\Delta x}{\Delta t}$ and $\dfrac{\Delta y}{\Delta t}$ approach $\dfrac{dx}{dt}$ and $\dfrac{dy}{dt}$, respectively. Similarly, $\dfrac{\Delta z}{\Delta t}$ approaches $\dfrac{dz}{dt}$ as $\Delta t \to 0$. The fact that x and y are continuous on I (because they are differentiable there) means that $\Delta x \to 0$ and $\Delta y \to 0$ as $\Delta t \to 0$. Therefore, because $(\varepsilon_1, \varepsilon_2) \to (0, 0)$ as $(\Delta x, \Delta y) \to (0, 0)$, it follows that $(\varepsilon_1, \varepsilon_2) \to (0, 0)$ as $\Delta t \to 0$. Letting $\Delta t \to 0$, we have

$$\underbrace{\lim_{\Delta t \to 0} \frac{\Delta z}{\Delta t}}_{\frac{dz}{dt}} = \frac{\partial f}{\partial x} \underbrace{\lim_{\Delta t \to 0} \frac{\Delta x}{\Delta t}}_{\frac{dx}{dt}} + \frac{\partial f}{\partial y} \underbrace{\lim_{\Delta t \to 0} \frac{\Delta y}{\Delta t}}_{\frac{dy}{dt}} + \underbrace{\lim_{\Delta t \to 0} \underbrace{\varepsilon_1}_{\to 0} \frac{\Delta x}{\Delta t}}_{\to \frac{dx}{dt}} + \underbrace{\lim_{\Delta t \to 0} \underbrace{\varepsilon_2}_{\to 0} \frac{\Delta y}{\Delta t}}_{\to \frac{dy}{dt}}$$

or

$$\frac{dz}{dt} = \frac{\partial f}{\partial x} \frac{dx}{dt} + \frac{\partial f}{\partial y} \frac{dy}{dt}. \qquad \blacktriangleleft$$

THEOREM 12.14   Second Derivative Test

Suppose that the second partial derivatives of f are continuous throughout an open disk centered at the point (a, b) where $f_x(a, b) = f_y(a, b) = 0$. Let $D(x, y) = f_{xx}(x, y) f_{yy}(x, y) - (f_{xy}(x, y))^2$.

1. If $D(a, b) > 0$ and $f_{xx}(a, b) < 0$, then f has a local maximum value at (a, b).

2. If $D(a, b) > 0$ and $f_{xx}(a, b) > 0$, then f has a local minimum value at (a, b).

3. If $D(a, b) < 0$, then f has a saddle point at (a, b).

4. If $D(a, b) = 0$, then the test is inconclusive.

Proof: The proof relies on a two-variable version of Taylor's Theorem, which we prove first. Figure B.3 shows the open disk R on which the conditions of Theorem 12.14 are satisfied; it contains the points $P_0(a, b)$ and $P(a + \Delta x, b + \Delta y)$. The line ℓ through $P_0 P$ has a parametric description

$$\langle x(t), y(t) \rangle = \langle a + t\Delta x, b + t\Delta y \rangle,$$

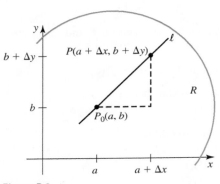

Figure B.3

where $t = 0$ corresponds to P_0 and $t = 1$ corresponds to P.

We now let $F(t) = f(a + t\Delta x, b + t\Delta y)$ be the value of f along that part of ℓ that lies in R. By the Chain Rule, we have

$$F'(t) = f_x \underbrace{x'(t)}_{\Delta x} + f_y \underbrace{y'(t)}_{\Delta y} = f_x \Delta x + f_y \Delta y.$$

Differentiating again with respect to t (f_x and f_y are differentiable), we use $f_{xy} = f_{yx}$ to obtain

$$F''(t) = \frac{\partial F'}{\partial x} \underbrace{x'(t)}_{\Delta x} + \frac{\partial F'}{\partial y} \underbrace{y'(t)}_{\Delta y}$$

$$= \frac{\partial}{\partial x}(f_x \Delta x + f_y \Delta y)\Delta x + \frac{\partial}{\partial y}(f_x \Delta x + f_y \Delta y)\Delta y$$

$$= f_{xx} \Delta x^2 + 2 f_{xy} \Delta x \Delta y + f_{yy} \Delta y^2.$$

Noting that F meets the conditions of Taylor's Theorem for one variable with $n = 1$, we write

$$F(t) = F(0) + F'(0)(t - 0) + \frac{1}{2} F''(c)(t - 0)^2,$$

where c is between 0 and t. Setting $t = 1$, it follows that

$$F(1) = F(0) + F'(0) + \frac{1}{2} F''(c), \qquad (1)$$

where $0 < c < 1$. Recalling that $F(t) = f(a + t\Delta x, b + t\Delta y)$ and invoking the condition $f_x(a, b) = f_y(a, b) = 0$, we have

$$F(1) = f(a + \Delta x, b + \Delta y)$$

$$= \underbrace{f(a, b) + f_x(a, b)\Delta x + f_y(a, b)\Delta y}_{F'(0) = 0}$$

$$+ \frac{1}{2}(f_{xx}\Delta x^2 + 2f_{xy}\Delta x\Delta y + f_{yy}\Delta y^2)\Big|_{(a + c\Delta x,\, b + c\Delta y)}$$

$$= f(a, b) + \underbrace{\frac{1}{2}(f_{xx}\Delta x^2 + 2f_{xy}\Delta x\Delta y + f_{yy}\Delta y^2)\Big|_{(a + c\Delta x,\, b + c\Delta y)}}_{H(c)}$$

$$= f(a, b) + \frac{1}{2}H(c).$$

The existence and type of extreme point at (a, b) is determined by the sign of $f(a + \Delta x, b + \Delta y) - f(a, b)$ (for example, if $f(a + \Delta x, b + \Delta y) - f(a, b) \geq 0$ for all Δx and Δy near 0, then f has a local minimum at (a, b)). Note that $f(a + \Delta x, b + \Delta y) - f(a, b)$ has the same sign as the quantity we have denoted $H(c)$. Assuming $H(0) \neq 0$, for Δx and Δy sufficiently small and nonzero, the sign of $H(c)$ is the same as the sign of

$$H(0) = f_{xx}(a, b)\Delta x^2 + 2f_{xy}(a, b)\Delta x\Delta y + f_{yy}(a, b)\Delta y^2$$

(because the second partial derivatives are continuous at (a, b) and $(a + c\Delta x, b + c\Delta y)$ can be made arbitrarily close to (a, b)). Multiplying both sides of the previous expression by f_{xx} and rearranging terms leads to

$$f_{xx}H(0) = f_{xx}^2\Delta x^2 + 2f_{xy}f_{xx}\Delta x\Delta y + f_{yy}f_{xx}\Delta y^2$$

$$= \underbrace{(f_{xx}\Delta x + f_{xy}\Delta y)^2}_{\geq 0} + \underbrace{(f_{xx}f_{yy} - f_{xy}^2)}_{D}\Delta y^2,$$

where all derivatives are evaluated at (a, b). Recall that the signs of $H(0)$ and $f(a + \Delta x, b + \Delta y) - f(a, b)$ are the same. Letting $D(a, b) = (f_{xx}f_{yy} - f_{xy}^2)\big|_{(a, b)}$, we reach the following conclusions:

- If $D(a, b) > 0$ and $f_{xx}(a, b) < 0$, then $H(0) < 0$ (for Δx and Δy sufficiently close to 0) and $f(a + \Delta x, b + \Delta y) - f(a, b) < 0$. Therefore, f has a local maximum value at (a, b).

- If $D(a, b) > 0$ and $f_{xx}(a, b) > 0$, then $H(0) > 0$ (for Δx and Δy sufficiently close to 0) and $f(a + \Delta x, b + \Delta y) - f(a, b) > 0$. Therefore, f has a local minimum value at (a, b).

- If $D(a, b) < 0$, then $H(0) > 0$ for some small nonzero values of Δx and Δy (implying $f(a + \Delta x, b + \Delta y) > f(a, b)$), *and* $H(0) < 0$ for other small nonzero values of Δx and Δy (implying $f(a + \Delta x, b + \Delta y) < f(a, b)$). (The relative sizes of $(f_{xx}\Delta x + f_{xy}\Delta y)^2$ and $(f_{xx}f_{yy} - f_{xy}^2)\Delta y^2$ can be adjusted by varying Δx and Δy.) Therefore, f has a saddle point at (a, b).

- If $D(a, b) = 0$, then $H(0)$ may be zero, in which case the sign of $H(c)$ cannot be determined. Therefore, the test is inconclusive.

◀

Answers

Section 6.1 Exercises, pp. 407–411

1. The position $s(t)$ is the location of the object relative to the origin. The displacement is the change in position between time $t = a$ and $t = b$. The distance traveled between $t = a$ and $t = b$ is $\int_a^b |v(t)|\,dt$, where $v(t)$ is the velocity at time t.   **3.** The displacement between $t = a$ and $t = b$ is $\int_a^b v(t)\,dt$.   **5.** $Q(t) = Q(0) + \int_0^t Q'(x)\,dx$ **7. a.** $[0, 1), (3, 5)$ **b.** -4 mi   **c.** 26 mi   **d.** 6 mi   **e.** 6 mi on the positive side of the initial position

9. a.

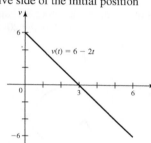

Positive direction for $0 \le t < 3$; negative direction for $3 < t \le 6$ **b.** 0   **c.** 18 m

11. a.

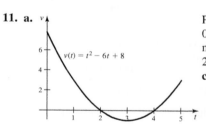

Positive direction for $0 \le t < 2$ and $4 < t < 5$; negative direction for $2 < t < 4$ **b.** 20/3 m   **c.** 28/3 m

13. a.

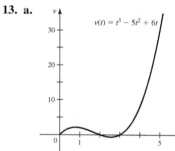

Positive direction for $0 < t < 2$ and $3 < t < 5$; negative direction for $2 < t < 3$

b. $\dfrac{275}{12}$ m   **c.** $\dfrac{95}{4}$ m

15. a.

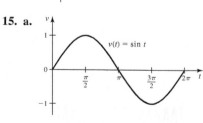

Positive direction for $0 < t < \pi$; negative direction for $\pi < t < 2\pi$

b. $s(t) = 2 - \cos t$ **c.**

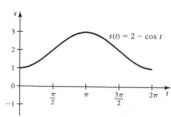

17. a.

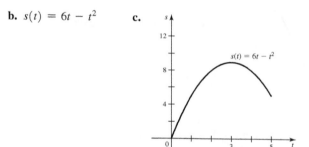

Positive direction for $0 \le t < 3$; negative direction for $3 < t \le 5$

b. $s(t) = 6t - t^2$ **c.**

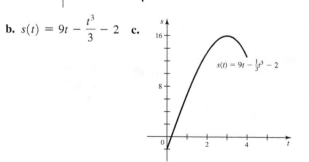

19. a.

Positive direction for $0 \le t < 3$; negative direction for $3 < t \le 4$

b. $s(t) = 9t - \dfrac{t^3}{3} - 2$ **c.**

21. a. $s(t) = 2 \sin \pi t$ **b.**   **c.** $\frac{3}{2}, \frac{7}{2}, \frac{11}{2}$

d. $\frac{1}{2}, \frac{5}{2}, \frac{9}{2}$

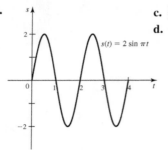

$s(t) = 2 \sin \pi t$

23. a. $s(t) = 10t(48 - t^2)$ **b.** 880 mi

c. $\dfrac{2720\sqrt{6}}{9} \approx 740.29$ mi

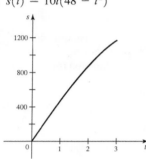

25.

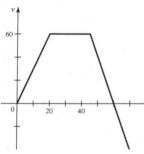

a. Velocity is a maximum for $20 \le t \le 45$; $v = 0$ at $t = 0$ and $t = 60$ **b.** 1200 m
c. 2550 m   **d.** 2100 m

27. $v(t) = -32t + 70$; $s(t) = -16t^2 + 70t + 10$
29. $v(t) = -9.8t + 20$; $s(t) = -4.9t^2 + 20t$
31. $v(t) = -\frac{1}{200}t^2 + 10$; $s(t) = -\frac{1}{600}t^3 + 10t$
33. $v(t) = \frac{1}{2}\sin 2t + 5$; $s(t) = -\frac{1}{4}\cos 2t + 5t + \frac{29}{4}$

35.

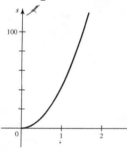

a. $s(t) = 44t^2$
b. 704 ft
c. $\sqrt{30} \approx 5.477$ s
d. $\dfrac{5\sqrt{33}}{11} \approx 2.611$ s
e. Approximately 180.023 ft

37. 6.154 mi; 1.465 mi   **39. a.** 27,250 barrels   **b.** 31,000 barrels
c. 4000 barrels   **41. a.** 2639 people   **b.** $P(t) = 250 + 20t^{3/2} + 30t$
people   **43. a.** 1897 cells; 1900 cells   **b.** $N(t) = -400e^{-0.25t} + 1900$
45. a. $96,875   **b.** $86,875   **47. a.** $69,583.33   **b.** $139,583.33
49. a. False   **b.** True   **c.** True   **d.** True

51. a. 3   **b.** $\frac{13}{3}$ **c.** 3

d. $s(t) = \begin{cases} -\dfrac{t^2}{2} + 2t, & 0 \le t \le 3 \\[2mm] \dfrac{3t^2}{2} - 10t + 18, & 3 < t \le 4 \\[2mm] -t^2 + 10t - 22, & 4 < t \le 5 \end{cases}$

53. $\dfrac{2}{3}$ **55.** $\dfrac{25}{3}$ **57. a.**

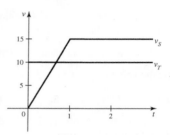

b. Theo   **c.** Sasha   **d.** Theo hits the 10-mi mark before Sasha; Sasha and Theo hit the 15-mi mark at the same time; Sasha hits the 20-mi mark before Theo.   **e.** Sasha   **f.** Theo
59. a. Abe initially runs into a headwind; Bess initially runs with a tailwind.

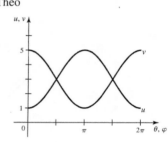

b. 3 mi/hr for both runners   **c.** $\pi\sqrt{5}/25$ hr for both runners
61. a. $\dfrac{10^7(1 - e^{-kt})}{k}$ **b.** $\dfrac{10^7}{k} =$ total number of barrels of
oil extracted if the nation extracts the oil indefinitely where
it is assumed that the nation has at least $\dfrac{10^7}{k}$ barrels of oil in

reserve   **c.** $k = \dfrac{1}{200} = 0.005$ **d.** Approximately 138.6 yr

63. a. $\dfrac{120}{\pi} + 40 \approx 78.20 \text{ m}^3$ **b.** $Q(t) = 20\left(t + \dfrac{12}{\pi}\sin\left(\dfrac{\pi}{12}t\right)\right)$

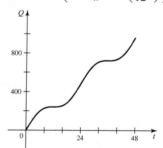

c. Approximately 122.6 hr

65. a. $V(t) = 5 + \cos\dfrac{\pi t}{2}$

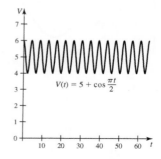

$V(t) = 5 + \cos\dfrac{\pi t}{2}$

b. 15 breaths/min   **c.** 2 L, 6 L

67. a. 7200 MWh or 2.592×10^{13} J   **b.** 16,000 kg; 5,840,000 kg
c. 450 g; 164,250 g   **d.** About 1500 turbines

69. $\displaystyle\int_a^b f'(x)\,dx = f(b) - f(a) = g(b) - g(a) = \int_a^b g'(x)\,dx$

Section 6.2 Exercises, pp. 416–420

1.

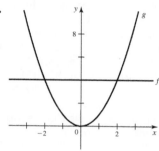

$\displaystyle\int_{-2}^{2} (f(x) - g(x))\,dx$ is the area between these curves.

3. See solution to Exercise 1.   **5.** $\dfrac{9}{2}$ **7.** $\dfrac{5}{2} - \dfrac{1}{\ln 2}$ **9.** $\dfrac{25}{2}$ **11.** $\dfrac{81}{32}$

13. $\pi - 2$ **15.** $2 - \sqrt{2}$ **17.** $\frac{1}{2} + \ln 2$ **19.** $\dfrac{7}{3}$ **21.** 3

23. 2   **25.** $\dfrac{125}{2}$ **27. a.** $\displaystyle\int_{-\sqrt{2}}^{-1} (2 - x^2)\,dx + \int_{-1}^{0} (-x)\,dx$

b. $\displaystyle\int_{-1}^{0} (y + \sqrt{y + 2})\,dy$

29. a. $\displaystyle 2\int_{-3}^{-2} \sqrt{x + 3}\,dx + \int_{-2}^{6} \left(\sqrt{x + 3} - \dfrac{x}{2}\right)dx$

b. $\displaystyle\int_{-1}^{3} (2y - (y^2 - 3))\,dy$

31. 9

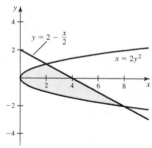

33. $\frac{64}{5}$ **35.** $\ln 2$ **37.** $\frac{5}{24}$ **39. a.** False   **b.** False   **c.** True
41. $\frac{1}{6}$ **43.** $\frac{9}{2}$ **45.** $\frac{32}{3}$ **47.** $\frac{63}{4}$ **49.** $\frac{15}{8} - 2\ln 2$

51. a. Area $(R_1) = \dfrac{p - 1}{2(p + 1)}$ for all positive integers p;

area $(R_2) = \dfrac{q - 1}{2(q + 1)}$ for all positive integers q; they are equal.

b. R_1 has greater area.   **c.** R_2 has greater area.   **53.** $\dfrac{17}{3}$

55. $\dfrac{81}{2}$ **57.** $\dfrac{n - 1}{2(n + 1)}$ **59.** $A_n = \dfrac{n - 1}{n + 1}$; $\displaystyle\lim_{n\to\infty} A_n = 1$; the region

approximates a square with side length of 1.   **61.** $k = 1 - \dfrac{1}{\sqrt{2}}$

63. $k = \dfrac{1}{2}$ **65. a.** The lowest $p\%$ of households owns exactly $p\%$ of the wealth for $0 \le p \le 100$.   **b.** The function must be one-to-one and its graph must lie below $y = x$ because the poorest $p\%$ cannot own more than $p\%$ of the wealth.   **c.** $p = 1.1$ is most equitable; $p = 4$ is least equitable.   **e.** $G(p) = \dfrac{p - 1}{p + 1}$ **f.** $0 \le G \le 1$ for $p \ge 1$

g. $\dfrac{5}{18}$ **67.** -1 **69.** $\frac{4}{9}$ **71. a.** $F(a) = ab^3/6 - b^4/12$; $F(a) = 0$ if $a \stackrel{1}{=} b/2$ **b.** Because $A'(b/2) = 0$ and $A''(b/2) > 0$, A has a minimum at $a = b/2$. The maximum value of $b^4/12$ occurs if $a = 0$ or $a = b$.

73. a.

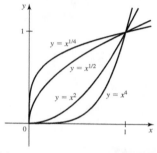

b. $A_n(x)$ is the net area of the region between the graphs of f and g from 0 to x.   **c.** $x = n^{n/(n^2 - 1)}$; the root decreases with n.

Section 6.3 Exercises, pp. 429–433

1. $A(x)$ is the area of the cross section through the solid at the point x.

3. $\displaystyle\int_0^2 \pi(4x^2 - x^4)\,dx$ **5.** The cross sections are disks, and $A(x)$ is the area of a disk.   **7.** $\dfrac{64}{15}$ **9.** 1   **11.** $\dfrac{1000}{3}$ **13.** $\dfrac{\pi}{3}$ **15.** $\dfrac{16\sqrt{2}}{3}$

17. 36π **19.** $\dfrac{15\pi}{32}$ **21.** $\dfrac{\pi^2}{2}$ **23.** $\dfrac{\pi^2}{6}$ **25.** $\dfrac{\pi^2}{2}$
27. $32\pi/3$ **29.** $5\pi/6$ **31.** $117\pi/5$ **33.** $(4\pi - \pi^2)/4$ **35.** 54π
37. $64\pi/5$ **39.** $32\pi/3$ **41.** Volumes are equal.   **43.** x-axis

45. $\dfrac{\pi}{6}$ **47.** $2\pi(8 + \pi)$ **49.** $(6\sqrt{3} - 2\pi)\pi$ **51.** 4π

53. a. False   **b.** True   **c.** True   **55.** $\pi \ln 3$ **57.** $\dfrac{\pi}{2}(e^4 - 1)$

59. $49\pi/2$ **61.** Volume $(S) = 8\pi a^{5/2}/15$; volume $(T) = \pi a^{5/2}/3$

63. a.   **b.**

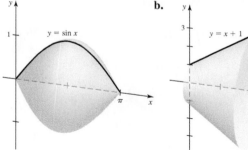

65. a. $\frac{1}{3}V_C$ **b.** $\frac{2}{3}V_C$ **67.** $24\pi^2$ **69. b.** $2/\sqrt{\pi}$ m

Section 6.4 Exercises, pp. 442–445

1. $\int_a^b 2\pi x(f(x) - g(x))\, dx$ **3.** $x; y$ **5.** $\dfrac{\pi}{6}$ **7.** $\pi \ln 5$ **9.** π

11. $\dfrac{\pi}{5}$ **13.** π **15.** 8π **17.** $\dfrac{32\pi}{3}$ **19.** $\dfrac{2\pi}{3}$ **21.** $\dfrac{81\pi}{2}$ **23.** 90π

25. π **27.** 24π **29.** 54π **31.** $\dfrac{16\sqrt{2}\,\pi}{3}$ **33.** $\dfrac{11\pi}{6}$ **35.** $\dfrac{23\pi}{15}$

37. $\dfrac{52\pi}{15}$ **39.** $\dfrac{36\pi}{5}$ **41.** $\dfrac{4\pi}{15}$; shell method   **43.** $\dfrac{8\pi}{27}$; shell

method   **45.** $\pi\,(\sqrt{e} - 1)^2$; shell method   **47.** $\dfrac{\pi}{9}$; washer method

49. a. True   **b.** False   **c.** True   **51.** $4\pi \ln 2$ **53.** $2\pi e(e - 1)$
55. $16\pi/3$ **57.** $608\pi/3$ **59.** $\pi/4$ **61.** $\pi/3$

63. a. $V_1 = \dfrac{\pi}{15}(3a^2 + 10a + 15)\ V_2 = \dfrac{\pi}{2}(a + 2)$

b. $V(S_1) = V(S_2)$ for $a = 0$ and $a = -\frac{5}{6}$ **67.** $\dfrac{\pi h^2}{3}(24 - h)$

69. $24\pi^2$ **73.** 10π **75. a.** $27\sqrt{3}\pi r^3/8$ **b.** $54\sqrt{2}/(3 + \sqrt{2})^3$
c. $500\pi/3$

Section 6.5 Exercises, pp. 450–451

1. Determine whether f has a continuous derivative on $[a, b]$. If so,

calculate $f'(x)$ and evaluate the integral $\int_a^b \sqrt{1 + f'(x)^2}\, dx$.

3. $\int_{-2}^5 \sqrt{1 + 9x^4}\, dx$ **5.** $\int_0^2 \sqrt{1 + 4e^{-4x}}\, dx$ **7.** $4\sqrt{5}$ **9.** $8\sqrt{65}$

11. 168   **13.** $\frac{4}{3}$ **15.** $\frac{123}{32}$ **17. a.** $\int_{-1}^1 \sqrt{1 + 4x^2}\, dx$ **b.** 2.96

19. a. $\int_1^4 \sqrt{1 + \dfrac{1}{x^2}}\, dx$ **b.** 3.34   **21. a.** $\int_3^4 \sqrt{\dfrac{4x - 7}{4x - 8}}\, dx$ **b.** 1.08

23. a. $\int_0^\pi \sqrt{1 + 4\sin^2 2x}\, dx$ **b.** 5.27   **25. a.** $\int_1^{10} \sqrt{1 + 1/x^4}\, dx$

b. 9.15   **27.** $7\sqrt{5}$ **29.** $\frac{123}{32}$ **31. a.** False   **b.** True   **c.** False
33. a. $f(x) = \pm 4x^3/3 + C$ **b.** $f(x) = \pm 3 \sin 2x + C$
35. $y = 1 - x^2$ **37.** Approximately 1326 m   **39. a.** $L/2$ **b.** L/c

Section 6.6 Exercises, pp. 457–459

1. 15π **3.** Evaluate $\int_a^b 2\pi f(x)\sqrt{1 + f'(x)^2}\, dx$ **5.** $156\sqrt{10}\pi$

7. $\dfrac{2912\pi}{3}$ **9.** $\dfrac{53\pi}{9}$ **11.** $\dfrac{\pi}{8}(16 + e^8 - e^{-8})$ **13.** $\dfrac{275\pi}{32}$

15. $\dfrac{9\pi}{125}\,\mathrm{m}^3$ **17.** $\dfrac{\pi}{9}(17^{3/2} - 1)$ **19.** $15\sqrt{17}\,\pi$

21. a. False   **b.** False   **c.** True   **d.** False   **23.** $\dfrac{48{,}143\pi}{48}$

25. $\dfrac{1{,}256{,}001\pi}{1024} \approx 3853.36$ **27. b.** Approximately 7.21

29. b. Approximately 3.84   **31.** $\dfrac{12\pi a^2}{5}$ **35. a.** $\dfrac{6}{a}$ **b.** $\dfrac{3}{a}$

c. $\dfrac{3}{2a} + \dfrac{3a}{2\sqrt{a^2 - 1}}\sin^{-1}\left(\dfrac{\sqrt{a^2 - 1}}{a}\right)$ **d.** The sphere
e. A sphere   **37. a.** $c^2 A$ **b.** A

Section 6.7 Exercises, pp. 467–471

1. 150 g   **3.** 25 J   **5.** Different volumes of water are moved different
distances.   **7.** 39,200 N/m^2 **9.** $\pi + 2$ **11.** 3   **13.** $(2\sqrt{2} - 1)/3$
15. 10   **17.** 9 J   **19. a.** $k = 150$ **b.** 12 J   **c.** 6.75 J   **d.** 9 J
21. a. 112.5 J   **b.** 12.5 J   **23. a.** 31.25 J   **b.** 312.5 J   **25. a.** 625 J
b. 391 J   **27.** 1.15×10^7 J   **29.** 3.94×10^6 J   **31. a.** $66{,}150\pi$ J
b. No   **33. a.** 2.10×10^8 J   **b.** 3.78×10^8 J   **35. a.** 32,667 J
b. Yes   **37.** 7.70×10^3 J   **39.** 1.47×10^7 N   **41.** 2.94×10^7 N
43. 6533 N   **45.** 8×10^5 N   **47.** 6737.5 N   **49. a.** True   **b.** True
c. True   **d.** False   **51. a.** Compared to a linear spring $F(x) = 16x$,
the restoring force is less for large displacements.   **b.** 17.87 J
c. 31.6 J   **53.** 0.28 J   **55. a.** 8.87×10^9 J
b. 500 $GMx/(R(x + R)) = (2 \times 10^{17})x/(R(x + R))$ J
c. GMm/R **d.** $v = \sqrt{2GM/R}$ **57. a.** 22,050 J   **b.** 36,750 J
61. Left: 16,730 N; right: 14,700 N   **63. a.** Yes   **b.** 4.296 m

Section 6.8 Exercises, pp. 480–481

1. $D = (0, \infty), R = (-\infty, \infty)$ **3.** $\dfrac{4^x}{\ln 4} + C$

5. $e^{x \ln 3}, e^{\pi \ln x}, e^{(\sin x)(\ln x)}$ **7.** 3   **9.** $\cos(\ln x)/x, x > 0$

11. $-\dfrac{5}{x(\ln 2x)^6}$ **13.** $6(1 - \ln 2)$ **15.** $\dfrac{3}{8}$ **17.** $\dfrac{1}{2}\ln(4 + e^{2x}) + C$

19. $\dfrac{1}{\ln 2} - \dfrac{1}{\ln 3}$ **21.** $4 - \dfrac{4}{e^2}$ **23.** $2e^{\sqrt{x}} + C$ **25.** $\ln|e^x - e^{-x}| + C$

27. $\dfrac{99}{10 \ln 10}$ **29.** 3   **31.** $\dfrac{6^{x+8}}{3 \ln 6} + C$ **33.** $4^{2x+1}x^{4x}(1 + \ln 2x)$

35. $(\ln 2)\,2^{x^2+1}\,x$ **37.** $2(x + 1)^{2x}\left(\dfrac{x}{x + 1} + \ln(x + 1)\right)$

39. $y^{\sin y}\left(\cos y \ln y + \dfrac{\sin y}{y}\right)$ **41. a.** True   **b.** False   **c.** False

d. False   **e.** False

43.

h	$(1 + 2h)^{1/h}$	h	$(1 + 2h)^{1/h}$
10^{-1}	6.1917	-10^{-1}	9.3132
10^{-2}	7.2446	-10^{-2}	7.5404
10^{-3}	7.3743	-10^{-3}	7.4039
10^{-4}	7.3876	-10^{-4}	7.3905
10^{-5}	7.3889	-10^{-5}	7.3892
10^{-6}	7.3890	-10^{-6}	7.3891

$\lim_{h \to 0}(1 + 2h)^{1/h} = e^2$

45.

x	$\dfrac{2^x - 1}{x}$	x	$\dfrac{2^x - 1}{x}$
10^{-1}	0.71773	-10^{-1}	0.66967
10^{-2}	0.69556	-10^{-2}	0.69075
10^{-3}	0.69339	-10^{-3}	0.69291
10^{-4}	0.69317	-10^{-4}	0.69312
10^{-5}	0.69315	-10^{-5}	0.69314
10^{-6}	0.69315	-10^{-6}	0.69315

$$\lim_{x \to 0} \frac{2^x - 1}{x} = \ln 2$$

47. a. No **b.** No **49.** $\dfrac{\ln p}{p - 1}, 0$ **51.** $-20xe^{-10x^2}$

53. $-(1/x)^x(1 + \ln x)$ **55.** $\left(-\dfrac{4}{x + 4} + \ln\left(\dfrac{x + 4}{x}\right)\right)\left(1 + \dfrac{4}{x}\right)^x$

57. $-\sin(x^{2 \sin x})x^{2 \sin x}\left(\dfrac{2 \sin x}{x} + 2 \cos x \ln x\right)$ **59.** $-\dfrac{1}{9^x \ln 9} + C$

61. $\dfrac{10^{x^3}}{3 \ln 10} + C$ **63.** $\dfrac{3 \cdot 3^{\ln 2} - 1}{\ln 3}$ **65.** $\dfrac{32}{3}$ **67.** $\dfrac{1}{3} \ln \dfrac{65}{16}$

69. $\dfrac{1}{2}(\ln 2 + 1) \approx 0.85$

73. $\ln 2 = \displaystyle\int_1^2 \dfrac{dt}{t} < L_2 = \dfrac{5}{6} < 1$

$\ln 3 = \displaystyle\int_1^3 \dfrac{dt}{t} > R_7$

$= 2\left(\dfrac{1}{9} + \dfrac{1}{11} + \dfrac{1}{13} + \dfrac{1}{15} + \dfrac{1}{17} + \dfrac{1}{19} + \dfrac{1}{21}\right) > 1$

Section 6.9 Exercises, pp. 488–490

1. The relative growth is constant. **3.** The time it takes a function to double in value **5.** $T_2 = (\ln 2)/k$ **7.** Compound interest, world population **9.** $\dfrac{df}{dt} = 10.5;\ \dfrac{dg}{dt} \cdot \dfrac{1}{g} = \dfrac{10e^{t/10}}{100e^{t/10}} = \dfrac{1}{10}$

11. $P(t) = 90{,}000e^{t \ln 1.024}$ people with $t = 0$ in 2010; 2039
13. $P(t) = 50{,}000e^{0.1t \ln 1.1}$ people; 60,500
15. $p(t) = 100e^{t \ln 1.03}$ dollars with $t = 0$ in 2005; $146.85
17. a. $T_2 \approx 87$ yr, 2050 pop ≈ 425 million **b.** $T_2 \approx 116$ yr, 2050 pop ≈ 393 million; $T_2 \approx 70$ yr, 2050 pop ≈ 460 million
19. About 33 million **21.** $H(t) = 800e^{t \ln 0.97}$ homicides with $t = 0$ in 2010; 2019 **23.** $a(t) = 20e^{(t/36) \ln 0.5}$ mg with $t = 0$ at midnight; 15.87 mg; 119.6 hr ≈ 5 days **25.** $P(t) = 9.94e^{(t/10) \ln 0.994}$ in millions with $t = 0$ in 2000; 9.82 million; the population decline may stop if the economy improves. **27.** 18,928 ft; 125,754 ft
29. 1.055 billion yr **31. a.** False **b.** False **c.** True
d. True **e.** True **33.** If $A(t) = A_0e^{kt}$ and $A(T) = 2A_0$, then $e^{kt} = 2$ and $T = (\ln 2)/k$. Therefore, the doubling time is a constant.
35. a. Bob; Abe **b.** $y = 4 \ln(t + 1)$ and $y = 8 - 8e^{-t/2}$; Bob

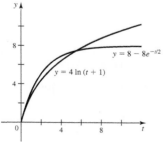

37. 10.034%; no **39.** 1.3 s **41.** 1044 days **43.** $50
45. $k = \ln(1 + r);\ r = 2^{(1/T_2)} - 1;\ T_2 = (\ln 2)/k$

Section 6.10 Exercises, pp. 502–506

1. $\cosh x = \dfrac{e^x + e^{-x}}{2};\ \sinh x = \dfrac{e^x - e^{-x}}{2}$ **3.** $\cosh^2 x - \sinh^2 x = 1$
5. $\sinh^{-1} x = \ln(x + \sqrt{x^2 + 1})$ **7.** Evaluate $\sinh^{-1} \frac{1}{5}$.
9. $\displaystyle\int \dfrac{dx}{16 - x^2} = \dfrac{1}{4} \coth^{-1} \dfrac{x}{4} + C$ when $|x| > 4$; in this case, the values in the interval of integration $6 \leq x \leq 8$ satisfy $|x| > 4$.
23. $2 \cosh x \sinh x$ **25.** $2 \tanh x \sech^2 x$ **27.** $-2 \tanh 2x$
29. $2x \cosh 3x(3x \sinh 3x + \cosh 3x)$ **31.** $(\sinh 2x)/2 + C$
33. $\ln(1 + \cosh x) + C$ **35.** $x - \tanh x + C$
37. $(\cosh^4 3 - 1)/12 \approx 856$ **39.** $\ln(5/4)$
41. $(x^2 + 1)/(2x) + C$ **43. a.** The values of $y = \coth x$ are close to 1 on $[5, 10]$. **b.** $\ln(\sinh 10) - \ln(\sinh 5) \approx 5.0000454$; $|\text{error}| \approx 0.0000454$
45.

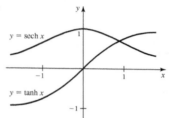

a. $x = \sinh^{-1} 1 = \ln(1 + \sqrt{2})$ **b.** $\pi/4 - \ln \sqrt{2} \approx 0.44$
47. $4/\sqrt{16x^2 - 1}$ **49.** $2v/\sqrt{v^4 + 1}$ **51.** $\sinh^{-1} x$
53. $\dfrac{1}{2\sqrt{2}} \coth^{-1}\left(\dfrac{x}{2\sqrt{2}}\right) + C$ **55.** $\tanh^{-1}(e^x/6)/6 + C$
57. $-\sech^{-1}(x^4/2)/8 + C$ **59.** $\sinh^{-1} 2 = \ln(2 + \sqrt{5})$
61. $-(\ln 5)/3 \approx -0.54$
63. $3 \ln\left(\dfrac{\sqrt{5} + 2}{\sqrt{2} + 1}\right) = 3(\sinh^{-1} 2 - \sinh^{-1} 1)$
65. $\dfrac{1}{15}\left(17 - \dfrac{8}{\ln(5/3)}\right) \approx 0.09$
67. a. $\text{sag} = f(50) - f(0) = a(\cosh(50/a) - 1) = 10$; now divide by a. **b.** $t \approx 0.08$ **c.** $a = 10/t \approx 125$; $L = 250 \sinh(2/5) \approx 102.7$ ft **69.** $\lambda \approx 32.81$ m
71. When $d/\lambda < 0.05$, $2\pi d/\lambda$ is small. Because $\tanh x \approx x$ for small values of x, $\tanh(2\pi d/\lambda) \approx 2\pi d/\lambda$; therefore,
$$v = \sqrt{\dfrac{g\lambda}{2\pi} \tanh\left(\dfrac{2\pi d}{\lambda}\right)} \approx \sqrt{\dfrac{g\lambda}{2\pi} \cdot \dfrac{2\pi d}{\lambda}} = \sqrt{gd}.$$
$v = \sqrt{gd}$ is a function of depth alone; when depth d decreases, v also decreases. **73. a.** False **b.** False **c.** False **d.** True **e.** False
75. a. 1 **b.** 0 **c.** Undefined **d.** 1 **e.** 13/12 **f.** 40/9
g. $\left(\dfrac{e^2 + 1}{2e}\right)^2$ **h.** Undefined **i.** $\ln 4$ **j.** 1 **77.** $x = 0$
79. $x = \pm \tanh^{-1}(1/\sqrt{3}) = \pm \ln(2 + \sqrt{3})/2 \approx \pm 0.658$
81. $\tan^{-1}(\sinh 1) - \pi/4 \approx 0.08$ **83.** Applying l'Hôpital's Rule twice brings you back to the initial limit; $\displaystyle\lim_{x \to \infty} \tanh x = 1$ **85.** $2/\pi$
87. 1 **89.** $-\csch z + C$ **91.** $\ln \sqrt{3} \cdot \ln(4/3) \approx 0.158$
93. $12(3 \ln(3 + \sqrt{8}) - \sqrt{8}) \approx 29.5$ **95. a.** ≈ 360.8 m
b. first 100 m: $t \approx 4.72$ s, $v_{av} \approx 21.2$ m/s; second 100 m: $t \approx 2.25$ s, $v_{av} \approx 44.5$ m/s **97. a.** $\sqrt{mg/k}$ **b.** $35\sqrt{3} \approx 60.6$ m/s
c. $t = \sqrt{\dfrac{m}{kg}} \tanh^{-1}(0.95) = \dfrac{1}{2}\sqrt{\dfrac{m}{kg}} \ln 39$ **d.** ≈ 736.5 m
109. $\ln(21/4) \approx 1.66$

Chapter 6 Review Exercises, pp. 507–510

1. a. True **b.** True **c.** True **d.** False **e.** False **f.** False
g. True   **3.** $s(t) = 20t - 5t^2$; displacement $= 20t - 5t^2$;
$$D(t) = \begin{cases} 20t - 5t^2 & \text{if } 0 \le t < 2 \\ 5t^2 - 20t + 40 & \text{if } 2 \le t \le 4 \end{cases}$$

5. a. $v(t) = -\dfrac{8}{\pi}\cos\dfrac{\pi t}{4}$; $s(t) = -\dfrac{32}{\pi^2}\sin\dfrac{\pi t}{4}$

b. Min value $= -\dfrac{32}{\pi^2}$; max value $= \dfrac{32}{\pi^2}$ **c.** 0; 0   **7. a.** $R(t) = 3t^{4/3}$

b. $R(t) = \begin{cases} 3t^{4/3} & \text{if } 0 \le t \le 8 \\ 2t + 32 & \text{if } t > 8 \end{cases}$ **c.** $t = 59$ min

9. a.

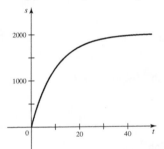

b. $10\ln 4 \approx 13.86$ s

c. $s(t) = 2000(1 - e^{-t/10})$ **d.** No

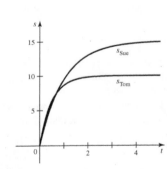

11. a. $s_{\text{Tom}}(t) = -10e^{-2t} + 10$
  $s_{\text{Sue}}(t) = -15e^{-t} + 15$

b. $t = 0$ and $t = \ln 2$ **c.** Sue   **13.** $\dfrac{7}{3}$

15. R_1: 17/6; R_2: 47/6; R_3: 11/2   **17.** 8   **19.** 1   **21.** $\dfrac{1}{3}$ **23.** $\dfrac{5}{6}$

25. $\dfrac{8}{15}$ **27.** $\dfrac{8\pi}{5}$ **29.** $\pi(e - 1)^2$ **31.** π **33.** $\dfrac{512\pi}{15}$

35. About $y = -2$: 80π; about $x = -2$: 112π
37. a. V_y **b.** V_y

c. $V_x = \begin{cases} \pi\left(\dfrac{a^{1-2p} - 1}{1 - 2p}\right) & \text{if } p \ne 1/2 \\ \pi\ln a & \text{if } p = 1/2 \end{cases}$

d. $V_y = \begin{cases} 2\pi\left(\dfrac{a^{2-p} - 1}{2 - p}\right) & \text{if } p \ne 2 \\ 2\pi\ln a & \text{if } p = 2 \end{cases}$

39. $c = 5$ **41.** 1   **43.** $2\sqrt{3} - \dfrac{4}{3}$

45. $\sqrt{b^2 + 1} - \sqrt{2} + \ln\left(\dfrac{(\sqrt{b^2 + 1} - 1)(1 + \sqrt{2})}{b}\right)$;

$b \approx 2.715$ **47. a.** 9π **b.** $\dfrac{9\pi}{2}$ **49. a.** $\dfrac{263{,}439\pi}{4096}$ **b.** $\dfrac{483}{64}$

c. $\dfrac{\pi}{8}(84 + \ln 2)$ **d.** $\dfrac{264{,}341\pi}{18{,}432}$ **51.** $\left(450 - \dfrac{450}{e}\right)$ g

53. a. 562.5 J   **b.** 56.25 J   **55.** 5.2×10^7 J   **57.** $\ln 4$
59. $\frac{1}{2}\ln(x^2 + 8x + 25) + C$
61. $\cosh^{-1}(x/3) + C = \ln(x + \sqrt{x^2 - 9}) + C$
63. $\tanh^{-1}(1/3)/9 = (\ln 2)/18 \approx 0.0385$ **65.** 48.37 yr
67. Local max at $x = -\frac{1}{2}(\sqrt{5} + 1)$; local min at $x = \frac{1}{2}(\sqrt{5} - 1)$;
inflection points at $x = -3$ and $x = 0$; $\displaystyle\lim_{x\to-\infty} f(x) = 0$;

$\displaystyle\lim_{x\to\infty} f(x) = \infty$

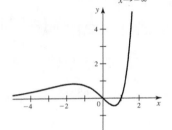

69. a.

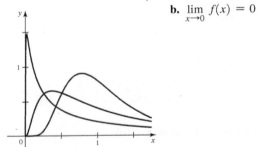

b. $\displaystyle\lim_{x\to 0} f(x) = 0$

d. $f(x^*) = \dfrac{1}{\sqrt{2\pi}}\dfrac{e^{\sigma^2/2}}{\sigma}$ **e.** $\sigma = 1$
71. a. $\cosh x$ **b.** $\text{sech}\,x(1 - x\tanh x)$
73. $L(x) = \frac{5}{3} + \frac{4}{3}(x - \ln 3)$; $\cosh 1 \approx 1.535$

CHAPTER 7

Section 7.1 Exercises, pp. 514–516

1. $u = 4 - 7x$ **3.** $\sin^2 x = \dfrac{1 - \cos 2x}{2}$

5. Complete the square in $x^2 - 4x + 5$.

7. $\dfrac{1}{15(3 - 5x)^3} + C$ **9.** $\dfrac{\sqrt{2}}{4}$

11. $\frac{1}{2}\ln^2 2x + C$ **13.** $\ln(e^x + 1) + C$ **15.** $\frac{1}{2}\ln|e^{2x} - 2| + C$
17. $\frac{32}{3}$ **19.** $-\frac{1}{5}\cot^5 x + C$ **21.** $x - \ln|x + 1| + C$
23. $\dfrac{1}{2}\ln(x^2 + 4) + \tan^{-1}\dfrac{x}{2} + C$

25. $\dfrac{\sec^2 t}{2} + \sec t + C$ or $\dfrac{\tan^2 t}{2} + \sec t + C$
27. $3\sqrt{1 - x^2} + 2\sin^{-1} x + C$ **29.** $x - 2\ln|x + 4| + C$
31. $\dfrac{t^3}{3} - \dfrac{t^2}{2} + t - 3\ln|t + 1| + C$ **33.** $\dfrac{1}{3}\tan^{-1}\left(\dfrac{x - 1}{3}\right) + C$
35. $\sin^{-1}\left(\dfrac{\theta + 3}{6}\right) + C$ **37.** $\tan\theta - \sec\theta + C$

39. $-x - \cot x - \csc x + C$ **41. a.** False **b.** False **c.** False **d.** False **43.** $\dfrac{\ln 4 - \pi}{4}$ **45.** $\dfrac{2 \sin^3 x}{3} + C$ **47.** $2 \tan^{-1} \sqrt{x} + C$

49. $\dfrac{1}{2} \ln (x^2 + 6x + 13) - \dfrac{5}{2} \tan^{-1} \left(\dfrac{x + 3}{2} \right) + C$

51. $-\dfrac{1}{e^x + 1} + C$ **53.** $\frac{1}{2}$ **55. a.** $\dfrac{\tan^2 x}{2} + C$ **b.** $\dfrac{\sec^2 x}{2} + C$

c. The antiderivatives differ by a constant.

57. a. $\frac{1}{2}(x + 1)^2 - 2(x + 1) + \ln |x + 1| + C$

b. $\dfrac{x^2}{2} - x + \ln |x + 1| + C$ **c.** The antiderivatives differ by a

constant. **59.** $\dfrac{\ln 26}{3}$ **61. a.** $\dfrac{14\pi}{3}$ **b.** $\dfrac{2}{3}(5\sqrt{5} - 1)\pi$

63. $\dfrac{2048 + 1763\sqrt{41}}{9375}$ **65.** $\pi\left(\dfrac{9}{2} - \dfrac{5\sqrt{5}}{6}\right)$

Section 7.2 Exercises, pp. 520–523

1. Product Rule **3.** $u = x^n$ **5.** Products for which the choice for dv is easily integrated and when the resulting new integral is no more difficult than the original
7. $x \sin x + \cos x + C$ **9.** $te^t - e^t + C$

11. $\dfrac{2}{3}(x - 2)\sqrt{x + 1} + C$ **13.** $\dfrac{x^3}{3} (\ln x^3 - 1) + C$

15. $\dfrac{x^3}{9} (3 \ln x - 1) + C$ **17.** $-\dfrac{1}{9x^9}\left(\ln x + \dfrac{1}{9}\right) + C$

19. $x \tan^{-1} x - \frac{1}{2} \ln (x^2 + 1) + C$ **21.** $\dfrac{1}{8} \sin 2x - \dfrac{x}{4} \cos 2x + C$

23. $-e^{-t}(t^2 + 2t + 2) + C$ **25.** $-\dfrac{e^{-x}}{17} (\sin 4x + 4 \cos 4x) + C$

27. $\dfrac{e^x}{2} (\sin x + \cos x) + C$ **29.** $\frac{1}{4}(1 - 2x^2) \cos 2x + \frac{1}{2} x \sin 2x + C$

31. π **33.** $-\frac{1}{2}$ **35.** $\frac{1}{9} (5e^6 + 1)$

37. $\left(\dfrac{2\sqrt{3} - 1}{12}\right)\pi + \dfrac{1 - \sqrt{3}}{2}$ **39.** $\pi(1 - \ln 2)$ **41.** $\dfrac{2\pi}{27} (13e^6 - 1)$

43. a. False **b.** True **c.** True **45.** Let $u = x^n$ and $dv = \cos ax\, dx$. **47.** Let $u = \ln^n x$ and $dv = dx$.

49. $\dfrac{x^2 \sin 5x}{5} + \dfrac{2x \cos 5x}{25} - \dfrac{2 \sin 5x}{125} + C$

51. $x \ln^4 x - 4x \ln^3 x + 12x \ln^2 x - 24x \ln x + 24x + C$
53. $(\tan x + 2) \ln (\tan x + 2) - \tan x + C$

55. $\displaystyle\int \log_b x\, dx = \int \dfrac{\ln x}{\ln b}\, dx = \dfrac{1}{\ln b} (x \ln x - x) + C$

57. $2\sqrt{x} \sin \sqrt{x} + 2 \cos \sqrt{x} + C$ **59.** $2e^3$ **61.** $\pi(\pi - 2)$

63. x-axis: $\dfrac{\pi^2}{2}$; y-axis: $2\pi^2$ **65. a.** Let $u = x$ and $dv = f'(x)\, dx$.

b. $\dfrac{e^{3x}}{9} (3x - 1) + C$ **67.** Use $u = \sec x$ and $dv = \sec^2 x\, dx$.

69. a. $t = k\pi$, for $k = 0, 1, 2, \ldots$

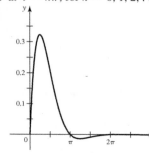

b. $\dfrac{e^{-\pi} + 1}{2\pi}$

c. $(-1)^n \left(\dfrac{e^\pi + 1}{2\pi e^{(n+1)\pi}}\right)$

d. $a_n = a_{n-1} \cdot \dfrac{1}{e^\pi}$

71. c. $\int f(x)g(x)dx = f(x)G_1(x) - f'(x)G_2(x) + f''(x)G_3(x) - \int f'''(x)G_3(x)dx$

f and its derivatives	g and its integrals
$f(x)$ $+$	$g(x)$
$f'(x)$ $-$	$G_1(x)$
$f''(x)$ $+$	$G_2(x)$
$f'''(x)$ $-$	$G_3(x)$

d. $\int x^2 e^{0.5x} dx = 2x^2 e^{0.5x} - 8xe^{0.5x} + 16e^{0.5x} + C$

f and its derivatives	g and its integrals
x^2 $+$	$e^{0.5x}$
$2x$ $-$	$2e^{0.5x}$
2 $+$	$4e^{0.5x}$
0 $-$	$8e^{0.5x}$

$\dfrac{d^{(n)}}{dx}(x^2) = 0$, for $n \geq 3$, so all entries in the left column of the table beyond row three are 0, which results in no additional contribution to the antiderivative.

e. $x^3 \sin x + 3x^2 \cos x - 6x \sin x - 6 \cos x + C$; five rows are needed because $\dfrac{d^{(n)}}{dx}(x^3) = 0$, for $n \geq 4$.

f. $\dfrac{d^{(k)}}{dx}(p_n(x)) = 0$, for $k \geq n + 1$

73. a. $\int e^x \cos x\, dx = e^x \sin x + e^x \cos x - \int e^x \cos x\, dx$
b. $\frac{1}{2}(e^x \sin x + e^x \cos x) + C$ **c.** $-\frac{3}{13}e^{-2x} \cos 3x - \frac{2}{13}e^{-2x} \sin 3x + C$
75. Let $u = x$ and $dv = f''(x)\, dx$ **77. a.** $I_1 = -\frac{1}{2}e^{-x^2} + C$
b. $I_3 = -\frac{1}{2}e^{-x^2}(x^2 + 1) + C$ **c.** $I_5 = -\frac{1}{2} e^{-x^2}(x^4 + 2x^2 + 2) + C$

Section 7.3 Exercises, pp. 529–531

1. $\sin^2 x = \frac{1}{2} (1 - \cos 2x); \cos^2 x = \frac{1}{2} (1 + \cos 2x)$
3. Rewrite $\sin^3 x$ as $(1 - \cos^2 x) \sin x$.
5. A reduction formula expresses an integral with a power in the integrand in terms of another integral with a smaller power in the integrand. **7.** Let $u = \tan x$. **9.** $\frac{x}{2} - \frac{1}{4} \sin 2x + C$

11. $\sin x - \dfrac{\sin^3 x}{3} + C$ **13.** $-\cos x + \frac{2}{3} \cos^3 x - \dfrac{\cos^5 x}{5} + C$

15. $\frac{1}{8} x - \frac{1}{32} \sin 4x + C$ **17.** $\dfrac{\cos^5 x}{5} - \dfrac{\cos^3 x}{3} + C$

19. $\frac{2}{5} \sin^{3/2}x - \frac{2}{7} \sin^{7/2} x + C$ **21.** $\sec x + 2 \cos x - \dfrac{\cos^3 x}{3} + C$

23. $\dfrac{\sin^3 2x}{48} + \frac{1}{16} x - \frac{1}{64} \sin 4x + C$ **25.** $\tan x - x + C$

27. $-\dfrac{\cot^3 x}{3} + \cot x + x + C$

29. $4 \tan^5 x - \frac{20}{3} \tan^3 x + 20 \tan x - 20x + C$ **31.** $\tan^{10} x + C$

33. $\dfrac{\sec^3 x}{3} + C$ **35.** $\frac{1}{8} \tan^2 4x + \frac{1}{4} \ln |\cos 4x| + C$

37. $\frac{2}{3} \tan^{3/2} x + C$ **39.** $\tan x - \cot x + C$ **41.** $\frac{4}{3}$ **43.** $\frac{4}{3} - \ln \sqrt{3}$

45. a. True **b.** False **49.** $\frac{1}{2} \ln (\sqrt{2} + \frac{3}{2})$

51. $\frac{1}{3} \tan^3 (\ln \theta) + \tan (\ln \theta) + C$ **53.** $\ln 4$ **55.** $8\sqrt{2}/3$

57. $\ln |\sec (e^x + 1) + \tan (e^x + 1)| + C$
59. $\sqrt{2}$ **61.** $2\sqrt{2}/3$ **63.** $\ln (\sqrt{2} + 1)$ **65.** $\frac{1}{2} - \ln \sqrt{2}$

67. $\frac{\cos 4x}{8} - \frac{\cos 10x}{20} + C$ **69.** $\frac{\sin x}{2} - \frac{\sin 5x}{10} + C$

73. a. $\frac{\pi}{2}; \frac{\pi}{2}$ **b.** $\frac{\pi}{2}$ for all n **d.** Yes **e.** $\frac{3\pi}{8}$ for all n

Section 7.4 Exercises, pp. 537–540

1. $x = 3 \sec \theta$ **3.** $x = 10 \sin \theta$ **5.** $\sqrt{4 - x^2}/x$ **7.** $\pi/6$

9. $25\left(\frac{2\pi}{3} - \frac{\sqrt{3}}{2}\right)$ **11.** $\frac{\pi}{12} - \frac{\sqrt{3}}{8}$ **13.** $\sin^{-1}\frac{x}{4} + C$

15. $-3 \ln\left|\frac{\sqrt{9 - x^2} + 3}{x}\right| + \sqrt{9 - x^2} + C$

17. $\frac{x}{2}\sqrt{64 - x^2} + 32 \sin^{-1}\frac{x}{8} + C$ **19.** $\frac{x}{\sqrt{1 - x^2}} + C$

21. $\frac{-\sqrt{x^2 + 9}}{9x} + C$ **23.** $\sin^{-1}\frac{x}{6} + C$

25. $\ln\left(\sqrt{x^2 - 81} + x\right) + C$ **27.** $x/\sqrt{1 + 4x^2} + C$

29. $8 \sin^{-1}(x/4) - x\sqrt{16 - x^2}/2 + C$

31. $\sqrt{x^2 - 9} - 3 \sec^{-1}(x/3) + C$

33. $\frac{x}{2}\sqrt{4 + x^2} - 2 \ln(x + \sqrt{4 + x^2}) + C$

35. $\sin^{-1}\left(\frac{x + 1}{2}\right) + C$ **37.** $\frac{9}{10}\cos^{-1}\frac{5}{3x} - \frac{\sqrt{9x^2 - 25}}{2x^2} + C$

39. $\frac{1}{10}\left(\tan^{-1}\frac{x}{5} - \frac{5x}{25 + x^2}\right) + C$

41. $x/\sqrt{100 - x^2} - \sin^{-1}(x/10) + C$

43. $81/(2(81 - x^2)) + \ln\sqrt{81 - x^2} + C$

45. $-1/\sqrt{x^2 - 1} - \sec^{-1}x + C$ **47.** $\ln\left(\frac{1 + \sqrt{17}}{4}\right)$

49. $2 - \sqrt{2}$ **51.** $\frac{1}{3} + \frac{\ln 3}{4}$ **53.** $\sqrt{2}/6$

55. $\frac{1}{16}[1 - \sqrt{3} - \ln(21 - 12\sqrt{3})]$ **57. a.** False **b.** True

c. False **d.** False **59.** $\frac{1}{3}\tan^{-1}\left(\frac{x + 3}{3}\right) + C$

61. $\left(\frac{x - 1}{2}\right)\sqrt{x^2 - 2x + 10}$

$-\frac{9}{2}\ln(x - 1 + \sqrt{x^2 - 2x + 10}) + C$

63. $\frac{x - 4}{\sqrt{9 + 8x - x^2}} - \sin^{-1}\left(\frac{x - 4}{5}\right) + C$ **65.** $\frac{\pi\sqrt{2}}{48}$

67. a. $\frac{r^2}{2}(\theta - \sin\theta)$ **69. a.** $\ln 3$ **b.** $\frac{\pi}{3}\tan^{-1}\frac{4}{3}$ **c.** 4π

71. $\frac{1}{4a}\left(20a\sqrt{1 + 400a^2} + \ln(20a + \sqrt{1 + 400a^2})\right)$

73. $\frac{1}{81} + \frac{\ln 3}{108}$

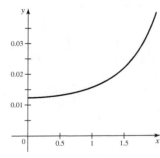

75. $25\left(\sqrt{3} - \ln\sqrt{2 + \sqrt{3}}\right)$

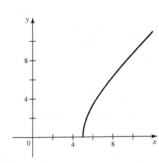

77. $\ln((2 + \sqrt{3})(\sqrt{2} - 1))$ **79.** $192\pi^2$

81. b. $\lim_{L \to \infty}\frac{kQ}{a\sqrt{a^2 + L^2}} = \lim_{L \to \infty} 2\rho k\frac{1}{a\sqrt{\left(\frac{a}{L}\right)^2 + 1}} = \frac{2\rho k}{a}$

83. a. $\frac{1}{\sqrt{g}}\left(\frac{\pi}{2} - \sin^{-1}\left(\frac{2\cos b - \cos a + 1}{\cos a + 1}\right)\right)$

b. For $b = \pi$, the descent time is $\frac{\pi}{\sqrt{g}}$, a constant.

87. $\pi - 3\sqrt{3}$

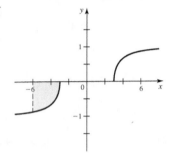

Section 7.5 Exercises, pp. 549–551

1. Rational functions **3. a.** $\frac{A}{x - 3}$ **b.** $\frac{A_1}{x - 4}, \frac{A_2}{(x - 4)^2}, \frac{A_3}{(x - 4)^3}$

c. $\frac{Ax + B}{x^2 + 2x + 6}$ **5.** $\frac{1/3}{x - 4} - \frac{1/3}{x + 2}$ **7.** $\frac{2}{x - 1} + \frac{3}{x - 2}$

9. $\frac{1/2}{x - 4} + \frac{1/2}{x + 4}$ **11.** $-\frac{3}{x - 1} + \frac{1}{x} + \frac{2}{x - 2}$ **13.** $\ln\left|\frac{x - 1}{x + 2}\right| + C$

15. $3 \ln\left|\frac{x - 1}{x + 1}\right| + C$ **17.** $-\ln 4$ **19.** $\ln|(x - 6)^6(x + 4)^4| + C$

21. $\ln\left|\frac{(x - 2)^2(x + 1)}{(x + 2)^2(x - 1)}\right| + C$ **23.** $\ln\left|\frac{x(x - 2)^3}{(x + 2)^3}\right| + C$

25. $\ln\left|\frac{(x - 3)^{1/3}(x + 1)}{(x + 3)^{1/3}(x - 1)}\right|^{1/16} + C$ **27.** $\frac{9}{x} + \ln\left|\frac{x - 9}{x}\right| + C$

29. $\ln 2 - \frac{3}{4}$ **31.** $-\frac{2}{x} + \ln\left|\frac{x + 1}{x}\right|^2 + C$

33. $\frac{5}{x} + \ln\left|\frac{x}{x + 1}\right|^6 + C$ **35.** $-\frac{6}{x - 3} + \ln\left|\frac{(x - 2)^2}{x - 3}\right| + C$

37. $\frac{3}{x - 1} + \ln\left|\frac{(x - 1)^5}{x^4}\right| + C$ **39.** $\frac{A}{x - 1} + \frac{B}{(x - 1)^2} + \frac{Cx + D}{x^2 + 1}$

41. $\frac{A}{x - 4} + \frac{B}{(x - 4)^2} + \frac{Cx + D}{x^2 + 3x + 4}$

43. $\ln|x + 1| + \tan^{-1}x + C$ **45.** $\ln(x + 1)^2 + \tan^{-1}(x + 1) + C$

47. $\ln\left|\frac{(x - 1)^2}{x^2 + 4x + 5}\right| + 14 \tan^{-1}(x + 2) + C$

49. $\ln|(x - 1)^{1/5}(x^2 + 4)^{2/5}| + \frac{2}{5}\tan^{-1}\frac{x}{2} + C$ **51. a.** False

b. False   **c.** False   **d.** True   **53.** $\ln 6$

55. $4\sqrt{2} + \frac{1}{3} \ln \left(\frac{3 - 2\sqrt{2}}{3 + 2\sqrt{2}} \right)$ **57.** $\left(\frac{24}{5} - 2 \ln 5 \right) \pi$

59. $\frac{2}{3} \pi \ln 2$ **61.** $2\pi \left(3 + \ln \frac{2}{5} \right)$ **63.** $x - \ln(1 + e^x) + C$

65. $3x + \ln \frac{(x - 2)^{14}}{|x - 1|} + C$ **67.** $\frac{1}{2} \left(t - \ln \left(2 + e^t \right) \right)$

69. $\frac{1}{4} \ln \left(\frac{1 + \sin t}{1 - \sin t} - \frac{2}{1 + \sin t} \right) + C$

71. $\ln \left| \frac{e^x - 1}{e^x + 2} \right|^{1/3} + C$ **73.** $-\frac{1}{2(e^{2x} + 1)} + C$

77. $\frac{4}{3}(x + 2)^{3/4} - 2(x + 2)^{1/2} + 4(x + 2)^{1/4}$
$- \ln \left((x + 2)^{1/4} + 1 \right)^4 + C$

79. $2\sqrt{x} - 3\sqrt[3]{x} + 6\sqrt[6]{x} - \ln \left(\sqrt[6]{x} + 1 \right)^6 + C$

81. $\frac{4}{3} \sqrt{1 + \sqrt{x}} \left(\sqrt{x} - 2 \right) + C$ **83.** $\ln \left(\frac{x^2}{x^2 + 1} \right) + \frac{1}{x^2 + 1} + C$

85. $\frac{1}{50} \left(\frac{5(3x + 4)}{x^2 + 2x + 2} + 11 \tan^{-1}(1 + x) + \ln \left| \frac{(x - 1)^2}{x^2 + 2x + 2} \right| \right) + C$

87. $\ln \sqrt{\left| \frac{x - 1}{x + 1} \right|} + C$ **89.** $\tan x - \sec x + C = -\frac{2}{\tan(x/2) + 1}$

91. $-\cot x - \csc x + C = -\cot(x/2) + C$

93. $\frac{1}{\sqrt{2}} \ln \frac{\sqrt{2} + 1}{\sqrt{2} - 1}$ **95. a.** Car A   **b.** Car C

c. $S_A(t) = 88t - 88 \ln |t + 1|$;

$S_B(t) = 88 \left(t - \ln(t + 1)^2 - \frac{1}{t + 1} + 1 \right)$;

$S_C(t) = 88(t - \tan^{-1} t)$

d. Car C   **97.** Because $\frac{x^4(1 - x)^4}{1 + x^2} > 0$ on $(0, 1)$,

$\int_0^1 \frac{x^4(1 - x^4)}{1 + x^2} \, dx > 0$; thus, $\frac{22}{7} > \pi$.

Section 7.6 Exercises, pp. 555–557

1. Substitutions, integration by parts, partial fractions
3. The CAS may not include the constant of integration, and it may use a trigonometric identity or other algebraic simplification.
5. $x \cos^{-1} x - \sqrt{1 - x^2} + C$ **7.** $\ln(x + \sqrt{16 + x^2}) + C$

9. $\frac{3}{4}(2u - 7 \ln|7 + 2u|) + C$ **11.** $-\frac{1}{4} \cot 2x + C$

13. $\frac{1}{12}(2x - 1)\sqrt{4x + 1} + C$ **15.** $\frac{1}{3} \ln \left| x + \sqrt{x^2 - \left(\frac{10}{3} \right)^2} \right| + C$

17. $\frac{x}{16\sqrt{16 + 9x^2}} + C$ **19.** $-\frac{1}{12} \ln \left| \frac{12 + \sqrt{144 - x^2}}{x} \right| + C$

21. $2x + x \ln^2 x - 2x \ln x + C$

23. $\frac{x + 5}{2}\sqrt{x^2 + 10x} - \frac{25}{2} \ln |x + 5 + \sqrt{x^2 + 10x}| + C$

25. $\frac{1}{3} \tan^{-1} \left(\frac{x + 1}{3} \right) + C$ **27.** $\ln x - \frac{1}{10} \ln(x^{10} + 1) + C$

29. $2 \ln(\sqrt{x - 6} + \sqrt{x}) + C$ **31.** $\ln(e^x + \sqrt{4 + e^{2x}}) + C$

33. $-\frac{1}{2} \ln \left| \frac{2 + \sin x}{\sin x} \right| + C$ **35.** $-\frac{\tan^{-1} x^3}{3x^3} + \ln \left| \frac{x}{(x^6 + 1)^{1/6}} \right| + C$

37. $\frac{2 \ln^2 x - 1}{4} \sin^{-1}(\ln x) + \frac{\ln x \sqrt{1 - \ln^2 x}}{4} + C$

39. $4\sqrt{17} + \ln(4 + \sqrt{17})$ **41.** $\sqrt{5} - \sqrt{2} + \ln \left(\frac{2 + 2\sqrt{2}}{1 + \sqrt{5}} \right)$

43. $\frac{128\pi}{3}$ **45.** $\frac{\pi^2}{4}$ **47.** $\frac{(x - 3)\sqrt{3 + 2x}}{3} + C$

49. $\frac{1}{3} \tan 3x - x + C$

51. $\frac{(x^2 - a^2)^{3/2}}{3} - a^2\sqrt{x^2 - a^2} + a^3 \cos^{-1} \frac{a}{x} + C$

53. $-\frac{x}{8}(2x^2 - 5a^2)\sqrt{a^2 - x^2} + \frac{3a^4}{8} \sin^{-1} \frac{x}{a} + C$ **55.** $\frac{\left(\frac{4}{5} \right)^9 - \left(\frac{2}{3} \right)^9}{9}$

57. $\frac{1540 + 243 \ln 3}{8}$ **59.** $\frac{\pi}{4}$ **61.** $2 - \frac{\pi^2}{12} - \ln 4$ **63. a.** True

b. True   **67.** $\frac{1}{8} e^{2x}(4x^3 - 6x^2 + 6x - 3) + C$

69. $\frac{\tan^3 3y}{9} - \frac{\tan 3y}{3} + y + C$

71. $\frac{1}{16} \left((8x^2 - 1) \sin^{-1} 2x + 2x\sqrt{1 - 4x^2} \right) + C$

73. $-\frac{\tan^{-1} x}{x} + \ln \left(\frac{|x|}{\sqrt{x^2 + 1}} \right) + C$ **75. b.** $\frac{\pi}{8} \ln 2$

77. a.

θ_0	T
0.10	6.27927
0.20	6.26762
0.30	6.24854
0.40	6.22253
0.50	6.19021
0.60	6.15236
0.70	6.10979
0.80	6.06338
0.90	6.01399
1.00	5.96247

b. All are within 10%.

79. $\frac{1}{a^2}(ax - b \ln|b + ax|) + C$

81. $\frac{1}{a^2} \left(\frac{(ax + b)^{n+2}}{n + 2} - \frac{b(ax + b)^{n+1}}{n + 1} \right) + C$

83. b. $\frac{63\pi}{512}$ **c.** Decrease

Section 7.7 Exercises, pp. 566–569

1. $\frac{1}{2}$ **3.** The Trapezoid Rule approximates areas under curves using trapezoids.   **5.** $-1, 1, 3, 5, 7, 9$ **7.** 1.59×10^{-3}; 5.04×10^{-4}
9. 1.72×10^{-3}; 6.32×10^{-4} **11.** 576; 640; 656   **13.** 0.643950551
15. 704; 672; 664   **17.** 0.622   **19.** $M(25) = 0.63703884$,
$T(25) = 0.63578179$; 6.58×10^{-4}, 1.32×10^{-3}
21.

n	$M(n)$	$T(n)$	Error in $M(n)$	Error in $T(n)$
4	99	102	1.00	2.00
8	99.75	100.5	0.250	0.500
16	99.9375	100.125	6.3×10^{-2}	0.125
32	99.984375	100.03125	1.6×10^{-2}	3.1×10^{-2}

23.

n	$M(n)$	$T(n)$	Error in $M(n)$	Error in $T(n)$
4	1.50968181	1.48067370	9.7×10^{-3}	1.9×10^{-2}
8	1.50241228	1.49517776	2.4×10^{-3}	4.8×10^{-3}
16	1.50060256	1.49879502	6.0×10^{-4}	1.2×10^{-3}
32	1.50015061	1.49969879	1.5×10^{-4}	3.0×10^{-4}

25.

n	$M(n)$	$T(n)$	Error in $M(n)$	Error in $T(n)$
4	-1.96×10^{-16}	0	2.0×10^{-16}	0
8	7.63×10^{-17}	-1.41×10^{-16}	7.6×10^{-17}	1.4×10^{-16}
16	1.61×10^{-16}	1.09×10^{-17}	1.6×10^{-16}	1.1×10^{-17}
32	6.27×10^{-17}	-4.77×10^{-17}	6.3×10^{-17}	4.8×10^{-17}

27. 54.5, Trapezoid Rule   **29.** 35.0, Trapezoid Rule
31. a. Left sum: 204.917; right sum: 261.375; Trapezoid Rule: 233.146; the approximations measure the average temperature of the curling iron on $[0, 120]$.   **b.** Left sum: underestimate; right sum: overestimate; Trapezoid Rule: underestimate   **c.** 305°F is the change in temperature over $[0, 120]$.   **33. a.** 5907.5   **b.** 5965   **c.** 5917
35. a. $T(25) = 3.19623162$
  $T(50) = 3.19495398$
  b. $S(50) = 3.19452809$
  c. $e_T(50) = 4.3 \times 10^{-4}$
  $e_S(50) = 4.5 \times 10^{-8}$
37. a. $T(50) = 1.00008509$
  $T(100) = 1.00002127$
  b. $S(100) = 1.00000000$
  c. $e_T(100) = 2.1 \times 10^{-5}$
  $e_S(100) = 4.6 \times 10^{-9}$

39.

n	$T(n)$	$S(n)$	Error in $T(n)$	Error in $S(n)$
4	1820.0000	—	284	—
8	1607.7500	1537.0000	71.8	1
16	1553.9844	1536.0625	18.0	6.3×10^{-2}
32	1540.4990	1536.0039	4.50	3.9×10^{-3}

41.

n	$T(n)$	$S(n)$	Error in $T(n)$	Error in $S(n)$
4	0.46911538	—	5.3×10^{-2}	—
8	0.50826998	0.52132152	1.3×10^{-2}	2.9×10^{-4}
16	0.51825968	0.52158957	3.4×10^{-3}	1.7×10^{-5}
32	0.52076933	0.52160588	8.4×10^{-4}	1.1×10^{-6}

43. a. True   **b.** False   **c.** True

45.

n	$M(n)$	$T(n)$	Error in $M(n)$	Error in $T(n)$
4	0.40635058	0.40634782	1.4×10^{-6}	1.4×10^{-6}
8	0.40634920	0.40634920	7.6×10^{-10}	7.6×10^{-10}
16	0.40634920	0.40634920	6.6×10^{-13}	6.6×10^{-13}
32	0.40634920	0.40634920	8.9×10^{-16}	7.8×10^{-16}

47.

n	$M(n)$	$T(n)$	Error in $M(n)$	Error in $T(n)$
4	4.72531819	4.72507878	1.2×10^{-4}	1.2×10^{-4}
8	4.72519850	4.72519849	9.1×10^{-9}	9.1×10^{-9}
16	4.72519850	4.72519850	0.	8.9×10^{-16}
32	4.72519850	4.72519850	0.	8.9×10^{-16}

53. Approximations will vary; exact value is 38.753792 ….
55. Approximations will vary; exact value is 68.26894921 ….
57. a. Approximately 1.6×10^{11} barrels
  b. Approximately 6.8×10^{10} barrels
59. a. $T(40) = 0.874799972\ldots$
  b. $f''(x) = e^x \cos e^x - e^{2x} \sin e^x$ $E_T \le \dfrac{1}{3200}$
63. Overestimate

Section 7.8 Exercises, pp. 578–581

1. The interval of integration is infinite or the integrand is unbounded on the interval of integration.
3. $\displaystyle\int_0^1 \frac{1}{\sqrt{x}}\,dx = \lim_{b\to 0^+}\int_b^1 \frac{1}{\sqrt{x}}\,dx$ **5.** 1   **7.** 1   **9.** Diverges   **11.** $\frac{1}{2}$
13. $\dfrac{1}{a}$ **15.** $\dfrac{1}{(p-1)\,2^{p-1}}$ **17.** 0   **19.** $\dfrac{1}{\pi}$ **21.** $\dfrac{\pi}{4}$ **23.** $\ln 2$
25. Diverges   **27.** $\dfrac{1}{4}$ **29.** $\dfrac{\pi}{3}$ **31.** $3\pi/2$ **33.** $\pi/\ln 2$ **35.** 6
37. 2   **39.** Diverges   **41.** $2(e-1)$ **43.** Diverges   **45.** $4\cdot 10^{3/4}/3$
47. -4 **49.** π **51.** 2π **53.** $\dfrac{72\cdot 2^{1/3}\,\pi}{5}$ **55.** Does not exist
57. 0.76   **59.** 10 mi   **61. a.** True   **b.** False   **c.** False   **d.** True
e. True   **63. a.** 2   **b.** 0   **65.** 0.886227   **67.** $-\frac{1}{4}$
69. $\frac{1}{2}$; $\sqrt{\pi}/4 \approx 0.443$ **71.** $1/b - 1/a$
73. a. $A(a,b) = \dfrac{e^{-ab}}{a}$,   for $a > 0$ **b.** $b = g(a) = -\dfrac{1}{a}\ln 2a$
c. $b^* = -2/e$ **75. a.** $p < \frac{1}{2}$ **b.** $p < 2$ **81.** \$41,666.67
85. 20,000 hr   **87. a.** $6.28 \times 10^7 m$ J   **b.** 11.2 km/s   **c.** ≤ 9 mm
89. a.
  b. $\sqrt{2\pi},\ \sqrt{\pi},\ \sqrt{\pi/2}$
  c. $e^{(b^2-4ac)/(4a)}\sqrt{\pi/a}$

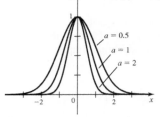

95. a. π **b.** $\pi/(4e^2)$ **97.** $p > 1$ **101.** $a^a - 1$

Section 7.9 Exercises, pp. 589–592

1. Second order   **3.** Two
5. Can be written in the form $g(y)y'(t) = h(t)$
7. Integrate both sides with respect to t and convert integral on left side to an integral with respect to y.
17. $y = t^3 - 2t^2 + 10t + 20$ **19.** $y = t^2 + 4\ln t + 1$
21. $y = Ce^{3t} + \frac{4}{3}$ **23.** $y = Ce^{-2x} - 2$ **25.** $y = 7e^{3t} + 2$
27. $y = 2e^{-2t} - 2$ **29. a.** $y = 150(1 - e^{-0.02t})$ **b.** 150 mg

c. $t = \dfrac{\ln 10}{0.02}$ hr $\approx$ 115 hr

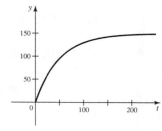

31. $y = \pm\sqrt{2t^3 + C}$ **33.** $y = -2\ln\left(\tfrac{1}{2}\cos t + C\right)$

35. Not separable   **37.** $y = \sqrt{e^t - 1}$ **39.** $y = \ln(e^x + 2)$

41. a. $P = \dfrac{200}{3e^{-0.08t} + 1}$ **b.** 200

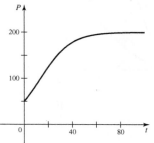

43.

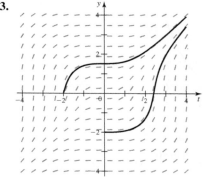

45. A–c, B–b, C–d, D–a   **47.**

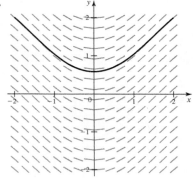

49. a. False   **b.** False   **c.** False   **d.** True

51. a. $y = 0$ **b, c.**

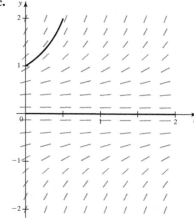

53. a. Equilibrium solutions $y = 0$ and $y = 3$

b.

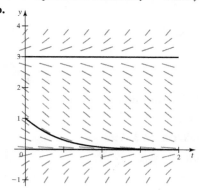

55. a. Equilibrium solutions $y = 0$, $y = 3$, and $y = -2$

b.

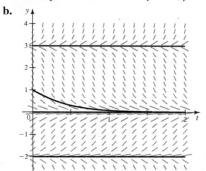

57. $p = 4e^{1 - 1/t} - 1$ **59.** $w = \tan^{-1}(t^2 + 1)$

61. a. $y = \dfrac{y_0}{(1 - y_0)e^{-kt} + y_0}$ **b.**

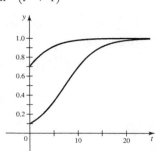

c. For any $0 < y_0 < 1$, $\lim\limits_{t \to \infty} y(t) = 1$. Eventually, everyone knows the rumor.

63. b. $v = \dfrac{mg}{R}$ **c.** $v = \dfrac{g}{b}(1 - e^{-bt})$

d.

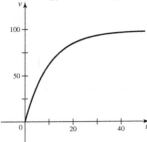

65. a. General solution $y = Ce^{-kt}$ **b.** $y = \dfrac{1}{kt + 1/y_0}$

c.

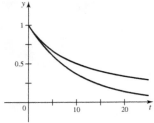

67. a. $B = 20{,}000 - 5000e^{0.05t}$; balance decreases
b. $m = \$2500$; constant balance $= \$50{,}000$

Chapter 7 Review Exercises, pp. 593–595

1. a. True   **b.** False   **c.** False   **d.** True   **e.** False
3. $2(x - 8)\sqrt{x + 4} + C$ **5.** $\pi/4$
7. $\sqrt{t - 1} - \tan^{-1}\sqrt{t - 1} + C$ **9.** $\dfrac{1}{3}\sqrt{x + 2}(x - 4) + C$
11. $x \cosh x - \sinh x + C$ **13.** $\dfrac{4}{105}$ **15.** $\dfrac{1}{5}\tan^5 t + C$
17. $\frac{1}{5}\sec^5 \theta - \frac{1}{3}\sec^3 \theta + C$ **19.** $\sqrt{3} - 1 - \pi/12$
21. $\frac{1}{3}(x^2 - 8)\sqrt{x^2 + 4} + C$ **23.** $2 \ln |x| + 3 \tan^{-1}(x + 1) + C$
25. $\dfrac{1}{x + 1} + \ln |(x + 1)(x^2 + 4)| + C$
27. $\dfrac{\sqrt{6}}{3}\tan^{-1}\sqrt{\dfrac{2x - 3}{3}} + C$
29. $\frac{1}{4}\sec^3 x \tan x + \frac{3}{8}\sec x \tan x + \frac{3}{8}\ln |\sec x + \tan x| + C$
31. 1.196288 **33. a.** $T(6) = 9.125, M(6) = 8.9375$
b. $T(12) = 9.03125, M(12) = 8.984375$ **35.** 1 **37.** $\pi/2$
39. $-\cot \theta + \csc \theta + C$ **41.** $\dfrac{e^x}{2}(\sin x - \cos x) + C$
43. $\dfrac{\theta}{2} + \dfrac{1}{16}\sin 8\theta + C$ **45.** $(\sec^5 z)/5 + C$
47. $(256 - 147\sqrt{3})/480$ **49.** $\sin^{-1}(x/2) + C$
51. $-\dfrac{1}{9y}\sqrt{9 - y^2} + C$ **53.** $\pi/9$ **55.** $-\operatorname{sech} x + C$ **57.** $\pi/3$
59. $\dfrac{1}{8}\ln \left|\dfrac{x - 5}{x + 3}\right| + C$ **61.** $\dfrac{\ln 2}{4} + \dfrac{\pi}{8}$ **63.** 3
65. $\dfrac{1}{3}\ln \left|\dfrac{x - 2}{x + 1}\right| + C$ **67.** $2(x - 2 \ln |x + 2|) + C$
69. $e^{2t}/2\sqrt{1 + e^{4t}} + C$ **71.** $\pi(e - 2)$ **73.** $\dfrac{\pi}{2}(e^2 - 3)$
75. y-axis   **77. a.** 1.603 **b.** 1.870 **c.** $b \ln b - b = a \ln a - a$
d. Decreasing   **79.** $20/(3\pi)$ **81.** 1901 cars

83. a. $I(p) = \dfrac{1}{(p - 1)^2}(1 - pe^{1-p})$ if $p \neq 1, I(1) = \dfrac{1}{2}$

b. $0, \infty$ **c.** $I(0) = 1$ **85.** 0.4054651 **87.** $n = 2$
89. a. $V_1(a) = \pi(a \ln^2 a - 2a \ln a + 2(a - 1))$
b. $V_2(a) = \dfrac{\pi}{2}(2a^2 \ln a - a^2 + 1)$
c. $V_2(a) > V_1(a)$ for all $a > 1$

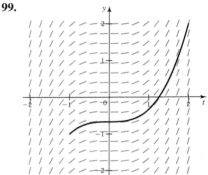

91. $a = \ln 2/(2b)$ **93.** $y = 10e^{2t} - 2$ **95.** $y = \sqrt{t + \ln t + 15}$
97. $\pi/2$
99.

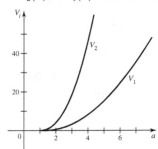

101. $t = \dfrac{-s - 5 \ln s + 50 + 5 \ln 50}{10}$, where $C \approx 70$
$\displaystyle\lim_{t \to \infty} s(t) = 0$

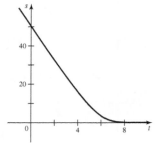

CHAPTER 8

Section 8.1 Exercises, pp. 604–606

1. A sequence is an ordered list of numbers. Example: $1, \frac{1}{3}, \frac{1}{9}, \frac{1}{27}, \ldots$
3. $1, 1, 2, 6, 24$ **5.** Given a sequence $\{a_1, a_2, \ldots\}$, an infinite series
is the sum $a_1 + a_2 + a_3 + \ldots$. Example: $\displaystyle\sum_{k=1}^{\infty} \dfrac{1}{k^2}$ **7.** $1, 5, 14, 30$
9. $\frac{1}{10}, \frac{1}{100}, \frac{1}{1000}, \frac{1}{10{,}000}$ **11.** $-\frac{1}{2}, \frac{1}{4}, -\frac{1}{8}, \frac{1}{16}$ **13.** $\frac{4}{3}, \frac{8}{5}, \frac{16}{9}, \frac{32}{17}$
15. $2, 1, 0, 1$ **17.** $2, 4, 8, 16$ **19.** $10, 18, 42, 114$ **21.** $0, 2, 15, 679$
23. a. $\frac{1}{32}, \frac{1}{64}$ **b.** $a_1 = 1, a_{n+1} = \dfrac{1}{2}a_n$, for $n \geq 1$

c. $a_n = \dfrac{1}{2^{n-1}}$, for $n \geq 1$ **25. a.** $-5, 5$ **b.** $a_1 = -5$,

$a_{n+1} = -a_n$ for $n \geq 1$ **c.** $a_n = (-1)^n \cdot 5$, for $n \geq 1$
27. a. $32, 64$ **b.** $a_1 = 1, a_{n+1} = 2a_n$, for $n \geq 1$ **c.** $a_n = 2^{n-1}$,
for $n \geq 1$ **29. a.** $243, 729$ **b.** $a_1 = 1, a_{n+1} = 3a_n$, for $n \geq 1$
c. $a_n = 3^{n-1}$, for $n \geq 1$ **31.** $9, 99, 999, 9999$; diverges
33. $\frac{1}{10}, \frac{1}{100}, \frac{1}{1000}, \frac{1}{10,000}$; converges to 0 **35.** $-\frac{1}{2}, \frac{1}{4}, -\frac{1}{8}, \frac{1}{16}$; converges to 0
37. $2, 2, 2, 2$; converges to 2 **39.** $54.545, 54.959, 54.996, 55.000$;
converges to 55 **41.** 0 **43.** Diverges   **45.** 1 **47. a.** $\frac{5}{2}, \frac{9}{4}, \frac{17}{8}, \frac{33}{16}$ **b.** 2
49. 4 **51.** Diverges   **53.** 4 **55. a.** $20, 10, 5, \frac{5}{2}$ **b.** $h_n = 20\left(\frac{1}{2}\right)^n$,
for $n \geq 0$ **57. a.** $30, \frac{15}{2}, \frac{15}{8}, \frac{15}{32}$ **b.** $h_n = 30\left(\frac{1}{4}\right)^n$, for $n \geq 0$
59. $S_1 = 0.3, S_2 = 0.33, S_3 = 0.333, S_4 = 0.3333; \frac{1}{3}$
61. $S_1 = 4, S_2 = 4.9, S_3 = 4.99, S_4 = 4.999; 5$

63. a. $\frac{2}{3}, \frac{4}{5}, \frac{6}{7}, \frac{8}{9}$ **b.** $S_n = \dfrac{2n}{2n+1}$ **c.** $\lim\limits_{n \to \infty} S_n = 1$

65. a. $\frac{1}{3}, \frac{2}{5}, \frac{3}{7}, \frac{4}{9}$ **b.** $S_n = \dfrac{n}{2n+1}$ **c.** $\lim\limits_{n \to \infty} S_n = \frac{1}{2}$

67. a. True **b.** False **c.** True   **69. a.** $40, 70, 92.5, 109.375$ **b.** 160
71. a. $0.9, 0.99, 0.999, 0.9999$ **b.** 1 **73. a.** $\frac{1}{3}, \frac{4}{9}, \frac{13}{27}, \frac{40}{81}$ **b.** $\frac{1}{2}$
75. a. $-1, 0, -1, 0$ **b.** Does not exist   **77. a.** $0.3, 0.33, 0.333,$
0.3333 **b.** $\frac{1}{3}$ **79. a.** $20, 10, 5, \frac{5}{2}, \frac{5}{4}$ **b.** $M_n = 20\left(\frac{1}{2}\right)^n$, for $n \geq 0$
c. $M_0 = 20, M_{n+1} = \frac{1}{2}M_n$, for $n \geq 0$ **d.** $\lim\limits_{n \to \infty} a_n = 0$
81. a. $200, 190, 180.5, 171.475, 162.90125$
b. $d_n = 200(0.95)^n$, for $n \geq 0$ **c.** $d_0 = 200, d_{n+1} = (0.95)d_n$,
for $n \geq 0$ **d.** $\lim\limits_{n \to \infty} d_n = 0$.

Section 8.2 Exercises, pp. 616–619

1. $a_n = \dfrac{1}{n}, \quad n \geq 1$ **3.** $a_n = \dfrac{n}{n+1}, \quad n \geq 1$ **5.** Converges for
$-1 < r \leq 1$, diverges otherwise   **7.** $\{e^{n/100}\}$ grows faster than $\{n^{100}\}$.
9. 0 **11.** $3/2$ **13.** 3 **15.** $\pi/2$ **17.** 0 **19.** e^2 **21.** $e^{1/4}$ **23.** 0
25. 1 **27.** 0 **29.** 0 **31.** 6 **33.** Does not exist   **35.** Does not
exist   **37.** 0 **39.** 2 **41.** 0 **43.** Does not exist   **45.** Converges
monotonically; 0 **47.** Converges, oscillates; 0 **49.** Diverges
monotonically   **51.** Diverges, oscillates   **53.** 0 **55.** 0 **57.** 0
59. a. $d_{n+1} = \frac{1}{2}d_n + 80, \quad n \geq 1$ **b.** 160 mg
61. a. $\$0, \$100, \$200.75, \$302.26, \$404.53$
b. $B_{n+1} = 1.0075B_n + 100$, for $n \geq 0$ **c.** During the 43rd month
63. 0 **65.** Diverges   **67.** 0 **69.** Given a tolerance $\varepsilon > 0$, look
beyond a_N where $N > 1/\varepsilon$.   **71.** Given a tolerance $\varepsilon > 0$, look
beyond a_N where $N > \frac{1}{4}\sqrt{3/\varepsilon}$, provided $\varepsilon < \frac{3}{4}$ **73.** Given a tolerance $\varepsilon > 0$, look beyond a_N where $N > c/(\varepsilon b^2)$.   **75. a.** True
b. False **c.** True **d.** True **e.** False **f.** True
77. $\{n^2 + 2n - 17\}_{n=3}^{\infty}$ **79.** 0 **81.** 1 **83.** 1
85. Diverges   **87.** $1/2$ **89.** 0 **91.** $n = 4, n = 6, n = 25$
93. a. $h_n = (200 + 5n)(0.65 - 0.01n) - 0.45n$, for $n \geq 0$
b. The profit is maximized after 8 days.   **95.** 0.607
97. b. $1, 1.4142, 1.5538, 1.5981, 1.6119$ **c.** Approx. 1.618
e. $\dfrac{1 + \sqrt{1 + 4p}}{2}$ **99. b.** $1, 2, 1.5, 1.6667, 1.6$

c. Approx. 1.618 **e.** $\dfrac{a + \sqrt{a^2 + 4b}}{2}$

101. a. $1, 1, 2, 3, 5, 8, 13, 21, 34, 55$ **b.** No   **105. d.** 3
107. $\{a_n\}; n = 36$ **109.** $\{a_n\}; n = 19$ **111.** $a < 1$

Section 8.3 Exercises, pp. 623–626

1. The next term in the series is generated by multiplying the
previous term by the constant r (the ratio of the series). Example:

$2 + 1 + \frac{1}{2} + \frac{1}{4} + \cdots$ **3.** The constant r in the series $\sum\limits_{k=0}^{\infty} ar^k$

5. No   **7.** 9841 **9.** Approx. 1.1905 **11.** Approx. 0.5392

13. $\dfrac{1 - \pi^7}{1 - \pi}$ **15.** 1 **17.** $\frac{1093}{2916}$ **19.** $\frac{4}{3}$ **21.** 10 **23.** Diverges

25. $\dfrac{1}{e^2 - 1}$ **27.** $\dfrac{1}{7}$ **29.** $\dfrac{1}{500}$ **31.** $\dfrac{\pi}{\pi - e}$ **33.** $\dfrac{2500}{19}$ **35.** $\dfrac{10}{19}$

37. $\dfrac{3\pi}{\pi + 1}$ **39.** $\dfrac{9}{460}$ **41.** $0.\overline{3} = \sum\limits_{k=1}^{\infty} 3(0.1)^k = \frac{1}{3}$

43. $0.\overline{1} = \sum\limits_{k=1}^{\infty} (0.1)^k = \frac{1}{9}$ **45.** $0.\overline{09} = \sum\limits_{k=1}^{\infty} 9(0.01)^k = \frac{1}{11}$

47. $0.\overline{037} = \sum\limits_{k=1}^{\infty} 37(0.001)^k = \frac{1}{27}$ **49.** $0.\overline{12} = \sum\limits_{k=0}^{\infty} 0.12(0.01)^k = \dfrac{4}{33}$

51. $0.\overline{456} = \sum\limits_{k=0}^{\infty} 0.456(0.001)^k = \dfrac{152}{333}$

53. $0.00\overline{952} = \sum\limits_{k=0}^{\infty} 0.00952(0.001)^k = \dfrac{238}{24,975}$

55. $S_n = \dfrac{n}{2n+4}; \dfrac{1}{2}$ **57.** $S_n = \dfrac{1}{7} - \dfrac{1}{n+7}; \dfrac{1}{7}$

59. $S_n = \dfrac{1}{9} - \dfrac{1}{4n+1}; \dfrac{1}{9}$ **61.** $S_n = \ln(n+1)$; diverges

63. $S_n = \dfrac{1}{p+1} - \dfrac{1}{n+p+1}; \dfrac{1}{p+1}$

65. $S_n = \left(\dfrac{1}{\sqrt{2}} + \dfrac{1}{\sqrt{3}}\right) - \left(\dfrac{1}{\sqrt{n+2}} + \dfrac{1}{\sqrt{n+3}}\right); \dfrac{1}{\sqrt{2}} + \dfrac{1}{\sqrt{3}}$

67. $S_n = -\dfrac{n+1}{4n+3}; -\dfrac{1}{4}$ **69. a.** True   **b.** True   **c.** False

d. True **e.** True   **71.** $-\dfrac{2}{15}$ **73.** $\dfrac{1}{\ln 2}$ **75. a, b.** $\dfrac{4}{3}$

77. $\sum\limits_{k=0}^{\infty} \left(\dfrac{1}{4}\right)^k A_1 = \dfrac{A_1}{1 - 1/4} = \dfrac{4}{3}A_1$ **79.** 462 months

81. 0 **83.** There will be twice as many children.

85. $\sqrt{\dfrac{20}{g}\left(\dfrac{1 + \sqrt{p}}{1 - \sqrt{p}}\right)}$ s   **87. a.** $L_n = 3\left(\dfrac{4}{3}\right)^n$, so $\lim\limits_{n \to \infty} L_n = \infty$

b. $\lim\limits_{n \to \infty} A_n = \dfrac{2\sqrt{3}}{5}$

89. $R_n = S - S_n = \dfrac{1}{1-r} - \left(\dfrac{1-r^n}{1-r}\right) = \dfrac{r^n}{1-r}$

91. a. 60 **b.** 9 **93. a.** 13 **b.** 15 **95. a.** $1, \frac{5}{6}, \frac{2}{3}$, undefined,
undefined   **b.** $(-1, 1)$ **97.** Converges for x in $(-\infty, -2)$ or
$(0, \infty); x = \frac{1}{2}$
99. a.

r	-0.9	-0.7	-0.5	-0.2	0	0.2	0.5	0.7	0.9
$f(r)$	0.526	0.588	0.667	0.833	1	1.250	2	3.333	10

b.

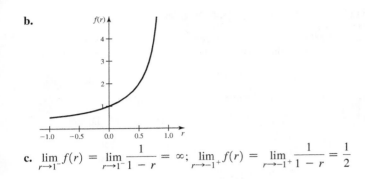

c. $\lim\limits_{r \to 1^-} f(r) = \lim\limits_{r \to 1^-} \dfrac{1}{1 - r} = \infty$; $\lim\limits_{r \to -1^+} f(r) = \lim\limits_{r \to -1^+} \dfrac{1}{1 - r} = \dfrac{1}{2}$

Section 8.4 Exercises, pp. 638–640

1. The series diverges. **3.** Yes, if the terms are positive and decreasing. **5.** Converges for $p > 1$ and diverges for $p \le 1$
7. $R_n = S - S_n$ **9.** Diverges **11.** Diverges **13.** Inconclusive
15. Diverges **17.** Diverges **19.** Converges **21.** Converges
23. Diverges **25.** Converges **27.** Test does not apply
29. Converges **31.** Converges **33.** Diverges

35. a. $\dfrac{1}{5n^5}$ **b.** 3 **c.** $L_n = S_n + \dfrac{1}{5(n + 1)^5}$; $U_n = S_n + \dfrac{1}{5n^5}$

d. $(1.017342754, 1.017343512)$ **37. a.** $\dfrac{3^{-n}}{\ln 3}$ **b.** 7

c. $L_n = S_n + \dfrac{3^{-n-1}}{\ln 3}$; $U_n = S_n + \dfrac{3^{-n}}{\ln 3}$

d. $(0.499996671, 0.500006947)$

39. a. $\dfrac{2}{\sqrt{n}}$ **b.** $4 \times 10^6 + 1$ **c.** $L_n = S_n + \dfrac{2}{\sqrt{n + 1}}$;

$U_n = S_n + \dfrac{2}{\sqrt{n}}$ **d.** $(2.598359182, 2.627792025)$

41. a. $\dfrac{1}{2n^2}$ **b.** 23 **c.** $L_n = S_n + \dfrac{1}{2(n + 1)^2}$; $U_n = S_n + \dfrac{1}{2n^2}$

d. $(1.201664217, 1.202531986)$ **43.** $\dfrac{4}{11}$ **45.** -2 **47.** $\dfrac{113}{30}$

49. $\dfrac{17}{10}$ **51. a.** True **b.** True **c.** False **d.** False **e.** False
f. False **53.** Converges **55.** Diverges **57.** Converges

59. a. $p > 1$ **b.** $\sum\limits_{k=2}^{\infty} \dfrac{1}{k(\ln k)^2}$ converges faster.

65. $\zeta(3) \approx 1.202, \zeta(5) \approx 1.037$ **67.** $\dfrac{\pi^2}{8}$ **69. a.** $\dfrac{1}{2}, \dfrac{7}{12}, \dfrac{37}{60}$

71. a. $\sum\limits_{k=2}^{n} \dfrac{1}{k}$ **b.** The distance can be made arbitrarily large.

Section 8.5 Exercises, pp. 647–649

1. Take the limit of the ratio of consecutive terms of the series as $n \to \infty$. The value of the limit determines whether the series converges.
3. Find an appropriate comparison series. Then take the limit of the ratio of the terms of the given series and the comparison series as $n \to \infty$. The value of the limit determines whether the series converges.
5. Ratio Test **7.** $S_{n+1} - S_n = a_{n+1} > 0$; therefore, $S_{n+1} > S_n$.
9. Converges **11.** Converges **13.** Converges **15.** Diverges

17. Converges **19.** Diverges **21.** Converges **23.** Converges
25. Converges **27.** Converges **29.** Diverges **31.** Converges
33. Converges **35.** Diverges **37.** Diverges **39. a.** False
b. True **c.** True **d.** True **41.** Diverges **43.** Converges
45. Converges **47.** Diverges **49.** Diverges **51.** Converges
53. Diverges **55.** Converges **57.** Converges **59.** Converges
61. Diverges **63.** Converges **65.** Diverges **67.** Converges
69. Converges **71.** $p > 1$ **73.** $p > 1$ **75.** $p < 1$
77. Diverges for all p **79.** Diverges if $|r| \ge 1$ **83.** $0 \le x < 1$
85. $0 \le x \le 1$ **87.** $0 \le x < 2$ **89. a.** e^2 **b.** 0

Section 8.6 Exercises, pp. 656–658

1. Because $S_{n+1} - S_n = (-1)^n a_{n+1}$ alternates sign
3. Because the remainder $R_n = S - S_n$ alternates sign
5. $|R_n| = |S - S_n| \le |S_{n+1} - S_n| = a_{n+1}$ **7.** No; if a series of positive terms converges, if does so absolutely and not conditionally.

9. Yes, $\sum\limits_{k=1}^{\infty} \dfrac{(-1)^k}{k^2}$ has this property. **11.** Converges **13.** Diverges

15. Converges **17.** Converges **19.** Diverges **21.** Diverges
23. Converges **25.** Diverges **27.** Converges **29.** 10,000
31. 5000 **33.** 10 **35.** 3334 **37.** 6 **39.** -0.973 **41.** -0.269
43. -0.783 **45.** Converges conditionally **47.** Converges
absolutely **49.** Converges absolutely **51.** Diverges
53. Diverges **55.** Converges absolutely **57. a.** False **b.** True
c. True **d.** True **e.** False **f.** True **g.** True **61.** The conditions

of the Alternating Series Test are met; therefore, $\sum\limits_{k=1}^{\infty} r^k$ converges for

$-1 < r < 0$. **65.** x and y are divergent series.

Chapter 8 Review Exercises, pp. 658–660

1. a. False **b.** False **c.** True **d.** False **e.** True **f.** False
g. False **h.** True **3.** 0 **5.** 1 **7.** $1/e$ **9.** Diverges

11. a. $\dfrac{1}{3}, \dfrac{11}{24}, \dfrac{21}{40}, \dfrac{17}{30}$ **b.** $S_1 = \dfrac{1}{3}, S_n = \dfrac{1}{2}\left(\dfrac{3}{2} - \dfrac{1}{n + 1} - \dfrac{1}{n + 2}\right), n \ge 1$

c. $3/4$ **13.** Diverges **15.** 1 **17.** 3 **19.** $2/9$ **21. a.** Yes; 1.5
b. Convergence uncertain **c.** Appears to diverge **23.** Diverges
25. Converges **27.** Converges **29.** Converges **31.** Converges
33. Converges **35.** Converges **37.** Converges **39.** Diverges
41. Diverges **43.** Converges absolutely **45.** Converges absolutely
47. Converges absolutely **49.** Diverges **51. a.** 0 **b.** $\dfrac{5}{9}$
53. $a_k = \dfrac{1}{k}$ **55. a.** Yes; $\lim\limits_{k \to \infty} a_k = 1$ **b.** No; $\lim\limits_{k \to \infty} a_k \ne 0$

57. $\lim\limits_{k \to \infty} a_k = 0, \lim\limits_{n \to \infty} S_n = 8$ **59.** $0 < p \le 1$

61. $0.25; 6.5 \times 10^{-15}$ **63.** 100

65. a. 803 m, 1283 m, $2000(1 - 0.95^N)$ m **b.** 2000 m

67. a. $\dfrac{\pi}{2^{n-1}}$ **b.** 2π **69. a.** $B_{n+1} = 1.0025B_n + 100, B_0 = 100$

b. $B_n = 40{,}000(1.0025^{n+1} - 1)$ **71. a.** $T_1 = \dfrac{\sqrt{3}}{16}, T_2 = \dfrac{7\sqrt{3}}{64}$

b. $T_n = \dfrac{\sqrt{3}}{4}\left(1 - \left(\dfrac{3}{4}\right)^n\right)$ **c.** $\lim\limits_{n \to \infty} T_n = \dfrac{\sqrt{3}}{4}$ **d.** 0

CHAPTER 9

Section 9.1 Exercises, pp. 672–675

1. $f(0) = p_2(0)$, $f'(0) = p_2'(0)$, and $f''(0) = p_2''(0)$
3. 1, 1.05, 1.04875   **5.** $R_n(x) = f(x) - p_n(x)$
7. a. $p_1(x) = 8 + 12(x - 1)$
b. $p_2(x) = 8 + 12(x - 1) + 3(x - 1)^2$

c. 9.2; 9.23   **9. a.** $p_1(x) = 1 - x$ **b.** $p_2(x) = 1 - x + \dfrac{x^2}{2}$

c. 0.8, 0.82   **11. a.** $p_1(x) = 1 - x$ **b.** $p_2(x) = 1 - x + x^2$
c. 0.95, 0.9525   **13. a.** $p_1(x) = 2 + \frac{1}{12}(x - 8)$
b. $p_2(x) = 2 + \frac{1}{12}(x - 8) - \frac{1}{288}(x - 8)^2$

c. $1.958\overline{3}$, 1.95747   **15. a.** $p_0(x) = 1$, $p_1(x) = 1$, $p_2(x) = 1 - \dfrac{x^2}{2}$
b.

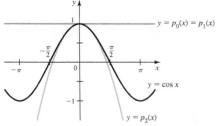

17. a. $p_0(x) = 0$, $p_1(x) = -x$, $p_2(x) = -x - \dfrac{x^2}{2}$

b.

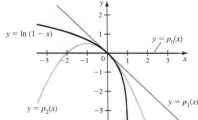

19. a. $p_0(x) = 0$, $p_1(x) = x$, $p_2(x) = x$
b.

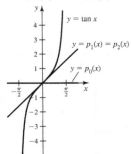

21. a. $p_0(x) = 1$, $p_1(x) = 1 - 3x$, $p_2(x) = 1 - 3x + 6x^2$
b.

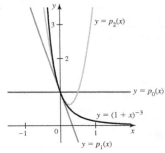

23. a. 1.0247   **b.** 7.6×10^{-6} **25. a.** 0.9624   **b.** 1.5×10^{-4}
27. a. 0.8613   **b.** 5.4×10^{-4}
29. a. $p_0(x) = 1$, $p_1(x) = 1 + 3(x - 1)$,
$p_2(x) = 1 + 3(x - 1) + 3(x - 1)^2$
b.

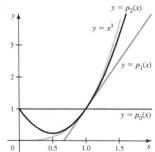

31. a. $p_0(x) = \dfrac{\sqrt{2}}{2}$, $p_1(x) = \dfrac{\sqrt{2}}{2} + \dfrac{\sqrt{2}}{2}\left(x - \dfrac{\pi}{4}\right)$,
$p_2(x) = \dfrac{\sqrt{2}}{2} + \dfrac{\sqrt{2}}{2}\left(x - \dfrac{\pi}{4}\right) - \dfrac{\sqrt{2}}{4}\left(x - \dfrac{\pi}{4}\right)^2$

b.

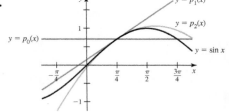

33. a. $p_0(x) = 3$, $p_1(x) = 3 + \dfrac{(x - 9)}{6}$,
$p_2(x) = 3 + \dfrac{(x - 9)}{6} - \dfrac{(x - 9)^2}{216}$

b.

35. a. $p_0(x) = 1$, $p_1(x) = 1 + \dfrac{x - e}{e}$,
$p_2(x) = 1 + \dfrac{x - e}{e} - \dfrac{(x - e)^2}{2e^2}$
b.

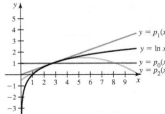

37. a. $p_0(x) = 2 + \dfrac{\pi}{4}, p_1(x) = 2 + \dfrac{\pi}{4} + \dfrac{5}{2}(x-1),$

$p_2(x) = 2 + \dfrac{\pi}{4} + \dfrac{5}{2}(x-1) + \dfrac{3}{4}(x-1)^2$

b.

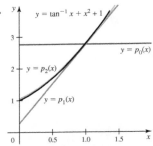

39. a. 1.12749 **b.** 8.9×10^{-6} **41. a.** -0.100333 **b.** 1.3×10^{-6}
43. a. 1.029564 **b.** 4.9×10^{-7} **45. a.** 10.04987563
b. 3.9×10^{-9} **47. a.** 0.520833 **b.** 2.6×10^{-4}

49. $R_n(x) = \dfrac{\sin^{(n+1)}(c)}{(n+1)!} x^{n+1}$, for c between x and 0.

51. $R_n(x) = \dfrac{(-1)^{n+1} e^{-c}}{(n+1)!} x^{n+1}$, for c between x and 0.

53. $R_n(x) = \dfrac{\sin^{(n+1)}(c)}{(n+1)!}\left(x - \dfrac{\pi}{2}\right)^{n+1}$, for c between x and $\dfrac{\pi}{2}$.

55. 2.0×10^{-5} **57.** 1.6×10^{-5} ($e^{0.25} < 2$) **59.** 2.6×10^{-4}
61. With $n = 4$, $|\text{error}| \le 2.5 \times 10^{-3}$
63. With $n = 2$, $|\text{error}| \le 4.2 \times 10^{-2}$ ($e^{0.5} < 2$)
65. With $n = 2$, $|\text{error}| \le 5.4 \times 10^{-3}$
67. 4 **69.** 3 **71.** 1   **73. a.** False **b.** True **c.** True
d. True **75. a.** C **b.** E **c.** A **d.** D **e.** B **f.** F
77. a. $0.1; 1.7 \times 10^{-4}$ **b.** $0.2; 1.3 \times 10^{-3}$
79. a. $0.995; 4.2 \times 10^{-6}$ **b.** $0.98; 6.7 \times 10^{-5}$
81. a. $1.05; 1.3 \times 10^{-3}$ **b.** $1.1; 5 \times 10^{-3}$
83. a. $1.1; 10^{-2}$ **b.** $1.2; 4 \times 10^{-2}$
85. a.

x	$|\sec x - p_2(x)|$	$|\sec x - p_4(x)|$
-0.2	3.4×10^{-4}	5.5×10^{-6}
-0.1	2.1×10^{-5}	8.5×10^{-8}
0.0	0	0
0.1	2.1×10^{-5}	8.5×10^{-8}
0.2	3.4×10^{-4}	5.5×10^{-6}

b. The error increases as $|x|$ increases.
87. a.

x	$|e^{-x} - p_1(x)|$	$|e^{-x} - p_2(x)|$
-0.2	2.1×10^{-2}	1.4×10^{-3}
-0.1	5.2×10^{-3}	1.7×10^{-4}
0.0	0	0
0.1	4.8×10^{-3}	1.6×10^{-4}
0.2	1.9×10^{-2}	1.3×10^{-3}

b. The error increases as $|x|$ increases.

89. a.

x	$|\tan x - p_1(x)|$	$|\tan x - p_3(x)|$
-0.2	2.7×10^{-3}	4.3×10^{-5}
-0.1	3.3×10^{-4}	1.3×10^{-6}
0.0	0	0
0.1	3.3×10^{-4}	1.3×10^{-6}
0.2	2.7×10^{-3}	4.3×10^{-5}

b. The error increases as $|x|$ increases.   **91.** Centered at $x = 0$
for all n **93. a.** $y = f(a) + f'(a)(x - a)$

95. a. $p_5(x) = x - \dfrac{x^3}{6} + \dfrac{x^5}{120}$;

$q_5(x) = -(x - \pi) + \dfrac{1}{6}(x - \pi)^3 - \dfrac{1}{120}(x - \pi)^5$

b.

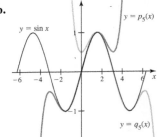

p_5 is a better approximation on $[-\pi, \pi/2]$; q_5 is a better
approximation on $(\pi/2, 2\pi]$.

c.

x	$|\sin x - p_5(x)|$	$|\sin x - q_5(x)|$
$\pi/4$	3.6×10^{-5}	7.4×10^{-2}
$\pi/2$	4.5×10^{-3}	4.5×10^{-3}
$3\pi/4$	7.4×10^{-2}	3.6×10^{-5}
$5\pi/4$	2.3	3.6×10^{-5}
$7\pi/4$	20	7.4×10^{-2}

d. p_5 is a better approximation at $x = \pi/4$; at $x = \pi/2$ the
errors are equal.

97. a. $p_1(x) = 6 + \dfrac{1}{12}(x - 36); q_1(x) = 7 + \dfrac{1}{14}(x - 49)$

b.

x	$|\sqrt{x} - p_1(x)|$	$|\sqrt{x} - q_1(x)|$
37	5.7×10^{-4}	6.0×10^{-2}
39	5.0×10^{-3}	4.1×10^{-2}
41	1.4×10^{-2}	2.5×10^{-2}
43	2.6×10^{-2}	1.4×10^{-2}
45	4.2×10^{-2}	6.1×10^{-3}
47	6.1×10^{-2}	1.5×10^{-3}

c. p_1 is a better approximation at $x = 37, 39, 41$.

Section 9.2 Exercises, pp. 682–684

1. $c_0 + c_1 x + c_2 x^2 + c_3 x^3$ **3.** Ratio and Root Tests   **5.** The radius
of convergence does not change. The interval of convergence may
change.   **7.** $|x| < \dfrac{1}{4}$ **9.** $R = \dfrac{1}{2}; \left(-\dfrac{1}{2}, \dfrac{1}{2}\right)$ **11.** $R = 1; [0, 2)$
13. $R = 0; \{x : x = 0\}$ **15.** $R = \infty; (-\infty, \infty)$
17. $R = 3; (-3, 3)$ **19.** $R = \infty; (-\infty, \infty)$ **21.** $R = \infty; (-\infty, \infty)$

23. $R = \sqrt{3}$; $(-\sqrt{3}, \sqrt{3})$ **25.** $R = 1$; $(0, 2)$

27. $R = \infty$; $(-\infty, \infty)$ **29.** $\displaystyle\sum_{k=0}^{\infty}(3x)^k$; $\left(-\frac{1}{3}, \frac{1}{3}\right)$

31. $2\displaystyle\sum_{k=0}^{\infty}x^{k+3}$; $(-1, 1)$ **33.** $4\displaystyle\sum_{k=0}^{\infty}x^{k+12}$; $(-1, 1)$

35. $-\displaystyle\sum_{k=1}^{\infty}\frac{(3x)^k}{k}$; $\left[-\frac{1}{3}, \frac{1}{3}\right)$ **37.** $-\displaystyle\sum_{k=1}^{\infty}\frac{x^{k+1}}{k}$; $[-1, 1)$

39. $-2\displaystyle\sum_{k=1}^{\infty}\frac{x^{k+6}}{k}$; $[-1, 1)$ **41.** $g(x) = 2\displaystyle\sum_{k=1}^{\infty}k(2x)^{k-1}$; $\left(-\frac{1}{2}, \frac{1}{2}\right)$

43. $g(x) = \displaystyle\sum_{k=3}^{\infty}\frac{k(k-1)(k-2)}{6}x^{k-3}$; $(-1, 1)$

45. $g(x) = -\displaystyle\sum_{k=1}^{\infty}\frac{3^k x^k}{k}$; $\left[-\frac{1}{3}, \frac{1}{3}\right)$ **47.** $\displaystyle\sum_{k=0}^{\infty}(-x^2)^k$; $(-1, 1)$

49. $\displaystyle\sum_{k=0}^{\infty}\left(-\frac{x}{3}\right)^k$; $(-3, 3)$ **51.** $\ln 2 - \frac{1}{2}\displaystyle\sum_{k=1}^{\infty}\frac{x^{2k}}{k4^k}$; $(-2, 2)$

53. a. True **b.** True **c.** True **d.** True **55.** e

57. $\displaystyle\sum_{k=0}^{\infty}\frac{(-1)^k x^k}{k+1}$ **59.** $\displaystyle\sum_{k=1}^{\infty}\frac{(-x^2)^k}{k!}$ **61.** $|x - a| < R$

63. $f(x) = \dfrac{1}{3 - \sqrt{x}}$; $1 < x < 9$ **65.** $f(x) = \dfrac{e^x}{e^x - 1}$; $0 < x < \infty$

67. $f(x) = \dfrac{3}{4 - x^2}$; $-2 < x < 2$ **69.** $\displaystyle\sum_{k=0}^{\infty}\frac{(-x)^k}{k!}$; $-\infty < x < \infty$

71. $\displaystyle\sum_{k=0}^{\infty}\frac{(-3x)^k}{k!}$; $-\infty < x < \infty$

73. $\displaystyle\lim_{k\to\infty}\left|\frac{c_{k+1}x^{k+1}}{c_k x^k}\right| = \lim_{k\to\infty}\left|\frac{c_{k+1}x^{k+m+1}}{c_k x^{k+m}}\right|$, so by the Ratio Test, the two series have the same radius of convergence.

75. a. $f(x) \cdot g(x) = c_0 d_0 + (c_0 d_1 + c_1 d_0)x + (c_0 d_2 + c_1 d_1 + c_2 d_0)x^2 + \cdots$. **b.** $\displaystyle\sum_{k=0}^{n}c_k d_{n-k}$ **77. b.** $n = 112$

Section 9.3 Exercises, pp. 694–696

1. The nth Taylor polynomial is the nth partial sum of the corresponding Taylor series. **3.** Calculate $c_k = \dfrac{f^{(k)}(a)}{k!}$ for $k = 0, 1, 2, \ldots$.

5. Replace x with x^2 in the Taylor series for $f(x)$; $|x| < 1$.

7. The Taylor series for a function f converges to f on an interval if, for all x in the interval, $\displaystyle\lim_{n\to\infty}R_n(x) = 0$, where $R_n(x)$ is the remainder at x. **9. a.** $1 - x + \dfrac{x^2}{2!} - \dfrac{x^3}{3!}$ **b.** $\displaystyle\sum_{k=0}^{\infty}\frac{(-1)^k x^k}{k!}$ **c.** $(-\infty, \infty)$

11. a. $1 - x^2 + x^4 - x^6$ **b.** $\displaystyle\sum_{k=0}^{n}(-1)^k x^{2k}$ **c.** $(-1, 1)$

13. a. $1 + 2x + \dfrac{(2x)^2}{2!} + \dfrac{(2x)^3}{3!}$ **b.** $\displaystyle\sum_{k=0}^{\infty}\frac{(2x)^k}{k!}$ **c.** $(-\infty, \infty)$

15. a. $\dfrac{x}{2} - \dfrac{x^3}{3\cdot 2^3} + \dfrac{x^5}{5\cdot 2^5} - \dfrac{x^7}{7\cdot 2^7}$ **b.** $\displaystyle\sum_{k=0}^{\infty}\frac{(-1)^k x^{2k+1}}{(2k+1)2^{2k+1}}$ **c.** $[-2, 2]$

17. a. $1 + (\ln 3)x + \dfrac{\ln^2 3}{2}x^2 + \dfrac{\ln^3 3}{6}x^3$ **b.** $\displaystyle\sum_{k=0}^{\infty}\frac{\ln^k 3}{k!}x^k$ **c.** $(-\infty, \infty)$

19. a. $1 + \dfrac{(3x)^2}{2} + \dfrac{(3x)^4}{24} + \dfrac{(3x)^6}{720}$ **b.** $\displaystyle\sum_{k=0}^{\infty}\frac{(3x)^{2k}}{(2k)!}$ **c.** $(-\infty, \infty)$

21. a. $1 - \dfrac{(x - \pi/2)^2}{2!} + \dfrac{(x - \pi/2)^4}{4!} - \dfrac{(x - \pi/2)^6}{6!}$

b. $\displaystyle\sum_{k=0}^{\infty}\frac{(-1)^k}{(2k)!}(x - \pi/2)^{2k}$

23. a. $1 - (x - 1) + (x - 1)^2 - (x - 1)^3$

b. $\displaystyle\sum_{k=0}^{\infty}(-1)^k(x - 1)^k$

25. a. $\ln 3 + \dfrac{(x - 3)}{3} - \dfrac{(x - 3)^2}{3^2\cdot 2} + \dfrac{(x - 3)^3}{3^3\cdot 3}$

b. $\ln 3 + \displaystyle\sum_{k=1}^{\infty}\frac{(-1)^{k+1}(x - 3)^k}{k3^k}$

27. a. $2 + 2(\ln 2)(x - 1) + (\ln^2 2)(x - 1)^2 + \dfrac{\ln^3 2}{3}(x - 1)^3$

b. $\displaystyle\sum_{k=0}^{\infty}\frac{2(x - 1)^k \ln^k 2}{k!}$ **29.** $x^2 - \dfrac{x^4}{2} + \dfrac{x^6}{3} - \dfrac{x^8}{4}$

31. $1 + 2x + 4x^2 + 8x^3$ **33.** $1 + \dfrac{x}{2} + \dfrac{x^2}{6} + \dfrac{x^3}{24}$

35. $1 - x^4 + x^8 - x^{12}$ **37.** $x^2 + \dfrac{x^6}{6} + \dfrac{x^{10}}{120} + \dfrac{x^{14}}{5040}$

39. a. $1 - 2x + 3x^2 - 4x^3$ **b.** 0.826

41. a. $1 + \frac{1}{4}x - \frac{3}{32}x^2 + \frac{7}{128}x^3$ **b.** 1.029

43. a. $1 - \frac{2}{3}x + \frac{5}{9}x^2 - \frac{40}{81}x^3$ **b.** 0.895

45. $1 + \dfrac{x^2}{2} - \dfrac{x^4}{8} + \dfrac{x^6}{16}$; $[-1, 1]$ **47.** $3 - \dfrac{3x}{2} - \dfrac{3x^2}{8} - \dfrac{3x^3}{16}$; $[-1, 1]$

49. $a + \dfrac{x^2}{2a} - \dfrac{x^4}{8a^3} + \dfrac{x^6}{16a^5}$; $|x| \le a$

51. $1 - 8x + 48x^2 - 256x^3$ **53.** $\dfrac{1}{16} - \dfrac{x^2}{32} + \dfrac{3x^4}{256} - \dfrac{x^6}{256}$

55. $\dfrac{1}{9} - \dfrac{2}{9}\left(\dfrac{4x}{3}\right) + \dfrac{3}{9}\left(\dfrac{4x}{3}\right)^2 - \dfrac{4}{9}\left(\dfrac{4x}{3}\right)^3$

57. $R_n(x) = \dfrac{f^{(n+1)}(c)}{(n+1)!}x^{n+1}$, where c is between 0 and x and $f^{(n+1)}(c) = \pm\sin c$ or $\pm\cos c$. Therefore, $|R_n(x)| \le \dfrac{|x|^{n+1}}{(n+1)!} \to 0$ as $n \to \infty$, for $-\infty < x < \infty$. **59.** $R_n(x) = \dfrac{f^{(n+1)}(c)}{(n+1)!}x^{n+1}$, where c is between 0 and x and $f^{(n+1)}(c) = (-1)^n e^{-c}$. Therefore, $|R_n(x)| \le \dfrac{|x|^{n+1}}{e^c(n+1)!} \to 0$, as $n \to \infty$, for $-\infty < x < \infty$.

61. a. False **b.** True **c.** False **d.** False **e.** True

63. a. $1 + \dfrac{x^2}{2!} + \dfrac{x^4}{4!} + \dfrac{x^6}{6!}$ **b.** $R = \infty$

65. a. $1 - \frac{2}{3}x^2 + \frac{5}{9}x^4 - \frac{40}{81}x^6$ **b.** $R = 1$

67. a. $1 - \frac{1}{2}x^2 - \frac{1}{8}x^4 - \frac{1}{16}x^6$ **b.** $R = 1$

69. a. $1 - 2x^2 + 3x^4 - 4x^6$ **b.** $R = 1$

71. 3.9149 **73.** 1.8989 **79.** $\displaystyle\sum_{k=0}^{\infty}\left(\frac{x - 4}{2}\right)^k$

81. $\dfrac{1\cdot 3\cdot 5\cdot 7}{2\cdot 4\cdot 6\cdot 8}x^4, \dfrac{-1\cdot 3\cdot 5\cdot 7\cdot 9}{2\cdot 4\cdot 6\cdot 8\cdot 10}x^5$ **83.** Use three terms of the Taylor series for $\cos x$ centered at $a = \pi/4$; 0.766

85. Use six terms of the Taylor series for $\sqrt[3]{x}$ centered at $a = 64$; 4.362 **87. a.** Use three terms of the Taylor series for $\sqrt[3]{125 + x}$ centered at $a = 0$; 5.03968 **b.** Use three terms of the Taylor series for $\sqrt[3]{x}$ centered at $a = 125$; 5.03968 **c.** Yes

Section 9.4 Exercises, pp. 702–704

1. Replace f and g with their Taylor series centered at a and evaluate the limit.   **3.** Substitute $x = -0.6$ into the Taylor series for e^x centered at 0. Because the resulting series is an alternating series, the error can be estimated.   **5.** $f'(x) = \sum\limits_{k=1}^{\infty} kc_k x^{k-1}$ **7.** 1   **9.** $\frac{1}{2}$

11. 2   **13.** $\frac{2}{3}$ **15.** $\frac{1}{3}$ **17.** $\frac{3}{5}$ **19.** $-\frac{8}{5}$ **21.** 1   **23.** $\frac{3}{4}$

25. a. $1 + x + \dfrac{x^2}{2!} + \cdots + \dfrac{x^n}{n!} + \cdots$ **b.** e^x **c.** $-\infty < x < \infty$

27. a. $1 - x + x^2 - \cdots (-1)^{n-1}x^{n-1} + \cdots$ **b.** $\dfrac{1}{1+x}$ **c.** $|x| < 1$

29. a. $-2 + 4x - 8 \cdot \dfrac{x^2}{2!} + \cdots + (-2)^n \dfrac{x^{n-1}}{(n-1)!} + \cdots$

b. $-2e^{-2x}$ **c.** $-\infty < x < \infty$ **31. a.** $1 - x^2 + x^4 - \cdots$

b. $\dfrac{1}{1+x^2}$ **c.** $-1 < x < 1$

33. a. $2 + 2t + \dfrac{2t^2}{2!} + \cdots + \dfrac{2t^n}{n!} + \cdots$ **b.** $y(t) = 2e^t$

35. a. $2 + 16t + 24t^2 + 24t^3 + \cdots + \dfrac{3^{n-1} \cdot 16}{n!}t^n + \cdots$

b. $y(t) = \frac{16}{3}e^{3t} - \frac{10}{3}$ **37.** 0.2448   **39.** 0.6958

41. $\dfrac{0.35^2}{2} - \dfrac{0.35^4}{12} \approx 0.0600$ **43.** 0.4994

45. $1 + 2 + \dfrac{2^2}{2!} + \dfrac{2^3}{3!}$ **47.** $1 - 2 + \dfrac{2}{3} - \dfrac{4}{45}$ **49.** $\frac{1}{2} - \frac{1}{8} + \frac{1}{24} - \frac{1}{64}$

51. $e - 1$ **53.** $\sum\limits_{k=1}^{\infty} \dfrac{(-1)^{k+1}x^k}{k}$ for $-1 < x \le 1$; $\ln 2$

55. $\dfrac{2}{2-x}$ **57.** $\dfrac{4}{4+x^2}$ **59.** $-\ln(1-x)$ **61.** $-\dfrac{3x^2}{(3+x)^2}$

63. $\dfrac{6x^2}{(3-x)^3}$ **65. a.** False   **b.** False   **c.** True   **67.** $\frac{a}{b}$ **69.** $e^{-1/6}$

71. $f^{(3)}(0) = 0$; $f^{(4)}(0) = 4e$ **73.** $f^{(3)}(0) = 2$; $f^{(4)}(0) = 0$
75. 2   **77. a.** 1.575 using four terms
b. At least three   **c.** More terms would be needed.
79. a. $S'(x) = \sin x^2$; $C'(x) = \cos x^2$
b. $\dfrac{x^3}{3} - \dfrac{x^7}{7 \cdot 3!} + \dfrac{x^{11}}{11 \cdot 5!} - \dfrac{x^{15}}{15 \cdot 7!}$; $x - \dfrac{x^5}{5 \cdot 2!} + \dfrac{x^9}{9 \cdot 4!} - \dfrac{x^{13}}{13 \cdot 6!}$
c. $S(0.05) \approx 0.00004166664807$; $C(-0.25) \approx -0.2499023614$
d. 1   **e.** 2   **81. a.** $1 - \dfrac{x^2}{4} + \dfrac{x^4}{64} - \dfrac{x^6}{2304}$ **b.** $-\infty < x < \infty$, $R = \infty$

83. a. The Maclaurin series for $\cos x$ consists of even powers of x, which are even functions.   **b.** The Maclaurin series for $\sin x$ consists of odd powers of x, which are odd functions.

Chapter 9 Review Exercises, pp. 705–706

1. a. True   **b.** False   **c.** True   **d.** True   **3.** $p_2(x) = 1$

5. $p_3(x) = x - \dfrac{x^2}{2} + \dfrac{x^3}{3}$ **7.** $p_2(x) = (x-1) - \dfrac{(x-1)^2}{2}$

9. $p_3(x) = \dfrac{5}{4} + \dfrac{3}{4}(x - \ln 2) + \dfrac{5}{8}(x - \ln 2)^2 + \dfrac{1}{8}(x - \ln 2)^3$

11. a. $p_2(x) = 1 + x + \dfrac{x^2}{2}$

b.

n	$p_n(x)$	Error
0	1	7.7×10^{-2}
1	0.92	3.1×10^{-3}
2	0.9232	8.4×10^{-5}

13. a. $p_2(x) = \dfrac{\sqrt{2}}{2} + \dfrac{\sqrt{2}}{2}\left(x - \dfrac{\pi}{4}\right) - \dfrac{\sqrt{2}}{4}\left(x - \dfrac{\pi}{4}\right)^2$

b.

n	$p_n(x)$	Error
0	0.7071	1.2×10^{-1}
1	0.5960	8.2×10^{-3}
2	0.5873	4.7×10^{-4}

15. $|R_3| < \dfrac{\pi^4}{4!}$ **17.** $(-\infty, \infty)$, $R = \infty$ **19.** $(-\infty, \infty)$, $R = \infty$

21. $(-9, 9)$, $R = 9$ **23.** $[-4, 0)$, $R = 2$ **25.** $\sum\limits_{k=0}^{\infty} x^{2k}$; $(-1, 1)$

27. $\sum\limits_{k=0}^{\infty}(-5x)^k$; $(-\frac{1}{5}, \frac{1}{5})$ **29.** $\sum\limits_{k=1}^{\infty}k(10x)^{k-1}$; $(-\frac{1}{10}, \frac{1}{10})$

31. $1 + 3x + \dfrac{9x^2}{2!}$; $\sum\limits_{k=0}^{\infty} \dfrac{(3x)^k}{k!}$

33. $-(x - \pi/2) + \dfrac{(x - \pi/2)^3}{3!} - \dfrac{(x - \pi/2)^5}{5!}$;

$\sum\limits_{k=0}^{\infty}(-1)^{k+1}\dfrac{(x - \pi/2)^{2k+1}}{(2k+1)!}$

35. $4x - \dfrac{(4x)^3}{3} + \dfrac{(4x)^5}{5}$; $\sum\limits_{k=0}^{\infty}\dfrac{(-1)^k(4x)^{2k+1}}{2k+1}$

37. $1 + \dfrac{9x^2}{2!} + \dfrac{81x^4}{4!}$; $\sum\limits_{k=0}^{\infty}\dfrac{(3x)^{2k}}{(2k)!}$ **39.** $1 + \dfrac{x}{3} - \dfrac{x^2}{9} + \cdots$

41. $1 - \dfrac{3}{2}x + \dfrac{3}{2}x^2 - \cdots$ **43.** $R_n(x) = \dfrac{(-1)^{n+1}e^{-c}}{(n+1)!}x^{n+1}$, where

c is between 0 and x. $\lim\limits_{n \to \infty}|R_n(x)| = \lim\limits_{n \to \infty}\dfrac{|x^{n+1}|}{e^{|x|}} \cdot \dfrac{1}{(n+1)!} = 0$ for

$-\infty < x < \infty$.   **45.** $R_n(x) = \dfrac{(-1)^n(1+c)^{-(n+1)}}{n+1}x^{n+1}$

where c is between 0 and x.

$\lim\limits_{n \to \infty}|R_n(x)| = \lim\limits_{n \to \infty}\left(\left(\dfrac{|x|}{1+c}\right)^{n+1} \cdot \dfrac{1}{n+1}\right) < \lim\limits_{n \to \infty}\left(1^{n+1} \cdot \dfrac{1}{n+1}\right)$

$= 0$, for $|x| \le \frac{1}{2}$.   **47.** $\frac{1}{24}$ **49.** $\frac{1}{8}$ **51.** $\frac{1}{6}$ **53.** 0.4615   **55.** 0.3819

57. $11 - \dfrac{1}{11} - \dfrac{1}{2 \cdot 11^3} - \dfrac{1}{2 \cdot 11^5}$ **59.** $-\dfrac{1}{3} + \dfrac{1}{3 \cdot 3^3} - \dfrac{1}{5 \cdot 3^5} + \dfrac{1}{7 \cdot 3^7}$

61. $y = 4 + 4x + \dfrac{4^2}{2!}x^2 + \dfrac{4^3}{3!}x^3 + \cdots + \dfrac{4^n}{n!}x^n + \cdots = 3 + e^{4x}$

63. a. $\sum\limits_{k=1}^{\infty}\dfrac{(-1)^{k+1}}{k}$ **b.** $\sum\limits_{k=1}^{\infty}\dfrac{1}{k2^k}$ **c.** $2\sum\limits_{k=0}^{\infty}\dfrac{x^{2k+1}}{2k+1}$

d. $x = \dfrac{1}{3}$; $2\sum\limits_{k=0}^{\infty}\dfrac{1}{3^{2k+1}(2k+1)}$ **e.** Series in part (d)

CHAPTER 10

Section 10.1 Exercises, pp. 715–719

1. Plotting $\{(f(t), g(t)): a \le t \le b\}$ generates a curve in the xy-plane.   **3.** $x = R \cos(\pi t/5), y = -R \sin(\pi t/5)$

5. $x = t, y = t^2, -\infty < t < \infty$ **7.** $y = \dfrac{3}{4}(1-x)^2$ **9.** Compute

$g'(a)/f'(a)$ and interpret the cases in which $f'(a) = 0$.

11. a.

t	-10	-4	0	4	10
x	-20	-8	0	8	20
y	-34	-16	-4	8	26

b.

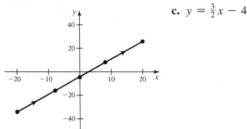

c. $y = \frac{3}{2}x - 4$

d. A line segment rising to the right as t increases
13. a.

t	-5	-2	0	2	5
x	11	8	6	4	1
y	-18	-9	-3	3	12

b.

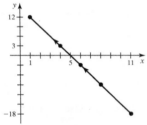

c. $y = -3x + 15$

d. A line segment rising to the left as t increases
15. a. $y = 3x - 12$ **b.** A line segment starting at $(4, 0)$
and ending at $(8, 12)$ **17. a.** $y = 1 - x^2, -1 \le x \le 1$
b. A parabola opening downward with a vertex at $(0, 1)$ starting at
$(1, 0)$ and ending at $(-1, 0)$ **19. a.** $y = (x + 1)^3$ **b.** A cubic
function rising to the right as r increases   **21.** $x^2 + y^2 = 9$; center
$(0, 0)$; radius 3; lower half of circle generated counterclockwise
23. $x^2 + (y - 1)^2 = 1$; center $(0, 1)$; radius 1; circle generated
counterclockwise starting at $(1, 1)$ **25.** $x^2 + y^2 = 49$; center
$(0, 0)$; radius 7; circle generated counterclockwise   **27.** $x = 4 \cos t$,
$y = 4 \sin t, 0 \le t \le 2\pi$: $x^2 + y^2 = 16$

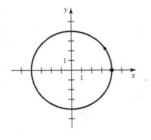

29. $x = \cos t + 2, y = \sin t + 3, 0 \le t \le 2\pi$;
$(x - 2)^2 + (y - 3)^2 = 1$

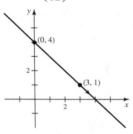

31. $x = 8 \sin t - 2, y = 8 \cos t - 3, 0 \le t \le 2\pi$;
$(x + 2)^2 + (y + 3)^2 = 64$

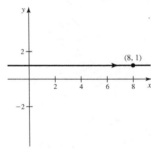

33. $x = 400 \cos\left(\dfrac{4\pi t}{3}\right), y = 400 \sin\left(\dfrac{4\pi t}{3}\right), 0 \le t \le 1.5$

35. $x = 50 \cos\left(\dfrac{\pi t}{12}\right), y(t) = 50 \sin\left(\dfrac{\pi t}{12}\right), 0 \le t \le 24$

37. Slope: -1; point: $(3, 1)$

39. Slope: 0; point: $(8, 1)$

41. $x = 2t, y = 8t, 0 \le t \le 1$
43. $x = -1 + 7t, y = -3 - 13t, 0 \le t \le 1$
45. $x = t, y = 2t^2 - 4, -1 \le t \le 5$ (not unique)

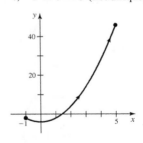

47. $x = 4t - 2, y = -6t + 3, 0 \le t \le 1;$
$x = t + 1, y = 8t - 11, 1 \le t \le 2$ (not unique)

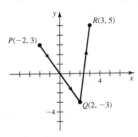

49.

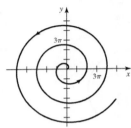

51.

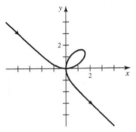

53.

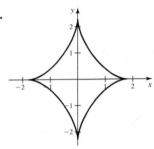

55.

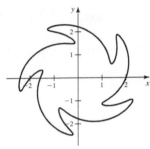

57.

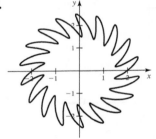

59. a. $\dfrac{dy}{dx} = -2; -2$ **b.**

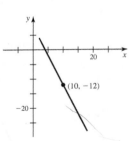

61. a. $\dfrac{dy}{dx} = -8 \cot t; 0$ **b.**

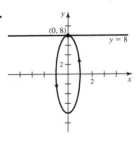

63. a. $\dfrac{dy}{dx} = \dfrac{t^2 + 1}{t^2 - 1}, t \ne 0;$ undefined   **b.**

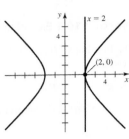

65. a. False   **b.** True   **c.** False   **d.** True   **e.** True
67. $y = \dfrac{13}{4}x + \dfrac{1}{4}$ **69.** $y = x - \dfrac{\pi\sqrt{2}}{4}$ **71.** $x = 1 + 2t, y = 1 + 4t,$
$-\infty < t < \infty$ **73.** $x = t^2, y = t, t \ge 0$
75. $0 \le t \le 2\pi$

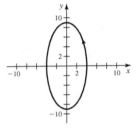

77. $x = 3 \cos t, y = \frac{3}{2} \sin t, 0 \le t \le 2\pi; \left(\dfrac{x}{3}\right)^2 + \left(\dfrac{2y}{3}\right)^2 = 1;$ in the

counterclockwise direction

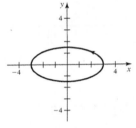

79. $x = 15 \cos t - 2, y = 10 \sin t - 3, 0 \le t \le 2\pi;$
$\left(\dfrac{x + 2}{15}\right)^2 + \left(\dfrac{y + 3}{10}\right)^2 = 1;$ in the counterclockwise direction

81. a. Lines intersect at $(1, 0)$.   **b.** Lines are parallel.   **c.** Lines
intersect at $(4, 6)$.   **83.** $x^2 + y^2 = 4$ **85.** $y = \sqrt{4 - x^2}$
87. $y = x^2$ **89.** $\left(-\dfrac{4}{\sqrt{5}}, \dfrac{8}{\sqrt{5}}\right)$ and $\left(\dfrac{4}{\sqrt{5}}, -\dfrac{8}{\sqrt{5}}\right)$ **91.** There is no
such point.   **93.** $a = p, b = p + \dfrac{2\pi}{3}$, for all real p **95. a.** $(0, 2)$
and $(0, -2)$ **b.** $(1, \sqrt{2}), (1, -\sqrt{2}), (-1, \sqrt{2}), (-1, -\sqrt{2})$
97. a. $x = \pm a \cos^{2/n} t, y = \pm b \sin^{2/n} t$ **c.** The curves become
more rectangular as n increases.

103. a.

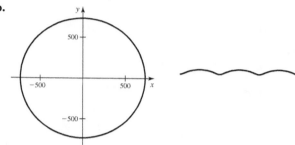

b.

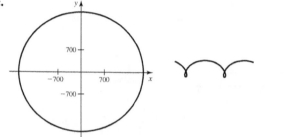

c.

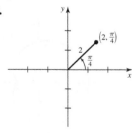

105. Approx. 2857 m

Section 10.2 Exercises, pp. 728–732

1.

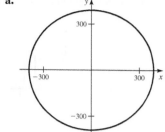

$(-2, -5\pi/6), (2, 13\pi/6);$
$(3, \pi/2), (3, 5\pi/2)$

3. $r^2 = x^2 + y^2, \tan \theta = \dfrac{y}{x}$ **5.** $r \cos \theta = 5$ or $r = 5 \sec \theta$

7. x-axis symmetry occurs if (r, θ) on the graph implies $(r, -\theta)$ is on the graph. y-axis symmetry occurs if (r, θ) on the graph implies $(r, \pi - \theta) = (-r, -\theta)$ is on the graph. Symmetry about the origin occurs if (r, θ) on the graph implies $(-r, \theta) = (r, \theta + \pi)$ is on the graph.

9.

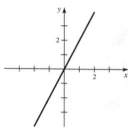

11.

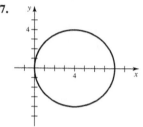

$(-2, -3\pi/4), (2, 9\pi/4)$

$(1, 2\pi/3), (1, 8\pi/3)$

13.

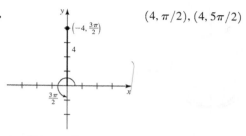

$(4, \pi/2), (4, 5\pi/2)$

15. $(3\sqrt{2}/2, 3\sqrt{2}/2)$ **17.** $(1/2, -\sqrt{3}/2)$ **19.** $(2\sqrt{2}, -2\sqrt{2})$
21. $(2\sqrt{2}, \pi/4), (-2\sqrt{2}, 5\pi/4)$ **23.** $(2, \pi/3), (-2, 4\pi/3)$
25. $(8, 2\pi/3), (-8, -\pi/3)$ **27.** $x = -4$; vertical line passing
through $(-4, 0)$ **29.** $x^2 + y^2 = 4$; circle centered at $(0, 0)$ of radius 2
31. $(x - 1)^2 + (y - 1)^2 = 2$; circle of radius $\sqrt{2}$ centered at $(1, 1)$
33. $x^2 + (y - 1)^2 = 1$; circle of radius 1 centered at $(0, 1)$ and
$x = 0$; y-axis   **35.** $x^2 + (y - 4)^2 = 16$; circle of radius 4
centered at $(0, 4)$

37.

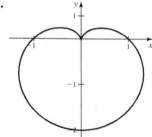

39.

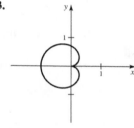

41.

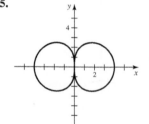

43.

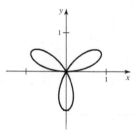

45.

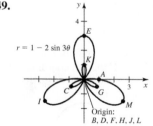

47.

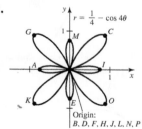

49.

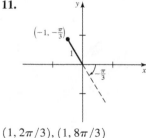

51.

53. $[0, 8\pi]$

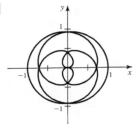

55. $[0, 2\pi]$

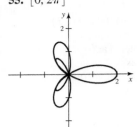

57. $[0, 5\pi]$

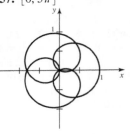

59. $[0, 2\pi]$

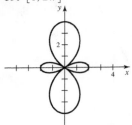

61. a. True **b.** True **c.** False **d.** True **e.** True
63. $r = \tan\theta \sec\theta$ **65.** $r^2 = \sec\theta \csc\theta$ or $r^2 = 2\csc 2\theta$

67.

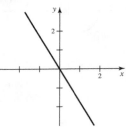

69.

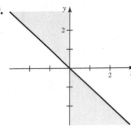

71.

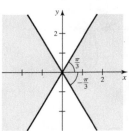

73.

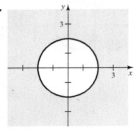

77. A circle of radius 4 and center $(2, \pi/3)$ (polar coordinates)

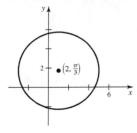

79. A circle of radius 4 centered at $(2, 3)$ (Cartesian coordinates)

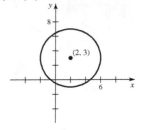

81. A circle of radius 3 centered at $(-1, 2)$ (Cartesian coordinates)

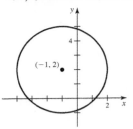

83. a. Same graph on all three intervals

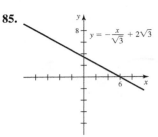

85.

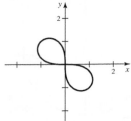

$y = -\dfrac{x}{\sqrt{3}} + 2\sqrt{3}$

87.

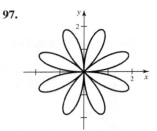

$y = 4x + 3$

89. a. A **b.** C **c.** B **d.** D **e.** E **f.** F
91.

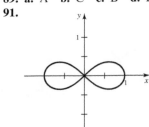

93.

95.

97.

101.

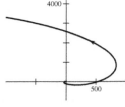

For $a = -1$, the spiral winds inward toward the origin.

103. $(2, 0)$ and $(0, 0)$
105. $(0, 0)$, $\left(\dfrac{2 - \sqrt{2}}{2}, 3\pi/4\right)$, $\left(\dfrac{2 + \sqrt{2}}{2}, 7\pi/4\right)$

107. a.

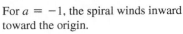

109. a.

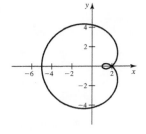

111. $r = a\cos\theta + b\sin\theta = \dfrac{a}{r}(r\cos\theta) + \dfrac{b}{r}(r\sin\theta) = \dfrac{a}{r}x + \dfrac{b}{r}y$;

therefore, $\left(x - \dfrac{a}{2}\right)^2 + \left(y - \dfrac{b}{2}\right)^2 = \dfrac{a^2 + b^2}{4}$. Center: $\left(\dfrac{a}{2}, \dfrac{b}{2}\right)$;

radius: $\dfrac{\sqrt{a^2 + b^2}}{2}$ **113.** Symmetry about the x-axis

Section 10.3 Exercises, pp. 738–740

1. $x = f(\theta)\cos\theta, y = f(\theta)\sin\theta$ **3.** The slope of the tangent line
is the rate of change of the vertical coordinate with respect to the hori-
zontal coordinate.   **5.** $0; \theta = \pi/2$ **7.** $-\sqrt{3}; \theta = 0$ **9.** Undefined,
undefined; the curve does not intersect the origin.   **11.** 0 at $(-4, \pi/2)$
and $(-4, 3\pi/2)$, undefined at $(4, 0)$ and $(4, \pi); \theta = \pi/4, \theta = 3\pi/4$
13. $\pm 1; \theta = \pm\pi/4$ **15.** Horizontal: $(2\sqrt{2}, \pi/4), (-2\sqrt{2}, 3\pi/4)$;
vertical: $(0, \pi/2), (4, 0)$ **17.** Horizontal: $(0, 0)$ $(0.943, 0.955)$,
$(-0.943, 2.186), (0.943, 4.097), (-0.943, 5.328)$; vertical: $(0, 0)$,
$(0.943, 0.615), (-0.943, 2.526), (0.943, 3.757), (-0.943, 5.668)$
19. Horizontal: $\left(\dfrac{1}{2}, \dfrac{\pi}{6}\right), \left(\dfrac{1}{2}, \dfrac{5\pi}{6}\right), \left(2, \dfrac{3\pi}{2}\right)$; vertical:
$\left(\dfrac{3}{2}, \dfrac{7\pi}{6}\right), \left(\dfrac{3}{2}, \dfrac{11\pi}{6}\right), \left(0, \dfrac{\pi}{2}\right)$

21. 1
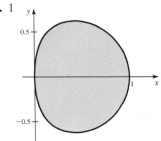

23. 16π
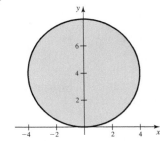

25. $9\pi/2$
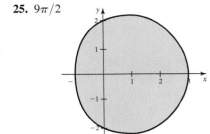

27. $\dfrac{\pi}{12}$
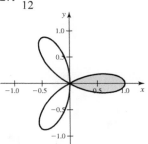

29. $\dfrac{1}{24}(3\sqrt{3} + 2\pi)$
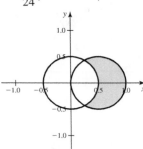

31. $\dfrac{1}{4}(2 - \sqrt{3}) + \dfrac{\pi}{12}$
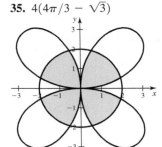

33. $\pi/20$
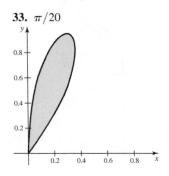

35. $4(4\pi/3 - \sqrt{3})$
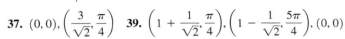

37. $(0, 0), \left(\dfrac{3}{\sqrt{2}}, \dfrac{\pi}{4}\right)$ **39.** $\left(1 + \dfrac{1}{\sqrt{2}}, \dfrac{\pi}{4}\right), \left(1 - \dfrac{1}{\sqrt{2}}, \dfrac{5\pi}{4}\right), (0, 0)$

41. $\dfrac{9}{8}(\pi - 2)$ **43.** $\dfrac{3\pi}{2} - 2\sqrt{2}$ **45. a.** False   **b.** False

47. $2\pi/3 - \sqrt{3}/2$ **49.** $9\pi + 27\sqrt{3}$
51. Horizontal: $(0, 0), (4.05, 2.03), (9.83, 4.91)$; vertical:
$(1.72, 0.86), (6.85, 3.43), (12.87, 6.44)$
53. a. $A_n = \dfrac{1}{4e^{(4n+2)\pi}} - \dfrac{1}{4e^{4n\pi}} - \dfrac{1}{4e^{(4n-2)\pi}} + \dfrac{1}{4e^{(4n-4)\pi}}$ **b.** 0
c. $e^{-4\pi}$ **55.** 6   **57.** 18π **59.** $(a^2 - 2)\theta^* + \pi - \sin 2\theta^*$, where
$\theta^* = \cos^{-1}(a/2)$ **61.** $a^2(\pi/2 + a/3)$

Section 10.4 Exercises, pp. 750–753

1. A parabola is the set of all points in a plane equidistant from a fixed
point and a fixed line.   **3.** A hyperbola is the set of all points in a plane
whose distances from two fixed points have a constant difference.

5. Parabola:

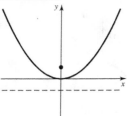

Hyperbola:

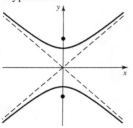

Ellipse:

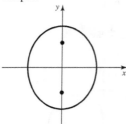

7. $\left(\dfrac{x}{a}\right)^2 + \dfrac{y^2}{a^2 - c^2} = 1$ **9.** $(\pm ae, 0)$ **11.** $y = \pm\dfrac{b}{a}x$

13.

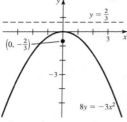

15.

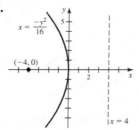

17.

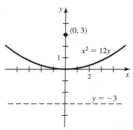

19. $y^2 = 16x$ **21.** $y^2 = 12x$

23. $x^2 = -\dfrac{2}{3}y$ **25.** $y^2 = 4(x + 1)$

27.

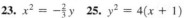

Vertices: $(\pm 2, 0)$; foci: $(\pm\sqrt{3}, 0)$; major axis has length 4; minor axis has length 2.

29.

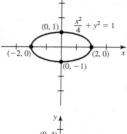
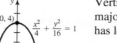
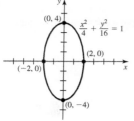

Vertices: $(0, \pm 4)$; foci: $(0, \pm 2\sqrt{3})$; major axis has length 8; minor axis has length 4.

31.

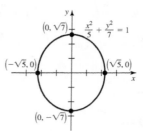

Vertices: $(0, \pm\sqrt{7})$; foci: $(0, \pm\sqrt{2})$; major axis has length $2\sqrt{7}$; minor axis has length $2\sqrt{5}$.

33.

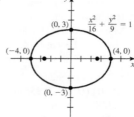

Foci: $(\pm\sqrt{7}, 0)$

35.

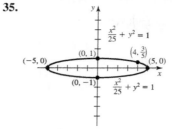

Foci: $(\pm 2\sqrt{6}, 0)$

37. $\dfrac{x^2}{4} + \dfrac{y^2}{9} = 1$

39.

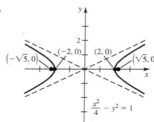

Vertices: $(\pm 2, 0)$; foci: $(\pm\sqrt{5}, 0)$; asymptotes: $y = \pm\dfrac{1}{2}x$

41.

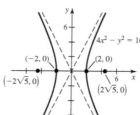

Vertices: $(\pm 2, 0)$; foci: $(\pm 2\sqrt{5}, 0)$; asymptotes: $y = \pm 2x$

43.

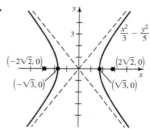

Vertices: $(\pm\sqrt{3}, 0)$; foci: $(\pm 2\sqrt{2}, 0)$; asymptotes: $y = \pm\sqrt{\dfrac{5}{3}}x$

45.

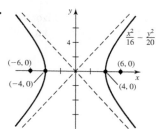

Vertices: $(\pm 4, 0)$; foci: $(\pm 6, 0)$; asymptotes: $y = \pm \dfrac{\sqrt{5}}{2} x$

$\dfrac{x^2}{16} - \dfrac{y^2}{20} = 1$

47.

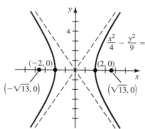

Vertices: $(\pm 2, 0)$; foci: $(\pm \sqrt{13}, 0)$; asymptotes: $y = \pm \dfrac{3}{2} x$

$\dfrac{x^2}{4} - \dfrac{y^2}{9} = 1$

49. $\dfrac{x^2}{16} - \dfrac{y^2}{9} = 1$

51. $\dfrac{x^2}{81} + \dfrac{y^2}{72} = 1$ Directrices: $x = \pm 27$

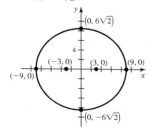

53. $x^2 - \dfrac{y^2}{8} = 1$

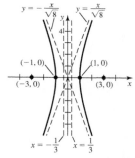

55.

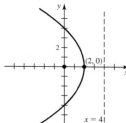

Vertex: $(2, 0)$; focus: $(0, 0)$; directrix: $x = 4$

57.

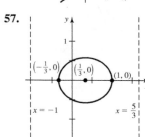

Vertices: $(1, 0)$, $\left(-\dfrac{1}{3}, 0\right)$; center: $\left(\dfrac{1}{3}, 0\right)$; foci: $(0, 0)$, $\left(\dfrac{2}{3}, 0\right)$; directrices: $x = -1, x = \dfrac{5}{3}$

59.

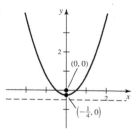

Vertex: $\left(0, -\dfrac{1}{4}\right)$; focus: $(0, 0)$; directrix: $y = -\dfrac{1}{2}$

61.

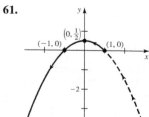

The parabola starts at $(1, 0)$ and goes through quadrants I, II, and III for θ in $[0, 3\pi/2]$; then it approaches $(1, 0)$ by traveling through quadrant IV on $(3\pi/2, 2\pi)$.

63.

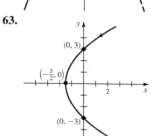

The parabola begins in the first quadrant and passes through the points $(0, 3)$ and then $\left(-\dfrac{3}{2}, 0\right)$ and $(0, -3)$ as θ ranges from 0 to 2π.

65. The parabolas open to the right if $p > 0$, open to the left if $p < 0$, and are more vertically compressed as $|p|$ decreases. **67. a.** True **b.** True **c.** True **d.** True **69.** $y = 2x + 6$ **71.** $y = \dfrac{-3}{40} x - \dfrac{4}{5}$

73. $r = \dfrac{4}{1 - 2\sin\theta}$ **77.** $\dfrac{dy}{dx} = -\dfrac{b^2 x}{a^2 y}$, so $\dfrac{y - y_0}{x - x_0} = -\dfrac{b^2 x_0}{a^2 y_0}$, which is equivalent to the given equation. **79.** $\dfrac{4\pi b^2 a}{3}; \dfrac{4\pi a^2 b}{3}$; yes, if $a \neq b$ **81. a.** $\dfrac{\pi b^2}{3a^2} \cdot (a - c)^2(2a + c)$ **b.** $\dfrac{4\pi b^4}{3a}$ **91.** $2p$

97. a. $u(m) = \dfrac{2m^2 - \sqrt{3m^2 + 1}}{m^2 - 1}$; $v(m) = \dfrac{2m^2 + \sqrt{3m^2 + 1}}{m^2 - 1}$; 2 intersection points for $|m| > 1$ **b.** $\dfrac{5}{4}, \infty$ **c.** 2, 2 **d.** $2\sqrt{3} - \ln(\sqrt{3} + 2)$

Chapter 10 Review Exercises, pp. 754–756

1. a. False **b.** False **c.** True **d.** False **e.** True **f.** True

3. a.

b. $y = 3/x^2$

c. The right branch of the function $y = 3/x^2$. **d.** -6

5. a. 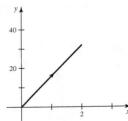   **b.** $y = 16x$

c. A line segment from $(0, 0)$ to $(2, 32)$ **d.** 16

7. $\dfrac{x^2}{16} + \dfrac{y^2}{9} = 1$; ellipse generated counterclockwise

9. $(x + 3)^2 + (y - 6)^2 = 1$; right half of a circle centered at $(-3, 6)$ of radius 1 generated clockwise   **11.** $x = 3 \sin t, y = 3 \cos t$, for $0 \le t \le 2\pi$ **13.** $x = 3 \cos t, y = 2 \sin t$, for $-\pi/2 \le t \le \pi/2$ **15.** $x = -1 + 2t, y = t$, for $0 \le t \le 1$; $x = 1 - 2t, y = 1 - t$, for $0 \le t \le 1$

17. At $t = \pi/6$: $y = (2 + \sqrt{3})x + \left(2 - \dfrac{\pi}{3} - \dfrac{\pi\sqrt{3}}{6}\right)$; at $t = \dfrac{2\pi}{3}$: $y = \dfrac{x}{\sqrt{3}} + 2 - \dfrac{2\pi}{3\sqrt{3}}$

19.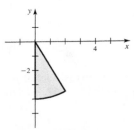

21. Liz should choose $r = 1 - \sin\theta$.

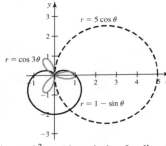

23. $(x - 3)^2 + (y + 1)^2 = 10$; a circle of radius $\sqrt{10}$ centered at $(3, -1)$ **25.** $r = 8 \cos\theta, 0 \le \theta \le \pi$

27. a. 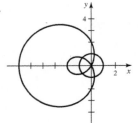   4 intersection points

b. $(1, \pm 1.32), (-1, \pm 0.7)$

29. a. Vertical tangents at $(4.73, 2.77), (4.73, 0.37)$; horizontal tangents at $(6, \pi/2), (2, 3\pi/2)$ **b.** There is no point at the origin.

c.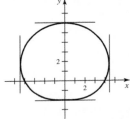

31. a. Horizontal tangent lines at $(1, \pi/6), (1, 5\pi/6), (1, 7\pi/6)$, and $(1, 11\pi/6)$; vertical tangent lines at $(\sqrt{2}, 0)$ and $(\sqrt{2}, \pi)$
b. Tangent lines at the origin have slopes ± 1.

c.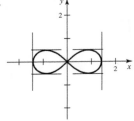

33. $\dfrac{19\pi}{2}$

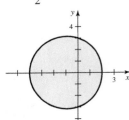

35. $\dfrac{1}{4}\left(\sqrt{255} - \cos^{-1}\dfrac{1}{16}\right)$

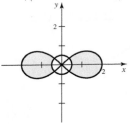

37. 4

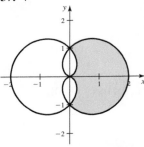

39. a. Hyperbola   **b.** Foci $(\pm\sqrt{3}, 0)$, vertices $(\pm 1, 0)$, directrices $x = \pm\dfrac{1}{\sqrt{3}}$ **c.** $e = \sqrt{3}$ **d.**

41. a. Hyperbola **b.** Foci $(0, \pm 2\sqrt{5})$, vertices $(0, \pm 4)$, directrices
$y = \pm \dfrac{8}{\sqrt{5}}$ **c.** $e = \dfrac{\sqrt{5}}{2}$ **d.**

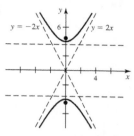

43. a. Ellipse **b.** Foci $(\pm \sqrt{2}, 0)$, vertices $(\pm 2, 0)$, directrices
$x = \pm 2\sqrt{2}$ **c.** $e = \dfrac{\sqrt{2}}{2}$ **d.**

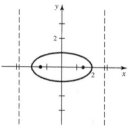

45. $y = \dfrac{3}{2}x - 2$ **47.** $y = -\dfrac{3}{5}x - 10$

49.

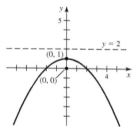

51.

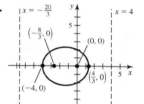

53. a. $x^2 - y^2 = 1$; hyperbola

b. $(\pm 1, 0), (\pm \sqrt{2}, 0); x = \pm \dfrac{1}{\sqrt{2}}; e = \sqrt{2}$

c.

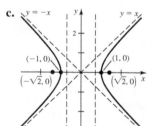

55. $\dfrac{y^2}{16} + \dfrac{25x^2}{336} = 1$; foci: $\left(0, \pm \dfrac{8}{5}\right)$

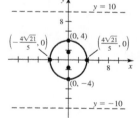

57. $\dfrac{y^2}{4} - \dfrac{x^2}{12} = 1$

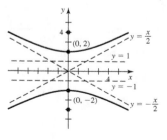

59. $e = 2/3, y = \pm 9, (\pm 2\sqrt{5}, 0)$ **61.** $(0, 0), (0.97, 0.97)$
63. $(0, 0)$ and $(r, \theta) = ((2n - 1)\pi, 0), n = 1, 2, 3, \ldots$
65. $\dfrac{2a}{\sqrt{2}} \cdot \dfrac{2b}{\sqrt{2}}; 2ab$ **67.** $m = \dfrac{b}{a}$ **71.** $r = \dfrac{3}{3 - \sin\theta}$

CHAPTER 11

Section 11.1 Exercises, pp. 767–770

3.

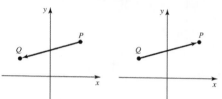

5. There are infinitely many vectors with the same direction and
length as **v**. **7.** If the scalar c is positive, scale the given vector
by a scaling factor c in the same direction. If $c < 0$, reverse the
direction of the vector and scale it by a factor $|c|$.
9. $\mathbf{u} + \mathbf{v} = \langle u_1 + v_1, u_2 + v_2 \rangle$ **11.** $|\langle v_1, v_2 \rangle| = \sqrt{v_1^2 + v_2^2}$
13. If P has coordinates (p_1, p_2) and Q has coordinates (q_1, q_2) then
the magnitude of $\overrightarrow{PQ}$ is given by $\sqrt{(q_1 - p_1)^2 + (q_2 - p_2)^2}$.
15. Divide **v** by its length and multiply the result by 10. **17.** a, c, e
19. a. 3**v** **b.** 2**u** **c.** −3**u** **d.** −2**u** **e.** **v** **21. a.** 3**u** + 3**v**
b. **u** + 2**v** **c.** 2**u** + 5**v** **d.** −2**u** + 3**v** **e.** 3**u** + 2**v**
f. −3**u** − 2**v** **g.** −2**u** − 4**v** **h.** **u** − 4**v** **i.** −**u** − 6**v**
23. a.

$\overrightarrow{OP} = \langle 3, 2 \rangle = 3\mathbf{i} + 2\mathbf{j}$
$|\overrightarrow{OP}| = \sqrt{13}$

b.

$\overrightarrow{QP} = \langle -1, 0 \rangle = -\mathbf{i}$
$|\overrightarrow{QP}| = 1$

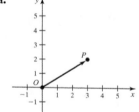

c.

$\overrightarrow{RQ} = \langle 10, 3 \rangle = 10\mathbf{i} + 3\mathbf{j}$
$|\overrightarrow{RQ}| = \sqrt{109}$

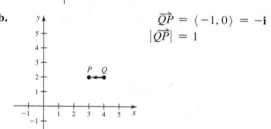
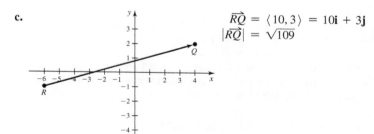

25. $\vec{QU} = \langle 7, 2 \rangle, \vec{PT} = \langle 7, 3 \rangle, \vec{RS} = \langle 2, 3 \rangle$

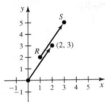

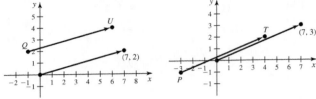

27. $\vec{QT}$ **29.** $\langle -4, 10 \rangle$ **31.** $\langle 12, -10 \rangle$ **33.** $\langle -28, 82 \rangle$
35. $2\sqrt{2}$ **37.** $\sqrt{194}$ **39.** $\langle 3, 3 \rangle, \langle -3, -3 \rangle$ **41.** $\mathbf{w} - \mathbf{u}$

43. $-\mathbf{i} + 10\mathbf{j}$ **45.** $\pm \dfrac{1}{\sqrt{61}} \langle 6, 5 \rangle$

47. $\left\langle -\dfrac{28}{\sqrt{74}}, \dfrac{20}{\sqrt{74}} \right\rangle, \left\langle \dfrac{28}{\sqrt{74}}, -\dfrac{20}{\sqrt{74}} \right\rangle$

49. $5\sqrt{65}$ km/hr ≈ 40.3 km/hr   **51.** 349.43 mi/hr in the direction
4.64° south of west   **53.** 1 m/s in the direction 30° east of north
55. a. $\langle 20, 20\sqrt{3} \rangle$ **b.** Yes   **c.** No   **57.** $250\sqrt{2}$ lb   **59. a.** True
b. True   **c.** False   **d.** False   **e.** False   **f.** False   **g.** False

h. True   **61. a.** $\left\langle \dfrac{3}{5}, -\dfrac{4}{5} \right\rangle$ and $\left\langle -\dfrac{3}{5}, \dfrac{4}{5} \right\rangle$ **b.** $b = \pm \dfrac{2\sqrt{2}}{3}$

c. $a = \pm \dfrac{3}{\sqrt{10}}$ **63.** $\mathbf{x} = \left\langle \dfrac{1}{5}, -\dfrac{3}{10} \right\rangle$ **65.** $\mathbf{x} = \left\langle \dfrac{4}{3}, -\dfrac{11}{3} \right\rangle$

67. $4\mathbf{i} - 8\mathbf{j}$ **69.** $\langle a, b \rangle = \left(\dfrac{a + b}{2} \right) \mathbf{u} + \left(\dfrac{b - a}{2} \right) \mathbf{v}$

71. $\mathbf{u} = \frac{1}{5}\mathbf{i} + \frac{3}{5}\mathbf{j}, \mathbf{v} = \frac{1}{5}\mathbf{i} - \frac{2}{5}\mathbf{j}$ **73.** $\left\langle \dfrac{15}{13}, -\dfrac{36}{13} \right\rangle$ **75.** $\langle 9, 3 \rangle$

77. a. 0   **b.** The 6:00 vector   **c.** Sum any six consecutive vectors.
d. A vector pointing from 12:00 to 6:00 with a length 12 times the
radius of the clock   **79.** 50 lb in the direction 36.87° north of east
81. $\mathbf{u} + \mathbf{v} = \langle u_1, u_2 \rangle + \langle v_1, v_2 \rangle = \langle u_1 + v_1, u_2 + v_2 \rangle$
$\qquad = \langle v_1 + u_1, v_2 + u_2 \rangle = \langle v_1, v_2 \rangle + \langle u_1, u_2 \rangle$
$\qquad = \mathbf{v} + \mathbf{u}$
83. $a(c\mathbf{v}) = a(c \langle v_1, v_2 \rangle) = a \langle cv_1, cv_2 \rangle$
$\qquad = \langle acv_1, acv_2 \rangle = \langle (ac)v_1, (ac)v_2 \rangle$
$\qquad = ac \langle v_1, v_2 \rangle = (ac)\mathbf{v}$
85. $(a + c)\mathbf{v} = (a + c) \langle v_1, v_2 \rangle$
$\qquad = \langle (a + c)v_1, (a + c)v_2 \rangle$
$\qquad = \langle av_1 + cv_1, av_2 + cv_2 \rangle$
$\qquad = \langle av_1, av_2 \rangle + \langle cv_1, cv_2 \rangle$
$\qquad = a \langle v_1, v_2 \rangle + c \langle v_1, v_2 \rangle$
$\qquad = a\mathbf{v} + c\mathbf{v}$
89. a. $\{ \mathbf{u}, \mathbf{v} \}$ are linearly dependent. $\{ \mathbf{u}, \mathbf{w} \}$ and $\{ \mathbf{v}, \mathbf{w} \}$ are linearly
independent.   **b.** Two linearly dependent vectors are parallel. Two
linearly independent vectors are not parallel.   **91. a.** $\frac{5}{3}$ **b.** -15

Section 11.2 Exercises, pp. 777–781

1. Move 3 units from the origin in the direction of the positive
x-axis, then 2 units in the direction of the negative y-axis, and then
1 unit in the direction of the positive z-axis.   **3.** It is parallel to the
yz-plane and contains the point $(4, 0, 0)$.   **5.** $\mathbf{u} + \mathbf{v} = \langle 9, 0, -6 \rangle$;
$3\mathbf{u} - \mathbf{v} = \langle 3, 20, -22 \rangle$ **7.** $(0, 0, -4)$ **9.** $A(3, 0, 5), B(3, 4, 0),$
$C(0, 4, 5)$ **11.** $A(3, -4, 5), B(0, -4, 0), C(0, -4, 5)$

13. a. 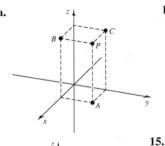   **b.**

c. 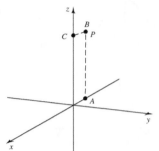   **15.**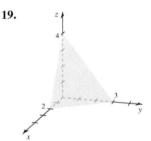

17. 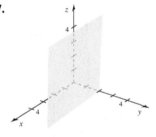   **19.**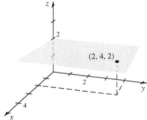

21.

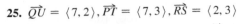

23. $(x - 1)^2 + (y - 2)^2 + (z - 3)^2 = 16$
25. $(x + 2)^2 + y^2 + (z - 4)^2 \le 1$
27. $\left(x - \frac{3}{2} \right)^2 + \left(y - \frac{3}{2} \right)^2 + (z - 7)^2 = \frac{13}{2}$ **29.** A sphere centered
at $(1, 0, 0)$ with radius 3   **31.** A sphere centered at $(0, 1, 2)$ with
radius 3   **33.** All points on or outside the sphere with center $(0, 7, 0)$
and radius 6   **35.** The ball centered at $(4, 7, 9)$ with radius 15
37. The single point $(1, -3, 0)$ **39.** $\langle 12, -7, 2 \rangle; \langle 16, -13, -1 \rangle; 5$
41. a. $\langle -4, 5, -4 \rangle$ **b.** $\langle -9, 3, -9 \rangle$ **c.** $3\sqrt{2}$
43. a. $\langle -15, 23, 22 \rangle$ **b.** $\langle -31, 49, 33 \rangle$ **c.** $3\sqrt{5}$
45. a. $\vec{PQ} = \langle 2, 6, 2 \rangle = 2\mathbf{i} + 6\mathbf{j} + 2\mathbf{k}$ **b.** $|\vec{PQ}| = 2\sqrt{11}$
c. $\left\langle \dfrac{1}{\sqrt{11}}, \dfrac{3}{\sqrt{11}}, \dfrac{1}{\sqrt{11}} \right\rangle$ and $\left\langle -\dfrac{1}{\sqrt{11}}, -\dfrac{3}{\sqrt{11}}, -\dfrac{1}{\sqrt{11}} \right\rangle$
47. a. $\vec{PQ} = \langle 0, -5, 1 \rangle = -5\mathbf{j} + \mathbf{k}$ **b.** $|\vec{PQ}| = \sqrt{26}$
c. $\left\langle 0, -\dfrac{5}{\sqrt{26}}, \dfrac{1}{\sqrt{26}} \right\rangle$ and $\left\langle 0, \dfrac{5}{\sqrt{26}}, -\dfrac{1}{\sqrt{26}} \right\rangle$
49. a. $\vec{PQ} = \langle -2, 4, -2 \rangle = -2\mathbf{i} + 4\mathbf{j} - 2\mathbf{k}$ **b.** $|\vec{PQ}| = 2\sqrt{6}$
c. $\left\langle -\dfrac{1}{\sqrt{6}}, \dfrac{2}{\sqrt{6}}, -\dfrac{1}{\sqrt{6}} \right\rangle$ and $\left\langle \dfrac{1}{\sqrt{6}}, -\dfrac{2}{\sqrt{6}}, \dfrac{1}{\sqrt{6}} \right\rangle$
51. a. $20\mathbf{i} + 20\mathbf{j} - 10\mathbf{k}$;   **b.** 30 mi/hr

53. The speed of the plane is approximately 220 mi/hr; the direction is slightly south of east and upward.

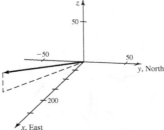

55. $5\sqrt{6}$ knots to the east, $5\sqrt{6}$ knots to the north, 10 knots upward
57. a. False **b.** False **c.** False **d.** True **59.** All points in $\mathbb{R}^3$ except those on the coordinate axes **61.** A circle of radius 1 centered at $(0, 0, 0)$ in the xy-plane

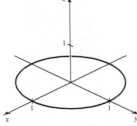

63. A circle of radius 2 centered at $(0, 0, 1)$ in the horizontal plane $z = 1$ **65.** $(x - 2)^2 + (z - 1)^2 = 9, y = 4$ **67.** $\langle 12, -16, 0 \rangle$, $\langle -12, 16, 0 \rangle$ **69.** $\langle -\sqrt{3}, -\sqrt{3}, \sqrt{3} \rangle, \langle \sqrt{3}, \sqrt{3}, -\sqrt{3} \rangle$
71. a. Collinear; Q is between P and R. **b.** Collinear; P is between Q and R. **c.** Noncollinear **d.** Noncollinear **73.** $\sqrt{29}$ ft
75. $\dfrac{250}{3} \left\langle -\dfrac{1}{\sqrt{3}}, 1, 2 \right\rangle, \dfrac{250}{3} \left\langle -\dfrac{1}{\sqrt{3}}, -1, -2 \right\rangle, \dfrac{500}{3} \left\langle \dfrac{1}{\sqrt{3}}, 0, -1 \right\rangle$
77. $(3, 8, 9), (-1, 0, 3)$, or $(1, 0, -3)$

Section 11.3 Exercises, pp. 788–791

1. $\mathbf{u} \cdot \mathbf{v} = |\mathbf{u}||\mathbf{v}| \cos \theta$ **3.** -40
5. $\cos \theta = \dfrac{\mathbf{u} \cdot \mathbf{v}}{|\mathbf{u}||\mathbf{v}|}$, so $\theta = \cos^{-1}\left(\dfrac{\mathbf{u} \cdot \mathbf{v}}{|\mathbf{u}||\mathbf{v}|}\right)$
7. $\mathrm{scal}_\mathbf{v}\,\mathbf{u}$ is the signed length of the $\mathrm{proj}_\mathbf{v}\,\mathbf{u}$.
9. $\dfrac{\pi}{2}$; 0 **11.** 100; $\dfrac{\pi}{4}$ **13.** $\dfrac{1}{2}$ **15.** 0; $\dfrac{\pi}{2}$
17. 1; $\pi/3$ **19.** -2; 93.2° **21.** 2; 87.2° **23.** -4; 104° **25.** $\langle 3, 0 \rangle$; 3
27. $\langle 0, 3 \rangle$; 3 **29.** $\dfrac{6}{5} \langle -2, 1 \rangle$; $\dfrac{6}{\sqrt{5}}$ **31.** $\langle -1, 1, -2 \rangle$; $-\sqrt{6}$
33. $\dfrac{14}{19} \langle -1, -3, 3 \rangle$; $-\dfrac{14}{\sqrt{19}}$ **35.** $-\mathbf{i} + \mathbf{j} - 2\mathbf{k}$; $\sqrt{6}$
37. $750\sqrt{3}$ ft-lb **39.** $25\sqrt{2}$ J **41.** 400 J **43.** $\langle 5, -5 \rangle, \langle -5, -5 \rangle$
45. $\dfrac{1}{2}\langle 5\sqrt{3}, -15 \rangle, \dfrac{1}{2}\langle -5\sqrt{3}, -5 \rangle$ **47. a.** False **b.** True **c.** True
d. False **e.** False **f.** True **49.** $\{\langle 1, a, 4a - 2 \rangle : a \in \mathbb{R}\}$
51. $\left\langle \dfrac{1}{\sqrt{2}}, \dfrac{1}{\sqrt{2}}, 0 \right\rangle, \left\langle -\dfrac{1}{\sqrt{2}}, \dfrac{1}{\sqrt{2}}, 0 \right\rangle, \langle 0, 0, 1 \rangle$ (one possibility)
53. a. $\mathrm{proj}_\mathbf{k}\mathbf{u} = |\mathbf{u}| \cos 60° \left(\dfrac{\mathbf{k}}{|\mathbf{k}|}\right) = \dfrac{1}{2}\mathbf{k}$ for all such $\mathbf{u}$ **b.** Yes
55. The heads of the vectors lie on the line $y = 3 - x$.
57. The heads of the vectors lie on the plane $z = 3$.
59. $\mathbf{u} = \left\langle -\dfrac{4}{5}, -\dfrac{2}{5} \right\rangle + \left\langle -\dfrac{6}{5}, \dfrac{12}{5} \right\rangle$
61. $\mathbf{u} = \left\langle 1, \dfrac{1}{2}, \dfrac{1}{2} \right\rangle + \left\langle -2, \dfrac{3}{2}, \dfrac{5}{2} \right\rangle$ **63. e.** $|\mathbf{w}| = \dfrac{28\sqrt{5}}{5}$
65. e. $|\mathbf{w}| = \sqrt{\dfrac{326}{109}}$

67. $\mathbf{I} = \dfrac{1}{\sqrt{2}}\mathbf{i} + \dfrac{1}{\sqrt{2}}\mathbf{j}, \mathbf{J} = -\dfrac{1}{\sqrt{2}}\mathbf{i} + \dfrac{1}{\sqrt{2}}\mathbf{j};$
$$\mathbf{i} = \dfrac{1}{\sqrt{2}}(\mathbf{I} - \mathbf{J}), \mathbf{j} = \dfrac{1}{\sqrt{2}}(\mathbf{I} + \mathbf{J})$$
69. a. $|\mathbf{I}| = |\mathbf{J}| = |\mathbf{K}| = 1$ **b.** $\mathbf{I} \cdot \mathbf{J} = 0, \mathbf{I} \cdot \mathbf{K} = 0, \mathbf{J} \cdot \mathbf{K} = 0$
c. $\langle 1, 0, 0 \rangle = \dfrac{1}{2}\mathbf{I} - \dfrac{1}{\sqrt{2}}\mathbf{J} + \dfrac{1}{2}\mathbf{K}$ **71.** $\angle P = 78.8°$,
$\angle Q = 47.2°, \angle R = 54.0°$ **73. a.** The faces on $y = 0$ and $z = 0$
b. The faces on $y = 1$ and $z = 1$ **c.** The faces on $x = 0$ and $x = 1$
d. 0 **e.** 1 **f.** 2 **75. a.** $\left(\dfrac{2}{\sqrt{3}}, 0, \dfrac{2\sqrt{2}}{\sqrt{3}}\right)$ **b.** $\mathbf{r}_{OP} = \langle \sqrt{3}, -1, 0 \rangle$,
$\mathbf{r}_{OQ} = \langle \sqrt{3}, 1, 0 \rangle, \mathbf{r}_{PQ} = \langle 0, 2, 0 \rangle, \mathbf{r}_{OR} = \left\langle \dfrac{2}{\sqrt{3}}, 0, \dfrac{2\sqrt{2}}{\sqrt{3}} \right\rangle$,
$\mathbf{r}_{PR} = \left\langle -\dfrac{\sqrt{3}}{3}, 1, \dfrac{2\sqrt{2}}{\sqrt{3}} \right\rangle$
83. a. $\cos^2 \alpha + \cos^2 \beta + \cos^2 \gamma$
$$= \left(\dfrac{\mathbf{v} \cdot \mathbf{i}}{|\mathbf{v}||\mathbf{i}|}\right)^2 + \left(\dfrac{\mathbf{v} \cdot \mathbf{j}}{|\mathbf{v}||\mathbf{j}|}\right)^2 + \left(\dfrac{\mathbf{v} \cdot \mathbf{k}}{|\mathbf{v}||\mathbf{k}|}\right)^2$$
$$= \dfrac{a^2}{a^2 + b^2 + c^2} + \dfrac{b^2}{a^2 + b^2 + c^2} + \dfrac{c^2}{a^2 + b^2 + c^2} = 1$$
b. $\langle 1, 1, 0 \rangle$, 90° **c.** $\left\langle \dfrac{1}{\sqrt{2}}, \dfrac{1}{\sqrt{2}}, 1 \right\rangle$, 45° **d.** No. If so,
$$\left(\dfrac{\sqrt{3}}{2}\right)^2 + \left(\dfrac{\sqrt{3}}{2}\right)^2 + \cos^2 \gamma = 1,$$ which has no solution. **e.** 54.7°
85. $|\mathbf{u} \cdot \mathbf{v}| = 33 = \sqrt{33} \cdot \sqrt{33} < \sqrt{70} \cdot \sqrt{74} = |\mathbf{u}||\mathbf{v}|$

Section 11.4 Exercises, pp. 797–799

1. $|\mathbf{u} \times \mathbf{v}| = |\mathbf{u}||\mathbf{v}|\sin \theta$, where $0 \le \theta \le \pi$ is the angle between $\mathbf{u}$ and $\mathbf{v}$ **3.** 0 **5.** $\mathbf{u} \times \mathbf{v} = \begin{vmatrix} \mathbf{i} & \mathbf{j} & \mathbf{k} \\ u_1 & u_2 & u_3 \\ v_1 & v_2 & v_3 \end{vmatrix}$ **7.** $15\mathbf{k}$

9. 0

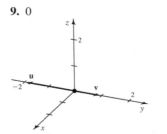

11. 18

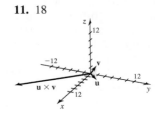

13. $\sqrt{2}/2$ **15.** $\mathbf{i}$

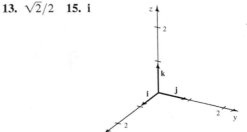

17. $-\mathbf{i}$ **19.** $6\mathbf{j}$

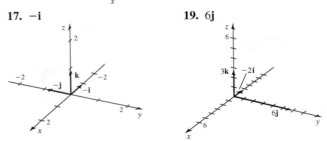

21. 11 **23.** $3\sqrt{10}$ **25.** $\sqrt{11}/2$ **27.** $4\sqrt{2}$
29. $\mathbf{u} \times \mathbf{v} = \langle -30, 18, 9 \rangle, \mathbf{v} \times \mathbf{u} = \langle 30, -18, -9 \rangle$

31. $\mathbf{u} \times \mathbf{v} = \langle 6, 11, 5 \rangle$, $\mathbf{v} \times \mathbf{u} = \langle -6, -11, -5 \rangle$
33. $\mathbf{u} \times \mathbf{v} = \langle 8, 4, 10 \rangle$, $\mathbf{v} \times \mathbf{u} = \langle -8, -4, -10 \rangle$ **35.** $\langle 3, -4, 2 \rangle$
37. $\langle -8, -40, 16 \rangle$ **39.** $5/\sqrt{2}$ N-m   **41.** $\langle 0, 20, -20 \rangle$
43. The force $\mathbf{F} = 5\mathbf{i} - 5\mathbf{k}$ produces the greater torque.
45. The magnitude is $20\sqrt{2}$ at a $135°$ angle with the positive x-axis in the xy-plane.

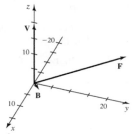

47. 4.53×10^{-14} kg-m/s^2 **49. a.** False   **b.** False   **c.** False
d. True   **e.** False   **51.** Not collinear   **53.** $\langle b^2 - a^2, 0, a^2 - b^2 \rangle$.
The vectors are parallel when $a = \pm b \neq 0$.   **55.** $9\sqrt{2}$ **57.** $\dfrac{7\sqrt{6}}{2}$
59. $\{\langle u_1, u_1 + 2, u_1 + 1 \rangle : u_1 \in \mathbb{R}\}$ **61.** $\dfrac{\sqrt{(ab)^2 + (ac)^2 + (bc)^2}}{2}$
63. a. $|\mathbf{u} \cdot (\mathbf{v} \times \mathbf{w})| = |\mathbf{u}||\mathbf{v} \times \mathbf{w}||\cos\theta|$, where $|\mathbf{v} \times \mathbf{w}|$ is the area of the base of the parallelepiped and $|\mathbf{u}||\cos\theta|$ is its height.   **b.** 46
65. $|\tau| = 26.4$ N-m; direction: into the page   **67.** 1.76×10^7 m/s

Section 11.5 Exercises, pp. 805–808

1. One   **3.** Its output is a vector.
5. $\langle x, y, z \rangle = \langle x_0, y_0, z_0 \rangle + t\langle x_1 - x_0, y_1 - y_0, z_1 - z_0 \rangle$
7. $\lim\limits_{t \to a} \mathbf{r}(t) = \langle \lim\limits_{t \to a} f(t), \lim\limits_{t \to a} g(t), \lim\limits_{t \to a} h(t) \rangle$
9. $\mathbf{r}(t) = \langle 0, 0, 1 \rangle + t\langle 4, 7, 0 \rangle$
11. $\langle x, y, z \rangle = \langle 0, 0, 1 \rangle + t\langle 0, 1, 0 \rangle$ **13.** $\langle x, y, z \rangle = t\langle 1, 2, 3 \rangle$
15. $\langle x, y, z \rangle = \langle -3, 4, 6 \rangle + t\langle 8, -5, -6 \rangle$
17. $\mathbf{r}(t) = t\langle -2, 8, -4 \rangle$ **19.** $\mathbf{r}(t) = t\langle -2, -1, 1 \rangle$
21. $\mathbf{r}(t) = \langle -2, 5, 3 \rangle + t\langle 0, 2, -1 \rangle$
23. $\mathbf{r}(t) = \langle 1, 2, 3 \rangle + t\langle -4, 6, 14 \rangle$ **25.** $\langle x, y, z \rangle = t\langle 1, 2, 3 \rangle$, $0 \leq t \leq 1$ **27.** $\langle x, y, z \rangle = \langle 2, 4, 8 \rangle + t\langle 5, 1, -5 \rangle$, $0 \leq t \leq 1$

29.

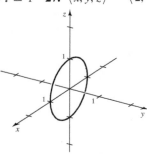

31.

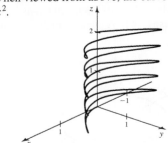

33.

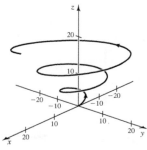

35.

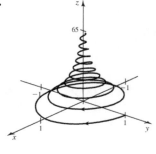

37.

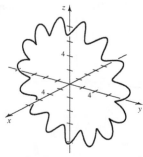

39. When viewed from above, the curve is a portion of the parabola $y = x^2$.

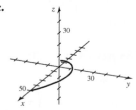

41. $-\mathbf{i} - 4\mathbf{j} + \mathbf{k}$ **43.** $-2\mathbf{j} + \dfrac{\pi}{2}\mathbf{k}$ **45.** $\mathbf{i}$ **47. a.** True   **b.** False
c. True   **d.** True   **49.** $\mathbf{r}(t) = \langle 4, 3, 3 \rangle + t\langle 0, -9, 6 \rangle$
51. The lines intersect at $(1, 3, 2)$.   **53.** Skew
55. These equations describe the same line.   **57.** $\{t : |t| \leq 2\}$
59. $\{t : 0 \leq t \leq 2\}$ **61.** $(21, -6, 4)$ **63.** $(16, 0, -8)$
65. $(4, 8, 16)$ **67. a.** E   **b.** D   **c.** F   **d.** C   **e.** A   **f.** B
69. a. $(50, 0, 0)$ **b.** $5\mathbf{k}$ **c.**

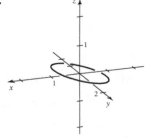

d. $x^2 + y^2 = (50e^{-t})^2$ so $r = 50e^{-t}$. Therefore, $z = 5 - 5e^{-t} = 5 - \dfrac{r}{10}$.

71. a.

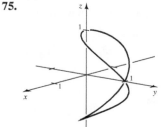

b. Curve is a tilted circle of radius 1 centered at the origin.
73. $\langle cf - ed, be - af, ad - bc \rangle$ or any scalar multiple
75. The curve lies on the sphere $x^2 + y^2 + z^2 = 1$.

77. $\dfrac{2\pi}{(m,n)}$, where $(m,n) = $ greatest common factor of m and n

81. 13

Section 11.6 Exercises, pp. 814–816

1. $\mathbf{r}'(t) = \langle f'(t), g'(t), h'(t) \rangle$ **3.** $\mathbf{T}(t) = \dfrac{r'(t)}{|r'(t)|}$

5. $\displaystyle\int \mathbf{r}(t)\,dt = \left(\int f(t)\,dt\right)\mathbf{i} + \left(\int g(t)\,dt\right)\mathbf{j} + \left(\int h(t)\,dt\right)\mathbf{k}$

7. $\langle -\sin t, 2t, \cos t \rangle$ **9.** $\left\langle 6t^2, \dfrac{3}{\sqrt{t}}, -\dfrac{3}{t^2} \right\rangle$ **11.** $e^t\mathbf{i} - 2e^{-t}\mathbf{j} - 8e^{2t}\mathbf{k}$

13. $\langle e^{-t}(1-t), 1 + \ln t, \cos t - t\sin t \rangle$ **15.** $\langle 1, 6, 3 \rangle$

17. $\langle 1, 0, 0 \rangle$ **19.** $8\mathbf{i} + 9\mathbf{j} - 10\mathbf{k}$ **21.** $\langle 2/3, 2/3, 1/3 \rangle$

23. $\dfrac{\langle 0, -\sin 2t, 2\cos 2t \rangle}{\sqrt{1 + 3\cos^2 2t}}$ **25.** $\dfrac{t^2}{\sqrt{t^4 + 4}}\left\langle 1, 0, -\dfrac{2}{t^2} \right\rangle$

27. $\langle 0, 0, -1 \rangle$ **29.** $\left\langle \dfrac{2}{\sqrt{5}}, 0, -\dfrac{1}{\sqrt{5}} \right\rangle$

31. $\langle 30t^{14} + 24t^3, 14t^{13} - 12t^{11} + 9t^2 - 3, -96t^{11} - 24 \rangle$

33. $4t(2t^3 - 1)(t^3 - 2)\langle 3t(t^3 - 2), 1, 0 \rangle$

35. $e^t(2t^3 + 6t^2) - 2e^{-t}(t^2 - 2t - 1) - 16e^{-2t}$

37. $5te^t(t + 2) - 6t^2e^{-t}(t - 3)$

39. $-3t^2\sin t + 6t\cos t + 2\sqrt{t}\cos 2t + \dfrac{1}{2\sqrt{t}}\sin 2t$

41. $\langle 2, 0, 0 \rangle, \langle 0, 0, 0 \rangle$ **43.** $\langle -9\cos 3t, -16\sin 4t, -36\cos 6t \rangle$, $\langle 27\sin 3t, -64\cos 4t, 216\sin 6t \rangle$

45. $\left\langle -\dfrac{1}{4}(t+4)^{-3/2}, -2(t+1)^{-3}, 2e^{-t^2}(1 - 2t^2) \right\rangle$, $\left\langle \dfrac{3}{8}(t+4)^{-5/2}, 6(t+1)^{-4}, -4te^{-t^2}(3 - 2t^2) \right\rangle$

47. $\left\langle \dfrac{t^5}{5} - \dfrac{3t^2}{2}, t^2 - t, 10t \right\rangle + \mathbf{C}$

49. $\left\langle 2\sin t, -\dfrac{2}{3}\cos 3t, \dfrac{1}{2}\sin 8t \right\rangle + \mathbf{C}$

51. $\frac{1}{3}e^{3t}\mathbf{i} + \tan^{-1}t\,\mathbf{j} - \sqrt{2t}\,\mathbf{k} + \mathbf{C}$

53. $\mathbf{r}(t) = \langle e^t + 1, 3 - \cos t, \tan t + 2 \rangle$

55. $\mathbf{r}(t) = \langle t + 3, t^2 + 2, t^3 - 6 \rangle$

57. $\mathbf{r}(t) = \left\langle \frac{1}{2}e^{2t} + \frac{1}{2}, 2e^{-t} + t - 1, t - 2e^t + 3 \right\rangle$

59. $\langle 2, 0, 2 \rangle$ **61.** $\mathbf{i}$ **63.** $\langle 0, 0, 0 \rangle$ **65.** $(e^2 + 1)\langle 1, 2, -1 \rangle$

67. a. False   **b.** True   **c.** True   **69.** $\langle 2 - t, 3 - 2t, \pi/2 + t \rangle$

71. $\langle 2 + 3t, 9 + 7t, 1 + 2t \rangle$ **73.** $\langle 2e^{2t}, -2e^t, 0 \rangle$

75. $\left\langle 4, -\dfrac{2}{\sqrt{t}}, 0 \right\rangle$ **77.** $\langle 1 + 6t^2, 4t^3, -2 - 3t^2 \rangle$ **79.** $(1, 0)$

81. $(1, 0, 0)$ **83.** $\mathbf{r}(t) = \langle a_1t, a_2t, a_3t \rangle$ or $\mathbf{r}(t) = \langle a_1e^{kt}, a_2e^{kt}, a_3e^{kt} \rangle$, where a_i and k are real numbers

Section 11.7 Exercises, pp. 826–830

1. $\mathbf{v}(t) = \mathbf{r}'(t)$, speed $= |\mathbf{r}'(t)|$, $\mathbf{a}(t) = \mathbf{r}''(t)$ **3.** $m\mathbf{a}(t) = \mathbf{F}$

5. $\mathbf{v}(t) = \displaystyle\int \mathbf{a}(t)\,dt = \langle v_1(t), v_2(t) \rangle + \mathbf{C}$. Use initial conditions to find $\mathbf{C}$.   **7. a.** $\langle 6t, 8t \rangle, 10t$ **b.** $\langle 6, 8 \rangle$ **9. a.** $\mathbf{v}(t) = \langle 2, -4 \rangle$, $|\mathbf{v}(t)| = 2\sqrt{5}$ **b.** $\mathbf{a}(t) = \langle 0, 0 \rangle$ **11. a.** $\mathbf{v}(t) = \langle 8\cos t, -8\sin t \rangle$, $|\mathbf{v}(t)| = 8$ **b.** $\mathbf{a}(t) = \langle -8\sin t, -8\cos t \rangle$ **13. a.** $\langle 2t, 2t, t \rangle, 3t$ **b.** $\langle 2, 2, 1 \rangle$ **15. a.** $\mathbf{v}(t) = \langle 1, -4, 6 \rangle, |\mathbf{v}(t)| = \sqrt{53}$ **b.** $\mathbf{a}(t) = \langle 0, 0, 0 \rangle$ **17. a.** $\mathbf{v}(t) = \langle 0, 2t, -e^{-t} \rangle$, $|\mathbf{v}(t)| = \sqrt{4t^2 + e^{-2t}}$ **b.** $\mathbf{a}(t) = \langle 0, 2, e^{-t} \rangle$ **19. a.** $[c, d] = [0, 1]$

b. $\langle 1, 2t \rangle, \langle 2, 8t \rangle$

c.

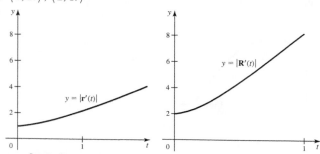

21. a. $\left[0, \frac{2\pi}{3} \right]$ **b.** $\mathbf{V_r}(t) = \langle -\sin t, 4\cos t \rangle$, $\mathbf{V_R}(t) = \langle -3\sin 3t, 12\cos 3t \rangle$

c.

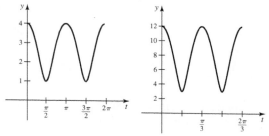

23. a. $[1, e^{36}]$

b. $\mathbf{V_r}(t) = \langle 2t, -8t^3, 18t^5 \rangle$, $\mathbf{V_R}(t) = \left\langle \dfrac{1}{t}, -\dfrac{4}{t}\ln t, \dfrac{9}{t}\ln^2 t \right\rangle$

c.

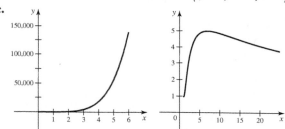

25. $\mathbf{r}(t)$ lies on a circle of radius 8; $\langle -16\sin 2t, 16\cos 2t \rangle \cdot \langle 8\cos 2t, 8\sin 2t \rangle = 0$.

27. $\mathbf{r}(t)$ lies on a sphere of radius 2; $\langle \cos t - \sqrt{3}\sin t, \sqrt{3}\cos t + \sin t \rangle \cdot \langle \sin t + \sqrt{3}\cos t, \sqrt{3}\sin t - \cos t \rangle = 0$.

29. $\mathbf{r}(t)$ does not lie on a sphere.

31. $\mathbf{v}(t) = \langle 2, t + 3 \rangle, \mathbf{r}(t) = \left\langle 2t, \dfrac{t^2}{2} + 3t \right\rangle$

33. $\mathbf{v}(t) = \langle 0, 10t + 5 \rangle, \mathbf{r}(t) = \langle 1, 5t^2 + 5t - 1 \rangle$

35. $\mathbf{v}(t) = \langle \sin t, -2\cos t + 3 \rangle$, $\mathbf{r}(t) = \langle -\cos t + 2, -2\sin t + 3t \rangle$

37. a. $\mathbf{v}(t) = \langle 30, -9.8t + 6 \rangle, \mathbf{r}(t) = \langle 30t, -4.9t^2 + 6t \rangle$

b.

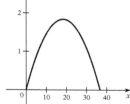

c. $T \approx 1.22$ s, range ≈ 36.7 m   **d.** 1.84 m

39. a. $\mathbf{v}(t) = \langle 80, 10 - 32t \rangle, \mathbf{r}(t) = \langle 80t, -16t^2 + 10t + 6 \rangle$
b.

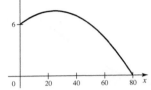

c. 1 s, 80 ft
d. max height ≈ 7.56 ft

41. a. $\mathbf{v}(t) = \langle 125, -32t + 125\sqrt{3} \rangle$,
$\mathbf{r}(t) = \langle 125t, -16t^2 + 125\sqrt{3}t + 20 \rangle$
b.   **c.** 13.6 s, 1702.5 ft   **d.** 752.4 ft

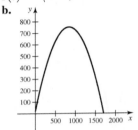

43. $\mathbf{v}(t) = \langle 1, 5, 10t \rangle, \mathbf{r}(t) = \langle t, 5t + 5, 5t^2 \rangle$
45. $\mathbf{v}(t) = \langle -\cos t + 1, \sin t + 2, t \rangle$,

$\mathbf{r}(t) = \left\langle -\sin t + t, -\cos t + 2t + 1, \dfrac{t^2}{2} \right\rangle$

47. a. $\mathbf{v}(t) = \langle 200, 200, -9.8t \rangle, \mathbf{r}(t) = \langle 200t, 200t, -4.9t^2 + 1 \rangle$
b.   **c.** 0.452 s, 127.8 m   **d.** 1 m

49. a. $\mathbf{v}(t) = \langle 60 + 10t, 80, 80 - 32t \rangle$,
$\mathbf{r}(t) = \langle 60t + 5t^2, 80t, 80t - 16t^2 + 3 \rangle$
b.   **c.** 5.04 s, 589 ft
d. 103 ft

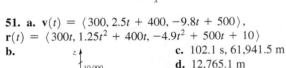

51. a. $\mathbf{v}(t) = \langle 300, 2.5t + 400, -9.8t + 500 \rangle$,
$\mathbf{r}(t) = \langle 300t, 1.25t^2 + 400t, -4.9t^2 + 500t + 10 \rangle$
b.   **c.** 102.1 s, 61,941.5 m
d. 12,765.1 m

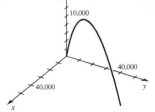

53. a. False   **b.** True   **c.** False   **d.** True   **e.** False   **f.** True
g. True   **55.** 15.3 s, 1988.3 m, 287.0 m   **57.** 21.7 s, 4330.1 ft, 1875 ft
59. Approximately 27.4° and 62.6°   **61. a.** The direction of $\mathbf{r}$ does
not change.   **b.** Constant in direction, not in magnitude

63. a. $\left[0, \dfrac{2\pi}{\omega} \right]$ **b.** $\mathbf{v}(t) = \langle -A\omega \sin \omega t, A\omega \cos \omega t \rangle$ is not constant;
$|\mathbf{v}(t)| = |A\omega|$ is constant.   **c.** $\mathbf{a}(t) = \langle -A\omega^2 \cos \omega t, -A\omega^2 \sin \omega t \rangle$
d. $\mathbf{r}$ and $\mathbf{v}$ are orthogonal; $\mathbf{r}$ and $\mathbf{a}$ are in opposite directions.
e.

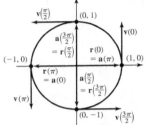

65. a. $\mathbf{r}(t) = \langle 5 \sin (\pi t/6), 5 \cos (\pi t/6) \rangle$
b. $\mathbf{r}(t) = \left\langle 5 \sin \left(\dfrac{1 - e^{-t}}{5} \right), 5 \cos \left(\dfrac{1 - e^{-t}}{5} \right) \right\rangle$
67. a. $\mathbf{v}(t) = \langle -a \sin t, b \cos t \rangle$; $|\mathbf{v}(t)| = \sqrt{a^2 \sin^2 t + b^2 \cos^2 t}$
b.

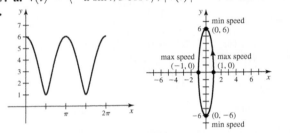

c. Yes   **d.** max $\left\{ \dfrac{a}{b}, \dfrac{b}{a} \right\}$
69. a. $\mathbf{r}(0) = \langle 50, 0, 0 \rangle$, $\lim_{t \to \infty} \mathbf{r}(t) = \langle 0, 0, 5 \rangle$ **b.** At $t = 0$
c.

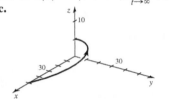

71. Approximately 23.5° or 59.6°   **73.** 113.4 ft/s   **75. a.** 1.2 ft,
0.46 s   **b.** 0.88 ft/s   **c.** 0.85 ft   **d.** More curve in the second half

e. $c = 28.17$ ft/s²   **77.** $T = \dfrac{|\mathbf{v}_0| \sin \alpha + \sqrt{|\mathbf{v}_0|^2 \sin^2 \alpha + 2gy_0}}{g}$,

range $= |\mathbf{v}_0| (\cos \alpha) T$, max height $= y_0 + \dfrac{|\mathbf{v}_0|^2 \sin^2 \alpha}{2g}$

79. $\{ (\cos t, \sin t, c \sin t) : t \in \mathbb{R} \}$ satisfies the equations $x^2 + y^2 = 1$
and $z - cy = 0$ so that $\langle \cos t, \sin t, c \sin t \rangle$ lies on the intersection of
a right circular cylinder and a plane, which is an ellipse.
83. b. $a^2 + c^2 + e^2 = b^2 + d^2 + f^2$ and $ab + cd + ef = 0$

Section 11.8 Exercises, pp. 838–840

1. $\sqrt{5}(b - a)$ **3.** $\displaystyle\int_a^b |\mathbf{v}(t)| \, dt$ **5.** 20π **7.** If the parameter t
used to describe a trajectory also measures the arc length s of the curve
that is generated, we say the curve has been parameterized by its arc length.

9. 5   **11.** 3π **13.** $\dfrac{\pi^2}{8}$ **15.** $5\sqrt{34}$ **17.** $4\pi\sqrt{65}$ **19.** 9

21. $\dfrac{3}{2}$ **23.** $3t^2\sqrt{30}$; $64\sqrt{30}$ **25.** 26; 26π **27.** 19.38   **29.** 32.50

31. πa **33.** $\frac{8}{3} \left((1 + \pi^2)^{3/2} - 1 \right)$ **35.** 32   **37.** $63\sqrt{5}$

39. $\dfrac{2\pi - 3\sqrt{3}}{8}$ **41.** Yes

43. No; $\mathbf{r}(s) = \left\langle \dfrac{s}{\sqrt{5}}, \dfrac{2s}{\sqrt{5}} \right\rangle, 0 \le s \le 3\sqrt{5}$

45. No; $\mathbf{r}(s) = \left\langle 2\cos\dfrac{s}{2}, 2\sin\dfrac{s}{2} \right\rangle, 0 \le s \le 4\pi$

47. No; $\mathbf{r}(s) = \langle \cos s, \sin s \rangle, 0 \le s \le \pi$

49. No; $\mathbf{r}(s) = \left\langle \dfrac{s}{\sqrt{3}} + 1, \dfrac{s}{\sqrt{3}} + 1, \dfrac{s}{\sqrt{3}} + 1 \right\rangle, s \ge 0$

51. a. True **b.** True **c.** True **d.** False **53. a.** If $a^2 = b^2 + c^2$, then $|\mathbf{r}(t)|^2 = (a\cos t)^2 + (b\sin t)^2 + (c\sin t)^2 = a^2$ so that $\mathbf{r}(t)$ is a circle centered at the origin of radius $|a|$. **b.** $2\pi a$ **c.** If $a^2 + c^2 + e^2 = b^2 + d^2 + f^2$ and $ab + cd + ef = 0$, then $\mathbf{r}(t)$ is a circle of radius $\sqrt{a^2 + c^2 + e^2}$ and its arc length is

$2\pi\sqrt{a^2 + c^2 + e^2}$. **55. a.** $\displaystyle\int_a^b \sqrt{(Ah'(t))^2 + (Bh'(t))^2}\, dt$

$= \displaystyle\int_a^b \sqrt{(A^2 + B^2)(h'(t))^2}\, dt = \sqrt{A^2 + B^2}\displaystyle\int_a^b |h'(t)|\, dt$

b. $64\sqrt{29}$ **c.** $\dfrac{7\sqrt{29}}{4}$ **57.** $\dfrac{\sqrt{1 + a^2}}{a}$ (where $a > 0$) **59.** 12.85

61. 26.73 **63. a.** 5.102 s **b.** $\displaystyle\int_0^{5.102} \sqrt{400 + (25 - 9.8t)^2}\, dt$

c. 124.43 m **d.** 102.04 m **65.** $|\mathbf{v}(t)| = \sqrt{a^2 + b^2 + c^2} = 1$, if $a^2 + b^2 + c^2 = 1$.

67. $\displaystyle\int_a^b |\mathbf{r}'(t)|\, dt = \displaystyle\int_a^b \sqrt{(cf'(t))^2 + (cg'(t))^2}\, dt$

$= |c|\displaystyle\int_a^b \sqrt{(f'(t))^2 + (g'(t))^2}\, dt = |c| L$

69. If $\mathbf{r}(t) = \langle t, f(t) \rangle$, then by definition, the arc length is $\displaystyle\int_a^b \sqrt{(t')^2 + f'(t)^2}\, dt = \displaystyle\int_a^b \sqrt{1 + f'(t)^2}\, dt$

$= \displaystyle\int_a^b \sqrt{1 + f'(x)^2}\, dx.$

Section 11.9 Exercises, pp. 852–854

1. 0 **3.** $\kappa = \dfrac{1}{|\mathbf{v}|}\left|\dfrac{d\mathbf{T}}{dt}\right|$ or $\kappa = \dfrac{|\mathbf{v} \times \mathbf{a}|}{|\mathbf{v}|^3}$ **5.** $\mathbf{N} = \dfrac{d\mathbf{T}/dt}{|d\mathbf{T}/dt|}$

7. These three unit vectors are mutually orthogonal at all points of the curve. **9.** The torsion measures the rate at which the curve rises or twists out of the **TN**-plane at a point. **11.** $\mathbf{T} = \dfrac{\langle 1, 2, 3 \rangle}{\sqrt{14}}, \kappa = 0$

13. $\mathbf{T} = \dfrac{\langle 1, 2\cos t, -2\sin t \rangle}{\sqrt{5}}, \kappa = \dfrac{1}{5}$

15. $\mathbf{T} = \dfrac{\langle \sqrt{3}\cos t, \cos t, -2\sin t \rangle}{2}, \kappa = \dfrac{1}{2}$

17. $\mathbf{T} = \dfrac{\langle 1, 4t \rangle}{\sqrt{1 + 16t^2}}, \kappa = \dfrac{4}{(1 + 16t^2)^{3/2}}$

19. $\mathbf{T} = \left\langle \cos\left(\dfrac{\pi t^2}{2}\right), \sin\left(\dfrac{\pi t^2}{2}\right) \right\rangle, \kappa = \pi t$

21. $\dfrac{1}{3}$ **23.** $\dfrac{2}{(4t^2 + 1)^{3/2}}$ **25.** $\dfrac{2\sqrt{5}}{(20\sin^2 t + \cos^2 t)^{3/2}}$

27. $\mathbf{T} = \langle \cos t, -\sin t \rangle, \mathbf{N} = \langle -\sin t, -\cos t \rangle$

29. $\mathbf{T} = \dfrac{\langle t, -3, 0 \rangle}{\sqrt{t^2 + 9}}, \mathbf{N} = \dfrac{\langle 3, t, 0 \rangle}{\sqrt{t^2 + 9}}$

31. $\mathbf{T} = \langle -\sin t^2, \cos t^2 \rangle, \mathbf{N} = \langle -\cos t^2, -\sin t^2 \rangle$

33. $\mathbf{T} = \dfrac{\langle 2t, 1 \rangle}{\sqrt{4t^2 + 1}}, \mathbf{N} = \dfrac{\langle 1, -2t \rangle}{\sqrt{4t^2 + 1}}$ **35.** $a_N = a_T = 0$

37. $a_T = \sqrt{3}\, e^t; a_N = \sqrt{2}e^t$ **39.** $\mathbf{a} = \dfrac{6t}{\sqrt{9t^2 + 4}}\mathbf{N} + \dfrac{18t^2 + 4}{\sqrt{9t^2 + 4}}\mathbf{T}$

41. $\mathbf{B}(t) = \langle 0, 0, -1 \rangle, \tau = 0$ **43.** $\mathbf{B}(t) = \langle 0, 0, 1 \rangle, \tau = 0$

45. $\mathbf{B}(t) = \dfrac{\langle -\sin t, \cos t, 2 \rangle}{\sqrt{5}}, \tau = -\dfrac{1}{5}$

47. $\mathbf{B}(t) = \dfrac{\langle 5, 12\sin t, -12\cos t \rangle}{13}, \tau = \dfrac{12}{169}$ **49. a.** False

b. False **c.** False **d.** True **e.** False **f.** False **g.** False

51. $\kappa = \dfrac{2}{(1 + 4x^2)^{3/2}}$ **53.** $\kappa = \dfrac{x}{(x^2 + 1)^{3/2}}$

57. $\kappa = \dfrac{|ab|}{(a^2\cos^2 t + b^2\sin^2 t)^{3/2}}$ **59.** $\kappa = \dfrac{2|a|}{(1 + 4a^2 t^2)^{3/2}}$

61. b. $\mathbf{v}_A(t) = \langle 1, 2, 3 \rangle, \mathbf{a}_A(t) = \langle 0, 0, 0 \rangle$ and $\mathbf{v}_B(t) = \langle 2t, 4t, 6t \rangle$, $\mathbf{a}_B(t) = \langle 2, 4, 6 \rangle$; A has constant velocity and zero acceleration while B has increasing speed and constant acceleration. **c.** $\mathbf{a}_A(t) = 0\mathbf{N} + 0\mathbf{T}, \mathbf{a}_B(t) = 0\mathbf{N} + 2\sqrt{14}\,\mathbf{T}$; both normal components are zero since the path is a straight line ($\kappa = 0$). **63. b.** $\mathbf{v}_A(t) = \langle -\sin t, \cos t \rangle, \mathbf{a}_A(t) = \langle -\cos t, -\sin t \rangle$
$\mathbf{v}_B(t) = \langle -2t\sin t^2, 2t\cos t^2 \rangle$
$\mathbf{a}_B(t) = \langle -4t^2\cos t^2 - 2\sin t^2, -4t^2\sin t^2 + 2\cos t^2 \rangle$
c. $\mathbf{a}_A(t) = \mathbf{N} + 0\mathbf{T}, \mathbf{a}_B(t) = 4t^2\mathbf{N} + 2\mathbf{T}$; for A, the acceleration is always normal to the curve, but this is not true for B.

65. b. $\kappa = \dfrac{1}{2\sqrt{2(1 - \cos t)}}$ **c.**

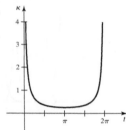

d. Minimum curvature at $t = \pi$ **67. b.** $\kappa = \dfrac{1}{t(1 + t^2)^{3/2}}$

c.

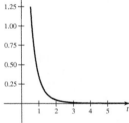

d. No maximum or minimum curvature

69. $\kappa = \dfrac{e^x}{(1 + e^{2x})^{3/2}}, \left(-\dfrac{\ln 2}{2}, \dfrac{1}{\sqrt{2}} \right), \dfrac{2\sqrt{3}}{9}$

71. $\dfrac{1}{\kappa} = \dfrac{1}{2}; x^2 + \left(y - \dfrac{1}{2} \right)^2 = \dfrac{1}{4}$

73. $\dfrac{1}{\kappa} = 4; (x - \pi)^2 + (y + 2)^2 = 16$

75. $\kappa\left(\dfrac{\pi}{2n} \right) = n^2; \kappa$ increases as n increases.

77. a. Speed $= \sqrt{V_0^2 - 2V_0\, gt \sin \alpha + g^2 t^2}$

b. $\kappa(t) = \dfrac{g V_0 \cos \alpha}{(V_0^2 - 2V_0\, gt \sin \alpha + g^2 t^2)^{3/2}}$

c. Speed has a minimum at $t = \dfrac{V_0 \sin \alpha}{g}$ and $\kappa(t)$ has a maximum at

$t = \dfrac{V_0 \sin \alpha}{g}$.   **79.** $\kappa = \dfrac{1}{|\mathbf{v}|} \cdot \left| \dfrac{d\mathbf{T}}{dt} \right|$, where $\mathbf{T} = \dfrac{\langle b, d, f \rangle}{\sqrt{b^2 + d^2 + f^2}}$ and

b, d, f are constant. Therefore, $\dfrac{d\mathbf{T}}{dt} = \mathbf{0}$ so $\kappa = 0$.

81. a. $\kappa_1(x) = \dfrac{2}{(1 + 4x^2)^{3/2}}$

$\kappa_2(x) = \dfrac{12x^2}{(1 + 16x^6)^{3/2}}$

$\kappa_3(x) = \dfrac{30x^4}{(1 + 36x^{10})^{3/2}}$

b.

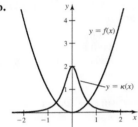

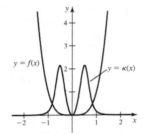

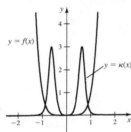

c. κ_1 has its maximum at $x = 0$, κ_2 has its maxima at $x = \pm\sqrt[6]{\frac{1}{56}}$,

κ_3 has its maxima at $x = \pm\sqrt[10]{\frac{1}{99}}$.   **d.** $\lim\limits_{n \to \infty} z_n = 1$; the graphs of

$y = f_n(x)$ show that as $n \to \infty$, the point corresponding to maximum curvature gets arbitrarily close to the point $(1, 0)$

Chapter 11 Review Exercises, pp. 854–857

1. a. True **b.** False **c.** True **d.** True **e.** False **f.** False

3.

5.

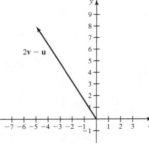

7. $\sqrt{221}$ **9.** $\pm\left\langle -\dfrac{60}{\sqrt{35}}, \dfrac{100}{\sqrt{35}}, \dfrac{20}{\sqrt{35}} \right\rangle$

11. $2\langle 29, 13, 22 \rangle, -2\langle 29, 13, 22 \rangle, 3\sqrt{166}$

13. a. $\mathbf{v} = -275\sqrt{2}\mathbf{i} + 275\sqrt{2}\mathbf{j}$ **b.** $-275\sqrt{2}\mathbf{i} + (275\sqrt{2} + 40)\mathbf{j}$

15. $\{(x, y, z): (x - 1)^2 + y^2 + (z + 1)^2 = 16\}$

17. $\{(x, y, z): x^2 + (y - 1)^2 + z^2 > 4\}$ **19.** A ball centered at

$(\frac{1}{2}, -2, 3)$ of radius $\frac{3}{2}$ **21.** All points outside a sphere of radius

10 centered at $(3, 0, 10)$ **23.** 50.15 m/s; 85.4° below the horizontal

in the northerly horizontal direction   **25.** A circle of radius 1 centered

at $(0, 2, 0)$ in the vertical plane $y = 2$ **27. a.** 0.68 radian

b. $\dfrac{7}{9}\langle 1, 2, 2 \rangle; \dfrac{7}{3}$ **c.** $\dfrac{7}{3}\langle -1, 2, 2 \rangle; 7$ **29.** $\pm\left\langle \dfrac{12}{\sqrt{197}}, \dfrac{7}{\sqrt{197}}, \dfrac{2}{\sqrt{197}} \right\rangle$

31. $T(\theta) = 39.2 \sin \theta$ has a maximum value of 39.2 N-m (when

$\theta = \pi/2$) and a minimum value of 0 N-m when $\theta = 0$. Direction

does *not* change.   **33.** $\langle x, y, z \rangle = \langle 0, -3, 9 \rangle + t\langle 2, -5, -8 \rangle$,

$0 \le t \le 1$ **35.** $\langle t, 1 + 6t, 1 + 2t \rangle$ **37.** 11

39.

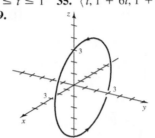

41.

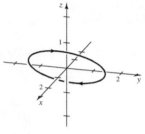

43. a. $\langle 1, 0 \rangle; \langle 0, 1 \rangle$ **b.** $\left\langle -\dfrac{2}{(2t + 1)^2}, \dfrac{1}{(t + 1)^2} \right\rangle; \langle -2, 1 \rangle$

c. $\left\langle \dfrac{8}{(2t + 1)^3}, -\dfrac{2}{(t + 1)^3} \right\rangle$ **d.** $\left\langle \dfrac{1}{2} \ln|2t + 1|, t - \ln|t + 1| \right\rangle + \mathbf{C}$.

45. a. $\langle 0, 3, 0 \rangle$; does not exist

b. $\langle 2 \cos 2t, -12 \sin 4t, 1 \rangle; \langle 2, 0, 1 \rangle$ **c.** $\langle -4 \sin 2t, -48 \cos 4t, 0 \rangle$

d. $\left\langle -\dfrac{1}{2} \cos 2t, \dfrac{3}{4} \sin 4t, \dfrac{1}{2}t^2 \right\rangle + \mathbf{C}$ **47. a.** $(116, 30)$ **b.** 39.1 ft

c. 2.315 s   **d.** $\displaystyle\int_0^{2.315} \sqrt{50^2 + (-32t + 50)^2}\, dt$ **e.** 129 ft

f. 41.4° to 79.4°   **49.** 25.6 ft/s   **51.** 12

53. a. $\mathbf{v}(t) = \mathbf{i} + t\sqrt{2}\mathbf{j} + t^2\mathbf{k}$ **b.** 12   **55.** 40.09

57. $\mathbf{r}(s) = \left\langle (\sqrt{1 + s} - 1)^2, \dfrac{4\sqrt{2}}{3}(\sqrt{1 + s} - 1)^{3/2}, 2(\sqrt{1 + s} - 1) \right\rangle$,

for $s \ge 0$ **59. a.** $\mathbf{v} = \langle -6 \sin t, 3 \cos t \rangle, \mathbf{T} = \dfrac{\langle -2 \sin t, \cos t \rangle}{\sqrt{1 + 3 \sin^2 t}}$

b. $\kappa(t) = \dfrac{2}{3(1 + 3 \sin^2 t)^{3/2}}$

c. $\mathbf{N} = \left\langle -\dfrac{\cos t}{\sqrt{1 + 3 \sin^2 t}}, -\dfrac{2 \sin t}{\sqrt{1 + 3 \sin^2 t}} \right\rangle$

d. $|\mathbf{N}| = \sqrt{\dfrac{\cos^2 t + 4 \sin^2 t}{1 + 3 \sin^2 t}} = \sqrt{\dfrac{(\cos^2 t + \sin^2 t) + 3 \sin^2 t}{1 + 3 \sin^2 t}} = 1$;

$\mathbf{T} \cdot \mathbf{N} = \dfrac{2 \sin t \cos t - 2 \sin t \cos t}{1 + 3 \sin^2 t} = 0$

e.

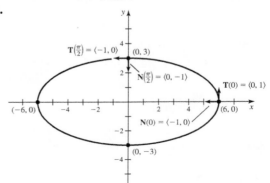

61. a. $\mathbf{v}(t) = \langle -\sin t, -2 \sin t, \sqrt{5} \cos t \rangle$,

$$\mathbf{T}(t) = \left\langle -\frac{1}{\sqrt{5}} \sin t, -\frac{2}{\sqrt{5}} \sin t, \cos t \right\rangle$$ **b.** $\kappa(t) = \frac{1}{\sqrt{5}}$

c. $\mathbf{N}(t) = \left\langle -\frac{1}{\sqrt{5}} \cos t, -\frac{2}{\sqrt{5}} \cos t, -\sin t \right\rangle$

d. $|\mathbf{N}(t)| = \sqrt{\frac{1}{5} \cos^2 t + \frac{4}{5} \cos^2 t + \sin^2 t} = 1$;

$$\mathbf{T} \cdot \mathbf{N} = \left(\frac{1}{5} \cos t \sin t + \frac{4}{5} \cos t \sin t \right) - \sin t \cos t = 0$$

e.

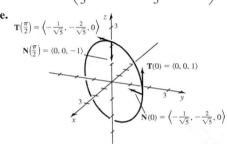

63. a. $\mathbf{a}(t) = 2\mathbf{N} + 0\mathbf{T} = 2\langle -\cos t, -\sin t \rangle$
b.

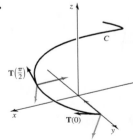

65. a. $a_T = \frac{2t}{\sqrt{t^2 + 1}}$ and $a_N = \frac{2}{\sqrt{t^2 + 1}}$

b.

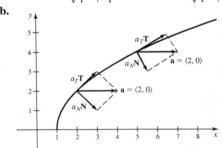

67. a. $a(x - x_0) + b(y - y_0) = 0$ **b.** $a(y - y_0) - b(x - x_0) = 0$
69. $\mathbf{B}(1) = \frac{\langle 3, -3, 1 \rangle}{\sqrt{19}}; \tau = \frac{3}{19}$

71. a. $\mathbf{T}(t) = \frac{1}{5}\langle 3 \cos t, -3 \sin t, 4 \rangle$ **b.** $\mathbf{N}(t) = \langle -\sin t, -\cos t, 0 \rangle$;

$\kappa = \frac{3}{25}$ **c.**

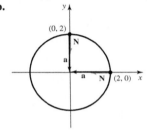

d. Yes **e.** $\mathbf{B}(t) = \frac{1}{5}\langle 4 \cos t, -4 \sin t, -3 \rangle$ **f.** See graph in part (c).

g. Check that $\mathbf{T}, \mathbf{N},$ and $\mathbf{B}$ have unit length and are mutually

orthogonal. **h.** $\tau = -\frac{4}{25}$ **73. a.** Let $\mathbf{r}(t) = \langle x(t), y(t), z(t) \rangle$

and show there are constants $a, b,$ and c such that $ax + by + cz = 1$, for all t in the interval. **b. B** is always normal to the plane and has

length 1. Therefore, $\frac{d\mathbf{B}}{ds} = \mathbf{0}$ and $\tau = 0$. **c.** $x + y - z = 4$

CHAPTER 12

Section 12.1 Exercises, pp. 870–873

1. A point and a normal vector   **3.** $x = -6, y = -4, z = 3$
5. z-axis; x-axis; y-axis   **7.** Intersection of the surface with a plane parallel to one of the coordinate planes   **9.** Ellipsoid
11. $x + y - z = 4$ **13.** $-x + 2y - 3z = 4$
15. $2x + y - 2z = -2$ **17.** $7x + 2y + z = 10$
19. $4x + 27y + 10z = 21$ **21.** Intercepts $x = 2, y = -3, z = 6$; $3x - 2y = 6, z = 0; -2y + z = 6, x = 0;$ and $3x + z = 6, y = 0$

23. Intercepts $x = 30, y = 10, z = -6; x + 3y = 30, z = 0;$
$x - 5z = 30, y = 0;$ and $3y - 5z = 30, x = 0$

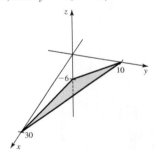

25. Orthogonal   **27.** Neither   **29.** Q and T are identical; $Q, R,$ and T are parallel; S is orthogonal to $Q, R,$ and T.
31. $-x + 2y - 4z = -17$ **33.** $4x + 3y - 2z = -5$
35. $x = t, y = 1 + 2t, z = -1 - 3t$
37. $x = \frac{7}{5} + 2t, y = \frac{9}{5} + t, z = -t$
39. a. x-axis   **41. a.** y-axis
b.

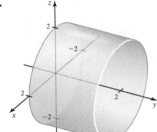

43. a. z-axis   **b.**

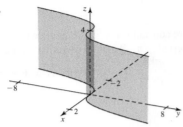

45. a. x-axis   **b.**

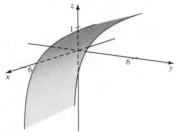

47. a. $x = \pm 1, y = \pm 2, z = \pm 3$ **b.** $x^2 + \dfrac{y^2}{4} = 1, x^2 + \dfrac{z^2}{9} = 1,$
$\dfrac{y^2}{4} + \dfrac{z^2}{9} = 1$ **c.**

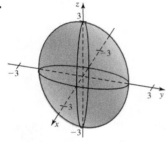

49. a. $x = \pm 3, y = \pm 1, z = \pm 6$ **b.** $\dfrac{x^2}{3} + 3y^2 = 3, \dfrac{x^2}{3} + \dfrac{z^2}{12} = 3,$
$3y^2 + \dfrac{z^2}{12} = 3$ **c.**

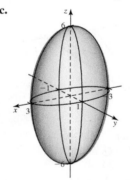

51. a. $x = y = z = 0$ **b.** $x = y^2, x = z^2$, origin
c.

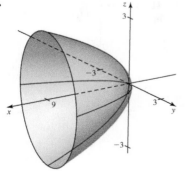

53. a. $x = y = z = 0$ **b.** Origin, $x - 9y^2 = 0, 9x - \dfrac{z^2}{4} = 0$
c.

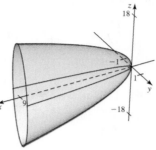

55. a. $x = \pm 5, y = \pm 3$, no z-intercept
b. $\dfrac{x^2}{25} + \dfrac{y^2}{9} = 1, \dfrac{x^2}{25} - z^2 = 1, \dfrac{y^2}{9} - z^2 = 1$

c.

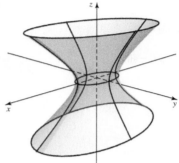

57. a. No x-intercept, $y = \pm 12, z = \pm \dfrac{1}{2}$ **b.** $-\dfrac{x^2}{4} + \dfrac{y^2}{16} = 9,$
$-\dfrac{x^2}{4} + 36z^2 = 9, \dfrac{y^2}{16} + 36z^2 = 9$

c.

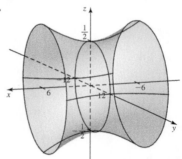

59. a. $x = y = z = 0$ **b.** $\dfrac{x^2}{9} - y^2 = 0, z = \dfrac{x^2}{9}, z = -y^2$

c.

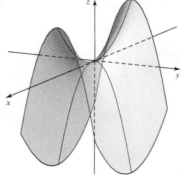

61. a. $x = y = z = 0$

b. $5x - \dfrac{y^2}{5} = 0, 5x + \dfrac{z^2}{20} = 0, -\dfrac{y^2}{5} + \dfrac{z^2}{20} = 0$

c.

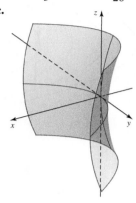

63. a. $x = y = z = 0$ **b.** Origin, $\dfrac{y^2}{4} = z^2$, $x^2 = z^2$

c.

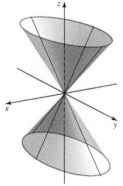

65. a. $x = y = z = 0$ **b.** $\dfrac{y^2}{18} = 2x^2, \dfrac{z^2}{32} = 2x^2$, origin

c.

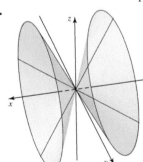

67. a. No x-intercept, $y = \pm 2$, no z-intercept   **b.** $-x^2 + \dfrac{y^2}{4} = 1$, no xz-trace, $\dfrac{y^2}{4} - \dfrac{z^2}{9} = 1$

c.

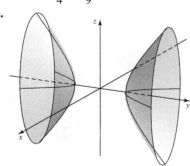

69. a. No x-intercept, $y = \pm\dfrac{\sqrt{3}}{3}$, no z-intercept

b. $-\dfrac{x^2}{3} + 3y^2 = 1$, no xz-trace, $3y^2 - \dfrac{z^2}{12} = 1$

c.

71. a. True   **b.** False   **c.** False   **d.** True   **e.** False   **f.** False
g. False   **73.** $\mathbf{r}(t) = \langle 2 + 2t, 1 - 4t, 3 + t \rangle$ **75.** $6x - 4y + z = d$
77. The planes intersect in the point $(3, 6, 0)$.   **79. a.** D   **b.** A
c. E   **d.** F   **e.** B   **f.** C   **81.** Hyperbolic paraboloid   **83.** Elliptic
paraboloid   **85.** Hyperboloid of one sheet   **87.** Hyperbolic cylinder
89. Hyperboloid of two sheets   **91.** $(3, 9, 27)$ and $(-5, 25, 75)$
93. $\left(\dfrac{6\sqrt{10}}{5}, \dfrac{2\sqrt{10}}{5}, \dfrac{3\sqrt{10}}{10} \right)$ and $\left(-\dfrac{6\sqrt{10}}{5}, -\dfrac{2\sqrt{10}}{5}, -\dfrac{3\sqrt{10}}{10} \right)$
95. $\theta = \cos^{-1}\left(-\dfrac{\sqrt{105}}{14} \right) \approx 2.392$ rad; $137°$ **97.** All except the
hyperbolic paraboloid   **99. a.**

b. Positive   **c.** $2x + y = 40$, line in the xy-plane   **101. a.** $z = cy$
b. $\theta = \tan^{-1} c$ **103. a.** The length of the orthogonal projection of
$\overrightarrow{PQ}$ onto the normal vector $\mathbf{n}$ is the magnitude of the scalar component
of $\overrightarrow{PQ}$ in the direction of $\mathbf{n}$, which is $\dfrac{|\overrightarrow{PQ} \cdot \mathbf{n}|}{|\mathbf{n}|}$.   **b.** $\dfrac{13}{\sqrt{14}}$

Section 12.2 Exercises, pp. 882–885

1. Independent: x and y; dependent: z
3. $D = \{(x, y): x \neq 0 \text{ and } y \neq 0\}$ **5.** Three   **7.** Circles   **9.** $n = 6$
11. $\mathbb{R}^2$ **13.** $\{(x, y): x^2 + y^2 \leq 25\}$ **15.** $D = \{(x, y): y \neq 0\}$
17. $D = \{(x, y): y < x^2\}$
19. $D = \{(x, y): xy \geq 0, (x, y) \neq (0, 0)\}$

21. Plane; domain $= \mathbb{R}^2$, range $= \mathbb{R}$

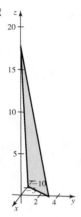

23. Hyperbolic paraboloid; domain $= \mathbb{R}^2$, range $= \mathbb{R}$

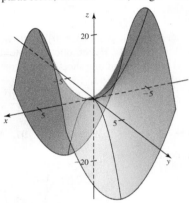

25. Lower part of a hyperboloid of two sheets; domain $= \mathbb{R}^2$, range $= (-\infty, -1]$

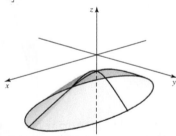

27. Upper half of a hyperboloid of one sheet; domain $= \{(x, y): x^2 + y^2 \geq 1\}$, range $= [0, \infty)$

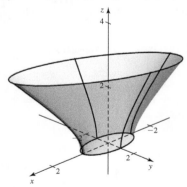

29. a. A   **b.** D   **c.** B   **d.** C   **31.**

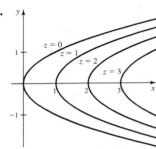

33.

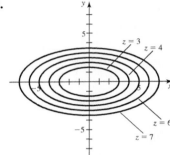

35.

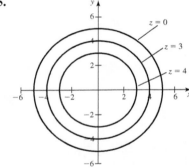

37.

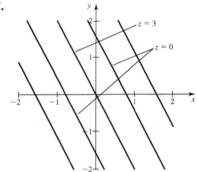

39. a.

b. $D = \{(r, h): r > 0, h > 0\}$ **c.** $h = 300/(\pi r^2)$

41. a.

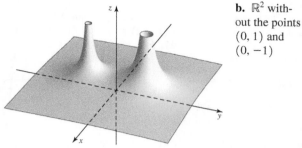

b. $\mathbb{R}^2$ without the points $(0, 1)$ and $(0, -1)$

c. $\varphi(2, 3)$ is greater. **d.**

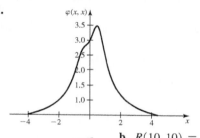

43. a.

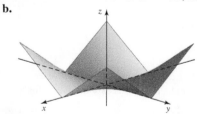

b. $R(10, 10) = 5$
c. $R(x, y) = R(y, x)$

45. a.

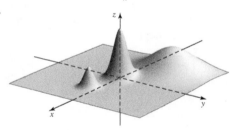

b. $(0, 0), (-5, 3), (4, -1)$
c. $f(0, 0) = 10.17, f(-5, 3) = 5.00, f(4, -1) = 4.00$
47. $D = \{(x, y, z): x \neq z\}$; all points not on the plane $x = z$
49. $D = \{(x, y, z): y \geq z\}$; all points on or below the plane $y = z$
51. $D = \{(x, y, z): x^2 \leq y\}$; all points on the side of the vertical cylinder $y = x^2$ that contains the positive y-axis **53. a.** False
b. False **c.** True **55. a.** $D = \mathbb{R}^2$, range $= [0, \infty)$
b.

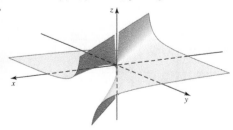

57. a. $D = \{(x, y): x \neq y\}$, range $= \mathbb{R}$
b.

59. a. $D = \{(x, y): y \neq x + \pi/2 + n\pi$ for any integer $n\}$, range $= [0, \infty)$ **b.**

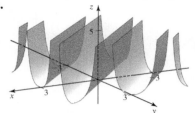

61. Peak at the origin **63.** Depression at $(1, 0)$ **65.** The level curves are $ax + by = d - cz_0$, where z_0 is a constant, which are lines with slope $-a/b$ if $b \neq 0$ or vertical lines if $b = 0$.
67. $z = x^2 + y^2 - C$; paraboloids with vertices at $(0, 0, -C)$
69. $x^2 + 2z^2 = C$; elliptic cylinders parallel to the y-axis
71. a. $P = \dfrac{20{,}000r}{(1 + r)^{240} - 1}$ **b.** $P = \dfrac{Br}{(1 + r)^{240} - 1}$, with

$B = 5000, 10{,}000, 15{,}000, 25{,}000$

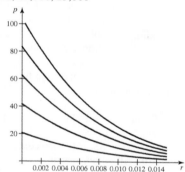

73. a.

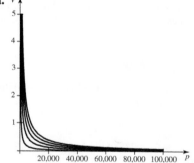

b.

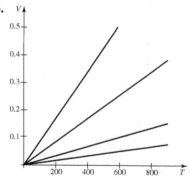

c.

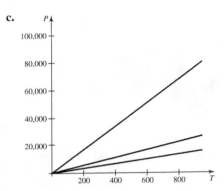

75. $D = \{(x, y): x - 1 \le y \le x + 1\}$
77. $D = \{(x, y, z): (x \le z \text{ and } y \ge -z) \text{ or } (x \ge z \text{ and } y \le -z)\}$

Section 12.3 Exercises, pp. 892–894

1. The values of $f(x, y)$ are arbitrarily close to L for all (x, y) sufficiently close to (a, b).   **3.** Because polynomials of n variables are continuous on all of $\mathbb{R}^n$, limits of polynomials can be evaluated with direct substitution.   **5.** If the function approaches different values along different paths, the limit does not exist.   **7.** f must be defined, the limit must exist, and the limit must equal the function value.
9. At any point where the denominator is nonzero   **11.** 101   **13.** 27
15. $1/(2\pi)$ **17.** 2   **19.** 6   **21.** -1 **23.** 2   **25.** $1/(2\sqrt{2}) = \sqrt{2}/4$
27. $L = 1$ along $y = 0$, and $L = -1$ along $x = 0$ **29.** $L = 1$ along $x = 0$, and $L = -2$ along $y = 0$ **31.** $L = 2$ along $y = x$, and $L = 0$ along $y = -x$ **33.** $\mathbb{R}^2$ **35.** All points except $(0, 0)$
37. $\{(x, y): x \ne 0\}$ **39.** All points except $(0, 0)$ **41.** $\mathbb{R}^2$
43. $\mathbb{R}^2$ **45.** $\mathbb{R}^2$ **47.** All points except $(0, 0)$ **49.** $\mathbb{R}^2$ **51.** $\mathbb{R}^2$
53. 6   **55.** -1 **57.** 2   **59. a.** False   **b.** False   **c.** True   **d.** False
61. $\frac{1}{2}$ **63.** 0   **65.** Does not exist   **67.** $\frac{1}{4}$ **69.** 0   **71.** 1   **73.** $b = 1$
77. 1   **79.** 1   **81.** 0

Section 12.4 Exercises, pp. 904–907

1. $f_x(a, b)$ is the slope of the surface in the direction parallel to the positive x-axis, $f_y(a, b)$ is the slope of the surface in the direction parallel to the positive y-axis, both taken at (a, b).
3. $f_x(x, y) = \cos xy - xy \sin xy; f_y(x, y) = -x^2 \sin xy$
5. Think of x and y as being fixed, and take the derivative with respect to the variable z.   **7.** $f_x(x, y) = 5y; f_y(x, y) = 5x$
9. $f_x(x, y) = \dfrac{1}{y}; f_y(x, y) = -\dfrac{x}{y^2}$ **11.** $f_x(x, y) = 6x; f_y(x, y) = 12y^2$
13. $f_x(x, y) = 6xy; f_y(x, y) = 3x^2$ **15.** $f_x(x, y) = e^y; f_y(x, y) = xe^y$
17. $g_x(x, y) = -2y \sin 2xy; g_y(x, y) = -2x \sin 2xy$
19. $f_x(x, y) = 2xye^{x^2y}; f_y(x, y) = x^2e^{x^2y}$ **21.** $f_w(w, z) = \dfrac{z^2 - w^2}{(w^2 + z^2)^2}$;
$f_z(w, z) = -\dfrac{2wz}{(w^2 + z^2)^2}$ **23.** $s_y(y, z) = z^3 \sec^2 yz$;
$s_z(y, z) = 2z \tan yz + yz^2 \sec^2 yz$ **25.** $G_s(s, t) = \dfrac{\sqrt{st}(t - s)}{2s(s + t)^2}$;
$G_t(s, t) = \dfrac{\sqrt{st}(s - t)}{2t(s + t)^2}$ **27.** $f_x(x, y) = 2yx^{2y-1}; f_y(x, y) = 2x^{2y} \ln x$
29. $h_{xx}(x, y) = 6x; h_{xy}(x, y) = 2y; h_{yx}(x, y) = 2y; h_{yy}(x, y) = 2x$
31. $f_{xx}(x, y) = 2y^3; f_{xy}(x, y) = f_{yx}(x, y) = 6xy^2; f_{yy}(x, y) = 6x^2y$
33. $f_{xx}(x, y) = -16y^3 \sin 4x; f_{xy}(x, y) = 12y^2 \cos 4x$;
$f_{yx}(x, y) = 12y^2 \cos 4x; f_{yy}(x, y) = 6y \sin 4x$
35. $p_{uu}(u, v) = \dfrac{-2u^2 + 2v^2 + 8}{(u^2 + v^2 + 4)^2}; p_{uv}(u, v) = -\dfrac{4uv}{(u^2 + v^2 + 4)^2}$;
$p_{vu}(u, v) = -\dfrac{4uv}{(u^2 + v^2 + 4)^2}; p_{vv}(u, v) = \dfrac{2u^2 - 2v^2 + 8}{(u^2 + v^2 + 4)^2}$

37. $F_{rr}(r, s) = 0; F_{rs}(r, s) = e^s; F_{sr}(r, s) = e^s; F_{ss}(r, s) = re^s$
39. $f_{xy} = 0 = f_{yx}$ **41.** $f_{xy} = -(xy \cos xy + \sin xy) = f_{yx}$
43. $f_{xy} = e^{x+y} = f_{yx}$ **45.** $f_x(x, y, z) = y + z; f_y(x, y, z) = x + z; f_z(x, y, z) = x + y$ **47.** $h_x(x, y, z) = h_y(x, y, z) = h_z(x, y, z) = -\sin(x + y + z)$
49. $F_u(u, v, w) = \dfrac{1}{v + w}; F_v(u, v, w) = F_w(u, v, w) = -\dfrac{u}{(v + w)^2}$
51. $f_w(w, x, y, z) = 2wxy^2; f_x(w, x, y, z) = w^2y^2 + y^3z^2$;
$f_y(w, x, y, z) = 2w^2xy + 3xy^2z^2; f_z(w, x, y, z) = 2xy^3z$
53. $h_w(w, x, y, z) = \dfrac{z}{xy}; h_x(w, x, y, z) = -\dfrac{wz}{x^2y}$;
$h_y(w, x, y, z) = -\dfrac{wz}{xy^2}; h_z(w, x, y, z) = \dfrac{w}{xy}$ **55. a.** $\dfrac{\partial V}{\partial P} = -\dfrac{kT}{P^2}$;
volume decreases with pressure at fixed temperature   **b.** $\dfrac{\partial V}{\partial T} = \dfrac{k}{P}$;
volume increases with temperature at fixed pressure

c.

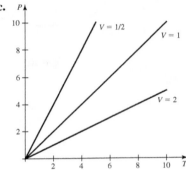

57. a. No   **b.** No.   **c.** $f_x(0, 0) = f_y(0, 0) = 0$ **d.** f_x and f_y are not continuous at $(0, 0)$.   **59. a.** False   **b.** False   **c.** True
61. 1.41   **63.** 1.55 (answer will vary)
65. $f_x(x, y) = -\dfrac{2x}{1 + (x^2 + y^2)^2}; f_y(x, y) = -\dfrac{2y}{1 + (x^2 + y^2)^2}$
67. $h_x(x, y, z) = z(1 + x + 2y)^{z-1}; h_y(x, y, z) = 2z(1 + x + 2y)^{z-1}$;
$h_z(x, y, z) = (1 + x + 2y)^z \ln(1 + x + 2y)$
69. a. $z_x(x, y) = \dfrac{1}{y^2}; z_y(x, y) = -\dfrac{2x}{y^3}$

b.

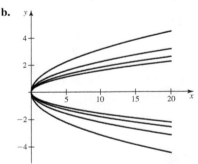

c. z increases as x increases.   **d.** z increases as y increases when $y < 0$, z is undefined for $y = 0$, and z decreases as y increases for $y > 0$.   **71. a.** $\dfrac{\partial c}{\partial a} = \dfrac{2a - b}{2\sqrt{a^2 + b^2 - ab}}; \dfrac{\partial c}{\partial b} = \dfrac{2b - a}{2\sqrt{a^2 + b^2 - ab}}$;
b. $\dfrac{\partial c}{\partial a} = \dfrac{2a - b}{2c}; \dfrac{\partial c}{\partial b} = \dfrac{2b - a}{2c}$ **c.** $a > \frac{1}{2}b$
73. a. $\varphi_x(x, y) = -\dfrac{2x}{(x^2 + (y - 1)^2)^{3/2}} - \dfrac{x}{(x^2 + (y + 1)^2)^{3/2}}$;
$\varphi_y(x, y) = -\dfrac{2(y - 1)}{(x^2 + (y - 1)^2)^{3/2}} - \dfrac{y + 1}{(x^2 + (y + 1)^2)^{3/2}}$

b. They both approach zero.   **c.** $\varphi_x(0, y) = 0$

d. $\varphi_y(x, 0) = \dfrac{1}{(x^2 + 1)^{3/2}}$

75. a. $\dfrac{\partial R}{\partial R_1} = \dfrac{R_2^2}{(R_1 + R_2)^2}; \dfrac{\partial R}{\partial R_2} = \dfrac{R_1^2}{(R_1 + R_2)^2}$

b. $\dfrac{\partial R}{\partial R_1} = \dfrac{R^2}{R_1^2}; \dfrac{\partial R}{\partial R_2} = \dfrac{R^2}{R_2^2}$ **c.** Increase   **d.** Decrease

77. $\dfrac{\partial^2 u}{\partial t^2} = -4c^2 \cos(2(x + ct)) = c^2 \dfrac{\partial^2 u}{\partial x^2}$

79. $\dfrac{\partial^2 u}{\partial t^2} = c^2 A f''(x + ct) + c^2 B g''(x - ct) = c^2 \dfrac{\partial^2 u}{\partial x^2}$

81. $u_{xx} = 6x \quad u_{yy} = -6x$

83. $u_{xx} = \dfrac{2(x - 1)y}{((x - 1)^2 + y^2)^2} - \dfrac{2(x + 1)y}{((x + 1)^2 + y^2)^2};$

$u_{yy} = -\dfrac{2(x - 1)y}{((x - 1)^2 + y^2)^2} + \dfrac{2(x + 1)y}{((x + 1)^2 + y^2)^2}$

85. $u_t = -16e^{-4t} \cos 2x = u_{xx}$ **87.** $u_t = -a^2 A e^{-a^2 t} \cos ax = u_{xx}$

89. $\varepsilon_1 = \Delta y, \varepsilon_2 = 0$ or $\varepsilon_1 = 0, \varepsilon_2 = \Delta x$ **91. a.** f is continuous at $(0, 0)$.   **b.** f is not differentiable at $(0, 0)$.   **c.** $f_x(0, 0) = f_y(0, 0) = 0$ **d.** f_x and f_y are not continuous at $(0, 0)$.   **e.** Theorem 12.5 does not apply because f_x and f_y are not continuous at $(0, 0)$; Theorem 12.6 does not apply because f is not differentiable at $(0, 0)$.   **93. a.** $f_x(x, y) = -h(x); f_y(x, y) = h(y)$ **b.** $f_x(x, y) = yh(xy); f_y(x, y) = xh(xy)$

Section 12.5 Exercises, pp. 913–916

1. One dependent, two intermediate, and one independent variable
3. Multiply each of the partial derivatives of w by the t-derivative of the corresponding function and add all these expressions.
5.

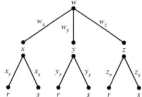

7. $4t^3 + 3t^2$ **9.** $z'(t) = 2t \sin 4t^3 + 12t^4 \cos 4t^3$
11. $w'(t) = -\sin t \sin 3t^4 + 12t^3 \cos t \cos 3t^4$
13. $w'(t) = 20t^4 \sin(t + 1) + 4t^5 \cos(t + 1)$
15. $U'(t) = \dfrac{1 + 2t + 3t^2}{t + t^2 + t^3}$
17. a. $V'(t) = 2\pi r(t)h(t)r'(t) + \pi r(t)^2 h'(t)$ **b.** $V'(t) = 0$
c. The volume remains constant.   **19.** $z_s = 2(s - t) \sin t^2;$
$z_t = 2(s - t)(t(s - t) \cos t^2 - \sin t^2)$
21. $z_s = 2s - 3s^2 - 2st + t^2; z_t = -s^2 - 2t + 2st + 3t^2$
23. $z_s = (t + 1)e^{st+s+t}; z_t = (s + 1)e^{st+s+t}$
25. $w_s = -\dfrac{2t(t + 1)}{(st + s - t)^2}; w_t = \dfrac{2s}{(st + s - t)^2}$
27.

$$\frac{dw}{dt} = \frac{dw}{dz}\left(\frac{\partial z}{\partial x}\frac{dx}{dt} + \frac{\partial z}{\partial y}\frac{dy}{dt}\right)$$

29.

$$\frac{\partial u}{\partial z} = \frac{du}{dv}\left(\frac{\partial v}{\partial w}\frac{dw}{dz} + \frac{\partial v}{\partial x}\frac{\partial x}{\partial z} + \frac{\partial v}{\partial y}\frac{\partial y}{\partial z}\right)$$

31. $\dfrac{dy}{dx} = \dfrac{x}{2y}$ **33.** $\dfrac{dy}{dx} = -\dfrac{y}{x}$ **35.** $\dfrac{dy}{dx} = -\dfrac{x + y}{2y^3 + x}$

37. $\dfrac{\partial s}{\partial x} = \dfrac{2x}{\sqrt{x^2 + y^2}}; \dfrac{\partial s}{\partial y} = \dfrac{2y}{\sqrt{x^2 + y^2}}$ **39. a.** False   **b.** False

41. $z'(t) = -\dfrac{2t + 2}{(t + 2t)} - \dfrac{3t^2}{(t^3 - 2)}$ **43.** $w'(t) = 0$

45. $\dfrac{\partial z}{\partial x} = -\dfrac{z^2}{x^2}$ **47. a.** $w'(t) = af_x + bf_y + cf_z$

b. $w'(t) = ayz + bxz + cxy = 3abct^2$

c. $w'(t) = \sqrt{a^2 + b^2 + c^2}\,\dfrac{t}{|t|}$

d. $w''(t) = a^2 f_{xx} + b^2 f_{yy} + c^2 f_{zz} + 2abf_{xy} + 2acf_{xz} + 2bcf_{yz}$

49. $\dfrac{\partial z}{\partial x} = -\dfrac{y + z}{x + y}; \dfrac{\partial z}{\partial y} = -\dfrac{x + z}{x + y}$ **51.** $\dfrac{\partial z}{\partial x} = -\dfrac{yz + 1}{xy - 1}; \dfrac{\partial z}{\partial y} = -\dfrac{xz + 1}{xy - 1}$

53. a. $z'(t) = -2x \sin t + 8y \cos t = 3 \sin 2t$ **b.** $0 < t < \pi/2$ and $\pi < t < 3\pi/2$ **55. a.** $z'(t) = \dfrac{(x + y)e^{-t}}{\sqrt{1 - x^2 - y^2}} = \dfrac{2e^{-2t}}{\sqrt{1 - 2e^{-2t}}}$

b. All $t \geq \tfrac{1}{2}\ln 2$ **57.** $E'(t) = mx'x'' + my'y'' + mgy' = 0$
59. a. The volume increases.   **b.** The volume decreases.

61. a. $\dfrac{\partial P}{\partial V} = -\dfrac{P}{V}; \dfrac{\partial T}{\partial P} = \dfrac{V}{k}; \dfrac{\partial V}{\partial T} = \dfrac{k}{P}$ **b.** Follows directly from part (a)

63. a. $w'(t) = \dfrac{2t(t^2 + 1)\cos 2t - (t^2 - 1)\sin 2t}{2(t^2 + 1)^2}$

b. Max value of $t \approx 0.838$, $(x, y, z) \approx (0.669, 0.743, 0.838)$

65. a. $z_x = \dfrac{x}{r}z_r - \dfrac{y}{r^2}z_\theta; z_y = \dfrac{y}{r}z_r + \dfrac{x}{r^2}z_\theta$

b. $z_{xx} = \dfrac{x^2}{r^2}z_{rr} + \dfrac{y^2}{r^4}z_{\theta\theta} - \dfrac{2xy}{r^3}z_{r\theta} + \dfrac{y^2}{r^3}z_r + \dfrac{2xy}{r^4}z_\theta$

c. $z_{yy} = \dfrac{y^2}{r^2}z_{rr} + \dfrac{x^2}{r^4}z_{\theta\theta} + \dfrac{2xy}{r^3}z_{r\theta} + \dfrac{x^2}{r^3}z_r - \dfrac{2xy}{r^4}z_\theta$

d. Add the results from (b) and (c).   **67. a.** $\left(\dfrac{\partial z}{\partial x}\right)_y = -\dfrac{F_x}{F_z}$

b. $\left(\dfrac{\partial y}{\partial z}\right)_x = -\dfrac{F_z}{F_y}; \left(\dfrac{\partial x}{\partial y}\right)_z = -\dfrac{F_y}{F_x}$ **c.** Follows from (a) and (b) by multiplication   **d.** $\left(\dfrac{\partial w}{\partial x}\right)_{y,z}\left(\dfrac{\partial z}{\partial w}\right)_{x,y}\left(\dfrac{\partial y}{\partial z}\right)_{x,w}\left(\dfrac{\partial x}{\partial y}\right)_{z,w} = 1$

69. a. $\left(\dfrac{\partial w}{\partial x}\right)_y = f_x + f_z\dfrac{dz}{dx} = 18$ **b.** $\left(\dfrac{\partial w}{\partial x}\right)_z = f_x + f_y\dfrac{dy}{dx} = 8$

d. $\left(\dfrac{\partial w}{\partial y}\right)_x = -5; \left(\dfrac{\partial w}{\partial y}\right)_z = 4; \left(\dfrac{\partial w}{\partial z}\right)_x = \dfrac{5}{2}; \left(\dfrac{\partial w}{\partial z}\right)_y = \dfrac{9}{2}$

Section 12.6 Exercises, pp. 925–928

1. Form the dot product between the unit direction vector **u** and the gradient of the function.   **3.** Direction of steepest ascent   **5.** The gradient is orthogonal to the level curves of f.

7. a.

	$(a,b) = (2,0)$	$(a,b) = (0,2)$	$(a,b) = (1,1)$
$\mathbf{u} = \langle \frac{\sqrt{2}}{2}, \frac{\sqrt{2}}{2} \rangle$	$-\sqrt{2}$	$-2\sqrt{2}$	$-3\sqrt{2}/2$
$\mathbf{v} = \langle -\frac{\sqrt{2}}{2}, \frac{\sqrt{2}}{2} \rangle$	$\sqrt{2}$	$-2\sqrt{2}$	$-\sqrt{2}/2$
$\mathbf{w} = \langle -\frac{\sqrt{2}}{2}, -\frac{\sqrt{2}}{2} \rangle$	$\sqrt{2}$	$2\sqrt{2}$	$3\sqrt{2}/2$

b. The function is decreasing at $(2, 0)$ in the direction of $\mathbf{u}$ and increasing at $(2, 0)$ in the directions of $\mathbf{v}$ and $\mathbf{w}$.
9. $\nabla f(x, y) = \langle 6x, -10y \rangle$, $\nabla f(2, -1) = \langle 12, 10 \rangle$
11. $\nabla g(x, y) = \langle 2(x - 4xy - 4y^2), -4x(x + 4y) \rangle$,
$\nabla g(-1, 2) = \langle -18, 28 \rangle$ **13.** $\nabla f(x, y) = e^{2xy} \langle 1 + 2xy, 2x^2 \rangle$,
$\nabla f(1, 0) = \langle 1, 2 \rangle$ **15.** $\nabla F(x, y) = -2e^{-x^2 - 2y^2} \langle x, 2y \rangle$,
$\nabla F(-1, 2) = 2e^{-9} \langle 1, -4 \rangle$ **17.** -6 **19.** $\frac{27}{2} - 6\sqrt{3}$

21. $-\dfrac{2}{\sqrt{5}}$ **23.** -2 **25.** 0 **27. a.** Direction of steepest

ascent: $\dfrac{1}{\sqrt{65}} \langle 1, 8 \rangle$; direction of steepest descent: $-\dfrac{1}{\sqrt{65}} \langle 1, 8 \rangle$

b. $\langle -8, 1 \rangle$ **29. a.** Direction of steepest ascent: $\dfrac{1}{\sqrt{5}} \langle -2, 1 \rangle$;

direction of steepest descent: $\dfrac{1}{\sqrt{5}} \langle 2, -1 \rangle$ **b.** $\langle 1, 2 \rangle$

31. a. Direction of steepest ascent: $\dfrac{1}{\sqrt{2}} \langle 1, -1 \rangle$;

direction of steepest descent: $\dfrac{1}{\sqrt{2}} \langle -1, 1 \rangle$ **b.** $\langle 1, 1 \rangle$

33. a. $\nabla f(3, 2) = -12\mathbf{i} - 12\mathbf{j}$ **b.** Direction of max increase,
$\theta = \dfrac{5\pi}{4}$; direction of max decrease, $\theta = \dfrac{\pi}{4}$; directions of no change,
$\theta = \dfrac{3\pi}{4}, \dfrac{7\pi}{4}$ **c.** $g(\theta) = -12 \cos \theta - 12 \sin \theta$ **d.** $\theta = \frac{5\pi}{4}$,
$g(\frac{5\pi}{4}) = 12\sqrt{2}$ **e.** $\nabla f(3, 2) = 12\sqrt{2} \langle \cos \frac{5\pi}{4}, \sin \frac{5\pi}{4} \rangle$,
$|\nabla f(3, 2)| = 12\sqrt{2}$ **35. a.** $\nabla f(\sqrt{3}, 1) = \frac{\sqrt{6}}{6} \langle \sqrt{3}, 1 \rangle$
b. Direction of max increase, $\theta = \frac{\pi}{6}$; direction of max
decrease, $\theta = \frac{7\pi}{6}$; directions of no change, $\theta = \frac{2\pi}{3}, \frac{5\pi}{3}$

c. $g(\theta) = \frac{\sqrt{2}}{2} \cos \theta + \frac{\sqrt{6}}{6} \sin \theta$ **d.** $\theta = \frac{\pi}{6}, g(\frac{\pi}{6}) = \frac{\sqrt{6}}{3}$
e. $\nabla f(\sqrt{3}, 1) = \frac{\sqrt{6}}{3} \langle \cos \frac{\pi}{6}, \sin \frac{\pi}{6} \rangle$, $|\nabla f(\sqrt{3}, 1)| = \frac{\sqrt{6}}{3}$
37. a. $\nabla F(-1, 0) = \frac{2}{e}\mathbf{i}$ **b.** Direction of max increase, $\theta = 0$;
direction of max decrease, $\theta = \pi$; directions of no change,
$\theta = \pm\frac{\pi}{2}$ **c.** $g(\theta) = \frac{2}{e} \cos \theta$ **d.** $\theta = 0, g(0) = \frac{2}{e}$
e. $\nabla F(-1, 0) = \frac{2}{e} \langle \cos 0, \sin 0 \rangle$, $|\nabla F(-1, 0)| = \frac{2}{e}$
39.

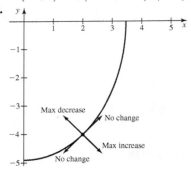

41.

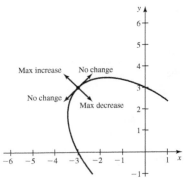

43. $y' = 0$ **45.** Vertical tangent   **47.** $y' = -2/\sqrt{3}$ **49.** Vertical
tangent   **51. a.** $\nabla f = \langle 1, 0 \rangle$ **b.** $x = 4 - t, y = 4, t \geq 0$
53. a. $\nabla f = \langle -2x, -4y \rangle$ **b.** $y = x^2, x \geq 1$
55. a. $\nabla f(x, y, z) = 2x\mathbf{i} + 4y\mathbf{j} + 8z\mathbf{k}, \nabla f(1, 0, 4) = 2\mathbf{i} + 32\mathbf{k}$

b. $\dfrac{1}{\sqrt{257}}(\mathbf{i} + 16\mathbf{k})$ **c.** $2\sqrt{257}$ **d.** $17\sqrt{2}$ **57. a.** $\nabla f(x, y, z) = $
$4yz\mathbf{i} + 4xz\mathbf{j} + 4xy\mathbf{k}, \nabla f(1, -1, -1) = 4\mathbf{i} - 4\mathbf{j} - 4\mathbf{k}$

b. $\dfrac{1}{\sqrt{3}}(\mathbf{i} - \mathbf{j} - \mathbf{k})$ **c.** $4\sqrt{3}$ **d.** $\dfrac{4}{\sqrt{3}}$

59. a. $\nabla f(x, y, z) = \cos (x + 2y - z)(\mathbf{i} + 2\mathbf{j} - \mathbf{k})$,
$\nabla f\left(\dfrac{\pi}{6}, \dfrac{\pi}{6}, -\dfrac{\pi}{6}\right) = -\dfrac{1}{2}\mathbf{i} - \mathbf{j} + \dfrac{1}{2}\mathbf{k}$ **b.** $\dfrac{1}{\sqrt{6}}(-\mathbf{i} - 2\mathbf{j} + \mathbf{k})$

c. $\sqrt{6}/2$ **d.** $-\dfrac{1}{2}$

61. a. $\nabla f(x, y, z) = \dfrac{2}{1 + x^2 + y^2 + z^2}(x\mathbf{i} + y\mathbf{j} + z\mathbf{k})$,
$\nabla f(1, 1, -1) = \dfrac{1}{2}\mathbf{i} + \dfrac{1}{2}\mathbf{j} - \dfrac{1}{2}\mathbf{k}$ **b.** $\dfrac{1}{\sqrt{3}}(\mathbf{i} + \mathbf{j} - \mathbf{k})$ **c.** $\dfrac{\sqrt{3}}{2}$

d. $\dfrac{5}{6}$ **63. a.** False   **b.** False   **c.** False   **d.** True   **65.** $\pm\dfrac{1}{\sqrt{5}}(\mathbf{i} - 2\mathbf{j})$

67. $\pm\dfrac{1}{\sqrt{2}}(\mathbf{i} + \mathbf{j})$ **69.** $x = x_0 + at, y = y_0 + bt$

71. a. $\nabla f(x, y, z) = \langle 2x, 2y, 2z \rangle, \nabla f(1, 1, 1) = \langle 2, 2, 2 \rangle$
b. $x + y + z = 3$ **73. a.** $\nabla f(x, y, z) = e^{x+y-z} \langle 1, 1, -1 \rangle$,
$\nabla f(1, 1, 2) = \langle 1, 1, -1 \rangle$ **b.** $x + y - z = 0$
75. a.

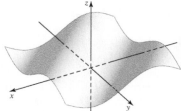

b. $\mathbf{v} = \pm \langle 1, 1 \rangle$ **c.** $\mathbf{v} = \pm \langle 1, -1 \rangle$
79. $\langle u, v \rangle = \langle \pi \cos \pi x \sin 2\pi y, 2\pi \sin \pi x \cos 2\pi y \rangle$

83. $\nabla f(x, y) = \dfrac{1}{(x^2 + y^2)^2} \langle y^2 - x^2 - 2xy, x^2 - y^2 - 2xy \rangle$

85. $\nabla f(x, y, z) = -\dfrac{1}{\sqrt{25 - x^2 - y^2 - z^2}} \langle x, y, z \rangle$

87. $\nabla f(x, y, z) = \dfrac{(y + xz) \langle 1, z, y \rangle - (x + yz) \langle z, 1, x \rangle}{(y + xz)^2}$

$= \dfrac{1}{(y + xz)^2} \langle y(1 - z^2), x(z^2 - 1), y^2 - x^2 \rangle$

Section 12.7 Exercises, pp. 935–938

1. The gradient of f is a multiple of $\mathbf{n}$.
3. $F_x(a, b, c)(x - a) + F_y(a, b, c)(y - b) + F_z(a, b, c)(z - c) = 0$
5. Multiply the change in x by $f_x(a, b)$ and the change in y by $f_y(a, b)$, and add both terms to f.   **7.** $dz = f_x(a, b)\, dx + f_y(a, b)\, dy$
9. $2x + y + z = 4; 4x + y + z = 7$
11. $x + y + z = 6; 3x + 4y + z = 12$
13. $x + \dfrac{1}{2}y + \sqrt{3}z = 2 + \dfrac{\sqrt{3}\pi}{6}$ and $\dfrac{1}{2}x + y + \sqrt{3}z = \dfrac{5\sqrt{3}\pi}{6} - 2$
15. $\frac{1}{2}x + \frac{2}{3}y + 2\sqrt{3}z = -2$ and $x - 2y + 2\sqrt{14}z = 2$
17. $z = -8x - 4y + 16$ and $z = 4x + 2y + 7$
19. $z = y + 1$ and $z = x + 1$ **21.** $z = 8x - 4y - 4$ and $z = -x - y - 1$ **23.** $z = \frac{7}{25}x - \frac{1}{25}y - \frac{2}{5}$ and $z = -\frac{7}{25}x + \frac{1}{25}y + \frac{6}{5}$
25. a. $L(x, y) = 4x + y - 6$ **b.** $L(2.1, 2.99) = 5.39$
27. a. $L(x, y) = -6x - 4y + 7$ **b.** $L(3.1, -1.04) = -7.44$
29. a. $L(x, y) = x + y$ **b.** $L(0.1, -0.2) = -0.1$
31. $dz = -6dx - 5dy = -0.1$ **33.** $dz = dx + dy = 0.05$
35. a. The surface area decreases.   **b.** Impossible to say
c. $dS \approx 53.3$ **d.** $dS = 33.95$ **e.** $RdR = rdr$ **37.** $\dfrac{dA}{A} = 3.5\%$
39. $dw = (y^2 + 2xz)\, dx + (2xy + z^2)\, dy + (x^2 + 2yz)\, dz$
41. $dw = \dfrac{dx}{y + z} - \dfrac{u + x}{(y + z)^2}\, dy - \dfrac{u + x}{(y + z)^2}\, dz + \dfrac{du}{y + z}$
43. a. $dc = 0.035$ **b.** When $\theta = \dfrac{\pi}{20}$ **45. a.** True   **b.** True
c. False   **47.** $z = \dfrac{1}{2}x + \dfrac{1}{2}y + \dfrac{\pi}{4} - 1$
49. $\dfrac{1}{6}(x - \pi) + \dfrac{\pi}{6}(y - 1) + \pi\left(z - \dfrac{1}{6}\right) = 0$ **51.** $(1, -1, 1)$
and $(1, -1, -1)$ **53.** Points with $x = 0, \pm\dfrac{\pi}{2}, \pm\pi$ and $y = \pm\dfrac{\pi}{2}$, or
points with $x = \pm\dfrac{\pi}{4}, \pm\dfrac{3\pi}{4}$ and $y = 0, \pm\pi$ **55. a.** $dS = 0.749$
b. More sensitive to changes in r **57. a.** $dA = \dfrac{2}{1225} = 0.00163$
b. No. The batting average increases more if he gets a hit than it would decrease if he fails to get a hit.   **c.** Yes. The answer depends on whether A is less than 0.500 or greater than 0.500.
59. a. $dV = \dfrac{21}{5000} = 0.0042$ **b.** $\dfrac{dV}{V} = -4\%$ **c.** $2p\%$
61. a. $f_r = n(1 - r)^{n-1}, f_n = -(1 - r)^n \ln(1 - r)$
b. $\Delta P \approx 0.027$ **c.** $\Delta P \approx 2 \times 10^{-20}$ **63.** $dR = 7/540 \approx 0.013\Omega$
65. a. Apply the Chain Rule.   **b.** Follows directly from (a)
c. $d(\ln(xy)) = \dfrac{dx}{x} + \dfrac{dy}{y}$ **d.** $d(\ln(x/y)) = \dfrac{dx}{x} - \dfrac{dy}{y}$
e. $\dfrac{df}{f} = \dfrac{dx_1}{x_1} + \dfrac{dx_2}{x_2} + \cdots + \dfrac{dx_n}{x_n}$

Section 12.8 Exercises, pp. 948–951

1. It is locally the highest point on the surface; you cannot get to a higher point in any direction.   **3.** The partial derivatives are both zero or do not exist.   **5.** The discriminant is a determinant; it is defined as $D(a, b) = f_{xx}(a, b)f_{yy}(a, b) - f_{xy}^2(a, b)$.   **7.** f has an absolute minimum value on R at (a, b) if $f(a, b) \leq f(x, y)$ for all (x, y) in R
9. $(0, 0)$ **11.** $(\frac{2}{3}, 4)$ **13.** $(0, 0), (2, 2)$, and $(-2, -2)$
15. $(0, 2), (\pm 1, 2)$ **17.** $(-3, 0)$ **19.** Local min at $(0, 0)$
21. Saddle point at $(0, 0)$ **23.** Saddle point at $(0, 0)$; local min at $(1, 1)$ and at $(-1, -1)$ **25.** Local min at $(2, 0)$ **27.** Saddle point at $(0, 0)$; local max at $\left(\dfrac{1}{\sqrt{2}}, \dfrac{1}{\sqrt{2}}\right)$ and $\left(-\dfrac{1}{\sqrt{2}}, -\dfrac{1}{\sqrt{2}}\right)$; local min at

$\left(\dfrac{1}{\sqrt{2}}, -\dfrac{1}{\sqrt{2}}\right)$ and $\left(-\dfrac{1}{\sqrt{2}}, \dfrac{1}{\sqrt{2}}\right)$ **29.** Local min: $(-1, 0)$; local max: $(1, 0)$ **31.** Saddle point: $(0, 1)$; local min: $(\pm 2, 0)$ **33.** Saddle point at $(0, 0)$ **35.** Height $= 32$ in, base is 16 in $\times$ 16 in; volume is 8192 in^3 **37.** 2 m $\times$ 2 m $\times$ 1 m   **39.** Critical point at $(0, 0), D(0, 0) = 0$, absolute min   **41.** Critical points along the x- and y-axes, all absolute min   **43.** Absolute min: $0 = f(0, 1)$; absolute max: $9 = f(0, -2)$ **45.** Absolute min: $4 = f(0, 0)$; absolute max: $7 = f(\pm 1, \pm 1)$ **47.** Absolute min: $0 = f(1, 0)$; absolute max: $3 = f(1, 1) = f(1, -1)$ **49.** Absolute min: $1 = f(1, -2) = f(1, 0)$; absolute max: $4 = f(1, -1)$ **51.** Absolute min: $0 = f(0, 0)$; absolute max: $\dfrac{7}{8} = f\left(\dfrac{1}{\sqrt{2}}, \sqrt{2}\right)$ **53.** Absolute min: $-4 = f(0, 0)$; no absolute max on R **55.** Absolute max: $2 = f(0, 0)$; no absolute min on R
57. $P\left(-\dfrac{5}{3}, \dfrac{4}{3}, \dfrac{13}{3}\right)$ **59.** $\left(\dfrac{1}{2}, \dfrac{1}{4}\right); \left(\dfrac{7}{8}, -\dfrac{1}{8}\right)$ **61. a.** True   **b.** False
c. True   **d.** True   **63.** Local min at $(0.3, -0.3)$; saddle point at $(0, 0)$ **65.** $P(\frac{4}{3}, \frac{2}{3}, \frac{4}{3})$ **67. a.–d.** $x = y = z = \dfrac{200}{3}$
69. a. $P\left(1, \frac{1}{3}\right)$ **b.** $P\left(\frac{1}{3}(x_1 + x_2 + x_3), \frac{1}{3}(y_1 + y_2 + y_3)\right)$
c. $P(\bar{x}, \bar{y})$, where $\bar{x} = \dfrac{1}{n}\displaystyle\sum_{k=1}^{n} x_k$ and $\bar{y} = \dfrac{1}{n}\displaystyle\sum_{k=1}^{n} y_k$
d. $d(x, y) = \sqrt{x^2 + y^2} + \sqrt{(x - 2)^2 + y^2} + \sqrt{(x - 1)^2 + (y - 1)^2}$. The absolute min of this function is $1 + \sqrt{3} = f\left(1, \dfrac{1}{\sqrt{3}}\right)$.   **73.** $y = \dfrac{22}{13}x + \dfrac{46}{13}$ **75.** $a = b = c = 3$
77. a. $\nabla d_1(x, y) = \dfrac{x - x_1}{d_1(x, y)}\mathbf{i} + \dfrac{y - y_1}{d_1(x, y)}\mathbf{j}$
b. $\nabla d_2(x, y) = \dfrac{x - x_2}{d_2(x, y)}\mathbf{i} + \dfrac{y - y_2}{d_2(x, y)}\mathbf{j}$;
$\nabla d_3(x, y) = \dfrac{x - x_3}{d_3(x, y)}\mathbf{i} + \dfrac{y - y_3}{d_3(x, y)}\mathbf{j}$
c. Follows from $\nabla f = \nabla d_1 + \nabla d_2 + \nabla d_3$ **d.** Three unit vectors add to zero.   **e.** P is the vertex at the large angle.   **f.** $P(0.255457, 0.304504)$
79. a. Local max at $(1, 0), (-1, 0)$ **b.** $(1, 0)$ and $(-1, 0)$

Section 12.9 Exercises, pp. 957–959

1. The level curve of f must be tangent to the curve $g = 0$ at the optimal point; therefore, the gradients are parallel.   **3.** $2x = 2\lambda$, $2y = 3\lambda, 2z = -5\lambda, 2x + 3y - 5z + 4 = 0$ **5.** Min: $-2\sqrt{5}$ at $\left(-\dfrac{2}{\sqrt{5}}, -\dfrac{4}{\sqrt{5}}\right)$; max: $2\sqrt{5}$ at $\left(\dfrac{2}{\sqrt{5}}, \dfrac{4}{\sqrt{5}}\right)$ **7.** Min: -2 at $(-1, -1)$; max: 2 at $(1, 1)$ **9.** Min: -3 at $(-\sqrt{3}, \sqrt{3})$ and $(\sqrt{3}, -\sqrt{3})$; max: 9 at $(3, 3)$ and $(-3, -3)$ **11.** Min: e^{-16} at $(2\sqrt{2}, -2\sqrt{2})$ and $(-2\sqrt{2}, 2\sqrt{2})$; max: e^{16} at $(-2\sqrt{2}, -2\sqrt{2})$ and $(2\sqrt{2}, 2\sqrt{2})$ **13.** Min: -16 at $(\pm 2, 0)$; max: 2 at $(0, \pm\sqrt{2})$ **15.** Min: $-2\sqrt{11}$ at $\left(-\dfrac{2}{\sqrt{11}}, -\dfrac{6}{\sqrt{11}}, \dfrac{2}{\sqrt{11}}\right)$; max: $2\sqrt{11}$ at $\left(\dfrac{2}{\sqrt{11}}, \dfrac{6}{\sqrt{11}}, -\dfrac{2}{\sqrt{11}}\right)$ **17.** Min: $-\dfrac{\sqrt{5}}{2}$ at $\left(-\dfrac{\sqrt{5}}{2}, 0, \dfrac{1}{2}\right)$; max: $\dfrac{\sqrt{5}}{2}$ at $\left(\dfrac{\sqrt{5}}{2}, 0, \dfrac{1}{2}\right)$ **19.** Min: $\dfrac{1}{3}$ at $\left(-\dfrac{1}{\sqrt{6}}, \dfrac{1}{\sqrt{6}}, 0\right)$ and $\left(\dfrac{1}{\sqrt{6}}, -\dfrac{1}{\sqrt{6}}, 0\right)$; max: 1 at $(0, 0, \pm 1)$
21. Min: -10 at $(-5, 0, 0)$; max: $\dfrac{29}{2}$ at $\left(2, 0, \pm\sqrt{\dfrac{21}{2}}\right)$
23. Min: $6\sqrt[3]{2} = f(\pm\sqrt[3]{4}, \pm\sqrt[3]{4}, \pm\sqrt[3]{4})$; no max
25. 18 in $\times$ 18 in $\times$ 36 in   **27.** Min: 0.6731; max: 1.1230

29. 2×1 **31.** $\left(-\dfrac{3}{17}, \dfrac{29}{17}, -3\right)$ **33.** Min: $\sqrt{38 - 6\sqrt{29}}$
(or $\sqrt{29} - 3$); max: $\sqrt{38 + 6\sqrt{29}}$ (or $\sqrt{29} + 3$)   **35.** $\ell = 3$
and $g = \frac{3}{2}$; $U = 15\sqrt{2}$ **37.** $\ell = \frac{16}{5}$ and $g = 1$; $U = 20.287$

39. a. True   **b.** False   **41.** $\dfrac{\sqrt{6}}{3}$ m $\times \dfrac{\sqrt{6}}{3}$ m $\times \dfrac{\sqrt{6}}{6}$ m

43. $2 \times 1 \times \frac{2}{3}$ **45.** $P\left(\frac{4}{3}, \frac{2}{3}, \frac{4}{3}\right)$ **47.** Min: $-\dfrac{7 + \sqrt{661}}{2}$;

max: $\dfrac{\sqrt{661} - 7}{2}$ **49.** Min: 0; max: $6 + 4\sqrt{2}$ **51.** Min: 1; max: 8

53. $K = 7.5$ and $L = 5$ **55.** $K = aB/p$ and $L = (1 - a)B/q$
57. Max: 8   **59.** Max: $\sqrt{a_1{}^2 + a_2{}^2 + a_3{}^2 + \cdots + a_n{}^2}$
61. a. Gradients are perpendicular to level surfaces.   **b.** If the gradient
was not in the plane spanned by ∇g and ∇h, f could be increased
(decreased) by moving the point slightly.   **c.** ∇f is a linear combination of ∇g and ∇h, since it belongs to the plane spanned by these two
vectors.   **d.** The gradient condition from part (c), as well as the constraints, must be satisfied.   **63.** Min: $2 - 4\sqrt{2}$; max: $2 + 4\sqrt{2}$
65. Min: $\frac{5}{4} = f\left(\frac{1}{2}, 0, 1\right)$; max: $\frac{125}{36} = f\left(-\frac{5}{6}, 0, \frac{5}{3}\right)$

Chapter 12 Review Exercises, pp. 959–962

1. a. False   **b.** False   **c.** False   **d.** False   **e.** True
3. a. $18x - 9y + 2z = 6$ **b.** $x = \frac{1}{3}, y = -\frac{2}{3}, z = 3$
c.

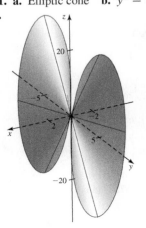

5. $x = t, y = 12 - 9t, z = -6 + 6t$ **7.** $3x + y + 7z = 4$
9. a. Hyperbolic paraboloid   **b.** $y^2 = 4x^2, z = \dfrac{x^2}{36}, z = -\dfrac{y^2}{144}$
c. $x = y = z = 0$
d.

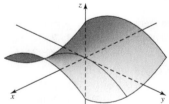

11. a. Elliptic cone   **b.** $y^2 = 4x^2$, origin, $y^2 = \dfrac{z^2}{25}$ **c.** Origin
d.

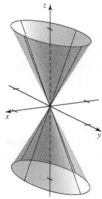

13. a. Elliptic paraboloid   **b.** Origin, $z = \dfrac{x^2}{16}, z = \dfrac{y^2}{36}$ **c.** Origin
d.

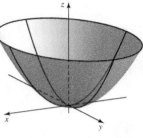

15. a. Hyperboloid of one sheet   **b.** $y^2 - 2x^2 = 1, 4z^2 - 2x^2 = 1,$
$y^2 + 4z^2 = 1$ **c.** No x-intercept, $y = \pm 1, z = \pm\frac{1}{2}$
d.

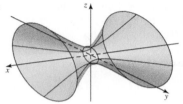

17. a. Hyperboloid of one sheet
b. $\dfrac{x^2}{4} + \dfrac{y^2}{16} = 4, \dfrac{x^2}{4} - z^2 = 4, \dfrac{y^2}{16} - z^2 = 4$
c. $x = \pm 4, y = \pm 8$, no z-intercept
d.

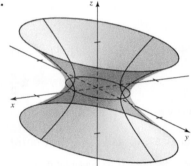

19. a. Ellipsoid   **b.** $\dfrac{x^2}{4} + \dfrac{y^2}{16} = 4, \dfrac{x^2}{4} + z^2 = 4, \dfrac{y^2}{16} + z^2 = 4$
c. $x = \pm 4, y = \pm 8, z = \pm 2$
d.

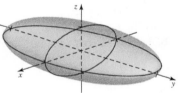

21. a. Elliptic cone   **b.** Origin, $\dfrac{x^2}{9} = \dfrac{z^2}{64}, \dfrac{y^2}{49} = \dfrac{z^2}{64}$.   **c.** Origin
d.

23. $D = \{(x, y) : (x, y) \neq (0, 0)\}$

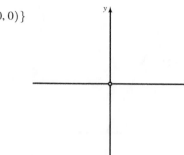

25. $D = \{(x, y) : x \geq y^2\}$

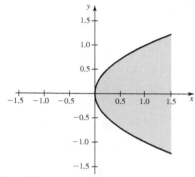

27. a. A **b.** D **c.** C **d.** B **29.**

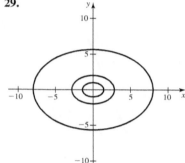

31. 2 **33.** Does not exist **35.** $\frac{2}{3}$ **37.** 4

39. $f_x = 6xy^5; f_y = 15x^2y^4$ **41.** $f_x = \dfrac{2xy^2}{(x^2 + y^2)^2}; f_y = -\dfrac{2x^2y}{(x^2 + y^2)^2}$

43. $f_x = y(1 + xy)e^{xy}; f_y = x(1 + xy)e^{xy}$ **45.** $f_x = e^{x+2y+3z}$;

$f_y = 2e^{x+2y+3z}; f_z = 3e^{x+2y+3z}$ **47.** $\dfrac{\partial^2 u}{\partial x^2} = 6y = -\dfrac{\partial^2 u}{\partial y^2}$ **49. a.** V

increases with R if r is fixed, $V_R > 0$; V decreases if r increases and R is fixed, $V_r < 0$. **b.** $V_r = -4\pi r^2$; $V_R = 4\pi R^2$ **c.** The volume increases more if R is increased. **51.** $w'(t) = -\dfrac{\cos t \sin t}{\sqrt{1 + \cos^2 t}}$

53. $w_r = \dfrac{3r + s}{r(r + s)}; w_s = \dfrac{r + 3s}{s(r + s)}; w_t = \dfrac{1}{t}$

55. $\dfrac{dy}{dx} = -\dfrac{2xy}{2y^2 + (x^2 + y^2)\ln(x^2 + y^2)}$

57. a. $z'(t) = -24 \sin t \cos t = -12 \sin 2t$

b. $z'(t) > 0$ for $\dfrac{\pi}{2} < t < \pi$ and $\dfrac{3\pi}{2} < t < 2\pi$

59. a.

	$(a, b) = (0, 0)$	$(a, b) = (2, 0)$	$(a, b) = (1, 1)$
$\mathbf{u} = \langle \frac{\sqrt{2}}{2}, \frac{\sqrt{2}}{2} \rangle$	0	$4\sqrt{2}$	$-2\sqrt{2}$
$\mathbf{v} = \langle -\frac{\sqrt{2}}{2}, \frac{\sqrt{2}}{2} \rangle$	0	$-4\sqrt{2}$	$-6\sqrt{2}$
$\mathbf{w} = \langle -\frac{\sqrt{2}}{2}, -\frac{\sqrt{2}}{2} \rangle$	0	$-4\sqrt{2}$	$2\sqrt{2}$

b. The function is increasing at $(2, 0)$ in the direction of $\mathbf{u}$ and decreasing at $(2, 0)$ in the directions of $\mathbf{v}$ and $\mathbf{w}$.
61. $\nabla g = \langle 2xy^3, 3x^2y^2 \rangle$; $\nabla g(-1, 1) = \langle -2, 3 \rangle$; $D_\mathbf{u}\, g(-1, 1) = 2$
63. $\nabla h = \left\langle \dfrac{x}{\sqrt{2 + x^2 + 2y^2}}, \dfrac{2y}{\sqrt{2 + x^2 + 2y^2}} \right\rangle$;

$\nabla h(2, 1) = \left\langle \dfrac{\sqrt{2}}{2}, \dfrac{\sqrt{2}}{2} \right\rangle$; $D_\mathbf{u}\, h(2, 1) = \dfrac{7\sqrt{2}}{10}$

65. $\nabla f = \langle \cos(x + 2y - z),$
$2\cos(x + 2y - z), -\cos(x + 2y - z) \rangle$;
$\nabla f \left(\dfrac{\pi}{6}, \dfrac{\pi}{6}, -\dfrac{\pi}{6} \right) = \left\langle -\dfrac{1}{2}, -1, \dfrac{1}{2} \right\rangle$; $D_\mathbf{u} f\left(\dfrac{\pi}{6}, \dfrac{\pi}{6}, -\dfrac{\pi}{6} \right) = -\dfrac{1}{2}$

67. a. Direction of steepest ascent: $\mathbf{u} = \dfrac{\sqrt{2}}{2}\mathbf{i} - \dfrac{\sqrt{2}}{2}\mathbf{j}$;

direction of steepest descent: $\mathbf{u} = -\dfrac{\sqrt{2}}{2}\mathbf{i} + \dfrac{\sqrt{2}}{2}\mathbf{j}$

b. No change: $\mathbf{u} = \pm\left(\dfrac{\sqrt{2}}{2}\mathbf{i} + \dfrac{\sqrt{2}}{2}\mathbf{j} \right)$

69. Tangent line is vertical; $\nabla f(2, 0) = -8\mathbf{i}$

71. $E = \dfrac{kx}{x^2 + y^2}\mathbf{i} + \dfrac{ky}{x^2 + y^2}\mathbf{j}$

73. $y = 2$ and $12x + 3y - 2z = 12$
75. $16x + 2y + z - 8 = 0$ and $8x + y + 8z + 16 = 0$
77. $z = \ln 3 + \dfrac{2}{3}(x - 1) + \dfrac{1}{3}(y - 2)$;

$z = \ln 3 - \dfrac{1}{3}(x + 2) - \dfrac{2}{3}(y + 1)$ **79. a.** $L(x, y) = x + 5y$

b. $L(1.95, 0.05) = 2.2$ **81.** -4% **83. a.** $dV = -0.1\pi$ m^3
b. $dS = -0.05\pi$ m^2 **85.** Saddle point at $(0, 0)$; local min at $(2, -2)$
87. Saddle points at $(0, 0)$ and $(-2, 2)$; local max at $(0, 2)$; local min at $(-2, 0)$ **89.** Absolute min: $-1 = f(1, 1) = f(-1, -1)$; absolute max: $49 = f(2, -2) = f(-2, 2)$ **91.** Absolute min:

$-\dfrac{1}{2} = f\left(-\dfrac{1}{\sqrt{2}}, \dfrac{1}{\sqrt{2}} \right)$; absolute max: $\dfrac{1}{2} = f\left(\dfrac{1}{\sqrt{2}}, \dfrac{1}{\sqrt{2}} \right)$

93. Max: $\dfrac{29}{2} = f\left(\dfrac{5}{3}, \dfrac{7}{6} \right)$; min: $\dfrac{23}{2} = f\left(\dfrac{1}{3}, \dfrac{5}{6} \right)$

95. Max: $f\left(\dfrac{\sqrt{6}}{6}, \dfrac{\sqrt{6}}{3}, -\dfrac{\sqrt{6}}{6} \right) = \sqrt{6}$;

min: $f\left(-\dfrac{\sqrt{6}}{6}, -\dfrac{\sqrt{6}}{3}, \dfrac{\sqrt{6}}{6} \right) = -\sqrt{6}$

97. $\dfrac{2a^2}{\sqrt{a^2 + b^2}}$ by $\dfrac{2b^2}{\sqrt{a^2 + b^2}}$

99. $x = \dfrac{1}{2} + \dfrac{\sqrt{10}}{20}, y = \dfrac{3}{2} + \dfrac{3\sqrt{10}}{20} = 3x, z = \dfrac{1}{2} + \dfrac{\sqrt{10}}{2} = \sqrt{10}x$

CHAPTER 13

Section 13.1 Exercises, pp. 970–973

1. $\displaystyle\int_0^2 \int_1^3 xy\, dy\, dx$ or $\displaystyle\int_1^3 \int_0^2 xy\, dx\, dy$ **3.** $\displaystyle\int_{-2}^4 \int_1^5 f(x, y)\, dy\, dx$ or

$\displaystyle\int_1^5 \int_{-2}^4 f(x, y)\, dx\, dy$ **5.** 4 **7.** $\dfrac{32}{3}$ **9.** 4 **11.** $\dfrac{224}{9}$ **13.** 7

15. $10 - 2e$ **17.** $\dfrac{117}{2}$ **19.** 15 **21.** $\dfrac{4}{3}$ **23.** $\dfrac{9 - e^2}{2}$ **25.** $\dfrac{4}{11}$

27. $e^2 - 3$ **29.** $e^{16} - 17$ **31.** $\ln\dfrac{5}{3}$ **33.** $\dfrac{1}{2\ln 2}$ **35.** $\dfrac{8}{3}$

37. a. True **b.** False **c.** True **39.** **a.** 1475 **b.** The sum of products of population densities and areas is a Riemann sum. **41.** 60

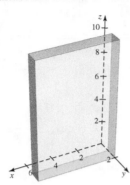

43. $\frac{1}{2}$ **45.** $10\sqrt{5} - 4\sqrt{2} - 14$ **47.** 3 **49.** 136 **51.** $a = \pi/6, 5\pi/6$
53. $a = \sqrt{6}$ **55. a.** $\frac{1}{2}\pi^2 + \pi$ **b.** $\frac{1}{2}\pi^2 + \pi$ **c.** $\frac{1}{2}\pi^2 + 2$
57. $\int_c^d \int_a^b f(x)\, dy\, dx = (c - d) \int_a^b f(x)\, dx$. The integral is the area of the cross section of S. **59.** $f(a, b) - f(a, 0) - f(0, b) + f(0, 0)$
61. Use substitution ($u = x^r y^s$ and then $v = x^r$).

Section 13.2 Exercises, pp. 980–984

1.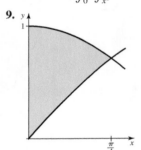

3. $dx\, dy$ **5.** $\int_0^1 \int_{x^2}^{\sqrt{x}} f(x, y)\, dy\, dx$ **7.** $\int_0^2 \int_{x^3}^{4x} f(x, y)\, dy\, dx$

9. 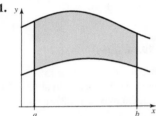 $\int_0^{\pi/4} \int_{\sin x}^{\cos x} f(x, y)\, dy\, dx$

11. 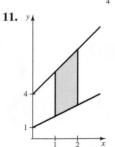 $\int_1^2 \int_{x+1}^{2x+4} f(x, y)\, dy\, dx$

13. 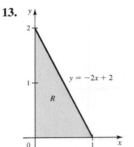 $\int_0^1 \int_0^{-2x+2} f(x, y)\, dy\, dx$

15. 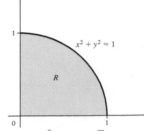 $\int_0^1 \int_0^{\sqrt{1-x^2}} f(x, y)\, dy\, dx$

17. 2 **19.** $\frac{8}{3}$ **21.** $\sqrt{2}$ **23.** 0 **25.** $e - 1$ **27.** 2 **29.** 12

31. $\int_0^{18} \int_{y/2}^{(y+9)/3} f(x, y)\, dx\, dy$

33. 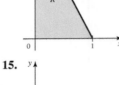 $\int_0^{23} \int_{(y-3)/2}^{(y+7)/3} f(x, y)\, dx\, dy$

35. 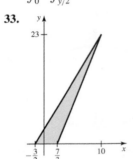 $\int_1^4 \int_0^{4-y} f(x, y)\, dx\, dy$

37. 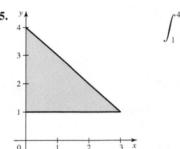 $\int_0^1 \int_y^{2-y} f(x, y)\, dx\, dy$

39. 9 **41.** 0 **43.** $\dfrac{\ln^3 2}{6}$ **45.** 2 **47.** 5 **49.** 14 **51.** 32 **53.** $\dfrac{32}{3}$

55. 12π **57.** $\int_0^4 \int_{y/2}^{\sqrt{y}} f(x, y)\, dx\, dy$ **59.** $\int_0^{\ln 2} \int_{1/2}^{e^{-x}} f(x, y)\, dy\, dx$

61. $\int_0^{\pi/2} \int_0^{\cos x} f(x, y)\, dy\, dx$

63. $\frac{1}{2}(e-1)$

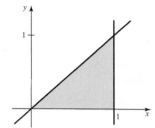

65. 0

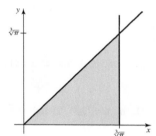

67. $\frac{2}{3}$

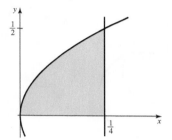

69. $\frac{2}{3}$ **71.** $\frac{81\pi}{2}$ **73.** $\frac{43}{6}$

75. $\frac{32}{3}$

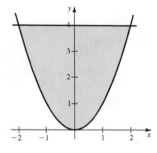

77. 1

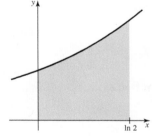

79. $\frac{140}{3}$

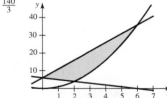

81. a. False   **b.** False   **c.** False   **83.** $\frac{9}{8}$ **85.** $\frac{1}{4}\ln 2$

87. $\displaystyle\int_1^e \int_{-\ln x}^{\ln x} f(x,y)\, dy\, dx$

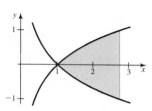

89. $\frac{a}{3}$ **91. a.**

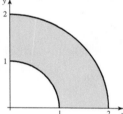

b. $\dfrac{15}{4} + 4\ln 2$

c. $2\ln 2 - \dfrac{5}{64}$

93. $\dfrac{3}{8e^2}$ **95.** 1   **97.** 30   **99.** 16   **101.** $4a\pi$

103. The integral over R_1

Section 13.3 Exercises, pp. 991–994

1. It is called a polar rectangle because each of r and θ vary between two constants.

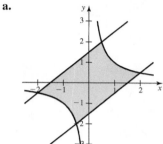

3.

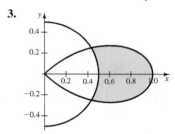

5. Evaluate the integral $\displaystyle\int_\alpha^\beta \int_{g(\theta)}^{h(\theta)} r\, dr\, d\theta$.

7.

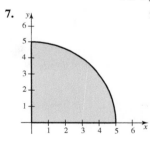

9.

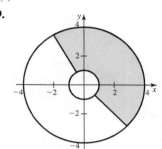

11. $\dfrac{7\pi}{2}$ **13.** $\dfrac{9\pi}{2}$ **15.** $\dfrac{62 - 10\sqrt{5}}{3}\pi$ **17.** $\dfrac{37\pi}{3}$ **19.** π

21. $\pi/2$ **23.** 128π

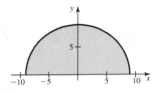

25. 0

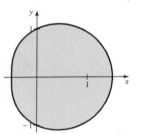

27. $(2 - \sqrt{3})\pi$

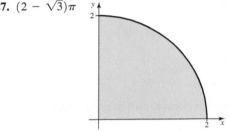

29. $(8 - 24e^{-2})\pi$ **31.** $\dfrac{15{,}625\pi}{3}$

33.

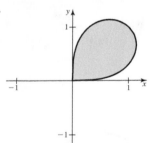

$$\int_0^{2\pi} \int_0^{1+\frac{1}{2}\cos\theta} f(r,\theta)r\,dr\,d\theta$$

35.

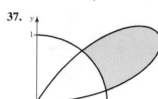

$$\int_0^{\pi/2} \int_0^{\sqrt{2\sin 2\theta}} f(r,\theta)r\,dr\,d\theta$$

37.

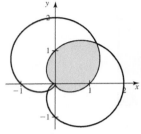

$$\int_{\pi/18}^{5\pi/18} \int_1^{2\sin 3\theta} f(r,\theta)r\,dr\,d\theta$$

39. $3\pi/2$

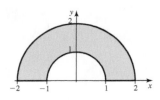

41. π

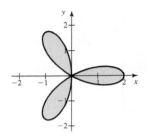

43. $\dfrac{3\pi}{2} - 2\sqrt{2}$

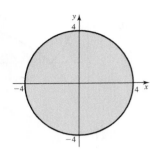

45. $2a/3$ **47.** $5/2$ **49. a.** False **b.** True **c.** True   **51.** $2\pi/5$
53. $\frac{1}{3}$ **55.** $\frac{14\pi}{3}$ **57.** $2\pi\left(1 - 2\ln\frac{3}{2}\right)$
59. The hyperboloid $\left(V = \frac{112\pi}{3}\right)$
61. a. $R = \{(r,\theta): -\pi/4 \le \theta \le \pi/4 \text{ or } 3\pi/4 \le \theta \le 5\pi/4\}$

b. $\dfrac{a^4}{4}$ **63.** 1   **65.** $\pi/4$ **67. a.** $9\pi/2$ **b.** $\pi + 3\sqrt{3}$

c. $\pi - 3\sqrt{3}/2$ **69.** $30\pi + 42$ **71. b.** $\sqrt{\pi}/2, 1/2,$ and $\sqrt{\pi}/4$

73. a. $I = \dfrac{\sqrt{2}}{2}\tan^{-1}\dfrac{\sqrt{2}}{2}$

b. $I = \dfrac{\sqrt{2}}{4}\tan^{-1}\dfrac{\sqrt{2}a}{2} + \dfrac{a}{2\sqrt{a^2+1}}\tan^{-1}\dfrac{1}{\sqrt{a^2+1}}$ **c.** $\dfrac{\sqrt{2}\pi}{8}$

Section 13.4 Exercises, pp. 1002–1006

1.

3. $\displaystyle\int_{-9}^{9} \int_{-\sqrt{81-x^2}}^{\sqrt{81-x^2}} \int_{-\sqrt{81-x^2-y^2}}^{\sqrt{81-x^2-y^2}} f(x,y,z)\,dz\,dy\,dx$

5. $\displaystyle\int_0^1 \int_0^{\sqrt{1-z^2}} \int_0^{\sqrt{1-z^2-x^2}} f(x,y,z)\,dy\,dx\,dz$

7. 24   **9.** 8   **11.** $\dfrac{2}{\pi}$ **13.** 0   **15.** 8   **17.** $\dfrac{32(\sqrt{2}-1)}{3}\pi$

19. $\dfrac{16}{3}$ **21.** $\dfrac{2\pi(1 + 19\sqrt{19} - 20\sqrt{10})}{3}$

23. 12π **25.** $\dfrac{2}{3}$ **27.** 128π **29.** $(10\sqrt{10} - 1)\dfrac{\pi}{6}$

31. $\dfrac{3\ln 2}{2} + \dfrac{e}{16} - 1$ **33.** $\dfrac{256}{9}$ **35.** $\dfrac{5}{12}$

37. 8   **39.** $\int_0^4 \int_{y/4-1}^0 \int_0^5 dz\,dx\,dy = 10$

41. $\int_0^1 \int_0^{\sqrt{1-x^2}} \int_0^{\sqrt{1-x^2}} dz\,dy\,dx = \dfrac{2}{3}$ **43.** $\dfrac{7}{\ln^3 2}$ **45.** $\dfrac{10}{3}$ **47.** $\dfrac{3}{2}$

49. a. False   **b.** False   **c.** False   **51.** 1   **53.** $\frac{16}{3}$ **55.** 2

57. $\int_0^1 \int_0^2 \int_0^{1-y} dz\,dx\,dy,$

$\int_0^2 \int_0^1 \int_0^{1-z} dy\,dz\,dx, \int_0^1 \int_0^2 \int_0^{1-z} dy\,dx\,dz,$

$\int_0^1 \int_0^{1-y} \int_0^2 dx\,dz\,dy, \int_0^1 \int_0^{1-z} \int_0^2 dx\,dy\,dz$

59. $\dfrac{224}{3}$ and $\dfrac{160}{3}$ **61.** $V = \dfrac{\pi r^2 h}{3}$ **63.** $V = \dfrac{\pi h^2}{3}(3R - h)$

65. $V = \dfrac{4\pi abc}{3}$ **67.** $\dfrac{1}{24}$

Section 13.5 Exercises, pp. 1019–1023

1. r measures the distance from the point to the z axis, θ is the angle that the segment from the point to the z-axis makes with the positive xz-plane, and z is the directed distance from the point to the xy-plane.
3. A cone   **5.** It approximates the volume of the cylindrical wedge formed by the changes Δr, $\Delta\theta$, and Δz.

7. $\int_\alpha^\beta \int_{g(\theta)}^{h(\theta)} \int_{G(r,\theta)}^{H(r,\theta)} f(r,\theta,z)\,r\,dz\,dr\,d\theta$ **9.** Cylindrical coordinates

11. 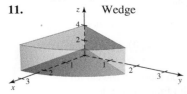 Wedge

13. 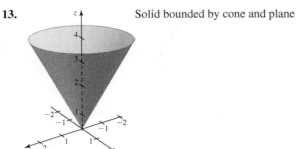 Solid bounded by cone and plane

15. 2π **17.** $4\pi/5$ **19.** $\pi(1 - e^{-1})/2$ **21.** $9\pi/4$
23. 560π **25.** 396π **27.** The paraboloid ($V = 44\pi/3$)
29. $\dfrac{2\pi + 14\pi\sqrt{17}}{3}$ **31.** $\dfrac{(16 + 17\sqrt{29})\pi}{3}$ **33.** $\dfrac{1}{3}$
35. 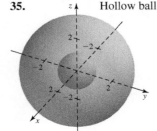 Hollow ball

37.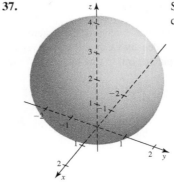
Sphere of radius $r = 2$, centered at $(0, 0, 2)$

39. $\dfrac{\pi}{2}$ **41.** $4\pi \ln 2$ **43.** $\pi\left(\dfrac{188}{9} - \dfrac{32\sqrt{3}}{3}\right)$ **45.** $\dfrac{32\pi\sqrt{3}}{9}$

47. $\dfrac{5\pi}{12}$ **49.** $\dfrac{8\pi}{3}$ **51.** $\dfrac{8\pi}{3}(9\sqrt{3} - 11)$ **53. a.** True   **b.** True

55. $z = \sqrt{x^2 + y^2 - 1}$; upper half of a hyperboloid of one sheet

57. $\dfrac{8\pi}{3}(1 - e^{-512}) \approx \dfrac{8\pi}{3}$ **59.** 32π

61.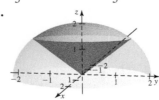

$\int_0^{2\pi} \int_0^{\sqrt{2}} \int_r^{\sqrt{4-r^2}} f(r,\theta,z)\,r\,dz\,dr\,d\theta,$

$\int_0^{2\pi} \int_0^{\sqrt{2}} \int_0^z f(r,\theta,z)\,r\,dr\,dz\,d\theta$

$+ \int_0^{2\pi} \int_{\sqrt{2}}^2 \int_0^{\sqrt{4-z^2}} f(r,\theta,z)\,r\,dr\,dz\,d\theta,$

$\int_0^{\sqrt{2}} \int_r^{\sqrt{4-r^2}} \int_0^{2\pi} f(r,\theta,z)\,r\,d\theta\,dz\,dr$

63.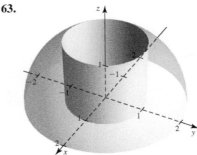

$\int_{\pi/6}^{\pi/2} \int_0^{2\pi} \int_{\csc\varphi}^2 f(\rho,\varphi,\theta)\,\rho^2 \sin\varphi\,d\rho\,d\theta\,d\varphi,$

$\int_{\pi/6}^{\pi/2} \int_{\csc\varphi}^2 \int_0^{2\pi} f(\rho,\varphi,\theta)\,\rho^2 \sin\varphi\,d\theta\,d\rho\,d\varphi$

65. $32\sqrt{3}\pi/9$ **67.** $2\sqrt{2}/3$ **69.** $7\pi/2$ **71.** $16/3$ **73.** 95.6036

77. $V = \dfrac{\pi r^2 h}{3}$ **79.** $V = \dfrac{\pi}{3}(R^2 + rR + r^2)h$

81. $V = \dfrac{\pi R^3(8r - 3R)}{12r}$

Section 13.6 Exercises, pp. 1031–1033

1. The pivot should be located at the center of mass of the system.
3. Use a double integral. Integrate the density function over the region occupied by the plate.   **5.** Use a triple integral to find the mass of the object and the three moments.

7. 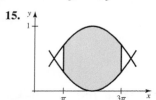 $\frac{27}{13}$ **9.** Mass is $2 + \pi$; $\bar{x} = \frac{\pi}{2}$

11. Mass is $\frac{20}{3}$; $\bar{x} = \frac{9}{5}$ **13.** Mass is 10; $\bar{x} = \frac{8}{3}$

15. 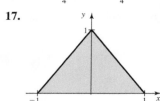 $\left(\frac{\pi}{2}, \frac{1}{2}\right)$

17.  $\left(0, \frac{1}{3}\right)$

19. 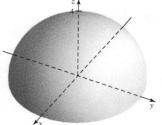 $\left(\frac{1}{4}(e^2 + 1), \frac{e}{2} - 1\right) \approx (2.10, 0.36)$

21. $\left(\frac{7}{3}, 1\right)$; density increases to the right.   **23.** $\left(\frac{16}{11}, \frac{16}{11}\right)$; density increases toward the hypotenuse of the triangle.

25. $\left(0, \dfrac{16 + 3\pi}{16 + 12\pi}\right) \approx (0, 0.4735)$; density increases away from the x-axis.

27. 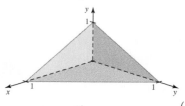 $\left(0, 0, \frac{3}{2}\right)$

29. 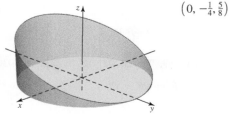 $\left(\frac{1}{4}, \frac{1}{4}, \frac{1}{4}\right)$

31. $\left(0, -\frac{1}{4}, \frac{5}{8}\right)$

33. $\left(\frac{7}{3}, \frac{1}{2}, \frac{1}{2}\right)$ **35.** $\left(0, 0, \frac{198}{85}\right)$ **37.** $\left(\frac{2}{3}, \frac{7}{3}, \frac{1}{3}\right)$ **39. a.** False   **b.** True

c. False   **d.** False   **41.** $\bar{x} = \dfrac{\ln(1 + L^2)}{2 \tan^{-1} L}$, $\lim_{L \to \infty} \bar{x} = \infty$

43. $\left(0, \frac{8}{9}\right)$ **45.** $\left(0, \frac{8}{3\pi}\right)$ **47.** $\left(\frac{5}{6}, 0\right)$ **49.** $\left(\dfrac{128}{105\pi}, \dfrac{128}{105\pi}\right)$

51. On the line of symmetry, $2a/\pi$ units above the diameter

53. $\left(\dfrac{2a}{3(4 - \pi)}, \dfrac{2a}{3(4 - \pi)}\right)$ **55.** $h/4$ units   **57.** $h/3$ units, where h

is the height of the triangle   **59.** $3a/8$ units

61. a. $\left(0, \dfrac{4(1 + a + a^2)}{3(1 + a)\pi}\right)$

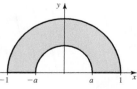

b. $a = \dfrac{1}{2}\left(-1 + \sqrt{1 + \dfrac{16}{3\pi - 4}}\right) \approx 0.4937$

63. Depth $= \dfrac{40\sqrt{10} - 4}{333}$ cm ≈ 0.3678 cm

65. a. $(\bar{x}, \bar{y}) = \left(\dfrac{-r^2}{R + r}, 0\right)$ (origin at center of large circle);

$(\bar{x}, \bar{y}) = \left(\dfrac{R^2 + Rr + r^2}{R + r}, 0\right)$ (origin at common point of the circles)

b. *Hint:* Solve $\bar{x} = R - 2r$.

Section 13.7 Exercises, pp. 1043–1045

1. The image of S is the 2×2 square with vertices at $(0, 0)$, $(2, 0)$, $(2, 2)$, and $(0, 2)$.   **3.** $\displaystyle\int_0^1 \int_0^1 f(u + v, u - v)\, 2\, du\, dv$

5. The rectangle with vertices at $(0, 0)$, $(2, 0)$, $\left(2, \frac{1}{2}\right)$, and $\left(0, \frac{1}{2}\right)$
7. The square with vertices at $(0, 0)$, $\left(\frac{1}{2}, \frac{1}{2}\right)$, $(1, 0)$, and $\left(\frac{1}{2}, -\frac{1}{2}\right)$
9. The region above the x-axis and bounded by the curves
$y^2 = 4 \pm 4x$ **11.** The upper half of the unit circle

13.

15.

17. -9 **19.** $-4(u^2 + v^2)$ **21.** -1
23. $x = (u + v)/3, y = (2u - v)/3$; $-1/3$
25. $x = -(u + 3v), y = -(u + 2v)$; -1

27. a.

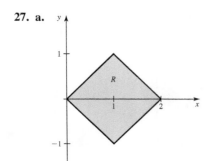

b. $0 \leq u \leq 1, 0 \leq v \leq 1$ **c.** $J(u, v) = -2$ **d.** 0

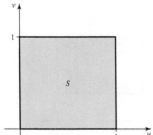

29. a.

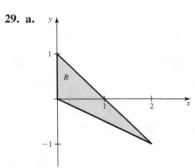

b. $0 \leq u \leq 1, 0 \leq v \leq 1 - u$ **c.** $J(u, v) = 2$ **d.** $256\sqrt{2}/945$

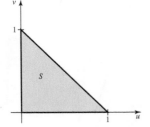

31. $4\sqrt{2}/3$

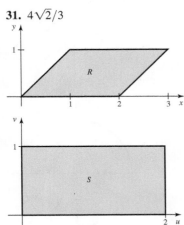

33. 3844/5625

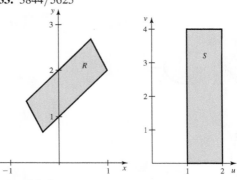

35. $\dfrac{15 \ln 3}{2}$

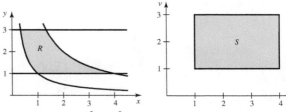

37. 2   **39.** $2w(u^2 - v^2)$ **41.** 5   **43.** $1024\pi/3$
45. a. True   **b.** True   **c.** True

47. *Hint:* $J(\rho, \varphi, \theta) = \begin{vmatrix} \sin\varphi\cos\theta & \rho\cos\varphi\cos\theta & -\rho\sin\varphi\sin\theta \\ \sin\varphi\sin\theta & \rho\cos\varphi\sin\theta & \rho\sin\varphi\cos\theta \\ \cos\varphi & -\rho\sin\varphi & 0 \end{vmatrix}$

49. $a^2b^2/2$ **51.** $(a^2 + b^2)/4$ **53.** $4\pi abc/3$

55. $(\bar{x}, \bar{y}, \bar{z}) = \left(0, 0, \dfrac{3c}{8}\right)$ **57. a.** $x = a^2 - \dfrac{y^2}{4a^2}$

b. $x = \dfrac{y^2}{4b^2} - b^2$ **c.** $J(u, v) = 4(u^2 + v^2)$ **d.** $\dfrac{80}{3}$ **e.** 160

f. Vertical lines become parabolas opening downward with vertices on the positive y-axis, and horizontal lines become parabolas opening upward with vertices on the negative y-axis.   **59. a.** S is stretched in the positive u- and v-directions but not in the w-direction. The amount of stretching increases with u and v.   **b.** $J(u, v, w) = ad$

c. Volume $= ad$ **d.** $\left(\dfrac{a + b + c}{2}, \dfrac{d + e}{2}, \dfrac{1}{2}\right)$

Chapter 13 Review Exercises, pp. 1046–1049

1. a. False   **b.** True   **c.** False   **d.** False   **3.** $\frac{26}{3}$

5. $\displaystyle\int_0^1 \int_{-\sqrt{y}}^{\sqrt{y}} f(x, y)\, dx\, dy$ **7.** $\displaystyle\int_0^1 \int_0^{\sqrt{1-x^2}} f(x, y)\, dy\, dx$

9. $\dfrac{304}{3}$

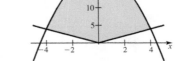

11. $\dfrac{\sqrt{17} - \sqrt{2}}{2}$

13. 8π **15.** $\dfrac{2}{7\pi^2}$ **17.** $\dfrac{1}{5}$

19. $\dfrac{9\pi}{2}$

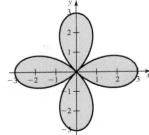

21. $6\pi - 16$

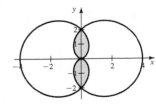

23. 2   **25.** $\displaystyle\int_0^4 \int_0^{\sqrt{16-z^2}} \int_0^{\sqrt{16-y^2-z^2}} f(x, y, z)\, dx\, dy\, dz$ **27.** $\pi - \dfrac{4}{3}$

29. $8 \sin^2 2 = 4(1 - \cos 4)$ **31.** $\dfrac{848}{9}$ **33.** $\dfrac{16}{3}$ **35.** $\dfrac{128}{3}$

37. $\dfrac{\pi}{6} - \dfrac{\sqrt{3}}{2} + \dfrac{1}{2}$ **39. a.** $\dfrac{512}{15}$ **b.** Five   **c.** $\dfrac{2^{pq+q+1}}{q(p+1)^2 + p + 1}$

41. $\frac{1}{3}$ **43.** π **45.** 4π **47.** $\dfrac{28\pi}{3}$ **49.** $\dfrac{2048\pi}{105}$

51.

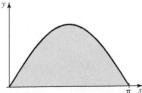

$(\bar{x}, \bar{y}) = \left(\dfrac{\pi}{2}, \dfrac{\pi}{8}\right)$

53.

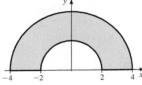

$(\bar{x}, \bar{y}) = \left(0, \dfrac{56}{9\pi}\right)$

55. $(\bar{x}, \bar{y}, \bar{z}) = (0, 0, 24)$ **57.** $(\bar{x}, \bar{y}, \bar{z}) = \left(0, 0, \dfrac{63}{10}\right)$ **59.** $\dfrac{h}{3}$

61. $\dfrac{1}{6}\sqrt{4s^2 - b^2} = \dfrac{h}{3}$, where h is the height of the triangle.

63. a. $\dfrac{4\pi}{3}$ **b.** $\dfrac{16Q}{3}$ **65.** $R = \{0 \le x \le 1, 0 \le y \le 1\}$

67. The square with vertices at $(0, 0)$, $\left(\frac{1}{2}, -\frac{1}{2}\right)$, $(1, 0)$, and $\left(\frac{1}{2}, \frac{1}{2}\right)$.
69. 10   **71.** 6

73. a.

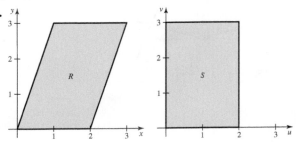

b. $0 \le u \le 2, 0 \le v \le 3$ **c.** $J(u, v) = 1$ **d.** $\frac{63}{2}$

75. a.

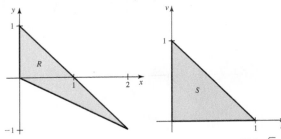

b. $0 \le u \le 1, 0 \le v \le 1 - u$ **c.** $J(u, v) = 2$ **d.** $\dfrac{256\sqrt{2}}{945}$

77. 42

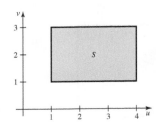

79. $-\dfrac{7}{16}$

CHAPTER 14

Section 14.1 Exercises, pp. 1057–1060

1. $\mathbf{F} = \langle f, g, h \rangle$ evaluated at (x, y, z) is the velocity vector of an air particle at (x, y, z) at a fixed point in time.   **3.** At selected points (a, b), plot the vector $\langle f(a, b), g(a, b) \rangle$.   **5.** It shows the direction in which the temperature increases the fastest and the amount of increase.

7.

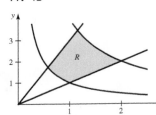

9.

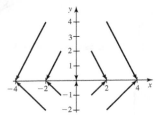

11.

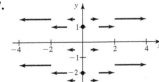

13.

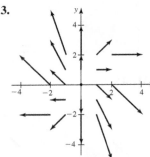

15.

17.

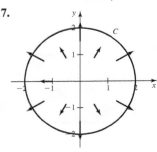

Normal at all points of C

19.

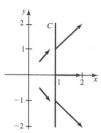

Normal to C at $(1, 0)$

21.

43.

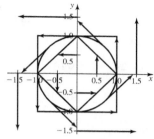

a. For S and D, the vectors with maximum magnitude occur at the vertices; on C, all vectors on the boundary have the same maximum magnitude ($|\mathbf{F}| = 1$).   **b.** For S and D, the field is directed out of the region on line segments between any vertex and the midpoint of the boundary line when proceeding in a counterclockwise direction; on C, the vector field is tangent to the boundary curve everywhere.   **45.** $\mathbf{F} = \langle -y, x \rangle$ or $\mathbf{F} = \langle -1, 1 \rangle$

47. $\mathbf{F}(x, y) = \dfrac{\langle x, y \rangle}{\sqrt{x^2 + y^2}} = \dfrac{\mathbf{r}}{|\mathbf{r}|}, \mathbf{F}(0,0) = \mathbf{0}$

49. a. $\mathbf{E} = \dfrac{c}{x^2 + y^2} \langle x, y \rangle$ **b.** $|\mathbf{E}| = \left| \dfrac{c}{|\mathbf{r}|^2} \mathbf{r} \right| = \dfrac{c}{r}$

c. *Hint:* The equipotential curves are circles centered at the origin.
51. The slope of the streamline at (x, y) is $y'(x)$, which equals the slope of the vector $\mathbf{F}(x, y)$, which is g/f. Therefore, $y'(x) = g/f$.

23.

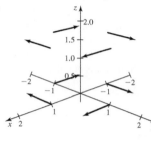

25. $\nabla \varphi(x, y) = 2\langle x, y \rangle$

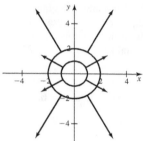

27. $\nabla \varphi = \langle 1, 1 \rangle$

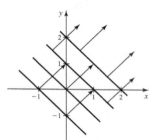

29. $\nabla \varphi(x, y) = \langle 2xy - y^2, x^2 - 2xy \rangle$
31. $\nabla \varphi(x, y) = \langle 1/y, -x/y^2 \rangle$ **33.** $\nabla \varphi(x, y, z) = \langle x, y, z \rangle = \mathbf{r}$

35. $\nabla \varphi(x, y, z) = -(x^2 + y^2 + z^2)^{-3/2} \langle x, y, z \rangle = -\dfrac{\mathbf{r}}{|\mathbf{r}|^3}$

37. a. $\nabla \varphi(x, y) = \langle 2, 3 \rangle$ **b.** $y' = -2/3, \langle 1, -\frac{2}{3} \rangle \cdot \nabla \varphi(1, 1) = 0$
c. $y' = -2/3, \langle 1, -\frac{2}{3} \rangle \cdot \nabla \varphi(x, y) = 0$ **d.**

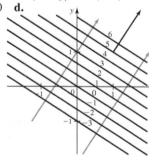

39. a. $\nabla \varphi(x, y) = \langle e^{x-y}, -e^{x-y} \rangle = e^{x-y} \langle 1, -1 \rangle$
b. $y' = 1, \langle 1, 1 \rangle \cdot \nabla \varphi(1, 1) = 0$
c. $y' = 1, \langle 1, 1 \rangle \cdot \nabla \varphi(x, y) = 0$
d.

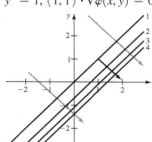

41. a. True   **b.** False   **c.** True

53.

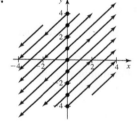

$y = x + C$

55.

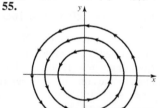

$x^2 + y^2 = C$

57. For $\theta = 0$: $\mathbf{u}_r = \mathbf{i}$ and $\mathbf{u}_\theta = \mathbf{j}$
for $\theta = \frac{\pi}{2}$: $\mathbf{u}_r = \mathbf{j}$ and $\mathbf{u}_\theta = -\mathbf{i}$
for $\theta = \pi$: $\mathbf{u}_r = -\mathbf{i}$ and $\mathbf{u}_\theta = -\mathbf{j}$
for $\theta = \frac{3\pi}{2}$: $\mathbf{u}_r = -\mathbf{j}$ and $\mathbf{u}_\theta = \mathbf{i}$

59.

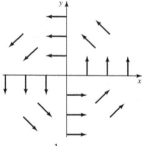

$\mathbf{F} = \dfrac{1}{\sqrt{x^2 + y^2}} \langle -y, x \rangle$

61.

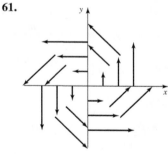

$\mathbf{F} = r\, \mathbf{u}_\theta$

Section 14.2 Exercises, pp. 1075–1078

1. A line integral is taken along a curve; an ordinary single-variable integral is taken along an interval.   **3.** $\sqrt{1 + 4t^2}$ **5.** The integrand of the alternative form is a dot product of $\mathbf{F}$ and $\mathbf{T}\, ds$.   **7.** Take the line integral of $\mathbf{F} \cdot \mathbf{T}$ along the curve with arc length as the parameter.
9. Take the line integral of $\mathbf{F} \cdot \mathbf{n}$ along the curve with arc length as the parameter, where $\mathbf{n}$ is the outward normal vector of the curve.
11. 0   **13.** $-\frac{32}{3}$ **15. a.** $\mathbf{r}(t) = \langle 4 \cos t, 4 \sin t \rangle, 0 \le t \le 2\pi$
b. $|\mathbf{r}'(t)| = 4$ **c.** 128π **17. a.** $\mathbf{r}(t) = \langle t, t \rangle, 1 \le t \le 10$

b. $|\mathbf{r}'(t)| = \sqrt{2}$ **c.** $\dfrac{\sqrt{2}}{2} \ln 10$ **19. a.** $\mathbf{r}(t) = \langle 2\cos t, 4\sin t \rangle$,
$0 \le t \le \dfrac{\pi}{2}$ **b.** $|\mathbf{r}'(t)| = 2\sqrt{1 + 3\cos^2 t}$ **c.** $\dfrac{112}{9}$
21. $\dfrac{15}{2}$ **23.** $\dfrac{1431}{268}$ **25.** 0   **27.** $\dfrac{3\sqrt{14}}{2}$ **29.** $-2\pi^2\sqrt{10}$
31. $\sqrt{101}$ **33.** $\dfrac{17}{2}$ **35.** 49   **37.** $\dfrac{3}{4\sqrt{10}}$ **39.** 0   **41.** 16

43. 0   **45.** $\dfrac{3\sqrt{3}}{10}$ **47. b.** 0   **49. a.** Negative   **b.** -4π
51. a. True   **b.** True   **c.** True   **d.** True   **53. a.** Both paths
require the same work: $W = 28{,}200$.   **b.** Both paths require the same
work: $W = 28{,}200$.   **55. a.** $\dfrac{5\sqrt{5}-1}{12}$ **b.** $\dfrac{5\sqrt{5}-1}{12}$
c. The results are identical.

57. *Hint:* Show that $\displaystyle\int_C \mathbf{F} \cdot \mathbf{T}\, ds = \pi r^2(c - b)$.

59. *Hint:* Show that $\displaystyle\int_C \mathbf{F} \cdot \mathbf{n}\, ds = \pi r^2(a + d)$.

61. The work equals zero for all three paths.   **63.** 409.5   **65. a.** $\ln a$
b. No   **c.** $\dfrac{1}{6}\left(1 - \dfrac{1}{a^2}\right)$ **d.** Yes   **e.** $W = \dfrac{3^{1-p/2}}{2 - p}(a^{2-p} - 1)$, for
$p \ne 2$; otherwise, $W = \ln a$.   **f.** $p > 2$ **67.** ab

Section 14.3 Exercises, pp. 1084–1086

1. A simple curve has no self-intersections; the initial and terminal
points of a closed curve are identical.   **3.** Test for equality of partial
derivatives as given in Theorem 14.3.   **5.** Integrate f with respect
to x and make the constant of integration a function of y to obtain
$\varphi = \int f\, dx + h(y)$; finally, set $\frac{\partial \varphi}{\partial y} = g$ to determine h.   **7.** 0
9. Conservative   **11.** Conservative   **13.** Conservative
15. $\varphi(x, y) = \frac{1}{2}(x^2 + y^2)$ **17.** Not conservative
19. $\varphi(x, y) = \sqrt{x^2 + y^2}$ **21.** $\varphi(x, y, z) = xz + y$
23. $\varphi(x, y, z) = xy + yz + zx$ **25.** $\varphi(x, y) = \sqrt{x^2 + y^2 + z^2}$
27. a, b. 0   **29. a, b.** 4   **31. a, b.** 2   **33.** 0   **35.** 0   **37.** 0
39. a. False   **b.** True   **c.** True   **d.** True   **e.** True   **41.** $-\frac{1}{2}$
43. 0   **45.** 10   **47.** 25   **49.** C_1 negative, C_2 positive
53. a. Compare partial derivatives.
b. $\varphi(x, y, z) = \dfrac{GMm}{\sqrt{x^2 + y^2 + z^2}} = \dfrac{GMm}{|\mathbf{r}|}$

c. $\varphi(B) - \varphi(A) = GMm\left(\dfrac{1}{r_2} - \dfrac{1}{r_1}\right)$ **d.** No

55. a. $\dfrac{\partial}{\partial y}\left(\dfrac{-y}{(x^2+y^2)^{p/2}}\right) = \dfrac{-x^2 + (p-1)y^2}{(x^2+y^2)^{1+p/2}}$ and

$\dfrac{\partial}{\partial x}\left(\dfrac{x}{(x^2+y^2)^{p/2}}\right) = \dfrac{-(p-1)x^2 + y^2}{(x^2+y^2)^{1+p/2}}$
b. The two partial derivatives in (a) are equal if $p = 2$.
c. $\varphi(x, y) = \tan^{-1}(y/x)$ **59.** $\varphi(x, y) = \frac{1}{2}(x^2 + y^2)$
61. $\varphi(x, y) = \frac{1}{2}(x^4 + x^2 y^2 + y^4)$

Section 14.4 Exercises, pp. 1097–1100

1. In both forms, the integral of a *derivative* is computed from bound-
ary data.   **3.** y^2 **5.** Area $= \frac{1}{2}\oint_C (x\, dy - y\, dx)$, where C encloses the
region   **7.** The integral in the flux form of Green's Theorem vanishes.

9. $\mathbf{F} = \langle y, x \rangle$

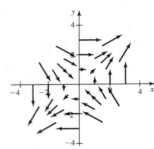

11. a. 0   **b.** Both integrals equal zero.   **c.** Yes   **13. a.** -4
b. Both integrals equal -8.   **c.** No   **15. a.** 0   **b.** Both integrals
equal zero.   **c.** Yes   **17.** 25π **19.** 16π **21.** 32   **23. a.** 2
b. Both integrals equal 8π.   **c.** No   **25. a.** 0   **b.** Both integrals
equal zero.   **c.** Yes   **27. a.** 0   **b.** Both integrals equal zero.

c. Yes   **29.** 6   **31.** $\dfrac{8}{3}$ **33.** $8 - \dfrac{\pi}{2}$ **35. a.** 0

b. 3π **37. a.** 0   **b.** $-\dfrac{15\pi}{2}$ **39. a.** True   **b.** False

c. True   **41. a.** 0   **b.** 2π **43. a.** 5702.4   **b.** 0.

45. Note: $\dfrac{\partial f}{\partial y} = 0 = \dfrac{\partial g}{\partial x}$ **47.** The integral becomes $\iint_R 2\, dA$.

49. a. $f_x = g_y = 0$ **b.** $\psi(x, y) = -2x + 4y$
51. a. $f_x = e^{-x}\sin y = -g_y$ **b.** $\psi(x, y) = e^{-x}\cos y$
53. a. *Hint:* $f_x = e^x\cos y$, $f_y = -e^x\sin y$,
$g_x = -e^x\sin y$, $g_y = -e^x\cos y$
b. $\varphi(x, y) = e^x\cos y$, $\psi(x, y) = e^x\sin y$

55. a. *Hint:* $f_x = -\dfrac{y}{x^2+y^2}$, $f_y = \dfrac{x}{x^2+y^2}$,

$g_x = \dfrac{x}{x^2+y^2}$, $g_y = \dfrac{y}{x^2+y^2}$

b. $\varphi(x, y) = x\tan^{-1}\dfrac{y}{x} + \dfrac{y}{2}\ln(x^2+y^2) - y$,

$\psi(x, y) = y\tan^{-1}\dfrac{y}{x} - \dfrac{x}{2}\ln(x^2+y^2) + x$

57. a.

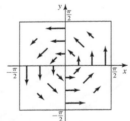

$\mathbf{F} = \langle -4\cos x\sin y, 4\sin x\cos y \rangle$ **b.** Yes, the divergence equals zero.
c. No, the two-dimensional curl equals $8\cos x\cos y$.   **d.** 0   **e.** 32
61. c. The vector field is undefined at the origin.
63.

Basic ideas: Let C_1 and C_2 be two smooth simple curves from A to B.

$$\int_{C_1} \mathbf{F} \cdot \mathbf{n}\, ds - \int_{C_2} \mathbf{F} \cdot \mathbf{n}\, ds = \oint_C \mathbf{F} \cdot \mathbf{n}\, ds = \iint_R \text{div } \mathbf{F}\, dA = 0$$

and $\displaystyle\int_{C_1} \mathbf{F} \cdot \mathbf{n}\, ds = \int_{C_1} \psi_x\, dx + \psi_y\, dy = \int_{C_1} d\psi = \psi(B) - \psi(A)$

65. Use $\nabla\varphi \cdot \nabla\psi = \langle f, g \rangle \cdot \langle -g, f \rangle = 0$

Section 14.5 Exercises, pp. 1107–1110

1. Compute $f_x + g_y + h_z$. **3.** There is no source or sink.
5. It indicates the axis and the angular speed of the circulation at a point. **7.** 0 **9.** 3 **11.** 0 **13.** $2(x + y + z)$
15. $\dfrac{x^2 + y^2 + 3}{(1 + x^2 + y^2)^2}$ **17.** $\dfrac{1}{|\mathbf{r}|^2}$ **19.** $-\dfrac{1}{|\mathbf{r}|^4}$ **21. a.** Positive for

both points **b.** div $\mathbf{F} = 2$ **c.** Outward everywhere **d.** Positive
23. a. curl $\mathbf{F} = 2\mathbf{i}$ **b.** $|\text{curl } \mathbf{F}| = 2$ **25. a.** curl $\mathbf{F} = 2\mathbf{i} - 2\mathbf{j} + 2\mathbf{k}$
b. $|\text{curl } \mathbf{F}| = 2\sqrt{3}$ **27.** $3y\,\mathbf{k}$ **29.** $-4z\,\mathbf{j}$ **31.** 0 **33.** 0
35. Follows from partial differentiation of $\dfrac{1}{(x^2 + y^2 + z^2)^{3/2}}$
37. Combine Exercise 36 with Theorem 14.8. **39. a.** False
b. False **c.** False **d.** False **e.** False **41. a.** No **b.** No
c. Yes, scalar function **d.** No **e.** No **f.** No **g.** Yes, vector field
h. No **i.** Yes, vector field **43. a.** At $(0, 1, 1)$, $\mathbf{F}$ points in the positive x-direction; at $(1, 1, 0)$, $\mathbf{F}$ points in the negative z-direction; at $(0, 1, -1)$, $\mathbf{F}$ points in the negative x-direction; and at $(-1, 1, 0)$, $\mathbf{F}$ points in the positive z-direction. These vectors circle the y-axis in the counterclockwise direction looking along $\mathbf{a}$ from head to tail. **b.** The argument in part (a) can be repeated in any plane perpendicular to the y-axis to show that the vectors of $\mathbf{F}$ circle the y-axis in the counterclockwise direction looking along $\mathbf{a}$ from head to tail. Alternatively, computing the cross product, we find that $\mathbf{F} = \mathbf{a} \times \mathbf{r} = \langle z, 0, -x \rangle$, which is a rotation field in any plane perpendicular to $\mathbf{a}$.
45. Compute an explicit expression for $\mathbf{a} \times \mathbf{r}$ and then take the required partial derivatives. **47.** div $\mathbf{F}$ has a maximum value of 6 at $(1, 1, 1)$, $(1, -1, -1)$, $(-1, 1, 1)$, and $(-1, -1, -1)$.
49. $\mathbf{n} = \langle a, b, 2a + b \rangle$, where a and b are real numbers
51. $\mathbf{F} = \frac{1}{2}(y^2 + z^2)\,\mathbf{i}$; no **53. a.** The wheel does not spin.
b. Clockwise, looking in the positive y-direction **c.** The wheel does not spin. **55.** $\omega = \dfrac{10}{\sqrt{3}}$, or $\dfrac{5}{\sqrt{3}\pi} \approx 0.9189$ revolutions per unit time
57. $\mathbf{F} = -200k e^{-x^2 + y^2 + z^2}(-x\,\mathbf{i} + y\,\mathbf{j} + z\,\mathbf{k})$
$\nabla \cdot \mathbf{F} = -200k(1 + 2(x^2 + y^2 + z^2))e^{-x^2 + y^2 + z^2}$
59. a. $\mathbf{F} = -\dfrac{GMm\mathbf{r}}{|\mathbf{r}|^3}$ **b.** See Theorem 14.9.

61. $\rho\left(\dfrac{\partial u}{\partial t} + u\dfrac{\partial u}{\partial x} + v\dfrac{\partial u}{\partial y} + w\dfrac{\partial u}{\partial z}\right) = -\dfrac{\partial p}{\partial x} + \mu\left(\dfrac{\partial^2 u}{\partial x^2} + \dfrac{\partial^2 u}{\partial y^2} + \dfrac{\partial^2 u}{\partial z^2}\right)$

$\rho\left(\dfrac{\partial v}{\partial t} + u\dfrac{\partial v}{\partial x} + v\dfrac{\partial v}{\partial y} + w\dfrac{\partial v}{\partial z}\right) = -\dfrac{\partial p}{\partial y} + \mu\left(\dfrac{\partial^2 v}{\partial x^2} + \dfrac{\partial^2 v}{\partial y^2} + \dfrac{\partial^2 v}{\partial z^2}\right)$

$\rho\left(\dfrac{\partial w}{\partial t} + u\dfrac{\partial w}{\partial x} + v\dfrac{\partial w}{\partial y} + w\dfrac{\partial w}{\partial z}\right) = -\dfrac{\partial p}{\partial z} + \mu\left(\dfrac{\partial^2 w}{\partial x^2} + \dfrac{\partial^2 w}{\partial y^2} + \dfrac{\partial^2 w}{\partial z^2}\right)$

63. a. Use $\nabla \times \mathbf{B} = -Ak \cos(kz - \omega t)\,\mathbf{i}$ and $\dfrac{\partial \mathbf{E}}{\partial t} = -A\omega \cos(kz - \omega t)\,\mathbf{i}$. **b.**

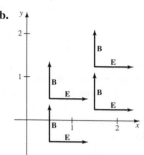

Section 14.6 Exercises, pp. 1123–1126

1. $\mathbf{r}(u, v) = \langle a \cos u, a \sin u, v \rangle, 0 \le u \le 2\pi, 0 \le v \le h$
3. $\mathbf{r}(u, v) = \langle a \sin u \cos v, a \sin u \sin v, a \cos u \rangle, 0 \le u \le \pi$, $0 \le v \le 2\pi$ **5.** Use the parameterization from Exercise 3 and compute $\displaystyle\int_0^\pi \int_0^{2\pi} f(a \sin u \cos v, a \sin u \sin v, a \cos u)\, a^2 \sin u\, dv\, du$.
7. Use the parametrization from Exercise 3 and compute
$\displaystyle\int_0^\pi \int_0^{2\pi} a^2 \sin u\,(f \sin u \cos v + g \sin u \sin v + h \cos u)\, dv\, du$.
9. The normal vectors point outward. **11.** $\langle u, v, \frac{1}{3}(16 - 2u + 4v) \rangle$, $|u| < \infty, |v| < \infty$ **13.** $\langle v \cos u, v \sin u, v \rangle, 0 \le u \le 2\pi$,
$2 \le v \le 8$ **15.** $\langle 3 \cos u, 3 \sin u, v \rangle, 0 \le u \le \dfrac{\pi}{2}, 0 \le v \le 3$
17. The plane $z = 2x + 3y - 1$ **19.** Part of the upper half of the cone $z^2 = 16x^2 + 16y^2$ of height 12 and radius 3 (with $y \ge 0$)
21. 28π **23.** $16\sqrt{3}$ **25.** $\pi r\sqrt{r^2 + h^2}$ **27.** 1728π **29.** 0
31. $4\pi\sqrt{5}$ **33.** $8\sqrt{17} + 2\ln(\sqrt{17} + 4) = 37.1743$ **35.** $\dfrac{2\sqrt{3}}{3}$
37. $\dfrac{1250\pi}{3}$ **39.** $\dfrac{1}{48}(e - e^{-5} - e^{-7} + e^{-13})$ **41.** $\dfrac{1}{4\pi}$ **43.** -8
45. 0 **47.** 4π **49. a.** True **b.** False **c.** True **d.** True
51. $8\pi(4\sqrt{17} + \ln(\sqrt{17} + 4))$ **53.** $8\pi a$ **55. a.** 8
b. $4\pi - 8$ **57. a.** 0 **b.** 0; the flow is tangent to the surface (radial flow). **59.** $2\pi ah$ **61.** $-400\left(e - \dfrac{1}{e}\right)^2$ **63.** $8\pi a$
65. a. $4\pi(b^3 - a^3)$ **b.** The net flux is zero. **67.** $\left(0, 0, \frac{2}{3}h\right)$
69. $\left(0, 0, \frac{7}{6}\right)$ **73.** Flux $= \displaystyle\iint_S \mathbf{F} \cdot \mathbf{n}\, dS = \iint_R dA$

Section 14.7 Exercises, pp. 1133–1135

1. The integral measures the circulation along the closed curve C.
3. Under certain conditions, the accumulated rotation of the vector field over the surface S equals the net circulation on the boundary of S.
5. Both integrals equal -2π. **7.** Both integrals equal zero.
9. Both integrals equal -18π. **11.** -24π **13.** $-\frac{128}{3}$ **15.** 15π
17. 0 **19.** 0 **21.** $\nabla \times \mathbf{v} = \langle 1, 0, 0 \rangle$; a paddle wheel with its axis aligned with the x-axis will spin with maximum angular speed counterclockwise (looking in the negative x-direction) at all points.

23. $\nabla \times \mathbf{v} = \langle 0, -2, 0 \rangle$; a paddle wheel with its axis aligned with the y-axis will spin with maximum angular speed clockwise (looking in the negative y-direction) at all points.   **25. a.** False   **b.** False   **c.** True   **d.** True   **27.** 0   **29.** 0   **31.** 2π **33.** $\pi(\cos\varphi - \sin\varphi)$; maximum for $\varphi = 0$ **35.** The circulation is 48π; it depends on the radius of the circle but not on the center.   **37. a.** The normal vectors point toward the z-axis on the curved surface of S and in the direction of $\langle 0, 1, 0 \rangle$ on the flat surface of S.   **b.** 2π **c.** 2π **39.** The integral is π for all a.   **41. a., b.** 0   **43. b.** 2π for any circle of radius r centered at the origin   **c.** $\mathbf{F}$ is not differentiable along the z-axis.   **45.** Apply the Chain Rule.

47. $\displaystyle\int_C \mathbf{F} \cdot d\mathbf{r} = \iint_R \left(\frac{\partial h}{\partial y} - \frac{\partial g}{\partial z} \right) dA$

Section 14.8 Exercises, pp. 1144–1147

1. The surface integral measures the flow across the boundary.
3. The flux across the boundary equals the cumulative expansion or contraction of the vector field inside the region.   **5.** 32π
7. The outward fluxes are equal.   **9.** Both integrals equal 96π.
11. Both integrals equal zero.   **13.** 0   **15.** 0
17. $16\sqrt{6}\pi$ **19.** $\frac{2}{3}$ **21.** $-\frac{128}{3}\pi$ **23.** 24π
25. -224π **27.** 12π **29.** 20   **31. a.** False
b. False   **c.** True   **33.** 0   **35.** $\frac{3}{2}$ **37. b.** The net flux between the two spheres is $4\pi(a^2 - \varepsilon^2)$.   **39. b.** Use $\nabla \cdot \mathbf{E} = 0$.
c. The flux across S is the sum of the contributions from the individual charges.   **d.** For an arbitrary volume, we find

$$\frac{1}{\varepsilon_0} \iiint_D q(x, y, z)\, dV = \iint_S \mathbf{E} \cdot \mathbf{n}\, dS = \iiint_S \nabla \cdot \mathbf{E}\, dV.$$

e. Use $\nabla^2 \varphi = \nabla \cdot \nabla \varphi$.   **41.** 0   **43.** $e^{-1} - 1$
45. $800\pi a^3 e^{-a^2}$

Chapter 14 Review Exercises, pp. 1147–1150

1. a. False   **b.** True   **c.** False   **d.** False   **e.** True
3. $\nabla \varphi = \langle 2x, 8y \rangle$

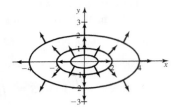

5. $-\dfrac{\mathbf{r}}{|\mathbf{r}|^3}$ **7. a.** $\mathbf{n} = \frac{1}{2}\langle x, y \rangle$ **b.** 0   **c.** $\frac{1}{2}$

9. $\dfrac{\sqrt{46}}{4}\left(e^{6(\ln 8)^2} - 1\right)$ **11.** Both integrals equal zero.

13. 0   **15.** The circulation is -4π; the outward flux is zero.

17. The circulation is zero; the outward flux is 2π.   **19.** $\dfrac{4v_0 L^3}{3}$

21. $\varphi(x, y, z) = xy + yz^2$ **23.** $\varphi(x, y, z) = xye^z$
25. 0 for both methods   **27. a.** $-\pi$ **b.** $\mathbf{F}$ is not conservative.
29. 0   **31.** $\frac{20}{3}$ **33.** 8π **35.** The circulation is zero; the outward flux equals 2π.   **37. a.** $b = c$ **b.** $a = -d$ **c.** $a = -d$ and $b = c$ **39.** $\nabla \cdot \mathbf{F} = 4\sqrt{x^2 + y^2 + z^2} = 4|\mathbf{r}|$, $\nabla \times \mathbf{F} = \mathbf{0}$, $\nabla \cdot \mathbf{F} \neq 0$; irrotational but not source free   **41.** $\nabla \cdot \mathbf{F} = 2y + 12xz^2$, $\nabla \times \mathbf{F} = \mathbf{0}$, $\nabla \cdot \mathbf{F} \neq 0$; irrotational but not source free   **43. a.** -1 and 0

b. $\mathbf{n} = \dfrac{1}{\sqrt{3}}\langle -1, 1, 1 \rangle$ **45.** 18π **47.** $4\sqrt{3}$ **49.** $\dfrac{8\sqrt{3}}{3}$

51. 8π **53.** $4\pi a^2$ **55. a.** Use $x = y = 0$ to confirm the highest

point; use $z = 0$ to confirm the base.   **b.** The hemisphere S has the greater surface area—$2\pi a^2$ for S versus $\dfrac{5\sqrt{5} - 1}{6}\pi a^2$ for T.

57. 0   **59.** 99π **61.** 0   **63.** $\dfrac{972}{5}\pi$ **65.** $\dfrac{124}{5}\pi$ **67.** $\dfrac{32}{3}$

APPENDIX A

Exercises, pp. 1157–1158

1. The set of real numbers greater than -4 and less than or equal to 10; $(-4, 10]$;

3. $|x| = \begin{cases} x & \text{if } x \geq 0 \\ -x & \text{if } x < 0 \end{cases}$ **5.** $2x - 4 \geq 3$ or $2x - 4 \leq -3$

7. Take the square root of the sum of the squares of the differences of the x- and y-coordinates.   **9.** $y = \sqrt{36 - x^2}$

11. $m = \dfrac{y + 2}{x - 4}$ or $y = m(x - 4) - 2$ **13.** They are equal.

15. 4   **17.** $4uv$ **19.** $-\dfrac{h}{x(x + h)}$ **21.** $(y - y^{-1})(y + y^{-1})$

23. $u = \pm\sqrt{2}, \pm 3$ **25.** $3x^2 + 3xh + h^2$

27. $(1, 5)$

29. $(-\infty, 4] \cup [5, 6)$

31. $\{x : x < -4/3 \text{ or } x > 4\}$; $\left(-\infty, -\frac{4}{3}\right) \cup (4, \infty)$

33. $\{x : -2 < x < -1 \text{ or } 2 < x < 3\}$; $(-2, -1) \cup (2, 3)$

35. $y = 2 - \sqrt{9 - (x + 1)^2}$

37. $y = \dfrac{5}{3}x + 4$

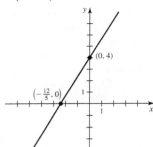

39. $y = \dfrac{4}{5}x - 4$

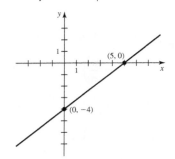

41. $x + 2y = 24$

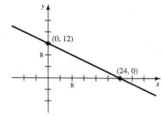

43. $y = \dfrac{1}{3}x - 7$ **45. a.** False **b.** True **c.** False **d.** False

e. False **f.** True **g.** False **47.** $\{x: |x - 1| \geq 3\}$

49.

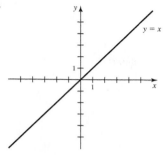

Index

TABLE OF INTEGRALS

Substitution Rule	Integration by Parts
$\displaystyle\int f(g(x))g'(x)\,dx = \int f(u)\,du \quad (u = g(x))$	$\displaystyle\int u\,dv = uv - \int v\,du$
$\displaystyle\int_a^b f(g(x))g'(x)\,dx = \int_{g(a)}^{g(b)} f(u)\,du$	$\displaystyle\int_a^b uv'\,dx = uv\Big|_a^b - \int_a^b vu'\,dx$

Basic Integrals

1. $\displaystyle\int x^n\,dx = \frac{1}{n+1}x^{n+1} + C;\ n \neq -1$

2. $\displaystyle\int \frac{dx}{x} = \ln|x| + C$

3. $\displaystyle\int \cos ax\,dx = \frac{1}{a}\sin ax + C$

4. $\displaystyle\int \sin ax\,dx = -\frac{1}{a}\cos ax + C$

5. $\displaystyle\int \tan x\,dx = \ln|\sec x| + C$

6. $\displaystyle\int \cot x\,dx = \ln|\sin x| + C$

7. $\displaystyle\int \sec x\,dx = \ln|\sec x + \tan x| + C$

8. $\displaystyle\int \csc x\,dx = -\ln|\csc x + \cot x| + C$

9. $\displaystyle\int e^{ax}\,dx = \frac{1}{a}e^{ax} + C$

10. $\displaystyle\int b^{ax}\,dx = \frac{1}{a\ln b}b^{ax} + C;\ b > 0, b \neq 1$

11. $\displaystyle\int \ln x\,dx = x\ln x - x + C$

12. $\displaystyle\int \log_b x\,dx = \frac{1}{\ln b}(x\ln x - x) + C$

13. $\displaystyle\int \frac{dx}{\sqrt{a^2 - x^2}} = \sin^{-1}\frac{x}{a} + C$

14. $\displaystyle\int \frac{dx}{x^2 + a^2} = \frac{1}{a}\tan^{-1}\frac{x}{a} + C$

15. $\displaystyle\int \frac{dx}{x\sqrt{x^2 - a^2}} = \frac{1}{a}\sec^{-1}\left|\frac{x}{a}\right| + C$

16. $\displaystyle\int \sin^{-1}x\,dx = x\sin^{-1}x + \sqrt{1 - x^2} + C$

17. $\displaystyle\int \cos^{-1}x\,dx = x\cos^{-1}x - \sqrt{1 - x^2} + C$

18. $\displaystyle\int \tan^{-1}x\,dx = x\tan^{-1}x - \frac{1}{2}\ln(1 + x^2) + C$

19. $\displaystyle\int \sec^{-1}x\,dx = x\sec^{-1}x - \ln(x + \sqrt{x^2 - 1}) + C$

20. $\displaystyle\int \sinh x\,dx = \cosh x + C$

21. $\displaystyle\int \cosh x\,dx = \sinh x + C$

22. $\displaystyle\int \operatorname{sech}^2 x\,dx = \tanh x + C$

23. $\displaystyle\int \operatorname{csch}^2 x\,dx = -\coth x + C$

24. $\displaystyle\int \operatorname{sech} x\tanh x\,dx = -\operatorname{sech} x + C$

25. $\displaystyle\int \operatorname{csch} x\coth x\,dx = -\operatorname{csch} x + C$

26. $\displaystyle\int \tanh x\,dx = \ln\cosh x + C$

27. $\displaystyle\int \coth x\,dx = \ln|\sinh x| + C$

28. $\displaystyle\int \operatorname{sech} x\,dx = \tan^{-1}\sinh x + C = \sin^{-1}\tanh x + C$

29. $\displaystyle\int \operatorname{csch} x\,dx = \ln|\tanh(x/2)| + C$

Trigonometric Integrals

30. $\displaystyle\int \cos^2 x\,dx = \frac{x}{2} + \frac{\sin 2x}{4} + C$

31. $\displaystyle\int \sin^2 x\,dx = \frac{x}{2} - \frac{\sin 2x}{4} + C$

32. $\displaystyle\int \sec^2 ax\,dx = \frac{1}{a}\tan ax + C$

33. $\displaystyle\int \csc^2 ax\,dx = -\frac{1}{a}\cot ax + C$

34. $\displaystyle\int \tan^2 x\,dx = \tan x - x + C$

35. $\displaystyle\int \cot^2 x\,dx = -\cot x - x + C$

36. $\displaystyle\int \cos^3 x\,dx = -\frac{1}{3}\sin^3 x + \sin x + C$

37. $\displaystyle\int \sin^3 x\,dx = \frac{1}{3}\cos^3 x - \cos x + C$

38. $\int \sec^3 x \, dx = \frac{1}{2} \sec x \tan x + \frac{1}{2} \ln |\sec x + \tan x| + C$

39. $\int \csc^3 x \, dx = -\frac{1}{2} \csc x \cot x - \frac{1}{2} \ln |\csc x + \cot x| + C$

40. $\int \tan^3 x \, dx = \frac{1}{2} \tan^2 x - \ln |\sec x| + C$

41. $\int \cot^3 x \, dx = -\frac{1}{2} \cot^2 x - \ln |\sin x| + C$

42. $\int \sec^n ax \tan ax \, dx = \frac{1}{na} \sec^n ax + C; \; n \neq 0$

43. $\int \csc^n ax \cot ax \, dx = -\frac{1}{na} \csc^n ax + C; \; n \neq 0$

44. $\int \frac{dx}{1 + \sin ax} = -\frac{1}{a} \tan \left(\frac{\pi}{4} - \frac{ax}{2} \right) + C$

45. $\int \frac{dx}{1 - \sin ax} = \frac{1}{a} \tan \left(\frac{\pi}{4} + \frac{ax}{2} \right) + C$

46. $\int \frac{dx}{1 + \cos ax} = \frac{1}{a} \tan \frac{ax}{2} + C$

47. $\int \frac{dx}{1 - \cos ax} = -\frac{1}{a} \cot \frac{ax}{2} + C$

48. $\int \sin mx \cos nx \, dx = -\frac{\cos (m + n)x}{2(m + n)} - \frac{\cos (m - n)x}{2(m - n)} + C; \; m^2 \neq n^2$

49. $\int \sin mx \sin nx \, dx = \frac{\sin (m - n)x}{2(m - n)} - \frac{\sin (m + n)x}{2(m + n)} + C; \; m^2 \neq n^2$

50. $\int \cos mx \cos nx \, dx = \frac{\sin (m - n)x}{2(m - n)} + \frac{\sin (m + n)x}{2(m + n)} + C; \; m^2 \neq n^2$

Reduction Formulas for Trigonometric Functions

51. $\int \cos^n x \, dx = \frac{1}{n} \cos^{n-1} x \sin x + \frac{n - 1}{n} \int \cos^{n-2} x \, dx$

52. $\int \sin^n x \, dx = -\frac{1}{n} \sin^{n-1} x \cos x + \frac{n - 1}{n} \int \sin^{n-2} x \, dx$

53. $\int \tan^n x \, dx = \frac{\tan^{n-1} x}{n - 1} - \int \tan^{n-2} x \, dx; \; n \neq 1$

54. $\int \cot^n x \, dx = -\frac{\cot^{n-1} x}{n - 1} - \int \cot^{n-2} x \, dx; \; n \neq 1$

55. $\int \sec^n x \, dx = \frac{\sec^{n-2} x \tan x}{n - 1} + \frac{n - 2}{n - 1} \int \sec^{n-2} x \, dx; \; n \neq 1$

56. $\int \csc^n x \, dx = -\frac{\csc^{n-2} x \cot x}{n - 1} + \frac{n - 2}{n - 1} \int \csc^{n-2} x \, dx; \; n \neq 1$

57. $\int \sin^m x \cos^n x \, dx = -\frac{\sin^{m-1} x \cos^{n+1} x}{m + n} + \frac{m - 1}{m + n} \int \sin^{m-2} x \cos^n x \, dx; \; m \neq -n$

58. $\int \sin^m x \cos^n x \, dx = \frac{\sin^{m+1} x \cos^{n-1} x}{m + n} + \frac{n - 1}{m + n} \int \sin^m x \cos^{n-2} x \, dx; \; m \neq -n$

59. $\int x^n \sin ax \, dx = -\frac{x^n \cos ax}{a} + \frac{n}{a} \int x^{n-1} \cos ax \, dx; \; a \neq 0$

60. $\int x^n \cos ax \, dx = \frac{x^n \sin ax}{a} - \frac{n}{a} \int x^{n-1} \sin ax \, dx; \; a \neq 0$

Integrals Involving $a^2 - x^2; \; a > 0$

61. $\int \sqrt{a^2 - x^2} \, dx = \frac{x}{2} \sqrt{a^2 - x^2} + \frac{a^2}{2} \sin^{-1} \frac{x}{a} + C$

62. $\int \frac{dx}{x \sqrt{a^2 - x^2}} = -\frac{1}{a} \ln \left| \frac{a + \sqrt{a^2 - x^2}}{x} \right| + C$

63. $\int \frac{dx}{x^2 \sqrt{a^2 - x^2}} = -\frac{\sqrt{a^2 - x^2}}{a^2 x} + C$

64. $\int x^2 \sqrt{a^2 - x^2} \, dx = \frac{x}{8} (2x^2 - a^2) \sqrt{a^2 - x^2} + \frac{a^4}{8} \sin^{-1} \frac{x}{a} + C$

65. $\int \frac{\sqrt{a^2 - x^2}}{x^2} \, dx = -\frac{1}{x} \sqrt{a^2 - x^2} - \sin^{-1} \frac{x}{a} + C$

66. $\int \frac{x^2}{\sqrt{a^2 - x^2}} \, dx = -\frac{x}{2} \sqrt{a^2 - x^2} + \frac{a^2}{2} \sin^{-1} \frac{x}{a} + C$

67. $\int \frac{dx}{a^2 - x^2} = \frac{1}{2a} \ln \left| \frac{x + a}{x - a} \right| + C$

Integrals Involving $x^2 - a^2; \; a > 0$

68. $\int \sqrt{x^2 - a^2} \, dx = \frac{x}{2} \sqrt{x^2 - a^2} - \frac{a^2}{2} \ln |x + \sqrt{x^2 - a^2}| + C$

69. $\int \frac{dx}{\sqrt{x^2 - a^2}} = \ln |x + \sqrt{x^2 - a^2}| + C$

70. $\int \frac{dx}{x^2 \sqrt{x^2 - a^2}} = \frac{\sqrt{x^2 - a^2}}{a^2 x} + C$

71. $\int x^2 \sqrt{x^2 - a^2} \, dx = \frac{x}{8} (2x^2 - a^2) \sqrt{x^2 - a^2} - \frac{a^4}{8} \ln |x + \sqrt{x^2 - a^2}| + C$

72. $\int \frac{\sqrt{x^2 - a^2}}{x^2} \, dx = \ln |x + \sqrt{x^2 - a^2}| - \frac{\sqrt{x^2 - a^2}}{x} + C$

73. $\int \frac{x^2}{\sqrt{x^2 - a^2}} \, dx = \frac{a^2}{2} \ln |x + \sqrt{x^2 - a^2}| + \frac{x}{2} \sqrt{x^2 - a^2} + C$

74. $\int \frac{dx}{x^2 - a^2} = \frac{1}{2a} \ln \left| \frac{x - a}{x + a} \right| + C$

75. $\int \frac{dx}{x(x^2 - a^2)} = \frac{1}{2a^2} \ln \left| \frac{x^2 - a^2}{x^2} \right| + C$

Integrals Involving $a^2 + x^2$; $a > 0$

76. $\displaystyle\int \sqrt{a^2 + x^2}\, dx = \frac{x}{2}\sqrt{a^2 + x^2} + \frac{a^2}{2}\ln\left(x + \sqrt{a^2 + x^2}\right) + C$

77. $\displaystyle\int \frac{dx}{\sqrt{a^2 + x^2}} = \ln\left(x + \sqrt{a^2 + x^2}\right) + C$

78. $\displaystyle\int \frac{dx}{x\sqrt{a^2 + x^2}} = \frac{1}{a}\ln\left|\frac{a - \sqrt{a^2 + x^2}}{x}\right| + C$

79. $\displaystyle\int \frac{dx}{x^2\sqrt{a^2 + x^2}} = -\frac{\sqrt{a^2 + x^2}}{a^2 x} + C$

80. $\displaystyle\int x^2\sqrt{a^2 + x^2}\, dx = \frac{x}{8}(a^2 + 2x^2)\sqrt{a^2 + x^2} - \frac{a^4}{8}\ln\left(x + \sqrt{a^2 + x^2}\right) + C$

81. $\displaystyle\int \frac{\sqrt{a^2 + x^2}}{x^2}\, dx = \ln\left|x + \sqrt{a^2 + x^2}\right| - \frac{\sqrt{a^2 + x^2}}{x} + C$

82. $\displaystyle\int \frac{x^2}{\sqrt{a^2 + x^2}}\, dx = -\frac{a^2}{2}\ln\left(x + \sqrt{a^2 + x^2}\right) + \frac{x\sqrt{a^2 + x^2}}{2} + C$

83. $\displaystyle\int \frac{\sqrt{a^2 + x^2}}{x}\, dx = \sqrt{a^2 + x^2} - a\ln\left|\frac{a + \sqrt{a^2 + x^2}}{x}\right| + C$

84. $\displaystyle\int \frac{dx}{(a^2 + x^2)^{3/2}} = \frac{x}{a^2\sqrt{a^2 + x^2}} + C$

85. $\displaystyle\int \frac{dx}{x(a^2 + x^2)} = \frac{1}{2a^2}\ln\left(\frac{x^2}{a^2 + x^2}\right) + C$

Integrals Involving $ax \pm b$; $a \neq 0, b > 0$

86. $\displaystyle\int (ax + b)^n\, dx = \frac{(ax + b)^{n+1}}{a(n + 1)} + C;\ n \neq -1$

87. $\displaystyle\int \left(\sqrt{ax + b}\right)^n dx = \frac{2}{a}\frac{\left(\sqrt{ax + b}\right)^{n+2}}{n + 2} + C;\ n \neq -2$

88. $\displaystyle\int \frac{dx}{x\sqrt{ax - b}} = \frac{2}{\sqrt{b}}\tan^{-1}\sqrt{\frac{ax - b}{b}} + C;\ b > 0$

89. $\displaystyle\int \frac{dx}{x\sqrt{ax + b}} = \frac{1}{\sqrt{b}}\ln\left|\frac{\sqrt{ax + b} - \sqrt{b}}{\sqrt{ax + b} + \sqrt{b}}\right| + C;\ b > 0$

90. $\displaystyle\int \frac{x}{ax + b}\, dx = \frac{x}{a} - \frac{b}{a^2}\ln|ax + b| + C$

91. $\displaystyle\int \frac{x^2}{ax + b}\, dx = \frac{1}{2a^3}\left((ax + b)^2 - 4b(ax + b) + 2b^2\ln|ax + b|\right) + C$

92. $\displaystyle\int \frac{dx}{x^2(ax + b)} = -\frac{1}{bx} + \frac{a}{b^2}\ln\left|\frac{ax + b}{x}\right| + C$

93. $\displaystyle\int x\sqrt{ax + b}\, dx = \frac{2}{15a^2}(3ax - 2b)(ax + b)^{3/2} + C$

94. $\displaystyle\int \frac{x}{\sqrt{ax + b}}\, dx = \frac{2}{3a^2}(ax - 2b)\sqrt{ax + b} + C$

95. $\displaystyle\int x(ax + b)^n\, dx = \frac{(ax + b)^{n+1}}{a^2}\left(\frac{ax + b}{n + 2} - \frac{b}{n + 1}\right) + C;\ n \neq -1, -2$

96. $\displaystyle\int \frac{dx}{x(ax + b)} = \frac{1}{b}\ln\left|\frac{x}{ax + b}\right| + C$

Integrals with Exponential and Trigonometric Functions

97. $\displaystyle\int e^{ax}\sin bx\, dx = \frac{e^{ax}(a\sin bx - b\cos bx)}{a^2 + b^2} + C$

98. $\displaystyle\int e^{ax}\cos bx\, dx = \frac{e^{ax}(a\cos bx + b\sin bx)}{a^2 + b^2} + C$

Integrals with Exponential and Logarithmic Functions

99. $\displaystyle\int \frac{dx}{x\ln x} = \ln|\ln x| + C$

100. $\displaystyle\int x^n \ln x\, dx = \frac{x^{n+1}}{n + 1}\left(\ln x - \frac{1}{n + 1}\right) + C;\ n \neq -1$

101. $\displaystyle\int xe^x\, dx = xe^x - e^x + C$

102. $\displaystyle\int x^n e^{ax}\, dx = \frac{1}{a}x^n e^{ax} - \frac{n}{a}\int x^{n-1}e^{ax}\, dx;\ a \neq 0$

103. $\displaystyle\int \ln^n x\, dx = x\ln^n x - n\int \ln^{n-1} x\, dx$

Miscellaneous Formulas

104. $\displaystyle\int x^n \cos^{-1} x\, dx = \frac{1}{n + 1}\left(x^{n+1}\cos^{-1}x + \int \frac{x^{n+1}dx}{\sqrt{1 - x^2}}\right);\ n \neq -1$

105. $\displaystyle\int x^n \sin^{-1} x\, dx = \frac{1}{n + 1}\left(x^{n+1}\sin^{-1} x - \int \frac{x^{n+1}dx}{\sqrt{1 - x^2}}\right);\ n \neq -1$

106. $\displaystyle\int x^n \tan^{-1} x\, dx = \frac{1}{n + 1}\left(x^{n+1}\tan^{-1} x - \int \frac{x^{n+1}dx}{x^2 + 1}\right);\ n \neq -1$

107. $\displaystyle\int \sqrt{2ax - x^2}\, dx = \frac{x - a}{2}\sqrt{2ax - x^2} + \frac{a^2}{2}\sin^{-1}\left(\frac{x - a}{a}\right) + C;\ a > 0$

108. $\displaystyle\int \frac{dx}{\sqrt{2ax - x^2}} = \sin^{-1}\left(\frac{x - a}{a}\right) + C;\ a > 0$

GRAPHS OF ELEMENTARY FUNCTIONS

Linear functions

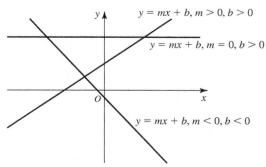

Quadratic functions

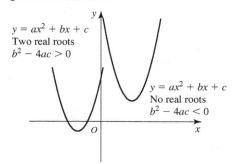

Positive even powers

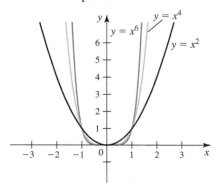

Positive odd powers

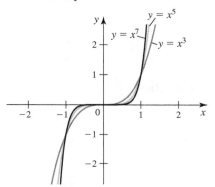

Negative even powers

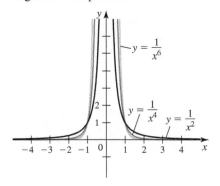

Negative odd powers

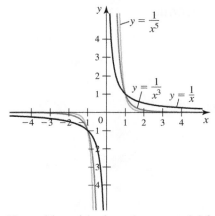

Exponential functions

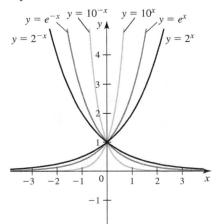

Natural logarithmic and exponential functions

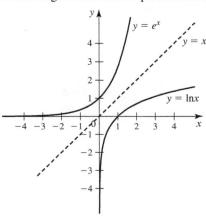

DERIVATIVES

General Formulas

$$\frac{d}{dx}(c) = 0$$

$$\frac{d}{dx}(cf(x)) = cf'(x)$$

$$\frac{d}{dx}(f(x) + g(x)) = f'(x) + g'(x)$$

$$\frac{d}{dx}(f(x) - g(x)) = f'(x) - g'(x)$$

$$\frac{d}{dx}(f(x)g(x)) = f'(x)g(x) + f(x)g'(x)$$

$$\frac{d}{dx}\left(\frac{f(x)}{g(x)}\right) = \frac{g(x)f'(x) - f(x)g'(x)}{(g(x))^2}$$

$$\frac{d}{dx}(x^n) = nx^{n-1}, \text{ for real numbers } n$$

$$\frac{d}{dx}[f(g(x))] = f'(g(x)) \cdot g'(x)$$

Trigonometric Functions

$$\frac{d}{dx}(\sin x) = \cos x$$

$$\frac{d}{dx}(\cos x) = -\sin x$$

$$\frac{d}{dx}(\tan x) = \sec^2 x$$

$$\frac{d}{dx}(\cot x) = -\csc^2 x$$

$$\frac{d}{dx}(\sec x) = \sec x \tan x$$

$$\frac{d}{dx}(\csc x) = -\csc x \cot x$$

Inverse Trigonometric Functions

$$\frac{d}{dx}(\sin^{-1} x) = \frac{1}{\sqrt{1 - x^2}}$$

$$\frac{d}{dx}(\cos^{-1} x) = -\frac{1}{\sqrt{1 - x^2}}$$

$$\frac{d}{dx}(\tan^{-1} x) = \frac{1}{1 + x^2}$$

$$\frac{d}{dx}(\cot^{-1} x) = -\frac{1}{1 + x^2}$$

$$\frac{d}{dx}(\sec^{-1} x) = \frac{1}{|x|\sqrt{x^2 - 1}}$$

$$\frac{d}{dx}(\csc^{-1} x) = -\frac{1}{|x|\sqrt{x^2 - 1}}$$

Exponential and Logarithmic Functions

$$\frac{d}{dx}(e^x) = e^x$$

$$\frac{d}{dx}(b^x) = b^x \ln b$$

$$\frac{d}{dx}(\ln |x|) = \frac{1}{x}$$

$$\frac{d}{dx}(\log_b x) = \frac{1}{x \ln b}$$

Hyperbolic Functions

$$\frac{d}{dx}(\sinh x) = \cosh x$$

$$\frac{d}{dx}(\cosh x) = \sinh x$$

$$\frac{d}{dx}(\tanh x) = \text{sech}^2 x$$

$$\frac{d}{dx}(\coth x) = -\text{csch}^2 x$$

$$\frac{d}{dx}(\text{sech } x) = -\text{sech } x \tanh x$$

$$\frac{d}{dx}(\text{csch } x) = -\text{csch } x \coth x$$

Inverse Hyperbolic Functions

$$\frac{d}{dx}(\sinh^{-1} x) = \frac{1}{\sqrt{x^2 + 1}}$$

$$\frac{d}{dx}(\cosh^{-1} x) = \frac{1}{\sqrt{x^2 - 1}} \quad (x > 1)$$

$$\frac{d}{dx}(\tanh^{-1} x) = \frac{1}{1 - x^2} \quad (|x| < 1)$$

$$\frac{d}{dx}(\coth^{-1} x) = \frac{1}{1 - x^2} \quad (|x| > 1)$$

$$\frac{d}{dx}(\text{sech}^{-1} x) = -\frac{1}{x\sqrt{1 - x^2}} \quad (0 < x < 1)$$

$$\frac{d}{dx}(\text{csch}^{-1} x) = -\frac{1}{|x|\sqrt{1 + x^2}} \quad (x \neq 0)$$

FORMS OF THE FUNDAMENTAL THEOREM OF CALCULUS

Fundamental Theorem of Calculus	$\displaystyle \int_a^b f'(x)\,dx = f(b) - f(a)$
Fundamental Theorem of Line Integrals	$\displaystyle \int_C \nabla f \cdot d\mathbf{r} = f(B) - f(A)$ (A and B are the initial and final points of C.)
Green's Theorem	$\displaystyle \iint_R (g_x - f_y)\,dA = \oint_C f\,dx + g\,dy$ $\displaystyle \iint_R (f_x + g_y)\,dA = \oint_C f\,dy - g\,dx$
Stokes' Theorem	$\displaystyle \iint_S (\nabla \times \mathbf{F}) \cdot \mathbf{n}\,dS = \oint_C \mathbf{F} \cdot d\mathbf{r}$
Divergence Theorem	$\displaystyle \iiint_D \nabla \cdot \mathbf{F}\,dV = \iint_S \mathbf{F} \cdot \mathbf{n}\,dS$

FORMULAS FROM VECTOR CALCULUS

Assume $\mathbf{F}(x, y, z) = f(x, y, z)\,\mathbf{i} + g(x, y, z)\,\mathbf{j} + h(x, y, z)\,\mathbf{k}$, where f, g, and h are differentiable on a region D of $\mathbb{R}^3$.

Gradient: $\displaystyle \nabla f(x, y, z) = \frac{\partial f}{\partial x}\mathbf{i} + \frac{\partial f}{\partial y}\mathbf{j} + \frac{\partial f}{\partial z}\mathbf{k}$

Divergence: $\displaystyle \nabla \cdot \mathbf{F}(x, y, z) = \frac{\partial f}{\partial x} + \frac{\partial g}{\partial y} + \frac{\partial h}{\partial z}$

Curl: $\displaystyle \nabla \times \mathbf{F}(x, y, z) = \begin{vmatrix} \mathbf{i} & \mathbf{j} & \mathbf{k} \\ \dfrac{\partial}{\partial x} & \dfrac{\partial}{\partial y} & \dfrac{\partial}{\partial z} \\ f & g & h \end{vmatrix}$

$\nabla \times (\nabla f) = \mathbf{0} \qquad \nabla \cdot (\nabla \times \mathbf{F}) = 0$

$\mathbf{F}$ conservative on $D \Leftrightarrow \mathbf{F} = \nabla \varphi$ for some potential function φ

$\qquad \Leftrightarrow \displaystyle \oint_C \mathbf{F} \cdot d\mathbf{r} = 0$ over closed paths C in D

$\qquad \Leftrightarrow \displaystyle \int_C \mathbf{F} \cdot d\mathbf{r}$ is independent of path for C in D

$\qquad \Leftrightarrow \nabla \times \mathbf{F} = \mathbf{0}$ on D